The Art Sales Index 1991/92

24th annual edition

Volume II

Oil Paintings, Watercolours, Drawings and Miniatures
Artists L - Z

Sculptures, Bronzes and Three Dimensional Works of Art
Artists A - Z

Edited by
Richard Hislop

Published by

ART SALES INDEX LTD
1 THAMES STREET, WEYBRIDGE, SURREY, ENGLAND

ISBN 0 903872 44 7

Published, computer composition and typeset by
Art Sales Index Ltd
1, Thames Street, Weybridge, Surrey

Printed and bound by
BPCC Wheatons Ltd
Hennock Road, Marsh Barton, Exeter

Contents

The ASI
Enquiry Service

The full ASI Data Bank is available to you: International art auction sale results, from 1970, price and detail of over 1,400,000 works by 120,000 artists and sculptors.

Answers to questions on:-

artists/sculptors -
names dates nationality
named groups or schools

prices
individual or overall totals
highest - lowest - average
by square inch or centimetre
most recent prices
by auction season or calendar year
by currency or country

titles of pictures
tracing words - names or people - family names -
ships - towns - lakes - rivers - places - sports - activities
(every word in every title is indexed)

dimensions
in inches or centimetres
exactly or within size ranges

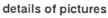

details of pictures
medium, whether signed, dated, inscribed
whether illustrated in the auction catalogue

auctioneers
date and place of auctions

Write for details to:-

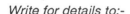

Art Sales Index Ltd.,
1 Thames Street, Weybridge, Surrey KT13 8JG, UK.
tel: (0932) 856426   fax: (0932) 842482

Index

Oil paintings, watercolours, drawings and miniatures
sold during the auction season are covered
by this book

Artists L - Z

STARTING PRICES

Oil Paintings - £500
Miniatures - £300
Watercolours and drawings - £400
National or regional "schools" - £1000

*(Sculpture prices are listed in a separate section
at the end of Volume II)*

L I (?) ?
£1058 $1884   (28-Apr-92 RAS.K656) Sunset over Gripsholm (51x80cm-20x31in) init.d.1838
    (D.KR 12000)

LAABS, Hans (1915-) Polish
£1049   *$1867*   *(30-Nov-91 VG.B811/R) Autumn by the sea (47x62cm-19x24in) s.d.1957*
    gouache W/C (DM 3000)

LAAGE, Wilhelm (1868-1930) German
£951 $1721   (3-Dec-91 FN.S2292/R) Windy corner with trees in Alb landscape
    (57x74cm-22x29in) s.d.1920 i.verso (DM 2700)

LAAN, Gerard van der (1844-1915) Dutch
£486 $846   (17-Sep-91 CH.AM268) Hooge Zee (24x47cm-9x19in) s. i. verso panel
    (D.FL 1600)

LAANEN, Jasper van der (1592-1626) Flemish
£5091 $9011   (10-Nov-91 ZZ.F68/R) Paysage anime. Paysage forestier avec bergers
    (17x22cm-7x9in) copper pair (F.FR 50500)

LAANEN, Jasper van der (style) (1592-1626) Flemish
£1800 $3222   (11-Nov-91 S548/R) Wooded landscape with huntsman (23x45cm-9x18in) panel

LAAR, Pieter Jacobsz van (c.1582-1642) Dutch
£926 $1575   (27-Oct-91 E.LA73) Le cavalier (48x38cm-19x15in) panel (F.FR 9200)

LAAR, Pieter Jacobsz van (circle) (c.1582-1642) Dutch
£4900 $8820   (30-Jan-92 TL25/R) Figures and goats in an Italianate landscape
    (59x53cm-23x21in) pair

LABILLE-GUIARD, Madame Adelaide (1749-1803) French
£25355 $44625   (10-Apr-92 AT.P47/R) Portrait de Madame Elisabeth (103x84cm-41x33in)
    (F.FR 250000)

LABILLE-GUIARD, Madame Adelaide (attrib) (1749-1803) French
£1524 $2652   (13-Apr-92 AT.P121/R) Portrait de gentilhomme (73x59cm-29x23in) oval
    (F.FR 15000)
£410 $741   *(22-May-92 GB.B5628) Portrait of young woman (50x38cm-20x15in) chl ochre*
    htd.white (DM 1200)

LABILLE-GUIARD, Madame Adelaide (circle) (1749-1803) French
£5874 $10396   (7-Nov-91 D.V189/R) Portrait of young boy with feathered hat holding
    cherries (61x50cm-24x20in) oval (A.S 120000)

LABILLE-GUIARD, Madame Adelaide (style) (1749-1803) French
£1000 $1790   (13-Nov-91 CG577/R) Portrait of a woman wearing a white and pink ribboned
    dress (65x53cm-26x21in) oval

LABISSE, Felix (1905-1982) French
£1236 $2237   (20-May-92 FB.P160) Exorcisme contre les incubes (54x73cm-21x29in) s.
    s.d.1957 verso (F.FR 12200)
£1236 $2237   (20-May-92 FB.P158) Envoutements exorcismes (73x60cm-29x24in) s. s.d.1969
    verso (F.FR 12200)
£2240 $4145   (10-Jun-92 LD.P138/R) Le seigneur des baux (80x60cm-31x24in) s. isorel
    (F.FR 22000)
£3000 $5730   (29-Jun-92 CSK132/R) Le tresor de Tijuca (61x50cm-24x20in) s. s.i.d.1972
    verso
£5092 $9420   (10-Jun-92 LD.P137/R) Le mot (73x91cm-29x36in) s. s.d.1951verso
    (F.FR 50000)
£8333 $14333   (12-Oct-91 KV.L455/R) Bay the fair at Ostend (72x59cm-28x23in) s.d.31
    (B.FR 500000)
£9174 $16147   (7-Apr-92 C.A160/R) The visitation (100x81cm-39x32in) s.d.1970
    (B.FR 550000)
£550   *$946*   *(12-Oct-91 KV.L175) Le port (32x48cm-13x19in) s. gouache (B.FR 33000)*
£973   *$1800*   *(12-Jun-92 SY.NY42/R) Praying mantisses (49x64cm-19x25in) s.d.43 gouache*
    paper laid down on board
£1454   *$2632*   *(7-Dec-91 KV.L189) Decor de theatre (19x27cm-7x11in) s. gouache*
    (B.FR 85000)

LABO, Savinio (1899-1976) Italian
£998 $1857   (16-Jun-92 F.M74) Tempo grigio, Milano (39x30cm-15x12in) s.d.1944 canvas
    on board (I.L 2200000)
£1361 $2532   (16-Jun-92 F.M61) Marina con figure (50x100cm-20x39in) s. panel
    (I.L 3000000)
£1361 $2532   (16-Jun-92 F.M62) Paesaggio fluviale (50x100cm-20x39in) s. (I.L 3000000)

LABORDE, Guillermo (?) ?
£860 $1600   (17-Jun-92 CAS.M33/R) El Maestro Educacionista Agustin Scarone en el
    estudio des artista (150x150cm-59x59in)

LABORNE, Edme Emile (1837-1913) French
£669 $1145   (22-Mar-92 LT.P202) Promeneur le long de la riviere (27x38cm-11x15in) s.
    (F.FR 6500)
£5814 $10000   (17-Oct-91 SY.NY218/R) Place des Vosges (70x99cm-28x39in) s.

LABOULAYE, Paul de (19th C) French
£3642 $6374   (5-Apr-92 CSC.P76/R) Jeune femme en rouge (67x54cm-26x21in) s.d.1903
                      (F.FR 35000)

LABOUREUR, Jean Emile (1877-1943) French
£692 $1315   (25-Jun-92 GK.B419) Le diner chez le bistrot (15x14cm-6x6in) s.d.1923 pen
                      (S.FR 1800)
£692 $1315   (25-Jun-92 GK.B418) Les trois Pommes (11x13cm-4x5in) s.d.1921 pencil
                      (S.FR 1800)
£769 $1462   (25-Jun-92 GK.B417) La fenetre canadienne (16x20cm-6x8in) s.d.1914 indian
                      ink pen brush wash (S.FR 2000)
£846 $1608   (25-Jun-92 GK.B420) Adelaide, jeune Voisine, fait secher ses Vetements
                      chez Pierre Bazan (13x10cm-5x4in) s.i.d.1925 pencil col.pencil
                      (S.FR 2200)
£1385 $2631   (25-Jun-92 GK.B416) Cafedjy au Bazar de Smyrne (17x21cm-7x8in) s.i.d.1910
                      chl (S.FR 3600)

LABRADOR, Jose Maria (1890-?) Spanish
£1044 $1880   (20-Nov-91 DUR.M1003/R) Flores (80x100cm-31x39in) s. (S.P 190000)

LABRUZZI, Pietro (circle) (1739-1805) Italian
£6000 $10680   (30-Oct-91 S158/R) Portrait of gentleman. Portrait of lady
                      (94x70cm-37x28in) pair

LACAMERA, Fortunato (1887-1951) Argentinian
£1099 $2000   (11-Dec-91 RO.BA227) Vaso con flores (43x35cm-17x14in) s.
£1648 $3000   (11-Dec-91 RO.BA229) Composicion (34x49cm-13x19in) s.
£1860 $3200   (9-Oct-91 RO.BA201/R) Interior (38x28cm-15x11in) s.
£2604 $5000   (4-Aug-92 V.BA61) Paisaje (40x50cm-16x20in) 63
£2907 $5000   (9-Oct-91 RO.BA202/R) Naturaleza muerta (35x46cm-14x18in) s.i.
£3073 $5500   (6-May-92 V.BA58/R) Paisaje (30x40cm-12x16in)
£5376 $10000   (16-Jun-92 RO.BA34) Calle de la Boca (36x50cm-14x20in)
£6720 $12500   (16-Jun-92 RO.BA3) El patio de Victorica (50x35cm-20x14in)
£6989 $13000   (16-Jun-92 RO.BA26) Escena Boquense (35x50cm-14x20in)
£7184 $12500   (19-Sep-91 V.BA57/R) Composicion (50x70cm-20x28in)
£7267 $12500   (9-Oct-91 RO.BA200/R) Riachuelo en gris (50x71cm-20x28in) s.
£8140 $14000   (9-Oct-91 RO.BA34/R) La pagina blanca (50x70cm-20x28in) s.
£8602 $16000   (16-Jun-92 RO.BA33) Naturaleza muerta (50x60cm-20x24in)
£11047 $19000   (9-Oct-91 RO.BA34 b) Rincon de mi patio (96x70cm-38x28in) s. panel

LACASSE, Joseph (1894-1975) Belgian
£1250 $2150   (17-Oct-91 C9) Untitled (49x40cm-19x16in) s.d.1933 gouache oil

LACH, A (?) ?
£3400 $5882   (3-Oct-91 CSK130/R) A bird's nest and roses on a bank (33x43cm-13x17in)
                      s.

LACH, Andreas (1817-1882) Austrian
£1963 $3729   (25-Jun-92 D.V430/R) Alpine flowers (41x32cm-16x13in) s. panel
                      (A.S 40000)
£3996 $7193   (21-Nov-91 D.V119/R) Alpine flowers and view of Dachstein
                      (47x38cm-19x15in) s. (A.S 80000)
£1279 $2200   (15-Oct-91 CE.NY122/R) A cobblestone street and a winter path
                      (28x37cm-11x15in) s. W/C board

LACH, Fritz (1868-1933) Austrian
£687 $1305   (25-Jun-92 D.V555/R) Ennstal landscape (26x20cm-10x8in) s. W/C
                      (A.S 14000)
£1066 $1941   (27-May-92 D.V668/R) View of Badgastein (21x32cm-8x13in) s. pen indian
                      ink W/C (A.S 22000)
£1221 $2101   (10-Oct-91 D.V240) Muhlen in St Martin (20x29cm-8x11in) s.i.d.1912 W/C
                      (A.S 25000)

LACHAISE, Gaston (1882-1935) French
£2171 $3800   (26-Sep-91 CH.NY210/R) Egyptian dancer (58x46cm-23x18in) s. pencil

LACHIEZE-REY, Henri (20th C) French
£3086 $5864   (24-Jun-92 GL.P244 b/R) Les toits de Lyon (73x100cm-29x39in) s.d.60
                      (F.FR 30000)

LACHMAN, Harry (1886-1974) American/French
£1754 $3000   (12-Mar-92 CH.NY159/R) Hillside village in winter (48x61cm-19x24in)
                      s.d.14

LACOMBE, Pierre (20th C) French
£2518 $4481   (30-Oct-91 QWA.P32/R) La magicienne (22x27cm-9x11in) s. wood (F.FR 25000)
£2518 $4481   (30-Oct-91 QWA.P33/R) Le paradis retrouve (33x41cm-13x16in) s. wood
                      (F.FR 25000)

LACOUR, Simone (1926-) Belgian
£733 $1261   (12-Oct-91 KV.L177/R) Plumes de Venise (81x54cm-32x21in) s.i.
                      (B.FR 44000)

LACOUTURE, H (19th C) French
£1132 $2048   (4-Dec-91 LD.P66/R) L'avocate libertine et le geai (30x15cm-12x6in)
       s.d.90 gold sheet on panel (F.FR 11000)

LACROIX DE MARSEILLE (18/19th C) French
£6354 $11500   (22-May-92 SY.NY159/R) Waterfall landscape with two women and two men
       fishing, castle beyond (56x81cm-22x32in)

LACROIX DE MARSEILLE (style) (18/19th C) French
£3371 $5899   (24-Feb-92 ARC.P73/R) Scenes de peche et de bateaux dans un port
       (248x120cm-98x47in) (F.FR 33000)

LACROIX DE MARSEILLE, Charles Francois (1720-c.1782) French
£3906 $6914   (5-Nov-91 GF.L2087/R) Rocky coastal landscape (55x80cm-22x31in)
       (S.FR 10000)
£7200 $12600   (31-Mar-92 PH21/R) Coastal landscape with fishermen and woman with child
       in arms (28x42cm-11x17in)
£13374 $25412   (26-Jun-92 AT.P28/R) Naufrage sur la cote mediterraneenne
       (123x175cm-48x69in) (F.FR 130000)
£15213 $26775   (10-Apr-92 AT.P54/R) Pecheurs pres d'une cote mediterraneenne
       (23x31cm-9x12in) s.d. copper (F.FR 150000)
£19000 $34580   (10-Dec-91 PH48/R) Fishermen launching craft within Mediterranean harbour
       (46x62cm-18x24in) s.d.1760
£19547 $35381   (5-Dec-91 SY.MO173/R) Marines (24x31cm-9x12in) s.d.1760 pair
       (F.FR 190000)
£19757 $35760   (22-May-92 LD.P73/R) Baigneuses sur le bord de la mer (106x148cm-42x58in)
       s.d.1774 (F.FR 195000)
£35000 $62300   (30-Oct-91 S200/R) Mediterranean harbour scene at sunset
       (36x47cm-14x19in) s.d.1772 copper
£1272   *$2327*   *(15-May-92 AT.P154) Deux vues de port (12x18cm-5x7in) one s.d.1757 pen*
       wash pair (F.FR 12500)

LACROIX DE MARSEILLE, Charles Francois (attrib) (1720-c.1782) French
£2484 $4247   (18-Mar-92 D.V262/R) Southern coastal landscape with figures angling
       (20x41cm-8x16in) panel (A.S 50000)

LACROIX DE MARSEILLE, Charles Francois (circle) (1720-c.1782) French
£4144 $7500   (21-May-92 CH.NY215/R) Fisherfolk and washerwoman on riverbank, view of
       Tivoli beyond (39x60cm-15x24in)

LACROIX DE MARSEILLE, Charles Francois (style) (1720-c.1782) French
£850 $1513   (29-Oct-91 PH2) A Mediterranean coast scene (24x29cm-9x11in) panel
£1500 $2880   (9-Jul-92 CSK273/R) Coastal landscape with anglers on rocks by waterfall
       (71x91cm-28x36in)

LACROIX, Eugene (19th C) ?
£1117 $2000   (14-Nov-91 CE.NY191) Hanging fruit (46x35cm-18x14in) s.d.63

LACROIX, H (19th C) ?
£604 $1100   (13-Dec-91 S.W1421) Clamdiggers (66x53cm-26x21in) s.

LACROIX, Paul (fl.1858-1869) French?
£7989 $14300   (14-Nov-91 GRO.B107/R) Nature's bounty (76x64cm-30x25in) s.i.d.62

LACY, C J de (fl.1885-1918) British
£560   *$969*   *(6-Sep-91 BW413) River Thames off Chelsea with barges in foreground*
       (20x46cm-8x18in) s. W/C

LADAS, Anneliese (1941-) German
£619 $1076   (17-Sep-91 FN.S2411) Chiemsee landscape with peasant family harvesting
       (30x60cm-12x24in) s. panel (DM 1800)

LADBROOKE, John Berney (1803-1879) British
£1400 $2520   (30-Jan-92 TL68/R) Cottage on Mousehold heath (32x24cm-13x9in) board pair
£3200 $5504   (11-Oct-91 K519/R) Travelling fish monger, boy with ponies in wooded
       landscape near cottage (58x71cm-23x28in) mono. i.verso
£5500 $10505   (15-Jul-92 S72/R) Lane near Norwich (76x101cm-30x40in)

LADBROOKE, John Berney (attrib) (1803-1879) British
£1100 $2068   (19-Dec-91 C160/R) Wayside chat (76x63cm-30x25in) bears indist.sig.

LADBROOKE, John Berney (circle) (1803-1879) British
£800 $1528   (15-Jul-92 S202/R) Farmhouse and cattle watering in landscape
       (26x35cm-10x14in) panel

LADBROOKE, Robert (attrib) (1770-1842) British
£800 $1424   (28-Apr-92 PH82/R) Cattle and figures before farmstead, landscape beyond
       (59x74cm-23x29in)

LADDAGA, Angel (1911-) Argentinian
£674 $1200   (1-Nov-91 PO.BA69) Pasado amoroso (37x48cm-15x19in) s.d.1973 hardboard

LADELL, Edward (1821-1886) British
£3000 $5310   (6-Nov-91 S105/R) Still life of fruit and flowers in basket
       (20x26cm-8x10in) mono. panel

LADELL, Edward (1821-1886) British-cont.
£5495	$10000	(28-May-92 SY.NY301/R) Still life with Rhenish Westerwald jug (69x58cm-27x23in) mono.
£16500	$30525	(12-Jun-92 C189/R) Grapes, peaches, plums, pear and glass of wine with Red Admiral (35x30cm-14x12in) mono.
£19000	$32300	(25-Oct-91 C70/R) Grapes, plums and other fruit with glass of wine on wooden ledge (43x35cm-17x14in) mono
£21802	$37500	(17-Oct-91 SY.NY77/R) Still life with fruit and game, landscape beyond (138x124cm-54x49in) mono.
£25000	$44500	(28-Apr-92 PH36/R) Still life with fruit, glass of wine and ivory casket (43x35cm-17x14in) mono.

LADELL, Edward (circle) (1821-1886) British
| £1400 | $2408 | (4-Mar-92 S98/R) Still life of fruit with flagon and shell (75x61cm-30x24in) |

LADELL, Ellen (19th C) British
| £1600 | $2720 | (22-Oct-91 SWS312/R) Still life with chrysanthemums, roses, nest, stuffed birds under bell jar on marble ledge (44x34cm-17x13in) s. |
| £2600 | $4472 | (4-Mar-92 S94/R) Still life of birds, fruit, roses and bird's nest (46x35cm-18x14in) s. |

LAER, Alexander T van (1857-?) American
| £585 | $1000 | (13-Mar-92 S.BM223/R) Autumnal fields (56x91cm-22x36in) s. |
| £765 | $1400 | (9-Feb-92 LIT.L234) Elms, Catlin's Meadows, Litchfield, Ct (107x89cm-42x35in) s. |

LAER, Pieter van (c.1582-c.1642) Dutch
| £13692 | $24097 | (10-Apr-92 AGS.P15/R) Bergers gardant leurs troupeaux (37x49cm-15x19in) i.verso pair (F.FR 135000) |

LAER, Pieter van (attrib) (c.1582-c.1642) Dutch
| £3168 | $5766 | (28-May-92 F.M9) Scena di bivacco (51x41cm-20x16in) (I.L 7000000) |

LAER, Pieter van (circle) (c.1582-c.1642) Dutch
| £3591 | $6500 | (22-May-92 SY.NY156/R) Peasants dancing and making merry in Italianate landscape (49x65cm-19x26in) |
| £17956 | $32500 | (22-May-92 SY.NY82 a/R) Necromancer threatened (70x93cm-28x37in) |

LAESSOE, T (1816-1898) Danish
| £660 | $1109 | (27-Aug-91 RAS.K410) View of the Bay of Naples (24x31cm-9x12in) (D.KR 7500) |

LAESSOE, Thorald (1816-1898) Danish
£718	$1271	(11-Feb-92 RAS.K109) View from Arricia (20x23cm-8x9in) (D.KR 8000)
£1013	$1793	(23-Apr-92 RAS.V841/R) View of the Campagna and Ponte Nomentane and Monte-Sacer (46x64cm-18x25in) s. (D.KR 11500)
£1488	$2692	(3-Dec-91 AB.S4724/R) The Roman Campagna (66x97cm-26x38in) s.i.d.1853 (S.KR 15500)
£2197	$3932	(6-May-92 KH.K129/R) Near Karlsbrucke in Prague with St. Nicolas church (31x22cm-12x9in) s.d.1843 (D.KR 25000)
£2800	$5068	(22-May-92 C25/R) Villa Borghese, Rome (38x57cm-15x22in)

LAESSOE, Thorald (attrib) (1816-1878) Danish
| £1242 | $2273 | (5-Feb-92 KH.K83/R) View of the Bay of Naples towards Vesuvius (44x69cm-17x27in) (D.KR 13800) |

LAEZZA, Giuseppe (?-1905) Italian
| £7369 | $13412 | (12-Dec-91 F.M83/R) Marina con figure (52x93cm-20x37in) s.d.1887 (I.L 16000000) |
| £10998 | $19466 | (7-Nov-91 F.M77/R) Marina con pescatori (52x93cm-20x37in) s.d.1887 (I.L 24000000) |

LAFAGE, Raymond (1656-1690) French
£400	$728	(11-Dec-91 PH174/R) Virtue slaying Evil. Venus conquering Time (15x19cm-6x7in) i. pen wash
£650	$1183	(11-Dec-91 PH69/R) Battle engagement outside city walls (19x28cm-7x11in) s. pen wash chk
£700	$1274	(11-Dec-91 PH74/R) The Rape of the Sabine Women. Sketches of figures and children (39x28cm-15x11in) i. pen over chk double-sided

LAFARGE, John (1835-1910) American
£14365	$26000	(5-Dec-91 SY.NY29/R) Camellia in Japanese bowl (15x22cm-6x9in) panel
£1143	$2000	(26-Sep-91 CH.NY219/R) Virgil-study for Class of 1880 Memorial window, Harvard University (27x10cm-11x4in) s.i.d.1882 pencil chl
£1628	$2800	(13-Oct-91 H.C12/R) Head of Christ (33x25cm-13x10in) chl pencil
£1923	$3500	(28-May-92 CH.NY90/R) Study for St Elizabeth (16x9cm-6x4in) s.d.1883 gouache W/C paper on board
£2286	$4000	(26-Sep-91 CH.NY67/R) Moonlight over snow - study from nature (14x9cm-6x4in) W/C
£2880	$5500	(3-Jul-92 S.W3098/R) Great Pali (20x36cm-8x14in) i. W/C
£4094	$7000	(12-Mar-92 CH.NY90/R) Adoring angel, study for Ascension mural (70x52cm-28x20in) s.i.d.87 W/C gouache pencil
£4192	$7000	(20-Aug-91 RB.HY121/R) Song of the Siren (23x13cm-9x5in) W/C

LAFARGE, John (1835-1910) American-cont.
£4571 $8000   (26-Sep-91 CH.NY68/R) Apple blossoms and butterfly (12x12cm-5x5in) W/C
                  paper on board painted circle
£9392 $17000   (6-Dec-91 CH.NY132/R) The harpist (31x26cm-12x10in) W/C gouache pencil
                  painted arch
£13812 $25000   (5-Dec-91 SY.NY28/R) Crater of Kilauea, sunrise (19x36cm-7x14in) i.d.1890
                  W/C gouache

LAFITE, Carl (1830-1900) Austrian
£1249 $2248   (21-Nov-91 D.V156/R) View of Berchtesgaden and Watzmann (21x30cm-8x12in)
                  s. i.verso paper on board (A.S 25000)

LAFITTE, Charles (?) ?
£1800 $3204   (28-Nov-91 CSK177) Elegant figures promenading on the coast
                  (31x52cm-12x20in) s. pair

LAFON, Francois (19th C) French
£1029 $1800   (18-Feb-92 CE.NY164) Cupid's touch (34x27cm-13x11in) s.d.1886 panel
£1738 $3093   (28-Nov-91 D.V3/R) Women bathing in castle park (60x73cm-24x29in) s.
                  (A.S 35000)

LAFON, Henri (19th C) French
£2747 $5000   (26-May-92 CE.NY103/R) Reading. A sip of tea (25x20cm-10x8in) s.d.1852
                  panel pair

LAFON, Wyatt (19th C) ?
£814 $1489   (15-May-92 AT.P156) La Glaneuse (40x29cm-16x11in) s.d.1884 pastel
                  (F.FR 8000)

LAFORET, Eugene (19/20th C) ?
£872 $1500   (16-Oct-91 D.NY65) Gondalas on the Grand Canal (41x51cm-16x20in) s.

LAFORGUE, Alexander de (1878-?) German
£893 $1573   (11-Apr-92 AW.H1833/R) Goats in high mountains and thunderstorm rising
                  (79x124cm-31x49in) s.i.d.1905 (DM 2600)

LAFOSSE, Charles de (1636-1716) French
£8287 $15000   (21-May-92 CH.NY120/R) God the Father supported by angels and surrounded
                  by symbols of Evangelists (82x63cm-32x25in) paper on canvas
£2100 $3654   (13-Apr-92 S201/R) Design for pendentive - St. Luke with ox and figure,
                  among clouds (28x48cm-11x19in) bears i. pen col.chk

LAFOSSE, Charles de (circle) (1636-1716) French
£4119 $7745   (18-Dec-91 AT.P186/R) Joseph et la femme de Putiphar (76x64cm-30x25in)
                  (F.FR 40000)

LAFRENSEN, Nicolas (elder-attrib) (1698-1756) Swedish
£5218 $9549   (14-May-92 BU.S92/R) Portrait of Gustav III as a child (19x13cm-7x5in)
                  gouache (S.KR 55000)

LAFRENSEN, Nicolas (younger) (1737-1807) Swedish
£5525 $10000   (22-May-92 SY.NY37/R) Elegant ladies in park, with young boy meeting two
                  commedia dell'arte figures (27x23cm-11x9in) panel
£720 $1303   (5-Dec-91 SY.MO21/R) Jeunes elegants prenant le the (26x20cm-10x8in) pen
                  wash blk.chk. (F.FR 7000)

LAGAGE, Pierre (1911-1977) French
£1703 $3082   (19-May-92 AB.S5266/R) Femme au citron (72x59cm-28x23in) s. (S.KR 18000)
£4028 $6848   (27-Oct-91 P.V11/R) Composition (81x65cm-32x26in) s.d.Nov.55 (F.FR 40000)
£5144 $9774   (26-Jun-92 FB.P30/R) Braga (130x95cm-51x37in) s.d.61 (F.FR 50000)

LAGAR, Celso (1891-1966) Spanish
£861 $1559   (18-May-92 AT.P118) Port sous la neige (26x35cm-10x14in) studio st. board
                  (F.FR 8500)
£941 $1674   (26-Jan-92 FE.P210) L'Eglise (54x65cm-21x26in) s. (F.FR 9200)
£1230 $2251   (13-May-92 FER.M174/R) Entrando a picar (22x27cm-9x11in) s. (S.P 225000)
£3434 $6079   (24-Apr-92 CN.P179) Bord de mer (53x72cm-21x28in) s. (F.FR 34000)
£3543 $6200   (27-Feb-92 CE.NY62/R) Clown avec son chien (46x38cm-18x15in) s.
£3553 $6040   (22-Oct-91 DUR.M72/R) Bodegon (38x56cm-15x22in) s. (S.P 650000)
£3955 $7000   (5-Nov-91 CE.NY187/R) Circus performers (34x41cm-13x16in) s.
£4800 $8688   (2-Dec-91 CSK129/R) Village aux pyrenees (60x72cm-24x28in) s.
£6096 $10668   (18-Feb-92 DUR.M31/R) Gente de circo (34x41cm-13x16in) s. (S.P 1100000)
£8199 $13938   (22-Oct-91 DUR.M73/R) Puerto (46x55cm-18x22in) s. (S.P 1500000)
£8500 $15385   (2-Dec-91 CSK130/R) Cirque Forain (39x40cm-15x16in) s. board
£9244 $16455   (28-Apr-92 EP.M1/R) Le Pont Neuf (61x73cm-24x29in) s. (S.P 1700000)
£21000 $38010   (2-Dec-91 CSK127/R) L'ecuyere (97x124cm-38x49in) s. s.d.1943verso
£495 $871   (9-Apr-92 ANS.M84/R) Desnudo sentado (26x20cm-10x8in) s. W/C chl
                  (S.P 90000)
£831 $1471   (12-Feb-92 ANS.M29/R) Desnudo sentado (26x20cm-10x8in) s. W/C chl
                  (S.P 150000)
£1016 $1768   (19-Apr-92 ZZ.F132/R) Nature morte a la coupe de fruits (17x22cm-7x9in)
                  s. oil ink (F.FR 10000)
£1101 $1971   (14-Nov-91 ANS.M55/R) Desnudo sentado (26x20cm-10x8in) s. W/C chl
                  (S.P 200000)

LAGAR, Celso (1891-1966) Spanish-cont.

£1500	$2715	(2-Dec-91 CSK132/R) Clown se Maquillant (34x28cm-13x11in) s. W/C gouache pencil
£1937	$3312	(17-Mar-92 FER.M195/R) La troupe (31x41cm-12x16in) s. gouache (S.P 350000)
£2049	$3689	(2-Feb-92 ZZ.F266/R) Le cirque (44x33cm-17x13in) s. gouache (F.FR 20000)
£2200	$3982	(2-Dec-91 CSK131/R) Deux clowns (21x27cm-8x11in) s. gouache pencil pen paper on card
£2260	$4000	(5-Nov-91 CE.NY92/R) Circus performers (44x34cm-17x13in) s. gouache pencil pen paper on board
£2400	$4200	(27-Feb-92 CE.NY66/R) Au cirque (32x42cm-13x17in) s. oil ink
£3784	$7000	(12-Jun-92 SY.NY56/R) Marseille bordello with monkey (49x62cm-19x24in) s.i. W/C gouache Indian ink pencil chl

LAGARDE, A G (19th C) ?

| £1517 | $2700 | (22-Jan-92 SY.NY431/R) Still life of roses with butterfly and bee (42x27cm-17x11in) s.d. panel |

LAGATTA, John (1894-1977) American

| £787 | $1400 | (2-Nov-91 IH.NY65/R) Couple in formal attire (56x38cm-22x15in) s. chl |

LAGAZE, Pierre (1816-1884) German

| £556 | $1006 | (19-May-92 GF.L2468/R) The secret admirer (56x46cm-22x18in) s.d.1877 panel (S.FR 1500) |

LAGERHOLM, Wilhelmina (1826-1917) Swedish

| £566 | $1002 | (5-Nov-91 BA.S109/R) Evening prayer (55x45cm-22x18in) s.i.d.1859 (S.KR 6000) |

LAGERSTAM, Berndt (1868-1930) Finnish

| £541 | $984 | (11-Dec-91 HOR.H56) Wooded path (51x64cm-20x25in) s. (F.M 4200) |

LAGLENNE, Jean Francis (1899-1962) French

| £615 | $1100 | (6-May-92 D.NY112/R) Tulipe et Asphodele (46x38cm-18x15in) s. i.verso |

LAGNEAU (16/17th C) French

| £1200 | $2184 | (11-Dec-91 PH102/R) Portrait of lady in linen head-dress (23x18cm-9x7in) chk. |
| £1397 | $2500 | (14-Jan-92 SY.NY23/R) Portrait of scholar, wearing hat, in profile (24x17cm-9x7in) black red chk htd white yellow stumping |

LAGNEAU, Nicolas (16/17th C) French

| £7000 | $13440 | (7-Jul-92 C44/R) Portrait of bearded man (42x29cm-17x11in) chk wash |

LAGOOR, Jan van (17th C) Dutch

£1900	$3648	(7-Jul-92 PH102/R) Interior with peasants playing cards at table (30x26cm-12x10in) s. panel
£2500	$4800	(7-Jul-92 PH168/R) Rest on flight into Egypt (24x31cm-9x12in) indist.s. panel
£2736	$5006	(12-May-92 SY.AM29/R) Nymphs bathing in pool and spied by satyrs (27x38cm-11x15in) (D.FL 9000)
£3726	$6371	(18-Mar-92 D.V390/R) Wooded river landscape with rowing boat and traveller (55x43cm-22x17in) panel (A.S 75000)

LAGOOR, Jan van (attrib) (17th C) Dutch

| £4000 | $7280 | (13-Dec-91 C203/R) Peasant in landscape with cottage among trees beyond (29x37cm-11x15in) panel |

LAGORIO, Lev Feliksovich (1827-1905) Russian

£524	$1000	(16-Jul-92 SY.NY461/R) Along the Crimean coast (24x28cm-9x11in) s.d.1888 canvas on board
£524	$1000	(16-Jul-92 SY.NY459/R) Kavkas landscape (24x30cm-9x12in) s.d.1889 canvas on board
£949	$1736	(14-May-92 BU.S191/R) Coastal landscape with vessel at anchor (38x65cm-15x26in) s.d.1901 (S.KR 10000)
£1214	$2160	(29-Apr-92 D.V831/R) Rocky coastal landscape with shipwreck and figures (24x36cm-9x14in) s.i.d.1895 (A.S 25000)

LAGRANGE, Jacques (1917-) French

| £624 | $1093 | (5-Apr-92 R.P208) Les jardiniers dans les arbres (34x48cm-13x19in) s.d.57verso (F.FR 6000) |
| £708 | $1238 | (5-Apr-92 R.P129) Carnaval combat (52x66cm-20x26in) s. W/C (F.FR 6800) |

LAGRENEE, Anthelme Francois (1774-1832) French

| £1111 | $2011 | (21-May-92 SY.G35/R) Portrait of General J E D Perruquet de Montrichard (9x?cm-4x?in) min.s. stamped gilt metal frame (S.FR 3000) |

LAGRENEE, Jean Jacques (1739-1821) French

£1943	$3400	(18-Feb-92 CE.NY26/R) Young girl with doll (61x49cm-24x19in) s. canvas on board
£16760	$30000	(17-Jan-92 SY.NY57/R) Minerva and Apollo crowning the arts (67x135cm-26x53in) s.d.1773 pair
£1600	$3072	(7-Jul-92 C241/R) Rinaldo abandoning Armida (33x45cm-13x18in) i. chk pen wash htd white

LAGRENEE, Jean Jacques (attrib) (1739-1821) French
£514 $873   (25-Oct-91 AT.P97) Le Sacrifice d'Abraham (28x23cm-11x9in) panel
                          (F.FR 5100)

LAGRENEE, Jean Jacques (circle) (1739-1821) French
£471 $900   *(16-Jul-92 SY.NY5/R) King David sacrificing at an altar*
                          (68x100cm-27x39in) i.verso pen wash

LAGRENEE, Louis Jean Francois (1725-1805) French
£6145 $11000   (17-Jan-92 SY.NY148/R) Cupid and Psyche (47x38cm-19x15in) s.d.1778 oval
£30864 $55864   (7-Dec-91 CH.MO44/R) L'architecture. L'Inspiration poetique
                          (87x73cm-34x29in) s.d.1774 oval pair (F.FR 300000)
£36623 $65554   (17-Nov-91 LT.P7/R) La lettre d'amour (52x64cm-20x25in) s. panel
                          (F.FR 360000)

LAGUNA Y PEREZ, Jose (19th C) Spanish
£1385 $2424   (18-Feb-92 DUR.M17/R) Discusion filosofica en un patio de la Alhambra
                          (26x20cm-10x8in) s.d.1871 (S.P 250000)

LAHARRAGUE, Carlos (20th C) Spanish
£829 $1559   (17-Dec-91 DUR.M94/R) Rincon madrileno (50x65cm-20x26in) s.d.1982
                          (S.P 150000)

LAHEY, Frances Vida (20th C) Australian
£1532 $2711   (26-Apr-92 SY.ME406) Bathers (14x18cm-6x7in) s. canvas on board
                          (A.D 3600)
£940   *$1674*   *(27-Apr-92 J.M65/R) Wattle blossom (47x40cm-19x16in) s. W/C (A.D 2200)*
£3084   *$5551*   *(24-Nov-91 SY.S328/R) Indian rug (54x64cm-21x25in) s.d.1935 W/C*
                          (A.D 7000)

LAHNER, Emile (1893-1980) French
£512 $922   (2-Feb-92 ZZ.F224/R) Paysage de Vallauris (55x46cm-22x18in) s.
                          (F.FR 5000)

LAHS, Curt (1893-1958) German
£684   *$1232*   *(23-Nov-91 N.M181/R) Abstract (48x62cm-19x24in) s. ochre ck (DM 1950)*
£1536   *$2795*   *(25-May-92 WK.M760/R) Abstract composition (63x47cm-25x19in) s.d.1953 oil*
                          pastel gouache (DM 4500)

LAHUERTA, G (20th C) Spanish
£997 $1725   (26-Mar-92 DUR.M1033/R) Masias levantinos (17x25cm-7x10in) s. canvas laid
                          down on board (S.P 180000)

LAI FONG (fl.1890-1910) Chinese
£950 $1691   (1-May-92 PHE85) Three masted sailing ship Woolton (43x59cm-17x23in)
                          s.i.d.1892

LAIDLAW, Nicol (1886-?) British
£550 $995   (5-Dec-91 CG174/R) Knight of the Revel (102x76cm-40x30in) s.d.1926

L'AIN, Girod de (?) ?
£578 $1000   (25-Mar-92 D.NY28) Harmonie jaune (117x81cm-46x32in) s. i.verso

LAINE, Olavi (1922-) Finnish
£507 $887   (25-Sep-91 HOR.H58) Mother and child (81x65cm-32x26in) s. (F.M 3600)
£521 $912   (25-Sep-91 HOR.H59) Returning home (81x65cm-32x26in) s. (F.M 3700)

LAING, James Garden (1852-1915) British
£520   *$931*   *(13-Nov-91 CG608/R) Pull's ferry, Norwich (42x53cm-17x21in) s.d.89 W/C*
                          htd.bodycol.
£600   *$1086*   *(5-Dec-91 CG1/R) Square in Granada (13x23cm-5x9in) s.i.d.92 s.i.verso W/C*

LAING, Tomson (fl.1890-1904) British
£600 $1068   (28-Apr-92 S154/R) Highland cattle (30x46cm-12x18in) s.indist.d
£900 $1602   (28-Apr-92 S203/R) Ploughing (38x53cm-15x21in) s. canvas laid down on
                          board

LAING, William Wardlaw (fl.1873-98) British
£1000   *$1790*   *(5-May-92 SWS118/R) The bird's nest (84x58cm-33x23in) s.i.stretcher W/C*
                          htd bodycol.

LAIRESSE, Gerard de (1641-1711) Flemish
£1748 $2990   (18-Mar-92 N.M436/R) Murder of bishop saint, possibly St Lambert
                          (124x93cm-49x37in) mono. i.verso (DM 5000)
£7263 $13000   (17-Jan-92 SY.NY117/R) Queen Esther accusing Haman in the presence of
                          Ahasuerus (94x130cm-37x51in)
£8629 $15532   (23-Nov-91 SO.S562/R) Interior with figures (146x176cm-57x69in)
                          (S.KR 90000)
£66860 $115000   (9-Oct-91 CH.NY195/R) Merucry ordering Calypso to release Ulysses
                          (91x114cm-36x45in)
£932   *$1658*   *(25-Nov-91 CH.AM92/R) The Golden Age, Aetas Aurea (29x35cm-11x14in) chk*
                          wash two joined sheets (D.FL 3000)

LAIRESSE, Gerard de (after) (1641-1711) Flemish
£1087 $1870   (7-Mar-92 CH.AM249/R) Finding of Erichthonius (109x86cm-43x34in) with
       sig. canvas on board (D.FL 3500)

LAIRESSE, Gerard de (circle) (1641-1711) Flemish
£2762 $5000   (21-May-92 CH.NY196/R) Triumph of Bacchus (95x138cm-37x54in)

LAIRESSE, Gerard de (style) (1641-1711) Flemish
£1474 $2564   (13-Apr-92 AT.P81) Narcisse (59x78cm-23x31in) panel (F.FR 14500)

LAIRESSE, Jan (1674-?) Dutch
£1100 $1958   (29-Oct-91 PH32) The sacrifice of Iphigenia (58x71cm-23x28in)

LAISSEMENT, Henri Adolphe (?-1921) French
£1100 $1947   (13-Feb-92 CSK206/R) Chez le Notare (22x23cm-9x9in) s. panel
£1900 $3439   (22-May-92 C159/R) Pinch of snuff (26x20cm-10x8in) s.d.1891 panel
£5000 $8750   (20-Feb-92 SY.NY155/R) Good book (41x29cm-16x11in) s. cradled panel
£7000 $12110   (4-Oct-91 C51/R) Word from on high (62x56cm-24x22in) s. panel

LAITILA, Atte (1893-1972) Finnish
£931 $1658   (1-Dec-91 HOR.H136) Still life (54x65cm-21x26in) s.d.1946 (F.M 7200)

LAJOUE, Jacques de (1687-1761) French
£41195 $77446   (18-Dec-91 AT.P60/R) Paysage avec en obelisque (78x119cm-31x47in)
       (F.FR 400000)

LAJOUE, Jacques de (school) (1687-1761) French
£1424 $2549   (15-Nov-91 SD.P13) Trois enfants en barque sur un bassin pres d'une
       fontaine (65x95cm-26x37in) (F.FR 14000)

LALAUME-DUPRE, Andre see   LAUME-DUPRE, Andre la

LAKHOVSKY, Arnold Borisovich (1880-1937) Russian
£1900 $3534   (16-Jun-92 S66/R) Russian provincial town in winter (61x50cm-24x20in) s.

LALAUZE, Alphonse (1872-?) French
£730 $1300   (22-Jan-92 SY.NY400/R) Lancetre (114x89cm-45x35in) s.d.1902

LALLEMAND, Jean Baptiste (1710-1805) French
£22657 $42595   (16-Dec-91 AGS.P57/R) Le concert dans le parc (61x81cm-24x32in)
       (F.FR 220000)
£450 $819   (10-Dec-91 C213) Peasants on a track before a ruined structure
       (25x39cm-10x15in) W/C
£1100 $1914   (13-Apr-92 S360/R) Architectural fantasy with triumphal arch
       (38x52cm-15x20in) pen wash htd gouache over black red chk
£5301 $9859   (20-Jun-92 CH.MO273/R) Une vue du Forum, Rome, avec la Statue d'Apollon
       Citharedos sur la gauche (37x45cm-15x18in) s. black chk gouache
       (F.FR 52000)
£5879 $10289   (3-Apr-92 AGS.P145) Jardin Italien avec des ruines antiques
       (34x47cm-13x19in) s. gouache (F.FR 56500)

LALLEMAND, Jean Baptiste (attrib) (1710-1805) French
£3058 $5688   (20-Jun-92 CH.MO64/R) Couples pres d'une fontaine (46x56cm-18x22in)
       (F.FR 30000)
£3911 $7000   (16-Jan-92 CH.NY97/R) Two women amongst ruins resting on stone beside
       antique urn (41x33cm-16x13in) painted oval
£4800 $8544   (30-Oct-91 S129/R) Capriccio landscape with the Temple of Vesta and other
       classical ruins (76x122cm-30x48in)

LALLEMAND, Jean Baptiste (circle) (1710-1805) French
£2762 $5000   (21-May-92 CH.NY249/R) Capriccio of Colosseum, Trajan's Column, Pyramid
       and Arch of Constantine and figures to fore (114x92cm-45x36in)

LAM QUA (studio) (19th C) Oriental
£2000 $3400   (23-Oct-91 S348/R) The Praya Grande, Macao (27x43cm-11x17in)

LAM, Wilfredo (1902-1982) Cuban
£8763 $15160   (29-Mar-92 P.V67/R) La fuite de l'ame (35x45cm-14x18in) s.d.1975
       (F.FR 85000)
£10299 $17611   (22-Mar-92 I.N47/R) Sans titre (45x35cm-18x14in) s. (F.FR 100000)
£13796 $24695   (14-Nov-91 F.M112/R) Totem (46x38cm-18x15in) s.d.1970 s.d.verso
       (I.L 30000000)
£14829 $26395   (26-Nov-91 SY.MI208/R) Composizione (50x60cm-20x24in) s.d.1970 s.d.verso
       (I.L 32000000)
£23642 $40664   (8-Oct-91 CC.P33/R) Le bien habille (92x72cm-36x28in) s.d.1968
       (F.FR 235000)
£38889 $70000   (19-Nov-91 CH.NY50/R) Figuras caribenas (75x49cm-30x19in) s.
£60773 $110000   (18-May-92 CH.NY36/R) Untitled (63x79cm-25x31in) s. paper on board
£83333 $150000   (18-Nov-91 SY.NY41/R) Figure (127x110cm-50x43in) s.d.1961
£98333 $177000   (19-Nov-91 CH.NY42/R) Foret (55x46cm-22x18in)
£165746 $300000   (18-May-92 CH.NY12/R) La Serre - el Invernadero (85x107cm-33x42in)
       s.d.1944 linen
£1601 $2786   (17-Sep-91 RAS.K84/R) Oiseaux fabuleux (28x42cm-11x17in) s. collage paper
       cut out felt-tip pen (D.KR 18000)
£2073 $3772   (9-Dec-91 CH.R26/R) Totem (48x33cm-19x13in) s.d.1974 pastel (I.L 4500000)

LAM, Wilfredo (1902-1982) Cuban-cont.

£2285	$4342	(23-Jun-92 F.M88) Totem (69x49cm-27x19in) s.d.1970 pastel cardboard (I.L 5000000)
£3659	$6366	(14-Apr-92 CSC.P45/R) Oiseau (35x34cm-14x13in) s.d.1977 pastel (F.FR 36000)
£5767	$9862	(19-Mar-92 CSC.P27/R) Totem (62x47cm-24x19in) s.d.1970 pastel (F.FR 56000)
£6392	$11058	(29-Mar-92 P.V66/R) Untitled (56x75cm-22x30in) s. pastel (F.FR 62000)
£7992	$14385	(2-Feb-92 CSC.P101/R) Totem (74x55cm-29x22in) s. pastel chl. (F.FR 78000)
£8333	$15000	(19-Nov-91 CH.NY137/R) Diablo (73x51cm-29x20in) s.d.1947 chl
£9945	$18000	(18-May-92 CH.NY77/R) Femme cheval (73x56cm-29x22in) s. s.d.1970 verso pastel
£13889	$25000	(18-Nov-91 SY.NY113/R) Untitled (64x48cm-25x19in) s.d.1965 gouache
£15353	$27329	(30-Nov-91 FB.P20/R) Sans titre (66x48cm-26x19in) s. pasterl paper laid down on canvas (F.FR 150000)
£27778	$50000	(19-Nov-91 CH.NY19/R) Autoretrato (90x63cm-35x25in) gouache W/C paper on canvas
£38889	$70000	(19-Nov-91 CH.NY20/R) Dos figuras (90x121cm-35x48in) gouache W/C paper on canvas
£47222	$85000	(19-Nov-91 CH.NY11/R) Femme cheval (89x64cm-35x25in) s.d.1947 gouache

LAMA, Giulia (1681-1747) Italian

| £13812 | $25000 | (22-May-92 SY.NY136/R) Girl holding trumpet (52x42cm-20x17in) |

LAMA, Giulia (attrib) (1681-1747) Italian

| £843 | $1500 | (30-Oct-91 D.NY67) Courtesan and old woman (51x64cm-20x25in) |

LAMB, Charles Vincent (1893-1965) Irish

£888	$1536	(25-Mar-92 A.D76) Landscape with cottage, Carraroe (25x36cm-10x14in) s. board (E.P 950)
£950	$1644	(24-Mar-92 CG793) Road among hills, Connemara (27x39cm-11x15in) s. board
£1182	$2045	(2-Oct-91 A.D192) Connemara coastal landscape (25x33cm-10x13in) bears sig. board (E.P 1300)
£1308	$2264	(25-Mar-92 A.D19) Carraroe Cottage (25x33cm-10x13in) s. board (E.P 1400)
£1400	$2436	(18-Sep-91 CG119) Sketch for bringing home Seaweed (16x21cm-6x8in) s. i.verso board
£2222	$4044	(11-Dec-91 A.D134/R) Colin - the Head of Connemara (38x30cm-15x12in) s. (E.P 2400)
£2336	$4042	(25-Mar-92 A.D120) Figures on the beach (53x38cm-21x15in) s. board (E.P 2500)
£5200	$9048	(18-Sep-91 CG192/R) Figures on quay, Carraroe (27x35cm-11x14in) s. panel

LAMB, F Mortimer (1861-1936) American

£528	$950	(22-Nov-91 S.BM118/R) Autumn landscape (46x53cm-18x21in) s. paperboard
£628	$1200	(19-Jul-92 JRB.C263/R) Winter landscape (33x48cm-13x19in) s. board
£833	$1500	(22-Nov-91 S.BM159/R) Still life with mixwed flowers (76x64cm-30x25in) s.
£479	$800	(20-Aug-91 RB.HY104/R) Winter landscape - The Blue Hills near Boston (48x66cm-19x26in) s.

LAMB, Henry (1883-1960) British

£800	$1528	(23-Jul-92 CSK22/R) Portrait of Dr Buchanan (77x56cm-30x22in) s.d.46
£855	$1521	(27-Apr-92 J.M308) Gathering hay (28x23cm-11x9in) s. board (A.D 2000)
£2200	$3894	(7-Nov-91 C32/R) Family group (48x59cm-19x23in) canvasboard
£2500	$4300	(6-Mar-92 C78/R) Brittany landscape (44x59cm-17x23in) s.d.38 canvas on board
£6800	$12240	(20-Nov-91 S171/R) Landscape in Westmeath (51x61cm-20x24in) s.d.34 canvas on board

LAMB, Oscar Hermann (1876-1947) Austrian

| £534 | $950 | (28-Apr-92 D.V172/R) Evening in Venice (60x45cm-24x18in) s.d.1921 W/C gouache (A.S 11000) |
| £981 | $1865 | (25-Jun-92 D.V651/R) Portrait of lady (93x63cm-37x25in) s.d.1935 pencil W/C (A.S 20000) |

LAMBDIN, George Cochran (1830-1896) American

£573	$1100	(31-Jul-92 E.EDM95/R) Calla lily (43x36cm-17x14in) s.
£1061	$1900	(6-May-92 D.NY22/R) Corner of the poppy field (46x76cm-18x30in) s.
£1383	$2600	(18-Dec-91 SY.NY49/R) Still life of roses (54x44cm-21x17in) s.d.79
£4386	$7500	(12-Mar-92 CH.NY41 a/R) Pink and yellow roses. Roses and wild colombine s.d.76 panel pair
£6145	$11000	(14-Nov-91 CE.NY192/R) Pink and yellow roses (61x46cm-24x18in) s.
£7018	$12000	(12-Mar-92 CH.NY43/R) Roses in full bloom (61x30cm-24x12in) s.d.78 panel pair

LAMBERGER, Henriette (1859-?) Austrian

| £1754 | $3158 | (22-Nov-91 SA.A1743/R) Still life with lobster (39x31cm-15x12in) s.i.d.1884 (DM 5000) |

LAMBERT, Camille Nicholas (1876-?) Belgian

£1404	$2526	(22-Nov-91 SA.A1741/R) Sweets (39x29cm-15x11in) s. (DM 4000)
£1501	$2642	(7-Apr-92 C.A162/R) The bathers (42x60cm-17x24in) s. (B.FR 90000)
£13687	$24773	(7-Dec-91 KV.L467/R) The masked ball (81x101cm-32x40in) s.d.1918 (B.FR 800000)

LAMBERT, Clement (c.1855-1925) British
£440 $840   (1-Jul-92 B54) View of 9 King's Gardens, Hove (16x26cm-6x10in) s. pencil W/C

LAMBERT, George (1710-1765) British
£9000 $16110   (13-Nov-91 S65/R) Italianate river landscape with figures (66x99cm-26x39in) s.d.1763
£37791 $65000   (13-Oct-91 H.C26/R) Landscape with travellers resting (201x196cm-79x77in) s.d.1760
£6500 $11635   (12-Nov-91 C7/R) Falls of the River Tees, Durham. Classical river landscape s.i.d.1746 pastel latter circle of G Lambert two

LAMBERT, George (circle) (1710-1765) British
£1400 $2492   (21-Jan-92 PH12/R) Classical landscape with figures in foreground (91x156cm-36x61in)
£3500 $6685   (17-Jul-92 C76/R) Arcadian landscape with shepherds, villa beyond (103x127cm-41x50in)

LAMBERT, George Washington (1873-1930) Australian
£4038 $7713   (19-Jul-92 SY.ME11/R) Still life of flowers (46x26cm-18x10in) init. board (A.D 10500)
£577 $1102   (19-Jul-92 SY.ME32) Seated lady (23x20cm-9x8in) init.d.1904 pencil (A.D 1500)
£1033 $1725   (19-Aug-91 SY.ME129) Study of soldier standing with rifle (33x20cm-13x8in) s. pencil (A.D 2200)

LAMBERT, Jacques Henri Jean (1877-?) French
£1585 $2662   (27-Aug-91 RAS.K434/R) Cavalier by his easel (73x90cm-29x35in) s. (D.KR 18000)

LAMBERT-RUCKI, Jean (1888-1967) French
£1442 $2465   (19-Mar-92 CSC.P11) La porteuse de cruche (21x15cm-8x6in) s.d.1919 oil wax board (F.FR 14000)
£1728 $3006   (14-Apr-92 CSC.P33 b) L'arbre vert (15x27cm-6x11in) s.d.1926 oil wax panel (F.FR 17000)
£2033 $3537   (14-Apr-92 CSC.P33/R) Trois silhouettes dans la ville (35x23cm-14x9in) s. oil wax board (F.FR 20000)
£2236 $3890   (14-Apr-92 CSC.P32) L'arbre au baiser (20x14cm-8x6in) s.d.1923 oil wax panel (F.FR 22000)
£2820 $5019   (28-Oct-91 GL.P199/R) Homme a la cigarette (29x21cm-11x8in) s.d.1926 waxed board (F.FR 28000)
£2869 $5164   (2-Feb-92 CSC.P54/R) L'homme a la canne (28x23cm-11x9in) s. oil wax board (F.FR 28000)
£3528 $6104   (4-Oct-91 CSC.P9/R) Statue dans la ville (56x39cm-22x15in) s. oil wax board (F.FR 35000)
£3550 $6460   (25-May-92 D.P166) Composition au trefle a quatre feuilles (50x65cm-20x26in) s.d.1926 board (F.FR 35000)
£3564 $6594   (12-Jun-92 ARC.P20) Le couple a l'oranger (81x65cm-32x26in) s.d.1923 panel (F.FR 35000)
£3726 $6632   (28-Oct-91 GL.P197/R) Homme a la guitare (41x29cm-16x11in) s.d.1920 waxed board (F.FR 37000)
£3913 $6692   (19-Mar-92 CSC.P10/R) Personnages dans la ville (57x43cm-22x17in) s. oil wax board (F.FR 38000)
£10299 $17611   (19-Mar-92 CSC.P12/R) Scenes de la vie parisienne (116x89cm-46x35in) s.d.1919 i.verso oil wax panel (F.FR 100000)
£1818 $3218   (22-Apr-92 ZZ.F121/R) Farandole de masques (44x36cm-17x14in) s.d.62 plaster polychrome (F.FR 18000)

LAMBERTS, Gerrit (1776-1850) Dutch
£621 $1106   (25-Nov-91 CH.AM222/R) View of street in Antwerp with cathedral beyond (37x29cm-15x11in) s. i.verso chk W/C (D.FL 2000)

LAMBILLOTTE, George (1915-) Belgian
£1170 $1988   (22-Oct-91 C.A213) Composition (100x80cm-39x31in) s. (B.FR 70000)

LAMBINET, Emile (1815-1877) French
£936 $1600   (22-Mar-92 LIT.L148) Barbizon landscape (30x46cm-12x18in) s. panel
£1400 $2422   (3-Oct-91 CSK53/R) Cattle in a meadow (33x43cm-13x17in) s.
£2022 $3600   (2-May-92 W.W22/R) Pres de la ferme (25x33cm-10x13in) s. i.verso board
£3143 $5500   (18-Feb-92 CE.NY145/R) Au bords de la riviere (84x130cm-33x51in) s.d.1875
£3297 $6000   (28-May-92 SY.NY159/R) Au bord du canal (43x74cm-17x29in) s.d.1877 cradled panel
£3846 $7000   (27-May-92 CH.NY191/R) Tending the fields (51x73cm-20x29in) s.
£4571 $8000   (23-Sep-91 S.SL257) Picking apples (89x145cm-35x57in) s.d.1859
£4825 $8250   (13-Mar-92 S.BM162/R) La Seine a Bougival (43x74cm-17x29in) s.d.1877 i.verso panel
£5723 $10016   (5-Apr-92 CSC.P79/R) Bord de riviere (84x100cm-33x39in) s.d.1874 (F.FR 55000)

LAMBINET, Emile (attrib) (1815-1877) French
£585 $1000   (21-Mar-92 W.W8/R) Country cottage (23x33cm-9x13in) s.

LAMBRECHTS, Jan Baptist (1680-1731) Flemish
£900 $1728   (10-Jul-92 PH58/R) Kitchen interior with seated woman peeling turnips (30x24cm-12x9in)

LAMBRECHTS, Jan Baptist (1680-1731) Flemish-cont.
£928	$1614	(18-Sep-91 N.M422/R) Figures at table eating meal (31x27cm-12x11in) i. panel (DM 2700)
£2115	$3785	(7-May-92 CH.AM78/R) Carnival revellers in interior (42x50cm-17x20in) with init. (D.FL 7000)
£3000	$5250	(3-Apr-92 C33/R) Smoker with maidservants in kitchen (41x30cm-16x12in)
£4400	$8008	(11-Dec-91 S180/R) Figures taking refreshment outside house (82x87cm-32x34in)
£19547	$37140	(26-Jun-92 AGS.P46) La Collation (29x23cm-11x9in) (F.FR 190000)

LAMBRECHTS, Jan Baptist (attrib) (1680-1731) Flemish
| £481 | $871 | (19-May-92 GF.L2690) Interior with woman seated (29x23cm-11x9in) canvas on panel (S.FR 1300) |

LAMBRECHTS, Jan Baptist (circle) (1680-1731) Flemish
| £3074 | $5533 | (27-Jan-92 CSC.P44) Le joyeux buveur (49x44cm-19x17in) (F.FR 30000) |

LAMBRECHTS, Jan Baptist (school) (1680-1731) Flemish
| £1445 | $2558 | (5-Nov-91 GF.L2384/R) Wine drinker in tavern interior (39x35cm-15x14in) indis.i.verso (S.FR 3700) |

LAMBRECHTS, Jan Baptist (style) (1680-1731) Flemish
| £697 | $1268 | (11-Dec-91 N.M337/R) Maid cleaning vegetables and cavaliers in kitchen interior (40x33cm-16x13in) i.verso (DM 2000) |
| £1750 | $3360 | (9-Jul-92 CSK325) Peasants dancing in interior (48x64cm-19x25in) |

LAMBUSSETI (19th C) Italian
| £419 | $800 | *(16-Jul-92 SY.NY603/R) Jester in the wine cellar (67x99cm-26x39in) s.i. W/C* |

LAME, Biagio dalle see PUPINI, Biagio

LAMEN, Christoffel Jacobsz van der (c.1606-1651) Flemish
| £3500 | $6125 | (31-Mar-92 PH76/R) Elegant company feasting at table before hearth (49x64cm-19x25in) panel |

LAMEN, Christoffel Jacobsz van der (circle) (c.1606-1651) Flemish
| £3198 | $5500 | (10-Oct-91 SY.NY127/R) Elegant figures gathered in a garden (57x72cm-22x28in) panel |

LAMEN, Jasper van der see LAANEN, Jasper van der

LAMERS, Johann Herman Joseph (circle) (1814-1847) Dutch
| £2800 | $4984 | (28-Nov-91 B183/R) Mending the nets (53x43cm-21x17in) |

LAMEYER Y BERENGUER, Francisco (1825-1877) Spanish
| £821 | $1569 | *(2-Jul-92 ANS.M142/R) Escena marroqui (32x22cm-13x9in) W/C (S.P 150000)* |
| £1205 | $2301 | *(2-Jul-92 ANS.M143) Rincon marroqui (32x22cm-13x9in) W/C (S.P 220000)* |

LAMI, Eugene Louis (1800-1890) French
£462	$883	*(1-Jul-92 CD.P13/R) Fermiere et militaires (23x17cm-9x7in) s.d.1889 W/C gouache (F.FR 4500)*
£500	$905	*(19-May-92 PH110/R) L'Arc de Triomphe (24x33cm-9x13in) indis.s.d.1842 W/C htd.white over pencil*
£800	$1424	*(27-Nov-91 S223/R) Cavalry officer (112x16cm-44x6in) s.d.1820 pen W/C*
£1405	$2458	*(3-Apr-92 AGS.P147) Illustration pour les caprices de Marianne (11x15cm-4x6in) mono. W/C (F.FR 13500)*
£2464	$4435	*(22-Nov-91 AGS.P100) La Representation (18x25cm-7x10in) s. W/C (F.FR 24000)*
£2497	$4645	*(19-Jun-92 CN.P35/R) Etude de cavalieres montant en amazone (21x16cm-8x6in) crayon double-sided (F.FR 24500)*
£3055	$5560	*(11-Dec-91 LD.P23/R) La jolie cavaliere (25x17cm-10x7in) mono. lead pencil W/C (F.FR 30000)*
£4124	$7134	*(26-Mar-92 PIC.P2/R) Scene de bal costume (13x27cm-5x11in) s.d.1855 W/C gouache (F.FR 40000)*
£7500	$13950	*(17-Jun-92 S421/R) Le chahut au bal de l'opera (15x23cm-6x9in) s.d.1851 W/C*

LAMI, G E (19th C) French
| £871 | $1585 | *(11-Dec-91 N.M286/R) Portrait of lady wearing low cut dress (6x5cm-2x2in) min. s.d.1811 W/C gouache ivory oval brass frame (DM 2500)* |

LAMI, Victor (?) ?
| £719 | $1294 | (20-Nov-91 CN.P185) Fillette au soufflet (46x37cm-18x15in) s. panel (F.FR 7000) |

LAMOND, William B (1857-1924) British
£500	$870	(11-Sep-91 PHG31) On the east coast (18x25cm-7x10in) s.d.94 board
£700	$1176	(26-Aug-91 S1063/R) Seascape, Auchmithie (35x45cm-14x18in) s. i.stretcher
£900	$1512	(26-Aug-91 S1052/R) Calves watering (35x53cm-14x21in) s.
£1100	$1892	(4-Mar-92 S155) Fieldwork (35x45cm-14x18in) s.
£1500	$2685	(13-Nov-91 CG648) Gathering wrech (25x30cm-10x12in) s.
£1600	$2688	(26-Aug-91 S1039/R) Rolling (20x30cm-8x12in) s.d.1901
£1600	$2688	(26-Aug-91 S986/R) Fifeshire landscape (35x45cm-14x18in) s.

LAMOND, William B (1857-1924) British-cont.
£1600 $2688   (26-Aug-91 S951/R) Watering the horses (24x30cm-9x12in) s. indist.d.
                          canvas board
£2800 $4704   (26-Aug-91 S1054/R) Watching ducks (25x36cm-10x14in) s.d.1890

LAMORE, Chet Harmon (1908-) American
£1056 $1900   (22-Nov-91 S.BM218/R) Necromancer, 1943 (102x76cm-40x30in) s. with
                          i.verso

LAMORINIERE, Jean Pierre Francois (1828-1911) Belgian
£857 $1500   (18-Feb-92 CE.NY142/R) Verdant landscape (72x106cm-28x42in) s.d.1873
                          panel

LAMPI, Francesco (1782-1852) Italian
£2290 $4168   (15-Dec-91 REM.W21) Portrait of Mieroszewski (77x67cm-30x26in)
                          (P.Z 45000000)

LAMPI, Johann Baptist (elder) (1751-1830) Italian
£10989 $19780   (21-Nov-91 D.V135/R) Portrait of Feldmarschall Johann Josef Furst von und
                          zu Liechtenstein (79x63cm-31x25in) (A.S 220000)

LAMPI, Johann Baptist (elder-circle) (1751-1830) Italian
£1000 $1780   (29-Oct-91 PH131/R) Portrait of Constantine, son of Paul I, Tsar of
                          Russia (82x67cm-32x26in) with painted oval
£1300 $2314   (29-Oct-91 PH40/R) Portrait of Catherine the Great, in Imperial robes
                          (81x63cm-32x25in)

LAMPI, Johann Baptist (younger) (1775-1837) Italian
£3945 $7101   (19-Nov-91 F.R48/R) Ritratto di donna (73x54cm-29x21in) s.d.1811
                          (I.L 8500000)

LAMPISUO, Antti (1926-) Finnish
£948 $1669   (12-Apr-92 HOR.H140) Porcelain bowl (50x61cm-20x24in) s.d.1989 (F.M 7500)
£1264 $2225   (12-Apr-92 HOR.H139) Coral flower (50x60cm-20x24in) s.d.1989 (F.M 10000)

LAMPLOUGH, A O (1877-1930) British
£474 $854   (19-Nov-91 GS.B3564) Street in Cairo (35x25cm-14x10in) s.i. W/C
*   (S.FR 1200)*
£785 $1500   (3-Jul-92 S.W3839) Arab village near Cairo (41x58cm-16x23in) s.d.14.4.03
*   W/C*

LAMPLOUGH, Augustus Osborne (1877-1930) British
£400 $680   (24-Oct-91 CSK28) Fayoum from the desert (18x28cm-7x11in) s.i. W/C
£420 $806   (9-Jul-92 B150/R) Figures in desert sunset (51x76cm-20x30in) s. W/C
£420 $714   (6-Aug-91 OT372) Creeping shadows (21x59cm-8x23in) s. W/C
£450 $770   (18-Mar-92 CSK49) Sandstorm in the desert (51x74cm-20x29in) s. pencil W/C
£500 $925   (12-Jun-92 K327/R) Mosque with figures by river (56x46cm-22x18in) s. W/C
£522 $930   (25-Nov-91 W.T1823/R) Arabian village near Cairo (42x61cm-17x24in)
*   s.d.1903 W/C (C.D 1050)*
£550 $963   (23-Sep-91 PHB6) On the banks of the River Nile (22x60cm-9x24in) s. W/C
£550 $935   (24-Oct-91 CSK32) A camel train emerging from a sandstorm
*   (48x71cm-19x28in) s. W/C htd.white*
£700 $1197   (12-Mar-92 B87/R) Desert afterglow (23x58cm-9x23in) s.i. W/C
£700 $1190   (23-Oct-91 S248/R) View of the Pyramids, Giza (22x58cm-9x23in) s. W/C
*   htd.bodycol*
£850 $1445   (24-Oct-91 CSK25/R) Figures on the banks of the Nile, Pyramids beyond
*   (48x71cm-19x28in) s. W/C htd.bodycol.*
£1000 $1850   (11-Jun-92 CSK20/R) Fishing dhow on the Nile (51x71cm-20x28in) s. pencil
*   W/C*
£1200 $2052   (12-Mar-92 CSK43) Island of Philae on the Nile (64x97cm-25x38in) s.
*   pencil W/C*
£1700 $2890   (23-Oct-91 S256/R) Feluccas by the Nile. Ruins near Luxor, time of
*   Inundation. Upper Nile (21x58cm-8x23in) s. two i.d.1905 and 1919 W/C*
*   over pencil three*

LAMPRECHT, Anton (1901-) ?
£632 $1080   (13-Mar-92 FN.S2535/R) Lake landscape with boats (69x90cm-27x35in)
                          s.d.1959 (DM 1800)
£5263 $9474   (23-Nov-91 N.M182/R) Park in Nizza (60x80cm-24x31in) s. (DM 15000)

LAMUNIERE, Gaspard (1810-1865) Swiss
£750 $1290   (4-Mar-92 C40/R) Gentleman, in black coat, white waistcoat and balck
*   cravat (6x?cm-2x?in) min. s. enamel gilt frame oval*

LANCASTER, Alfred Dobree (?-1909) British
£2600 $4524   (12-Sep-91 CSK259/R) At the helm (124x81cm-49x32in) i.verso

LANCASTER, Hume (?-1850) British
£1200 $2052   (19-Mar-92 B48/R) A Dutch Estuary Scene (61x97cm-24x38in) s.d.1849

LANCASTER, John (20th C) British
£800 $1432   (5-May-92 SWS501/R) The glory of the garden (35x44cm-14x17in) s.d.1960
                          board

LANCASTER, Osbert (1908-) British
£420 $802   (16-Jul-92 B100/R) Lord Berners grappling with muse (22x17cm-9x7in)
       gouache
£850 $1598   (18-Dec-91 C94/R) Set design for l'Italian Algeri (28x38cm-11x15in) W/C
       collage

LANCASTER, Percy (1878-1951) British
£1400 $2562   (4-Jun-92 CSK57/R) Port St Mary, Isle of Man (71x91cm-28x36in) s.
       s.i.verso board
£400 $716   (11-Nov-91 PH204/R) The flower seller (23x32cm-9x13in) s.mono. W/C
£420 $781   (18-Jun-92 CSK133) South Porch, Quimperle (33x23cm-13x9in) mono
       s.i.d.12verso pencil W/C
£460 $837   (10-Dec-91 SWS451) The fruit shop (23x34cm-9x13in) s. W/C over pencil
£480 $922   (28-Jul-92 RJ158) Shepherd in marshland scene (33x48cm-13x19in) s. W/C

LANCASTER, Richard Hume (1773-1853) British
£1500 $2715   (20-May-92 S23/R) Unloading the cargo (44x61cm-17x24in) panel
£1700 $2992   (8-Apr-92 S232/R) Welsh river landscape with figures crossing bridge
       (41x41cm-16x16in) i.stretcher

LANCE, G (1802-1864) British
£650 $1157   (1-May-92 BW397) Still life study of various fruits (38x48cm-15x19in)
       s.d.1854 board

LANCE, George (1802-1864) British
£700 $1211   (4-Sep-91 BT285/R) Interior with girl and fruit (20x18cm-8x7in) s.d.1851
       board
£1200 $2136   (28-Apr-92 PH37/R) Still life of fruit and flowers (61x50cm-24x20in)
       indist.s.d.1831
£1310 $2200   (1-Sep-91 PO.BA20) Naturaleza muerta (35x45cm-14x18in) s.
£2500 $4450   (28-Apr-92 PH38/R) Fruit and still life (36x46cm-14x18in) init.d.1842
£3300 $5742   (11-Sep-91 MMB355/R) Still life of fruit and a bird's nest
       (43x36cm-17x14in) init.d.1859
£3500 $6230   (27-Apr-92 PHB273/R) Still life of mixed fruit (51x50cm-20x20in) s.d.1860
       panel
£30000 $51000   (25-Oct-91 C39/R) The village coquette (110x86cm-43x34in) s.

LANCE, George (style) (1802-1864) British
£1600 $2896   (18-May-92 HS358) Still life of fruit and flowers on table top, landscape
       beyond (61x74cm-24x29in)

LANCELEY, Colin (1938-) New Zealander
£766 $1356   (26-Apr-92 SY.ME474 c/R) Metung, where all rivers meet, 1990
       (124x179cm-49x70in) acrylic collage board (A.D 1800)
£4701 $8368   (28-Apr-92 CH.ME20/R) Up the Bonza Lairo (122x87cm-48x34in) s.d.63
       s.i.d.verso assemblage mixed media board (A.D 11000)
£5634 $9408   (19-Aug-91 SY.ME218/R) Harvest (85x134cm-33x53in) s.i.d.1983 verso oil
       assemblage canvas (A.D 12000)

LANCEROTTO, Egisto (1848-1916) Italian
£6000 $10500   (20-Feb-92 SY.NY297/R) Una Donna con fiore (150x75cm-59x30in) s.indist.i.
£10174 $17500   (17-Oct-91 SY.NY338/R) Italian lovers (112x75cm-44x30in) s.

LANCKOW, Ludwig (19th C) German
£1047 $1800   (15-Oct-91 CE.NY62/R) A hunter in a wooded winter forest
       (51x41cm-20x16in) s.d.9/7/71 board

LANCRET, Nicolas (1690-1743) French
£30864 $55864   (5-Dec-91 SY.MO189/R) Jeune femme sur son canape (23x31cm-9x12in) panel
       (F.FR 300000)
£121547 $220000   (22-May-92 SY.NY41/R) Sleeping shepherdess (28x23cm-11x9in) panel
£131048 $231956   (7-Nov-91 AT.P76/R) Autoportrait (89x72cm-35x28in) (F.FR 1300000)
£524 $1000   (3-Jul-92 S.W3701/R) Nobleman (10x8cm-4x3in) sepia chk
£2793 $5000   (14-Jan-92 SY.NY175) Woman seen from behind (23x16cm-9x6in) red chk
£3000 $5760   (6-Jul-92 S87/R) Study of man in full-length coat (27x18cm-11x7in) chk.
£3500 $6720   (6-Jul-92 S12/R) Study of lady dancing (19x17cm-7x7in) chk.
£3608 $6242   (27-Mar-92 CN.P13/R) Etude de trois gentilshommmes (17x22cm-7x9in)
       sanguine (F.FR 35000)
£4200 $8064   (7-Jul-92 C54/R) Study of man looking down (25x13cm-10x5in) chk
£8939 $16000   (14-Jan-92 SY.NY60/R) Study of gentleman sitting on ground. Study of feet
       and dress of seated lady (16x20cm-6x8in) red chk htd white double-sided
£13408 $24000   (15-Jan-92 CH.NY76/R) Study of man with outstretched arms and studies of
       hands. Figure study (16x20cm-6x8in) red chk double-sided

LANCRET, Nicolas (after) (1690-1743) French
£8721 $15000   (10-Oct-91 SY.NY124/R) Musicians and dancers in a landscape with
       fountains (178x152cm-70x60in)

LANCRET, Nicolas (attrib) (1690-1743) French
£560 $1036   (12-Jun-92 ARC.P129) Jeune homme allonge, jeune homme agenouille
       (28x23cm-11x9in) num.203 verso black chk htd white chk (F.FR 5500)

LANCRET, Nicolas (circle) (1690-1743) French
£1852 $3352   (5-Dec-91 SY.MO375/R) Jeux d'enfants (32x40cm-13x16in) (F.FR 18000)

LANCRET, Nicolas (circle) (1690-1743) French-cont.
£1966 $3500 (22-Jan-92 SY.NY153/R) Two women and man gardening by fountain
(70x98cm-28x39in)

LANCRET, Nicolas (school) (1690-1743) French
£960 $1700 (23-Apr-92 S.BM590) Garden concert (28x36cm-11x14in)

LANCRET, Nicolas (style) (1690-1743) French
£718 $1300 (20-May-92 D.NY21) Pastoral couples at harvest time (74x140cm-29x55in)
£750 $1350 (21-Nov-91 CSK244) Elegant couple making music in wooded glade before
Term of Pan (84x61cm-33x24in)
£2361 $4251 (21-Nov-91 BL.P48) Concert avec Pierrot et Arlequin (57x77cm-22x30in)
(F.FR 23000)

LANDALUZE, Victor Patricio (1828-1889) Cuban
£10497 $19000 (19-May-92 SY.NY83/R) Vendedor de Loteria (36x27cm-14x11in) s.
£11050 $20000 (19-May-92 SY.NY82/R) Mujer fumando (36x27cm-14x11in) s.

LANDAU, Zygmunt (1898-1962) Polish
£700 $1218 (19-Sep-91 CSK55) View of lakeside town (61x77cm-24x30in) s.d.1923
£732 $1340 (17-May-92 GL.P74) Fillette ecrivant (46x37cm-18x15in) s. isorel
(F.FR 7200)
£1812 $3406 (21-Dec-91 PSA.W9) Still life of fruits (65x78cm-26x31in) s.
(P.Z 35000000)

LANDELLE, Charles Zacharie (1812-1908) French
£11628 $20000 (16-Oct-91 CH.NY37/R) Femme Fellah (129x87cm-51x34in) s.d.1869

LANDENBERGER, Christian (1862-1927) German
£2405 $4402 (2-Jun-92 FN.S2641/R) Study for Descent from the Cross (59x52cm-23x20in)
s.d.1910 i.verso (DM 7000)
*£584 $1016 (17-Sep-91 FN.S2415) Portrait of elegant young lady (65x57cm-26x22in)
s.d.1916 ochre (DM 1700)*

LANDER, B (19th C) British
£902 $1533 (23-Oct-91 GD.B1127/R) Fox hunt (29x39cm-11x15in) s. panel (S.FR 2300)

LANDER, Benjamin (19th C) American
£584 $1045 (6-May-92 GD.B734/R) Fox hunt (45x60cm-18x24in) s. panel (S.FR 1600)

LANDER, John St Helier (1869-1944) British
£1600 $2960 (11-Jun-92 CSK199/R) Portrait of Guy Repton as young boy
(101x76cm-40x30in) s.i. verso

LANDERSET, Theresa Maria de (c.1829-?) Swiss
£950 $1720 (20-May-92 B241/R) Roses (38x56cm-15x22in) s. W/C over pencil

LANDHEER, Hugo (1896-?) Dutch
£864 $1573 (11-Dec-91 CH.AM27) Dorpsgezicht met brug en wandelaar (53x73cm-21x29in)
s.d.1927 (D.FL 2800)

LANDI, Ricardo Verdugo (1871-1930) Spanish
£1374 $2473 (19-Nov-91 DUR.M127/R) Manifestacion en San Petesburgo (55x38cm-22x15in)
s. (S.P 250000)
£3284 $5977 (27-May-92 DUR.M440/R) Paisaje costero (100x185cm-39x73in) s.d.24
(S.P 600000)

LANDIN, Bengt (1933-) Swedish
£859 $1529 (27-Nov-91 BU.S72/R) Signs in the sky (59x50cm-23x20in) indist.init.
(S.KR 9000)

LANDINI, Jacopo (1297-1358) Italian
£23464 $42000 (16-Jan-92 CH.NY2/R) Saint Reparata. Saint John the Baptist
(27x22cm-11x9in) tempera gold ground panel pair
£93923 $170000 (22-May-92 SY.NY101/R) Madonna and child (43x32cm-17x13in) gold ground
tempera panel pointed top

LANDSEER (after) (19th C) British
£1453 $2500 (10-Oct-91 FA.PH722) Highlanders (64x76cm-25x30in)

LANDSEER (style) (19th C) British
£3700 $6512 (7-Apr-92 LS470/R) Study of boy seated on rock feeding lamb with ewe and
collie nearby (109x84cm-43x33in) bears sig. canvas on board

LANDSEER, Jessica (1810-1880) British
£800 $1416 (13-Feb-92 B192) Dove Dale, Derbyshire (14x20cm-6x8in) i.d.1831verso W/C

LANDSEER, Sir Edwin (1802-1873) British
£16000 $28640 (15-Nov-91 C87/R) Dead Blackcock and grey hen (50x66cm-20x26in) panel
£19000 $33440 (8-Apr-92 S124/R) Poacher (46x61cm-18x24in) panel
£19126 $35000 (5-Jun-92 SY.NY151/R) Dog looking out of a kennel (30x22cm-12x9in)
£130000 $228800 (10-Apr-92 C80/R) Scarbro, the Old Cover Hack (122x152cm-48x60in)
*£850 $1522 (14-Jan-92 B224/R) A dog retrieving a woodcock (24x32cm-9x13in)
mono.d.1830 pencil pastel gum arabic*

LANDSEER, Sir Edwin (1802-1873) British-cont.
*£8500 $14620   (4-Mar-92 S312/R) Dash (25x25cm-10x10in) init.d.1825 pencil pastel
                        gouache*

LANDSEER, Sir Edwin (after) (1802-1873) British
£2600 $4446   (12-Mar-92 CSK149 a) Shoeing (142x112cm-56x44in) s.Swingler i.d.1890

LANDSEER, Sir Edwin (attrib) (1802-1873) British
£462 $882   (16-Jul-92 S42) Stag and other studies (28x37cm-11x15in) col.crayons

LANDSEER, Sir Edwin (circle) (1802-1873) British
£1400 $2492   (28-Apr-92 PH110/R) Working dogs (52x69cm-20x27in) bears init.

LANDSHEER, Jan de (1750-1828) Flemish
£750 $1313   (25-Sep-91 CSK349) Portrait of a gentleman in a black jacket holding a
                        top hat (81x64cm-32x25in) s.d.1810

LANDSTROM, Bjorn (1917-) Scandinavian
*£683 $1202   (12-Apr-92 HOR.H142) On fairy island (42x33cm-17x13in) s.d.1944 gouache
                        (F.M 5400)*

LANDT, Frants (1885-1976) Danish
£492 $895   (12-Dec-91 RAS.V740) Entrance to Copenhagen harbour (71x109cm-28x43in)
                        s.d.1938 (D.KR 5500)
£900 $1629   (20-May-92 S61/R) Three-masted barque following skiff (61x84cm-24x33in)
                        s.

LANDUYT, Octave (1922-) Belgian
£2167 $3727   (12-Oct-91 KV.L180/R) The patriarch (23x19cm-9x7in) s. panel
                        (B.FR 130000)
*£751 $1321   (7-Apr-92 C.A478) Cordons ombiliaux (40x29cm-16x11in) s. dr.
                        (B.FR 45000)*

LANDWEHR-PRAGENAU, Ottokar von (1905-) Austrian
£616 $1060   (8-Oct-91 ZEL.L1571/R) Portrait of dark haired woman with folded arms
                        (96x71cm-38x28in) s. board (DM 1800)

LANE, Fitz Hugh (1804-1865) American
£164835 $300000   (28-May-92 CH.NY26/R) Beached for repairs, Duncan's Point, Gloucester
                        (41x56cm-16x22in)
£372928 $675000   (5-Dec-91 SY.NY19/R) Camden Mountains from the south entrance to harbour
                        (56x91cm-22x36in) s.d.1859

LANE, Samuel (1780-1859) British
£650 $1131   (12-Sep-91 CSK112) Portrait of the Very Reverend George Peacock, Dean of
                        Ely (143x112cm-56x44in) s. indist.i.verso
£1150 $1978   (8-Oct-91 PH44/R) Portrait of William Henchman Crowfoot. Mrs William
                        Crowfoot (36x28cm-14x11in) panel pair

LANE, Theodore (1800-1828) British
£550 $1007   (7-Feb-92 K527) Figure resting with dog on river bank (20x25cm-8x10in) s.

LANFANT DE METZ, Francois Louis (1814-1892) French
£1800 $3204   (26-Nov-91 PH201) The new arrival (25x31cm-10x12in) s. panel
£2000 $3720   (17-Jun-92 S438/R) On ferry (18x29cm-7x11in) s. panel
£2135 $3800   (1-Nov-91 PO.BA12) Travesuras infantiles (40x32cm-16x13in) s.
£2749 $4784   (17-Sep-91 FN.S416/R) Children watching cock fight on staircase in palace
                        gardens (36x26cm-14x10in) s. (DM 8000)
£3000 $5190   (4-Oct-91 C49/R) La glissade (36x18cm-14x7in) s. panel
£3310 $6024   (11-Dec-91 WE.MU175) Children sliding down stairs (36x18cm-14x7in) s.
                        panel (DM 9500)
£3909 $7428   (22-Jun-92 AT.P59/R) Le livre d'images (43x35cm-17x14in) s. (F.FR 38000)
£6067 $10800   (1-Nov-91 PO.BA13) Ninos leyendo y ninos marchando (26x34cm-10x13in) s.
                        pair
£6687 $12706   (22-Jun-92 AT.P58/R) La permission galante (65x54cm-26x21in) s.
                        (F.FR 65000)

LANFRANCO (?) Italian
£511 $960   (19-Dec-91 F.M122) L'isola del sale (80x65cm-31x26in) s. (I.L 1100000)
£511 $960   (19-Dec-91 F.M85) Scavi in galleria (89x70cm-35x28in) s. i.verso
                        (I.L 1100000)

LANFRANCO, Giovanni (1582-1647) Italian
£16760 $30000   (16-Jan-92 CH.NY7/R) Samson and lion (142x110cm-56x43in)
*£900 $1566   (13-Apr-92 S257/R) Design for spandrel - sibyl and prophet (9x14cm-4x6in)
                        pen wash*

LANFRANCO, Giovanni (after) (1582-1647) Italian
£950 $1663   (25-Feb-92 PH94/R) Mary Magdalen in glory (65x48cm-26x19in)

LANFRANCO, Giovanni (circle) (1582-1647) Italian
£800 $1424   (29-Oct-91 PH13) The Madonna and Child with St. Francis (64x48cm-25x19in)
£850 $1632   (10-Jul-92 PH7) Angel appearing to St Peter (30x22cm-12x9in)

LANG, Johann (19th C) German
£1761 $2958   (27-Aug-91 RAS.K191/R) Still life of grapes, peaches, nuts and wineglass on ledge (31x39cm-12x15in) s.d.1849 (D.KR 20000)

LANG, L (19th C) ?
£600 $1032   (16-Oct-91 FER.M120/R) Parada morisca para beber (40x66cm-16x26in) s.d.1886 (S.P 110000)

LANGASKENS, Maurice (1884-1946) Belgian
£1407 $2547   (23-May-92 KV.L190/R) The cartographer (72x56cm-28x22in) s. (B.FR 85000)

LANGBERG, Emily (1851-1935) Norwegian
£792 $1393   (8-Apr-92 GWP.O122) Woman at sewing machine in farmroom (92x70cm-36x28in) s. (N.KR 9000)

LANGE, Frederik (1870-1941) Danish
£1579 $2842   (22-Nov-91 SA.A1656/R) Landscape with view of town and figure pulling sledge with children (121x160cm-48x63in) s.d.1912 (DM 4500)

LANGE, Johann Gustav (1811-1887) German
£1384 $2630   (24-Jun-92 KM.K1163) Figures before timber framed houses in snow covered landscape (95x76cm-37x30in) s. (DM 4000)
£2048 $3706   (21-May-92 L.K440/R) Winter landscape at sunset with huntsman amongst trees (100x135cm-39x53in) s. (DM 6000)

LANGE, Ludwig (attrib) (1808-1868) German
£2509 $4566   (12-Dec-91 L.K613/R) View of Cologne with Siebengebirge beyond (50x63cm-20x25in) (DM 7200)

LANGE, Niels Erik (1890-1919) Danish
£528 $914   (2-Sep-91 BU.K82/R) Chickens (76x91cm-30x36in) s. (D.KR 6000)

LANGE, Otto (1879-1944) German
£542 $965   (25-Nov-91 WK.M630) Horse-drawn cart (27x37cm-11x15in) s.i.d.1921 board W/C over pencil (DM 1550)
£546 $994   (25-May-92 WK.M761/R) Evening glow at Lake Constance (38x52cm-15x20in) s. W/C (DM 1600)
£546 $988   (23-May-92 GB.B6796) St Tropez (35x45cm-14x18in) s. W/C over pen monotype paper on board (DM 1600)
£842 $1516   (23-Nov-91 N.M572) Southern town (38x50cm-15x20in) s.i. W/C indian ink brush (DM 2400)

LANGENBERGH, Dre van den (1903-1976) Belgian
£501 $852   (22-Oct-91 C.A990) The artist (100x64cm-39x25in) s.d.1938 (B.FR 30000)
£501 $852   (22-Oct-91 C.A988/R) Beside the window (75x54cm-30x21in) (B.FR 30000)

LANGENDYK, Dirk (1748-1805) Dutch
£1235 $2210   (14-Nov-91 CH.AM23) Mare and goat in landscape with herdsman and cattle on bridge (21x26cm-8x10in) s.d.1780 panel (D.FL 4000)

LANGENDYK, Dirk (attrib) (1748-1805) Dutch
£679 $1215   (12-Nov-91 SY.AM353/R) Skirmish at sea (19x25cm-7x10in) i.verso pen wash after Lingelbach (D.FL 2200)

LANGENDYK, Jan Anthonie (1780-1818) Dutch
£1850 $3367   (11-Dec-91 MMB184/R) Skirmish in Napoleonic Wars s.d.1813 W/C pair
£2123 $3800   (15-Jan-92 CH.NY163/R) Flower market in Rotterdam - summer (30x45cm-12x18in) s.d.1804 black chk wash ink
£2346 $4200   (15-Jan-92 CH.NY164/R) Fish market in Rotterdam - winter (30x45cm-12x18in) s.d.1805 black chk pen wash htd white

LANGER, Viggo (1860-1942) Danish
£528 $887   (27-Aug-91 RAS.K402) Flowering shrub on garden wall, Menton (40x47cm-16x19in) s.i. (D.KR 6000)
£1100 $1991   (21-May-92 CSK118) Wooded landscape with drover and cattle (63x91cm-25x36in) s.
£1220 $2111   (3-Oct-91 D.V62/R) Chickens and ducks (48x66cm-19x26in) s.d.1930 (A.S 25000)
£1625 $2924   (19-Nov-91 RAS.K108/R) The low house in Hellebaek (50x67cm-20x26in) s.d.1916 (D.KR 18000)
£2200 $3982   (22-May-92 C21/R) Cottage garden (47x63cm-19x25in) s.d.1918
£2326 $4000   (14-Oct-91 H.C83/R) Blossoming trees in spring (64x89cm-25x35in) s.d.1907

LANGEROCK, Henri (?-1885) Belgian
£816 $1461   (5-May-92 ZEL.L1404/R) Lion on outcrop in landscape (34x42cm-13x17in) s. (DM 2400)
£419 $800   (3-Jul-92 S.W2740) Mosques, Egypt (43x25cm-17x10in) s. i.verso W/C gouache

LANGEROCK, J (?) ?
£520 $925   (26-Jan-92 LIT.L285) Garden of Allah (25x43cm-10x17in) s. W/C

LANGETTI, Giovanni Battista (1625-1676) Italian
£3322 $5747   (25-Mar-92 KM.K978) Classical scene with Hermes and Zeus (108x140cm-43x55in) (DM 9500)

LANGETTI, Giovanni Battista (1625-1676) Italian-cont.
£10225 $18508   (5-Dec-91 F.M64/R) Giuseppe spiega i sogni. Giobbe deriso
            (?x100cm-?x39in) pair (I.L 22000000)

LANGETTI, Giovanni Battista (attrib) (1625-1676) Italian
£2266 $4260   (18-Dec-91 AT.P134/R) Vierge de douleur (68x54cm-27x21in) (F.FR 22000)

LANGEVELD, Frans (1877-1939) Dutch
£1818 $3218   (22-Apr-92 CH.AM49/R) Building-site, Amsterdam (69x115cm-27x45in) s.
            (D.FL 6000)
£1835 $3193   (14-Apr-92 SY.AM196/R) View on the Bridge by Het Singel in Amsterdam
            (46x77cm-18x30in) s. (D.FL 6000)

LANGEVIN, Claude (1942-) Canadian
£746 $1328   (26-Nov-91 JOY.T239/R) Village de la Cote Nord (50x60cm-20x24in) s.
            (C.D 1500)

LANGHAMMER, Arthur (1854-1901) German
£7167 $12973   (21-May-92 L.K441) Young peasant woman and cattle in field
            (60x80cm-24x31in) s. (DM 21000)

LANGHAMMER, Carl (1868-?) German
£576 $1042   (3-Dec-91 AB.S4725/R) Summer landscape with road (100x125cm-39x49in) s.
            (S.KR 6000)

LANGHANS, Jorg (1966-) German
£418 $764   *(5-Jun-92 CB.P63/R) Personnage (46x38cm-18x15in) s.d.1990 ink acrylic
            pastel board (F.FR 4100)*

LANGKER, Sir Erik (1898-1982) Australian
£594 $1039   (23-Sep-91 AAA.S97) Valley landscape (37x45cm-15x18in) s. board
            (A.D 1300)
£607 $1098   (19-May-92 JRL.S221/R) Coastal scene (57x88cm-22x35in) s. board
            (A.D 1450)
£1026 $1826   (28-Apr-92 CH.ME163/R) Suburban landscape (60x75cm-24x30in) s. s.i.verso
            canvasboard (A.D 2400)

LANGKO, Dietrich (attrib) (1819-1896) German
£1049 $1794   (18-Mar-92 N.M579/R) Woodland stream (59x46cm-23x18in) i.stretcher
            (DM 3000)

LANGLADE, Pierre (1812-1909) French
£2405 $4402   (3-Jun-92 L.K260/R) Port de la Rochelle (46x55cm-18x22in) s. (DM 7000)

LANGLAIS, Bernard (1921-1977) American
£2443 $4250   *(15-Sep-91 JRB.C42/R) Last train up river (61x122cm-24x48in) s. wood
            construction*

LANGLET, Alexander (1870-1953) Swedish
£457 $832   (14-Dec-91 BA.S37/R) Carolean on horseback in snowstorm (40x30cm-16x12in)
            s.d.45 (S.KR 4800)
£522 $955   (12-May-92 GO.G73) Spring farming with horse (30x40cm-12x16in) s.
            (S.KR 5500)
£664 $1215   (12-May-92 GO.G74) Farming with horses (43x58cm-17x23in) s.d.50
            (S.KR 7000)
£672 $1216   (3-Dec-91 AB.S4630/R) Workhorse pulling timber, winter (41x51cm-16x20in)
            s. (S.KR 7000)

LANGLEY, Walter (1852-1922) British
£720 $1253   (17-Sep-91 PH11/R) A reverie (61x35cm-24x14in) s. i. label
£1207 $2076   (16-Oct-91 KM.K1251) Portrait of fisherboy (80x35cm-31x14in) s. canvas on
            panel (DM 3500)
£2600 $4550   (27-Feb-92 L215/R) A reverie (61x36cm-24x14in) s.
£367 $672   *(1-Jun-92 W.T1279) Mill pond with old lady at spring (38x55cm-15x22in) s.
            W/C (C.D 800)*
£600 $1068   *(28-Nov-91 L75/R) Portrait of young woman in flower decorated hat
            (23x18cm-9x7in) s.i. pastel*
£680 $1156   *(22-Oct-91 SWS196/R) Old fisherwoman (23x15cm-9x6in) s. W/C*
£1100 $1870   *(22-Oct-91 SWS171/R) Two figures looking across harbour (35x25cm-14x10in)
            s.*
£2000 $3560   *(28-Nov-91 L209/R) Figures on quayside before cottages, Polperro Harbour,
            Cornwall (36x25cm-14x10in) s. W/C*
£2200 $3784   *(10-Oct-91 L350/R) Woman and children in courtyard before punt
            (33x48cm-13x19in) s.d.1881 W/C*
£3000 $5490   *(5-Jun-92 C16/R) A moment's rest (39x38cm-15x15in) s. W/C bodycol.*

LANGLEY, William (19th C) British
£520 $868   (22-Aug-91 CSK87) Colwyn Bay (51x76cm-20x30in) s.
£550 $957   (19-Sep-91 TL519) Highland cattle by a loch (29x49cm-11x19in) s.
£1600 $2736   (12-Mar-92 CSK227) The Thames from Richmond Hill (51x76cm-20x30in) s.
            i.verso

LANGLOIS, M W (19th C) British
£600 $1032   (4-Mar-92 CBB25) Two terriers ratting in a stable (25x30cm-10x12in)

LANGLOIS, Mark W (19th C) British

£520	$900	(6-Sep-91 S.BM140/R) The toy seller (20x15cm-8x6in) s. panel
£650	$1118	(4-Mar-92 S75/R) Toy boat (53x43cm-21x17in) s.
£650	$1157	(1-May-92 PHE58/R) Pet rabbits (21x15cm-8x6in) s. panel
£650	$1164	(14-Nov-91 CSK260) The shared meal (135x109cm-53x43in) s.
£679	$1256	(9-Jun-92 FB.M70) Taking salute (53x43cm-21x17in) s. (C.D 1500)
£700	$1197	(12-Mar-92 CSK254/R) The fruit seller (53x43cm-21x17in) s.
£900	$1674	(18-Jun-92 B153/R) Children playing with rabbits (21x15cm-8x6in) s. panel
£1000	$1720	(4-Mar-92 S152/R) Pet rabbit. First recital (53x43cm-21x17in) s.
£1100	$1958	(30-Apr-92 CSK72) Grandfather playing the flute. Buying apples on the way home (53x44cm-21x17in) s. pair
£1228	$2211	(22-Nov-91 SA.A1736/R) Woman and girl watching geese (76x60cm-30x24in) s. (DM 3500)
£1350	$2403	(28-Apr-92 PH144/R) Happy moments. Roadside inn (53x43cm-21x17in) init. pair
£2400	$4104	(18-Mar-92 WAW329/R) Little navigator. Itinerant musician (51x41cm-20x16in) one s.i.verso one init. pair
£4600	$7912	(11-Oct-91 C29/R) The village fair (71x91cm-28x36in) init. s.i.verso

LANINO, Bernardino (1510-1578) Italian

£4000	$7680	(7-Jul-92 C122/R) Flagellation of St Catherine (51x37cm-20x15in) i. chk wash htd white arched top

LANNOY, Aristide de (?) ?

£400	$708	(13-Feb-92 B255/R) Portrait of a lady, wearing a feather boa (79x58cm-31x23in) s. pastel

LANOUE, Felix Hippolyte (1812-1872) French

£2577	$4459	(27-Mar-92 CN.P59/R) Vue des ruines romaines a Arles (45x36cm-18x14in) s.d.1851 (F.FR 25000)

LANSAC, Francois-Emile de (1803-1890) French

£666	$1199	(29-Jan-92 LC.P19) Portrait equestre d'un roi croise (59x71cm-23x28in) s. (F.FR 6500)

LANSDOWNE, James Fenwick (1937-) Canadian

£4948	$8411	(23-Oct-91 MA.V100) The Golden Crown Kinglets (48x43cm-19x17in) s.d.1975 W/C (C.D 9500)

LANSIL, Walter Franklin (1846-1925) American

£729	$1400	(31-Jul-92 E.EDM101/R) The harbour front, Boston (43x56cm-17x22in) s.
£2639	$4750	(22-Nov-91 S.BM65/R) Calm in vineyard sound (25x76cm-10x30in) s.d.1883
£3892	$7200	(10-Jun-92 CE.NY238/R) Fete night, Venice (70x102cm-28x40in) s.d.1906 s.i.d.1906 verso

LANSKOY, Andre (1902-1976) Russian/French

£1027	$1848	(19-Nov-91 FB.P39/R) Le village (60x81cm-24x32in) (F.FR 10000)
£1405	$2458	(5-Apr-92 ZZ.F238/R) L'atelier du peintre (24x31cm-9x12in) s. (F.FR 13500)
£1717	$3005	(5-Apr-92 ZZ.F228/R) Composition (18x24cm-7x9in) init. (F.FR 16500)
£1824	$3301	(18-May-92 AT.P115/R) Sur le banc (25x36cm-10x14in) s. (F.FR 18000)
£2100	$3633	(26-Mar-92 C25/R) Tournant interieur (22x27cm-9x11in) s. d.1944verso
£2599	$4990	(7-Jul-92 ARC.P57/R) Composition (46x55cm-18x22in) s. (F.FR 25000)
£4120	$7333	(29-Apr-92 G.Z102/R) Scene de village (50x65cm-20x26in) s. paper on canvas (S.FR 11000)
£4494	$8000	(29-Apr-92 G.Z83/R) Le repas (60x81cm-24x32in) s. (S.FR 12000)
£5842	$10808	(11-Jun-92 HN.H302/R) Solo pour flute (65x21cm-26x8in) s. i.verso (DM 17000)
£6179	$10566	(21-Mar-92 AT.P40/R) La nuit s'approche (50x73cm-20x29in) s. i.verso (F.FR 60000)
£6857	$12000	(26-Sep-91 SY.I69/R) Vase of flowers (99x64cm-39x25in) s.
£7514	$13000	(2-Oct-91 SY.NY75/R) Composition (80x54cm-31x21in) s.
£7569	$13699	(19-May-92 AB.S5267/R) Reproches inutiles - 1959 (60x72cm-24x28in) s. (S.KR 80000)
£7684	$13832	(2-Feb-92 CSC.P83/R) Ni moi, ni toi (55x33cm-22x13in) s. i.d.60verso (F.FR 75000)
£7800	$13494	(26-Mar-92 S11/R) Composition (56x65cm-22x26in) s.
£8656	$15840	(3-Jun-92 PIC.P89/R) Composition (60x73cm-24x29in) s. d.1959verso (F.FR 85000)
£9734	$17520	(2-Feb-92 ZZ.F196/R) Composition (73x91cm-29x36in) s. (F.FR 95000)
£10288	$19547	(26-Jun-92 FB.P15/R) Habitation de l'Arlequin (99x72cm-39x28in) s. (F.FR 100000)
£10571	$18500	(28-Feb-92 SY.NY273/R) Composition in blue and grey (77x51cm-30x20in) s.
£11500	$19895	(26-Mar-92 C18/R) La neige rose (60x73cm-24x29in) s.i.d.58verso
£12029	$22373	(15-Jun-92 GL.P91/R) Composition (96x54cm-29x24in) s. (F.FR 118000)
£13500	$23355	(26-Mar-92 C11/R) Biographie d'un papillon (101x72cm-40x28in) s.i.d.58verso
£13714	$24000	(25-Feb-92 SY.NY133/R) Untitled (99x65cm-39x26in) s.d.71verso
£16185	$28000	(2-Oct-91 SY.NY78/R) Angle du jardin (99x127cm-39x50in) s. d.61 verso
£18156	$32500	(14-Nov-91 SY.NY287/R) Sombre et decit (146x96cm-57x38in) s.d. 58 verso
£19920	$36056	(4-Dec-91 G.Z145/R) Composition (65x46cm-26x18in) s. (S.FR 50000)
£31219	$53072	(27-Oct-91 P.V17/R) Le jardin vagabone (114x146cm-45x57in) s. i.verso (F.FR 310000)
£813	$1415	(16-Apr-92 FB.P169/R) Composition (15x19cm-6x7in) mono. ink gouache paper laid down on canvas (F.FR 8000)

LANSKOY, Andre (1902-1976) Russian/French-cont.
£865	$1600	(12-Jun-92 SY.NY253/R) Three figures (13x17cm-5x7in) s. gouache
£2270	$4040	(29-Apr-92 F.F113/R) Senza titolo (66x48cm-26x19in) s. mixed media paper on canvas (I.L 5000000)
£2270	$4040	(29-Apr-92 F.F114) Senza titolo (66x48cm-26x19in) s. mixed media paper on canvas (I.L 5000000)
£3086	$5586	(2-Dec-91 CC.P13/R) Sans titre (63x49cm-25x19in) s. gouache (F.FR 30000)
£3093	$5351	(29-Mar-92 P.V20/R) Composition a fond noir (48x63cm-19x25in) s. gouache (F.FR 30000)
£4571	$8000	(25-Feb-92 SY.NY92/R) Abstrait (65x50cm-26x20in) s. gouache pastel
£5714	$10000	(25-Feb-92 SY.NY89/R) Untitled (65x50cm-26x20in) s. gouache pastel
£5960	$10788	(23-May-92 KV.L442/R) Composition (57x40cm-22x16in) s. gouache (B.FR 360000)
£6000	$10320	(12-Oct-91 KV.L420/R) Composition (49x31cm-19x12in) s. gouache (B.FR 360000)
£6179	$10566	(19-Mar-92 CSC.P31/R) Composition sur fond noir (40x64cm-16x25in) s. gouache ink (F.FR 60000)
£7560	$13835	(3-Jun-92 L.K261/R) Composition (48x64cm-19x25in) s. gouache (DM 22000)

LANSYER, Emmanuel (1835-1893) French
| £712 | $1302 | (12-May-92 GO.G226) Wooded landscape with figure on road (60x45cm-24x18in) s.d.78 (S.KR 7500) |
| £2113 | $3634 | (7-Oct-91 CSC.P124/R) Le Chateau de Chenonceaux (64x44cm-25x17in) s.d.81 (F.FR 21000) |

LANTARA, Simon Mathurin (1729-1778) French
| £3080 | $5359 | (13-Sep-91 C159/R) Wooded landscape with peasant watching over cattle, sheep and horse by river (40x52cm-16x20in) s.d. |
| £1631 | $3034 | (20-Jun-92 CH.MO238/R) Le Guet d'une riviere menant a un village masque par la pluie (25x38cm-10x15in) s.d.1767 black chk htd white red chk (F.FR 16000) |

LANTARA, Simon Mathurin (attrib) (1729-1778) French
| £1147 | $2099 | (3-Jun-92 R.T189/R) Landscape - man washing feet in fountain (89x102cm-35x40in) s. after Poussin (C.D 2500) |

LANTE, Louis Marie (attrib) (1789-?) French
| £513 | $924 | (22-Nov-91 AGS.P102) Promenade au Palais Royal (18x124cm-7x49in) pen sepia wash (F.FR 5000) |

LANTOINE, Fernand (1876-1936) French
£538	$1000	(17-Jun-92 CAS.M62) Puerto de la Selva, Espana (18x25cm-7x10in) board
£829	$1517	(12-May-92 C.A191) Congolese Harbour (70x104cm-28x41in) s. (B.FR 50000)
£1009	$1736	(20-Oct-91 I.N86/R) Village Africain (60x73cm-24x29in) s. (F.FR 10000)
£1337	$2272	(22-Oct-91 GM.B555/R) Calanques (24x34cm-9x13in) s. wood (B.FR 80000)
£2018	$3471	(20-Oct-91 I.N85) Scene Africaine (70x81cm-28x32in) s. (F.FR 20000)
£3500	$6230	(27-Nov-91 S295/R) Au spectacle (36x48cm-14x19in) s.

LANTS, Gerrard (1927-) Australian
£881	$1568	(26-Nov-91 J.M832) last chapter (58x49cm-23x19in) s. (A.D 2000)
£1111	$1978	(27-Apr-92 J.M45) The dancers (49x59cm-19x23in) s. canvas on board (A.D 2600)
£661	$1176	(26-Nov-91 J.M816) Afternoon outing s. W/C (A.D 1500)

LANYON, Peter (1918-1964) British
£880	$1522	(3-Oct-91 DLY717/R) Fish eye (8x15cm-3x6in) i.verso card
£3500	$6300	(20-Nov-91 S64/R) Foggia guitar (29x35cm-11x14in) s.d.44 s.i.d.1944 verso oil linen map on board
£14000	$25200	(20-Nov-91 S192/R) Strange coast (114x44cm-45x17in) s. s.i.d.1960verso board
£15000	$27000	(20-Nov-91 S191/R) Inland water (47x54cm-19x21in) s.d.52 s.l.verso board
£32000	$57600	(20-Nov-91 S67/R) Antigone (183x122cm-72x48in) s.d.62 i.stretcher
£660	$1135	(10-Oct-91 L53) Churchtown (30x25cm-12x10in) s.i.d.1948 silkscreen gouache
£2400	$4272	(28-Nov-91 L290/R) Abstract form (23x28cm-9x11in) s. mixed media
£4200	$7434	(5-Nov-91 PH64/R) Sea birds (79x58cm-31x23in) s.i.d.Oct.61verso gouache

LANZ (19th C) Austrian?
| £890 | $1557 | (20-Feb-92 D.V457/R) Farmstead (44x55cm-17x22in) s. i.d.1846verso (A.S 18000) |

LANZA, G G (?) Italian
| £1087 | $2011 | (8-Jun-92 CH.R629) Contadini presso i templi di Paestum (43x74cm-17x29in) s. W/C (I.L 2400000) |

LANZA, Giovanni (1827-?) Italian
| £2400 | $4152 | (4-Oct-91 C141/R) Bay of Naples (44x75cm-17x30in) s. W/C |

LANZA, Luigi (19th C) Italian
£580	$992	(17-Mar-92 PH230) The Grand Canal, Venice (25x35cm-10x14in) s.
£1224	$2093	(18-Mar-92 N.M580/R) Canale Grande, Venice (36x53cm-14x21in) s. (DM 3500)
£2208	$4195	(25-Jun-92 D.V442/R) Canale Grande with Rialto Bridge (36x53cm-14x21in) s. (A.S 45000)

LANZA, Vicenzo (?) Italian
£1300 $2210   (23-Oct-91 S132/R) View of the Parthenon, Athens (18x25cm-7x10in) s.i. W/C over pencil
£3000 $5190   (4-Oct-91 C137/R) Temple of Zeus with Acropolis. The Parthenon, Athens (24x36cm-9x14in) s. pencil W/C one htd.white pair

LANZANI, Polidoro (after) (1515-1565) Italian
£950 $1710   (22-Nov-91 SWS144) The Holy Family in a landscape (87x125cm-34x49in)

LANZANI, Polidoro (style) (1515-1565) Italian
£2800 $5040   (21-Nov-91 C116/R) Holy Family with infant St John the Baptist (61x75cm-24x30in) panel

LANZONI, P (19th C) Italian
£2000 $3540   (7-Nov-91 PHC742) Dainty morsel (38x29cm-15x11in) s. panel pair

LAPAYESE DEL RIO, Jose (1926-) Spanish
£1762 $3154   (14-Nov-91 ANS.M59/R) Bodegon de la naranja (54x75cm-21x30in) s. s.i.verso mixed media (S.P 320000)

LAPCHINE, Georges (20th C) Russian
£1025 $1844   (2-Feb-92 ZZ.F11/R) Terrasse fleurie sur la Mediterranee (60x73cm-24x29in) s. (F.FR 10000)

LAPICQUE, Charles (1898-1988) French
£1927 $3391   (8-Apr-92 FB.P99/R) Composition (63x49cm-25x19in) s.d.44 gouache pastel (F.FR 19000)
£3347 $5890   (8-Apr-92 FB.P102/R) Joseph et la femme de putiphar (50x65cm-20x26in) s.d.72 i.verso (F.FR 33000)
£6110 $11120   (15-Dec-91 P.V48/R) Villa Venitienne (51x32cm-20x13in) s. paper laid down on canvas (F.FR 60000)
£7216 $12485   (29-Mar-92 P.V62/R) Epave ancienne en Hollande (65x81cm-26x32in) s.d.1974 s.i.d.verso acrylic (F.FR 70000)
£7809 $13744   (8-Apr-92 FB.P108/R) Oedipe (54x73cm-21x29in) s.d.64 i.verso (F.FR 77000)
£8239 $14089   (22-Mar-92 I.N45/R) Figure (100x65cm-39x26in) s.d.1950 gouache (F.FR 80000)
£13505 $23364   (23-Mar-92 GL.P186/R) Le tennis (81x116cm-32x46in) s.d.1965 i.verso (F.FR 131000)
£15979 $27644   (23-Mar-92 GL.P187/R) La matinee d'un Seigneur (46x61cm-18x24in) s.d.1960 i.verso (F.FR 155000)
£17241 $30345   (8-Apr-92 FB.P90/R) Les derniers conseils (50x100cm-20x39in) s.d.50 i.verso (F.FR 170000)
£18557 $32103   (29-Mar-92 P.V73/R) Le Mont Palatin (92x73cm-36x29in) s.d.1958 (F.FR 180000)
£511 $936   (5-Feb-92 FB.P153) Personnage et chevaux (37x27cm-15x11in) s. Indian ink (F.FR 5000)
£514 $982   (3-Jul-92 GL.P88) Le cavalier (30x45cm-12x18in) s.d.1950 pencil dr (F.FR 5000)
£536 $916   (22-Mar-92 I.N71/R) Sans titre (27x21cm-11x8in) s.d.1982 crayolor (F.FR 5200)
£822 $1414   (4-Mar-92 AT.P62) Voiliers (31x49cm-12x19in) s.d.51 chl.htd.gouache (F.FR 8000)
£862 $1517   (8-Apr-92 FB.P107/R) Composition aux personnages (64x48cm-25x19in) s.d.73 chl.oil pastel (F.FR 8500)
£979 $1694   (29-Mar-92 P.V51/R) Untitled (33x24cm-13x9in) s. mixed media (F.FR 9500)
£979 $1694   (29-Mar-92 P.V50/R) Untitled (33x24cm-13x9in) s.d.1962 mixed media (F.FR 9500)
£1153 $1972   (22-Mar-92 I.N26/R) L'animateur (65x50cm-26x20in) s.d.1973 lead pencil oil pastel (F.FR 11200)
£1281 $2305   (27-Jan-92 GL.P43/R) Composition (62x46cm-24x18in) s.d.1947n gouache (F.FR 12500)
£1512 $2676   (10-Nov-91 ZZ.F220/R) Les tigres (18x27cm-7x11in) s.d.1961 mixed media board laid down on canvas (F.FR 15000)

LAPINE, Andreas Christian Gottfried (1868-1952) Canadian
£498 $886   (25-Nov-91 W.T1593/R) River scene with sunlit village (76x91cm-30x36in) s. board (C.D 1000)
£700 $1239   (6-Nov-91 SY.T30) Lumber Mill (49x60cm-19x24in) s. board (C.D 1400)

LAPINO, Marco (?) ?
£850 $1454   (17-Mar-92 SWS1108) The Oyster gatherers (78x107cm-31x42in)

LAPIRA see also PIRA, la

LAPIRA (?) Italian
£2513 $4472   (29-Oct-91 PH.T47/R) Isola di Procida (41x62cm-16x24in) s. gouache (C.D 5000)

LAPIRA (attrib) (?) Italian
£2600 $4628   (27-Nov-91 S315/R) Fishermen casting nets (65x94cm-26x37in) gouache
£3000 $5340   (27-Nov-91 S316) Vesuvius erupting (51x73cm-20x29in) gouache W/C
£5500 $9405   (19-Mar-92 B19/R) Naples from the Mergellina (61x94cm-24x37in) gouache

LAPIRA (circle) (?) Italian
£1200 $2052   (19-Mar-92 B8/R) The Bay of Naples (41x48cm-16x19in) gouache

LAPIRA (circle) (?) Italian-cont.
£1600 $2848   (27-Nov-91 B1) Bay of Naples (41x48cm-16x19in) gouache

LAPIRA, P (?) Italian
£1937 $3254   (27-Aug-91 RAS.K663) Isola di Procida (46x63cm-18x25in) s. gouache
    (D.KR 22000)
£11271 $20063   (25-Nov-91 BU.K66/R) Prospect views of Bay of Naples (45x64cm-18x25in) s.
    gouache three (D.KR 125000)

LAPORTE, C (20th C) ?
£790 $1375   (17-Sep-91 CH.AM295) Elegant ladies conversing on a beach
    (60x100cm-24x39in) s.i. board (D.FL 2600)

LAPORTE, George Henry (1799-1873) German
£1714 $3000   (18-Feb-92 CE.NY62/R) Over hill (58x77cm-23x30in) s.

LAPORTE, George Henry (attrib) (1799-1873) German
£1138 $1900   (25-Aug-91 LIT.L274) Fox hunting scene (30x46cm-12x18in) s.

LAPORTE, Georges (1926-) French
£533 $959   (2-Feb-92 CSC.P27) Petite Bretagne (19x24cm-7x9in) s. d.fevrier 89verso
    (F.FR 5200)
£566 $969   (18-Mar-92 LT.P36) Petite neige (22x27cm-9x11in) s. (F.FR 5500)
£717 $1291   (2-Feb-92 CSC.P25) Le plat d'huitres (33x41cm-13x16in) s. (F.FR 7000)
£1332 $2398   (2-Feb-92 CSC.P29/R) Bord de mer en Bretagne (73x100cm-29x39in) s.
    (F.FR 13000)
£1339 $2289   (18-Mar-92 LT.P39/R) Cote sauvage (65x92cm-26x36in) s. (F.FR 13000)
£2869 $5164   (2-Feb-92 CSC.P44 b/R) Neige pres de Zurich (80x100cm-31x39in) s.d.1967
    (F.FR 28000)
£2869 $5164   (2-Feb-92 CSC.P33/R) Hiver en Bretagne (55x73cm-22x29in) s. (F.FR 28000)

LAPOSTOLET, Charles (1824-1890) French
£550 $1007   (5-Feb-92 ZZ.B211) Harbour scene (28x22cm-11x9in) s.d.1882 panel
£1486 $2600   (18-Feb-92 CE.NY39/R) French village (41x32cm-16x13in) s.
£1600 $2896   (22-May-92 C116/R) Il Redentore, Venice (32x40cm-13x16in) s.
£1758 $3200   (26-May-92 CE.NY205/R) Le Canal de la Guidecca, Venise (31x40cm-12x16in)
    s.i. panel

LAPRADE, Pierre (1875-1932) French
£937 $1639   (5-Apr-92 ZZ.F116/R) Monastere a la lisiere de la foret (43x24cm-17x9in)
    s. (F.FR 9000)
£4948 $8561   (23-Mar-92 GL.P199/R) Jeune fille au carton a desin (65x54cm-26x21in) s.
    (F.FR 48000)
£509 $942   (11-Jun-92 ARC.P9/R) Femme se coiffant (30x24cm-12x9in) studio st. pen
    lead pencil (F.FR 5000)
£514 $915   (29-Nov-91 GAB.G2780/R) Femme peignant (31x28cm-12x11in) s. W/C
    (S.FR 1300)
£811 $1467   (18-May-92 AT.P196) La couturiere (35x18cm-14x7in) s. W/C (F.FR 8000)
£817 $1445   (8-Nov-91 LGB.P94) Vue de Volterra (19x39cm-7x15in) s. W/C gouache
    (F.FR 8100)

LAQUY, Willem Joseph (1738-1798) German
£3400 $5950   (1-Apr-92 S117/R) Interior with woman spinning (53x42cm-21x17in) s. panel

LARA, Edwina (19th C) British
£650 $1190   (7-Feb-92 K471/R) Busy beach scene with fisherman sorting catch
    (43x58cm-17x23in) s.

LARA, Georgina (19th C) British
£1050 $1869   (21-Jan-92 PH128) Village life (20x33cm-8x13in) s.
£2000 $3700   (11-Jun-92 CSK126/R) Figures with haycart in village landscape
    (33x48cm-13x19in) s.
£2000 $3800   (24-Jun-92 MMB396) Rural landscapes with figures before farmhouses
    (25x36cm-10x14in) s.d.1860verso pair
£2300 $3933   (12-Mar-92 CSK189/R) The village street (51x76cm-20x30in)
£2500 $4250   (24-Oct-91 CSK155/R) The village street (51x76cm-20x30in)
£6200 $11160   (19-Nov-91 PH93/R) Farmyard scenes (23x34cm-9x13in) s.d.1866 pair

LARA, P Leslie (19th C) British
£600 $1110   (11-Jun-92 CSK139/R) Harvesting (30x40cm-12x16in) s.

LARCHE, Raoul (1860-1912) French
£705 $1255   (31-Oct-91 LD.P189) La Trinite, rue de village (55x38cm-22x15in) s.
    i.d.1907verso (F.FR 7000)

LARCO, Jorge (1897-1967) Argentinian
£391 $750   (4-Aug-92 V.BA63) Arboles (32x40cm-13x16in) W/C
£447 $800   (6-May-92 V.BA62) Patio (66x50cm-26x20in) W/C
£838 $1500   (6-May-92 V.BA61) Paisaje (68x48cm-27x19in) W/C
£1075 $2000   (16-Jun-92 RO.BA101) Miguel Angel (67x51cm-26x20in) W/C

LARCOMBE, Ethel (?) ?
£900 $1548   (4-Mar-92 S326/R) Fantasia (16x33cm-6x13in) mono. W/C gold paint
    semi-circular

LARDOY, Francois (?) Belgian?
£1021 $1838   (19-Nov-91 GM.B339/R) Italienne buvant a la source (30x55cm-12x22in) s.
       (B.FR 60000)

LARGILLIERE, Nicolas de (1656-1746) French
£4297 $7605   (5-Nov-91 GF.L2084/R) Portrait of young woman (82x66cm-32x26in)
       (S.FR 11000)
£6166 $11778   (1-Jul-92 CD.P21/R) Portrait du Marquis de Brisay en Saint Jean-Baptiste
       (79x62cm-31x24in) (F.FR 60000)
£9250 $17667   (1-Jul-92 CD.P20/R) Portrait de la Marquise de Brisay sur fond de paysage
       (79x62cm-31x24in) (F.FR 90000)
£10194 $18960   (18-Jun-92 SY.MO230/R) Portrait de femme (80x64cm-31x25in) s.d.1699verso
       oval (F.FR 100000)
£12000 $21360   (30-Oct-91 S133/R) Portrait of gentleman said to be The Marquis de las
       Cases (81x64cm-32x25in) oval
£18127 $30816   (21-Oct-91 ARC.P6/R) Portrait d'une jeune femme au ruban rose
       (77x62cm-30x24in) (F.FR 180000)
£54381 $92447   (24-Oct-91 D.P22 b/R) Portrait de Madame Titon, nee Marguerite Becaille
       (137x105cm-54x41in) (F.FR 540000)
*£5464 $9344   (18-Mar-92 D.V45/R) Portrait of sculptor Jean Thierry le jeune
       (92x72cm-36x28in) pastel chk paper on canvas (A.S 110000)*

LARGILLIERE, Nicolas de (circle) (1656-1746) French
£925 $1767   (1-Jul-92 CD.P18) Portrait de Pierre de Brisay, Comte de Denonville
       (64x48cm-25x19in) (F.FR 9000)
£1826 $3250   (22-Jan-92 SY.NY61/R) Portrait of gentleman in armour (69x56cm-27x22in)
£2523 $4339   (16-Oct-91 AT.P106/R) Portrait d'un gentilhomme (91x73cm-36x29in)
       (F.FR 25000)
£2575 $4840   (16-Dec-91 AGS.P56/R) Portrait de jeune femme en robe d'apparat
       (81x64cm-32x25in) (F.FR 25000)

LARGILLIERE, Nicolas de (school) (1656-1746) French
£976 $1865   (3-Jul-92 SD.P96) Portrait de femme en buste (72x59cm-28x23in)
       (F.FR 9500)
£2117 $3705   (25-Sep-91 CSC.P26/R) Portrait d'homme vu en buste (81x64cm-32x25in) oval
       (F.FR 21000)
£3736 $6500   (16-Sep-91 B.SF2001/R) Portraits of Marie Therese and Marie Anne de
       Bourbon (34cm-13ins circular) pair

LARGILLIERE, Nicolas de (studio) (1656-1746) French
£785 $1335   (24-Oct-91 D.P11/R) Portrait de femme vue en buste (80x60cm-31x24in) oval
       (F.FR 7800)
£2367 $4023   (24-Oct-91 D.P17/R) Portrait de femme vue en buste (80x60cm-31x24in)
       (F.FR 23500)

LARGILLIERE, Nicolas de (style) (1656-1746) French
£1100 $1980   (21-Nov-91 CSK238) Portrait of nobleman in armour with lace jabot and
       cloak (73x68cm-29x27in) oval
£2100 $3654   (15-Apr-92 PHL211/R) Portrait of King James II, in armour, with Ribbon of
       Garter (124x101cm-49x40in)
£2949 $5250   (30-Oct-91 D.NY63) La Marquise de l'Isle Rouet (130x97cm-51x38in)
£7000 $12740   (11-Dec-91 S122/R) Portrait of lady, said to be Duchesse de Valier in
       masquerade costume (137x105cm-54x41in)

LARI, J P (19/20th C) Italian
£1400 $2394   (17-Mar-92 PH233) Shepherd girl and boy with flock (69x109cm-27x43in) s.

LARIONOV, Mikhail (1881-1964) Russian
£857 $1500   (28-Feb-92 SY.NY97/R) Fish in motion (24x37cm-9x15in) s.d.1906 paper on
       board
£2287 $3979   (14-Apr-92 ZZ.F106/R) Visage et main (33x33cm-13x13in) mono. s.verso
       paper (F.FR 22500)
£4573 $7957   (14-Apr-92 ZZ.F111/R) Nature morte a la bouteille de Benedictine
       (45x81cm-18x32in) s. i.verso (F.FR 45000)
£6098 $10610   (14-Apr-92 ZZ.F73/R) Composition a la table et aux pains
       (59x77cm-23x30in) s.verso (F.FR 60000)
£6098 $10610   (14-Apr-92 ZZ.F110/R) Deux cerises (45x81cm-18x32in) mono.
       s.i.d.1907verso (F.FR 60000)
£7714 $13500   (25-Feb-92 CH.NY30/R) La chaise d'osier (59x44cm-23x17in) init.
£18293 $31829   (14-Apr-92 ZZ.F109/R) Composition rayonniste bleue (52x43cm-20x17in)
       s.verso board (F.FR 180000)
£27439 $47744   (14-Apr-92 ZZ.F81/R) Autoportrait (98x102cm-39x40in) s.i.verso
       (F.FR 270000)
*£559 $973   (14-Apr-92 ZZ.F86/R) Baigneurs devant une barque et la mer
       (21x17cm-8x7in) mono. W/C (F.FR 5500)*
*£823 $1432   (14-Apr-92 ZZ.F84/R) Femme a l'eventail (30x19cm-12x7in) s. blk.crayon
       squared paper (F.FR 8100)*
£872 $1500   (12-Oct-91 SY.NY61/R) Composition (21x27cm-8x11in) init. ink wash
*£1931 $3360   (14-Apr-92 ZZ.F82/R) Les deux amies (45x55cm-18x22in) s.d.1908 lead
       pencil (F.FR 19000)*
*£2213 $3807   (12-Oct-91 SY.MO183/R) Portrait de Boris Kochno (14x13cm-6x5in) pencil
       (F.FR 22000)*

LARIVE-GODEFROY, Pierre Louis de (1735-1817) Swiss
£9630 $17430   (19-May-92 GF.L2242/R) Phantastic landscape (52x69cm-20x27in) s.d.1802
  (S.FR 26000)
£11952 $21633   (5-Dec-91 SY.Z12/R) Vue de Frascati prise du bas avec architectures a
  l'antique, personnages et animaux (143x175cm-56x69in) s.d.1786
  (S.FR 30000)

LARIVE-GODEFROY, Pierre Louis de (attrib) (1735-1817) Swiss
£2407 $4357   (19-May-92 GF.L2449/R) Savoy alpine landscape with peasants harvesting
  and thunderstorm rising (50x73cm-20x29in) panel (S.FR 6500)
£3600 $6300   (31-Mar-92 PH122/R) Horsemen with farm animals within barn
  (44x65cm-17x26in) panel

LARK, Tremayne (fl.1882-1885) British
£1700 $3077   (5-Dec-91 CSK186/R) Mrs Fitz-George dancing at Monte Carlo
  (114x89cm-45x35in) s.

LARKIN, William (attrib) (17th C) British
£15000 $28650   (15-Jul-92 S11/R) Portrait of Ludovick Stuart 2nd Duke of Lennox and his
  wife Frances (75x112cm-30x44in) panel

LARKWAY, G (20th C) ?
£680   *$1176*   *(25-Mar-92 PHI502) The link man (23x31cm-9x12in) indis.s.i.d.1911 chk*
  htd.W/C

LAROCHE, Armand (1826-1903) French
£787 $1400   (22-Jan-92 SY.NY389/R) Death of messenger (45x119cm-18x47in) s.

LAROCHE, Ernesto (?) Uruguayan
£519 $950   (4-Jun-92 GOM.M61) Paisaje con Rancho (12x16cm-5x6in) s. panel
£694 $1200   (30-Sep-91 GC.M16/R) Arroyo y Monte Criollo (17x12cm-7x5in) s. panel
£718 $1300   (2-Dec-91 GC.M75) La Canada (37x48cm-15x19in) s.
£751 $1300   (30-Sep-91 GC.M14/R) Paisaje con camino (14x18cm-6x7in) s. panel
£1742 $3100   (28-Oct-91 GC.M26/R) Paisaje rural (70x100cm-28x39in) s.

LAROCHE, Robert (?) French?
£1050 $1827   (12-Sep-91 GSP339) Seascape La Rochelle (43x53cm-17x21in) s.d.1949

LAROON, Marcellus (17/18th C) British
£1200   *$2112*   *(9-Apr-92 S28) Figure drawings - including mounted drummer, sportsman and*
  peddlar (8x5cm-3x2in) mono. pen four framed together

LAROON, Marcellus (circle) (17/18th C) British
£800 $1408   (8-Apr-92 S191/R) Musical soiree (42x36cm-17x14in) panel

LAROT, Dina (1943-) Austrian
£440   *$765*   *(12-Sep-91 D.V138) Girl wearing yellow dress (55x42cm-22x17in) s.d.1978*
  ochre W/C (A.S 9000)

LARPENTEUR, J D (19th C) French
£1093 $2000   (5-Jun-92 SY.NY217/R) A halt in the woods. Stag hunt (45x37cm-18x15in) s.
  panel pair

LARRANAGA, Enrique de (1900-1956) Argentinian
£517 $900   (19-Sep-91 V.BA59) Pescadores Avenida Costanera (42x51cm-17x20in) d.1955
£722 $1300   (20-Nov-91 V.BA56) Payaso (31x23cm-12x9in) tempera
£955 $1700   (28-Apr-92 PO.BA36) Paisaje (85x99cm-33x39in) s.d.1924
£2688 $5000   (16-Jun-92 RO.BA64) Arlequin (100x70cm-39x28in)
£2809 $5000   (28-Apr-92 PO.BA37) Paisaje de Cordoba (95x100cm-37x39in) s.d.1924

LARRAVIDE, Manuel (1871-1910) Uruguayan
£611 $1100   (20-Nov-91 V.BA57) Barco (15x33cm-6x13in) d.1902
£867 $1500   (30-Sep-91 GC.M22/R) Fragata (100x185cm-39x73in) s.d.98
£950 $1700   (6-May-92 CAS.M38) Marina (59x33cm-23x13in)
£1209 $2200   (11-Dec-91 RO.BA264) Pescadores de Montevideo (93x65cm-37x26in) s.
£1285 $2300   (6-May-92 V.BA64) Puerto de Buenos Aires (35x48cm-14x19in)
£2191 $3900   (28-Oct-91 GC.M25) Fragata (100x185cm-39x73in) s.d.98

LARRAZ, Julio (1944-) Cuban
£11111 $20000   (19-Nov-91 CH.NY71/R) Sinforosa's mirrored wall (153x101cm-60x40in)
  s.d.76
£12155 $22000   (18-May-92 CH.NY80/R) Listening (76x122cm-30x48in) s.d.83 masonite

LARRIEU, Gaston (1908-) French
£813 $1415   (13-Apr-92 GL.P128) Paysage de riviere (97x130cm-38x51in) s. (F.FR 8000)

LARRUMBIDE, Alberto (1909-) Spanish
£443   *$757*   *(17-Mar-92 FER.M204) El estudio - Tema de Fragonard (8x6cm-3x2in) min. s.*
  (S.P 80000)
£821   *$1461*   *(29-Oct-91 BRO.B370) Hechizo (9x7cm-4x3in) min. s. (S.P 150000)*
£875   *$1601*   *(13-May-92 FER.M211/R) El tepidarium (8x5cm-3x2in) min. s.d.1944*
  (S.P 160000)
£876   *$1558*   *(29-Oct-91 BRO.B339) Alfonso XIII (10x8cm-4x3in) min. s. (S.P 160000)*
£985   *$1753*   *(29-Oct-91 BRO.B309) Autorretrato con Saskia (11x9cm-4x4in) min. s.*
  (S.P 180000)

LARRUMBIDE, Alberto (1909-) Spanish-cont.
£1204 $2143   (29-Oct-91 BRO.B271) Bodegon (9x12cm-4x5in) min. s. (S.P 220000)

LARSEN, Adolph (1856-1942) Danish
£573 $1020   (28-Apr-92 RAS.K478) Harrestrup river (68x94cm-27x37in) s. (D.KR 6500)
£1144 $1923   (27-Aug-91 RAS.K481/R) Frederiksberg Avenue (49x65cm-19x26in) s.
                     (D.KR 13000)
£6977 $12000   (17-Oct-91 SY.NY283/R) Sunset over marsh (93x126cm-37x50in) s.d.1909

LARSEN, Alfred (1860-1946) Danish
£842 $1516   (22-Nov-91 SA.A1775/R) The little water carriers (50x70cm-20x28in) s.
                     (DM 2400)

LARSEN, Carl Frederick Emanuel see LARSEN, Emanuel

LARSEN, Emanuel (1823-1859) Danish
£968 $1627   (28-Aug-91 KH.K127/R) Landscape from Sognefjord, Iceland (19x28cm-7x11in)
                     (D.KR 11000)
£1764 $3139   (28-Apr-92 RAS.K374/R) View from Sonderborg (18x29cm-7x11in) s.d.1849
                     (D.KR 20000)
£2646 $4709   (28-Apr-92 RAS.K115/R) View of Kronborg (34x38cm-13x15in) s.d.1850
                     (D.KR 30000)

LARSEN, Ferdinand (1830-1892) Danish
£772 $1389   (22-Nov-91 SA.A1641/R) River landscape with farmhouse, evening
                     (28x36cm-11x14in) s.d.1885 (DM 2200)

LARSEN, Johannes (1867-1961) Danish
£624 $1073   (16-Oct-91 KH.K162) Birds in flight (39x47cm-15x19in) mono.d.25
                     (D.KR 7000)
£758 $1410   (16-Jun-92 RAS.K224/R) Wood pigeons in flight (33x44cm-13x17in) mono.d.29
                     (D.KR 8500)
£802 $1380   (16-Oct-91 KH.K161) Birds in flight over field (34x44cm-13x17in)
                     mono.d.43 (D.KR 9000)
£880 $1479   (27-Aug-91 RAS.K152/R) Swedish landscape with elk, cranes and birds
                     (95x190cm-37x75in) mono. sketch for fresco, Odense Town Hall
                     (D.KR 10000)
£1499 $2668   (28-Apr-92 RAS.K428/R) Pointer in heather landscape (90x120cm-35x47in)
                     init.d.1897-98-99 (D.KR 17000)
£2228 $3832   (16-Oct-91 KH.K50/R) Mallards in swimming and flight (60x80cm-24x31in)
                     mono.d.1924 (D.KR 25000)
£2230 $4148   (16-Jun-92 RAS.K234/R) Swans in flight over the fjord (60x80cm-24x31in)
                     mono.d.1914 (D.KR 25000)
*£427 $747   (1-Apr-92 KH.K125) Summer day by watermill (50x64cm-20x25in) mono.i.d.38
                     W/C (D.KR 4700)*
*£624 $1161   (16-Jun-92 RAS.K341) Gate in Kerteminde (35x45cm-14x18in) mono.d.43 pen
                     W/C (D.KR 7000)*
*£1606 $2987   (16-Jun-92 RAS.K363/R) Seagulls in flight along the coast
                     (49x64cm-19x25in) mono. pen W/C (D.KR 18000)*
*£1873 $3484   (16-Jun-92 RAS.K371/R) Ducks swimming (49x64cm-19x25in) mono. pen W/C
                     (D.KR 21000)*

LARSEN, Karl (1897-1977) Danish
£490 $843   (16-Oct-91 KH.K174) Nature morte. Figure study (47x55cm-19x22in)
                     init.d.21 double-sided (D.KR 5500)
£492 $895   (10-Dec-91 RAS.K131) Still life of two fish and lemon (90x130cm-35x51in)
                     init.d.26 (D.KR 5500)
£534 $929   (17-Sep-91 RAS.K650) Still life (60x73cm-24x29in) s. (D.KR 6000)
£590 $1033   (1-Apr-92 KH.K129) Nature morte (65x77cm-26x30in) (D.KR 6500)

LARSEN, Knud (1865-1922) Danish?
£2817 $4732   (27-Aug-91 RAS.K593/R) Market day in Holbaek (63x86cm-25x34in)
                     mono.d.1889 (D.KR 32000)

LARSEN, Lars (1876-1955) Norwegian
£789 $1468   (15-Jun-92 B.O99/R) Landscape from Hurum (58x80cm-23x31in) s.i.d.1925
                     (N.KR 9000)

LARSEN, Martin (?) ?
£948 $1669   (12-Apr-92 HOR.H21) Eagles (80x120cm-31x47in) s. (F.M 7500)

LARSEN, Oscar (1882-1972) Austrian
£874 $1555   (28-Apr-92 D.V240/R) Bacchanal (39x44cm-15x17in) s.d.948 (A.S 18000)
£981 $1865   (25-Jun-92 D.V643/R) Madonna with Child and angel (85x75cm-33x30in)
                     s.d.1950 (A.S 20000)
£993 $1768   (28-Nov-91 D.V103/R) Diana (76x100cm-30x39in) s.d.1920 (A.S 20000)
*£499 $892   (15-Jan-92 D.V150/R) The love ship (31x41cm-12x16in) s.d.1918 i.verso
                     mixed media (A.S 10000)*
£519 $991   (4-Jul-92 BOD.P608) The rest (31x47cm-12x19in) s. mixed media (DM 1500)
*£544 $952   (19-Feb-92 D.V198/R) Das Standchen (15x14cm-6x6in) s.d.1922 mixed media
                     (A.S 11000)*
*£544 $952   (19-Feb-92 D.V199/R) Artist and models (15x14cm-6x6in) s.d.1928 mixed
                     media (A.S 11000)*
*£1026 $1826   (28-Apr-92 CH.ME249) Moses parting the Red Sea (66x96cm-26x38in) s. mixed
                     media (A.D 2400)*

LARSEN, Oscar (1882-1972) Austrian-cont.
£1246 $2231 *(15-Jan-92 D.V151/R) Bacchanale (71x100cm-28x39in) s. mixed media board on board (A.S 25000)*

LARSON, Marcus (1825-1864) Swedish
£5758 $10422 *(3-Dec-91 AB.S4631/R) Sailing vessels by Kronborg Palace, moonlit night (92x127cm-36x50in) s.d.1850 (S.KR 60000)*
£5977 $10938 *(14-May-92 BU.S35/R) Lake landscape with figures walking, fishing and rowing (70x84cm-28x33in) s.d.1848 (S.KR 63000)*
£6055 $10959 *(19-May-92 AB.S4911/R) Moonlit seascape with steamship on fire (73x108cm-29x43in) s.d.1857 (S.KR 64000)*

LARSON, Nils (1872-1914) Swedish
£2347 $4224 *(19-Nov-91 RAS.K279/R) Interior with women sewing (57x80cm-22x31in) s.d.09 (D.KR 26000)*

LARSSEN, Ansgar (1897-1967) Norwegian?
£966 $1661 *(7-Oct-91 B.O83/R) Man with concertina (57x49cm-22x19in) s.d.32 (N.KR 11000)*

LARSSON, Carl (1853-1919) Swedish
£566 $1002 *(5-Nov-91 BA.S223/R) Bjornstjerne Bjornson (15x13cm-6x5in) init. Indian ink (S.KR 6000)*
£667 $1213 *(14-Dec-91 BA.S151) Portrait of old woman (9x6cm-4x2in) init. Indian ink (S.KR 7000)*
£1139 $2083 *(14-May-92 BU.S95/R) School boy (58x21cm-23x8in) init. pencil (S.KR 12000)*
£1823 $3300 *(3-Dec-91 AB.S4632/R) Landscape from Vasteras with the Cathedral (26x23cm-10x9in) s. wash (S.KR 19000)*
£13283 $24307 *(14-May-92 BU.S94/R) The angel (62x40cm-24x16in) mono.d.1898 W/C (S.KR 140000)*
£28937 $52955 *(12-May-92 GO.G264/R) Karin Larsson reading in the long green grass (22x27cm-9x11in) s.i.d.1883 W/C htd white (S.KR 305000)*
£49057 $87811 *(7-May-92 RAS.S44/R) Girl by window (74x68cm-29x27in) init.d.1912 W/C (S.KR 520000)*
£55028 $100702 *(11-May-92 NOR.S40/R) Martina by the open fire (50x71cm-20x28in) init.d.1908 W/C (S.KR 580000)*
£67362 $123273 *(14-May-92 BU.S93/R) The fence (64x63cm-25x25in) init.d.1904 W/C (S.KR 710000)*
£85389 $156262 *(11-May-92 NOR.S32/R) Playing hide-and-seek (94x62cm-37x24in) init. W/C (S.KR 900000)*
£96226 $172245 *(7-May-92 RAS.S45/R) Now it's Christmas again (58x147cm-23x58in) init.d.1907 W/C (S.KR 1020000)*

LARSSON, Hans (1910-1973) Swedish
£576 $1042 *(3-Dec-91 AB.S5079/R) Still life of green bottle (54x36cm-21x14in) s.d.52 (S.KR 6000)*
£713 $1276 *(16-Nov-91 FAL.M190/R) Still life of musical instruments and jug (43x55cm-17x22in) s.d.59 (S.KR 7500)*
£1901 $3403 *(16-Nov-91 FAL.M186/R) Houses - view from the artist's studio (76x91cm-30x36in) s.d.36 (S.KR 20000)*

LARSSON, Marcus (1825-1864) Swedish
£2087 $3820 *(11-May-92 NOR.S3/R) Fjord landscape with sailing vessel (32x48cm-13x19in) s.d.1852 (S.KR 22000)*

LARTER, Richard (1929-) Australian
£1502 $2509 *(19-Aug-91 SY.ME299/R) Untitled abstract (121x181cm-48x71in) init.d.1967 board (A.D 3200)*
£1613 $3000 *(21-Jun-92 SY.ME55/R) Scatter shift (183x142cm-72x56in) init.d.1980 acrylic (A.D 4000)*
£1878 $3136 *(19-Aug-91 SY.ME321/R) Gabari No. 5 (179x124cm-70x49in) init.d.12.1983 i.verso acrylic canvas (A.D 4000)*
£2419 $4500 *(21-Jun-92 SY.ME28/R) Dead eye glitter (135x84cm-53x33in) s.d.1974 i.verso acrylic (A.D 6000)*
£3052 $5096 *(19-Aug-91 SY.ME335/R) Kind of nasty (182x114cm-72x45in) s.d.2.77 i.verso acrylic canvas (A.D 6500)*
£3226 $6000 *(21-Jun-92 SY.ME100/R) Luddenham evocation (178x155cm-70x61in) s.d.1973 acrylic (A.D 8000)*

LARTIGUE, Jacques Henri (1894-1986) French
£912 $1650 *(20-May-92 I.N136) Vase de fleurs (73x92cm-29x36in) s. (F.FR 9000)*
£1026 $1836 *(19-Jan-92 PPB.P151/R) Bouquet (97x74cm-38x29in) s. (F.FR 10000)*

LARUE, Andre Leon (1785-1834) French
£850 $1462 *(4-Mar-92 C19/R) Lady, in purple dress, lace collar and shawl, lace bonnet, wearing Order (6x?cm-2x?in) min. s.d.1818 gilt-metal mount oval*
£1365 $2471 *(22-May-92 L.K1103/R) Portrait of Austrian Hungarian nobleman wearing uniform (4x3cm-2x1in) min.s. oval (DM 4000)*

LARUS, Eliane (1944-) French
£1220 $2122 *(14-Apr-92 CSC.P78) Enfant au rateau (92x73cm-36x29in) s. acrylic panel (F.FR 12000)*

LARWIL, David (1956-) Australian

£2511	$4444	(26-Apr-92 SY.ME372/R) Evening. Untitled (116x150cm-46x59in) double-sided (A.D 5900)
£2553	$4519	(26-Apr-92 SY.ME382/R) Here to learn (183x152cm-72x60in) s.i.d.1987 stretcher (A.D 6000)
£1101	*$1960*	*(26-Nov-91 J.M230/R) Untitled (75x101cm-30x40in) init. i.verso oil collage canvas (A.D 2500)*

LARWIN, Johann (1873-1938) Austrian

£674	$1200	(22-Jan-92 SY.NY408/R) Hunger (51x43cm-20x17in) s. board
£674	$1200	(22-Jan-92 SY.NY427/R) Taking wounded to rear (44x62cm-17x24in) s.d.1916 indist.i.d.1916 verso paper on board
£730	$1300	(22-Jan-92 SY.NY406/R) Cossack (63x42cm-25x17in) s.d.1917 paper on board
£787	$1400	(22-Jan-92 SY.NY424/R) Front trench (41x55cm-16x22in) s.d.1916 canvas on board
£899	$1600	(22-Jan-92 SY.NY429/R) After battle (42x56cm-17x22in) s. indist.i.d.1915 verso board
£955	$1700	(22-Jan-92 SY.NY422/R) Machine gunners (33x42cm-13x17in) s.d.1918 paper on board
£976	$1689	(3-Oct-91 D.V135/R) Gypsy girl (32x25cm-13x10in) s. board (A.S 20000)
£1011	$1800	(22-Jan-92 SY.NY425/R) In trenches (48x61cm-19x24in) s.d.1916 indist.i.d.1916 verso canvas on board
£1067	$1900	(22-Jan-92 SY.NY423/R) Life in trenches (36x49cm-14x19in) s.d.1916 paper on board
£1292	$2300	(22-Jan-92 SY.NY412/R) Refugees (36x49cm-14x19in) s. indist.i.d.1915 verso board
£1348	$2400	(22-Jan-92 SY.NY426/R) Soup kitchen (110x110cm-43x43in) s.
£3933	$7000	(22-Jan-92 SY.NY411/R) Death directs bullet (100x100cm-39x39in) s.

LASARD, L Albert (20th C) German

£3714	$6500	(26-Sep-91 SY.I43/R) Port scene, Berlin (68x93cm-27x37in) s.

LASCANO, Juan (1947-) Argentinian

£17778	$32000	(19-Nov-91 CH.NY204/R) Virgo (130x100cm-51x39in) s.i.d.90

LASCAUX, Elie (1888-1969) French

£811	$1500	(12-Jun-92 SY.NY220/R) La route de Sacre-Coeur (45x61cm-18x24in) s.
£1400	$2534	(2-Dec-91 CSK80/R) La lune sur la mer (60x73cm-24x29in) s.d.54 s.i.d.verso

LASELLAZ, Gustave Francois (19th C) French

£4000	$7000	(20-Feb-92 SY.NY70/R) Sur la plage (24x33cm-9x13in) s.

LASKE, Oskar (1874-1951) Austrian

£4847	$8822	(26-May-92 D.V146/R) After the circus performance (38x50cm-15x20in) s.d.48 (A.S 100000)
£534	*$950*	*(28-Apr-92 D.V236/R) Portrait of lady seated (45x34cm-18x13in) s.d.1947 W/C board (A.S 11000)*
£551	*$998*	*(5-Dec-91 D.V216) Shipwrecked, illustrations for Shakespeare's Storm (31x23cm-12x9in) s. pencil W/C (A.S 11000)*
£1359	*$2419*	*(28-Apr-92 D.V264/R) Beach of Hoorn (47x37cm-19x15in) s.i. mixed media (A.S 28000)*
£1738	*$3093*	*(28-Nov-91 D.V108/R) Figures for opera Maruf by Wolf Ferrari, stage design (34x42cm-13x17in) s.i. W/C gouache (A.S 35000)*
£2731	*$4861*	*(28-Nov-91 D.V213/R) Kiew street scene (36x50cm-14x20in) s.i. W/C gouache (A.S 55000)*
£2921	*$5345*	*(3-Jun-92 L.K263/R) Still life of flowers (64x43cm-25x17in) s.d.1944 gouache bodycol (DM 8500)*
£3904	*$6755*	*(3-Oct-91 D.V248/R) Bunch of flowers (38x29cm-15x11in) s. gouache (A.S 80000)*
£5958	*$10606*	*(28-Nov-91 D.V107/R) Grundlsee s.i. W/C gouache (A.S 120000)*

LASKER, Jonathan (1948-) American

£4749	$8500	(9-May-92 CE.NY205/R) Beer culture (61x76cm-24x30in) s.d.1988verso linen
£6286	$11000	(27-Feb-92 CE.NY258/R) For small country (76x61cm-30x24in) s.d.1987 verso
£14525	$26000	(5-May-92 CH.NY104/R) Standards of expression (152x213cm-60x84in) s.d.1989verso
£17143	$30000	(27-Feb-92 CH.NY75/R) Mantra to a distracted God (183x140cm-72x55in) s.d.1990verso

LASKO, Hans (1900-) German

£410	*$741*	*(23-May-92 GB.B6799) Rider and walkers on avenue in park (27x41cm-11x16in) s. col.pastel linen (DM 1200)*

LASSALLE, Louis see CABAILLOT, Louis Simon

LASSCHER, Sofy (20th C) ?

£800	$1368	(17-Mar-92 PH108) Still life of mixed flowers in silver vase (61x51cm-24x20in) s.

LASSEN, Hans August (1857-?) German

£922	$1677	(26-May-92 KF.M388/R) Wine tasting in vault (35x54cm-14x21in) s.d.1894 (DM 2700)
£1180	$2100	(22-Jan-92 SY.NY277/R) Blowing bubbles (62x76cm-24x30in) s.d.1888

LASSEN, Hans August (1857-?) German-cont.
£2055 $3534 (8-Oct-91 ZEL.L1578/R) Three gentleman seated in cellar tasting new vintage (50x40cm-20x16in) s.i.d.1908 (DM 6000)

LASSNIG, Maria (20th C) Austrian
£1939 $3529 (26-May-92 D.V218/R) Untitled (50x65cm-20x26in) s.d.60 chl paper on board (A.S 40000)
£3393 $6175 (26-May-92 D.V219/R) Untitled (50x65cm-20x26in) s.d.59 W/C (A.S 70000)

LASZLO DE LOMBOS, Philip Alexius de (1869-1937) British
£17000 $31110 (13-May-92 S36/R) Portrait of Dame Gwen Ffrangcon-Davies as Mary Queen of Scots (91x71cm-36x28in) s.i.d.1934

LATAPIE, Louis (1891-1972) French
£716 $1310 (5-Feb-92 FB.P154) Femme allongee. Nu allongee (46x38cm-18x15in) s. paper double-sided (F.FR 7000)
£760 $1375 (20-May-92 FB.P163) Nature morte (27x35cm-11x14in) s. (F.FR 7500)
£803 $1437 (6-May-92 GD.B739/R) Composition au melone (54x73cm-21x29in) s.i.verso (S.FR 2200)
£811 $1467 (20-May-92 I.N137/R) Le modele nu (66x25cm-26x10in) s. paper on canvas (F.FR 8000)
£922 $1660 (2-Feb-92 CSC.P124) Nature morte (33x39cm-13x15in) s. (F.FR 9000)
£2926 $5033 (20-Oct-91 I.N173/R) Nu cubiste (65x25cm-26x10in) s. paper laid down on canvas (F.FR 29000)
£436 $789 (20-May-92 FB.P166) En devissant (24x31cm-9x12in) s. studio st.verso ink wash (F.FR 4300)
£773 $1338 (29-Mar-92 FE.P31) Les roses de Rochard s. W/C (F.FR 7500)

LATASTER, Ger (1920-) Dutch
£4630 $8380 (2-Dec-91 CC.P26/R) Deux vents (65x90cm-26x35in) s.d.1962 (F.FR 45000)
£576 $1042 (21-May-92 SY.AM370/R) Untitled (55x75cm-22x30in) s.d.90 W/C col.chk (D.FL 1900)
£617 $1123 (12-Dec-91 SY.AM243) Het brood (45x58cm-18x23in) s.d.82 W/C col.chk (D.FL 2000)
£1296 $2359 (12-Dec-91 SY.AM290/R) Untitled (69x99cm-27x39in) s.d.76 W/C col.pencil (D.FL 4200)

LATHAM, James (style) (1696-1747) British
£1300 $2327 (13-Nov-91 S121/R) Portrait of Elizabeth Kettle standing by fountain holding parakeet (121x96cm-48x38in)
£1400 $2506 (13-Nov-91 S129/R) Portrait of John Dawson Damer, 1st Earl of Portarlington (74x61cm-29x24in) painted oval

LATHAM, Molly M (fl.1935-1938) British
£4400 $8448 (28-Jul-92 SWS151/R) The Crawley and Horsham Hunt outside Knepp Castle (90x135cm-35x53in) s.d.1938

LATHANGUE, Henry Herbert (1859-1929) British
£6500 $11310 (17-Sep-91 PH29/R) A deserted rose garden in Provence (61x72cm-24x28in) s.i. stretcher

LATHION, Luc (1931-) Swiss?
£471 $800 (23-Oct-91 GD.B438/R) View of town (50x39cm-20x15in) s.d.1957verso pavatex (S.FR 1200)

LATHROP, Francis (1849-1909) American
£1600 $2800 (3-Apr-92 S.W2471/R) Little seamstress (104x86cm-41x34in) s.

LATHROP, William Langson (1859-1938) American
£833 $1400 (28-Aug-91 MFA.C205/R) Landscape (36x51cm-14x20in) s. with letter
£914 $1600 (26-Sep-91 CH.NY103/R) Sketching near Easton (41x36cm-16x14in) i.d.1900 stretcher

LATOIX, Gaspard (fl.1882-1903) British
£4420 $8000 (5-Dec-91 SY.NY39/R) Apache Indian on horseback (61x51cm-24x20in) s.
£851 $1600 (18-Dec-91 SY.NY376/R) Cowboy on horseback (50x38cm-20x15in) s. W/C paper on board

LATOUCHE, Gaston de (1854-1913) French
£1520 $2751 (18-May-92 AT.P119) Le gue (39x39cm-15x15in) s. panel (F.FR 15000)
£1955 $3714 (22-Jun-92 AT.P60) Le carrosse (49x41cm-19x16in) paper on panel (F.FR 19000)

LATOUR, Georges de (1593-1652) French
£1229 $2200 (13-Jan-92 CE.NY192) Saint Jerome (99x75cm-39x30in)
£1700000 $3094000 (13-Dec-91 C54/R) Blind hurdy-gurdy player in profile to left (85x61cm-33x24in)

LATOUR, Georges de (circle) (1593-1652) French
£2616 $4500 (10-Oct-91 SY.NY65/R) Saint Paul the Apostle (67x51cm-26x20in)

LATOUR, Maurice Quentin de (1704-1788) French
£203874 $379205 (18-Jun-92 SY.MO60/R) Portrait du Marechal de Belle-Isle (69x49cm-27x19in) pastel (F.FR 2000000)

LAUBIES, Rene (1924-) French
£595	$1100	(12-Jun-92 SY.NY240/R) Untitled (100x64cm-39x25in) s.d.1964 board on canvas
£924	$1663	(19-Nov-91 FB.P183/R) Composition (34x26cm-13x10in) s. paper laid down on canvas (F.FR 9000)

L'AUBINIERE, C M de (fl.1880-1889) Canadian
£488	$878	(19-Nov-91 FP.M36) Sunset over Lower Town, Quebec (26x35cm-10x14in) s.d.1888 board (C.D 1000)
£732	$1317	(19-Nov-91 FP.M153) Harbour view, Quebec (25x35cm-10x14in) s.d.1888 board (C.D 1500)

L'AUBINIERE, G M de (19/20th C) ?
£400	*$696*	*(20-Sep-91 CBB243) Wooded valley scape with meandering river (48x76cm-19x30in) s. W/C*

LAUBSER, Maggie (1886-1973) South African
£907	$1606	(4-Nov-91 SY.J290/R) Sailing boat in harbour (34x27cm-13x11in) s.d.24 board (SA.R 4500)
£1491	$2594	(13-Apr-92 SY.J362/R) Flower and cormorants (49x39cm-19x15in) s. board (SA.R 7500)
£3579	$6227	(13-Apr-92 SY.J363/R) Still life with Arum lilies (45x55cm-18x22in) s.d.23 canvas on board (SA.R 18000)
£4435	$7851	(4-Nov-91 SY.J292/R) Landscape with wood carrier (45x40cm-18x16in) s. board (SA.R 22000)
£7056	$12490	(4-Nov-91 SY.J293/R) Indian girl with sari (59x55cm-23x22in) s. board (SA.R 35000)
£8468	$14988	(4-Nov-91 SY.J294/R) Woman with yellow doek and red flowers (50x39cm-20x15in) init. canvas on board (SA.R 42000)
£9274	$16415	(4-Nov-91 SY.J291/R) Flamingoes (44x54cm-17x21in) s.d.36 board (SA.R 46000)

LAUDER, Charles James (?-1920) British
£580	$1038	(14-Jan-92 SWS155/R) The flower market (23x17cm-9x7in) s. canvas on card squared
£1500	$2610	(11-Sep-91 PHG23/R) By the quayside (90x60cm-35x24in) s.
£400	*$760*	*(23-Jun-92 CG632/R) Eton College and chapel from river (42x33cm-17x13in) s. W/C htd bodycol*
£820	*$1451*	*(6-Nov-91 S240) Fishing boats in the lagoon, Venice (27x37cm-11x15in) s. W/C htd.white*

LAUDER, Robert Scott (1803-1869) British
£12000	$21360	(28-Apr-92 S140/R) The Penance of Jane Shore (134x180cm-53x71in) bears sig.indist.i.verso arched top

LAUDY, J (?) Belgian
£1194	$2244	(18-Dec-91 GM.B4069/R) Portrait de femme (74x62cm-29x24in) s. (B.FR 70000)

LAUDY, Jean (1877-1956) Belgian
£2649	$4795	(23-May-92 KV.L192/R) Seated nude (88x58cm-35x23in) s. (B.FR 160000)
£3083	$5303	(12-Oct-91 KV.L375/R) Flowers in an interior (80x68cm-31x27in) s. panel (B.FR 185000)
£8725	$15880	(26-May-92 D.V20/R) Roses (71x90cm-28x35in) s. (A.S 180000)

LAUER, Josef (1818-1881) Austrian
£1488	$2500	(1-Sep-91 PO.BA22) Vaso con flores (38x27cm-15x11in) s.

LAUGE, Achille (1861-1944) French
£4733	$8992	(26-Jun-92 CSC.P98/R) Bouquet de fleurs (53x71cm-21x28in) s.d.16 (F.FR 46000)

LAUGEE, Georges (1853-?) French
£596	$1091	(1-Jun-92 W.T1435 a) Les jeune moissoneurs (46x53cm-18x21in) s. (C.D 1300)
£2261	$4319	(1-Jul-92 FB.P70/R) La moisson (65x54cm-26x21in) s. (F.FR 22000)
£3000	$5220	(16-Sep-91 TAY672/R) Mother with child in country landscape (130x86cm-51x34in) indist.s.d.1883
£3729	$6750	(2-Dec-91 S.SL290/R) Scene in wheat field with peasant woman calling unseen person to lunch (66x81cm-26x32in) s.d.1883
£4670	$8500	(28-May-92 SY.NY146/R) La moisson (84x58cm-33x23in) s.

LAUGHEED, Robert (20th C) American
£632	$1075	(11-Aug-91 LIT.L106) Hunt (51x61cm-20x24in) s.

LAULIE, Joseph (1928-) French
£515	$968	(18-Dec-91 LGB.P138) Le cafe des colonnes a Biarritz (33x41cm-13x16in) s.d.79 (F.FR 5000)

LAUMANS, Fanny (19th C) ?
£1300	$2314	(26-Nov-91 PH157) A helping hand (63x53cm-25x21in) s.d.1883

LAUME-DUPRE, Andre la (c.1915-) French
£22177	$38367	(4-Oct-91 CSC.P11/R) Elegantes au Pre Catelan (73x93cm-29x37in) s. (F.FR 220000)

LAUNOIS, Jean (1898-1942) French
£819 $1458   (27-Nov-91 AT.P40) Trois personnages (58x46cm-23x18in) s. W/C htd.pastel gouache (F.FR 8000)

LAUPHEIMER, Anton (1848-1927) German
£906 $1649   (12-Dec-91 L.K615) Young peasant girl wearing costume (27x21cm-11x8in) s. panel (DM 2600)

LAUR, Marie Yvonne (1879-?) French
£700 $1246   (28-Nov-91 CSK105) Tabby kitten (43x64cm-17x25in) s.indis.d.1904
£791 $1400   (13-Feb-92 S.W2116/R) Luring the kittens (33x23cm-13x9in) s.

LAUREN, Per Ake (1879-1951) Finnish
£553 $1007   (11-Dec-91 HOR.H57) Green landscape (37x43cm-15x17in) s.d.1934 (F.M 4300)
£620 $1097   (6-Nov-91 HOR.H67) Green landscape (51x64cm-20x25in) s.d.1922 (F.M 4400)

LAURENCE (?) ?
£1850 $3533   (1-Jul-92 FB.P168) Natures mortes aux raisins et aux cerises (46x38cm-18x15in) s. pair (F.FR 18000)

LAURENCE, Sydney (1865-1940) American
£1105 $2000   (4-Dec-91 D.NY94/R) View of St. Ives (30x41cm-12x16in) s.i. board
£3352 $6000   (13-Nov-91 B.SF2737/R) Early evening, Mount McKinley (54x65cm-21x26in) s.
£5143 $9000   (25-Sep-91 SY.NY36/R) Alaska Indian Cache. Springtime (20x25cm-8x10in) s. masonite pair
£5143 $9000   (25-Sep-91 SY.NY37/R) Mount McKinley (41x51cm-16x20in) s.
£6077 $11000   (6-Dec-91 CH.NY112/R) Mount McKinley from the Susitna Valley (30x40cm-12x16in) s. board
£670 $1200   (13-Nov-91 B.SF2739/R) Venice (43x29cm-17x11in) s. W/C

LAURENCIN, Marie (1885-1956) French
£1421 $2672   (16-Dec-91 AT.P49/R) Vase de fleurs (41x33cm-16x13in) paper laid down on canvas (F.FR 13800)
£4098 $7377   (2-Feb-92 ZZ.F153/R) Vase de tulipes et de pivoines (41x33cm-16x13in) paper laid down on canvas (F.FR 40000)
£13078 $22495   (12-Oct-91 SY.MO28/R) Cavaliere sur un chemin (20x25cm-8x10in) s. board (F.FR 130000)
£17486 $32000   (13-May-92 CH.NY209/R) Autoportrait (40x30cm-16x12in) s.d.1904 panel
£19244 $35216   (3-Jun-92 L.K264/R) Portrait of Madame Auclair (33x24cm-13x9in) s.d.1955 (DM 56000)
£33898 $60000   (7-Nov-91 SY.NY227/R) Autoportrait (41x33cm-16x13in) s.d.1946 s.i.d.verso
£35000 $60550   (24-Mar-92 C55/R) Les deux amies (35x27cm-14x11in) s.
£38000 $68780   (3-Dec-91 C274/R) Vase de fleurs (55x46cm-22x18in) s.d.1939
£45714 $80000   (25-Feb-92 SY.NY54/R) Fille couronnee de feuilles (41x33cm-16x13in) s.
£49180 $90000   (14-May-92 SY.NY310/R) Vase de fleurs avec lys (63x53cm-25x21in) s.d.1933
£57000 $103170   (4-Dec-91 S168/R) Deux filles a la guitare (41x33cm-16x13in) s.
£65574 $120000   (14-May-92 SY.NY311/R) Femme a la guitare (54x46cm-21x18in) s. canvas on board
£101695 $180000   (7-Nov-91 SY.NY225/R) Comme un betail pensif (61x50cm-24x20in) s.
£767 $1403   (5-Feb-92 FB.P156) Trois danseuses (20x27cm-8x11in) st.mono. lead pencil (F.FR 7500)
£1006 $1730   (12-Oct-91 SY.MO208/R) Cour de maison - projet de decor (25x30cm-10x12in) pencil col.crayons (F.FR 10000)
£1380 $2526   (5-Feb-92 FB.P157/R) Femme au chapeau (13x13cm-5x5in) bears st.mono lead pencil (F.FR 13500)
£1629 $2965   (12-Dec-91 CSC.P355/R) Portrait de femme au collier de perles (30x21cm-12x8in) st.mono. crayon (F.FR 16000)
£3800 $6536   (16-Oct-91 S102/R) Jeune fille (16x11cm-6x4in) init. W/C pencil
£3850 $6969   (22-May-92 BL.P75/R) Jeune femme au chapeau, voile rose (17x13cm-7x5in) s. W/C (F.FR 38000)
£5102 $9336   (3-Jun-92 PIC.P71/R) Jeune femme a l'eventail (16x12cm-6x5in) s. W/C (F.FR 50100)
£5714 $10000   (25-Feb-92 CH.NY43/R) Tete de jeune fille (14x11cm-6x4in) s. W/C over pencil
£7771 $14221   (3-Feb-92 SD.P136/R) Jeune femme a la guirlande (24x19cm-9x7in) s. col.crayons (F.FR 76000)
£8000 $14480   (3-Dec-91 C186/R) Autoportrait (20x15cm-8x6in) pencil col.crayon
£8000 $14480   (3-Dec-91 C187/R) Tete de jeune fille (32x26cm-13x10in) s. W/C pencil paper laid on board
£8147 $15071   (10-Jun-92 ZZ.F25/R) Elegante au foulard (37x27cm-15x11in) s. W/C (F.FR 80000)
£9000 $17190   (29-Jun-92 CSK39/R) Jeune femme au collier de Perles (55x45cm-22x18in) s. W/C
£9040 $16000   (6-Nov-91 CH.NY161/R) Femme a l'oiseau (21x16cm-8x6in) s. W/C brush india ink over pencil
£10000 $17400   (19-Sep-91 TL522/R) Girl with floer in her hair (26x21cm-10x8in) s. pencil crayon paper on board
£12346 $23457   (24-Jun-92 GL.P140 b/R) Portrait au foulard (30x25cm-12x10in) s. W/C (F.FR 120000)
£14124 $25000   (6-Nov-91 CH.NY154/R) Portrait de femme (31x26cm-12x10in) s. W/C over pencil
£22000 $38060   (25-Mar-92 S64/R) Trois filles debout et une fille asise avec chien (36x44cm-14x17in) s. ink pencil W/C
£24294 $43000   (6-Nov-91 CH.NY153/R) La ronde d'enfants (34x45cm-13x18in) s. W/C over pencil

LAURENG, Theodor (1879-1929) Norwegian
£479 $863   (19-Nov-91 GO.G231) Interior with woman and white tulips (102x132cm-40x52in) s.d.04 (S.KR 5000)
£668 $1156   (23-Mar-92 B.O78/R) Summer landscape (67x86cm-26x34in) s.d.1905 (N.KR 7500)

LAURENS, Albert (1864-?) French
£7000 $13020   (19-Jun-92 C92/R) Sea nymphs (100x160cm-39x63in) s.

LAURENS, Henri (1885-1954) French
£2014 $3585   (28-Oct-91 GL.P128) Femme assis (17x13cm-7x5in) mono. lead pencil (F.FR 20000)
£24565 $43726   (28-Nov-91 FB.P19/R) Composition cubiste (27x18cm-11x7in) s.d.1917verso pen (F.FR 240000)
£39817 $72865   (3-Jun-92 PIC.P58/R) Untitled (51x36cm-20x14in) s.d.1918 chk collage chl board (F.FR 391000)
£76503 $140000   (11-May-92 CH.NY18/R) Tete (52x29cm-20x11in) s.d.1919 gouache collage graphite chk board
£102354 $182190   (28-Nov-91 FB.P14/R) Bouteille de beaune (38x26cm-15x10in) s.d.1916 chk.chl. cut paper on board (F.FR 1000000)

LAURENS, Jean Paul (1838-1921) French
£659 $1200   (26-May-92 CE.NY97/R) Gentleman in red velvet coat (45x38cm-18x15in) s.
£1423 $2476   (15-Apr-92 CB.P15/R) Les supplicies (36x27cm-14x11in) mono. Indian ink wash brush pen (F.FR 14000)

LAURENS, Jules Joseph Augustin (1825-1901) French
£662 $1211   (2-Jun-92 AT.P175) Mosquees et voiliers a Constantinople (23x32cm-9x13in) s. W/C (F.FR 6500)
£1000 $1700   (23-Oct-91 S217/R) Tombeau de la Inttane Valide a Scutari, Constantinople (50x35cm-20x14in) i.verso W/C htd.bodycol gum arabic gold

LAURENT, Bruno Emile (20th C) French
£511 $894   (23-Feb-92 FE.P31) Rue de l'Abreuvoir (73x55cm-29x22in) s. i.verso (F.FR 5000)
£562 $983   (23-Feb-92 FE.P32) Le lapin agile (55x47cm-22x19in) s. i.verso (F.FR 5500)

LAURENT, Jean (20th C) French
£540 $961   (29-Oct-91 SWS157/R) Garden party (45x60cm-18x24in) s.
£540 $961   (29-Oct-91 SWS155) Slide (34x54cm-13x21in) s.
£540 $961   (29-Oct-91 SWS154) See-saw (35x55cm-14x22in) s.
£580 $1032   (29-Oct-91 SWS156/R) On beach (39x54cm-15x21in) s.
£705 $1256   (28-Apr-92 RAS.K251) Seascape (40x50cm-16x20in) i. (D.KR 8000)
£880 $1610   (6-Feb-92 DLY273) Figures on beach (23x36cm-9x14in) s.
£1083 $1949   (19-Nov-91 RAS.K510) Seascape with sailship off the coast (40x60cm-16x24in) s. panel (D.KR 12000)

LAURENT, Jean Antoine (1763-1832) French
£584 $993   (25-Oct-91 AT.P100) Jeune femme assise, dessinant dans un paysage (20x15cm-8x6in) gouache vellum (F.FR 5800)

LAURENT, Robert (1890-1970) American
£977 $1700   (15-Sep-91 JRB.C144/R) Composition cubiste aux insects (36x46cm-14x18in) s.

LAURENTI, Cesare (1854-1937) Italian
£34286 $60000   (19-Feb-92 CH.NY102/R) Blind Man's Bluff (70x98cm-28x39in) s.d.1886

LAURER, Johann (1892-1949) Austrian
£748 $1338   (15-Jan-92 D.V167/R) Technisches Museum, Vienna (58x81cm-23x32in) (A.S 15000)
£894 $1591   (28-Nov-91 D.V224/R) Meierei im Stadtpark, Wien (65x90cm-26x35in) (A.S 18000)
£894 $1591   (28-Nov-91 D.V223/R) Modling, Herzoggasse with view of Pestsaule (52x72cm-20x28in) (A.S 18000)
£1097 $1963   (15-Jan-92 D.V168/R) Belvedere Garten with view of Salesianerinnenkirche (52x73cm-20x29in) st.sig.verso (A.S 22000)

LAURET, Francois (1820-1868) French
£1700 $2890   (23-Oct-91 S72/R) View from Terrace, Algiers (28x43cm-11x17in) s.d.1851 board
£4258 $7750   (28-May-92 SY.NY175/R) Jeune homme au chapeau (66x54cm-26x21in) s.d.1851

LAURI, Filippo (1623-1694) Italian
£4800 $8544   (30-Oct-91 S177/R) Christ on the road to Calvary (50x65cm-20x26in) init. i.d.1675verso
£4979 $9061   (28-May-92 F.M57/R) Galatea (60x74cm-24x29in) (I.L 11000000)

LAURI, Filippo (attrib) (1623-1694) Italian
£3680 $6330   (15-Oct-91 CH.R68/R) Tancredi battezza Clorinda (96x73cm-38x29in) (I.L 8000000)
£430 $765   (29-Nov-91 ARC.P2) Porjet decoratif (18x26cm-7x10in) i. pen wash pierre noire (F.FR 4200)

LAURI, Filippo (style) (1623-1694) Italian
£1000 $1780   (31-Oct-91 B60/R) Hebe (75x60cm-30x24in)
£2000 $3560   (30-Oct-91 S25) The Martyrdom of St Stephen (46x66cm-18x26in)
£4000 $7000   (28-Feb-92 C10/R) Putti with flora in grounds of Italian villa
                          (65x98cm-26x39in)

LAURI, Filippo and GRIMALDI, Giovanni Francesco (attrib) (17th C) Italian
£13014 $23556   (5-Dec-91 F.M97/R) Battesimo di Cristo (180x145cm-71x57in) (I.L 28000000)

LAURITZ, Paul (1889-1975) American
£618 $1100   (26-Nov-91 MOR.P106 a) Landscape (30x38cm-12x15in) s. board
£674 $1200   (26-Nov-91 MOR.P64) Winter landscape (76x102cm-30x40in) s.
£698 $1200   (20-Oct-91 HG.C43) Spring landscape (51x61cm-20x24in) s.
£789 $1500   (24-Jun-92 B.SF6425/R) Oregon autumn (61x86cm-24x34in) s. board
£947 $1800   (23-Jun-92 MOR.P56 a) Boats in boatyard (41x51cm-16x20in) s.
£1011 $1800   (26-Nov-91 MOR.P106) Sierra mountains - Big Pine Creek (51x61cm-20x24in)
                          s.

LAUSEN, Uwe (1941-1970) ?
£1604 $2919   (25-May-92 WK.M767/R) Himmler and Kaltenbrunner (30x60cm-12x24in) s.
                          (DM 4700)
£1433   *$2609*   *(26-May-92 KF.M996/R) Family life (42x61cm-17x24in) s.i.d.1966 indian ink*
                          W/C over pencil (DM 4200)

LAUSTNER, J (jnr) (19th C) German
£692 $1315   (27-Jun-92 FN.L1141) Stag and does by a mountain lake (88x69cm-35x27in)
                          s.d.1884 (DM 2000)

LAUTERBURG, Martin (1891-1960) Swiss
£1445 $2687   (19-Jun-92 ZOF.Z1992/R) Expectations, reclining female nude and
                          marionette above (99x104cm-39x41in) (S.FR 3800)

LAUTERS, Paul (1806-1876) Belgian
£480   *$859*   *(16-Jan-92 B137) Extensive woodland landscape with figures resting by*
                          stream (53x75cm-21x30in) s.d.78 W/C bodycol

LAUVRAY, Abel (1870-1950) French
£1931 $3360   (15-Apr-92 PLF.P82) Campagne avignonaise (38x55cm-15x22in) s.
                          (F.FR 19000)
£2445 $4279   (5-Apr-92 ZZ.F115/R) Paysage d'Ile-de-France (38x55cm-15x22in) s. panel
                          (F.FR 23500)

LAUX, August (1847-1921) American
£823 $1375   (25-Aug-91 LIT.L186) Cat and kittens (10x15cm-4x6in) s. panel
£862 $1500   (15-Apr-92 SY.NY34/R) Still life with cherries in basket (20x25cm-8x10in)
                          s.
£884 $1600   (21-May-92 S.W2941/R) Chickens outside stable (25x36cm-10x14in) s.
£2924 $5000   (12-Mar-92 CH.NY61/R) Basket of apples (36x51cm-14x20in) s.
£3143 $5500   (26-Sep-91 CH.NY14/R) Gooseberries (25x35cm-10x14in) s.

LAVAGNA, Francesco (18th C) Italian
£8399 $14949   (28-Apr-92 F.R34/R) Vaso di fiori (32x41cm-13x16in) (I.L 18500000)
£19500 $37440   (8-Jul-92 S153/R) Still lifes of fruit and flowers in landscapes
                          (63x49cm-25x19in) s. pair

LAVAGNA, Francesco (attrib) (18th C) Italian
£20000 $38400   (8-Jul-92 S231/R) Still life of flowers in basket upon pedestal and fruit
                          in landscape (63x99cm-25x39in)

LAVAGNA, Francesco and Giuseppe (18th C) Italian
£15448 $29042   (18-Dec-91 AT.P21/R) Vase de fleurs sur un entablement devant un paysage
                          (72x97cm-28x38in) (F.FR 150000)

LAVAL, Fernand (1895-) French
£863 $1467   (23-Oct-91 GD.B1132/R) Rue de village (45x60cm-18x24in) s.d.1955
                          (S.FR 2200)

LAVALLE, John (1896-?) American
£1111 $2000   (22-Nov-91 S.BM175/R) Miss Laetitia Orlandini (102x76cm-40x30in) s.d.1928
                          s.verso

LAVALLEE-POUSSIN, Etienne de (1733-1793) French
£750   *$1440*   *(7-Jul-92 C303/R) Sacrifice to Priapus (17x21cm-7x8in) i. chk pen wash*
£7500   *$14400*   *(7-Jul-92 C63/R) Le rendez-vous de chasse (41x66cm-16x26in) i. chk pen*
                          wash

LAVALLEY, J J (19th C) American
£681 $1300   (24-Jul-92 DOU.M1) Peaches with leaves (48x33cm-19x13in)
£785 $1500   (24-Jul-92 DOU.M2) Grapes, peaches and copper ewer (53x41cm-21x16in)
£1623 $3100   (24-Jul-92 DOU.M8) Peaches with leaves (48x33cm-19x13in)
£1728 $3300   (24-Jul-92 DOU.M7) Raspberries in a bowl (48x33cm-19x13in)

LAVALLEY, Jonas Joseph (1858-1930) American
£1229 $2200   (14-Nov-91 GRO.B105/R) Still life with peaches and grapes
                          (25x36cm-10x14in) s.

LAVERENC, Gustav (1851-1906) German
£4985 $8923   (16-Jan-92 D.V28/R) Brother. Sister (42x27cm-17x11in) s.i.d.1875 panel
                      pair (A.S 100000)

LAVERENZ, C (19th C) German
£1193 $2147   (22-Nov-91 SA.A1679/R) Summer flowers in glass vase (39x28cm-15x11in) s.
                      panel (DM 3400)

LAVERGNE, Georges (1863-1942) French
£1133 $1937   (18-Mar-92 PIC.P56) Natures mortes au lapin et au faisan
                      (54x65cm-21x26in) s.d.1885,86 two (F.FR 11000)
£1194 $2244   (17-Dec-91 GM.B914/R) Gondoles a Venice (37x46cm-15x18in) s. (B.FR 70000)

LAVERIE, C (attrib) (19/20th C) ?
£1012 $1701   (27-Aug-91 RAS.K403) Party scene with figures wearing roccoco costumes
                      (57x80cm-22x31in) s. (D.KR 11500)

LAVERNIA (20th C) ?
£1208 $2054   (27-Oct-91 LT.P129) Le Chardonneret (61x73cm-24x29in) s. (F.FR 12000)

LAVERY, Sir John (1856-1941) British
£2210 $4000   (21-May-92 GRO.B99/R) Portrait of lady, Miss L (76x64cm-30x25in)
                      s.i.d.1907 s.verso
£2736 $4871   (25-Nov-91 W.T1922/R) Landscape with figures, Tangiers (25x35cm-10x14in)
                      s. i.verso board (C.D 5500)
£3200 $5728   (13-Nov-91 CG565/R) Portrait of Margaret Jean Fairlie Dunn
                      (46x35cm-18x14in) later sig.d.89
£6800 $12240   (20-Nov-91 S120/R) The turquoise sea, Mimizan (61x73cm-24x29in) s.
                      s.i.d.1917verso
£7000 $12460   (1-May-92 PHE95/R) Beaulieu (63x76cm-25x30in) s.i.d.1921verso
£7000 $12810   (5-Jun-92 C11/R) Tangier Bay (24x33cm-9x13in) s. board
£7200 $12312   (11-Mar-92 S28/R) Portrait of Miss Elaine Coggeshall (62x39cm-24x15in) s.
                      s.i.d.1924 verso panel
£8636 $14941   (2-Oct-91 A.D57/R) Market, Tangier (28x41cm-11x16in) s. (E.P 9500)
£9500 $16340   (6-Mar-92 C11/R) Eileen Lavery holding tennis racket (76x63cm-30x25in)
                      i.d.1909
£10000 $17300   (2-Oct-91 S27/R) Street in Rabat, Morocco (25x30cm-10x12in) s.
                      s.i.d.1920verso panel
£11500 $19320   (26-Aug-91 S1010/R) Portrait of lady (36x26cm-14x10in) s.i. canvas board
£12000 $21600   (20-Nov-91 S84/R) Portrait of Stella Donner (35x25cm-14x10in) s.
                      canvasboard
£12500 $22250   (1-May-92 PHE37/R) A Japanese garden (61x75cm-24x30in) s.i.d.1916
£13000 $23790   (13-May-92 S13 a/R) Lady in sables (80x67cm-31x26in) s.
£15000 $25800   (6-Mar-92 C16/R) The end of the day, Tangier Bay (63x76cm-25x30in) s.
£16484 $30000   (28-May-92 SY.NY132/R) Sands (63x76cm-25x30in) s. s.d.1917 verso
£24000 $43920   (5-Jun-92 C10/R) Sirocco, Tangier (63x76cm-25x30in) s.i.d.1921 verso
£27429 $48000   (19-Feb-92 CH.NY174/R) Rain in distance (63x76cm-25x30in) s. s.i.d.1919
                      verso
£32000 $58560   (13-May-92 S16/R) Portrait of Patrick William Adam in his studio
                      (127x101cm-50x40in) s. s.i.d.1918 verso
£32000 $56640   (5-Nov-91 PH26/R) The terrace at Cannes (51x61cm-20x24in) s.
                      i.d.1931verso canvasboard
£35000 $64050   (13-May-92 S15/R) A winter afternoon (63x58cm-25x23in) s. s.i.d.1913
                      verso
£62857 $110000   (19-Feb-92 CH.NY172/R) Golf links, North Berwick (63x76cm-25x30in) s.
                      s.i.d.1919 verso
£62857 $110000   (19-Feb-92 CH.NY166/R) Veranda (64x76cm-25x30in) s. s.i.d.1912 verso

LAVES, Werner (1903-1972) German
£580 $1050   (23-May-92 GB.B6800) Bridge in St Malo, Northern Brittany
                      (78x102cm-31x40in) (DM 1700)

LAVIE, Raffi (1937-) Israeli
£973 $1800   (8-Jun-92 GG.TA173/R) Untitled (81x100cm-32x39in) s.d.67
£1000 $1800   (6-Jan-92 GG.TA416/R) Untitled (65x93cm-26x37in) s.d.1967 s.d.verso
*£486 $900   (8-Jun-92 GG.TA174/R) Untitled (73x73cm-29x29in) s.d.68 oil collage mixed
                      media canvas*
*£851 $1600   (5-Jan-92 GG.TA237/R) Untitled (120x90cm-47x35in) s.d.1976 oil collage
                      board*

LAVIEILLE, Eugene (1820-1889) French
£1826 $3213   (10-Apr-92 AGS.P32/R) Rochers a Fontainebleau (21x36cm-8x14in) s. panel
                      (F.FR 18000)
*£765 $1422   (21-Jun-92 LT.P48) Rue de la Chausee a la Ferte-Milon (33x24cm-13x9in)
                      s.d.1865 oil Indian ink (F.FR 7500)*

LAVILLE, Joy (1923-) British
£7778 $14000   (19-Nov-91 CH.NY99/R) Woman on two rocks (130x160cm-51x63in) s.
                      s.d.1990verso
£1105 $2000   (19-May-92 SY.NY154/R) Desnudo (33x48cm-13x19in) s.d.73 pastel

LAVOINE, L P Robert (1916-) French
£566 $969   (22-Mar-92 LT.P210) Rue animee aupres du Sacre-Coeur (47x32cm-19x13in) s.
                      W/C (F.FR 5500)

LAVOINE, L P Robert (1916-) French-cont.

£806	$1427	(10-Nov-91 LT.P2/R) Paysage en neige a Saint-Mamme (46x55cm-18x22in) s. (F.FR 8000)
£820	$1475	(2-Feb-92 ZZ.F236/R) Honfleur, la Lieutenance et le Port (46x61cm-18x24in) s. (F.FR 8000)
£892	$1597	(19-Jan-92 PPB.P155) Rue Lepic (30x39cm-12x15in) s.i. (F.FR 8700)
£916	$1677	(7-Jun-92 LT.P175 b) Le Moulin de la Galette (33x41cm-13x16in) s. (F.FR 9000)
£916	$1677	(7-Jun-92 LT.P82) Le port de Rouen sous la neige (46x61cm-18x24in) s. (F.FR 9000)
£937	$1639	(3-Apr-92 ZZ.F97) Montmartre (38x46cm-15x18in) s. (F.FR 9000)
£963	$1742	(20-May-92 I.N138) La rue Lepic a Montmartre (54x65cm-21x26in) s. (F.FR 9500)
£1309	$2226	(27-Oct-91 LT.P68) La Rue Lepic sous la neige (50x61cm-20x24in) s. (F.FR 13000)
£1310	$2320	(10-Nov-91 ZZ.F242/R) Moulin a Montmartre (50x61cm-20x24in) s. (F.FR 13000)
£1364	$2414	(26-Apr-92 FE.P44) Rue a Montmartre (65x82cm-26x32in) panel (F.FR 13500)
£1379	$2413	(23-Feb-92 LT.P60 b) Place Blanche (F.FR 13500)
£1416	$2534	(10-May-92 LT.P132) Ruelle a Saint Ouen (46x61cm-18x24in) s.d.41 (F.FR 14000)
£1443	$2482	(20-Oct-91 LT.P39/R) Le Moulin de la Galette sous la neige (61x50cm-24x20in) s. (F.FR 14300)
£1788	$3128	(23-Feb-92 LT.P51 b) Le Moulin de la Galette en ete (50x61cm-20x24in) (F.FR 17500)
£404	$694	*(20-Oct-91 LT.P23) Bateau a Quistreham (32x47cm-13x19in) s. W/C (F.FR 4000)*
£407	$745	*(7-Jun-92 LT.P99/R) La Rue Norvins a Montmartre (31x46cm-12x18in) s. W/C (F.FR 4000)*
£407	$745	*(7-Jun-92 LT.P123) La maison de Mimi Pinson (31x47cm-12x19in) s. W/C (F.FR 4000)*
£409	$715	*(23-Feb-92 LT.P101) Le Port de Honfleur (33x46cm-13x18in) s. W/C (F.FR 4000)*
£427	$747	*(5-Apr-92 ZZ.F292/R) Estuaire sur la cote Normande (35x48cm-14x19in) s. W/C (F.FR 4100)*
£506	$905	*(10-May-92 LT.P135) Voiliers dans le port de Honfleur (32x47cm-13x19in) s. W/C (F.FR 5000)*
£695	$1216	*(23-Feb-92 LT.P80 b) Bateaux a Etretat (31x46cm-12x18in) W/C (F.FR 6800)*

LAVOUE, H (?) Australian

£1014	$1764	(17-Sep-91 JRL.S386) Lady bathers (161x112cm-63x44in) s. hessian (A.D 2200)

LAVREINCE, Nicolas (younger) see LAFRENSEN, Nicolas (younger)

LAVRENKO, Boris (1920-) Russian

£508	$884	(13-Apr-92 ARC.P117/R) Le peintre et son modele (65x81cm-26x32in) s. (F.FR 5000)
£614	$1093	(25-Nov-91 ARC.P28/R) La table des invites (90x70cm-35x28in) s. (F.FR 6000)
£617	$1117	(6-Dec-91 ARC.P201/R) Les pommes (60x75cm-24x30in) s. (F.FR 6000)
£669	$1210	(6-Dec-91 ARC.P200/R) Nature morte a la poupee (80x100cm-31x39in) s. (F.FR 6500)
£691	$1202	(13-Apr-92 ARC.P115/R) En famille (30x18cm-12x7in) s. board (F.FR 6800)
£716	$1275	(25-Nov-91 ARC.P25/R) Nature morte a la nappe (100x75cm-39x30in) s. (F.FR 7000)
£716	$1275	(25-Nov-91 ARC.P27/R) Nature morte au melon (51x49cm-20x19in) s. (F.FR 7000)
£716	$1275	(25-Nov-91 ARC.P26) Nature morte aux fruits (50x60cm-20x24in) s. (F.FR 7000)
£732	$1273	(13-Apr-92 ARC.P118/R) A l'ombre d'un parasol (35x50cm-14x20in) s. board (F.FR 7200)
£741	$1341	(6-Dec-91 ARC.P209/R) Sur le gueridon (100x73cm-39x29in) s. (F.FR 7200)
£915	$1591	(13-Apr-92 ARC.P113/R) Nature morte au samovar (75x102cm-30x40in) s. (F.FR 9000)
£1049	$1899	(6-Dec-91 ARC.P203/R) Beaute russe (116x89cm-46x35in) s. (F.FR 10200)
£2006	$3631	(6-Dec-91 ARC.P198/R) Le tableau (120x73cm-47x29in) s. (F.FR 19500)

LAW, Anthony (20th C) Canadian

£800	$1400	(22-Feb-92 YFA.M128/R) Winter in Quebec City, 1939 (30x41cm-12x16in) s. s.i.verso board

LAW, David (1831-1901) British

£530	$1007	(24-Jun-92 MMB297) Thames at Windsor (25x46cm-10x18in) s.
£700	$1281	(14-May-92 TL101) Dittisham on the Dart (48x89cm-19x35in) s.verso
£450	$833	*(11-Jun-92 CSK43/R) Punting on the river by the Swan Inn (33x51cm-13x20in) s. pencil W/C htd.white*

LAW, Denys (20th C) British?

£520	$952	(4-Jun-92 DLY354/R) Summertime at Lamorna (51x61cm-20x24in) s.

LAW, R (?) ?

£450	$765	*(24-Oct-91 CSK29) The fish market, Venice (36x51cm-14x20in) s. pencil W/C*

LAWES, Harold (fl.1890's) British
£367	$672	(1-Jun-92 W.T1279 a) Sussex lane (23x35cm-9x14in) s.i. W/C (C.D 800)
£423	$753	(25-Nov-91 W.T1828) Old English cottage with figures and dove cote (52x35cm-20x14in) s. W/C (C.D 850)
£520	$993	(16-Jul-92 CSK147/R) At village pond (25x37cm-10x15in) s.i. pencil W/C htd white
£645	$1142	(4-Nov-91 SY.J40/R) English country garden near Godalming, Surrey (44x67cm-17x26in) s. W/C (SA.R 3200)

LAWLESS, C E (?) American
| £730 | $1300 | (26-Jan-92 JRB.C55/R) Reflected birches (38x38cm-15x15in) s. canvas on board |

LAWLESS, Carl (1894-1934) American
£500	$900	(22-Nov-91 S.BM158/R) Batik - still life (38x38cm-15x15in) s.
£632	$1100	(13-Sep-91 DOU.M7) Flowers (56x56cm-22x22in)
£690	$1200	(13-Sep-91 DOU.M2) Daffodils (43x43cm-17x17in)
£690	$1200	(13-Sep-91 DOU.M4) Asters (56x56cm-22x22in)
£785	$1500	(24-Jul-92 DOU.M6) Colorado landscape in winter (43x43cm-17x17in)
£3216	$5500	(12-Mar-92 CH.NY190/R) Clear winter day (77x76cm-30x30in) s.

LAWLEY, Douglas (1906-1971) Canadian
| £1194 | $2125 | (26-Nov-91 JOY.T38/R) Horse-drawn sleighs hauling logs, village in distance (62x80cm-24x31in) s. (C.D 2400) |
| £1220 | $2195 | (19-Nov-91 FP.M174) Lookout, Montreal (41x51cm-16x20in) s. board (C.D 2500) |

LAWLOR, Adrian (1890-) Australian
| £3404 | $6026 | (26-Apr-92 SY.ME408/R) Profile (45x33cm-18x13in) s. cardboard (A.D 8000) |

LAWRANSON, Thomas (18th C) British
| £1800 | $3222 | (13-Nov-91 S150/R) Portrait of Jeremiah Brandreth. His wife (72x59cm-28x23in) i.d.1763verso painted oval pair |

LAWRENCE (style) (?) ?
| £760 | $1322 | (11-Sep-91 PHL61) Portrait of lady wearing white dress and tiara (55x45cm-22x18in) painted oval |

LAWRENCE, George (attrib) (c.1758-1802) British
| £421 | $720 | (13-Mar-92 FN.S358/R) Portrait of gentleman wearing green jacket with cravat (6x5cm-2x2in) min. gouache ivory oval medaillon (DM 1200) |

LAWRENCE, George Feather (1901-1981) Australian
£529	$952	(19-Nov-91 JRL.S228) Old Sydney (19x24cm-7x9in) s. board (A.D 1200)
£655	$1146	(30-Mar-92 AAA.S98) Beach at Womberal (19x34cm-7x13in) s. board (A.D 1500)
£684	$1238	(2-Dec-91 AAA.S89) Trafalgar Square (46x61cm-18x24in) s. board (A.D 1600)
£731	$1279	(23-Sep-91 AAA.S91) Terrace houses (28x37cm-11x15in) s. board (A.D 1600)
£781	$1492	(29-Jun-92 AAA.S115) Across the Parramatta (37x50cm-15x20in) s.d.49 board (A.D 2000)
£855	$1547	(2-Dec-91 AAA.S122/R) The city from Northbridge (38x56cm-15x22in) s. board (A.D 2000)
£1025	$1855	(19-May-92 JRL.S34/R) Dusk, Bald Head (37x44cm-15x17in) s.d.1950 board (A.D 2450)
£1135	$1987	(30-Mar-92 AAA.S118) Old Pyrmont (30x38cm-12x15in) s.d.62 board (A.D 2600)
£1240	$2369	(21-Jul-92 JRL.S154) Timeless land (20x24cm-8x9in) s.d.72 board (A.D 3200)
£1444	$2470	(17-Mar-92 JRL.S190) Village in snow (39x49cm-15x19in) s. board (A.D 3250)
£1659	$2887	(16-Sep-91 CH.ME48) Marie Santry in studio (39x47cm-15x19in) s.d.54 canvas on board (A.D 3600)
£2907	$5552	(21-Jul-92 JRL.S153/R) Harbour from Woolwich (65x100cm-26x39in) s.d.65 board (A.D 7500)
£3521	$5880	(19-Aug-91 SY.ME305/R) Picton (59x90cm-23x35in) s.d.1967 board (A.D 7500)

LAWRENCE, Jacob (1917-) American
| £2527 | $4750 | (18-Dec-91 SY.NY341/R) Underground railroad - fording a stream (41x58cm-16x23in) s.i.d.1948 India ink pencil |

LAWRENCE, Sir Thomas (1769-1830) British
£8000	$14240	(28-Apr-92 RG2561/R) Portrait of William First Lord Auckland (43x33cm-17x13in)
£10000	$19100	(15-Jul-92 S47/R) Portrait of Miss Louisa Hornby (108x88cm-43x35in)
£10000	$17900	(13-Nov-91 S54/R) Portrait of gentleman, probably the Hon William Lamb (76x63cm-30x25in)
£38000	$68020	(15-Nov-91 C32/R) Portrait of Hon. Sophia Upton, in white dress, with holly in hair (76x65cm-30x26in) painted oval
£550	$985	(12-Nov-91 C32) The descent from the cross (114x73cm-45x29in) pastel vellum after Daniele da Volterra
£733	$1400	(16-Jul-92 SY.NY297/R) Portrait study of James, Viscount Hamilton (37x38cm-15x15in) pencil chk
£766	$1394	(11-Dec-91 FER.M41/R) Perfil de joven mujer (24x21cm-9x8in) pencil dr (S.P 140000)

LAWRENCE, Sir Thomas (1769-1830) British-cont.

£1200	$2136	(1-Nov-91 S451/R) Portrait of gentleman (22x17cm-9x7in) s. pencil htd red chk oval
£1500	$2865	(14-Jul-92 C32/R) Portrait, possibly of Margaret Noble, wearing shawl and bonnet (21x17cm-8x7in) s.d. pencil col.chk
£1816	$3250	(13-Nov-91 B.SF2156/R) Portrait of the artist's wife (26x22cm-10x9in) pencil
£15000	$28650	(14-Jul-92 C31/R) Portrait of Lady Selina Meade, seated (37x27cm-15x11in) init.d.1819 pencil black red chk
£75000	$132000	(7-Apr-92 C54/R) Portrait of Mrs. Ayscoghe Boucherett with two eldest children Emilia and half-sister Juliana Angerst (51x41cm-20x16in) init.i.d.1794 pastel

LAWRENCE, Sir Thomas (after) (1769-1830) British

£1100	$1969	(11-Nov-91 S561/R) Portrait of George Howard, 6th Earl of Carlisle, wearing Peer's robes (59x49cm-23x19in)
£760	$1292	(22-Oct-91 SWS34/R) Portrait of Sir George Beaumont, wearing red coat (71x59cm-28x23in) pastel pencil

LAWRENCE, Sir Thomas (attrib) (1769-1830) British

£1242	$2124	(18-Mar-92 D.V260/R) Female playing harp (32x19cm-13x7in) panel (A.S 25000)
£2447	$4332	(7-Nov-91 D.V375/R) Portrait of gentleman said to be Charles, II Earl Grey (76x61cm-30x24in) (A.S 50000)
£2600	$4654	(15-Nov-91 C186/R) Head of child - sketch (22x26cm-9x10in)

LAWRENCE, Sir Thomas (circle) (1769-1830) British

£1067	$1900	(22-Jan-92 SY.NY116/R) Portrait of Lady Sophia (74x61cm-29x24in) pastel
£1124	$2000	(22-Jan-92 SY.NY239/R) Portrait of two young women (31x26cm-12x10in)
£1600	$2848	(31-Oct-91 D149/R) Portrait of gentleman wearing white stock and brown coat (74x61cm-29x24in)
£1854	$3300	(22-Jan-92 SY.NY233/R) Portrait of young lady (72x59cm-28x23in)

LAWRENCE, Sir Thomas (style) (1769-1830) British

£750	$1290	(16-Oct-91 CSK170) Portrait of Viscount Canterbury, standing holding letter (121x94cm-48x37in)
£850	$1581	(18-Jun-92 CSK188) Portrait of Benjamin West (58x51cm-23x20in)
£880	$1531	(12-Sep-91 CSK103) Portrait of lady in brown dress with gold wrap (71x60cm-28x24in)
£1450	$2625	(20-May-92 BT183) Ladsy, seated, wearing white dress, landscape beyond (91x71cm-36x28in)
£12000	$21480	(13-Nov-91 S61/R) Portrait of William Hanbury as boy seated with fishing rod in landscape (152x122cm-60x48in)

LAWRENCE, W (19th C) ?

£950	$1739	(15-May-92 TE386/R) Shipping off Gibraltar (56x122cm-22x48in) s.d.1879

LAWRIE, Hamish (20th C) British

£850	$1547	(29-May-92 PHG17) Night ferry, St. Mark's Basin, Venice (64x90cm-25x35in) s. s.i.d.77 verso board

LAWSON, Alexander (fl.1890-1903) British

£1000	$1720	(4-Mar-92 S236) Bonfire (28x33cm-11x13in) s. W/C
£1300	$2288	(6-Apr-92 PH122) Morning - Conway Castle (68x119cm-27x47in) s.i.verso W/C

LAWSON, Constance B (fl.1880-1903) British

£450	$824	(14-May-92 CSK72) Still life of red roses in vase (30x41cm-12x16in) s. pencil W/C

LAWSON, Ernest (1873-1939) American

£3315	$6000	(21-May-92 S.W2892/R) Waterfall (36x28cm-14x11in) s. i.verso board on panel
£10286	$18000	(26-Sep-91 CH.NY93/R) Biltmore Hotel, Palm Beach (52x62cm-20x24in) s.
£40936	$70000	(11-Mar-92 SY.NY70/R) Boathouses along river (53x67cm-21x26in) s.
£46961	$85000	(5-Dec-91 SY.NY66/R) River scene in winter (76x76cm-30x30in) s.

LAWSON, Fred (1888-?) British

£500	$925	(12-Jun-92 TE596/R) Redmire (25x30cm-10x12in) s.i.d.1935 pen W/C
£500	$905	(6-Dec-91 TE486) Grinton Church, with horse-drawn carts (18x25cm-7x10in) s.d.1913 W/C

LAXEIRO (20th C) Spanish

£4130	$7393	(14-Nov-91 ANS.M62/R) Rostro (47x34cm-19x13in) s. paper on canvas (S.P 750000)
£1094	$1992	(11-Dec-91 FER.M42/R) Maternidad (31x21cm-12x8in) s.d.91 sanguine (S.P 200000)
£2187	$4002	(13-May-92 FER.M176/R) Monstruo (54x36cm-21x14in) s.d.1957 gouache (S.P 400000)

LAZERGES, Hippolyte (19th C) ?

£1561	$2825	(19-May-92 AB.S4346/R) Maroccan boy with basket of flowers (40x28cm-16x11in) s.d.1879 panel (S.KR 16500)

LAZERGES, Jean Raymond Hippolyte (1817-1887) French
£5339 $9610   (18-Nov-91 AT.P361/R) Le cafe maure (38x56cm-15x22in) s. panel
         (F.FR 52000)

LAZERGES, Paul Jean Baptiste (1845-1902) French
£580 $998   (3-Mar-92 SWS1693) Lady in black (18x15cm-7x6in) s. panel
£1606 $2938   (3-Jun-92 R.T123/R) Arab caravan outside village (65x54cm-26x21in)
         s.d.1892 (C.D 3500)
£2921 $5082   (21-Sep-91 SA.A1761/R) Oasis with camels and caravan (47x61cm-19x24in)
         s.d.1896 (DM 8500)
£3500 $6195   (14-Feb-92 C87/R) Arab encampment by moonlight (81x100cm-32x39in) s.
£8727 $15708   (18-Nov-91 AT.P357/R) Caravane a Bou-Saada (53x65cm-21x26in) s.
         (F.FR 85000)

LAZNICKA, Wilhelm (19th C) Austrian
£909 $1618   (29-Nov-91 ZEL.L1061/R) Still life of roses, fruit and food on table
         before drapes (80x120cm-31x47in) s. (DM 2600)

LAZZARI, Bice (20th C) Italian
£635 $1162   (12-May-92 F.R115) Senza titolo (48x65cm-19x26in) s.d.1964 tempera
         (I.L 1400000)
£1394 $2524   (3-Dec-91 F.R220/R) Composizione (50x64cm-20x25in) s.d.1955verso
         (I.L 3000000)
£2324 $4206   (3-Dec-91 F.R194) Senza titolo (89x100cm-35x39in) s.d.1964verso
         (I.L 5000000)

LAZZARINI, Gregorio (circle) (1655-1730) Italian
£681 $1300   (16-Jul-92 SY.NY205/R) Sacrifice of Noah (40x33cm-16x13in)

LAZZELL, Blanche (20th C) American
£5278 $9500   (24-Nov-91 JRB.C53/R) Abstraction no.1 (58x46cm-23x18in) s.d.1944 panel

LE PHO (1907-) Vietnamese
£526 $900   (13-Mar-92 WOL.C759) Flowers in Chinese vase (36x23cm-14x9in) s.
£559 $1000   (9-May-92 CE.NY30/R) Femmes dans le jardin (81x65cm-32x26in) s.
£670 $1200   (9-May-92 CE.NY31/R) Vase de fleurs (81x65cm-32x26in) s.
£686 $1200   (19-Feb-92 D.NY65) Femme aux fleurs (53x74cm-21x29in) s.
£1189 $2200   (12-Jun-92 SY.NY218/R) La Cueillette des Parots (54x64cm-21x25in) s.

LEA, Nancy (?) British?
£1250 $2275   (10-Dec-91 HAR732/R) Still lifes with flowers (48x38cm-19x15in) s. board
         pair

LEACH, Bernard (1887-?) British
£450   *$801*   *(28-Nov-91 L133) Goose and flying bird in river landscape*
         (25x23cm-10x9in) init.i.d.1948 ink wash

LEACH-JONES, Alun (1937-) Australian
£1210 $2250   (21-Jun-92 SY.ME78) Romance of death (229x185cm-90x73in) i.d.1981verso
         acrylic (A.D 3000)
£1452 $2700   (21-Jun-92 SY.ME107/R) Celtic ritual (122x113cm-48x44in) s.d.1963 i.verso
         (A.D 3600)

LEADER, Benjamin Williams (1831-1923) British
£600 $1032   (3-Mar-92 H302/R) To let or sale - derelict thatched cottage and figure
         at wicket gate (46x36cm-18x14in)
£800 $1424   (27-Apr-92 PHB297) Lock gates (40x61cm-16x24in) s.d.1881
£900 $1665   (11-Jun-92 CSK124) On the Llugwy (32x43cm-13x17in) s.d.1910 board on
         panel
£1000 $1710   (19-Mar-92 B124/R) Gleaners returning, evening (32x42cm-13x17in) s.d.1906
         i.verso
£1100 $1892   (5-Mar-92 D119/R) Edge of wood (38x58cm-15x23in) s.d.1897
£1147 $2099   (1-Jun-92 W.T1348/R) Sketch on the Jarratt (34x44cm-13x17in) s.d.1887
         i.verso (C.D 2500)
£1800 $3456   (29-Jul-92 PHC405/R) Angler on the bend of a river (42x60cm-17x24in)
         board
£2000 $3800   (24-Jun-92 MMB331/R) Cattle watering at the Lledr (30x46cm-12x18in)
         s.d.1896
£2356 $4500   (16-Jul-92 SY.NY513/R) On the river Conway at Bettws-y-Coed
         (33x43cm-13x17in) s.d.1899 board
£2400 $4128   (11-Oct-91 C167/R) Near Rosenlaui (61x51cm-24x20in) s.d.1876 s.i.verso
£2907 $5000   (14-Oct-91 H.C51/R) Capel Curing (51x76cm-20x30in) s.
£3000 $5490   (3-Jun-92 S44/R) An old southern port (61x102cm-24x40in) s.d.1901
£3107 $5500   (9-Nov-91 W.W108/R) English seaport (61x102cm-24x40in) s.d.1901
£3200 $5856   (3-Jun-92 S30/R) Summer time at Burrows Cross (31x42cm-12x17in) s.d.1916
         board
£3400 $6018   (6-Nov-91 S37/R) Near Northwich, Cheshire (37x46cm-15x18in) s.d.1861
         s.i.verso
£4800 $8496   (6-Nov-91 S49/R) Welsh barley field (40x61cm-16x24in) s.d.1874 s.i.verso
         board
£5800 $9918   (13-Mar-92 C121/R) On the Terne at Bransford Bridge, Worcestershire
         (41x61cm-16x24in) s.d.1865 i.verso board
£6000 $10620   (6-Nov-91 S45/R) The old church, Whittington, Worcester (51x76cm-20x30in)
         s.d.1887 s.i.stretcher

LEADER, Benjamin Williams (1831-1923) British-cont.

£6200	$10974	(6-Nov-91 S44/R) Sunny morning on the river Conway (56x91cm-22x36in) s.d.1866 i.stretcher
£6500	$11180	(4-Mar-92 S13/R) Path by river near Capel Curig, North Wales (51x76cm-20x30in) s.d.1875 s.i.stretcher
£7000	$12040	(11-Oct-91 C107/R) Evening light (152x122cm-60x48in) s.d.1902 s.i.stretcher
£8242	$15000	(27-May-92 CH.NY269/R) Bettws-y-Coed Church on the River Conway (61x92cm-24x36in) s.d.1864
£8800	$16104	(14-May-92 TL93/R) Summertime, Llandulas, North Wales (41x61cm-16x24in) s.d.1878 board
£10000	$17100	(13-Mar-92 C120/R) Summer afternoon by the river (102x152cm-40x60in) s.d.1871
£11000	$18920	(11-Oct-91 C16/R) On the Llugwy, North Wales (41x61cm-16x24in) s.d.1880
£15429	$27000	(20-Feb-92 SY.NY256/R) Stream in summer time - Bettys-y-Coed, North Wales (76x132cm-30x52in) s.
£20000	$37000	(12-Jun-92 C177/R) Passing clouds near Capel Curig, N. Wales (89x137cm-35x54in) s.d.1872

LEADER, Charles (attrib) (19th C) British

£1300	$2483	(29-Jun-92 PHB169/R) Valley of Llangollen, North Wales (61x91cm-24x36in)

LEAKEY, James (1775-1865) British

£650	$1118	(4-Mar-92 C73/R) Officer, in gold-bordered scarlet coat with gold epaulettes (10x?cm-4x?in) min. gilt-wood gesso frame rec.

LEANDRE, Charles (1862-1930) French

£1727	$3023	(5-Apr-92 CSC.P26) Le repas de l'ogre (32x28cm-13x11in) s. oil crayon W/C (F.FR 16600)

LEAR, Edward (1812-1888) British

£7600	$14516	(15-Jul-92 S76/R) Olive trees, Corfu (46x58cm-18x23in) i. panel
£9400	$17954	(15-Jul-92 S77/R) Olive trees, Corfu (44x55cm-17x22in) s. board
£420	$748	(27-Nov-91 B108) Coastal view with hilltop castle (17x26cm-7x10in) i. pencil
£450	$792	(7-Apr-92 C191/R) Grunwald (50x35cm-20x14in) i.d. pencil
£480	$859	(12-Nov-91 C140) Indian partridges (20x15cm-8x6in) s.i. pencil W/C
£495	$945	(16-Jul-92 S165) Jaffa (5x13cm-2x5in) i.d.1858 pen W/C over pencil
£540	$918	(22-Oct-91 SWS113/R) Sunrise, Cerigo (8x14cm-3x6in) i.d.1863 W/C pen
£550	$979	(27-Nov-91 B98) Monks by pine trees in coastal landscape (20x28cm-8x11in) i. chk
£620	$1104	(27-Nov-91 B102) Fortified villa by trees (33x23cm-13x9in) i. pencil
£620	$1104	(27-Nov-91 B112) Frankfurt (28x19cm-11x7in) i.d. pencil htd.white
£650	$1144	(7-Apr-92 C188/R) Philae (8x16cm-3x6in) mono.i.d.1869 pencil pen
£700	$1246	(27-Nov-91 B97) Italian villa with pine tree (24x16cm-9x6in) s.i.
£700	$1253	(12-Nov-91 C142/R) Olevano (21x32cm-8x13in) s.i.d.1839 pencil
£800	$1464	(15-May-92 TE316/R) Bridge at Kirkby Lonsdale, Westmorland (23x33cm-9x13in) i. pencil htd white
£1100	$1958	(30-Apr-92 CG803/R) Stromboli, Lipari Islands (7x22cm-3x9in) i.d.1864 ink W/C
£1100	$2090	(23-Jun-92 CG603/R) Khanea, Crete (15x23cm-6x9in) i.num.32 pencil pen W/C
£1200	$2136	(27-Nov-91 B99/R) Florence from S.Miniato (26x17cm-10x7in) s.i.d. pencil htd.white
£1300	$2210	(23-Oct-91 S142) Corfu. Cephalonia (24x36cm-9x14in) i. sepia over pencil two
£1300	$2314	(27-Nov-91 B100/R) Olive trees by Italian lake (24x36cm-9x14in) s.i.d.1838 chk htd.white
£1500	$2640	(9-Apr-92 S98/R) Ghats at Benares, India (10x20cm-4x8in) W/C over pencil htd white
£1800	$3204	(27-Nov-91 B101/R) View of Bay of Naples (22x38cm-9x15in) s.indis.i. chk htd.white
£1800	$3078	(18-Mar-92 WI1178) View in Roman Campana (10x30cm-4x12in) s.d.1838 W/C
£2000	$3520	(9-Apr-92 S99/R) Wadi Halfeh on Nile (16x34cm-6x13in) i. pen W/C over pencil
£2000	$3580	(11-Nov-91 PH134) Studies of Arabs standing, sitting and walking near the pyramids (12x20cm-5x8in) ink W/C
£2000	$3580	(11-Nov-91 PH135/R) Group of Arabs near the pyramids (15x28cm-6x11in) i.d.1849 ink W/C
£2400	$4296	(12-Nov-91 C141/R) Ponte del Ammiraglio, Palermo (25x44cm-10x17in) i.d.12.July.1847 pencil ink W/C
£2800	$4928	(9-Apr-92 S25/R) Folio of drawings of Wadi Feiran, near Mount Sinai (31x51cm-12x20in) i.d.1849 num.117 to 123 pen over pencil four
£2800	$4928	(9-Apr-92 S26/R) Folio drawings in Sinai Peninsula d.1849 num.82 83 and 138 pen three
£3200	$5728	(12-Nov-91 C144/R) The beach at Cannes (16x40cm-6x16in) i.d.8.April 1865 pencil ink W/C htd.white
£3300	$5874	(27-Nov-91 B104/R) View of buildings in Rome. Views in the environs of Rome i. pencil three in one frame
£3410	$6513	(16-Jul-92 S166/R) Masada (15x22cm-6x9in) i. pen W/C htd bodycol
£3500	$6265	(11-Nov-91 S564/R) Ioannina, Greece (9x19cm-4x7in) s. W/C
£4000	$7040	(7-Apr-92 C189/R) Red fort at Agra, from banks of river Jumna (27x39cm-11x15in) mono.d.1875 i.v. pencil W/C gum arabic htd wht
£4200	$7476	(27-Nov-91 B106/R) Palermo (32x48cm-13x19in) i.d.1847 pen gouache
£4400	$8404	(16-Jul-92 S164/R) Eze, France (17x23cm-7x9in) i.d.1864 pen W/C

LEAR, Edward (1812-1888) British-cont.

£4500	$8055	(11-Nov-91 S562/R) Soracte from Civita Castellana (27x42cm-11x17in) s.i. black crayon htd white
£4500	$7920	(7-Apr-92 C187/R) Cerigo (16x26cm-6x10in) mono. pencil W/C bodycol gum arabic
£4500	$8010	(30-Apr-92 CG802/R) Paxus, Ionian Islands (30x51cm-12x20in) init.indist.i.d.85 ink W/C htd white
£4700	$8366	(27-Nov-91 B109/R) S.Salvador, Corfu. Views of Corfu i.d.1862 pen wash five in one frame
£5400	$9666	(14-Nov-91 S175/R) View from St Hospice, France (13x35cm-5x14in) s. W/C over pencil
£5500	$9845	(11-Nov-91 S563/R) Cerigo, Corfu (16x25cm-6x10in) mono. indist.i.verso W/C
£5600	$9968	(27-Nov-91 B111/R) Catania (32x48cm-13x19in) i.d.1847 pen gouache
£8200	$14596	(27-Nov-91 B110/R) Malta near St Angelo Hal Far, 1 pm (37x53cm-15x21in) i.d.1866 pen W/C htd.white
£10500	$17850	(23-Oct-91 S154/R) Gate of Canea, Crete (11x18cm-4x7in) mono.i.d.1864 W/C bodycol
£11000	$19690	(14-Nov-91 S174/R) Corfu from Vonitsa (29x54cm-11x21in) s.i.d.1856 W/C htd.bodycol pen
£11000	$19690	(14-Nov-91 S173/R) Constantinople from Ayoub (29x45cm-11x18in) s.i.d.1848/1856 pen W/C htd.bodycol
£12000	$21480	(12-Nov-91 C143/R) The Alps and Italy all s.i.d.1844 pencil ink wash set of twelve
£15500	$27745	(14-Nov-91 S172/R) Masada on the Dead Sea, Palestine (29x45cm-11x18in) mono.i.d.1859 W/C bodycol over pencil

LEASON, Percival Alexander (1889-1959) Australian

£586	$1119	(29-Jun-92 AAA.S95) Backyard clothesline (45x38cm-18x15in) s. (A.D 1500)

LEAVER, Charles (19th C) British

£1900	$3648	(28-Jul-92 SWS321/R) Glade in Savenake Forest (100x125cm-39x49in) s.d.1866
£3000	$5190	(4-Oct-91 BW410) Winter scene with figures and cottages (51x76cm-20x30in) s.d.

LEAVER, Noel Harry (1889-1951) British

£420	$777	(11-Jun-92 B170/R) Arab street scene with figures outside mosque (25x36cm-10x14in) s. W/C
£440	$845	(9-Jul-92 B160/R) Street scene, Rothenburg (35x25cm-14x10in) s. W/C bodycol
£500	$870	(9-Sep-91 PH12) A city gate, Palestine (26x37cm-10x15in) s. i. verso W/C
£520	$915	(9-Apr-92 B196/R) Siena, Italy (18x25cm-7x10in) s. W/C
£540	$923	(19-Mar-92 T180/R) Surrey Common (18x25cm-7x10in) s. W/C
£560	$1075	(28-Jul-92 SWS262) Continental town by a lake (35x51cm-14x20in) s. W/C gouache
£580	$1114	(28-Jul-92 SWS265) Arab merchants in a square (24x36cm-9x14in) s. W/C gouache
£600	$1086	(5-Dec-91 CG30/R) Figures by gateway to Spanish town (25x36cm-10x14in) s. W/C htd.bodycol
£600	$1152	(28-Jul-92 SWS261/R) Broughton Mills, Furness (36x52cm-14x20in) s. W/C gouache
£640	$1229	(28-Jul-92 SWS266) Street in Old Plyumouth (27x44cm-11x17in) s. W/C over pencil
£700	$1260	(27-Jan-92 PH62/R) Ancient mosque (38x26cm-15x10in) s. i.verso W/C bodycol
£734	$1343	(1-Jun-92 W.T1282/R) Outside a mosque (25x17cm-10x7in) s. W/C (C.D 1600)
£820	$1574	(28-Jul-92 SWS263/R) An old watermill (37x53cm-15x21in) s. W/C gouache
£900	$1530	(23-Oct-91 S260/R) Gateway in North African town (27x37cm-11x15in) s. W/C over pencil
£1000	$1850	(12-Jun-92 C16/R) Moorish archway (30x53cm-12x21in) s. pencil W/C
£1000	$1700	(23-Oct-91 S259/R) Mosque in North African town (35x50cm-14x20in) s. W/C over pencil
£1050	$1901	(19-May-92 CD106) Moorish street scene with archway (25x18cm-10x7in) s. W/C
£1061	$1900	(13-Nov-91 B.SF2216/R) Mosque in Cairo (36x26cm-14x10in) s. W/C
£1100	$1991	(19-May-92 CD105/R) Moorish street scene with archway (25x18cm-10x7in) s. W/C
£1150	$2208	(28-Jul-92 SWS264/R) Market at Leyden, Holland (26x36cm-10x14in) s. W/C gouache
£1194	$2125	(25-Nov-91 W.T1829/R) Arabian town with figures outside mosque (27x44cm-11x17in) s. W/C
£1250	$2238	(5-May-92 SWS170/R) Algerian mosque. Algerian archway (35x50cm-14x20in) s. W/C over pencil pair
£1400	$2688	(28-Jul-92 SWS260/R) Cumbrian landscape (54x72cm-21x28in) s. W/C gouache
£1450	$2625	(19-May-92 CD104) Rouen street scene with figures and timbered houses (36x25cm-14x10in) s. W/C
£1571	$3000	(3-Jul-92 S.W3068/R) Street scene, Tunis (28x43cm-11x17in) s. W/C
£1600	$2720	(23-Oct-91 S261/R) The courtyard, El Aghar (36x51cm-14x20in) s. W/C over pencil
£1700	$3145	(9-Jun-92 LW1798/R) Panoramic view of Derwentwater (23x36cm-9x14in) s. W/C
£1850	$3552	(28-Jul-92 SWS267/R) Italian market scene (35x51cm-14x20in) s. W/C gouache over pencil

LEAVER, Noel Harry (1889-1951) British-cont.
£2000 $3400   (23-Oct-91 S262/R) Mosque in Tunisia. On the edge of the desert. View of North African town (17x26cm-7x10in) s. two i.verso W/C over pencil three

LEAVITT, Edward C (1842-1904) American
£556	$1000	(22-Nov-91 S.BM87/R) Still life with raspberries and leaf (30x61cm-12x24in) s.d.1893 s.i.verso
£556	$1000	(22-Nov-91 S.BM80/R) Basket of roses (61x76cm-24x30in) s.d.1900
£952	$1600	(28-Aug-91 MFA.C64) Hanging grapes (56x28cm-22x11in) s.
£1117	$2000	(14-Nov-91 CE.NY99/R) Still life with dead game (51x42cm-20x17in) s.d.1872
£1186	$2100	(10-Nov-91 LIT.L10) Still life of melon (23x28cm-9x11in) s.d.1864 board
£2128	$4000	(18-Dec-91 SY.NY51/R) Still life of pink and yellow roses (61x73cm-24x29in) s.d.1895

LEBARON-DESVES, Augusta (1804-?) French
£928 $1698   (2-Jun-92 FN.S2645) Portrait of young girl wearing Sunday outfit (25x20cm-10x8in) s.d.1835 board (DM 2700)

LEBAS, Gabriel-Hippolyte (1812-1880) French
£801 $1441   (20-Nov-91 CN.P54 b) Bord de mer (54x42cm-21x17in) s.d.1867 W/C gouache (F.FR 7800)

LEBASQUE, Henri (1865-1937) French
£4630	$8796	(24-Jun-92 GL.P161) Femme et enfant devant une table fleurie (46x55cm-18x22in) s. (F.FR 45000)
£5155	$8918	(23-Mar-92 GL.P194/R) Le pod de rhododendron (77x60cm-30x24in) s. (F.FR 50000)
£6000	$11460	(29-Jun-92 CSK33/R) Les rhododendrons (77x60cm-30x24in) s.
£6079	$11003	(18-May-92 AT.P205/R) Fleurs dans un vase (55x46cm-22x18in) s. (F.FR 60000)
£6660	$11988	(2-Feb-92 ZZ.F124/R) Nu allonge dans un fauteuil (46x55cm-18x22in) s. (F.FR 65000)
£8197	$15000	(14-May-92 SY.NY256/R) Scene de plage (27x41cm-11x16in) s.
£11000	$21010	(29-Jun-92 CSK38/R) Les baigneuses au bord de la riviere (38x45cm-15x18in) s.
£14208	$26000	(14-May-92 SY.NY335/R) Nu au fauteuil (44x53cm-17x21in) s.
£15819	$28000	(6-Nov-91 CH.NY270/R) Nu allonge (33x55cm-13x22in) s.
£16949	$30000	(6-Nov-91 CH.NY274/R) Le gouter des enfants (78x138cm-31x54in) s.
£38000	$68780	(3-Dec-91 C217/R) Les Bords de la Marne (54x65cm-21x26in) s.
£45000	$85950	(1-Jul-92 S137/R) Femme nue assise de dos (76x63cm-30x25in) s.
£55276	$92864	(16-Aug-91 ZZ.F86/R) Jeunes filles dans un paysage (54x65cm-21x26in) s. (F.FR 550000)
£62000	$112220	(3-Dec-91 C222/R) Port de Saint Tropez (73x92cm-29x36in) s.d.1906
£385	$685	(25-Nov-91 WK.M635/R) Five men resting. Female nude seen from behind (19x26cm-7x10in) s. pencil (DM 1100)
£512	$922	(27-Jan-92 GL.P8) Voiles et barques (24x42cm-9x17in) s. W/C lead pencil (F.FR 5000)
£514	$977	(24-Jun-92 GL.P109) Effet de soleil sur la mer (16x24cm-6x9in) s. W/C (F.FR 5000)
£514	$977	(24-Jun-92 GL.P108) Barque sur une plage (16x24cm-6x9in) s. W/C (F.FR 5000)
£562	$1029	(5-Feb-92 FB.P158/R) Femme nue au bouquet (27x17cm-11x7in) mono. crayon (F.FR 5500)
£1127	$2029	(27-Jan-92 GL.P4) Jeunes femmes assises dans la vallee (27x40cm-11x16in) s. chl.W/C (F.FR 11000)
£1373	$2458	(13-Nov-91 PIC.P67/R) Femme lisant (15x16cm-6x6in) s. W/C (F.FR 13500)
£1426	$2595	(12-Dec-91 CSC.P343/R) Jeune fille (21x16cm-8x6in) s. W/C crayon (F.FR 14000)
£1486	$2674	(27-Jan-92 GL.P7) Femme a la robe jaune (17x21cm-7x8in) s.d.1921 crayon W/C (F.FR 14500)
£1537	$2766	(27-Jan-92 GL.P6) Les trois baigneuses (18x24cm-7x9in) s.i. chl.W/C (F.FR 15000)
£1600	$2800	(28-Feb-92 SY.NY6/R) Girl reading book. Young girl seated in armchair (22x16cm-9x6in) s. pastel pencil double-sided
£1639	$2951	(27-Jan-92 GL.P5/R) Bateaux au port (25x42cm-10x17in) s. W/C (F.FR 16000)
£1742	$3135	(27-Jan-92 GL.P9) Les voiles rouges (22x40cm-9x16in) s. chl.W/C (F.FR 17000)
£1742	$3135	(27-Jan-92 GL.P3) Le port a Maree Basse (27x44cm-11x17in) s. W/C (F.FR 17000)
£2077	$3946	(25-Jun-92 GK.B439) Jeune femme nue etendue sur un divan (15x25cm-6x10in) s. W/C over pencil (S.FR 5400)
£2400	$4344	(2-Dec-91 CSK92/R) Les voiliers, souvenir de Prefailles (26x35cm-10x14in) s.i.d.1922 W/C pencil
£2541	$4421	(19-Apr-92 ZZ.F24/R) Femme sur la plage (18x21cm-7x8in) s.d.1921 W/C (F.FR 25000)
£2571	$4500	(27-Feb-92 CE.NY4/R) Midinette au divan bleu (24x35cm-9x14in) s. W/C pencil paper on board
£3122	$5463	(5-Apr-92 ZZ.F88/R) Le port de Saint-Tropez (25x41cm-10x16in) s. W/C (F.FR 30000)
£3642	$6374	(5-Apr-92 ZZ.F100/R) Voiliers a maree basse (27x44cm-11x17in) s. W/C (F.FR 35000)
£3850	$6738	(5-Apr-92 ZZ.F104/R) Jeune femme assise dans un paysage de Provence (27x39cm-11x15in) s. W/C (F.FR 37000)

LEBASQUE, Henri (1865-1937) French-cont.
£3954 $6920 (5-Apr-92 ZZ.F108/R) Barque dans le Golfe de Saint-Tropez
      (22x40cm-9x16in) s. W/C (F.FR 38000)

LEBDUSKA, Lawrence (1894-1966) American
£554 $975 (9-Apr-92 FA.PH764) Still life with banana (30x41cm-12x16in) s.d.47 board
£805 $1400 (15-Apr-92 SY.NY264/R) Jungle sunset (63x76cm-25x30in) s.
£2793 $5000 (14-Nov-91 CE.NY461/R) Garden of Eden (138x213cm-54x84in) s.d.2-62

LEBEDEW, Wladimir W (1875-1946) Russian
£524 $934 (30-Nov-91 VG.B813/R) In the street (21x14cm-8x6in) indian ink pen
      gouache map of SU verso (DM 1500)
£619 $1144 (12-Jun-92 HN.H516/R) Composition with jongleur (33x24cm-13x9in) pen
      col.stamp (DM 1800)
£629 $1120 (30-Nov-91 VG.B816/R) Man with pistol (24x17cm-9x7in) indian ink pen
      gouache map of Upper Italy verso (DM 1800)
£699 $1245 (30-Nov-91 VG.B819/R) Meeting (21x15cm-8x6in) pen over pencil gouache map
      verso (DM 2000)
£699 $1245 (30-Nov-91 VG.B814/R) Two women (24x16cm-9x6in) indian ink pen gouache
      map of South Sweden verso (DM 2000)
£699 $1245 (30-Nov-91 VG.B817/R) Cleaning woman (25x17cm-10x7in) indian ink gouache
      map of South of France verso (DM 2000)
£699 $1245 (30-Nov-91 VG.B818/R) Mechaniker (25x17cm-10x7in) indian ink pen gouache
      map of Florida verso (DM 2000)
£756 $1399 (12-Jun-92 HN.H515/R) Composition with figures (34x25cm-13x10in) pen
      col.stamp (DM 2200)
£874 $1556 (30-Nov-91 VG.B815/R) Two gentlemen meeting (21x14cm-8x6in) indian ink
      pen gouache Russian map verso (DM 2500)

LEBEDJEV, Vladimir (1891-1967) Russian
£458 $829 (6-Dec-91 GB.B6748) Abstract figures, woman with shovel (26x21cm-10x8in)
      indian ink pen (DM 1300)
£528 $956 (6-Dec-91 GB.B6747) Abstract couple dancing (27x21cm-11x8in) indian ink
      pen (DM 1500)
£614 $1112 (23-May-92 GB.B6804) Abstract couple (28x16cm-11x6in) indian ink pen
      (DM 1800)
£683 $1235 (23-May-92 GB.B6803/R) Dancing couple (33x22cm-13x9in) indian ink pen
      (DM 2000)

LEBEL, Antoine (1705-1793) French
£7202 $13683 (22-Jun-92 PIC.P20/R) Paysage avec scene de chasse aux oies sauvages
      s.d.1793 (F.FR 70000)

LEBEL, Edmond (1834-1909) French
£627 $1141 (12-Dec-91 L.K425) Two Italian girls selling fruit and nuts
      (22x27cm-9x11in) s.d.1869 W/C (DM 1800)

LEBENSTEIN, Jan (1930-) Polish/French
£375 $667 (29-Apr-92 G.Z151/R) Composition (80x29cm-31x11in) mixed media W/C indian
      ink (S.FR 1000)

LEBIER, Daniel (1941-) French
£911 $1640 (19-Nov-91 GO.G232) French balcony (160x100cm-63x39in) s. (S.KR 9500)

LEBLANC, Walter (1932-1986) Belgian
£735 $1250 (22-Oct-91 C.A220) Composition (40x50cm-16x20in) s.d.1959 paper
      (B.FR 44000)
£1337 $2272 (22-Oct-91 C.A219/R) Composition (65x81cm-26x32in) s.d.1958 (B.FR 80000)

LEBOURG, Albert (1849-1928) French
£2642 $4598 (19-Apr-92 ZZ.F110/R) Rouen, bateaux a quais (17x27cm-7x11in) s. panel
      (F.FR 26000)
£3714 $6500 (25-Feb-92 CH.NY4/R) Le quai de l'Amiraute a Alger (46x38cm-18x15in) s.i.
      canvas on masonite
£4630 $8796 (22-Jun-92 AT.P62/R) Bouquet de fleurs (41x27cm-16x11in) s. studio
      st.verso panel (F.FR 45000)
£5123 $9221 (2-Feb-92 ZZ.F126/R) Paris - la Seine - Notre-Dame et les Bouquinistes
      (20x31cm-8x12in) s. panel (F.FR 50000)
£6110 $11303 (12-Jun-92 AT.P14/R) Brouillard sur la Meuse, a Delft (36x65cm-14x26in)
      s. (F.FR 60000)
£6936 $12000 (2-Oct-91 SY.NY5/R) Les laveuses a Pont-du-Chateau (51x85cm-20x33in) s.
£7558 $13000 (12-Oct-91 SY.NY17/R) Environs de Clermont-Ferrand (41x74cm-16x29in) s.
£8475 $15000 (7-Nov-91 SY.NY114/R) Le bassin a Dieppe (31x58cm-12x23in) s.indist.d.
£10000 $17200 (16-Oct-91 S7/R) Bord d'Etang de Chalou-Moulineux, environs d'Etampes
      (54x81cm-21x32in) s.
£10682 $19120 (13-Nov-91 PIC.P68) La Seine a Rouen (51x65cm-20x26in) s. (F.FR 105000)
£11000 $21010 (1-Jul-92 S118/R) Bords de riviere (50x65cm-20x26in) s.
£12860 $24434 (24-Jun-92 GL.P155/R) La Seine a Rouen vue du Pre-aux-Loups
      (54x81cm-21x32in) s. (F.FR 125000)
£13306 $23685 (28-Nov-91 FB.P23/R) La Seine aux environs de Paris (46x76cm-18x30in) s.
      (F.FR 130000)
£14837 $25817 (19-Apr-92 ZZ.F70/R) Le Val de la Haye (46x85cm-18x33in) s. (F.FR 146000)
£16113 $27392 (21-Oct-91 ARC.P19/R) Canal en Hollande (37x60cm-15x24in) s.
      (F.FR 160000)

LEBOURG, Albert (1849-1928) French-cont.

£20000	$36200	(4-Dec-91 S124/R) Le Pont de Neuilly, pres Paris (46x76cm-18x30in) s.d.1888
£36687	$63835	(19-Apr-92 ZZ.F108/R) Le chevet de Notre-Dame de Paris vu des quais (61x82cm-24x32in) s. (F.FR 361000)
£666	$1199	(2-Feb-92 ZZ.F240/R) Arbres au bord de la riviere (20x31cm-8x12in) s. chl. (F.FR 6500)
£930	$1600	(12-Oct-91 SY.NY35/R) Seascape (32x22cm-13x9in) s. W/C paper on board
£1024	$1822	(27-Nov-91 AT.P42/R) Paris - La Seine a l'Institut (15x25cm-6x10in) s. W/C (F.FR 10000)
£1335	$2402	(20-Nov-91 CN.P52/R) Paris, une rue (18x28cm-7x11in) s. W/C gouache (F.FR 13000)
£1524	$2652	(19-Apr-92 ZZ.F19/R) Le port de Rouen (30x48cm-12x19in) s. W/C (F.FR 15000)
£1524	$2652	(19-Apr-92 ZZ.F4) Paris, Notre-Dame et les quais (14x17cm-6x7in) s. W/C (F.FR 15000)
£1773	$3209	(20-May-92 I.N139) Voilier a quai (18x26cm-7x10in) s. W/C (F.FR 17500)
£2018	$3471	(20-Oct-91 I.N213/R) Rouen, vapeur a quai (31x48cm-12x19in) s. W/C (F.FR 20000)

LEBOURG, Albert (attrib) (1849-1928) French

£794	$1413	(28-Apr-92 RAS.K245) Harbour scene, Dieppe (39x54cm-15x21in) s. (D.KR 9000)

LEBRET, Frans (1820-1909) Dutch

£608	$1100	(21-May-92 GRO.B23/R) Farmyard with ox cart (58x76cm-23x30in) s.

LEBRUN (?) ?

£1700	$3009	(13-Feb-92 CSK145) Preparing to bathe (177x114cm-70x45in) s.

LEBRUN, Andre Jean (1737-1811) French

£1631	$3034	(20-Jun-92 CH.MO237/R) Diane au bain chk ink wash (F.FR 16000)

LEBRUN, Charles (1619-1690) French

£733	$1400	(3-Jul-92 S.W3734/R) Military trophies for Gallerie de Glace at Versailles (15x23cm-6x9in) i. ink wash

LEBRUN, Charles (after) (1619-1690) French

£1047	$2000	(16-Jul-92 SY.NY71/R) Mary Magdalene (40x25cm-16x10in) copper

LEBRUN, Charles (circle) (1619-1690) French

£4200	$8064	(10-Jul-92 C202/R) Moses preparing tablets of Law to Children of Israel (199x195cm-78x77in)

LEBRUN, Charles (school) (1619-1690) French

£1758	$3111	(5-Nov-91 GF.L2333/R) Alexander the Great and Darius visiting tents (65x93cm-26x37in) (S.FR 4500)

LEBRUN, Charles (studio) (1619-1690) French

£1226	$2145	(19-Feb-92 D.P1/R) Poupe de navire (35x49cm-14x19in) pierre noire wash sanguine (F.FR 12000)

LEBRUN, Charles (style) (1619-1690) French

£1300	$2496	(9-Jul-92 CSK107/R) Adoration of the Shepherds (61x48cm-24x19in)
£1400	$2450	(27-Feb-92 CSK75/R) The Triumph of David. The capture of the Ark by the Philistines (37x49cm-15x19in) pair
£2281	$3900	(13-Mar-92 FN.S2845/R) Mythological scene with young woman seated before jewellery box (100x83cm-39x33in) i.verso (DM 6500)
£2600	$4550	(27-Feb-92 CSK90/R) Lot and his daughters (47x64cm-19x25in) oval

LEBRUN, Christopher (20th C) ?

£2743	$4800	(27-Feb-92 CE.NY221/R) Untitled (159x109cm-63x43in) s. s.d.1985 paper
£5143	$9000	(27-Feb-92 CE.NY231/R) Cloud and tree (197x149cm-78x59in) s.d.27.6.85 31.10.85 17.11.85 verso
£8939	$16000	(5-May-92 CH.NY143/R) Helm (256x381cm-101x150in) s.d.85verso s.d.stretcher
£9143	$16000	(27-Feb-92 CH.NY66/R) Pillar, banner, fire (259x366cm-102x144in) s.i.d.82verso
£15000	$28650	(2-Jul-92 C2 a/R) Amphion (249x213cm-98x84in) s.i.d.21.2.81 7/81 6.10.81 2.10.81 verso

LEBRUN, Piotr (1802-1879) Polish

£1463	$2546	(19-Sep-91 D.V136/R) Gentleman riding horse (66x52cm-26x20in) i.d.1838verso (A.S 30000)

LEBRUN, Rico (1900-1964) Italian/American

£459	$850	(10-Jun-92 CE.NY568/R) Weeping nun (61x47cm-24x19in) s.d.1948 pen

LECK, Bart van der (1876-1958) Dutch

£2121	$3839	(19-May-92 CH.AM209/R) Abstract composition (38x31cm-15x12in) pencil W/C htd.white (D.FL 7000)
£2424	$4388	(19-May-92 CH.AM208/R) Volksuniversiteit (58x49cm-23x19in) pencil pen W/C htd. white (D.FL 8000)
£2469	$4494	(11-Dec-91 CH.AM276/R) Four designs for tapestries (35x30cm-14x12in) pencil W/C double-sided (D.FL 8000)

LECK, Bart van der (1876-1958) Dutch-cont.
£3086 $5617   (11-Dec-91 CH.AM275/R) De Maaier, study of reaper (76x85cm-30x33in)
                  st.studio i.verso pencil chk (D.FL 10000)
£3704 $6741   (11-Dec-91 CH.AM273/R) Ueber allen Gipfeln ist Ruh (65x50cm-26x20in)
                  i.verso pencil pen W/C double-sided (D.FL 12000)

LECLAIRE, Leon Louis (1829-?) French
£411 $707   (6-Mar-92 ARC.P16) Vision de Saint-Hubert (54x140cm-21x55in) s.d.1875
                  crayon pen wash paper laid down canvas (F.FR 4000)

LECLERC, Sebastien Jacques see LECLERC DES GOBELINS, Sebastian

LECLERC DES GOBELINS, Sebastian (1734-1785) French
£2675 $4842   (2-Dec-91 CK.P7/R) Les baigneuses surprises (31x40cm-12x16in) panel
                  (F.FR 26000)
£67039 $120000 (17-Jan-92 SY.NY64/R) An elegant company listening to a hurdy-gurdy
                  player. Amorous coupleswith shepherds in a landscape (48x59cm-19x23in)
                  pair

LECLERC, Sebastien (elder) (1637-1714) French
£400 $728   (10-Dec-91 C47/R) Saints Quiricus and Julitta led to martyrdom
                  (15x19cm-6x7in) red chk.wash

LECLERC, Sebastien (younger-attrib) (1676-1763) French
£2854 $5309   (20-Jun-92 CH.MO75/R) Fete galante (40x33cm-16x13in) panel (F.FR 28000)

LECOMTE, Emile (1866-1938) Belgian
£700 $1246   (28-Nov-91 CSK126) Arab on donkey at oasis (41x33cm-16x13in) s.d.1859

LECOMTE, Hippolyte (1781-1857) French
£892 $1659   (16-Jun-92 RAS.V824 a/R) North African battle scene with Arabs and
                  Frenchmen (40x53cm-16x21in) indist.s. (D.KR 10000)
£3436 $6289   (3-Jun-92 DO.H2340/R) Reception at the French Court (42x57cm-17x22in)
                  s.d.1832 (DM 10000)

LECOMTE, Paul (1842-1920) French
£720 $1368   (22-Jun-92 AT.P63) Retour de peche (61x120cm-24x47in) s. (F.FR 7000)
£820 $1475   (2-Feb-92 ZZ.F71/R) Bord de Seine a Paris (27x35cm-11x14in) s. panel
                  (F.FR 8000)
£1700 $3009   (14-Feb-92 C8/R) Une ferme au bord d'une riviere (37x60cm-15x24in) s.
£411 $739   (20-Nov-91 CN.P66 c) Paysage d'hiver (25x37cm-10x15in) s. W/C (F.FR 4000)
£461 $830   (2-Feb-92 ZZ.F239/R) Voiliers (24x35cm-9x14in) s. W/C (F.FR 4500)
£615 $1107   (2-Feb-92 ZZ.F242/R) Paquebot dans la Rade (22x28cm-9x11in) s. W/C
                  (F.FR 6000)

LECOMTE, Paul Emile (1877-1950) French
£863 $1467   (23-Oct-91 GD.B1134/R) House amongst trees (38x45cm-15x18in) s. panel
                  (S.FR 2200)
£2800 $4956   (13-Feb-92 CSK119/R) Marche aux fleurs (63x93cm-25x37in) s.
£3637 $6547   (2-Feb-92 ZZ.F56/R) Port Breton (46x55cm-18x22in) s. (F.FR 35500)
£4273 $7648   (17-Nov-91 FB.P197) Port Breton (64x81cm-25x32in) s. (F.FR 42000)
£7429 $13000   (20-Feb-92 SY.NY135/R) Scene de marche (63x79cm-25x31in) s.
£8656 $15754   (15-Dec-91 T.B190/R) Vue de l'Ile d'Yeu - Port-Joinville
                  (65x92cm-26x36in) s. (F.FR 85000)
£416 $728   (5-Apr-92 ZZ.F291/R) Le jardin fleuri (28x37cm-11x15in) s. W/C
                  (F.FR 4000)
£1034 $1800   (11-Sep-91 D.NY54/R) Concarneau (38x53cm-15x21in) s. i.verso W/C

LECOMTE, Victor (1856-1920) French
£3634 $6250   (17-Oct-91 SY.NY194 a/R) Story time (43x58cm-17x23in) s.d.1888

LECOMTE-VERNET, Charles Emile (1821-1900) French
£550 $1007   (5-Feb-92 CSK165) Figures on beach (14x18cm-6x7in) s. board

LECONTE (18/19th C) ?
£1180 $2100   (22-Jan-92 SY.NY16/R) Marine soleil levant. Marine soleil couchant
                  (25x34cm-10x13in) s.d.1790 ink wash gouache pair

LECOSSOIS, Victor (1897-1976) Belgian
£753 $1363   (7-Dec-91 KV.L209) Tavern interior (50x60cm-20x24in) s. (B.FR 44000)

LECOURT, Raymond (1882-1946) French
£1020 $1785   (30-Mar-92 ZZ.F100) Vaches au pre (41x54cm-16x21in) s. canvas laid down
                  on panel (F.FR 9800)
£9124 $16332   (6-May-92 GD.B756/R) Moisson aux Murrets (47x73cm-19x29in) s.
                  (S.FR 25000)

LEDER, Heinrich (attrib) (19th C) German
£756 $1315   (19-Sep-91 N.M2778/R) Knight in armour riding horse (63x53cm-25x21in)
                  i.d.1843verso panel (DM 2200)

LEDESMA, Blas de (after) (16th C) Spanish
£820 $1500   (5-Feb-92 D.NY7) Bird picking cherries out of Delft bowl
                  (33x36cm-13x14in)

LEDESMA, Blas de (after) (16th C) Spanish-cont.
| £1163 | $2000 | (16-Oct-91 D.NY4) Birds with cherries framed by two floral bouquets (74x99cm-29x39in) |
| £2105 | $4000 | (24-Jun-92 D.NY54) Birds on perches above still life of flowers and cherries (99x170cm-39x67in) |

LEDESMA, Blas de (circle) (16th C) Spanish
| £5200 | $9984 | (7-Jul-92 PH30/R) Still life of grapes and apples on pewter plate on ledge (30x45cm-12x18in) |

LEDESMA, Blas de (studio) (16th C) Spanish
| £7871 | $13538 | (15-Oct-91 PPB.P28/R) Cartouches a volutes et feuilles d'acanthe decores de fruits, oiseaux et fleurs (55x81cm-22x32in) pair (F.FR 78000) |

LEDESMA, Gabriel Fernandez (1900-1983) Mexican
£1860	$3200	(14-Oct-91 H.C192/R) Serenade (64x71cm-25x28in) s.
£2762	$5000	(19-May-92 SY.NY127/R) Serenata (63x70cm-25x28in) s.
£8333	$15000	(19-Nov-91 CH.NY67/R) La familia (90x70cm-35x28in) s.d.1926

LEDOULX, P F (1730-1807) Flemish
| £1000 | $1910 | (20-Jul-92 WW34/R) Four putti building house of cards (56x89cm-22x35in) s.d.1779 |

LEDOUX, Jeanne Philiberte (1767-1840) French
| £4115 | $7449 | (5-Dec-91 SY.MO355/R) La reveuse (43x35cm-17x14in) (F.FR 40000) |

LEDUC, Fernand (1916-) Canadian
| £3653 | $6685 | (14-May-92 SY.T156/R) Abstract composition (63x67cm-25x26in) s.d.52 (C.D 8000) |

LEDUC, Paul (1876-1943) Belgian
| £1832 | $3407 | (16-Jun-92 SY.B339/R) A Mediterranean terrace (59x43cm-23x17in) s. (B.FR 110000) |

LEDUC, Victor Viollet see   VIOLLET LE DUC, Victor

LEE, Doris (20th C) American
| £690 | $1200 | (15-Apr-92 SY.NY268/R) Landscape with cows (28x41cm-11x16in) s. canvasboard |
| £4888 | $8750 | (6-May-92 D.NY36 a) The barn dance, Oklahoma (50x72cm-20x28in) s. |

LEE, Frederick Richard (1798-1879) British
| £8000 | $14080 | (8-Apr-92 S89/R) Fulford Park, Exeter, Devon (70x90cm-28x35in) s. i.verso |
| £10000 | $17900 | (15-Nov-91 C99/R) English river fish on bank (74x102cm-29x40in) s.d.1834 |

LEE, Frederick Richard (attrib) (1798-1879) British
| £600 | $1146 | (17-Jul-92 C98 a) Angler in wooded river landscape (36x51cm-14x20in) |

LEE, Frederick Richard and COOPER, Thomas Sidney (19th C) British
| £1350 | $2498 | (11-Jun-92 CSK113/R) Sheep in wooded landscape (35x48cm-14x19in) s.i. canvas on board |

LEE, John J (19th C) British
| £92000 | $156400 | (25-Oct-91 C51/R) The bookstall (102x81cm-40x32in) s.d.1863 |

LEE, Nancy (20th C) ?
| £526 | $900 | (13-Mar-92 FN.S2846) Still life of roses in vase on marble ledge (24x18cm-9x7in) s. panel (DM 1500) |
| £671 | $1221 | (12-Dec-91 RAS.V741) Still life of flowers in vase on ledge (50x40cm-20x16in) s. (D.KR 7500) |

LEE, William (1810-1865) British
| £950 | $1691 | (29-Oct-91 C54/R) Hide and seek (53x61cm-21x24in) pencil W/C |

LEE-HANKEY, William (1869-1952) British
£2400	$4152	(2-Oct-91 S26/R) The ploughman (51x61cm-20x24in) s.
£2793	$5000	(13-Nov-91 B.SF2430/R) Montreuil sur Mer (63x76cm-25x30in) s.
£2863	$5097	(26-Nov-91 J.M61 a) Vegetable stall (29x35cm-11x14in) s. (A.D 6500)
£3600	$6444	(14-Jan-92 PH48/R) Idle moment (48x56cm-19x22in) s.
£3800	$6574	(2-Oct-91 S41/R) Solitary supper (127x140cm-50x55in) s.
£3800	$6954	(14-May-92 C207/R) Near mouth of Seine (51x61cm-20x24in) s. s.i.verso
£4000	$7520	(18-Dec-91 C112/R) The river Conway, North Wales (61x76cm-24x30in) s. s.i.verso
£4000	$7320	(14-May-92 C208/R) Spaniards Inn, Hampstead (63x76cm-25x30in) s. s.i.verso
£4400	$7788	(5-Nov-91 PH88/R) Sospel (51x61cm-20x24in) s.
£4500	$8235	(14-May-92 C206/R) Ferry, Concarneau (51x61cm-20x24in) s. s.i.verso
£5200	$8996	(2-Oct-91 S28/R) Near Notre Dame, Paris (63x76cm-25x30in) s. s.i.verso
£5500	$10065	(14-May-92 C209/R) River Rance at Dinan, Normandy (51x61cm-20x24in) s. s.i.stretcher
£6500	$11895	(14-May-92 C205/R) Mussel harvest, Honfleur (51x61cm-20x24in) s. s.i.verso
£400	$708	(7-Nov-91 CSK133) Marshland with copse beyond (29x44cm-11x17in) s.d.01 W/C

LEE-HANKEY, William (1869-1952) British-cont.

£500	$870	(16-Apr-92 PHX321) Summer landscape, nr Findon, Sussex (25x33cm-10x13in) s.i.verso with d.1936 W/C over pencil
£800	$1384	(6-Sep-91 BW286) By the window, interior scene with figures (30x28cm-12x11in) s. W/C
£920	$1610	(27-Sep-91 C110/R) The stile (37x26cm-15x10in) s. i. verso W/C bodycol.
£1200	$2136	(28-Nov-91 L235/R) Girl with staff (23x33cm-9x13in) s. W/C
£1900	$3249	(11-Mar-92 S20/R) Mother and child (46x33cm-18x13in) s. W/C
£2000	$3540	(7-Nov-92 C11/R) The young shepherdess (27x35cm-11x14in) s.d.1902 W/C bodycol.
£5100	$9129	(14-Jan-92 SWS104/R) Lunch in the garden (29x21cm-11x8in) s.d.1902 W/C htd.gum arabic
£7000	$12530	(14-Jan-92 SWS105/R) By the stile (29x21cm-11x8in) s.d.02 W/C bodycol htd.gum arabic

LEE-SMITH, Hughie (1910-) American

£1862	$3500	(17-Dec-91 BG.M686/R) Portrait of the artist's wife nude (61x46cm-24x18in) s.d.48
£1935	$3250	(16-Aug-91 DM.D2007) Woman by seashore (51x41cm-20x16in) s.
£4261	$7500	(10-Apr-92 DM.D2006/R) Woman by seashore (46x61cm-18x24in) s.d.57 board
£4464	$7500	(16-Aug-91 DM.D2006/R) Reader (46x61cm-18x24in) s.
£4520	$8000	(14-Feb-92 DM.D2004/R) Man in courtyard (56x76cm-22x30in) s.d.53 masonite

LEECH, William John (1881-1968) British

£2083	$3792	(11-Dec-91 A.D16) The boat (18x23cm-7x9in) s. board (E.P 2250)
£9813	$16977	(25-Mar-92 A.D122/R) The Orchard (36x46cm-14x18in) s. board (E.P 10500)

LEEKE, Ferdinand (1859-?) German

£515	$943	(2-Jun-92 FN.S2646) Hillside stony field with rare flowers and edge of the wood beyond (45x65cm-18x26in) s. (DM 1500)
£1774	$3086	(14-Apr-92 SY.AM134/R) Wood nymph (132x89cm-52x35in) s.d.1905 (D.FL 5800)
£2095	$3813	(14-Dec-91 BA.S40) Mythological scene (100x119cm-39x47in) s.d.1910 (S.KR 22000)

LEEMPOELS, Jef (1867-?) Belgian

£633	$1177	(16-Jun-92 GM.B566/R) Village brabancon (32x47cm-13x19in) s. (B.FR 38000)

LEEMPUTTEN, Cornelis van (1841-1902) Belgian

£620	$1153	(16-Jun-92 PH24 a) Ducks and poultry (18x20cm-7x8in) s. panel
£797	$1450	(15-Dec-91 LIT.L284) Interior barn scene with sheep and chickens (18x23cm-7x9in) s.
£859	$1495	(18-Sep-91 N.M601/R) Sheep, goats and chicken in landscape (18x24cm-7x9in) s. panel (DM 2500)
£979	$1674	(18-Mar-92 N.M581/R) Sheep and chicken in stable (16x24cm-6x9in) s. panel (DM 2800)
£1500	$2565	(17-Mar-92 PH26/R) Poultry in landscape (27x36cm-11x14in) s. s.i.d.1862verso panel
£2200	$3806	(4-Oct-91 C67/R) Chickens, ducks and rabbits by pond (25x35cm-10x14in) s.d.1867 two
£9890	$18000	(28-May-92 SY.NY24/R) Return of flock (142x208cm-56x82in) s.

LEEMPUTTEN, J F van (19th C) Belgian

£729	$1269	(17-Sep-91 CH.AM445) Poultry in a field near a fence (25x35cm-10x14in) s.d.1865 panel (D.FL 2400)

LEEMPUTTEN, Jef Louis van (c.1865-1948) Belgian

£663	$1214	(12-May-92 C.A347) Sheep in a stall (38x50cm-15x20in) s. (B.FR 40000)
£680	$1183	(11-Sep-91 PHL74/R) Poultry in extensive landscape (23x35cm-9x14in) s.indist.d. panel
£855	$1548	(3-Dec-91 C.A338) The shepherd (60x50cm-24x20in) s. (B.FR 50000)
£887	$1543	(14-Apr-92 SY.AM224) Poultry by river (33x48cm-13x19in) s.d.1869 panel (D.FL 2900)
£3488	$6000	(16-Oct-91 CH.NY238/R) Het Vaderland Bezet (101x151cm-40x59in) s.i.d.1914-1918

LEEN, Willem van (1753-1825) Dutch

£6000	$10920	(13-Dec-91 C187/R) Slice of melon, peach, grapes, pomegranate and flowers on marble ledge (47x37cm-19x15in) s.

LEEN, Willem van (style) (1753-1825) Dutch

£2623	$4696	(12-Nov-91 SY.AM124/R) Fruit arranged on ledge with view of park beyond (49x36cm-19x14in) bears indis.sig. (D.FL 8500)

LEES, Edwin (19th C) ?

£608	$1142	(3-Jan-92 DUR.M89/R) Paisaje escoces (41x61cm-16x24in) s. (S.P 110000)

LEEST, Johannes Theodorus van der (1907-) Dutch

£508	$899	(5-Nov-91 GF.L2699/R) View of Amsterdam (60x70cm-24x28in) s. d.1966verso (S.FR 1300)

LEEUW, Alexis de (fl.1848-1883) British

£1000	$1860	(18-Jun-92 B63/R) Blacksmith shoeing a carthorse (58x87cm-23x34in) s.
£2416	$4300	(27-Apr-92 S.SL491/R) Snowy winter landscape with children tending sheep in twilight (89x119cm-35x47in) s.

LEEUW, Bert de (1926-) Belgian
£1337 $2272   (22-Oct-91 C.A484) Rider (95x142cm-37x56in) s.d.1959 mixed media
        (B.FR 80000)

LEEUW, Pieter van de (1647-1679) Dutch
£3509 $6000   (13-Mar-92 FN.S2847/R) Market square of southern town with figures and
        cattle (92x100cm-36x39in) (DM 10000)

LEEUW, Pieter van de (attrib) (1647-1679) Dutch
£994 $1699   (18-Mar-92 D.V366/R) Riders and cows by ford (46x60cm-18x24in)
        (A.S 20000)

LEEVENDIG, Floris Johan (1901-) Dutch
£679 $1188   (18-Feb-92 CH.AM94) View of the Reguliersgracht, Amsterdam, with the
        Amstelkerk (52x73cm-20x29in) s. panel (D.FL 2200)
£1049 $1836   (18-Feb-92 CH.AM86/R) A red cat (60x79cm-24x31in) s. another painting by
        H J Ansingh (D.FL 3400)

LEEWENS, Will (1923-) Dutch
£758 $1371   (19-May-92 CH.AM407) Abstract composition (80x100cm-31x39in) s.
        (D.FL 2500)
£818 $1481   (21-May-92 SY.AM359/R) Blakend blond en blauw (80x100cm-31x39in)
        s.i.stretcher (D.FL 2700)
£988 $1798   (12-Dec-91 SY.AM135/R) Still life (50x41cm-20x16in) s.d.43 (D.FL 3200)
£1389 $2528   (11-Dec-91 CH.AM187) Vera Cruz (47x65cm-19x26in) s. i.verso board
        (D.FL 4500)
£455 $823   (19-May-92 CH.AM377) Abstract composition (35x51cm-14x20in) s.d.84
        gouache (D.FL 1500)

LEFEBVRE, Claude (1632-1675) French
£15448 $26416   (20-Mar-92 ZZ.F8/R) Portrait presume du Chancelier d'Aguesseau
        (189x129cm-74x51in) (F.FR 150000)

LEFEBVRE, Jules Joseph (1836-1911) French
£705 $1256   (28-Apr-92 RAS.K246) Young girl praying (57x45cm-22x18in) s. (D.KR 8000)
£8571 $15000   (20-Feb-92 SY.NY41/R) Reclining nude (15x32cm-6x13in) s. panel

LEFEBVRE, Maurice Jean (1873-1954) Belgian
£733 $1261   (12-Oct-91 KV.L182) Scene de plage (24x34cm-9x13in) s. board (B.FR 44000)
£1490 $2697   (23-May-92 KV.L194) Reclining nude (38x61cm-15x24in) s. (B.FR 90000)

LEFEVRE (?) ?
£1119 $2048   (15-May-92 AT.P160) Portrait d'homme (64x54cm-25x21in) s.d.1746 i.verso
        pastel (F.FR 11000)

LEFEVRE, Edmond (?) French
£510 $948   (17-Jun-92 I.N211) Scene de plage (19x27cm-7x11in) s. panel (F.FR 5000)
£686 $1180   (20-Oct-91 I.N291) Conversation sur la plage (19x27cm-7x11in) s. panel
        (F.FR 6800)
£1418 $2567   (22-May-92 BL.P77) Baigneuse (21x16cm-8x6in) s. (F.FR 14000)

LEFEVRE, Robert Jacques Francois (circle) (1755-1830) French
£1028 $1829   (29-Nov-91 GAB.G3075/R) Portrait de femme a mi-corps dans un paysage
        (73x60cm-29x24in) (S.FR 2600)
£2884 $5421   (16-Dec-91 AGS.P63/R) Portrait de Femme. Portrait d'Homme
        (68x54cm-27x21in) pair (F.FR 28000)

LEFLER, Franz (1831-1898) Czechoslovakian
£1429 $2500   (18-Feb-92 CE.NY25) Bacchanale (44x122cm-17x48in) s.
£2472 $4325   (20-Feb-92 D.V307/R) Allegory of Constitution (86x115cm-34x45in) s.
        (A.S 50000)
£8140 $14000   (17-Oct-91 SY.NY287/R) Putti singing. Putti with flowers. Putti with
        tambourine (89x129cm-35x51in) s. three

LEFORT, H (20th C) ?
£750 $1373   (15-May-92 S254) The can-can (39x49cm-15x19in) s.

LEFORT, Jean (1875-1954) French
£8791 $16000   (27-May-92 CH.NY59/R) Elegant gathering in the Bois de Boulogne
        (34x68cm-13x27in) s. oil pastel on paper

LEFTWICH DODGE, William de (1867-1935) American
£1453 $2600   (14-Nov-91 CE.NY295/R) Sunset near Paris (38x54cm-15x21in) s.i.d.1888
£6044 $11000   (27-May-92 SY.NY60/R) Woman by sea (119x81cm-47x32in) s.d.1925 num.15
        verso

LEGA, Silvestro (1826-1895) Italian
£8707 $15411   (7-Nov-91 F.M4/R) La musica sacra (149x102cm-59x40in) s.d.1859
        (I.L 19000000)

LEGARES, Josep Olivet (1885-1956) Spanish
£5472 $9740   (29-Oct-91 BRO.B337/R) Paisaje de la comarca de Olot (74x93cm-29x37in) s.
        s.i.verso (S.P 1000000)

LEGAT, Leon (1829-?) French
£13736 $25000   (28-May-92 SY.NY33/R) Le chemin au bord de la riviere (81x132cm-32x52in) s.

LEGEAY, Jean Laurent (1710-1786) French
£2235 $4000   (15-Jan-92 CH.NY99/R) Capriccio with figures beneath ruined temple, obelisk, rotunda, pyramid (43x32cm-17x13in) red chk wash

LEGER, Fernand (1881-1955) French
£59063 $107495   (13-Dec-91 ZZ.F83/R) Le signal dans le paysage (65x50cm-26x20in) d.1955verso (F.FR 580000)
£79430 $144562   (13-Dec-91 ZZ.F82/R) Nature morte aux six fruits (54x65cm-21x26in) s.d.38 (F.FR 780000)
£80000 $152800   (29-Jun-92 C50/R) Composition avec figure (65x46cm-26x18in) s.d.31 s.verso
£101695 $180000   (6-Nov-91 CH.NY305/R) Le motif bleu (50x65cm-20x26in) s.d.38 s.i.d.verso
£105000 $190050   (3-Dec-91 S51/R) Composition (54x65cm-21x26in) s.d.46
£180000 $343800   (30-Jun-92 S58/R) Composition aux trois profils (89x130cm-35x51in) s.d.37
£197740 $350000   (5-Nov-91 CH.NY51/R) Les deux femmes au vase bleu (54x65cm-21x26in) s.d.35 s.i.d.verso
£210728 $364559   (28-Mar-92 F.L86/R) Composition a la feuille jaune (65x92cm-26x36in) s.d.1930 (S.FR 550000)
£260000 $470600   (2-Dec-91 C44/R) Personnages et Plantes (74x90cm-29x35in) s.d.38
£3954802 $7000000   (5-Nov-91 CH.NY10/R) Le petit dejeuner (96x129cm-38x51in) s.d.21
£1368 $2476   (18-May-92 AT.P17) David triomphant (31x24cm-12x9in) s.d.36 gouache (F.FR 13500)
£1372 $2387   (15-Apr-92 PLF.P83/R) Femme nue (30x21cm-12x8in) mono.d.06 ink dr (F.FR 13500)
£2541 $4421   (13-Apr-92 GL.P74/R) Projet de sculpture polychrome ceramique (32x49cm-13x19in) st.sig. gouache (F.FR 25000)
£2673 $4651   (17-Sep-91 JRL.S382/R) Composition with figure (26x35cm-10x14in) s.d.6.38 gouache stencil (A.D 5800)
£3055 $5652   (12-Jun-92 ARC.P17/R) Les batisseurs (41x35cm-16x14in) mono. Indian ink crayon (F.FR 30000)
£3708 $6340   (18-Mar-92 PIC.P58/R) La danse (43x62cm-17x24in) studio st. Indian ink crayon dr (F.FR 36000)
£3955 $7000   (6-Nov-91 CH.NY179/R) Element mecanique (30x23cm-12x9in) init.d.44 pen brush paper squared for transfer
£5220 $9500   (28-May-92 BG.M555/R) Voici le temps des assassins (33x25cm-13x10in) init.d.1950 gouache
£5500 $9955   (3-Dec-91 C162/R) Composition (34x26cm-13x10in) gouache ink
£5658 $10242   (6-Dec-91 GL.P164 b/R) Une femme americaine (33x25cm-13x10in) gouache (F.FR 55000)
£6687 $12104   (6-Dec-91 GL.P165/R) Projet pour une sculpture polychrome (44x22cm-17x9in) st.init.st.sig. gouache (F.FR 65000)
£7104 $13000   (11-May-92 CH.NY16/R) Nu debout (32x23cm-13x9in) init. pen
£7650 $14000   (11-May-92 CH.NY71/R) Maquette pour couverture d'un catalogue (32x24cm-13x9in) s. gouache over pencil
£8743 $16000   (11-May-92 CH.NY63/R) Maquette pour couverture d'un catalogue (32x24cm-13x9in) s. gouache pencil
£9000 $15480   (16-Oct-91 S73/R) Visage (32x24cm-13x9in) init.d.30 pen indian ink over pencil
£10169 $18000   (7-Nov-91 SY.NY166/R) Tete de femme (42x35cm-17x14in) init.d.40 brush ink over pencil paper on board
£10169 $18000   (6-Nov-91 CH.NY167/R) Paysage (25x32cm-10x13in) st.init. gouache over pencil paper on board
£10370 $18770   (20-May-92 GK.Z5057/R) Construction mecanique (31x24cm-12x9in) mono.d.1949 mixed media (S.FR 28000)
£11429 $20000   (25-Feb-92 CH.NY85/R) La ville (42x63cm-17x25in) st.sig. gouache indian ink over pencil on board
£11475 $21000   (14-May-92 SY.NY167/R) L'ecuyere dans le cirque (42x32cm-17x13in) init.i.d.48 gouache ink wash over pencil board
£12000 $20760   (25-Mar-92 S70/R) Projet de decor - Bolivar (22x31cm-9x12in) init.i.d.49 gouache
£12000 $22920   (30-Jun-92 C126/R) Etude pour La Partie de Cartes (17x22cm-7x9in) s.i.d.A16 pen indian ink
£12000 $20760   (24-Mar-92 C67/R) Personnage de la grande parade, le clown au banjo (45x32cm-18x13in) init.d.53 gouache
£12429 $22000   (7-Nov-91 SY.NY215/R) Design for United Nations General Assembly Hall Mural (22x45cm-9x18in) init.d.52 gouache over pencil
£12568 $23000   (14-May-92 SY.NY170/R) Composition (36x30cm-14x12in) s.i. gouache ink wash pencil squared
£13078 $22495   (7-Oct-91 RY.P77/R) Composition a l'homme et a l'oiseau (23x17cm-9x7in) init.d.41 gouache (F.FR 130000)
£13525 $24344   (2-Feb-92 ZZ.F191/R) Portrait de femme et bouquet de fleurs (59x50cm-23x20in) mono.d.1951 gouache (F.FR 132000)
£14208 $26000   (14-May-92 SY.NY166/R) Etude pour la ville, la vitrine (48x63cm-19x25in) st.sig. gouache ink wash
£15000 $25950   (24-Mar-92 C105/R) Le veston (48x41cm-19x16in) init.d.34 gouache pencil
£15301 $28000   (11-May-92 CH.NY44/R) Femme avec main devant son visage (39x32cm-15x13in) init.d.39 pen brush indian ink over pencil
£16393 $30000   (13-May-92 CH.NY263/R) Composition abstraite (32x23cm-13x9in) init.d.37 gouache over pencil
£18311 $32777   (17-Nov-91 GL.P15/R) L'homme a la nature morte (32x39cm-13x15in) mono. gouache (F.FR 180000)

LEGER, Fernand (1881-1955) French-cont.

£18644	$33000	(7-Nov-91 SY.NY162/R) Composition a l'oiseau (56x76cm-22x30in) init. brush ink over pencil
£19774	$35000	(7-Nov-91 SY.NY167/R) Etude pour l'anniversaire (21x16cm-8x6in) init.d.50 gouache ink wash
£20765	$38000	(11-May-92 CH.NY51/R) Les gants (32x25cm-13x10in) init.d.33 pen indian ink
£21779	$38767	(26-Nov-91 SY.MI200/R) Composizione (32x25cm-13x10in) mono.d.49 gouache indian ink (I.L 47000000)
£21858	$40000	(11-May-92 CH.NY9/R) Etude pour Abondance (31x19cm-12x7in) pen
£21858	$40000	(11-May-92 CH.NY8/R) Les deux tues (12x9cm-5x4in) init.d.24-10-16 pen over pencil
£22951	$42000	(14-May-92 SY.NY171/R) Etude, composition murale, masurel (42x36cm-17x14in) init. gouache ink wash over pencil
£24000	$45840	(1-Jul-92 S213/R) Les deux matelots (35x30cm-14x12in) inits.d.50 gouache W/C over pencil
£25458	$47098	(12-May-92 AT.P38/R) Femme a la rose (53x42cm-21x17in) st.inits. gouache (F.FR 250000)
£25989	$46000	(6-Nov-91 CH.NY158/R) La danseuse (48x63cm-19x25in) init.d.31 pencil double-sided
£27429	$48000	(25-Feb-92 CH.NY40/R) Figure polychrome (49x35cm-19x14in) init. gouache brush indian ink
£28807	$54733	(24-Jun-92 GL.P176/R) La mere et l'enfant (65x50cm-26x20in) init. gouache (F.FR 280000)
£30000	$51900	(25-Mar-92 S71/R) Couple au chien (45x32cm-18x13in) s. pencil gouache brush indian ink
£30041	$55575	(12-Jun-92 AT.P37/R) Nu allonge (24x32cm-9x13in) init.d.1920 W/C (F.FR 295000)
£32922	$62551	(24-Jun-92 GL.P177/R) Les deux amoureux (66x50cm-26x20in) init. gouache (F.FR 320000)
£38066	$72325	(24-Jun-92 GL.P180/R) La grande parade (38x48cm-15x19in) init.d.1952 gouache (F.FR 370000)
£38251	$70000	(11-May-92 CH.NY4/R) Les foreurs (23x14cm-9x6in) s. gouache W/C pen
£46448	$85000	(11-May-92 CH.NY46/R) Nature morte avec cafetiere (32x24cm-13x9in) init.d.24 pencil
£48023	$85000	(6-Nov-91 CH.NY155/R) Nature morte au compotier (24x31cm-9x12in) init.d.25 W/C brush india ink over pencil
£51913	$95000	(11-May-92 CH.NY41/R) Composition a l'echiquier (48x42cm-19x17in) init.d.26 gouache brush indian ink over pencil
£53640	$92797	(28-Mar-92 F.L50/R) Le cafe (45x65cm-18x26in) s. gouache (S.FR 140000)
£60109	$110000	(14-May-92 SY.NY169/R) L'anniversaire (65x49cm-26x19in) init.d.53 W/C gouache ink wash
£60109	$110000	(11-May-92 CH.NY38/R) Le siphon (26x18cm-10x7in) init. pencil pen indian ink W/C
£63158	$108000	(13-Mar-92 FN.S2540/R) Untitled (39x56cm-15x22in) mono.i.d.1952 gouache (DM 180000)
£73446	$130000	(6-Nov-91 CH.NY189/R) Les constructeurs (56x76cm-22x30in) init.d.50 gouache brush india ink
£81967	$150000	(11-May-92 CH.NY26/R) Nature morte au buste (31x25cm-12x10in) init.d.24 pencil col.pencil W/C
£89159	$161378	(24-May-92 GL.P20/R) Composition mecanique (32x24cm-13x9in) s. W/C paper laid down on board (F.FR 880000)
£96045	$170000	(6-Nov-91 SY.NY64/R) Les cyclistes (28x40cm-11x16in) init.d.44 gouache India ink
£98361	$180000	(14-May-92 SY.NY143/R) Etude pour le dejeuner (26x33cm-10x13in) init.d.21 W/C ink wash
£98361	$180000	(11-May-92 CH.NY50/R) Le constructeur, etude de jambes (63x49cm-25x19in) init.d.51 pen brush indian ink paper on panel
£98361	$180000	(13-May-92 SY.NY36/R) Etude pour le remorqueur (25x33cm-10x13in) init.d.18 W/C ink
£125683	$230000	(11-May-92 CH.NY34/R) Deux hommes dans un escalier (29x25cm-11x10in) init.d.24 pencil
£153005	$280000	(11-May-92 CH.NY29/R) Trois femmes (31x42cm-12x17in) init.d.21 pencil

LEGER, Nadia (20th C) ?

£834	$1485	(27-Nov-91 F.M206) Composizione (20x13cm-8x5in) s. ink (I.L 1800000)

LEGGE, Russell (20th C) ?

£500	$900	(10-Jan-92 DM.D1044/R) Figural scenes (53x36cm-21x14in) s.i.d.29 pencil

LEGGETT, Alexander (19th C) British

£1200	$2064	(3-Mar-92 AG264/R) His boat in sight (60x44cm-24x17in) s.i.verso
£2647	$4500	(25-Oct-91 S.W2787/R) Cuckoo clock (81x107cm-32x42in) i.stretcher
£3500	$6230	(28-Apr-92 S176/R) The cuckoo clock (81x107cm-32x42in)

LEGGETT, Miss Rowley (fl.1904-1919) British

£906	$1550	(12-Mar-92 MFA.C140) Wild flowers (46x36cm-18x14in) s. board

LEGILLON, Jean Francois (1739-1797) Flemish

£838	$1500	(15-Jan-92 CH.NY116/R) Studies of horses' heads and tails and study of boy seated on rock (23x19cm-9x7in) s.i.d.1784 num.22 black lead

LEGLER, Wilhelm (1875-1951) Italian

£699	$1210	(25-Mar-92 KM.K1281) Still life of flowers in vase on draped table (54x48cm-21x19in) s. (DM 2000)

LEGNANI, Stefano Maria (1660-1715) Italian
£6000 $11520   (7-Jul-92 PH67/R) Madonna and child (99x81cm-39x32in) painted oval

LEGORA, Giovanni Cappa (1887-?) Italian
£2975 $5087   (19-Mar-92 F.M128/R) Piove nel porto (35x45cm-14x18in) s.i.d.1934 board
           (I.L 6400000)

LEGOUT-GERARD, Fernand (1856-1924) French
£659 $1200   (26-May-92 CE.NY337) Marketplace (12x12cm-5x5in) s. panel oval
£1739 $3096   (29-Nov-91 GAB.G2131 a) Scene animee sur les quais a Concarneau
           (46x55cm-18x22in) s. (S.FR 4400)
£2405 $4474   (20-Jun-92 BM.B854/R) Harbour scene with fish market, Brittanny
           (46x38cm-18x15in) s. (DM 7000)
£2610 $4750   (28-May-92 SY.NY200/R) Le port de la Rochelle (22x27cm-9x11in) s.d.1919
           panel
£2917 $5192   (27-Nov-91 AT.P161/R) Marine (35x50cm-14x20in) s.d.01 panel (F.FR 28500)
£3000 $5250   (20-Feb-92 SY.NY136/R) Breton fishing village (27x22cm-11x9in) s. panel
£3500 $6055   (4-Oct-91 C7/R) The Market Place, Concarneau (21x27cm-8x11in) s. panel
£5429 $9500   (20-Feb-92 SY.NY138/R) Breton fishing harbour at sunset (53x64cm-21x25in)
           s.
£6977 $12000   (17-Oct-91 SY.NY169/R) Market place (50x61cm-20x24in) s.
£8970 $16685   (21-Jun-92 LT.P50/R) Jour de Marche en Bretagne aux Halles de Faouet
           (55x65cm-22x26in) s. (F.FR 88000)
£9116 $16500   (4-Dec-91 NA.BA3/R) Port de peche en Bretagne (50x61cm-20x24in) s.
£9295 $16267   (21-Feb-92 LC.P56/R) Le depart des pecheurs (55x65cm-22x26in) s.
           (F.FR 91000)

LEGRAND, Louis Auguste Mathieu (1863-1951) French
£3905 $6717   (4-Mar-92 AT.P166/R) Deux filles de joie (54x65cm-21x26in) s.
           (F.FR 38000)
£2000 $3620   (2-Dec-91 CSK117/R) La ballerine (19x25cm-7x10in) s. W/C pencil

LEGRAND, Pierre Nicolas (1758-1829) Swiss
£471 $800   (23-Oct-91 GD.B444/R) Portrait of woman (69x57cm-27x22in) s.d.1823
           (S.FR 1200)

LEGRAND, Rene (1923-) French
£600 $1074   (14-Jan-92 SWS279/R) The rockpool (40x50cm-16x20in) s.
£880 $1575   (14-Jan-92 SWS277/R) Summer's day (51x71cm-20x28in) s.
£900 $1611   (14-Jan-92 SWS278/R) On the beach (61x86cm-24x34in) s.

LEGROS, Alphonse (1837-1911) French
£2682 $4800   (11-Nov-91 GC.M68/R) Franciscanos Agradeciendo el Pan (62x93cm-24x37in)
           s.

LEGUEULT, Raymond (1898-1971) French
£10267 $18480   (22-Nov-91 PIC.P31/R) Le printemps (116x73cm-46x29in) s.d.1937-38
           s.i.d.verso (F.FR 100000)
£812 $1420   (5-Apr-92 ZZ.F252/R) Portrait de jeune fille (26x20cm-10x8in) s. W/C
           (F.FR 7800)

LEHMANN, Edvard (1815-1892) Danish
£926 $1648   (27-Apr-92 BU.K58/R) Two girls reading letter (30x24cm-12x9in) panel
           (D.KR 10500)
£1276 $2144   (27-Aug-91 RAS.K406) From the fairytale 'The crow and Regnar Lodbrog'
           (78x98cm-31x39in) s.d.1849 (D.KR 14500)

LEHMANN, Henri (1814-1882) French
£559 $996   (26-Nov-91 KF.M229) Portrait of young noble man (24x18cm-9x7in) s.d.1851
           pencil (DM 1600)

LEHMANN, Herbert (1890-?) German
£631 $1123   (28-Apr-92 D.V77/R) Lady wearing hat with veil (26x21cm-10x8in) s.d.20
           pencil W/C (A.S 13000)

LEHMANN, Jean (1885-1969) ?
£859 $1521   (5-Nov-91 GF.L2664/R) View of monastery at dusk. Wooded landscape, autumn
           (51x60cm-20x24in) s.i.d.1917 i.stretcher double-sided (S.FR 2200)

LEHMANN, Karl Ernest Rodolphe Heinrich Salem see   LEHMANN, Henri

LEHMANN, Wilhelm Ludwig (1861-1932) Swiss
£586 $1038   (6-Nov-91 N.M1078) Landscape with hay stooks (33x45cm-13x18in) canvas on
           board (DM 1700)

LEHMBRUCK, Wilhelm (1881-1919) German
£893 $1635   (3-Jun-92 L.K265/R) Portrait of Ludwig Rubiner (22x17cm-9x7in) indian ink
           brush (DM 2600)

LEHMDEN, Anton (1929-) Austrian
£776 $1412   (26-May-92 D.V238/R) Vogelflug (19x36cm-7x14in) s. pen indian ink
           (A.S 16000)
£874 $1555   (28-Apr-92 D.V324) Gussing (31x22cm-12x9in) s. indian ink pen (A.S 18000)
£3393 $6175   (26-May-92 D.V234/R) Vogelflug (47x22cm-19x9in) s. mixed media oil panel
           (A.S 70000)

LEHTO, Nikolai (1905-) Finnish
£607 $1068   (12-Apr-92 HOR.H144) Guardian Angel (29x21cm-11x8in) s.d.1979 (F.M 4800)
£1201 $2114   (12-Apr-92 HOR.H143) The whole family (36x45cm-14x18in) s.d.1985
     (F.M 9500)

LEIBL, W (1844-1900) German
£600 $1038   (26-Mar-92 LE215) Head and shoulder portrait of an elderly woman
     (23x15cm-9x6in) pencil dr.

LEIBL, Wilhelm (1844-1900) German
£13500 $25110   (19-Jun-92 C22/R) An old woman (21x16cm-8x6in) pencil

LEICKERT, Charles (1818-1907) Belgian
£1368 $2380   (17-Sep-91 CH.AM598) A stormy winter landscape with skaters on the ice,
     windmill beyond (23x41cm-9x16in) s. panel (D.FL 4500)
£2080 $3702   (30-Oct-91 CH.AM30) Winter landscape with skaters on frozen river
     (13x17cm-5x7in) s. panel (D.FL 6800)
£2446 $4355   (30-Oct-91 CH.AM184/R) Skaters pushing sledge in winter landscape with
     windmill beyond (21x33cm-8x13in) s. panel (D.FL 8000)
£2446 $4257   (14-Apr-92 SY.AM243/R) Figures in Dutch town (33x26cm-13x10in) s. panel
     (D.FL 8000)
£2576 $4559   (22-Apr-92 CH.AM106/R) Winterlandscape with peasants and a
     horse-drawn-sledge by a windmill (39x51cm-15x20in) s.d.73 (D.FL 8500)
£2727 $4827   (22-Apr-92 CH.AM139/R) View in a town in winter with villagers in a snowy
     street (36x27cm-14x11in) with sig. panel (D.FL 9000)
£2879 $5095   (22-Apr-92 CH.AM98/R) Winterlandscape with skaters on a frozen waterway,
     windmills in distance (17x24cm-7x9in) s. panel (D.FL 9500)
£3030 $5364   (22-Apr-92 CH.AM199/R) View in a town with several figures on a square
     (20x27cm-8x11in) s. panel (D.FL 10000)
£3040 $5289   (17-Sep-91 CH.AM488/R) Stormy weather approaching (23x28cm-9x11in) s.
     panel (D.FL 10000)
£3531 $6250   (6-Nov-91 D.NY20/R) Skaters in winter landscape (22x27cm-9x11in) s. panel
£3670 $6385   (14-Apr-92 SY.AM303/R) Winter landscape with figures by cottage
     (16x21cm-6x8in) s. panel (D.FL 12000)
£3976 $7037   (5-Nov-91 SY.AM33/R) View of town with figures on quay (28x39cm-11x15in)
     s. panel (D.FL 13000)
£4200 $7182   (18-Mar-92 S10/R) Winter scene in a village (29x35cm-11x14in) s.
£4545 $8045   (22-Apr-92 CH.AM129/R) View in a town with washerwomen along a canal
     (24x17cm-9x7in) indist.s. panel (D.FL 15000)
£4587 $8119   (5-Nov-91 SY.AM248/R) River landscape with figures in boat and
     washerwomen by mill (52x67cm-20x26in) s. (D.FL 15000)
£4918 $8852   (2-Feb-92 ZZ.F27/R) Village sous la neige (22x27cm-9x11in) s. panel
     (F.FR 48000)
£5500 $9405   (18-Mar-92 S2/R) Fisherfolk on the beach at Scheveningen
     (40x58cm-16x23in) s. canvas laid down on board
£5842 $10165   (21-Sep-91 SA.A1898/R) Market scene before town gates in snow covered
     square (42x34cm-17x13in) s. panel (DM 17000)
£6000 $10740   (14-Jan-92 SWS208/R) Dutch winter landscape (44x59cm-17x23in) s.
     s.i.verso
£6857 $12000   (20-Feb-92 SY.NY194/R) Village market (32x25cm-13x10in) s. panel
£7429 $13000   (20-Feb-92 SY.NY193/R) Winter landscape (56x90cm-22x35in) s.
£7492 $13111   (5-Apr-92 ZZ.F45/R) Village et moulin sous la neige (45x65cm-18x26in) s.
     (F.FR 72000)
£8563 $14899   (14-Apr-92 SY.AM84/R) Summer landscape with boats on river
     (20x28cm-8x11in) s. panel (D.FL 28000)
£9091 $16091   (22-Apr-92 CH.AM142 a/R) Riverlandscape with moored rowing boats in a
     village (43x60cm-17x24in) s.indist.d.68 (D.FL 30000)
£9786 $17419   (30-Oct-91 CH.AM144/R) View of town with figures conversing on bridge
     over canal (24x21cm-9x8in) s.d.51 panel (D.FL 32000)
£9884 $17000   (17-Oct-91 SY.NY7/R) Lomer (30x41cm-12x16in) s. panel
£12000 $20520   (17-Mar-92 PH10/R) Figures in river landscape (49x72cm-19x28in) s.d.66
£12232 $21651   (5-Nov-91 SY.AM218/R) Winter landscape with figures and sledge on frozen
     river (41x55cm-16x22in) s. (D.FL 40000)
£18349 $32477   (5-Nov-91 SY.AM89/R) Dutch winter scene (80x114cm-31x45in) s.d.75
     (D.FL 60000)
£19266 $33523   (14-Apr-92 SY.AM208/R) Winter landscape with figures by a 'Koek en Zopie'
     (69x99cm-27x39in) s. (D.FL 63000)
£31000 $57660   (17-Jun-92 S271/R) Figures and skaters on frozen river (96x134cm-38x53in)
     s.d.68
£31429 $55000   (20-Feb-92 SY.NY5/R) River landscape in summer (63x95cm-25x37in) s.d.63
£450 $815   (6-Dec-91 TE506/R) Medinblik Harbour, Holland (30x41cm-12x16in) s. W/C

LEICKERT, Charles (circle) (1818-1907) Belgian
£900 $1602   (28-Nov-91 B39/R) Winter landscape (46x65cm-18x26in) bears sig.

LEICKERT, Charles and ROCHUSSEN, Charles (19th C) Belgian/Dutch
£9174 $16239   (5-Nov-91 SY.AM77/R) Winter landscape with skaters and horse-drawn sledge
     on frozen river (44x73cm-17x29in) s. panel (D.FL 30000)

LEIER, Grant (1956-) American
£683 $1229   (18-Nov-91 HO.ED118/R) Untitled - women and budgies (96x76cm-38x30in)
     mixed media board (C.D 1400)

LEIGH, William R (1866-1955) American
£1287 $2200   (13-Mar-92 WOL.C450/R) Desert landscape (33x38cm-13x15in) s. board

LEIGH, William R (1866-1955) American-cont.
£2105	$3600	(13-Mar-92 WOL.C455/R) Desert landscape (20x28cm-8x11in) s. board
£10234	$17500	(11-Mar-92 SY.NY26/R) Niagara Falls (76x66cm-30x26in)
£10989	$20000	(28-May-92 CH.NY124/R) The Grand Canyon (56x84cm-22x33in) s.
£12155	$22000	(6-Dec-91 CH.NY111/R) Rainbow Bridge by moonlight (91x121cm-36x48in) s.
£65934	$120000	(28-May-92 CH.NY127/R) Looking for strays (71x57cm-28x22in) s.d.1913
£80111	$145000	(6-Dec-91 CH.NY108/R) Ready to shoot (101x76cm-40x30in) s.
£6704	$12000	(13-Nov-91 B.SF2712/R) Seated Navajo (43x49cm-17x19in) s.d.1951 pencil
£9064	$15500	(11-Mar-92 SY.NY31/R) Horse in desert landscape (37x53cm-15x21in) s.i.d.1937 W/C paperboard

LEIGH-PEMBERTON, John (fl.1934-1938) British
£1050	$1880	(14-Jan-92 PH85/R) At cricket match (33x43cm-13x17in) s.d.48 canvasboard

LEIGHTON (?) British
£550	$941	(11-Mar-92 B171) In the New Forest (76x94cm-30x37in) i.verso

LEIGHTON, Alfred Crocker (1901-1965) British
£1827	$3197	(17-Feb-92 HO.ED110/R) Gibbon Falls (32x43cm-13x17in) s. W/C (C.D 3800)
£537	$966	(18-Nov-91 HO.ED145) Sidney, Vancouver Island (28x36cm-11x14in) W/C (C.D 1100)

LEIGHTON, Edmund Blair (1853-1922) British
£500	$865	(25-Mar-92 PHI565) The nap (12x17cm-5x7in) init.i. i.verso board
£1000	$1830	(3-Jun-92 S158/R) A pink bonnet (21cm-8ins circular) init. panel
£1500	$2775	(9-Jun-92 RG2381) Girl walking on Cornish cliff top track (28x20cm-11x8in) mono.d.93 panel
£7500	$13875	(12-Jun-92 C239/R) A wet Sunday morning (101x70cm-40x28in) s.d.1896
£11500	$22080	(28-Jul-92 SWS343/R) A favour (90x49cm-35x19in) s.d.1898

LEIGHTON, F (20th C) American
£1086	$1900	(18-Feb-92 CE.NY24) Blowing bubbles (30x19cm-12x7in) s.d.92 panel
£520	$926	(27-Nov-91 B177/R) Gathering primroses (35x25cm-14x10in) s.d.1881 W/C
£550	$979	(27-Nov-91 B178) The rose garden (35x25cm-14x10in) s.d.1881 W/C

LEIGHTON, Kathryn Woodman (1876-1952) American
£1117	$2000	(13-Nov-91 B.SF2814/R) Old Indian deep in thought (112x91cm-44x36in) s.

LEIGHTON, Lord Frederic (1830-1896) British
£16000	$28480	(30-Apr-92 CG861/R) Type of Beauty (43x30cm-17x12in) i.verso
£18502	$33304	(24-Nov-91 SY.S251/R) Type of beauty (43x30cm-17x12in) i.verso (A.D 42000)
£210000	$359100	(13-Mar-92 C85/R) Lady Sybil Primrose (122x87cm-48x34in)
£800	$1416	(6-Nov-91 S33/R) Studies for figures Science Literature and Arts from Jubilee Medal (25x29cm-10x11in) chk
£800	$1416	(6-Nov-91 S326/R) Study for music (26x33cm-10x13in) chk
£2200	$4136	(19-Dec-91 C4/R) Study of young girl who posed for 'Wide Wondering Eyes' (21x15cm-8x6in) s.i.d.1874 black and white chk
£4000	$7160	(11-Nov-91 S605) Botanical studies (28x42cm-11x17in) one i. pencil W/C four
£7000	$12530	(11-Nov-91 S606) Hercules wrestling with death for body of Alceste (13x28cm-5x11in) black white chk
£9302	$16000	(17-Oct-91 SY.NY322/R) Head of young girl (22x16cm-9x6in) mono.i.d.1853 pencil

LEIGHTON, Scott (1847-1898) American
£1040	$1800	(29-Mar-92 MY.F83/R) Tending the flock (76x102cm-30x40in) s.
£1934	$3500	(21-May-92 GRO.B81/R) Horses grazing and watering (69x112cm-27x44in) s.
£8036	$13500	(14-Aug-91 B.P187/R) Racing home through a Maine snow storm (61x91cm-24x36in) s.
£18713	$32000	(12-Mar-92 CH.NY53/R) Seal skin brigade (81x138cm-32x54in) s.

LEINARDI, Ermanno (1933-) Italian
£958	$1657	(23-Mar-92 AB.L138/R) La o supli seii (100x100cm-39x39in) s.d.1979verso acrylic collage canvas (S.FR 2500)

LEIPOLD, Karl (1864-?) German
£523	$951	(11-Dec-91 N.M506/R) River landscape with sailing boats and windmill (70x81cm-28x32in) s. i.d.1818-19stretcher (DM 1500)

LEISNER, V (19th C) ?
£673	$1192	(11-Feb-92 RAS.K106) House in Jaegersborg Dyrehave (125x156cm-49x61in) s.d.1885 (D.KR 7500)

LEIST, Frederick William (1878-1946) Australian
£714	$1243	(17-Sep-91 JRL.S446) Portrait of lady (76x64cm-30x25in) s. (A.D 1550)
£3191	$5649	(26-Apr-92 SY.ME412/R) Golfers (49x59cm-19x23in) s. (A.D 7500)
£3524	$6344	(24-Nov-91 SY.S330/R) Blossom time (48x59cm-19x23in) s. (A.D 8000)

LEISTIKOW, Walter (1865-1908) Russian
£5944	$10580	(30-Nov-91 VG.B133/R) House behind trees (23x33cm-9x13in) s. board (DM 17000)
£20478	$37270	(29-May-92 VG.B8/R) Wooded Mark lake landscape (63x76cm-25x30in) s. (DM 60000)

LEISTIKOW, Walter (1865-1908) Russian-cont.
£22526	$40997	(29-May-92 VG.B7/R) House in wooded landscape (73x93cm-29x37in) s. (DM 66000)
£24390	$44390	(11-Dec-91 N.M507/R) Wooded Schlachtensee landscape near Berlin (66x80cm-26x31in) s. (DM 70000)
£3631	$6500	(13-Nov-91 B.SF2329/R) Wooded pool in spring (31x48cm-12x19in) s. W/C gouache
£3780	$6993	(12-Jun-92 HN.H520/R) Mark landscape (33x40cm-13x16in) s. W/C bodycol. board (DM 11000)
£32168	$57259	(30-Nov-91 VG.B134/R) Mark lake landscape (48x64cm-19x25in) s. pastel board (DM 92000)

LEITCH, William Leighton (1804-1883) British
£600	$1116	(18-Jun-92 B40/R) SShrine of Santa Rosalia on Monte Pelegrino (23x32cm-9x13in) pencil W/C htd.white
£900	$1611	(11-Nov-91 PH137) Southampton Water, sunset (13x22cm-5x9in) init.d.1873 W/C
£900	$1611	(11-Nov-91 PH138/R) View of Piazza della Bocco della Verita, Rome (29x49cm-11x19in) W/C bodycol
£1100	$1925	(1-Apr-92 B59/R) Scottish landscape with castle by loch and cattle (80x65cm-31x26in) s.d.1865 W/C
£1600	$2896	(5-Dec-91 CG43/R) Vieolo della frezzo vitimo piano, Roma (33x46cm-13x18in) mono.i.d.1852 W/C htd.white

LEITGEB, Franz (?) ?
£588	$1053	(15-Nov-91 ZOF.Z1402/R) Still life of flowers (40x29cm-16x11in) s. panel (S.FR 1500)

LEITH-ROSS, Harry (1886-1973) American
£1050	$1900	(22-May-92 S.BM119/R) Through the trees, Woodstock (25x20cm-10x8in) s. board
£1977	$3400	(10-Oct-91 FA.PH923/R) Horse farm Delaware County (56x81cm-22x32in) s.
£2762	$4750	(10-Oct-91 FA.PH920/R) Early spring (56x81cm-22x32in) s.

LEITNER, Franz (attrib) (18th C) ?
£894	$1529	(18-Mar-92 D.V275/R) River landscape with stone bridge (16x22cm-6x9in) metal (A.S 18000)

LEITNER, Thomas (1876-1948) Austrian
£834	$1585	(25-Jun-92 D.V679) Chapel in winter (26x34cm-10x13in) s.d.1915 panel (A.S 17000)
£878	$1520	(3-Oct-91 D.V56/R) Corn stooks (40x29cm-16x11in) s.d.1907 board (A.S 18000)
£890	$1557	(19-Feb-92 D.V130/R) North Sea, Holland (36x57cm-14x22in) s.d.1913 panel (A.S 18000)

LEJEUNE, A A (18/19th C) French
£2793	$5000	(14-Jan-92 SY.NY156/R) Trompe l'oeil of revolutionary assignats (51x77cm-20x30in) s.i.d.1796 pen gouache htd white

LEJEUNE, Adolphe Frederic (fl.1879-1912) French
£3905	$7459	(1-Jul-92 FB.P162) L'Odalisque (45x63cm-18x25in) s.d.1870 W/C gouache (F.FR 38000)

LEJEUNE, Emile (1885-1964) Swiss
£784	$1333	(23-Oct-91 GD.B448/R) Cagnes, autumn (60x72cm-24x28in) s.d.1928 (S.FR 2000)
£1000	$1730	(24-Mar-92 C110/R) Le hameau provencal (27x35cm-11x14in) s.d.40
£2000	$3460	(24-Mar-92 C109/R) Cagnes-sur-Mer (60x73cm-24x29in)
£3000	$5190	(24-Mar-92 C115/R) Le jardin exotique (73x60cm-29x24in) s.d.1940

LEKEGIAN, G (?) ?
£800	$1360	(23-Oct-91 S213) Street musicians, Stambul (61x45cm-24x18in) s. W/C over pencil

LELEUX, Adolphe (1812-1891) French
£851	$1541	(19-May-92 AB.S4348/R) Woman with distaff in interior (72x51cm-28x20in) s.d.1866 (S.KR 9000)
£7500	$13950	(19-Jun-92 C64/R) Kaiserin Eugenie, wife of Napoleon III watching Victory Parade (40x68cm-16x27in) s. oval
£8140	$14000	(17-Oct-91 SY.NY196/R) Enfants conduisant les oies (100x74cm-39x29in) s.d.1855

LELEUX, Armand-Hubert-Simon (1818-1885) French
£726	$1300	(11-Nov-91 GC.M46/R) El Relojero (23x17cm-9x7in) s. panel

LELIE, Adriaen de (1755-1820) Dutch
£3509	$6000	(13-Mar-92 FN.S2849/R) Figures gathered around table watching card player (60x52cm-24x20in) s.d.1810 panel (DM 10000)
£4587	$8119	(5-Nov-91 SY.AM249/R) Figures by fish-stand (53x69cm-21x27in) s.d.1820 (D.FL 15000)

LELIENBERGH, Cornelis van (1626-c.1676) Dutch
£5149	$9681	(18-Dec-91 AT.P166/R) Trophees de chasse a la trompe et au fusil (81x62cm-32x24in) s. (F.FR 50000)

LELLOUCHE, Jules (1903-1963) French
£916	$1675	(17-May-92 GL.P172) Le rabbin de Djerba (46x38cm-18x15in) s.d.1939 board (F.FR 9000)
£1119	$2048	(17-May-92 GL.P173) Vue de Sidi-Bou-Said (55x46cm-22x18in) s. (F.FR 11000)

LELLOUCHE, Ofer (1947-) Israeli
£585	$1100	(5-Jan-92 GG.TA259/R) Mediterranean landscape (40x50cm-16x20in) s.d.1988 canvas on board
£798	$1500	(5-Jan-92 GG.TA260/R) Figures in field (41x51cm-16x20in) s.d.1988 canvas on board
£1081	$2000	(8-Jun-92 GG.TA181/R) Still life (50x60cm-20x24in) s.d.89

LELOIR, Alexandre Louis (1843-1884) French
£7000	$11970	(18-Mar-92 S98/R) The strolling players (56x107cm-22x42in) s.
£1117	*$2000*	*(6-May-92 D.NY59/R) Flamenco dancer (34x23cm-13x9in) s.d.1876 W/C*
£3200	*$5664*	*(14-Apr-92 C88/R) La Belle Exotique (25x33cm-10x13in) s.d.76 pencil W/C htd white card*

LELOIR, Maurice (1853-1940) French
£3429	*$6000*	*(20-Feb-92 SY.NY169/R) Les sept peches capitaux (76x55cm-30x22in) s.d.1891 W/C*

LELONG (17/19th C) French
£10198	$18663	(4-Jun-92 F.M237/R) Natura morte con carte geografiche. Tazzae caffetiera. Melone e bottigliePiatto di prugne. Fucile e (15x22cm-6x9in) tempera paper set of five (I.L 22500000)
£2000	*$3500*	*(27-Feb-92 CSK184/R) A globe, books, navigational instruments and other objects (15x21cm-6x8in) gouache*
£3154	*$5771*	*(15-May-92 AT.P162) Deux natures mortes (15x20cm-6x8in) gouache pair (F.FR 31000)*

LELONG, Rene (19th C) French?
£7136	$13272	(18-Jun-92 SY.MO381/R) Promenade sur la cote, pres de Monaco (38x38cm-15x15in) s. (F.FR 70000)

LELU, Pierre (1741-1810) French
£1927	*$3507*	*(25-May-92 ARC.P54/R) La fontaine (45x34cm-18x13in) s.d.1787 pen wash sanguine htd white (F.FR 19000)*

LELU, Pierre (attrib) (1741-1810) French
£764	*$1413*	*(12-Jun-92 ARC.P133) Paysage ave personnages au bord d'une riviere (39x53cm-15x21in) i. pen wash (F.FR 7500)*

LELY, Sir Peter (1618-1680) British
£1700	$2992	(10-Apr-92 C93/R) Portrait of Lady Sarah Cowper seated (120x101cm-47x40in) i.
£6800	$12988	(15-Jul-92 S13/R) Portrait of a lady (74x62cm-29x24in) in painted cartouche
£9000	$16110	(13-Nov-91 S25/R) Portrait of Elizabeth Hamilton, Comtesse de Grammont (127x101cm-50x40in) mono.
£17000	$29920	(8-Apr-92 S16/R) Portrait of Lady Jane Noel, seated in landscape (119x95cm-47x37in) i.
£46000	$80960	(8-Apr-92 S15/R) Portrait of Sir Richard Sprignell Bt of Coppenthorp, York, when boy (77x64cm-30x25in) oval
£52000	$91520	(8-Apr-92 S21/R) Portrait of Barbara Villiers, Countess of Castlemaine and Duchess of Cleveland, seated by red curtai (213x131cm-84x52in)
£800	*$1432*	*(14-Nov-91 S6) Portrait of head of old woman (21x16cm-8x6in) bears i. chk*
£5000	*$8800*	*(9-Apr-92 S32/R) Landscape with small figures (15x21cm-6x8in) s. wash pen*

LELY, Sir Peter (after) (1618-1680) British
£800	$1440	(22-Nov-91 SWS240) Portrait of Bishop Morley (124x99cm-49x39in)
£1419	$2569	(19-May-92 AB.S4349) Portrait of Nell Gwynne dressed in red (127x104cm-50x41in) (S.KR 15000)
£1500	$2865	(15-Jul-92 S117/R) Portrait of young girl in red hat (73x60cm-29x24in) painted oval
£1800	$3438	(15-Jul-92 S132/R) Portrait of the Duchess de Mazarin (90x68cm-35x27in)
£1800	$3060	(22-Oct-91 S252/R) Portrait of Charles II, wearing armour (71x61cm-28x24in) painted oval cartouche

LELY, Sir Peter (attrib) (1618-1680) British
£760	$1414	(18-Jun-92 DOL.Z204/R) Portrait of a Queen (125x103cm-49x41in) (S.FR 2000)
£2060	$3750	(13-Dec-91 S.W2627/R) Portrait of lady (127x102cm-50x40in)
£3448	$6000	(13-Sep-91 S.W2778/R) Portrait of Mary Duchess of Richmond (213x130cm-84x51in)
£11000	$19690	(11-Nov-91 S491/R) Portrait of Frances, Duchess of Newcastle as Diana (221x126cm-87x50in)

LELY, Sir Peter (circle) (1618-1680) British
£920	$1656	(22-Nov-91 SWS253/R) Portrait of a lady (61x49cm-24x19in)
£1268	$2296	(3-Dec-91 R.T213/R) Jephtha's return from war greeted by suitors (97x154cm-38x61in) (C.D 2600)
£1600	$2848	(28-Apr-92 PH4/R) Portrait of lady, seated, holding posy of flowers, landscape beyond (46x38cm-18x15in)

LELY, Sir Peter (circle) (1618-1680) British-cont.

£2000	$3440	(8-Oct-91 PH42/R) Portrait of a lady wearing a green satin dress (117x101cm-46x40in)
£2800	$5348	(17-Jul-92 C3/R) Portrait of lady with shpherd's crook and pet lamb (122x100cm-48x39in)
£2800	$5040	(19-Nov-91 PH10/R) Portrait of gentleman said to be Charles Lennox, Duke of Richmond (129x106cm-51x42in) i.
£3200	$5504	(8-Oct-91 PH31/R) Portrait of a lady wearing a brown dress and blue mantle (118x101cm-46x40in)
£3300	$5874	(27-Apr-92 PHB267/R) Portrait of Countess of Castlemaine, wearing feather hat (127x101cm-50x40in)
£3600	$6912	(9-Jul-92 B79/R) Portrait of 1st Duke of St. Albans, aged 9, in silk robes with earring (76x65cm-30x26in) i. canvas on board oval
£3800	$6498	(12-Mar-92 CSK102/R) Portrait of young gentleman said to be James Carr Clarke (76x63cm-30x25in)
£3800	$6688	(10-Apr-92 C83 a/R) Portrait of Henry Wilmot seated by stone plinth with bust (129x103cm-51x41in)
£4000	$7120	(28-Apr-92 PH5/R) Portrait of young girl, pearls in hair, holding bow and arrow, landscape beyond (125x99cm-49x39in)
£4600	$8096	(8-Apr-92 S156/R) Portrait of young child, seated wearing gown and bonnet, holding charm (72x61cm-28x24in)
£7000	$12320	(10-Apr-92 C15/R) Portrait of King James II in Garter robes (231x145cm-91x57in)
£9790	$17327	(7-Nov-91 D.V196/R) Juno and Venus (233x153cm-92x60in) (A.S 200000)

LELY, Sir Peter (studio) (1618-1680) British

£3000	$5280	(10-Apr-92 C88/R) Portrait of King Charles II in classical dress holding baton (128x102cm-50x40in)
£3867	$7000	(22-May-92 SY.NY310/R) Portrait of lady (125x99cm-49x39in)
£4000	$7640	(2-Jul-92 D178/R) Portrait of lady seated in landscape (124x99cm-49x39in) mono

LELY, Sir Peter (style) (1618-1680) British

£520	$900	(4-Sep-91 BT238/R) Young lady with curling brown hair adorned with flowers (38x30cm-15x12in) panel
£760	$1376	(20-May-92 BT192) Gentleman, seated wearing full wig and brown coat (122x99cm-48x39in)
£1000	$1750	(27-Feb-92 B148) Portrait of a lady wearing a gold satin dress (76x62cm-30x24in)
£1400	$2548	(13-Dec-91 C125/R) Portrait of girl wearing white dress with grey wrap (53x46cm-21x18in)
£1800	$3168	(8-Apr-92 S161/R) Portrait of lady, said to be Venetia Stanley (61x53cm-24x21in)
£2500	$4375	(2-Apr-92 CSK50/R) Reclining female nude (53x76cm-21x30in)
£2800	$4928	(10-Apr-92 C92/R) Portrait of lady seated listening to boy singing and gentleman with lute (121x94cm-48x37in)
£2800	$5376	(9-Jul-92 B82/R) Portrait of Prince Henry Stuart, Duke of Gloucester, wearing armour (113x94cm-44x37in)
£10000	$17900	(15-Nov-91 C11/R) Portrait of Mary, 2nd Viscountess Massereene, by orange tree in urn, column and landscape beyond (128x101cm-50x40in)

LEMAIRE, Denise (1925-) French

£588	$1000	(23-Oct-91 GD.B1136) Still life with apples and flowers (34x27cm-13x11in) mono. (S.FR 1500)

LEMAIRE, Jean (circle) (17/18th C) French

£2700	$4941	(12-May-92 SWS603/R) Classical landscape with infancy of Jupiter (78x62cm-31x24in)

LEMAIRE, Madeleine (1845-1928) French

£9945	$18000	(22-May-92 S.BM79/R) Tennis (56x46cm-22x18in) s. panel
£427	$765	(17-Nov-91 FB.P31) Jeune femme fleurissant un autel (57x38cm-22x15in) mono. W/C (F.FR 4200)
£681	$1300	(16-Jul-92 SY.NY330/R) Still life of violets. Study of carnations (46x60cm-18x24in) s. W/C pair
£917	$1706	(18-Jun-92 SY.MO515/R) Roses et livre (35x51cm-14x20in) s. W/C (F.FR 9000)
£1324	$2449	(10-Jun-92 ZZ.F29) Roses dans un panier (38x53cm-15x21in) W/C pair (F.FR 13000)
£1404	$2500	(1-Nov-91 PO.BA28) Canasta con violetas (40x54cm-16x21in) s. W/C

LEMAITRE, Maurice (1929-) French

£700	$1337	(16-Jul-92 B29) Champs inondes a Soignolles en Brie (33x55cm-13x22in) s.
£705	$1255	(28-Oct-91 GL.P248) Questin a l'amateur letriste (65x54cm-26x21in) s.d.1987 i.verso (F.FR 7000)
£705	$1255	(28-Oct-91 GL.P249) Propos de createur (61x50cm-24x20in) s.d.1988 (F.FR 7000)
£758	$1357	(10-May-92 LT.P43) Ete a Pezarches (27x35cm-11x14in) s. panel (F.FR 7500)
£1246	$2181	(23-Feb-92 LT.P118) Mas aux Eygalieres (24x33cm-9x13in) s. panel (F.FR 12200)
£1342	$2308	(20-Oct-91 LT.P75/R) Maree Basse a Kerity (27x35cm-11x14in) s. (F.FR 13300)
£1430	$2503	(23-Feb-92 LT.P67/R) Juin a Beauvais (27x35cm-11x14in) s. (F.FR 14000)
£1430	$2503	(23-Feb-92 LT.P84/R) Voiliers a Vaires-sur-Marne (50x65cm-20x26in) s. (F.FR 14000)

LEMAITRE, Maurice (1929-) French-cont.

£1512	$2676	(10-Nov-91 LT.P1/R) Promeneuses a Rochecolombe (46x61cm-18x24in) s. (F.FR 15000)
£1527	$2795	(7-Jun-92 LT.P96/R) Paysage a Saint-Felix (27x35cm-11x14in) s. (F.FR 15000)
£1769	$3167	(10-May-92 LT.P49/R) Pecheurs au bord de la Sevre Niortaise (33x46cm-13x18in) s. (F.FR 17500)
£1873	$3278	(5-Apr-92 ZZ.F144/R) Paysage d'ete dans la Vienne (46x65cm-18x26in) s. (F.FR 18000)
£2018	$3471	(20-Oct-91 LT.P53/R) Barques a Kerity (38x55cm-15x22in) s. (F.FR 20000)
£2043	$3575	(23-Feb-92 LT.P73/R) Paysage a Orgon (33x46cm-13x18in) s. (F.FR 20000)
£2240	$4100	(7-Jun-92 LT.P46/R) Dans le jardin aux Moutiers sur le Lay (46x55cm-18x22in) s. (F.FR 22000)
£2326	$4163	(10-May-92 LT.P70/R) En Briere (46x61cm-18x24in) s. (F.FR 23000)
£2349	$4111	(23-Feb-92 LT.P46/R) Pecheurs en barque a Ecourt Saint-Quentin (46x61cm-18x24in) s. (F.FR 23000)
£2451	$4290	(23-Feb-92 I.N214) Hiver a Saint-Augustin (46x65cm-18x26in) s. (F.FR 24000)
£2523	$4339	(20-Oct-91 LT.P64/R) Bords de la Sevre Niortaise (46x65cm-18x26in) s. (F.FR 25000)
£2758	$4826	(23-Feb-92 LT.P69) Printemps a Saints (50x65cm-20x26in) s. (F.FR 27000)
£2778	$4862	(23-Feb-92 LT.P50/R) Le haut d'Eygalieres (46x65cm-18x26in) s. (F.FR 27200)
£3473	$6078	(23-Feb-92 LT.P54/R) Neige a Lavanderie (65x100cm-26x39in) s. (F.FR 34000)

LEMAN, Robert (1799-1863) British

| *£960* | *$1632* | *(22-Oct-91 SWS104/R) Woodland track (33x49cm-13x19in) i. W/C over pencil* |

LEMAN, Ulrich (19/20th C) German

| *£893* | *$1635* | *(3-Jun-92 L.K269) Mallorca (47x67cm-19x26in) s.i.d.1939 W/C (DM 2600)* |

LEMARCHAND, Anne (19th C) French

| £1442 | $2711 | (18-Dec-91 PR.P42) Fleurs et fruits (72x59cm-28x23in) s.d.77 (F.FR 14000) |

LEMATTE, Fernand (?) French

| £854 | $1546 | (4-Dec-91 CB.P117) Italienne endormie (22x40cm-9x16in) s. (F.FR 8300) |

LEMBECK, Jack (1942-) American

| £3314 | $5800 | (27-Feb-92 CE.NY277/R) Toy anatomy (72x92cm-28x36in) s. s.d.1988 verso acrylic shaped |

LEMECHEV, Vladimir (1932-) Russian

| £608 | $1100 | (20-May-92 ARC.P222/R) Anastassia (55x70cm-22x28in) s. (F.FR 6000) |

LEMERCIER, Charles Nicolas (1797-1859) French

| £807 | $1388 | (16-Oct-91 AT.P144) Portrait d'un homme en habit noir (92x73cm-36x29in) s.d.1848 (F.FR 8000) |

LEMEUNIER, Basile (1852-?) French

| £6110 | $11303 | (12-Jun-92 ARC.P14/R) La foire du Trone (60x45cm-24x18in) s. (F.FR 60000) |

LEMIEUX, Jean Paul (1904-1990) Canadian

£3425	$6233	(26-May-92 JOY.T219/R) Les docteurs (25x20cm-10x8in) s. (C.D 7500)
£3731	$6642	(26-Nov-91 JOY.T121/R) Young girl and boy (25x20cm-10x8in) s. (C.D 7500)
£7306	$13297	(26-May-92 JOY.T154/R) La mer (52x36cm-20x14in) s. (C.D 16000)
£14500	$25665	(6-Nov-91 SY.T97/R) La femme au collier (63x41cm-25x16in) s. (C.D 29000)
£19900	$35423	(26-Nov-91 JOY.T101/R) Enfant a la tuque (45x35cm-18x14in) s.d.59 (C.D 40000)
£30000	$53100	(6-Nov-91 SY.T98/R) Hommage a Katie Fusch (124x51cm-49x20in) s.i.d.1971 s.i.verso (C.D 60000)
£39801	$70846	(26-Nov-91 JOY.T68/R) Night meeting (100x67cm-39x26in) s.d.62 (C.D 80000)
£45000	$79650	(6-Nov-91 SY.T131/R) Le Silence (77x283cm-30x111in) with sig. (C.D 90000)
£70000	$123900	(6-Nov-91 SY.T130/R) La Nativite (71x102cm-28x40in) s.d.66 panel (C.D 140000)
£1791	*$3188*	*(26-Nov-91 JOY.T106/R) Le couple (45x59cm-18x23in) s. ink (C.D 3600)*
£5366	*$9659*	*(19-Nov-91 FP.M56/R) Lady wearing necklace (66x51cm-26x20in) s. ink canvas (C.D 11000)*

LEMMEN, Georges (1865-1916) Belgian

£2339	$3977	(22-Oct-91 C.A222/R) Young girl in an interior before a fireplace (37x44cm-15x17in) mono.d.1903 board (B.FR 140000)
£4200	$7602	(2-Dec-91 CSK19/R) La dormeuse (59x48cm-23x19in) st.studio s.d.1898verso
£5081	$8841	(15-Apr-92 PLF.P84/R) Femme nue assise (88x62cm-35x24in) st.mono. paper laid down on canvas (F.FR 50000)
£5347	$9089	(22-Oct-91 C.A223/R) Rocky coast with turquoise sea (40x59cm-16x23in) mono. canvas on panel (B.FR 320000)
£7263	$13000	(6-May-92 D.NY70/R) La Hulpe (44x61cm-17x24in) mono.i.1889 and 1907 i.stretcher
£11000	$21010	(1-Jul-92 S142/R) Vase de fleurs (71x60cm-28x24in) mono.
£13687	$24773	(7-Dec-91 KV.L389/R) Baigneuses au bord de la mer (50x62cm-20x24in) st.mono.board (B.FR 800000)
£505	*$894*	*(22-Apr-92 ZZ.F57) Baigneuses (39x48cm-15x19in) mono.d.1909 pastel (F.FR 5000)*

LEMMEN, Georges (1865-1916) Belgian-cont.
£528 $956 (6-Dec-91 GB.B5905) Garden corner (28x19cm-11x7in) st.sig.d.1890 pen indian ink wash (DM 1500)

LEMMENS, Theophile Victor Emile (1821-1867) French
£523 $900 (16-Oct-91 D.NY66) A Big Splash (15x23cm-6x9in) s. panel
£2163 $4066 (18-Dec-91 FB.P127) Les indiens (32x40cm-13x16in) s. (F.FR 21000)
£2171 $3800 (18-Feb-92 CE.NY211/R) Cat on prowl (18x27cm-7x11in) s. panel

LEMMERS, Georges (1871-1944) Belgian
£1198 $2168 (7-Dec-91 KV.L213) Cap Martin (33x44cm-13x17in) s. (B.FR 70000)
£1327 $2428 (12-May-92 C.A193) Village church (50x60cm-20x24in) s. (B.FR 80000)
£5004 $8807 (7-Apr-92 C.A165/R) Woman by open window (40x31cm-16x12in) s. panel (B.FR 300000)
£416 $728 (30-Mar-92 ZZ.F6) Petit lapin (30x24cm-12x9in) s. oil crayon chl. (F.FR 4000)

LEMMI, Angiolo (19/20th C) Italian
£11429 $20000 (19-Feb-92 CH.NY106/R) Nydia, blind flower girl of Pompei (220x166cm-87x65in) s. d.1903 verso

LEMOINE, Jacques (1751-1824) French
£1700 $2958 (13-Apr-92 S167/R) La jeune convalescent (19x16cm-7x6in) black red white chk
£2800 $5376 (7-Jul-92 C.A245/R) Lady writing letter in landscape (27x23cm-11x9in) s.i. chk wash oval

LEMOINE, Marie Victoire (1754-1820) French
£9465 $17984 (26-Jun-92 AT.P37/R) Portrait d'un jeune homme en habit bleu (71x58cm-28x23in) s.d.1789 oval (F.FR 92000)
£760 $1375 (20-May-92 CSC.P6 b) L'offrande sur l'autel de l'amour (25x19cm-10x7in) s. gouache vellum (F.FR 7500)
£1159 $2052 (6-Nov-91 LT.P58) L'offrande sur l'autel de l'amour (25x19cm-10x7in) s. gouache vellum (F.FR 11500)

LEMONNIER, Anicet Charles Gabriel (1743-1824) French
£460 $800 (14-Apr-92 C167/R) Allegorical female figure and studies of architectural details. Figures (27x20cm-11x8in) chk double-sided

LEMORDANT, Jean Julien (1882-1968) French
£1109 $2029 (17-May-92 T.B385/R) L'Esclave (52x70cm-20x28in) s. W/C (F.FR 10900)

LEMOYNE, Pierre Antoine (1605-1665) French
£141988 $249899 (10-Apr-92 AT.P39/R) Grappes de raisins, figues et grenades sur un entablement (84x69cm-33x27in) s. (F.FR 1400000)

LEMPEREUR, Edmond (1876-1909) French
£1733 $3223 (18-Jun-92 CB.P95) Dans la corrida (50x61cm-20x24in) s. (F.FR 17000)

LEMPEREUR-HAUT, Marcel (1898-1986) Belgian
£1440 $2607 (6-Dec-91 GL.P283) Sans titre (97x41cm-38x16in) s.d.1923 three on same mount (F.FR 14000)

LEMPICKA, Tamara de (1898-1980) Polish
£1130 $2000 (5-Nov-91 CE.NY229/R) Composition abstraite (41x30cm-16x12in) s.
£1243 $2200 (5-Nov-91 CE.NY227/R) Composition abstraite (41x30cm-16x12in) s.d.1960
£1564 $2800 (9-May-92 CE.NY177/R) Composition in blue no 2 (51x41cm-20x16in) s. s.i.verso
£2260 $4000 (5-Nov-91 CE.NY102/R) Vase de fleurs (41x33cm-16x13in) s.
£2260 $4000 (5-Nov-91 CE.NY101/R) Le fruit (30x41cm-12x16in) s. s.i.verso
£2642 $4598 (15-Apr-92 PLF.P85/R) Composition geometrique (79x56cm-31x22in) (F.FR 26000)
£3226 $5581 (4-Oct-91 CSC.P66) Composition (45x36cm-18x14in) s. (F.FR 32000)
£5431 $9885 (25-May-92 CH.R48/R) La femme au turban rouge (27x21cm-11x8in) (I.L 12000000)
£6215 $11000 (5-Nov-91 CE.NY192/R) Femme au turban (42x33cm-17x13in)
£7429 $13000 (28-Feb-92 SY.NY125/R) Femme nue (74x49cm-29x19in)
£8571 $15000 (25-Feb-92 CH.NY86/R) Composition abstraite (86x106cm-34x42in) s.
£10000 $19100 (29-Jun-92 CSK127/R) Femme nu aux cheveux roux - copie d'apres Suzanne au bain 1941 (81x54cm-32x21in)
£10286 $18000 (25-Feb-92 CH.NY64/R) L'automne (86x107cm-34x42in) s.
£10857 $19000 (25-Feb-92 CH.NY53/R) Portrait de la belle M (92x60cm-36x24in)
£54000 $103140 (1-Jul-92 S235/R) Femme a la rose noire (185x60cm-73x24in) s.d.23
£207650 $380000 (14-May-92 SY.NY274/R) Portrait de Mademoiselle Poum Rachou (92x46cm-36x18in)
£1676 $3000 (9-May-92 CE.NY45/R) Femme au chapeau a voile (38x25cm-15x10in) s.d.1925 gouache W/C over pencil board
£2123 $3800 (9-May-92 CE.NY93/R) Femme assise (37x29cm-15x11in) s. pencil paper on paper
£2222 $4000 (24-Nov-91 LIT.L27) Magnolias in stoneware bottle (48x36cm-19x14in) s. mixed media
£2373 $4200 (5-Nov-91 CE.NY75/R) Femme nue assise (12x15cm-5x6in) W/C pencil

LEMTTER, E R (20th C) Belgian
£674 $1200 (1-Nov-91 PO.BA26) Naturaleza muerta con cobres (19x27cm-7x11in) s. board

LEMZAKOV, Nikolai (1919-) Russian
£1270 $2210 (13-Apr-92 ARC.P17/R) Trois copains (76x158cm-30x62in) s. (F.FR 12500)

LENAIN (circle) (16/17th C) French
£14403 $26070 (5-Dec-91 SY.MO112/R) Portrait d'homme (24x18cm-9x7in) panel
    (F.FR 140000)

LENAIN, Mathieu (style) (1607-1677) French
£1800 $3240 (22-Nov-91 SWS69/R) Musicians playing in a tavern (44x62cm-17x24in)

LENBACH (19th C) German
£1818 $3236 (29-Nov-91 GAB.G2131 b) Nu (70x58cm-28x23in) s. (S.FR 4600)

LENBACH, Franz von (1836-1904) German
£650 $1125 (3-Oct-91 CSK147) A harem girl (51x43cm-20x17in) s. board
£1638 $2965 (21-May-92 L.K445) Susannah bathing (68x93cm-27x37in) board (DM 4800)
£12857 $22500 (20-Feb-02 SY.NY64/R) Portrait of young girl holding fruit
    (76x69cm-30x27in) s.d.1903 board
£699 *$1245* *(25-Nov-91 WK.M642/R) Eleonora Duse (10x6cm-4x2in) s.i.d.1887 ochre*
    (DM 2000)
£1154 *$1973* *(18-Mar-92 N.M293) Otto Furst von Bismarck with cap (47x34cm-19x13in)*
    i.d.1891 pen board (DM 3300)
£1259 *$2279* *(19-May-92 GF.L2455/R) Eleonore Duse with Marion von Lenbach*
    (40x32cm-16x13in) mono.i. ochre (S.FR 3400)

LENCIEWICZ, Robert (?) ?
£850 $1488 (27-Feb-92 L275/R) Young girl and a terrier dog (76x48cm-30x19in) s.

LENDORFF, Hans (1863-1946) Swiss
£475 $884 (19-Jun-92 ZOF.Z1993/R) Portrait of young Italian woman (49x44cm-19x17in)
    s. (S.FR 1250)

LENEPVEU, Jules Eugene (1819-1898) French
£3652 $6500 (22-Jan-92 SY.NY346/R) Narcissus (25x38cm-10x15in) s.d.1869 panel
£8086 $14393 (27-Nov-91 CB.P46/R) Velleda (231x131cm-91x52in) s.d.1883 (F.FR 79000)

L'ENGLE, Lucy Brown (1889-?) American
£2000 $3500 (26-Sep-91 CH.NY196/R) Turtle dance, Taos (77x102cm-30x40in) s.d.1941
    s.i.stretcher

LENIER (?) French
£1387 $2650 (3-Jul-92 SD.P19) Vue d'un port de l'Empire Ottoman (42x93cm-17x37in) s.
    (F.FR 13500)

LENK, Franz (1898-1968) German
£1754 $3000 (13-Mar-92 FN.S2541/R) Bleak coastal landscape (32x40cm-13x16in)
    mono.d.1954 tempera (DM 5000)
£3780 $6993 (12-Jun-92 HN.H521/R) Winter landscape (51x43cm-20x17in) s.d.1924 panel
    (DM 11000)
£6826 $12423 (26-May-92 KF.M1002/R) House by the Baltic Sea, Zempin (53x75cm-21x30in)
    s.d.1936 oil egg tempera canvas on panel (DM 20000)
£1375 *$2543* *(12-Jun-92 HN.H522/R) Mud flats (47x34cm-19x13in) s.d.1927 W/C (DM 4000)*

LENKIEWICZ, Robert O (?) ?
£500 $860 (10-Oct-91 L154) Painter with Ann Grey, St Anthony theme
    (46x41cm-18x16in) s.verso
£800 $1376 (10-Oct-91 L150/R) Painter with Joanne, St Anthony theme
    (41x30cm-16x12in) s.verso board

LENOIR, Charles Amable (1861-?) French
£14535 $25000 (17-Oct-91 SY.NY183/R) Contemplation (125x82cm-49x32in) s.

LENOIR, Marcel (1872-1931) French
£6275 $11231 (15-Nov-91 GK.Z5230/R) Nu assis et la danse (41x32cm-16x13in) s. panel
    (S.FR 16000)
£7843 $14039 (15-Nov-91 GK.Z5229/R) Still life of grapes, peaches and pears
    (33x59cm-13x23in) s. panel (S.FR 20000)

LENOIR, Simon Bernard (1729-1791) French
£1742 *$3100* *(22-Jan-92 SY.NY57/R) Portrait of lady (55x46cm-22x18in) s.d.1762 pastel*
    paper on canvas

LENS, Andrew Bernard (style) (?) ?
£1000 $1750 (3-Apr-92 C73) Couple at horseplay (32x40cm-13x16in) panel

LENS, Andries (1739-1822) Flemish
£710 $1249 (10-Apr-92 AGS.P16/R) Adam et Eve (62x50cm-24x20in) bears i. (F.FR 7000)
£8000 $14240 (1-Nov-91 C79/R) Hero crowned with wreaths by nymphs (120x94cm-47x37in)

LENS, Andries (circle) (1739-1822) Flemish
£1100 $2002 (13-Dec-91 C139/R) Meleager presenting the Head of the Calydonian Boar to
    Atalanta (31x30cm-12x12in)

LENS, Bernard (17/18th C) British
£500 $860   (4-Mar-92 C99/R) Lady, in blue dress with striped white underslip, hair over shoulder (8x?cm-3x?in) min. gilt frame spiral border oval

LENS, Bernard (style) (17/18th C) British
£1000 $1750   (27-Feb-92 CSK190/R) Soldiers by ramparts (28x28cm-11x11in) canvas laid down on board

LENS, Bernard III (attrib) (1682-1740) British
£950 $1701   (12-Nov-91 C2/R) Prospect of Woburn Farm, Surrey (16x21cm-6x8in) init. W/C bodycol.

LENTINI, Rocco (1858-1943) Italian
£787 $1362   (24-Mar-92 CH.R80) Venezia, Calle Vendramin (18x32cm-7x13in) s. panel (I.L 1700000)

LENTULOV, Aristarkh (1882-1943) Russian
£1000 $1860   (16-Jun-92 S10/R) South Russian town (44x64cm-17x25in) s. W/C over chl
£1226 $2121   (28-Mar-92 F.L67/R) Paesaggio (36x30cm-14x12in) gouache (S.FR 3200)
£1839 $3182   (28-Mar-92 F.L70/R) Costume teatrale per i Racconti di Hoffman (53x37cm-21x15in) i.verso pencil tempera (S.FR 4800)

LENTZ, Carl Libert August (1827-1898) German
£687 $1196   (18-Sep-91 N.M602/R) Canale Grande, Venice (27x40cm-11x16in) s.d.1878 paper on canvas (DM 2000)
£909 $1573   (25-Mar-92 KM.K1282 a) Canale Grande, Venice (27x40cm-11x16in) s.d.1873 paper on canvas (DM 2600)
£1963 $3729   (25-Jun-92 D.V443/R) Canale Grande, Venice (27x40cm-11x16in) s.d.73 paper on canvas (A.S 40000)

LENZ, G (19th C) German
£550 $979   (26-Nov-91 PH127) Lady in interior (68x31cm-27x12in) s.

LENZ, Maximilien (1860-1948) Austrian
£679 $1235   (26-May-92 D.V36/R) Still life with crossbow (99x73cm-39x29in) s.d.1872 (A.S 14000)
£824 $1500   (26-May-92 D.V75/R) Interior (85x72cm-33x28in) (A.S 17000)

LEOMPORRI, Raffaele (1926-1974) Italian
£5884 $10708   (25-May-92 CH.R49/R) Senza titolo (115x91cm-45x36in) s. s.d.1960verso (I.L 13000000)

LEON Y ESCOSURA, Ignacio de (1834-1901) Spanish
£4800 $8496   (14-Feb-92 C77/R) Preparing for the duel (33x47cm-13x19in) s.d.1873 panel
£7663 $13946   (26-May-92 DUR.M12/R) Los duelistas (33x46cm-13x18in) s.d.1878 panel (S.P 1400000)
£11059 $20791   (17-Dec-91 DUR.M6/R) Un rato de lectura sosegada (32x40cm-13x16in) s.d.1881 panel (S.P 2000000)

LEON, Omar de (20th C) South American
£1163 $2000   (12-Oct-91 SY.NY208/R) Naturaleza muerta con melon (72x91cm-28x36in) s.d.1957 masonite

LEONARD, Jos (20th C) Swiss?
£652 $1161   (29-Nov-91 GAB.G2773/R) ABC (23x18cm-9x7in) mono. s.d.1925verso collage (S.FR 1650)
£652 $1161   (29-Nov-91 GAB.G2772/R) Navigation (22x18cm-9x7in) mono. s.d.1925verso collage (S.FR 1650)

LEONARD, Patrick (1918-) British
£500 $865   (2-Oct-91 A.D167) Near Tramore (41x51cm-16x20in) s. board (E.P 550)
£727 $1258   (2-Oct-91 A.D64) Women on pier (56x46cm-22x18in) s. board (E.P 800)
£773 $1337   (2-Oct-91 A.D171) Potato sellers (43x33cm-17x13in) s. board (E.P 850)

LEONARDO DA PISTOIA (style) (fl.1516-1540) Italian
£6275 $11357   (5-Dec-91 F.M42) Sacra famiglia con San Giovannino (98x88cm-39x35in) panel (I.L 13500000)

LEONARDO DA VINCI (after) (1452-1519) Italian
£1359 $2514   (8-Jun-92 CH.R746/R) Ritratto di dama, La Belle Ferroniere (55x46cm-22x18in) panel (I.L 3000000)
£1500 $2745   (12-May-92 SWS629/R) Mona Lisa (79x52cm-31x20in) panel
£2200 $3828   (13-Sep-91 C54/R) Mona Lisa (77x56cm-30x22in)

LEONARDO DA VINCI (circle) (1452-1519) Italian
£1800 $3456   (7-Jul-92 C3/R) Grotesque male head (13x10cm-5x4in) pen htd white after Leonardo

LEONARDO DA VINCI (style) (1452-1519) Italian
£2760 $4748   (15-Oct-91 CH.R81) Ritratto di Mona Lisa (74x60cm-29x24in) panel (I.L 6000000)

LEONE, Andrea di (1596-1677) Italian
£14403 $26070   (5-Dec-91 SY.MO265/R) Choc de cavalerie (43x92cm-17x36in) (F.FR 140000)

LEONE, Andrea di (attrib) (1596-1677) Italian
£49724 $90000   (21-May-92 CH.NY101/R) Rebecca and Eliezar (142x182cm-56x72in)

LEONE, Romolo (19th C) French
£921 $1676   (12-Dec-91 F.M82) Casa rustica a Napoli. Cascinale a Napoli
                 (35x49cm-14x19in) s. panel pair (I.L 2000000)
£3978 $7200   (18-May-92 SY.MI62/R) Veduta della campagna Napoletana (79x110cm-31x43in)
                 s. (I.L 8800000)

LEONI, Ottavio (1587-1630) Italian
£950 $1729   *(10-Dec-91 C138) Portrait of a gentleman, bust length (18x13cm-7x5in)*
                 blk.white chk.

LEONI, Ottavio (attrib) (1587-1630) Italian
£1955 $3500   *(14-Jan-92 SY.NY11) Portrait of young man (22x15cm-9x6in) bears i.*
                 col.chk

LEONI, Ottavio (circle) (1587-1630) Italian
£750 $1305   *(13-Apr-92 S64/R) Portrait of small girl holding flower (20x14cm-8x6in)*
                 i. black col.chk

LEOPOLD DA TIVOLI (19th C) ?
£1573 $2691   (18-Mar-92 N.M585/R) Shepherdess with herd before Rome (37x48cm-15x19in)
                 s.d.1874 i.stretcher (DM 4500)

LEOPOLD, V (19/20th C) German
£1049 $1794   (18-Mar-92 N.M584/R) Chiemsee with Fraueninsel (47x92cm-19x36in) s.i.
                 (DM 3000)

LEOPOLD-LEVY (1882-1966) French
£916 $1675   *(17-May-92 GL.P133) Paysage (49x63cm-19x25in) s.d.1946 W/C (F.FR 9000)*

LEOPOLDT, Johannes (1877-1948) Dutch
£747 $1300   (15-Apr-92 B.SF3528/R) Still life with gladiolas, china pot and china
                 bowl (81x61cm-32x24in) s.d.1941

LEOPOLSKI, Wilhelm (1830-1892) Polish
£723 $1293   (17-Nov-91 REM.W17) Portrait of Jozef Brzostowski (43x37cm-17x15in)
                 (P.Z 14000000)

LEPAGE, Jules Bastien (1848-1884) French
£1061 $1877   (22-Apr-92 CH.AM183) Washerwomen in a hilly meadow (13x22cm-5x9in) init.
                 panel (D.FL 3500)

LEPAIXE (20th C) ?
£608 $1100   *(20-May-92 FB.P172) Aspirante, aspiration (114x146cm-45x57in) s. s.d.1989*
                 verso mixed media canvas (F.FR 6000)

LEPAPE, George (1887-1971) French
£594 $1057   (27-Nov-91 CB.P84/R) Portrait de femme (27x35cm-11x14in) panel
                 (F.FR 5800)
£635 $1130   (27-Nov-91 CB.P78/R) Fauteuil dans un jardin (27x35cm-11x14in) panel
                 (F.FR 6200)
£1075 $1913   (27-Nov-91 CB.P86/R) Femme a la balancelle (27x35cm-11x14in) board
                 (F.FR 10500)
£1126 $2004   (27-Nov-91 CB.P85/R) Femme assis dans un jardin (27x35cm-11x14in) board
                 (F.FR 11000)
£921 $1640   *(27-Nov-91 CB.P74) Parasol sur la plage (21x27cm-8x11in) W/C (F.FR 9000)*
£946 $1816   *(7-Jul-92 ARC.P60 a) La toque rouge, couverture de Vogue*
                 (30x25cm-12x10in) s.d.1928 gouache (F.FR 9100)
£959 $1649   *(15-Oct-91 PPB.P55/R) La biche blanche (36x24cm-14x9in) s.i.d. gouache*
                 (F.FR 9500)
£1009 $1736   *(15-Oct-91 PPB.P48) Les canards sauvages (36x22cm-14x9in) s.i.d. gouache*
                 (F.FR 10000)
£1106 $1980   *(14-Nov-91 GRO.B154/R) Elegant lady (30x25cm-12x10in) s.d.1920 gouache*
£2515 $4326   *(12-Oct-91 SY.MO219/R) Portrait de Paul Poiret (23x20cm-9x8in) s.d.1920*
                 gouache pencil (F.FR 25000)
£2817 $4845   *(12-Oct-91 SY.MO220/R) Vue de la maison de Monsieur Paul Poiret*
                 (21x19cm-8x7in) s.i. pen W/C with tracing two wood-cuts paper
                 (F.FR 28000)

LEPAULLE, Francois Gabriel (1804-1886) French
£20325 $35366   (13-Apr-92 AT.P193/R) Le Pacha et son harem (92x73cm-36x29in) s.
                 (F.FR 200000)

LEPELTIER, Robert (1913-) French
£566 $969   (18-Mar-92 PIC.P60) Detente au salon (33x41cm-13x16in) s. (F.FR 5500)
£1236 $2113   (18-Mar-92 PIC.P59/R) Marie-Claire (61x49cm-24x19in) s. (F.FR 12000)

LEPERE, Auguste (1849-1918) French
£512 $927   *(22-May-92 GB.B5954/R) Landscape with stream (30x20cm-12x8in) s. chl*
                 (DM 1500)

LEPICIE, Michel Nicolas Bernard (1735-1784) French
£6314 $11680   (12-Jun-92 ARC.P62/R) Les joies de famille (33x27cm-13x11in) i.verso oval
                 (F.FR 62000)
£8230 $14897   (5-Dec-91 SY.MO309/R) Jeune dessinateur (79x63cm-31x25in) (F.FR 80000)
£49419 $85000   (9-Oct-91 CH.NY9/R) Portrait of young boy, wearing grey velvet coat and
                 brown velvet cap, carrying portfolio (45x37cm-18x15in)
*£1900 $3382   (1-Nov-91 S400/R) Study of man seated at table (41x30cm-16x12in) black
                 chk htd white red chk*
*£2854 $5309   (20-Jun-92 CH.MO236/R) Sainte Cecile. Deux anges musiciens
                 (21x16cm-8x6in) i. pencil ink wash two mounted together (F.FR 28000)*

LEPICIE, Michel Nicolas Bernard (circle) (1735-1784) French
£1233 $2356   (1-Jul-92 CD.P22) Portrait de fillette (39x31cm-15x12in) (F.FR 12000)
£2678 $5034   (16-Dec-91 AGS.P58/R) L'enrolement des jeunes paysans (45x54cm-18x21in)
                 sketch (F.FR 26000)

LEPIE, Ferdinand (1824-1883) Czechoslovakian
£732 $1273   (19-Sep-91 D.V53/R) View of town, winter (73x101cm-29x40in)
                 s.indis.d.1870 (A.S 15000)
£732 $1245   (24-Oct-91 D.V15/R) Rhine landscape with castle surrounded by water
                 (55x68cm-22x27in) s. (A.S 15000)
£1074 $1826   (24-Oct-91 D.V203/R) View of Vienna seen from Belvedere (45x65cm-18x26in)
                 s. (A.S 22000)
£1074 $1826   (24-Oct-91 D.V103/R) View of Maria della Salute, Venice (24x48cm-9x19in)
                 s. (A.S 22000)
£1718 $2990   (18-Sep-91 N.M603/R) Fugen in Zillertal (55x68cm-22x27in) s. (DM 5000)
£1939 $3529   (27-May-92 D.V604/R) View of Hallstatt (55x68cm-22x27in) (A.S 40000)

LEPINE, Stanislas (1835-1892) French
£1235 $2247   (12-Dec-91 SY.AM29/R) Coastal landscape (15x23cm-6x9in) s. cardboard
                 (D.FL 4000)
£1490 $2533   (23-Oct-91 GD.B1137/R) Riverside fishing village (34x24cm-13x9in) s.
                 (S.FR 3800)
£7202 $13683   (26-Jun-92 AGS.P15/R) Mariage a Saint-Etienne du Mont (24x14cm-9x6in) s.
                 panel (F.FR 70000)
£7630 $13657   (13-Nov-91 PIC.P69/R) La Seine a Courbevoie (14x23cm-6x9in) s. panel
                 (F.FR 75000)
£12000 $21000   (20-Feb-92 SY.NY123/R) Les bords de la Marne pres de Creteil
                 (46x56cm-18x22in) indist.s.

L'EPLATTENIER, Charles (1874-1946) Swiss
£1679 $3005   (6-May-92 GD.B728/R) Le Doubs pres au saut (81x100cm-32x39in) s.d.1930
                 mono.i.d.verso (S.FR 4600)
£2390 $4327   (5-Dec-91 SY.Z151/R) Etang aux franches montagnes (81x101cm-32x40in)
                 mono.s.i.d.verso (S.FR 6000)
*£717 $1298   (5-Dec-91 SY.Z156/R) Le serment (61x34cm-24x13in) s.d.1939 pastel
                 (S.FR 1800)*

LEPOITTEVIN, Eugene (1806-1870) French
£562 $1000   (22-Jan-92 SY.NY316/R) Fisherman with net (28x36cm-11x14in) s. panel
£1825 $3395   (19-Jun-92 ZOF.Z1604/R) Les pecheurs d'Etretat (28x36cm-11x14in) s.
                 (S.FR 4800)
£2000 $3500   (18-Feb-92 CE.NY143/R) Victory (51x61cm-20x24in) s.
£6694 $11781   (10-Apr-92 AGS.P29/R) La baignade a Etretat (21x48cm-8x19in) panel
                 (F.FR 66000)

LEPPIEN, Jean (1910-) German
£1107 $1970   (29-Nov-91 GAB.G2788 a) Composition en bleu (64x54cm-25x21in) i.verso
                 (S.FR 2800)
£3093 $5722   (11-Jun-92 HN.H305/R) Composition LX (65x54cm-26x21in) s.
                 mono.i.d.1950verso (DM 9000)
£19392 $35294   (25-May-92 WK.M773/R) Composition (100x81cm-39x32in) s.d.1954
                 mono.i.d.verso hessian (DM 56820)
*£1120 $2050   (3-Jun-92 CSC.P57/R) Composition (39x34cm-15x13in) s. ink W/C
                 (F.FR 11000)*

LEPRI, Stanislao (1905-1980) Italian
£1290 $2347   (9-Dec-91 CH.R91/R) Jeux aquatiques (73x50cm-29x20in) s.d.1965
                 (I.L 2800000)
£2286 $4000   (28-Feb-92 SY.NY92/R) La tour mysogine le Bruse. Tower of seated men
                 (74x28cm-29x11in) s.d.47 one s.d.1947 verso panel pair
£4024 $6922   (12-Oct-91 SY.MO201/R) Le bal des blanchisseuses (35x25cm-14x10in) s.d.46
                 tempera panel (F.FR 40000)

LEPRIN, Marcel (1891-1933) French
£2669 $4805   (19-Nov-91 FB.P49/R) L'Arc de Triomphe (38x46cm-15x18in) s. (F.FR 26000)
£4179 $7774   (19-Jun-92 ARC.P33/R) Village et vergers (65x54cm-26x21in) s.
                 (F.FR 41000)
£4321 $8210   (22-Jun-92 AT.P131/R) La fermette (54x73cm-21x29in) s. (F.FR 42000)
£5015 $9078   (18-May-92 AT.P123/R) Bouquet varie (73x54cm-29x21in) s. (F.FR 49500)
£5657 $10523   (19-Jun-92 ARC.P31/R) L'etaliere (52x65cm-20x26in) s. (F.FR 55500)
£6104 $11170   (13-May-92 LC.P54) Marseille, la montee des accoules (46x36cm-18x14in) s.
                 board (F.FR 60000)
£6296 $11017   (5-Apr-92 ZZ.F161/R) Vase de fleurs (65x54cm-26x21in) s. (F.FR 60500)
£6660 $11655   (5-Apr-92 ZZ.F125/R) Vase de fleurs (65x54cm-26x21in) s. (F.FR 64000)

LEPRIN, Marcel (1891-1933) French-cont.

£8537	$14854	(15-Apr-92 PLF.P86/R) La terrasse de l'auberge (54x73cm-21x29in) s. (F.FR 84000)
£8619	$15256	(10-Nov-91 ZZ.F172/R) Saint Pierre de Montmartre (50x65cm-20x26in) s. (F.FR 85500)
£8669	$15345	(10-Nov-91 ZZ.F179/R) Vue du village de Mailly-le-Chateau (65x81cm-26x32in) s. (F.FR 86000)
£9054	$16569	(13-May-92 LC.P51/R) Marche sur la place du village (61x50cm-24x20in) s. (F.FR 89000)
£9259	$17593	(22-Jun-92 AT.P130/R) Bouquet varie (65x64cm-26x25in) s. (F.FR 90000)
£10181	$18021	(10-Nov-91 ZZ.F184/R) Vue d'Avallon (73x100cm-29x39in) s. (F.FR 101000)
£669	$1145	(22-Mar-92 LT.P179) Animation pres du Sacre-Coeur (15x25cm-6x10in) s.d.21 lead pencil (F.FR 6500)
£814	$1489	(13-May-92 LC.P52/R) Le bal du 14 Juillet, vers 1922 (14x25cm-6x10in) s. wax crayon col.crayons (F.FR 8000)
£2520	$4461	(10-Nov-91 ZZ.F170/R) Le moulin de la galette (42x32cm-17x13in) s. mixed media board laid down on canvas (F.FR 25000)

LEPRINCE, Auguste Xavier (1799-1826) French

£5144	$9774	(26-Jun-92 AT.P91/R) Le marche sur la place du bourg (46x38cm-18x15in) s.d.1824 (F.FR 50000)

LEPRINCE, Auguste Xavier (circle) (1799-1826) French

£1724	$3034	(10-Apr-92 AGS.P30/R) Fete paysanne (35x42cm-14x17in) panel (F.FR 17000)

LEPRINCE, Jean Baptiste (1734-1781) French

£14271	$26544	(18-Jun-92 SY.MO48/R) Portrait de jeune fille (52x37cm-20x15in) (F.FR 140000)
£14330	$25507	(29-Nov-91 ARC.P30/R) Portrait d'un enfant en costume de fantasie (50x37cm-20x15in) (F.FR 140000)
£873	$1571	(21-Nov-91 BL.P16) Village de pecheurs en Russie (25x33cm-10x13in) pen sepia wash htd.white gouache (F.FR 8500)

LEPRINCE, Jean Baptiste (attrib) (1734-1781) French

£559	$1000	(15-Jan-92 CH.NY100/R) Studies of heads of Russian priest, Orinetals and servant girl (23x15cm-9x6in) black chk two sheets paper
£1000	$1740	(14-Apr-92 C45 a) Young couple (15x13cm-6x5in) red chk lower right corner made up

LEPRINCE, Leopold (1800-1847) French

£565	$1016	(21-Nov-91 BL.P49) Paysage montagneux (27x41cm-11x16in) s.d.1822 (F.FR 5500)

LEPSIUS, Reinhold (1857-1922) German

£548	$982	(16-Jan-92 D.V151/R) Sleeping Beauty (120x80cm-47x31in) s.d.81 chl (A.S 11000)

LEPSIUS, Sabine (1864-?) German

£2041	$3653	(5-May-92 ZEL.L1411/R) Portrait of young woman seated wearing evening dress (160x100cm-63x39in) s. (DM 6000)

LERAY, Prudent Louis (1820-1879) French

£1243	$2250	(21-May-92 S.W2999) Brief rest (9x13cm-4x5in) s. board
£1644	$2827	(8-Oct-91 ZEL.L1584/R) Two page boys with dog on stairs of palace (40x31cm-16x12in) s. panel (DM 4800)

LERCH, Franz (1895-) Austrian

£1092	$1944	(28-Nov-91 D.V192/R) Portrait of woman (73x55cm-29x22in) s.d.39 (A.S 22000)
£4965	$8838	(28-Nov-91 D.V175/R) Blue boats before red house (60x80cm-24x31in) s. (A.S 100000)
£485	$882	(26-May-92 D.V120/R) Suburb (44x62cm-17x24in) s. W/C gouache (A.S 10000)
£894	$1591	(28-Nov-91 D.V204/R) Lake landscape (36x54cm-14x21in) s.d.36 W/C gouache (A.S 18000)
£969	$1764	(26-May-92 D.V137/R) Beach scene (35x42cm-14x17in) W/C pencil (A.S 20000)

LERCHE, Vincent Stoltenberg (1837-1892) Norwegian

£1300	$2223	(19-Mar-92 B78/R) The secret (33x25cm-13x10in) s.d.73 board
£1900	$3363	(13-Feb-92 CSK61/R) Carnival Masqueraders boarding gondola (37x27cm-15x11in) s.d.70 pencil W/C

LERFELDT, Hans Henrik (20th C) Scandinavian

£534	$929	(18-Sep-91 KH.K149) Composition (22x27cm-9x11in) s.d.1972-73verso (D.KR 6000)
£991	$1705	(4-Mar-92 KH.K137) Model (30x23cm-12x9in) s.d.1978verso (D.KR 11000)
£1041	$1884	(4-Dec-91 KH.K117) Model (24x19cm-9x7in) s.d.1978verso (D.KR 11500)
£495	$852	(4-Mar-92 KH.K139) Dawn (31x23cm-12x9in) s.d.83 W/C (D.KR 5500)
£543	$983	(4-Dec-91 KH.K125) Figure composition (31x26cm-12x10in) W/C gouache (D.KR 6000)
£1131	$2048	(4-Dec-91 KH.K124) Model (26x20cm-10x8in) s. pencil (D.KR 12500)
£1173	$2006	(10-Mar-92 RAS.K98/R) Portrait of lady and fly (36x24cm-14x9in) s. W/C (D.KR 13000)
£1396	$2402	(4-Mar-92 KH.K262/R) It's blue world around us (32x24cm-13x9in) s.d.84 crayon (D.KR 15500)

LERFELDT, Hans Henrik (20th C) Scandinavian-cont.

£1538	$2785	(4-Dec-91 KH.K35/R) Double image (59x35cm-23x14in) s.d.80-81 W/C (D.KR 17000)
£2534	$4586	(4-Dec-91 KH.K33/R) Punk model (65x47cm-26x19in) s.d.86 W/C (D.KR 28000)

LERGAARD, Niels (1893-1982) Danish

£537	$977	(10-Dec-91 RAS.K155) View of Gudhjem (65x79cm-26x31in) init.d.32 (D.KR 6000)
£1272	$2225	(1-Apr-92 KH.K77/R) The town, evening (55x65cm-22x26in) s. (D.KR 14000)
£1961	$3373	(16-Oct-91 KH.K155/R) Salene road by Gudhjem (50x65cm-20x26in) s. (D.KR 22000)
£1961	$3373	(16-Oct-91 KH.K114/R) Town by the sea, Gudhjem 1977 (55x65cm-22x26in) s. (D.KR 22000)
£2076	$3550	(12-Mar-92 RAS.K706/R) Evening in Spellingmosen, Gudhjem (66x80cm-26x31in) s. (D.KR 23000)
£2135	$3715	(17-Sep-91 RAS.K652/R) Figure in hilly landscape, sea in background (94x107cm-37x42in) (D.KR 24000)

LERICHE (18/19th C) ?

£9790	$17327	(7-Nov-91 D.V207/R) Roses, peonies, lilac and other flowers in metal vase on ledge (34x48cm-13x19in) (A.S 200000)

LERMITE (20th C) ?

£852	$1542	(20-May-92 GK.Z5167) Window design (33x33cm-13x13in) s.d.1972 i.verso col.pencil paper on panel (S.FR 2300)

LEROUX (?) French?

£730	$1307	(6-May-92 GD.B754/R) Still life of white grapes and peaches (33x40cm-13x16in) s. (S.FR 2000)
£1204	$2156	(6-May-92 GD.B753/R) Still life of blue grapes and pears (41x32cm-16x13in) s. (S.FR 3300)

LEROUX, A (?) ?

£510	$867	(23-Oct-91 GD.B1138/R) Portrait of young lady with flower hat and other figures beyond (40x32cm-16x13in) s. pavatex (S.FR 1300)

LEROUX, Andre (1911-) French

£565	$1080	(3-Jul-92 RY.P189) Chien a la balle (50x61cm-20x24in) s. (F.FR 5500)
£565	$1080	(3-Jul-92 RY.P180) Portrait d'homme a la tunique jaune (61x50cm-24x20in) s. (F.FR 5500)
£596	$1139	(3-Jul-92 RY.P233) Nature morte a la lettre cachetee (28x35cm-11x14in) s. (F.FR 5800)
£617	$1178	(3-Jul-92 RY.P210/R) Nature morte aux chataignes (60x81cm-24x32in) s. (F.FR 6000)
£617	$1178	(3-Jul-92 RY.P175/R) Composition aux etoffes (81x65cm-32x26in) s. (F.FR 6000)
£617	$1178	(3-Jul-92 RY.P172/R) Portrait d'une espagnole (55x46cm-22x18in) s. (F.FR 6000)
£617	$1178	(3-Jul-92 RY.P218/R) Nature morte a la mandoline (60x81cm-24x32in) s. (F.FR 6000)
£668	$1276	(3-Jul-92 RY.P212) Bouquet de pivoines roses et blanches (81x60cm-32x24in) s.d.1970 (F.FR 6500)
£699	$1335	(3-Jul-92 RY.P186/R) Hamelet (81x100cm-32x39in) s.d.1975 (F.FR 6800)
£822	$1570	(3-Jul-92 RY.P174) Serenite (89x117cm-35x46in) (F.FR 8000)
£822	$1570	(3-Jul-92 RY.P187) Danseuse de Flamenco (92x67cm-36x26in) s. (F.FR 8000)
£976	$1865	(3-Jul-92 RY.P226/R) Bouquet de pivoines (92x65cm-36x26in) s.d.1968 (F.FR 9500)
£1131	$2159	(3-Jul-92 RY.P214/R) Antonio (93x74cm-37x29in) s.d.1946 (F.FR 11000)
£1850	$3533	(3-Jul-92 RY.P188) Nature morte au bouquet de pivoines (73x92cm-29x36in) s. oil htd chk (F.FR 18000)

LEROUX, Auguste (1871-1954) French

£524	$1001	(3-Jul-92 RY.P105/R) Elegante au miroir (101x81cm-40x32in) (F.FR 5100)
£534	$1021	(3-Jul-92 RY.P59) Interieur de Musee (33x24cm-13x9in) s.d.1900 panel (F.FR 5200)
£545	$1040	(3-Jul-92 RY.P73) Allegorie des sports, projet de decoration (81x60cm-32x24in) (F.FR 5300)
£565	$1080	(3-Jul-92 RY.P67) Parc a la statue antique (61x50cm-24x20in) panel (F.FR 5500)
£576	$1099	(3-Jul-92 RY.P114) L'age heureux (55x46cm-22x18in) s. (F.FR 5600)
£596	$1139	(3-Jul-92 RY.P106) Place de la Concorde (89x117cm-35x46in) s.d.1918 (F.FR 5800)
£596	$1139	(3-Jul-92 RY.P45/R) Statue d'athlete antique (81x100cm-32x39in) s. (F.FR 5800)
£617	$1178	(3-Jul-92 RY.P39/R) Portrait d'Andre a la palette (100x81cm-39x32in) (F.FR 6000)
£617	$1178	(3-Jul-92 RY.P96/R) L'arbre jaune (81x100cm-32x39in) s. (F.FR 6000)
£719	$1374	(3-Jul-92 RY.P94) Femme en noir (160x100cm-63x39in) s. (F.FR 7000)
£874	$1669	(3-Jul-92 RY.P85/R) Parc fleuri a la statue antique (101x81cm-40x32in) s. (F.FR 8500)
£874	$1669	(3-Jul-92 RY.P83/R) Homme au torse nu (81x99cm-32x39in) s.verso (F.FR 8500)
£925	$1767	(3-Jul-92 RY.P108) Vue de Brouage (80x200cm-31x79in) s.d.1923 (F.FR 9000)

LEROUX, Auguste (1871-1954) French-cont.

£1028	$1963	(3-Jul-92 RY.P36/R) Reflet de femme a la jupe verte (146x97cm-57x38in) paper laid down on canvas (F.FR 10000)
£1233	$2356	(3-Jul-92 RY.P71/R) Au musee de Cluny (114x64cm-45x25in) s.d.1901 (F.FR 12000)
£1233	$2356	(3-Jul-92 RY.P62) Seance de croquis au parc (46x61cm-18x24in) (F.FR 12000)
£1285	$2454	(3-Jul-92 RY.P115/R) L'entracte (81x100cm-32x39in) s. (F.FR 12500)
£1542	$2945	(3-Jul-92 RY.P40) Domestique au bouquet de fleurs (81x65cm-32x26in) (F.FR 15000)
£1747	$3337	(3-Jul-92 RY.P80/R) Nu au livre (82x105cm-32x41in) s. (F.FR 17000)
£1747	$3337	(3-Jul-92 RY.P111/R) Promeneurs au parc s. (F.FR 17000)
£2467	$4711	(3-Jul-92 RY.P58/R) Peintre en bord de mer (81x65cm-32x26in) s. (F.FR 24000)
£2569	$4908	(3-Jul-92 RY.P66/R) Reflet de nu au miroir (83x123cm-33x48in) s. (F.FR 25000)
£3494	$6674	(3-Jul-92 RY.P89/R) Reflets (130x90cm-51x35in) s. (F.FR 34000)
£5242	$10011	(3-Jul-92 RY.P24) Rousse au miroir (177x137cm-70x54in) s. (F.FR 51000)
£565	$1080	(3-Jul-92 RY.P60 b) Jeune fille au bonnet (57x47cm-22x19in) s. pastel oval (F.FR 5500)

LEROUX, Francois (1943-) French

£624	$1093	(5-Apr-92 R.P149) Sans titre (104x74cm-41x29in) s. mixed media (F.FR 6000)

LEROUX, Georges (1877-1957) French

£1852	$3352	(4-Dec-91 LD.P55/R) Le Moulin et les peintres (28x34cm-11x13in) W/C gouache (F.FR 18000)
£2675	$4842	(4-Dec-91 LD.P59/R) Le concert rouge, decembre 1901 (22x34cm-9x13in) s.i.d.1901 blk.crayon gouache (F.FR 26000)
£2778	$5028	(4-Dec-91 LD.P58/R) A la Gaite Montparnasse (28x42cm-11x17in) s.i.d.1903 pastel (F.FR 27000)
£3086	$5586	(4-Dec-91 LD.P60/R) Le Moulin de la Galette (31x48cm-12x19in) s.i.d.janvier 1905 blk.crayon W/C gouache (F.FR 30000)
£4218	$7635	(4-Dec-91 LD.P61/R) Le Moulin de la Galette (37x55cm-15x22in) s.i.d.novembre 1904 blk.crayon W/C gouache (F.FR 41000)

LEROUX, Louis Hector (1829-1900) French

£1100	$1903	(3-Oct-91 CSK247/R) Maidens at the shrine of Ascelpius (66x43cm-26x17in) s. panel

LEROUX, Lucienne (1903-1981) French

£976	$1865	(3-Jul-92 RY.P145/R) Baigneuse (100x81cm-39x32in) s. (F.FR 9500)
£976	$1865	(3-Jul-92 RY.P125/R) Jeune paysanne Espagnole (101x81cm-40x32in) s. (F.FR 9500)

LEROUX, Marie-Guillaume-Charles (1814-1895) French

£838	$1500	(13-Nov-91 B.SF2254/R) Bridge and ford on shallow river (29x36cm-11x14in) panel

LEROY (?) French

£556	$1006	(21-May-92 GK.Z1706/R) Portrait of young gentleman wearing brown coat with lace jabot (3x3cm-1x1in) min.s.d.1779 oval ivory box (S.FR 1500)
£661	$1184	(13-Nov-91 PIC.P119/R) Famille en promenade au bord d'un cours d'eau ombrage (20x26cm-8x10in) s. gouache (F.FR 6500)

LEROY, Etienne (1828-?) French

£800	$1448	(21-May-92 CSK210/R) Vanity (34x25cm-13x10in) s.

LEROY, Eugene (1910-) French

£14359	$25703	(19-Jan-92 CC.P56/R) Ciel (73x100cm-29x39in) s.verso (F.FR 140000)

LEROY, Francois (fl.1864-70) French

£3600	$6552	(28-May-92 C62/R) Various camp scenes in Mauritius (18x27cm-7x11in) s. two d.1865 one d.1864 W/C four

LEROY, Jules (19/20th C) French

£950	$1625	(17-Mar-92 PH193/R) Cat and two kittens on gold cushion (18x32cm-7x13in) s. panel
£1400	$2394	(17-Mar-92 PH195/R) Hide and seek (33x41cm-13x16in) s.
£1453	$2500	(15-Oct-91 CE.NY157/R) Le tic tac (55x46cm-22x18in) s.i.
£1600	$2736	(17-Mar-92 PH192/R) Standing guard (41x33cm-16x13in) s.
£1600	$2736	(17-Mar-92 PH198/R) Cat and two kittens on red and gold cushion (33x46cm-13x18in) s.
£1676	$3000	(13-Nov-91 B.SF2297/R) Kittens making mischief (43x49cm-17x19in) s.
£1933	$3537	(17-May-92 T.B176/R) Chatons sur le fauteuil (65x54cm-26x21in) s. (F.FR 15000)
£4000	$7160	(19-Jan-92 CSC.P116/R) Les chatons (46x65cm-18x26in) s. (F.FR 39000)

LEROY, Jules (attrib) (19/20th C) French

£963	$1743	(19-May-92 GF.L2551/R) Cat with kittens (23x30cm-9x12in) (S.FR 2600)
£4167	$7000	(12-Aug-91 SG.M601/R) Cat and kittens (74x91cm-29x36in) s. i.verso

LEROY, Patrick (1948-) French
£512 $922   (2-Feb-92 ZZ.F208/R) Jeune femme a l'ombrelle et au levrier
     (70x51cm-28x20in) s. panel (F.FR 5000)
£520 $911   (5-Apr-92 ZZ.F220/R) Elegantes pres de la vasque fleurie
     (89x69cm-35x27in) s. panel (F.FR 5000)

LEROY, Paul Alexandre Alfred (1860-1942) French
£2846 $4951   (13-Apr-92 AT.P192/R) La brodeuse (41x33cm-16x13in) s. (F.FR 28000)
£15707 $30000   (30-Jun-92 PO.BA7) Interior de harem con personajes (169x181cm-67x71in)
     s.d.1908

LERSY, Roger (1920-) French
£945 $1625   (16-Oct-91 G.Z141/R) Pont de Tancarville (98x147cm-39x58in) s.d.1961
     (S.FR 2400)

LESAINT, Charles Louis (1795-?) French
£1646 $2979   (3-Dec-91 CN.P36/R) Personnage dans les ruines (68x52cm-27x20in) s.d.1826
     (F.FR 16000)
£26504 $49297   (18-Jun-92 SY.MO78/R) Vue d'un atelier de peintre (31x40cm-12x16in) s.
     (F.FR 260000)

LESBROS, Alfred (1873-1940) French
£1009 $1736   (20-Oct-91 I.N31/R) Maison jaune (52x37cm-20x15in) s. board (F.FR 10000)
£1917 $3298   (20-Oct-91 I.N30) La Chartreuse de Villeneuve-les-Avignon
     (54x73cm-21x29in) s. (F.FR 19000)
£2243 $4171   (17-Jun-92 I.N71/R) La Vierge au jardin (73x53cm-29x21in) s. studio
     st.verso board (F.FR 22000)

LESIEUR, Pierre (1922-) French
£1081 $2000   (12-Jun-92 SY.NY217/R) Jardin des Tuileries (160x160cm-63x63in) s.d.65
£1117 $2000   (9-May-92 CE.NY98/R) Coquillages (81x76cm-32x30in) s.d.70
£1423 $2476   (13-Apr-92 GL.P154) Plage (46x60cm-18x24in) s.d.1967 (F.FR 14000)
£1440 $2607   (6-Dec-91 GL.P232) Interieur (65x54cm-26x21in) s.d.1980 (F.FR 14000)
£1543 $2793   (6-Dec-91 GL.P231) Plage (38x45cm-15x18in) s. (F.FR 15000)
£1712 $3047   (28-Oct-91 GL.P207/R) Paysage (65x53cm-26x21in) s.d.1960 (F.FR 17000)
£2417 $4302   (28-Oct-91 GL.P214/R) Petite Galine (40x40cm-16x16in) s.d.1963
     (F.FR 24000)
£2575 $4403   (17-Mar-92 FB.P44/R) Femme devant la fenetre (162x130cm-64x51in) s.d.58
     (F.FR 25000)
£2703 $5000   (12-Jun-92 SY.NY210/R) Nu devant la glace (139x139cm-55x55in) s.d.63
£2881 $5214   (6-Dec-91 GL.P230/R) Village de Tunise (58x71cm-23x28in) s.d.1967
     (F.FR 28000)
£4943 $8453   (17-Mar-92 FB.P18/R) Mosaique (200x200cm-79x79in) s.d.74 (F.FR 48000)
£7114 $12378   (13-Apr-92 GL.P155) Personnage endormi dans un paysage
     (220x220cm-87x87in) s.d.1970 (F.FR 70000)
£7700 $13860   (19-Nov-91 FB.P85/R) Les coquillages (157x157cm-62x62in) s.d.67
     (F.FR 75000)

LESLIE, Alfred (1927-) American
£22346 $40000   (6-May-92 CH.NY284/R) Pythoness (173x220cm-68x87in) s.d.1959 verso
£432   *$800*   *(12-Jun-92 SY.NY242/R) Collage (19x15cm-7x6in) oil collage fabric on*
     board
£459   *$850*   *(12-Jun-92 SY.NY243/R) Collage (17x19cm-7x7in) s.d.53 oil collage canvas*
£2027   *$3750*   *(12-Jun-92 SY.NY245/R) Untitled (47x61cm-19x24in) s.i.d.1953 gouache*
     collage

LESLIE, Charles (19th C) British
£650 $1209   (17-Jun-92 B111) Highland Loch view at sunset (39x59cm-15x23in) s.
£650 $1242   (30-Jun-92 RJ130/R) Llyn Dinas with figures and sheep by bank
     (28x58cm-11x23in) s.indist.d.
£681 $1226   (19-Nov-91 GM.B548) Scene du vicaire de Wakerfield (78x63cm-31x25in) s.
     (B.FR 40000)
£1000 $1720   (4-Mar-92 S19/R) Rush gatherers (61x101cm-24x40in) indist.s.

LESLIE, Charles Robert (1794-1859) British
£1500 $2655   (6-Nov-91 S151/R) Farewell (68x48cm-27x19in) s. s.indis.i.stretcher
£1600 $2736   (12-Mar-92 CSK274/R) Leaving the room (67x47cm-26x19in) s.

LESLIE, P (1877-) British
£500 $905   (21-May-92 B353) Fishermen in wooded river landscape (51x76cm-20x30in) s.

LESLIE, Peter (1877-?) British
£681 $1225   (23-Nov-91 SO.S434/R) Landscape with houses and chickens
     (44x80cm-17x31in) s. (S.KR 7100)

LESOURD-BEAUREGARD, Ange Louis Guillaume (1800-1885) French
£7099 $12495   (10-Apr-92 AT.P58/R) Nature morte de fruits disposes sur un entablement
     de marbre (32x41cm-13x16in) (F.FR 70000)
£8000 $14880   (19-Jun-92 C12/R) Peaches, grapes, melon, convulvuli and other flowers in
     landscape (59x51cm-23x20in) s. panel
£2000   *$3480*   *(14-Apr-92 C175) Hibiscus with bee (32x24cm-13x9in) s. lead W/C bodycol*
     vellum on panel

ESREL, Adolphe Alexandre (1839-1929) French
£550 $1007   (15-May-92 TE356) Smoker (36x25cm-14x10in) s.d.1914 panel

LESREL, Adolphe Alexandre (1839-1929) French-cont.
£1235 $2346   (22-Jun-92 AT.P67) Quimperle (41x33cm-16x13in) s.d.1916 panel
              (F.FR 12000)
£2469 $4691   (22-Jun-92 AT.P66/R) Fileuses a Lorient (46x37cm-18x15in) s.d.1916 panel
              (F.FR 24000)
£13736 $25000   (28-May-92 SY.NY74/R) Bacchante enivree (87x200cm-34x79in) s.d.1882

LESSER-URY see URY, Lesser

LESSI, Giovanni (1852-1922) Italian
£9530 $17726   (16-Jun-92 F.M262/R) In Place de L'Opera a Parigi (25x19cm-10x7in) s.
              canvas on board (I.L 21000000)

LESSI, Tito (1858-1917) Italian
£2299 $4116   (14-Nov-91 CH.R162/R) Dopo il pasto (27x21cm-11x8in) s.d.1884 panel
              (I.L 5000000)
£402 $700   *(10-Sep-91 BG.M705/R) Standing gentleman (30x15cm-12x6in) s.i.d.1881 W/C*

LESSING, Karl Friedrich (1808-1880) German
£559 $968   (25-Mar-92 KM.K1284/R) Portrait of girl en face wearing white lace collar
              on black dress (52x45cm-20x18in) mono.1852 (DM 1600)
£10239 $18635   (27-May-92 PH.DU28/R) Riders in landscape before ruins
              (111x138cm-44x54in) mono.d.1845 (DM 30000)
£2160 $3932   *(12-Dec-91 L.K429/R) Portrait of artist's wife (38x26cm-15x10in)*
              mono.d.1844 W/C over pencil (DM 6200)

LESSORE, Emile (1805-1876) French
£872 $1561   (19-Jan-92 CSC.P119) Enfants se desalterant pres de la fontaine
              (57x43cm-22x17in) s. (F.FR 8500)
£400 $764   *(14-Jul-92 DR438) Street scene with seated figures (38x20cm-15x8in) s.*
              W/C bodycol

LESSORE, Jules (1849-1892) French/British
£1220 $2195   *(19-Nov-91 FP.M98/R) Rouen (74x53cm-29x21in) s. W/C (C.D 2500)*

LESSORE, Therese (1884-1945) French
£1800 $3150   (27-Sep-91 C134/R) Girl resting on a chaise lounge (49x59cm-19x23in)
              s.d.1922
£440 $761   *(4-Sep-91 BT34/R) Bruges Market (28x23cm-11x9in) s.d.1921 W/C*

LESUR, Henri Victor (1863-1900) French
£4000 $7000   (19-Feb-92 CH.NY50/R) Gentleman and flower girl near book stalls by Seine
              (39x32cm-15x13in) s. panel

LETENDRE, Rita (1929-) Canadian
£1442 $2524   (17-Feb-92 HO.ED167) Shemesh (107x168cm-42x66in) s.i.d.1975verso acrylic
              (C.D 3000)

LETERREUX, Gervaix (20th C) French
£613 $1073   (23-Feb-92 FE.P155) Port en Bessin (38x46cm-15x18in) s. (F.FR 6000)

LETH, Harald (1899-?) Danish
£620 $1128   (25-May-92 RAS.K173) Green sunset (23x39cm-9x15in) s.d.c.1960verso
              masonite (D.KR 7000)
£664 $1209   (25-May-92 RAS.K172) Boy with calf (51x60cm-20x24in) s. on stretcher
              (D.KR 7500)
£980 $1686   (16-Oct-91 KH.K182) Poultry yard, Asminderod (65x80cm-26x31in) init.
              (D.KR 11000)

LETHBRIDGE, John (1948-) Australian
£585 $1088   *(21-Jun-92 SY.ME79/R) Subtle winds and coarse bodies (168x168cm-66x66in)*
              s.i.d.1983verso acrylic chl (A.D 1450)

LETHIERE, Guillaume-Guillon (1760-1832) French
£5028 $9000   *(14-Jan-92 SY.NY149/R) Metellus spared by Octavian (46x60cm-18x24in) s.*
              pen wash over black chk

LETHIERE, Guillaume-Guillon (attrib) (1760-1832) French
£3399 $6389   (18-Dec-91 AT.P233/R) Ulysse et l'epreuve du tir a l'arc contre les
              pretendants (44x71cm-17x28in) (F.FR 33000)

LETIN, Jacques Ninet de (1597-1661) French
£12346 $22346   (5-Dec-91 SY.MO147/R) L'apparition du Christ aux disciples d'Emmaus
              (141x124cm-56x49in) (F.FR 120000)

LETO, Antonino (1844-1913) Italian
£1563 $2766   (5-Nov-91 GF.L2496/R) Rainy Italian street scene (22x30cm-9x12in) s.
              (S.FR 4000)
£8552 $14624   (19-Mar-92 F.M82/R) Spiaggia con barche (36x57cm-14x22in) s.
              (I.L 18400000)
£36000 $64080   (29-Nov-91 C104/R) Un pomeriggio d'Estate (39x64cm-15x25in) s.i.

LETOCT, Christian (20th C) ?
£645 $1129   (5-Apr-92 R.P223/R) Sans espoir de retour David Karadine
              (73x60cm-29x24in) s. (F.FR 6200)

LETOCT, Christian (20th C) ?-cont.
£814 $1457   (17-Nov-91 R.P244) Michey Rourke (73x60cm-29x24in) s. (F.FR 8000)

LETTE, G de (19th C) Italian
£400 $700   (18-Feb-92 CE.NY271) Venezia, Canal Grande-Palazzo Rerronico dove e Morto
                 Poete Browning (48x34cm-19x13in) s. i.verso W/C paperboard

LEU, August Wilhelm (1819-1897) German
£687 $1196   (18-Sep-91 N.M607/R) Alpine summer farm with goats (20x29cm-8x11in)
                 i.stretcher board (DM 2000)
£962 $1750   (13-Dec-91 DM.D2008/R) Bavarian landscape (66x81cm-26x32in)

LEU, Oscar (1864-1942) German
£772 $1320   (12-Mar-92 GK.Z113) Alpine landscape with mill by stream
                 (60x81cm-24x32in) s. (S.FR 2000)

LEURS, J (?) ?
£1000 $1810   (21-May-92 CSK149/R) Dutch coastal landscape (61x89cm-24x35in) s.

LEURS, Johannes Karel (1865-1938) Dutch
£785 $1500   (16-Jul-92 SY.NY478/R) Landscape with windmills and cows
                 (40x60cm-16x24in) s.
£909 $1609   (22-Apr-92 CH.AM31) View in a village (60x45cm-24x18in) s. (D.FL 3000)
£550 $995   (21-May-92 CSK15) Shepherd returning home with flock (37x55cm-15x22in) s.
                 W/C htd white
£580 $1032   (27-Nov-91 B31) Drover and cattle in wooded landscape (53x37cm-21x15in)
                 s. W/C

LEUTERITZ, Paul (1867-1919) German
£415 $789   (27-Jun-92 FN.L1143) Four Spanish sparows looking for food
                 (26x36cm-10x14in) s. W/C (DM 1200)

LEUTZE, Emmanuel (after) (1816-1868) German
£1638 $2900   (22-Apr-92 D.NY70) Washington crossing the Delaware (51x102cm-20x40in)

LEUTZE, Emmanuel (style) (1816-1868) German
£1519 $2750   (21-May-92 S.W3001) Mother and child (36x29cm-14x11in)

LEVANON, Mordechai (1901-1968) Israeli
£479 $900   (5-Jan-92 GG.TA243/R) Vase and flowers (35x29cm-14x11in) s.d.1938 paper
£1011 $1900   (5-Jan-92 GG.TA238/R) Village in Galilee (30x45cm-12x18in) s.d.1963
£1135 $2100   (8-Jun-92 GG.TA176/R) Street in Rosh Pina (30x35cm-12x14in) s.d.38 board
£4865 $9000   (9-Jun-92 GG.TA278/R) Safed (92x65cm-36x26in) s.d.50
£595 $1100   (9-Jun-92 GG.TA348/R) Family (58x45cm-23x18in) s.d.50 gouache
£851 $1600   (5-Jan-92 GG.TA242/R) Landscape (49x68cm-19x27in) s.twice gouache
£851 $1600   (5-Jan-92 GG.TA240/R) Safed (50x69cm-20x27in) s.d.1962 W/C gouache
£865 $1600   (9-Jun-92 GG.TA347/R) Safed (34x48cm-13x19in) s.d.61 gouache
£957 $1800   (5-Jan-92 GG.TA241/R) Ein Karem, landscape and figures (48x68cm-19x27in)
                 s.d.1963twice gouache W/C
£1405 $2600   (8-Jun-92 GG.TA175/R) Safed (75x55cm-30x22in) s.d.60 gouache

LEVECQ, Jacobus (attrib) (1634-1675) Dutch
£5556 $9944   (12-Nov-91 SY.AM194/R) Two elegant ladies near fountain on terrace
                 (77x96cm-30x38in) (D.FL 18000)

LEVEE, John (1924-) American
£996 $1733   (16-Apr-92 FB.P173/R) Juin V (72x60cm-28x24in) s.d.1955 i.verso
                 (F.FR 9800)
£1355 $2452   (4-Dec-91 G.Z146) Composition (26x33cm-10x13in) s.d.1953 mixed media
                 (S.FR 3400)

LEVEILLE, Andre (1880-1963) French
£1676 $3000   (13-Nov-91 B.SF2373/R) Paysage au bord de la riviere (41x49cm-16x19in) s.
                 panel

LEVER, Richard Hayley (1876-1958) American
£503 $900   (6-May-92 D.NY50) Fireworks on the Hudson (13x20cm-5x8in) s.s. board
£517 $900   (14-Sep-91 LAE.L261/R) Sunset, Porthmeor Beach, St. Ives (20x30cm-8x12in)
                 s. i.verso board
£610 $1050   (10-Oct-91 FA.PH826) Floral still life (41x51cm-16x20in)
£649 $1200   (10-Jun-92 CE.NY434 a) Sunday morning, St. Ives, Cornwall (20x24cm-8x9in)
                 s.
£746 $1350   (7-Dec-91 LAE.L52/R) House by river with tug boat and boats
                 (23x33cm-9x13in) s.
£773 $1400   (4-Dec-91 D.NY92/R) Returning of fishing fleet, St. Ives, Cornwall
                 (25x33cm-10x13in) s. i.stretcher
£1006 $1800   (6-May-92 D.NY40/R) Rough seas, Brandt Rock (41x51cm-16x20in) s.
£1006 $1800   (6-May-92 D.NY43 a/R) Cottages of Concarneau, Brittany (28x36cm-11x14in)
                 s.d.1908
£1341 $2400   (14-Nov-91 CE.NY337 a/R) Fishing boats at anchor, Gloucester,
                 Massachusetts (16x24cm-6x9in) s.
£1366 $2431   (26-Nov-91 J.M432) Seascape (41x59cm-16x23in) s. (A.D 3100)
£1494 $2600   (15-Apr-92 SY.NY148/R) Woodstock, New York (27x30cm-11x12in) s. d.1933
                 verso board
£1514 $2800   (10-Jun-92 CE.NY604/R) Drying laundry (41x51cm-16x20in) s.

LEVER, Richard Hayley (1876-1958) American-cont.

£1816	$3250	(6-May-92 D.NY41 a/R) Morning mist, St Ives, Cornwall (41x51cm-16x20in) s. s.i.verso
£2235	$4000	(14-Nov-91 CE.NY349 a/R) St. Ives, Cornwall (33x41cm-13x16in) s. board
£2674	$4600	(14-Oct-91 H.C157/R) Harbour with moored boats (33x41cm-13x16in) s.d.1915
£3107	$5500	(9-Nov-91 W.W257/R) Early morning, Central Park (64x76cm-25x30in) s.d.33 i.verso
£12000	$21000	(25-Sep-91 SY.NY71/R) J boats racing, Larchmont, New York (76x102cm-30x40in) s.
£405	$750	(10-Jun-92 CE.NY443 a) View of city (21x27cm-8x11in) s.d.1926 W/C pencil board
£523	$900	(20-Oct-91 HG.C19) Bridges of New York (33x48cm-13x19in) s. W/C
£526	$900	(13-Mar-92 S.BM265/R) Village street (25x30cm-10x12in) s. mixed media canvas on board

LEVERD, Rene (1872-1938) French

£408	$758	(21-Jun-92 LT.P27 b) La gardienne d'oie (36x54cm-14x21in) s. W/C (F.FR 4000)
£453	$770	(27-Oct-91 LT.P44) Les moissons dans le Pas-de-Calais (28x38cm-11x15in) s. W/C (F.FR 4500)
£478	$875	(17-May-92 LT.P111 b) Sur la Place de la Concorde (24x32cm-9x13in) W/C (F.FR 4700)
£529	$968	(17-May-92 LT.P117) Fete Nationale a la Concorde en 1918 (13x18cm-5x7in) s. W/C (F.FR 5200)
£610	$1117	(17-May-92 LT.P71 b) Promeneur a Saint-Mames (37x54cm-15x21in) W/C (F.FR 6000)
£631	$1154	(17-May-92 LT.P79/R) Dieppe (20x30cm-8x12in) s. W/C (F.FR 6200)
£651	$1191	(17-May-92 LT.P59/R) Marins dans un port pres de Boulogne (31x48cm-12x19in) s. W/C (F.FR 6400)
£695	$1181	(27-Oct-91 LT.P31) Paris, le Pont Saint Louis (21x31cm-8x12in) s. W/C (F.FR 6900)
£712	$1303	(17-May-92 LT.P77/R) La Grande Rue a Avallon (36x55cm-14x22in) s. W/C (F.FR 7000)
£763	$1396	(17-May-92 LT.P27/R) Automne a Moret-sur-Loing (23x31cm-9x12in) s. W/C (F.FR 7500)
£814	$1489	(17-May-92 LT.P57 b) Voiliers a Chioggia (46x64cm-18x25in) W/C (F.FR 8000)
£997	$1824	(17-May-92 LT.P62/R) Le que a Vardes (38x56cm-15x22in) s. W/C (F.FR 9800)
£1279	$2277	(27-Nov-91 AT.P45) Paris, les bouquinistes (45x64cm-18x25in) s. W/C (F.FR 12500)
£3052	$5585	(17-May-92 LT.P25) Quai de la Seine a Paris en hiver (79x105cm-31x41in) s. gouache W/C (F.FR 30000)

LEVERE, Paul (19th C) French

£728	$1275	(5-Apr-92 ZZ.F98/R) Rivage mediterraneen (40x65cm-16x26in) s. (F.FR 7000)
£749	$1311	(5-Apr-92 ZZ.F136/R) Rocher boise pres du rivage (41x65cm-16x26in) s. (F.FR 7200)

LEVI, Carlo (1902-1975) Italian

£834	$1485	(29-Nov-91 F.F75) Ritratto (18x13cm-7x5in) panel (I.L 1800000)
£834	$1485	(29-Nov-91 F.F76) Natura morta (18x13cm-7x5in) panel (I.L 1800000)
£2324	$4206	(3-Dec-91 F.R222/R) Natura morta con melograno (50x70cm-20x28in) s.d.1969verso (I.L 5000000)
£2722	$4981	(12-May-92 F.R135/R) Natura morta (50x70cm-20x28in) s.d.1966 (I.L 6000000)
£3254	$5889	(3-Dec-91 F.R256/R) Natura morta con crostacei de conchiglia sulla spiaggia (50x60cm-20x24in) s.verso (I.L 7000000)
£3486	$6310	(3-Dec-91 F.R165/R) Paesaggio di Alassio (73x92cm-29x36in) s.verso (I.L 7500000)
£3629	$6641	(12-May-92 F.R175/R) Bosco (73x100cm-29x39in) s.d.1972 s.verso (I.L 8000000)
£3856	$7056	(12-May-92 F.R192/R) Natura morta con fichi e granoturco (50x70cm-20x28in) s.d.1970 s.verso (I.L 8500000)

LEVI, Julian E (1900-) American

£556	$950	(13-Mar-92 S.BM246/R) Route 22, Connecticut (23x46cm-9x18in) s.d.37

LEVIER, Charles (20th C) French

£543	$950	(27-Feb-92 CE.NY81) Rue de ville (38x76cm-15x30in) s.
£565	$1000	(5-Nov-91 CE.NY144/R) Le tarn (76x101cm-30x40in) s. s.i.verso
£571	$1000	(27-Feb-92 CE.NY140/R) Le refuge (76x101cm-30x40in) s.
£571	$1000	(28-Feb-92 SY.NY225/R) Mediterranee (102x76cm-40x30in) s.
£571	$1000	(27-Feb-92 CE.NY141/R) Port-en-Bessin (76x102cm-30x40in) s.
£649	$1124	(29-Mar-92 FE.P79) Le jardin (60x90cm-24x35in) s. (F.FR 6300)
£657	$1176	(10-May-92 LT.P147 b) A la campagne (50x60cm-20x24in) (F.FR 6500)
£669	$1271	(28-Jun-92 FE.P73) A la campagne (50x61cm-20x24in) s. (F.FR 6500)
£670	$1200	(9-May-92 CE.NY152/R) Mois de mai (76x102cm-30x40in) s. s.i.verso
£670	$1200	(9-May-92 CE.NY158/R) Le quais (101x76cm-40x30in) s. s.i.verso
£670	$1200	(9-May-92 CE.NY159/R) Femmes au bar (102x76cm-40x30in) s. s.i.verso
£674	$1200	(1-Dec-91 DU.E1127) Fleurs des champs (76x61cm-30x24in) s.
£686	$1200	(27-Feb-92 CE.NY135/R) Tournesols (102x76cm-40x30in) s.
£806	$1370	(27-Oct-91 LT.P128/R) Le bouquet aupres de la fenetre (101x76cm-40x30in) s. (F.FR 8000)
£809	$1400	(2-Oct-91 D.NY54) Le fleuve (61x122cm-24x48in) s. s.i.verso
£914	$1600	(27-Feb-92 CE.NY78/R) Fleurs sauvages (122x61cm-48x24in) s.

LEVIER, Charles (20th C) French-cont.
£1006	$1800	(6-May-92 D.NY124/R) Provence (76x102cm-30x40in) s. s.i.verso
£1017	$1800	(6-Nov-91 D.NY119/R) Le poisson (76x112cm-30x44in) s. s.i.stretcher
£1017	$1800	(6-Nov-91 D.NY117/R) Venise (76x101cm-30x40in) s. s.i.verso
£1029	$1800	(28-Feb-92 SY.NY166/R) Le port (76x102cm-30x40in) s.
£1117	$2000	(13-Nov-91 B.SF2368/R) Moored sailing boats (52x152cm-20x60in) s. board
£1117	$2000	(13-Nov-91 B.SF2369/R) Still life with mandolin (38x111cm-15x44in) s. board
£1130	$2000	(6-Nov-91 D.NY116/R) Sortie du music hall (76x102cm-30x40in) s. s.i.verso
£1143	$2000	(27-Feb-92 CE.NY80/R) La table blanche (122x61cm-48x24in) s.
£1163	$2000	(12-Oct-91 SY.NY145/R) Still life (76x61cm-30x24in) s.
£1221	$2100	(12-Oct-91 SY.NY166/R) Saltimbanque (112x40cm-44x16in) s. s.d.57 verso
£1229	$2200	(6-May-92 D.NY123/R) Le manteau rouge (76x102cm-30x40in) s. s.i.verso
£1243	$2200	(5-Nov-91 CE.NY190/R) A la fenetre (102x76cm-40x30in) s. s.i.verso
£1277	$2400	(5-Jan-92 LIT.L277) Le poisson (74x109cm-29x43in) s.
£1279	$2200	(12-Oct-91 SY.NY165/R) Les filles (102x76cm-40x30in) s.
£1714	$3000	(27-Feb-92 CE.NY116/R) Fleurs sur la mer (101x76cm-40x30in) s.
£608	$1100	*(21-May-92 S.W2748) Flowers along the promenade (53x74cm-21x29in) s. W/C*

LEVINE, David (20th C) American
£531	$950	*(14-Nov-91 CE.NY436) Woman in peach burnoose (46x36cm-18x14in) s.d.79 W/C pencil*
£629	$1100	*(28-Feb-92 SY.NY86/R) Caricature of George Balanchine (35x28cm-14x11in) s.d.78 pen indian ink*
£703	$1300	*(12-Jun-92 SY.NY290/R) Young man in tied shirt (45x24cm-18x9in) s.d.78 W/C*
£710	$1300	*(11-May-92 CH.NY85/R) Portrait of Douglas Cooper (35x28cm-14x11in) s.d.85 indian ink over pencil*
£743	$1300	*(26-Sep-91 CH.NY256/R) Boardwalk at Coney Island (37x55cm-15x22in) s.d. W/C pencil*

LEVINE, David and PENNEY, James (20th C) American
£1086	$1900	*(26-Sep-91 CH.NY265/R) Dressmakers. Beach scene (41x61cm-16x24in) one s.d. pastel one s. oil masonite pair*

LEVINE, J (?) American
£1366	$2500	(7-Jun-92 LIT.L198) Beach scene (41x51cm-16x20in) s. masonite

LEVINE, Jack (1915-) American
£773	$1400	(22-May-92 S.BM222/R) Mardi Gras (51x41cm-20x16in) s.d.59

LEVINE, Sherrie (1947-) American
£4469	$8000	*(7-May-92 SY.NY174/R) Broad stripe no.9 (61x50cm-24x20in) s.d.1985 num.9 verso casein wax wood*
£6704	$12000	*(14-Nov-91 SY.NY186/R) Untitled - Check no.2 (61x51cm-24x20in) s.d.1985 num.verso casein mahogany*

LEVINSEN, S (1869-1943) French
£757	$1302	(20-Oct-91 I.N52) Les Martigues (28x36cm-11x14in) s. (F.FR 7500)

LEVINSEN, Sophus (1869-1943) French
£741	$1407	(26-Jun-92 CSC.P97) Cour de ferme (26x34cm-10x13in) s. panel (F.FR 7200)

LEVIS, Maurice (1860-1940) French
£920	$1600	(11-Sep-91 D.NY55) Nossi Be - vue de Mouillage (23x33cm-9x13in) s. i.verso board
£1988	$3538	(30-Oct-91 CH.AM241/R) Le printemps bords de la Selune (13x21cm-5x8in) s. s.i.verso panel (D.FL 6500)
£2035	$3642	(17-Nov-91 FB.P194) Un coin de bassin, Boulogne (51x65cm-20x26in) s. board laid down on canvas (F.FR 20000)
£2356	$4500	(16-Jul-92 SY.NY349/R) Petite ferme a St Leonard (45x64cm-18x25in) s.
£4500	$8370	(17-Jun-92 S462/R) River Canche at Etaples (23x33cm-9x13in) s. panel

LEVIS, Max (1863-?) German
£1456	$2592	(29-Apr-92 D.V754/R) The model (123x92cm-48x36in) (A.S 30000)

LEVITAN, Isaac Ilyitch (1860-1900) Russian
£1158	$2061	(31-Oct-91 LD.P140) Le pont sur le lac (18x27cm-7x11in) canvas laid down on board (F.FR 11500)
£2800	$4984	(28-Nov-91 S505/R) Country path (27x19cm-11x7in) panel
£7568	$14000	(9-Jun-92 GG.TA280/R) Country path (27x19cm-11x7in) s. panel
£10465	$18000	(17-Oct-91 SY.NY281/R) Riverbank (46x65cm-18x26in) s.

LEVRAC-TOURNIERES, Robert (1667-1752) French
£4630	$8380	(5-Dec-91 SY.MO306/R) Portrait de Gregoire de Saint Genies (51x38cm-20x15in) s.d.1734 panel (F.FR 45000)
£5078	$8988	(5-Nov-91 GF.L2404/R) Portrait of gentleman. Portrait of lady (122x97cm-48x38in) one s. pair (S.FR 13000)
£36290	$64234	(5-Nov-91 GGL.L1/R) Portrait d'un magistrat (216x138cm-85x54in) s.d.1716 (F.FR 360000)

LEVRAC-TOURNIERES, Robert (attrib) (1667-1752) French
£2854	$5309	(19-Jun-92 CN.P55/R) Portrait de femme tenant une fleur rouge (79x62cm-31x24in) oval (F.FR 28000)

LEVRAC-TOURNIERES, Robert (attrib) (1667-1752) French-cont.
£3568 $6636   (19-Jun-92 CN.P56/R) Portrait de femme a la robe rouge (81x65cm-32x26in)
                    (F.FR 35000)

LEVY, Alexander (1881-1947) American
£1547 $2800   (7-Dec-91 LAE.L24/R) Woman in red dress (102x76cm-40x30in) s.

LEVY, Emile (1826-1890) French
£1815 $3212   (10-Nov-91 ZZ.F127/R) Reve antique (60x41cm-24x16in) s. panel
                    (F.FR 18000)

LEVY, Nat (1896-1984) American
£857 $1500   (31-Mar-92 MOR.P85) Barns in landscape (36x48cm-14x19in) s. W/C
£1271 $2250   (12-Feb-92 B.SF634/R) Old blacksmith shop (71x89cm-28x35in) s. W/C

LEVY, Rudolf (1875-1943) German
£1706 $3106   (30-May-92 VG.B793/R) Portrait of the painter Curt Craemer
                    (81x61cm-32x24in) (DM 5000)
£5965 $10737   (21-Nov-91 L.K274/R) Portrait of the author Wolfgang Hellmert
                    (160x125cm-63x49in) (DM 17000)
£13402 $24526   (3-Jun-92 L.K270) Still life of pumpkin (65x54cm-26x21in) s.d.1907
                    (DM 39000)

LEVY, William Auerbach (1889-?) American
£1224 $2117   (25-Mar-92 KM.K1287) Portrait of young boy in profile (36x31cm-14x12in)
                    s. (DM 3500)

LEVY-DHURMER, Lucien (1865-1953) French
£442 $801   (2-Dec-91 CK.P19/R) Pins parasols (49x70cm-19x28in) s. ink wash
                    (F.FR 4300)
£524 $1000   (16-Jul-92 SY.NY324/R) The embrace (60x41cm-24x16in) i. pastel chl.
                    double-sided
£1800 $3114   (4-Oct-91 C37/R) Head of girl (41x33cm-16x13in) s.i.d.79 pastel paper on
                    board
£7194 $13741   (1-Jul-92 FB.P163/R) Jeune fille rousse (48x36cm-19x14in) s. pastel
                    (F.FR 70000)

LEWENSTEIN, Daniel (1860-?) ?
£1905 $3410   (5-May-92 ZEL.L1412/R) Female nude reclining on tigerskin
                    (54x71cm-21x28in) s.d.1899 panel (DM 5600)

LEWERS, Margo (1908-) Australian
£847 $1575   (21-Jun-92 SY.ME8/R) Deviations (66x85cm-26x33in) s. board (A.D 2100)

LEWIN, Stephen (fl.1890-1910) British
£2000 $3760   (19-Dec-91 C148/R) The stag (61x81cm-24x32in) s.d.1903
£3000 $5190   (23-Mar-92 HS232/R) Sincere and upright (70x90cm-28x35in) s.d.1905

LEWIS, A (?) British
£500 $925   (11-Jun-92 CSK131/R) Cattle watering in Highland river landscape
                    (50x76cm-20x30in) s.d.10

LEWIS, Aletta (1904-) British
£2423 $4361   (24-Nov-91 SY.S301/R) Factories on Yarra (44x36cm-17x14in) s.d.1928
                    plywood (A.D 5500)

LEWIS, Arthur James (1824-1901) British
£3800 $6802   (5-May-92 SWS418/R) The last number (57x37cm-22x15in) mono.d.1865
                    s.i.stretcher

LEWIS, Charles James (1830-1892) British
£500 $975   (15-Jan-92 CSK328) Trysting tree (52x37cm-20x15in) s.i.verso board backed
                    panel
£836 $1496   (6-May-92 DS.W19/R) Trifling with his affection (18x14cm-7x6in) s.
                    i.verso (NZ.D 2800)
£4000 $7080   (6-Nov-91 S68/R) At the back of the mill (61x118cm-24x46in) s.d.1889
                    s.i.stretcher
£5200 $9620   (12-Jun-92 C232/R) Coming thro' the rye (25x40cm-10x16in) s.i. card

LEWIS, Edmund Darch (1835-1910) American
£531 $950   (6-May-92 B.P149) Vermont landscape (76x51cm-30x20in) s.
£894 $1600   (14-Nov-91 CE.NY168/R) Ships by lighthouse (24x51cm-9x20in) s.d.1891 W/C
                    gouache paperboard
£1352 $2420   (14-Nov-91 GRO.B53/R) Along river (56x91cm-22x36in) s.d.1873
£11696 $20000   (12-Mar-92 CH.NY46/R) View of the Centennial Exhibition, Philadelphia
                    (91x152cm-36x60in) s.d.1876
£367 $660   (23-Nov-91 YFA.M182/R) Seascape (23x51cm-9x20in) s.d.1890 W/C gouache
£475 $850   (14-Nov-91 CE.NY334) Rocky coast with sailboats in distance
                    (23x48cm-9x19in) s.d.1888 W/C paper on board
£670 $1200   (14-Nov-91 CE.NY77) Italianate villa on lake (47x72cm-19x28in) s.d.1882
                    W/C paperboard
£811 $1500   (10-Jun-92 CE.NY244) Sailboat off rocky coast (25x52cm-10x20in) s.d.1884
                    W/C paperboard
£894 $1600   (13-Nov-91 B.SF2765/R) View of Narragansett (25x52cm-10x20in) s.d.1902
                    W/C

LEWIS, Edmund Darch (1835-1910) American-cont.
£1135 $2100   (10-Jun-92 CE.NY229/R) Town by sea (23x52cm-9x20in) s.d.1878 W/C paper on board

LEWIS, George Lennard see LEWIS, Lennard

LEWIS, Harry Emerson (1892-1958) American
£543 $950   (31-Mar-92 MOR.P114) Our coast (71x89cm-28x35in) s. board
£686 $1200   (31-Mar-92 MOR.P108) Palm Canyon, Borrego Valley (51x61cm-20x24in) s. i.verso masonite
£857 $1500   (31-Mar-92 MOR.P107) The artists afield, La Quinta Canyon (56x71cm-22x28in) s. i.verso masonite

LEWIS, Jeanette Maxfield (1894-1982) American
£479 $900   (18-Dec-91 SY.NY219/R) Street scene (40x50cm-16x20in) s. board

LEWIS, John (18th C) British
£2477 $4261   (7-Oct-91 CH.E227/R) Portrait of Jane Magendie, seated, playing lute (78x58cm-31x23in) s.d.1769 (E.P 2700)

LEWIS, John Frederick (1805-1876) British
£1798 $3200   (22-Jan-92 SY.NY495/R) Halt in desert (26x36cm-10x14in) W/C graphite
£3000 $5280   (7-Apr-92 C196/R) Study for 'Halt in Desert' (24x34cm-9x13in) pencil W/C htd white
£3080 $5883   (16-Jul-92 S150/R) Jewish woman of Gibraltar in festa dress (35x23cm-14x9in) W/C over pencil htd white
£8000 $14080   (9-Apr-92 S114/R) Spanish peasants (30x42cm-12x17in) W/C over pencil htd bodycol gum arabic
£8500 $15215   (12-Nov-91 C136/R) Study of an Arab Sheikh (28x20cm-11x8in) s. col.chks.W/C bodycol.htd.gum arabic

LEWIS, Lennard (1826-1913) British
£1000 $1850   (12-Jun-92 C34/R) Shelstone farmhouse near Gidleigh, Dartmoor (33x54cm-13x21in) s.i. pencil W/C

LEWIS, Martin (1883-1962) American
£3226 $5775   (14-Nov-91 GRO.B179/R) Spectators (53x38cm-21x15in) s. W/C

LEWIS, Percy Wyndham (1882-1957) British
£1200 $2196   (5-Jun-92 C65/R) Portrait of Bernard Rowland (28x21cm-11x8in) s.d.1921 pencil
£1900 $3477   (5-Jun-92 C60/R) Estelle with kerchiefed head (34x44cm-13x17in) s.d.1942 pencil crayon W/C
£3500 $6195   (7-Nov-91 C25/R) Crouching nude (28x25cm-11x10in) s.d.1919 pencil W/C
£3800 $6954   (5-Jun-92 C64/R) Portrait of artist's future wife, Froanna (49x35cm-19x14in) s.d.1922 pencil col.crayon W/C
£7500 $13725   (5-Jun-92 C63 a/R) Head of Ezra Pound (30x22cm-12x9in) init. crayon

LEWITT, Sol (1928-) American
£571 $1000   (28-Feb-92 SY.NY349/R) Untitled (25x25cm-10x10in) s.d.10/81 ink wash pencil
£1483 $2639   (29-Nov-91 F.F129/R) Composizione (28x28cm-11x11in) s.d.1987 gouache cardboard (I.L 3200000)
£1676 $3000   (6-May-92 SY.NY351/R) Grid eighth inch (41x41cm-16x16in) s.d.1971 ink
£2235 $4000   (12-Nov-91 CE.NY130/R) Irregular forms (38x55cm-15x22in) s.i.d.88 gouache
£2259 $4066   (19-Nov-91 FB.P236 a) Sans titre (45x55cm-18x22in) s.d.1985 ink gouache (F.FR 22000)
£2286 $4000   (25-Feb-92 SY.NY204/R) Untitled (34x50cm-13x20in) init. s.d.69verso ink
£2286 $4000   (25-Feb-92 SY.NY213/R) Untitled (28x28cm-11x11in) s.i. W/C pencil
£2570 $4600   (9-May-92 CE.NY294/R) Untitled s. one i.d.1989 one 90 gouache set of 3
£2682 $4800   (13-Nov-91 CH.NY222/R) Untitled (38x38cm-15x15in) s.d.Feb.10 1975 ink graphite
£3073 $5500   (7-May-92 SY.NY164/R) Blue lines from centre and red lines from lower left corner (50x50cm-20x20in) s.d.1975 ink pencil
£3073 $5500   (6-May-92 SY.NY356/R) Untitled (57x57cm-22x22in) s. brush ink
£3073 $5500   (6-May-92 SY.NY355/R) Untitled (57x57cm-22x22in) s. brush ink
£3631 $6500   (13-Nov-91 CH.NY219/R) Untitled (28x28cm-11x11in) s.d.1971 pen col.inks
£3659 $6366   (16-Apr-92 FB.P241/R) Sans titre (28x75cm-11x30in) s.d.11987 W/C crayon (F.FR 36000)
£3911 $7000   (13-Nov-91 CH.NY279/R) Untitled (56x56cm-22x22in) s.d.8/82 ink
£3911 $7000   (14-Nov-91 SY.NY158 a/R) Location of several lines (56x56cm-22x22in) s.d.1974 pencil ink
£3911 $7000   (14-Nov-91 SY.NY169/R) Lines from midpoint of lines (46x46cm-18x18in) s. ink on plastic
£7263 $13000   (14-Nov-91 SY.NY161/R) Wall drawing No.91 col.pencil
£13295 $23000   (3-Oct-91 SY.NY105/R) Wall Drawing no.99 col.pencil
£18436 $33000   (7-May-92 SY.NY152/R) Wall drawing No.12 - drawing series I 1-A and B and III 1-A and B (122x13cm-48x5in) black pencil four drawings two rows
£19553 $35000   (6-May-92 CH.NY363/R) Folding screen (183x383cm-72x151in) indian ink wash paper on board 2-sided 5 panel
£20112 $36000   (13-Nov-91 CH.NY191/R) Folding screen (183x382cm-72x150in) india ink wash paper mounted board five panels
£41899 $75000   (6-May-92 SY.NY51/R) Wall drawing no 1, drawing series II 18 A and B (122x122cm-48x48in) pencil two

LEWY, Kurt (1898-1963) Belgian
£1083	$1863	(12-Oct-91 KV.L186) Beach houses (50x65cm-20x26in) mono. (B.FR 65000)
£464	$839	(23-May-92 KV.L197) Composition (46x35cm-18x14in) mono.d.54 W/C chl. (B.FR 28000)
£535	$909	(22-Oct-91 C.A651) Composition (40x60cm-16x24in) mono. W/C (B.FR 32000)
£550	$1006	(3-Jun-92 L.K271) Abstract composition (65x50cm-26x20in) mono.d.1959 W/C (DM 1600)

LEXMOND, Johannes van (1769-1838) Dutch
| £1180 | $2101 | (25-Nov-91 CH.AM221/R) View of courtyard in city with maids cleaning (20x14cm-8x6in) s. pencil pen W/C (D.FL 3800) |

LEY, Hans Christian Clausen (1828-1875) Danish
| £1533 | $2729 | (25-Nov-91 BU.K7/R) View from the Royal stables (36x48cm-14x19in) s.d.1859 i.verso (D.KR 17000) |

LEY, S van der (19th C) Dutch
| £1300 | $2379 | (15-May-92 TE410/R) Street scene, Rotterdam (53x43cm-21x17in) s.i. panel |

LEYDEN, Aertgen van see CLAESZ, Aert

LEYDEN, Ernest van (1892-) Dutch
| £790 | $1375 | (17-Sep-91 CH.AM32) A landscape in Sicily (83x90cm-33x35in) s.i.d.24 (D.FL 2600) |
| £868 | $1554 | (15-Nov-91 KM.K512/R) Positive statement (110x120cm-43x47in) s.d.66 s.i.verso col.fabric cotton on canvas (DM 2500) |

LEYDEN, Lucas van (attrib) (1494-1538) Dutch
| £8811 | $15595 | (7-Nov-91 D.V121/R) Loth with his daughters (30x41cm-12x16in) panel (A.S 180000) |

LEYDEN, Lucas van (school) (1494-1538) Dutch
| £2222 | $4022 | (19-May-92 GF.L2345/R) Church interior with priest and parish members (75x52cm-30x20in) i. panel (S.FR 6000) |

LEYDEN, Lucas van (style) (1494-1538) Dutch
| £1888 | $3228 | (18-Mar-92 D.V281/R) Joseph interpreting the dreams of prisoners (33x77cm-13x30in) panel after Lucas van Leyden (A.S 38000) |

LEYEN, S van der (19th C) Dutch?
| £2600 | $4966 | (21-Jul-92 PH240/R) Figures in Dutch street scene (76x63cm-30x25in) s. panel |

LEYENDECKER, Joseph C (1874-1951) American
£730	$1300	(2-May-92 IH.NY35/R) Men in hats in profile, man's head in cameo (53x33cm-21x13in)
£798	$1500	(18-Dec-91 SY.NY206/R) Illustrative studies (61x81cm-24x32in) mono.
£843	$1500	(2-May-92 W.W125/R) Campers beside river (53x76cm-21x30in) mono.

LEYENDECKER, Mathias (1822-1871) French
| £1300 | $2249 | (4-Oct-91 C104/R) Thrush hanging from hook (35x22cm-14x9in) s.d.1869 |

LEYENDECKER, Paul Joseph (1842-?) French
| £3906 | $6914 | (5-Nov-91 GF.L2145/R) Southern landscape with figures (92x133cm-36x52in) (S.FR 10000) |

LEYMAN, A (1856-1933) British
| £750 | $1305 | (12-Sep-91 CSK77) Figures on road by cottages at Gittisham, near Honiton, Devon (36x53cm-14x21in) s. pencil W/C |

LEYMAN, Alfred (1856-1933) British
£800	$1368	(19-Mar-92 T208) Canal Banks, Exeter (25x51cm-10x20in) s.d.1890 W/C
£820	$1402	(19-Mar-92 T253) Kingswear looking towards Dartmouth (36x53cm-14x21in) s. W/C
£840	$1462	(13-Sep-91 MAX318/R) Rural village street with pony and trap and cattle (46x71cm-18x28in) s. W/C
£920	$1684	(6-Feb-92 T248) Dittisham, Devon (38x56cm-15x22in) s.d.1904 W/C
£1060	$1940	(6-Feb-92 T260/R) Gittisham, near Honiton (38x56cm-15x22in) s.d.1904 W/C
£1100	$1958	(29-Nov-91 T310/R) Stepcote Hill, Exeter (53x36cm-21x14in) s. W/C

LEYPOLD, Karl Julius von (1806-1874) German
| £1379 | $2372 | (16-Oct-91 KM.K1256) View of snow covered farmhouses (25x33cm-10x13in) mono. board on panel (DM 4000) |

LEYS, Baron Hendrik (1815-1869) Belgian
| £673 | $1211 | (30-Jan-92 RAS.V645) Town scene with figures by watermill (20x24cm-8x9in) s.d.1856 (D.KR 7500) |
| £4643 | $8498 | (12-May-92 C.A195/R) The letter (55x70cm-22x28in) s. panel (B.FR 280000) |

LEYSHORN-WHITE, Cyril (?) Australian?
| £661 | $1176 | (26-Nov-91 J.M730) Dandenong Ranges (18x27cm-7x11in) s. W/C (A.D 1500) |

LEYSING, Piet (1883-1933) German
| £2098 | $3629 | (25-Mar-92 KM.K188/R) Two work horses in shade of tree before farmhouse (80x122cm-31x48in) s. (DM 6000) |

LEYTENS, Gysbrecht see LYTENS, Gysbrecht

LEZAY-MARNESIA DE NETTANCOURT, Marie Claudine de (?-c.1793) French
£3000 $5340   (1-Nov-91 C65/R) Ruined castle on river (18x24cm-7x9in) s. panel

L'HAY, Michele-Eudes de (19th C) French
£511 $894   (23-Feb-92 I.N175) Bord de mer (39x56cm-15x22in) s.d.82 (F.FR 5000)

LHERMITTE, Leon (1844-1925) French
£6517	$11927	(5-Jun-92 D.P13/R) Les lavandieres (46x35cm-18x14in) s. (F.FR 64000)
£20571	$36000	(20-Feb-92 SY.NY17/R) Maternite (41x33cm-16x13in) s.
£23352	$42500	(28-May-92 SY.NY31/R) Jeune mere (55x41cm-22x16in) s.
£279070	$480000	(17-Oct-91 SY.NY17/R) La Fenaison - Haymakers (216x264cm-85x104in) s.d.1887
£409	$729	(27-Nov-91 BL.P134) Etude de moissonneuse pour La Moisson (32x49cm-13x19in) lead pencil (F.FR 4000)
£409	$729	(27-Nov-91 BL.P25) Vue d'une eglise bertonne (34x47cm-13x19in) bears st.init. lead pencil (F.FR 4000)
£430	$765	(27-Nov-91 BL.P66) Pecheur breton (32x47cm-13x19in) bears st.init. lead pencil (F.FR 4200)
£430	$765	(27-Nov-91 BL.P89) Breton a genoux (47x30cm-19x12in) bears st.init. lead pencil (F.FR 4200)
£430	$765	(27-Nov-91 BL.P64) Berton a genoux (30x47cm-12x19in) bears st.init. lead pencil (F.FR 4200)
£461	$820	(27-Nov-91 BL.P86) Etude pour Le Pardon de Ploumanach (45x30cm-18x12in) bears st.init. lead pencil (F.FR 4500)
£461	$820	(27-Nov-91 BL.P75) Etude pour le Marche de Chateau-Thierry (30x46cm-12x18in) bears st.init. blk.crayon (F.FR 4500)
£491	$875	(27-Nov-91 BL.P94) Etude pour Le Pardon de Ploumanach (46x31cm-18x12in) bears st.init. lead pencil (F.FR 4800)
£512	$911	(27-Nov-91 BL.P87) Etude pour le Pardon de Ploumanach (46x30cm-18x12in) bears st.init. lead pencil htd.white chk. (F.FR 5000)
£512	$911	(27-Nov-91 BL.P56) Interieur de l'Eglise de Pont-Christ (31x42cm-12x17in) bears st.init. chl.lead pencil htd.white chk. (F.FR 5000)
£512	$911	(27-Nov-91 BL.P27/R) Interieur de l'eglise St Meleine a Morlaix (31x47cm-12x19in) st.init. chl. (F.FR 5000)
£512	$911	(27-Nov-91 BL.P160) Etude pour Le Repos (25x23cm-10x9in) init. chl. (F.FR 5000)
£532	$947	(27-Nov-91 BL.P150) Repos des faneurs ou moissonneurs (25x36cm-10x14in) st.init. chl. (F.FR 5200)
£563	$1002	(27-Nov-91 BL.P54) Vue de la Place St Thomas de Cantorbery de Landerneau (23x42cm-9x17in) bears st.init. lead pencil (F.FR 5500)
£584	$993	(25-Oct-91 AT.P104) Paysan vu de trois-quarts vers la gauche (32x24cm-13x9in) mono. pastel (F.FR 5800)
£716	$1275	(27-Nov-91 BL.P34/R) Tour Landerneau de St Thomas de Cantorbery a Landerneau (49x32cm-19x13in) bears st.init. blk.crayon (F.FR 7000)
£747	$1330	(27-Nov-91 BL.P84/R) Breton agenouille (32x47cm-13x19in) bears st.init. crayon (F.FR 7300)
£768	$1366	(27-Nov-91 BL.P100) Etude pour le portrait d'Amaury-Duval (30x23cm-12x9in) bears st.init. lead pencil htd.white chk. (F.FR 7500)
£811	$1467	(22-May-92 BL.P79/R) Enfant dormant (31x48cm-12x19in) studio st. pencil dr htd white chk (F.FR 8000)
£819	$1458	(27-Nov-91 BL.P82/R) Etude pour le Pardon de Ploumanach (47x31cm-19x12in) bears st.init. lead pencil htd.white chk. (F.FR 8000)
£901	$1603	(27-Nov-91 BL.P70) Pecheurs (46x63cm-18x25in) bears st.init. chl. (F.FR 8800)
£1800	$3204	(27-Nov-91 S212/R) Portrait of old woman (59x43cm-23x17in) s. chl
£2000	$3500	(20-Feb-92 SY.NY137/R) Les faucheurs (25x32cm-10x13in) s. pastel
£2559	$4555	(27-Nov-91 BL.P14/R) Etude pour Le Pelerinage a la Vierge du Pilier (32x51cm-13x20in) st.init. chl.htd.white chk. (F.FR 25000)
£2809	$5000	(28-Apr-92 PO.BA16) Paisajes (54x65cm-21x26in) s. pastel board two
£2866	$5101	(27-Nov-91 BL.P91/R) Etude pour Le Pardon de Ploumanach (47x62cm-19x24in) bears st.init. chl. (F.FR 28000)
£2907	$5000	(16-Oct-91 CH.NY84/R) Portrait of a young girl. Head study (31x24cm-12x9in) s. pastel ink chk. double-sided
£3153	$5611	(27-Nov-91 BL.P123/R) Souper le soir en famille (34x47cm-13x19in) s. chl. (F.FR 30800)
£3714	$6500	(20-Feb-92 SY.NY132/R) Le repas dans la cuisine (40x46cm-16x18in) s. chl
£3779	$6500	(16-Oct-91 CH.NY85/R) Rue a Arachon (33x25cm-13x10in) s. pastel paper laid on board
£3992	$7105	(27-Nov-91 BL.P50/R) Portrait d'Amedee Jullien (60x48cm-24x19in) bears st.init. chl. (F.FR 39000)
£4429	$7750	(20-Feb-92 SY.NY134/R) L'Hyeurette, deux pecheurs (44x34cm-17x13in) s. pastel
£4606	$8199	(27-Nov-91 BL.P20/R) Esquisse de tableau - Chez les humbles (28x25cm-11x10in) s.i. pastel paper laid down on canvas (F.FR 45000)
£4913	$8745	(27-Nov-91 BL.P165/R) Tisserand et ses filles a Laren (34x50cm-13x20in) s. chl. (F.FR 48000)
£6977	$12000	(17-Oct-91 SY.NY21/R) Le chateau d'Armentieres sur Ourcq (32x40cm-13x16in) s. pastel
£7429	$13000	(20-Feb-92 SY.NY23/R) Fenaison (37x28cm-15x11in) s. brown crayon conte crayon
£8571	$15000	(20-Feb-92 SY.NY18/R) Glaneuses (34x44cm-13x17in) s. pastel
£9091	$16091	(22-Apr-92 CH.AM310/R) Les Dentellieres (34x40cm-13x16in) s. i.verso pastel (D.FL 30000)

LHERMITTE, Leon (1844-1925) French-cont.
£13953 $24000   (16-Oct-91 CH.NY86/R) Paysanne dans un champ de ble (30x46cm-12x18in) s. pastel paper laid down on canvas
£16484 $30000   (27-May-92 CH.NY202/R) Le Soir au jardin a Charteves (44x57cm-17x22in) s.d.1893 pastel

L'HOEST, Engelbert (1919-) Dutch
£1212 $2194   (19-May-92 CH.AM362/R) Landscape (70x59cm-28x23in) s. board (D.FL 4000)

LHOMME, Damien (circle) (17th C) French?
£5301 $9859   (20-Jun-92 CH.MO56/R) Vanite (35x49cm-14x19in) (F.FR 52000)

LHOTE, Andre (1885-1962) French
£2567 $4620   (20-Nov-91 CN.P191/R) Portrait de femme (16x13cm-6x5in) s. panel (F.FR 25000)
£4107 $7392   (19-Nov-91 FB.P24/R) Vallee du Rhone, vue sur le Teil (38x46cm-15x18in) s. (F.FR 40000)
£4771 $8492   (28-Nov-91 BU.S100/R) Spring landscape (48x60cm-19x24in) s. panel (S.KR 50000)
£5857 $10250   (25-Feb-92 SY.NY22/R) Village en automne (36x50cm-14x20in) s.
£6256 $10761   (20-Oct-91 I.N160/R) Femme assise (33x23cm-13x9in) board (F.FR 62000)
£7104 $13000   (14-May-92 SY.NY273/R) Paysage (36x51cm-14x20in) s.
£7650 $14000   (13-May-92 CH.NY219/R) Trois femmes dans un paysage (47x61cm-19x24in) s. paper on board
£7700 $13860   (20-Nov-91 CN.P190/R) Nu accroupi (38x46cm-15x18in) s. i.d.1930verso (F.FR 75000)
£8500 $16235   (30-Jun-92 C132/R) Le village (72x91cm-28x36in) s.
£10000 $17200   (16-Oct-91 S51/R) Personnages dans un paysage (49x64cm-19x25in) s.
£10000 $18100   (20-May-92 GK.Z5054/R) Woman knitting (73x60cm-29x24in) s.d.1922 (S.FR 27000)
£10571 $18500   (25-Feb-92 CH.NY71/R) Paysage (51x61cm-20x24in) s.
£11000 $21010   (30-Jun-92 C133/R) Paysage du Bassin d'Arcachon (60x74cm-24x29in) s.
£11429 $20000   (25-Feb-92 CH.NY63/R) Maison a travers les arbres (54x65cm-21x26in) s. burlap
£12994 $23000   (6-Nov-91 CH.NY294/R) Voilier a Bordeaux (41x60cm-16x24in) s.
£14374 $25873   (22-Nov-91 PIC.P25/R) La Baignade (54x81cm-21x32in) s. (F.FR 140000)
£15000 $25800   (16-Oct-91 S106/R) Nu a la psyche (72x59cm-28x23in) s.
£17000 $29410   (25-Mar-92 S35/R) Le jardin (65x48cm-26x19in) s.
£18424 $32794   (28-Nov-91 FB.P47/R) Nature morte a la theiere et a la bouteille de suze (50x63cm-20x25in) s. Arche paper laid down on canvas (F.FR 180000)
£19447 $34616   (28-Nov-91 FB.P11/R) Composition a la bouteille et au pichet (35x27cm-14x11in) s. (F.FR 190000)
£407 $745   (17-May-92 T.B264/R) Marin de dos (31x20cm-12x8in) s. chl (F.FR 4000)
£463 $880   (28-Jun-92 FE.P7) Nu assis (20x14cm-8x6in) s. dr (F.FR 4500)
£511 $936   (5-Feb-92 FB.P171) Meules a Mirmande (22x28cm-9x11in) bears st.sig. Indian ink (F.FR 5000)
£748 $1293   (25-Mar-92 A.D118/R) Art Ancien (28x38cm-11x15in) s. W/C (E.P 800)
£813 $1415   (19-Apr-92 ZZ.F45) Femme nue debout (30x19cm-12x7in) s. crayon dr. (F.FR 8000)
£1469 $2659   (20-May-92 I.N144) Interieur (28x38cm-11x15in) s. W/C (F.FR 14500)
£1543 $2932   (24-Jun-92 GL.P172/R) Nu assis (39x30cm-15x12in) s.d.1935 gouache (F.FR 15000)
£1543 $2793   (6-Dec-91 GL.P160/R) La fenetre ouverte (32x24cm-13x9in) s. W/C (F.FR 15000)
£1561 $2732   (5-Apr-92 ZZ.F214/R) Portrait de Jean Cocteau (26x20cm-10x8in) s. Indian ink dr (F.FR 15000)
£1561 $2732   (5-Apr-92 ZZ.F146/R) Nu en buste de profil (60x47cm-24x19in) s. pastel (F.FR 15000)
£1665 $2914   (5-Apr-92 ZZ.F192/R) Scene d'interieur (29x38cm-11x15in) s. W/C (F.FR 16000)
£1665 $2914   (5-Apr-92 ZZ.F207/R) Paysage des Alpilles (23x35cm-9x14in) s. pastel (F.FR 16000)
£1717 $3039   (22-Apr-92 ZZ.F58) Le Picquay (24x36cm-9x14in) s.d.1938 pen dr. (F.FR 17000)
£1769 $3096   (5-Apr-92 ZZ.F169/R) Le bois de sapin (39x28cm-15x11in) s. W/C (F.FR 17000)
£2542 $4500   (5-Nov-91 CE.NY40/R) Le village (27x39cm-11x15in) s. gouache W/C paper on board
£2542 $4500   (5-Nov-91 CE.NY78/R) Paysage (29x39cm-11x15in) s. gouache W/C paper on board
£2758 $4826   (23-Feb-92 I.N98/R) Paysage au clocher (20x29cm-8x11in) s. W/C (F.FR 27000)
£3018 $5191   (8-Oct-91 CC.P7/R) Paysage (29x38cm-11x15in) s. W/C (F.FR 30000)
£3498 $6646   (24-Jun-92 GL.P174/R) Arbres (31x24cm-12x9in) st.sig. W/C (F.FR 34000)
£8354 $14202   (22-Oct-91 C.A226/R) Cubistic landscape (47x64cm-19x25in) s. pastel (B.FR 500000)

L'HUILLIER, Jacques (1867-?) French
£5495 $10000   (28-May-92 SY.NY150/R) Soleil levant sur la Seine (109x208cm-43x82in) s.

LHUILLIER, Suzanne see PERREGAUX, Suzanne

LI CHE-FAN (1907-1989) Chinese
£5563 $9513   (22-Mar-92 SY.TA27/R) Roses (39x27cm-15x11in) s.d.1984 W/C (T.D 242000)

LI FANGYING (1696-1755) Chinese
£2684 $4750   (7-Nov-91 B.SF1252/R) Banana tree, bamboo and rock (112x48cm-44x19in) s. ink scroll

LI HUASHENG (1944-) Chinese
£480 $850   (7-Nov-91 B.SF1239/R) Country landscape (67x68cm-26x27in) s.i. ink colour scroll
£847 $1500   (7-Nov-91 B.SF1238/R) Landscape with cormorant fishermen (135x67cm-53x26in) s.d.1982 ink colour scroll
£904 $1600   (7-Nov-91 B.SF1209/R) Landscape with figure (150x82cm-59x32in) s.d.1984 ink colour scroll

LI KERAN (1907-1989) Chinese
£1412 $2500   (7-Nov-91 B.SF1216/R) Herdboys and water buffaloes (68x45cm-27x18in) s. ink colour
£1977 $3500   (7-Nov-91 B.SF1253/R) Chong mountain range (41x59cm-16x23in) ink colour
£4438 $7766   (30-Mar-92 CH.HK133/R) Buffalo in springtime (68x45cm-27x18in) s.i.d.1982 ink W/C hanging scroll (HK.D 60000)
£5917 $10355   (30-Mar-92 CH.HK132/R) Old man seated beneath Wisteria vines (50x37cm-20x15in) s.i.d.1946 ink W/C scroll (HK.D 80000)
£8136 $14238   (30-Mar-92 CH.HK134/R) Laughing monk (68x45cm-27x18in) s.i.d.1984 ink W/C hanging scroll (HK.D 110000)
£11834 $20710   (30-Mar-92 CH.HK261/R) Morning in mountains (33x30cm-13x12in) i. ink W/C scroll (HK.D 160000)
£16272 $28476   (30-Mar-92 CH.HK136/R) Mountains of Li Jiang (68x81cm-27x32in) s.i.d.1979 ink W/C hanging scroll (HK.D 220000)
£33284 $58247   (30-Mar-92 CH.HK262/R) Landscape after rain (68x95cm-27x37in) s.i.d.1984 ink W/C scroll (HK.D 450000)

LI KUCHAN (1898-1983) Chinese
£3955 $7000   (7-Nov-91 B.SF1208/R) Pair of eagles (175x93cm-69x37in) s.d.1978 ink colour scroll

LI MEI-SHU (1902-1983) Chinese
£88506 $151345   (22-Mar-92 SY.TA62/R) San-Hsia landscape (50x65cm-20x26in) (T.D 3850000)

LI SHIH-CHIAO (1908-) Chinese
£70805 $121076   (22-Mar-92 SY.TA50/R) View of old postal building (74x77cm-29x30in) s.d.1958 board (T.D 3080000)
£91034 $155669   (22-Mar-92 SY.TA25/R) Green lake (65x80cm-26x31in) s.d.1981 (T.D 3960000)

LI YONGSEN (1898-?) Chinese
£5310 $9081   (22-Mar-92 SY.TA56/R) Scenes of France (26x34cm-10x13in) one s.verso board pair (T.D 231000)

LIADOVSKII, Nikolai (1923-) Russian
£1722 $3118   (20-May-92 ARC.P104/R) Les voiliers (60x70cm-24x28in) s. (F.FR 17000)

LIANI, Francesco (1712-1780) Italian
£14388 $25899   (19-Nov-91 F.R167/R) Ritratto della Marchesa di Campolattaro Blanch. Ritratto del marchese (100x72cm-39x28in) oval pair (I.L 31000000)

LIAO CHI-CHUN (1902-1976) Chinese
£136552 $233503   (22-Mar-92 SY.TA41/R) Still life in blue (61x73cm-24x29in) s. (T.D 5940000)
£161839 $276745   (22-Mar-92 SY.TA66/R) Kuei-Shan Island (72x91cm-28x36in) s. (T.D 7040000)

LIAUSU, Camille (1894-1975) French
£988 $1709   (6-Oct-91 LT.P3/R) Le modele nu a la source (65x40cm-26x16in) s. panel (F.FR 9800)
£403 $698   (6-Oct-91 LT.P8) La chaise longue (30x26cm-12x10in) s. W/C ink (F.FR 4000)
£554 $959   (6-Oct-91 LT.P7/R) Le toreador (91x63cm-36x25in) s. gouache (F.FR 5500)
£696 $1203   (6-Oct-91 LT.P9) Nu parmi les fleurs (38x27cm-15x11in) s.d.1930 gouache (F.FR 6900)

LIBALT, Gottfried (fl.1649-1666) Dutch
£1450 $2596   (7-May-92 CH.AM11/R) Gentlemen playing at cards in forest, valley beyond (72x98cm-28x39in) s.d.1656 (D.FL 4800)

LIBERA, Giovanni Battista della (1826-1886) Italian
£460 $842   (5-Feb-92 ZZ.B219) Cathedral interior (53x41cm-21x16in) s. W/C bodycol

LIBERI, Marco (1640-1687) Italian
£9761 $17667   (5-Dec-91 F.M57/R) Venere e la Pace disarmano Cupido (95x205cm-37x81in) (I.L 21000000)

LIBERI, Pietro (1614-1687) Italian
£19553 $35000   (17-Jan-92 SY.NY138/R) Allegory of the constancy of love (117x154cm-46x61in)
£22099 $40000   (21-May-92 CH.NY32/R) Allegory of Prudence (91x77cm-36x30in)
£61792 $116169   (18-Dec-91 AT.P13/R) Le Temps enchainant la Beaute (201x150cm-79x59in) (F.FR 600000)
£1000 $1920   (9-Jul-92 B1/R) Interior of Foundling's Hospital (16x26cm-6x10in) bears i. pen wash

LIBERI, Pietro (attrib) (1614-1687) Italian
£2941 $5000   (23-Oct-91 GD.B1145/R) Allegory of sculpture (96x72cm-38x28in)
          (S.FR 7500)
£5295 $9637   (11-Dec-91 LD.P42/R) Saint Antoine repoussant la tentation
          (80x100cm-31x39in) (F.FR 52000)
£13903 $23774   (20-Mar-92 ZZ.F29/R) Allegorie de la fortune (132x172cm-52x68in)
          (F.FR 135000)

LIBERI, Pietro (circle) (1614-1687) Italian
£6077 $11000   (21-May-92 CH.NY99/R) Decorative frieze (110x243cm-43x96in)

LIBERI, Pietro (school) (1614-1687) Italian
£1485 $2673   (19-Nov-91 F.R41) Venere e putto (71x55cm-28x22in) (I.L 3200000)

LIBERI, Pietro (style) (1614-1687) Italian
£7200 $12816   (1-Nov-91 C51/R) Personification of Vanity (126x194cm-50x76in)

LIBERT, G E (1820-1908) Danish
£705 $1256   (28-Apr-92 RAS.K493) Coastal landscape, Mons Klint (25x36cm-10x14in)
          s.d.55 (D.KR 8000)
£1761 $2958   (27-Aug-91 RAS.K122/R) Norwegian mountainous landscape with waterfall
          (91x134cm-36x53in) s.d.1840 (D.KR 20000)
£2817 $4732   (27-Aug-91 RAS.K247/R) Landscape from Heidelberg (50x75cm-20x30in) s.
          (D.KR 32000)

LIBERT, Georg Emil (1820-1908) Danish
£612 $1064   (14-Apr-92 SY.AM207/R) The Hardangerfjorden (91x130cm-36x51in) s.
          (D.FL 2000)
£628 $1112   (11-Feb-92 RAS.K16/R) Coastal landscape with sunset over Kullen
          (100x155cm-39x61in) s.d.1880 (D.KR 7000)
£628 $1112   (11-Feb-92 RAS.K223) Moonlit coastal cliffs (30x23cm-12x9in) s.
          (D.KR 7000)
£718 $1271   (11-Feb-92 RAS.K221/R) View of Sundet from a balcony (39x59cm-15x23in)
          s.d.86 (D.KR 8000)
£1354 $2315   (12-Mar-92 RAS.V936/R) Sunset near Kullen (100x155cm-39x61in) s.d.1880
          (D.KR 15000)
£1700 $3026   (27-Nov-91 S57/R) Fishing on fjord (90x133cm-35x52in) s.d.1846
£1805 $3249   (19-Nov-91 RAS.K184/R) Dutch canal landscape with mills, winter
          (79x115cm-31x45in) s. (D.KR 20000)
£2373 $4247   (6-May-92 KH.K119/R) From Heidelberg Palace and town seen from Road to
          Wolfsbrunnen (47x64cm-19x25in) s.d.59 (D.KR 27000)
£4225 $7648   (3-Dec-91 FN.S2306/R) View of Heidelberg with figures (49x74cm-19x29in)
          s. (DM 12000)

LIBERTI, F (17th C) Italian
£4070 $7000   (9-Oct-91 CH.NY188/R) Putti frolicking among garlands of flowers in park
          (51x59cm-20x23in) s.indist.d.

LIBERTS, Ludolfs (1895-1945) Russian
£877 $1579   (23-Nov-91 N.M187/R) Paris at night with Champs Elysees (64x90cm-25x35in)
          s. board (DM 2500)
£2793 $5000   (13-Nov-91 B.SF2343/R) Paris street scene at night (89x60cm-35x24in) s.

LICATA, Riccardo (1929-) Italian
£556 $990   (29-Nov-91 F.F67/R) Paesaggio (8x9cm-3x4in) s.d.1959 board (I.L 1200000)
£1382 $2515   (9-Dec-91 CH.R30/R) Composizione (81x65cm-32x26in) s. egg tempera
          (I.L 3000000)
*£817 $1455   (29-Apr-92 F.F88/R) Primavera (33x33cm-13x13in) s.d.1987 mixed media
          board (I.L 1800000)*
*£908 $1616   (29-Apr-92 F.F87) Senza titolo (27x37cm-11x15in) d.1967 mixed media
          (I.L 2000000)*

LICHERIE, Louis (attrib) (1629-1687) French
£2551 $4515   (10-Feb-92 GL.P6/R) Deux prophetes sur fond de paysage (58x29cm-23x11in)
          panel pair (F.FR 25000)
£3229 $5554   (16-Oct-91 AT.P93/R) La Naissance de la Vierge (130x163cm-51x64in)
          (F.FR 32000)

LICHT, Hans (1876-1935) German
£699 $1245   (30-Nov-91 VG.B828/R) Wooded landscape (51x63cm-20x25in) s.i. board
          (DM 2000)
£825 $1534   (20-Jun-92 BM.B946/R) Landscape before rain (66x87cm-26x34in) s. i.verso
          board (DM 2400)

LICHTENSTEIN, Roy (1923-) American
*£1852 $3352   (2-Dec-91 CC.P58/R) Seascape (31x41cm-12x16in) s.d.67 serigraph collage
          (F.FR 18000)*
*£3955 $7000   (6-Nov-91 D.NY6/R) Landscape (35x53cm-14x21in) s.d.1965verso mixed media
          cardboard*
*£8671 $15000   (3-Oct-91 SY.NY63/R) Landscape (38x51cm-15x20in) s.d.1965verso mixed
          media paper plastic collage*
*£11173 $20000   (13-Nov-91 CH.NY167/R) Untitled (72x56cm-28x22in) s.verso rowlux magna
          board*
*£13408 $24000   (12-Nov-91 CH.NY16/R) Study for drawing (14x14cm-6x6in) init.d.64
          graphite col.pencils*

LICHTENSTEIN, Roy (1923-) American-cont.

£14525	$26000	(6-May-92 CH.NY309/R) Study for modern painting with sun rays (10x15cm-4x6in) init. graphite col.pencil
£45714	$80000	(27-Feb-92 CH.NY26/R) Ohh ... alright (15x15cm-6x6in) s.d.1964verso col.crayons graphite
£50279	$90000	(6-May-92 CH.NY306/R) Study for sweet dreams, baby (14x13cm-6x5in) init. graphite col.felt-tip pen col.pencil
£111732	$200000	(14-Nov-91 SY.NY372 a/R) Path through forest (102x127cm-40x50in) s.d.84 verso oil magna canvas
£279330	$500000	(13-Nov-91 SY.NY53/R) In deep thought (127x152cm-50x60in) s.d.80 verso oil magna canvas
£474860	$850000	(13-Nov-91 SY.NY46/R) Non objective I (142x122cm-56x48in) magna canvas

LICINI, Osvaldo (1894-1958) Italian

£4972	$9000	(21-May-92 F.M166/R) Composizione (17x26cm-7x10in) pencil (I.L 11000000)

LICINIO, Bernardino (attrib) (1489-1565) Italian

£4070	$7000	(10-Oct-91 SY.NY12/R) Portrait of a man holding gloves (86x64cm-34x25in)

LICINIO, Bernardino (style) (1489-1565) Italian

£3254	$5889	(4-Dec-91 CH.R100) Ritratto di giovanne donna (39x33cm-15x13in) panel (I.L 7000000)

LICK, Armand van der (1897-1985) Belgian?

£4003	$7046	(7-Apr-92 C.A249/R) Young woman by the sea (107x123cm-42x48in) s. (B.FR 240000)

LICOURT, Paul (19th C) French

£706	$1200	(23-Oct-91 GD.B1147/R) Farmstead by edge of wood (27x35cm-11x14in) s. (S.FR 1800)

LIDBERG, Sven (1929-1985) Swedish

£565	$1006	(28-Oct-91 AB.S123) Elderly couple in garden (53x44cm-21x17in) s. panel (S.KR 6000)

LIDDERDALE (1831-1895) British

£600	$1098	(5-Jun-92 BW427) Portrait study of your lady (91x71cm-36x28in) mono.

LIDDERDALE, Charles Sillem (1831-1895) British

£500	$960	(29-Jul-92 CSK295) A country girl (31x25cm-12x10in) mono. board
£900	$1548	(11-Oct-91 C66/R) Una senorita (47x39cm-19x15in) init.d.70
£2000	$3440	(4-Mar-92 S120/R) Rustic beauty (51x40cm-20x16in) mono.
£4587	$8394	(3-Jun-92 R.T151/R) Country girl in forest (70x46cm-28x18in) mono.d.85 (C.D 10000)
£480	$888	(10-Jun-92 HAR414) Portrait of girl in yellow headscarf and blue beads (53x41cm-21x16in) init. W/C
£2050	$3547	(25-Mar-92 AH169) Portrait of young lady (43x36cm-17x14in) W/C

LIE, Edvarda (1910-1983) Norwegian

£878	$1510	(7-Oct-91 B.O85/R) Woman and lamb (57x63cm-22x25in) init.d.48 (N.KR 10000)
£3336	$5738	(7-Oct-91 B.O84/R) Interior with three women (100x150cm-39x59in) init.d.53 (N.KR 38000)

LIE, Jonas (1880-1940) American

£838	$1500	(13-Nov-91 B.SF2642/R) Windswept trees (76x64cm-30x25in) s.
£1620	$2900	(6-May-92 P.44/R) At landing (30x41cm-12x16in) s.
£3488	$6000	(13-Oct-91 H.C5/R) Northern Hills (25x36cm-10x14in) s. board
£3801	$6500	(12-Mar-92 CH.NY179/R) Safe harbour (91x76cm-36x30in) s.

LIE-JORGENSEN, Thorbjorn (1900-1961) Norwegian

£658	$1224	(15-Jun-92 B.O101/R) Boat harbour, Hellnes Island (35x50cm-14x20in) s.d.1948 panel (N.KR 7500)

LIEBER, Edvard (1948-) American

£1061	$1900	(9-May-92 CE.NY257/R) Point, John Cage playing chess (41x51cm-16x20in) s.d.1980verso ink gouache graphite

LIEBERMANN, Ernst (1869-?) German

£586	$1038	(6-Nov-91 N.M1083/R) Woman resting in landscape (100x120cm-39x47in) s.i. (DM 1700)
£702	$1200	(13-Mar-92 FN.S2851) Nude girl seated (50x40cm-20x16in) s.i. board (DM 2000)

LIEBERMANN, Max (1847-1935) German

£3515	$6398	(25-May-92 WK.M784/R) Portrait Dr Julius Elias (43x37cm-17x15in) s.d.1920 (DM 10300)
£5000	$8900	(1-Nov-91 PO.BA24) Figura femenina (70x90cm-28x35in) s.
£6667	$12000	(23-Nov-91 N.M188/R) Portrait of gentleman with cigar (111x84cm-44x33in) s.d.1924 (DM 19000)
£26163	$45000	(17-Oct-91 SY.NY132/R) Konzert in der Berliner Oper (42x51cm-17x20in) s.d.1921 panel
£31359	$57073	(11-Dec-91 WE.MU259/R) Field workers resting (34x45cm-13x18in) s. panel (DM 90000)

LIEBERMANN, Max (1847-1935) German-cont.

£54608	$99386	(29-May-92 VG.B6/R) Attending church in Laren, Sunday afternoon (46x75cm-18x30in) s.d.1894 i.verso (DM 160000)
£62937	$112028	(29-Nov-91 VG.B3/R) Children playing - the siblings (37x5cm-15x2in) (DM 180000)
£80420	$143147	(29-Nov-91 VG.B4/R) Idyllic village scene (43x60cm-17x24in) s.d.1879 panel (DM 230000)
£94286	$165000	(26-Sep-91 SY.I7/R) House and garden (59x71cm-23x28in) s.
£476	$852	(5-May-92 ZEL.L1156/R) Orchard (19x30cm-7x12in) s. chl (DM 1400)
£478	$865	(23-May-92 GB.B6827) Man reading seated on chair (17x12cm-7x5in) s. pen chk (DM 1400)
£1365	$2471	(23-May-92 GB.B6825/R) Children and woman on beach (12x19cm-5x7in) s. chl (DM 4000)
£1965	$3537	(22-Nov-91 SA.A410/R) Portrait of man smoking pipe (14x13cm-6x5in) s. pencil (DM 5600)
£2372	$4246	(6-May-92 GD.B770/R) Woodland interior (16x10cm-6x4in) s. pastel (S.FR 6500)
£2538	$4823	(25-Jun-92 GK.B446 a) Two women in yard with stairs (32x25cm-13x10in) s. chl (S.FR 6600)
£3509	$6316	(21-Nov-91 L.K282/R) Landscape near Nordwyk (12x17cm-5x7in) s. pencil (DM 10000)
£4571	$8000	(19-Feb-92 CH.NY77/R) Children playing at beach (30x36cm-12x14in) s. W/C over pencil
£4895	$8713	(30-Nov-91 VG.B142/R) Dutch canal landscape (12x19cm-5x7in) s. chl chk (DM 14000)
£5000	$9500	(25-Jun-92 GK.B446/R) View of Dutch canal with farmhouses and windmill (28x45cm-11x18in) s. chk (S.FR 13000)
£5286	$9250	(20-Feb-92 SY.NY238/R) Das Meer (29x36cm-11x14in) s. W/C
£6857	$12000	(20-Feb-92 SY.NY239/R) Unter den baumen (11x17cm-4x7in) s. pastel
£8000	$14000	(19-Feb-92 CH.NY76/R) Self-portrait of artist in studio. Study of trees (23x30cm-9x12in) s. W/C htd wht over pencil blk chk double-sided
£9898	$18014	(25-May-92 WK.M785/R) Jungfernstieg in Hamburg (26x35cm-10x14in) s. chk (DM 29000)
£10385	$19731	(25-Jun-92 GK.B447/R) Riders on beach (12x19cm-5x7in) s. pastel (S.FR 27000)
£19113	$34785	(30-May-92 VG.B132/R) Rowing boat (23x30cm-9x12in) s. pastel (DM 56000)
£23368	$43230	(12-Jun-92 HN.H525/R) Wannsee landscape (24x29cm-9x11in) s. pastel (DM 68000)

LIEBERS, A (?) American?

£3488	$6000	(20-Oct-91 HG.C55) Flowered hat (64x48cm-25x19in) s.

LIEDER, Franz (1780-1859) Austrian

£900	$1728	(8-Jul-92 PH108/R) Seated lady and child in elegant setting on balcony, view of town (24x19cm-9x7in) s. gouache gum arabic vellum

LIEGE SCHOOL (?) Belgian

£4124	$7175	(17-Sep-91 FN.S2631/R) Maria Lactans nursing Jesus (16x11cm-6x4in) c.1500 panel arched top (DM 12000)

LIEGOIS, Paul (attrib) (17th C) French?

£4733	$8992	(26-Jun-92 AT.P87/R) Nature morte de peches sur un entablement de marbre (19x24cm-7x9in) panel (F.FR 46000)

LIENDER, Jacobus van (1696-1759) Flemish

£559	$995	(25-Nov-91 CH.AM201 a) Hilly wooded landscape with castle (11x18cm-4x7in) pen W/C (D.FL 1800)

LIENDER, Paul van (1731-1797) Dutch

£2795	$4975	(25-Nov-91 CH.AM203/R) View of church by square in town (22x27cm-9x11in) s.d.1777 pen W/C (D.FL 9000)
£4348	$7739	(25-Nov-91 CH.AM202 a/R) View of the Oude Kerk, Amsterdam from the Enge Kerksteeg (22x18cm-9x7in) init. pen W/C (D.FL 14000)

LIER, Adolf (1826-1882) German

£1568	$2854	(11-Dec-91 N.M508/R) Young Dachau woman with rake and water jug in flowering meadow (32x24cm-13x9in) s.d.1869 (DM 4500)

LIER, Adolf (attrib) (1826-1882) German

£697	$1268	(11-Dec-91 N.M510) Mountainous lake landscape with traveller and peasant woman (32x41cm-13x16in) mono. (DM 2000)
£767	$1395	(11-Dec-91 N.M509/R) Hay harvest in alpine landscape (21x44cm-8x17in) s.i. canvas on board (DM 2200)

LIESEGANG, Helmut (1858-1945) German

£2273	$3932	(25-Mar-92 KM.K1290/R) Dordrecht harbour scene (64x52cm-25x20in) s. (DM 6500)
£2273	$3932	(25-Mar-92 KM.K1291) Shepherd and flock in landscape (30x40cm-12x16in) s. (DM 6500)
£2405	$4474	(20-Jun-92 BM.B858/R) Dutch coastal landscape with peasant women working (40x50cm-16x20in) s. (DM 7000)

LIESLER, Josef (1912-) Czechoslovakian?

£1192	$2121	(29-Nov-91 D.V161/R) Fast eine Geburt des Phonix (46x55cm-18x22in) s.d.83 panel (A.S 24000)

LIESTE, Cornelis (1817-1861) Dutch
£2446 $4330   (5-Nov-91 SY.AM91/R) Little girl on heath (55x78cm-22x31in) s. panel
(D.FL 8000)

LIEVENS, Jan (after) (1607-1674) Dutch
£1235 $2210   (14-Nov-91 CH.AM80/R) Portrait of Admiral Maerten Harpertsz Tromp
standing, naval scene beyond (39x33cm-15x13in) panel (D.FL 4000)

LIEVENS, Jan (circle) (1607-1674) Dutch
£2500 $4450   (29-Oct-91 PH72/R) The sacrifice of Isaac (208x169cm-82x67in)
£726   *$1300*   *(15-Jan-92 CH.NY140) Wooded river landscape with church and other
buildings (14x34cm-6x13in) with i.verso black chk pen*

LIEVIN (19th C) French
£1221 $2234   (13-May-92 LC.P29) Vapeurs le long des quais (43x65cm-17x26in) s.
(F.FR 12000)

LIEVIN, Jacques (1850-?) French
£1022 $1820   (26-Jan-92 FE.P223) Paysage fermier (46x33cm-18x13in) s. (F.FR 10000)
£1041 $1821   (5-Apr-92 ZZ.F79/R) Paysannes au bord de la route (32x46cm-13x18in) s.
(F.FR 10000)
£1639 $2951   (2-Feb-92 ZZ.F55/R) Grange et village sous un ciel d'ete
(39x64cm-15x25in) s. (F.FR 16000)
£5827 $10198   (5-Apr-92 CSC.P82/R) Paysage a l'etang (65x100cm-26x39in) s.d.91
(F.FR 56000)
£2058   *$3909*   *(22-Jun-92 AT.P72/R) Paris, Place Clichy (18x30cm-7x12in) s. gouache
(F.FR 20000)*

LIEVRE, Lucien (1878-?) French
£1461 $2600   (2-May-92 W.W23/R) Dock scene in Holland s.

LIEZEN-MAYER, Alexander von (1839-1898) Austrian
£800 $1368   (19-Mar-92 B60/R) In the churchyard (117x81cm-46x32in) s.

LIFSHITZ, Uri (1936-) Israeli
£851 $1600   (5-Jan-92 GG.TA255/R) Figure (93x65cm-37x26in) s.
£1081 $2000   (8-Jun-92 GG.TA180/R) Figures (100x80cm-39x31in) s.
£3243 $6000   (9-Jun-92 GG.TA281/R) Black widow (98x116cm-39x46in) s.
£3617 $6800   (5-Jan-92 GG.TA254/R) Figures (131x100cm-52x39in) s.d.1969
£691   *$1300*   *(5-Jan-92 GG.TA256/R) Fisherman (100x68cm-39x27in) s. mixed media*

LIGHTBODY, L A (19th C) British
£1937 $3254   (27-Aug-91 RAS.K422/R) Children flying a kite in summer (61x51cm-24x20in)
s.d.1891 (D.KR 22000)

LIGNIS, Pierre de (style) (?-1627) Flemish
£1000 $1750   (27-Feb-92 CSK24) The Martydom of a Saint (28x21cm-11x8in) copper

LIGNON, Bernard (20th C) French
£471 $800   (23-Oct-91 GD.B1151/R) Street scene (54x45cm-21x18in) s.indis.d.1950
(S.FR 1200)
£667 $1133   (23-Oct-91 GD.B1150/R) Paris street scene (54x45cm-21x18in) s.i.
(S.FR 1700)
£1244 $2276   (12-May-92 C.A196/R) The Moulin Rouge in Paris (46x55cm-18x22in) s.
(B.FR 75000)

LIGORIO, Pirro (attrib) (1513-1583) Italian
£1957   *$3679*   *(18-Dec-91 AT.P100/R) Allegorie de l'Ancien et Nouveau Testament
(47x32cm-19x13in) pen wash htd.white (F.FR 19000)*

LIGOZZI, Jacopo (1547-1632) Italian
£154696 $280000   (22-May-92 SY.NY85/R) Adoration of Magi (34x24cm-13x9in) s. copper

LIGOZZI, Jacopo (circle) (1547-1632) Italian
£1024   *$1863*   *(26-May-92 KF.M147/R) The reign of death (44x32cm-17x13in) pen wash htd
white (DM 3000)*

LIGTELIJN, Evert Jan (1893-) Dutch
£545 $965   (22-Apr-92 CH.AM56) View of Loenen aan de Vecht, with a washerwoman in
the foreground (51x41cm-20x16in) s. (D.FL 1800)

LILJEBLADH, Birgitta (1924-) Swedish
£1233 $2257   (13-May-92 BU.S107/R) Flowers (61x54cm-24x21in) s.d.1973 panel
(S.KR 13000)

LILJEFORS, Bruno (1860-1939) Swedish
£771 $1333   (28-Mar-92 UA.U485/R) Rock (127x160cm-50x63in) st.verso (S.KR 8000)
£997 $1735   (13-Apr-92 AB.S132) Seagull and grey sky (21x27cm-8x11in) st. panel
(S.KR 10500)
£1423 $2604   (12-May-92 GO.G81) Eagle hunting duck at dawn (42x65cm-17x26in)
(S.KR 15000)
£2453 $4391   (7-May-92 RAS.S46/R) White tailed eagles (23x35cm-9x14in) init. sketch
panel (S.KR 26000)
£3263 $5906   (3-Dec-91 AB.S4637/R) Geese on beach (15x25cm-6x10in) s.i.d.1907
(S.KR 34000)

LILJEFORS, Bruno (1860-1939) Swedish-cont.

£3700	$6771	(12-May-92 GO.G82/R) Late winter landscape with deer (51x70cm-20x28in) s. (S.KR 39000)
£4364	$7987	(14-May-92 BU.S42/R) Elk in autumn landscape (71x85cm-28x33in) i.verso (S.KR 46000)
£4541	$8219	(19-May-92 AB.S4236/R) Winter landscape with hare by fence (35x45cm-14x18in) s. (S.KR 48000)
£4906	$8683	(25-Apr-92 SO.S451/R) River's edge at sunset (50x65cm-20x26in) s.verso (S.KR 52000)
£5298	$9589	(19-May-92 AB.S4233/R) Mallards in flight (70x100cm-28x39in) st.verso (S.KR 56000)
£5676	$10274	(19-May-92 AB.S4232/R) Ducks in snow (59x74cm-23x29in) st.i.verso (S.KR 60000)
£5932	$10559	(28-Oct-91 AB.S124/R) Duck in flight at sunset, Osterby (31x41cm-12x16in) s.d.1924 panel (S.KR 63000)
£6667	$12000	(24-Nov-91 LIT.L35) Ducks on lake shore (48x64cm-19x25in) s.d.1920
£7400	$13543	(14-May-92 BU.S40/R) Fox being hunted by dogs in winter landscape (35x50cm-14x20in) s. (S.KR 78000)
£7414	$13272	(16-Nov-91 FAL.M196/R) Hare in snow (40x60cm-16x24in) s.d.1924 (S.KR 78000)
£7569	$13699	(19-May-92 AB.S4234/R) Winter landscape with hare (35x50cm-14x20in) s. (S.KR 80000)
£7590	$13890	(11-May-92 NOR.S23/R) Swans in flight (34x50cm-13x20in) s. (S.KR 80000)
£7678	$13896	(3-Dec-91 AB.S4636/R) Wooded landscape with geese in flight, sunset (70x105cm-28x41in) s.d.91 (S.KR 80000)
£7862	$14151	(19-Nov-91 GO.G90/R) Capercaillie in wood (108x200cm-43x79in) (S.KR 82000)
£8065	$14758	(11-May-92 NOR.S21/R) Eagle with catch in mountain landscape (36x55cm-14x22in) s. (S.KR 85000)
£8396	$14861	(25-Apr-92 SO.S450/R) Wild geese (35x50cm-14x20in) s. (S.KR 89000)
£8491	$15198	(7-May-92 RAS.S30/R) Fox chasing partridge (35x50cm-14x20in) s. (S.KR 90000)
£9488	$17362	(14-May-92 BU.S41/R) Two English setters (40x53cm-16x21in) s.d.1892 (S.KR 100000)
£9488	$17362	(14-May-92 BU.S38/R) Fox creeping up on ducklings (45x65cm-18x26in) s.d.1935 (S.KR 100000)
£10436	$19099	(11-May-92 NOR.S9/R) Cat in winter landscape (22x16cm-9x6in) s.i.d.1884 panel (S.KR 110000)
£11321	$20264	(7-May-92 RAS.S59/R) Fox chasing crows (35x50cm-14x20in) s. (S.KR 120000)
£11321	$20264	(7-May-92 RAS.S1/R) Cat on fence (24x14cm-9x6in) s.d.84 panel (S.KR 120000)
£11826	$21405	(19-May-92 AB.S4230/R) Field landscape with curlew by water hole (55x80cm-22x31in) s.d.1927 (S.KR 125000)
£13283	$24307	(14-May-92 BU.S39/R) Bird-shooting (51x70cm-20x28in) s.d.1891 (S.KR 140000)
£13757	$25176	(12-May-92 GO.G79/R) Autumn landscape with geeses by marshes (60x90cm-24x35in) s.d.1922 (S.KR 145000)
£15094	$27019	(7-May-92 RAS.S11/R) Fox and hare in winter landscape (50x63cm-20x25in) s.d.84 (S.KR 160000)
£15180	$27780	(11-May-92 NOR.S24/R) Black grouse (69x99cm-27x39in) s.d.1908 (S.KR 160000)
£16509	$29552	(7-May-92 RAS.S21/R) Capercaillie displaying (50x35cm-20x14in) s.d.1890 (S.KR 175000)
£16981	$30057	(5-Nov-91 BA.S102/R) Eiderducks in breakers (52x75cm-20x30in) s.d.1926 (S.KR 180000)
£17078	$31252	(11-May-92 NOR.S26/R) Winter landscape with hare (50x74cm-20x29in) s.d.1927 (S.KR 180000)
£17466	$31614	(3-Dec-91 AB.S4633/R) Winter trees with bullfinches (65x50cm-26x20in) s.d.1923 (S.KR 182000)
£18027	$32989	(11-May-92 NOR.S34/R) Blackgrouse in snowy landscape (70x100cm-28x39in) s.d.1909 (S.KR 190000)
£18130	$32271	(28-Nov-91 BU.S24/R) Sparrows in the snow (24x33cm-9x13in) s.d.1891 panel (S.KR 190000)
£18217	$32790	(19-Nov-91 GO.G91/R) Wooded landscape with ducks by water's edge (70x100cm-28x39in) s.d.1917 (S.KR 190000)
£19924	$36461	(11-May-92 NOR.S35/R) Fox being hunted by hounds (69x98cm-27x39in) s.d.1909 (S.KR 210000)
£21698	$38840	(7-May-92 RAS.S10/R) Hawk attacking capercaillie (86x110cm-34x43in) s.d.1881 (S.KR 230000)
£26565	$48615	(14-May-92 BU.S36/R) Fox and blackgrouse (50x70cm-20x28in) s.d.1892 (S.KR 280000)
£27804	$50048	(19-Nov-91 GO.G92/R) Autumn landscape with foxes by fence (71x100cm-28x39in) s.d.1924 (S.KR 290000)
£28149	$50105	(28-Nov-91 BU.S25/R) Blackgrouse in autumn (88x117cm-35x46in) s.d.1908 (S.KR 295000)
£31309	$57296	(12-May-92 GO.G78/R) Summer landscape with family of foxes and duck by tarn (65x100cm-26x39in) s.d.1922 (S.KR 330000)
£404	*$695*	*(8-Mar-92 BU.M133) Woodcock (6x9cm-2x4in) mono. pencil (S.KR 4200)*
£759	*$1389*	*(12-May-92 GO.G265) Martten in tree (27x36cm-11x14in) s. pencil (S.KR 8000)*
£1408	*$2366*	*(27-Aug-91 RAS.K667/R) Three crows by waterhole init. pen wash (D.KR 16000)*
£2838	*$5137*	*(19-May-92 AB.S4235/R) Jeppe, the cat, among leaves near bird's nest (17x27cm-7x11in) s. W/C (S.KR 30000)*

LILJEFORS, Bruno (1860-1939) Swedish-cont.
£7547 $13509   *(7-May-92 RAS.S47/R) Cat by bird's nest (44x29cm-17x11in) s.d.86 Indian ink dr (S.KR 80000)*

LILJEFORS, Bruno (attrib) (1860-1939) Swedish
£1412 $2514   (28-Oct-91 AB.S125) Wooded autumn landscape (39x70cm-15x28in) (S.KR 15000)

LILJEFORS, Lindorm (1909-1985) Swedish
£612 $1089   (28-Oct-91 AB.S127) Bog in autumn landscape (45x53cm-18x21in) s.d.52 panel (S.KR 6500)
£617 $1074   (13-Apr-92 AB.S135) Autumn landscape with brook (45x37cm-18x15in) s.d.37 panel (S.KR 6500)
£732 $1267   (28-Mar-92 UA.U489) Cranes in flight (18x26cm-7x10in) s. panel (S.KR 7600)
£823 $1490   (19-May-92 AB.S4240/R) Coastal landscape with tree and birds (33x44cm-13x17in) s.d.76 panel (S.KR 8700)
£1060 $1833   (28-Mar-92 UA.U488/R) Early spring landscape, Uppland (38x46cm-15x18in) s.d.35 panel (S.KR 11000)
£1187 $2066   (13-Apr-92 AB.S134) Winter landscape with horse and sleigh (44x53cm-17x21in) s.d.40 panel (S.KR 12500)
£1330 $2313   (13-Apr-92 AB.S133) Northern winter landscape with horse and sleigh (45x53cm-18x21in) s.d.39 panel (S.KR 14000)
£1423 $2448   (19-Oct-91 UA.U383/R) Large stone in pine forest (46x38cm-18x15in) s.i.d.1934 panel (S.KR 15000)
£1879 $3231   (19-Oct-91 UA.U382/R) Jays in autumn landscape (60x73cm-24x29in) s.d.1946 panel (S.KR 19800)
£1887 $3340   (5-Nov-91 BA.S106/R) Winter landscape with jays in bushes (46x55cm-18x22in) s.d.50 panel (S.KR 20000)
£1934 $3423   (5-Nov-91 BA.S107 a/R) Elk and dog in landscape (41x56cm-16x22in) s.d.72 panel (S.KR 20500)
£2264 $4008   (5-Nov-91 BA.S105/R) Golden-eyes in flight (41x56cm-16x22in) s. panel (S.KR 24000)
£2547 $4508   (5-Nov-91 BA.S104/R) Mergansers in flight (60x90cm-24x35in) s. (S.KR 27000)
£3083 $5333   (28-Mar-92 UA.U487) Elk and elkhounds (41x46cm-16x18in) one s.d.39 panel diptych (S.KR 32000)
£3208 $5742   (7-May-92 RAS.S71/R) Field landscape with pheasants (46x55cm-18x22in) s.d.46 panel (S.KR 34000)
£3263 $5906   (3-Dec-91 AB.S4638/R) Wooded landscape with elk running (65x90cm-26x35in) s.d.42 panel (S.KR 34000)
£3500 $6336   (19-May-92 AB.S4239/R) Coastal landscape with crows on beach in sunshine (72x91cm-28x36in) s.d.43 panel (S.KR 37000)
£3774 $6755   (7-May-92 RAS.S73/R) Pheasant hunt (60x72cm-24x28in) s.d.51 panel (S.KR 40000)
£5561 $10010   (19-Nov-91 GO.G93/R) Lake landscape with mallards landing (60x73cm-24x29in) s.d.52 panel (S.KR 58000)

LILJELUND, Arvid (19th C) Swedish
£14877 $26481   (1-Dec-91 HOR.H137) Harbour bay (44x66cm-17x26in) s. (F.M 115000)

LILLONI, Umberto (1898-1980) Italian
£2741 $4769   (14-Apr-92 F.M62/R) Bosco (20x30cm-8x12in) s. s.i.d.1978verso (I.L 6000000)
£4634 $8248   (26-Nov-91 SY.MI81/R) Bardonecchia (34x55cm-13x22in) s.init.d.53 (I.L 10000000)
£5253 $9140   (14-Apr-92 F.M153/R) Vele sulla laguna (38x54cm-15x21in) s.d.1948 (I.L 11500000)
£5329 $9486   (29-Nov-91 F.F161 h) Spogliarello (60x40cm-24x16in) s. s.i.d.1969verso (I.L 11500000)
£6033 $11342   (19-Dec-91 F.M157/R) Fiori dal vaso cinese (70x60cm-28x24in) s. (I.L 13000000)
£8341 $14847   (26-Nov-91 SY.MI190/R) Venezia (50x73cm-20x29in) s.d.54 (I.L 18000000)
£394 $701   *(27-Nov-91 F.M60) Bordonecchia (33x24cm-13x9in) s.i.d.1951 crayon (I.L 850000)*

LIM KAC-KEONG (1901-) Chinese
£12138 $20756   (22-Mar-92 SY.TA16/R) At source (61x50cm-24x20in) s. board (T.D 528000)

LIMBACH, Hans Jorg (1928-1990) Swiss
£646 $1202   (19-Jun-92 G.Z477) The rice farmer (40x35cm-16x14in) mono.d.1955 (S.FR 1700)
£837 $1556   (19-Jun-92 G.Z476) Japanese No-Mask (45x39cm-18x15in) mono.d.1953 (S.FR 2200)

LIMBORCH, Hendrik van (1681-1759) Dutch
£3200 $6144   (7-Jul-92 PH186/R) Diana bathing attended by servants (65x81cm-26x32in)

LIMOUSE, Roger (1894-1990) French
£791 $1407   (29-Nov-91 GAB.G2789/R) Le repas s.i.d.1950 (S.FR 2000)
£1537 $2766   (2-Feb-92 ZZ.F223/R) Vase de fleurs (55x46cm-22x18in) s. (F.FR 15000)
£1815 $3212   (10-Nov-91 ZZ.F203/R) Vase d'anemones (61x50cm-24x20in) s. (F.FR 18000)
£1865 $3301   (10-Nov-91 ZZ.F204/R) Pot de fleurs sur en entablement (61x50cm-24x20in) s. (F.FR 18500)

LIMOUSE, Roger (1894-1990) French-cont.
£2043 $3575   (21-Feb-92 LC.P53) Composition au bouquet de fleurs (61x50cm-24x20in) s.
(F.FR 20000)

LIN FENGMIAN (1900-1991) Chinese
£14161 $24215   (22-Mar-92 SY.TA35/R) Opera figures (58x45cm-23x18in) s. (T.D 616000)
£42989 $73510   (22-Mar-92 SY.TA6/R) Autumn landscape (59x72cm-23x28in) s. (T.D 1870000)
£60690 $103779   (22-Mar-92 SY.TA36/R) Fish market (71x90cm-28x35in) s. (T.D 2640000)
£3672 $6500   (7-Nov-91 B.SF1212/R) Herons and reeds (82x69cm-32x27in) s. ink colour
scroll
£5178 $9061   (30-Mar-92 CH.HK303/R) Landscape (107x34cm-42x13in) s.d.1946 ink W/C
hanging scroll (HK.D 70000)
£6657 $11649   (30-Mar-92 CH.HK243/R) Goose flying amidst reeds (67x67cm-26x26in) s. ink
W/C scroll (HK.D 90000)
£8876 $15533   (30-Mar-92 CH.HK242/R) Lotus pond (44x54cm-17x21in) s. ink W/C scroll
(HK.D 120000)
£8876 $15533   (30-Mar-92 CH.HK245/R) Fishing boats (70x65cm-28x26in) s. ink W/C scroll
(HK.D 120000)
£10355 $18121   (30-Mar-92 CH.HK247/R) Bridge by bank with willows (66x66cm-26x26in) s.
ink W/C scroll (HK.D 140000)
£11834 $20710   (30-Mar-92 CH.HK153/R) Seated lady (68x69cm-27x27in) s. ink W/C scroll
(HK.D 160000)
£14793 $25888   (30-Mar-92 CH.HK246/R) Autumn landscape (69x68cm-27x27in) s. ink W/C
scroll (HK.D 200000)
£16272 $28476   (30-Mar-92 CH.HK150/R) Sailboats (37x65cm-15x26in) s. ink W/C scroll
(HK.D 220000)
£16272 $28476   (30-Mar-92 CH.HK152/R) Still life (63x62cm-25x24in) s. ink W/C scroll
(HK.D 220000)

LIN YUAN (1913-1991) Chinese
£3287 $5621   (22-Mar-92 SY.TA44/R) Cow (65x80cm-26x31in) s.d.1991 (T.D 143000)

LIN, Hermann van (17th C) Dutch
£5525 $10000   (21-May-92 CH.NY117/R) Cavalry skirmish (17x22cm-7x9in) s.panel

LIN, Richard (1933-) British
£1098 $1965   (15-Nov-91 GK.Z5730) White parallel forms, Windsor yellow
(56x96cm-22x38in) s.i.d.1969verso (S.FR 2800)
£795 $1438   (23-May-92 KV.L200) From BPG to ER (96x101cm-38x40in) aluminium oil on
canvas (B.FR 48000)
£828 $1498   (23-May-92 KV.L199) And it came to pass (76x102cm-30x40in) aluminium oil
on canvas (B.FR 50000)

LINARD, Jacques (1600-1645) French
£45918 $81276   (10-Feb-92 GL.P13/R) Vanite au papillon (32x43cm-13x17in) panel
(F.FR 450000)

LINARD, Jacques (style) (1600-1645) French
£3000 $5460   (11-Dec-91 S131/R) Still life of plums in bowl, book, knife and pitcher,
half draped table (38x44cm-15x17in)
£4000 $7120   (30-Oct-91 S110/R) Still life of tulips in glass vase on table
(40x29cm-16x11in) panel

LINCK, J A (1766-1843) Swiss
£1100 $1980   (28-Jan-92 RG2761) Continental mountainous landscape with figures and
goats (46x56cm-18x22in) s. W/C

LINDAU, Dietrich Wilhelm (1799-1862) German
£2286 $4000   (18-Feb-92 CE.NY93/R) Outdoor revelry (52x71cm-20x28in) s.d.1854

LINDAUER, Gottfried (1839-1926) New Zealander
£1532 $2711   (26-Apr-92 SY.ME280/R) Maori portrait (38x29cm-15x11in) (A.D 3600)
£3917 $6816   (16-Sep-91 SY.ME59/R) Portrait of Maori (50x39cm-20x15in) s.i. (A.D 8500)

LINDBERG, Alf (1905-1990) Swedish
£569 $1042   (12-May-92 GO.G87) Landscape from Sunnero, Mjorn (50x37cm-20x15in) s.
(S.KR 6000)
£576 $1042   (3-Dec-91 AB.S5081/R) Park study (17x29cm-7x11in) s.d.36 panel
(S.KR 6000)
£767 $1381   (19-Nov-91 GO.G95) Man seated at table (125x86cm-49x34in) s. (S.KR 8000)
£828 $1424   (8-Mar-92 BU.M334) Town scene (50x65cm-20x26in) s. (S.KR 8600)
£1518 $2778   (12-May-92 GO.G86/R) Flowers in a vase (66x50cm-26x20in) s. (S.KR 16000)

LINDBERG, Harald (1901-1976) Swedish
£503 $920   (12-May-92 GO.G90) Night time (46x38cm-18x15in) s.d.1943 panel
(S.KR 5300)
£684 $1190   (13-Apr-92 AB.S138) Windy day, vessels by the coast (24x36cm-9x14in) s.
panel (S.KR 7200)

LINDE, Ossip L (19/20th C) American
£2000 $3500   (31-Mar-92 MOR.P68) Landscape, golden folia (76x76cm-30x30in) s.

LINDELL, Lage (1920-1980) Scandinavian
£643 $1164   (3-Dec-91 AB.S5083/R) Arabian street scene (14x18cm-6x7in) s.d.47 crayon
(S.KR 6700)

INDEMANN-FROMMEL, Karl (1819-1891) German
£23000 $39330   (18-Mar-92 S79/R) View of Rome (92x179cm-36x70in) s.d.1872
£550 $968   *(11-Apr-92 AW.H605/R) Woodland steps in Ariccia with memorial by rocks*
               (25x35cm-10x14in) i.d.1845 brush over pencil (DM 1600)

INDENAU, Erich (1889-1955) German
£1568 $2854   (13-Dec-91 BM.B845/R) Still life of pears on wooden table
               (64x80cm-25x31in) mono. (DM 4500)

INDENAU, Heinrich (1858-?) German
£859 $1495   (21-Sep-91 SA.A552/R) Still life of flowers (67x98cm-26x39in) s. board
               (DM 2500)

INDENBERG, Robert (19th C) German
£912 $1642   (22-Nov-91 SA.A1684/R) Frisian girl knitting standing in interior
               (32x24cm-13x9in) s. panel (DM 2600)

INDENMUTH, Tod (1855-?) American
£1236 $2200   (26-Jan-92 JRB.C71/R) Coastal landscape (28x36cm-11x14in) s. canvasboard

INDENSCHMIT, Hermann (style) (1857-1939) German
£1972 $3293   (19-Aug-91 SY.ME177/R) Game of cards (47x58cm-19x23in) (A.D 4200)

INDER, P (19th C) British
£2907 $5000   (17-Oct-91 SY.NY306/R) Feeding ducks (47x61cm-19x24in) s.
£2907 $5000   (17-Oct-91 SY.NY305/R) Teatime (47x61cm-19x24in) s.

INDER, Philippe Jacques (19th C) French
£718 $1300   (22-May-92 S.BM33/R) La coquette (33x23cm-13x9in) s. panel

INDERUM, Richard (1851-?) German
£500 $895   (15-Jan-92 BT184/R) The recital (25x20cm-10x8in) s. panel
£2205 $3924   (28-Apr-92 RAS.K139/R) Woman by fountain (61x44cm-24x17in) s.d.82
               (D.KR 25000)

INDGREEN, K (?) ?
£769 $1331   (25-Mar-92 KM.K1292) Reading girl reclining on bed (25x40cm-10x16in) s.
               (DM 2200)

INDGREN, Emil (1866-1940) Swedish
£522 $955   (17-May-92 BU.M324) Young lady with burning light and bouquet of flowers
               (90x72cm-35x28in) s.d.1929 (S.KR 5500)
£570 $991   (13-Apr-92 AB.S145) Interior with girl wearring Dala-Flod costume
               (88x66cm-35x26in) s.d.1928 (S.KR 6000)
£807 $1405   (13-Apr-92 AB.S144) Harvesters at Grisslehamn (79x109cm-31x43in) s.d.1917
               (S.KR 8500)

INDH, Bror (1877-1941) Swedish
£2075 $3715   (7-May-92 RAS.S70/R) Winter night II Varmland (56x76cm-22x30in) s. panel
               (S.KR 22000)
£3019 $5404   (7-May-92 RAS.S68/R) Winter atmosphere (100x125cm-39x49in) s.
               (S.KR 32000)

INDHOLM, Berndt (1841-1914) Finnish
£767 $1381   (19-Nov-91 GO.G98) Pasture (26x33cm-10x13in) s. (S.KR 8000)
£3359 $6080   (3-Dec-91 AB.S4728/R) Coastal landscape (31x25cm-12x10in) s. (S.KR 35000)
£4010 $7138   (1-Dec-91 HOR.H142) Breakers (13x31cm-5x12in) s. (F.M 31000)
£6718 $12159 (3-Dec-91 AB.S4727/R) Mountainous landscape with trees (66x48cm-26x19in)
               s.d.91 (S.KR 70000)
£7762 $13816 (1-Dec-91 HOR.H141) Coastal breakers (34x50cm-13x20in) s.d.1904
               (F.M 60000)
£10367 $18245 (12-Apr-92 HOR.H153/R) Light and shade, leafy wood (39x54cm-15x21in)
               s.d.1882 (F.M 82000)
£12334 $22571 (12-May-92 GO.G92/R) West coast landscape with children fishing
               (40x65cm-16x26in) s. (S.KR 130000)
£13274 $23363 (12-Apr-92 HOR.H152/R) Trees at base of mountain (66x48cm-26x19in)
               s.d.1891 (F.M 105000)
£16435 $28925 (12-Apr-92 HOR.H150/R) Admiring the ocean (47x70cm-19x28in) s.d.1888
               (F.M 130000)
£20228 $35601 (12-Apr-92 HOR.H149/R) Beach landscape (44x63cm-17x25in) s. (F.M 160000)
£22756 $40051 (12-Apr-92 HOR.H148/R) Stony shore (62x95cm-24x37in) s. (F.M 180000)
£33635 $59871 (1-Dec-91 HOR.H138/R) Gulls on rocks by the sea (98x129cm-39x51in)
               s.d.1894 (F.M 260000)

INDI (1904-) Swiss
£657 $1176   (6-May-92 GD.B773/R) Ragusa (65x54cm-26x21in) mono.d.32 s.i.d.verso
               (S.FR 1800)
£1020 $1733   (23-Oct-91 GD.B453/R) View of Palma, Mallorca (39x56cm-15x22in) s.d.1959
               (S.FR 2600)

INDIN, Carl Olof Eric (1869-1942) American
£787 $1400   (2-May-92 W.W102/R) Docked boats at dusk (71x51cm-28x20in) s.

1106

LINDKVIST, Jonas (1889-1955) Swedish
£778 $1338   (19-Oct-91 UA.U385/R) From Tingshojden, Vaksala (67x98cm-26x39in)
                 s.d.1941 (S.KR 8200)

LINDMAN, Axel (1848-1930) Swedish
£660 $1169   (5-Nov-91 BA.S112/R) Silhouettes at Soder (24x33cm-9x13in) init.d.1886
                 panel (S.KR 7000)

LINDNER, Ernest (1897-1988) Canadian
£3000 $5310   (6-Nov-91 SY.T205/R) Cornucopia (75x60cm-30x24in) s.d.1964 board
                 (C.D 6000)

LINDNER, Richard (1901-1978) American/German
£162011 $290000 (12-Nov-91 CH.NY44/R) The couple (183x198cm-72x78in) s.d.1971
£922 $1677   (26-May-92 KF.M1013/R) Self portrait in mirror (10x13cm-4x5in) s.d.1974
                 pencil chk (DM 2700)
£9497 $17000   (6-May-92 CH.NY375/R) Confrontation (57x41cm-22x16in) s.d.1977 W/C
                 ball-point pen paper collage
£16600 $28551   (12-Oct-91 GL.P9/R) Two profiles (127x97cm-50x38in) s.d.1977 pastel lead
                 pencil (F.FR 165000)

LINDON, J D (attrib) (?) ?
£1156 $1942   (27-Aug-91 GM.B575/R) The Benediction (64x126cm-25x50in) (B.FR 70000)

LINDQVIST, Arne (1919-) Swedish
£547 $990   (8-Dec-91 SO.S438) Birds in flight (45x54cm-18x21in) s. (S.KR 5700)

LINDQVIST, Axel Hjalmar (1843-1917) Swedish
£477 $839   (11-Apr-92 FAL.M258/R) Setting out the nets (21x48cm-8x19in) s.
                 (S.KR 5000)
£537 $955   (28-Oct-91 AB.S134) Beech wood - winter landscape (46x59cm-18x23in) s.
                 panel (S.KR 5700)
£667 $1174   (11-Apr-92 FAL.M257/R) Horse and cart in wooded landscape
                 (38x50cm-15x20in) s. (S.KR 7000)

LINDQVIST, Carl Magnus (1884-) Swedish
£494 $859   (13-Apr-92 AB.S149) Autumn landscape with Lapplander and girl by lake
                 (48x60cm-19x24in) s. (S.KR 5200)
£518 $922   (28-Oct-91 AB.S137) Northern farm by river in autumn (40x49cm-16x19in)
                 s.d.1933 (S.KR 5500)

LINDQVIST, Herman (1868-1923) Swedish
£2642 $4675   (5-Nov-91 BA.S113/R) Sunny winter's day, Skeppsholmen (66x45cm-26x18in)
                 s.d.1919 (S.KR 28000)

LINDSAY, H (?) ?
£474 $900   (24-Jun-92 D.NY56) Darning socks (76x51cm-30x20in) init.d.94

LINDSAY, Norman Alfred Williams (1879-1970) Australian
£2447 $4331   (26-Apr-92 SY.ME35/R) Kneeling nude (22x29cm-9x11in) s. canvas on board
                 (A.D 5750)
£2553 $4519   (26-Apr-92 SY.ME346/R) Revery (57x49cm-22x19in) (A.D 6000)
£3965 $7137   (24-Nov-91 SY.S422/R) Moonlight sonata (30x25cm-12x10in) s. (A.D 9000)
£4255 $7532   (26-Apr-92 SY.ME432) Green bracelet (57x54cm-22x21in) s. (A.D 10000)
£13178 $25171   (21-Jul-92 JRL.S84/R) Reclining nude (67x100cm-26x39in) s. (A.D 34000)
£29915 $53248   (28-Apr-92 CH.ME208/R) Rita (75x60cm-30x24in) s.d.1938 (A.D 70000)
£441 $784   (26-Nov-91 J.M1287) Proposition (40x30cm-16x12in) pencil wash (A.D 1000)
£463 $796   (14-Oct-91 MGS.S58) The deathless gods (55x71cm-22x28in) s. pencil
                 (A.D 1400)
£598 $1065   (28-Apr-92 CH.ME70) Two horsemen (31x26cm-12x10in) s. pencil wash
                 (A.D 1400)
£659 $1259   (21-Jul-92 JRL.S38) Courtesan (45x34cm-18x13in) dr. (A.D 1700)
£661 $1189   (24-Nov-91 SY.S36) Cartoon - Strikes and Profiteering (37x37cm-15x15in)
                 s. ink (A.D 1500)
£812 $1470   (2-Dec-91 CH.ME298/R) Great Scott - what queer looking couple
                 (26x38cm-10x15in) s.i. chl (A.D 1900)
£936 $1657   (26-Apr-92 SY.ME14/R) Welcome home (43x51cm-17x20in) s. pencil (A.D 2200)
£1282 $2282   (28-Apr-92 CH.ME91) Summer (28x24cm-11x9in) s. W/C (A.D 3000)
£1422 $2432   (17-Mar-92 JRL.S58) Reclining nude (33x26cm-13x10in) s. W/C (A.D 3200)
£1434 $2739   (21-Jul-92 JRL.S77/R) Reclining nude (72x53cm-28x21in) pencil (A.D 3700)
£1500 $2670   (28-Nov-91 C33/R) Young lovers (22x23cm-9x9in) s. pencil W/C htd white
£1938 $3702   (21-Jul-92 JRL.S113) Repose (26x22cm-10x9in) s. W/C (A.D 5000)
£2340 $4143   (26-Apr-92 SY.ME297/R) Study for spring wood fantasy (70x66cm-28x26in)
                 init. pencil (A.D 5500)
£4264 $8143   (21-Jul-92 JRL.S115/R) The plunderers (53x44cm-21x17in) s.d.1934 W/C
                 (A.D 11000)
£7364 $14066   (21-Jul-92 JRL.S121/R) Afternoon bathers (51x38cm-20x15in) s. W/C
                 (A.D 19000)
£9692 $17251   (26-Nov-91 J.M185/R) Destiny's buffoon (44x42cm-17x17in) s. W/C with
                 drawing init. pencil (A.D 22000)

LINDSAY, Percy (1870-1952) Australian
£1145 $2062   (24-Nov-91 SY.S27) Tributary - to Hawkesbury River (18x23cm-7x9in) s.
                 i.verso board (A.D 2600)
£1603 $2853   (27-Apr-92 J.M2) Picnic (17x30cm-7x12in) s. board (A.D 3750)

LINDSAY, Percy (1870-1952) Australian-cont.
£10500 $18690   (28-Nov-91 C14/R) Fossacking for gold (41x30cm-16x12in)

LINDSAY, Sir Coutts (1824-1907) British
£1000 $1730   (4-Sep-91 PHK107) Loch Awe (50x74cm-20x29in) s.i.verso

LINDSAY, Sir Daryl Ernest (1889-1976) Australian
£641 $1141   (27-Apr-92 J.M302) Still life (49x44cm-19x17in) s. canvas on board
             (A.D 1500)
£876 $1524   (16-Sep-91 CH.ME175 a) Big Bob (34x29cm-13x11in) s. canvas on board
             (A.D 1900)
£1923 $3423   (27-Apr-92 J.M68/R) The pack team, Northern Territory (36x64cm-14x25in)
             s.d.62 board (A.D 4500)

LINDSAY, Sir Lionel (1874-1961) Australian
£427 $761   (28-Apr-92 CH.ME130) Ruined palace, Jaipur (28x39cm-11x15in) s.i. W/C
             (A.D 1000)
£446 $745   (19-Aug-91 SY.ME124) Perugia in springtime (20x30cm-8x12in) s. conte
             crayon W/C bodycol (A.D 950)
£504 $962   (21-Jul-92 JRL.S223) Palace and wine boat (29x38cm-11x15in) s. W/C
             (A.D 1300)
£704 $1176   (19-Aug-91 SY.ME145 a) Lady of Pluckup (49x65cm-19x26in) s.i. W/C htd
             bodycol (A.D 1500)

LINDSAY, Thomas Corwin (1845-1907) American
£771 $1350   (3-Apr-92 S.W2040) Rocky coastline (69x86cm-27x34in) s.

LINDSTROM, Arvid Mauritz (1849-1923) Swedish
£1230 $2226   (19-May-92 AB.S4243/R) Coastal landscape with deer on beach at dusk
             (37x71cm-15x28in) s.d.1876 (S.KR 13000)
£1965 $3538   (19-Nov-91 GO.G101/R) Lake landscape, evening light (76x130cm-30x51in) s.
             (S.KR 20500)
£2933 $5308   (19-May-92 AB.S4242/R) Swedish autumn landscape with trees by water
             (75x128cm-30x50in) s. (S.KR 31000)

LINDSTROM, Bengt (1925-) Swedish
£694 $1207   (17-Sep-91 RAS.K86) Composition (69x54cm-27x21in) s. acrylic paper on
             canvas (D.KR 7800)
£746 $1387   (15-Jun-92 B.O102/R) Composition s. paper (N.KR 8500)
£752 $1256   (25-Aug-91 BU.M216) Mandolin players (73x45cm-29x18in) s.d.1950 panel
             (S.KR 8000)
£869 $1590   (5-Feb-92 FB.P174) Composition (71x97cm-28x38in) bears sig.apocryphal
             (F.FR 8500)
£883 $1598   (3-Dec-91 AB.S5088/R) Animated landscape II (33x24cm-13x9in) s.
             (S.KR 9200)
£1132 $2004   (25-Apr-92 SO.S457/R) Police (75x56cm-30x22in) s. acrylic (S.KR 12000)
£1240 $2208   (27-Nov-91 BU.S53/R) Composition 1953 (46x51cm-18x20in) s. (S.KR 13000)
£1328 $2431   (13-May-92 BU.S111/R) Figure and animal (40x32cm-16x13in) s. (S.KR 14000)
£1613 $2952   (13-May-92 BU.S110/R) The face (46x38cm-18x15in) s. (S.KR 17000)
£1751 $2994   (21-Mar-92 AT.P91/R) La boule de cristal (46x38cm-18x15in) s. acrylic
             (F.FR 17000)
£1957 $3346   (18-Mar-92 LT.P102/R) Personnage assis (76x56cm-30x22in) s. acrylic paper
             (F.FR 19000)
£2006 $3651   (12-Dec-91 SY.AM269/R) Untitled (46x38cm-18x15in) s.d.77 verso board
             (D.FL 6500)
£2053 $3696   (19-Nov-91 FB.P145/R) Composition aux personnages (56x76cm-22x30in) s.i.
             paper laid down on hardboard (F.FR 20000)
£2111 $3821   (3-Dec-91 AB.S5089/R) Green figures (50x61cm-20x24in) s. (S.KR 22000)
£2317 $4124   (26-Nov-91 SY.MI38/R) Chasse sauvage (37x45cm-15x18in) s. (I.L 5000000)
£2342 $4333   (13-Jun-92 AT.P48/R) Le charbonnier (100x50cm-39x20in) s.d.69
             (F.FR 23000)
£2483 $4495   (23-May-92 KV.L503/R) Figure (75x55cm-30x22in) s. acrylic (B.FR 150000)
£2491 $4335   (17-Sep-91 RAS.K85/R) Attacked by yellow devil (66x56cm-26x22in) s.
             (D.KR 28000)
£2590 $4687   (4-Dec-91 G.Z165/R) Three heads (54x73cm-21x29in) s. (S.FR 6500)
£2823 $4883   (4-Oct-91 CSC.P103/R) La femme sauvage (105x75cm-41x30in) s. acrylic
             paper laid down on canvas (F.FR 28000)
£3071 $5559   (3-Dec-91 AB.S5086/R) Figure composition (81x65cm-32x26in) s.
             (S.KR 32000)
£3259 $5963   (3-Jun-92 CSC.P110/R) Rouge et vert (107x75cm-42x30in) s. acrylic paper
             on panel (F.FR 32000)
£3279 $5902   (2-Feb-92 CSC.P123/R) L'eclat (105x75cm-41x30in) s. acrylic paper laid
             down on canvas (F.FR 32000)
£3296 $5635   (19-Mar-92 CSC.P53/R) Grand personnage (107x77cm-42x30in) s. acrylic
             paper laid down on panel (F.FR 32000)
£3528 $6104   (4-Oct-91 CSC.P104) Femme assis a la robe ruge (105x75cm-41x30in) s.
             acrylic paper laid down on canvas (F.FR 35000)
£3625 $6453   (28-Oct-91 GL.P161/R) Trois figures (91x73cm-36x29in) s. (F.FR 36000)
£3827 $6812   (28-Oct-91 GL.P162/R) Tendre dialogue (116x89cm-46x35in) s. (F.FR 38000)
£4599 $8232   (14-Nov-91 F.M122/R) Figure (57x46cm-22x18in) s. (I.L 10000000)
£4955 $8523   (4-Mar-92 KH.K1221/R) Composition (145x114cm-57x45in) s. (D.KR 55000)
£5133 $9290   (7-Dec-91 KV.L438/R) Figures with an umbrella (73x60cm-29x24in) s.
             (B.FR 300000)
£5338 $9288   (17-Sep-91 RAS.K11/R) Composition with red monster (100x81cm-39x32in) s.
             (D.KR 60000)

LINDSTROM, Bengt (1925-) Swedish-cont.
£5943	$10697	(2-Feb-92 CSC.P118/R) Grande tete (130x97cm-51x38in) s. acrylic (F.FR 58000)
£9346	$15981	(21-Mar-92 KV.L486/R) Drole de Bete (100x73cm-39x29in) s. (B.FR 550000)
£9597	$17370	(3-Dec-91 AB.S5084/R) Composition with polycrome figures (122x606cm-48x239in) s. panel cut up into six pieces (S.KR 100000)
£13594	$23246	(21-Mar-92 KV.L419/R) L'Amphibie (98x131cm-39x52in) s.d.1965 verso (B.FR 800000)
£14073	$25472	(23-May-92 KV.L456/R) Man with dog (147x112cm-58x44in) s. (B.FR 850000)
£389	*$669*	*(15-Oct-91 GO.G1230) Composition in black (73x53cm-29x21in) s.d.60 gouache (S.KR 4100)*
£1135	*$2055*	*(19-May-92 AB.S5268/R) Figure composition (76x57cm-30x22in) s. gouache (S.KR 12000)*

LINDSTROM, Fritz (1874-1962) Swedish
£565	$1006	(28-Oct-91 AB.S139) Self portrait (33x23cm-13x9in) s.i. (S.KR 6000)
£2591	$4690	(3-Dec-91 AB.S4640/R) Landscape from Varmland (40x60cm-16x24in) s.d.25 panel (S.KR 27000)

LINDSTROM, Rikard (1882-1943) Swedish
£1139	$2083	(14-May-92 BU.S43/R) 'Nocturne' (73x59cm-29x23in) s.d.1899 (S.KR 12000)

LINDSTROM, Sven Otto (1883-1932) Scandinavian
£1235	*$2148*	*(13-Apr-92 AB.S376) Harbour scene from Normandy (118x147cm-46x58in) s.d.1915 gouache (S.KR 13000)*

LINER, Carl (jnr) (1914-) Swiss
£876	$1586	(4-Dec-91 G.Z135/R) Abstract (73x60cm-29x24in) s.d.1956 (S.FR 2200)
£1195	$2163	(4-Dec-91 G.Z895/R) Summer landscape (61x81cm-24x32in) s. (S.FR 3000)
£1490	$2667	(15-Nov-91 GK.Z5336/R) Southern village landscape (30x44cm-12x17in) s. pavatex (S.FR 3800)
£2037	$3687	(20-May-92 GK.Z5135) Women bathing (34x51cm-13x20in) s.d.1947 pavatex (S.FR 5500)
£2431	$4133	(23-Oct-91 GD.B454/R) Appenzell landscape (65x81cm-26x32in) s. (S.FR 6200)
£4074	$7374	(20-May-92 GK.Z5134/R) Scene with figures, Provence (81x116cm-32x46in) s.d.1955 (S.FR 11000)
£1176	*$2000*	*(23-Oct-91 GD.B456/R) Wooded landscape (42x28cm-17x11in) s.d.51 mixed media (S.FR 3000)*

LINER, Carl August (1871-1946) Swiss
£41353	$75677	(4-Jun-92 SY.Z354/R) Procession (71x101cm-28x40in) s.d.14 (S.FR 110000)

LINES, Henry H (1800-1889) British
£2000	$3560	(28-Apr-92 PH142/R) Conway Castle, North Wales (76x63cm-30x25in) s.i.stretcher

LINFORD, Charles (1846-1897) American
£538	$925	(10-Oct-91 FA.PH883) View of forest at sunset (114x76cm-45x30in) s. canvas on board

LINGELBACH, Johannes (1622-1674) Dutch
£12000	$21840	(11-Dec-91 S166/R) Italianate harbour with figures loading livestock onto small vessel (51x68cm-20x27in)
£24000	$46080	(9-Jul-92 B171/R) Capriccio view of Roman Piazza with numerous figures and activities (104x72cm-41x28in) panel

LINGELBACH, Johannes (attrib) (1622-1674) Dutch
£1739	$2973	(18-Mar-92 D.V368/R) Riders in landscape (35x46cm-14x18in) (A.S 35000)
£5594	$9678	(25-May-92 KM.K979/R) Hunting party in Roman landscape with classical architecture (81x133cm-32x52in) (DM 16000)

LINGELBACH, Johannes (circle) (1622-1674) Dutch
£4074	$7374	(19-May-92 GF.L2364/R) Castle ruins and shepherd scene (74x94cm-29x37in) (S.FR 11000)

LINGELBACH, Johannes (style) (1622-1674) Dutch
£2111	$3821	(3-Dec-91 AB.S4729/R) Town scene with figures (48x40cm-19x16in) (S.KR 22000)
£6500	$11375	(27-Feb-92 CSK150/R) Travellers and dockhands in Levantine harbour (66x90cm-26x35in)

LINGEMAN, Lambertus (1829-1894) Dutch
£3517	$6119	(14-Apr-92 SY.AM77/R) The artist's studio (43x53cm-17x21in) s.d.1871 panel (D.FL 11500)

LINGNER, Otto (1856-?) German
£760	$1361	(16-Nov-91 FAL.M203/R) Nude model (90x70cm-35x28in) s.d.1922 (S.KR 8000)

LINKE, Simon (1958-) American
£5587	$10000	(13-Nov-91 CH.NY307/R) Ed Ruscha, October 1986 (183x183cm-72x72in) linen
£5587	$10000	(7-May-92 SY.NY185/R) Lee Krasner, October 1986 (183x183cm-72x72in)
£6704	$12000	(14-Nov-91 SY.NY212/R) Jean Michel Basquiat, December 1985 (152x152cm-60x60in) s.d.1987 verso linen

INNELL, James Thomas (1826-1905) British
£2800 $5124   (3-Jun-92 S11/R) Boys fishing, Somersetshire (53x77cm-21x30in) s.d.1899

INNELL, John (1792-1882) British
£1100 $1980   (19-Nov-91 PH91/R) North Wales, fine evening after rain (19x32cm-7x13in)
                        s. i.verso paper on panel
£1270 $2209   (14-Sep-91 BU.O282) Landscape with man fishing (16x18cm-6x7in) s.
                        (N.KR 14500)
£2400 $4176   (12-Sep-91 CSK137) Extensive wooded mountainous landscape with David and
                        the Lion (139x217cm-55x85in) s.d.1850
£3200 $5472   (13-Mar-92 C118/R) David (71x99cm-28x39in) s.d.1871
£3500 $6300   (19-Nov-91 PH20/R) Portrait of Henry Petty-Fitzmaurice third Marquis of
                        Lansdowne (38x31cm-15x12in) s.d.1840 panel
£5000 $8850   (5-Nov-91 CD564/R) Shepherds conversing in wooded landscape with sheep
                        (36x28cm-14x11in)
£5200 $9152   (8-Apr-92 S78/R) Gleaners return (33x45cm-13x18in) s.d.1856 panel
£6500 $11050   (25-Oct-91 C73/R) Welsh dairy farm (27x41cm-11x16in) s.d.1847 panel
*£800 $1408   (9-Apr-92 S53) Rooks Hill, near Shoreham, Kent (17x12cm-7x5in) s. pen
                        pencil*
*£2200 $3872   (9-Apr-92 S54) View of Mouse Bridge at foot of Hanson Toot, Derbyshire
                        (15x22cm-6x9in) pen W/C*

INNELL, John (attrib) (1792-1882) British
£660 $1161   (8-Apr-92 GWP.O124) Landscape with man fishing (16x18cm-6x7in) s.
                        (N.KR 7500)
£682 $1200   (8-Apr-92 D.NY52) Harvesters coming in from fields (61x97cm-24x38in)
                        bears sig.

INNELL, William (1826-1910) British
£700 $1239   (6-Nov-91 S41/R) Sandpits near Dorking (46x61cm-18x24in) s.d.1863

INNIG, Egidius (1821-1860) Belgian
£582 $1053   (3-Dec-91 C.A157) Boat launching at Kattendijk boatyard (20x26cm-8x10in)
                        d.1854 panel (B.FR 34000)
£4286 $7500   (18-Feb-92 CE.NY34) Shipping off jetty (55x78cm-22x31in) s.d.1853 with
                        sig.verso panel

INNIG, Willem (elder) (1819-1885) Belgian
£900 $1593   (13-Feb-92 CSK215) Outside the poulterers (55x41cm-22x16in) s.d.1858
                        panel

INNOVAARA, Juhani (1934-) Finnish
£7332 $12905   (12-Apr-92 HOR.H155) Quiet moment (80x75cm-31x30in) s.d.1962 (F.M 58000)
£15653 $27863   (1-Dec-91 HOR.H143/R) Here I come (162x130cm-64x51in) s.d.1988
                        (F.M 121000)
£22756 $40051   (12-Apr-92 HOR.H154/R) Sign of night (150x195cm-59x77in) s.d.1988-1989
                        (F.M 180000)
*£3161 $5563   (12-Apr-92 HOR.H156) Outdone (95x65cm-37x26in) s.d.1984 gouache
                        (F.M 25000)*
£4657 $8290   (1-Dec-91 HOR.H145/R) Frightened (74x54cm-29x21in) s. gouache (F.M 36000)

INNQVIST, Hilding (1891-1984) Swedish
£6149 $11131   (19-May-92 AB.S5269/R) Siesta - view from Bastugatan's Park, Stockholm
                        (81x60cm-32x24in) s. (S.KR 65000)

INS, Adolf (1856-1927) German
£6529 $11491   (11-Apr-92 AW.H1884/R) Cows and geese by stream (59x79cm-23x31in) s.
                        (DM 19000)

INSON, Corwin Knapp (1864-1959) American
£957 $1800   (18-Dec-91 SY.NY176/R) Autumn glow (55x45cm-22x18in) s. canvas on board
£3191 $6000   (18-Dec-91 SY.NY172/R) Views of Jordan, Jerusalem and Bethany
                        (16x22cm-6x9in) s.i.d.1898 and 1899 board five
£3720 $6250   (14-Aug-91 B.P88/R) Winter in New England (30x41cm-12x16in) s.indist.d.

INT, Hendrik van (1684-1763) Flemish
£6000 $11520   (8-Jul-92 S324/R) Coastal landscape with figures beside cascade and
                        fortified town beyond (21x26cm-8x10in)
£25484 $47401   (18-Jun-92 SY.MO38/R) Vue d'un lavoir antique (35x46cm-14x18in) s.
                        (F.FR 250000)
£40000 $69600   (15-Apr-92 C55/R) The Vatican from Monte Mario (33x43cm-13x17in)
£70000 $134400   (7-Jul-92 PH80/R) Mercury delivering infant Bacchus to Mount Nysa. Diana
                        resting after hunt (46x70cm-18x28in) s.d.1744 pair
£105000 $201600   (10-Jul-92 C31/R) Bacino di San Marco, Venice, with masqueraders and
                        gentry on Isola di S. Giorgio to fore (58x110cm-23x43in) s.d.

INT, Hendrik van (circle) (1684-1763) Flemish
£1900 $3648   (9-Jul-92 B148/R) Italianate pastoral landscape with figures on bridge
                        above waterfall (28x25cm-11x10in) indist.init. panel
£3916 $6931   (7-Nov-91 D.V140/R) River landscape with shepherds and animals
                        (24x35cm-9x14in) copper one of pair (A.S 80000)
£3916 $6931   (7-Nov-91 D.V139/R) River landscape with travellers (24x35cm-9x14in)
                        copper one of pair (A.S 80000)

LINT, Hendrik van (style) (1684-1763) Flemish
£900	$1620	(21-Nov-91 C49/R) Waterfall in wooded landscape (13x18cm-5x7in) panel
£1100	$1980	(21-Nov-91 C50) Horseman on track by cottage (13x18cm-5x7in) copper
£1300	$2327	(14-Nov-91 CSK312) Classical figures by lake in Italianate landscape (58x91cm-23x36in)
£2000	$3500	(3-Apr-92 C143) Wooded Italianate landscape with peasants on track by ruins (74x100cm-29x39in)
£2439	$4512	(13-Jun-92 CH.AM174/R) Arcadian landscape with Apollo playing the lyre to nymphs (88x118cm-35x46in) (D.FL 8000)
£4500	$7875	(28-Feb-92 C58/R) Extensive winter landscape (15x22cm-6x9in) copper pair

LINT, Louis van (1909-1987) Belgian
£6364	$11518	(21-May-92 SY.AM265/R) Meandres a dinard (113x146cm-44x57in) s.i.d.1973 (D.FL 21000)
£10909	$19745	(21-May-92 SY.AM264/R) Le marche de nabeul (130x200cm-51x79in) s. (D.FL 36000)
£13636	$24682	(21-May-92 SY.AM239/R) Soleil revelateur (148x200cm-58x79in) s.d.68 i.verso (D.FL 45000)

LINT, Peter van (1609-1690) Flemish
£3909	$7428	(26-Jun-92 AT.P93/R) Une jeune femme a son miroir (35x24cm-14x9in) mono. panel (F.FR 38000)

LINT, Peter van (attrib) (1609-1690) Flemish
£3100	$5673	(12-May-92 SWS738/R) Presentation in temple (114x171cm-45x67in)
£23464	$42000	(16-Jan-92 CH.NY79/R) Holy Family with Saint Anne (126x117cm-50x46in)
£410	*$741*	*(21-May-92 L.K296/R) Southern landscape with town (17x26cm-7x10in) pen sepia wash (DM 1200)*

LINTON, Sir James Dromgole (1840-1916) British
£750	*$1335*	*(29-Oct-91 C60/R) Seated woman holding fan (25x35cm-10x14in) inits.d.89 pencil W/C*

LINTON, William (1791-1876) British
£1000	$1790	(13-Nov-91 S209/R) On the Lune, Sedbergh, Yorkshire (30x42cm-12x17in) i.verso board

LINTON, William (attrib) (1791-1876) British
£3200	$5728	(13-Nov-91 CG515/R) An extensive view of a Spanish City, possibly Salamanca (61x129cm-24x51in)

LINTOTT, Bernard (1875-1951) British
£904	$1700	(18-Dec-91 SY.NY147/R) Promenade in the park (63x76cm-25x30in) s.

LINTZ, Ferdinand Ernst (1833-1909) Dutch
£545	*$965*	*(22-Apr-92 CH.AM332) Farmers on a horse and cart on a snowy track (41x62cm-16x24in) s. W/C bodycol. (D.FL 1800)*

LINTZ, Frederik (1824-1909) Dutch
£1273	$2253	(22-Apr-92 CH.AM197/R) The winetasters (32x25cm-13x10in) s. panel (D.FL 4200)

LIOTARD, Jean-Etienne (1702-1789) Swiss
£11111	*$20111*	*(21-May-92 SY.G33/R) Portraits of the Dauphin. His consort Marie-Josephe de Saxe (6x?cm-2x?in) min.pair gilt metal frames fitted case (S.FR 30000)*

LIOTARD, Jean-Etienne (after) (1702-1789) Swiss
£788	$1363	(7-Sep-91 CH.AM183/R) The chocolate girl (87x56cm-34x22in) (D.FL 2600)

LIOTARD, Jean-Etienne (circle) (1702-1789) Swiss
£30523	$52500	(10-Oct-91 SY.NY44/R) Young woman reading in oriental costume (45x52cm-18x20in)

LIOTARD, Jean-Etienne (school) (1702-1789) Swiss
£1056	$1912	(3-Dec-91 FN.S2312/R) Portrait of Moritz von Sachsen standing before entrance of tent (49x61cm-19x24in) s. (DM 3000)
£550	*$946*	*(4-Mar-92 C25/R) Lady, in decollete fur bordered blue dress, black feather aigrette hair (5x?cm-2x?in) min. vellum gilt mount rec*

LIOTARD, Jean-Etienne (style) (1702-1789) Swiss
£4444	*$8044*	*(19-May-92 GF.L2446/R) Portrait of Reichgraf von Kauniz. His wife (69x56cm-27x22in) pastel board pair (S.FR 12000)*

LIPCHITZ, Jacques (1891-1973) French
£2000	*$3620*	*(2-Dec-91 CSK54/R) Study for the sculpture Arrival (43x49cm-17x19in) s. gouache ink crayon*
£3107	*$5500*	*(5-Nov-91 CE.NY109/R) Etude pour mere et enfant (65x49cm-26x19in) s. pen brush chl*
£3429	*$6000*	*(25-Feb-92 CH.NY90/R) Study for sculpture - Couple (65x61cm-26x24in) s. brush ink wash gessoed masonite*
£65574	*$120000*	*(13-May-92 SY.NY14/R) Guitariste (27x22cm-11x9in) s. gouache oil sand panel*

LIPMAN, M (?) ?
£600 $1074   (11-Nov-91 PH213/R) American street scene (37x48cm-15x19in) s. W/C

LIPPENS, Piet (1890-1981) Belgian
£1159 $2098   (23-May-92 KV.L203) Caravan (55x46cm-22x18in) s. (B.FR 70000)

LIPPI, Lorenzo (attrib) (1606-1665) Italian
£1321 $2299   (13-Apr-92 AT.P22) La Charite Romaine (61x50cm-24x20in) (F.FR 13000)
£20994 $38000   (21-May-92 CH.NY83/R) Rebecca and Eliezer (208x269cm-82x106in)

LIPPI, Lorenzo (circle) (1606-1665) Italian
£3395 $6077   (12-Nov-91 SY.AM202/R) Mary Magdalene (47x35cm-19x14in) (D.FL 11000)
£6000 $10500   (25-Feb-92 PH40/R) Crucifixion with the Virgin, Mary Magdelene and St
                                      John the Evangelist (188x101cm-74x40in)

LIPPINE (19th C) American
£2151 $3700   (10-Oct-91 FA.PH726 a) Landscape (20x30cm-8x12in) s. panel

LIPPS, Richard (1857-1926) German
£919 $1608   (3-Apr-92 BM.B676/R) Venetian courtyard and women fetching water
                                      (30x20cm-12x8in) s.i. panel (DM 2600)
£1229 $2224   (21-May-92 L.K447) Peasant garden with goats (47x55cm-19x22in) s.
                                      (DM 3600)
£7514 $13000   (6-Sep-91 S.BM148/R) Marketplace, Venice (112x81cm-44x32in) s.
£8571 $15000   (19-Feb-92 CH.NY69/R) Piazza della Erbe, Verona (112x81cm-44x32in) s.
£430 $770   (14-Nov-91 GRO.B35/R) Reading in cloister (61x46cm-24x18in) s. W/C

LIPTAI, Arthur (1893-?) German
£1923 $3327   (25-Mar-92 KM.K1294/R) Cows grazing by edge of wood and peasant family
                                      harvesting (100x140cm-39x55in) s. (DM 5500)

LIPTON, Seymour (20th C) American
£3073 $5500   (12-Nov-91 CE.NY2/R) Untitled (21x27cm-8x11in) one s.d.53 one s.d.61 chl
                                      graphite two

LIRA, Pedro (19th C) Chilean
£4124 $7175   (21-Sep-91 SA.A1923/R) Flowers from an admirer (121x70cm-48x28in) s.
                                      (DM 12000)
£6686 $11500   (17-Oct-91 SY.NY359/R) Lady Jennifer (140x90cm-55x35in) s.d.1877

LISAERT, Pieter (attrib) (16th C) Flemish
£2400 $4272   (29-Oct-91 PH106/R) The Annunciation (51x33cm-20x13in) panel

LISIEWSKA, Anna Dorothea (attrib) (1721-1782) German
£2035 $3500   (9-Oct-91 CH.NY70/R) Young woman, in costume, wearing wreath flowers,
                                      holding parrot, tazza (70x86cm-28x34in)
£2907 $5000   (10-Oct-91 SY.NY34/R) Allegory of wisdom triumphing over ignorance
                                      (56x71cm-22x28in)

LISIO, Arnaldo de (1869-?) Italian
£546 $1000   (16-May-92 HG.C192) Young maiden (86x58cm-34x23in) s.

LISMER, Arthur (1885-1969) Canadian
£1500 $2655   (6-Nov-91 SY.T180/R) Junk on derelict, Cape Breton (30x41cm-12x16in)
                                      i.d.48 init.verso panel (C.D 3000)
£1791 $3188   (26-Nov-91 JOY.T184/R) Tide coming in on Long Beach, Vancouver Island,
                                      West coast (30x40cm-12x16in) s. panel (C.D 3600)
£2388 $4251   (26-Nov-91 JOY.T79/R) Light in forest, Vancouver Island (40x30cm-16x12in)
                                      s.d.58 panel (C.D 4800)
£2500 $4425   (6-Nov-91 SY.T177/R) Still life with pears (30x43cm-12x17in) s.d.45
                                      s.d.1945 verso panel double-sided pencil (C.D 5000)
£3980 $7085   (26-Nov-91 JOY.T10/R) Lake Macarthur, Canadian Rockies (32x40cm-13x16in)
                                      s. board (C.D 8000)
£4110 $7521   (14-May-92 SY.T48/R) Glacier, Moraine Lake (22x29cm-9x11in) s. s.i.verso
                                      board (C.D 9000)
£6500 $11505   (6-Nov-91 SY.T94/R) Pine tree, Georgian Bay (23x31cm-9x12in) s.verso
                                      panel (C.D 13000)
£8676 $15877   (14-May-92 SY.T73/R) Little Cove, Macgregor Bay (31x39cm-12x15in) s.
                                      s.i.d.1930 verso board (C.D 19000)
£11872 $21726   (14-May-92 SY.T70/R) Algoma (23x31cm-9x12in) s. d.1922 verso panel
                                      (C.D 26000)
£413 $756   (2-Jun-92 R.T541/R) Cape Breton Island (23x28cm-9x11in) st.sig. d. estate
                                      st.verso conte crayon (C.D 900)
£463 $839   (2-Dec-91 R.T235/R) Milk maid in farmyard (31x47cm-12x19in) s. W/C
                                      graphite (C.D 950)
£721 $1262   (17-Feb-92 HO.ED128/R) Forest giants, Vancouver Island, B C
                                      (19x13cm-7x5in) s. ink chl. (C.D 1500)

LISMONDE, Jules (1908-) Belgian
£2506 $4261   (22-Oct-91 C.A229/R) The silence of spring (100x73cm-39x29in) s.d.1965
                                      panel (B.FR 150000)
£468 $795   (22-Oct-91 C.A233) Composition (64x15cm-25x6in) s.d.1973 ink dr.
                                      (B.FR 28000)
£476 $814   (21-Mar-92 KV.L188) Composition (52x31cm-20x12in) s. wash (B.FR 28000)

LISMONDE, Jules (1908-) Belgian-cont.
£535   *$909*   *(22-Oct-91 C.A232) Composition (48x63cm-19x25in) s.d.1968 chl. (B.FR 32000)*
£535   *$909*   *(22-Oct-91 C.A231) Valtellina III (47x70cm-19x28in) s.d.1964 dr. (B.FR 32000)*
£1170   *$1988*   *(22-Oct-91 C.A230) Perspectives autres IV (65x49cm-26x19in) s.d.1974 dr. (B.FR 70000)*

LISS, Jan (attrib) (c.1595-1629) Dutch
£1778 $3218   (19-May-92 GF.L2359/R) The evangelist Matthew (72x63cm-28x25in) (S.FR 4800)

LISS, Jan (style) (c.1595-1629) Dutch
£1300 $2275   (27-Feb-92 CSK97) Diana bathing with her Nymphs (23x25cm-9x10in) panel oval

LISSANDRINO, Alessandro see MAGNASCO, Alessandro

LISSE, Dirck van der (?-1669) Dutch
£2600 $4680   (21-Nov-91 C155/R) Actaeon discovering Diana and nymphs bathing (22x32cm-9x13in) mono. copper on panel
£2616 $4500   (10-Oct-91 SY.NY96/R) Landscape with nymphs dancing around a herm (31x27cm-12x11in) panel
£9302 $16000   (9-Oct-91 CH.NY88/R) Diana and Actaeon in mountainous river landscape (113x150cm-44x59in)

LISSE, Dirck van der (style) (?-1669) Dutch
£750 $1373   (12-May-92 SWS781) River landscape with nymphs bathing (18x23cm-7x9in) panel

LISSITZKY, El (1890-1941) Russian
£68259   *$124232*   *(29-May-92 VG.B50/R) Proun-star (55x44cm-22x17in) s. i.verso collage ind.ink gouache over pencil (DM 200000)*

LISTER, William Lister (1859-1943) Australian
£669 $1212   (19-May-92 JRL.S55) Twilight (35x45cm-14x18in) s. board (A.D 1600)
£1542 $2775   (19-Nov-91 JRL.S274) North Narabeen (32x75cm-13x30in) s. (A.D 3500)
£598   *$1065*   *(27-Apr-92 J.M300 a) By the Hawkesbury (36x56cm-14x22in) s. W/C (A.D 1400)*
£619   *$1033*   *(21-Aug-91 DS.W1) Seaside with distant ships (24x37cm-9x15in) s. W/C (NZ.D 1800)*
£684   *$1217*   *(27-Apr-92 J.M538) Coastal cliffs (40x42cm-16x17in) s. W/C (A.D 1600)*
£766   *$1356*   *(26-Apr-92 SY.ME132/R) River landscape (33x49cm-13x19in) s. W/C (A.D 1800)*
£907   *$1688*   *(15-Jun-92 MGS.S83) River scene (42x48cm-17x19in) s. W/C (A.D 2250)*
£1202   *$2295*   *(21-Jul-92 JRL.S133) Morning walk (27x50cm-11x20in) s. W/C (A.D 3100)*

LITTLE, John C (1928-) Canadian
£1000 $1770   (6-Nov-91 SY.T257/R) Last year of Lachine Canal, Montreal (30x39cm-12x15in) s. s.i.d.74 stretcher (C.D 2000)
£2740 $5014   (14-May-92 SY.T15/R) Epicerie Poulin - Quebec (60x75cm-24x30in) s. s.d.75 stretcher (C.D 6000)

LITTLE, Philip (1857-1942) American
£833 $1400   (14-Aug-91 B.P154/R) Green Island, Sheepscot River (76x102cm-30x40in) s. i.d.1925 verso
£4670 $8500   (28-May-92 CH.NY178/R) Rainy night in Washington (76x76cm-30x30in) s.d.1910

LITTLEJOHNS, John (1874-?) British
£474 $868   (12-May-92 GO.G227) Landscape (52x62cm-20x24in) s.d.1920 (S.KR 5000)

LITTROW, Leo von (1860-1914) Italian
£494 $865   (19-Feb-92 D.V28/R) Flowering coastal landscape, Bay of Naples (47x44cm-19x17in) i.verso (A.S 10000)
£692 $1211   (19-Feb-92 D.V29/R) Fishing boats before southern harbour (24x46cm-9x18in) i.verso (A.S 14000)
£732 $1266   (3-Oct-91 D.V109/R) Southern coastal landscape with view of town (53x79cm-21x31in) (A.S 15000)
£1214 $2160   (28-Apr-92 D.V102/R) Phlox and tagetes (48x37cm-19x15in) mono panel (A.S 25000)

LITVINIENKO, Vladimir (1930-) Russian
£510 $948   (17-Jun-92 ARC.P186/R) Les iris (70x94cm-28x37in) s. (F.FR 5000)
£528 $920   (13-Apr-92 ARC.P49/R) Venise (65x85cm-26x33in) s. (F.FR 5200)
£589 $1026   (13-Apr-92 ARC.P50/R) Au bord de la mer (73x85cm-29x33in) s. (F.FR 5800)
£628 $1137   (20-May-92 ARC.P44/R) Au jardin public (62x73cm-24x29in) s. (F.FR 6200)
£713 $1304   (3-Jun-92 ARC.P125/R) Journee de printemps a Odessa (85x91cm-33x36in) s. (F.FR 7000)
£963 $1742   (20-May-92 ARC.P45/R) La foret en hiver (68x99cm-27x39in) s. (F.FR 9500)
£1474 $2564   (13-Apr-92 ARC.P48/R) Dimanche au parc (100x90cm-39x35in) s. (F.FR 14500)
£1520 $2751   (20-May-92 ARC.P42/R) Bouquet pres de la fenetre (100x56cm-39x22in) s. (F.FR 15000)

LITVINOVSKY, Pinchas (1894-1985) Israeli
£620 $1128   (11-Dec-91 ZZ.B247) Peasant girl (55x46cm-22x18in) s.verso
£649 $1200   (9-Jun-92 GG.TA390/R) Seated man (60x46cm-24x18in) board
£649 $1200   (9-Jun-92 GG.TA393/R) Rabbi (66x46cm-26x18in) s. board
£649 $1200   (9-Jun-92 GG.TA388/R) Women gathering wood (36x30cm-14x12in) board
£919 $1700   (9-Jun-92 GG.TA391/R) Head of woman and flowers (45x29cm-18x11in) s. board
£1167 $2100   (6-Jan-92 GG.TA419/R) Musicians (60x65cm-24x26in) s.
£4167 $7500   (6-Jan-92 GG.TA418/R) Two seated Arabs (130x97cm-51x38in)
£15135 $28000   (9-Jun-92 GG.TA387/R) Woman and donkey (73x92cm-29x36in) s.
£378 $700   (8-Jun-92 GG.TA50/R) Nude (67x103cm-26x41in) s. pastel
£378 $700   (9-Jun-92 GG.TA392/R) Nudes (38x28cm-15x11in) s. gouache

LITVINSKI, Petr (1927-) Russian
£564 $1014   (27-Jan-92 ARC.P70/R) Interieur aux icones (65x50cm-26x20in) s. board (F.FR 5500)
£1361 $2382   (24-Sep-91 ARC.P30/R) Devant l'aquarium (92x68cm-36x27in) s.d.56 (F.FR 13500)

LIU CHAN-HUNG (1953-) Chinese
£1770 $3027   (22-Mar-92 SY.TA83/R) Temple doors (42x53cm-17x21in) s.d.1991 (T.D 77000)

LIU CHI-WEI (1912-) Chinese
£5057 $8648   (22-Mar-92 SY.TA76/R) Evening call (60x47cm-24x19in) s.d.1980 mixed media (T.D 220000)

LIU GUOSONG (1932-) Chinese
£6287 $11002   (30-Mar-92 CH.HK327/R) Water and clouds at Lake Wangmu (84x81cm-33x32in) s.d.1986 ink W/C hanging scroll (HK.D 85000)

LIU JIAN (1961-) Chinese
£5816 $9946   (22-Mar-92 SY.TA86/R) Abstract architectural structure (180x96cm-71x38in) artist seal mixed media (T.D 253000)

LIVESAY, Richard (attrib) (?-1823) British
£1600 $3056   (15-Jul-92 S150/R) Portrait of young girl (41x33cm-16x13in)

LIVINGSTON, John (fl.1827-1834) British
£5500 $9680   (10-Apr-92 C38/R) Portrait of three children with dog cart in landscape (113x90cm-44x35in) s.d.1832

LIZCANO Y MONEDERO, Angel (19th C) Spanish
£2589 $4454   (7-Oct-91 ANS.M130/R) Descanso en el camino (47x29cm-19x11in) s.d.92 (S.P 475000)

LIZCANO, Angel (?) Spanish
£887 $1552   (18-Feb-92 DUR.M65/R) Lancero medieval (21x11cm-8x4in) s. panel (S.P 160000)

LJUBA (1934-) Yugoslavian
£1232 $2218   (19-Nov-91 FB.P154/R) Le mythe de promehee (41x33cm-16x13in) s.i.d.1980verso (F.FR 12000)

LJUNGBERG, Sigge (20th C) Swedish
£493 $903   (17-May-92 BU.M479) Coffee after the funeral (21x28cm-8x11in) s.d.1958 panel (S.KR 5200)

LJUNGGREN, Reinhold (1920-) Swedish
£1583 $2866   (3-Dec-91 AB.S5091/R) Southern street scene (65x54cm-26x21in) s. (S.KR 16500)
£3321 $6077   (13-May-92 BU.S112/R) Winter day by Trosa river (39x55cm-15x22in) s. panel (S.KR 35000)

LJUNGQUIST, Birger (1898-1965) Swedish
£575 $1035   (23-Nov-91 SO.S446/R) Woman behind tree (31x23cm-12x9in) s.d.1955 W/C (S.KR 6000)

LJUTICA, Zoran (20th C) ?
£615 $1102   (19-Jan-92 ZZ.F194/R) Metamorphose 1 (103x65cm-41x26in) s. (F.FR 6000)
£718 $1285   (19-Jan-92 ZZ.F50/R) Metamorphose 2 (116x89cm-46x35in) s. (F.FR 7000)
£769 $1377   (19-Jan-92 ZZ.F234/R) La tete alchimice (130x97cm-51x38in) s. (F.FR 7500)

LLAMAS, Millan (20th C) Spanish
£547 $1040   (23-Jun-92 DUR.M984/R) Quite por veronicas (50x61cm-20x24in) s.d.10-57 (S.P 100000)

LLAVERIAS LABRO, Joan (1865-1938) Spanish
£681 $1172   (7-Oct-91 ANS.M64/R) Puerto mediterraneo (30x42cm-12x17in) s.d.1902 W/C (S.P 125000)
£887 $1569   (12-Feb-92 ANS.M30/R) Barcas (24x34cm-9x13in) s. W/C (S.P 160000)

LLONA, Ramiro (1947-) Peruvian
£9945 $18000   (18-May-92 CH.NY207/R) Still hour of crysalis (173x203cm-68x80in)

LLOPIS, Carlos Ruano (1878-1950) Spanish
£678 $1200   (9-Nov-91 W.W48/R) Bull fight (38x53cm-15x21in) s. canvas mounted on panel
£1374 $2473   (19-Nov-91 DUR.M32/R) Picador (154x106cm-61x42in) s. (S.P 250000)

LLORENS, Jose Navarro see   NAVARRO LLORENS, Jose

LLOVERAS, Federico (1912-1983) Spanish
£1261 $2244   (26-Nov-91 BRO.B371) La modelo (92x60cm-36x24in) s. s.i.d.1974verso (S.P 230000)
£657 $1169   *(29-Oct-91 BRO.B316) Paseo de Isabel II, Barcelona (35x50cm-14x20in) s.d.45 W/C (S.P 120000)*

LLOYD, Frederick John see   STREVENS, John

LLOYD, Tom see   LLOYD, Thomas James

LLOYD JONES, Sir Charles (1878-1958) Australian
£5385 $10285   (19-Jul-92 SY.ME16/R) Caretaker's cottage (50x60cm-20x24in) s. (A.D 14000)

LLOYD OF ELLESMERE, Edward (19th C) British
£1100 $1947   (5-Nov-91 CD571/R) Stable scene with stallion and mare (61x74cm-24x29in) s.d.1867 board
£1300 $2301   (5-Nov-91 CD572/R) Stable interior with stallion (61x74cm-24x29in) s.d.1867 board

LLOYD, Marcia (20th C) American
£1796 $3000   (25-Aug-91 JRB.C84) Arboretum summer II, 1987 (102x168cm-40x66in)

LLOYD, Norman (1897-1985) Australian
£513 $913   (28-Apr-92 CH.ME127) Ripening corn (31x39cm-12x15in) s. board (A.D 1200)
£798 $1333   (19-Aug-91 SY.ME7/R) Oasis (62x73cm-24x29in) s. i.verso canvas on board (A.D 1700)
£881 $1568   (26-Nov-91 J.M132) Springtime (74x95cm-29x37in) s. (A.D 2000)
£1322 $2379   (24-Nov-91 SY.S18/R) Darling Harbour (44x54cm-17x21in) s. (A.D 3000)

LLOYD, R Malcolm (fl.1879-1907) British
£500 $950   (24-Jun-92 MMB263) Estuary scene with fishermen (25x51cm-10x20in) s.d.1889
£500 $900   *(27-Jan-92 PH44) Fishing fleet returning to port (17x48cm-7x19in) s.i. W/C*
£580 $1027   *(6-Nov-91 S228/R) Harbour entrance (34x49cm-13x19in) s.indis.i.d. W/C htd.white*

LLOYD, T Ivester (19/20th C) British
£550 $1051   (16-Jul-92 HB611) Horses taking fence at point-to-point (36x58cm-14x23in) s.
£800 $1536   *(28-Jul-92 SWS129/R) Mares and a foal in a field (59x75cm-23x30in) s.*
£400 $700   *(17-Feb-92 HS190/R) Toll gate (23x34cm-9x13in) s.i. W/C*

LLOYD, Thomas James (1849-1910) British
£1100 $2013   (3-Jun-92 S54/R) The Lord of the Manor (29x53cm-11x21in) s. board
£580 $1061   *(14-May-92 B275/R) Gathering blackberries (29x51cm-11x20in) s.d.79 W/C*
£800 $1384   *(23-Mar-92 HS171/R) Autumnal landscape with lady and pet dog in foreground (19x34cm-7x13in) s.d.1896*
£800 $1432   *(15-Jan-92 BT87/R) The cottage on the marsh (20x46cm-8x18in) s.d.1906 W/C*
£940 $1598   *(22-Oct-91 SWS201/R) Road to farm (12x26cm-5x10in) s.d.1896 W/C bodycol*
£1200 $2124   *(6-Nov-91 S276/R) On the river bank (15x35cm-6x14in) s.d.1901 W/C htd.white*
£1400 $2562   *(6-Feb-92 T170/R) Figures and geese by thatched cottage (23x48cm-9x19in) s.d.1906 W/C*
£2200 $3938   *(14-Jan-92 SWS87/R) Evening stroll (38x69cm-15x27in) s.d.1906 W/C bodycol*
£2500 $4575   *(3-Jun-92 S275/R) Gathering roses (29x69cm-11x27in) s.d.1903 W/C*
£6000 $10800   *(27-Jan-92 PH128/R) August - scene is Wembury, twelve miles from Plymouth (54x120cm-21x47in) s.d.1889 i.verso W/C bodycol*

LLOYD, W Stuart (fl.1875-1929) British
£629 $1089   (25-Mar-92 KM.K1295) Scottish lake landscape with cattle grazing (67x40cm-26x16in) s.d.1884 (DM 1800)
£420 $777   *(11-Jun-92 CSK53) Fishermen preparing their boats, Clovelly (48x69cm-19x27in) s. pencil W/C htd. white*
£500 $870   *(12-Sep-91 CSK41/R) Lincoln Cathedral (36x71cm-14x28in) s.d.1911 pencil W/C htd white*
£550 $1018   *(11-Jun-92 CSK40/R) A barge on the river at Ilford Bridge (48x74cm-19x29in) s. W/C bodycol.*
£700 $1232   *(10-Apr-92 K475) Tranquil evening river scene with figure fishing from punt (71x53cm-28x21in) s.d.1885 W/C*
£700 $1281   *(15-May-92 MAI293) The duck pond, Brading s. W/C*
£800 $1504   *(19-Dec-91 C38/R) Waiting for the ferry (29x65cm-11x26in) s.d.1902 pencil W/C htd white*
£894 $1600   *(13-Nov-91 B.SF2338/R) Brittany coast at sunset (28x64cm-11x25in) s.d.1906 W/C*
£980 $1882   *(28-Jul-92 SWS259/R) Crossing the bridge (30x65cm-12x26in) s. W/C over pencil*

LLOYD, W Stuart (fl.1875-1929) British-cont.
£1000 $1710   *(12-Mar-92 CSK28/R) Fishing fleet at Caernarvon (30x89cm-12x35in) s. pencil W/C htd.white*
£1150 $2001   *(13-Sep-91 MAX319/R) Fishbourne Mill, river landscape with fishing boats landing catch (48x74cm-19x29in) s. W/C*

LLULL, Jose Pinelo (1861-1922) Spanish
£1910 $3400   (1-Nov-91 PO.BA23) Paisaje fluvial (32x41cm-13x16in) s.d.1912 panel
£5179 $8907   (7-Oct-91 ANS.M93/R) Rincon de Guadalcanal (68x100cm-27x39in) s.d.1902 (S.P 950000)

LO-A-NJOE, Clyde (1937-) ?
£926 $1685   (11-Dec-91 CH.AM159/R) Alice in Lop-Lop land (120x99cm-47x39in) s.i.d.1990verso acrylic (D.FL 3000)

LOATES, Glen (1945-) Canadian
£450 $797   *(6-Nov-91 SY.T181/R) Ring-necked pheasant (36x28cm-14x11in) s.d.1974 pencil framed with reproduction (C.D 900)*

LOBLEY, James (19th C) British
£1550 $2666   (16-Oct-91 PHL232/R) Key (34x44cm-13x17in) s.

LOBO, Balthazar (1911-) Spanish
£636 $1195   *(16-Dec-91 ANS.M219/R) Dama con mantilla (50x33cm-20x13in) s.d.1948 W/C (S.P 115000)*
£1254 $2156   *(7-Oct-91 ANS.M54/R) Dama con mantilla (50x33cm-20x13in) s.d.1948 W/C (S.P 230000)*

LOCARDI, Gerard (1915-) French
£1778 $3095   *(15-Apr-92 PLF.P88/R) Couples (185x62cm-73x24in) s.d.53 gouache three-panelled screen (F.FR 17500)*

LOCATELLI, Andrea (1693-1741) Italian
£7901 $14302   (3-Dec-91 SY.MI201/R) Paesaggi (22x30cm-9x12in) oval pair (I.L 17000000)
£8336 $14422   (25-Mar-92 CH.R9/R) Paesaggio lacustre con pescatori (40x55cm-16x22in) (I.L 18000000)
£16672 $28843   (25-Mar-92 CH.R111/R) Contadini che giocano a carte con rovine romane e viandanti sullo sfondo (64x75cm-25x30in) mono. (I.L 36000000)
£17197 $31127   (4-Dec-91 CH.R98/R) Capriccio di rovine antiche con urna e soldati (99x75cm-39x30in) (I.L 37000000)
£27000 $49140   (13-Dec-91 C267/R) Mountainous landscape with shepherd and peasant girl (75x98cm-30x39in)

LOCATELLI, Andrea (attrib) (1693-1741) Italian
£4972 $9000   (21-May-92 CH.NY176/R) Mountainous river landscape with washerwoman and herdsman by cascade (98x73cm-39x29in)
£12400 $23684   (20-Jul-92 WW10/R) Classical Italianate landscape with figures (62x75cm-24x30in)
£31600 $58777   (20-Jun-92 CH.MO8/R) Paysage du Latium (81x119cm-32x47in) (F.FR 310000)

LOCATELLI, Andrea (circle) (1693-1741) Italian
£3600 $6408   (29-Oct-91 PH98/R) Shepherds conversing with a soldier before a river estuary (59x74cm-23x29in)
£6077 $11000   (22-May-92 SY.NY175/R) Italianate landscape with figures along country road (59x72cm-23x28in)
£10500 $18375   (25-Feb-92 PH65/R) Italianate river landscape with figures fishing before stone bridge (71x98cm-28x39in)

LOCATELLI, Andrea (style) (1693-1741) Italian
£1300 $2496   (9-Jul-92 CSK264/R) Travellers fording stream in landscape (57x73cm-22x29in) panel
£1400 $2450   (2-Apr-92 CSK66/R) Drover with goats and sheep in Italianate landscape (69x90cm-27x35in)
£1450 $2538   (27-Feb-92 CSK93/R) Elijah and the Ravens (48x60cm-19x24in)
£2300 $4025   (28-Feb-92 C42) Italianate landscape with traveller by classical ruins (53x42cm-21x17in)
£2495 $4516   (3-Dec-91 AB.S4730/R) Italian river landscape with figures (40x50cm-16x20in) (S.KR 26000)

LOCATELLI, Giovan Francesco (1810-1882) Italian
£2037 $3707   (28-May-92 F.M60) Ritratto di fanciulla con specchio (74x64cm-29x25in) s. (I.L 4500000)

LOCCA, Albert (1895-1966) Swiss
£1176 $2000   (23-Oct-91 GD.B461/R) Still life with thistles and glass decanter (46x40cm-18x16in) s. (S.FR 3000)

LOCCA, Jimmy (1940-) Swiss
£471 $800   *(23-Oct-91 GD.B464/R) La Suisse (80x100cm-31x39in) s. oil collage canvas (S.FR 1200)*

LOCHER, Carl (1851-1915) Danish
£528 $887   (28-Aug-91 KH.K130) English warship in the Channel (33x47cm-13x19in) s. (D.KR 6000)

LOCHER, Carl (1851-1915) Danish-cont.
£542	$975	(19-Nov-91 RAS.K219) Gathering seaweed (23x33cm-9x13in) mono.d.91 (D.KR 6000)
£575	$1017	(11-Feb-92 RAS.K89) Coastal landscape with fishermen tending nets, morning (34x47cm-13x19in) init.d.87 (D.KR 6400)
£617	$1099	(28-Apr-92 RAS.K252) Winter night with full moon, Osterby, Skagen (33x41cm-13x16in) s.d.1901 (D.KR 7000)
£704	$1183	(28-Aug-91 KH.K129) Landscape with church, Hornbaek (41x55cm-16x22in) s.d.1855 (D.KR 8000)
£879	$1573	(6-May-92 KH.K124) Seascape with sailship (41x58cm-16x23in) s. (D.KR 10000)
£882	$1570	(28-Apr-92 RAS.K201/R) In full sail (48x72cm-19x28in) s.d.76 (D.KR 10000)
£1077	$1907	(11-Feb-92 RAS.K88/R) Herringboats in Sundet (35x60cm-14x24in) s.d.84 (D.KR 12000)
£1163	$2116	(12-Dec-91 RAS.V743/R) Seascape with sailship (35x54cm-14x21in) s. (D.KR 13000)
£1525	$2744	(30-Jan-92 RAS.V646/R) Seascape with vessels at sea (42x57cm-17x22in) s.d.98 (D.KR 17000)
£1852	$3296	(28-Apr-92 RAS.K299/R) Fishermen on edge of water (57x82cm-22x32in) s. (D.KR 21000)
£2113	$3549	(27-Aug-91 RAS.K504/R) Fishermen pulling nets out of the sea (47x66cm-19x26in) s. (D.KR 24000)
£2205	$3924	(28-Apr-92 RAS.K301/R) Fishingboats in sunshine (63x97cm-25x38in) s. (D.KR 25000)
£2437	$4386	(19-Nov-91 RAS.K48/R) Seascape with rowingboat (46x60cm-18x24in) s.d.1902 (D.KR 27000)
£3081	$5176	(28-Aug-91 KH.K128/R) The lifeboat going out (76x130cm-30x51in) s. (D.KR 35000)
£3785	$6359	(27-Aug-91 RAS.K52/R) The lifeboat going out (55x80cm-22x31in) s. (D.KR 43000)
£4665	$7838	(27-Aug-91 RAS.K61 a/R) Seascape with sailship off coast of North Sjaelland (73x110cm-29x43in) s.d.84 (D.KR 53000)

LOCHERT, J (19th C) British
£720	$1303	(20-May-92 BT235/R) Zodiac of Whitby - Captain W Mansell (48x74cm-19x29in) s.i.d.1866

LOCHHEAD, John (1866-1921) British
£1100	$1969	(6-May-92 MMB411) Village pond with ducks, horse cart and figures (38x76cm-15x30in) s.d.03

LOCHHEAD, Kenneth (1926-) American
£1122	$2020	(18-Nov-91 HO.ED100) Quiet morning (61x81cm-24x32in) board (C.D 2300)

LOCKERBY, Mabel I (1887-?) Canadian
£1484	$2716	(14-May-92 SY.T198/R) Red sails (22x29cm-9x11in) s. d.1928 verso panel (C.D 3250)
£1507	$2742	(26-May-92 JOY.T264/R) Three boats (22x30cm-9x12in) s. panel (C.D 3300)

LOCKHART, William Ewart (1846-1900) British
£8000	$13440	(26-Aug-91 S835/R) Orange harvest, Majorca (62x86cm-24x34in) s.d.1875

LODDER, W P J (fl.1783-1804) British
£800	*$1424*	*(27-Nov-91 C249/R) Portrait of lady wearing coral necklace (7x?cm-3x?in) min.s.i.d.1802verso gold frame oval*

LODER OF BATH, James (1784-1860) British
£1400	$2520	(22-Nov-91 SWS296/R) Study of a grey horse in a stable (56x71cm-22x28in) s.d.1834

LODER OF BATH, James (attrib) (1784-1860) British
£3600	$6336	(8-Apr-92 S213/R) Study of two hounds (23x64cm-9x25in)

LODER, James see LODER OF BATH, James

LODER, Matthaus (1781-1828) Australian
£922	*$1668*	*(22-May-92 GB.B5960) Portrait of Napoleon and Marie Louise (50x43cm-20x17in) s. brush (DM 2700)*

LODGE, G E (1860-1954) British
£460	*$810*	*(6-Apr-92 WW104) Norwegian scene (27x36cm-11x14in) i.verso gouache*

LODGE, George Edward (1860-1954) British
£1500	$2520	(26-Aug-91 S930/R) Rough-legged buzzard (15x23cm-6x9in) s. panel
£2000	$3500	(25-Feb-92 C116/R) Peregrine falcon on rocky outcrop (39x59cm-15x23in) s. canvasboard
£2600	$4550	(25-Feb-92 C184/R) Woodcock shooting (14x24cm-6x9in) s.d.1885 with i.verso panel
£9000	$16020	(28-Apr-92 S208/R) Iceland Gyr-Falcon (81x122cm-32x48in) s.d.1916 i.stretcher
£1100	*$1892*	*(4-Mar-92 DR78/R) Pheasant in flight (28x43cm-11x17in) s. bodycol*
£1272	*$2200*	*(2-Oct-91 D.NY56) Curious quail. Snow grouse in sun spot (38x58cm-15x23in) s. W/C pair*
£1400	*$2450*	*(25-Feb-92 C131/R) Pheasants in flight (28x44cm-11x17in) s. pencil W/C bodycol*

LODGE, George Edward (1860-1954) British-cont.

£1500	$2640	(6-Apr-92 WW105/R) Dark breasted barn owl (29x23cm-11x9in) s. gouache
£1600	$2800	(25-Feb-92 C37/R) Marsh tit (23x15cm-9x6in) s. i.verso pencil W/C bodycol
£1700	$2975	(25-Feb-92 C16/R) Slender-billed Nutcracker (28x22cm-11x9in) s. i.verso pencil W/C htd white
£1750	$3360	(28-Jul-92 SWS51/R) Grouse in flight (27x41cm-11x16in) s. W/C htd. bodycol.
£1800	$3258	(21-May-92 B409/R) Pheasant flying out of wood. Cock and hen pheasant perched on fence (28x43cm-11x17in) s. gouache pair
£2100	$3696	(6-Apr-92 WW106/R) Pheasant Phasianns Calchicus - Melanistic Mutant (23x30cm-9x12in) s. gouache
£2200	$4070	(12-Jun-92 C61/R) Woodcock over the Moors (27x44cm-11x17in) s. W/C bodycol.
£2200	$4070	(12-Jun-92 C60/R) Covey of partridge in a field of stubble (27x44cm-11x17in) s. W/C bodycol.
£2500	$4200	(26-Aug-91 S947/R) Grouse (28x44cm-11x17in) s. W/C htd bodycol.
£2500	$4200	(26-Aug-91 S889/R) Partridge amongst the stubble (28x44cm-11x17in) s. gouache
£2500	$4375	(25-Feb-92 C154/R) Great Snipe (23x30cm-9x12in) s. pencil W/C bodycol
£2500	$4200	(26-Aug-91 S892/R) High flyers (29x43cm-11x17in) s. gouache
£2500	$4200	(26-Aug-91 S894/R) Grouse in snow (29x44cm-11x17in) s. W/C htd bodycol.
£2500	$4200	(26-Aug-91 S891/R) Grouse in flight (29x44cm-11x17in) s. gouache
£3200	$5600	(25-Feb-92 C36/R) Willow Warbler. Chiffchaff (29x20cm-11x8in) s. i.verso pencil W/C bodycol pair
£4000	$7000	(25-Feb-92 C141/R) Ptarmigan in flight (28x43cm-11x17in) s. bodycol
£5800	$10150	(25-Feb-92 C135/R) Red grouse on heathland (29x50cm-11x20in) s. bodycol

LODGE, Reginald B (fl.1881-1890) British

| £3279 | $6000 | (5-Jun-92 SY.NY314/R) Icelandic Falcon. Atlantic Osprey (87x74cm-34x29in) 1 init. pair |

LODI, Gaetano (19th C) Italian

| £1271 | $2300 | (2-Dec-91 S.SL513/R) Genre subjects, children playing (43x51cm-17x20in) s. pair |
| £3022 | $5500 | (26-May-92 CE.NY166/R) Sneaking a smoke. A brawl (41x52cm-16x20in) s. pair |

LODI, Gilardo da (19th C) Italian

| £18000 | $32760 | (13-Dec-91 C261/R) Vine hanging over potplant, parrot and funghi, rocky landscape beyond (88x113cm-35x44in) |

LOEB, Louis (1866-1909) American

| £2162 | $4000 | (10-Jun-92 CE.NY419/R) Lady standing in breeze (36x25cm-14x10in) s. panel |

LOEB, Pierre (20th C) French

| £832 | $1597 | (6-Jul-92 HC.P51/R) Nature morte a la figue (61x46cm-24x18in) s. (F.FR 8000) |

LOEBER, Lou (1894-1983) Dutch

| £1364 | $2468 | (19-May-92 CH.AM1/R) Wervelend landscape (55x55cm-22x22in) init.d.61 board (D.FL 4500) |

LOEFFLER, Carl Friedrich (1823-1905) Austrian

| £1739 | $2973 | (18-Mar-92 D.V233/R) Holy Family (41x32cm-16x13in) s.d.1900 panel after Leonardo da Vinci (A.S 35000) |

LOEMANS, A F (19th C) American

| £621 | $1100 | (10-Nov-91 LIT.L107) Indian encampment in mountains (30x46cm-12x18in) s. |

LOEMANS, Alexander Francois (19th C) American

| £1277 | $2400 | (18-Dec-91 SY.NY41/R) Mountain ravine with rushing stream (121x81cm-48x32in) s.i. |
| £6667 | $12000 | (19-Nov-91 CH.NY216/R) Monte Chimborazo (76x123cm-30x48in) s. |

LOEWIG, Roger (1930-) German

| £769 | $1369 | (30-Nov-91 VG.B847/R) Lonely angel (37x61cm-15x24in) s.d.1966 indian ink pen board (DM 2200) |

LOFFLER, August (1822-1866) German

| £4983 | $8670 | (21-Sep-91 SA.A1793/R) Heroic mountain landscape with shepherds and sheep (127x98cm-50x39in) mono.d.1845 (DM 14500) |

LOFFLER, Franz Karl (1875-1955) German

£680	$1218	(5-May-92 ZEL.L1413/R) Portrait of sleeping baby on christening pillow (35x41cm-14x16in) s. board (DM 2000)
£816	$1461	(5-May-92 ZEL.L1415/R) Small child with dummy in mouth sleeping (38x33cm-15x13in) s. (DM 2400)
£822	$1414	(8-Oct-91 ZEL.L1587/R) Lake landscape near Wasserburg with snow covered Alps beyond, spring (23x33cm-9x13in) s. board (DM 2400)
£909	$1618	(29-Nov-91 ZEL.L1064/R) View of Wasserburg (23x34cm-9x13in) s. panel (DM 2600)
£909	$1618	(29-Nov-91 ZEL.L1065) View of Wasserburg, evening (23x33cm-9x13in) s. board (DM 2600)
£952	$1705	(5-May-92 ZEL.L1416/R) Lake Constance landscape with view of orchard and houses (34x45cm-13x18in) canvas on board (DM 2800)

LOFFLER, Hugo (1859-1935) German
£710 $1300   (3-Jun-92 D.NY58) Nymph and Pan (119x81cm-47x32in) s.

LOFFLER-RADYMNO, Leopold and KRATZMANN, Gustav Philipp (19th C) Austrian/Czech
£2062 $3588   (18-Sep-91 N.M593/R) Girl seated on grandmother's lap looking at rabbit
                   held by father (63x50cm-25x20in) s.d.1862 (DM 6000)

LOFFTZ, Ludwig von (1845-1910) German
£1742 $3171   (11-Dec-91 WE.MU66/R) Fishermen in Vierwaldstatter See landscape
                   (58x87cm-23x34in) s.d.68 (DM 5000)
£6529 $11361   (21-Sep-91 SA.A1818/R) Traveller walking downhill in wooded landscape
                   (59x96cm-23x38in) s.i.d.1879 (DM 19000)

LOFTUS, Peter (20th C) American
£760 $1300   (18-Mar-92 GRO.B60) Evening glow-emerald and copper (112x173cm-44x68in)
                   s.d.84

LOGAN, George (20th C) British
£750   *$1358*   *(5-Dec-91 CG35/R) Woodland recital (30x46cm-12x18in) s. pencil W/C*
                   htd.white

LOGAN, Maurice (1886-1977) American
£4237 $7500   (12-Feb-92 B.SF486/R) Mudflat homes (76x91cm-30x36in) s.
£506   *$900*   *(26-Nov-91 MOR.P60 a) House in landscape - Porta Costa (56x74cm-22x29in)*
                   s. W/C
£629   *$1100*   *(31-Mar-92 MOR.P86) Boats in slips (28x41cm-11x16in) s. W/C*
£678   *$1200*   *(12-Feb-92 B.SF627/R) Yachts in harbour. Rocky coastline*
                   (53x74cm-21x29in) s. W/C double-sided
£684   *$1300*   *(24-Jun-92 B.SF6519/R) Old storefronts (53x75cm-21x30in) s. W/C*
£789   *$1500*   *(24-Jun-92 B.SF6517/R) Loading dock (51x70cm-20x28in) s. W/C*

LOGHI, Kimon (1871-?) Yugoslavian
£1100 $1881   (17-Mar-92 PH98/R) Woman in the sun (78x37cm-31x15in) s.

LOGSDAIL, William (1859-1944) British
£2000 $3840   (28-Jul-92 SWS150/R) The terrier man (63x43cm-25x17in) mono.
£2000 $3500   (18-Feb-92 CE.NY240/R) Fisherman of Venice (44x35cm-17x14in) s.indist.d.
                   i.verso

LOGVINE, Ivan (1923-) Russian
£527 $954   (20-May-92 ARC.P204/R) Les vieux greements (39x30cm-15x12in) s.
                   (F.FR 5200)

LOHR, August (1843-1919) German
£19444 $35000   (18-Nov-91 SY.NY9/R) Paisaje Mexicano (59x80cm-23x31in) s.d.1914

LOHSE, Carl (20th C) German?
£704   *$1275*   *(6-Dec-91 GB.B6785/R) Head of man (53x56cm-21x22in) s. W/C (DM 2000)*

LOHSE, Richard Paul (1902-) Swiss
£11121 $19796   (26-Nov-91 SY.MI173/R) Vier Farbfelder auf weissem Kreuz
                   (48x47cm-19x19in) s.i.d.1952/68verso acrylic (I.L 24000000)

LOIR, Luigi (1845-1916) French
£553 $952   (11-Oct-91 HC.P29) Jardin public (19x24cm-7x9in) s. panel (F.FR 5500)
£1209 $2200   (26-May-92 CE.NY198/R) Village by a stream (13x22cm-5x9in) s.i. canvas on
                   panel
£1439 $2748   (1-Jul-92 FB.P71 a) Le parc (18x23cm-7x9in) s. panel (F.FR 14000)
£4651 $8000   (17-Oct-91 SY.NY212/R) L'Ile de la Cite (36x41cm-14x16in) s.
£5814 $10000   (17-Oct-91 SY.NY211/R) Boulevard in winter (16x22cm-6x9in) s. panel
£2473   *$4500*   *(28-May-92 SY.NY199/R) Scene de peche. Navire a l'horizon*
                   (24x33cm-9x13in) s. pencil W/C gouache pair

LOIR, Marianne (18th C) French
£15702 $29833   (23-Jun-92 D.V56/R) Portrait of Gebriel Nicolas Silvain de Montaignac
                   d'Estansanne, aged 10 (60x72cm-24x28in) s.i.verso (A.S 320000)

LOIR, Nicolas (1624-1679) French
£11156 $19635   (10-Apr-92 AT.P26/R) Alexandre devant la tente de Darius
                   (71x95cm-28x37in) after Charles Le Brun (F.FR 110000)

LOIR, Nicolas (attrib) (1624-1679) French
£418   *$761*   *(12-Dec-91 L.K430/R) The Visitation of Mary (14x19cm-6x7in) pen over*
                   ochre wash (DM 1200)

LOIR, Nicolas (circle) (1624-1679) French
£3144 $5533   (11-Apr-92 AT.P78/R) L'enfance de Jupiter (103x115cm-41x45in)
                   (F.FR 31000)

LOIRE (?) French
£1222 $2261   (13-Jun-92 AT.P94) Untitled (160x135cm-63x53in) s.d.12-91 acrylic panel
                   (F.FR 12000)

LOISEAU, Gustave (1865-1935) French

£639	$1200	(16-Dec-91 AT.P29/R) Vases de fleurs et pommes (55x46cm-22x18in) s. board (F.FR 6200)
£721	$1355	(16-Dec-91 AT.P31/R) Falaises de Saint-Jouin (61x73cm-24x29in) s.d.1907 (F.FR 7000)
£1114	$2017	(18-May-92 AT.P129) Nature morte (41x53cm-16x21in) board (F.FR 11000)
£2088	$3799	(11-Dec-91 ZZ.F27/R) Petit bras de Seine a Conelles, Eure (65x81cm-26x32in) s. (F.FR 20500)
£17490	$31656	(2-Dec-91 CK.P20/R) Jardin et maisons a la campagne (54x65cm-21x26in) s. (F.FR 170000)
£18786	$32500	(2-Oct-91 SY.NY18/R) Le Quai de l'Oise Pontoise (46x61cm-18x24in) s.d.1906
£26000	$44980	(25-Mar-92 S31/R) Belle-Isle, la Cote Sauvage (66x81cm-26x32in) s.
£26012	$45000	(2-Oct-91 SY.NY16/R) Les Falaises du Cap Frehel (66x92cm-26x36in) s.d.1905
£32000	$61120	(1-Jul-92 S119 a/R) Les falaises de Puy (60x73cm-24x29in) s.d.01
£35242	$62731	(26-Nov-91 J.M21/R) Riviere en Normandie, Eure (63x78cm-25x31in) s.d.1921 i.stretcher (A.D 80000)
£38136	$67500	(7-Nov-91 SY.NY121/R) Tournant de riviere, l'eure a Saint Cyr-Du-Vaudreuil (68x92cm-27x36in) s.d.1904
£38251	$70000	(14-May-92 SY.NY233/R) Gelee blanche, environs de pontoise (60x92cm-24x36in) s.d.1906
£39817	$72865	(3-Jun-92 PIC.P59/R) Paris - Rue Clignancourt (65x54cm-26x21in) s. (F.FR 391000)
£60000	$108600	(3-Dec-91 C218/R) Falaises en Normandie (60x73cm-24x29in) s.d.1901
£1322	*$2420*	*(17-May-92 T.B58) Mauvais temps a Fecamp (28x35cm-11x14in) init.d.1925 W/C (F.FR 13000)*

LOJACONO, Francesco (1841-1915) Italian

£9341	$17000	(28-May-92 SY.NY316/R) Pastoral landscape (43x84cm-17x33in) s.
£27473	$50000	(28-May-92 SY.NY118/R) Gathering sticks (47x96cm-19x38in) s.

LOJACONO, Francesco (attrib) (1841-1915) Italian

£732	$1273	(19-Sep-91 D.V230/R) Donkey cart in coastal landscape (47x88cm-19x35in) (A.S 15000)
£1945	$3365	(24-Mar-92 CH.R98) Marina col Monte Pellegrino (14x32cm-6x13in) rem.sig. board (I.L 4200000)

LOKHORST, Dirk Pieter van (1848-?) Dutch

£729	$1269	(17-Sep-91 CH.AM609) An inn along a country lane (38x50cm-15x20in) s. (D.FL 2400)

LOLMO, Giovanni Paolo (1550-1593) Italian

£8741	$15034	(15-Oct-91 CH.R59/R) La cattura di Sansone (130x205cm-51x81in) (I.L 19000000)

LOMAKIN, Oleg (1924-) Russian

£510	$948	(17-Jun-92 ARC.P69/R) Modele sur un fauteuil (70x60cm-28x24in) s. (F.FR 5000)
£594	$1057	(25-Nov-91 ARC.P165) Dans le jardin (60x50cm-24x20in) s. (F.FR 5800)
£661	$1149	(13-Apr-92 ARC.P151/R) La chambre rose (55x46cm-22x18in) s. (F.FR 6500)
£663	$1232	(17-Jun-92 ARC.P71/R) Bouquet de printemps (73x54cm-29x21in) s. (F.FR 6500)
£737	$1312	(25-Nov-91 ARC.P164/R) La fille du sud (79x60cm-31x24in) s. (F.FR 7200)
£793	$1379	(13-Apr-92 ARC.P152/R) Sur le gueridon (60x73cm-24x29in) s. (F.FR 7800)
£811	$1467	(20-May-92 ARC.P38/R) La robe bleue (54x73cm-21x29in) s. (F.FR 8000)
£864	$1503	(13-Apr-92 ARC.P153/R) Ludmilla (55x46cm-22x18in) s. (F.FR 8500)
£864	$1503	(13-Apr-92 ARC.P154) Nu au divan (50x61cm-20x24in) s. (F.FR 8500)
£874	$1583	(6-Dec-91 ARC.P216/R) Le matin (80x60cm-31x24in) s. (F.FR 8500)
£977	$1769	(6-Dec-91 ARC.P213/R) Dans la chambre (80x60cm-31x24in) s. (F.FR 9500)
£1114	$2017	(20-May-92 ARC.P39/R) Bouquet dans un vase blanc (73x54cm-29x21in) s. (F.FR 11000)
£1169	$2034	(13-Apr-92 ARC.P149/R) Pres du paravent (100x73cm-39x29in) s. (F.FR 11500)
£1183	$2141	(6-Dec-91 ARC.P211/R) Pres de la fenetre (80x60cm-31x24in) s. (F.FR 11500)
£1223	$2275	(17-Jun-92 ARC.P70/R) Reve (70x60cm-28x24in) s. (F.FR 12000)
£1351	$2405	(25-Nov-91 ARC.P165 a/R) La barrette (79x60cm-31x24in) s. (F.FR 13200)
£1418	$2567	(20-May-92 ARC.P37/R) Le matin (79x59cm-31x23in) s. (F.FR 14000)
£1492	$2700	(6-Dec-91 ARC.P214/R) Katioucha (50x40cm-20x16in) s. (F.FR 14500)
£1903	$3445	(6-Dec-91 ARC.P212/R) Nu allonge (63x100cm-25x39in) s. (F.FR 18500)
£2337	$4067	(13-Apr-92 ARC.P150/R) Nu au fauteuil (73x54cm-29x21in) s. (F.FR 23000)
£3122	$5557	(25-Nov-91 ARC.P163/R) Filette au bouquet (70x50cm-28x20in) s. (F.FR 30500)

LOMAKINE, Misha (1970-) Russian

£629	$1144	(27-May-92 GL.P19/R) Natascha (80x60cm-31x24in) s.verso (F.FR 6200)

LOMAS, William (19th C) British

£3500	$6020	(4-Mar-92 S130/R) Music (112x81cm-44x32in) s.d.82 s.i.overlap

LOMAX, John Arthur (1857-1923) British

£769	$1400	(26-May-92 CE.NY243/R) Enjoying the story (31x42cm-12x17in) s. board
£800	$1432	(6-May-92 ZZ.B164) The spinning wheel (61x46cm-24x18in) s.
£820	$1460	(21-Jan-92 PH139) Spinning wheel (61x46cm-24x18in) s.

1120

LOMAX, John Arthur (1857-1923) British-cont.
£988 $1700   (20-Oct-91 HG.C52) Smoking by fireplace (58x36cm-23x14in) s.
£3000 $5400   (19-Nov-91 PH59/R) The connoisseurs (39x28cm-15x11in) s. panel
£3000 $5340   (21-Jan-92 PH130) Huntsmen at dining room table (61x76cm-24x30in) s.
£5800 $10614   (3-Jun-92 S169/R) The dice players (40x30cm-16x12in) s. panel
£1250 $2238   (5-May-92 SWS252/R) Driving cattle. Geese by river (37x54cm-15x21in) s.
*   one d.1886 W/C htd white pair*

LOMBARD SCHOOL, 16th C Italian
£4416 $7992   (5-Dec-91 F.M12/R) Nativita (180x140cm-71x55in) (I.L 9500000)
£12500 $21875   (1-Apr-92 S20/R) Head of warrior (47x44cm-19x17in) tempera panel

LOMBARD SCHOOL, 17th C Italian
£5876 $10636   (18-May-92 SY.MI244/R) Tamira con la testa di Ciro (132x126cm-52x50in)
    (I.L 13000000)
£8599 $15651   (28-May-92 F.M31/R) Fuga in Egitto. Riposo nella fuga in Egitto
    (25x27cm-10x11in) panel pair (I.L 19000000)
£9528 $17246   (5-Dec-91 F.M61) Susanna e i vecchioni (85x165cm-33x65in) (I.L 20500000)
£39246 $72997   (18-Jun-92 SY.MO175/R) Le Bon Samaritain (113x154cm-44x61in)
    (F.FR 385000)

LOMBARD SCHOOL, 18th C Italian
£3486 $6310   (5-Dec-91 F.M36/R) Nativita (90x119cm-35x47in) (I.L 7500000)

LOMBARD SCHOOL, 19th C Italian
£5578 $9538   (19-Mar-92 F.M7/R) Val d'Intelvi. La punta di Bellagio (35x55cm-14x22in)
    paper on canvas pair (I.L 12000000)

LOMBARD, Lambert (1506-1566) Flemish
£7247 $13407   (8-Jun-92 CH.R739/R) Psiche involata dagli amorini (99x77cm-39x30in)
    panel (I.L 16000000)

LOMI, Giovanni (1889-1969) Italian
£679 $1257   (8-Jun-92 CH.R570) Rustico Terricciola (22x15cm-9x6in) s. panel
    (I.L 1500000)
£770 $1425   (8-Jun-92 CH.R572) La torre di Recanati (22x16cm-9x6in) s. panel
    (I.L 1700000)
£861 $1592   (8-Jun-92 CH.R569) Vecchia Roma (16x22cm-6x9in) s. s.i.verso masonite
    (I.L 1900000)
£1359 $2514   (8-Jun-92 CH.R573) Campiglia case antiche. Viareggio Darsena
    (18x23cm-7x9in) s. panel two (I.L 3000000)
£2092 $3577   (19-Mar-92 F.M98) Marina con barche (39x75cm-15x30in) s. panel
    (I.L 4500000)
£2789 $4769   (19-Mar-92 F.M50/R) Marina con pescatori (50x70cm-20x28in) s.
    (I.L 6000000)
£2979 $5272   (7-Nov-91 F.M62/R) Marina con barche al tramonto (50x70cm-20x28in) s.
    (I.L 6500000)

LOMME, Bert (20th C) French
£1753 $3049   (21-Sep-91 SA.A583/R) Model at morning toilet (60x46cm-24x18in) s.i.
    (DM 5100)

LOMMEN, Wilhelm (1838-1895) German
£1223 $2128   (14-Apr-92 SY.AM286/R) Cattle on a dike (94x152cm-37x60in) s.d.1880
    (D.FL 4000)

LONBLAD, Emilia (1865-1946) Scandinavian
£472 $835   (5-Nov-91 BA.S117/R) Portrait of Elisabeth Keyser (33x27cm-13x11in) s.
    (S.KR 5000)
£3416 $6250   (14-May-92 BU.S46/R) Small girl among wilting lilies (97x66cm-38x26in) s.
    (S.KR 36000)

LONCELLO, F (?) Italian
£633 $1145   (18-May-92 SY.MI34/R) Porto di Livorno (24x50cm-9x20in) s. W/C
*   (I.L 1400000)*

LONCLE, Emile (1818-?) French
£1438 $2474   (8-Oct-91 ZEL.L1589/R) Female nudes bathing in woodland pond
    (29x47cm-11x19in) s. (DM 4200)

LONDONIO, Francesco (1723-1783) Italian
£4648 $8413   (3-Dec-91 SY.MI266) Studi di teste di capre (50x73cm-20x29in)
    (I.L 10000000)

LONDONIO, Francesco (style) (1723-1783) Italian
£2600 $4550   (1-Apr-92 S193/R) Pastoral landscapes (20x41cm-8x16in) panel pair

LONG, Charles (19th C) British
£900 $1530   (23-Oct-91 S73) The British troops on duty, September 1815
    (26x39cm-10x15in) i.d.verso panel

LONG, Christopher (20th C) American
£16763 $29000   (3-Oct-91 SY.NY61/R) We're off we're off (168x168cm-66x66in)

LONG, Edwin (1829-1891) British
£1500 $2775   (12-Jun-92 C131/R) Head of an Arab girl (62x47cm-24x19in)
£3500 $6580   (19-Dec-91 C167/R) The new dress (61x46cm-24x18in) s.d.1872

LONG, Edwin (style) (1829-1891) British
£1100 $1958   (30-Apr-92 CSK63) Holding up the shroud (117x163cm-46x64in)

LONG, Leonard (1911-) Australian
£756 $1292   (16-Mar-92 MGS.S109) Goulburn Valley (40x50cm-16x20in) s. board (A.D 1700)
£793 $1411   (26-Nov-91 J.M85) In Northern territory (39x49cm-15x19in) s.d.70 canvas on board (A.D 1800)
£833 $1433   (14-Oct-91 MGS.S77) Morning light, Murray river (39x49cm-15x19in) s.d.1991 canvas on board (A.D 1800)
£833 $1433   (14-Oct-91 MGS.S342) Evening at Bellambi Creek, NSW (59x75cm-23x30in) s. (A.D 1800)
£933 $1596   (16-Mar-92 MGS.S108) Morning light Murray River (40x50cm-16x20in) s. board (A.D 2100)
£1085 $2073   (21-Jul-92 JRL.S107) After the rains (59x90cm-23x35in) s.d.1985 board (A.D 2800)
£2074 $3608   (16-Sep-91 CH.ME162/R) Valley of Goodradigbee (113x152cm-44x60in) s.d.1971 (A.D 4500)
£2203 $3965   (24-Nov-91 SY.S479/R) Rawnsley Bluff, Gums, Flinders Ranges, South Australia (110x149cm-43x59in) s.d.1984 board (A.D 5000)
£2203 $3965   (24-Nov-91 SY.S480/R) Summer muster (90x120cm-35x47in) s.d.1985 board (A.D 5000)

LONG, Marion (1882-1970) Canadian
£697 $1240   (26-Nov-91 JOY.T105/R) Maroon jacket (105x87cm-41x34in) s. (C.D 1400)

LONG, Richard (1945-) American
£14000 $24220   (26-Mar-92 S91/R) Mud hand Africa map (112x82cm-44x32in) s. st.mono.d.1985 River Avon mud
£19553 $35000   (14-Nov-91 SY.NY190/R) Untitled (42x31cm-17x12in) River Avon mud paper ten parts

LONG, Sydney (1872-1955) Australian
£1240 $2369   (21-Jul-92 JRL.S82) Central Railway Station (46x66cm-18x26in) s. (A.D 3200)
£1778 $3040   (17-Mar-92 JRL.S168/R) Landscape with trees and lake (29x49cm-11x19in) s. canvasboard (A.D 4000)
£1883 $3408   (19-May-92 JRL.S53/R) Landscape with apple blossom (24x35cm-9x14in) s. board (A.D 4500)
£2128 $3766   (26-Apr-92 SY.ME282/R) Narrabeen Lake (29x33cm-11x13in) s. i.d.1940 verso board (A.D 5000)
£2383 $4218   (26-Apr-92 SY.ME445/R) River landscape with boat (28x44cm-11x17in) s. board (A.D 5600)
£3991 $6664   (19-Aug-91 SY.ME224/R) Among bushes (45x29cm-18x11in) s.d.1933 i.verso board (A.D 8500)
£5556 $9889   (28-Apr-92 CH.ME14) Narrabeen lake (43x53cm-17x21in) s.d.1944 board (A.D 13000)
£8120 $14453   (28-Apr-92 CH.ME199/R) Flamingoes (30x41cm-12x16in) s. board (A.D 19000)
£8462 $16162   (19-Jul-92 SY.ME6/R) Griffith's Farm (29x14cm-11x6in) s. panel (A.D 22000)
£1282 $2282   (28-Apr-92 CH.ME239) Flamingoes (26x36cm-10x14in) s.d.1910 W/C (A.D 3000)
£1496 $2662   (27-Apr-92 J.M331) Moonrise (23x28cm-9x11in) s.d.1910 W/C (A.D 3500)
£2423 $4313   (26-Nov-91 J.M107 a) Passing storm (43x34cm-17x13in) s.d.1916 W/C (A.D 5500)
£7234 $12804   (26-Apr-92 SY.ME299/R) Pink flamingoes (38x72cm-15x28in) s. W/C (A.D 17000)

LONG, Sydney (attrib) (1872-1955) Australian
£598 $1065   (27-Apr-92 J.M469) Blossom (40x29cm-16x11in) s. canvas on board (A.D 1400)

LONGHI, Barbara (attrib) (1552-1638) Italian
£1011 $1800   (22-Jan-92 SY.NY133/R) St. Cecelia (38x31cm-15x12in) canvas on board

LONGHI, Luca (1507-1580) Italian
£6704 $12000   (16-Jan-92 CH.NY14/R) Portrait of gentleman, standing in armour, hand resting on helmet (132x94cm-52x37in) i.

LONGHI, Luca (style) (1507-1580) Italian
£2500 $4800   (9-Jul-92 CSK24/R) The Deposition (83x98cm-33x39in) canvas laid down on panel

LONGHI, Pietro (1702-1785) Italian
£15470 $28000   (21-May-92 CH.NY124/R) Young lady winding wool and old lady spinning wool, accompanied by young men (62x51cm-24x20in)

LONGHI, Pietro (circle) (1702-1785) Italian
£1242 $2124   (18-Mar-92 D.V194/R) Portrait of young Venetian woman (22x17cm-9x7in) canvas on panel (A.S 25000)
£1934 $3500   (22-May-92 SY.NY182/R) Interior of parlour with young man sleeping, three women looking on (62x51cm-24x20in)

LONGHI, Pietro (studio) (1702-1785) Italian
£2039 $3792 (18-Jun-92 SY.MO115) Scenes d'interieur (42x24cm-17x9in) pair
          (F.FR 20000)

LONGHI, Pietro (style) (1702-1785) Italian
£1000 $1780 (31-Oct-91 B57) Venetian gentlefolk visiting girls in convent
          (62x89cm-24x35in)
£1934 $3500 (22-May-92 SY.NY181/R) Masked figures (41x31cm-16x12in)

LONGO, Robert (1953-) American
£25140 $45000 (6-May-92 CH.NY253/R) Men in cities (152x315cm-60x124in) graphite three
           panels

LONGOBARDI, Nino (1953-) Italian
£700 $1211 (26-Mar-92 C108/R) Untitled (76x56cm-30x22in) s.d.1987verso gouache
          chl.col.crayon
£700 $1211 (26-Mar-92 C107/R) Untitled (76x56cm-30x22in) s.d.1987verso acrylic
          chl.collage

LONGONI, Emilio (1859-1933) Italian
£7261 $13506 (16-Jun-92 F.M293/R) Tramonto sul lago (30x39cm-12x15in) s. canvas on
          board (I.L 16000000)
£12085 $21873 (3-Dec-91 SY.MI149/R) Paesaggio montano (26x43cm-10x17in) s. panel
          (I.L 26000000)
£23028 $41911 (12-Dec-91 F.M69/R) Pizzo Bernina (67x97cm-26x38in) s. canvas on panel
          (I.L 50000000)
£1380 $2470 (14-Nov-91 CH.R193) Paesaggio montano (26x42cm-10x17in) pastel
          (I.L 3000000)
£3254 $5889 (3-Dec-91 SY.MI71/R) Paesaggio (59x81cm-23x32in) s. pastel (I.L 7000000)

LONGPRE, Paul de (1855-1911) French
£4213 $7500 (22-Jan-92 SY.NY348/R) Still life with pink peonies (75x60cm-30x24in)
          s.d.1884
£1105 $2000 (22-May-92 S.BM82/R) Still life of roses and apple blossoms
          (28x71cm-11x28in) s.d.1897 W/C
£1264 $2250 (26-Nov-91 MOR.P137) Bunch of cherries (46x33cm-18x13in) s.d.1903 W/C
          mixed media
£2684 $4750 (12-Feb-92 B.SF436/R) Roses and bumble bees (47x30cm-19x12in) s.d.1908
          W/C

LONGPRE, Raoul de (19/20th C) American
£442 $800 (22-May-92 S.BM80/R) Still life of roses and white lilacs
          (51x36cm-20x14in) s. gouache paperboard
£538 $1000 (19-Jun-92 S.BM190) Still life with lilacs and roses (61x46cm-24x18in)
          gouache paperboard
£745 $1400 (18-Dec-91 SY.NY50/R) Bouquet of lavender and white lilac
          (55x40cm-22x16in) s.d.1870
£1124 $2000 (2-May-92 W.W86/R) Still life of white roses and lilacs (66x48cm-26x19in)
          s. gouache
£1724 $3000 (15-Apr-92 SY.NY42/R) White and red roses (69x41cm-27x16in) s. gouache
£2542 $4500 (12-Feb-92 B.SF432/R) Daisies (51x63cm-20x25in) s. gouache

LONGSDON, David (fl.1867-1901) British
£1600 $2848 (31-Oct-91 D126/R) Whitmans Mill, North Mill, Easebourne, Midhurst,
          Sussex (71x89cm-28x35in) s.

LONGSTAFF, Sir John (1862-1941) Australian
£1197 $2130 (27-Apr-92 J.M545) Villa in France (20x10cm-8x4in) s. (A.D 2800)

LONGSTAFFE, E (19th C) ?
£600 $1086 (6-Dec-91 K503) Welsh mountain landscape with cattle resting on bank
          (48x66cm-19x26in) mono.

LONGSTAFFE, Edgar (1849-1912) British
£571 $982 (7-Oct-91 B.O88/R) Cattle in landscape (31x46cm-12x18in) init.d.1903
          panel (N.KR 6500)
£700 $1344 (28-Jul-92 SWS314/R) Angler in a punt on a still pool (49x75cm-19x30in)
          mono.

LONNBERG, William (1887-1949) Finnish
£528 $960 (11-Dec-91 HOR.H62) View of the sea (50x61cm-20x24in) s. (F.M 4100)

LONNER, Max (20th C) German
£997 $1824 (2-Jun-92 FN.S2654) Climbing rose on stone wall (92x61cm-36x24in) s.
          (DM 2900)

LONNING, Terkel Eriksen (1762-1823) Danish
£1435 $2583 (30-Jan-92 RAS.V650/R) Battle at Copenhagen's Rehd, 11 April MDCCCI
          (55x77cm-22x30in) s.i. W/C (D.KR 16000)

LONNROTH, Arvid Fredrik (1823-1880) Swedish
£1518 $2778 (14-May-92 BU.S47/R) Runaway horse (50x61cm-20x24in) s. (S.KR 16000)

LONSDALE, G H (19th C) British
£550 $941 (19-Mar-92 B74) Still life of plums and dates (30x46cm-12x18in) s.

ONZA, Antonio (1846-?) Italian
£2143 $3900   (11-Dec-91 RO.BA274) Porgendo l'aqua (88x63cm-35x25in) s.

OO, Amedee van (1719-1795) French
£5226 $9512   (12-Dec-91 L.K103/R) Portrait of Konig Friedrich II of Prussia
                     (80x65cm-31x26in) oval (DM 15000)

OO, Carle van (1705-1765) French
£1424 $2549   (15-Nov-91 SD.P17) La halte de chasse (80x113cm-31x44in) (F.FR 14000)
£2762 $5000   (21-May-92 CH.NY200/R) portrait of lady, wearing satin dress with cloak,
                     fireplace beyond (81x64cm-32x25in)
£7202 $13035   (7-Dec-91 CH.MO50/R) Saint Jean Baptiste (65x54cm-26x21in) s.
                     (F.FR 70000)
£4639 $8026   (26-Mar-92 PIC.P5/R) Tete d'homme de profil vers la gauche
                     (25x21cm-10x8in) sanguine (F.FR 45000)

OO, Carle van (after) (1705-1765) French
£4321 $8210   (22-Jun-92 PIC.P11/R) Le dejeuner de chasse (96x126cm-38x50in)
                     (F.FR 42000)
£4500 $8010   (29-Oct-91 PH61/R) Three children making music in an interior
                     (96x127cm-38x50in)
£12000 $21360   (1-Nov-91 C64/R) Allegories of painting, sculpture, architecture and
                     music (98x129cm-39x51in) four

OO, Carle van (attrib) (1705-1765) French
£7645 $14220   (18-Jun-92 SY.MO229/R) Portrait de femme en vestale (142x109cm-56x43in)
                     (F.FR 75000)

OO, Carle van (circle) (1705-1765) French
£2949 $5250   (22-Jan-92 D.NY37) Portrait of Comtess de Melfort (74x58cm-29x23in) oval

OO, Carle van (studio) (1705-1765) French
£7209 $12327   (20-Mar-92 ZZ.F13/R) Allegorie de la Sculpture. Allegorie de la Musique
                     (86x131cm-34x52in) pair (F.FR 70000)

OO, Carle van (style) (1705-1765) French
£1309 $2500   (16-Jul-92 SY.NY223/R) Portrait of a lady (40x31cm-16x12in)
£1715 $2951   (16-Oct-91 AT.P110/R) Tete de Bacchus (59x47cm-23x19in) painted oval
                     (F.FR 17000)
£1966 $3500   (22-Jan-92 SY.NY158/R) Nymph and satyr in landscape (74x105cm-29x41in)
£2000 $3500   (3-Apr-92 C154/R) Personification of Fortitude (71x83cm-28x33in)
£5000 $8750   (28-Feb-92 C96/R) A sultan and his harem being entertained by a dancer
                     (48x56cm-19x22in)

OO, Jacob van (1614-1670) Dutch
£11628 $20000   (9-Oct-91 CH.NY147/R) Portrait of lady, standing holding fan, before red
                     curtain on balustrade (105x93cm-41x37in) s.

OO, Jacob van (attrib) (1614-1670) Dutch
£3122 $5463   (1-Apr-92 CSC.P15/R) Paysage avec femmes au bain (64x50cm-25x20in)
                     (F.FR 30000)
£82305 $148971   (7-Dec-91 CH.MO21/R) Portrait d'une petite fille, un chien a ses pieds
                     (120x90cm-47x35in) (F.FR 800000)

OO, Jean Baptiste van (1684-1745) French
£3600 $6408   (1-Nov-91 S430/R) Portrait of gentleman. Portrait of lady
                     (73x59cm-29x23in) oval sold with another English School 18th C

OO, Jean Baptiste van (attrib) (1684-1745) French
£8000 $14080   (8-Apr-92 S30/R) Portrait of Hon. Sir James Campbell of Lawers, standing
                     wearing armour (124x99cm-49x39in)

OO, Jean Baptiste van (school) (1684-1745) French
£2138 $3892   (11-Dec-91 LD.P35) Lous, troisieme Duc d'Orleans, fils du Regent
                     (61x51cm-24x20in) (F.FR 21000)

OO, Jules Cesar Denis van (1743-1821) French
£4144 $7500   (21-May-92 CH.NY135/R) Snowy winter landscape with woodcutters and
                     figures before bonfire (63x77cm-25x30in)
£7000 $13440   (8-Jul-92 S172/R) Winter landscape with figures entering cottage at night
                     (54x72cm-21x28in) s.d.x
£9500 $18240   (8-Jul-92 S171/R) Winter landscape with figures crossing bridge near
                     monastery (60x73cm-24x29in) s.d.X

OO, Louis-Michel van (1707-1771) French
£2840 $4998   (11-Apr-92 AT.P97/R) Portrait de jeune femme a la robe bleue
                     (61x49cm-24x19in) oval (F.FR 28000)
£20000 $38400   (8-Jul-92 S67/R) Portrait of Marechal de France, said to be James
                     Fitzjames (198x121cm-78x48in)

OO, Louis-Michel van (circle) (1707-1771) French
£4330 $7491   (27-Mar-92 CD.P8/R) Portrait de jeune femme (60x48cm-24x19in) oval
                     (F.FR 42000)

LOO, Pieter van (1731-1784) Dutch
£8380 $15000   *(14-Jan-92 SY.NY70/R) Still life of flowers and fruit (53x39cm-21x15in)*
                                  s. W/C gouache gum arabic over black chk

LOOBY, Keith (1940-) Australian
£2621 $4875   (21-Jun-92 SY.ME102) Kelly (165x240cm-65x94in) d.1981 (A.D 6500)

LOOMIS, Andrew (1892-1959) American
£1977 $3500   (14-Feb-92 DM.D2016/R) Apple kiss (76x81cm-30x32in) s.

LOON, Gustaaf van (1912-1980) Belgian
£728 $1319   (23-May-92 KV.L363) Cow in river landscape (24x25cm-9x10in) s. canvas on
                               panel (B.FR 44000)
£821 $1486   (7-Dec-91 KV.L332) Landscape (22x25cm-9x10in) s. canvas on panel
                               (B.FR 48000)

LOOP, Henry Augustus (1831-1895) American
£601 $1100   (3-Jun-92 D.NY59) Portrait of young girl in white with striped sash
                               (61x51cm-24x20in) s.d.72 i.d.1872 verso

LOOS, Friedrich (1797-1890) Austrian
£683 $1235   *(21-May-92 L.K297/R) Near Salzburg (17x26cm-7x10in) s.d.1831 pencil*
                               (DM 2000)

LOOS, Henry (19/20th C) Belgian
£4500 $8100   (22-Nov-91 C86/R) Three-masted Norwegian barque Victoria off the
                               Eddystone Lighthouse (66x97cm-26x38in) s.d.1893

LOOS, John F (circle) (19th C) Belgian
£2000 $3520   (6-Apr-92 WW10/R) Three masted clipper (46x66cm-18x26in)

LOOSE, Basile de (1809-1885) Dutch
£1300 $2353   (21-May-92 CSK243/R) Forty winks (41x30cm-16x12in) s.d.1829 panel
£4775 $8500   (22-Jan-92 SY.NY447/R) Pranksters (81x69cm-32x27in) s.
£14124 $25000   (6-Nov-91 D.NY30/R) Learning their lessons (62x75cm-24x30in) s.d.1864
                               panel

LOOSE, Max (1869-?) German
£592 $1078   (11-Dec-91 N.M512/R) Peasant boy on rocky path (46x30cm-18x12in) s.d.1895
                               canvas on board (DM 1700)

LOOY, H Hendrik van (20th C) Dutch?
£1648 $3098   *(18-Dec-91 PR.P44/R) Amsterdam (90x153cm-35x60in) s.d.1911 pastel*
                               (F.FR 16000)

LOPEZ LEAO DE LAGUNA, Baruch (1864-1943) Dutch
£795 $1415   (30-Oct-91 CH.AM140) Still life with violets in vase (57x40cm-22x16in) s.
                               (D.FL 2600)
£2141 $3789   (5-Nov-91 SY.AM20/R) Girl knitting in kitchen interior (59x44cm-23x17in)
                               s. (D.FL 7000)
£2424 $4411   (27-May-92 D.V608/R) At the end of the day (54x45cm-21x18in) s.
                               (A.S 50000)

LOPEZ PAMIES, Antonio (?) Spanish
£876 $1594   (27-May-92 DUR.M343/R) Pescadoras (60x81cm-24x32in) s. (S.P 160000)

LOPEZ ROMAN (20th C) Spanish
£554 $997   *(29-Jan-92 FER.M227/R) Dia de mercado en el pueblo (36x28cm-14x11in) s.*
                               W/C (S.P 100000)

LOPEZ SAENZ, Antonio (1936-) Mexican
£5249 $9500   (18-May-92 CH.NY227/R) Sonando un viaje (130x100cm-51x39in) s.d.89

LOPEZ Y PORTANA, Vicente (1772-1850) Spanish
£19396 $33943   (20-Feb-92 EP.M18/R) Retratos de Dona Concepcion de Elvira de Escofet e
                               de Don Vicente Escofet y Ferrer de la Torre (81x65cm-32x26in) one
                               s.d.1845 two (S.P 3500000)

LOPEZ, Alberto (?) Spanish
£608 $1142   (3-Jan-92 DUR.M79/R) Panoramica de Toledo (65x81cm-26x32in) s.
                               (S.P 110000)

LOPEZ, Gasparo (1650-1732) Italian
£6630 $12000   (22-May-92 SY.NY192/R) Still life of urn and basket of flowers, two other
                               urns, all in landscape (74x49cm-29x19in)
£10769 $20569   (15-Jul-92 CH.S765/R) Swags of flowers, vase, melons and parrot by ruined
                               pillar (72x98cm-28x39in) (A.D 28000)
£12860 $23277   (5-Dec-91 SY.MO232/R) Bouquets de fleurs dans un paysage
                               (46x32cm-18x13in) pair (F.FR 125000)
£18000 $32760   (10-Dec-91 PH38/R) Vase of mixed flowers and overturned basket of apples
                               in garden, with fountain (116x146cm-46x57in)
£24691 $44691   (7-Dec-91 CH.MO3/R) Natures mortes de vases et de guirlandes de fleurs
                               pres de fontainesdans un paysage boise (55x70cm-22x28in) pair
                               (F.FR 240000)

LOPEZ, Gasparo (circle) (1650-1732) Italian
£1963 $3750   (16-Jul-92 SY.NY102/R) Still life of flowers in vase (40x28cm-16x11in)
£2809 $5000   (22-Jan-92 SY.NY93/R) Still life with flowers (46x36cm-18x14in)
£3058 $5688   (18-Jun-92 SY.MO321/R) Fleurs dans un paysage (43x82cm-17x32in)
        (F.FR 30000)

LOPEZ, Gasparo (style) (1650-1732) Italian
£1621 $2804   (25-Mar-92 CH.R34) Natura morta di fiori in vaso su piano di pietra
        (58x73cm-23x29in) (I.L 3500000)
£3000 $5490   (12-May-92 SWS686/R) Still life studies of mixed flowers in vase on
        ledge, fruit, flowers, porcelain and parrot below (44x37cm-17x15in)
        panel pair
£3315 $6000   (22-May-92 SY.NY226/R) Still life of flowers and fruits in park landscape
        (82x120cm-32x47in)

LOPEZ, Gasparo and MATTEIS, Paolo de (17th C) Italian
£14607 $26000   (22-Jan-92 D.NY106/R) Mythological reliefs surrounded by garlands of
        flowers (66x74cm-26x29in) i. pair

LOPEZ, Vicente (17/18th C?) ?
£8854 $15141   (17-Mar-92 FER.M110/R) Virgen del Rosario (86x73cm-34x29in) (S.P 1600000)

LOPEZ-CABRERA, Ricardo (1866-1950) Spanish
£682 $1234   (20-May-92 ANS.M164/R) Sierras de Tanti (32x41cm-13x16in) s. board
        (S.P 125000)
£711 $1301   (13-May-92 FER.M124/R) La dama de los ojos verdes (95x70cm-37x28in)
        s.d.1917 (S.P 130000)
£770 $1355   (9-Apr-92 ANS.M145/R) Bodegon de uvas (25x36cm-10x14in) s. panel
        (S.P 140000)
£774 $1455   (18-Dec-91 DUR.M635/R) Melocotones (24x35cm-9x14in) s. panel (S.P 140000)
£1385 $2424   (18-Feb-92 DUR.M11/R) Serrania de Ronda (31x40cm-12x16in) s. board
        (S.P 250000)
£1700 $3026   (27-Nov-91 S338/R) Sunlit view of Alcala River (59x74cm-23x29in) s.i.
£900 $1602   *(26-Nov-91 PH230/R) Tambourine girl (51x34cm-20x13in) s.i.d.88 W/C*

LOPPE, Gabriel (1825-1913) French
£1500 $2685   (11-Nov-91 S656/R) Travellers in Alps (59x44cm-23x17in) s.

LORCK, Karl Julius (1829-1882) Norwegian
£1754 $3263   (18-Jun-92 GWP.O67/R) The pilot and his wife (19x13cm-7x5in) s.d.1881
        i.verso panel (N.KR 20000)

LORDON, Pierre Jerome (1780-1838) French
£1545 $2904   (18-Dec-91 AT.P236/R) Leonidas aux Thermopyles (46x65cm-18x26in) s.
        (F.FR 15000)

LORENTSON, Waldemar (1899-1982) Swedish
£658 $1099   (25-Aug-91 BU.M490) Emancipation (16x23cm-6x9in) s. d.1955verso panel
        (S.KR 7000)
£713 $1233   (28-Mar-92 UA.U352/R) Surrealistic beach formation (27x35cm-11x14in) s.
        (S.KR 7400)
£959 $1726   (19-Nov-91 GO.G102) Construction of boat (24x19cm-9x7in) s. (S.KR 10000)
£1630 $2934   (19-Nov-91 GO.G103) Blue sea (21x23cm-8x9in) s. (S.KR 17000)
£2015 $3648   (3-Dec-91 AB.S5094/R) Purse-net and keep-net (34x38cm-13x15in) s.d.34
        (S.KR 21000)
£2111 $3821   (3-Dec-91 AB.S5093/R) Tema maritim scen (25x20cm-10x8in) s. panel
        (S.KR 22000)
£1344 $2432   *(3-Dec-91 AB.S5095/R) Figure composition (36x28cm-14x11in) s. crayon
        pencils (S.KR 14000)*

LORENTZEN, C A (1749-1828) Danish
£1338 $2489   (16-Jun-92 RAS.V825/R) Portrait of Charlotte Lindholm (72x56cm-28x22in)
        oval (D.KR 15000)
£2641 $4437   (27-Aug-91 RAS.K98/R) Street scene with figures and horses, Lyngbyegnen
        (70x85cm-28x33in) s.d.1806 (D.KR 30000)
£4401 $7394   (27-Aug-91 RAS.K244/R) Landscape with figures on bench, Lyngbyegnen
        (70x85cm-28x33in) s.d.1808 (D.KR 50000)

LORENTZEN, Christian August (attrib) (1749-1828) Danish
£485 $863   (28-Apr-92 RAS.K255) Portrait of Hans Lindholm (38x31cm-15x12in)
        (D.KR 5500)

LORENZ, R (19th C) German
£828 $1465   (6-Nov-91 N.M1087/R) Fishing boats by lake shore (86x111cm-34x44in)
        s.d.1899 (DM 2400)

LORENZ, Richard (1858-1915) German
£2048 $3727   (27-May-92 PH.DU125/R) River landscape (85x110cm-33x43in) s.d.1899
        (DM 6000)

LORENZ, Willi (1901-1981) German
£550 $1023   (20-Jun-92 BM.B947) Fox with kill in undergrowth (70x102cm-28x40in) s.
        s.verso (DM 1600)
£385 $665   *(25-Mar-92 KM.K1745) Antelopes in prairie (50x70cm-20x28in) s.d.73 chl
        (DM 1100)*

LORENZ-MUROWANA, Ernst Hugo (1872-?) German
£494 $865   (19-Feb-92 D.V93/R) Fishing boats (70x100cm-28x39in) s.d.44 (A.S 10000)

LORENZI, Francesco (attrib) (1723-1787) Italian
£6500 $12480   (10-Jul-92 C294/R) Madonna and child with saints Luigi Gonzaga and
    Gaetano Thiene (99x49cm-39x19in) painted arched top

LORENZO MONACO (style) (c.1370-c.1425) Italian
£1000 $1830   (12-May-92 SWS697/R) Madonna and child (47x33cm-19x13in) gold ground
    panel

LORI, Guglielmo Amedeo (1866-1913) Italian
£3616 $6545   (18-May-92 SY.MI117/R) Betulle (108x40cm-43x16in) s.d.98 (I.L 8000000)

LORIA, Vincenzo (1850-?) Italian
£1297 $2243   (24-Mar-92 CH.R118 a) Marina con pescatori (29x42cm-11x17in) s. canvas on
    board (I.L 2800000)
£2747 $5000   (28-May-92 SY.NY315/R) Bringing in catch (55x75cm-22x30in) s.
£450   *$815*   *(21-May-92 CSK48) Figures by gateway to fort (53x25cm-21x10in) s.i.
    pencil W/C*

LORIMER, John Henry (1856-1936) British
£1341 $2415   (19-Nov-91 FP.M204/R) Portrait of young girl holding branch
    (117x76cm-46x30in) mono.d.1881 (C.D 2750)

LORJOU, Bernard (1908-1986) French
£1366 $2500   (17-May-92 DU.E1108/R) Romeo et Juliet (99x99cm-39x39in) s. s.i.d.53verso
£2053 $3696   (20-Nov-91 CN.P194/R) Nature morte au lapin (60x75cm-24x30in) s. board
    (F.FR 20000)
£2541 $4421   (16-Apr-92 FB.P81/R) Bouquet de fleurs (65x50cm-26x20in) s. board laid
    down on canvas (F.FR 25000)
£2875 $5175   (19-Nov-91 FB.P5/R) Nature morte a l'ananas (50x65cm-20x26in) s.
    (F.FR 28000)
£3093 $5351   (23-Mar-92 GL.P189/R) Scene de cirque (55x75cm-22x30in) s. board
    (F.FR 30000)
£3814 $6599   (23-Mar-92 GL.P191/R) La cariole (89x116cm-35x46in) s. (F.FR 37000)
£3953 $7115   (22-Nov-91 EA.Z87) Roses rouges (93x60cm-37x24in) s. (S.FR 10000)
£3969 $6866   (23-Mar-92 GL.P193/R) L'ecuyer (75x55cm-30x22in) s. board (F.FR 38500)
£4032 $6976   (6-Oct-91 BG.P52/R) L'oie (116x89cm-46x35in) s.d.1954 (F.FR 40000)
£4124 $7134   (23-Mar-92 GL.P188/R) Ecuyer et chevaux de cirque (81x100cm-32x39in) s.
    (F.FR 40000)
£4587 $8118   (10-Nov-91 ZZ.F201/R) Nature morte aux fruits et au pichet
    (81x65cm-32x26in) s. (F.FR 45500)
£6048 $10464   (6-Oct-91 BG.P187/R) L'assissinat de Sharon Tate (150x250cm-59x98in) s.
    (F.FR 60000)
£1041   *$1821*   *(5-Apr-92 ZZ.F213/R) Le cavalier (76x60cm-30x24in) s. mixed media
    (F.FR 10000)*

LORRAINE SCHOOL, 17th C French
£7500 $13650   (10-Dec-91 PH57/R) Gamblers (96x137cm-38x54in)

LORSAY, Louis Alexandre Eustache (1822-?) French
£1900 $3363   (14-Feb-92 C10/R) The celebration (37x46cm-15x18in) s. panel

LORTEL, Leberecht (c.1818-1901) French
£474 $854   (19-Nov-91 GS.B3197) Lake Geneva landscape (28x36cm-11x14in) i.verso
    (S.FR 1200)
£941 $1600   (23-Oct-91 GD.B466/R) Bern landscape with Wetterhorn (33x50cm-13x20in) s.
    (S.FR 2400)
£2407 $4357   (19-May-92 GF.L2245/R) Torrent in wooded landscape with view of
    Wetterhorn (90x65cm-35x26in) s.d.1871 (S.FR 6500)

LORY, Gabriel Ludwig (1763-1840) Swiss
£1059 $1800   (23-Oct-91 GD.B467/R) Berner Oberland landscape with farmhouse in wooded
    river valley (30x40cm-12x16in) indis.s.d.1820 panel (S.FR 2700)

LORY, Matthias Gabriel (1784-1846) Swiss
£2578   *$4693*   *(12-Dec-91 L.K431/R) Foothills of the Alps with view of snow covered
    mountains, Switzerland (27x40cm-11x16in) s. W/C (DM 7400)*

LOSADA, Manuel (1865-1949) Spanish
£600   *$1032*   *(16-Oct-91 FER.M139/R) Paseo en burro por el pueblo (25x42cm-10x17in) s.
    pastel (S.P 110000)*

LOSSI, T (19th C) Italian
£1826   *$3250*   *(22-Jan-92 SY.NY520/R) Lady with Oriental parasol (27x16cm-11x6in)
    s.d.1881 W/C*

LOTH, Johann Karl (1632-1698) German
£3000 $5340   (30-Oct-91 S90/R) Salome with head of St John the Baptist
    (110x90cm-43x35in)
£8147 $14827   (28-May-92 F.M7/R) Abramo e l'angelo (95x158cm-37x62in) (I.L 18000000)
£12371 $21526   (18-Sep-91 N.M424/R) St Sebastian nursed by St Irene and other women
    (112x117cm-44x46in) (DM 36000)

LOTH, Johann Karl (school) (1632-1698) German
£1797 $3180   (5-Nov-91 GF.L2332/R) The penitent Mary Magdalen (117x96cm-46x38in)
                   (S.FR 4600)

LOTH, Johann Karl (style) (1632-1698) German
£2235 $3823   (18-Mar-92 D.V219/R) Pieta with angels (116x103cm-46x41in) (A.S 45000)

LOTH, Wilhelm (1920-) German?
£412 $755   (2-Jun-92 L.K770) Reclining female nude (33x51cm-13x20in) s.d.1947 W/C
                 (DM 1200)
£437 $778   (25-Nov-91 WK.M658/R) Female torso (68x38cm-27x15in) s.d.1989 indian ink
                 brush W/C (DM 1250)

LOTIRON, Robert (1886-1966) French
£1007 $1712   (24-Oct-91 D.P139/R) Rue de village (27x35cm-11x14in) s. (F.FR 10000)
£1112 $1991   (10-May-92 LT.P149) Le Hameau, 1960 (27x48cm-11x19in) (F.FR 11000)
£1143 $2000   (28-Feb-92 SY.NY170/R) Rural landscape (34x46cm-13x18in) s.
£1243 $2300   (12-Jun-92 SY.NY24/R) Batteuse (28x35cm-11x14in) s.
£1340 $2292   (11-Mar-92 LGB.P164) Un port (38x46cm-15x18in) s. (F.FR 13000)
£3150 $5482   (19-Apr-92 ZZ.F121/R) Paris, les quais (33x41cm-13x16in) s. (F.FR 31000)

LOTT, F T (fl.1852-1879) British
£560 $980   (25-Sep-91 RB657) Plemont Bay, Jersey (30x69cm-12x27in) s.

LOTT, Frederick Tully (fl.1852-1879) British
£520 $920   (11-Feb-92 GA61/R) Canterbury Cathedral from meadows (18x48cm-7x19in) s.
£500 $855   (12-Mar-92 CSK60) Wash day (46x66cm-18x26in) s. pencil W/C

LOTTO, Lorenzo (1480-1556) Italian
£22346 $40000   (14-Jan-92 SY.NY34/R) Study of head of bearded man (17x13cm-7x5in) bears
                 i. black chk

LOTTO, Lorenzo (after) (1480-1556) Italian
£2937 $5198   (7-Nov-91 D.V213/R) Lucretia (89x86cm-35x34in) panel (A.S 60000)

LOTTO, Lorenzo (style) (1480-1556) Italian
£2500 $4450   (1-Nov-91 C157/R) Portrait of bearded man, wearing black hat
                 (30x35cm-12x14in) panel

LOTZ, Anna (1861-1945) ?
£620 $1111   (6-May-92 GD.B788/R) Portrait of girl wearing costume (90x73cm-35x29in)
                 s. (S.FR 1700)

LOTZ, Mathilde (1858-1923) American
£2825 $5000   (12-Feb-92 B.SF411/R) Friends (62x81cm-24x32in) s.d.1890

LOU BOAN (1947-) Chinese
£4808 $8413   (30-Mar-92 CH.HK339/R) Landscape after rain (68x96cm-27x38in) s.i.d.1991
                 ink W/C scroll (HK.D 65000)

LOUBON, Emile Charles Joseph (1809-1863) French
£2366 $4496   (22-Jun-92 AT.P96/R) Bergers donnant l'aubade aupres d'un oratoire
                 (62x50cm-24x20in) s. (F.FR 23000)
£8138 $14568   (17-Nov-91 FB.P84/R) Le retour de la transhumance (73x133cm-29x52in) s.
                 (F.FR 80000)

LOUCHE, Constant (19th C?) French
£1524 $2652   (13-Apr-92 AT.P196/R) Vue de Boghari (42x124cm-17x49in) s.d.33
                 (F.FR 15000)
£1848 $3326   (18-Nov-91 AT.P359/R) Vue de Bohari (42x123cm-17x48in) s.d.1929
                 (F.FR 18000)
£3760 $6543   (13-Apr-92 AT.P195/R) La grande Kasbah a Iril Ali Akbou
                 (65x165cm-26x65in) s. (F.FR 37000)

LOUDAN, William Mouat (1868-1925) British
£5500 $9405   (19-Mar-92 B54/R) A portrait group (198x162cm-78x64in) s.d.1903 i.label
                 verso

LOUDEN, Albert (1943-) British
£1200 $2064   (5-Mar-92 CSK171/R) Another conversation (53x80cm-21x31in) pastel

LOUDERBACK, Walt (1887-1941) American
£2388 $4250   (2-Nov-91 IH.NY108/R) Young couple under trees with dog (76x61cm-30x24in)
                 s.

LOUDON, Terence (fl.1921-1940) British
£600 $1086   (20-May-92 B361) Still life of summer flowers in vase (59x48cm-23x19in)
                 s.
£2200 $3916   (30-Apr-92 CSK84) Still life of flowers in urn with apples, plums and
                 gourd on ledge (91x76cm-36x30in) s.

LOUGHEED, Robert Elmer (1910-1981) Canadian
£1978 $3520   (2-May-92 IH.NY218/R) Men racing speed boats (66x8cm-26x3in) board
£2701 $4700   (15-Apr-92 SY.NY222/R) Toclat country - Alaska (30x41cm-12x16in) s. board

LOUIS, Morris (1912-1962) American
£4286 $7500   *(27-Feb-92 CE.NY154/R) Ladder (41x61cm-16x24in) s.d.50 magna canvas*
£111732 $200000   *(13-Nov-91 SY.NY20/R) Number 1-70 (207x125cm-81x49in) magna canvas*

LOUIS, Seraphine see SERAPHINE DE SENLIS

LOUND, Thomas (1802-1861) British
£3000 $5280   (8-Apr-92 S93/R) On Yare, Norfolk (27x47cm-11x19in) s.verso artist
           st.stretcher

LOURENCO, Armand (c.1925-) French
£565 $972   (20-Oct-91 LT.P134) Paris sous la neige (33x41cm-13x16in) s. (F.FR 5600)
£595 $1024   (20-Oct-91 LT.P144) Le Faubourg Saint-Antoine (46x55cm-18x22in) s.
           (F.FR 5900)

LOUSTAUNAU, Louis Auguste Georges (1846-1898) French
£2145 $3754   (24-Feb-92 CSC.P55) Le repos de l'officier (28x35cm-11x14in) s.i.
           (F.FR 21000)

LOUTHERBOURG (circle) (18/19th C) French
£942 $1800   (16-Jul-92 SY.NY121/R) Landing the British troops in Aboukir Bay
           (99x127cm-39x50in)

LOUTHERBOURG, Jacques Philippe de (1740-1812) French
£9365 $16389   (1-Apr-92 CSC.P18/R) Scene de naufrage (86x122cm-34x48in) (F.FR 90000)
£12707 $23000   (22-May-92 SY.NY268/R) Shepherd and sheperdess at rest with animals in
           wooded river landscape (67x104cm-26x41in) s.d.
£1004 $1717   *(12-Mar-92 GK.Z367) Interior of barn with peasant servant and domestic
           animals (26x37cm-10x15in) pen (S.FR 2600)*

LOUTHERBOURG, Jacques Philippe de (after) (1740-1812) French
£6000 $11460   (17-Jul-92 C183/R) The Battle of Trafalgar (119x178cm-47x70in)

LOUTHERBOURG, Jacques Philippe de (circle) (1740-1812) French
£850 $1573   (11-Jun-92 CSK89) Figures in winter landscape (68x91cm-27x36in)
£5000 $9100   (13-Dec-91 C214/R) Frigate in storm off castle on rocky coast
           (67x87cm-26x34in)

LOUTHERBOURG, Philip James de (18th C) French
£14000 $25480   (12-Dec-91 B111/R) Battle of Ushant, The Glorious First of June 1794
           (80x105cm-31x41in) canvas laid down on panel
£400 $764   *(1-Jul-92 B8) Figures and ponies on Welsh mountain track (22x31cm-9x12in)
           s. pen W/C htd with oil*

LOUTTRE, Marc Antoine (1926-) French
£561 $993   (12-Feb-92 GL.P61) Composition (60x73cm-24x29in) s. (F.FR 5500)

LOUVET, Emile (19th C) Italian
£512 $922   (2-Feb-92 ZZ.F259/R) Jeune femme revenant du marche (66x55cm-26x22in)
           s.d.1860 (F.FR 5000)

LOUVRIER, M (20th C) French
£3024 $5353   (10-Nov-91 LT.P4) La Seine au Pre-aux-Loups (73x92cm-29x36in) s.
           (F.FR 30000)

LOUVRIER, Maurice (20th C) French
£1016 $1768   (19-Apr-92 ZZ.F63/R) Paysage aux grands arbres (32x41cm-13x16in) s.
           (F.FR 10000)
£1955 $3500   (9-May-92 CE.NY15/R) Voiliers sur la Seine (46x55cm-18x22in) s.

LOUYOT, Edmond (19th C) German
£525 $950   (22-May-92 S.BM104 a/R) Winter river (79x58cm-31x23in) s.
£880 $1593   (3-Dec-91 FN.S2317) Rocky coastal landscape with fortified castle and
           figures, St Margherita (140x126cm-55x50in) s. i.verso (DM 2500)

LOVATI, Gusto (?) Italian
£1300 $2210   (22-Oct-91 SWS335/R) Introduction (53x72cm-21x28in) s.

LOVATTI, August (1852-1921) Italian
£883 $1678   *(25-Jun-92 D.V520/R) Garden with agaves (25x17cm-10x7in) s.i.d.1891 W/C
           (A.S 18000)*

LOVATTI, E A (1816-?) Italian
£1571 $3000   (16-Jul-92 SY.NY610/R) Monk in Capri (53x33cm-21x13in) s.i.
£2037 $3687   (19-May-92 GF.L2531/R) Surf near Capri (96x141cm-38x56in) s.i. panel
           (S.FR 5500)

LOVATTI, E Augusto (1816-?) Italian
£2400 $4464   (16-Jun-92 PH79/R) Coastal view with beached fishing boats, Capri
           (17x28cm-7x11in) s.i. panel
£2808 $5195   (9-Jun-92 F.R95) I Faraglioni di Capri (35x51cm-14x20in) s.d.1898
           (I.L 6200000)
£3333 $5700   (13-Mar-92 WOL.C464 a/R) Two children, coast of Capri (36x51cm-14x20in)
           s.i.

LOVEJOY, Rupert (attrib) (1885-1975) American
£763 $1450   (22-Jun-92 SG.M582) Gloucester Harbour, Mass (48x56cm-19x22in) s.verso

LOVELL, Tom (1909-) American
£1676 $3000   (13-Nov-91 B.SF2745/R) Saratoga Trunk (58x79cm-23x31in) s.d.41
£1685 $3000   (2-May-92 IH.NY207/R) Woman looking in phone book as man looks on
                        (43x64cm-17x25in) s. masonite
£2107 $3750   (2-Nov-91 IH.NY61/R) Four people in swimsuits on rock over ocean
                        (43x53cm-17x21in) s. board

LOVERIDGE, Clinton (19th C) British
£843 $1500   (26-Nov-91 MOR.P110) Cows at stream (30x25cm-12x10in) s.
£1520 $2600   (13-Mar-92 S.BM172/R) Lake Erie. Autumn on Lake George (15x30cm-6x12in)
                        s. init.i.verso board
£1714 $3000   (31-Mar-92 MOR.P126) Cows in pasture (30x41cm-12x16in) s.

LOW, Will Hicock (1853-1932) American
£798 $1500   (18-Dec-91 SY.NY74/R) The arched bridge (55x46cm-22x18in) s.d.1874

LOWCOCK, Charles Frederick (fl.1878-1922) British
£800 $1448   (6-Dec-91 TE588/R) The favourite chair (46x36cm-18x14in) mono.

LOWE, M C (?) ?
£684 $1239   (3-Dec-91 C.A159) Beside the fire (63x78cm-25x31in) s. (B.FR 40000)

LOWELL, Milton H (1848-1927) American
£1173 $2100   (6-May-92 D.NY18/R) Mountain pass, autumn (46x102cm-18x40in) s.

LOWENSBERG, Verena (1912-1986) Swiss
£4323 $7912   (4-Jun-92 SY.Z452/R) Composition (96x63cm-38x25in) s.d.64 (S.FR 11500)

LOWER RHINE SCHOOL, 16th C German
£7500 $13650   (10-Dec-91 PH54/R) Virgin and child enthroned (40x25cm-16x10in) panel

LOWITH, Wilhelm (1861-?) Austrian
£859 $1495   (21-Sep-91 SA.A1918/R) A little friend (16x12cm-6x5in) s.d.1889 panel
                        (DM 2500)
£1348 $2400   (22-Jan-92 SY.NY254/R) Toast (10x14cm-4x6in) s.d.1889 panel
£1990 $3542   (25-Nov-91 W.T2007/R) Awaiting an audience (19x10cm-7x4in) s. board
                        (C.D 4000)
£3500 $5985   (18-Mar-92 S65/R) Smoking with somer friends. Tasting the wine
                        (16x21cm-6x8in) s.d.1884 panel pair

LOWRY, Laurence Stephen (1887-1976) British
£10000 $17200   (6-Mar-92 C83/R) Old house boat at Aldeburgh (31x41cm-12x16in) s.d.1954
£10000 $17700   (7-Nov-91 C114/R) People walking towards the sea (51x76cm-20x30in)
                        s.d.1965
£13000 $22360   (6-Mar-92 C84/R) Old house (25x46cm-10x18in) s.d.1953
£17021 $30128   (26-Apr-92 SY.ME223/R) Tankers entering Tyne (48x74cm-19x29in) s.d.1967
                        s.i.d.verso (A.D 40000)
£40000 $70800   (7-Nov-91 C116/R) Ferry boats (30x40cm-12x16in) s.d.1960 i.stretcher
£47000 $83190   (7-Nov-91 C115/R) Northern river scene (51x76cm-20x30in) s.d.1959
£120000 $219600   (13-May-92 S65/R) The football match (71x91cm-28x36in) s.d.1949
£155000 $283650   (13-May-92 S66/R) Industrial landscape (114x152cm-45x60in) s.d.1952
£750 $1313   *(27-Sep-91 C6/R) Deal Sands (16x24cm-6x9in) init.i.d.24/9/12 blk.white*
                        crayon
£1200 $2292   *(23-Jul-92 CSK100/R) Street in Crewe (28x20cm-11x8in) s.i.d.1960 ink*
                        crayon
£1300 $2379   *(5-Jun-92 C102/R) Children sitting on a bench (15x25cm-6x10in)*
                        init.d.1972 pencil
£1400 $2548   *(12-Dec-91 CSK278) Street in Crewe (28x20cm-11x8in) s.i.d.1960 blk.crayon*
£1600 $2768   *(2-Oct-91 S91/R) The bomb-site (24x34cm-9x13in) s.d.1960 pencil*
£1800 $3114   *(2-Oct-91 S127/R) Seaham Harbour (25x34cm-10x13in) s.d.1964 pencil*
£2200 $4026   *(5-Jun-92 C103/R) Figures on a pier (28x41cm-11x16in) s.d.1969 pencil*
£2600 $4602   *(7-Nov-91 PHC662/R) On promenade (29x40cm-11x16in) s.d.1971 pencil chl*
£5500 $10065   *(5-Jun-92 C101/R) The auction (26x37cm-10x15in) s.d.1936 pencil*
£6000 $10260   *(11-Mar-92 S107/R) Accident (38x28cm-15x11in) s.d.1929 pencil*

LOXTON, John S (1903-) Australian
£783 $1363   (16-Sep-91 CH.ME163) Delphiniums (67x54cm-26x21in) s. (A.D 1700)
£1057 $1882   (26-Nov-91 J.M140/R) Adjusting plough (62x74cm-24x29in) s. (A.D 2400)
£1322 $2352   (26-Nov-91 J.M144/R) Delphiniums (67x54cm-26x21in) s. (A.D 3000)
£385 $685   *(27-Apr-92 J.M986) Road to Flowerdale, Victoria (35x49cm-14x19in) s. W/C*
                        (A.D 900)
£427 $774   *(2-Dec-91 AAA.S7) Droving to the West (37x45cm-15x18in) s. W/C (A.D 1000)*
£563 $941   *(19-Aug-91 SY.ME138) Ploughing (35x42cm-14x17in) s. W/C (A.D 1200)*
£705 $1255   *(26-Nov-91 J.M439) Gondolars, Venice (46x55cm-18x22in) s. W/C (A.D 1600)*

LOY, E (20th C) ?
£691 $1257   (10-Dec-91 F.R106) La modella (52x38cm-20x15in) s. (I.L 1500000)

LOZANO, Francisco (20th C) Spanish
£2078 $3637   (19-Feb-92 DUR.M806/R) Mediterraneo (16x22cm-6x9in) s. panel (S.P 375000)
£2175 $3872   (28-Apr-92 DUR.M519/R) Paisaje (33x24cm-13x9in) s.d.77 s.i.d.verso
                        (S.P 400000)

LOZANO, Francisco (20th C) Spanish-cont.
£2719 $4840   (28-Apr-92 DUR.M39/R) Mediterraneo, Primavera (21x26cm-8x10in) s.
                   (S.P 500000)

LOZANO, Josep M Martinez (1923-) Mexican?
£1095 $1960   (6-May-92 GD.B789/R) Paquet de 3 toiles (109x115cm-43x45in) s.d.1959/1962
                   (S.FR 3000)

LU YANSHAO (1909-) Chinese
£2367 $4142   (30-Mar-92 CH.HK282/R) Western Tian Hu Mountains (68x48cm-27x19in)
                   s.i.d.1962 ink W/C scroll (HK.D 32000)
£2959 $5178   (30-Mar-92 CH.HK106/R) Waterfall in cloudy valley (82x34cm-32x13in) s.
                   ink W/C hanging scroll (HK.D 40000)
£3698 $6472   (30-Mar-92 CH.HK107/R) Mount Emei in winter snow (100x30cm-39x12in)
                   s.i.d.1963 ink W/C hanging scroll (HK.D 50000)
£5178 $9061   (30-Mar-92 CH.HK218/R) Waterfall of Yandang Mountains (96x43cm-38x17in)
                   s.i.d.1979 ink W/C hanging scroll (HK.D 70000)
£5547 $9708   (30-Mar-92 CH.HK219/R) Landscape (89x48cm-35x19in) s. ink W/C hanging
                   scroll (HK.D 75000)
£6657 $11649   (30-Mar-92 CH.HK217/R) Landscapes (45x33cm-18x13in) s.i. nine d.1988 ink
                   album twelve leaves (HK.D 90000)

LU YONGQI (1938-) Chinese
£1627 $2848   (30-Mar-92 CH.HK254/R) Scholar gazing at waterfall (119x59cm-47x23in)
                   s.d.1989 ink W/C hanging scroll (HK.D 22000)

LUARD, John Dalbiac (c.1830-1860) British
£1050 $1806   (4-Mar-92 S191/R) Welcome arrival (17x22cm-7x9in) panel

LUBBERS, Holger (1855-1928) Danish
£514 $926   (19-Nov-91 RAS.K228) Seascape with sailship (28x44cm-11x17in) s.d.1907
                   (D.KR 5700)
£617 $1048   (8-Aug-91 RAS.V954/R) Sailship and steamers off Kullen (43x64cm-17x25in)
                   s.d.1917 (D.KR 7000)
£704 $1218   (2-Sep-91 BU.K40/R) Sailship in Copenhagen harbour (37x60cm-15x24in) s.
                   (D.KR 8000)
£749 $1326   (23-Apr-92 RAS.V840/R) Two woman and man with baskets on beach
                   (38x48cm-15x19in) mono. (D.KR 8500)
£1346 $2383   (11-Feb-92 RAS.K9/R) Seascape with the frigatte Jylland (90x80cm-35x31in)
                   s. (D.KR 15000)
£2000 $3620   (20-May-92 S189/R) The Straits at Messina (52x78cm-20x31in) s.
                   i.stretcher
£2300 $4163   (20-May-92 S189 a) Danish frigate (101x94cm-40x37in) s.d.1882

LUBBERS, Thomas Christian (attrib) (1797-1873) Danish
£791 $1416   (6-May-92 KH.K252/R) Portrait of Joseph Hambro (10x8cm-4x3in) min. pencil
                   W/C oval (D.KR 9000)

LUBIN, Arieh (1897-1980) Israeli
£811 $1500   (9-Jun-92 GG.TA364/R) Head of woman (30x26cm-12x10in) s.d.39
£1027 $1900   (9-Jun-92 GG.TA357/R) Landscape, house and trees (33x41cm-13x16in) s.
£1277 $2400   (5-Jan-92 GG.TA245/R) Landscape with cypress trees (46x38cm-18x15in) s.
£1596 $3000   (5-Jan-92 GG.TA244/R) Goldberg House, Ramat Gan Grove (54x65cm-21x26in)
                   s.d.1939 i.verso
£1730 $3200   (9-Jun-92 GG.TA354/R) View of city from roof (40x50cm-16x20in) s.d.31
£2162 $4000   (9-Jun-92 GG.TA351/R) Labourers resting (37x45cm-15x18in) s.d.28 board
£2162 $4000   (9-Jun-92 GG.TA350/R) Still life (46x46cm-18x18in) s.d.27
£2378 $4400   (9-Jun-92 GG.TA356/R) Landscape (45x62cm-18x24in) s.
£2811 $5200   (9-Jun-92 GG.TA355/R) Landscape, trees and house (41x54cm-16x21in) s.d.34
£2811 $5200   (9-Jun-92 GG.TA349/R) Milkman (62x45cm-24x18in)
£3243 $6000   (9-Jun-92 GG.TA375/R) Village women (60x80cm-24x31in)
£4686 $8200   (26-Sep-91 SY.I62/R) The Jordan valley (54x73cm-21x29in) s.d.47
£378 $700   (9-Jun-92 GG.TA385/R) Woman holding apple (36x32cm-14x13in) s. pastel
£378 $700   (9-Jun-92 GG.TA361/R) Outskirts of town (23x37cm-9x15in) s. W/C pencil
£432 $800   (9-Jun-92 GG.TA362/R) Landscape (25x35cm-10x14in) s. W/C pencil
£486 $900   (9-Jun-92 GG.TA369/R) Synagogue in Safed (35x50cm-14x20in) s.i.d.48 W/C
                   pencil
£541 $1000   (9-Jun-92 GG.TA370/R) Synagogue in Safed (35x50cm-14x20in) s. W/C pencil
£541 $1000   (9-Jun-92 GG.TA373/R) Oriental cafe (30x39cm-12x15in) s. W/C col.crayons
£649 $1200   (9-Jun-92 GG.TA367/R) Three women (49x44cm-19x17in) s. W/C
£649 $1200   (9-Jun-92 GG.TA384/R) Narghile smoker (44x32cm-17x13in) s. gouache
£691 $1300   (5-Jan-92 GG.TA246/R) The Jars' Market (54x69cm-21x27in) s.d.1970 gouache
£757 $1400   (9-Jun-92 GG.TA386/R) Three women (42x68cm-17x27in) s. pastel
£811 $1500   (9-Jun-92 GG.TA352/R) Women on beach (20x19cm-8x7in) s. W/C mixed media
£865 $1600   (9-Jun-92 GG.TA353/R) Women on beach (18x18cm-7x7in) s. W/C mixed media
£865 $1600   (9-Jun-92 GG.TA380/R) Nudes (98x67cm-39x26in) s. pastel chl
£865 $1600   (9-Jun-92 GG.TA379/R) Women with urns (99x68cm-39x27in) s. pastel chl
£865 $1600   (9-Jun-92 GG.TA377/R) Group of women (69x99cm-27x39in) s. pastel
£919 $1700   (9-Jun-92 GG.TA378/R) Narghile smokers (69x99cm-27x39in) s. pastel
£1027 $1900   (9-Jun-92 GG.TA358/R) Hill village (19x30cm-7x12in) s. W/C
£1081 $2000   (9-Jun-92 GG.TA381/R) Oriental cafe (24x46cm-9x18in) s. gouache
£1117 $2100   (5-Jan-92 GG.TA247/R) Oriental figures (42x65cm-17x26in) s. W/C gouache
£1405 $2600   (9-Jun-92 GG.TA368/R) Acre (35x50cm-14x20in) s.d.48 W/C pencil
£1622 $3000   (9-Jun-92 GG.TA382/R) Oriental cafe (24x78cm-9x31in) s. gouache
£3027 $5600   (9-Jun-92 GG.TA376/R) Oriental cafe (46x60cm-18x24in) s. W/C

LUBITCH, Ossip (1896-1986) French
£1017 $1862   (17-May-92 GL.P224 b) Paysage de Banyuls (55x46cm-22x18in) s.
                      (F.FR 10000)
£1831 $3351   (17-May-92 GL.P153/R) Danseuse au miroir (90x60cm-35x24in) s.
                      (F.FR 18000)

LUCA, R de (19th C) Italian
£1000 $1780   (26-Nov-91 PH277) Coastal view, Capri (61x92cm-24x36in) s.

LUCANDER, Anitra (1918-) Finnish
£4678 $8233   (12-Apr-92 HOR.H157) The violinist (65x55cm-26x22in) s. (F.M 37000)

LUCAS Y PADILLA, Eugenio (1824-1870) Spanish
£7293 $13200   (4-Dec-91 NA.BA6/R) Una juerga en los barrios bajos (63x49cm-25x19in)

LUCAS Y PADILLA, Eugenio (attrib) (1824-1870) Spanish
£1923 $3500   (11-Dec-91 RO.BA62/R) El dialogo (60x50cm-24x20in)
£2099 $3800   (21-May-92 CH.NY234/R) Portrait of lady, standing in lace trimmed dress
                      with fan, by balcony (183x106cm-72x42in)

LUCAS Y VILLAAMIL, Eugenio (1858-1918) Spanish
£820 $1468   (14-Jan-92 SWS226/R) Off to market (21x11cm-8x4in) s. panel
£1649 $2968   (19-Nov-91 DUR.M33/R) Sentados en la pradera (13x24cm-5x9in) panel
                      (S.P 300000)
£1649 $2968   (19-Nov-91 DUR.M34/R) Galanteo (13x25cm-5x10in) s. panel (S.P 300000)
£2077 $3593   (24-Mar-92 DUR.M577/R) Pareja de figuras de epoca (29x15cm-11x6in) s.
                      panel (S.P 375000)
£3571 $6500   (13-Dec-91 S.BM502 a/R) In the salon (56x102cm-22x40in) s.
£3732 $7017   (16-Dec-91 ANS.M113/R) Llevando el Santisimo (38x31cm-15x12in) s. tin
                      (S.P 675000)
£5456 $9875   (20-May-92 ANS.M100/R) La pradera de San Isidro (42x77cm-17x30in)
                      (S.P 1000000)
£6096 $10668   (18-Feb-92 DUR.M18/R) Paseando por Versalles (23x45cm-9x18in) s. panel
                      (S.P 1100000)
£6541 $11251   (7-Oct-91 ANS.M99/R) Fiesta campestre (34x48cm-13x19in) s. panel
                      (S.P 1200000)
£9302 $16000   (17-Oct-91 SY.NY357/R) Wedding party (38x56cm-15x22in) s.d.90 canvas on
                      board
£13854 $24245   (18-Feb-92 DUR.M19/R) Saludando a los novios (38x57cm-15x22in) s.
                      d.indist. canvas laid down on panel (S.P 2500000)

LUCAS Y VILLAAMIL, Eugenio (attrib) (1858-1918) Spanish
£1367 $2501   (13-May-92 FER.M108/R) Escena de la Inquisicion. El sacamuelas
                      (18x23cm-7x9in) pair (S.P 250000)

LUCAS Y VILLAAMIL, Eugenio (style) (1858-1918) Spanish
£15698 $27000   (10-Oct-91 SY.NY13/R) Battle scene (55x89cm-22x35in)

LUCAS, Albert Durer (1828-1918) British
£750 $1283   (12-Mar-92 CSK245) Dahlias, fuchsias and daisies with ferns
                      (51x36cm-20x14in) indis.s.d.1871
£900 $1665   (11-Jun-92 CSK178) Exotic ferns (47x35cm-19x14in) s.i.d.1864
£1000 $1780   (31-Oct-91 D137/R) Green moth amidst heather and other flowers
                      (18x13cm-7x5in) s.d.1888 i.verso board
£1191 $2109   (26-Apr-92 SY.ME229) Butterfly with flowers and bracken. Butterflies,
                      grasshopper and flowers (24x19cm-9x7in) s.d.1878 board pair (A.D 2800)
£2000 $3580   (5-May-92 SWS423/R) Still lives with butterflies and flowers
                      (19x14cm-7x6in) s.d.1889 s.i.d.verso board pair
£2000 $3440   (11-Oct-91 C26/R) Heather in flower (25x20cm-10x8in) s.d.1901 s.i.d.verso
£2200 $3872   (6-Apr-92 WW42/R) At mountains foot, study group of orchids with humming
                      bird (77x63cm-30x25in) s.d.1889
£4400 $7744   (6-Apr-92 WW41/R) Group of orchids painted from specimens at Messrs.
                      Veitch nursery for Exotics London (77x63cm-30x25in) s.d.1881
£759 $1389   (14-May-92 BU.S96/R) Flower study (22x17cm-9x7in) s.d.1878 W/C oval
                      (S.KR 8000)

LUCAS, Edward George Handel (1861-1936) British
£524 $934   (29-Nov-91 ZEL.L1066/R) Spanish woman seated on chair wearing Sunday
                      outfit in park landscape (24x18cm-9x7in) s. panel (DM 1500)

LUCAS, Felix Hippolyte see   HIPPOLYTE-LUCAS, Marie Felix

LUCAS, George (19th C) British
£750 $1350   *(27-Jan-92 PH34) Harvest time (66x101cm-26x40in) s. W/C htd white*

LUCAS, H F L (?-1943) British
£3600 $6588   (3-Jun-92 S92/R) Barsac. Roughside - Race horses (71x91cm-28x36in) s.i.
                      one d.96 one d.99 pair

LUCAS, Henry Frederick Lucas (?-1943) British
£874 $1600   (5-Jun-92 SY.NY51/R) Rugby, a black horse with groom by a barn
                      (59x76cm-23x30in) s.d.1879
£1600 $2848   (21-Jan-92 PH120/R) Fox hounds in stable (28x37cm-11x15in) s.d.92
£1900 $3648   (28-Jul-92 SWS120/R) Mrs Stead, a bay. Sunset, a bay. Dappled grey
                      (22x29cm-9x11in) s.d.92 panel three

LUCAS, Jean Paul (?-1808) French
£550 $963   (27-Feb-92 CSK62) The Mystic Marriage of Saint Catherine (23x17cm-9x7in)
        i.verso copper after Correggio

LUCAS, John (1807-1874) British
£880 $1681   (14-Jul-92 DR404) Portrait of General Sir George Higginson in military
        dress (139x190cm-55x75in) s.i.d.1852 verso

LUCAS, John Seymour (1849-1923) British
£1366 $2323   (24-Oct-91 DUR.M1002/R) Mrs. Graham Harris (140x100cm-55x39in) s.
        (S.P 250000)
£1581 $2846   (19-Nov-91 GS.B3575/R) Drawing the longbow (51x77cm-20x30in) s.d.1879
        s.i.d.verso (S.FR 4000)
£9000 $15480   (11-Oct-91 C63/R) The call to arms (65x99cm-26x39in) s.d.1894
£1650 $2920   (7-Nov-91 F.M71) Corsia dei Servi, Milano (41x30cm-16x12in) s. W/C
        (I.L 3600000)

LUCAS, John Templeton (1836-1880) British
£580 $998   (8-Oct-91 PH119/R) Sculling (30x25cm-12x10in) s.d.1868

LUCAS, Ralph W (19th C) British
£3700 $6956   (19-Dec-91 C130) Wooded landscape with woodmen, Windsor Castle seen
        through clearing (112x88cm-44x35in) s.

LUCAS, Wilhelm (1884-1918) German
£699 $1210   (25-Mar-92 KM.K1297) Landscape with view of town (14x16cm-6x6in) s. paper
        (DM 2000)
£1661 $3156   (24-Jun-92 KM.K1174) Beach scene with figures by sailing boat
        (32x50cm-13x20in) s. board (DM 4800)
£3793 $6524   (16-Oct-91 KM.K1262/R) Landscape with view of windmill and church tower
        (90x150cm-35x59in) s.d.05 (DM 11000)

LUCAS-ROBIQUET, Marie Aimee (1864-?) French
£6000 $11160   (19-Jun-92 C84/R) Arab smoking in doorway (77x100cm-30x39in) s.

LUCCA SCHOOL (?) Italian
£3867 $7000   (21-May-92 CH.NY28/R) Crucifixion with Virgin and Saint John the Baptist
        (66x41cm-26x16in) possibly 20th C copy tempera panel

LUCCHESI, Giorgio (1855-1941) Italian
£10556 $19000   (22-Nov-91 S.BM50/R) Passing of autumn - still life with dried flowers,
        apples and grapes (99x71cm-39x28in) s.d.1904

LUCCHESI, P (19th C) Italian
£789 $1500   (26-Jun-92 WOL.C868/R) Reading the note (76x61cm-30x24in) s.

LUCE, Maximilien (1858-1941) French
£1947 $3504   (2-Feb-92 ZZ.F140/R) Vaches dans un pre au soleil couchant
        (16x27cm-6x11in) s. panel (F.FR 19000)
£2252 $4008   (27-Nov-91 AT.P164/R) La Seine a Rolleboise (33x50cm-13x20in) bears
        studio st. paper laid down on canvas (F.FR 22000)
£2317 $4356   (16-Dec-91 AGS.P20/R) L'Eglise Americaine - Quai d'Orsay (19x26cm-7x10in)
        s. panel (F.FR 22500)
£2459 $4426   (2-Feb-92 ZZ.F109/R) La plage (22x27cm-9x11in) s. panel (F.FR 24000)
£2569 $4418   (7-Oct-91 CH.E249/R) Portrait of Charles Angrand seated at table
        (33x26cm-13x10in) s.i. board (E.P 2800)
£2835 $4905   (23-Mar-92 CC.P10/R) Bretagne, paysage (27x41cm-11x16in) s. (F.FR 27500)
£3144 $5533   (10-Apr-92 AGS.P33/R) Bords de la Loire (38x55cm-15x22in) s. (F.FR 31000)
£3500 $6055   (25-Mar-92 S184/R) Paysage (34x53cm-13x21in) s. paper laid down on canvas
£3827 $6812   (28-Oct-91 GL.P225/R) Les bateleurs (52x67cm-20x26in) s. board
        (F.FR 38000)
£4000 $7640   (29-Jun-92 CSK13/R) Bords de la Loire, Saint-Ay (38x55cm-15x22in) s.
        i.stretcher
£4630 $8380   (2-Dec-91 CC.P1/R) Honfleur (38x50cm-15x20in) st.sig. paper pasted on
        canvas (F.FR 45000)
£4800 $8304   (25-Mar-92 S183/R) Conversation sous l'arbre - Rolleboise
        (37x48cm-15x19in) s. oil paper laid down on canvas
£5800 $10498   (2-Dec-91 CSK13/R) Paysage aux Pommiers (25x39cm-10x15in) s. board
£6061 $10727   (22-Apr-92 ZZ.F123/R) Mere et enfant a la campagne (26x32cm-10x13in)
        (F.FR 60000)
£6557 $12000   (14-May-92 SY.NY261/R) Rolleboise, baigneuses au bord de la Seine
        (33x50cm-13x20in) s.d. paper on canvas
£6857 $12000   (25-Feb-92 CH.NY20/R) Le barrage sur la Seine (27x36cm-11x14in) s. paper
        on canvas
£6900 $12972   (16-Dec-91 AGS.P21/R) L'entree du village (37x50cm-15x20in) s. board
        (F.FR 67000)
£7187 $12936   (19-Nov-91 FB.P97/R) Le quai d'Orsay et le Trocadero (46x65cm-18x26in) s.
        (F.FR 70000)
£7451 $12667   (23-Oct-91 GD.B1155/R) Wooded lake landscape with sailing boats
        (24x34cm-9x13in) s.d.1936 panel (S.FR 19000)
£7879 $14261   (19-May-92 CH.AM185/R) La Rue Denfert, les toits sous la neige
        (31x41cm-12x16in) s. panel (D.FL 26000)
£9000 $15570   (25-Mar-92 S177/R) Bords de la Seine, Bonnieres (54x65cm-21x26in) s.
        i.verso

LUCE, Maximilien (1858-1941) French-cont.

£9119	$16505	(24-May-92 GL.P60/R) La rue Reaumur, le percement (33x27cm-13x11in) s.d.1896 board (F.FR 90000)
£9605	$17000	(7-Nov-91 SY.NY122/R) Chevres sur la falaise, le treport (45x81cm-18x32in) s.d.35
£10000	$18100	(3-Dec-91 C258/R) Vase de Dahlias (45x38cm-18x15in) s. paper laid on canvas
£10286	$18000	(25-Feb-92 SY.NY12/R) Les travailleurs (50x65cm-20x26in) s.
£11190	$20031	(13-Nov-91 PIC.P71/R) Paysage de Bessy/Cure, Yonne (65x81cm-26x32in) s.d.1906 (F.FR 110000)
£14754	$27000	(14-May-92 SY.NY257/R) Bessy sur Cure, le village (63x81cm-25x32in) s.d.1906
£14754	$27000	(14-May-92 SY.NY238/R) Paysanne sur la route de moulineux (36x49cm-14x19in) s.
£16000	$28000	(25-Feb-92 CH.NY15/R) La baignade (60x93cm-24x37in) s.
£19000	$32680	(16-Oct-91 S23/R) Au bord de la route (38x45cm-15x18in) s.d.1905
£22000	$39820	(4-Dec-91 S125/R) Guernes, la passerelle sur le bras de Seine (54x73cm-21x29in) s.d.24
£25956	$47500	(14-May-92 SY.NY250/R) Paysage mediterraneen (26x40cm-10x16in) board
£35519	$65000	(14-May-92 SY.NY255/R) Saint Tropez, les pins (99x65cm-39x26in) s.
£39106	$70000	(11-Nov-91 GC.M59/R) Le Pont au Change (65x81cm-26x32in) s.d.1912
£42000	$76020	(3-Dec-91 C215/R) Les Tanneries de la Bievre (59x72cm-23x28in) s.d.87
£237288	$420000	(6-Nov-91 SY.NY14/R) Eragny, le verger de Pissarro (81x100cm-32x39in) s.d.95
£416	$728	(5-Apr-92 ZZ.F103/R) Arbre au bord du chemin (21x16cm-8x6in) s. pastel (F.FR 4000)
£453	$807	(31-Oct-91 LD.P105) Le clocher (27x21cm-11x8in) studio st. blk.crayon ink wash (F.FR 4500)
£454	$781	(20-Oct-91 I.N112) Scenes de port (13x19cm-5x7in) s. ink (F.FR 4500)
£457	$800	(2-Apr-92 BG.M445/R) Landscape with trees, cart and house (25x36cm-10x14in) india ink graphite
£483	$860	(31-Oct-91 LD.P91/R) Mere et enfant (27x21cm-11x8in) studio st. blk.crayon ink wash (F.FR 4800)
£512	$922	(2-Feb-92 ZZ.F243/R) Les quais de Seine a Rouen (15x25cm-6x10in) st.sig. chl. (F.FR 5000)
£512	$922	(2-Feb-92 ZZ.F103/R) Arbre au bord de la riviere (16x13cm-6x5in) s. pastel (F.FR 5000)
£520	$911	(5-Apr-92 ZZ.F99/R) Rivere dans la vallee (15x23cm-6x9in) st.sig. pastel (F.FR 5000)
£584	$1040	(31-Oct-91 LD.P71/R) La baignade (21x27cm-8x11in) studio st. blk.crayon ink wash (F.FR 5800)
£624	$1111	(31-Oct-91 LD.P72) Berger et son troupeau (21x27cm-8x11in) studio st. blk.crayon ink wash (F.FR 6200)
£705	$1255	(31-Oct-91 LD.P106) La Tamise a Londres (21x27cm-8x11in) studio st. blk.crayon ink wash (F.FR 7000)
£820	$1475	(2-Feb-92 ZZ.F99/R) Chemin pres des grands arbres (33x46cm-13x18in) s. pastel (F.FR 8000)
£886	$1577	(31-Oct-91 LD.P68/R) Ferme a Rolleboise (20x27cm-8x11in) studio st. blk.crayon ink wash (F.FR 8800)
£915	$1591	(19-Apr-92 ZZ.F2/R) Bord de Seine a Herblay (17x23cm-7x9in) s. crayon htd.white chk. (F.FR 9000)
£1154	$2054	(26-Nov-91 KF.M822/R) Imprimerie (25x18cm-10x7in) s.i. chk (DM 3300)
£1179	$2111	(19-Jan-92 CSC.P60) Personnage devant une statue (15x22cm-6x9in) s. ink (F.FR 11500)

LUCE, Percival de (1847-1914) American

£758	$1350	(26-Jan-92 LIT.L177) Still life with cup and saucer (20x15cm-8x6in) s.

LUCEBERT (1924-) Dutch

£1068	$1858	(17-Sep-91 RAS.K4/R) Senator II (40x30cm-16x12in) s.d.69 (D.KR 12000)
£1335	$2322	(17-Sep-91 RAS.K109/R) The prophetess (50x70cm-20x28in) s.d.72 (D.KR 15000)
£1423	$2533	(29-Nov-91 GAB.G2795) Figures (48x62cm-19x24in) s.d.75 XII 28 acrylic paper laid down on canvas (S.FR 3600)
£4023	$6960	(23-Mar-92 AB.L131/R) Untitled (92x65cm-36x26in) s.d.1988 (S.FR 10500)
£4305	$7791	(23-May-92 KV.L511/R) De wereld als voorstelling (130x100cm-51x39in) s.d.89 (B.FR 260000)
£6061	$10970	(19-May-92 CH.AM317/R) Pyromaan (40x60cm-16x24in) s.d.60 (D.FL 20000)
£7562	$13158	(17-Sep-91 RAS.K36/R) Snake's shield (107x75cm-42x30in) s.d.63 (D.KR 85000)
£10762	$19478	(23-May-92 KV.L460/R) In a Persian garden (200x150cm-79x59in) s.d.88 (B.FR 650000)
£10802	$19660	(11-Dec-91 CH.AM345/R) Verloren meisje, little girl lost (98x60cm-39x24in) s. board (D.FL 35000)
£11728	$21346	(11-Dec-91 CH.AM346/R) Nieuwe bruiloftsdans (130x100cm-51x39in) s.d.67 i.verso (D.FL 38000)
£14286	$25000	(25-Feb-92 SY.NY139/R) Thessaurier baby (100x80cm-39x31in) s.d.60
£18182	$32909	(19-May-92 CH.AM292/R) Tataar met huisgoden (100x80cm-39x31in) s.d.63 (D.FL 60000)
£26235	$47747	(12-Dec-91 SY.AM235/R) Macbeth with witches (130x200cm-51x79in) s.d.64 d.verso (D.FL 85000)
£432	$786	(11-Dec-91 CH.AM186) Angry faces (32x23cm-13x9in) s.d.26 pen brush col.pastels (D.FL 1400)
£500	$881	(7-Apr-92 C.A167) Louis XIV (48x60cm-19x24in) s.d.1975 W/C (B.FR 30000)

LUCEBERT (1924-) Dutch-cont.

£556	$1011	(11-Dec-91 CH.AM141) Man and horse (17x20cm-7x8in) s.d.50 pen brush ink (D.FL 1800)
£800	$1376	(17-Oct-91 S121/R) Mother of desert (48x36cm-19x14in) s.d.15.IX.70 pencil pastel
£802	$1460	(12-Dec-91 SY.AM232/R) Droom van een dorpsgek (34x46cm-13x18in) s.d.74.3.14 gouache W/C (D.FL 2600)
£917	$1615	(7-Apr-92 C.A168) Composition (48x60cm-19x24in) s.d.1975 W/C (B.FR 55000)
£986	$1785	(6-Dec-91 GB.B6786) Figures standing (63x49cm-25x19in) s.d.1965 indian ink pen brush (DM 2800)
£1152	$2084	(19-May-92 CH.AM299 b) Animal (26x34cm-10x13in) s. pencil brush ink gouache (D.FL 3800)
£1335	$2322	(18-Sep-91 KH.K34/R) Figure composition (31x21cm-12x8in) s.d.51 W/C Indian ink (D.KR 15000)
£1379	$2399	(18-Sep-91 KH.K11/R) Figure composition (27x21cm-11x8in) s.i.d.51 crayon Indian ink (D.KR 15500)
£1515	$2742	(19-May-92 CH.AM295) Personnage (64x49cm-25x19in) s.d.1983 gouache (D.FL 5000)
£1879	$3401	(21-May-92 SY.AM222/R) Satyr met Venus der Cyclopen (75x100cm-30x39in) s.d.12 acrylic W/C col.chk (D.FL 6200)
£1970	$3565	(21-May-92 SY.AM244/R) Untitled (70x100cm-28x39in) s.d.77 gouache W/C wax crayon (D.FL 6500)
£2182	$3949	(21-May-92 SY.AM252) Untitled (45x60cm-18x24in) s.d.52 gouache cardboard (D.FL 7200)
£2315	$4213	(11-Dec-91 CH.AM385/R) Three figures (48x63cm-19x25in) s. gouache (D.FL 7500)
£2833	$4873	(12-Oct-91 KV.L485/R) Composition with figures (66x98cm-26x39in) s. acrylic pastel (B.FR 170000)
£5152	$9324	(19-May-92 CH.AM293/R) An animal (47x63cm-19x25in) s.d.1959 gouache (D.FL 17000)

LUCIANI, Ascanio (1700-?) Italian

| £13014 | $23556 | (4-Dec-91 CH.R160/R) Scena di melodramma entro ruderi di edifici antichi (102x135cm-40x53in) s. (I.L 28000000) |

LUCIENTES, Francisco Jose de see GOYA Y LUCIENTES, Francisco Jose de

LUCIONI, Luigi (1900-1988) American

| £694 | $1200 | (6-Sep-91 S.BM245/R) House among the trees (15x23cm-6x9in) s. indist.d. masonite |
| £1147 | $2065 | (23-Nov-91 YFA.M186/R) Old red barn (15x20cm-6x8in) s.d.1950 board |

LUCK, Bruno (20th C) German

| £1220 | $2220 | (13-Dec-91 BM.B776/R) Village fair (91x100cm-36x39in) s.d.38 (DM 3500) |

LUCKEROTH, Jupp (1919-) German

| £982 | $1768 | (19-Nov-91 L.K888/R) Wellensturz (80x60cm-31x24in) s.d.1960 s.i.d.verso oil resin canvas (DM 2800) |

LUCKX, Frans (1802-1849) Belgian

| £8721 | $15000 | (17-Oct-91 SY.NY40/R) Pleading for justice (89x117cm-35x46in) s.d.1836 |

LUCY, Charles (1814-1873) British

| £700 | $1204 | (4-Mar-92 S114) Puritan emigrants, English pastor's family (41x53cm-16x21in) s. arched top |
| £850 | $1479 | (12-Sep-91 CSK268/R) Portrait of young Italian peasant girl (27x20cm-11x8in) mono.d.1856 panel |

LUDEKENS, Fred (1900-1982) American

| £733 | $1400 | (3-Jul-92 S.W3847/R) Incident at ballgame (23x74cm-9x29in) s. W/C |

LUDLOW, Hal see LUDLOW, Henry Stephen

LUDLOW, Henry Stephen (1861-?) British

| £560 | $980 | (23-Sep-91 HS172/R) Pas seul - study of dancer wearing chiffon dress (38x22cm-15x9in) s.i. W/C |

LUDOVICI, Albert (1820-1894) British

£550	$1023	(18-Jun-92 B53) A serving maid (29x24cm-11x9in) mono.d.1874
£1250	$2288	(6-Feb-92 PHF177/R) Young girl seated on grassy bank before woodland, holding aloft bonnet (60x44cm-24x17in) mono.d.1884
£2200	$4070	(12-Jun-92 C225/R) The new hat (59x44cm-23x17in) mono.d.1884
£2200	$4070	(12-Jun-92 C227/R) Play time (45x28cm-18x11in) indis.s.d.1880 board

LUDOVICI, Albert (jnr) (1852-1932) British

| £2000 | $3760 | (19-Dec-91 C177/R) The proposal. Unwanted suitor (31x41cm-12x16in) s. pair |

LUDWIG, Auguste (1834-?) German

| £16000 | $27360 | (17-Mar-92 PH46/R) The first pipe (108x82cm-43x32in) s.i. |

LUDWIG, Louis (?) Belgian?

| £602 | $1023 | (22-Oct-91 C.A780) Working in the fields (30x40cm-12x16in) s. canvas on panel (B.FR 36000) |

LUEG, Konrad (1939-) German
£825 $1509 (2-Jun-92 L.K773) Untitled (50x50cm-20x20in) s.i.d.1966verso foil mixed
        media pair (DM 2400)

LUEG-FISCHER, Konrad (20th C) German
£2793 $5000 (13-Nov-91 SY.NY123/R) Boxers (136x100cm-54x39in) s.d.64verso oil pencil
        canvas

LUEGER, Michael (1804-1883) German
£535 $996 (16-Jun-92 RAS.V825 a) Alpine landscape with cottage and horses
        (32x47cm-13x19in) s.d.1871 (D.KR 6000)
£756 $1315 (18-Sep-91 N.M611/R) Farmhouse in mountain valley and cattle on path
        (28x35cm-11x14in) s.d.1863 (DM 2200)
£5575 $10146 (11-Dec-91 WE.MU70/R) View of Wurzburg (64x89cm-25x35in) mono. (DM 16000)

LUERZER, Friderick (1858-1917) German
£1023 $1800 (8-Apr-92 D.NY53) Children playing beside rushing mountain stream
        (76x127cm-30x50in) s.d.89

LUGARDON, Albert (1827-1909) French
£1963 $3553 (20-May-92 GK.Z5116/R) Lake Geneva landscape with cattle, shepherd boys
        and sailing boat beyond (63x97cm-25x38in) s. (S.FR 5300)
£2964 $5277 (29-Nov-91 GAB.G2135/R) Sur l'alpage (90x130cm-35x51in) s.d.1878
        (S.FR 7500)

LUGINBUHL, Bernhard (1929-) Swiss
£526 $947 (19-Nov-91 L.K891) Zwei Doppelpoller (30x42cm-12x17in) s.d.1980 felt tip
        pen (DM 1500)
£1385 $2631 (25-Jun-92 GK.B454/R) Le Crocrodome de Zic et Puce (21x30cm-8x12in)
        s.d.1977 felt tip pen (S.FR 3600)

LUGO, Emil (1840-1902) German
£6529 $11948 (2-Jun-92 FN.S2657) Artist's garden in Baden-Baden (52x72cm-20x28in)
        mono.d.1876 (DM 19000)
£1568 $2854 (11-Dec-91 N.M515/R) Classical scenes with Orpheus and Eurydike
        (59x89cm-23x35in) mixed media board triptych pair (DM 4500)

LUGO, Emil (attrib) (1840-1902) German
£1408 $2549 (3-Dec-91 FN.S2318) Young peasant with goats resting on hill near cottage
        beneath trees (46x35cm-18x14in) (DM 4000)

LUIGI, Mario de (1908-) Italian
£741 $1320 (29-Nov-91 F.F68/R) Composizione (13x10cm-5x4in) s. s.d.1965 paper on
        panel (I.L 1600000)
£1051 $1997 (23-Jun-92 F.M82/R) G.V. 206 (38x45cm-15x18in) s.i.d.1974verso mixed
        media graffiti (I.L 2300000)
£4402 $7836 (29-Nov-91 F.F136/R) Senza titolo (117x73cm-46x29in) s. mixed media
        cardboard (I.L 9500000)

LUIGINI, F-J (1870-1943) French
£800 $1416 (13-Feb-92 CSK74/R) Bassin a Concarneau. Automne dans la campagne
        (49x60cm-19x24in) one s. W/C bodycol. pair

LUIGINI, Ferdinand-Jean (1870-1943) French
£813 $1415 (13-Apr-92 AT.P197) L'anier a la fontaine (49x65cm-19x26in) s.d.92
        (F.FR 8000)

LUINI, Bernardino (circle) (1475-1532) Italian
£3486 $6310 (3-Dec-91 SY.MI241/R) Madonna col Bambino (48x37cm-19x15in) (I.L 7500000)
£19337 $35000 (21-May-92 CH.NY77/R) Music-making angels (58x49cm-23x19in) fresco
        transferred canvas
£20349 $35000 (10-Oct-91 SY.NY143/R) Orpheus playing the viola da braccio, calming the
        wild beasts (79x148cm-31x58in) panel

LUINI, Bernardino (school) (1475-1532) Italian
£3056 $5500 (22-Nov-91 S.BM8/R) Holy Family with John the Baptist in landscape
        (99x71cm-39x28in)

LUINI, Bernardino (style) (1475-1532) Italian
£750 $1260 (29-Aug-91 CG98) The three ages of man (61x76cm-24x30in)
£3500 $6230 (1-Nov-91 C32/R) Madonna and Child (41x28cm-16x11in) copper

LUKA, Madeleine (20th C) French
£596 $1025 (4-Mar-92 AT.P169) Je prefere les rouseaux aux lys (55x46cm-22x18in) s.
        (F.FR 5800)
£1527 $2826 (10-Jun-92 LD.P112) Auberge des iles a l'Isle Adam (50x61cm-20x24in) s.
        (F.FR 15000)
£25589 $45548 (27-Nov-91 AT.P165) Je prefere les roseaux aux lys (55x46cm-22x18in) s.
        (F.FR 250000)

LUKASCHEWSKI, Rolf (1947-) German
£1546 $2675 (23-Mar-92 CC.P140/R) Schone Aussicht (124x129cm-49x51in) s.d.1983
        i.verso (F.FR 15000)

LUKASIEWICZ, Jozef Ignacy (1789-1850) Lithuanian
£598 $1029   (20-Oct-91 UNI.W5) Portrait of young Russian Officer (21x16cm-8x6in)
      (P.Z 11500000)

LUKE, John (1906-1975) British
£5000 $8700   (18-Sep-91 CG185/R) McArt's Fort (38x56cm-15x22in) s.d.34 panel
£750   *$1305*   *(18-Sep-91 CG56) House on Lagan (23x32cm-9x13in) s. W/C*

LUKER, William (jnr) (1867-1951) British
£650 $1105   (22-Oct-91 SWS275/R) Walberswick Ferry (25x39cm-10x15in) s.d.07 board
£1700 $2924   (4-Mar-92 S86/R) Scottish terrier (50x61cm-20x24in) s.d.1906

LUKER, William (snr) (1828-1905) British
£500 $860   (16-Oct-91 HAR427) Highland landscape with cattle (28x48cm-11x19in)
      s.d.1889
£600 $1074   (14-Jan-92 B250/R) Two spaniels in a kennel (51x61cm-20x24in) s.d.1845
£1150 $1955   (23-Oct-91 LJ265) Woodland road with flock of sheep (36x66cm-14x26in)
      s.d.
£7500 $12750   (23-Oct-91 S70/R) Camel drivers at Karnak, Egypt (110x140cm-43x55in)
      s.d.1860

LUKER, William (style) (19/20th C) British
£1200 $2124   (6-Nov-91 S100/R) Bay horse and two dogs (63x76cm-25x30in)

LUKIS DE GUERIN, A (19/20th C) ?
£1500   *$2685*   *(11-Nov-91 S645/R) Seditious meeting - birds of feather (21x36cm-8x14in)*
      s. W/C

LUKOVICZKI, Endre (20th C) Hungarian
£605 $1041   (14-Oct-91 AT.P2) Musique (100x70cm-39x28in) s.d.1990 board (F.FR 6000)
£807 $1388   (14-Oct-91 AT.P3/R) Eclipse de soleil (100x70cm-39x28in) s.d.1990 board
      (F.FR 8000)
£807 $1388   (14-Oct-91 AT.P4) La danse du Shaman (127x97cm-50x38in) s.d.1990
      (F.FR 8000)

LUKS, George (1867-1933) American
£1977 $3500   (9-Nov-91 W.W221/R) Summer field (89x102cm-35x40in) s.
£32044 $58000   (6-Dec-91 CH.NY173/R) The black hat (69x51cm-27x20in) s.
£747 $1300   (15-Apr-92 SY.NY203/R) Figure studies (16x11cm-6x4in) st. num.62 40 verso
      pencil dbl-sided two sheets
£995 $1900   (3-Jul-92 S.W3119/R) Penta Delgada (43x18cm-17x7in) s.d.1893 W/C
£1029 $1800   (26-Sep-91 CH.NY243/R) Woolworth building (46x30cm-18x12in) pencil
£1437 $2500   (15-Apr-92 SY.NY131/R) Art students (25x20cm-10x8in) s. black crayon
      paper on board
£4386 $7500   (12-Mar-92 CH.NY240/R) Country road (35x50cm-14x20in) s.verso W/C chl

LUKS, George (attrib) (1867-1933) American
£847 $1500   (22-Apr-92 D.NY71) By camp fire (51x41cm-20x16in) bears sig. i.verso
      board
£718 $1300   (7-Dec-91 LAE.L32/R) Unemployment line (23x30cm-9x12in) s. W/C crayon chl

LUMINAIS, Evariste-Vital (1822-1896) French
£488 $878   (19-Nov-91 FP.M102) Reading of will (23x29cm-9x11in) s.verso board
      (C.D 1000)
£515 $912   (26-Apr-92 FE.P104) Portrait de femme (37x28cm-15x11in) s. panel
      (F.FR 5100)
£1606 $2874   (6-May-92 GD.B796/R) Mother pouring milk for children (37x45cm-15x18in)
      s. (S.FR 4400)

LUMIS, Harriet Randall (1870-?) American
£1497 $2500   (23-Aug-91 DOU.M3) Foggy morning (53x66cm-21x26in)
£1967 $3600   (15-May-92 DOU.M3) Mountain landscape in autumn (69x58cm-27x23in)
£2077 $3800   (15-May-92 DOU.M4) The hill road (69x58cm-27x23in)
£2131 $3900   (15-May-92 DOU.M1) Rainy day (64x51cm-25x20in)
£2240 $4100   (15-May-92 DOU.M2) Autumn hillside (69x58cm-27x23in)
£2787 $5100   (15-May-92 DOU.M5) Woodland scene (69x58cm-27x23in)
£2994 $5000   (23-Aug-91 DOU.M4) Old house by sea (56x46cm-22x18in)
£3593 $6000   (23-Aug-91 DOU.M2) Road to sea (61x71cm-24x28in)
£3593 $6000   (23-Aug-91 DOU.M6) Bowl of flowers (51x46cm-20x18in)
£4192 $7000   (23-Aug-91 DOU.M7) Hillside maples (71x61cm-28x24in)
£4192 $7000   (23-Aug-91 DOU.M5) Inner harbour (66x53cm-26x21in)

LUND, Bjarne (1896-1931) Norwegian
£590 $1033   (1-Apr-92 KH.K137) Farmyard with horse and figures (59x73cm-23x29in) s.
      (D.KR 6500)
£624 $1073   (16-Oct-91 KH.K190) Norwegian mountain landscape (54x64cm-21x25in)
      s.d.1920 (D.KR 7000)

LUND, Emil (1855-1928) Danish
£794 $1413   (28-Apr-92 RAS.K206) Summer day by Holmen's Canal (49x81cm-19x32in)
      s.d.1912 (D.KR 9000)

LUND, F C (1826-1901) Danish
£485 $863   (28-Apr-92 RAS.K259) View towards Hammershus (40x64cm-16x25in) s.d.1854
      (D.KR 5500)

LUND, Henrik (1879-1935) Scandinavian
£789 $1468   (15-Jun-92 B.O105/R) Man wearing straw hat (53x45cm-21x18in) s.d.1907
                 (N.KR 9000)
£980 $1696   (23-Mar-92 B.O81/R) Portrait of the Danish author Carl Ewald
                 (76x63cm-30x25in) s.d.1906 (N.KR 11000)
£2018 $3753   (18-Jun-92 GWP.O68/R) Hans Jaeger and two Danish authors
                 (48x72cm-19x28in) s.indist.d. (N.KR 23000)
£4035 $7505   (15-Jun-92 B.O104/R) Portrait of Crown Princess Martha (66x50cm-26x20in)
                 s.d.31 (N.KR 46000)
£4456 $7709   (23-Mar-92 B.O80/R) Landscape with white house, Skatoy 1914
                 (100x90cm-39x35in) s.d.1914 (N.KR 50000)
£7932 $13723   (23-Mar-92 B.O79/R) Summer landscape, Skatoy 1920 (97x104cm-38x41in)
                 s.d.20 (N.KR 89000)
£2195 $3775   *(10-Oct-91 BU.O16/R) Female nude (63x48cm-25x19in) s. chl canvas*
                 (N.KR 25000)

LUND, Johan Ludvig (1777-1867) Danish
£2166 $3899   (19-Nov-91 RAS.K30/R) Portrait of Eleanor Anastatia Hage seated in wooded
                 landscape (54x45cm-21x18in) s. (D.KR 24000)

LUND, Liv (1923-) Norwegian
£531 $967   (14-Dec-91 BU.O67/R) Still life of jugs (50x38cm-20x15in) s.d.55
                 (N.KR 6000)
£798 $1412   (15-Feb-92 BU.O86) Model (54x45cm-21x18in) (N.KR 9000)
£1149 $2011   (25-Feb-92 UL.T214/R) Interior with woman 1936 (67x45cm-26x18in)
                 (N.KR 13000)
£1949 $3547   (14-Dec-91 BU.O91/R) Blond model (68x40cm-27x16in) s.d.1956 s.i.verso
                 (N.KR 22000)

LUNDBERG, August Frederick (1878-1928) American
£621 $1100   (13-Feb-92 S.W2139) Winter morning (61x51cm-24x20in) s.d.1924

LUNDBERG, Gustaf (1695-1786) Swedish
£5693 $10417   (11-May-92 NOR.S111/R) Marie Anne de Bourbon-Conde (136x104cm-54x41in)
                 i.verso after Jean Baptiste Santerre (S.KR 60000)
£3069 $5523   *(19-Nov-91 RAS.K29/R) Portrait of scantily dressed female with flowers in*
                 her hair (57x45cm-22x18in) s. pastel (D.KR 34000)
£4364 $7987   *(14-May-92 BU.S97/R) Portrait of a young man (64x53cm-25x21in) pastel*
                 (S.KR 46000)
£6623 $11987   *(19-May-92 AB.S4244/R) Portrait of Christina Holmcreutz (65x50cm-26x20in)*
                 pastel (S.KR 70000)

LUNDBERG, Gustaf (style) (1695-1786) Swedish
£1135 $2055   *(19-May-92 AB.S4245/R) Portrait of young girl (66x50cm-26x20in) pastel*
                 (S.KR 12000)

LUNDBERG, Lars-Gosta (1938-) Scandinavian
£759 $1389   (13-May-92 BU.S113/R) Our silent world (116x131cm-46x52in)
                 s.indist.d.196. (S.KR 8000)
£946 $1712   (19-May-92 AB.S5270/R) Blue stars (130x97cm-51x38in) (S.KR 10000)
£461 $834   *(3-Dec-91 AB.S5096/R) Paper nude No.15 (89x56cm-35x22in) s.d.1981 mixed*
                 media (S.KR 4800)

LUNDBOHM, Sixten (1895-1982) Swedish
£712 $1239   (13-Apr-92 AB.S156) Mountainous French landscape (54x74cm-21x29in)
                 s.d.1935verso (S.KR 7500)
£759 $1389   (12-May-92 GO.G94) Still life of flowers in jug (82x67cm-32x26in) s.
                 (S.KR 8000)
£768 $1390   (3-Dec-91 AB.S5098/R) Mountain landscape with lake (33x87cm-13x34in) s.
                 (S.KR 8000)
£949 $1736   (13-May-92 BU.S115/R) Still life of flowers and vases (75x65cm-30x26in)
                 s. s.d.1935verso (S.KR 10000)
£1082 $1860   (19-Oct-91 UA.U306/R) Tossa de Mar (47x61cm-19x24in) s. (S.KR 11400)
£1200 $2171   (3-Dec-91 AB.S5097/R) Beech wood (113x70cm-44x28in) s. d.1949verso
                 (S.KR 12500)
£1233 $2257   (13-May-92 BU.S116/R) Apples (72x64cm-28x25in) s. panel (S.KR 13000)

LUNDBYE, J T (1818-1848) Danish
£748 $1257   *(28-Aug-91 KH.K264/R) Peasant woman knitting (23x19cm-9x7in)*
                 mono.i.d.1844 pen W/C (D.KR 8500)
£1625 $2924   *(19-Nov-91 RAS.K97/R) Cattle grazing by thatched barn, summer*
                 (20x33cm-8x13in) mono.i.d.1847 pen W/C (D.KR 18000)

LUNDBYE, Johan Thomas (1818-1848) Danish
£1499 $2668   (28-Apr-92 RAS.K596/R) Standing brown horse (22x29cm-9x11in) mono.d.47
                 study (D.KR 17000)
£2888 $5199   (19-Nov-91 RAS.K31/R) Study for 'Hankehoj at Vallekilde Prestegardsmark
                 (17x22cm-7x9in) mono.d.46 (D.KR 32000)
£529 $942   *(28-Apr-92 RAS.K689) Donkey rider (18x28cm-7x11in) s. pen (D.KR 6000)*

LUNDE, Anders (1809-1886) Danish
£1220 $2220   (11-Dec-91 N.M516/R) View of Amalfi (37x54cm-15x21in) s.i. (DM 3500)
£1675 $2982   (28-Apr-92 RAS.K379/R) Cypresses in a monastery (53x37cm-21x15in) s.i.
                 (D.KR 19000)

LUNDE, Anders (1809-1886) Danish-cont.
£4328 $7704   (25-Nov-91 BU.K19/R) Italian landscape with aqueduct (41x53cm-16x21in)
                                s.i. (D.KR 48000)

LUNDEBY, Alf (1870-1961) Norwegian
£624 $1079   (23-Mar-92 B.O82/R) Landscape from Lillehammer (63x79cm-25x31in) s.
                                (N.KR 7000)
£753 $1370   (14-Dec-91 BU.O4/R) Landscape, Anticoli, Italy (43x50cm-17x20in)
                                s.i.d.1929 (N.KR 8500)
£7401 $13321   (19-Nov-91 RAS.K64/R) The outskirts of Rome (64x100cm-25x39in) s.i.d.99
                                (D.KR 82000)

LUNDEGARD, Justus (1860-1924) Swedish
£903 $1616   (16-Nov-91 FAL.M205/R) Wooded landscape with road (53x45cm-21x18in)
                                s.d.98 (S.KR 9500)
£2657 $4861   (14-May-92 BU.S44/R) Walking by the canal (79x114cm-31x45in) s.d.1889
                                (S.KR 28000)

LUNDENS, Gerrit (1622-1677) Dutch
£800 $1528   (21-Jul-92 PH239/R) Peasants eating shellfish in interior
                                (28x23cm-11x9in)
£2432 $4450   (12-May-92 SY.AM100/R) Peasants in interior playing game of Le Main Chaud
                                (27x29cm-11x11in) panel (D.FL 8000)
£7599 $13906   (12-May-92 SY.AM113/R) Married couple leading dance at wedding feast
                                (62x53cm-24x21in) mono. (D.FL 25000)

LUNDGREN, Egron Sillif (1815-1875) Swedish
£425   *$751*   *(5-Nov-91 BA.S226/R) Indian prisoners in English service (19x30cm-7x12in)*
                                init. W/C (S.KR 4500)
£580   *$1114*   *(8-Jul-92 PH136/R) Study of seated lady holding fan (35x24cm-14x9in) red*
                                chk wash
£728   *$1319*   *(19-May-92 AB.S4246/R) Portrait of Spanish girl (237x23cm-93x9in) s. W/C*
                                (S.KR 7700)

LUNDGREN, Johan Edvin (1920-) Swedish
£779 $1355   (13-Apr-92 AB.S159) Early spring landscape, Nordingra (86x87cm-34x34in)
                                s. (S.KR 8200)

LUNDGREN, Johan Erik (1822-1895) Swedish
£3890 $7119   (14-May-92 AB.S45/R) View of Stockholm (82x125cm-32x49in) s.d.1860
                                (S.KR 41000)

LUNDH, Theodor (1812-1896) Swedish
£652 $1174   (19-Nov-91 GO.G105) Still life of flowers and bird (62x50cm-24x20in)
                                s.indist.d.18 (S.KR 6800)
£1534 $2761   (19-Nov-91 GO.G106/R) Still life of dead game (71x50cm-28x20in) s.d.90
                                (S.KR 16000)

LUNDQVIST, Evart (1904-) Swedish
£949 $1736   (13-May-92 BU.S122/R) Portrait of Harald (33x28cm-13x11in) s.
                                (S.KR 10000)
£1233 $2257   (13-May-92 BU.S121/R) Portrait of woman (27x24cm-11x9in) s. (S.KR 13000)
£2087 $3820   (11-May-92 NOR.S99/R) The queue (50x62cm-20x24in) init. s.i.d.1963verso
                                (S.KR 22000)
£2087 $3820   (11-May-92 NOR.S93/R) Landscape, Grasberg, Dalarne (65x59cm-26x23in)
                                s.d.1933verso (S.KR 22000)
£4031 $7296   (3-Dec-91 AB.S5099/R) Woman - figure composition (49x89cm-19x35in) s.
                                (S.KR 42000)
£5123 $9376   (13-May-92 BU.S119/R) The man on the hill (65x54cm-26x21in) init.
                                  s.d.1974verso (S.KR 54000)
£9488 $17362   (11-May-92 NOR.S100/R) The rock (100x89cm-39x35in) init. s.d.1972verso
                                  (S.KR 100000)
£12334 $22571   (13-May-92 BU.S118/R) Through the mortar opening (90x100cm-35x39in)
                                  s.d.1961verso (S.KR 130000)
£15655 $28648   (11-May-92 NOR.S94/R) Still life with copper saucepan (80x100cm-31x39in)
                                init. s.verso (S.KR 165000)

LUNDSTEDT, Kristian (1894-1959) Swedish
£522 $955   (12-May-92 GO.G95) Late summer (85x100cm-33x39in) s. (S.KR 5500)

LUNDSTROM, Knut (1892-1945) Swedish
£1135 $2055   (19-May-92 AB.S5271/R) Chalk cliffs near Seine (48x64cm-19x25in) s.i.
                                panel (S.KR 12000)

LUNDSTROM, Vilhelm (1893-1950) Danish
£980 $1686   (16-Oct-91 KH.K219/R) Landscape, Amager (28x43cm-11x17in) s. (D.KR 11000)
£2147 $3907   (10-Dec-91 RAS.K162/R) Still life of glass bonbonniere (31x31cm-12x12in)
                                (D.KR 24000)
£9083 $15895   (1-Apr-92 KH.K87/R) Still life of yellow jug and stand (80x62cm-31x24in)
                                init.d.46verso (D.KR 100000)
£10676 $18577   (17-Sep-91 RAS.K121/R) Still life with red cylinder (81x62cm-32x24in)
                                init.d.46verso (D.KR 120000)
£11566 $20125   (17-Sep-91 RAS.K116/R) Still life of yellow bowl and blue jug
                                (81x65cm-32x26in) init.d.1939verso (D.KR 130000)

LUNDSTROM, Vilhelm (1893-1950) Danish-cont.
£11586	$19929	(16-Oct-91 KH.K130/R) Still life (100x80cm-39x31in) init.d.38verso (D.KR 130000)
£18100	$32760	(4-Dec-91 KH.K4/R) Still life of yellow jug and black bottle (102x80cm-40x31in) (D.KR 200000)
£19838	$35311	(25-Nov-91 BU.K50/R) Still life, 1924 (90x117cm-35x46in) (D.KR 220000)
£20499	$35258	(16-Oct-91 KH.K168/R) Still life, Cagnes 1923 (114x146cm-45x57in) init.d.23 (D.KR 230000)
£44563	$76649	(16-Oct-91 KH.K112/R) Still life of white jugs (140x105cm-55x41in) (D.KR 500000)

LUNOIS, Alexandre (1863-1916) French
£1006	$1800	(11-Nov-91 GC.M30/R) Pastoreo (110x131cm-43x52in) s.d.90
£756	*$1300*	*(12-Oct-91 SY.NY103/R) Bullfight (63x84cm-25x33in) s. pastel gouache*

LUNS, Huib (1881-1942) Dutch
£578	$1005	(17-Sep-91 CH.AM46) The four seasons (120x20cm-47x8in) s.d.1912 (D.FL 1900)

LUNSTROTH, F M (?) ?
£629	$1076	(19-Mar-92 N.M2794) Farmhouse parlour (84x98cm-33x39in) s. (DM 1800)

LUNY, Thomas (1759-1837) British
£600	$1008	(15-Aug-91 B387) Shipping in storm (19x28cm-7x11in) bears sig.d. bears i.verso board
£1200	$2016	(15-Aug-91 B405/R) Bringing in catch (22x30cm-9x12in) s.d.1822 panel
£1250	$2238	(5-May-92 SWS301/R) Coastal scene with fishermen pulling in nets in foreground (24x34cm-9x13in) indist.s.d.1827 panel
£1600	$2896	(20-May-92 S22/R) Harbour by moonlight (38x53cm-15x21in) canvas on board
£1700	$2856	(15-Aug-91 B389) Shipping off fort, at sunset (25x36cm-10x14in) s.d.1826 board
£1800	$3240	(9-Jan-92 B312/R) Going Free (30x27cm-12x11in) s. i.verso panel
£2000	$3460	(4-Sep-91 BT307/R) View from Teignmouth Beach (25x30cm-10x12in) s.d.1826 panel
£2000	$3560	(28-Apr-92 PH75/R) Fishing boats in storm off coast with castle ruin on cliff top (61x86cm-24x34in) s.d.1835
£2400	$4320	(22-Nov-91 C34/R) Harbour in the Bosphorous with Turkish traders (38x51cm-15x20in) s.d.1822
£2500	$4325	(4-Sep-91 BT301/R) Unloading the catch (23x28cm-9x11in) s.indist.d. panel
£2800	$4984	(28-Apr-92 PH74/R) Figures rescuing survivors from shipwreck in storm (61x86cm-24x34in) s.d.1835
£3100	$5363	(4-Sep-91 BT306/R) Frigate with pilot cutter entering bay (20x28cm-8x11in) s.d.1828 panel
£3200	$5376	(15-Aug-91 B419/R) Royal Navy cutter and other vessels on moonlit sea (43x65cm-17x26in) s.indist.d.
£3500	$6055	(4-Sep-91 BT305/R) Limekilns by river, probably the Tamar (30x38cm-12x15in) s.d.1829 panel
£3867	$7000	(22-May-92 S.BM41/R) Putting ashore (46x71cm-18x28in) s.d.1792
£4000	$7600	(24-Jun-92 DR182/R) Thames near Royal Dockyard at Millwall (51x71cm-20x28in) s.
£4600	$7958	(4-Sep-91 BT299/R) Entrance to the River Dart (28x38cm-11x15in) s.
£5200	$8996	(4-Sep-91 BT298/R) Coaster beached at Teignmouth (48x69cm-19x27in) s.d.1834
£5249	$9500	(22-May-92 S.BM43/R) Harbour view (46x71cm-18x28in) s.d.1792
£6000	$10080	(15-Aug-91 B397/R) St Michael's Mount (57x69cm-22x27in) s.d.1831
£6000	$10440	(14-Apr-92 CSK106/R) Two-decker making sail from anchorage in Plymouth harbour. Shipping off South Downs (38x51cm-15x20in) one s.d.1831 pair
£6000	$10800	(22-Nov-91 C134/R) The Battle of Toulon, 11 February 1744 (43x60cm-17x24in) s.d.1780 i.verso
£6800	$11424	(15-Aug-91 B403/R) Unloading catch (45x65cm-18x26in) s.d.1807
£7000	$12530	(15-Nov-91 C74/R) Sailing vessels in choppy waters off Ramsgate with figures on quayside (37x51cm-15x20in) s.d.1830 panel
£7200	$12960	(9-Jan-92 B276/R) Shipping off Dover (61x102cm-24x40in) s.d.1801
£60000	$114600	(15-Jul-92 S6/R) The bombardment of Algiers - II (119x179cm-47x70in) s.

LUNY, Thomas (attrib) (1759-1837) British
£4118	$7000	(6-Aug-91 RB.HY97/R) British frigate - two views (58x91cm-23x36in)

LUNY, Thomas (circle) (1759-1837) British
£550	$946	(10-Oct-91 CSK14/R) Shipping in rough seas off rocks (23x33cm-9x13in)
£1100	$1980	(22-Nov-91 SWS280/R) Fishing boats and sailing vessels in an estuary (57x108cm-22x43in)
£3200	$5376	(15-Aug-91 B402/R) Engagement between H.M.S. Iris and Citoyenne - Francaise, 13th May, 1793 (48x69cm-19x27in)

LUNY, Thomas (style) (1759-1837) British
£580	$974	(15-Aug-91 B343) Shipping off fort (57x72cm-22x28in)

LUO YITONG (1960-) Chinese
£3107	*$5436*	*(30-Mar-92 CH.HK321/R) Mountain village in Italy (68x136cm-27x54in) s.i.d.1991 ink W/C scroll (HK.D 42000)*

LUO ZHONGLI (1948-) Chinese
£13149	$22486	(22-Mar-92 SY.TA31/R) Girl with two white horses (63x79cm-25x31in) s. (T.D 572000)

LUPERTZ, Markus (1941-) Czechoslovakian

£1440	$2606	(3-Dec-91 AB.S5100/R) Green composition (40x29cm-16x11in) s. paper (S.KR 15000)
£1100	$2034	(11-Jun-92 HN.H320) Fish (60x78cm-24x31in) s. col.chk gouache (DM 3200)
£2218	$4038	(30-May-92 VG.B419/R) Untitled, Babylon Dithyrambisch (61x44cm-24x17in) mono distemper canvas on board (DM 6500)
£2346	$4200	(6-May-92 CH.NY230/R) Lupolis (42x56cm-17x22in) s. black white chk W/C
£2500	$4300	(17-Oct-91 C103/R) Untitled (70x49cm-28x19in) init. W/C chl gouache pencil
£2560	$4659	(30-May-92 VG.B418/R) Untitled (63x45cm-25x18in) s. gouache chk (DM 7500)
£2596	$4674	(19-Nov-91 L.K890/R) Untitled (38x64cm-15x25in) s. col.wax crayons (DM 7400)
£3780	$6918	(2-Jun-92 L.K775/R) Untitled (100x70cm-39x28in) mono gouache oil pastel chk chl pencil (DM 11000)
£3925	$7143	(30-May-92 VG.B420/R) Corn ears (59x79cm-23x31in) s. col.grease chk over pencil (DM 11500)

LUPIANEZ Y CARRASCO, Jose (1864-1933) Spanish

| £3007 | $5503 | (13-May-92 FER.M120/R) Llenando el cantaro en la fuente (50x90cm-20x35in) s. (S.P 550000) |
| £9408 | $16087 | (17-Mar-92 FER.M130/R) Vista de Madrid desde el Puente de Segovia (30x50cm-12x20in) s.i.d.1907 panel (S.P 1700000) |

LUPO (20th C) Italian

| £1180 | $2100 | (1-Nov-91 PO.BA8) Calle con personajes (40x30cm-16x12in) |

LUPO, Alessandro (1876-1953) Italian

£1394	$2384	(19-Mar-92 F.M11/R) Capobianco, Ponza (40x50cm-16x20in) s. (I.L 3000000)
£1394	$2384	(19-Mar-92 F.M46/R) I due Jumeaux. Tramonto sul lago s. panel pair (I.L 3000000)
£1520	$2766	(12-Dec-91 F.M56/R) Baite a Rheme Notre Dame (30x35cm-12x14in) board (I.L 3300000)
£1766	$3020	(19-Mar-92 F.M9/R) Casolari (50x40cm-20x16in) s. board (I.L 3800000)
£1812	$3352	(9-Jun-92 F.R125) Rose (35x42cm-14x17in) s. board (I.L 4000000)
£1934	$3521	(12-Dec-91 F.M85/R) Foro romano (50x40cm-20x16in) s.d.43 i.verso panel (I.L 4200000)
£2062	$3650	(7-Nov-91 F.M8) Baite in Val Ferret (50x40cm-20x16in) s. i.verso (I.L 4500000)
£2395	$4359	(12-Dec-91 F.M86/R) Zinnie (50x39cm-20x15in) s. i.verso board (I.L 5200000)
£2749	$4867	(7-Nov-91 F.M7) Sera Rheme Notre Dame (40x50cm-16x20in) s. board (I.L 6000000)

LURCAT, Jean (1892-1966) French

£1017	$1800	(5-Nov-91 CE.NY55/R) Aux bords de la mer (27x53cm-11x21in) s.
£2229	$3900	(29-Sep-91 LIT.L357) Abstract still life (33x56cm-13x22in) s.
£2400	$4584	(29-Jun-92 CSK78/R) Paysage (46x73cm-18x29in) s.d.27
£2429	$4250	(28-Feb-92 SY.NY43/R) Still life with four fruit (33x61cm-13x24in) s.
£2429	$4250	(28-Feb-92 SY.NY44/R) Still life with fruit on ledge (27x41cm-11x16in) s.d.27
£3000	$5250	(28-Feb-92 SY.NY47/R) Nature morte (55x38cm-22x15in) s.d.25
£14736	$25640	(14-Apr-92 ZZ.F58/R) L'attente (99x82cm-39x32in) s.d.20 canvas laid down on hardboard (F.FR 145000)
£700	$1198	(18-Mar-92 PIC.P63) Les tortues (67x121cm-26x48in) s.d.1948 W/C (F.FR 6800)
£887	$1570	(8-Nov-91 LGB.P95/R) Trois baigneuses sur la plage (24x32cm-9x13in) s.d.1933 gouache (F.FR 8800)
£900	$1629	(2-Dec-91 CSK82/R) Le gresivaudan (61x66cm-24x26in) s.i. gouache board
£1000	$1910	(29-Jun-92 CSK81/R) Nature morte a la pomme (33x49cm-13x19in) s.d.1925 wax crayons board
£1629	$2982	(3-Jun-92 CSC.P47/R) Poeme (48x65cm-19x26in) s.d.50 gouache pencil (F.FR 16000)
£1739	$3096	(29-Nov-91 GAB.G2795 a) Porjet pour une tapisserie (49x65cm-19x26in) s. gouache (S.FR 4400)

LUST, Antoni de (mid17th C) Dutch

| £14918 | $27001 | (5-Dec-91 SY.MO123/R) Composition aux cerises et groseilles (62x52cm-24x20in) (F.FR 145000) |
| £30426 | $53550 | (10-Apr-92 AT.P36/R) Bouquet de fleurs dans un vase sur un entablement (50x44cm-20x17in) traces sig. (F.FR 300000) |

LUTI, Benedetto (1666-1724) Italian

| £14199 | $24990 | (10-Apr-92 AT.P4/R) Le Repas chez Simon (174x184cm-69x72in) (F.FR 140000) |
| £10000 | $19200 | (7-Jul-92 C38/R) Bearded apostle reading (41x33cm-16x13in) s.d.1712verso pastel |

LUTI, Benedetto (attrib) (1666-1724) Italian

| £3764 | $6888 | (15-May-92 AT.P168) Tete du Christ (54x40cm-21x16in) with i. black chk sanguine htd pastel (F.FR 37000) |

LUTI, Benedetto (circle) (1666-1724) Italian

| £2200 | $4224 | (7-Jul-92 C188/R) Head of man looking upwards (44x33cm-17x13in) chk pastel |

UTTEROTH, Ascan (1842-1923) German
£769 $1315   (18-Mar-92 N.M589/R) Upper Italian lake landscape, possibly Lake Como near Bellaggio (42x60cm-17x24in) s. (DM 2200)
£1166 $2041   (3-Apr-92 BM.B677/R) Italian lake landscape with figures, possibly Lake Garda (59x101cm-23x40in) s. (DM 3300)
£2174 $4022   (9-Jun-92 F.R109) Veduta di Capri (54x88cm-21x35in) s. (I.L 4800000)

UTTICH, Mila von (20th C) German
£1697 $3088   (26-May-92 D.V3/R) Goldregen (27x21cm-11x8in) mono mixed media paper on board (A.S 35000)

UTTICHUYS, Isaak (1616-1673) Dutch
£4360 $7500   (9-Oct-91 CH.NY148/R) Portrait of lady, standing holding rose before balustrade (127x100cm-50x39in)

UTTICHUYS, Isaak (attrib) (1616-1673) Dutch
£1100 $1925   (3-Apr-92 C113/R) Portrait of gentleman, in coat and lace cravat (47x34cm-19x13in) painted oval

UTTICHUYS, Simon (1610-1662) Dutch
£18500 $31635   (16-Mar-92 WHB60/R) Still life of glass of wine and tankard on silver tankard with cherries and loaf (43x36cm-17x14in) init.

UTTROW, Leo (19th C) ?
£1552 $2747   (6-Nov-91 N.M1088/R) Girl on terrace planting pots (39x26cm-15x10in) s.indis.d.897 panel (DM 4500)

UTYENS, Charles Augustus Henry (1829-1915) British
£600 $1026   (18-Mar-92 CSK258) Putti desporting with garlands of flowers (38x91cm-15x36in) s. pair
£780 $1388   (21-Jan-92 PH69) Putti (19x24cm-7x9in) indist.s.
£850 $1513   (21-Jan-92 PH62) Putti with garland of flowers (30x25cm-12x10in) s.

UTZ, Dan (1906-1978) American
£508 $900   (12-Feb-92 B.SF626/R) Grand portal (61x46cm-24x18in) s.d.52

UYKEN, Jan (1649-1712) Dutch
£776 $1382   (25-Nov-91 CH.AM93) Carpenters working on building in city (10x13cm-4x5in) i. pen ink wash (D.FL 2500)
£2243 $4171   (20-Jun-92 CH.MO257/R) L'Exode (28x53cm-11x21in) black chk ink wash htd white (F.FR 22000)

UYPAERT, Jean (1893-1954) Belgian
£667 $1174   (7-Apr-92 C.A504) Interior of Veurne Townhall (58x75cm-23x30in) s. (B.FR 40000)

UYTEN, Henri (1859-1945) Belgian
£2335 $4110   (7-Apr-92 C.A169/R) Horse and cart (100x130cm-39x51in) s. (B.FR 140000)
£2600 $4446   (18-Mar-92 S32/R) Girl mending a fishing net (97x125cm-38x49in) s.d.X-03
£2800 $4788   (18-Mar-92 S34/R) Portrait of a mother and her son (150x100cm-59x39in) s.d.9-IV-II

UZURIAGA, Juan Ramon (1938-) Spanish?
£498 $936   (17-Dec-91 DUR.M104/R) Portugalete (41x33cm-16x13in) s. s.i.d.1976verso (S.P 90000)
£526 $921   (18-Feb-92 DUR.M69/R) Ribera de Deusto (46x38cm-18x15in) s. s.i.d.1976verso (S.P 95000)
£550 $989   (19-Nov-91 DUR.M35/R) Boya y gabarra (41x33cm-16x13in) s. s.d.1977verso (S.P 100000)
£553 $984   (21-Jan-92 DUR.M49/R) Bar de Ondarroa (46x38cm-18x15in) s. s.i.d.1975verso (S.P 100000)
£657 $1195   (26-May-92 DUR.M99/R) Nuevo dia (55x46cm-22x18in) s. s.i.d.1977 (S.P 120000)

UZZI, Cleto (19/20th C) Italian
£2107 $3750   (22-Jan-92 SY.NY533/R) Gondola ride (74x100cm-29x39in) s.

UZZO (?) Italian?
£800 $1448   (20-May-92 S145/R) Topsail schooner Gilbert off Venice (33x53cm-13x21in) W/C

UZZO, Giovanni (19/20th C) Italian
£600 $1086   (20-May-92 S78) S.S. Somersby, Stockton, Genova (40x61cm-16x24in) s.i.d.1913 W/C htd.white

YALL, Laura Adeline (1860-1930) Canadian
£639 $1163   (26-May-92 JOY.T225/R) Study of young girl (45x40cm-18x16in) (C.D 1400)
£2189 $3897   (25-Nov-91 W.T1568) Portrait of young girl (56x46cm-22x18in) s. (C.D 4400)
£6849 $12534   (14-May-92 SY.T87/R) Mother and child (69x89cm-27x35in) d.1895 verso (C.D 15000)

YCKE, Oscar (1877-1972) Swedish
£550 $1007   (17-May-92 BU.M397) Winter landscape, sunset (86x145cm-34x57in) s. (S.KR 5800)

LYCKE, Oscar (1877-1972) Swedish-cont.
| £802 | $1419 | (5-Nov-91 BA.S115/R) Ski-tracks in winter (76x102cm-30x40in) s. (S.KR 8500) |
| £989 | $1760 | (28-Oct-91 AB.S146) At sunset, Vallsjon, Angermanland (80x118cm-31x46in) s. (S.KR 10500) |

LYDIS, Mariette (1890-1970) Austrian
£676	$1297	(7-Jul-92 ARC.P65) Jeune fille en blanc (72x60cm-28x24in) s.d.1966 (F.FR 6500)
£1099	$2000	(11-Dec-91 RO.BA242) Ninas (19x24cm-7x9in) s.d.1953 panel
£1500	$2865	(29-Jun-92 CSK106/R) Portrait de jeune fille aux papillons (46x37cm-18x15in) s.d.1938 panel
£1860	$3200	(9-Oct-91 RO.BA400) Nuevo destino (73x60cm-29x24in) s.d.1965
£2616	$4500	(9-Oct-91 RO.BA399/R) Figuras de ninos (55x46cm-22x18in) s.d.1964
£3226	$6000	(16-Jun-92 RO.BA65) Figura de nino (73x60cm-29x24in)

LYLE, Thomas Byron (fl.1880-1890) British
| £800 | $1384 | (24-Mar-92 CG773) The bird's nest (46x36cm-18x14in) s.d.1880 |

LYMAN, John Goodwin (1886-1967) Canadian
| £597 | $1063 | (26-Nov-91 JOY.T208) Fort Duvernette, St. Vincent (12x17cm-5x7in) s. board (C.D 1200) |

LYMBURNER, Francis (1916-) Australian
£1315	$2195	(19-Aug-91 SY.ME12) Bus stop (27x43cm-11x17in) s. (A.D 2800)
£1690	$2823	(19-Aug-91 SY.ME8/R) Drama (48x58cm-19x23in) s. s.i.verso (A.D 3600)
£2535	$4410	(16-Sep-91 CH.ME99/R) Girl undressing (60x50cm-24x20in) s. (A.D 5500)
£2555	$4599	(24-Nov-91 SY.S322/R) Departure (50x60cm-20x24in) s. s.i.verso (A.D 5800)
£3404	$6026	(26-Apr-92 SY.ME469/R) Blue stockings (90x70cm-35x28in) s. i.verso (A.D 8000)
£504	$962	(21-Jul-92 JRL.S244/R) Circus elephants (21x28cm-8x11in) s.d.53 pen wash (A.D 1300)
£563	$941	(19-Aug-91 SY.ME19) Seated nude (38x31cm-15x12in) s. ink wash (A.D 1200)
£577	$1027	(28-Apr-92 CH.ME43) Seated figure (25x19cm-10x7in) st.sig. i.verso ink wash (A.D 1350)
£578	$988	(17-Mar-92 JRL.S91) Viaduct on Wales (35x45cm-14x18in) s.d.1962 ink (A.D 1300)
£620	$1103	(28-Apr-92 CH.ME38) Couple in room (19x27cm-7x11in) s. i.verso ink wash (A.D 1450)
£684	$1217	(28-Apr-92 CH.ME65) Standing couple (26x14cm-10x6in) s. i.verso ink wash (A.D 1600)

LYNAS-GRAY, John Abernethy (1869-?) British
£410	$709	(6-Sep-91 T301/R) Girl and geese by thatched cottage (25x18cm-10x7in) s.d.1913 W/C
£420	$727	(6-Sep-91 T300/R) Girl and poultry outside thatched cottage (25x18cm-10x7in) s.d.1913 W/C
£580	$1114	(29-Jul-92 PHC279/R) At the cottage door (18x26cm-7x10in) s.d.1911 W/C
£620	$1190	(29-Jul-92 PHC280/R) Feeding the hens (18x26cm-7x10in) s.d.1914 W/C
£720	$1382	(29-Jul-92 PHC281/R) Playing with the puppies (18x26cm-7x10in) s.d.1913 W/C
£800	$1464	(3-Jun-92 S271) Seaside village (28x45cm-11x18in) s.d.1912 W/C
£800	$1432	(14-Jan-92 SWS60/R) Feeding chickens on country lane (28x46cm-11x18in) s.d.1912 W/C
£880	$1522	(27-Mar-92 HC311) Eveing at Tanfield, on the Gare (43x69cm-17x27in) mono.d.1905 W/C
£1200	$2100	(1-Apr-92 B104/R) Small girl in cottage garden (27x43cm-11x17in) s.d.1917 W/C bodycol pair

LYNCH, Albert (1851-?) Peruvian
£1832	$3500	(16-Jul-92 SY.NY386/R) Portrait of lady wearing black hat (61x50cm-24x20in) s.
£3202	$5700	(3-May-92 LIT.L165) Portrait of beautiful lady (46x36cm-18x14in) s.
£3543	$6200	(19-Feb-92 CH.NY57/R) Winter celebration (65x45cm-26x18in) s.
£7143	$12500	(20-Feb-92 SY.NY300/R) Portrait of girl (65x54cm-26x21in) s.
£16484	$30000	(27-May-92 CH.NY23/R) The letter (73x55cm-29x22in) s. panel
£617	$1178	(1-Jul-92 FB.P100) La servante (47x31cm-19x12in) s. W/C (F.FR 6000)
£650	$1183	(28-May-92 C28/R) Lady seated in profile (24x10cm-9x4in) s. pencil pen wash htd white
£3571	$6500	(27-May-92 CH.NY25/R) Gathering in the drawing room (31x63cm-12x25in) s. gouache W/C over chk gum arabic lunette

LYNCH, Justo (1870-1953) Argentinian
£814	$1400	(9-Oct-91 RO.BA763) Barcas junto a la costa (21x25cm-8x10in) s.
£1092	$1900	(19-Sep-91 V.BA62) El puerto (19x22cm-7x9in)
£5769	$10500	(11-Dec-91 RO.BA451) Marina (78x64cm-31x25in) s.d.1926

LYNE, Michael (1912-1989) British
£500	$895	(5-May-92 SWS496/R) Studies of Arkle, No.11 (49x59cm-19x23in) s.i.
£6011	$11000	(5-Jun-92 SY.NY291/R) Mme de Rothschild's stag hounds at La Michelette (71x106cm-28x42in) s.
£1000	$1710	(13-Mar-92 C41/R) Duke of Beaufort with Beaufort Hunt in Wraxhall Park (34x51cm-13x20in) s.d.1946 pencil W/C bodycol
£1913	$3500	(5-Jun-92 SY.NY288 a/R) The Marches, Middlebury, Connecticut - The Litchfield County Hounds (35x53cm-14x21in) s.d.1950 W/C gouache

LYNE, Michael (1912-1989) British-cont.
£4000 $7000   *(27-Sep-91 C113/R) The Heythrop (42x59cm-17x23in) s.i.d.1956 pencil W/C bodycol.*

LYNN, Elwyn Augustus (1917-) Australian
£922 $1604   *(16-Sep-91 CH.ME85/R) Posted (102x102cm-40x40in) s.d.1966 verso mixed media canvas (A.D 2000)*

LYNN, John (19th C) British
£1500 $2865   (17-Jul-92 C167/R) View of gibraltar from the North (22x30cm-9x12in) s.d.1837 panel

LYON, Corneille de see   CORNEILLE DE LYON

LYON, Harold (1930-) Canadian
£1154 $2019   (17-Feb-92 HO.ED60/R) Noon and done a day's work (61x91cm-24x36in) s. i.verso (C.D 2400)

LYON, John Howard (?) ?
£1800 $3204   (28-Apr-92 S312/R) Glen Ogle (76x127cm-30x50in) s.

LYRE, Adolphe la (1850-?) French
£514 $884   (4-Mar-92 AT.P162) Le modele (38x27cm-15x11in) s. board (F.FR 5000)
£923 $1652   (19-Jan-92 CSC.P114) Scene de plage (36x52cm-14x20in) s. (F.FR 9000)
£1915 $3390   (5-Nov-91 ZZ.F104/R) Naiades (106x69cm-42x27in) s.d.MDCCCCXVI (F.FR 19000)

LYSSAK, Nikolai (1951-) Russian
£515 $881   (13-Mar-92 ARC.P139/R) Conversation sur la terrasse (75x84cm-30x33in) s.verso (F.FR 5000)
£615 $1107   (27-Jan-92 ARC.P142/R) Serenade (79x100cm-31x39in) s. (F.FR 6000)
£619 $1058   (13-Mar-92 ARC.P141/R) L'heure du the (79x79cm-31x31in) s.verso (F.FR 6000)
£717 $1291   (27-Jan-92 ARC.P140/R) Femme a l'eventail (98x99cm-39x39in) s. (F.FR 7000)
£717 $1291   (27-Jan-92 ARC.P141/R) Sous la veranda (85x120cm-33x47in) s. (F.FR 7000)
£768 $1383   (27-Jan-92 ARC.P138/R) Avant le spectacle (80x69cm-31x27in) s. (F.FR 7500)
£1025 $1844   (27-Jan-92 ARC.P139/R) Le reveil (99x88cm-39x35in) s.verso (F.FR 10000)
£1159 $2029   (24-Sep-91 ARC.P169/R) Sous la tonnelle (79x79cm-31x31in) s. verso (F.FR 11500)
£1443 $2468   (13-Mar-92 ARC.P140/R) Le restaurant en plein air (80x90cm-31x35in) s.verso (F.FR 14000)
£1935 $3541   (3-Jun-92 ARC.P91/R) Jeunes femmes aux eventails (160x56cm-63x22in) s.verso two (F.FR 19000)

LYTENS, Gysbrecht (17th C) Flemish
£58000 $105560   (11-Dec-91 S53/R) Wooded landscape in winter with wood gatherers (55x77cm-22x30in) panel

LYTENS, Gysbrecht (attrib) (17th C) Flemish
£3909 $7428   (26-Jun-92 AT.P100/R) Des chasseurs dans un paysage de riviere (26x36cm-10x14in) panel (F.FR 38000)

LYTTON, Neville Stephen (1879-1951) British
£700 $1218   (11-Sep-91 PHG50/R) The white dress (89x55cm-35x22in) mono.

LYTZEN, Niels Aagaard (1826-1890) Danish
£2000 $3420   (13-Mar-92 C140/R) Golden retriever on path in wooded landscape (124x152cm-49x60in) s.d.1853

M E (?) ?
£1600 $2896   (22-May-92 C17/R) Study (51x36cm-20x14in) init.

M G (?) ?
£638   *$1130*   *(26-Apr-92 SY.ME126) Micelago, New South Wales (27x38cm-11x15in) init. W/C htd white (A.D 1500)*

M L (?) ?
£794 $1413   (28-Apr-92 RAS.K585) Roses and bindweed on ledge (26x35cm-10x14in) init.d.1857 (D.KR 9000)
£1000 $1810   (6-Dec-91 TE586/R) Reflections (69x53cm-27x21in) mono.

M de R (18th C) ?
£2460 $4181   (22-Oct-91 DUR.M5/R) Inmaculada (200x125cm-79x49in) s. (S.P 450000)

MAANEN, A van (18th C) Dutch
£512 $927   *(21-May-92 L.K298) Riverside farmhouses (34x50cm-13x20in) s.d.1799 W/C (DM 1500)*

MAAR, Dora (20th C) French
£2732 $5000   *(11-May-92 CH.NY79/R) Paysage. Peche. Composition abstraite*
                      (24x32cm-9x13in) s. W/C gouache three
£5650 $10000   *(7-Nov-91 SY.NY138/R) Figural studies (31x24cm-12x9in) s.d.1940 pencil*
                      three

MAAREL, Marinus van der (1857-1921) Dutch
£912 $1587   (17-Sep-91 CH.AM294) Children playing at a beach (26x19cm-10x7in) s.
                     panel (D.FL 3000)

MAARNI, Elvi (1907-) Finnish
£1517 $2670   (12-Apr-92 HOR.H159) Girl with knitting (23x23cm-9x9in) s. (F.M 12000)
£479 $848   (6-Nov-91 HOR.H75) Madonna (21x29cm-8x11in) s. W/C (F.M 3400)
£582 $1024   (12-Apr-92 HOR.H160) Violin players (18x15cm-7x6in) s. chk (F.M 4600)
£1544 $2811   (11-Dec-91 HOR.H63) Violas (29x21cm-11x8in) s. col chk (F.M 12000)
£1690 $2958   (25-Sep-91 HOR.H63/R) The violin player (26x21cm-10x8in) s. col chk
                     (F.M 12000)

MAAS, Dirck (1659-1717) Dutch
£2210 $4000   (20-May-92 D.NY42/R) At the blacksmith's (46x61cm-18x24in)
£3136 $5707   (11-Dec-91 N.M338/R) Hunters resting in river landscape with sailing
                     boats (66x60cm-26x24in) (DM 9000)
£500 $910   (11-Dec-91 PH25/R) Soldiers taking prisoners in a valley. Fallen soldier
                     (20x30cm-8x12in) chk. double-sided
£528 $940   (25-Nov-91 CH.AM39/R) Upland landscape with mule train and cavalrymen by
                     lake (16x20cm-6x8in) s. chk W/C (D.FL 1700)

MAAS, Dirck (attrib) (1659-1717) Dutch
£3677 $6619   (30-Jan-92 RAS.V658/R) Landscape with riders and figures
                     (55x64cm-22x25in) (D.KR 41000)
£4938 $8840   (12-Nov-91 SY.AM169/R) Cavalier fleeing bandits (60x85cm-24x33in) panel
                     (D.FL 16000)

MAAS, Dirck (style) (1659-1717) Dutch
£1235 $2210   (12-Nov-91 SY.AM211) Cavaliers meeting outside encampment
                     (40x48cm-16x19in) (D.FL 4000)

MAAS, Ernst (1904-1971) Swiss
£1176 $2106   *(15-Nov-91 ZOF.Z1792/R) It wasn't the cat (46x61cm-18x24in) s.d.1960*
                     i.verso collage (S.FR 3000)

MAAS, Paul (1890-1962) Belgian
£1076 $1948   (23-May-92 KV.L209) Seated nude (67x34cm-26x13in) s. paper (B.FR 65000)
£1105 $2000   (22-May-92 S.BM223/R) Les vacances (119x79cm-47x31in) s.
£2152 $3896   (23-May-92 KV.L431/R) Albert Plage (70x92cm-28x36in) s. (B.FR 130000)
£2168 $3817   (7-Apr-92 C.A170) Beach at Cannes (51x65cm-20x26in) s.d.1958 paper on
                     canvas (B.FR 130000)
£2318 $4195   (23-May-92 KV.L486/R) Menigte (65x92cm-26x36in) studio st.verso
                     (B.FR 140000)
£834 $1468   *(7-Apr-92 C.A171) Under the plane trees (24x32cm-9x13in) s. W/C*
                     (B.FR 50000)

MAASS, David (?) ?
£2105 $3600   (13-Mar-92 S.BM258/R) Winged bullets, canvasbacks (51x61cm-20x24in) s.
                     masonite

MAATSCH, Thilo (1900-) German
£2062 $3814   (12-Jun-92 HN.H545/R) Composition 148 (81x99cm-32x39in) s.i.d.1928verso
                     panel (DM 6000)

MABE, Manabu (1924-) Brazilian
£2924 $5000   (21-Mar-92 W.W109/R) Untitled (69x48cm-27x19in) s. s.i.d.64 verso
£4386 $7500   (21-Mar-92 W.W73/R) Abstract in red, black, blue and white
                     (130x99cm-51x39in) s.d.1959
£6433 $11000   (21-Mar-92 W.W114/R) Yellow abstract (152x127cm-60x50in) s.d.65 s.d.1965
                     verso i.stretcher

MABUSE, Jan see GOSSAERT, Jan

MACAFFEE, Ila (1897-) American
£1117 $2000   (13-Nov-91 B.SF2811/R) Indians on horseback (30x41cm-12x16in) s. board

MACALLUM, Hamilton (1841-1896) British
£3600 $6192   (10-Oct-91 L470) The shrimpers, three men wading off foreshore with nets
                     and boats (56x107cm-22x42in) s.d.1885
£520 $926   *(29-Nov-91 T245) Hauling in the nets (38x71cm-15x28in) s.d.1867 W/C*

MACARA, Andrew (1944-) British
£500 $940   (18-Dec-91 C36/R) Ilfracombe, Devon (51x102cm-20x40in) s.d.1990 i.d.verso
£500 $940   (18-Dec-91 C37/R) Late afternoon, Woolacombe (39x49cm-15x19in) s.d.1989
                     i.d.verso i.stretcher
£600 $1128   (18-Dec-91 C38/R) Mundy Pool, Marketon Park, Derby (42x76cm-17x30in)
                     s.d.1990 i.verso

MACAULEY, Kate (fl.1880-1896) British
£460 $879   (30-Jun-92 RJ161) Harbour scene with boats (48x30cm-19x12in) s. W/C

MACAVOY, Edouard (1905-1991) French
£788 $1395   (26-Apr-92 FE.P49) Gondole a Venise (28x37cm-11x15in) s. panel
       (F.FR 7800)
£1561 $2732   (5-Apr-92 ZZ.F167/R) Venise - La Misericorda (55x40cm-22x16in) s.d.1938
       (F.FR 15000)
£1636 $2994   (5-Feb-92 FB.P178/R) Personnage au chateau (26x21cm-10x8in) s. gouache
       (F.FR 16000)
£2354 $4190   (27-Nov-91 AT.P165 b) Fenetre sur le port (116x89cm-46x35in) s.d.36
       (F.FR 23000)
£3347 $5723   (22-Mar-92 LT.P48/R) Arlequin (80x45cm-31x18in) s.d.63 (F.FR 32500)

MACBETH, James (1847-1891) British
£2203 $3921   (26-Nov-91 J.M170) National Park, New South Wales (72x49cm-28x19in)
       s.i.d.1888 W/C (A.D 5000)

MACBETH, Robert Walker (1848-1910) British
£720 $1224   (23-Oct-91 B82/R) Pretty young girl bottle-feeding a lamb at a cottage
       door (39x29cm-15x11in) indist.s.d.1881
£5000 $9150   (3-Jun-92 S66/R) Cutting reeds (58x79cm-23x31in) init.d.1900
£800 $1424   (28-Apr-92 S266/R) Flower seller (34x25cm-13x10in) s.d.1907 W/C

MACBETH-RAEBURN, Marjorie May (1902-1988) British
£550 $946   (5-Mar-92 CSK5) Study of jockeys and racehorses at start
       (46x57cm-18x22in) board in studio Sir Alfred Munnings

MACBRIDE, William (19th C) British
£1055 $1931   (1-Jun-92 W.T1311) Woodcutters in copse (53x43cm-21x17in) s. (C.D 2300)

MACBRYDE, Robert (1913-1966) British
£2000 $3600   (20-Nov-91 S8/R) Yellow still life (51x61cm-20x24in) s.

MACCABE, Gladys (?) Irish
£540 $934   (5-Oct-91 TA.B532) French cafe scene (38x30cm-15x12in) s.

MACCARI, Mino (1898-1989) Italian
£1188 $2258   (23-Jun-92 F.M91) Due volti (29x25cm-11x10in) s. s.d.1968verso
       canvasboard (I.L 2600000)
£1297 $2310   (29-Nov-91 F.F79/R) Volti (24x30cm-9x12in) s. (I.L 2800000)
£1453 $2586   (29-Apr-92 F.F101/R) Il cliente (30x20cm-12x8in) s. (I.L 3200000)
£1576 $2804   (29-Nov-91 F.F80) Maschere Venezia (25x35cm-10x14in) s. (I.L 3400000)
£1764 $3315   (19-Dec-91 F.M80/R) Due figure (40x30cm-16x12in) s. (I.L 3800000)
£1840 $3293   (14-Nov-91 F.M29/R) Figura (35x25cm-14x10in) s. panel (I.L 4000000)
£2228 $4188   (19-Dec-91 F.M109/R) La coppia (40x30cm-16x12in) s. panel (I.L 4800000)
£2270 $4040   (29-Apr-92 F.F174) Due volti (40x27cm-16x11in) s. panel (I.L 4800000)
£2353 $4283   (26-May-92 SY.MI63/R) Ritratto (39x30cm-15x12in) s. canvasboard
       (I.L 5200000)
£2716 $4942   (25-May-92 CH.R47/R) Senza titolo (35x50cm-14x20in) s. paper on canvas
       (I.L 6000000)
£2989 $5351   (14-Nov-91 F.M47/R) Senza titolo (60x40cm-24x16in) s.d.1968 s.d.verso
       panel (I.L 6500000)
£3254 $5889   (3-Dec-91 F.R154/R) La contesa (35x50cm-14x20in) s.d.1978 (I.L 7000000)
£3405 $6061   (29-Apr-92 F.F173/R) Quattro figure su sfondo verde (40x50cm-16x20in) s.
       (I.L 7500000)
£4145 $7544   (9-Dec-91 CH.R181/R) Il domatore (40x50cm-16x20in) s. (I.L 9000000)
£4313 $7677   (29-Apr-92 F.F175/R) Stanza d'albergo (30x40cm-12x16in) s. (I.L 9500000)
£5670 $10377   (12-May-92 F.R216/R) Passeggiata (40x50cm-16x20in) s.d.1950 board on
       canvas (I.L 12500000)
£463 $825   (27-Nov-91 F.M133) Due volti (24x35cm-9x14in) W/C chl (I.L 1000000)
£633 $1145   (21-May-92 F.M36) Testa (24x18cm-9x7in) s. W/C crayon (I.L 1400000)
£649 $1155   (29-Nov-91 F.F81) Figure (30x40cm-12x16in) s. chl gouache (I.L 1400000)
£678 $1227   (21-May-92 F.M31) Due teste (24x33cm-9x13in) s. W/C pencil (I.L 1500000)
£1946 $3464   (27-Nov-91 F.M218/R) Personaggi (35x50cm-14x20in) s. W/C chl
       (I.L 4200000)
£2138 $3870   (3-Dec-91 F.R101/R) Lei scherza troppo (34x34cm-13x13in) s. indian ink
       sold with 2 dr by Renato Guttuso (I.L 4600000)
£2722 $4981   (12-May-92 F.R60/R) Personaggi di una fiaba (50x70cm-20x28in) s. mixed
       media paper on canvas (I.L 6000000)

MACCHERONI, Henri (20th C) ?
£821 $1469   (19-Jan-92 CC.P3) Sans titre (60x60cm-24x24in) s.d.1987 (F.FR 8000)
£916 $1677   (3-Jun-92 CSC.P165) Archeologies (65x50cm-26x20in) s.d.1972 paper on
       board (F.FR 9000)
£1527 $2795   (3-Jun-92 CSC.P164/R) Archeologies bleues, de la preserie des Egypte-Bleu
       (54x60cm-21x24in) s.d.1974 W/C indian ink board (F.FR 15000)

MACCIO, Romulo (1931-) Argentinian
£3591 $6500   (18-May-92 CH.NY212/R) Untitled (99x90cm-39x35in) s.

MACCO, Georg (1863-1933) German
£777 $1360   (3-Apr-92 BM.B678/R) Lake Chiemsee with view of Fraueninsel
       (30x48cm-12x19in) s.d.1915 i.verso (DM 2200)
£787 $1400   (29-Nov-91 MFA.C175) Swiss winter snow scene (76x114cm-30x45in) s.d.1932

MACCO, Georg (1863-1933) German-cont.
£648 $1174   (21-May-92 L.K299) Spring in Wimpfen on the Neckar (39x51cm-15x20in) s. W/C oil board (DM 1900)

MACCULLOCH, James (?-1915) British
£400 $692   (4-Sep-91 BT138/R) Scuir na Gillean from Loch-an-eillan, Skye (46x74cm-18x29in) s. s.i.label back panel W/C

MACDONALD, Alfred (fl.1868-1903) British
£620 $1184   (14-Jul-92 DR393) My farewell inspection of Grenadier Guards (46x71cm-18x28in) s.d.1871 monochrome

MACDONALD, J Tim (19/20th C) British
£750 $1313   (1-Apr-92 B160/R) Westminster (23x36cm-9x14in) s.d.23 W/C
£800 $1400   (1-Apr-92 B69/R) Piccadilly Circus (33x19cm-13x7in) s.d.23 W/C

MACDONALD, James Edward Hervey (1873-1932) Canadian
£1368 $2435   (25-Nov-91 W.T1584/R) Bathsheba Coast, Barbados (22x27cm-9x11in) s.i.d.1932verso board (C.D 2750)
£1625 $2876   (6-Nov-91 SY.T202/R) Barbados (22x27cm-9x11in) s.d.32 verso estate st.verso board (C.D 3250)
£2055 $3760   (14-May-92 SY.T135) Barbados, coastal scene (21x26cm-8x10in) panel (C.D 4500)
£2169 $3969   (14-May-92 SY.T16) Banks of Humber (15x20cm-6x8in) init. i.verso board (C.D 4750)
£2439 $4415   (2-Dec-91 R.T275/R) Rockies (20x26cm-8x10in) init. s.i.verso board (C.D 5000)
£2985 $5313   (25-Nov-91 W.T1579/R) Logs coming down narrows, Turtle Lake, Ontario (22x27cm-9x11in) s.i.verso board (C.D 6000)
£3881 $7103   (14-May-92 SY.T69/R) Logs coming down narrows, Turtle Lake, Ont (21x25cm-8x10in) s. board (C.D 8500)
£4726 $8413   (26-Nov-91 JOY.T119/R) Our barn at Thornhill, 1914 (16x23cm-6x9in) board (C.D 9500)
£5936 $10804   (26-May-92 JOY.T100 d) Poplar point, Sturgeon Bay (21x26cm-8x10in) init.d.31 board (C.D 13000)
£868 $1588   (14-May-92 SY.T38) Winding stream (23x28cm-9x11in) s. pencil (C.D 1900)
£1468 $2686   (2-Jun-92 R.T127/R) Autumn sunshine (20x13cm-8x5in) init.d.1897 W/C (C.D 3200)

MACDONALD, James W G (1897-1960) Canadian
£1990 $3542   (26-Nov-91 JOY.T15/R) Abstract fantasy (35x44cm-14x17in) s. W/C (C.D 4000)

MACDONALD, John Blake (1829-1901) British
£850 $1428   (26-Aug-91 S806 a) Haymaking (21x25cm-8x10in) s.indist.d. board

MACDONALD, Manly Edward (1889-1971) Canadian
£488 $883   (2-Dec-91 R.T220/R) Autumn (12x16cm-5x6in) s. canvasboard (C.D 1000)
£498 $886   (26-Nov-91 JOY.T214) Autumn landscape (26x34cm-10x13in) s. board (C.D 1000)
£498 $886   (26-Nov-91 JOY.T194) Trees at water's edge (26x34cm-10x13in) s. board (C.D 1000)
£502 $914   (26-May-92 JOY.T233) Overlooking Picton Bay (30x40cm-12x16in) s. canvas on board (C.D 1100)
£800 $1416   (6-Nov-91 SY.T34/R) Rouge River (41x51cm-16x20in) s. board (C.D 1600)
£875 $1549   (6-Nov-91 SY.T36) Horses with plough (22x27cm-9x11in) s. board (C.D 1750)
£1095 $1948   (26-Nov-91 JOY.T19/R) Country road, autumn (45x60cm-18x24in) s. (C.D 2200)
£1125 $1991   (6-Nov-91 SY.T21/R) Don valley (30x40cm-12x16in) s. board (C.D 2250)
£1171 $2119   (2-Dec-91 R.T219/R) Boy fishing (40x51cm-16x20in) s. (C.D 2400)
£1279 $2327   (26-May-92 JOY.T151/R) Farm in winter, Roslin, Ontario (30x40cm-12x16in) s. canvasboard (C.D 2800)
£1294 $2302   (26-Nov-91 JOY.T107/R) Village in winter (30x40cm-12x16in) s. canvasboard (C.D 2600)
£1375 $2434   (6-Nov-91 SY.T38/R) River view, autumn (49x65cm-19x26in) s. (C.D 2750)
£1826 $3342   (14-May-92 SY.T22/R) Bridge on Scootama (60x75cm-24x30in) s. (C.D 4000)
£1950 $3568   (1-Jun-92 W.T1107/R) Welland furnaces (71x91cm-28x36in) s. (C.D 4250)
£1990 $3542   (26-Nov-91 JOY.T42/R) Bay of Quinte (50x65cm-20x26in) s. (C.D 4000)
£2625 $4646   (6-Nov-91 SY.T122/R) Two boys fishing (60x75cm-24x30in) s. (C.D 5250)

MACDONALD, Murray (fl.1889-1910) British
£540 $988   (12-May-92 LV161) Balgonie Castle with cattle and drover to the fore (38x48cm-15x19in) s.d.1890

MACDONALD, W Alister (fl.1893-1910) British
£750 $1433   (13-Jul-92 PH115/R) St Paul's from the river (51x35cm-20x14in) init.d.1902 W/C gouache

MACDONALD, William (fl.1884-1938) British
£580 $1032   (1-May-92 PHE47) Blue door, convento do San Antonio (76x63cm-30x25in) s.

MACFARLANE, Stewart (20th C) Australian
£523 $947   (19-May-92 JRL.S188) Shoot (120x172cm-47x68in) s. (A.D 1250)

MACGEORGE, William Stewart (1861-1931) British
£4000 $7240   (4-Dec-91 S191/R) Playing on beach (30x40cm-12x16in) s.
£4200 $7602   (4-Dec-91 S190/R) On Solway (30x40cm-12x16in) s. board
£800 $1424   *(28-Apr-92 S271/R) Chopping faggots (27x38cm-11x15in) s. W/C*

MACGINNIS, Robert E (1926-) American
£983 $1700   (6-Sep-91 S.BM202/R) Kyle Nolan's Camp (41x102cm-16x40in) i. verso board
£2107 $3750   *(2-May-92 IH.NY7/R) Woman with arms raised kneeling by urn (51x38cm-20x15in) s. gouache*

MACGOUN, Hannah C Preston (1864-1913) British
£650 $1157   *(28-Apr-92 S270/R) Thoughtful (30x22cm-12x9in) s.d.1901 W/C*

MACGREGOR, John (1944-) Canadian
£507 $917   *(24-May-92 AT.P132) Train (56x76cm-22x30in) s. acrylic collage (F.FR 5000)*

MACHADO, Emilio (1936-) Spanish
£1637 $2962   (20-May-92 ANS.M138/R) Paginas de ultima hora (122x98cm-48x39in) s.d.90 s.i.d.verso (S.P 300000)
£1637 $2962   (20-May-92 ANS.M137/R) Pagina de los horoscopos (122x89cm-48x35in) s.d.90 (S.P 300000)

MACHELBACH (19th C) ?
£1309 $2500   (3-Jul-92 S.W3122/R) Jester and barmaid (30x23cm-12x9in) s. panel

MACHEN, William H (1832-1911) American
£546 $1000   (15-May-92 DM.D2033/R) Two game birds (43x36cm-17x14in) s.

MACHEREN, Philip van (attrib) (17th C) Dutch
£2209 $3800   (9-Oct-91 CH.NY113/R) Naval battle. Warships anchored in harbour (36x96cm-14x38in) pair

MACHI, Mariano (?) ?
£831 $1437   (24-Mar-92 DUR.M562/R) Vendimiadores (81x65cm-32x26in) s. (S.P 150000)

MACHOLM, Niels (20th C) Scandinavian
£620 $1128   (25-May-92 RAS.K93) Having a sweet tooth (70x100cm-28x39in) s.verso masonite (D.KR 7000)

MACHUCA, Pedro (circle) (?-1550) Spanish
£4303 $7961   (8-Jun-92 CH.R761/R) Cristo e gli apostoli in gloria (58x171cm-23x67in) (I.L 9500000)

MACK, Andre (?) ?
£580 $1050   (20-May-92 LJ236) Le Plage de St. Aubin (46x53cm-18x21in) s.

MACK, Heinz (1931-) German?
£2800 $4816   *(17-Oct-91 S52/R) Wave relief (60x53cm-24x21in) s.d.67 verso aluminium board*

MACKAY, Edwin Murray (?-1926) American
£2707 $4900   (24-May-92 LIT.L54) Garden party (46x56cm-18x22in) s.

MACKAY, Florence (fl.1890-1920) British
£640 $1139   *(21-Jan-92 SWS1273) In cottage garden (17x24cm-7x9in) s.d.1921 W/C bodycol*
£1143 $2000   *(18-Feb-92 CE.NY293) Thatched cottage with flowering garden (25x20cm-10x8in) s. W/C board*

MACKAY, James M (19/20th C) British
£1500 $2520   (26-Aug-91 S991/R) Mill pool (61x91cm-24x36in) s.d.1904

MACKAY, John (19th C) ?
£2800 $5124   (4-Jun-92 CSK153/R) Urban landscape (102x117cm-40x46in) s.i.

MACKAY, Thomas (19/20th C) British
£460 $810   *(6-Apr-92 PH127) The convent garden (19x27cm-7x11in) s.i. W/C htd white*
£500 $925   *(11-Jun-92 CSK45/R) In the cottage garden (13x10cm-5x4in) s.d.09 pencil W/C htd.white*
£1250 $2175   *(11-Sep-91 MMB107/R) A young lady at the water's edge (20x13cm-8x5in) s. bodycol.*
£1400 $2632   *(19-Dec-91 C16/R) Girl with ducks by stream (20x32cm-8x13in) s. pencil W/C scratching out*
£1550 $2775   *(5-May-92 SWS267/R) Where the minnows are (16x21cm-6x8in) s.d.1907 W/C gouache scratching out*
£1850 $3145   *(22-Oct-91 SWS180/R) Harvest time (13x20cm-5x8in) s. W/C bodycol*
£1850 $3312   *(14-Jan-92 SWS101/R) The village street (19x29cm-7x11in) s. W/C bodycol*
£2500 $4250   *(22-Oct-91 SWS252/R) Ashow church, on Avon near Kenilworth (25x42cm-10x17in) s.d.1895 W/C bodycol*

MACKE, August (1887-1914) German
£6873 $12715   (12-Jun-92 HN.H548/R) Man reading seated on chair, Claus Cito (51x41cm-20x16in) d.1907 board (DM 20000)

MACKE, August (1887-1914) German-cont.

£10997	$20344	(12-Jun-92 HN.H547/R) Women working in field (47x35cm-19x14in) s.d.1907 board (DM 32000)
£10997	$20344	(12-Jun-92 HN.H549/R) Grandmother in garden. Four studies (49x39cm-19x15in) d.1907 board double-sided (DM 32000)
£1399	$2490	(30-Nov-91 VG.B856/R) Forms III (39x24cm-15x9in) i.d.1913verso indian ink brush wash vellum (DM 4000)
£2730	$4969	(30-May-92 VG.B184/R) Girl bathing (25x22cm-10x9in) pencil over col.brush (DM 8000)
£2971	$5200	(26-Sep-91 SY.I106/R) Figures on the beach (16x24cm-6x9in) i.d.1911 verso brush ink over pencil
£3654	$6942	(25-Jun-92 GK.B456) Park entrance (14x8cm-6x3in) i.d.1914verso col.pencil (S.FR 9500)
£4561	$8211	(23-Nov-91 N.M199/R) Riverside street and horse-drawn coach (8x14cm-3x6in) d.1912 col.chk over chl (DM 13000)
£5965	$10737	(21-Nov-91 L.K292/R) Lakeside village with church (17x10cm-7x4in) chl (DM 17000)

MACKE, Helmuth (1891-1936) German

£634	$1147	(6-Dec-91 GB.B6789) Lake Constance landscape (35x50cm-14x20in) s.d.1935 W/C over pencil (DM 1800)
£1203	$2201	(3-Jun-92 L.K279/R) Martin Buber (29x23cm-11x9in) s.i.d.1931 W/C bodycol indian ink pen (DM 3500)
£1748	$3112	(30-Nov-91 VG.B273/R) Rhine landscape with Drachenfels (26x33cm-10x13in) W/C over pencil (DM 5000)

MACKELLAR, Duncan (1849-1908) British

£500	$890	(1-Nov-91 PHE22) Fishing boat on highland loch (29x44cm-11x17in) init.d.75

MACKENZIE, Alexander (1923-) British

£620	$1079	(11-Sep-91 MMB324) Granite - White June 1961 (79x61cm-31x24in) s.i.d. verso board

MACKENZIE, Alfred (?) British

£500	$955	(14-Jul-92 DR394) Room at Gyldenscroft with figures (33x53cm-13x21in) s. W/C

MACKENZIE, Frederick (1787-1854) British

£1163	$2000	(7-Mar-92 LAE.L17/R) Vespers in Christ Church, Oxford (38x33cm-15x13in) W/C

MACKENZIE, J Hamilton (1875-1926) British

£800	$1392	(11-Sep-91 PHG60) A Scotch lassie (29x24cm-11x9in) s.mono. i. label
£900	$1629	(4-Dec-91 S314/R) Scotch lassie (30x25cm-12x10in) s. s.i.stretcher
£540	$934	(4-Oct-91 BW384/R) Shepherd and sheep in turnip field (23x36cm-9x14in) s. pastel

MACKENZIE, M H (1878-1961) Dutch

£547	$991	(3-Dec-91 C.A160) Coaches in winter (50x60cm-20x24in) s. (B.FR 32000)

MACKENZIE, Marie Henrie (1878-1961) Dutch

£795	$1407	(5-Nov-91 SY.AM79) Building-site in Amsterdam (43x58cm-17x23in) s. (D.FL 2600)

MACKEPRANG, A (1833-1911) Danish

£704	$1183	(27-Aug-91 RAS.K552/R) Horses in a farmyard (70x98cm-28x39in) mono.d.62 (D.KR 8000)
£792	$1331	(27-Aug-91 RAS.K382/R) Driving donkeys on dusty road (46x79cm-18x31in) mono. (D.KR 9000)
£808	$1430	(11-Feb-92 RAS.K332/R) Deer and stag in Dyrehaven (88x123cm-35x48in) mono.d.1910 (D.KR 9000)
£1235	$2198	(28-Apr-92 RAS.K112/R) Deer on the run (88x137cm-35x54in) s. (D.KR 14000)

MACKEPRANG, Adolf (1833-1911) Danish

£698	$1200	(15-Oct-91 CE.NY277/R) Landscape with ducks by a pond (52x70cm-20x28in) s.d.1857

MACKIE, Charles H (1862-1930) British

£3500	$6230	(28-Apr-92 S235/R) A night promenade (73x108cm-29x43in) s.d.1905

MACKINTOSH, Margaret MacDonald (fl.1900-1940) British

£3600	$6408	(1-May-92 PHE94/R) Sheep grazing on rocky headland (38x43cm-15x17in) i.verso pastel

MACKNIGHT, Dodge (1860-?) American

£444	$800	(22-Nov-91 S.BM147/R) Quiet stroll through village (38x48cm-15x19in) s. W/C
£576	$1100	(19-Jul-92 JRB.C117) Andalusia, Spain (36x53cm-14x21in) s. W/C
£703	$1300	(10-Jun-92 CE.NY291) Marshy landscape (40x56cm-16x22in) s.d.1924 W/C
£734	$1300	(25-Apr-92 YFA.M216/R) Moonlight over Point (36x51cm-14x20in) s. W/C
£760	$1300	(13-Mar-92 S.BM263/R) Dunes in bloom and distant sea (38x53cm-15x21in) s. W/C graphite
£833	$1500	(22-Nov-91 S.BM213/R) Buttes in afternoon sunlight, Sidona, Arizona (38x53cm-15x21in) s. W/C

MACKRILL, Martyn R (?) ?
£500 $905   (20-May-92 S269/R) Casting off (36x54cm-14x21in) s.i.d.91 W/C

MACLAREN, Peter (1964-) British
£800 $1416   (10-Feb-92 B124/R) The cyclist (222x206cm-87x81in) board

MACLEAN, Alexander (1867-1940) British
£4800 $8544   (28-Apr-92 S195/R) Watermeadows at twilight (101x151cm-40x59in) s.

MACLEAN, Will (1941-) British
£700 $1274   (28-May-92 B292) Wheelhouse (216x122cm-85x48in) s.d.80 mixed media
     triptych
£1300 $2301   (8-Nov-91 C294 a/R) Death fish study (26x41cm-10x16in) s.i.d.83 mixed
     media relief

MACLEAY, McNeil (19th C) British
£1400 $2492   (1-May-92 PHE40/R) Loch Lubnaig near Callender with shoulder of Ben Ledi
     (45x76cm-18x30in) s.d.1868 i.verso

MACLEAY, Robert McNeil (?) British
£1000 $1770   (15-Feb-92 TA.B396) Children by bridge in landscape (61x74cm-24x29in) s.

MACLEOD, Pegi Nichol (1904-1949) Canadian
£500 $885   (6-Nov-91 SY.T256) View of city street from verandah (60x49cm-24x19in)
     panel (C.D 1000)
£731 $1337   (14-May-92 SY.T226/R) Study of child (60x48cm-24x19in) estate st.verso
     panel (C.D 1000)
£1095 $1948   (26-Nov-91 JOY.T118/R) Under El, New York (42x27cm-17x11in) (C.D 2200)
£1463 $2649   (2-Dec-91 R.T204/R) Houses and church, Hull, Quebec. Autumnal trees
     (30x30cm-12x12in) panel double-sided (C.D 3000)
£1750 $3098   (6-Nov-91 SY.T45/R) Still life of flowers with woman in background.
     Mother and two children (60x65cm-24x26in) panel double-sided (C.D 3500)
£2100 $3823   (26-May-92 JOY.T170/R) Rock pool reflections (50x50cm-20x20in) s. panel
     (C.D 4600)

MACLET, Elisee (1881-1962) French
£766 $1341   (26-Feb-92 CK.P44) Viaduc (49x64cm-19x25in) s. board (F.FR 7500)
£1134 $1962   (27-Mar-92 PPB.P49) Bouquet (34x24cm-13x9in) s. board (F.FR 11000)
£1418 $2567   (18-May-92 AT.P132) Rue a Montmartre (32x41cm-13x16in) s. board
     (F.FR 14000)
£1500 $2865   (29-Jun-92 CSK99/R) Montmartre, Paris (22x27cm-9x11in) s.
£1714 $3034   (12-Feb-92 GL.P62 b) Le lapin agile (38x46cm-15x18in) s. board
     (F.FR 16800)
£1839 $3218   (23-Feb-92 FE.P87) Rue de lAbreuvoir a Montmartre (35x27cm-14x11in) s.
     (F.FR 18000)
£1880 $3271   (13-Apr-92 BG.P119/R) La maison de Mimi Pinson (27x34cm-11x13in) s.
     i.stretcher (F.FR 18500)
£2043 $3575   (23-Feb-92 I.N176/R) Le canal (41x27cm-16x11in) s. (F.FR 20000)
£2123 $3800   (9-May-92 CE.NY60/R) Le Vieux moulin (30x40cm-12x16in) s.
£2160 $4105   (24-Jun-92 GL.P237) Le lapin a Gille (22x31cm-9x12in) s. board
     (F.FR 21000)
£2222 $4022   (20-May-92 GK.Z5037) White roses (55x61cm-22x24in) s. (S.FR 6000)
£2447 $4600   (5-Jan-92 LIT.L246) French town (48x61cm-19x24in) s.
£2559 $4555   (27-Nov-91 AT.P170) Bateaux au port (38x55cm-15x22in) s. (F.FR 25000)
£2846 $4951   (19-Apr-92 ZZ.F81/R) Montmartre le Sacre-Coeur (32x27cm-13x11in) st.sig.
     board (F.FR 28000)
£2846 $4951   (13-Apr-92 GL.P150/R) Port mediterraneen (33x46cm-13x18in) s.
     (F.FR 28000)
£3049 $5305   (19-Apr-92 ZZ.F115/R) Paysage mediterraneen (42x65cm-17x26in) s. board
     (F.FR 30000)
£3049 $5305   (16-Apr-92 FB.P52/R) Rue a Montmartre (73x50cm-29x20in) s. (F.FR 30000)
£3143 $5500   (27-Feb-92 CE.NY94/R) Le pont sur le Canal Chippillu (39x54cm-15x21in) s.
£3955 $7000   (5-Nov-91 CE.NY67/R) Le port (50x61cm-20x24in) s.
£4200 $7602   (2-Dec-91 CSK109/R) La maison de Mimi-Pinson (46x55cm-18x22in) s. board
£4571 $8000   (27-Feb-92 CE.NY61/R) Moulin de la galette (63x46cm-25x18in) s.
£4885 $8500   (16-Sep-91 B.SF2007/R) La Rue Mont-Cenis, Montmartre (50x65cm-20x26in) s.
     board
£4942 $8500   (12-Oct-91 SY.NY95/R) Vue de la Seine et Notre Dame (46x55cm-18x22in) s.
£5800 $10498   (2-Dec-91 CSK107/R) Le Moulin de la Galette (44x54cm-17x21in) s. board
£5814 $10000   (12-Oct-91 SY.NY94/R) Le vieux port de Cassis (46x55cm-18x22in) s.
£7955 $14000   (10-Apr-92 DM.D2014/R) Paris street scene (48x64cm-19x25in) s. board
£8130 $14146   (19-Apr-92 ZZ.F97/R) Montmartre (75x104cm-30x41in) s. board (F.FR 80000)
£8700 $15486   (27-Nov-91 AT.P168/R) Paris, Montmartre, rue Ravignan (38x46cm-15x18in)
     s. (F.FR 85000)
£416 $728   (5-Apr-92 ZZ.F177/R) Maison au bord de la riviere (21x27cm-8x11in) s. W/C
     (F.FR 4000)
£460 $842   (5-Feb-92 FB.P179) Le Lapin Agile (30x37cm-12x15in) s. W/C (F.FR 4500)
£565 $972   (4-Mar-92 AT.P70) Bateaux amarres (30x23cm-12x9in) s. W/C (F.FR 5500)
£971 $1700   (28-Feb-92 SY.NY134/R) Rooftops of Paris (19x26cm-7x10in) s. W/C pen
     Indian ink
£1086 $1900   (28-Feb-92 SY.NY141/R) Jardins a Montmartre (20x26cm-8x10in) s. W/C pen
     indian ink
£1337 $2300   (12-Oct-91 SY.NY93/R) Riverboat (26x36cm-10x14in) s. W/C
£1714 $3033   (10-Nov-91 ZZ.F247/R) Le port de Dieppe (29x26cm-11x10in) s. W/C
     (F.FR 17000)

MACLIAMMOIR, Michael (19/20th C) British
£435 $792   *(11-Dec-91 A.D125) Study for Romeo and Juliet (25x30cm-10x12in) W/C (E.P 470)*
£727 $1258   *(2-Oct-91 A.D139) Paris by night (23x23cm-9x9in) s. W/C (E.P 800)*
£864 $1494   *(2-Oct-91 A.D123) Changelings (36x25cm-14x10in) s. W/C (E.P 950)*

MACLISE, Daniel (1806-1870) British
£5500 $10175   (12-Jun-92 C112/R) And in the first career they ran........ (63x49cm-25x19in)
£10465 $18000   (17-Oct-91 SY.NY87/R) Visit to printing house (102x142cm-40x56in) s.
£700 $1253   *(12-Nov-91 C57/R) Three children playing with a pug (28x22cm-11x9in) mono. pencil htd.W/C*
£1800 $3204   *(29-Oct-91 C36/R) The Mock Duenna (32x49cm-13x19in) s.d.1853 i.verso W/C bodycol.*

MACLISE, Daniel (circle) (1806-1870) British
£1050 $1880   (14-Jan-92 SWS123/R) Figures in the garden of Pitti Palace (84x116cm-33x46in)

MACNAB, Iain (1890-1967) British
£600 $1044   (19-Sep-91 B118/R) Still life of tulips (91x71cm-36x28in) s.

MACNAIR, Frances (1874-1921) British
£1500 $2745   *(5-Feb-92 C8/R) Design for jewellery, depicting woman's face within medallion (12x18cm-5x7in) pencil ink*

MACNAUGHTON, John H (?) Canadian?
£547 $974   *(26-Nov-91 JOY.T199) Returning from hunt (21x15cm-8x6in) s. W/C (C.D 1100)*
£597 $1063   *(26-Nov-91 JOY.T198) Snow plough pulled by three horses passing habitant home (13x20cm-5x8in) s. W/C (C.D 1200)*

MACNEE, Robert Russell (1880-1952) British
£500 $870   (19-Sep-91 B178/R) Young boy with wheelbarrow in village (46x35cm-18x14in) s.
£500 $865   (1-Oct-91 SWS1604/R) Footbridge (44x34cm-17x13in) s.
£650 $1131   (11-Sep-91 PHG4) Fishing at dusk (43x34cm-17x13in) s.
£850 $1428   (26-Aug-91 S830/R) Cattle in orchard (45x75cm-18x30in) s.d.90
£1300 $2262   (11-Sep-91 PHL121/R) Feeding chickens (35x45cm-14x18in) s.
£1500 $2715   (4-Dec-91 S346) Feeding chickens (35x46cm-14x18in) s.
£2000 $3580   (13-Nov-91 CG625/R) Thatched cottages in a sunlit landscape (35x46cm-14x18in) s.d.17 indist.i.stretcher
£2000 $3360   (26-Aug-91 S938/R) Chickens (24x34cm-9x13in) s.d.19
£2200 $3916   (28-Apr-92 S190/R) Loading the cart (71x108cm-28x43in) s.d.23
£3000 $5370   (13-Nov-91 CG638/R) The grey of the morn (41x60cm-16x24in) s.d.23
£6000 $10080   (26-Aug-91 S1120/R) Feeding the chickens (49x59cm-19x23in) s.d.21
£700 $1246   *(28-Apr-92 S191) Landscape with cottages and sheep (38x25cm-15x10in) s. W/C*
£700 $1246   *(28-Apr-92 S192) Chickens by cottage (34x24cm-13x9in) s. W/C*

MACNICOL, Bessie (1869-1904) British
£1400 $2352   (26-Aug-91 S1132/R) A fine view of the harbour (25x34cm-10x13in) init. canvas board
£2500 $4525   (4-Dec-91 S309/R) Lady with fan (36x27cm-14x11in) s.d.1904 panel

MACPHERSON, J (19th C) British
£500 $865   *(25-Mar-92 AH185) Longmoor Pool Sutton Park (25x38cm-10x15in) W/C*

MACPHERSON, John (19th C) British
£530 $970   *(6-Feb-92 T360/R) River landscape with cattle, horses and figures by village (36x58cm-14x23in) s.d.1871 W/C*
£580 $1032   *(29-Nov-91 T228) Cattle watering in river (28x51cm-11x20in) s. W/C*
£900 $1593   *(6-Nov-91 S305/R) The land of summer (37x48cm-15x19in) s. i.verso W/C*

MACPHERSON, John and FAULKNER, John (19th C) British
£1500 $2550   *(22-Oct-91 SWS176/R) Dodagh Strand, Achill, C. Mayo (42x77cm-17x30in) s.i. W/C over pencil*

MACPHERSON, Neil (1954-) British
£600 $1092   *(29-May-92 PHG30) Two dogs (69x49cm-27x19in) s. acrylic paper*
£580 $1056   *(29-May-92 PHG94/R) Man with dogs (95x94cm-37x37in) s. mixed media collage*

MACQUEEN, Kenneth (1897-) Australian
£1795 $3195   *(28-Apr-92 CH.ME209/R) Homestead on weathercock farm (38x47cm-15x19in) s.d.1925 W/C (A.D 4200)*
£2222 $3956   *(28-Apr-92 CH.ME75/R) Coastal landscape (37x47cm-15x19in) s. W/C (A.D 5200)*
£2350 $4184   *(28-Apr-92 CH.ME93/R) Rural landscape with dam (38x47cm-15x19in) s. W/C (A.D 5500)*
£2564 $4564   *(28-Apr-92 CH.ME171/R) Tranquil dam (38x39cm-15x15in) s. W/C (A.D 6000)*

MACRAE, Emma Fordyce (1887-1974) American
£851 $1600   (18-Dec-91 SY.NY256/R) Four of a kind (66x45cm-26x18in) s. masonite

MACRAE, Emma Fordyce (1887-1974) American-cont.
£2171 $3800   (26-Sep-91 CH.NY153/R) Belgian girl (77x64cm-30x25in) s. oil pencil canvas on panel

MACREAU, Michel (1935-) French
£1169 $2034   (16-Apr-92 FB.P211/R) Le couple (108x74cm-43x29in) mono.d.81 chl.pastel (F.FR 11500)
£8351 $14446   (29-Mar-92 P.V58/R) Ecriture pour une surface blanc kace (130x162cm-51x64in) s.d.1962verso oil mixed media canvas (F.FR 81000)
£9072 $15695   (29-Mar-92 P.V57/R) La faune humaine (192x116cm-76x46in) s. s.i.d.1961verso oil mixed media (F.FR 88000)

MACTAGGART, Sir William (1903-1981) British
£950 $1691   (30-Apr-92 CG932) Towards Soutra (18x25cm-7x10in) s.d.64 board
£1300 $2327   (13-Nov-91 CG684) The estuary (10x15cm-4x6in) s. canvas board
£1300 $2314   (1-May-92 PHE62) Red house by river (47x58cm-19x23in) s. board
£1900 $3382   (28-Apr-92 S320/R) Cottages at Fisherrow (21x28cm-8x11in) s. s.i.d.1949verso board
£2000 $3480   (11-Sep-91 PHG9) Across the sound (19x26cm-7x10in) s. board
£2400 $4272   (1-May-92 PHE5/R) The road to Lasswade (35x48cm-14x19in) s. board
£2800 $5012   (13-Nov-91 CG688/R) Drummond Place, Edinburgh, from the artist's studio (46x53cm-18x21in) s. i.verso board
£3000 $5040   (26-Aug-91 S1107/R) Still life with bottle, grapes and pears (60x59cm-24x23in) s. studio st.verso board
£3400 $6086   (11-Nov-91 S691/R) Shore (38x49cm-15x19in) s. board
£3846 $7346   (19-Jul-92 SY.ME39/R) Still life of flowers in vase (75x54cm-30x21in) s. board (A.D 10000)
£4000 $7120   (1-May-92 PHE57/R) Harvest landscape (30x44cm-12x17in) s. board
£8000 $14320   (13-Nov-91 CG683/R) Sunset (63x76cm-25x30in) s.
£12000 $20160   (26-Aug-91 S1116/R) Afterglow, East Lothian (81x51cm-32x20in) s. indist.d.

MACWHIRTER, John (1839-1911) British
£600 $1026   (17-Mar-92 SWS1236) The ravine (50x34cm-20x13in) init. i.verso panel
£1700 $3077   (4-Dec-91 S130) Tay at Dunkeld (51x76cm-20x30in) s.
£2700 $4536   (26-Aug-91 S821/R) Running waters, Glen Cannich (124x84cm-49x33in) s. s.i.backboard canvas laid down on board
£5000 $8900   (30-Apr-92 CG898/R) In Glen Affric (152x104cm-60x41in) s.i.d.1897verso
£400 $680   (22-Oct-91 SWS174/R) Tete noir from Finhants (17x12cm-7x5in) init. W/C

MADDOX, Alan (20th C) New Zealander?
£859 $1435   (21-Aug-91 DS.W80/R) Crosses on Scrim (76x70cm-30x28in) acrylic (NZ.D 2500)
£515 $861   (21-Aug-91 DS.W9) Untitled (86x80cm-34x31in) crayon gouache (NZ.D 1500)

MADDOX, Conroy (1912-) British
£750 $1328   (5-Nov-91 PH129/R) A manual of childhood (61x78cm-24x31in) s.d.83 i.verso
£1930 $3474   (19-Nov-91 L.K905/R) Theatre of displacement (101x71cm-40x28in) s.d.66 s.i.d.verso (DM 5500)
£420 $790   (18-Dec-91 C177) Finishing school (26x37cm-10x15in) s.d.66 s.i.d.verso oil wash collage

MADELAIN, Gustave (1867-1944) French
£1714 $3000   (28-Feb-92 SY.NY101/R) Parisian street scene (46x32cm-18x13in) s. s.d.1867 verso panel
£1951 $3512   (19-Nov-91 FP.M101/R) La porte Saint-Denis (46x31cm-18x12in) s.d.1919 board (C.D 4000)
£2357 $4242   (2-Feb-92 ZZ.F125/R) Paris, eglise Saint-Germain l'Auxerrois (49x65cm-19x26in) s. (F.FR 23000)
£2593 $4693   (19-May-92 GF.L2559/R) View of the Seine with tugboats, Paris (32x46cm-13x18in) s. panel (S.FR 7000)
£3078 $5294   (15-Oct-91 PPB.P59) Peniches a quai (36x55cm-14x22in) s. panel (F.FR 30500)
£3125 $5531   (10-Nov-91 ZZ.F134/R) Rue animee pres de la cathedrale (92x60cm-36x24in) s. panel (F.FR 31000)
£4472 $7780   (15-Apr-92 PLF.P90/R) Quai de l'Hotel de Ville (51x38cm-20x15in) s. panel (F.FR 44000)
£5040 $8921   (10-Nov-91 ZZ.F144/R) Bateaux sur la Seine et vue de l'ancien trocadero (62x43cm-24x17in) s. (F.FR 50000)

MADELINE, Paul (1863-1920) French
£2152 $3873   (2-Feb-92 ZZ.F117/R) Ruisseau corse en Saintonge (38x46cm-15x18in) st.sig. (F.FR 21000)
£3831 $6780   (10-Nov-91 ZZ.F143/R) L'entree du village (54x54cm-21x21in) s. (F.FR 38000)
£4008 $6894   (4-Mar-92 AT.P171/R) Bord de riviere (54x65cm-21x26in) s. (F.FR 39000)
£5133 $9240   (20-Nov-91 CN.P193/R) L'ecluse (51x65cm-20x26in) s.d.06 (F.FR 50000)
£5200 $9412   (2-Dec-91 CSK21/R) Pins au bord de la mer (59x73cm-23x29in) s.
£5252 $8981   (18-Mar-92 PIC.P65/R) Sur la route du village (50x65cm-20x26in) s. (F.FR 51000)

MADOU, Jean Baptiste (1796-1877) Belgian
£802 $1404   (18-Feb-92 CH.AM178) Peasant woman in wooded landscape holding basket with eggs (56x42cm-22x17in) s.d.1857 panel (D.FL 2600)

MADOU, Jean Baptiste (1796-1877) Belgian-cont.
£847 $1500   (9-Nov-91 W.W21/R) Gentleman in a bookshop (33x18cm-13x7in) s.d.1873 panel
£464   *$850*   *(12-May-92 C.A203) Quarrel in the tavern (26x38cm-10x15in) s.d.1839 wash (B.FR 28000)*
£621 $1068   (16-Oct-91 KM.K1680) Tavern scene with landlady asking drunken guest to leave (34x27cm-13x11in) s.d.1873 pencil (DM 1800)

MADQUICK, C (20th C) ?
£531 $914   (19-Oct-91 UA.U309) Landscape with riders and dogs (60x90cm-24x35in) s. (S.KR 5600)

MADRAZO Y GARRETA, Raimundo de (1841-1920) Spanish
£750 $1395   (16-Jun-92 PH74) Portrait of gentleman seated before landscape (130x97cm-51x38in) s.
£4000 $6840   (17-Mar-92 PH206/R) Young lady with cockatoo (100x75cm-39x30in) canvas on board
£5542 $9809   (12-Feb-92 ANS.M84/R) Sagrada Familia (23x17cm-9x7in) s. copper (S.P 1000000)
£17442 $30000   (16-Oct-91 CH.NY162/R) Portrait of Mrs Edwin C Post (101x82cm-40x32in) s.i.d.1901
£21864 $37169   (22-Oct-91 DUR.M20/R) Aline tocando la guitarra (60x42cm-24x17in) s. (S.P 4000000)
£1314   *$2510*   *(2-Jul-92 ANS.M39/R) Retrato de dama (30x22cm-12x9in) chl albayalde (S.P 240000)*

MADRILENA SCHOOL, 17th C Spanish
£8177 $14064   (7-Oct-91 ANS.M96/R) Retrato del Rey Carlos II (202x101cm-80x40in) s. (S.P 1500000)

MADRITSCH, Karl (1908-) Swiss
£444   *$804*   *(22-May-92 EA.Z81) Seated woman (45x24cm-18x9in) s. chl (S.FR 1200)*

MADSEN, Karl (1855-1938) Danish
£1761 $2958   (27-Aug-91 RAS.K4/R) The artist Anna Ancher by her easel (36x31cm-14x12in) init. (D.KR 20000)

MADSEN, Mads (20th C) Danish
£588 $1065   (4-Dec-91 KH.K129) Performance II (140x100cm-55x39in) s.d.89verso (D.KR 6500)

MADSEN-OHLSEN, Jeppe (1891-1948) Danish
£3381 $5883   (17-Sep-91 RAS.K656/R) The two wise men (70x80cm-28x31in) s.d.1940 (D.KR 38000)

MADURA, J (19/20th C) Italian
£1500 $2715   (21-May-92 CSK323/R) Italianate town with figures by riverside (69x106cm-27x42in) s.

MAEHLE, Ole (1904-1990) Norwegian
£709 $1290   (14-Dec-91 BU.O75/R) November day near Mesna (60x73cm-24x29in) s. s.i.d.1962verso panel (N.KR 8000)
£1229 $2114   (10-Oct-91 BU.O104/R) March evening (70x80cm-28x31in) s.d.79 s.i.verso (N.KR 14000)

MAELLA, Mariano Salvador de (1739-1819) Spanish
£4153 $7475   (28-Jan-92 EP.M1/R) Angeles (32x54cm-13x21in) (S.P 750000)
£8380 $15000   (16-Jan-92 CH.NY114/R) Esau selling birthright (239x156cm-94x61in)
£2187   *$4002*   *(13-May-92 FER.M5/R) Personaje clasico portando la antorcha (50x39cm-20x15in) s.i.d.1759 sanguine (S.P 400000)*

MAES, Dirk see MAAS, Dirck

MAES, Eugene Remy (1849-1931) Belgian
£950 $1805   (23-Jun-92 CG718/R) Cockerel, hens and wood pigeons in farmyard (18x30cm-7x12in) s. panel
£1009 $1847   (1-Jun-92 W.T1237/R) Poultry and chickens on hay rick (25x35cm-10x14in) s. panel (C.D 2200)
£3429 $6000   (18-Feb-92 CE.NY337/R) Battle for corn (61x92cm-24x36in) s.d.1869 s.i.verso
£6395 $11000   (14-Oct-91 H.C7/R) Chickens and ducks (84x119cm-33x47in) s.
£6993 $12587   (21-Nov-91 D.V20/R) Chicken yard (61x91cm-24x36in) s. (A.S 140000)

MAES, Giacomo (19th C) Italian
£667   *$1133*   *(23-Oct-91 GD.B1156/R) Bridge across river (24x32cm-9x13in) s.i.d.1865 W/C (S.FR 1700)*

MAES, Godfried (1649-1700) Flemish
£762 $1326   (13-Apr-92 AT.P69) La Nativite (31x24cm-12x9in) s.d.17.. (F.FR 7500)

MAES, Jacques (1905-1968) Belgian
£850 $1539   (2-Dec-91 CSK71 a/R) L'homme a la barque (80x65cm-31x26in) s. s.i.verso
£2207 $3774   (10-Mar-92 GM.B554/R) Nature morte aux Poires et Prunes (65x81cm-26x32in) s. (B.FR 130000)

MAES, Nicolaes (1632-1693) Dutch

£3200	$5600	(1-Apr-92 S110/R) Portrait of lady, said to be Barbara Beerning, daughter Willem Elsevier (41x31cm-16x12in) bears i.verso panel painted oval
£3229	$5554	(16-Oct-91 AT.P57/R) Portrait d'une jeune femme avec un collier de perles (64x52cm-25x20in) (F.FR 32000)
£4321	$7735	(14-Nov-91 CH.AM184 a/R) Portrait of Duyfje van Loten seated leaning on fountain, landscape beyond (46x38cm-18x15in) indis.s. i.stretcher (D.FL 14000)
£5740	$10275	(7-May-92 CH.AM92/R) Portrait of Anna Rees, standing on terrace by curtain, holding basket (140x110cm-55x43in) s.i.d.1652 (D.FL 19000)
£6000	$10920	(11-Dec-91 S121/R) Portrait of lady wearing red dress (63x50cm-25x20in) s.
£7263	$13000	(17-Jan-92 SY.NY122/R) Portrait of a young man, said to be the Prince of Orange (44x31cm-17x12in) s.d.1675 painted oval
£8000	$15360	(8-Jul-92 S309/R) Portrait of young boy as Adonis (61x49cm-24x19in) s.
£8200	$14596	(30-Oct-91 S159/R) Portrait of Lady. Portrait of gentleman (91x70cm-36x28in) one bears sig.d.1650 panel pair rounded tops
£8587	$16315	(23-Jun-92 D.V89/R) Portrait of gentleman (68x57cm-27x22in) one of pair (A.S 175000)
£8587	$16315	(23-Jun-92 D.V88/R) Portrait of lady (68x57cm-27x22in) s. one of pair (A.S 175000)
£12500	$24000	(10-Jul-92 C148/R) Portrait of Gerbrand de Vicq as Ganymede (99x84cm-39x33in)
£14684	$25991	(7-Nov-91 D.V107/R) Portrait of warlord in armour with black page boy (124x100cm-49x39in) (A.S 300000)
£16000	$28480	(30-Oct-91 S203/R) Portrait of young boy with pet spaniel and bird (90x72cm-35x28in) s.d.1671
£17877	$32000	(16-Jan-92 CH.NY6/R) Portrait of gentleman, leaning on rock in landscape. Portrait of lady, seated by waterfall (68x56cm-27x22in) one s. one bears sig. pair
£22000	$42240	(10-Jul-92 C18/R) Portrait of gentleman, leaning on capital in landscape. Portrait of lady in landscape (57x46cm-22x18in) s. pair
£27933	$50000	(16-Jan-92 CH.NY58/R) Young boy, in costume and plumed hat, holding sprig fruit by plinth with peaches (71x64cm-28x25in)
£55249	$100000	(21-May-92 CH.NY47/R) Interior of cottage with young serving maid plucking duck, with young man by window (68x86cm-27x34in) s.d.1655

MAES, Nicolaes (attrib) (1632-1693) Dutch

£1500	$2880	(7-Jul-92 C87/R) Standing man wearing fur cap (14x8cm-6x3in) pen

MAES, Nicolaes (style) (1632-1693) Dutch

£899	$1600	(22-Jan-92 SY.NY101/R) Portrait of gentleman (116x85cm-46x33in)
£1050	$1890	(22-Nov-91 SWS132/R) Portrait of a young boy as a mercury with two dogs in a landscape (34x25cm-13x10in) panel
£1500	$2745	(12-May-92 SWS705) Portrait of young boy as Mercury with two dogs in landscape (34x25cm-13x10in) panel
£2315	$4144	(14-Nov-91 CH.AM77/R) Young woman sewing in interior (27x20cm-11x8in) panel (D.FL 7500)

MAESTOSI, Guido (20th C) Italian

£2000	$3460	(4-Oct-91 C182/R) Sala dell Iliade, Pitti Palace, Florence (80x105cm-31x41in) s.

MAESTRI, Michelangelo (?-1812) Italian

£787	$1400	(30-Oct-91 D.NY7) Trionfo de Sileno (43x61cm-17x24in) i. bodycol
£1348	$2400	(30-Oct-91 D.NY9) Maenads dancing (41x30cm-16x12in) bodycol pair
£1348	$2400	(30-Oct-91 D.NY8) Maenads covorting with centaurs (41x53cm-16x21in) i. bodycol pair
£1852	$3352	(5-Dec-91 SY.MO80/R) Venus sur son char et Apollon sur son char (38x45cm-15x18in) gouache pen pair (F.FR 18000)
£1977	$3400	(15-Oct-91 CE.NY294/R) Putti driving chariots (37x52cm-15x20in) gouache
£2907	$5000	(15-Oct-91 CE.NY292/R) Classical figures (38x28cm-15x11in) gouache

MAESTRI, Michelangelo (attrib) (?-1812) Italian

£1400	$2492	(27-Nov-91 S369/R) Classical nymphs (43x33cm-17x13in) W/C gouache pair
£1800	$3114	(4-Oct-91 C199/R) Muses (41x30cm-16x12in) pen ink bodycol pair
£1846	$3526	(15-Jul-92 CH.S792/R) Love, pride and war - maiden entertaining three putti (40x30cm-16x12in) bodycol (A.D 4800)
£2000	$3560	(27-Nov-91 S372/R) Europa and bull. Roman sacrifice (31x70cm-12x28in) W/C pair
£2400	$4152	(4-Oct-91 C203/R) Persephone with Charon being sought out by Ceres (46x51cm-18x20in) bodycol sold with another picture red
£2600	$4498	(4-Oct-91 C201/R) Mythological scenes (43x31cm-17x12in) pen ink bodycol set of four
£4500	$8010	(27-Nov-91 S371/R) Muses (45x35cm-18x14in) W/C gouache nine
£6000	$10680	(27-Nov-91 S373/R) Classical nymphs and deities (38x72cm-15x28in) W/C gouache eight
£6200	$10726	(4-Oct-91 C204/R) Mythological scenes (52x83cm-20x33in) pen ink bodycol set of four

MAESTRI, Michelangelo (circle) (?-1812) Italian

£1700	$3026	(28-Nov-91 CSK1/R) Figures on prancing horses, studies after Pompeiian frescoes (46x51cm-18x20in) pen W/C bodycol decorated border

MAETZEL, Emil (1877-1955) German
£526 $947   *(23-Nov-91 N.M206/R) Group of eight children before fence. Landscape study (38x54cm-15x21in) s.d.1929 gouache W/C over indian ink double-side (DM 1500)*
£616 $1060   *(11-Oct-91 AW.H2558/R) Squatting female nude washing (22x17cm-9x7in) s.d.1918 W/C over carpenter's pencil (DM 1800)*
£775 $1402   *(4-Dec-91 DO.H3292/R) Woman reading (50x32cm-20x13in) mono.d. W/C ove carpenter's pencil (DM 2200)*

MAETZEL-JOHANNSEN, Dorothea (1886-1930) German
£481 $847   *(11-Apr-92 AW.H1899/R) Female nude squatting (30x22cm-12x9in) mono.d.19 W/C col.pencil (DM 1400)*
£634 $1147   *(6-Dec-91 GB.B6799) Squatting nude girl with cat (20x18cm-8x7in) mono.d.1919 W/C over pencil (DM 1800)*

MAEXMONTAN, Frans (1847-1901) Finnish
£3161 $5563   *(12-Apr-92 HOR.H161/R) Fishing on the ice (65x81cm-26x32in) s.d.1896 (F.M 25000)*

MAFAI, Antonietta Raphael (1900-1975) Italian
£544 $996   *(12-May-92 F.R80) Le due signore (45x34cm-18x13in) s.d.1958 ink W/C (I.L 1200000)*

MAFAI, Mario (1902-1965) Italian
£24634 $44587   *(3-Dec-91 F.R243/R) Nudo femminile con scarpa rossa (55x40cm-22x16in) s.d.1945 (I.L 53000000)*
£27634 $50294   *(9-Dec-91 CH.R116/R) Demolizione (42x60cm-17x24in) s.d.1935 panel (I.L 60000000)*
£2224 $3959   *(29-Nov-91 F.F91) Natura morta (22x36cm-9x14in) s. W/C paper on canvas (I.L 4800000)*

MAFFEI, Dario (19th C) Italian
£780 $1396   *(6-May-92 MMB316) Dante and Beatrice on a street in Verona (86x117cm-34x46in) s.*

MAFFEY, C D (19th C) ?
£1000 $1770   *(13-Feb-92 CSK115) Town on the Rhone (30x74cm-12x29in) s.d.1853*

MAFLI, Walter (1915-) Swiss
£870 $1548   *(29-Nov-91 GAB.G2797) Ferme dans les environs de la vue des Alpes (38x46cm-15x18in) s. (S.FR 2200)*
£926 $1676   *(20-May-92 GK.Z5104) Shipping in Ouchy Harbour (62x50cm-24x20in) s.d.1944 (S.FR 2500)*
£2157 $3861   *(15-Nov-91 ZOF.Z1794) Jura village (80x130cm-31x51in) s.d.76 (S.FR 5500)*
£803 $1437   *(6-May-92 GD.B800/R) Farmhouses (47x67cm-19x26in) s.d.80 oil chk (S.FR 2200)*

MAGAFAN, Ethel (1916-) American
£936 $1600   *(13-Mar-92 S.BM248/R) Western slope, Colorado farm scene (15x69cm-6x27in) s.d.1936 s.i.verso masonite*

MAGANZA, Alessandro (1556-1630) Italian
£480 $922   *(8-Jul-92 PH225/R) Study of two kneeling figures. Sketch (12x7cm-5x3in) pen wash black chk double-sided*

MAGANZA, Giovanni Battista (elder) (1513-1586) Italian
£3621 $6590   *(28-May-92 F.M113/R) Deposizione (225x132cm-89x52in) arched top (I.L 8000000)*
£4190 $7500   *(14-Jan-92 SY.NY47/R) Study of soldier holding sword and spear, seen from behind (30x18cm-12x7in) pen wash*

MAGATTI, Pietro Antonio (circle) (1687-1768) Italian
£1236 $2200   *(30-Oct-91 D.NY26/R) The Assumption of the Virgin (36x43cm-14x17in)*

MAGEE, Alan (20th C) American
£4167 $7000   *(14-Aug-91 B.P149/R) Pumpkin stems (30x53cm-12x21in) s.*

MAGERER, H (20th C) ?
£650 $1151   *(13-Feb-92 CSK128 a/R) Dutch flower seller on quayside (61x91cm-24x36in) s.*
£800 $1464   *(14-May-92 CSK250) The flower market (91x64cm-36x25in) s.*
£1642 $2940   *(6-May-92 GD.B803/R) Fish market on beach (69x55cm-27x22in) s. (S.FR 4500)*

MAGES, Joseph (1728-1769) Austrian
£1490 $2548   *(18-Mar-92 D.V347/R) Apotheosis of St Joseph of Cupertino (66x51cm-26x20in) (A.S 30000)*

MAGGI (?) ?
£1229 $2200   *(11-Nov-91 GC.M8/R) Pastor con ovejas en los Apeninos (55x26cm-22x10in) s. fan-shaped*

MAGGI, Cesare (1881-1961) Italian
£2612 $4623   *(7-Nov-91 F.M59/R) Estate (28x20cm-11x8in) s. panel (I.L 5700000)*

AGGI, Cesare (1881-1961) Italian-cont.
£3254 $5889   (3-Dec-91 SY.MI67/R) Pascolo (30x41cm-12x16in) s.d.1912 panel
           (I.L 7000000)
£7261 $13506   (16-Jun-92 F.M212/R) Donne in riva a lago, Pian dei Gelsi
           (49x69cm-19x27in) s.d.1930 board (I.L 16000000)
£8966 $15421   (16-Oct-91 KM.K1265/R) Shepherd and flock in landscape with view of snow
           covered mountain range (150x200cm-59x79in) s. (DM 26000)
£13136 $24301   (9-Jun-92 F.R14/R) Il Monte Bianco da Entreves (100x70cm-39x28in) s.
           (I.L 29000000)
£15580 $27577   (7-Nov-91 F.M65/R) Il Cervino (100x70cm-39x28in) s. i.verso
           (I.L 34000000)
£15580 $27577   (7-Nov-91 F.M50/R) A San Mauro in una sera d'inverno (105x145cm-41x57in)
           s.d.1911 (I.L 34000000)
£19451 $33651   (24-Mar-92 CH.R48/R) Marina (32x43cm-13x17in) s.d.1921 board
           (I.L 42000000)
£32000 $56960   (28-Nov-91 CSK91/R) Winter in the Alps (381x511cm-150x201in) s.d.911

AGGIORANI, Luigi (19th C) Italian
£1700 $3043   (5-May-92 SWS406/R) Picnic on grassy slope (18x31cm-7x12in) s. panel

AGGIOTTO, Domenico (1713-1794) Italian
£10000 $17800   (1-Nov-91 C40/R) Personification of summer (58x45cm-23x18in)
£10000 $17800   (1-Nov-91 C41/R) Personification of spring (58x45cm-23x18in)

AGGIOTTO, Domenico (circle) (1713-1794) Italian
£2018 $3471   (16-Oct-91 AT.P13/R) Saint Philippe Neri (79x46cm-31x18in) painted arch
           (F.FR 20000)

AGGIOTTO, Domenico (studio) (1713-1794) Italian
£3477 $5946   (18-Mar-92 D.V5/R) Shepherd scene with sleeping woman (40x31cm-16x12in)
           oval (A.S 70000)

AGGIOTTO, Domenico (style) (1713-1794) Italian
£7500 $13125   (3-Apr-92 C163/R) Lot and daughters (80x109cm-31x43in)

AGGS, John Charles (1819-1896) British
£1257 $2200   (18-Feb-92 CE.NY31/R) Coach in snowstorm (44x67cm-17x26in)
£1639 $3000   (5-Jun-92 SY.NY154/R) London-Brimingham run - leaving London fully loaded
           (35x68cm-14x27in) s.indis.d.
£2747 $5000   (26-May-92 CE.NY23/R) Spread Eagle Tap. Copenhagen House
           (35x66cm-14x26in) s.i.d.1884 pair
£5000 $8600   (11-Oct-91 K511/R) Winter coaching scenes outside public house with
           passing travellers (36x64cm-14x25in) s.d.1898 pair
£11475 $21000   (5-Jun-92 SY.NY158/R) Outside the White Lion Hotel and Tavern
           (86x132cm-34x52in) s.d.1873

AGILL, L (fl.1891) British
£650 $1118   (8-Oct-91 PH161) A dandy Dinmont (61x51cm-24x20in) s.d.1891

AGINI, Carlo (1720-1806) Italian
£8819 $15874   (19-Nov-91 F.R16/R) Natura morta con zuppiera e uova al tegame
           (33x41cm-13x16in) (I.L 19000000)
£22634 $40967   (5-Dec-91 SY.MO102/R) Trompe-l'oeil aux vitraux (55x46cm-22x18in)
           (F.FR 220000)

AGISTRETTI, Emilio (1851-1936) Italian
£4375 $7963   (12-Dec-91 F.M53/R) Prove di canto (28x21cm-11x8in) s. canvas on board
           (I.L 9500000)

AGNASCO, A and TAVELLA, C A (school) (17/18th C) Italian
£2616 $4500   (9-Oct-91 CH.NY53/R) Monks praying in landscape (93x126cm-37x50in) canvas
           on board

AGNASCO, Alessandro (1667-1749) Italian
£1373 $2333   (23-Oct-91 GD.B1158/R) Figures on path and houses in wooded river
           landscape (70x58cm-28x23in) (S.FR 3500)
£2734 $4840   (5-Nov-91 GF.L2320/R) Monks in grotto (51x38cm-20x15in) canvas on board
           (S.FR 7000)
£11173 $20000   (17-Jan-92 SY.NY184/R) Self-portrait (63x48cm-25x19in)
£16709 $30077   (19-Nov-91 F.R74/R) Mensa di frati in un antro (58x72cm-23x28in)
           (I.L 36000000)
£26000 $47320   (11-Dec-91 S70/R) Temptation of Christ (35x27cm-14x11in)
£85502 $156468   (16-May-92 F.L30/R) Paesaggio con monaci in preghiera (96x132cm-38x52in)
           (S.FR 230000)
£750   *$1440*   *(7-Jul-92 C37/R) Three monks at table and one serving (24x34cm-9x13in)*
           chk bodycol

AGNASCO, Alessandro (attrib) (1667-1749) Italian
£1333 $2280   (13-Mar-92 FN.S2856/R) Wooded landscape with houses and soldiers resting
           beneath tree (53x77cm-21x30in) (DM 3800)
£4070 $7000   (10-Oct-91 SY.NY18/R) Pulcinello seated in an arcade eating a bowl of
           pasta, landscape beyond (38x34cm-15x13in)
£14000 $26880   (8-Jul-92 S119/R) Procession of monks (36x86cm-14x34in)
£493   *$942*   *(3-Jul-92 SD.P85) La Sainte Vierge soutenue par l'Ange (18x26cm-7x10in)*
           black chk wash (F.FR 4800)

MAGNASCO, Alessandro (circle) (1667-1749) Italian
£5874 $10396   (7-Nov-91 D.V63/R) Phantastic landscape with ruins, figures and monument of warrior (75x110cm-30x43in) (A.S 120000)

MAGNASCO, Alessandro (school) (1667-1749) Italian
£1105 $2000   (21-May-92 CH.NY178/R) Monk seated in landscape (61x50cm-24x20in)
£1215 $2200   (21-May-92 CH.NY126/R) Saint Francis of Assisi in ecstacy (37x27cm-15x11in) canvas on panel
£2361 $4250   (22-Nov-91 S.BM25/R) Day's labours (13x23cm-5x9in) panel
£4942 $8500   (9-Oct-91 CH.NY185/R) Two fishermen drawing in net (41x30cm-16x12in)
£16245 $29242   (19-Nov-91 RAS.K16/R) Pulcinella and Colombina with kneeling figure (52x40cm-20x16in) pair (D.KR 180000)

MAGNASCO, Alessandro (style) (1667-1749) Italian
£1300 $2275   (28-Feb-92 C114/R) Two monks - a study (18x24cm-7x9in) canvas laid down on panel
£1953 $3457   (5-Nov-91 GF.L2325/R) Landscapes (84x64cm-33x25in) pair (S.FR 5000)
£2116 $3767   (28-Apr-92 RAS.K525/R) Herders and cattle by well (55x40cm-22x16in) (D.KR 24000)
£4144 $7500   (20-May-92 D.NY101/R) Carnival procession outside the city's walls (58x71cm-23x28in)

MAGNASCO, Stefano (attrib) (1635-1681) Italian
£5500 $9625   (31-Mar-92 PH61/R) Doubting Thomas (78x112cm-31x44in)

MAGNELLI, Alberto (1888-1971) Italian
£16455 $31265   (23-Jun-92 F.M204/R) Sur fond sienne n.1 (46x55cm-18x22in) s.d.1963 s.i.d.verso (I.L 36000000)
£25720 $48868   (24-Jun-92 FB.P50/R) Persone al mare, Femmes au bord de la mer, Florence (125x100cm-49x39in) s.d.22 (F.FR 250000)
£39388 $70111   (26-Nov-91 SY.MI198/R) Conception dirigee, la ferrage (100x80cm-39x31in) s.d.68 s.i.d.verso (I.L 85000000)
£40527 $73354   (24-May-92 GL.P29/R) Attitude tranquille (100x82cm-39x32in) s.d.1945 s.i.d.verso (F.FR 400000)
£199234 $344674   (28-Mar-92 F.L76/R) La Foire (100x75cm-39x30in) s.d.1914 s.i.d.verso (S.FR 520000)
£3447 $6548   *(24-Jun-92 GL.P179/R) Composition geometrique (25x32cm-10x13in) s.d.1942 gouache ink (F.FR 33500)*
£3839 $6948   *(3-Dec-91 AB.S5104/R) Composition aux taches blanches (27x21cm-11x8in) s. W/C Indian ink (S.KR 40000)*
£3870 $7043   *(13-Dec-91 ZZ.F55) Composition (24x30cm-9x12in) s.d.41 Indain ink W/C htd.white chamois paper (F.FR 38000)*
£4571 $8685   *(23-Jun-92 F.M177/R) Composizione (27x21cm-11x8in) s.d.1941 gouache (I.L 10000000)*
£5601 $10193   *(13-Dec-91 ZZ.F56/R) Composition (24x31cm-9x12in) s.d.43 gouache chamois paper (F.FR 55000)*
£6856 $13027   *(23-Jun-92 F.M154/R) Composizione (31x23cm-12x9in) s. gouache cardboard (I.L 15000000)*
£7637 $13977   *(3-Jun-92 PIC.P85/R) Composition geometrique (64x49cm-25x19in) s.d.1963 oil felt pen (F.FR 75000)*
£8754 $14969   *(17-Mar-92 FB.P37/R) Ardoise (28x20cm-11x8in) s.d.37 gouache slate (F.FR 85000)*

MAGNI, Giuseppe (1869-?) Italian
£1449 $2681   (8-Jun-92 CH.R555) Bambina che cuce (38x30cm-15x12in) s. panel (I.L 3200000)
£6977 $12000   (17-Oct-91 SY.NY376/R) Admiring baby (52x66cm-20x26in) s.
£12571 $22000   (19-Feb-92 CH.NY104/R) Musical afternoon (56x80cm-22x31in) s.i.

MAGNUS, Camille (1850-?) French
£1745 $3123   (16-Jan-92 D.V47/R) Wooded landscape (38x45cm-15x18in) s. (A.S 35000)
£3846 $7000   (27-May-92 CH.NY157/R) Faggot gatherer in woodland clearing (89x130cm-35x51in) s.

MAGNUSSEN, Gustave Adolph (1868-1944) American
£618 $1100   (26-Nov-91 MOR.P61) Boats on bay (28x36cm-11x14in) s.

MAGNUSSON, Ragnvald (1904-) Swedish
£474 $868   (12-May-92 GO.G100) Interior with seated lady (55x42cm-22x17in) s. panel (S.KR 5000)
£575 $1035   (19-Nov-91 GO.G110) Autumn in the skerries (40x58cm-16x23in) s. panel (S.KR 6000)

MAGRATH, Georges-Achille de (19th C) French
£659   *$1200   (26-May-92 CE.NY146) A stop along the way (33x50cm-13x20in) s. W/C*

MAGRITTE, Rene (1898-1967) Belgian
£110169 $195000   (6-Nov-91 CH.NY306/R) Le montagnard (74x50cm-29x20in) s. i.d.1947verso
£327869 $600000   (13-May-92 SY.NY85/R) Les travaux d'Alexandre (58x49cm-23x19in) s.i.d.1950verso
£367232 $650000   (5-Nov-91 CH.NY57/R) L'image en soi (66x50cm-26x20in) s. s.i.d.1961verso
£1049 $1867   *(25-Nov-91 WK.M665/R) Study of male nude (18x26cm-7x10in) pencil (DM 3000)*
£2593 $4693   *(22-May-92 EA.Z107) Apple (15x20cm-6x8in) s. indian ink (S.FR 7000)*

MAGRITTE, Rene (1898-1967) Belgian-cont.
£3388	$6099	(20-Nov-91 CN.P57/R) La souche d'arbre (12x19cm-5x7in) s. ink (F.FR 33000)
£5650	$10000	(7-Nov-91 SY.NY168/R) Untitled (21x27cm-8x11in) s. pencil ball point pen
£6186	$10701	(23-Mar-92 CC.P17/R) Les trois graces (26x21cm-10x8in) s. dr (F.FR 60000)
£7000	$12110	(25-Mar-92 S48/R) Sans titre (24x30cm-9x12in) s.d.24 pen indian ink
£9000	$15570	(24-Mar-92 C64/R) Tete d'homme (23x18cm-9x7in) s. gouache
£12994	$23000	(7-Nov-91 SY.NY208/R) Une simple histoire d'armour (27x18cm-11x7in) s. pen
£36000	$65160	(4-Dec-91 S193/R) Le savoir (35x27cm-14x11in) s. pencil blk crayon W/C collage musical score
£50000	$95500	(29-Jun-92 C33/R) L'Empire de la Reflexion (34x49cm-13x19in) s. gouache
£60606	$109697	(19-May-92 CH.AM191/R) La Promesse (36x45cm-14x18in) s. i.d.1950 verso pencil gouache (D.FL 200000)
£80448	$147220	(3-Jun-92 PIC.P84/R) La magie noire (46x37cm-18x15in) s. gouache (F.FR 790000)
£85000	$162350	(30-Jun-92 S53/R) La philosophie dans le boudoir (44x35cm-17x14in) s. s.d.1948verso gouache
£85000	$153850	(3-Dec-91 C167/R) Le monde invisible (38x27cm-15x11in) s. i.d.1953verso gouache
£93000	$177630	(30-Jun-92 C171/R) Le geant (30x38cm-12x15in) s. gouache
£100000	$181000	(3-Dec-91 C168/R) Le partition (30x41cm-12x16in) s. pencil W/C pen collage
£115000	$219650	(30-Jun-92 S54/R) La main heureuse (25x33cm-10x13in) s. s.d.1955verso gouache

MAGROTTI, Ercole (1890-1958) Italian
£599	$1000	(19-Aug-91 GC.M34/R) Patio con barca (100x70cm-39x28in) s.

MAGUET, Joseph (1799-?) French
£1546	$2675	(27-Mar-92 CN.P70/R) La brodeuse (55x45cm-22x18in) s.d.1838 (F.FR 15000)

MAGUIRE, Helena (1860-1909) British
£570	$986	(4-Sep-91 PHK90) Portrait of young Scottish lad in Highland tartan, holding Balmoral bonnet (45x34cm-18x13in) s.
£1000	$1920	(28-Jul-92 SWS238/R) A bird in hand (46x33cm-18x13in) s.
£540	$961	(28-Apr-92 RG2471) Great expectations, farmyard scene of young boy and pigs (25x20cm-10x8in) s. W/C
£800	$1448	(2-Dec-91 B96/R) The caught rabbit (32x48cm-13x19in) s.d.1897 W/C
£2400	$4296	(5-May-92 SWS259/R) Animal friends (52x75cm-20x30in) s. W/C scratching out

MAHLKNECHT, Edmund (1820-1903) Austrian
£775	$1402	(3-Dec-91 FN.S2322) Lake landscape with animals and shepherd girls (35x45cm-14x18in) s. (DM 2200)
£900	$1602	(27-Apr-92 PHB262) Horse and chickens in stable yard (18x21cm-7x8in) init. board
£1463	$2546	(19-Sep-91 D.V175/R) Bull in landscape (26x34cm-10x13in) s. panel (A.S 30000)
£1595	$2855	(16-Jan-92 D.V133/R) Ox standing in field (25x30cm-10x12in) s. (A.S 32000)
£1717	$3263	(25-Jun-92 D.V411/R) Village view, Salzkammergut (17x21cm-7x8in) mono indis.d. panel (A.S 35000)
£2666	$4852	(27-May-92 D.V647/R) View of Dachstein (17x21cm-7x8in) mono.d.853 (A.S 55000)
£3878	$7058	(27-May-92 D.V629/R) Hallstatter See landscape (20x26cm-8x10in) s.d.840 panel (A.S 80000)
£7143	$13000	(28-May-92 SY.NY38/R) Farmyard scene (55x95cm-22x37in) s.
£9756	$17756	(11-Dec-91 N.M517/R) Shepherds with cattle and goats by mountain lake (37x57cm-15x22in) s. panel (DM 28000)

MAHLKNECHT, Edmund (attrib) (1820-1903) Austrian
£728	$1296	(29-Apr-92 D.V828) Animals in river landscape (36x45cm-14x18in) (A.S 15000)

MAHONEY, James (1816-1879) British
£981	$1698	(25-Mar-92 A.D137) The early morning wash (46x33cm-18x13in) s. W/C (E.P 1050)

MAHONEY, M (?) ?
£971	$1700	(19-Feb-92 D.NY56) The Feiseen (48x84cm-19x33in) s.

MAHRINGER, Anton (?) ?
£873	$1588	(26-May-92 D.V111/R) Female sleeping (40x36cm-16x14in) s.i.d.31 pencil (A.S 18000)
£2666	$4852	(26-May-92 D.V109/R) Trees. Nude (40x46cm-16x18in) s.d.1931 W/C pencil double-sided (A.S 55000)

MAHRMANN, Henry (?) ?
£1650	$2987	(20-May-92 BT242/R) Barque Kilmeny under sail (58x97cm-23x38in) s. i.stretcher

MAHU, Cornelis (1613-1689) Flemish
£7452	$12742	(18-Mar-92 D.V102/R) Peasants in tavern interior (24x31cm-9x12in) copper (A.S 150000)

MAIBACH, Karl Ludwig (1833-1886) Russian
£556 $1006   (22-May-92 EA.Z142) High mountain landscape, morning (33x47cm-13x19in)
                      s.d.1863 (S.FR 1500)

MAIDMENT, Henry (19/20th C) British
£550 $979   (28-Nov-91 B17/R) Lane near Dorking, Surrey (30x41cm-12x16in) mono.
                      i.verso
£600 $1038   (1-Oct-91 SWS1640/R) Evening (52x42cm-20x17in) mono.indist.d.
£620 $1054   (22-Oct-91 RG2486) Rural landscape with a figure and cattle by a cottage
                      (74x38cm-29x15in) s. board
£700 $1281   (14-May-92 CSK256/R) Girl feeding ducks by pond (20x41cm-8x16in)
£1350 $2444   (18-May-92 HS502/R) Sonning-on-Thames - White Hart Inn on far bank. River
                      Thames at Richmond (39x60cm-15x24in) s.i.d.1889 pair
£1800 $3384   (19-Dec-91 C123/R) Shepherd with flock on country lane. Cattle watering
                      in wooded river landscape (30x61cm-12x24in) mono.d.1904 pair
£1800 $3186   (6-Nov-91 S66/R) Near Leamington. Near Warwick (30x61cm-12x24in) mono.
                      i.verso pair

MAIGNAN, Albert (1845-1908) French
£7114 $12378   (13-Apr-92 BG.P133/R) Les Cathares ... (117x176cm-46x69in) s.d.1875
                      (F.FR 70000)

MAILLAUD, Fernand (1863-1948) French
£843 $1610   (3-Jul-92 GL.P100) Fermieres berrichonnes (27x35cm-11x14in) s. canvas
                      laid down on board (F.FR 8200)
£1118 $1945   (13-Apr-92 GL.P129/R) Paysage (33x40cm-13x16in) s. panel (F.FR 11000)
£1131 $2105   (21-Jun-92 LT.P30) Le labour (33x41cm-13x16in) s. panel (F.FR 11100)
£1873 $3278   (5-Apr-92 ZZ.F64/R) Cavalier Arabe dans la montagne (41x50cm-16x20in) s.
                      (F.FR 18000)
£1884 $3485   (10-Jun-92 ZZ.F28/R) Moissons dans la Creuse (54x65cm-21x26in) s.
                      (F.FR 18500)
£1900 $3534   (17-Jun-92 S514/R) ladies on beach (46x70cm-18x28in) s. panel
£1913 $3253   (23-Oct-91 LEB.P3/R) Les Bles. Creuse (37x53cm-15x21in) s. panel
                      (F.FR 19000)
£3243 $6000   (12-Jun-92 SY.NY138/R) Spring landscape with cottage (45x54cm-18x21in) s.
£4069 $7284   (17-Nov-91 FB.P179/R) Le bord de riviere (46x55cm-18x22in) s.
                      (F.FR 40000)
£6704 $12000   (13-Nov-91 B.SF2361/R) La Jerinette a Toulon (70x94cm-28x37in) s. i.verso
                      board

MAILLOL, Aristide (1861-1944) French
£1324 $2409   (11-Dec-91 ZZ.F42/R) Projet d'illustation. Femme nue dans un verger, une
                      esquisse de nu (16x19cm-6x7in) s. blk.crayon lead pencil double-sided
                      (F.FR 13000)
£1385 $2631   (25-Jun-92 GK.B461) Etude de nu (30x20cm-12x8in) mono chk (S.FR 3600)
£1440 $2737   (24-Jun-92 GL.P118/R) Nu de dos (29x38cm-11x15in) mono. sanguine
                      (F.FR 14000)
£1462 $2777   (25-Jun-92 GK.B458/R) Etude de nu, les bras leves (32x24cm-13x9in) mono
                      chl double-sided (S.FR 3800)
£1639 $3000   (13-May-92 CH.NY225/R) Femme nue, vue de dos (31x23cm-12x9in) mono.
                      pencil paper on board
£1646 $3128   (24-Jun-92 GL.P116/R) Nu assis (31x23cm-12x9in) st.mono. sanguine
                      (F.FR 16000)
£1857 $3250   (28-Feb-92 SY.NY8/R) Nu debout (32x22cm-13x9in) mono. chl paper on board
£3000 $5700   (25-Jun-92 GK.B459) Etude de nu, vu de dos (35x21cm-14x8in) mono pencil
                      htd chk double-sided (S.FR 7800)
£4913 $8500   (2-Oct-91 SY.NY35/R) Jeune femme debout de dos (38x24cm-15x9in) mono.
                      sanguine white chk
£5962 $11327   (25-Jun-92 GK.B460/R) Deux femmes nues (28x22cm-11x9in) mono ochre htd
                      white (S.FR 15500)
£8000 $14480   (3-Dec-91 C120/R) Nu couche de dos (33x43cm-13x17in) mono. sanguine
                      htd.white card laid on board
£203666 $372709   (3-Jun-92 PIC.P55/R) Jeune fille nue etendue sur le dos
                      (85x130cm-33x51in) mono. chl dr htd white chk (F.FR 2000000)

MAILLOL, Gaspard (1880-?) French
£411 $785   (3-Jul-92 GL.P101) Scene de restaurant (41x50cm-16x20in) mono. W/C pencil
                      (F.FR 4000)

MAILLOT, Philippe (1940-) French
£515 $881   (21-Mar-92 AT.P64/R) Sans titre (54x40cm-21x16in) s.d.1991 gouache
                      (F.FR 5000)

MAINARDI, Sebastiano (1460-1513) Italian
£58659 $105000   (17-Jan-92 SY.NY9/R) The Madonna and child and Saint Joseph adoring the
                      Christ child (80cm-31ins circular) tempera panel

MAINELLA, Raffaele (1858-?) Italian
£850 $1539   (21-May-92 CSK81) On lagoon, Venice. Venetian girl feeding pigeons
                      (32x16cm-13x6in) s.i. pencil W/C pair
£996 $1844   (9-Jun-92 F.R24) Gondole a Venezia (19x34cm-7x13in) s. ink W/C
                      (I.L 2200000)
£1100 $1881   (19-Mar-92 B28) Urchins bathing in the lagoon, an island in the distance
                      (16x32cm-6x13in) W/C

MAINERI, Giovanni Francesco (attrib) (15th C) Italian
£6996 $12663   (5-Dec-91 SY.MO201/R) Adoration (32x24cm-13x9in) panel (F.FR 68000)

MAINGAUD, Martin (17th C) French
£4500 $8595   (17-Jul-92 C5 a/R) Group portrait of three young ladies in satin gowns
                  trimmed with lace (127x101cm-50x40in) s.d.1721 verso

MAINSSIEUX (20th C) ?
£510 $948   (18-Jun-92 CB.P78) Paysage (60x73cm-24x29in) s.d.1937 (F.FR 5000)

MAIRE, Andre (1898-1985) French
£1016 $1768   (13-Apr-92 GL.P137) Bouquet (73x59cm-29x23in) s.d.1968 hardboard
                  (F.FR 10000)
£906 $1541   (23-Oct-91 LEB.P8/R) Jeunes femmes dans un paysage (48x62cm-19x24in)
                  s.d.1954 gouache (F.FR 9000)
£1184 $2025   (22-Mar-92 LT.P141/R) Femmes et enfants au marche en Indochine
                  (48x63cm-19x25in) s.d.1956 gouache (F.FR 11500)
£1249 $2185   (5-Apr-92 ZZ.F191/R) Les Tahitiennes (48x64cm-19x25in) s.d.1953 gouache
                  (F.FR 12000)

MAIRE, Ferdinand Henri (1901-1963) Swiss
£1314 $2352   (6-May-92 GD.B807/R) Two women sunbathing (80x94cm-31x37in) s.d.38
                  (S.FR 3600)

MAIROVICH, Zvi (1911-1973) Israeli
£486 $900   (9-Jun-92 GG.TA394 a/R) Vase of flowers (33x24cm-13x9in) s.
£523 $900   (12-Oct-91 SY.NY224/R) Jerusalem (25x33cm-10x13in) s. s.i.verso
£581 $1000   (12-Oct-91 SY.NY222/R) Abstract composition (49x61cm-19x24in) s.
£1081 $2000   (8-Jun-92 GG.TA186/R) Sun in desert (50x61cm-20x24in) s.
£1351 $2500   (8-Jun-92 GG.TA184/R) Still life in front of window (60x49cm-24x19in)
                  s.d.48 board
£1489 $2800   (5-Jan-92 GG.TA263/R) The artist's wife holding flowers (61x41cm-24x16in)
                  s.d.1948
£1489 $2800   (5-Jan-92 GG.TA262/R) Still life with blue flowers (61x50cm-24x20in) s.
                  board
£1489 $2800   (5-Jan-92 GG.TA265/R) Tel Aviv nights (50x101cm-20x40in) s.
£1568 $2900   (8-Jun-92 GG.TA185/R) Artist's wife in green blouse (65x50cm-26x20in) s.
£2286 $4000   (26-Sep-91 SY.I47/R) Still life before window (49x60cm-19x24in) s.
£1011 $1900   (5-Jan-92 GG.TA264/R) Dusk (30x32cm-12x13in) s.
£1027 $1900   (8-Jun-92 GG.TA187/R) Lone house in garden (34x36cm-13x14in) s. crayon
£4865 $9000   (8-Jun-92 GG.TA183/R) Autobiographical page, summer 1971
                  (100x100cm-39x39in) s. panda crayon
£5851 $11000   (5-Jan-92 GG.TA261/R) Boulevard with winy colour blossom
                  (98x98cm-39x39in) s.

MAISTRE, Roy de (1894-1968) Australian
£2778 $4944   (28-Apr-92 CH.ME72/R) Amaryllis (53x26cm-21x10in) s. i.d.1964verso
                  (A.D 6500)
£2800 $4984   (28-Nov-91 C50/R) Deposition (47x41cm-19x16in) s. board
£3846 $6846   (28-Apr-92 CH.ME8) Landscape, Sutton Forest (44x37cm-17x15in) s.d.1927
                  s.i.verso board (A.D 9000)
£7660 $13557   (26-Apr-92 SY.ME411/R) Royal Jubilee (39x44cm-15x17in) s. s.d.1935 verso
                  (A.D 18000)
£8462 $16162   (19-Jul-92 SY.ME23/R) Beach at St Jean de Luz (52x64cm-20x25in) s.d.1924
                  (A.D 22000)
£507 $882   (16-Sep-91 CH.ME127) St Jean de Luz (19x26cm-7x10in) studio st. W/C
                  (A.D 1100)

MAITLAND, Paul (1869-1909) British
£800 $1416   (5-Nov-91 PH98) Chelsea reach (25x30cm-10x12in)
£2200 $4026   (14-May-92 C15/R) Storm cloud, Kensington Gradens (25x35cm-10x14in)

MAJEWICZ, G (20th C) ?
£1263 $2274   (22-Nov-91 SA.A1598/R) Red deer in landscape, autumn (100x150cm-39x59in)
                  s. panel (DM 3600)

MAJORCAN SCHOOL, 17th/18th C Spanish
£3830 $6971   (11-Dec-91 FER.M133/R) Bodegon con flores y anades. Bodegon con flores y
                  ave (66x87cm-26x34in) canvas laid down on board pair (S.P 700000)

MAJORCHI (?) Italian
£1498 $2786   (16-Jun-92 F.M241/R) Piazzo duomo a Milano (16x24cm-6x9in) s. W/C
                  (I.L 3300000)

MAJORELLE, Jacques (1886-1962) French
£3058 $5688   (19-Jun-92 ARC.P35/R) Les deux modeles (48x61cm-19x24in) s. peinture a
                  l'essence paper (F.FR 30000)
£3071 $5466   (27-Nov-91 CB.P54/R) Dans le Souks de Marrakech (32x27cm-13x11in) s.
                  panel (F.FR 30000)
£9774 $17690   (4-Dec-91 LD.P91/R) Scene de village en Afrique (54x65cm-21x26in) s.
                  canvas laid down (F.FR 95000)
£3193 $6002   (16-Dec-91 BG.P108/R) Marrakech (53x64cm-21x25in) s. pastel (F.FR 31000)
£5203 $9105   (3-Apr-92 CB.P32/R) Une rue des souk a Marrakech (55x46cm-22x18in) s.
                  softened htd.gouache (F.FR 50000)
£6385 $12004   (16-Dec-91 BG.P109/R) Izounen (76x87cm-30x34in) s. gouache (F.FR 62000)

MAJORELLE, Jacques (1886-1962) French-cont.
£8700	*$15486*	*(27-Nov-91 CB.P53/R) Femme noire aux dattes (71x45cm-28x18in) s. W/C htd.gold dusting (F.FR 85000)*
£12794	*$22774*	*(27-Nov-91 CB.P52/R) La penetration Pacifique (48x61cm-19x24in) s.i. W/C htd.gold dusting (F.FR 125000)*
£20325	*$35366*	*(13-Apr-92 AT.P165/R) Irounen (77x88cm-30x35in) s. distemper panel (F.FR 200000)*

MAK, Paul (20th C) British?
£568	*$966*	*(22-Oct-91 C.A795) The winner (27x18cm-11x7in) s.d.1956 gouache (B.FR 34000)*

MAKAROVA, Irina (1950-) Russian
£512	$911	(25-Nov-91 ZZ.F32/R) Les pecheurs au village (124x105cm-49x41in) s. (F.FR 5000)
£512	$911	(25-Nov-91 ZZ.F28/R) Le soir (105x124cm-41x49in) s. (F.FR 5000)
£532	$947	(25-Nov-91 ZZ.F30/R) Les pecheurs (124x105cm-49x41in) s. (F.FR 5200)
£563	$1002	(25-Nov-91 ZZ.F7/R) La cueillette (32x43cm-13x17in) s.verso board (F.FR 5500)
£614	$1093	(25-Nov-91 ZZ.F29/R) Troupeaux en Montagne (106x94cm-42x37in) s. (F.FR 6000)
£614	$1093	(25-Nov-91 ZZ.F26/R) Le recital (80x80cm-31x31in) s. (F.FR 6000)
£972	$1731	(25-Nov-91 ZZ.F31/R) Le repas de chasse (170x353cm-67x139in) s.verso triptych (F.FR 9500)
£1024	$1822	(25-Nov-91 ZZ.F33/R) L'atelier de Sadky (240x300cm-94x118in) s. (F.FR 10000)
£5203	$9105	(30-Mar-92 ZZ.F23/R) L'enlevement des Sabines (180x444cm-71x175in) s.verso triptych (F.FR 50000)

MAKART, Hans (1840-1884) Austrian
£5817	$10587	(27-May-92 D.V580/R) Design for ceiling (20x69cm-8x27in) board arched top (A.S 120000)
£7000	$13020	(19-Jun-92 C67/R) The butcher's trade (63x285cm-25x112in) init.
£9990	$17982	(21-Nov-91 D.V88/R) Still life of flowers (181x104cm-71x41in) (A.S 200000)
£12209	$21000	(17-Oct-91 SY.NY83/R) Venus and Cupids (149x98cm-59x39in)
£619	*$1089*	*(11-Apr-92 AW.H609/R) Figure studies (28x34cm-11x13in) mono.i.d.1863 pencil (DM 1800)*
£1068	*$1901*	*(29-Apr-92 D.V560/R) Study of figures (55x44cm-22x17in) pencil (A.S 22000)*

MAKART, Hans (circle) (1840-1884) Austrian
£2329	$4005	(8-Oct-91 ZEL.L1602/R) Female nude with long hair standing at balustrade in park, evening (41x24cm-16x9in) panel (DM 6800)

MAKART, Hans (style) (1840-1884) Austrian
£3000	$5310	(13-Feb-92 CSK146/R) The Harem (112x190cm-44x75in)

MAKELA, Jukka (1949-) Finnish
£851	$1541	(19-May-92 AB.S5280/R) Composition (42x86cm-17x34in) s.d.89verso (S.KR 9000)

MAKIELSKI, Leon A (1885-?) American
£1871	$3200	(12-Mar-92 CH.NY235/R) Summer in Vermont (33x40cm-13x16in) s. st.studio i.verso panel

MAKIN, Jeffrey (1943-) Australian
£681	$1205	(26-Apr-92 SY.ME91) South Morang cutting (76x60cm-30x24in) s.d.1987 i.d.1987 verso (A.D 1600)

MAKOVSKI, Alexander (?) Russian
£2562	$4688	(14-May-92 BU.S192/R) Woman on bench in park landscape (26x41cm-10x16in) s. panel (S.KR 27000)

MAKOVSKY, Konstantin (1839-1915) Russian
£1797	$3180	(5-Nov-91 GF.L2486/R) Boy with orange seated (80x58cm-31x23in) s.i. (S.FR 4600)
£3100	$5518	(1-May-92 PHE62 a) Summer bouquet (40x26cm-16x10in) s. panel
£3839	$6948	(3-Dec-91 AB.S4731/R) The dancer (55x45cm-22x18in) s. panel (S.KR 40000)
£4000	$7440	(16-Jun-92 S62/R) Russian beauty (80x55cm-31x22in) s.
£30000	$53400	(27-Nov-91 S116/R) Toilet of Venus (244x372cm-96x146in)
£57143	$100000	(20-Feb-92 SY.NY84/R) Blind Man's Bluff (183x198cm-72x78in) s.

MAKOVSKY, Vladimir (1846-1920) Russian
£800	$1424	(26-Nov-91 PH164) Young woman seated in woodland (26x20cm-10x8in) s.indis.d.
£2600	$4628	(28-Nov-91 S523/R) Portrait of girl in peasant Sunday best (69x52cm-27x20in) s.d.1896
£2600	*$4836*	*(16-Jun-92 S67/R) Country market (37x52cm-15x20in) s.d.1895 W/C over pencil*

MAKOWSKI, Alexander W (1869-1924) Russian
£2000	$3560	(28-Nov-91 S396/R) Churches on river bank (40x51cm-16x20in) s.d.1910
£15000	$26700	(28-Nov-91 S422/R) Grand duchess Elena Pavlovna (142x106cm-56x42in) s.d.1896 verso after Robertson

MAKOWSKI, Tade (1882-1932) Polish
£3077 $5478   (3-Nov-91 PSA.W10) Two children in front of white house (24x32cm-9x13in)
        s. (P.Z 60000000)
£3590 $6391   (3-Nov-91 PSA.W11) Village de Merey (19x33cm-7x13in) s. (P.Z 70000000)
£25884 $48662   (21-Dec-91 PSA.W10) Phantastic garden (50x73cm-20x29in) (P.Z 500000000)
£763   *$1389*   *(15-Dec-91 REM.W22) Players (29x30cm-11x12in) W/C ink (P.Z 15000000)*

MAKOWSKI, Tehodore (1890-1971) ?
£513 $918   (19-Jan-92 PPB.P23) Hanouka (46x55cm-18x22in) s. (F.FR 5000)

MAKS, Cornelis Johannes (1876-1965) Dutch
£909 $1645   (19-May-92 CH.AM54/R) Circus (40x50cm-16x20in) s. board (D.FL 3000)
£1030 $1865   (21-May-92 SY.AM78/R) View of Ronda (46x68cm-18x27in) s. board
        (D.FL 3400)
£1235 $2247   (11-Dec-91 CH.AM12) Acrobat on horse in circus (30x39cm-12x15in) s. board
        (D.FL 4000)
£1364 $2468   (19-May-92 CH.AM4) Een hogeschoolrijdster (30x39cm-12x15in) s. board
        (D.FL 4500)
£1420 $2584   (12-Dec-91 SY.AM116/R) Ballerina (50x40cm-20x16in) s. board (D.FL 4600)
£1818 $3291   (19-May-92 CH.AM37/R) Hoogeschool rijden (30x40cm-12x16in) s. board
        (D.FL 6000)
£3939 $7130   (19-May-92 CH.AM167/R) Andre en Denise (84x84cm-33x33in) s. (D.FL 13000)
£4938 $8988   (12-Dec-91 SY.AM45/R) View of Prinseneiland (63x91cm-25x36in) s.
        (D.FL 16000)
£6364 $11518   (21-May-92 SY.AM130/R) De spaansche dansers Mercedes en Antonio Triana
        (118x147cm-46x58in) s. s.i.stretcher (D.FL 21000)
£16667 $30167   (21-May-92 SY.AM137/R) Op de panneau (195x310cm-77x122in) (D.FL 55000)

MALAGODI, Giuseppe (1890-1968) Italian
£604 $1094   (3-Dec-91 F.R142) Paesaggio con ponte (44x55cm-17x22in) s. s.verso oil
        faesite (I.L 1300000)
£1208 $2187   (3-Dec-91 F.R173) Operai in galleria (54x64cm-21x25in) s. faesite
        (I.L 2600000)
£1580 $2860   (3-Dec-91 F.R226/R) Cantiere (84x126cm-33x50in) s. (I.L 3400000)

MALAINE, Joseph Laurent (1745-1809) French
£3148 $5698   (19-May-92 GF.L2427/R) Still life of flowers (54x42cm-21x17in) panel
        (S.FR 8500)

MALANCA, Jose (1897-1967) Argentinian
£521 $1000   (4-Aug-92 V.BA67) Paisaje (30x37cm-12x15in)
£1095 $1840   (1-Sep-91 PO.BA29) Sombras en la iglesia (58x58cm-23x23in) s. i.d.38verso
£1179 $1980   (1-Sep-91 PO.BA30) Iglesia (59x58cm-23x23in) s.
£1309 $2500   (30-Jun-92 PO.BA24) Paisaje con casas (38x42cm-15x17in)
£1563 $3000   (4-Aug-92 V.BA68) Paisaje de La Serranita (43x46cm-17x18in)
£1563 $3000   (4-Aug-92 V.BA66) Esquina nortena (39x47cm-15x19in)
£1786 $3000   (1-Sep-91 PO.BA31) Camino en la huerta (66x66cm-26x26in) s.
£2151 $4000   (16-Jun-92 RO.BA80) Paisaje Riojano (42x44cm-17x17in)
£2291 $4100   (6-May-92 V.BA67/R) Paisaje de Cordoba (51x60cm-20x24in)
£3846 $7000   (11-Dec-91 RO.BA233/R) Patio Colonial (59x77cm-23x30in) s.
£4121 $7500   (11-Dec-91 RO.BA12/R) Las Puertas Verdes (66x66cm-26x26in) s.d.50
£5495 $10000   (11-Dec-91 RO.BA10/R) Pampa de Olaen, Cordoba (75x96cm-30x38in) s.
£6720 $12500   (16-Jun-92 RO.BA44) Atardecer en el valle (76x100cm-30x39in)
£6989 $13000   (16-Jun-92 RO.BA46) Sierras de Cordoba (56x69cm-22x27in)
£8242 $15000   (11-Dec-91 RO.BA232/R) Duraznos en flor (70x92cm-28x36in) s.d.53
£8602 $16000   (16-Jun-92 RO.BA42) Iglesia de Purmamarca (66x66cm-26x26in)
£10440 $19000   (11-Dec-91 RO.BA9/R) Paisaje serrano (79x90cm-31x35in) s.d.42
£10753 $20000   (16-Jun-92 RO.BA45) Paisaje de Siena, Italia (75x104cm-30x41in)
£11559 $21500   (16-Jun-92 RO.BA79) Atardecer (100x80cm-39x31in)
£11628 $20000   (9-Oct-91 RO.BA45/R) Paisaje Serrano (96x99cm-38x39in) s.d.47
£11828 $22000   (16-Jun-92 RO.BA50) Calle de Purmamarca (73x93cm-29x37in)
£12366 $23000   (16-Jun-92 RO.BA38) Tarde primavera (90x130cm-35x51in)
£13978 $26000   (16-Jun-92 RO.BA37) Dia luminoso (90x120cm-35x47in)
£15707 $30000   (30-Jun-92 PO.BA23) Campo arado (77x125cm-30x49in) s.
£16129 $30000   (16-Jun-92 RO.BA78) Paisaje serrano (65x80cm-26x31in)
£17033 $31000   (11-Dec-91 RO.BA11) La Chacra (75x86cm-30x34in) s.d.29
£18280 $34000   (16-Jun-92 RO.BA36) Paisaje Serrano (103x161cm-41x63in)
£28090 $50000   (28-Apr-92 PO.BA35) Paisaje serrano (129x264cm-51x104in) s.d.39

MALARD, Felix (1840-?) French
£5000 $8650   (4-Oct-91 C25/R) Elegant figures promenading by the sea (60x76cm-24x30in)
        s.

MALAVAL, Robert (1937-1980) French
£662 $1225   (13-Jun-92 AT.P87) Pluie soleil (72x92cm-28x36in) s.i.d.72verso acrylic
        (F.FR 6500)
£1469   *$2659*   *(20-May-92 FB.P182/R) La danse du fossile (45x26cm-18x10in) s. d.1960*
        verso mixed media canvas (F.FR 14500)
£2033   *$3537*   *(14-Apr-92 CSC.P66/R) Projet carnaval (49x64cm-19x25in) s.d.14/11/64*
        Indian ink col.ink (F.FR 20000)
£3521   *$6056*   *(7-Oct-91 RY.P81/R) Gold Falls I (65x50cm-26x20in) s.verso mixed media*
        pressed board (F.FR 35000)
£5634   *$9690*   *(7-Oct-91 RY.P82/R) Cicatrice Rock (56x77cm-22x30in) mixed media board*
        (F.FR 56000)

MALAVAL, Robert (1937-1980) French-cont.
£6996   *$12663*   *(2-Dec-91 CC.P27/R) Le veritable aliment blanc, hiver 11961*
                               (71x70cm-28x28in) s. mixed media panel (F.FR 68000)

MALBON, William (19th C) British
£600 $1068   (30-Apr-92 CSK80/R) Feeding the rabbit (61x53cm-24x21in) s.
£620 $1054   (24-Oct-91 CSK164) Feeding the rabbits (41x51cm-16x20in) s. panel

MALBONE, Edward Green (attrib) (1777-1807) American
£2924 $5000   (21-Mar-92 S.BM34/R) Portrait of Henry Loring, age 21 (5x5cm-2x2in) min.
                               gold oval pendant case woven hair verso

MALBRANCHE, Louis-Claude (1790-1838) French
£1000 $1860   (18-Jun-92 CSK290) Townsfolk skating on frozen river (30x51cm-12x20in) s.
£2393 $4188   (5-Apr-92 ZZ.F53/R) Eglise du village sous la neige (24x32cm-9x13in) s.
                               (F.FR 23000)
£2601 $4553   (5-Apr-92 ZZ.F54/R) Village sous la neige (24x32cm-9x13in) s.d.1829
                               (F.FR 25000)

MALCHE, Brigitta (20th C) Swiss?
£591 $1016   (16-Oct-91 G.Z39/R) SAIS (110x109cm-43x43in) s.d.1970 acrylic (S.FR 1500)

MALCHIN, Carl Wilhelm (1838-1923) German
£1031 $1887   (3-Jun-92 DO.H2347/R) Fishing boats on the Baltic Sea (16x34cm-6x13in) s.
                               board on board on panel (DM 3000)

MALCZEWSKI, Jacek (1854-1929) Polish
£814 $1482   (15-Dec-91 REM.W24) Young woman in landscape (64x97cm-25x38in) s. board
                               (P.Z 16000000)
£1476 $2686   (15-Dec-91 REM.W23) Stone cutters (16x35cm-6x14in) s. board
                               (P.Z 29000000)
£1767 $3181   (24-Nov-91 AG.W11) In a garden (29x58cm-11x23in) s. board (P.Z 35000000)
£3036 $5251   (8-Sep-91 REM.W17) Study of a garden (32x40cm-13x16in) s. (P.Z 58000000)
£5230 $8996   (13-Oct-91 REM.W14) Head of an old faun (39x27cm-15x11in) s. board
                               (P.Z 100000000)
£10065 $18015   (17-Nov-91 REM.W18) Susanne (150x54cm-59x21in) (P.Z 195000000)
£16413 $29215   (3-Nov-91 PSA.W13) Symbolic composition (123x73cm-48x29in) s.
                               (P.Z 320000000)
£25645 $45648   (3-Nov-91 PSA.W12) Salome with head of John the Baptist
                               (171x90cm-67x35in) s. (P.Z 500000000)
£37159 $64285   (8-Sep-91 REM.W16) Death of Ellenai (200x115cm-79x45in) s.
                               (P.Z 710000000)
£530   *$954*   *(24-Nov-91 AG.W13) Portrait of a man (28x24cm-11x9in) s. W/C*
                               (P.Z 10500000)
£555   *$1000*   *(24-Nov-91 AG.W12) Dancer (27x22cm-11x9in) s. W/C (P.Z 11000000)*

MALDARELLI, Federico (1826-1893) Italian
£30103 $52078   (24-Mar-92 CH.R119/R) La prova dell'abito (108x149cm-43x59in) s.d.1863
                               (I.L 65000000)

MALDON, William (?) British?
£750 $1358   (6-Dec-91 K565/R) Young boy playing with rabbits (43x48cm-17x19in) s.

MALEAS, Constantine (20th C) Greek?
£2429 $4250   (28-Feb-92 SY.NY98/R) Assouan (44x45cm-17x18in) s.d.1924 paper

MALEFYT, Johannes de Waal (1812-1851) Dutch
£2080 $3618   (14-Apr-92 SY.AM73/R) Figures in wooded landscape (49x61cm-19x24in) s.
                               (D.FL 6800)

MALENOTTI, Emilio (1913-) Italian
£726 $1293   (29-Apr-92 F.F102/R) Strada con figure che passegiano (70x50cm-28x20in)
                               s. (I.L 1600000)

MALET, A (1905-1986) French
£2039 $3792   (21-Jun-92 LT.P58 b) Paysage enneige (54x73cm-21x29in) (F.FR 20000)

MALET, Albert (1905-1986) French
£665 $1130   (27-Oct-91 LT.P150) Bord de Seine sous la neige (19x24cm-7x9in) s. panel
                               (F.FR 6600)
£1160 $1996   (20-Oct-91 LT.P88) Les oliviers sur la Colline (27x41cm-11x16in) s.
                               (F.FR 11500)
£1309 $2226   (27-Oct-91 LT.P57/R) Promenade sur l'Allee Ombragee (33x41cm-13x16in) s.
                               panel (F.FR 13000)
£1362 $2343   (20-Oct-91 LT.P66) Coucher de soleil sur la Seine (33x41cm-13x16in) s.
                               panel (F.FR 13500)
£1514 $2603   (20-Oct-91 LT.P44) Barques amarrees sur la Seine au couchant
                               (38x46cm-15x18in) s. panel (F.FR 15000)
£2016 $3569   (10-Nov-91 ZZ.F139/R) Bord de Seine au soleil couchant (46x65cm-18x26in)
                               s. (F.FR 20000)
£2236 $3890   (19-Apr-92 ZZ.F92/R) Les voiles blanches (46x65cm-18x26in) s.
                               (F.FR 22000)

MALEVICH, Kasimir (1878-1935) Russian
£2400   *$4584*   (30-Jun-92 C129/R) Suprematist composition (22x15cm-9x6in) pencil graph paper
£12000   *$22920*   (1-Jul-92 S155/R) Dancing maidens (23x24cm-9x9in) W/C gouache pencil card
£20000   *$38200*   (1-Jul-92 S154/R) The widow (14x14cm-6x6in) s.d.1908 W/C gouache over pencil card
£26000   *$49660*   (1-Jul-92 S170/R) Suprematist composition - aeroplane flying (18x21cm-7x8in) pencil brush Indian ink

MALFAIT, Hubert (1898-1971) Belgian
£1170 $1988   (22-Oct-91 C.A243) Woman and goat (20x26cm-8x10in) s. paper on wood (B.FR 70000)
£1334 $2349   (7-Apr-92 C.A172) Still life (103x76cm-41x30in) s. (B.FR 80000)
£596   *$1079*   (23-May-92 KV.L211) Stuiker (35x27cm-14x11in) s. chk. (B.FR 36000)

MALFANTI, Cesar (1895-?) Argentinian
£559 $1000   (6-May-92 V.BA68) Paisaje (48x62cm-19x24in)

MALFRAY, Charles Alexandre (1887-1940) French
£407   *$745*   (15-May-92 AT.P169) Femme nue allongee (29x41cm-11x16in) s. crayon (F.FR 4000)

MALFROY, Charles (1862-1918) French
£889 $1609   (19-May-92 GF.L2484/R) Stony coastal landscape (45x80cm-18x31in) s. (S.FR 2400)
£1810 $3348   (9-Jun-92 FB.M57/R) Bateaux (59x88cm-23x35in) s. (C.D 4000)
£2058 $3909   (22-Jun-92 AT.P71/R) Cassis (38x55cm-15x22in) s. (F.FR 20000)

MALFROY, Henry (1895-1944) French
£600   *$1062*   (13-Feb-92 CSK258) Italian harbour at sunset (23x32cm-9x13in) s.
£1016 $1768   (16-Apr-92 FB.P134/R) Village en Provence (46x55cm-18x22in) s. (F.FR 10000)
£1293 $2250   (13-Sep-91 S.W2047/R) Flower sellers along Avenue, Paris (28x33cm-11x13in) s.panel
£1332 $2398   (2-Feb-92 ZZ.F10/R) Petit port de peche en Mediterranee (27x46cm-11x18in) s. (F.FR 13000)
£1563 $2766   (5-Nov-91 GF.L2711/R) Fishing harbour near Martigues (38x55cm-15x22in) s. (S.FR 4000)
£1704 $3084   (19-May-92 GF.L2561/R) Busy quay in Martigues (46x65cm-18x26in) s.d.1919 (S.FR 4600)
£2575 $4403   (18-Mar-92 PIC.P70/R) Paris, le quai aux fleurs (27x41cm-11x16in) s. (F.FR 25000)
£2736 $4871   (25-Nov-91 W.T1991/R) Cassis, Provence, with schooner and other boats at anchor (60x90cm-24x35in) s.i.verso (C.D 5500)

MALHARRO, Martin (1865-1911) Argentinian
£889 $1600   (20-Nov-91 V.BA59) Paisaje de Francia (15x22cm-6x9in)
£1613 $3000   (16-Jun-92 RO.BA93) Quietud (15x23cm-6x9in)
£4301 $8000   (16-Jun-92 RO.BA29) Paisaje de Paris (16x24cm-6x9in) panel
£938   *$1800*   (4-Aug-92 V.BA69) Paisaje (17x26cm-7x10in) W/C
£944   *$1700*   (20-Nov-91 V.BA60) Paisaje (15x24cm-6x9in) W/C

MALHERBE, William (1884-1951) French
£3390 $6000   (5-Nov-91 CE.NY2/R) Nature morte aux fruits et fleurs (103x84cm-41x33in) s.

MALI, Christian (1832-1906) German
£1546 $2830   (2-Jun-92 FN.S2660/R) Staffelsee landscape (21x39cm-8x15in) d.1873 i.verso canvas on board (DM 4500)
£2749 $4784   (18-Sep-91 N.M614/R) Lake Constance near Kressbronn (30x55cm-12x22in) s.d.1878 (DM 8000)
£4467 $8175   (2-Jun-92 FN.S2659/R) Chiemsee landscape with view of Fraueninsel, evening (37x71cm-15x28in) s.i.d.1864 (DM 13000)
£8780 $15278   (19-Sep-91 D.V16/R) Shepherd boy with sheep (52x40cm-20x16in) s.d.1902 (A.S 180000)
£9859 $17845   (3-Dec-91 FN.S2324/R) Domestic animals resting in mountain lake landscape (37x48cm-15x19in) s.i.d.1900 (DM 28000)
£12324 $22306   (3-Dec-91 FN.S2323/R) Mountain lake landscape with cattle watering and shepherd girl with dog (59x79cm-23x31in) s.i. (DM 35000)
£18531 $31689   (18-Mar-92 N.M592/R) Shepherd with animals at lake shore, possibly Achensee (54x87cm-21x34in) s.i.d.1898 (DM 53000)
£25773 $44845   (18-Sep-91 N.M613/R) Tyrolean cattle market on rainy village street (82x137cm-32x54in) s.i.d.1873 (DM 75000)

MALI, Christian (attrib) (1832-1906) German
£6184 $11750   (22-Jun-92 SG.M631) Sheep in landscape (43x36cm-17x14in) s.

MALIAVINE, Philippe (1869-1939) Russian
£1625 $2924   (19-Nov-91 RAS.K88/R) Wooded landscape with fox (48x78cm-19x31in) s.d.1938 (D.KR 18000)
£3400 $6052   (28-Nov-91 S502/R) Peasant woman with distaff (40x45cm-16x18in) s.

MALINA, Milos (1904-) Czechoslovakian
£695 $1237   (29-Nov-91 D.V98/R) Still life with grapefruit (28x24cm-11x9in) s.d.48 (A.S 14000)

MALINCONICO, Nicola (attrib) (1654-1721) Italian
£24862 $45000   (21-May-92 CH.NY68/R) Flowers in sculpted urns, terracotta bust and parakeet amongst pediments figures on balcony beyond (93x135cm-37x53in)

MALINOWSKI, Wiktor Adam (19th C) Polish
£1569 $2699   (13-Oct-91 REM.W15) Winter landscape (45x73cm-18x29in) s. (P.Z 30000000)

MALINOWSKY, Lise (20th C) Danish?
£542 $926   (10-Mar-92 RAS.K244) Mumie No.5 (85x65cm-33x26in) init. oil acrylic canvas on chipboard (D.KR 6000)

MALINVERNO, Atilio (1890-1936) Argentinian
£962 $1750   (11-Dec-91 RO.BA450) Casona en la Serrania (34x42cm-13x17in) s.d.1926
£1067 $1900   (1-Nov-91 PO.BA47) Paisaje con casas (34x52cm-13x20in) s. board
£1613 $3000   (16-Jun-92 RO.BA88) El rancho

MALKINE, Georges (1898-1970) French
£4094 $7000   (21-Mar-92 W.W50/R) Le baiser (74x61cm-29x24in) s.d.27 s.d.1927 verso

MALKOWSKY, Heiner (1920-1988) German
£3881 $7063   (25-May-92 WK.M807/R) Abstract composition (63x93cm-25x37in) panel (DM 11370)
£4386 $7895   (22-Nov-91 SA.A471/R) Group of figures (145x145cm-57x57in) (DM 12500)
£478 $870   (25-May-92 WK.M809) Musician (30x18cm-12x7in) s.i.d.1948 chl (DM 1400)
£683 $1242   (25-May-92 WK.M808/R) Head of girl. Study (44x47cm-17x19in) s.d.1945 chl double-sided paper on board (DM 2000)
£5119 $9317   (30-May-92 VG.B357/R) Abstract composition (127x100cm-50x39in) s. st.studio verso tempera chk pencil canvas (DM 15000)

MALLET, Jean Baptiste (1759-1835) French
£14286 $26000   (28-May-92 SY.NY1/R) Une nymphe au bain, environnee d'amours (38x46cm-15x18in)
£10082 $18249   (5-Dec-91 SY.MO90/R) Scene d'interieur avec d'elegants personnes (37x53cm-15x21in) W/C htd.gouache (F.FR 98000)
£12346 $23457   (22-Jun-92 PIC.P13/R) Les blanchisseuses (31x39cm-12x15in) gouache (F.FR 120000)

MALLET, Jean Baptiste (attrib) (1759-1835) French
£1029 $1862   (5-Dec-91 SY.MO65) Scene d'interieur paysan (28x38cm-11x15in) blk.chk. wash htd.white gouache (F.FR 10000)

MALLEYN, Gerrit (1753-1816) Dutch
£40000 $70000   (1-Apr-92 S33/R) Hunting party approaching inn (170x131cm-67x52in)
£50000 $87500   (1-Apr-92 S32/R) Hunting party departing (171x121cm-67x48in)
£58000 $101500   (1-Apr-92 S31/R) Hunting party resting and taking refreshment (169x130cm-67x51in) s.d.1789

MALLO, Cristino (20th C) Spanish?
£830 $1419   (17-Mar-92 FER.M93/R) Mujer sentada (48x33cm-19x13in) s. W/C ink (S.P 150000)

MALMSTROM, Akke Hugh (1894-1968) Swedish
£477 $839   (11-Apr-92 FAL.M268/R) Cloudy landscape (92x100cm-36x39in) s.d.44 panel (S.KR 5000)

MALMSTROM, August (1829-1901) Swedish
£18448 $33392   (19-May-92 AB.S4248/R) Tell-tale, landscape with school children (69x100cm-27x39in) (S.KR 195000)

MALMSTROM, Henning (1890-1968) Swedish
£570 $1021   (16-Nov-91 FAL.M211/R) Still life of flowers (61x53cm-24x21in) s.d.18 (S.KR 6000)
£665 $1191   (16-Nov-91 FAL.M210 a/R) Still life of flowers in vase (60x73cm-24x29in) s.d.19 (S.KR 7000)

MALNOVITZER, Zvi (?) Israeli
£2848 $5213   (17-May-92 GL.P191/R) Simhat Thora (39x49cm-15x19in) s. panel (F.FR 28000)

MALSKAT, Lothar (1913-1988) German
£1045 $1902   (14-Dec-91 BOD.P729) River landscape (40x54cm-16x21in) mono (DM 3000)

MALTBY, Peg (?) Australian
£470 $837   (27-Apr-92 J.M450) Umbrella man (25x16cm-10x6in) W/C (A.D 1100)
£470 $837   (27-Apr-92 J.M449) On the toadstool (26x18cm-10x7in) s. W/C (A.D 1100)
£684 $1217   (27-Apr-92 J.M35) Fairy courtship (24x16cm-9x6in) s. W/C (A.D 1600)
£1282 $2282   (27-Apr-92 J.M266/R) The fairy dance (26x37cm-10x15in) s. W/C (A.D 3000)

MALTESE SCHOOL, 18th C
£18000 $32760   (12-Dec-91 B10 m) View of the Grand Harbour, Valetta (103x199cm-41x78in) pair

MALTON, Thomas (jnr) (1748-1804) British
£3500 $6160   (7-Apr-92 C112/R) Oriel College, Oxford, with St. Mary's Church in distance (32x46cm-13x18in) pen W/C

MALUDA (20th C) ?
£1424 $2606 (14-May-92 BG.P3) Maisons (34x42cm-13x17in) s.d.80 (F.FR 14000)

MAMBOUR, Auguste (1896-1968) Belgian
£1545 $2797 (19-May-92 CH.AM93) Young girl in profile (50x50cm-20x20in) s. panel
(D.FL 5100)

MAMMEN, Jeanne (1890-1976) German?
£402 $716 (30-Nov-91 VG.B859/R) Female nude standing with left arm raised
(47x23cm-19x9in) mono. pencil (DM 1150)
£420 $747 (30-Nov-91 VG.B858/R) Portrait of old prostitute (60x25cm-24x10in) mono.
pencil (DM 1200)
£741 $1348 (11-Dec-91 CH.AM293) Frauenkopf (47x32cm-19x13in) init. pencil
col.crayons (D.FL 2400)
£1718 $3179 (12-Jun-92 HN.H555/R) Young woman (43x31cm-17x12in) mono pencil (DM 5000)

MAMPASO, Manuel (1924-) Spanish
£1640 $2788 (24-Oct-91 DUR.M1042/R) Composicion (170x80cm-67x31in) s. (S.P 300000)
£1640 $2788 (24-Oct-91 DUR.M1041/R) Composicion (140x126cm-55x50in) s.d.57
(S.P 300000)

MAN-RAY (1890-1976) American
£11050 $20000 (6-Dec-91 CH.NY223/R) Landscape and houses (25x35cm-10x14in) s.d.1913
£27947 $48628 (14-Apr-92 ZZ.F55/R) Paysage urbain au viaduc et aux trains
(65x81cm-26x32in) (F.FR 275000)
£56497 $100000 (7-Nov-91 SY.NY211/R) La maree (38x47cm-15x19in) s.d.49 panel
£837 $1515 (19-May-92 JRL.S111/R) Landscape with cow (49x69cm-19x27in) s.verso mixed
media (A.D 2000)
£1955 $3500 (13-Nov-91 B.SF2418/R) Untitled (27x38cm-11x15in) s.d.1936 ink
£3012 $5361 (27-Nov-91 F.M255/R) L'attente (38x27cm-15x11in) s.d.1936 indian ink
(I.L 6500000)
£3200 $6112 (29-Jun-92 CSK124/R) Untitled (56x38cm-22x15in) s.d.54 gouache brush ink
W/C
£4119 $7044 (17-Mar-92 FB.P33/R) Man in the window (35x25cm-14x10in) s.d.1940 W/C ink
(F.FR 40000)
£7000 $12110 (25-Mar-92 S58/R) Le pied dans le pied (24x32cm-9x13in) s.i. W/C collage
leather shoe soles
£7104 $13000 (14-May-92 SY.NY136/R) Optical longings and illusions (35x24cm-14x9in)
s.i.d.1943 gouache ink wash collage paperboard
£8571 $15000 (25-Feb-92 SY.NY66/R) King Lear, Shakespeare Equation (30x41cm-12x16in)
init.d.48 W/C
£11500 $21965 (1-Jul-92 S194/R) Ombre de cuir (34x23cm-13x9in) s.d.1953 leather wood
corrugated cardboard.hessian

MANAGO, Vincent (1880-1936) French
£719 $1294 (18-Nov-91 AT.P364) Le marche au legumes (50x65cm-20x26in) s. (F.FR 7000)
£813 $1415 (13-Apr-92 AT.P198) Les palanquins au bord de l'oued (45x61cm-18x24in) s.
panel (F.FR 8000)

MANARESI, Ugo (1851-1917) Italian
£6807 $12662 (16-Jun-92 F.M228/R) Marina livornese con barca in secca e pescatori
(23x40cm-9x16in) s. (I.L 15000000)
£9041 $16363 (18-May-92 SY.MI120/R) Porto (41x61cm-16x24in) s. (I.L 20000000)

MANASS, J (19th C) ?
£2567 $4620 (18-Nov-91 AT.P275/R) Portrait du Sultan Murad V (26x19cm-10x7in)
min.s.d.1893verso gilt copper frame oval (F.FR 25000)

MANCADAN, Jacobus Sibrandi (1602-1680) Dutch
£1404 $2400 (13-Mar-92 FN.S2857/R) Shepherds with animals in autumnal mountain
landscape (50x80cm-20x31in) panel (DM 4000)
£23000 $40250 (1-Apr-92 S22/R) Landscape with goatherd resting with flock by well
(33x62cm-13x24in) mono. panel

MANCADAN, Jacobus Sibrandi (attrib) (1602-1680) Dutch
£4942 $8500 (10-Oct-91 SY.NY30/R) Horseman encountering a herdsman in an extensive
rocky landscape (53x82cm-21x32in) panel

MANCINI, Antonio (1852-1930) Italian
£1739 $3096 (29-Nov-91 GAB.G2798/R) Portrait d'un vieux Milanais (60x45cm-24x18in)
(S.FR 4400)
£1800 $3078 (17-Mar-92 PH234/R) Portrait of young woman with flowers in hair
(47x36cm-19x14in) s.
£7818 $13994 (14-Nov-91 CH.R130/R) Ritratto del padre (34x24cm-13x9in) s. panel
(I.L 17000000)
£32419 $56084 (24-Mar-92 CH.R11/R) Sotto i limoni (130x186cm-51x73in) s. (I.L 70000000)
£930 $1683 (3-Dec-91 SY.MI38/R) Studio di testa di donna (24x31cm-9x12in) s. chl
htd.white (I.L 2000000)
£930 $1683 (3-Dec-91 SY.MI41) Studio di donna (31x42cm-12x17in) s. chl chk
(I.L 2000000)
£1040 $1882 (18-May-92 SY.MI51) Studio di nudo maschile (39x23cm-15x9in) s. chl
sanguine htd white (I.L 2300000)
£1474 $2800 (26-Jun-92 WOL.C417) Bust of young peasant girl (28x20cm-11x8in) s. W/C
£3254 $5564 (19-Mar-92 F.M19/R) Ritratto in costume (59x30cm-23x12in) i. pastel paper
on cardboard (I.L 7000000)

1166

MANCINI, Antonio (1852-1930) Italian-cont.
£3904 $6676   (19-Mar-92 F.M49/R) Ritratto allo specchio (49x35cm-19x14in) s. pastel
                    (I.L 8400000)

MANCINI, Antonio (attrib) (1852-1930) Italian
£3171 $5866   (8-Jun-92 CH.R647) Busto di giovane donna seminuda (45x25cm-18x10in)
                    (I.L 7000000)

MANCINI, Francesco (18/19th C) Italian
£784 $1333   (23-Oct-91 GD.B1160/R) Seated nude (61x53cm-24x21in) s. (S.FR 2000)
£6200 $11222   (22-May-92 C244/R) Returning home (49x35cm-19x14in) s.d.1873

MANCINI, Francesco Longo (1880-?) Italian
£556 $1000   (24-Nov-91 LIT.L142) The dice game (69x51cm-27x20in) s. board
£2038 $3771   (8-Jun-92 CH.R659) Maternita (46x50cm-18x20in) s. canvas laid down on
                    board (I.L 4500000)
£3242 $5608   (24-Mar-92 CH.R111/R) Ritratto di donna sorridente (100x86cm-39x34in) s.
                    (I.L 7000000)

MANDELBAUM, Efraim (1885-1940) ?
£497 $855   (13-Oct-91 REM.W16) Harvesting (44x61cm-17x24in) s. board (P.Z 9500000)

MANDELLI, Pompilio (1912-) Italian
£1827 $3179   (14-Apr-92 F.M103) Immagine (70x50cm-28x20in) s.d.1962 acrylic cardboard
                    (I.L 4000000)
£2041 $3736   (12-May-92 F.R159) Figure fondo arancio (120x95cm-47x37in) s. s.i.d.1976
                    (I.L 4500000)

MANDER, Karel van (16/17th C) Dutch
£632 $1137   (19-Nov-91 RAS.K372/R) Old man (80x62cm-31x24in) (D.KR 7000)
£7000 $13440   (6-Jul-92 S159/R) Manasseh (18x14cm-7x6in) mono.d.1596 pen wash over chk.

MANDER, W H (fl.1880-1922) British
£2400 $4272   (1-Nov-91 MAI591) Mountain river landscape with children s.

MANDER, William Henry (fl.1880-1922) British
£500 $855   (20-Mar-92 CBB81) Country lane with figure and dog (20x41cm-8x16in) s.
                    board
£800 $1464   (3-Jun-92 S61/R) In the Lledr Valley, N.Wales (30x46cm-12x18in) s.
£1381 $2500   (21-May-92 S.W2910/R) In the Aberguynant Valley (46x36cm-18x14in) s.
                    s.i.d.1908verso
£1900 $3287   (4-Sep-91 BT321/R) Moel Siabod from the Llugwy (48x74cm-19x29in)
                    s.d.indist. s.i.verso
£4000 $7400   (12-Jun-92 C164/R) On the Severn, near Arley (60x96cm-24x38in) s.

MANDYN, Jan (style) (1500-1560) Dutch
£19000 $34580   (11-Dec-91 S191/R) Temptation of Saint Anthony (54x69cm-21x27in) panel

MANE KATZ (1894-1962) French
£2429 $4250   (28-Feb-92 SY.NY197/R) Mare with foal (30x25cm-12x10in) s.
£3000 $5730   (29-Jun-92 CSK55/R) Maison dans la neige (51x76cm-20x30in) s.
£3561 $6516   (17-May-92 GL.P206/R) Portrait d'adolescent (33x24cm-13x9in) s.
                    (F.FR 35000)
£3714 $6500   (28-Feb-92 SY.NY177/R) Young woman (46x30cm-18x12in) s.
£3768 $6970   (11-Jun-92 ARC.P10/R) Les deux hommes et l'enfant (46x38cm-18x15in) s.
                    (F.FR 37000)
£4625 $8834   (3-Jul-92 GL.P102) Nu (54x60cm-21x24in) s. (F.FR 45000)
£5714 $10000   (26-Sep-91 SY.I57/R) Beach scene (54x34cm-21x13in) s.
£7413 $12750   (12-Oct-91 SY.NY24/R) Nue assise (76x99cm-30x39in) s.d.42
£9000 $17190   (29-Jun-92 CSK54/R) Les cavaliers (50x65cm-20x26in) s.
£9143 $16000   (25-Feb-92 CH.NY45/R) Vase de fleurs (79x63cm-31x25in) s.d.39
£10857 $19000   (26-Sep-91 SY.I8/R) Girl beside fence (120x65cm-47x26in) s.d.26
£10857 $19000   (26-Sep-91 SY.I51/R) Landscape in the South of France (54x65cm-21x26in)
                    s.
£12000 $21720   (3-Dec-91 C266/R) Bouquet de Pavots (73x54cm-29x21in) s. canvas laid down
                    on board
£12000 $21000   (26-Sep-91 SY.I15/R) La ventana (74x92cm-29x36in) s.
£12963 $23463   (20-May-92 GK.Z5044/R) Rabbi with Thora (51x41cm-20x16in) s. (S.FR 35000)
£14286 $25000   (26-Sep-91 SY.I16/R) The prayer (72x59cm-28x23in) s.
£16431 $29084   (10-Nov-91 ZZ.F224/R) Bouquet de fleurs (100x81cm-39x32in) s.
                    (F.FR 163000)
£1977 $3500   (5-Nov-91 CE.NY114/R) Desert conversation (66x51cm-26x20in) s.d.35
                    gouache paper on board
£2971 $5200   (26-Sep-91 SY.I78/R) Beach scene (50x65cm-20x26in) s.d.61 gouache
£3667 $6600   (6-Jan-92 GG.TA420/R) Vase and flowers (49x34cm-19x13in) s. pastel
£3714 $6500   (26-Sep-91 SY.I89/R) Beach in the South of France (50x65cm-20x26in)
                    s.d.1924 gouache

MANESSIER, Alfred (1911-) French
£3189 $6060   (26-Jun-92 FB.P1/R) La nuit obscure (76x56cm-30x22in) s.d.59 paper
                    (F.FR 31000)
£4100 $7093   (26-Mar-92 S10/R) La vieille demeure - benauge (24x41cm-9x16in) s.
£5842 $10808   (11-Jun-92 HN.H326/R) Rythmes en gris (20x20cm-8x8in) s.d.1966
                    s.i.d.verso (DM 17000)

MANESSIER, Alfred (1911-) French-cont.

| £2236 | $3890 | (16-Apr-92 FB.P148/R) Le jardin sur fond bleu (43x34cm-17x13in) s.d.58 gouache (F.FR 22000) |
| £3285 | $5914 | (19-Nov-91 FB.P178/R) Port au soleil couchant (31x49cm-12x19in) s.d.76 W/C (F.FR 32000) |

MANET, Edouard (1832-1883) French

£983607	$1800000	(12-May-92 CH.NY110/R) Les travailleurs de la mer (63x79cm-25x31in) s.
£731	$1388	(25-Jun-92 GK.B463) Study after Italian madonna (30x22cm-12x9in) chk (S.FR 1900)
£22000	$39820	(4-Dec-91 S105/R) Soldat examinant son fusil (26x10cm-10x4in) pen sepia ink tracing paper on card
£191257	$350000	(12-May-92 CH.NY107/R) Jeune fille au chapeau marron (55x35cm-22x14in) s. pastel canvas

MANETTI, Rutilio (attrib) (1571-1639) Italian

| £1608 | $2911 | (19-May-92 AB.S4351/R) Garden of Eden with Eve giving Adam the apple (45x41cm-18x16in) (S.KR 17000) |

MANFREDI, Alberto (1930-) Italian

| £822 | $1431 | (14-Apr-92 F.M16) Nudo di donna (40x32cm-16x13in) s.d.1971 panel (I.L 1800000) |
| £407 | $736 | (21-May-92 F.M287) Volto femminile (31x21cm-12x8in) s.d.1992 W/C (I.L 900000) |

MANFREDI, Bartolomeo (style) (1580-1620) Italian

£2000	$3580	(11-Nov-91 S479) Lute player (96x94cm-38x37in)
£2000	$3840	(10-Jul-92 C252/R) Youth tuning stringed instrument (47x36cm-19x14in)
£2200	$3828	(13-Sep-91 C37) Youthful monk, head and shoulders (48x39cm-19x15in)
£4000	$7680	(10-Jul-92 C251/R) Youth pointing with right hand (47x36cm-19x14in)

MANFREDI, Giuseppe (1934-1987) Italian

| £590 | $1051 | (29-Apr-92 F.F98/R) Natura morta (50x70cm-20x28in) s. panel (I.L 1300000) |
| £681 | $1212 | (29-Apr-92 F.F53) Vaso con rose (70x50cm-28x20in) s. canvas on panel (I.L 1500000) |

MANGLARD, Adrien (1695-1760) French

£9945	$18000	(22-May-92 SY.NY84/R) Capriccio of southern port with ships and figures off-loading boat (95x128cm-37x50in) bears sig.d.
£69832	$125000	(17-Jan-92 SY.NY136/R) View of the Bay of Naples with Mt. Vesuvius in the distance (105x210cm-41x83in)
£712	$1303	(15-May-92 AT.P170) Vue d'un bateau en cale seche (17x24cm-7x9in) s. st. pen wash (F.FR 7000)

MANGLARD, Adrien (circle) (1695-1760) French

| £3997 | $7434 | (16-Jun-92 SY.B215/R) Shiiping in capriccio Italianate harbour (68x88cm-27x35in) (B.FR 240000) |

MANGLARD, Adrien (school) (1695-1760) French

| £2837 | $5135 | (23-May-92 G.SB462/R) Scene de tempete pres de la cote (72x105cm-28x41in) (F.FR 28000) |

MANGOLD, Josef (1884-1942) German

| £5263 | $9474 | (21-Nov-91 L.K295/R) Still life with playing card (41x32cm-16x13in) s. panel (DM 15000) |
| £7368 | $13263 | (21-Nov-91 L.K294/R) Poppies in grey jug (53x43cm-21x17in) s. i.d.1931verso (DM 21000) |

MANGOLD, Robert (1937-) American

£10615	$19000	(13-Nov-91 CH.NY237/R) A square within a square (34x33cm-13x13in) s.i.d.1974verso acrylic panel
£3018	$5191	(8-Oct-91 CC.P45/R) 3 squares within a triangle (57x79cm-22x31in) s.i.d.1975-1976 lead pencil green crayon (F.FR 30000)
£3143	$5500	(25-Feb-92 SY.NY212 a/R) Study for irregular no 5, ochre (76x56cm-30x22in) s.i.d.1986 acrylic chl
£3352	$6000	(12-Nov-91 CE.NY91/R) Distorted square-circle (30x28cm-12x11in) s.i.d.1972 graphite set of three
£4469	$8000	(12-Nov-91 CE.NY90/R) Untitled (28x35cm-11x14in) s.i.d.1972 and 1973 graphite set of four
£4571	$8000	(25-Feb-92 SY.NY203/R) Rectangle not totally within triangle (55x71cm-22x28in) s.i.d.1976 col.pencil
£12571	$22000	(27-Feb-92 CH.NY64/R) Red ellipse, ivory frame (76x113cm-30x44in) s.i.d.1989 acrylic graphite two sheets

MANGOLD, Sylvia (1938-) American

| £1229 | $2200 | (12-Nov-91 CE.NY100/R) Half window (75x86cm-30x34in) s.i.d.1972verso s.i.d.1972stretcher acrylic |

MANGUIN, Henri (1874-1949) French

£4798	$8685	(3-Dec-91 AB.S4732/R) Citron et nefles (27x35cm-11x14in) s. panel (S.KR 50000)
£5945	$10345	(15-Apr-92 CB.P33/R) La terrasse (33x27cm-13x11in) s. board (F.FR 58500)
£6890	$12470	(19-May-92 FB.P52/R) Paysage, le Jardin a Raincy, ete (55x46cm-22x18in) st.sig. (F.FR 68000)
£14000	$24220	(24-Mar-92 C96/R) Fleurs dans un vase (73x60cm-29x24in) st.sig.

MANGUIN, Henri (1874-1949) French-cont.

£15000	$25950	(24-Mar-92 C98/R) Le golfe de St Tropez (32x45cm-13x18in) s. canvas on board
£26000	$44980	(25-Mar-92 S27/R) La Mairesse - Colombier (63x80cm-25x31in) s.
£36008	$68416	(24-Jun-92 FB.P47/R) Grenades et Arbouses (73x92cm-29x36in) s. (F.FR 350000)
£46857	$82000	(25-Feb-92 CH.NY52/R) Femme dans un interieur - Jeanne (74x61cm-29x24in) s.
£50917	$93177	(3-Jun-92 PIC.P56/R) Nu debout au tapis bleu, Anita Champagne (100x73cm-39x29in) s. (F.FR 500000)
£71869	$129363	(22-Nov-91 PIC.P26/R) Femme s'essuyant, Anita Champagne (100x81cm-39x32in) s. (F.FR 700000)
£86000	$155660	(3-Dec-91 C234/R) Nu allonge, accoude (50x61cm-20x24in) s.
£462	*$795*	*(4-Mar-92 AT.P71) Modele de dos (21x27cm-8x11in) s. crayon (F.FR 4500)*
£782	*$1400*	*(6-May-92 D.NY88/R) Still life of roses and irises (74x46cm-29x18in) s. pastel*
£3913	*$6692*	*(18-Mar-92 PIC.P71/R) Vue de la chapelle Saint-Anne (36x48cm-14x19in) s.d.1924 W/C (F.FR 38000)*

MANGUIN, Pierre (1935-) French

£813	$1415	(13-Apr-92 GL.P225) Levitation (195x130cm-77x51in) s.d.1988 i.verso (F.FR 8000)

MANIATIS, Tonis (1937-) Greek

£859	$1495	(17-Sep-91 FN.S2040) Spring in Vaison la Romaine, Provence (88x97cm-35x38in) s.d.1983verso (DM 2500)

MANIATTY, S G (?) American

£800	$1400	(28-Feb-92 DOU.M2) Deep pool (74x48cm-29x19in)

MANKES, Jan (1889-1920) Dutch

£9091	$16455	(21-May-92 SY.AM121/R) Citroentjes (9x15cm-4x6in) canvas on panel (D.FL 30000)

MANLY, Charles MacDonald (1855-1924) Canadian

£550	$974	(6-Nov-91 SY.T4) Watering place (27x56cm-11x22in) s.d.96 W/C (C.D 1100)

MANN, Alexander (1853-1908) British

£1200	$2172	(4-Dec-91 S320/R) Lerici (25x35cm-10x14in) s.i.verso canvasboard
£1211	$2143	(5-Nov-91 GF.L2470/R) Portrait of young woman (32x26cm-13x10in) s. (S.FR 3100)

MANN, Gother Victor Fyers (1863-1948) Australian

£711	*$1216*	*(17-Mar-92 JRL.S26) Yachting Sydney Harbour (35x46cm-14x18in) s.d.1890 W/C (A.D 1600)*

MANN, Harrington (1864-1937) British

£1064	$2000	(18-Dec-91 SY.NY191/R) Portrait of Lord Duveen (101x76cm-40x30in) s.d.1921
£1400	$2506	(14-Jan-92 SWS260/R) Claire (74x62cm-29x24in) s.d.1907 s.i.verso
£3200	$5728	(13-Nov-91 CG597/R) Portrait of Cora Brown Potter, in a cream dress (72x56cm-28x22in) s.

MANN, Joshua Hargrave Sams (?-1886) British

£500	$860	(3-Mar-92 AG257) Gypsies camped by roadside (19x16cm-7x6in) i.verso board oval
£1000	$1850	(12-Jun-92 C182/R) Honeysuckle, peonies, lilies and other flowers in basket (35x52cm-14x20in) s.i. board

MANN, Joshua Hargrave Sams and KING, Haynes (19th C) British

£800	$1424	(1-May-92 PHE7/R) Spanish water carrier (83x58cm-33x23in) s.

MANNERS, William (fl.1885-c.1910) British

£550	$1018	(11-Jun-92 CSK144/R) Timber hauling (40x61cm-16x24in) s.
£670	$1193	(24-Jan-92 MAX323/R) Figures before cottage on river bank (30x18cm-12x7in) s.d.1892
£847	$1500	(9-Nov-91 W.W113/R) Timber hauling (41x61cm-16x24in) s.
£1000	$1710	(13-Mar-92 C108/R) Harvesters resting at Wharfedale near Grassington (20x32cm-8x13in) s.d.1895 board
£2600	$4810	(12-Jun-92 C162/R) Netting salmon (76x127cm-30x50in) s.d.1899
£400	*$696*	*(18-Sep-91 WI1147) A lane near Oxford (23x33cm-9x13in) s. W/C*
£500	*$960*	*(29-Jul-92 CSK123) Figures outside the village tavern (23x33cm-9x13in) s.d.1912 W/C bodycol.*
£725	*$1262*	*(15-Apr-92 HAR436) Wood cutters, Leyburn, Wensleydale (25x33cm-10x13in) s.d.1910 W/C*
£1600	*$2752*	*(16-Oct-91 PHL96/R) Returning from fields (29x44cm-11x17in) s. col.wash htd white bodycol pair*

MANNHEIM, Jean (1863-1945) German/American

£526	$1000	(23-Jun-92 MOR.P69) Zinnias in blue vase (51x61cm-20x24in) s.
£562	$1000	(26-Nov-91 MOR.P111 c) Zinnias in blue vase (51x61cm-20x24in) s. masonite
£730	$1300	(26-Nov-91 MOR.P111 b) Landscape (51x61cm-20x24in) s. masonite
£899	$1600	(26-Nov-91 MOR.P111 a) Coastal scene (51x61cm-20x24in) s. masonite
£1184	$2250	(24-Jun-92 B.SF6381/R) Woman reading (42x55cm-17x22in) s.
£1711	$3250	(24-Jun-92 B.SF6359/R) Old barn (30x41cm-12x16in) s. board

MANNHEIM, Jean (1863-1945) German/American-cont.
£3005 $5500 (6-Jun-92 LAE.L134/R) Girl with hand mirror (61x51cm-24x20in) s.

MANNIX, Max (1939-) Australian
£1336 $2325 (17-Sep-91 JRL.S248) Saturday morning in town (90x120cm-35x47in) s. acrylic canvas panel (A.D 2900)

MANNOURY, Armand Arsene (fl.1880-1893) French
£536 $1007 (16-Dec-91 BG.P97) Le chemin de l'eglise (33x55cm-13x22in) s. (F.FR 5200)

MANNUCCI, Cipriano (1882-1970) Italian
£2324 $3974 (19-Mar-92 F.M27/R) Bocca d'Asse (50x62cm-20x24in) s. panel (I.L 5000000)

MANOCCHI, Giuseppe (attrib) (c.1731-1782) Italian
£800 $1432 (14-Nov-91 S34/R) Design for chimney piece (35x48cm-14x19in) W/C pen

MANOLO (1872-1945) Spanish
£608 $1143 (17-Dec-91 BRO.B341) Mujer sentada arreglandose el cabello (19x15cm-7x6in) ink dr (S.P 110000)
£885 $1663 (17-Dec-91 BRO.B432) Desnudo femenino (32x22cm-13x9in) s. pencil dr (S.P 160000)

MANRIQUE, Cesar (20th C) Latin American
£2490 $4258 (17-Mar-92 FER.M191/R) Bodegon con jarron de flores (42x51cm-17x20in) s. mixed media (S.P 450000)

MANRUOLI, Egisto (after) (19th C) Italian
£1279 $2200 (12-Oct-91 DU.E245/R) Untitled (94x69cm-37x27in)

MANSFELD, Heinrich August (1816-1901) Austrian
£7271 $13233 (27-May-92 D.V525/R) Was it delivered by the stork (49x62cm-19x24in) s.d.1874 i.verso board (A.S 150000)

MANSFELD, Josef (1819-1894) Austrian
£1320 $2284 (2-Sep-91 BU.K71/R) Still life with Moet and Chandon champagne and objects on table (31x26cm-12x10in) s.d.1884 panel (D.KR 15000)
£2200 $3740 (22-Oct-91 SWS346/R) Table-top still life (39x29cm-15x11in) s.d.1883 panel

MANSFELD, Josef (attrib) (1819-1894) Austrian
£800 $1368 (19-Mar-92 B63) A still life of strawberries and other fruits with flowers and butterfly (21x17cm-8x7in) board

MANSFELD, Moritz (fl.1850-1890) Austrian
£1257 $2200 (18-Feb-92 CE.NY161/R) Ornate still life (26x20cm-10x8in) s.d.1883 panel

MANSION, Andre Leon Larue see LARUE, Andre Leon

MANSKIRCH, Bernhard Gottfried (1736-1817) German
£2767 $4980 (19-Nov-91 GS.B3582/R) Wooded landscape with figures on path and shepherd with cattle by stream (41x54cm-16x21in) s. panel (S.FR 7000)
£3093 $5351 (27-Mar-92 CD.P9/R) Paysage boise a la chaumiere (39x52cm-15x20in) s. (F.FR 30000)
£4000 $7000 (28-Feb-92 C145) Children on a path by a wood in an extensive landscape. River landscape with peasants on a bridge two
£5500 $10560 (10-Jul-92 C205/R) Extensive pastoral landscape at sunset with peasants returning home (101x127cm-40x50in)
£5500 $9625 (28-Feb-92 C138/R) A wooded landscape with children near timber-framed cottages (135x111cm-53x44in)
£7000 $12250 (28-Feb-92 C31) Wooded river landscape with peasants loading a punt by a cottage (129x167cm-51x66in)
£8000 $14000 (28-Feb-92 C146/R) An extensive landscape with children playing by a river (135x174cm-53x69in)
£13000 $22750 (28-Feb-92 C144/R) A river landscape with children fishing. An extensive landscape with a ruined castle (135x161cm-53x63in) pair

MANSON, James Bolivar (1879-1945) British
£650 $1105 (22-Oct-91 SWS377/R) At Cancale, Brittany (27x36cm-11x14in) s. i.verso

MANSOUROFF, Paul (1896-1983) French
£1132 $2150 (24-Jun-92 GL.P179 b) Spere rouges (80x25cm-31x10in) s. panel (F.FR 11000)
£5738 $10328 (2-Feb-92 CSC.P66/R) Peinture (106x77cm-42x30in) s. panel (F.FR 56000)
£1310 $2267 (4-Oct-91 CSC.P72/R) Les cercles gris (31x14cm-12x6in) s. oil pastel (F.FR 13000)

MANSSON, Carl (1892-?) Swedish
£584 $1039 (28-Oct-91 AB.S152) Summer landscape with farm by pond (31x43cm-12x17in) s. (S.KR 6200)
£989 $1760 (28-Oct-91 AB.S151) Swedish summer landscape with farm (50x70cm-20x28in) s. (S.KR 10500)

MANTEGAZZA, Giacomo (1853-1920) Italian
£6148 $11250 (17-May-92 DU.E1127/R) Chasing a mouse (84x53cm-33x21in) s.s. panel
£10000 $17800 (27-Nov-91 S334/R) Entertainer (83x120cm-33x47in) s.d.1884

MANTEGAZZA, Giacomo (attrib) (1853-1920) Italian
£465 $841   (3-Dec-91 SY.MI26) Maternita (28x17cm-11x7in) panel (I.L 1000000)

MANTELET, Albert Goguet (1858-?) French
£1686 $3018   (15-Nov-91 ZOF.Z1404/R) Water lilies (57x77cm-22x30in) s. (S.FR 4300)

MANTUA SCHOOL, 16th C Italian
£10000 $18200   (11-Dec-91 S144/R) Portrait of Vincenzo I Gonzaga, Duke of Mantua, in armour (138x108cm-54x43in)

MANUEL, Victor (1897-1969) Cuban
£4444 $8000   (18-Nov-91 SY.NY130/R) Gitana con manzana roja (55x47cm-22x19in) s.
£4696 $8500   (19-May-92 SY.NY209 a/R) Mujer con sombrero (45x36cm-18x14in) s. canvas laid down on board
£6077 $11000   (19-May-92 SY.NY178/R) Bohio (53x41cm-21x16in) s.
£1381 $2500   (19-May-92 SY.NY207/R) Mujer con fondo azul (38x28cm-15x11in) s. gouache ink col.pencil

MANZANA-PISSARRO, Georges (1871-1961) French
£1078 $1940   (19-Nov-91 FB.P29/R) Les deux orientales au chat (45x31cm-18x12in) s.d.1928 panel (F.FR 10500)
£2691 $4763   (5-Nov-91 SY.AM168/R) View of inner-Alstel, Hamburg, with present consulate of USA (21x35cm-8x14in) s. panel (D.FL 8800)
£1067 $1857   (13-Apr-92 GL.P14) Paysage de riviere (32x49cm-13x19in) s. pastel gold ink (F.FR 10500)

MANZANET, Riccardo (19th C) Spanish
£4646 $7898   (22-Oct-91 DUR.M49/R) Flores (100x61cm-39x24in) s.d.1888 (S.P 850000)

MANZONI, Ignacio (1799-1880) Italian
£500 $910   (11-Dec-91 ZZ.B245) Slave market (39x30cm-15x12in) s. panel
£546 $950   (19-Sep-91 V.BA66) Posada (35x26cm-14x10in)
£5143 $9000   (20-Feb-92 SY.NY276/R) Cavalier's repast (131x100cm-52x39in) s.

MANZONI, P (?) ?
£700 $1211   (3-Oct-91 CSK49) A faggot gatherer in a wooded landscape (130x155cm-51x61in) s.d.04

MANZONI, Piero (1933-1963) Italian
£21000 $36120   (17-Oct-91 S53/R) Senza titolo (81x100cm-32x39in) oil tar canvas
£7000 $12040   (17-Oct-91 S49/R) Impronte (61x50cm-24x20in) s. ink
£11315 $20593   (26-May-92 SY.MI227/R) Achrome (25x19cm-10x7in) cotton wool wads on panel (I.L 25000000)
£100000 $181000   (5-Dec-91 S22/R) Achrome (60x75cm-24x30in) s.verso kaolin canvas

MANZONI, Ridolfo (1675-1743) Italian
£4000 $7000   (27-Feb-92 B68/R) An allegory of sin (28x20cm-11x8in) s.i.d.1710 vellum laid down on panel

MANZU, Giacomo (1908-1991) Italian
£1842 $3353   (9-Dec-91 CH.R1/R) Per la pace (34x47cm-13x19in) s.i.d.1965 ink (I.L 4000000)
£1924 $3560   (12-Jun-92 HN.H556/R) Reclining figure (19x28cm-7x11in) s. pencil (DM 5600)
£2869 $5250   (13-May-92 SY.NY208/R) Artist and model (37x46cm-15x18in) s.i.d.1967 pen chk
£3390 $6000   (5-Nov-91 CE.NY180/R) Sonia Accovaciata (58x45cm-23x18in) s. brush ink wash
£3402 $6226   (12-May-92 F.R98/R) Ritratto di Inge (37x27cm-15x11in) s.d.70 chl board (I.L 7500000)
£3429 $6000   (27-Feb-92 CE.NY87/R) Piccone (31x44cm-12x17in) s. gouache over black wax crayon
£3672 $6500   (5-Nov-91 CE.NY178/R) Studio Donna (70x50cm-28x20in) s. gouache pencil
£3714 $6500   (27-Feb-92 CE.NY88/R) Ninfa (49x61cm-19x24in) s. pen wash

MANZUOLI, Egisto (?) Italian?
£1800 $3186   (13-Feb-92 CSK257) The Molo, Venice (45x74cm-18x29in) s.i. after Canaletto

MANZUOLI, Tommaso D'Antonio (attrib) (1536-1571) Italian
£7558 $13000   (10-Oct-91 SY.NY4/R) Portrait bust of a young man (43x37cm-17x15in) panel

MAO LIZI (1950-) Chinese
£9609 $16432   (22-Mar-92 SY.TA82/R) Door with graffiti (92x74cm-36x29in) init. board (T.D 418000)

MAPPLETHORPE, Robert (20th C) American
£12570 $22500   (7-May-92 SY.NY323/R) Calender guy (51x30cm-20x12in) s.d.69 mixed media paperboard

MAQHUBELA, Louis Khela (1939-) South African
£444 $785   (4-Nov-91 SY.J180/R) African dream (54x54cm-21x21in) s.d.73 pastel (SA.R 2200)

ARA, Pol (1920-) Belgian
2985	$5463	(12-May-92 C.A209/R) Through deep windows (100x80cm-39x31in) s.d.1981 verso (B.FR 180000)
3336	$5872	(7-Apr-92 C.A173/R) Column of an Oriental palace (195x162cm-77x64in) s.d.1975 (B.FR 200000)
3676	$6249	(22-Oct-91 C.A244/R) The three details for 'close up' (145x145cm-57x57in) s.d.1969-72 verso (B.FR 220000)
500	*$881*	*(7-Apr-92 C.A175) Pink-Point (110x73cm-43x29in) s.d.1970 W/C (B.FR 30000)*
501	*$852*	*(22-Oct-91 C.A247) Diana, Goddess of the Hunt (110x73cm-43x29in) s.d.1971 W/C (B.FR 30000)*
568	*$966*	*(22-Oct-91 C.A246) A green meadow (110x73cm-43x29in) s.d.1971 W/C (B.FR 34000)*
751	*$1321*	*(7-Apr-92 C.A174) Twin sisters (107x70cm-42x28in) s.d.1975 W/C (B.FR 45000)*

ARAIS, Jean (20th C) French
604	$1038	(12-Oct-91 SY.MO221) La chaumiere (23x33cm-9x13in) s.i. panel (F.FR 6000)

ARAIS-MILTON, V (1872-?) French
5263	$9000	(13-Mar-92 WOL.C416/R) Vieille chanson (53x64cm-21x25in) s.

ARAIS-MILTON, Victor (1872-?) French
2128	$3702	(17-Sep-91 CH.AM457/R) A cardinal error (48x38cm-19x15in) s. paper laid down on canvas (D.FL 7000)

ARANGIO, Carlo (1936-) Italian
614	$1093	(1-Dec-91 I.N16) Composition (92x73cm-36x29in) s.d.1973 (F.FR 6000)

ARANIELLO, Giuseppe (1945-) Italian
822	$1431	(14-Apr-92 F.M70) Senza titolo (50x40cm-20x16in) s.i.d.1981verso mixed media collage canvas (I.L 1800000)

ARASCO, Antonio (1886-?) Italian
1764	$3315	(19-Dec-91 F.M77/R) Anacapri, Chiesetta di S.Antonio (30x45cm-12x18in) s. canvasboard (I.L 3800000)
511	*$925*	*(3-Dec-91 F.R93/R) Uomo aereoplano (19x18cm-7x7in) mono. pencil (I.L 1100000)*

ARATTA, Carlo (1625-1713) Italian
3400	$5950	(25-Feb-92 PH92/R) Holy Family with Infant St John the Baptist (91x92cm-36x36in) painted tondo
7496	$13342	(28-Apr-92 RAS.K69/R) Orpheus playing to the women (94x130cm-37x51in) (D.KR 85000)
879	*$1512*	*(10-Oct-91 D.V27/R) Holy Family (22x16cm-9x6in) indis.s. pen bister (A.S 18000)*
1500	*$2880*	*(7-Jul-92 C183/R) Drapery study for the Madonna (41x27cm-16x11in) i. i.verso chk*
4000	*$7680*	*(7-Jul-92 C182/R) Studies of partly draped figure (27x42cm-11x17in) chk*
6969	*$12683*	*(12-Dec-91 L.K433/R) Nulla dies sine line (42x33cm-17x13in) graphite wash htd.white (DM 20000)*

ARATTA, Carlo (after) (1625-1713) Italian
950	$1729	(12-Dec-91 B12) St. John the Evangelist (56x41cm-22x16in)
1937	$3254	(27-Aug-91 RAS.K268/R) The Holy Family (41x31cm-16x12in) (D.KR 22000)

ARATTA, Carlo (attrib) (1625-1713) Italian
1966	$3500	(22-Jan-92 D.NY64) Artist's daughter Faustina as Cleopatra (109x84cm-43x33in)
3426	$6065	(7-Nov-91 D.V28/R) Holy Family in landscape (89x65cm-35x26in) (A.S 70000)
3916	$6931	(7-Nov-91 D.V35/R) The Presentation in the Temple (71x50cm-28x20in) (A.S 80000)
8939	$16000	(17-Jan-92 SY.NY132/R) The herdsman Faustulus bringing home Romulus and Remus (93x137cm-37x54in)

ARATTA, Carlo (circle) (1625-1713) Italian
1178	$2237	(23-Jun-92 D.V201/R) Madonna with Child and San Giovannino (24x19cm-9x7in) copper (A.S 24000)
7200	$12528	(15-Apr-92 C187/R) Holy Family with Sts Anne and Elizabeth and Infant John the Baptist (64x57cm-25x22in) copper

ARATTA, Carlo (studio) (1625-1713) Italian
2000	$3560	(31-Oct-91 B52/R) Annunciation (67x49cm-26x19in)
17387	$29732	(18-Mar-92 D.V46/R) Portrait of Clemens IX (94x74cm-37x29in) (A.S 350000)

ARATTA, Carlo (style) (1625-1713) Italian
825	$1436	(13-Sep-91 C39) Old man, head and shoulders (25x19cm-10x7in) copper oval
1050	$1838	(28-Feb-92 C76) The Mater Dolorosa (38x28cm-15x11in) copper
1100	$1980	(21-Nov-91 CSK5) The Annunciation (68x51cm-27x20in)
2800	$5040	(21-Nov-91 C133/R) The Holy Family with the Infant St John the Baptist (104x119cm-41x47in) oval
4577	$7690	(27-Aug-91 RAS.K227/R) The Holy Family (126x202cm-50x80in) (D.KR 52000)
5438	$9734	(7-May-92 CH.AM37 a/R) Jacob meeting Rachel at well (163x146cm-64x57in) with sig. (D.FL 18000)

MARATTA, Carlo and CITTADINI, Pier Francesco (style) (17th C) Italian
£3000 $5250   (28-Feb-92 C33/R) The Madonna and Child with putti and cherubs in a garland surround (74x61cm-29x24in)

MARATTA, Carlo and TAMM, Franz Werner (attrib) (17th C) Italian/German
£15897 $27183   (18-Mar-92 D.V60/R) Two women and putto decorating stone bust with flowers in park (160x115cm-63x45in) (A.S 320000)

MARC, Franz (1880-1916) German
£16140 $29053   (23-Nov-91 N.M211/R) Hay stooks (35x42cm-14x17in) board (DM 46000)
£23693 $43122   (14-Dec-91 BOD.P730/R) Two babies (46x58cm-18x23in) c.1911 mono verso (DM 68000)
£6143 $11119   (23-May-92 GB.B6873/R) Reclining female nude (12x21cm-5x8in) d.1910 pencil (DM 18000)
£13559 $24000   (6-Nov-91 CH.NY125/R) Kleines Madchen mit weissem Kragen (61x34cm-24x13in) s.d.1905 chl col.chk

MARC, Wilhelm (1839-1907) German
£3086 $5494   (28-Apr-92 RAS.K626/R) Shepherdess with lamb on her arm (55x42cm-22x17in) s.i. (D.KR 35000)

MARCA-RELLI, Conrad (1913-) American
£1714 $3000   (28-Feb-92 SY.NY336/R) Untitled (52x66cm-20x26in) s. collage canvas on panel
£5587 $10000   (6-May-92 CH.NY274/R) Composizione (66x84cm-26x33in) s. oil canvas collage on canvas
£15642 $28000   (13-Nov-91 CH.NY145/R) X-L-31-62 (152x152cm-60x60in) s. i.d.verso oil canvas collage canvas

MARCEGLIA, P (?) Italian?
£2200 $3982   (21-May-92 CSK209/R) In salon (56x68cm-22x27in) s. pair

MARCEL-CLEMENT, Amedee Julien (1873-?) French
£900 $1629   (21-May-92 CSK150) Fishing boats in calm (48x60cm-19x24in) s.
£1600 $2896   (21-May-92 CSK157/R) Evening calm (46x61cm-18x24in) s.

MARCESTEL (20th C) ?
£5086 $9105   (17-Nov-91 R.P159) Sring (148x116cm-58x46in) s. (F.FR 50000)
£5086 $9105   (17-Nov-91 R.P217) Dancing with the birds (148x116cm-58x46in) s. (F.FR 50000)

MARCH, Esteban (attrib) (?-1660) Spanish
£1309 $2500   (16-Jul-92 SY.NY126/R) Battle scenes (36x28cm-14x11in) panel pair

MARCH, Horacio (1899-1978) Argentinian
£517 $900   (19-Sep-91 V.BA68) Balcon de Mariquita Thompson (14x21cm-6x8in) tempera
£805 $1400   (19-Sep-91 V.BA67) Alto San Blas-Cuzco (20x27cm-8x11in) W/C

MARCH, Vicente (1859-1914) Spanish
£21512 $37000   (17-Oct-91 SY.NY84/R) Assignation in garden (36x60cm-14x24in) s.i.d.86

MARCHAL, Charles Francois (1825-1877) French
£9262 $16024   (24-Mar-92 CH.R64/R) Le secret (94x112cm-37x44in) s. (I.L 20000000)

MARCHAND DES RAUX (1902-) French
£635 $1130   (29-Nov-91 D.P145/R) Paysanne pres de la ferme (32x41cm-13x16in) s. d.1950verso panel (F.FR 6200)

MARCHAND, Andre (1907-) French
£843 $1500   (28-Apr-92 PO.BA22) Colette Baudoche (73x92cm-29x36in) s.d.1937
£843 $1500   (28-Apr-92 PO.BA23) Feb (73x92cm-29x36in) s.d.1930
£893 $1500   (1-Sep-91 PO.BA7) La mission (49x60cm-19x24in) s.
£1018 $1883   (9-Jun-92 FB.M58) Paysage (22x26cm-9x10in) s. board (C.D 2250)
£1966 $3500   (28-Apr-92 PO.BA21) Biribi (73x92cm-29x36in) s.d.1926
£2319 $4011   (6-Oct-91 BG.P186/R) Les trois pommes (46x55cm-18x22in) s. i.verso panel (F.FR 23000)
£2884 $4931   (18-Mar-92 PIC.P74) Silence dans la riziere (65x81cm-26x32in) s. s.i.verso (F.FR 28000)
£3193 $5459   (18-Mar-92 PIC.P73/R) La bouteille de bourgogne (46x55cm-18x22in) s. (F.FR 31000)
£3696 $6653   (22-Nov-91 PIC.P44/R) Le soleil qui se couche (46x55cm-18x22in) s. s.i.verso (F.FR 36000)
£4360 $7500   (12-Oct-91 SY.NY123/R) Le plein soleil dans les Foins-Provence (81x100cm-32x39in) s. s.d.73 verso
£4620 $8316   (22-Nov-91 PIC.P45/R) Naissance du Printemps (56x46cm-22x18in) s. i.d.1953verso (F.FR 45000)
£5943 $10697   (2-Feb-92 ZZ.F176/R) Le plein ete dans les files (81x100cm-32x39in) s. i.d.1973verso (F.FR 58000)
£7209 $12327   (18-Mar-92 PIC.P72/R) Vies silencieuses. Le tulipes (81x65cm-32x26in) s. (F.FR 70000)

MARCHAND, Charles see KAUFMANN, Karl

MARCHAND, Jean Hippolyte (1883-1940) French
£900 $1719   (29-Jun-92 CSK60/R) Bateaux a port (55x66cm-22x26in) s.

ARCHAND, Jean Hippolyte (1883-1940) French-cont.
.950	$1815	(29-Jun-92 CSK61/R) Femme au turban (74x60cm-29x24in) s. s.i.verso
1200	$2292	(29-Jun-92 CSK58/R) Route de village (55x74cm-22x29in) s.
.1400	$2534	(2-Dec-91 CSK70 a/R) Auto portrait (46x37cm-18x15in)
:1600	$2896	(2-Dec-91 CSK67/R) Auto portrait (65x50cm-26x20in) s.d.1909 paper on canvas
:2300	$4393	(29-Jun-92 CSK53/R) Renne moulins (38x53cm-15x21in) s.
:2600	$4706	(2-Dec-91 CSK70/R) L'eglise dans la neige (65x55cm-26x22in) s.verso
:3500	$6335	(2-Dec-91 CSK66/R) Nus au cupidon, Suzanne au bain (148x110cm-58x43in) s.d.1911

ARCHENCKO, Viacheslav (1952-) Russian
.492	$836	(24-Oct-91 DUR.M1197/R) Soldado (80x60cm-31x24in) s. (S.P 90000)

ARCHES SCHOOL, 15th C Italian
:11000	$21120	(8-Jul-92 S5/R) Virgin and Child (36x29cm-14x11in) tempera panel arched top gold ground
:25484	$47401	(18-Jun-92 SY.MO2/R) Vierge a l'Enfant. Saints (94x156cm-37x61in) tempera panel polyptich (F.FR 250000)

ARCHESCHI, Jean-Paul (20th C) French
832	*$1597*	*(6-Jul-92 HC.P52/R) 11000 nuits, fragment s.verso wax pastel felt pencil soot (F.FR 8000)*

ARCHESI, Salvatore (1852-1926) Italian
:12000	$20520	(18-Mar-92 S185/R) In the sacristy (104x67cm-41x26in) s.

ARCHESINI, Alessandro (1664-1738) Italian
:15363	$27500	(17-Jan-92 SY.NY137/R) Phaethon approaching his father Apollo (86x110cm-34x43in)

ARCHESINI, Alessandro (attrib) (1664-1738) Italian
2060	$3872	(18-Dec-91 AT.P138/R) Saint Roch et les pestiferes (34x23cm-13x9in) d.78verso copper (F.FR 20000)

ARCHETTI DA FAENZA, Marco (16th C) Italian
:2000	*$3640*	*(10-Dec-91 C117/R) A boar hunt (37x22cm-15x9in) mono. i.verso blk.chk.ink*

ARCHETTI DA FAENZA, Marco (attrib) (16th C) Italian
550	*$957*	*(13-Apr-92 S96/R) Passion of Christ (42x29cm-17x11in) pen wash over black chk*

ARCHETTI, Ludovico (1853-1909) Italian
650	$1209	(18-Jun-92 B100 a) Barges on the Seine (26x36cm-10x14in) s.i. panel
.1337	$2313	(23-Mar-92 B.O84/R) Still life of hare and pheasant (90x60cm-35x24in) s.d.1894 (N.KR 15000)
:3468	$6000	(29-Mar-92 MY.F63/R) The fair captive (28x38cm-11x15in) s. panel
:11190	$20031	(17-Nov-91 FB.P95/R) La conversation galante (43x60cm-17x24in) s. (F.FR 110000)

ARCHETTI, Ludovico (attrib) (1853-1909) Italian
.565	$1000	(9-Nov-91 W.W33/R) Maiden under a triumphal arch (28x20cm-11x8in) s.i. board

ARCHI, Mario Vellani (1895-1979) Italian
:2353	$4283	(26-May-92 SY.MI50/R) Natura morta con limoni (40x52cm-16x20in) s.d.29 panel (I.L 5200000)

ARCHI, Vincenzo (1818-1894) Italian
664	*$1247*	*(17-Dec-91 DUR.M5/R) Arco romano (24x37cm-9x15in) s. W/C (S.P 120000)*

ARCHINI, Lorenzo (19th C) Italian
:1812	$3352	(9-Jun-92 F.R98) Natura morta di cacciagione (72x90cm-28x35in) s.d.1876 (I.L 4000000)

ARCHIONI, Elisabetta (18th C) Italian
:44693	$80000	(17-Jan-92 SY.NY47/R) Still lives of tulips, roses peonies and other flowers (107x140cm-42x55in) pair

ARCHIS, Alessio de (?-1725) Italian
1121	*$2086*	*(20-Jun-92 CH.MO215/R) Une ville fortifiee pres d'un lac eclairee par des rayons de soleil (16x13cm-6x5in) i. red chk wash (F.FR 11000)*

ARCHISIO, Andrea (1850-1927) Italian
:1447	$2750	(26-Jun-92 WOL.C478) The long journey (41x61cm-16x24in) s.

ARCIL, Rene (1917-) Canadian
390	*$706*	*(2-Dec-91 R.T51/R) Femme aux jonquilles (46x59cm-18x23in) s.d.51 chl (C.D 800)*

ARCKE DE LUMMEN, Emile van (1827-1890) French
.1440	$2750	(16-Jul-92 SY.NY377/R) Cows grazing in a pasture (32x45cm-13x18in) s. panel
:4587	$8394	(3-Jun-92 R.T124/R) Bord d'Etang (67x100cm-26x39in) s. (C.D 10000)

MARCKS, Gerhard (1889-) ?
£526 $900   (13-Mar-92 FN.S2554/R) Female nude seated (32x22cm-13x9in) s. pencil
                   (DM 1500)

MARCOLA (18th C) Italian
£2600 $4992   (7-Jul-92 C41/R) The Raising of Lazarus (28x37cm-11x15in) chk pen wash by
                   Giovanni Battista or Marco

MARCOLA, Giovanni Battista (1711-1780) Italian
£1800 $3132   (13-Apr-92 S170/R) Roman soldiers and figures gathered by altar. Study of
                   male nude (28x42cm-11x17in) s.verso pen wash blk chk htd wht
                   double-sided

MARCON, Charles (1920-) French
£7558 $13000   (12-Oct-91 SY.NY121/R) L'homme qui semme pour les oiseaux
                   (100x65cm-39x26in) s.d.73 masonite

MARCOUSSIS, Louis (1883-1941) French
£19672 $36000   (13-May-92 CH.NY236/R) nature morte (30x74cm-12x29in) s. board on panel
£26000 $49660   (30-Jun-92 C140/R) Violin, raisin et cuiller (91x32cm-36x13in) s.
£28000 $53480   (1-Jul-92 S187/R) Instrument de musique sur gueridon (80x53cm-31x21in) s.
£3005 $5500   (14-May-92 SY.NY130/R) Paris (18x12cm-7x5in) s.d.1933 W/C
£18079 $32000   (7-Nov-91 SY.NY157/R) Nature morte devant la fenetre (43x31cm-17x12in) s.
                   gouache indian ink pencil

MARCUCCI, Mario (1910-) Italian
£1671 $3141   (19-Dec-91 F.M130/R) Natura morta (34x43cm-13x17in) s. panel
                   (I.L 3600000)

MARCUS, Kaete Ephraim (1892-1970) ?
£532 $1000   (5-Jan-92 GG.TA285/R) Fishing boats on the Sea of Galilee
                   (50x66cm-20x26in) s. s.verso canvas on masonite
£2486 $4600   (8-Jun-92 GG.TA203/R) Landscape and figures (60x80cm-24x31in) s.

MARCZELL, Gyorgy (1897-?) Hungarian
£1220 $2111   (3-Oct-91 D.V131/R) Fisher girl (100x120cm-39x47in) s. (A.S 25000)

MARDEN, Brice (1938-) American
£10615 $19000   (5-May-92 CH.NY159/R) Untitled (75x56cm-30x22in) oil graphite paper on
                   board
£189944 $340000   (13-Nov-91 SY.NY65/R) Nico painting (173x254cm-68x100in) s.d.1966 verso
                   oil wax canvas
£321229 $575000   (6-May-92 SY.NY29/R) The Dylan Karina painting (244x366cm-96x144in)
                   s.i.d.1969verso iuk wax canvas on panel
£418994 $750000   (13-Nov-91 SY.NY60/R) Grove Group II (183x274cm-72x108in) oil wax canvas
                   two panels
£1912 $3250   (23-Oct-91 B.SF3703/R) Untitled 12 (37x30cm-15x12in) s. ink
£36313 $65000   (7-May-92 SY.NY154/R) Untitled (66x101cm-26x40in) s.d.69 graphite wax

MAREC, Victor (1862-1920) French
£700 $1211   (3-Oct-91 CSK216) A tasty morsel (81x64cm-32x25in) s.d.1883
£5143 $9000   (23-Sep-91 S.SL259) Luxembourg gardens (61x43cm-24x17in) s.

MARECHAL, Claude (20th C) French
£1824 $3301   (21-May-92 CC.P35/R) Collines ensoleillees (59x45cm-23x18in) s.d.89 paper
                   collage japon nacre (F.FR 18000)
£4024 $6922   (8-Oct-91 CC.P4/R) Vallee fertile (65x56cm-26x22in) s.d.1984 torn paper
                   mixed media (F.FR 40000)

MAREES, Hans von (1837-1887) German
£2448 $4357   (30-Nov-91 VG.B107/R) Study of two horses and warriors (44x29cm-17x11in)
                   pencil (DM 7000)
£6993 $12448   (29-Nov-91 VG.B2/R) Riders (51x30cm-20x12in) ochre (DM 20000)
£8392 $14937   (30-Nov-91 VG.B106/R) Study for Bacchus (45x21cm-18x8in) ochre gouache
                   htd.white (DM 24000)
£16434 $29252   (29-Nov-91 VG.B1/R) Study for Volkmanns's amazone (48x40cm-19x16in)
                   d.1886 ochre (DM 47000)

MARESCA, G (?) Italian
£600 $1086   (21-May-92 CSK283) Serenade (38x24cm-15x9in) s.

MARESCA, M (19th C) Italian
£521 $885   (23-Oct-91 MA.V189) Capri waterfront (61x91cm-24x36in) s. (C.D 1000)

MARESCA, S (19th C) Italian
£747 $1300   (11-Sep-91 D.NY57) Friendly wager (36x61cm-14x24in) s.

MARESCALCO, Pietro (1503-1584) Italian
£46961 $85000   (21-May-92 CH.NY11/R) Madonna and child enthroned, flanked by Saints
                   James and Prosdocimus of Padua, with angel (163x124cm-64x49in)
                   s.i.d.M.D.LXIII
£1500 $2880   (7-Jul-92 C127/R) St John the Baptist and monastic saint. Justice, Diana
                   and two nymphs (33x23cm-13x9in) i.verso chk pen wash htd.white
                   double-sided

MAREVNA (20th C) French
£5500	$9515	(24-Mar-92 C59/R) Vase de fleurs des champs (55x38cm-22x15in) s.
£1500	$2595	*(25-Mar-92 S196/R) Nude. Two girls (63x48cm-25x19in) s.d.43*
		indist.i.verso W/C pencil two

MAREVNA, Marie (1892-1984) Russian
£869	$1590	(5-Feb-92 FB.P243) Portrait de jeune fille (40x30cm-16x12in) s.
		d.1974verso (F.FR 8500)
£3360	$5980	(29-Nov-91 GAB.G2800/R) Composition de fleurs des champs
		(55x38cm-22x15in) s.d.1932 (S.FR 8500)

MAREY (19th C) French
| £885 | $1514 | (17-Mar-92 FER.M57/R) Bodegon de jamon, ajos, panes y cantaro |
| | | (84x101cm-33x40in) s. (S.P 160000) |

MARFAING, Andre (1925-1987) French
£1468	$2554	(18-Sep-91 KH.K94/R) Composition (61x50cm-24x20in) s. i.verso
		(D.KR 16500)
£1538	$2785	(4-Dec-91 KH.K111/R) Composition (61x50cm-24x20in) s.d.74 (D.KR 17000)
£1874	$3393	(21-May-92 CC.P23/R) X-53 (60x73cm-24x29in) s.d.X-53verso (F.FR 18500)
£4938	$8938	(5-Dec-91 BG.P86) Composition (100x80cm-39x31in) s. (F.FR 48000)

MARGETSON, William Henry (1861-1940) British
£1000	$1850	(12-Jun-92 C241/R) The Annunciation to the Shepherds (44x23cm-17x9in)
		s.d.1906 panel
£2800	$5348	(29-Jun-92 PHB173/R) Nymph of waterfall (104x77cm-41x30in) s.
£4600	$8188	(28-Nov-91 B129/R) Harbingers of spring (61x25cm-24x10in) s.d.1911
£2000	$3580	*(5-May-92 SWS260/R) The linen maid (74x47cm-29x19in) s.d.1911 W/C*

MARGITSON, Marie (1857-1864) British
| £2200 | $3982 | (6-Dec-91 K530/R) Still life of mixed fruit on ledge |
| | | (36cm-14ins circular) s. |

MARI, Giovan Antonio (attrib) (?-1661) Italian
| £431 | $776 | *(22-Nov-91 AGS.P116) Martyre d'Ursule et des onze mille vierges a Cologne* |
| | | *(30x22cm-12x9in) i.verso pen (F.FR 4200)* |

MARIA, Nicola de (1954-) Italian
£4568	$7948	(14-Apr-92 F.M172/R) Senza titolo (20x14cm-8x6in) paper (I.L 10000000)
£10049	$17485	(14-Apr-92 F.M243/R) Sposa, fiore, luce - sentimenti molto isolati
		(30x40cm-12x16in) s.i.d.1985/86verso oil pigment (I.L 22000000)
£18286	$32000	(27-Feb-92 CH.NY44/R) AAA Testa-Polline I dipinti (115x87cm-45x34in)
		s.i.d.1982-1983verso s.i.stretcher
£19553	$35000	(5-May-92 CH.NY128/R) Giorni del secolo nuovo (189x230cm-74x91in) i.
		s.i.d.1981verso d.stretcher acrylic
£23000	$43930	(2-Jul-92 C57/R) 10 Fiori-Regno dei Fiori (149x263cm-59x104in)
		s.i.d.1984-85 overlap
£37255	$64078	(12-Oct-91 F.L245/R) Testa di fuoco (160x200cm-63x79in) i.verso
		(S.FR 95000)
£494	$899	*(11-Dec-91 CH.AM120) Celebration of music (23x26cm-9x10in) s. pastel*
		pencil (D.FL 1600)
£606	$1097	*(21-May-92 SY.AM236) Untitled (29x23cm-11x9in) s. wax crayon (D.FL 2000)*
£633	$1089	*(12-Oct-91 KV.L75) Regno dei Fiori (29x19cm-11x7in) s. pastel*
		(B.FR 38000)
£667	$1207	*(21-May-92 SY.AM235/R) Untitled (23x32cm-9x13in) s. wax crayon pencil*
		(D.FL 2200)
£727	$1316	*(19-May-92 CH.AM386) Flower power (29x23cm-11x9in) s. crayon (D.FL 2400)*
£733	$1261	*(12-Oct-91 KV.L74) Regno die Fiori (29x22cm-11x9in) s. pastel*
		(B.FR 44000)
£1296	$2359	*(12-Dec-91 SY.AM298/R) Untitled (24x23cm-9x9in) s. wax crayons pencil*
		(D.FL 4200)
£8380	$15000	*(12-Nov-91 CE.NY157/R) Angeli and mare and azzurri sentimenti*
		(30x40cm-12x16in) s.i.d.1985verso oil acrylic col.crayons canvas
£12849	$23000	*(6-May-92 CH.NY225/R) La Testa Allegra di un Angelo Bello*
		(50x40cm-20x16in) oil graphite paper collage canvas

MARIANI, Carlo Maria (1931-) Italian
| £5587 | $10000 | (13-Nov-91 CH.NY344/R) Ciparisso (60x44cm-24x17in) s.i.verso |

MARIANI, Pompeo (1857-1927) Italian
£1453	$2500	(15-Oct-91 CE.NY334/R) Breaking waves (47x69cm-19x27in) s.
£1852	$3205	(24-Mar-92 CH.R66) Nella neve (18x15cm-7x6in) s. panel (I.L 4000000)
£2566	$4542	(7-Nov-91 F.M4/R) Riposo di pastorelli nel bosco (36x52cm-14x20in)
		s.i.d.913 (I.L 5600000)
£2882	$4928	(19-Mar-92 F.M125/R) Mareggiata a Bordighera (29x20cm-11x8in) s.d.91
		board (I.L 6200000)
£3800	$6764	(28-Nov-91 B7/R) Olive trees by path (47x55cm-19x22in) s.i.d.1916 board
£4648	$7948	(19-Mar-92 F.M127/R) Incendio nel porto di Genova (26x35cm-10x14in)
		s.d.1900 board (I.L 10000000)
£4800	$8688	(22-May-92 C232/R) Wooded lake landscape (75x50cm-30x20in) s. panel
£5200	$9204	(14-Feb-92 C127/R) On the Nile (23x32cm-9x13in) s.i. panel
£6200	$10974	(14-Feb-92 C136/R) Mother and child in wooded landscape (18x30cm-7x12in)
		init.d.1887 panel four
£6484	$11217	(24-Mar-92 CH.R76/R) Coppia di Zelade (21x26cm-8x10in) s. one
		indis.d.1878 board pair (I.L 14000000)

MARIANI, Pompeo (1857-1927) Italian-cont.

£6500	$11505	(14-Feb-92 C138/R) Wooded lake landscape (75x48cm-30x19in) s. panel
£8278	$14817	(14-Nov-91 CH.R194/R) Scena di caccia. Scena di pesca (50x35cm-20x14in) board oval pair (I.L 18000000)
£9500	$16815	(14-Feb-92 C140/R) Shooting duck (72x93cm-28x37in) s.
£16000	$28320	(14-Feb-92 C139/R) Shipping in harbour at dawn (22x27cm-9x11in) s. panel sold with nine others
£23599	$43894	(16-Jun-92 F.M220/R) Paesaggio del Ticino (133x219cm-52x86in) s.d.1896 (I.L 52000000)
£681	*$1266*	*(16-Jun-92 F.M78) Cascinale in campagna (9x14cm-4x6in) s. W/C (I.L 1500000)*
£726	*$1351*	*(16-Jun-92 F.M48) Marina con pescatore (21x30cm-8x12in) mono.d.1886 chl pastel (I.L 1600000)*

MARIANI, Umberto (1936-) Italian

| £2299 | $4116 | (14-Nov-91 F.M44) In alta societa (116x89cm-46x35in) s.i.d.1972verso (I.L 5000000) |
| *£460* | *$823* | *(14-Nov-91 F.M3) Senza titolo (28x36cm-11x14in) s.d.1990 s.i.d.verso mixed media lead (I.L 1000000)* |

MARIENHOF, J A (17th C) Dutch

| £3800 | $6916 | (13-Dec-91 C201/R) Rocky landscape with bandits by outcrop (33x50cm-13x20in) s.d.1652 panel |

MARIESCHI (after) (18th C) Italian

| £4100 | $7831 | (14-Jul-92 DR402/R) Venice, scenes on Grand Canal, Rialto and Doges Palace (29x44cm-11x17in) pair |

MARIESCHI, Jacopo (1711-1791) Italian

| £12982 | $22848 | (10-Apr-92 AGS.P19/R) Abords d'une ville Italienne animes de bergers (55x73cm-22x29in) (F.FR 128000) |
| £30000 | $52500 | (31-Mar-92 PH123/R) Grand Canal, Venice - view from Rialto Bridge from south (71x117cm-28x46in) |

MARIESCHI, Jacopo (circle) (1711-1791) Italian

| £4000 | $7640 | (21-Jul-92 PH237) Elegant figures strolling amongst castle gardens (34x55cm-13x22in) |
| £15000 | $26250 | (31-Mar-92 PH27/R) View of Dogana and entrance to Grand Canal looking west with figures and gondolas (52x81cm-20x32in) |

MARIESCHI, Jacopo (studio) (1711-1791) Italian

| £5874 | $10396 | (7-Nov-91 D.V44/R) View of Venice (53x71cm-21x28in) (A.S 120000) |

MARIESCHI, Michele (1696-1743) Italian

£50000	$87000	(15-Apr-92 C56/R) The Doge's Palace, Piazzetta and the Prisons, Venice (55x85cm-22x33in)
£60000	$115200	(10-Jul-92 C32/R) Capriccio of ruined classical portico, statue of horse, with washerwoman and peasants and dog (56x84cm-22x33in)
£149171	$270000	(22-May-92 SY.NY55/R) Capriccio with Palladian church and domed chapel. Capriccio with ruins by water (46x70cm-18x28in) pair

MARIESCHI, Michele (circle) (1696-1743) Italian

£1581	$2814	(29-Nov-91 GAB.G3081/R) Vue fantasiste d'un port Mediterraneen (51x72cm-20x28in) (S.FR 4000)
£4238	$7290	(16-Oct-91 AT.P30/R) Paysage a l'obelisque et aux ruines antiques (61x92cm-24x36in) (F.FR 42000)
£4260	$7497	(11-Apr-92 AT.P19/R) Ruine dans un paysage de riviere (35x46cm-14x18in) (F.FR 42000)
£7182	$13000	(22-May-92 SY.NY135/R) Capriccio with equestrian monument and obelisk (68x93cm-27x37in)
£37037	$67037	(5-Dec-91 SY.MO216/R) Palais devant une vue de Venise (62x86cm-24x34in) (F.FR 360000)

MARIESCHI, Michele (style) (1696-1743) Italian

£950	$1710	(21-Nov-91 CSK270) Gondoliers off the Dogana, Venice (28x38cm-11x15in)
£5500	$10560	(9-Jul-92 CSK282) Santa Maria della Salute and the Dogana, Venice (90x133cm-35x52in)
£6500	$11700	(21-Nov-91 CSK275/R) Santa Maria della Salute and the Dogana, Venice (90x133cm-35x52in)
£6500	$11375	(28-Feb-92 C12/R) San Giorgio Maggiore, Venice with the Doge's Palace beyond (62x97cm-24x38in)
£11000	$21120	(8-Jul-92 S214/R) The Grand Canal at San Stae, Venice (54x72cm-21x28in)
£11050	$20000	(22-May-92 SY.NY56/R) View of Canareggio, Venice (62x102cm-24x40in)

MARILHAT, Prosper (1811-1847) French

| £1623 | $3100 | (16-Jul-92 SY.NY363/R) Bather at twilight (46x55cm-18x22in) |

MARIN BAGUES, Francisco (?) ?

| £2076 | $3738 | (29-Jan-92 FER.M196/R) Jovenes compesinas con un cesto de frutas (67x90cm-26x35in) s. (S.P 375000) |

MARIN, Claude (1924-) French

| £524 | $907 | (28-Mar-92 BOD.P994) Heath landscape in evening glow (64x99cm-25x39in) s. (DM 1500) |

MARIN, Enrique (19/20th C) Spanish?
£665	$1177	(12-Feb-92 ANS.M161/R) El porton (21x12cm-8x5in) s. panel (S.P 120000)
£442	$832	(17-Dec-91 DUR.M69/R) Granada (14x9cm-6x4in) s. W/C (S.P 80000)
£465	$850	(13-May-92 FER.M73/R) Calle toledana con balcon de flores (14x8cm-6x3in) s. W/C (S.P 85000)
£492	$900	(13-May-92 FER.M72/R) Campanario y balconada (14x8cm-6x3in) s. W/C (S.P 90000)
£498	$936	(17-Dec-91 DUR.M70/R) Granada (14x9cm-6x4in) s. W/C (S.P 90000)
£498	$936	(17-Dec-91 DUR.M67/R) Balcon en flor (14x9cm-6x4in) s. W/C (S.P 90000)
£498	$936	(17-Dec-91 DUR.M68/R) Toledo (14x9cm-6x4in) s. W/C (S.P 90000)
£875	$1601	(13-May-92 FER.M74/R) Calle granadina (34x24cm-13x9in) s. W/C (S.P 160000)
£1000	$1780	(27-Nov-91 S361/R) Laden donkey (44x32cm-17x13in) s.i. W/C
£1011	$1851	(13-May-92 FER.M75/R) Arqueria (32x23cm-13x9in) s. W/C (S.P 185000)
£1503	$2555	(22-Oct-91 DUR.M63/R) Carro en una calle de Toledo (13x8cm-5x3in) s. W/C (S.P 275000)
£1504	$2752	(13-May-92 FER.M76/R) Puerta granadina (32x23cm-13x9in) s. W/C (S.P 275000)
£1801	$3152	(18-Feb-92 DUR.M24/R) Calle toledana (47x32cm-19x13in) s. W/C (S.P 325000)
£2050	$3485	(22-Oct-91 DUR.M64/R) Rincon toledano (14x8cm-6x3in) s. W/C (S.P 375000)
£2186	$3717	(22-Oct-91 DUR.M66/R) Granada (33x23cm-13x9in) s. W/C (S.P 400000)
£2460	$4502	(13-May-92 FER.M130/R) Pelando la pava (68x45cm-27x18in) s. W/C (S.P 450000)
£2596	$4414	(22-Oct-91 DUR.M65/R) Calle toledana (13x8cm-5x3in) s. W/C (S.P 475000)

MARIN, John (1870-1953) American
£895	$1700	(26-Jun-92 WOL.C482/R) Mountain village scene (23x28cm-9x11in) s.d.08 pastel
£4000	$7000	(26-Sep-91 CH.NY212/R) Sunset (21x28cm-8x11in) s. W/C pencil
£8000	$14000	(25-Sep-91 SY.NY88/R) Downtown New York buildings (19x24cm-7x9in) s.d.12 W/C pencil
£10989	$20000	(27-May-92 SY.NY98/R) Berkshire Hills (35x42cm-14x17in) s.d.12 W/C
£99448	$180000	(6-Dec-91 CH.NY224/R) A street seeing (66x54cm-26x21in) s.d.28 W/C chl pencil

MARINARI, Onorio (style) (1627-1715) Italian
£1009	$1736	(15-Oct-91 PPB.P10) Vierge a l'Enfant (87x70cm-34x28in) (F.FR 10000)

MARINELLI, Mario (20th C) Italian
£853	$1553	(30-May-92 VG.B840/R) Rural scene (14x35cm-6x14in) s.d.1958 panel (DM 2500)

MARINELLI, Vincenzo (1820-1892) Italian
£2038	$3771	(9-Jun-92 F.R166/R) Pescatori davanti a Castel Sant'Elmo (18x25cm-7x10in) s. cardboard (I.L 4500000)

MARINI, Antonio (?) Italian
£14403	$26070	(5-Dec-91 SY.MO264/R) Paysage de bord de mer (89x114cm-35x45in) (F.FR 140000)

MARINI, Marino (1901-1980) Italian
£19067	$33939	(29-Apr-92 F.F239/R) Cavaliere (32x27cm-13x11in) s.d.1949 tempera cardboard (I.L 42000000)
£19774	$35000	(6-Nov-91 CH.NY313/R) Cavallo (93x72cm-37x28in) s.d.1950 paper on canvas
£35653	$67741	(23-Jun-92 F.M153/R) Cavaliere nero (100x75cm-39x30in) s.d.1950 paper on masonite (I.L 78000000)
£36318	$64646	(29-Apr-92 F.F240/R) Fantasia (88x63cm-35x25in) s.i.verso (I.L 80000000)
£90000	$171900	(29-Jun-92 C60/R) Grande teatro (179x179cm-70x70in) s.d.1958-60
£698	$1200	(20-Oct-91 HG.C1560) Heads (28x20cm-11x8in) s. ink W/C
£1816	$3232	(29-Apr-92 F.F241/R) Cavallo profilo (23x16cm-9x6in) indian ink (I.L 4000000)
£2270	$4040	(29-Apr-92 F.F242/R) Uomo con spada (30x21cm-12x8in) s. indian ink (I.L 5000000)
£2716	$4942	(26-May-92 SY.MI103/R) Nudo I (28x19cm-11x7in) s. ink (I.L 6000000)
£4171	$7424	(26-Nov-91 SY.MI28/R) Pomona (33x23cm-13x9in) s. mixed media (I.L 9000000)
£6000	$10380	(24-May-92 C62/R) Cavallo (48x35cm-19x14in) s. pen ink
£7634	$13588	(28-Nov-91 BU.S51/R) Portrait of a man (34x25cm-13x10in) s. gouache (S.KR 80000)
£7650	$14000	(13-May-92 CH.NY289/R) Cavallo (61x47cm-24x19in) s.d.1950 enamel paper
£8000	$15280	(1-Jul-92 S219/R) Quadriga leggera (39x52cm-15x20in) s.i.verso gouache collage
£9063	$16405	(3-Dec-91 F.R237/R) Cavalli e giocoliere (38x28cm-15x11in) mono. tepera graphite album page (I.L 19500000)
£10000	$19100	(1-Jul-92 S218/R) Mare lungo (39x52cm-15x20in) s. s.i.verso gouache collage
£13000	$22490	(24-Mar-92 C108/R) Cavaliere (50x35cm-20x14in) s. gouache col.crayon pen ink wash htd.white
£13661	$25000	(14-May-92 SY.NY302/R) Uomini e cavallo (63x44cm-25x17in) s.d.1953 oil ink paper on canvas
£18000	$31140	(25-Mar-92 S91/R) Cavallo e Cavaliere (91x71cm-36x28in) s. oil gouache W/C indian ink wash paper canvas
£19000	$32870	(25-Mar-92 S90/R) Cavaloo e Cavaliere (56x40cm-22x16in) s.d.1950 gouache brush ink

MARINI, Marino (1901-1980) Italian-cont.
£27429 $48000   (25-Feb-92 CH.NY76/R) Cavallo e cavaliere (86x62cm-34x24in) s.d.1955
               tempera gouache pen indian ink

MARINO, P di (19th C) Italian
£645 $1174   (10-Dec-91 F.R117) Il golfo di Napoli (24x34cm-9x13in) s. panel
               (I.L 1400000)

MARINO, Raffaello (1868-?) Italian
£5219 $9707   (16-Jun-92 F.M250/R) Sur le quai Voltaire (27x25cm-11x10in) s.d.1895
               (I.L 11500000)

MARINONI, Antonio (1796-1871) Italian
£3027 $5480   (19-May-92 AB.S4352/R) Landscape with waterfall and figures
               (99x75cm-39x30in) s.i.d.1858 (S.KR 32000)

MARIOTTI, Leopoldo (1848-1916) Italian
£553 $1006   (10-Dec-91 F.R103) Bufalo (22x38cm-9x15in) s. panel (I.L 1200000)

MARIOTTO DI CRISTOFANO (1393-1457) Italian
£13812 $25000   (22-May-92 SY.NY4/R) Annunciation (115x102cm-45x40in) tempera panel

MARIOTTO, Bernardino di (15th C) Italian
£46479 $84127   (5-Dec-91 F.M133/R) Angelo annunciante (44x23cm-17x9in) tempera panel
               shaped top (I.L 100000000)

MARIS, Jacob (1837-1899) Dutch
£950 $1700   (6-May-92 B.P91/R) Italian farm scene (20x18cm-8x7in) s. panel
£1590 $2815   (5-Nov-91 SY.AM164/R) View of Dutch town (24x35cm-9x14in) indist.s. panel
               (D.FL 5200)
£1835 $3248   (5-Nov-91 SY.AM83/R) Allotments in Hague (16x23cm-6x9in) s. panel
               (D.FL 6000)
£2446 $4355   (30-Oct-91 CH.AM281) The little bridge (21x53cm-8x21in) s. panel
               (D.FL 8000)
£4848 $8582   (22-Apr-92 CH.AM240/R) Windmill in a snowy landscape (48x35cm-19x14in) s.
               (D.FL 16000)
£5046 $8780   (14-Apr-92 SY.AM310/R) View of Dordrecht (65x84cm-26x33in) s.
               (D.FL 16500)
£5199 $9046   (14-Apr-92 SY.AM24/R) Het Jagertje (27x22cm-11x9in) s. panel (D.FL 17000)
£7951 $13835   (14-Apr-92 SY.AM105/R) Het Zieken, The Hague with figure on towpath
               (23x31cm-9x12in) s. (D.FL 26000)
£12727 $22527   (22-Apr-92 CH.AM169/R) An Italian girl picking oranges (53x33cm-21x13in)
               s.d.1868 (D.FL 42000)
£802 $1404   (18-Feb-92 CH.AM213/R) Small stream with two moored vessels near farm
               (26x21cm-10x8in) s. pencil W/C blk.chk. on concert programme
               (D.FL 2600)
£1223 $2177   (30-Oct-91 CH.AM305/R) View of outskirts of town with workers carrying
               wooden beams ashore (28x22cm-11x9in) s. W/C bodycol (D.FL 4000)
£2446 $4355   (30-Oct-91 CH.AM353/R) Moored boats in harbour at sunset
               (41x63cm-16x25in) s. W/C bodycol (D.FL 8000)

MARIS, Jacob (attrib) (1837-1899) Dutch
£550 $941   (18-Mar-92 CSK348) Boats in harbour (33x56cm-13x22in) bears sig. board

MARIS, Simon (1873-1935) Dutch
£608 $1058   (17-Sep-91 CH.AM378) A lady in a boudoir holding a mirror
               (51x40cm-20x16in) s. (D.FL 2000)
£700 $1197   (17-Mar-92 PH32/R) Young girl sewing by the sea (60x46cm-24x18in)
               s.i.d.1916 gouache canvas
£729 $1269   (17-Sep-91 CH.AM379) A nude standing (90x45cm-35x18in) s. (D.FL 2400)
£765 $1330   (14-Apr-92 SY.AM68) Portrait of lady in white dress (120x85cm-47x33in) s.
               (D.FL 2500)
£1468 $2598   (5-Nov-91 SY.AM207) On beach (23x17cm-9x7in) s. (D.FL 4800)
£6728 $11908   (5-Nov-91 SY.AM154/R) Children making flower garlands in dunes
               (86x108cm-34x43in) s. (D.FL 22000)
£683 $1216   (26-Nov-91 VN.R69) Woman seated in armchair (60x55cm-24x22in) s. mixed
               media (D.FL 2200)

MARIS, Willem (1844-1910) Dutch
£550 $980   (30-Oct-91 CH.AM206) Cow (41x28cm-16x11in) cardboard on panel (D.FL 1800)
£856 $1490   (14-Apr-92 SY.AM268) Holland pastures (34x45cm-13x18in) s. (D.FL 2800)
£1223 $2165   (5-Nov-91 SY.AM115/R) Flying ducks (35x24cm-14x9in) s. (D.FL 4000)
£1818 $3218   (22-Apr-92 CH.AM36) Watering cow in a meadow (44x33cm-17x13in) s.
               (D.FL 6000)
£1682 $2927   (14-Apr-92 SY.AM52/R) Duck with ducklings on waterfront (69x51cm-27x20in)
               s. W/C (D.FL 5500)
£1682 $2927   (14-Apr-92 SY.AM241) Cows in meadow (34x60cm-13x24in) s. W/C (D.FL 5500)

MARISOL (20th C) South American
£1676 $3000   (12-Nov-91 CE.NY84/R) My name is I Hate You (56x35cm-22x14in) s.i.d.1971
               graphite col.pencil

MARK, Lajos (1867-1942) Rumanian
£490 $847   (25-Mar-92 KM.K1304) Elegant lady wearing evening dress seated at table
               (78x58cm-31x23in) s. (DM 1400)

MARKES, Albert Ernest (1865-1901) British
£500 $855   *(13-Mar-92 C2) Shipping off the coast (22x28cm-9x11in) s. pencil W/C htd.white*
£1000 $1800   *(22-Nov-91 C20/R) Shipping docked in the Thames at moonlight. Barque in squall (26x37cm-10x15in) s. pencil W/C htd.white pair*
£1700 $3230   *(23-Jun-92 CG609/R) Fishing boats approaching shore. Shipping in estuary (32x48cm-13x19in) s.d.1884 W/C htd white pair*

MARKHAM, Charles C (1837-1907) American
£4396 $8000   *(28-May-92 CH.NY54/R) The little German band (35x30cm-14x12in) s.d.1874*

MARKHAM, Kyra (1891-?) American
£2557 $4500   *(12-Apr-92 LIT.L192) Spring over Halifax, Vermont (61x74cm-24x29in) s. glazed tempera*

MARKINO, Yoshio (1874-?) British
£1500 $2880   *(28-Jul-92 SWS273/R) Elegant lady in a park (27x17cm-11x7in) s.*
£800 $1440   *(27-Jan-92 PH22/R) Inner cloister, Westminster Abbey (27x36cm-11x14in) s. W/C over pencil*

MARKO, Andreas (1824-1895) Austrian
£5059 $9055   *(14-Nov-91 CH.R150/R) Lago Laziale (75x101cm-30x40in) s.d.1876 (I.L 11000000)*
£6448 $11735   *(10-Dec-91 F.R208/R) Al pascolo (46x74cm-18x29in) s.d.1879 (I.L 14000000)*
£9497 $17000   *(13-Nov-91 B.SF2250/R) Goatherders in Roman campagna (103x136cm-41x54in) s.d.1872*

MARKO, Andreas (circle) (1824-1895) Austrian
£1724 $2966   *(16-Oct-91 KM.K1268) Shepherd family with cattle in Italian landscape (40x66cm-16x26in) i.d.1885 (DM 5000)*

MARKO, Karl (19th C) Hungarian
£1453 $2500   *(15-Oct-91 CE.NY235/R) The return home (91x61cm-36x24in) s.*

MARKO, Karl (elder) (1791-1860) Hungarian
£2184 $3888   *(29-Apr-92 D.V808/R) Southern landscape with figures (18x27cm-7x11in) s. (A.S 45000)*
£4500 $8370   *(16-Jun-92 PH47/R) Classical ruins in Italianate landscape with baptism scene (33x49cm-13x19in) s.i.d.1849*
£7692 $14000   *(28-May-92 SY.NY261/R) Susannah and Elders (85x123cm-33x48in)*

MARKO, Karl (elder-attrib) (1791-1860) Hungarian
£1709 $2905   *(24-Oct-91 D.V75/R) Ruins in lake landscape (38x46cm-15x18in) (A.S 35000)*

MARKO, Karl (younger) (1822-1891) Hungarian
£2749 $4784   *(18-Sep-91 N.M615/R) Christ and Apostles on their way to Emmaus (54x79cm-21x31in) s. (DM 8000)*

MARKO, Serge (1925-) ?
£404 $694   *(20-Oct-91 PLF.P75) Breguet Alize (49x64cm-19x25in) s. W/C India ink (F.FR 4000)*

MARKOS, Andras (1950-) ?
£1195 $2174   *(25-May-92 WK.M839/R) Composition (89x99cm-35x39in) s. mixed media collage canvas (DM 3500)*
£1246 $2267   *(25-May-92 WK.M838/R) Die Entstehung eines Bogens (79x88cm-31x35in) s.d.1986 mixed media gauze on paper on board (DM 3650)*

MARKOWICZ (19th C) Polish
£520 $998   *(6-Jul-92 HC.P27/R) Les canards (38x50cm-15x20in) (F.FR 5000)*

MARKOWICZ, Arthur (1872-1934) Polish
£366 $634   *(8-Sep-91 REM.W20) Girl in front of a mirror (41x29cm-16x11in) s. pastel (P.Z 7000000)*
£378 $700   *(8-Jun-92 GG.TA62/R) Figures in park (21x29cm-8x11in) s.i.d.1919 pastel pencil*
£419 $724   *(8-Sep-91 REM.W18) At the table (28x37cm-11x15in) s. pastel (P.Z 8000000)*
£497 $860   *(8-Sep-91 REM.W19) At the table (33x26cm-13x10in) s. pastel (P.Z 9500000)*
£595 $1100   *(9-Jun-92 GG.TA285/R) Old woman reading (34x31cm-13x12in) s. pastel*
£1383 $2600   *(5-Jan-92 GG.TA283/R) Rabbi in his study (41x31cm-16x12in) s.i. pastel*

MARKS, Claude (19th C) ?
£3613 $6250   *(29-Mar-92 MY.F19/R) Grand Canal, Venice (97x81cm-38x32in) s.i.*

MARKS, George (fl.1876-1922) British
£950 $1815   *(1-Jul-92 B71/R) Summer evening-cornstooks in field near Downs (59x90cm-23x35in) s. W/C*
£1900 $3401   *(6-May-92 MMB261) On Shere Heath (30x41cm-12x16in) s.i. W/C*
£4500 $7650   *(23-Oct-91 MMB220/R) Water garden (38x51cm-15x20in) s. W/C*

MARKS, Henry Stacy (1829-1898) British
£5000 $9250   *(12-Jun-92 C196 a/R) Birds of prey (76x63cm-30x25in) s.*
£5714 $10000   *(20-Feb-92 SY.NY271/R) White stork in marshes (98x63cm-39x25in) s.*
£400 $716   *(14-Nov-91 B235/R) Lears Macaw (24x11cm-9x4in) init.i. W/C htd.white*

MARLET, Jean Henri (1771-1847) French
£504 $892   *(10-Nov-91 ZZ.F47/R) Allegorie a la gloire du citoyen rioufe*
                              (47x59cm-19x23in) pen wash indian ink htd.gouache (F.FR 5000)

MARLIAVE, Francois (1874-1953) French
£627 $1197   (29-Jun-92 CSC.P121) Le bassin a Bordeaux (23x17cm-9x7in) s. panel
                              (F.FR 6100)
£411 $785   (29-Jun-92 CSC.P114) Femme Man Tien, Chiem Hoa (22x20cm-9x8in) s.d.20 W/C
                              (F.FR 4000)
£421 $805   (29-Jun-92 CSC.P58) Ruines Egyptiennes (43x58cm-17x23in) s. gouache
                              (F.FR 4100)
£421 $805   (29-Jun-92 CSC.P102/R) Masque de Sorcier (23x17cm-9x7in) s. W/C
                              (F.FR 4100)
£432 $824   (29-Jun-92 CSC.P74) Le Vallon d'Annam (36x62cm-14x24in) s. W/C
                              (F.FR 4200)
£462 $883   (29-Jun-92 CSC.P77/R) Temple a Angkor (47x65cm-19x26in) s. W/C
                              (F.FR 4500)
£462 $883   (29-Jun-92 CSC.P8) Le marche (14x22cm-6x9in) s.d.43 W/C (F.FR 4500)
£576 $1099   (29-Jun-92 CSC.P113/R) Hue fete du printemps (21x14cm-8x6in) s.d.21 W/C
                              (F.FR 5600)
£596 $1139   (29-Jun-92 CSC.P75) Le Hameau d'Annam (41x65cm-16x26in) s. W/C
                              (F.FR 5800)
£822 $1570   (29-Jun-92 CSC.P48) Colonnes de Timgad (20x27cm-8x11in) s. W/C
                              (F.FR 8000)

MARLIER, Philippe de (circle) (c.1573-1668) Flemish
£5123 $9221   (27-Jan-92 CSC.P43/R) Corbeille de fleurs sur un entablement
                              (13x17cm-5x7in) alabaster (F.FR 50000)

MARLOW, William (1740-1813) British
£4000 $7040   (8-Apr-92 S67/R) Thames at Richmond with Cholmondeley House from river
                              (66x119cm-26x47in)
£4000 $7280   (12-Dec-91 B101/R) Italian landscape with houses near classical ruin
                              (43x53cm-17x21in)

MARLOW, William (attrib) (1740-1813) British
£2600 $4966   (21-Jul-92 PH271/R) View of Westminster Abbey from Lambeth Palace
                              (71x91cm-28x36in)

MARMION, Simon (circle) (1425-1489) French
£63536 $115000   (22-May-92 SY.NY64 a/R) Female donor with Saint Elizabeth of Hungary
                              (50x37cm-20x15in) panel right wing triptych

MARNY, Paul (1829-1914) British
£2286 $4000   (20-Feb-92 SY.NY139/R) Old Rouen (51x91cm-20x36in) s.
£440 $788   *(11-Nov-91 PH164) River in French town (21x32cm-8x13in) s. W/C ink arched*
                              top
£500 $860   *(15-Oct-91 CHAP293/R) Antwerp fromthe Tet de Flandre (51x91cm-20x36in) s.*
                              W/C
£580 $1044   *(27-Jan-92 PH172) Old clock tower, Rouen (45x30cm-18x12in) s. W/C*
£620 $1135   *(7-Feb-92 BW384) Town scene with figures (69x46cm-27x18in) s. W/C*
£700 $1253   *(11-Nov-91 PH166/R) Busy French port (17x33cm-7x13in) s. W/C ink*
£720 $1318   *(6-Feb-92 PHF141/R) View of Paris from near Port du Change*
                              (38x69cm-15x27in) s. W/C
£872 $1500   *(15-Oct-91 CE.NY92) Underneath the bridge (94x67cm-37x26in) s. W/C*
                              paperboard
£900 $1539   *(12-Mar-92 B99/R) Bridge over continental river, possibly the Seine,*
                              Paris (41x70cm-16x28in) s. W/C
£980 $1705   *(16-Sep-91 CHAP35/R) Shipping at the mouth of Scarborough Harbour*
                              (20x56cm-8x22in) s.d.1858 W/C
£1050 $1901   *(19-May-92 PH92) Rouen (59x97cm-23x38in) s. W/C ink over pencil*
£1300 $2301   *(6-Nov-91 S227/R) Saint Malo (34x64cm-13x25in) s.i. W/C htd.bodycol*
£1700 $3111   *(6-Feb-92 PHF142/R) View of Old Chartres and cathedral from river*
                              (49x90cm-19x35in) s. W/C

MAROHN, Ferdinand (19th C) French
£3586 $6455   (2-Feb-92 ZZ.F6/R) Scene animee au lavoir (53x81cm-21x32in) s.
                              (F.FR 35000)

MAROLD, Ludwig (1865-1898) Czechoslovakian
£777   *$1383*   *(29-Apr-92 D.V621/R) Young lady wearing hat and overcoat (25x14cm-10x6in)*
                              mono. W/C htd.white (A.S 16000)

MARON, Anton von (1733-1808) Austrian
£1224 $2166   (7-Nov-91 D.V316/R) Portrait of Doge Michelangelo Cambiaso of Genova
                              (38x27cm-15x11in) s.d.1792 (A.S 25000)
£14000 $25060   (13-Nov-91 S48/R) Portrait of Elizabeth Davers, Countess of Bristol,
                              seated holding book (95x70cm-37x28in) s.d.1779

MARONIEZ, Georges Philibert-ch (1865-1930) French
£1873 $3278   (5-Apr-92 CSC.P73) Coucher de soleil au bord de l'eau (26x40cm-10x16in)
                              s. board (F.FR 18000)

MAROT, Francois (1666-1719) French
£1067 $1921   (19-Nov-91 GS.B3584/R) Vertumnus and Pomona (53x65cm-21x26in) oval
   (S.FR 2700)
£4651 $8000   (9-Oct-91 CH.NY7/R) Terpsichore (91x126cm-36x50in)
£5658 $10242   (5-Dec-91 SY.MO215/R) Fruite en Egypte (97x72cm-38x28in) (F.FR 55000)

MARQUANT, Peter (1956-) Austrian
£449 $803   (15-Jan-92 D.V211/R) Landscape (42x99cm-17x39in) s.d.84 mixed media
   (A.S 9000)

MARQUES, Jose Maria (1862-1936) Spanish
£1374 $2473   (19-Nov-91 DUR.M111/R) En el rio (83x51cm-33x20in) s. (S.P 250000)

MARQUET, Albert (1875-1947) French
£16667 $31667   (24-Jun-92 FB.P34/R) Temps gris a Fontarabie (22x27cm-9x11in) s. panel
   (F.FR 162000)
£21000 $38010   (3-Dec-91 C248/R) Paris, les bords de la Seine (38x46cm-15x18in) s.
£22290 $40344   (24-May-92 GL.P56/R) Les Coteaux de l'Estaque (33x41cm-13x16in) s.
   (F.FR 220000)
£26342 $47680   (24-May-92 GL.P68/R) Laperlier a Alger (33x41cm-13x16in) s. panel
   (F.FR 260000)
£29835 $56687   (24-Jun-92 FB.P33/R) Villa Erlanger, Sidi Bou Said (33x41cm-13x16in) s.
   canvas laid down on panel (F.FR 290000)
£38384 $67939   (24-Apr-92 CN.P199/R) La douane a Alger (33x55cm-13x22in) s.
   (F.FR 380000)
£40692 $72838   (17-Nov-91 GL.P24/R) Nature morte au pichet et aux fruits
   (36x26cm-14x10in) s. (F.FR 400000)
£40733 $75356   (12-Jun-92 ARC.P41/R) Le port de Stockholm, Matin d'hiver
   (52x61cm-20x24in) s. (F.FR 400000)
£45317 $77039   (21-Oct-91 ARC.P17/R) Paris, le Pont Neuf (39x47cm-15x19in) s.
   (F.FR 450000)
£45593 $82523   (24-May-92 GL.P69/R) Les voiles, Audierne (32x41cm-13x16in) s. panel
   (F.FR 450000)
£46000 $79580   (24-Mar-92 C47/R) Le Port d'Alger (27x41cm-11x16in) s.
£50000 $90500   (3-Dec-91 C255/R) Le Port d'Alger (50x61cm-20x24in) s.
£60000 $108600   (3-Dec-91 C260/R) Alger, La Palais Consulaire et la Plaice du
   Gouvernement (50x61cm-20x24in) s.
£75000 $129750   (25-Mar-92 S63/R) Venise - San Giorgio Maggiore (46x55cm-18x22in) s.
£412 $713   (27-Mar-92 PPB.P50) Nu (19x13cm-7x5in) artist st. crayon (F.FR 4000)
£427 $743   (15-Apr-92 PLF.P91/R) Nu assis (22x16cm-9x6in) mono. crayon dr
   (F.FR 4200)
£433 $749   (27-Mar-92 PPB.P52) Nu couche Indian ink sketch same mount (F.FR 4200)
£590 $1056   (13-Nov-91 PIC.P75) Charrette attelee. Homme tirant une charrette
   (16x25cm-6x10in) init. Indian ink dr double-sided (F.FR 5800)
£676 $1184   (5-Apr-92 ZZ.F272/R) Le couple (15x8cm-6x3in) s. Indian ink dr
   (F.FR 6500)
£950 $1625   (12-Mar-92 B35) Le Port d'Oran (17x23cm-7x9in) s.i.d.1930 W/C over pencil
£1829 $3200   (27-Feb-92 CE.NY1/R) Terre rouge, Algers (12x17cm-5x7in) s. W/C over
   pencil
£2778 $5278   (24-Jun-92 FB.P87/R) Oran (16x22cm-6x9in) s.d.1930 W/C (F.FR 27000)
£3909 $7428   (26-Jun-92 AGS.P3 b/R) Vue de Vernet (21x25cm-8x10in) s.d.40 W/C
   (F.FR 38000)
£4198 $7473   (28-Nov-91 BU.S52/R) View of Stockholm, (24x36cm-9x14in) s.d.1938 W/C
   (S.KR 44000)

MARR, Carl Ritter von (1858-1936) German
£6977 $12000   (17-Oct-91 SY.NY271/R) Die flagellanten (107x88cm-42x35in) s. canvas on
   board

MARR, Joseph Heinrich Ludwig (1807-1871) German
£1224 $2093   (18-Mar-92 N.M593/R) Peasant with horse resting before alpine cottage
   (24x29cm-9x11in) s. i.stretcher (DM 3500)

MARREL, Jacob (attrib) (1614-1681) Dutch
£8287 $15000   (22-May-92 SY.NY184/R) Still life with flowers, candle, book, jewelled
   cross, staff, watch, coins and skull (51x40cm-20x16in) i.

MARSANO, L (19th C) Italian
£4000 $7240   (21-May-92 CSK208/R) Elegant company at recital (74x100cm-29x39in) s.
£6857 $12000   (19-Feb-92 CH.NY101/R) Grand entrance (68x103cm-27x41in) s.

MARSELIER, Louis see MASRELIEZ, Louis

MARSH, Arthur H (1842-1909) British
£480 $826   (3-Mar-92 AG200/R) Feeding time (106x72cm-42x28in) s. W/C

MARSH, Dale (1940-) Australian
£685 $1275   (15-Jun-92 MGS.S150) Ploughing (39x49cm-15x19in) s.d.1975 (A.D 1700)
£1282 $2282   (27-Apr-92 J.M186) Idyll chatter and golden sunlight (75x90cm-30x35in)
   s.i.d.1991 (A.D 3000)

MARSH, Lucille Patterson (1890-?) American
£899 $1600   (2-Nov-91 IH.NY27/R) Blonde haired baby peering out of crib
   (43x33cm-17x13in) s. canvasboard

MARSH, Reginald (1898-1954) American

£1117	$2000	(13-Nov-91 B.SF2707/R) Seated nude (61x36cm-24x14in) init.
£1995	$3750	(18-Dec-91 SY.NY279/R) On the boardwalk (25x20cm-10x8in) s.d.1950-53 masonite
£2281	$3900	(12-Mar-92 CH.NY203/R) Girl on carousel horse. Standing nude masonite pair
£2924	$5000	(12-Mar-92 CH.NY208/R) Two on horse (30x41cm-12x16in) s. tempera board
£4696	$8500	(5-Dec-91 SY.NY97/R) 14th Street shopper (41x30cm-16x12in) s.d.1950 tempera board
£5525	$10000	(6-Dec-91 CH.NY208/R) The boardwalk (42x31cm-17x12in) s.d.53 masonite
£5747	$10000	(15-Sep-91 JRB.C100 a) Two women tempera board
£5848	$10000	(11-Mar-92 SY.NY94/R) Shopper (41x30cm-16x12in) s.d.48 canvasboard
£5866	$10500	(6-May-92 D.NY31/R) Three women (56x38cm-22x15in) i.verso cardboard
£769	$1400	(28-May-92 BG.M557/R) Freighter with other boats (36x51cm-14x20in) s.d.1928 W/C
£1287	$2200	(12-Mar-92 CH.NY202/R) Tugboat at dock (35x50cm-14x20in) s.d.1931 W/C pencil
£1287	$2200	(12-Mar-92 CH.NY204/R) Summer manse (35x50cm-14x20in) s.d.1929 W/C pen
£1637	$2800	(12-Mar-92 CH.NY219/R) New York Harbour (35x51cm-14x20in) s. W/C pencil
£1868	$3250	(15-Apr-92 SY.NY201/R) Out for stroll (23x19cm-9x7in) s.d.53 d.1953 verso W/C
£2807	$4800	(12-Mar-92 CH.NY205/R) Cityscape, New York (36x50cm-14x20in) s.d.1931 W/(pencil
£2880	$5500	(17-Jul-92 DM.D2009/R) Beach scene (28x38cm-11x15in) s.d.1951 W/C
£4190	$7500	(13-Nov-91 B.SF2706/R) In surf (69x102cm-27x40in) s.d.1947 ink wash
£4971	$8500	(12-Mar-92 CH.NY206/R) Trainyards, New York (35x56cm-14x22in) s.d.1929 W/C pencil
£6044	$11000	(28-May-92 CH.NY217/R) Reading in Times Square (53x38cm-21x15in) s.d.38 W/C chl gouache
£8000	$14000	(26-Sep-91 CH.NY272/R) Skyscrapers (35x51cm-14x20in) s.d.1931 W/C
£13736	$25000	(28-May-92 CH.NY225/R) New York street scenes (55x75cm-22x30in) brush ink wash W/C double-sided

MARSHALL, Ben (1767-1835) British

£800	$1376	(3-Mar-92 SWS1636/R) A fighting cock (61x47cm-24x19in) canvas laid on panel
£3646	$6600	(4-Dec-91 NA.BA27) Sir Charles Bunbury's 'Eleanor', a bay racehorse (71x91cm-28x36in) s.
£19126	$35000	(5-Jun-92 SY.NY25/R) Portrait of the artist and his favourite Newfoundland (72x88cm-28x35in) s.d.1811
£36000	$63360	(8-Apr-92 S130/R) Gentleman on bay hunter in landscape (84x100cm-33x39in) s.d.1832

MARSHALL, Charles (1806-1896) British

£1300	$2379	(3-Jun-92 S43/R) Old bridge and country of the Test, Hants (20x40cm-8x16in) s.

MARSHALL, Charles Edward (fl.1872-1903) British

£500	$955	(16-Jul-92 CSK243/R) Sabrina (60x50cm-24x20in) s.d.1889 i.verso

MARSHALL, Herbert Menzies (1841-1913) British

£400	$760	(24-Jun-92 PHI510) Paddle steamers in the Thames estuary (14x24cm-6x9in) s.d.1894 W/C
£600	$1032	(15-Oct-91 CSK645) The Houses of Parliament from Lambeth (16x25cm-6x10in) s. W/C
£720	$1296	(27-Jan-92 PH196/R) Shadwell Reach (21x32cm-8x13in) s.d.1892 W/C
£800	$1376	(4-Mar-92 S214/R) Continental river (13x30cm-5x12in) s.d.1897 W/C
£800	$1376	(15-Oct-91 CSK648) Whitby Harbour (36x54cm-14x21in) s.d.1888 W/C
£850	$1462	(4-Mar-92 S218/R) Busy river (25x35cm-10x14in) s. W/C
£1100	$1892	(4-Mar-92 S210/R) Waiting for ferry (35x51cm-14x20in) s.d.1907 W/C htd white
£1300	$2210	(22-Oct-91 SWS207/R) Ludgate Hill from cathedral steps (35x25cm-14x10in) s.d.1895 i.verso W/C over pencil
£1700	$3043	(11-Nov-91 PH167/R) St Mary-le-Strand, London (29x20cm-11x8in) s. W/C over pencil
£2600	$4810	(12-Jun-92 C17/R) St Pancras (25x36cm-10x14in) s.i.d.1892 pencil W/C

MARSHALL, J G (19th C) British?

£1800	$3258	(20-May-92 S62/R) Portsmouth Harbour (21x28cm-8x11in) s.d.62

MARSHALL, J Miller (19th C) British

£2128	$3766	(26-Apr-92 SY.ME427/R) Picnic by river (61x74cm-24x29in) s.d.1890 (A.D 5000)
£400	$688	(11-Oct-91 K447) Reedham on the Yare (23x41cm-9x16in) s.d.1886 W/C

MARSHALL, John (fl.1840-1896) British

£750	$1290	(4-Mar-92 S74) Safe hiding place (23x30cm-9x12in) init. canvasboard
£2700	$4779	(6-Nov-91 S111/R) Still life of cherries and basket (33x44cm-13x17in) s.d.1888

MARSHALL, Lambert (attrib) (1810-1870) British

£3462	$6612	(15-Jul-92 CH.S786/R) Racehorse with groom in landscape (40x55cm-16x22in) (A.D 9000)

MARSHALL, Peter Paul (1830-1900) British
£6500 $11050   (25-Oct-91 C59/R) Countess Czerlaski and brother. Rev Amos Barton and family (51x40cm-20x16in) s. one indis.i.verso panel pair

MARSHALL, Roberto Angelo Kittermaster (1849-1902) British
£1005 $1789   (29-Oct-91 PH.T110/R) Near Haslemere, Surrey (34x49cm-13x19in) s. W/C (C.D 2000)
£1100 $1991   (20-May-92 BT70/R) Sheep grazing in sunlit meadow (33x58cm-13x23in) s. W/C
£1300 $2236   (16-Oct-91 HAR397/R) Extensive landscape with shepherd and flock (36x58cm-14x23in) s.
£1400 $2562   (3-Jun-92 S260/R) Near Haslemere, Surrey (34x49cm-13x19in) s. W/C
£1600 $2864   (14-Jan-92 SWS89/R) Near Wableton, Hants (33x58cm-13x23in) s. W/C
£1700 $3145   (12-Jun-92 C31/R) Sheep grazing in a meadow, Surrey (34x52cm-13x20in) s. pencil W/C
£2200 $4136   (19-Dec-91 C41/R) Landscape with sheep grazing by stream (36x53cm-14x21in) s. pencil W/C

MARSHALL, Thomas Falcon (1818-1878) British
£800 $1392   (12-Sep-91 CSK244) A moment's rest (61x51cm-24x20in) s.d.1848

MARSHALL, William Elstob (1837-1906) American
£2800 $4984   (28-Apr-92 PH101/R) Ptarmigan (51x62cm-20x24in) s.d.1870

MARSILLACH, Joaquim (1905-) Spanish
£711 $1266   (29-Oct-91 BRO.B360) Robles, Moixina (33x41cm-13x16in) s.d.68 i.verso tablex (S.P 130000)
£713 $1268   (26-Nov-91 BRO.B345) Carretera de la Moixina, Olot (33x46cm-13x18in) s.d.68 s.i.verso (S.P 130000)
£1051 $1975   (17-Dec-91 BRO.B407) Paisaje con figuras (46x55cm-18x22in) s. (S.P 190000)
£1096 $1951   (26-Nov-91 BRO.B409) Llansa, Puerto (21x43cm-8x17in) s.d.68 i.d.verso panel (S.P 200000)
£1423 $2532   (29-Oct-91 BRO.B289) Paisaje nevado (38x55cm-15x22in) s. (S.P 260000)
£1751 $3117   (29-Oct-91 BRO.B353) Puenta de la Moras con nieve, Olot (46x61cm-18x24in) s. i.verso (S.P 320000)
£5253 $9876   (17-Dec-91 BRO.B330) Paisaje panoramico (97x130cm-38x51in) s.d.67 (S.P 950000)

MARSTON, C (19/20th C) ?
£617 $1049   (21-Oct-91 SY.J373) Table Bay with shipping (25x65cm-10x26in) s. board (SA.R 3000)

MARSTON, Mabel G (fl.1885-1903) British
£675 $1181   (27-Feb-92 WAW362) Delphiniums, ramblers and scabious still life (51x41cm-20x16in) s. board

MARSTRAND, Wilhelm (1810-1873) Danish
£484 $813   (28-Aug-91 KH.K138) Young Italian girl with white headscarf (21x17cm-8x7in) (D.KR 5500)
£546 $917   (28-Aug-91 KH.K137) Rider on wooded path (24x29cm-9x11in) (D.KR 6200)
£617 $1099   (28-Apr-92 RAS.K169/R) Study of Italian lady with striped head scarf (46x37cm-18x15in) indist.s.d.1847 (D.KR 7000)
£1058 $1884   (28-Apr-92 RAS.K168/R) Study of a young girl (44x39cm-17x15in) i.d.1837 (D.KR 12000)
£1320 $2218   (27-Aug-91 RAS.K398/R) Interior with mother mending socks by sleeping child (34x22cm-13x9in) (D.KR 15000)
£1585 $2662   (27-Aug-91 RAS.K385/R) Young Italian dancing (37x21cm-15x8in) sketch (D.KR 18000)
£1761 $2958   (27-Aug-91 RAS.K178 a/R) Italian lady on balcony (40x29cm-16x11in) (D.KR 20000)
£2465 $4141   (27-Aug-91 RAS.K136/R) Seated Italian woman with red blouse (36x24cm-14x9in) (D.KR 28000)
£2662 $4764   (16-Nov-91 FAL.M212/R) Italian interior with mother and two children (46x37cm-18x15in) mono.d.40 (S.KR 28000)
£3081 $5176   (27-Aug-91 RAS.K81/R) Scene from an auction (21x30cm-8x12in) sketch (D.KR 35000)
£4401 $7394   (27-Aug-91 RAS.K137/R) Portrait of Ida Marie Louise Munster (34x27cm-13x11in) init.d.1835 (D.KR 50000)

MARTA, Luigi (19th C) Italian
£2000 $3400   (23-Oct-91 S140/R) Pensive Greek hero at seashore (27x21cm-11x8in) s. W/C over pencil htd.gum arabic

MARTCHENKO, Tatiana (1918-) Russian
£512 $911   (25-Nov-91 ARC.P57/R) Sous les tournesols (110x90cm-43x35in) s. (F.FR 5000)
£566 $1024   (6-Dec-91 ARC.P37/R) La branche de pommier (65x80cm-26x31in) s. hardboard (F.FR 5500)
£716 $1275   (25-Nov-91 ARC.P58/R) Bouquet de fleurs des champs (71x51cm-28x20in) s. hardboard (F.FR 7000)
£844 $1527   (6-Dec-91 ARC.P34/R) Travaux d'hiver (100x80cm-39x31in) s. (F.FR 8200)
£1126 $2004   (25-Nov-91 ARC.P59/R) Un insecte interssant (34x24cm-13x9in) s. board (F.FR 11000)

MARTEAU, Augusto (1890-?) Argentinian
£824 $1500   (11-Dec-91 RO.BA452) En la plaza (57x71cm-22x28in) s.

MARTEN, Elliot H (fl.1886) British
£400 $700   (1-Apr-92 B147) Harvesters in landscape (34x49cm-13x19in) s. W/C
£420 $739   (9-Apr-92 B45/R) Dorset coast near Lulworth (38x53cm-15x21in) s. W/C
£450 $774   (10-Oct-91 B195/R) Evening, Arun (26x18cm-10x7in) s. W/C

MARTENS, Conrad (1801-1878) Australian
£4405 $7930   (24-Nov-91 SY.S368/R) Invermien (23x36cm-9x14in) s. W/C pencil
                        (A.D 10000)
£513 $913   (28-Apr-92 CH.ME241) Study for Kangaroo Point (12x23cm-5x9in) W/C
                        (A.D 1200)
£775 $1481   (21-Jul-92 JRL.S101) Devonshire village (22x15cm-9x6in) W/C (A.D 2000)
£775 $1481   (21-Jul-92 JRL.S108) Afternoon, Hawkesbury River (14x21cm-6x8in) W/C
                        (A.D 2000)
£800 $1368   (17-Mar-92 JRL.S206) Bakers daughters (18x46cm-7x18in) init. W/C
                        (A.D 1800)
£4000 $7280   (28-May-92 C10/R) Approach to Montevideo Bay (20x30cm-8x12in) W/C
£9000 $15300   (22-Oct-91 C96/R) Sydney harbour looking towards North Head from
                        Rushcutters Bay (47x67cm-19x26in) s.d.1836 pencil W/C
£19500 $33150   (22-Oct-91 C101/R) View of Parramatta River from Wollstonecraft, with
                        Sydney in distance (45x66cm-18x26in) s. with i.verso W/C bodycol htd
                        gum arabic

MARTENS, Ernest (1865-?) French
£6395 $11000   (17-Oct-91 SY.NY224/R) Promenade en barque (60x73cm-24x29in) s.

MARTENS, Luise Henriette von (1828-1897) German
£5226 $9512   (12-Dec-91 L.K623/R) Portrait of little girl holding rabbit
                        (87x67cm-34x26in) s.d.1867 (DM 15000)

MARTENS, Willem Johannes (1838-1895) Dutch
£5758 $10191   (22-Apr-92 CH.AM294/R) Elegant beauty on a balcony (54x32cm-21x13in) s.i.
                        W/C bodycol. (D.FL 19000)

MARTIARENA, Ascensio (1883-?) Spanish
£2749 $4838   (9-Apr-92 ANS.M114/R) Autorretrato (123x100cm-48x39in) s. (S.P 500000)

MARTIN (?) ?
£737 $1260   (13-Mar-92 FN.S360/R) Portrait of young lady with one shoulder bare seen
                        from behind (9x7cm-4x3in) min.s.d.1802 gouache ivory oval (DM 2100)
£1437 $2557   (29-Nov-91 F.F131/R) Constellation I (71x103cm-28x41in) s.d.1960 oil
                        mixed media cardboard (I.L 3100000)
£1543 $2793   (3-Dec-91 CN.P32/R) Marine, avec le bateau Amiral de la flotte
                        Hollandaise (17x24cm-7x9in) s.d.1677 pen wash (F.FR 15000)

MARTIN, Agnes (1912-) American
£111732 $200000   (13-Nov-91 SY.NY57 a/R) Stone (183x183cm-72x72in) oil pencil canvas
£178771 $320000   (13-Nov-91 SY.NY36/R) Night sea (183x183cm-72x72in) s.d.63 verso canvas
                        with gold leaf
£3631 $6500   (12-Nov-91 CE.NY31/R) Aspiration (30x24cm-12x9in) pen ink
£81006 $145000   (6-May-92 SY.NY30/R) Untitled XXI (183x183cm-72x72in) d.1980 s.verso
                        acrylic gesso graphite canvas
£100559 $180000   (6-May-92 SY.NY52/R) Happy valley (183x183cm-72x72in) s.i.d.1967verso
                        acrylic pencil ink canvas

MARTIN, Andreas (18th C) Dutch
£8741 $14948   (18-Mar-92 N.M438/R) Encampment in river landscape with town beyond
                        (42x56cm-17x22in) s. panel (DM 25000)

MARTIN, Benito Quinquela see QUINQUELA MARTIN, Benito

MARTIN, David (1736-1798) British
£2907 $5000   (10-Oct-91 SY.NY26/R) Portrait of a young man said to be Archibald Seaton
                        (75x62cm-30x24in) s.d.1788
£1100 $1969   (11-Nov-91 S528/R) Portrait of Andrew Agnew when boy (44x37cm-17x15in)
                        pastel

MARTIN, E (?) ?
£1186 $2134   (21-Nov-91 SY.G6/R) Portrait of lady with roses in hair wearing low-cut
                        dress (9x?cm-4x?in) min.s.i.d.c.1835 oval gilt metal wood frame
                        (S.FR 3000)

MARTIN, Elias (1739-1818) Swedish
£1044 $1910   (14-May-92 BU.S98/R) St. John the Baptist preaching in the desert
                        (23x29cm-9x11in) W/C (S.KR 11000)

MARTIN, Etienne Philippe (1858-1945) French
£823 $1564   (22-Jun-92 AT.P93) Village fortifie en Haute-Provence (32x40cm-13x16in)
                        s. panel (F.FR 8000)
£1643 $2957   (18-Nov-91 AT.P365) La sortie des mauresques (101x60cm-40x24in) s.
                        (F.FR 16000)

MARTIN, Eugene-Louis (1880-1954) Swiss
£547 $980 (6-May-92 GD.B819/R) View of Lake Lugano with figures on lakeside path
              (24x46cm-9x18in) s. (S.FR 1500)
£1131 $1945 (4-Mar-92 AT.P172) Bretons dans un interieur (33x41cm-13x16in) s.
              (F.FR 11000)

MARTIN, Fletcher (1904-1979) American
£638 $1200 (18-Dec-91 SY.NY389/R) Stormy weather (50x38cm-20x15in) s. egg tempera
              board
£638 $1200 (18-Dec-91 SY.NY275/R) Profile of a sailor (50x40cm-20x16in)
£3509 $6000 (12-Mar-92 CH.NY218/R) Snug harbour (86x66cm-34x26in) s.d.33 s.i.verso
£838 $1500 (13-Nov-91 B.SF2753/R) Poker players (48x36cm-19x14in) s. W/C

MARTIN, Frances K (?) ?
£926 $1620 (17-Feb-92 AD.D63) Lady reading book beside lilac tree (61x74cm-24x29in)
              s. (E.P 1000)

MARTIN, H (?) ?
£920 *$1600* *(13-Sep-91 S.W2340/R) Venetian canal (38x66cm-15x26in) s. W/C*

MARTIN, Henri (1860-1943) French
£3354 $5835 (19-Apr-92 ZZ.F107/R) Les calanques de Cassis (24x33cm-9x13in) s.i. panel
              (F.FR 33000)
£8743 $16000 (13-May-92 CH.NY210/R) Portrait de Madame Henri Martin (51x37cm-20x15in)
              s.
£10405 $18000 (2-Oct-91 SY.NY25/R) Muse (65x46cm-26x18in) s.
£14754 $27000 (14-May-92 SY.NY266/R) Le Port de Marseille (35x78cm-14x31in) s.
£18145 $32117 (10-Nov-91 ZZ.F146/R) Reflets d'arbres sur la riviere pres de la Bastide
              du Vert (94x50cm-37x20in) s. (F.FR 180000)
£18955 $34119 (2-Feb-92 ZZ.F114/R) La petite eglise du village (83x50cm-33x20in) s.
              (F.FR 185000)
£32587 $59633 (3-Jun-92 HC.P34/R) Sous la pergola a Marquayrol (165x270cm-65x106in) s.
              (F.FR 320000)
£32787 $60000 (13-May-92 CH.NY216/R) Le bassin (82x82cm-32x32in) s.
£32830 $55811 (24-Oct-91 CSC.P20/R) La bastide du vert en automne (81x54cm-32x21in) s.
              (F.FR 326000)
£36885 $67500 (14-May-92 SY.NY262/R) Trois femmes dans le jardin (66x81cm-26x32in)
              st.sig.
£40000 $72400 (4-Dec-91 S121/R) Paysage du Lot (70x98cm-28x39in) s.
£4200 $7266 (25-Mar-92 S17/R) Paysanne tricotant (53x31cm-21x12in) s. pencil

MARTIN, Homer D (1836-1897) American
£1389 $2500 (24-Nov-91 JRB.C62/R) Moon at sunset (46x76cm-18x30in) s.

MARTIN, J (?) ?
£946 *$1626* *(4-Mar-92 AT.P73) La visite de Rome (70x52cm-28x20in) s. W/C gouache
              (F.FR 9200)*

MARTIN, Jacques (1844-1919) French
£593 $1055 (29-Nov-91 GAB.G2138) Le jardin (21x25cm-8x10in) studio st. paper
              (S.FR 1500)
£1178 $2250 (17-Jul-92 DM.D2000/R) Nature morte avec fleur (53x76cm-21x30in) s.
£1512 $2676 (5-Nov-91 GGL.L3/R) La robe blanche (73x45cm-29x18in) s.d.1908 board
              (F.FR 15000)

MARTIN, Jean Baptiste (1659-1735) French
£11111 $20111 (19-May-92 GF.L2086/R) Sharing of the loot in captured town
              (75x98cm-30x39in) (S.FR 30000)

MARTIN, John (1789-1854) British
£1092 $1900 (13-Sep-91 S.W2843/R) Venetian view (76x104cm-30x41in) s.d.1850
£1951 $3532 (2-Dec-91 R.T145/R) Winter morning (53x64cm-21x25in) s. (C.D 4000)
£390 *$706* *(2-Dec-91 R.T147/R) Disturbed cat (55x76cm-22x30in) s.i.d.1962verso
              (C.D 800)*
£642 $1175 (2-Jun-92 R.T426/R) McAvity (38x51cm-15x20in) s.d.1960 studio st.verso
              W/C (C.D 1400)
£1193 $2183 (2-Jun-92 R.T448/R) Stupidity Street (51x50cm-20x20in) s.d.53 copolymer
              masonite (C.D 2600)
£3652 $6500 (22-Jan-92 SY.NY474/R) Cornfield with distant church and shower
              (18x28cm-7x11in) s.d.1839 W/C

MARTIN, Jules (19th C) French
£612 $1083 (5-Nov-91 SY.AM81) Figures in street of town (33x24cm-13x9in) s. panel
              (D.FL 2000)

MARTIN, Maurice (19th C) Swiss
£650 $1183 (12-Dec-91 CSK192) Young boy fishing (53x66cm-21x26in) s.
£973 $1800 (12-Jun-92 SY.NY141/R) Road to the village (54x64cm-21x25in) s.
£3107 $5500 (6-Nov-91 D.NY41/R) Village in snow (88x100cm-35x39in) s. i.verso
              i.stretcher

MARTIN, P (?) ?
£697 *$1268* *(11-Dec-91 N.M287/R) Portrait of lady (7x6cm-3x2in) min. s. W/C gouache
              ivory oval brass frame (DM 2000)*

MARTIN, Philip (1927-) British
£568	$966	(22-Oct-91 C.A798) Affiche pour pompei (88x61cm-35x24in) s.d.1961 mixed media (B.FR 34000)
£1576	$2804	(26-Nov-91 SY.MI8/R) Winter quarters (67x91cm-26x36in) s.init.d.61 oil mixed media paper on panel (I.L 3400000)

MARTIN, Pierre Denis (1663-1742) French
£13388	$25170	(18-Dec-91 AT.P59/R) Vue du Chateau de Saint Germain en Laye avec le depart pour la chasse (59x89cm-23x35in) (F.FR 130000)

MARTIN, S R (?) ?
£1538	$2800	(26-May-92 CE.NY302/R) The Forum (49x71cm-19x28in) s. W/C

MARTIN, Sue Pettey (1896-?) American
£523	$900	(10-Oct-91 FA.PH841/R) Sleeping nude (97x119cm-38x47in) init. s.stretcher

MARTIN, Sylvester (19th C) British
£2500	$4575	(7-Feb-92 BW380/R) Study of poacher with pheasant and two hounds near wooded bank and fence (51x76cm-20x30in) i.verso
£2800	$4984	(28-Nov-91 B153/R) After a big day, Kenilworth (27x47cm-11x19in) s.i.d.1896 set of four

MARTIN, Thomas Mower (1838-1934) Canadian
£597	$1063	(26-Nov-91 JOY.T57/R) Cattle watering in stream (100x85cm-39x33in) s. (C.D 1200)
£365	$665	(26-May-92 JOY.T128) Lake scene, Northern Ontario (32x48cm-13x19in) s. W/C (C.D 800)
£896	$1594	(26-Nov-91 JOY.T30/R) Rocky Mountain vista (62x95cm-24x37in) s. W/C (C.D 1800)

MARTIN, Tomas (1858-1919) Spanish?
£660	$1187	(19-Nov-91 DUR.M140/R) Paisaje (12x22cm-5x9in) panel (S.P 120000)

MARTIN, Vicente (?) Uruguayan
£453	$860	(25-Jun-92 GOM.M55) Mujer (73x73cm-29x29in) s. enamel canvas
£537	$1020	(25-Jun-92 GOM.M54) Caballo y luna (72x72cm-28x28in) s. enamel canvas

MARTIN, William A K (1817-1867) American
£585	$1000	(21-Mar-92 S.BM23/R) U.S. Ship Ontario (25x36cm-10x14in) s.i.d.1848 with i.verso W/C ink

MARTIN-FERRIERES, Jac (1893-1972) French
£817	$1430	(23-Feb-92 I.N179) Composition florale (50x65cm-20x26in) s. (F.FR 8000)
£1012	$1802	(29-Apr-92 D.P141/R) Florence (38x46cm-15x18in) s. panel (F.FR 10000)
£1249	$2185	(5-Apr-92 ZZ.F127/R) Vue du Bois de Boulogne (38x46cm-15x18in) s. panel (F.FR 12000)
£1704	$3084	(20-May-92 GK.Z5050/R) View of Tolede (65x50cm-26x20in) s.i. (S.FR 4600)
£1778	$3218	(20-May-92 GK.Z5145/R) Mountainous Danish lake landscape (53x80cm-21x31in) s. (S.FR 4800)
£1852	$3352	(20-May-92 GK.Z5097/R) Church goers in Concarneau (54x65cm-21x26in) s. (S.FR 5000)
£2037	$3687	(20-May-92 GK.Z5049/R) Lakeside village in hilly landscape (60x81cm-24x32in) S. (S.FR 5500)
£2714	$4750	(28-Feb-92 SY.NY186/R) Reclining nude in bedroom (46x61cm-18x24in) s. masonite
£4651	$8000	(14-Oct-91 H.C89/R) Collioure (69x86cm-27x34in) s.
£8000	$14000	(25-Feb-92 CH.NY50/R) Chioggia (45x55cm-18x22in) s.d.24
£9143	$16000	(25-Feb-92 CH.NY66/R) Collioure (69x86cm-27x34in) s.

MARTIN-KAVEL, Francois (19/20th C) French
£1086	$2009	(9-Jun-92 FB.M189/R) Gitane (63x80cm-25x31in) s. (C.D 2400)

MARTINAU, Natalie (1845-1936) Finnish
£2276	$4005	(12-Apr-92 HOR.H163) The domino player (119x90cm-47x35in) s. (F.M 18000)

MARTINEAU, Edith (1842-1909) British
£460	$833	(19-May-92 SWS448) Horse and cart in moorland (18x35cm-7x14in) s. W/C bodycol
£1700	$2924	(4-Mar-92 S282/R) Wheelbarrow (26x34cm-10x13in) s.d.1884 W/C htd bodycol
£2200	$3894	(6-Nov-91 S291/R) Rustic courtship (28x37cm-11x15in) s.d.1888 W/C
£2700	$4752	(6-Apr-92 PH92/R) Potato harvest (49x61cm-19x24in) s,d,1888 W/C
£5500	$9460	(4-Mar-92 S268/R) Heard melodies are sweet but those unheard are sweeter - Keats (48x31cm-19x12in) s. s.i.verso W/C

MARTINELLI, Giovanni (1610-1659) Italian
£8000	$14560	(13-Dec-91 C259/R) Young woman painter enticed by old woman with money bag (96x78cm-38x31in)

MARTINELLI, Niccolo see TROMETTA, Nicolo

MARTINETTI, Angelo (19th C) Italian
£8854	$15141	(17-Mar-92 FER.M118/R) Los polluelos observando al saltamontes. Los polluelos cogiendo su presa (22x32cm-9x13in) s. panel pair (S.P 1600000)

ARTINETTI, Maria (19th C) Italian
£1047 $2000   (16-Jul-92 SY.NY599/R) The game (37x55cm-15x22in) s. W/C
£1100 $1881   (19-Mar-92 B3 a) A Ciocciara (66x51cm-26x20in) s.i. W/C

ARTINEZ CHECA, Fernando (?) Spanish
£831 $1455   (18-Feb-92 DUR.M64/R) Puente de Valmaseda, Pais vasco (65x131cm-26x52in)
                 s. (S.P 150000)
£2462 $4482   (11-Dec-91 FER.M147 a/R) Bodegon de claveles rojos y pensamientos
                 (90x129cm-35x51in) s. (S.P 450000)

ARTINEZ DE LEON, Andres (1895-1978) Spanish
£383 $732   (2-Jul-92 ANS.M32/R) Romeros del Rocio (23x34cm-9x13in) s. ink dr
                (S.P 70000)

ARTINEZ NOVILLO, Cirilo (1921-) Spanish
£774 $1455   (17-Dec-91 DUR.M85/R) Paisaje con arboles y casa (24x33cm-9x13in) gouache
                 (S.P 140000)

ARTINEZ PEDRO, Luis (1910-) Cuban
£1492 $2700   (19-May-92 SY.NY115/R) Figura (60x44cm-24x17in) s.d.48 gouache

ARTINEZ, Alfredo Ramos (1872-1946) Mexican
£35912 $65000   (18-May-92 CH.NY85/R) La India de las Floripondias (76x61cm-30x24in) s.
£11050 $20000   (19-May-92 SY.NY107/R) Tres mujeres (52x42cm-20x17in) s. gouache ink
                 newsprint laid down on board
£13260 $24000   (19-May-92 SY.NY26/R) Tres mujeres (56x43cm-22x17in) s. pastel chl
                 gouache newsprint on board

ARTINEZ, Antonio Nicolas (1883-?) Spanish
£763 $1313   (7-Oct-91 ANS.M167/R) Rincon rural (27x17cm-11x7in) s. panel (S.P 140000)

ARTINEZ, Enrique (19th C) Spanish
£1524 $2667   (18-Feb-92 DUR.M28/R) La Escalinata (39x24cm-15x9in) s. (S.P 275000)

RTINEZ, Gonzalo Bilbao (?) ?
£7692 $14000   (28-May-92 SY.NY125 a/R) La cigarreras (65x84cm-26x33in) s.

ARTINEZ, Julian (1897-1943) American
£378 $700   (14-Jun-92 S.BM19/R) Deer dancer (23x28cm-9x11in) s. gouache
£405 $750   (14-Jun-92 S.BM18/R) Deer dancer (25x30cm-10x12in) s. gouache
£464 $850   (8-Feb-92 S.BM22/R) Deer dancers (30x48cm-12x19in) s. gouache
£595 $1100   (14-Jun-92 S.BM13/R) Antelope dancers (23x28cm-9x11in) gouache

ARTINEZ, Ricardo (1918-) Mexican
£8287 $15000   (19-May-92 SY.NY155/R) La mujer verde (114x85cm-45x33in) s.d.61
£9444 $17000   (19-Nov-91 CH.NY66/R) Los musicos (80x105cm-31x41in) s.d.54
£9444 $17000   (19-Nov-91 CH.NY65/R) El Peregrino (60x55cm-24x22in) s.d.43 masonite
£12155 $22000   (19-May-92 SY.NY180/R) Figura con fondo azul (100x150cm-39x59in) s.d.81
£12778 $23000   (18-Nov-91 SY.NY165/R) Hombre en reposo (89x49cm-35x19in) s.d.60
£14365 $26000   (18-May-92 CH.NY110/R) Hombre primitivo (150x129cm-59x51in) s.d.60
£20556 $37000   (18-Nov-91 SY.NY69/R) Hombre (120x80cm-47x31in) s.d.55
£27624 $50000   (18-May-92 CH.NY14/R) Pareja Antigua (201x175cm-79x69in) s.d.68

ARTINEZ, S (19th C) Spanish
£1953 $3457   (5-Nov-91 GF.L2502/R) Soldier drinking (66x49cm-26x19in) s. (S.FR 5000)

ARTINEZ, Santiago (?) Spanish
£720 $1296   (29-Jan-92 FER.M231) Paseando junto a la Mezquita de Cordoba
                 (25x31cm-10x12in) s. (S.P 130000)
£997 $1794   (29-Jan-92 FER.M230/R) El Loreto (99x79cm-39x31in) s.i. (S.P 180000)
£1107 $1993   (29-Jan-92 FER.M229/R) Mediodia en la plaza de la Iglesia
                 (66x55cm-26x22in) s. (S.P 200000)

ARTINEZ-PEDRO, Luis (20th C) Cuban
£3867 $7000   (18-May-92 CH.NY117/R) Retrato con paisaje cubano (56x50cm-22x20in)
                 s.d.41 pencil

ARTINI, Alberto (1876-1954) Italian
£626 $1114   (27-Nov-91 F.M29) Dopo il temporale (30x42cm-12x17in) mono.d.1896 gouache
                 (I.L 1350000)
£814 $1473   (21-May-92 F.M274/R) Vulcano, illustrazione per La secchia rapita
                 (6x17cm-2x7in) mono indian ink (I.L 1800000)
£2741 $4769   (14-Apr-92 F.M71/R) Sorriso infernale (69x49cm-27x19in) s.d.1919 pastel
                 board (I.L 6000000)
£3168 $5766   (26-May-92 SY.MI33/R) Signora orientale nel palco (62x46cm-24x18in) s.
                 pastel board (I.L 7000000)
£4634 $8248   (27-Nov-91 F.M267/R) La carne e lo spirito (51x36cm-20x14in) s.i.d.1928
                 indian ink (I.L 10000000)

ARTINI, F (?) ?
£460 $833   (19-May-92 SWS467) The Spanish Steps, Rome (34x26cm-13x10in) s. W/C over
                pencil

ARTINI, Gaetano de (1845-?) Italian
£465 $800   (9-Oct-91 RO.BA197) Buena ventura (36x21cm-14x8in) s. W/C

MARTINI, Johann Gottfried (fl.1716-1759) German
£13000 $24960   (8-Jul-92 S278/R) Trompe l'oeil still life of leather folio with manuscript and book pages (66x96cm-26x38in) s.d.1757 pen W/C htd.gilt

MARTINI, Joseph de (1896-?) American
£805 $1400   (15-Apr-92 SY.NY156/R) Barges on river (51x76cm-20x30in) s. board

MARTINI, Simone (after) (c.1284-1344) Italian
£4437 $8031   (21-May-92 L.K89/R) Madonna with Child (74x40cm-29x16in) gold ground panel pointed top (DM 13000)

MARTINI, Simone (style) (c.1284-1344) Italian
£1648 $3000   (13-Dec-91 S.W2629/R) Annunciation (56x51cm-22x20in) mixed media gold leaf panel

MARTINI, Vivaldo (1908-1989) Italian
£912 $1633   (6-May-92 GD.B827/R) Seated nude by fountain (65x54cm-26x21in) s. (S.FR 2500)
£1277 $2286   (6-May-92 GD.B828/R) Composition (68x87cm-27x34in) s. panel (S.FR 3500)

MARTINO, Antonio Pietro (1902-1989) American
£1705 $3000   (9-Apr-92 FA.PH718/R) Houses in winter landscape (51x61cm-20x24in) s.
£2374 $4250   (6-May-92 B.P72/R) Rock (64x71cm-25x28in) s.d.1925
£2614 $4600   (9-Apr-92 FA.PH724/R) Winter landscape in Manayunk (76x91cm-30x36in) s. canvas on masonite

MARTINO, Edoardo (1838-1912) Italian
£650 $1131   (14-Apr-92 CSK171/R) Royal yacht Victoria and Albert III anchored off rocky headland (30x25cm-12x10in) indist.s.i.d.1907
£1500 $2700   (9-Jan-92 B289/R) A Man-o-War drying her hammocks in the Mediterranean (25x46cm-10x18in) s. board
£1800 $3132   (14-Apr-92 CSK173/R) Cunard liner S.S.Servia in Mersey (23x46cm-9x18in) s.i.d.81 i.verso
£1900 $3629   (17-Jul-92 C166/R) An English man-o-war off the Italian coast (22x42cm-9x17in) s. board
£6044 $11000   (11-Dec-91 RO.BA61/R) Marina (23x38cm-9x15in) s.d.85

MARTINSEN, Kaare (1912-1986) Norwegian
£482 $897   (15-Jun-92 B.O107/R) Landscape with farm and animals (54x46cm-21x18in) s. panel (N.KR 5500)

MARTRO, Andrey (20th C) ?
£665 $1150   (26-Mar-92 DUR.M954/R) Jovenes (80x63cm-31x25in) s.d.84 (S.P 120000)

MARUSSIG, Piero (1879-1937) Italian
£9282 $17450   (19-Dec-91 F.M164/R) Figure a passeggio (70x60cm-28x24in) s. (I.L 20000000)
£9296 $16825   (3-Dec-91 F.R197/R) Malinconia (124x190cm-49x75in) s. (I.L 20000000)
£510 $907   (29-Nov-91 F.F30/R) Paesaggio con figura seduta (21x26cm-8x10in) s. pencil (I.L 1100000)
£998 $1826   (12-May-92 F.R55) Vela all'isola di San Giorgio (39x35cm-15x14in) s. mixed media (I.L 2200000)

MARUYAMA (?) ?
£1937 $3700   (19-Jul-92 JRB.C251/R) Japanese farm (33x51cm-13x20in) s. W/C

MARVAL, Jacqueline (1866-1932) French
£2372 $4221   (29-Nov-91 GAB.G2803/R) Jeune femme au hamac (36x43cm-14x17in) s.i. (S.FR 6000)
£7179 $12851   (19-Jan-92 CSC.P117/R) Jeune femme au hamac (36x43cm-14x17in) s.i. (F.FR 70000)

MARX, Alphonse (19/20th C) French
£1500 $2565   (17-Mar-92 PH181) Kittens in the kitchen (33x41cm-13x16in) s.

MARX, Ernst Bernhard (1864-?) German
£5105 $9750   (16-Jul-92 SY.NY427/R) Reclining nude (127x204cm-50x80in) s.

MARX, Gustav (1855-1928) German
£2389 $4324   (21-May-92 L.K449/R) Kaiser Wilhelm II on horseback during manoeuvre (114x92cm-45x36in) s.d.89 (DM 7000)

MARX, John (19th C) ?
£521 $1000   (30-Jul-92 E.EDM206/R) Shipping off Quebec (56x91cm-22x36in) s.

MARXER, Alfred (1876-1945) Swiss
£1124 $2000   (29-Apr-92 G.Z160/R) View from studio over Kilchberg and Lake Zurich (49x41cm-19x16in) s. (S.FR 3000)
£1128 $2064   (4-Jul-92 SY.Z410/R) Am Obersee (80x100cm-31x39in) s.d.25 (S.FR 3000)
£1992 $3606   (5-Dec-91 SY.Z175/R) Garden in winter (60x70cm-24x28in) s.d.37 (S.FR 5000)

MARY, Guillaume (1962-) French
£509 $942   (13-Jun-92 AT.P18/R) Amphore (100x80cm-39x31in) s.i.d.90verso (F.FR 5000)

MARYAN (1927-1977) American
£1342 $2442 (10-Dec-91 RAS.K72/R) Personage (81x65cm-32x26in) s.d.58 (D.KR 15000)

MARYAN, Burstein Pinchas (1927-1977) American
£3918 $6777 (29-Mar-92 P.V10/R) Chevalier fleuri (116x89cm-46x35in) s.d.1959
                (F.FR 38000)
£1029 *$1862* *(5-Dec-91 BG.P40) Femme au chapeau (72x56cm-28x22in) s. col.oil crayons
                (F.FR 10000)*

MARZELLE, Jean (1916-) French
£670 $1146 (11-Mar-92 LGB.P167) Une route en Espagne (20x60cm-8x24in) s. (F.FR 6500)
£1009 $1736 (20-Oct-91 I.N208) Paysage (31x54cm-12x21in) s.d.55-58 (F.FR 10000)

MARZOHL, Johann Baptiste (1792-1862) Swiss
£392 *$702* *(12-Nov-91 GF.L5091) River landscape with wooden bridge and figures
                (30x42cm-12x17in) W/C over pencil (S.FR 1000)*

MASCART, Gustave (19th C) French
£1025 $1844 (2-Feb-92 ZZ.F54/R) La statue de Jeanne d'Arc et le jardin des tuileries
                (22x27cm-9x11in) s. panel (F.FR 10000)
£1109 $1963 (10-Nov-91 ZZ.F123/R) Maison au bord de la riviere (19x35cm-7x14in) s.
                panel (F.FR 11000)
£1210 $2141 (10-Nov-91 ZZ.F113/R) Pont a l'entree du village (21x35cm-8x14in) s.
                panel (F.FR 12000)
£1754 $3000 (21-Mar-92 W.W35/R) River town (64x91cm-25x36in) s.

MASCHEK, Franz (1797-1862) Czechoslovakian
£989 $1730 (20-Feb-92 D.V417/R) Portrait of gentleman with pipe (23x19cm-9x7in)
                s.d.1833 board (A.S 20000)

MASEREEL, Frans (1889-1972) Belgian
£513 $929 (7-Dec-91 KV.L233) L'Escaut a Tamise Remorqueurs et Chalands
                (33x50cm-13x20in) mono.d.1948 board (B.FR 30000)
£1001 $1761 (7-Apr-92 C.A179) Nude (55x45cm-22x18in) s. panel (B.FR 60000)
£1159 $2098 (23-May-92 KV.L213) The mermaid (50x45cm-20x18in) mono. paper on canvas
                (B.FR 70000)
£1375 $2515 (3-Jun-92 L.K300/R) Nu au miroir II (27x19cm-11x7in) mono.d.1944 i.verso
                board (DM 4000)
£1474 $2653 (21-Nov-91 L.K319/R) Avignon, les Remparts (47x30cm-19x12in) mono.d.1940
                W/C indian ink brush (DM 4200)
£1474 $2653 (21-Nov-91 L.K321/R) Palais des Papes (47x31cm-19x12in) mono.i.d.1940 W/C
                (DM 4200)
£1501 $2642 (7-Apr-92 C.A178) Woman on a balcony (50x60cm-20x24in) s. panel
                (B.FR 90000)
£1538 $2738 (30-Nov-91 VG.B871/R) Man walking on beach (65x50cm-26x20in) mono.d.1929
                s.d.verso (DM 4400)
£1930 $3474 (21-Nov-91 L.K318/R) Lot-et-Garonne. Femme en ruine (46x55cm-18x22in)
                mono.d.1947 s.i.d.verso board (DM 5500)
£2006 $3651 (12-Dec-91 SY.AM142/R) Harbour view (46x64cm-18x25in) init.d.1954
                s.d.verso (D.FL 6500)
£2062 $3773 (3-Jun-92 L.K301/R) Brune et blonde sur la plage I (49x64cm-19x25in)
                mono.d.1950 i.stretcher (DM 6000)
£2105 $3789 (21-Nov-91 L.K317/R) Torse nu sur fond vert. Still life of flowers
                (23x18cm-9x7in) mono.d.1945 board double-sided (DM 6000)
£5119 $9317 (27-May-92 PH.DU64/R) Coastal landscape (73x100cm-29x39in) mono.d.1929
                (DM 15000)
£5657 $10523 (21-Jun-92 LT.P66/R) Souvenir de Londres, Hyde Park (65x92cm-26x36in)
                mono. (F.FR 55500)
£397 *$719* *(23-May-92 KV.L215) Femme etendue dans le Ble (30x46cm-12x18in)
                mono.d.1961 brush dr. (B.FR 24000)*
£420 *$747* *(30-Nov-91 VG.B872/R) Man reclining on beach (24x40cm-9x16in) indian ink
                brush felt tip pen htd.white (DM 1200)*
£497 *$899* *(23-May-92 KV.L214) Benne et pecheur a la Ligne (38x46cm-15x18in)
                mono.d.1966 W/C (B.FR 30000)*
£500 *$881* *(7-Apr-92 C.A180) Two swans III (32x42cm-13x17in) mono.d.1958
                (B.FR 30000)*
£596 *$1074* *(21-Nov-91 L.K324) Rowing boat on beach (24x16cm-9x6in) mono. indian ink
                brush (DM 1700)*
£632 *$1137* *(21-Nov-91 L.K326) Portrait of Romain Rolland (24x18cm-9x7in) mono.d.1919
                pen (DM 1800)*
£770 *$1393* *(3-Dec-91 C.A516) Young girl (60x45cm-24x18in) mono.d.1959 gouache
                (B.FR 45000)*
£772 *$1320* *(13-Mar-92 FN.S2555) Harbour scene with steamship and figures
                (33x48cm-13x19in) mono.d.1927 indian ink brush (DM 2200)*
£1056 *$1912* *(6-Dec-91 GB.B6820) Market scene, Tunesia (37x45cm-15x18in) s.d.1911 W/C
                over chk (DM 3000)*
£1064 *$1851* *(17-Sep-91 CH.AM194) Who's the boss (49x64cm-19x25in)
                s.indist.i.d.F.M.1924 ink brush (D.FL 3500)*

MASLENNIKOV, Pavel (1914-) Russian
£1570 $2842 (20-May-92 ARC.P71/R) Coucher de soleil (62x100cm-24x39in) s.
                (F.FR 15500)

MASON, Barry (1947-) British
£1250 $2400 (28-Jul-92 SWS441/R) The Head Sea (72x90cm-28x35in) s.

MASON, Barry (1947-) British-cont.
£4000 $6960   (14-Apr-92 CSK182/R) Flying spray and blown Spume - Kaisow racing Norman Court (91x122cm-36x48in) s. s.i.verso

MASON, Benjamin Franklin (19th C) American
£1608 $2750   (21-Mar-92 S.BM143/R) Portrait of Mary Bradley Potter Babcock and George Reed Babcock (76x64cm-30x25in) pair

MASON, Frank H (1876-1965) British
£700 $1218   (15-Apr-92 PHL182) Fair wind for home - off Casquets - Channel Island (22x55cm-9x22in) s.d.1943 canvasboard
£747 $1300   (15-Sep-91 JRB.C70/R) Still life (76x91cm-30x36in) s.d.57
£950 $1815   (17-Jul-92 C157/R) Heading for shore (50x61cm-20x24in) s.d.1944
£1000 $1680   (15-Aug-91 B401/R) Outward bound - down Channel off Needles (51x61cm-20x24in) s.d.1947 bears i.verso
£1200 $2124   (7-Nov-91 PHC663/R) Fishing boats at quay (78x57cm-31x22in) tempera board pair
£8000 $14400   (22-Nov-91 C113/R) Ships of the Mediterranean Fleet lying in Valetta Harbour, Malta (87x103cm-34x41in) s. canvas on board
£400 $724   (19-May-92 PH54) Busy shipping lane (24x34cm-9x13in) s. W/C bodycol
£480 $864   (9-Jan-92 B135/R) A motor launch off the Coquet Lighthouse on the Northumberland coast (24x34cm-9x13in) s. W/C
£500 $840   (15-Aug-91 B219/R) Schooner yacht and barque in swell (30x42cm-12x17in) pencil W/C
£520 $894   (16-Oct-91 PHL128) Shrimps, pink and brown, Harwich (22x53cm-9x21in) s.i. gouache
£620 $1054   (22-Oct-91 SWS148/R) Coastwise (25x34cm-10x13in) s. i.verso W/C gouache
£650 $1183   (10-Dec-91 AG198/R) Frontier cities of Tuy and Valencia (24x36cm-9x14in) s.i. W/C
£700 $1225   (24-Sep-91 SWO5) View on the Thames with sailing boats and steamer (15x33cm-6x13in) s. W/C
£750 $1358   (20-May-92 S241/R) Venice (23x74cm-9x29in) s. W/C
£800 $1384   (2-Oct-91 RBB849/R) Off the foreland. End of the voyage (38x23cm-15x9in) s.i. W/C pair
£950 $1653   (14-Apr-92 CSK81/R) Berengaria (43x25cm-17x10in) s. pencil W/C htd white
£1050 $1880   (5-May-92 SWS109/R) Off Calais (36x53cm-14x21in) s. W/C gouache scratching out
£1200 $2016   (15-Aug-91 B359) View of Venice from Giardino Publico (15x32cm-6x13in) s. W/C htd white pair
£1350 $2403   (29-Apr-92 RBB742/R) Seascapes - Spanish barque making Tegus. Off Gibraltar, with vessels (23x30cm-9x12in) s. W/C pair
£1600 $2848   (28-Apr-92 RG568) In Harwich Roads. Outward bound (25x36cm-10x14in) s. W/C pair
£1800 $3384   (19-Dec-91 C58) Shipping off Quayside at Lowestoft. Off Bamborough. Shipping off pier (15x44cm-6x17in) s.d.1900 two i. pencil W/C htd white three
£1900 $3420   (22-Nov-91 C10/R) Clippers on the high seas (36x49cm-14x19in) s. pencil W/C bodycol htd.white two
£4500 $7740   (4-Mar-92 S194/R) Scarborough (49x74cm-19x29in) s.d.1909 W/C

MASQUERIER, John James (1778-1855) British
£800 $1424   (21-Jan-92 PH50/R) Portrait of lady, standing, right arm on ledge, by urn, landscape beyond (38x32cm-15x13in)

MASQUERIER, John James (attrib) (1778-1855) British
£1500 $2685   (15-Nov-91 C187/R) Portrait of gentleman, in coat and stock (62x51cm-24x20in)

MASRELIEZ, Louis (1748-1810) Swedish
£1526 $2731   (17-Nov-91 LT.P2/R) Le martyr de Saint Sebastien (33x31cm-13x12in) ink wash blk.crayon sanguine (F.FR 15000)

MASRIERA Y MANOVENS, Francisco (1842-1902) Spanish
£707 $1258   (28-Apr-92 DUR.M26/R) Figura (32x23cm-13x9in) s. board (S.P 130000)
£3857 $6750   (20-Feb-92 SY.NY311/R) Jeune femme aux Mimosas (46x38cm-18x15in) s.d.1885 panel
£4652 $8467   (26-May-92 DUR.M16/R) Joven con ramo di mimosas (46x38cm-18x15in) s.d.1885 panel (S.P 850000)
£9302 $16000   (17-Oct-91 SY.NY345/R) Young bride (46x37cm-18x15in) s.d.1885 panel
£10465 $18000   (16-Oct-91 CH.NY168 a/R) An exotic beauty (123x60cm-48x24in) s.d.1898
£11429 $20000   (20-Feb-92 SY.NY47/R) Mal des amores - odalisque (113x95cm-44x37in) s.d.1889
£23262 $42337   (26-May-92 DUR.M15/R) Ensenando el ajuar (53x65cm-21x26in) s.d.1877 panel (S.P 4250000)
£547 $996   (26-May-92 DUR.M68/R) Desnudo femenino (70x39cm-28x15in) s.d.1878 dr (S.P 100000)
£1366 $2323   (22-Oct-91 DUR.M21/R) Desnudo femenino, Academia (66x40cm-26x16in) s.d.1878 chl dr (S.P 250000)
£1366 $2323   (22-Oct-91 DUR.M22/R) Desnudo femenino, Academia (66x40cm-26x16in) s.d.1878 chl dr (S.P 250000)

MASRIERA, Luis (1872-1958) Spanish
£553 $1040   (17-Dec-91 BRO.B331) Interior con figuras (33x41cm-13x16in) s. (S.P 100000)
£900 $1566   (19-Sep-91 B115/R) Old man holding hen (81x66cm-32x26in)

MASSAGRANDE, Matteo (20th C) Italian
£681 $1212   (29-Apr-92 F.F168/R) Il tavolo (40x30cm-16x12in) d.1991 mixed media
                 canvas (I.L 1500000)

MASSANI, Pompeo (1850-1920) Italian
£1117 $2000   (13-Nov-91 B.SF2246/R) Il vecchio violinista (35x25cm-14x10in) s.i.
                 canvas laid down on board
£1450 $2596   (14-Jan-92 SWS217/R) The old musician (31x22cm-12x9in) s.
£1700 $3009   (13-Feb-92 CSK221/R) A bad brew (30x24cm-12x9in) s.
£2800 $5068   (22-May-92 C229/R) L'Accordatura (32x25cm-13x10in) s.i. i.verso
£2800 $4844   (4-Oct-91 C180/R) The card players (42x60cm-17x24in) s.
£500 $890   (26-Nov-91 PH251/R) A quiet read (31x24cm-12x9in) s.i. W/C over pencil

MASSARD, A (19th C) French
£1700 $3162   (17-Jun-92 S522/R) Still life with exotic fruit (60x73cm-24x29in) s.

MASSARI, Lucio (attrib) (1569-1633) Italian
£1006 $1800   (15-Jan-92 CH.NY20/R) Saint Sebastian (26x19cm-10x7in) with i.verso black
                 chk htd white

MASSE, Jean Baptiste (1687-1767) French
£1333 $2413   (21-May-92 SY.G6/R) Portrait of Marie Madelaine Masse, artist's
                 sister-in-law (7x?cm-3x?in) min. gilt metal frame (S.FR 3600)
£9630 $17430   (21-May-92 SY.G8) Portrait of Jacques Masse, artist's brother standing
                 holding book (9x?cm-4x?in) i.verso gilt metal frame (S.FR 26000)

MASSMANN, Hans (1887-1973) Rumanian
£589 $1119   (25-Jun-92 D.V676/R) Church square of Adriach (79x70cm-31x28in) s.d.1918
                 i.verso board (A.S 12000)

MASSON, Alexandre Charles (19th C) French
£1613 $2823   (5-Apr-92 ZZ.F48/R) Elegante sur les remparts devant la mer
                 (41x32cm-16x13in) s. (F.FR 15500)
£5000 $9300   (17-Jun-92 S493/R) Danae in shower of gold (51x74cm-20x29in)

MASSON, Andre (1896-1988) French
£5544 $9592   (4-Oct-91 CSC.P96/R) Coucher de soleil (42x28cm-17x11in) s. panel
                 (F.FR 55000)
£8763 $15160   (23-Mar-92 GL.P183/R) Paysage a la maniere Song (64x53cm-25x21in) s.verso
                 (F.FR 85000)
£11340 $19619   (23-Mar-92 GL.P179/R) La route au crepuscule (54x65cm-21x26in) s.
                 (F.FR 110000)
£14124 $25000   (6-Nov-91 CH.NY298/R) Orphee (38x28cm-15x11in) init.
£15979 $27644   (23-Mar-92 GL.P174/R) La chaise devant la mer (35x27cm-14x11in) init.
                 i.d.1938verso
£17000 $29410   (25-Mar-92 S94/R) Rencontre nocturne (65x56cm-26x22in) s.
£22518 $40082   (1-Dec-91 I.N47/R) L'oiseau noir (55x46cm-22x18in) s. (F.FR 220000)
£25000 $47750   (1-Jul-92 S217/R) Flore (80x64cm-31x25in) s. mono.i.d.76verso
£40000 $72400   (4-Dec-91 S196/R) Le migrateur (121x100cm-48x39in) s. i.d.1957 verso
£42373 $75000   (6-Nov-91 CH.NY35/R) Necromancie (146x114cm-57x45in) s.
                 s.i.d.1962stretcher
£48023 $85000   (6-Nov-91 CH.NY324/R) La chimere domptee (130x162cm-51x64in) s.
                 i.d.1960-1961stretcher
£48023 $85000   (6-Nov-91 CH.NY297/R) Bacchanale (35x57cm-14x22in) s.
£59063 $108086 (3-Jun-92 PIC.P87/R) Kermesse (100x81cm-39x32in) s. (F.FR 580000)
£248588 $440000 (7-Nov-91 SY.NY176/R) Femme paralytique (114x146cm-45x57in) s.
£453 $807   (28-Oct-91 GL.P145) Enee sauvant Anchise (49x31cm-19x12in) i. pastel
                 (F.FR 4500)
£520 $998   (7-Jul-92 ARC.P81/R) Nouveau combat de poissons (21x27cm-8x11in) mono.
                 Indian ink (F.FR 5000)
£572 $1098   (7-Jul-92 ARC.P78/R) Femme sur fond bleu (21x27cm-8x11in) col.crayons
                 (F.FR 5500)
£624 $1198   (7-Jul-92 ARC.P80/R) Metamorphoses (32x24cm-13x9in) s. Indian ink
                 (F.FR 6000)
£728 $1397   (7-Jul-92 ARC.P76/R) Le chat et la libellule (27x43cm-11x17in) crayon
                 (F.FR 7000)
£815 $1483   (25-May-92 CH.R17/R) Cris humains dand l'arbre (11x21cm-4x8in) mono i.
                 ink (I.L 1800000)
£957 $1703   (28-Oct-91 GL.P146) Dordrecht (44x32cm-17x13in) ink pastel (F.FR 9500)
£1016 $1768   (13-Apr-92 GL.P88) L'oiseau fantome (40x31cm-16x12in) s. wash dr.
                 (F.FR 10000)
£1321 $2299   (13-Apr-92 GL.P87/R) Sans titre (23x20cm-9x8in) s. pastel paper laid down
                 on canvas (F.FR 13000)
£1341 $2400   (9-May-92 CE.NY131/R) Arbre (31x23cm-12x9in) s.d.33 col.pencil wax crayon
                 pencil
£1437 $2587   (20-Nov-91 CN.P56/R) Sans titre (31x30cm-12x12in) s. Indian ink
                 (F.FR 14000)
£1440 $2607   (6-Dec-91 GL.P259/R) Sous les arbres (64x58cm-25x23in) pstel (F.FR 14000)
£1720 $3130   (25-May-92 CH.R7/R) La femme, la fleur, l'astre (27x21cm-11x8in) d.1949
                 pencil (I.L 3800000)
£1815 $3139   (4-Oct-91 CSC.P90/R) Composition (29x20cm-11x8in) s.d. 72 synthetic ink
                 (F.FR 18000)
£1931 $3360   (13-Apr-92 GL.P82/R) Phedre et Hyppolite, chute des amants
                 (42x25cm-17x10in) studio st.i. felt pen board (F.FR 19000)

MASSON, Andre (1896-1988) French-cont.

£2033	$3537	(13-Apr-92 GL.P81) Les delices de l'amour (44x28cm-17x11in) i. ball pen (F.FR 20000)
£2062	$3567	(23-Mar-92 GL.P108) Femme a la tete d'aigle (45x60cm-18x24in) init. ink gouache (F.FR 20000)
£2117	$3662	(4-Oct-91 CSC.P91) Composition (25x17cm-10x7in) init.d.72 Indian ink col.crayons (F.FR 21000)
£2134	$3713	(13-Apr-92 GL.P86/R) Oiseaux (52x42cm-20x17in) s. Indian ink col.crayons (F.FR 21000)
£2216	$3766	(24-Oct-91 CSC.P74) Les baigneuses a la cascade (48x31cm-19x12in) s.i. pastel (F.FR 22000)
£2266	$3874	(19-Mar-92 CSC.P38) La main ouverte (38x28cm-15x11in) Indian ink (F.FR 22000)
£2268	$3924	(23-Mar-92 GL.P109/R) Tete de martiniquaise (30x22cm-12x9in) s.d.1941 dr. (F.FR 22000)
£2388	$4155	(13-Apr-92 GL.P83) Composition (43x34cm-17x13in) s.d.1956 gouache (F.FR 23500)
£3018	$5191	(12-Oct-91 SY.MO41/R) Vue de Venise (30x40cm-12x16in) s.d.51 lithographic crayon paper on card (F.FR 30000)
£3049	$5305	(13-Apr-92 GL.P85/R) Proliferation (18x25cm-7x10in) moo.i.d.1955 gouache (F.FR 30000)
£3093	$5351	(23-Mar-92 GL.P106) Maelstrom (76x57cm-30x22in) s.d.1957 Indian ink brush (F.FR 30000)
£3605	$6164	(19-Mar-92 CSC.P34/R) Promethee (26x30cm-10x12in) lead pencil (F.FR 35000)
£3638	$6985	(7-Jul-92 ARC.P74/R) L'homme debout (50x23cm-20x9in) s. pen wash htd col. (F.FR 35000)
£3918	$6777	(23-Mar-92 GL.P107/R) Tauromachie (33x38cm-13x15in) s.d.1936 pen (F.FR 38000)
£4032	$7137	(10-Nov-91 ZZ.F241/R) Composition (62x49cm-24x19in) pastel (F.FR 40000)
£4737	$8101	(22-Mar-92 I.N40/R) La danse (48x31cm-19x12in) studio st. gouache lead pencil (F.FR 46000)
£4893	$9101	(15-Jun-92 GL.P14/R) Nu dans le vent (63x48cm-25x19in) s. Indian ink dr (F.FR 48000)
£5392	$9651	(17-Nov-91 LL.LH91/R) Agressivite (49x38cm-19x15in) s.d.1975 indian ink (F.FR 53000)
£6804	$11771	(23-Mar-92 GL.P105/R) Dessisn automatique (32x24cm-13x9in) s.i. Indian ink dr. (F.FR 66000)
£10499	$19529	(15-Jun-92 GL.P7/R) Le grain de ble (37x44cm-15x17in) s. chl pastel (F.FR 103000)
£10929	$20000	(13-May-92 CH.NY328/R) Trophee (73x60cm-29x24in) s. pastel paper on canvas
£11299	$20000	(6-Nov-91 CH.NY187/R) L'oeil du cyclope (50x65cm-20x26in) s. pastel paper on canvas
£11340	$19619	(23-Mar-92 GL.P148/R) Femme au tricorne (64x50cm-25x20in) pastel (F.FR 110000)
£12575	$21630	(12-Oct-91 SY.MO42/R) Lansquennets et courtisanes (33x26cm-13x10in) s. d.1964 verso W/C pen col.ink (F.FR 125000)
£12729	$23549	(12-Jun-92 AT.P42/R) Quatre dames (54x42cm-21x17in) s. gouache (F.FR 125000)
£13711	$23721	(23-Mar-92 GL.P149/R) La legende du mais (46x59cm-18x23in) s.i.d.Novembre 42 W/C (F.FR 133000)
£17010	$29428	(23-Mar-92 GL.P147/R) L'enfant au livre (47x41cm-19x16in) s. pastel (F.FR 165000)
£18362	$32500	(6-Nov-91 SY.NY45/R) Autoportrait (63x48cm-25x19in) s.i.d.1944verso chl.India ink
£59381	$103323	(14-Apr-92 F.M231/R) Paysage au lievre (88x115cm-35x45in) oil pencil (I.L 130000000)

MASSON, Henri L (1907-) Canadian

£679	$1256	(9-Jun-92 FB.M151) Gatineau hills (41x51cm-16x20in) s. (C.D 1500)
£683	$1229	(19-Nov-91 FP.M33) Joueuse de flute (30x25cm-12x10in) s. board (C.D 1400)
£800	$1416	(6-Nov-91 SY.T266/R) Street scene (24x29cm-9x11in) s.d.49 panel (C.D 1600)
£938	$1594	(23-Oct-91 MA.V99) Landscape with a house (30x41cm-12x16in) s. (C.D 1800)
£1095	$1948	(25-Nov-91 W.T1575/R) Rainy street (38x46cm-15x18in) s.d.50 (C.D 2200)
£1122	$2020	(19-Nov-91 FP.M46/R) Gaspe fishermen (38x46cm-15x18in) s. (C.D 2300)
£1370	$2493	(26-May-92 JOY.T139/R) Enfants de choeur (25x30cm-10x12in) s. board (C.D 3000)
£1465	$2563	(25-Sep-91 EA.M484 a) Nature morte aux raisins (40x51cm-16x20in) s. s.d.75 verso (C.D 2900)
£1500	$2655	(6-Nov-91 SY.T198/R) Suburbs with quarry, Hull, P.Q (45x53cm-18x21in) s. (C.D 3000)
£1616	$2828	(25-Sep-91 EA.M528 a) Petite vallee, Gaspesie (40x51cm-16x20in) s. (C.D 3200)
£1750	$3098	(6-Nov-91 SY.T77) Monks (30x25cm-12x10in) s. panel (C.D 3500)
£1791	$3188	(26-Nov-91 JOY.T11/R) Early spring, Alcove, Quebec (40x50cm-16x20in) s. (C.D 3600)
£1823	$3099	(23-Oct-91 MA.V98) Road near Lucerne (41x51cm-16x20in) s. board (C.D 3500)
£3234	$5756	(26-Nov-91 JOY.T115/R) Landscape in winter (60x75cm-24x30in) s. (C.D 6500)
£4087	$7151	(17-Feb-92 HO.ED69/R) Untitled landscape (64x85cm-25x33in) s.d.1962 board (C.D 8500)
£365	$665	(26-May-92 JOY.T239/R) Gatineau (26x36cm-10x14in) s. col.chk (C.D 800)

MASSON, Henri L (1907-) Canadian-cont.
£385	$673	(17-Feb-92 HO.ED57) Augers, Quebec (33x41cm-13x16in) s.i. ink (C.D 800)
£417	$708	(23-Oct-91 EA.M415) Antibes (26x28cm-10x11in) s. W/C wax crayon (C.D 800)
£502	$919	(14-May-92 SY.T181/R) Old houses, Venice (41x34cm-16x13in) s. d.1957 verso mixed media (C.D 1100)
£585	$1054	(18-Nov-91 HO.ED29/R) Block Lake - October (36x51cm-14x20in) W/C (C.D 1200)
£1279	$2327	(26-May-92 JOY.T126) Lower Town, Old Quebec (29x39cm-11x15in) s. W/C crayon ink (C.D 2800)

MASSON, Marcel (1911-1988) French
£556	$1006	(19-May-92 GF.L2653/R) Place Pigalle with Moulin Rouge (22x27cm-9x11in) s. (S.FR 1500)
£784	$1333	(23-Oct-91 GD.B1165/R) Montmartre street scene with Sacre Coeur beyond, winter (55x46cm-22x18in) s. (S.FR 2000)
£922	$1660	(2-Feb-92 ZZ.F233/R) Le Port de la Rochelle (54x73cm-21x29in) s. (F.FR 9000)
£1289	$2282	(5-Nov-91 GF.L2734/R) Village street (46x55cm-18x22in) s. (S.FR 3300)

MASSONI, Egisto (fl.1880's) Italian
£900	$1602	(28-Nov-91 B73/R) Venice (23x47cm-9x19in) s.i.
£431	$750	(10-Sep-91 BG.M703/R) Italian seashore with buildings, figures and animals (48x74cm-19x29in) s. W/C

MASSOT, Firmin (1766-1849) Swiss
£1304	$2322	(29-Nov-91 GAB.G2139/R) Portrait de Dorothee (16x14cm-6x6in) s.d.1802 panel oval (S.FR 3300)

MAST, Herman van der (attrib) (c.1550-1610) Dutch
£8025	$14364	(14-Nov-91 CH.AM133/R) Portrait of gentleman aged 36 standing. His wife aged 25 standing (95x67cm-37x26in) i.d.1587 panel pair (D.FL 26000)

MASTENBROEK, Johann Hendrik van (1875-1945) Dutch
£1117	$2000	(13-Nov-91 B.SF2227/R) Moored sailing boats. Along the canal (20x30cm-8x12in) s. panel pair
£1220	$2268	(16-Jun-92 VN.R160) 'Uit de dekking' (70x100cm-28x39in) s.d.1936 (D.FL 4000)
£1304	$2257	(24-Mar-92 VN.R54/R) 'Uit de dekkin' (70x100cm-28x39in) s.d.1936 (D.FL 4200)
£1863	$3224	(24-Mar-92 VN.R55/R) River scene with busy harbour beyond (27x39cm-11x15in) s.d.1903 (D.FL 6000)
£1988	$3459	(14-Apr-92 SY.AM212/R) The 'Zeeburgerpad', Amsterdam (27x38cm-11x15in) s.i.d.1901 (D.FL 6500)
£3517	$6119	(14-Apr-92 SY.AM58/R) Polder landscape with farm and figures in boat (45x33cm-18x13in) s.d.1920 (D.FL 11500)
£7339	$13064	(30-Oct-91 CH.AM75/R) Herinnering aan de verlichting op de tentoonstelling te Gent, 1913 (70x130cm-28x51in) s.d.1913 s.i.d.stretcher (D.FL 24000)
£7339	$12991	(5-Nov-91 SY.AM98/R) 'Aan de Kade (38x59cm-15x23in) s.d.1923 (D.FL 24000)
£870	$1504	(24-Mar-92 VN.R53) Harbour scene (22x31cm-9x12in) s.d. W/C (D.FL 2800)
£979	$1703	(14-Apr-92 SY.AM258/R) Sailing vessels on estuary (19x27cm-7x11in) s.d.1892 W/C (D.FL 3200)
£1101	$1916	(14-Apr-92 SY.AM107) Busy harbour (12x22cm-5x9in) s. W/C (D.FL 3600)
£1951	$3512	(19-Nov-91 FP.M96/R) Town river view at low tide (17x25cm-7x10in) s.d.1906 W/C (C.D 4000)
£8563	$14899	(14-Apr-92 SY.AM189/R) View of Rotterdam Harbour (52x70cm-20x28in) s.d.1907 W/C (D.FL 28000)
£8869	$15697	(5-Nov-91 SY.AM160/R) View of Rotterdam (49x71cm-19x28in) s.d.05 W/C (D.FL 29000)

MASTER OF 1310 (14th C) Italian
£413408	$740000	(17-Jan-92 SY.NY16/R) Scenes from the life of a Martyred female saint - Margaret of Antioch (91x127cm-36x50in) tempera panel gold ground Master of 1310

MASTER OF 1540 (16th C) Dutch
£30387	$55000	(21-May-92 CH.NY49/R) Portrait of gentleman, wearing fur trimmed jacket, shirt and cap (40x35cm-16x14in) i.d.1541 panel

MASTER OF FRANKFURT (c.1490-1515) Dutch
£15470	$28000	(22-May-92 SY.NY139/R) Saint James the Greater and female martyred saint, probably Saint Encratia of Saragossa (67x23cm-26x9in) panel shaped wings triptych

MASTER OF LOS BALBASES (15th C) Spanish
£65466	$118494	(19-May-92 EP.M2/R) La resurreccion (117x69cm-46x27in) tempera oil gold panel (S.P 12000000)
£65466	$118494	(19-May-92 EP.M1/R) La flagelacion (114x70cm-45x28in) tempera oil gold panel (S.P 12000000)

MASTER OF MARRADI (attrib) (15th C) Italian
£25720	$48868	(26-Jun-92 AT.P1/R) L'adoration de l'Enfant (32x22cm-13x9in) panel (F.FR 250000)

1194

MASTER OF MUHLDORF (attrib) (16th C) German
£7832 $13862   (7-Nov-91 D.V82/R) Christ Crowned with Thorns (88x71cm-35x28in) panel
                   (A.S 160000)

MASTER OF PALANQUINOS (16th C) Spanish
£20000 $36400   (29-May-92 C307/R) The Assumption of the Virgin with kneeling female
                   donor and St Thomas (136x92cm-54x36in) i. gold ground panel
£20930 $36000   (10-Oct-91 SY.NY145/R) Battle scene (124x89cm-49x35in) oil tempera panel

MASTER OF PEREA (fl.1490-1505) Spanish
£27933 $50000   (16-Jan-92 CH.NY81/R) Christ presenting Redeemed of Old Testament to
                   Mother (107x85cm-42x33in) gold ground panel
£280000 $509600   (29-May-92 C306/R) The Last Supper (266x283cm-105x111in) tempera gold
                   ground panel in three sections

MASTER OF PEREA (circle) (fl.1490-1505) Spanish
£1800 $3456   (10-Jul-92 C222/R) Ascension. Adoration of Magi (60x56cm-24x22in) tempera
                   gold ground panel altarpiece two parts

MASTER OF SAINT IVO (?) ?
£33520 $60000   (17-Jan-92 SY.NY1/R) The Madonna and child enthroned flanked by Saints
                   Peter and Lawrence (69x38cm-27x15in) tempera panel shaped top

MASTER OF SAINT SEVERIN (style) (16th C) German
£4321 $7735   (12-Nov-91 SY.AM59/R) Adoration of the Magi (80x75cm-31x30in) panel
                   (D.FL 14000)

MASTER OF SAN MARTINO A MENSOLA (?) Italian
£17391 $30957   (29-Nov-91 GAB.G3078/R) La Vierge et l'Enfant en trone entre
                   Saint-Antoine Abbe et Saint Catherine d'Alexandrine (56x37cm-22x15in)
                   panel (S.FR 44000)

MASTER OF STAFFOLO (circle) (15th C) Italian
£11602 $21000   (22-May-92 SY.NY170/R) Annunciation, resurrection, Trinity with saints,
                   Coronation of Virgin, adoration of magi (54x66cm-21x26in) tempera panel
                   triptych

MASTER OF THE APOLLO AND DAPHNE LEGEND (c.1480-c.1510) Italian
£19337 $35000   (22-May-92 SY.NY6/R) King David praying while Saul and Abner sleep and
                   Job mocked by friends (69x204cm-27x80in) oil tempera panel

MASTER OF THE CLAVELES (15th C) ?
£6500 $11570   (1-Nov-91 C54/R) Presentation in temple (111x80cm-44x31in) gold ground
                   panel

MASTER OF THE COUNTESS OF WARWICK (attrib) (?) British
£10500 $18585   (6-Nov-91 CB147/R) Portrait of Sir Gabriel Poyntz, aged 36 with coat of
                   arms (97x71cm-38x28in) i.d.1568 panel

MASTER OF THE EGMONT ALBUMS (?) ?
£9000   *$17280*   (7-Jul-92 C82/R) The Good Samaritan at the Inn (27x35cm-11x14in) chk pen

MASTER OF THE FEMALE HALF LENGTHS (16th C) Flemish
£4815 $8715   (19-May-92 GF.L2011/R) Magdalen reading (36x27cm-14x11in) panel
                   (S.FR 13000)

MASTER OF THE HALF-FIGURES (circle) (?) ?
£11317 $20484   (5-Dec-91 SY.MO204/R) Vierge a l'enfant (36x26cm-14x10in) panel
                   (F.FR 110000)

MASTER OF THE HARTFORD STILL LIFE (attrib) (17th C) ?
£43296 $77500   (17-Jan-92 SY.NY86/R) Still life of lilies and other flowers in a vase,
                   fruit on stepped ledges (76x88cm-30x35in)

MASTER OF THE HOLY BLOOD (16th C) Flemish
£3125 $5531   (5-Nov-91 GF.L2007/R) Lucretia commiting suicide (52x37cm-20x15in) panel
                   (S.FR 8000)

MASTER OF THE INCREDULITY OF SAINT THOMAS (16th C) Italian
£8287 $15000   (22-May-92 SY.NY7/R) Madonna and child in landscape (36x30cm-14x12in)
                   transferred from panel to canvas

MASTER OF THE JUDGMENT OF SOLOMON (attrib) (fl.1615-1625) Italian
£3200 $6144   (10-Jul-92 C242/R) Saint Paul (122x87cm-48x34in) canvas on board

MASTER OF THE LEONARDESQUE FEMALE PORTRAITS (16th C) ?
£167598 $300000   (16-Jan-92 CH.NY103/R) Portrait of lady, seated before window, landscape
                   beyond (60x44cm-24x17in) panel

MASTER OF THE LITOMERICE ALTARPIECE (fl.1495-1520) Czechoslovakian
£17000 $30940   (13-Dec-91 C51/R) The Massacre of the Innocents (57x35cm-22x14in) panel

MASTER OF THE LOMBARD FRUIT BOWL (17th C) Spanish
£150000 $273000   (29-May-92 C324/R) Artichokes with flowers in vase and fruit in basket on
                   stone pedestal (77x115cm-30x45in)

MASTER OF THE MAGDALEN LEGEND (circle) (15th C) Flemish
£20000 $35600   (1-Nov-91 C108/R) Virgin and Child (42x30cm-17x12in) panel

MASTER OF THE MISERICORDIA (15th C) Italian
£11000 $20020   (13-Dec-91 C234/R) Saint Anthony Abbot and a Deacon Martyr (21x9cm-8x4in)
          gold ground panel

MASTER OF THE PARROT (attrib) (16th C) Flemish
£94972 $170000   (16-Jan-92 CH.NY34/R) Saint Mary Magdalene before curtain supported by
          angels in niche (74x58cm-29x23in) i. panel

MASTER OF THE PRODIGAL SON (1530-1560) Flemish
£4500 $8640   (8-Jul-92 S251/R) Jacob's ladder (72x100cm-28x39in) panel
£19000 $34580   (11-Dec-91 S167/R) Ars Moriendi - angel and devil contending for soul of
          rich man (74x100cm-29x39in) panel

MASTER OF THE PRODIGAL SON (attrib) (1530-1560) Flemish
£4651 $8000   (10-Oct-91 SY.NY176/R) The Pieta (58x49cm-23x19in) panel

MASTER OF THE PRODIGAL SON (circle) (16th C) Flemish
£1500 $2670   (29-Oct-91 PH1/R) The death of Turnus outside the walls of a town
          (35x45cm-14x18in) panel

MASTER OF THE SAINT LOUIS MADONNA (fl.1480-1490) Italian
£15803 $28603   (5-Dec-91 F.M141/R) Madonna col Bambino e San Giovannino
          (70x41cm-28x16in) panel (I.L 34000000)

MASTER OF THE VANITAS (fl.1650-1670) Italian
£15803 $28603   (5-Dec-91 F.M104) Vanitas (59x82cm-23x32in) (I.L 34000000)

MASTER OF TORRALBA (15th C) Spanish
£47486 $85000   (16-Jan-92 CH.NY5/R) Crucifixion (105x82cm-41x32in) gold ground panel
          arched top

MASTERS, Edwin (19th C) British
£650 $1105   (22-Oct-91 SWS269/R) On country lane (26x44cm-10x17in) init.
£800 $1376   (4-Mar-92 S42/R) Small country hamlet (25x45cm-10x18in)
£2000 $3540   (6-Nov-91 S131/R) Outside inn (51x76cm-20x30in) s.

MASUCCI, Agostino (attrib) (18th C) Italian
£411 $739   (22-Nov-91 AGS.P117) Sait moine adorant la Vierge (27x13cm-11x5in) pen
          pierre noire (F.FR 4000)

MASUCCI, Agostino (style) (18th C) Italian
£1100 $1913   (17-Sep-91 FN.S2430/R) Allegory of Wisdom - portrait of young lady
          holding snake and mirror (49x43cm-19x17in) (DM 3200)
£1100 $1913   (17-Sep-91 FN.S2431) Allegory of Bravery - young lady holding sword over
          open fire (49x43cm-19x17in) i. (DM 3200)

MASUREL, Johannes Engel (1826-1915) Dutch
£729 $1269   (17-Sep-91 CH.AM323) A kitchen interior with a maid preparing a meal, a
          still life in theforeground (56x41cm-22x16in) s. (D.FL 2400)

MATAL, Bohumir (1922-1988) Czechoslovakian
£645 $1149   (29-Nov-91 D.V101/R) Shape (35x25cm-14x10in) s.d.81 panel (A.S 13000)

MATANIA, Fortunino (1881-?) Italian
£600 $1152   (28-Jul-92 SWS410/R) Cardinal by an altar (36x27cm-14x11in) s. canvas on
          board
£400 $712   (28-Nov-91 CSK41) Islamic law (33x51cm-13x20in) s. pencil W/C
£1900 $3306   (19-Sep-91 B7/R) Farewell (48x35cm-19x14in) s.d.1918 pencil W/C htd white

MATEJKO, Jan (1838-1893) Polish
£994 $1709   (13-Oct-91 REM.W17) Portrait of a man (14x10cm-6x4in) s. W/C
          (P.Z 19000000)

MATEOS, Francisco (1894-1976) Spanish
£3274 $5632   (16-Oct-91 FER.M265/R) Vendedoras de sandias (46x55cm-18x22in) s.
          (S.P 600000)
£4981 $8517   (17-Mar-92 FER.M197/R) El arbol quemado (81x100cm-32x39in) s.
          s.i.d.71verso (S.P 900000)
£5507 $9857   (14-Nov-91 ANS.M64/R) La maridada (81x100cm-32x39in) s.i.d.1971verso
          (S.P 1000000)
£409 $703   (7-Oct-91 ANS.M76/R) Mascaras (17x13cm-7x5in) s. W/C (S.P 75000)
£831 $1455   (18-Feb-92 DUR.M32/R) Mascaras y animales s. W/C four mounted together
          (S.P 150000)
£942 $1649   (18-Feb-92 DUR.M33/R) Musicos, mascaras y figuras s. W/C four mounted
          together (S.P 170000)
£1108 $1940   (18-Feb-92 DUR.M34/R) Mascaras y animales s. W/C four mounted together
          (S.P 200000)
£3283 $5975   (11-Dec-91 FER.M200/R) Aprendiendo a volar (64x48cm-25x19in) s.d.63 W/C
          (S.P 600000)

MATHAM, Jacob (1571-1631) Dutch
£2469 $4420   *(12-Nov-91 SY.AM289/R) Profile study of head. Two studies of heads*
      (16x11cm-6x4in) pen ink wash double-sided (D.FL 8000)
£10000 $19200   *(7-Jul-92 C81/R) Vanity (30x24cm-12x9in) s.i.d.1621 chk pen vellum*
£11728 $20994   *(12-Nov-91 SY.AM333/R) Danae (25x38cm-10x15in) i. chk (D.FL 38000)*

MATHELIN, Lucien (1905-1981) French
£692 $1260   (11-Dec-91 ZZ.F86/R) Les bonnes pommes (65x54cm-26x21in) s. (F.FR 6800)

MATHER, Arvid (1905-1950) German
£515 $959   (20-Jun-92 BM.B1053/R) Woman by water (40x30cm-16x12in) s. (DM 1500)

MATHER, John (1848-1916) British
£529 $941   (26-Nov-91 J.M444) On Stevenson River, Marysville (41x51cm-16x20in)
      s.d.1880 (A.D 1200)
£1000 $1700   (23-Oct-91 S308/R) Homestead in rocky landscape (35x53cm-14x21in)
      s.d.1882

MATHER, Sydney (1944-) Australian
£470 $837   (27-Apr-92 J.M1143) Morning near Maffra (51x76cm-20x30in) s. canvasboard
      (A.D 1100)
£529 $941   (26-Nov-91 J.M1219) Old house near Arnaud (50x75cm-20x30in) s.
      canvasboard (A.D 1200)
£556 $989   (27-Apr-92 J.M774) Near Cherry Tree National Park, Loch Sport
      (61x76cm-24x30in) s. canvasboard (A.D 1300)
£598 $1065   (27-Apr-92 J.M317) Old house, Cann River district (51x76cm-20x30in) s.
      canvasboard (A.D 1400)
£617 $1098   (26-Nov-91 J.M1212) Landscape near Bairnsdale (50x75cm-20x30in) s.
      canvasboard (A.D 1400)
£1141 $2031   (26-Nov-91 J.M146/R) Rising mist, Wallagaraugh River (89x120cm-35x47in)
      s. (A.D 2590)

MATHEWS, J (19th C) British
£1684 $3200   (24-Jun-92 D.NY57/R) Chestnut hunter in loose stall (58x76cm-23x30in)
      s.d.1888

MATHEWS, John Chester (fl.1884-1900) British
£920 $1766   (28-Jul-92 SWS87/R) Hollington, winner of Grand Military Gold Cup,
      Sandown 1891 (54x74cm-21x29in) s.d.1891

MATHEWS, Lucia Kleinhans (1870-1955) American
£6215 $11000   *(12-Feb-92 B.SF447/R) Monterey Pines (48x59cm-19x23in) s.d.39 W/C*

MATHEY, Paul (1844-?) French
£1111 $2011   (19-May-92 GF.L2508/R) Canal in landscape with farmhouse
      (46x55cm-18x22in) s. panel (S.FR 3000)
£5607 $10428   (18-Jun-92 SY.MO393/R) Portrait d'homme a la peinture de Degas
      (41x31cm-16x12in) s. panel (F.FR 55000)

MATHIE, James (fl.1897-1938) British
£550 $979   (1-May-92 PHE24) The marigold pool (35x45cm-14x18in) s.d.1907

MATHIESEN, Egon (1907-1976) Danish
£541 $930   (4-Mar-92 KH.K152) Composition (33x41cm-13x16in) init.d.63verso
      (D.KR 6000)
£541 $930   (4-Mar-92 KH.K151) Brittany (100x76cm-39x30in) init.d.74verso (D.KR 6000)
£3114 $5418   (17-Sep-91 RAS.K101/R) Nature morte (137x101cm-54x40in) init.
      s.d.1943verso (D.KR 35000)
£4253 $7699   (4-Dec-91 KH.K6/R) Nature morte (136x200cm-54x79in) init.d.1944verso
      (D.KR 47000)

MATHIEU, Georges (1921-) French
£4800 $8256   (17-Oct-91 S8/R) Untitled (51x65cm-20x26in) s.d.54 paper
£6085 $11075   (25-May-92 D.P174/R) Montaudou (34x92cm-13x36in) s. (F.FR 60000)
£6497 $12215   (19-Dec-91 F.M218/R) Composizione (76x57cm-30x22in) s. paper on canvas
      (I.L 14000000)
£9410 $17032   (7-Dec-91 KV.L492/R) Daon (92x60cm-36x24in) s.d.1969 (B.FR 550000)
£9579 $16571   (28-Mar-92 F.L104/R) Solitude Secrete (60x73cm-24x29in) s.d.1987
      (S.FR 25000)
£10000 $17200   (17-Oct-91 C41/R) Greau (54x92cm-21x36in) s.d.65
£11765 $20235   (12-Oct-91 F.L242/R) Obscur Ennemi (73x60cm-29x24in) (S.FR 30000)
£13000 $22360   (17-Oct-91 S5/R) Kergoat (89x145cm-35x57in) s.d.64
£14000 $24220   (26-Mar-92 C19/R) Serenite de Brunon, archeveque de Cologne
      (72x115cm-28x45in) s.d.54 i.stretcher
£15000 $25800   (17-Oct-91 C39/R) Charles d'Espagne Connectable tue dans son lit par le
      Roy de Navarre (88x146cm-35x57in) s.d.1957
£18786 $32500   (3-Oct-91 SY.NY27/R) Athanor (91x73cm-36x29in) s.d.67 i.stretcher
£18898 $32504   (16-Oct-91 G.Z66/R) Son du soir (70x57cm-28x22in) s. (S.FR 48000)
£20387 $37920   (15-Jun-92 GL.P27/R) Triomphe rouge (162x97cm-64x38in) s.d.1961
      (F.FR 200000)
£21788 $39000   (13-Nov-91 CH.NY103/R) Untitled (97x162cm-38x64in) s.stretcher
£30000 $57300   (2-Jul-92 S13/R) Composition rouge, noir, blanc (130x195cm-51x77in)
      s.d.52
£30242 $52319   (6-Oct-91 BG.P84/R) Tsimisian (119x160cm-47x63in) s. panel (F.FR 300000)

MATHIEU, Georges (1921-) French-cont.
£1668	$2936	(7-Apr-92 C.A186/R) Composition (44x72cm-17x28in) s.d.1959 W/C (B.FR 100000)
£2100	$3633	(26-Mar-92 S13/R) Composition (70x51cm-28x20in) s.d.65 W/C collage
£2800	$4816	(17-Oct-91 C1/R) Composition (56x76cm-22x30in) s.d.58 ink wash
£4305	$7791	(23-May-92 KV.L496/R) Composition (48x63cm-19x25in) s.d.54 gouache (B.FR 260000)

MATHIEU, Paul (1872-1932) Belgian
£915	$1575	(7-Oct-91 RY.P84/R) La port verte (38x46cm-15x18in) s. panel (F.FR 9100)
£1500	$2610	(19-Sep-91 CSK92/R) Scene de rue a Gent (41x56cm-16x22in) s. panel
£2778	$5056	(12-Dec-91 SY.AM52/R) Harbour at Ostende (41x56cm-16x22in) s. board (D.FL 9000)
£2907	$5000	(12-Oct-91 SY.NY27/R) En Hollande (51x70cm-20x28in) s.
£3600	$6264	(19-Sep-91 CSK142/R) Bateaux a Ostende (39x56cm-15x22in) s. board
£4003	$7046	(7-Apr-92 C.A187/R) The Seine in Paris (40x55cm-16x22in) s.d.1917 board (B.FR 240000)

MATHIS, Hans (1882-?) German
| £524 | $897 | (21-Mar-92 WK.M372/R) River landscape (45x50cm-18x20in) s. (DM 1500) |

MATHISON, John (20th C) British
| £500 | $905 | (5-Dec-91 CG157) Woods near Ardilistry, Islay (76x102cm-30x40in) s.d.1981 |

MATIGNON, Albert (1869-?) French
| £1223 | $2275 | (18-Jun-92 SY.MO418/R) Jeune fille au plat de fleurs (62x31cm-24x12in) s. (F.FR 12000) |

MATILLA Y MARINA, Segundo (1862-1937) Spanish
£2630	$4734	(28-Jan-92 EP.M41/R) La vuelta de la pesca (18x21cm-7x8in) s. board (S.P 475000)
£5473	$9962	(26-May-92 DUR.M40/R) Marina (33x36cm-13x14in) s. canvas laid down on board (S.P 1000000)
£6566	$11688	(29-Oct-91 BRO.B299/R) Marina (70x40cm-28x16in) s. (S.P 1200000)
£8208	$14610	(29-Oct-91 BRO.B298/R) Marisqueando (70x40cm-28x16in) s. (S.P 1500000)
£27907	$49674	(29-Oct-91 BRO.B367/R) Mar y rocas (81x102cm-32x40in) s. panel (S.P 5100000)

MATISSE, Camille (20th C) French
| £600 | $1116 | (16-Jun-92 SWS188/R) Still life of mixed flowers in vase (63x52cm-25x20in) s.i. board oval |

MATISSE, Henri (1869-1954) French
£86558	$157536	(15-Dec-91 P.V12/R) Cypres et oliviers, pres du castel des deux rois (33x41cm-13x16in) s. canvas pasted on board (F.FR 850000)
£231638	$410000	(6-Nov-91 SY.NY34/R) Portrait de femme (33x24cm-13x9in) s. panel
£240000	$458400	(30-Jun-92 S34/R) Nu au divan rouge (24x33cm-9x13in) s.
£1000000	$1810000	(3-Dec-91 S32/R) Anemones dans un vase a Godrons (46x55cm-18x22in) s.d.43
£1092896	$2000000	(13-May-92 SY.NY77/R) Nu debout devant la cheminee (46x36cm-18x14in) s.
£1532	$2681	(21-Feb-92 LC.P39) Composition abstraite (25x21cm-10x8in) s.i. ink (F.FR 15000)
£2247	$3933	(21-Feb-92 LC.P48 b) Portrait de Robert Rey (48x31cm-19x12in) s.d.16 mars 1947 crayon (F.FR 22000)
£2400	$4152	(24-Mar-92 C22/R) Femme nue assise. Tete d'homme (26x21cm-10x8in) pencil double-sided
£2800	$4844	(24-Mar-92 C23/R) Femme nue assise. Nu (26x21cm-10x8in) pencil double-sided
£3600	$6228	(24-Mar-92 C20/R) Femme nue assise. Nu de dos (26x21cm-10x8in) pencil double-sided
£4500	$7785	(24-Mar-92 C16/R) Nu debout (26x21cm-10x8in) pencil
£5200	$9412	(4-Dec-91 S139/R) Nu lisant (50x32cm-20x13in) init. lithographic pencil
£5295	$9690	(3-Jun-92 PIC.P63/R) Le modele allonge (27x44cm-11x17in) s.d.1928 crayon dr (F.FR 52000)
£5650	$10000	(7-Nov-91 SY.NY205 a/R) Visage d'une jeune femme, vue de profil a gauche dans un carrau (19x20cm-7x8in) init.i. brush ink gouache linen wove stationery
£5780	$10000	(2-Oct-91 SY.NY73/R) Costume design for Rouge et Noir for ballet Russe de Monte Carlo (26x20cm-10x8in) s.i. i.verso pencil ink double-sided
£6215	$11000	(7-Nov-91 SY.NY199/R) Medine - treillis fleuri (19x25cm-7x10in) s.i.d.1913 pen
£6557	$12000	(14-May-92 SY.NY110/R) Sketches from Collioure (22x17cm-9x7in) st.init. indian ink
£7345	$13000	(7-Nov-91 SY.NY205/R) Portail, mosquee de la Casbah I (26x17cm-10x7in) s.i.d.1912 pen
£8475	$15000	(7-Nov-91 SY.NY202/R) Rue de Tanger, deux passants. Rue de Tanger, trois passants (25x19cm-10x7in) s.i.d.1913 one pair
£8475	$15000	(7-Nov-91 SY.NY203/R) Paysage, pres de Tanger I. Paysage, pres de Tanger II (17x26cm-7x10in) one s.d.1912 one s.i.d.1912 pen pair
£8743	$16000	(13-May-92 SY.NY59/R) Nu assis sur un tabouret (35x22cm-14x9in) s. pencil
£9040	$16000	(7-Nov-91 SY.NY201/R) Palais du Sultan (25x19cm-10x7in) s.i.d.1913 pen
£11299	$20000	(7-Nov-91 SY.NY188/R) Vue de la fenetre, Tanger I (26x17cm-10x7in) s. pen gouache
£11864	$21000	(7-Nov-91 SY.NY187/R) Marocain, mi-corps (25x19cm-10x7in) s.d.1913 pencil
£11864	$21000	(7-Nov-91 SY.NY200/R) Vue de la Medine (21x27cm-8x11in) s.i.d.1912 pen
£11864	$21000	(7-Nov-91 SY.NY191/R) Deux vues de Tanger (25x19cm-10x7in) s.i.d.1913 pen

MATISSE, Henri (1869-1954) French-cont.

£12429	$22000	(7-Nov-91 SY.NY192/R) Portail, mosquee de la Casbah II (26x17cm-10x7in) s. pen
£12429	$22000	(7-Nov-91 SY.NY196/R) Marocain assis (25x20cm-10x8in) s.d.1913 pen
£12568	$23000	(14-May-92 SY.NY109/R) Costume designs for Rouge et Noir for le ballet russe de Monte Carlo (27x22cm-11x9in) s.init.i. pencil pen W/C pair one double-sided
£12994	$23000	(7-Nov-91 SY.NY193/R) Marocain assis, les bras croises. Soldat marocain et Hamido (25x19cm-10x7in) one s.i.d.1913 one s.d.1913 pen pair
£12994	$23000	(7-Nov-91 SY.NY197/R) Porte avec ane et personnage. Porte avec deux anes et leurs cavaliers (26x19cm-10x7in) s.i.d.1913 pen pair
£13115	$24000	(13-May-92 CH.NY294/R) Denise, tete dans la main (30x23cm-12x9in) init. chl
£13559	$24000	(7-Nov-91 SY.NY204/R) A la porte de la casbah (25x19cm-10x7in) s.i.d.1913 pen
£14124	$25000	(7-Nov-91 SY.NY195/R) Casbah - Marabout et drapeau (25x19cm-10x7in) s.i.d.1913 pen
£14689	$26000	(7-Nov-91 SY.NY190/R) Marocain, de trois-quarts (25x20cm-10x8in) s.d.1913 pen
£16949	$30000	(6-Nov-91 CH.NY184/R) Tete de femme (44x37cm-17x15in) s.d.1949 pen india ink
£17000	$29240	(16-Oct-91 S71/R) Nu debout de profil (64x50cm-25x20in) s.i.d. crayon
£19126	$35000	(14-May-92 SY.NY157/R) Zorah, tete dans les mains (24x31cm-9x12in) st.init. pen
£19774	$35000	(6-Nov-91 CH.NY186/R) Tete de femme (41x53cm-16x21in) s.i. pencil
£26836	$47500	(7-Nov-91 SY.NY212/R) Buste de femme (53x41cm-21x16in) s.d.47 pencil paper on board
£27322	$50000	(14-May-92 SY.NY158/R) Femme assise avec les bras croises (28x38cm-11x15in) s. pencil
£28249	$50000	(7-Nov-91 SY.NY189/R) Marocain assis, devant un fond fleuri (25x18cm-10x7in) s. pen
£31000	$53320	(16-Oct-91 S72/R) Le platane - nu debout de trois quarts (64x50cm-25x20in) s.i.d.1950 crayon
£32000	$55360	(25-Mar-92 S60/R) Jeune fille souriante (41x31cm-16x12in) s. pencil
£39548	$70000	(6-Nov-91 CH.NY118/R) Collioure (25x32cm-10x13in) init. W/C paper on board
£42726	$76480	(17-Nov-91 GL.P10/R) Le famille (44x55cm-17x22in) s.d.1939 pen (F.FR 420000)
£46000	$83260	(4-Dec-91 S191/R) Martiniquaise (52x40cm-20x16in) s.d.47 black crayon
£51913	$95000	(14-May-92 SY.NY164/R) Visage (43x33cm-17x13in) s.i.d.51 brush ink
£54645	$100000	(13-May-92 SY.NY28/R) Nu au repos (39x26cm-15x10in) s.init. india ink
£60109	$110000	(14-May-92 SY.NY165/R) Profil de femme (33x19cm-13x7in) s. brush ink
£62374	$107284	(12-Oct-91 SY.MO30/R) Fruits, coquillages et vase sur une table (53x41cm-21x16in) s.d.41 pen (F.FR 620000)
£120000	$229200	(30-Jun-92 S37/R) Femme assise a la guitare (47x31cm-19x12in) s. chl estompe
£125683	$230000	(13-May-92 SY.NY34/R) Nu allonge (38x56cm-15x22in) s.d.1935 pen
£150273	$275000	(13-May-92 SY.NY31/R) Antoinette etendue sur une chaise-longue (59x67cm-23x26in) s. pencil
£175141	$310000	(6-Nov-91 SY.NY29/R) Femma se repsant (53x40cm-21x16in) s.d.35 India ink
£191257	$350000	(13-May-92 SY.NY20/R) Jeune fille a la mantilla, etude pour l'espagnole aux fleurs (52x42cm-20x17in) s. chl estompe
£245902	$450000	(13-May-92 SY.NY29/R) Le chapeau aux plumes (35x29cm-14x11in) s.d.1919 pencil
£437158	$800000	(13-May-92 SY.NY32/R) Ballerine assise dans un fauteuil (61x46cm-24x18in) s.d.44 chl
£601093	$1100000	(13-May-92 SY.NY35/R) Femme assise en blouse roumaine motifs de broderie (66x51cm-26x20in) s.d.38 chl

MATO VILARO, Francisco (20th C) Uruguayan?

£497	$900	(2-Dec-91 GC.M45/R) Naturaleza muerta con jarras y botellas (47x49cm-19x19in) s.d.65 board

MATOSSY, Pierre (1891-1969) French

£920	$1638	(26-Jan-92 FE.P231) Fete Africaine (100x80cm-39x31in) s. (F.FR 9000)

MATSCH, Franz von (1861-1942) Austrian

£2028	$3610	(29-Nov-91 ZEL.L1074) Allegory of World Peace with child Jesus and cannons in landscape (110x75cm-43x30in) s. (DM 5800)
£437	$778	(29-Apr-92 D.V501/R) Reclining female nude (32x44cm-13x17in) chk htd.white (A.S 9000)

MATSIEVSKAYA, Yadviga (1916-) Russian

£570	$1044	(3-Jun-92 ARC.P51/R) Dans la baie (59x85cm-23x33in) s. (F.FR 5600)
£611	$1118	(3-Jun-92 ARC.P50/R) Pres du quai (60x80cm-24x31in) s. (F.FR 6000)
£615	$1107	(27-Jan-92 ARC.P134/R) La promenade du matin (50x60cm-20x24in) s. (F.FR 6000)
£697	$1254	(27-Jan-92 ARC.P136/R) La rive du Dnepr (45x90cm-18x35in) s. (F.FR 6800)
£812	$1420	(5-Apr-92 ARC.P147/R) Le paysage ukrainien (69x99cm-27x39in) s. (F.FR 7800)

MATSON, Alex (1888-1972) Finnish

£453	$806	(1-Dec-91 HOR.H152) The old bridge (48x60cm-19x24in) s.d.1919 (F.M 3500)

MATTA (1911-) Chilean

£12000	$20640	(17-Oct-91 S66/R) Untitled (65x54cm-26x21in) s.
£12222	$22000	(19-Nov-91 CH.NY143/R) Abstract composition (77x63cm-30x25in)
£13902	$24745	(26-Nov-91 SY.MI209/R) Voir plus loin (64x78cm-25x31in) s. (I.L 30000000)
£14000	$24220	(26-Mar-92 C58/R) Untitled (65x81cm-26x32in)
£15755	$28044	(26-Nov-91 SY.MI161/R) Composizione (80x84cm-31x33in) s. (I.L 34000000)
£17680	$32000	(18-May-92 CH.NY170/R) Untitled (107x87cm-42x34in) s. i.verso
£18000	$32580	(5-Dec-91 C28/R) Untitled (64x79cm-25x31in) s.
£19000	$36290	(2-Jul-92 C41/R) Un mot d'amour (37x139cm-15x55in) s.i.d.1967-68 verso
£20866	$38186	(12-May-92 F.R219/R) Exil du ciel (83x102cm-33x40in) s.d.1961 (I.L 46000000)
£21000	$36330	(26-Mar-92 C52/R) Untitled (100x81cm-39x32in) s.
£22099	$40000	(18-May-92 CH.NY78/R) Le dos du miroir (103x83cm-41x33in) s.
£22222	$40000	(19-Nov-91 CH.NY78/R) Yellow flame (104x98cm-41x39in) s.i. s.i.d.74verso linen
£25000	$45000	(19-Nov-91 CH.NY77/R) Composicion sin titulo (96x96cm-38x38in) s.
£27778	$50000	(18-Nov-91 SY.NY172/R) Untitled (62x73cm-24x29in) s.
£27778	$50000	(18-Nov-91 SY.NY123/R) Triptych (49x301cm-19x119in)
£32000	$61120	(2-Jul-92 S49/R) Composition (81x100cm-32x39in) s.d.56verso
£33149	$60000	(18-May-92 CH.NY79/R) Marajos (84x100cm-33x39in) s.
£35282	$61038	(4-Oct-91 CSC.P105/R) Composition (128x128cm-50x50in) s.d.69 (F.FR 350000)
£35605	$63733	(17-Nov-91 GL.P35/R) Les complices de l'oubli (81x100cm-32x39in) s.i.verso (F.FR 350000)
£36111	$65000	(19-Nov-91 CH.NY44/R) Sin titulo (92x73cm-36x29in) s.
£42632	$75885	(26-Nov-91 SY.MI186/R) Composizione (114x144cm-45x57in) (I.L 92000000)
£48780	$84878	(14-Apr-92 CSC.P59/R) Le dieu bleu (115x150cm-45x59in) s. (F.FR 480000)
£52000	$99320	(2-Jul-92 C33/R) L'Overture (112x144cm-44x57in) s.verso
£65000	$117650	(5-Dec-91 C27/R) Morning of morning (118x180cm-46x71in)
£72016	$136831	(26-Jun-92 FB.P19/R) Death in the afternoon (200x395cm-79x156in) s.i.verso (F.FR 700000)
£72222	$130000	(19-Nov-91 CH.NY33/R) Ouvre le feu (206x211cm-81x83in) s. i.verso
£94444	$170000	(18-Nov-91 SY.NY16/R) Les pommes de Cezanne (66x53cm-26x21in) s.d.42verso
£226519	$410000	(19-May-92 SY.NY32/R) Theorie de l'arbre (75x95cm-30x37in) i.d.1941stretcher
£932	$1687	(20-May-92 FB.P190/R) Untitled (60x47cm-24x19in) s. crayon (F.FR 9200)
£2039	$3629	(29-Nov-91 F.F120/R) Composizione (32x35cm-13x14in) s. mixed media collage cardboard (I.L 4400000)
£2533	$4585	(20-May-92 FB.P188/R) Aux etudiants (50x65cm-20x26in) s.d.68 pastel col.crayon (F.FR 25000)
£3168	$5766	(25-May-92 CH.R61/R) Burundasso (75x55cm-30x22in) i.d.1975verso pastel (I.L 7000000)
£3824	$6500	(23-Oct-91 B.SF3789/R) Composition (31x38cm-12x15in) s.i. crayon graphite col.pencil
£4444	$8000	(18-Nov-91 SY.NY154/R) Untitled (44x64cm-17x25in) s. graphite crayon
£4444	$8000	(19-Nov-91 CH.NY81/R) Baseball pitcher (25x35cm-10x14in) s. crayon pencil
£5556	$10000	(19-Nov-91 CH.NY82/R) Composicion (50x69cm-20x27in) crayon pencil
£7222	$13000	(18-Nov-91 SY.NY180/R) Untitled (37x41cm-15x16in) s.d.1955 oil gouache black crayon
£7500	$12975	(26-Mar-92 C16/R) Untitled (44x69cm-17x27in) oil pencil board
£7735	$14000	(18-May-92 CH.NY145/R) La Copa Negra (32x50cm-13x20in) i. pencil wax crayon
£8188	$14575	(30-Nov-91 FB.P19/R) Valer o morio o dos furibundos fendenties (129x153cm-51x60in) s. pastel paper laid down on canvas (F.FR 80000)
£8287	$15000	(19-May-92 SY.NY160/R) Contre la terreur sacre (50x65cm-20x26in) s. graphite crayon
£8333	$15000	(19-Nov-91 CH.NY142/R) Erotic composition (27x29cm-11x11in) indis.i. pencil wax crayon
£8745	$16615	(26-Jun-92 FB.P27/R) El mas extranio pensiamento que jamas dio loco en el mundo (130x150cm-51x59in) s. pastel paper laid down on canvas (F.FR 85000)
£8889	$16000	(19-Nov-91 CH.NY144/R) Composicion sin titulo (50x65cm-20x26in) s.d.56 pencil wax crayon
£11050	$20000	(19-May-92 SY.NY145/R) Degrees de solitude - Fonder son existence sur l'inexistances des otres (50x65cm-20x26in) i. graphite crayon
£11050	$20000	(19-May-92 SY.NY33/R) Sueno (21x28cm-8x11in) s.i. ink col.pencils
£11050	$20000	(19-May-92 SY.NY34/R) Desnudo (24x30cm-9x12in) s. gouache crayon

MATTEINI, Theodoro (attrib) (1754-1831) Italian

£4409	$7937	(19-Nov-91 F.R119/R) Scena di conversazione su sfondo di paesaggio (45x61cm-18x24in) (I.L 9500000)

MATTEIS, Paolo de (1662-1728) Italian

£1966	$3500	(22-Jan-92 SY.NY40/R) Madonna and Child (46x36cm-18x14in)
£3405	$6061	(28-Apr-92 F.R17/R) Le Marie al sepolcro. La Veronica (41x57cm-16x22in) oval pair (I.L 7500000)
£3532	$6463	(16-May-92 F.L7/R) Madonna col Bambino (48x34cm-19x13in) (S.FR 9500)
£10056	$18000	(17-Jan-92 SY.NY133/R) Erminia seeking refuge with the shepherds (53x114cm-21x45in)
£16000	$29120	(13-Dec-91 C251/R) Solomon and the Queen of Sheba (74x126cm-29x50in)
£23743	$42500	(17-Jan-92 SY.NY134/R) The Goddess Iris appearing to the Goddess Cybele (128x152cm-50x60in)
£51127	$92540	(4-Dec-91 CH.R109/R) Rinaldo e Armida (189x256cm-74x101in) (I.L 110000000)

MATTEIS, Paolo de (1662-1728) Italian-cont.
£66298 $120000   (21-May-92 CH.NY29/R) Journey of Rebecca (124x178cm-49x70in)

MATTEIS, Paolo de (attrib) (1662-1728) Italian
£4471 $7645   (18-Mar-92 D.V35/R) St Sebastian (104x57cm-41x22in) (A.S 90000)
£52000 $94640   (13-Dec-91 C233/R) Bathsheba at the Bath (150x204cm-59x80in)

MATTEIS, Paolo de (circle) (1662-1728) Italian
£1700 $2975   (31-Mar-92 PH4/R) Lot and daughters (35x47cm-14x19in)
£4065 $7073   (13-Apr-92 AT.P33/R) La Liberation de Saint Pierre (25x38cm-10x15in)
              copper (F.FR 40000)
£5500 $9570   (15-Apr-92 C174/R) Apollo and Daphne (64x91cm-25x36in)
£5500 $9570   (15-Apr-92 C173/R) Pan and Syrinx (64x91cm-25x36in)

MATTEIS, Paolo de (style) (1662-1728) Italian
£1359 $2514   (8-Jun-92 CH.R741 a) Annunciazione (74x56cm-29x22in) canvas laid down on
              panel oval (I.L 3000000)
£3500 $6720   (10-Jul-92 C266/R) Erminia and shepherds (46x63cm-18x25in)
£4000 $7000   (2-Apr-92 CSK40/R) Judgement of Paris (89x129cm-35x51in)

MATTEIS, Paolo de and LOPEZ, Gasparo (17th C) Italian
£14607 $26000   (22-Jan-92 D.NY106/R) Mythological reliefs surrounded by garlands of
              flowers (66x74cm-26x29in) i. pair

MATTHEWS, Edward (19/20th C) British
£400 $696   *(19-Sep-91 TL489) View of Ben Nevis (43x62cm-17x24in) s.d.1886 W/C*

MATTHEWS, James (19th C) British
£900 $1611   *(5-May-92 SWS173/R) At Slinfold, Sussex (34x52cm-13x20in) s.i. W/C*

MATTHEWS, Julia B (20th C) British
£480 $864   *(27-Jan-92 PH61) Arab girl (50x35cm-20x14in) W/C*

MATTHEWS, Marmaduke (1837-1913) Canadian
£411 $752   *(14-May-92 SY.T68 a) Two children tending cow by stream (50x77cm-20x30in)*
              s. W/C (C.D 900)
£750 $1328   *(6-Nov-91 SY.T229/R) Noonday rest - Empire News (37x54cm-15x21in) s. W/C*
              (C.D 1500)

MATTHEWS, Michael (?) ?
£1400 $2534   (6-Dec-91 CBS279) Ballooning over London (91x71cm-36x28in) s.

MATTHISON, William (fl.1883-1923) British
£1000 $1720   *(4-Mar-92 S220/R) Riverside path (55x92cm-22x36in) s. W/C*

MATTIASSON, Jens (1916-) Scandinavian
£598 $1028   (15-Oct-91 GO.G1101/R) Rich cultivation (52x93cm-20x37in) s. (S.KR 6300)

MATTINEN, Seppo (1930-) Finnish
£541 $930   (4-Mar-92 KH.K155) Composition (44x44cm-17x17in) s.d.73 masonite
              (D.KR 6000)

MATTIOLI, Carlo (1911-) Italian
£1998 $3556   *(29-Apr-92 F.F45/R) Paesaggio (46x62cm-18x24in) s.d.1957 mixed media*
              paper on canvas (I.L 4400000)
£2179 $3879   *(29-Apr-92 F.F46) Ritratto (58x47cm-23x19in) s. mixed media cardboard on*
              canvas (I.L 4800000)

MATTO, Francisco (1911-) Uruguayan
£5556 $10000   (18-Nov-91 SY.NY173/R) Constructivo con jarra y cabeza (50x70cm-20x28in)
              s. board

MATTO, N (20th C) Uruguayan?
£2210 $4000   (2-Dec-91 GC.M47/R) Constructivo (93x64cm-37x25in) s.d.1953

MATTONI DE LA FUENTE, Virgilio (1842-?) Spanish
£711 $1352   (23-Jun-92 DUR.M7/R) Boda real (19x25cm-7x10in) s. (S.P 130000)

MATULKA, Jan (1890-1969) American
£851 $1600   (18-Dec-91 SY.NY320/R) New York cityscape (35x50cm-14x20in)
£714 $1200   *(14-Aug-91 B.P152/R) House at the Lake George (41x51cm-16x20in) s. W/C*
£2339 $4000   *(12-Mar-92 CH.NY232/R) Village street scene (38x56cm-15x22in) s. W/C*
              pencil

MATULLA, Oskar (1900-1983) Austrian
£499 $892   (15-Jan-92 D.V210/R) Madchen aus Kona (82x103cm-32x41in) mono.d.1954verso
              (A.S 10000)

MAUCKNER, Georg (19th C) German
£2622 $4484   (18-Mar-92 N.M594/R) Isar valley with view of Burg Grunwald and Burg
              Schwaneck beyond (74x59cm-29x23in) s.i.d.1852 (DM 7500)

MAUFRA, Maxime (1861-1918) French
£4200 $7266   (24-Mar-92 C56/R) Marine (46x55cm-18x22in) init.

MAUFRA, Maxime (1861-1918) French-cont.
£6307 $11542   (17-May-92 T.B184/R) Paysage de Bretagne (47x55cm-19x22in) s.
            (F.FR 62000)
£7429 $13000   (25-Feb-92 CH.NY8/R) Au bord de la riviere d'Auray, Bretagne
            (38x55cm-15x22in) s.
£9836 $18000   (14-May-92 SY.NY232/R) Le torrent bleu, Vallee du Veneon, Oisans
            (60x74cm-24x29in) s.d.1904
£11000 $19030   (25-Mar-92 S175/R) Le Quai de la Rapee - Inondation de Paris
            (46x55cm-18x22in) s.d.1910
£11475 $21000   (14-May-92 SY.NY237/R) La gabarre anglaise, Le Havre (44x53cm-17x21in)
            s.d.1905
£11561 $20000   (2-Oct-91 SY.NY15/R) La marne a Champigny (65x81cm-26x32in) s.d.1902
£13225 $24201   (17-May-92 T.B185/R) Clair de lune par temps nuageux (54x65cm-21x26in)
            s.d.1900 (F.FR 130000)
£14000 $24220   (25-Mar-92 S32/R) Le Port du Croisic (60x73cm-24x29in) s.d.1906
            i.stretcher
£14857 $26000   (25-Feb-92 SY.NY10/R) La rentree des bateaux de peche (60x72cm-24x28in)
            s.
£15000 $28650   (1-Jul-92 S135/R) Soleil couchant sur le Loir, Lavardin, Loir-et-Cher
            (54x81cm-21x32in) s.d.1907
£19126 $35000   (14-May-92 SY.NY248/R) La plage (61x81cm-24x32in) s.d.1911
£22000 $39820   (3-Dec-91 C216/R) Les Pavilions, Paris Exposition Internationale, 1900 or
            La Ville ephemere (60x73cm-24x29in) s.d.1900
£22857 $40000   (25-Feb-92 SY.NY5/R) La jetee de Pontivy, Morbihan (60x81cm-24x32in)
            s.d.1909
£1233   *$2121*   *(4-Mar-92 AT.P74) Paysage (30x38cm-12x15in) s.mono. gouache (F.FR 12000)*
£1751   *$2994*   *(22-Mar-92 LT.P23/R) Saint-Michel en Greve (34x48cm-13x19in) s. pastel*
            gouache (F.FR 17000)
£1933   *$3537*   *(17-May-92 T.B60/R) Paysage boise (30x38cm-12x15in) s. W/C chl*
            (F.FR 19000)

MAUL, Friedrich (19th C) German
£871 $1585   (11-Dec-91 N.M522/R) Portrait of Amalie Wilhelmine Henriette Elisabeth
            Epping (82x70cm-32x28in) i.d.1830verso (DM 2500)

MAULBERTSCH, Franz Anton (attrib) (1724-1796) Austrian
£981 $1865   (23-Jun-92 D.V316/R) Study of angel seen from behind (16x12cm-6x5in)
            (A.S 20000)
£981 $1865   (23-Jun-92 D.V309/R) Putti and cherubs in clouds, study for painting
            (13x18cm-5x7in) (A.S 20000)

MAUPERCHE, Henri (1602-1686) French
£7716 $13966   (5-Dec-91 SY.MO320/R) Paysage avec la fuite en Egypte (73x120cm-29x47in)
            panel (F.FR 75000)

MAURA, Antonio (?) ?
£1093 $2001   (13-May-92 FER.M65/R) Lavanderas en el rio (22x48cm-9x19in) s. panel
            (S.P 200000)

MAURA, Francisco (?) Spanish
£765 $1401   (13-May-92 FER.M66/R) Pastores en el camino (40x76cm-16x30in) s.
            (S.P 140000)
£1037 $1783   (16-Oct-91 FER.M162/R) Poastor a la orilla de un rio (40x75cm-16x30in)
            (S.P 190000)
£1091 $1877   (16-Oct-91 FER.M161/R) Paisaje con pastores y rio (41x75cm-16x30in) s.
            (S.P 200000)
£2053 $3736   (26-May-92 DUR.M146/R) Las hermanas (151x80cm-59x31in) s.d.90
            (S.P 375000)

MAURER (?) ?
£2372   *$4269*   *(19-Nov-91 GS.B4494/R) Figures praying by wayside cross with view of*
            Gaster and Glarneralpen (30x42cm-12x17in) gouache (S.FR 6000)

MAURER, Alfred H (1868-1932) American
£7018 $12000   (12-Mar-92 CH.NY231/R) House in landscape (46x55cm-18x22in) s. board on
            canvas

MAURER, Eugen (1885-1961) Swiss
£588 $1053   (15-Nov-91 ZOF.Z1801) Lake landscape (27x33cm-11x13in) s.d.1916 canvas on
            board (S.FR 1500)

MAURER, Jacob (18/19th C) Dutch/German
£944 $1700   (22-Nov-91 S.BM14/R) Day's journey (46x64cm-18x25in) s.

MAURER, Jacob (1737-1780) Dutch
£1203 $2093   (18-Sep-91 N.M425/R) Portrait of lady and coat of arms (72x58cm-28x23in)
            s.d.1761 (DM 3500)

MAURUS, Hans (1901-1942) German
£476 $852   (5-May-92 ZEL.L1431/R) Zillertal landscape with chapel (60x80cm-24x31in)
            s. i.verso (DM 1400)
£690 $1221   (6-Nov-91 N.M1092) Farmstead in mountain landscape (75x60cm-30x24in) s.
            (DM 2000)
£919 $1608   (3-Apr-92 BM.B778) Berchtesgaden (60x81cm-24x32in) s.d.1925 (DM 2600)
£1134 $1973   (17-Sep-91 FN.S2432) Grossglockner (81x101cm-32x40in) s.i. (DM 3300)

MAURUS, Hans (1901-1942) German-cont.
| £1259 | $2152 | (19-Mar-92 N.M2798/R) St Cyprian, Rosengarten (80x65cm-31x26in) s.i. i.verso (DM 3600) |
| £1399 | $2420 | (25-Mar-92 KM.K1306/R) View of St Wolfgang (100x80cm-39x31in) s. (DM 4000) |

MAURY, Francois (1861-1933) French
| £1831 | $3278 | (17-Nov-91 FB.P182) Scene de parc (61x50cm-24x20in) s. panel (F.FR 18000) |

MAUVE, A (1838-1888) Dutch
| £1296 | $2269 | *(25-Feb-92 VN.R186) Two bathers (31x18cm-12x7in) dr. (D.FL 4200)* |

MAUVE, A R (1876-1962) Dutch
| £1273 | $2177 | (17-Mar-92 FER.M120/R) Costa holandesa (51x66cm-20x26in) s. (S.P 230000) |

MAUVE, Anton (1838-1888) Dutch
£508	$915	(23-Nov-91 SO.S455/R) Traveller on road (44x29cm-17x11in) s. (S.KR 5300)
£807	$1397	(24-Mar-92 VN.R56/R) Cow lying down (16x35cm-6x14in) s. (D.FL 2600)
£1672	$2909	(17-Sep-91 CH.AM559/R) A white terrier on a persian rug (58x47cm-23x19in) s. (D.FL 5500)
£5758	$10191	(22-Apr-92 CH.AM35) Shepherd and flock in a wooded landscape (61x79cm-24x31in) s. (D.FL 19000)
£5810	$10284	(5-Nov-91 SY.AM285/R) Shepherd with flock (35x50cm-14x20in) s. panel (D.FL 19000)
£9341	$17000	(27-May-92 CH.NY240/R) Peasant woman in farmyard (24x30cm-9x12in) s. panel
£17033	$31000	(28-May-92 SY.NY27/R) Potatoe pickers (61x81cm-24x32in) s.
£509	$875	*(20-Oct-91 HG.C1401) Interior scene (28x38cm-11x15in) s. pencil htd white*
£917	$1624	*(5-Nov-91 SY.AM350/R) Shepherd with sheep by stable (22x23cm-9x9in) s. W/C (D.FL 3000)*
£917	$1596	*(14-Apr-92 SY.AM472) Shepherd with his flock (18x22cm-7x9in) s. W/C (D.FL 3000)*
£1450	$2784	*(28-Jul-92 SWS228/R) Ploughing (20x36cm-8x14in) s. W/C*
£1515	$2682	*(22-Apr-92 CH.AM276/R) Little girl feeding chickens (28x37cm-11x15in) s. ink col.chk.W/C (D.FL 5000)*
£1905	$3410	*(14-Nov-91 GRO.B21) Woman with cattle (20x36cm-8x14in) s. W/C paper on board*
£5000	$9600	*(28-Jul-92 SWS229/R) The road to the sea. Shepherd and flock (31x51cm-12x20in) s.W/C gouache pair*

MAUVE, Anton (circle) (1838-1888) Dutch
| £850 | $1513 | (30-Apr-92 CG885) Shepherdess and sheep in wooded landscape (40x51cm-16x20in) |

MAUZUDI, Egisto (19th C) Italian
| £2641 | $4437 | (27-Aug-91 RAS.K325/R) Pastoral landscape with girls harvesting (102x135cm-40x53in) i. (D.KR 30000) |

MAVRO, Mania (1889-?) Russian
| £2213 | $3807 | (7-Oct-91 CSC.P132/R) Jeune fille pensive (126x160cm-50x63in) s.d.1911 (F.FR 22000) |

MAX, Gabriel von (1840-1915) Czechoslovakian
£414	$732	(6-Nov-91 N.M1093/R) Madonna with Child (48x40cm-19x16in) s.d.1888 (DM 1200)
£600	$1068	(1-Nov-91 PHE80) The red dress (34x26cm-13x10in) s.
£650	$1151	(13-Feb-92 CSK181) Portrait of girl (34x27cm-13x11in) s.
£685	$1178	(8-Oct-91 ZEL.L1610/R) Portrait of Stella (47x41cm-19x16in) s. (DM 2000)
£852	$1542	(22-May-92 EA.Z144/R) Head of young woman (44x37cm-17x15in) s. (S.FR 2300)
£1031	$1794	(18-Sep-91 N.M616) Monkey on blanket in cage (93x79cm-37x31in) s. (DM 3000)
£1279	$2200	(15-Oct-91 CE.NY182/R) Portrait of Else wearing a garland of flowers (41x30cm-16x12in) s.i.
£1742	$3171	(11-Dec-91 WE.MU188/R) Pensive thoughts (33x25cm-13x10in) s. (DM 5000)

MAX, Peter (1937-) American
| £2674 | $4600 | (14-Oct-91 H.C207/R) Grammy (91x61cm-36x24in) s. acrylic |
| £1067 | $1900 | *(2-Nov-91 IH.NY77/R) Man with raised fist on flag-draped podium (43x56cm-17x22in) s. gouache acetate overlay* |

MAXENCE, Edgard (1871-1954) French
| £7000 | $13020 | (17-Jun-92 S515/R) Bouquet of flowers (77x77cm-30x30in) s. panel |

MAXIMOUCHKINA, Vera (1923-) Russian
£508	$884	(13-Apr-92 ARC.P111) La petite fille (32x29cm-13x11in) s. (F.FR 5000)
£508	$884	(13-Apr-92 ARC.P106/R) Le petit lutin (36x25cm-14x10in) s. board (F.FR 5000)
£512	$911	(25-Nov-91 ARC.P87/R) Sur le bateau (48x35cm-19x14in) s. board (F.FR 5000)
£514	$931	(6-Dec-91 ARC.P64/R) Le petit dejeuner (100x125cm-39x49in) s. (F.FR 5000)
£530	$986	(17-Jun-92 ARC.P178/R) La jeune reveuse (28x37cm-11x15in) s. board (F.FR 5200)
£559	$973	(13-Apr-92 ARC.P103) Fillette (34x25cm-13x10in) s. board (F.FR 5500)
£561	$1043	(17-Jun-92 ARC.P179) Trois copains (35x28cm-14x11in) s. board (F.FR 5500)

AXIMOUCHKINA, Vera (1923-) Russian-cont.
563    $1002   (25-Nov-91 ARC.P89 b) Un deguisement (24x17cm-9x7in) s. board (F.FR 5500)
614    $1093   (25-Nov-91 ARC.P83/R) Les petites mains (100x149cm-39x59in) s.
                (F.FR 6000)
671    $1167   (13-Apr-92 ARC.P105/R) Auguste (50x34cm-20x13in) s. board (F.FR 6600)
691    $1202   (13-Apr-92 ARC.P104/R) Sous le soleil (17x22cm-7x9in) s. board
                (F.FR 6800)
711    $1238   (13-Apr-92 ARC.P108/R) Les devoirs d'ete (90x122cm-35x48in) s.
                (F.FR 7000)
772    $1397   (6-Dec-91 ARC.P61 a) Garcon en costume vert (43x30cm-17x12in) s.
                (F.FR 7500)
1034 $1840   (25-Nov-91 ARC.P86/R) Le jeune clown (50x35cm-20x14in) s. board
                (F.FR 10100)
1126 $2004   (25-Nov-91 ARC.P84/R) L'ecoliere (52x26cm-20x10in) s. board (F.FR 11000)
1126 $2004   (25-Nov-91 ARC.P85/R) La pettie ballerine (47x35cm-19x14in) s.
                (F.FR 11000)
1331 $2368   (25-Nov-91 ARC.P89/R) Preparations de fete (22x21cm-9x8in) s. board
                (F.FR 13000)
1524 $2652   (13-Apr-92 ARC.P102/R) Le reveillon des enfants (25x19cm-10x7in) s. board
                (F.FR 15000)
1996 $3553   (25-Nov-91 ARC.P82/R) Le livre interessant (76x93cm-30x37in) s. board
                (F.FR 19500)
3292 $5959   (6-Dec-91 ARC.P61/R) Les degisements de Noel (95x94cm-37x37in) s. board
                (F.FR 32000)
5453 $9869   (6-Dec-91 ARC.P60/R) Preparatifs pour la fete (35x35cm-14x14in) s. board
                (F.FR 53000)

AXWELL, John (1905-1962) British
900   *$1512*   *(26-Aug-91 S1115/R) The fairground (33x25cm-13x10in) ink*

AY, Arthur Dampier (fl.1872-1914) British
1250 $2163   (1-Oct-91 SWS1663) Portrait of lady (53x40cm-21x16in) s.d.98

AY, Brian (19th C) British?
520    $874   (15-Aug-91 B298/R) 20 Raters racing in 1896 (61x92cm-24x36in) s. i.verso

AY, Phil (1864-1903) British
500   *$895*   *(11-Nov-91 PH203) Notes by globe trotter at Monte Carlo (36x5cm-14x2in)*
                s.i.d.92 pen W/C

AY, Walter William (1831-1896) British
700    $1344   (28-Jul-92 SWS367/R) Falmouth (31x57cm-12x22in) s.d.84
800    $1536   (28-Jul-92 SWS366/R) On the thames (32x48cm-13x19in) s.d.83
500   *$955*   *(1-Jul-92 B122) Shipping in the Orwell Estuary with sheep in foreground*
                (19x33cm-7x13in) s.d.66 W/C
850   *$1530*   *(27-Jan-92 PH78/R) Off Dutch coast (54x86cm-21x34in) s.d.72 W/C over*
                pencil htd white

AYA CORTES, Antonio (1950-) Spanish
560    $1161   (9-Apr-92 ANS.M161/R) Paisaje (24x33cm-9x13in) s. panel (S.P 120000)
876    $1674   (2-Jul-92 ANS.M98/R) El primer gateo (39x49cm-15x19in) s. panel
                (S.P 160000)

AYAN, Theophile Henri (1860-?) French
745    $1267   (23-Oct-91 GD.B1170/R) Shepherd with herd in hilly dune landscape,
                Provence (21x26cm-8x10in) s. panel (S.FR 1900)

AYBURGER, Josef (1813-1908) Austrian
2670 $4752   (29-Apr-92 D.V874/R) View of Wolfgangsee (33x43cm-13x17in) s. (A.S 55000)

AYDELL, Baron Ernst von (1888-?) German
402   *$700*   *(10-Sep-91 BG.M697) Fashion Show (28x28cm-11x11in) s. pencil W/C*
402   *$700*   *(10-Sep-91 BG.M695) Still life of poppys and insects (25x23cm-10x9in) s.*
                pencil W/C
517   *$900*   *(10-Sep-91 BG.M696) Floral still life with frog and mouse conversing*
                (23x20cm-9x8in) s. pencil W/C

AYER, Auguste Etienne (1805-1890) French
5500 $12090   (17-Jun-92 S474) Naval engagement (61x90cm-24x35in) s.d.1853

AYER, Erich (1876-1960) South African
197    $865   (13-Apr-92 SY.J318/R) Letaba River, Kruger National Park
                (31x40cm-12x16in) s.d.1948 canvas on board (SA.R 2500)
766    $1356   (4-Nov-91 SY.J264/R) Ou huis in Groot Marico (17x24cm-7x9in) s.d.1958
                canvasboard (SA.R 3800)
766    $1356   (4-Nov-91 SY.J265/R) Bergsering in die Najaar (22x40cm-9x16in) s.d.1955
                board (SA.R 3800)
907    $1606   (4-Nov-91 SY.J267/R) De Korte Street, Johannesburg (23x31cm-9x12in)
                init.d.1920 board (SA.R 4500)
1008 $1784   (4-Nov-91 SY.J266/R) Women by river, Zimbabwe (29x38cm-11x15in) s.d.1947
                board (SA.R 5000)
1411 $2498   (4-Nov-91 SY.J263/R) Baobab tree (39x29cm-15x11in) s.d.1943 board
                (SA.R 7000)
766   *$1356*   *(4-Nov-91 SY.J268/R) Rustenburg Kloof (38x52cm-15x20in) s.d.1927 pencil*
                pastel (SA.R 3800)

MAYER, F (?) ?
£526 $900   (13-Mar-92 FN.S2861/R) Village scene with thunderstorm rising, Lower Bavaria (26x33cm-10x13in) s.d.1855 board (DM 1500)

MAYER, Friedrich (1825-1875) German
£2048 $3706   (21-May-92 L.K450) Chiemsee landscape with hay boat (37x31cm-15x12in) s. (DM 6000)
£13000 $23140   (27-Nov-91 S110/R) View of Rome (56x79cm-22x31in) s.d.1841
£20000 $35600   (27-Nov-91 S112/R) View of Bay of Naples and Vesuvius (56x79cm-22x31in)

MAYER, Friedrich Carl (1824-1903) German
£3833 $6976   (11-Dec-91 N.M523/R) View of Molveno, South Tyrol (85x92cm-33x36in) s. (DM 11000)
£5000 $9300   (19-Jun-92 C26/R) Der Hof des altern Pellerschen Hauses in Nurnberg mit der Aussicht auf die Burg (79x70cm-31x28in) s.

MAYER, Georg (1765-c.1830) Swiss
£650 $1157   (21-Jan-92 PH56) Portrait of Emile Algernon Arthur Keppel Cowell Stepney, aged 6 years (76x61cm-30x24in)
£850 $1530   (19-Nov-91 PH73/R) Portrait of Sir John Stepney Cowell Stepney wearing military uniform (72x61cm-28x24in)

MAYER, Gustav (1847-1900) German
£1742 $3171   (11-Dec-91 WE.MU186/R) Peasant woman before house (34x24cm-13x9in) s. (DM 5000)

MAYER, Luigi (style) (18th C) Italian
£1600 $2720   (23-Oct-91 S45/R) Excavations at the Temple of Amada, Nubia (59x105cm-23x41in)

MAYES, William Edward (1861-1952) British
£450   *$833*   *(12-Jun-92 K477/R) Wherry and yacht on the Broads (20x30cm-8x12in) s. W/C*

MAYET, Leon (1858-?) French
£732 $1245   (24-Oct-91 D.V194/R) Still life with pansies (51x65cm-20x26in) s. (A.S 15000)

MAYEUR, J le (?) ?
£4580 $8153   (28-Nov-91 BU.S99/R) The dancers - view from Bali (45x55cm-18x22in) s. (S.KR 48000)

MAYNARD, George Willoughby (1843-1923) American
£1229 $2200   (14-Nov-91 CE.NY270/R) Fort, Marblehead, Mass (20x39cm-8x15in) s.i.d.19 board

MAYNARD, Richard Field (19/20th C) American
£1989 $3600   (4-Dec-91 D.NY60/R) Young beauty holding gold fan (69x81cm-27x32in) s.d.1914

MAYNE, Henry (1891-) Swedish
£906 $1594   (11-Apr-92 FAL.M272/R) Three girls on beach (66x80cm-26x31in) s.d.1926 (S.KR 9500)

MAYNE, Jean (19th C) Belgian
£993 $1798   (23-May-92 KV.L218) Dutch farm (54x75cm-21x30in) s.d.1898 (B.FR 60000)

MAYNO, Juan Battista (after) (1569-1649) Spanish
£750 $1313   (27-Feb-92 CSK89/R) The Soriano Portrait (34x26cm-13x10in) copper

MAYO, Paolo de (1703-1784) Italian
£4982 $9218   (8-Jun-92 CH.R749/R) Cristo risuscita Lazzaro (125x182cm-49x72in) (I.L 11000000)

MAYOL, Salvador (1775-1834) Spanish
£1649 $2903   (9-Apr-92 ANS.M149/R) Escena de la Guerra de la Independencia (43x70cm-17x28in) canvas on panel (S.P 300000)

MAYR, Heinrich von (1806-1871) German
£1300   *$2210*   *(23-Oct-91 S139/R) Three Greek warriors looking towards Messalonghi (21x17cm-8x7in) i. W/C over pencil gum arabic gold*

MAYR, Karl Viktor (1881-1975) Austrian
£415   *$754*   *(10-Dec-91 F.R61) Campagna ad Aviano (45x58cm-18x23in) s.d.1918 W/C (I.L 900000)*

MAYR, Peter (1758-1836) German
£3497   *$5979*   *(18-Mar-92 N.M402/R) Portraits of Ludwig Konig von Bayern with family (7cm-3ins circular) min.s.d.1832 W/C bodycol four in one frame (DM 10000)*

MAYR, Wolfgang Christoph von (?-1776) German
£1951   *$3551*   *(12-Dec-91 L.K482/R) Family of Landgraf Friedrich II of Hessen-Kassel (42x32cm-17x13in) s.i.d.1772 pen wash painted with J.H.Tischbein (DM 5600)*

AYRSHOFER, Max (1875-1950) German
515	$897	(17-Sep-91 FN.S2434) Park landscape in spring (25x36cm-10x14in) s. board (DM 1500)
561	$1011	(23-Nov-91 N.M602) Still life of flowers (52x37cm-20x15in) s. i.verso board (DM 1600)

AYS, Brian (20th C) British
2600	$4966	(17-Jul-92 C147/R) Sailing off Cowes (61x91cm-24x36in) s.d.91

AZE, Paul (1887-1979) French
600	$1098	(14-May-92 C63/R) Loch Etive, Argyllshire (63x79cm-25x31in) s.d.1921
650	$1164	(13-Nov-91 CG550) First conception of trooping the colour 1910 (13x22cm-5x9in) s. panel
800	$1384	(24-Mar-92 CG760) Nasturtiums in a yellow basket (41x33cm-16x13in) s. board
4200	$7308	(17-Sep-91 SWS214/R) West Marden from the Hall (70x90cm-28x35in) s.
8000	$13920	(17-Sep-91 SWS213/R) The races (16x62cm-6x24in) s. board
15500	$26970	(17-Sep-91 SWS215/R) Flowers (70x90cm-28x35in) s.
400	$696	(17-Sep-91 SWS210) Snowdrops in black pot (19x24cm-7x9in) s.i.d.1957 W/C pencil with figure on horse verso
450	$806	(13-Nov-91 CG506) Mixed roses in a pottery vase (35x42cm-14x17in) s.d.39 pastel
600	$1098	(4-Jun-92 CSK107/R) French houses with red roofs, on river (23x30cm-9x12in) s. oil W/C paper on board
600	$1098	(4-Jun-92 CSK61) Landscape, Sussex (38x56cm-15x22in) s. pastel
600	$1020	(5-Aug-91 WW156) Ascot (30x38cm-12x15in) s. W/C
600	$1044	(17-Sep-91 SWS200) By the sea with trees (20x26cm-8x10in) s. pastel
600	$1026	(12-Mar-92 B76/R) Watching boats in the harbour (20x32cm-8x13in) W/C pencil
600	$1098	(4-Jun-92 CSK108/R) Fishermen on quay with bathers in shallows (25x35cm-10x14in) s. pastel
750	$1283	(12-Mar-92 B77) Woman seated in an interior (23x28cm-9x11in) s. pastel
750	$1305	(17-Sep-91 SWS194/R) Study of Nipee, a Pekinese (20x25cm-8x10in) s.i.d.1933 indist. red chk
800	$1392	(17-Sep-91 SWS195/R) Roses (12x32cm-5x13in) s. pastel
850	$1556	(14-May-92 C69/R) Summer landscape (53x76cm-21x30in) s. pastel
900	$1566	(17-Sep-91 SWS191/R) Landscape (54x75cm-21x30in) s. pastel
1000	$1740	(17-Sep-91 SWS192/R) The chapel grounds (56x76cm-22x30in) s. W/C
1050	$1827	(17-Sep-91 SWS190/R) River landscape (53x73cm-21x29in) s. pastel
1300	$2262	(17-Sep-91 SWS198/R) Harbour scene with yachts (19x31cm-7x12in) s.d.1959 pencil W/C
1800	$3132	(17-Sep-91 SWS197/R) In the paddock (23x32cm-9x13in) s. pastel
2600	$4524	(17-Sep-91 SWS196/R) Anemones (21x26cm-8x10in) s.i. pastel
3000	$5220	(17-Sep-91 SWS193/R) Majorca (36x54cm-14x21in) s. pastel
3226	$5775	(14-Nov-91 GRO.B163/R) Roses in crystal vase (56x76cm-22x30in) s. pastel
4200	$7308	(17-Sep-91 SWS203/R) Cows grazing on the downs (52x74cm-20x29in) s.d.1959 pastel
4200	$7308	(17-Sep-91 SWS199/R) Bosham (36x54cm-14x21in) s. pastel
5000	$8700	(17-Sep-91 SWS204/R) Tulips in pot (54x74cm-21x29in) s. pastel
6000	$10440	(17-Sep-91 SWS207/R) Still life with poppies (54x72cm-21x28in) s. pastel
7500	$13050	(17-Sep-91 SWS202/R) Tea by the pond (40x62cm-16x24in) s. pastel
7500	$13425	(5-May-92 SWS276/R) Roses in crystal vase (56x76cm-22x30in) s. pastel
7800	$13572	(17-Sep-91 SWS206/R) On the river (35x60cm-14x24in) s. pastel
8000	$13920	(17-Sep-91 SWS205/R) Hyde Park 1936 (52x70cm-20x28in) s. pastel
8400	$14616	(17-Sep-91 SWS201/R) Canal, France (53x72cm-21x28in) s.d.1955 pastel
18000	$31320	(17-Sep-91 SWS208/R) Still life with flowers in jug on table (53x74cm-21x29in) s. pastel
21000	$36540	(17-Sep-91 SWS209/R) Flowers on red tray (54x74cm-21x29in) s. pastel

AZER, Karl Peter (1807-1884) Swedish
6679	$11889	(28-Nov-91 BU.S28/R) Portrait of the artist's nieces Sigrid and Anna Mazer (75x60cm-30x24in) s.d.1858 (S.KR 70000)

AZINI (19th C) Italian
410	$750	(3-Jun-92 D.NY63) Gate keeper, Cairo (43x28cm-17x11in) s.i. W/C

AZO, Juan Bautista Martinez del (attrib) (1612-1667) Spanish
2618	$5000	(16-Jul-92 SY.NY111/R) Portrait of three boys (151x101cm-59x40in)

AZUR, Michael (1935-) American
1257	$2100	(25-Aug-91 JRB.C203) Amyrillus and Calla s.i.
719	$1200	(25-Aug-91 JRB.C107) Fall tress - neighbour's yard (76x69cm-30x27in) pastel
898	$1500	(25-Aug-91 JRB.C58) Wakeby, 1923 (112x112cm-44x44in) s. chl pastel
1018	$1700	(25-Aug-91 JRB.C4) Self-portrait (114x97cm-45x38in) s.d.86 pastel chl

AZZANTI, Lodovico (1679-1775) Italian
5042	$10937	(3-Dec-91 SY.MI221/R) Noli me tangere (57x41cm-22x16in) i.d.1774verso (I.L 13000000)

AZZETTI, Emo (1870-) Italian
1472	$2634	(14-Nov-91 CH.R202) Lago di Garda (49x64cm-19x25in) s. panel (I.L 3200000)

MAZZILINI, S (?) ?
£680 $1176   (3-Oct-91 CSK193) Setting out for the party (64x51cm-25x20in) indist.s.

MAZZOLA, Francesco (1503-1540) Italian
£32000 $55680   (14-Apr-92 C86/R) Two lovers (13x15cm-5x6in) i.verso pen

MAZZOLA, Francesco (after) (1503-1540) Italian
£3625 $6489   (7-May-92 CH.AM19/R) Madonna and Child with saints John Baptist, Jerome,
                     August and Margaret (59x47cm-23x19in) (D.FL 12000)

MAZZOLA, Francesco (attrib) (1503-1540) Italian
£4094 $7288   (29-Nov-91 ARC.P91/R) Groupe de personnages i. pen (F.FR 40000)
£28000 $53760   (6-Jul-92 S16/R) Seated male reaching out with one arm (28x31cm-11x12in)
                     pen

MAZZOLA, Francesco (style) (1503-1540) Italian
£614 $1112   (21-May-92 L.K304/R) St John writing (34x27cm-13x11in) ochre (DM 1800)

MAZZOLA, Girolamo Bedoli (circle) (1500-1569) Italian
£1366 $2472   (3-Dec-91 R.T214/R) Adoration of the Shepherds (58x35cm-23x14in)
                     (C.D 2800)

MAZZOLA, Girolamo Bedoli (style) (1500-1569) Italian
£2200 $3960   (21-Nov-91 C97/R) Madonna and Child with infant St John the Baptist
                     (50x35cm-20x14in)

MAZZOLA, Giuseppe (1748-1838) Italian
£697 $1192   (19-Mar-92 F.M100) Scena di famiglia (27x19cm-11x7in) s.d.1853 W/C
                     (I.L 1500000)

MAZZOLINI, G (19th C) Italian
£1800 $3258   (21-May-92 CSK301/R) Rest by pool (91x71cm-36x28in) s.
£2094 $4000   (16-Jul-92 SY.NY197/R) Allegory of Winter (62x49cm-24x19in) s.
£3198 $5500   (17-Oct-91 SY.NY383/R) Maternita (63x50cm-25x20in)
£3200 $5792   (21-May-92 CSK278/R) Watching over baby (100x74cm-39x29in) s.d.

MAZZOLINI, Giuseppe (19th C) Italian
£2198 $4000   (28-May-92 SY.NY307/R) La madre e suo bambino (102x75cm-40x30in) s.d.1867
£2300 $4094   (29-Oct-91 SWS56/R) Young hunter (105x88cm-41x35in) bears i.
£2421 $4600   (28-Jun-92 LIT.L170) Fleeing the storm (61x51cm-24x20in) s.verso
£3779 $6500   (15-Oct-91 CE.NY322/R) Rocking the baby asleep (102x75cm-40x30in) s.

MAZZOLINO, Ludovico (1480-1528) Italian
£80000 $153600   (8-Jul-92 S45/R) Holy Family with St Sebastian and St Roch
                     (39x35cm-15x14in) s.d.MCCCCCXI branded verso panel

MAZZONI, Sebastiano (?-1683) Italian
£61000 $111020   (11-Dec-91 S170/R) Sophonisba (113x99cm-44x39in)

MAZZOTTA, Federico (19th C) Italian
£5233 $9000   (16-Oct-91 CH.NY200/R) Playtime (80x54cm-31x21in) s.
£9000 $16740   (17-Jun-92 S579/R) Dispute (92x73cm-36x29in) s.

MAZZUCHELLI, Pietro Francesco (attrib) (1571-1626) Italian
£950 $1824   (8-Jul-92 PH101/R) Coronation of Virgin (14x10cm-6x4in) i. wash over
                     black chk htd white squared

MAZZUCHELLI, Pietro Francesco (circle) (1571-1626) Italian
£1840 $3165   (15-Oct-91 CH.R79/R) Gli angeli recano la corona del martirio alla
                     Maddalena penitente (39x45cm-15x18in) (I.L 4000000)

MAZZUOLI, Giuseppe (1536-1589) Italian
£16357 $29933   (16-May-92 F.L17/R) Lo sposalizio Mistico di Santa Caterina
                     (86x66cm-34x26in) (S.FR 44000)

McALPINE (?) ?
£1582 $2768   (20-Feb-92 D.V321/R) Seascape (25x51cm-10x20in) s. (A.S 32000)

McALPINE, William (19th C) British
£1100 $1892   (8-Oct-91 PH82) Trafalgar 21st October 1805 (61x107cm-24x42in) s.d.74

McAULAY, Charles (20th C) British?
£520 $884   (22-Oct-91 SWS387/R) Cattle grazing in valley (37x55cm-15x22in) s. board
£550 $957   (18-Sep-91 CG136) Rocky coastline, Co. Antrim (38x56cm-15x22in) s. board
£580 $1015   (17-Feb-92 HS291) Coshendall Bay, Antrim (41x60cm-16x24in) s. i.verso
£650 $1131   (18-Sep-91 CG135) Breakers, Co. Antrim (38x56cm-15x22in) s. board
£900 $1566   (18-Sep-91 CG134) Cattle grazing by bay, Co. Antrim (36x49cm-14x19in) s.
                     board
£900 $1566   (18-Sep-91 CG133/R) Unloading nets, Connemara (46x61cm-18x24in) s. board

McAULIFFE, J J (1848-1921) American
£2787 $5100   (9-Feb-92 LIT.L178) Trotter racing, possibly Long Island
                     (66x91cm-26x36in) s.

McBEY, James (1883-1959) British
£2100 $3801   (4-Dec-91 S237/R) Sussex fields (32x67cm-13x26in) s.d.1938 i.verso
£414 $750   (22-May-92 S.BM182/R) Stop along the river bank, Boston England
     (36x25cm-14x10in) s.i.d.1930 W/C ink graphite
£450 $864   (29-Jul-92 CSK104) Gypsy encampment, Niebla (27x48cm-11x19in) s.d.1932
     pen W/C
£450 $815   (5-Dec-91 CG93) Cowie (18x36cm-7x14in) s.i.d.1923 pen W/C
£500 $905   (5-Dec-91 CG103) Fishing boats (23x36cm-9x14in) s.i.d.1931 pencil pen W/C
£600 $1008   (26-Aug-91 S1135) West Mercea (27x45cm-11x18in) s.i.d.1957 W/C
£635 $1150   (5-Dec-91 FA.PH576) Lisbon Port (36x53cm-14x21in) s.i.d.1946 W/C
£700 $1267   (5-Dec-91 CG99/R) Afternoon after good Friday (13x25cm-5x10in) s.i.d.1914
     pen W/C

McCAIG, Norman J (?) Irish
£455 $786   (2-Oct-91 A.D90) Feeding ducks, St. Stephen's Green, Dublin
     (36x46cm-14x18in) s. (E.P 500)
£467 $808   (25-Mar-92 A.D181) Summer holiday, The Rosses, Donegal (41x51cm-16x20in)
     s. board (E.P 500)
£596 $1109   (17-Jun-92 A.D64) Springtime (36x46cm-14x18in) s. board (E.P 650)
£642 $1194   (17-Jun-92 A.D191) Roundstone harbour, Co. Galway (51x61cm-20x24in) s.
     (E.P 700)

McCALL, Charles (1907-1989) British
£540 $940   (17-Sep-91 PH106) Portobello Road (61x51cm-24x20in) s.d.62 i.verso
£800 $1424   (30-Apr-92 CG927) Pink dressing gown (56x30cm-22x12in) s.d.57 board
£850 $1488   (27-Sep-91 C77/R) Domestic interior (40x25cm-16x10in) s.d.57 board
£950 $1663   (27-Feb-92 L78) At the Milliners (48x58cm-19x23in)
£1000 $1720   (10-Oct-91 L198) At the Milliners, lady and assistant trying on hats
     (48x58cm-19x23in)
£1200 $2148   (13-Nov-91 CG670/R) The snack bar (61x46cm-24x18in) s.d.58 i.verso board

McCALLUM, Andrew (1821-1902) British
£950 $1615   (23-Oct-91 S74) The winter sun, Kom Ombo, Egypt (37x112cm-15x44in)
     s.d.1872 i.stretcher W/C

McCANNELL, Ursula (20th C) British
£850 $1505   (23-Apr-92 B80) The storm (93x78cm-37x31in) s.d.38 board

McCARTHY, Doris Jean (1910-) Canadian
£594 $1080   (26-May-92 JOY.T69) Hibb's Hole, NFLD (52x72cm-20x28in) s. W/C (C.D 1300)

McCAY, Winsor (1869-1934) American
£1573 $2800   (2-May-92 IH.NY142/R) Money burns a hole in man's pocket
     (48x33cm-19x13in) s. pen ink
£6742 $12000   (2-Nov-91 IH.NY152/R) Little Nemo fighting Indians, comic strip
     (71x56cm-28x22in) s. pen

McCHESNEY, Clara Taggart (1860-1928) American
£1117 $2000   (13-Nov-91 B.SF2620/R) Mother and child (41x33cm-16x13in) s. W/C gouache

McCLOSKEY, Jim (20th C) American
£769 $1400   (13-Dec-91 S.W2290/R) Protest outside White House (46x61cm-18x24in) s.

McCLOSKEY, William J (1859-1941) American
£170330 $310000   (27-May-92 SY.NY12 a/R) Wrapped oranges (26x43cm-10x17in) s.d.1901

McCLOY, Samuel (1831-1904) British
£900 $1566   (18-Sep-91 CG70/R) Two girls by bridge (53x76cm-21x30in) s. W/C htd
     bodycol
£1900 $3306   (18-Sep-91 CG19/R) Conversation by river (25x36cm-10x14in) s. W/C
£2100 $3654   (18-Sep-91 CG18) Flowers for teacher (38x27cm-15x11in) mono. W/C

McCLURE, David (1926-) British
£500 $905   (5-Dec-91 CG149) Donkey and cart (74x91cm-29x36in) s. board
£840 $1529   (29-May-92 PHG100 d) Self portrait in mirror with cat no. 1
     (48x58cm-19x23in) s.indist.d. s.i.verso panel

McCOLLUM, Allan (1944-) French
£5714 $10000   (27-Feb-92 CH.NY112/R) Collection of 30 drawings, no 8 graphite
     paperboard

McCORD, George (1848-1909) American
£600 $1098   (14-May-92 CSK268) Shipping on river at sunset (46x76cm-18x30in) s.
£745 $1400   (18-Dec-91 SY.NY73/R) The approaching storm (76x63cm-30x25in) s.
£1301 $2250   (29-Mar-92 MY.F95/R) Vesper hour (66x51cm-26x20in) s.
£1436 $2600   (7-Dec-91 LAE.L112/R) Harbour scene (46x76cm-18x30in) s.i.
£1514 $2800   (10-Jun-92 CE.NY206/R) Fisherfolk on coast (51x91cm-20x36in) s.
£2394 $4500   (18-Dec-91 SY.NY110/R) Landscape near Yonkers (23x46cm-9x18in) s.i. on
     stretcher
£2456 $4200   (12-Mar-92 CH.NY18/R) Sunset on Lake George (30x51cm-12x20in) s.
£3056 $5500   (24-Nov-91 JRB.C61/R) Hudson river landscape (58x119cm-23x47in) s.
£3216 $5500   (12-Mar-92 CH.NY79/R) The fisherman's return (46x76cm-18x30in) s.
£5525 $10000   (6-Dec-91 CH.NY73/R) A glimpse of Morristown, New Jersey
     (128x103cm-50x41in) s. canvas on masonite

McCORMACK, Thomas Arthur (1883-1973) New Zealander
£515   *$861*   *(21-Aug-91 DS.W69) Beach scene (17x24cm-7x9in) s. W/C (NZ.D 1500)*
£597   *$1069*   *(6-May-92 DS.W5) Ocean beach (36x57cm-14x22in) s. i.verso W/C (NZ.D 2000)*

McCORMACK, Tim (20th C) Australian
£922 $1604   (17-Sep-91 JRL.S455/R) Bush potato dreaming (238x183cm-94x72in) acrylic
     canvas (A.D 2000)

McCORMICK, A D (1860-1943) British
£420 $735   *(25-Sep-91 CSK13) Watching a regatta from the beach (20x25cm-8x10in)*
     s.d.90 pencil W/C

McCORMICK, Arthur David (1860-1943) British
£959 $1630   (6-Aug-91 UL.T155) The song of triumph (130x120cm-51x47in) (N.KR 11000)
£2600 $4472   (11-Oct-91 C33/R) A fine ale. A good smoke (61x46cm-24x18in) init. pair
£1000   *$1850*   *(11-Jun-92 CSK38/R) A Christmas Carol (51x74cm-20x29in) s. pencil W/C*

McCORMICK, Howard (1875-1943) American
£751 $1300   (6-Sep-91 S.BM199/R) Hopi Katchina (36x36cm-14x14in) s. panel

McCOY, Raymond A (1893-?) American
£877 $1500   (12-Mar-92 MFA.C120 a) Young girl in tree (61x46cm-24x18in) s.

McCRACKEN, Francis (1879-1959) British
£1940 $3473   (6-May-92 DS.W30/R) Sea of Forth (69x89cm-27x35in) (NZ.D 6500)
£358   *$641*   *(6-May-92 DS.W31) Reclining nude (40x50cm-16x20in) mixed media*
     (NZ.D 7000)
£1718   *$2869*   *(21-Aug-91 DS.W117) Cathedral at Quimper (74x53cm-29x21in) s. W/C crayon*
     (NZ.D 5000)

McCROSSAN, Mary (?-1934) British
£500   *$955*   *(16-Jul-92 B43) Evening, Port St Mary (38x47cm-15x19in) s.*
£620 $1116   (20-Nov-91 B183) Sailing vessels on river (46x60cm-18x24in) s.d.1923
£700 $1225   (27-Sep-91 C66/R) Padstow, Cornwall (39x32cm-15x13in) s. i. verso panel
£1800 $3150   (27-Sep-91 C117/R) Thames barges (33x41cm-13x16in) s.d.1928 i. label
     verso board

McCUBBIN, Frederick (1855-1917) Australian
£7234 $12804   (26-Apr-92 SY.ME344/R) Across Yarra to Richmond (24x34cm-9x13in) s.
     canvas on board (A.D 17000)
£13617 $24102   (26-Apr-92 SY.ME431/R) Reaper and haystack (23x34cm-9x13in) s. panel
     (A.D 32000)
£129032 $224516   (16-Sep-91 CH.ME147/R) Mountain cottage (74x100cm-29x39in) s.d.1915
     (A.D 280000)

McCULLOCH, George (fl.1855-1901) British
£450   *$783*   *(12-Sep-91 B158/R) The young harvester (40x30cm-16x12in) s.d.1977 W/C*

McCULLOCH, Horatio (1805-1867) British
£550 $957   (11-Sep-91 PHG17) Glencoe (42x50cm-17x20in) s.
£700 $1267   (4-Dec-91 S280/R) Glencoe (44x51cm-17x20in) s.
£800 $1448   (4-Dec-91 S278/R) Lochside road (55x97cm-22x38in) indist.s.d.1851
£800 $1464   (12-May-92 LV234/R) Wooded river landscape with ruin and small boat,
     moutains beyond (28x43cm-11x17in) s.d.1853
£857 $1500   (18-Feb-92 CE.NY110) Oak tree (35x47cm-14x19in) s. panel
£1000 $1830   (12-May-92 LV235/R) Gathering storm (20x33cm-8x13in) s.
£1200 $2016   (26-Aug-91 S771/R) Deer in the highlands (61x98cm-24x39in) s.
£1600 $2848   (28-Apr-92 S126/R) Bothwell Castle and Blantyre Priory (37x55cm-15x22in)
     s.
£1800 $3024   (26-Aug-91 S772/R) Deer in landscape (36x45cm-14x18in) s.

McCULLOCH, Horatio (attrib) (1805-1867) British
£2400 $4272   (30-Apr-92 CG915/R) View of Edinburgh from Corstophine (28x91cm-11x36in)

McCULLOCH, Horatio (circle) (1805-1867) British
£3000 $5370   (13-Nov-91 CG620/R) Prospect of Inverary looking South towards Inverary
     Castle (96x137cm-38x54in)

McCULLOCH, Horatio (style) (1805-1867) British
£1700 $3043   (13-Nov-91 CG629/R) View of Loch Lomond from Scout Hill looking north
     towards Ben Lomond (71x91cm-28x36in)

McCULLOCH, Wilfred Arthur (1910-1942) Australian
£1872 $3333   (26-Nov-91 J.M166/R) Peninsula landscape (39x46cm-15x18in) s. canvas on
     board (A.D 4250)

McDERMOTT and McGOUGH (20th C) American
£838 $1500   (12-Nov-91 CE.NY199/R) Untitled (66x30cm-26x12in) s.i.d.1763

McDOUGAL, John (fl.1877-1941) British
£460   *$819*   *(24-Jan-92 CBB238) North Wales - toll house and cottages*
     (38x58cm-15x23in) s.d.1882 W/C
£520   *$926*   *(29-Nov-91 T227) Sunlit sea, Porth Patrick Bay (20x33cm-8x13in) s.d.1921*
     W/C
£900   *$1593*   *(6-Nov-91 S237/R) Sheltered estuary (37x59cm-15x23in) s.d.1892 W/C*

McDOUGAL, John (fl.1877-1941) British-cont.

£900	$1647	(3-Jun-92 S215/R) Leaving harbour, Cemaes Bay (49x59cm-19x23in) s.d.1932 W/C htd.white
£1200	$2256	(3-Jan-92 BW376/R) Fishing boats setting out to sea from Newly (46x36cm-18x14in) s.d.1889 W/C
£1200	$2100	(31-Mar-92 RJ131) Sunset coastal scene with boats (28x48cm-11x19in) s.d.1888 W/C

McDOUGALL, John Alexander (1810-1894) ?

| £1073 | $1900 | (25-Apr-92 YFA.M221/R) Peeling vegetables (61x46cm-24x18in) s.i. |

McDUFF, Frederick H (1931-) American

| £497 | $900 | (21-May-92 S.W2454/R) Figures in summer landscape (30x41cm-12x16in) s. |
| £1243 | $2200 | (13-Feb-92 S.W2859) Figures along the shore (28x46cm-11x18in) s. |

McENTEE, Jervis (1828-1891) American

£539	$900	(20-Aug-91 RB.HY139/R) Trees in the forest (43x30cm-17x12in) canvas laid down on cardboard
£1098	$1900	(24-Mar-92 GRO.B42) Where trout run (30x46cm-12x18in) mono.indist.d.1871 s.d.verso canvas on board
£1649	$3100	(18-Dec-91 SY.NY40/R) The wood in autumn (40x27cm-16x11in) mono.d.83
£2034	$3600	(9-Nov-91 W.W139/R) View from sunset rock (20x28cm-8x11in) mono.init.d.Oct.71 bears i.verso board
£2222	$4000	(10-Jan-92 DM.D2009/R) Pool in autumn (30x36cm-12x14in) mono.s.i.verso
£2924	$5000	(12-Mar-92 CH.NY42/R) Morning glories (23x18cm-9x7in) board

McEVOY, A (1878-1927) British

| £500 | $840 | (16-Aug-91 K584) Portrait of young lady in blue dress (64x48cm-25x19in) s. |

McEVOY, Ambrose (1878-1927) British

£5500	$10065	(5-Jun-92 C7/R) Portrait of a lady (173x102cm-68x40in)
£700	$1218	(19-Sep-91 CSK42) San Giorgio Maggiore, Venice (28x44cm-11x17in) s.i.d.1923 pencil W/C bodycol
£10800	$18468	(11-Mar-92 S32/R) Portrait of Lady Diana Cooper (39x33cm-15x13in) s. pencil W/C

McEWAN, Tom (1846-1914) British

| £5000 | $8400 | (26-Aug-91 S849/R) Grannie's care (63x76cm-25x30in) s. s.i.verso |
| £2200 | $3696 | (26-Aug-91 S852/R) The spinner. Sewing (36x25cm-14x10in) both s. one s.i.verso W/C two |

McEWEN, Walter (1860-1943) British

| £4696 | $8500 | (4-Dec-91 D.NY18/R) Stad Herberg of Nieuw Amsterdam, New York (140x203cm-55x80in) s.i. |

McFARLANE, D (19th C) ?

| £620 | $1122 | (5-Dec-91 CSK144) Cattle in highland landscape (102x76cm-40x30in) s. |

McFEE, Henry Lee (1886-1953) American

| £2571 | $4500 | (26-Sep-91 CH.NY233/R) Still life with kitchen utensils (61x51cm-24x20in) s. |
| £3143 | $5500 | (26-Sep-91 CH.NY241/R) Still life with onions and lemons (54x41cm-21x16in) s.d. |

McGEEHAN, Jessie M (fl.1892-1913) British

| £1900 | $3382 | (27-Apr-92 PHB263/R) Little girl with basket of plums (54x45cm-21x18in) s.indist.d. |

McGHIE, John (1867-1941) British

£900	$1557	(24-Mar-92 PHC387/R) Harvester's rest (36x47cm-14x19in) s.
£2800	$4984	(30-Apr-92 CG940/R) East Coast fishwife (51x61cm-20x24in) s.
£7800	$13884	(30-Apr-92 CG941/R) Fisherfolk unloading boats (76x145cm-30x57in) s.
£8500	$14280	(26-Aug-91 S973/R) Cornfield by the sea (76x63cm-30x25in) s.

McGILL, Donald (?) British?

£420	$764	(11-Dec-91 CSK2) Waiter, there's an insect in this soup (18x13cm-7x5in) s. i.verso pencil W/C bodycol.
£420	$806	(10-Jul-92 CSK48) Is he fond of children. I don't know Mum I ain't fed on nothin' but biscuits so far (20x15cm-8x6in) s.i.verso pencil W/C bodycol
£420	$764	(11-Dec-91 CSK8) Pardon me, Madam - did you drop this (23x18cm-9x7in) s. i.verso pencil W/C bodycol.
£450	$819	(11-Dec-91 CSK12) I see the man next door kisses his wife good-bye every morning... (23x18cm-9x7in) s. i.verso pencil W/C bodycol.
£450	$819	(11-Dec-91 CSK7) You know you said that girl has something... (20x20cm-8x8in) s. i.verso pencil W/C bodycol.
£450	$819	(11-Dec-91 CSK1/R) Sorry, lady I'avent't got a fillet steak this morning.... (18x13cm-7x5in) s. i.verso pencil W/C bodycol.
£450	$819	(11-Dec-91 CSK4) They say it's freezing in exposed parts (20x15cm-8x6in) s. i.verso pencil W/C bodycol.
£450	$819	(11-Dec-91 CSK6) Yes, lassie, it's a new kilt... (20x15cm-8x6in) s. i.verso pencil W/C bodycol.
£480	$874	(11-Dec-91 CSK11) Oh, it's a bee (20x15cm-8x6in) s. i.verso pencil W/C bodycol.

McGILL, Donald (?) British?-cont.

£480	$874	(11-Dec-91 CSK3) I've got the sack from the tram depot (20x15cm-8x6in) s. i.verso pencil W/C bodycol.
£480	$874	(11-Dec-91 CSK14) If I find you've got two homes and one away, there's going to be trouble (23x18cm-9x7in) s. i.verso pencil W/C bodycol.
£480	$874	(11-Dec-91 CSK5) There you are, What did I tell you (13x25cm-5x10in) s. i.verso pencil W/C bodycol.
£600	$1146	(1-Jul-92 B144) Dont look now but I think we are being followed (12x25cm-5x10in) s. gouache
£680	$1238	(11-Dec-91 CSK9/R) This nudist used to love the Bees.... (23x18cm-9x7in) s. i.verso pencil W/C bodycol.
£700	$1337	(1-Jul-92 B152) Dont be silly that's only a fig leaf (21x15cm-8x6in) s. gouache
£800	$1456	(11-Dec-91 CSK13) Don't forget you promised to teach me to drive a car, too (13x25cm-5x10in) s. i.verso pencil W/C bodycol.

McGIVERN, Barbara (1950-) Canadian

£811	$1467	(24-May-92 AT.P50/R) Study in red (96x127cm-38x50in) s. acrylic (F.FR 8000)

McGONIGAL, Maurice (1900-1979) British

£917	$1706	(17-Jun-92 A.D176/R) Donkey foal going for walk (41x51cm-16x20in) s. board (E.P 1000)
£950	$1653	(18-Sep-91 CG183) Foal going for walk (41x51cm-16x20in) s. board
£2400	$4176	(18-Sep-91 CG182/R) Donkey and foal (46x61cm-18x24in) s. canvasboard
£2523	$4365	(25-Mar-92 A.D140) Cattle grazing, Phoenix Park (43x51cm-17x20in) s. board (E.P 2700)
£3519	$6404	(11-Dec-91 A.D49/R) Charlemont Mall, Dublin (61x71cm-24x28in) s. board (E.P 3800)
£3853	$7167	(17-Jun-92 A.D18/R) Cottages at Inverin, Connemara (30x41cm-12x16in) s. board (E.P 4200)
£6944	$12639	(11-Dec-91 A.D92 a) Cora ar Lochaig, Dingle Peninsula, Kerry (41x76cm-16x30in) s. s.i.d.1972verso board (E.P 7500)
£727	$1258	(2-Oct-91 A.D154) Errisbeag, West Connemara (20x53cm-8x21in) pen W/C (E.P 800)

McGOOGAN, Archibald (20th C) British

£500	$870	(18-Sep-91 CG90/R) Bather by stream (25x18cm-10x7in) W/C htd white

McGORAN, Kieran (?) British

£400	$696	(18-Sep-91 CG15) On coast (35x33cm-14x13in) s. pastel
£480	$835	(18-Sep-91 CG17) At start (38x49cm-15x19in) s. pastel
£700	$1218	(18-Sep-91 CG14) Under starter's orders (47x40cm-19x16in) s. pastel
£750	$1305	(18-Sep-91 CG16) Going down to beach (27x36cm-11x14in) s. pastel
£1300	$2262	(18-Sep-91 CG13/R) Picnic on beach (41x51cm-16x20in) s. pastel

McGOUGH and McDERMOTT see McDERMOTT and McGOUGH

McGREGOR, R (1848-1922) British

£780	$1490	(16-Jul-92 HB595) Young girl seated outside window shelling peas (61x46cm-24x18in) s. board

McGREGOR, Robert (1848-1922) British

£500	$890	(1-Nov-91 PHE31) Fisherfolk and boats (53x41cm-21x16in) s. canvas laid down
£700	$1253	(5-May-92 SWS337/R) Looking after baby (21x11cm-8x4in) init. board
£900	$1602	(30-Apr-92 CG929/R) The potato harvest (30x40cm-12x16in) s. canvas laid down on board
£1400	$2352	(26-Aug-91 S1040/R) Camp site (59x79cm-23x31in) s.d.1910
£1500	$2670	(30-Apr-92 CG860/R) Mother and child with cow at dusk (46x57cm-18x22in) s.
£1600	$2848	(28-Apr-92 S254/R) Midday repast (25x35cm-10x14in) s. s.i.verso
£1900	$3382	(1-May-92 PHE38/R) Shrimping (25x35cm-10x14in) s. board
£2600	$4810	(11-Jun-92 CSK230/R) The toy boat (71x91cm-28x36in) s.d.73
£4800	$8544	(30-Apr-92 CG946/R) Shrimping on French coast (67x84cm-26x33in) s.

McGUINNESS, Norah (1903-1980) British

£818	$1415	(2-Oct-91 A.D170) Still life - roses in window (51x36cm-20x14in) s. (E.P 900)
£1200	$2256	(18-Dec-91 C145/R) The black gate (29x38cm-11x15in) init.d.
£1589	$2749	(25-Mar-92 A.D183) Mud flats (51x71cm-20x28in) s. (E.P 1700)
£1727	$2988	(2-Oct-91 A.D161) Heron pool (41x56cm-16x22in) s. (E.P 1900)
£1727	$2988	(2-Oct-91 A.D147) Geese on salt marsh (51x91cm-20x36in) s. (E.P 1900)
£1750	$3290	(18-Dec-91 C144/R) Ochre and heather (51x61cm-20x24in) s.
£2593	$4719	(11-Dec-91 A.D138/R) Winter sun (69x91cm-27x36in) s. (E.P 2800)
£11818	$20445	(2-Oct-91 A.D66/R) Still life interior with vases and flowers on table (84x64cm-33x25in) (E.P 13000)
£364	$629	(2-Oct-91 A.D146) Three figures on cliff edge (30x23cm-12x9in) pen (E.P 400)
£370	$674	(11-Dec-91 A.D8) Wharfs (23x28cm-9x11in) gouache (E.P 400)
£382	$661	(2-Oct-91 A.D162) Blue cart (20x28cm-8x11in) init. gouache (E.P 420)
£413	$768	(17-Jun-92 A.D16) Artist with Denis Johnson (23x33cm-9x13in) with studio st. pencil W/C (E.P 450)
£463	$843	(11-Dec-91 A.D129) Warehouse at Ramelton (30x48cm-12x19in) s.d.1935 W/C gouache (E.P 500)

McGUINNESS, Norah (1903-1980) British-cont.

£545	$944	(2-Oct-91 A.D148) Priory, Rathmullan, Co. Donegal (25x36cm-10x14in) W/C (E.P 600)
£561	$970	(25-Mar-92 A.D2) Temple Street, Dublin (33x48cm-13x19in) s.d.1941 W/C (E.P 600)
£844	$1570	(15-Jun-92 AD.D80) Seagulls. Country scene with graveyard (46x58cm-18x23in) s. W/C pair (E.P 920)
£1101	$2048	(17-Jun-92 A.D91) Salmon weir, Galway (38x53cm-15x21in) s.d.1946 gouache (E.P 1200)
£1550	$2697	(18-Sep-91 CG35/R) Still life with potted primulas and hyacinths on table (55x44cm-22x17in) s.d.1947 W/C htd bodycol
£2407	$4381	(11-Dec-91 A.D168/R) Upton View, Monkstown, Co.Dublin with children playing in snow (43x53cm-17x21in) s.indist. gouache (E.P 2600)
£2500	$4550	(11-Dec-91 A.D122/R) Snow on the hills, Rockbrook (41x61cm-16x24in) s.d.47 gouache (E.P 2700)
£2909	$5033	(2-Oct-91 A.D71) New York harbour (36x48cm-14x19in) s.d.1933 gouache (E.P 3200)

McGUINNESS, William Bingham (?-1928) British

£450	$783	(18-Sep-91 CG69) Fisherman by tree-lined river (26x35cm-10x14in) s. W/C htd white
£650	$1131	(18-Sep-91 CG68) Market stalls beneath Arches (25x16cm-10x6in) s. W/C htd white
£800	$1392	(18-Sep-91 CG67) Windmill by canal (52x36cm-20x14in) s. W/C htd white
£1178	$2250	(16-Jul-92 SY.NY566/R) Ventian canal (88x53cm-35x21in) s.d.1890 W/C
£1600	$2784	(18-Sep-91 CG66/R) Zattere, Venice (38x54cm-15x21in) s. i.verso W/C htd white

McINNES, Robert (1801-1886) British

| £2500 | $4300 | (4-Mar-92 S110/R) Interior of English cottage (30x40cm-12x16in) s.i. panel |

McINNES, William Beckwith (1889-1939) Australian

£837	$1490	(26-Nov-91 J.M71) Farmyard scene (33x52cm-13x20in) s. (A.D 1900)
£900	$1602	(28-Nov-91 B170/R) In the shade (37x31cm-15x12in) s.d.1913 board
£1542	$2744	(26-Nov-91 J.M162/R) Bazaar in Cairo (28x38cm-11x15in) s. board (A.D 3500)
£2423	$4313	(26-Nov-91 J.M204 a) Bazaar in Morocco (41x57cm-16x22in) s. canvas on board (A.D 5500)
£2903	$5052	(16-Sep-91 CH.ME82/R) Quarry (50x60cm-20x24in) s.d.18 (A.D 6300)
£3524	$6273	(26-Nov-91 J.M227/R) French street scene (35x24cm-14x9in) s. board (A.D 8000)
£14978	$26960	(24-Nov-91 SY.S360/R) Hawkesbury River (74x125cm-29x49in) s.d.21 (A.D 34000)

McINNIS, Robert (1942-) Canadian

| £585 | $1054 | (18-Nov-91 HO.ED129/R) Blue sky and elevators (76x91cm-30x36in) (C.D 1200) |
| £634 | $1141 | (18-Nov-91 HO.ED91) West of Okotoks (61x76cm-24x30in) (C.D 1300) |

McINTYRE, Joseph Wrightson (19th C) British

| £1000 | $1730 | (4-Sep-91 BT309/R) Village and harbour of St.Abb's, Berwickshire (66x102cm-26x40in) s. s.i.verso |

McINTYRE, Peter (1910-) New Zealander

£515	$861	(21-Aug-91 DS.W177) Daydreaming (59x44cm-23x17in) s. (NZ.D 1500)
£567	$1015	(6-May-92 DS.W44) Summer in Antarctica (50x60cm-20x24in) s.d.1959 i.verso (NZ.D 1900)
£1358	$2431	(6-May-92 DS.W46) Junks, Hong Kong Harbour (64x85cm-25x33in) s. (NZ.D 4550)
£2062	$3443	(21-Aug-91 DS.W85/R) Purakunui (61x57cm-24x22in) s.d. (NZ.D 6000)
£2405	$4017	(21-Aug-91 DS.W90/R) North Canterbury (58x68cm-23x27in) s. (NZ.D 7000)

McINTYRE, Robert Finlay (fl.1892-1897) British

| £500 | $855 | (18-Mar-92 CSK250) London from Greenwich Park (36x61cm-14x24in) s. s.i. |

McKAIN, Bruce (1900-) American

| £526 | $900 | (13-Mar-92 S.BM276) Fisherman (64x76cm-25x30in) board |

McKAY, William Darling (1844-1924) British

£700	$1330	(23-Jun-92 PH173) Marquis of Teesdale sketched by artist while out shooting (62x81cm-24x32in) sd.1865
£800	$1424	(28-Apr-92 PH131/R) Seed drilling in landscape (51x77cm-20x30in) s.
£1900	$3192	(26-Aug-91 S1053/R) Woodcutters (27x41cm-11x16in) init. board
£1900	$3192	(26-Aug-91 S993/R) Carting potatoes (35x54cm-14x21in) init. s.i.label frame

McKEEVER, Ian (1946-) British

| £3073 | $5500 | (9-May-92 CE.NY196/R) Through the ice lens (221x170cm-87x67in) s.i.d.86verso oil poto collage canvas |
| £3352 | $6000 | (9-May-92 CE.NY195/R) Glacier III (220x170cm-87x67in) s.d.86verso oil photo collage canvas |

McKELVEY, Frank (1895-1974) British
£596 $1109   (17-Jun-92 A.D193) Pond, Bessbrook, Co. Down (23x33cm-9x13in) s. board
                         (E.P 650)
£4206 $7276   (25-Mar-92 A.D142) Gathering the turf in a lake and mountain landscape
                         (46x61cm-18x24in) s. (E.P 4500)
£8500 $15555   (13-May-92 S19/R) St Stephen's Green, Dublin (51x69cm-20x27in) s.
£8704 $15231   (17-Feb-92 AD.D29/R) Lake Reflections (41x51cm-16x20in) s. (E.P 9400)
£9346 $16168   (25-Mar-92 A.D45/R) Fishermen on Lake Shore, West of Ireland
                         (51x69cm-20x27in) s. (E.P 10000)
£13000 $23790   (13-May-92 S17/R) Picnic by the Lagan (51x69cm-20x27in) s.
£367 $683   (17-Jun-92 A.D96) Near Carrigart, Co. Donegal (23x33cm-9x13in) s. W/C
                         (E.P 400)
£750 $1305   (18-Sep-91 CG24) Atlantic Drive, Co. Donegal (26x36cm-10x14in) s. W/C
£818 $1415   (2-Oct-91 A.D63) Tearful farewell (36x25cm-14x10in) s.d.1914 W/C htd
                         white (E.P 900)
£1455 $2516   (2-Oct-91 A.D30) Gull Island from Rosses (38x56cm-15x22in) s. W/C
                         (E.P 1600)

McKEWAN, David Hall (19th C) British
£400 $696   (9-Sep-91 PH115) Mountain pass in Wales (33x51cm-13x20in) s. W/C

McKNIGHT, Thomas (?) ?
£719 $1200   (25-Aug-91 JRB.C149) Veranda view with watermelon (86x99cm-34x39in)
                         s.num.121/175

McLAREN, Peter (20th C) British
£550 $1001   (29-May-92 PHG16) Driving - figures in car (184x246cm-72x97in) s.verso
                         mixed media board

McLAUGHLIN, Isabel (1903-) Canadian
£872 $1595   (1-Jun-92 W.T1047) The corner house (48x51cm-19x20in) s.verso (C.D 1900)

McLAUGHLIN, John (1898-1976) American
£7821 $14000   (7-May-92 SY.NY252/R) No.7-1961 (122x152cm-48x60in) s.d.1961
£11429 $20000   (27-Feb-92 CH.NY54/R) No 20-1958 (152x97cm-60x38in) s.i.d.1958verso
£13408 $24000   (13-Nov-91 CH.NY139/R) Untitled no.17 (81x96cm-32x38in) s.d.Feb '54verso
                         masonite
£13408 $24000   (13-Nov-91 CH.NY152/R) No.11-1959 (152x111cm-60x44in) s.i.d.1959verso

McLEAN, Bruce (1944-) British
£500 $915   (14-May-92 C130) Untitled (76x54cm-30x21in) acrylic photographic paper
£1143 $2000   (27-Feb-92 CE.NY233/R) Untitled (200x149cm-79x59in) acrylic col.chk
                         canvas
£1397 $2500   (9-May-92 CE.NY232/R) Untitled (190x149cm-75x59in) acrylic chl canvas
£1745 $3142   (19-Nov-91 FB.P225/R) Personnage (241x154cm-95x61in) mixed media canvas
                         (F.FR 17000)

McLEAN, Jack Lee (1924-) Canadian
£1094 $1859   (23-Oct-91 MA.V93) Cowpony and Palisade Bunkhouse, Vidette Lake Area, B.C
                         (46x61cm-18x24in) s. board (C.D 2100)

McLELLAN, Charles A (1885-?) American
£4480 $7750   (29-Mar-92 MY.F114/R) Fisk tire illustration (66x112cm-26x44in) s.

McLEOD, Ewan (?) Australian?
£556 $950   (17-Mar-92 JRL.S246) Children in water (140x170cm-55x67in) s.d.2/89 verso
                         (A.D 1250)

McLEOD, Robert (20th C) New Zealander
£586 $1061   (4-Dec-91 DS.W23) Red yellow running (170x115cm-67x45in) s.i.d.1978
                         (NZ.D 1900)

McMANUS, George (1869-1954) American
£562 $1000   (2-May-92 IH.NY127/R) Bringing up father (53x41cm-21x16in) s. pen ink

McMASTER, James (1856-1913) British
£520 $900   (24-Mar-92 CG709) In Tayport Harbour (35x24cm-14x9in) s.i. W/C
                         htd.bodycol.
£580 $974   (29-Aug-91 CG36) Morning Ayr Harbour (33x25cm-13x10in) s.i. W/C
                         htd.bodycol.
£700 $1267   (4-Dec-91 S301/R) Shades of Eve (39x60cm-15x24in) s.i. W/C

McMINN, W K (fl.1854-1888) British
£3305 $5750   (11-Sep-91 D.NY59/R) Full rigged ship coming into harbour
                         (61x91cm-24x36in) s.

McMINN, William Kimmins (fl.1854-1880) British
£8500 $15300   (22-Nov-91 C97/R) Ship Shepherdess passing Perch Rock Fort and Lighthouse
                         in Mersey (61x91cm-24x36in) s.d.1856

McNALLY, Matthew James (1874-1943) Australian
£617 $1098   (26-Nov-91 J.M5) Farm en route Mt Macedon (23x29cm-9x11in) s.i.d.1916 W/C
                         (A.D 1400)
£705 $1255   (26-Nov-91 J.M150/R) By jetty (18x23cm-7x9in) s.d.1927 W/C (A.D 1600)

McNALLY, Matthew James (1874-1943) Australian-cont.
£1068 $1902   (27-Apr-92 J.M129/R) Sheep amongst the gums (28x36cm-11x14in) s. W/C (A.D 2500)
£1106 $1924   (16-Sep-91 CH.ME168) Balcombe Hill (32x38cm-13x15in) s.i.d.1910 pencil W/C (A.D 2400)
£1816 $3233   (27-Apr-92 J.M20/R) Bank Street (21x26cm-8x10in) s.i. W/C (A.D 4250)

McNEIL, George (20th C) American
£686 $1200   (28-Feb-92 SY.NY359/R) Dementia disco (173x142cm-68x56in) s.d.85 s.d.1985 verso
£872 $1500   (12-Oct-91 SY.NY347/R) Bird lady (122x112cm-48x44in) s.d.76 s.d.1976 verso
£2035 $3500   (12-Oct-91 SY.NY346/R) Idle fears (122x112cm-48x44in) s.d.79 s.d.1979 verso acrylic canvas
£2762 $4750   (12-Oct-91 SY.NY345/R) Shaman and magic birds (152x142cm-60x56in) s.d.80 s.d.1980 verso
£8939 $16000   (12-Nov-91 CE.NY19/R) The British Navy (168x168cm-66x66in) s.d.57 s.i.d.verso

McPHAIL, Roger (?) British
£3600 $6300   (25-Feb-92 C140/R) Grey partridge on bank (49x57cm-19x22in) s. W/C htd white
£4000 $7000   (25-Feb-92 C142/R) Driven grouse (51x67cm-20x26in) s. W/C htd white

McQUALTER, John (20th C) Australian
£881 $1568   (26-Nov-91 J.M221/R) Day at beach Rye (50x60cm-20x24in) s. canvasboard (A.D 2000)
£1322 $2352   (26-Nov-91 J.M152/R) Rosebud beach (75x100cm-30x39in) s. (A.D 3000)

McRAE, Dora (1908-) Australian
£1542 $2744   (26-Nov-91 J.M447) Flower arrangement (39x33cm-15x13in) s. board (A.D 3500)

McROBB, Charles (19th C) British
£2000 $3420   (13-Mar-92 C131/R) Water spaniel and fox terriers with hare and woodcock (69x84cm-27x33in) s.d.1821

McSWINEY, Eugene (1866-?) British
£1300 $2236   (17-Oct-91 HB549) Mother and daughter, by bridge over river, wodds and cottages beyond (43x61cm-17x24in) s.

McTAGGART, William (1835-1910) British
£4500 $8055   (13-Nov-91 CG634/R) Listen - the murmur of the shell (47x34cm-19x13in) s.d.1904
£10000 $17900   (13-Nov-91 CG600/R) Fishing in a ground swell (31x47cm-12x19in) s.d.1883
£1100 $1958   (30-Apr-92 CG828/R) Machrihanish from The Bathing Rock (33x51cm-13x20in) s.d.1876 W/C bodycol.
£1600 $2848   (30-Apr-92 CG837) Moonlight, Crail (23x36cm-9x14in) s. W/C htd white
£1600 $2896   (4-Dec-91 S141/R) Farm (24x36cm-9x14in) s.d.1865 W/C
£1800 $3204   (28-Apr-92 S178/R) Playing in the rocks (26x37cm-10x15in) s.d.76 W/C
£3200 $5696   (28-Apr-92 S179/R) On a footpath (23x33cm-9x13in) s.d.99 W/C
£5200 $8996   (26-Mar-92 RB616) Shoreline scene with children in boat and other figures (48x74cm-19x29in) s.d.1881 W/C

McTAGGART, William (attrib) (1835-1910) British
£1850 $3256   (10-Apr-92 K549) Coastal scene with children playing on rocks (23x33cm-9x13in) bears sig.

McWHANNEL, Isabel (1885-1918) Australian
£1410 $2537   (24-Nov-91 SY.S161/R) Windsor landscape (27x53cm-11x21in) s.d.1907 W/C (A.D 3200)

MEACCI, Ricciardo (1856-?) Italian
£500 $905   (21-May-92 CSK37) And He gathers prayers as he stands, and they change into flowers in his hands (30x41cm-12x16in) s.i. pencil W/C htd gold semi-circular
£700 $1302   (18-Jun-92 B2/R) The Annunciation (20x25cm-8x10in) W/C gold

MEADOWS, Arthur Joseph (1843-1907) British
£581 $1000   (15-Oct-91 CE.NY78/R) Peasants by a wooded river (41x81cm-16x32in) s.
£900 $1611   (5-May-92 SWS374/R) Scene on Continental lake (19x35cm-7x14in) s.d.1892 s. indist.i.verso panel
£1250 $2225   (28-Apr-92 PH77/R) Schiedam, early morning (51x61cm-20x24in) s.d.1904 s.i.d.verso
£1400 $2492   (28-Nov-91 B87/R) River scene on the Loire (23x46cm-9x18in) s.indis.d. indis.i.verso pair
£1500 $2565   (12-Mar-92 CSK295/R) Dutch fishing fleet (36x61cm-14x24in) s.d.1882 indis.i.verso
£1600 $2976   (18-Jun-92 B65) Coblentz (30x25cm-12x10in) s.i.verso
£1700 $2924   (11-Oct-91 C74/R) Dinant on the Meuse (30x51cm-12x20in) s.d.96 s.i.d.1896verso
£1761 $2958   (28-Aug-91 KH.K140/R) Seascape with sailboats near Dordrecht (25x36cm-10x14in) s.d.1886 (D.KR 20000)
£1900 $3268   (8-Oct-91 PH75) Herring boats off Gorleston (25x35cm-10x14in) s.d.1884
£2000 $3480   (15-Apr-92 HAR485/R) Pozzuoli, Bay of Naples (58x43cm-23x17in) s.d.1900

MEADOWS, Arthur Joseph (1843-1907) British-cont.
£2000	$3540	(6-Nov-91 EH1074) Fishing boats on the Rhone at Avignon (58x89cm-23x35in) s.d.1891
£2000	$3800	(23-Jun-92 PH155) Fishing vessels in breeze off coastline (30x57cm-12x22in) s.
£2064	$3778	(1-Jun-92 W.T1301) Coaster entering port in rough weather (36x61cm-14x24in) s.d.1882 (C.D 4500)
£2064	$3778	(1-Jun-92 W.T1302/R) Mackerel boats, Seaford Roads (36x61cm-14x24in) s.d.1882 (C.D 4500)
£2700	$5184	(28-Jul-92 SWS365/R) Fishing boats in the mouth of Dover Harbour (34x60cm-13x24in) s.d.1875
£2800	$5040	(22-Nov-91 C102/R) Fishing boats in Dunkerque Harbour (30x41cm-12x16in) s.d.1887 indis.i.stretcher
£3200	$5504	(4-Mar-92 S141/R) Old bridge, Verona (30x20cm-12x8in) s. s.i.verso panel
£3400	$5780	(22-Oct-91 SWS321/R) Scarboro' - with Grand Hotel. St. Lawrence Cathedral, Rotterdam (25x35cm-10x14in) s.d.1888 s.i.d.1888 verso pair
£3500	$5950	(22-Oct-91 SWS303/R) Palanza, lago Maggiore (29x49cm-11x19in) s.d.1896 s.i.d.verso
£3800	$6840	(22-Nov-91 C39/R) Race for the derelict (77x120cm-30x47in) s.d.1873 s.indis.i.stretcher
£4000	$6960	(15-Apr-92 HAR487/R) St Mark's Square, Venice (89x69cm-35x27in) s.d.1903
£4800	$8640	(19-Nov-91 PH32 a/R) On the Grand Canal, Venice (20x30cm-8x12in) s.d.1904 i.verso panel
£6908	$12573	(12-Dec-91 F.M25/R) Veduta del paese di Atrani dal mare (36x61cm-14x24in) s.d.1898 i.d.verso (I.L 15000000)
£8000	$15280	(17-Jul-92 C181/R) Off Yarmouth (39x66cm-15x26in) s.d.1873
£650	*$1170*	*(9-Jan-92 B268/R) Shipping off the South Coast (31x51cm-12x20in) s.d.1866 W/C bodycol. arched top*

MEADOWS, Christopher (fl.1883-1901) British
£1200	$2148	(14-Jan-92 B169/R) A Spaniel and two Yorkshire Terriers in an interior (51x76cm-20x30in) s.d.1902

MEADOWS, Edwin L (19th C) British
£1100	$1881	(13-Mar-92 C116/R) Carting timber (66x92cm-26x36in) s.d.75
£2286	$4000	(19-Feb-92 CH.NY175/R) View of Spofforth, Yorkshire (76x122cm-30x48in) s.i.d.78
£2924	$5000	(21-Mar-92 W.W127/R) Hay wagon in country landscape (51x76cm-20x30in) s.d.1858

MEADOWS, Gordon A (1868-?) British
£1700	$3111	(3-Jun-92 S7/R) The Dogana, Venice. San Giorgio, Venice (12x17cm-5x7in) s. one indis. canvas on board pair

MEADOWS, J E (19th C) British
£2100	$3759	(6-May-92 MMB410/R) Cart fording a stream (76x127cm-30x50in) s.d.1880

MEADOWS, James Edwin (1828-1888) British
£680	$1170	(4-Mar-92 S31/R) Country footpath (35x30cm-14x12in) s.d.1855
£849	$1503	(5-Nov-91 BA.S120/R) Wanderers in summer landscape (35x30cm-14x12in) s.d.1855 (S.KR 9000)
£1236	$2163	(20-Feb-92 D.V369) Landscape (43x73cm-17x29in) s. (A.S 25000)
£1800	$3258	(20-May-92 S226/R) Fishermen on the beach (61x107cm-24x42in) s.d.1868
£5500	$10340	(19-Dec-91 C115/R) Children on path by pond (76x122cm-30x48in) s.d.indist.1859
£6000	$10680	(28-Nov-91 B150/R) Haymaking in Hampshire (76x122cm-30x48in) s.
£12000	$20640	(11-Oct-91 C22/R) The harvesters' midday rest (76x122cm-30x48in) s.d.1866

MEADOWS, James Edwin (circle) (1828-1888) British
£1200	$2220	(12-Jun-92 C173/R) The little shepherds (76x157cm-30x62in)

MEADOWS, W G (19th C) British
£1050	$1785	(24-Oct-91 CSK95/R) Figures resting by cattle watering in an open river landscape (91x61cm-36x24in) s.d.1893

MEADOWS, William (fl.1870-1895) British
£520	$946	(10-Dec-91 SWS20) Venice (44x80cm-17x31in) s.
£550	$1007	(15-May-92 TE391/R) Grand Canal, Venice (51x76cm-20x30in) s.
£650	$1118	(8-Oct-91 PH96) View of Santa Maria salute (41x61cm-16x24in) s.
£1000	$1810	(6-Dec-91 TE569/R) The Grand Canal, Venice (51x76cm-20x30in) s.
£1700	$3026	(21-Jan-92 PH83) Venice (25x45cm-10x18in) s. pair
£1900	$3363	(6-Nov-91 S57/R) By windmill. Village street (51x76cm-20x30in) s. pair

MEAKIN, Louis Henry (1853-1917) American
£1073	$1900	(10-Nov-91 LIT.L147) Cape Anne, Rockport, Mass (53x84cm-21x33in) s.

MEARS, Henrietta Dunn (1877-?) American
£791	$1400	(12-Feb-92 B.SF511/R) Spring landscape (29x34cm-11x13in) s. canvasboard

MEDARD, Jules Ferdinand (1850-?) French
£15698	$27000	(17-Oct-91 SY.NY149/R) Corbeilles de fleurs (81x100cm-32x39in) s.

MEDINA, Sir John (circle) (c.1660-1711) British
£4200	$8022	(15-Jul-92 S122/R) Portraits of Sir John Morgan and his wife (73x61cm-29x24in) ovals pair

MEDIZ, Karl (1868-1944) Austrian
£777 $1383   (28-Apr-92 D.V1/R) View of glacier (34x58cm-13x23in) panel (A.S 16000)
£839 $1494   (29-Nov-91 ZEL.L1075) Surf near La Croma (34x56cm-13x22in) st.sig.i.verso
     (DM 2400)
£2208 $4195   (25-Jun-92 D.V719/R) Adria near Corfu (39x61cm-15x24in) board on panel
     (A.S 45000)
£2224 $3893   (19-Feb-92 D.V2/R) Glacier of Mittelberg (40x59cm-16x23in) i.d.1903verso
     (A.S 45000)
£4392 $7599   (3-Oct-91 D.V7/R) Gastgarten, Krokke (37x47cm-15x19in) d.1890 (A.S 90000)
£1092 $1944   (28-Nov-91 D.V26/R) Young Dachau woman in interior (58x44cm-23x17in)
     s.d.1889 chl (A.S 22000)

MEDIZ-PELIKAN, Emilie (1861-1908) Austrian
£680 $1218   (5-May-92 ZEL.L1433/R) Isonzo street scene with figures (26x18cm-10x7in)
     i. (DM 2000)
£1027 $1767   (8-Oct-91 ZEL.L1615/R) Study of flowering branch (30x50cm-12x20in)
     (DM 3000)
£1712 $2945   (8-Oct-91 ZEL.L1614/R) Nude girl standing (80x40cm-31x16in) (DM 5000)
£2466 $4241   (8-Oct-91 ZEL.L1613/R) Blue Coast of Duino (94x145cm-37x57in) s.
     i.d.1898verso (DM 7200)
£586 $1013   (3-Oct-91 D.V33/R) Nanerl (35x26cm-14x10in) s.d.1905 chk col.pencil
     (A.S 12000)
£1079 $2051   (25-Jun-92 D.V720/R) Mai in Duino (40x56cm-16x22in) s.d.1905 mixed media
     (A.S 22000)
£1092 $1944   (28-Nov-91 D.V6/R) Dachauer Moor landscape, winter (14x28cm-6x11in)
     s.d.92 grisaille mixed media board (A.S 22000)
£1092 $1944   (28-Nov-91 D.V21/R) Dawn (37x56cm-15x22in) s.i.d.1902 pastel (A.S 22000)
£1214 $2160   (28-Apr-92 D.V3/R) Coastal landscape near Duino, afternoon
     (44x57cm-17x22in) mono.i.d.1905 pastel chk (A.S 25000)

MEDLEY, Robert (1905-) British
£5500 $9900   (20-Nov-91 S5/R) Summer eclogue No. 1 - cyclists (130x160cm-51x63in)
     s.d.1950 s.i.verso

MEDLYCOTT, Sir Hubert (1841-1920) British
£420 $802   (30-Jun-92 SWS1729) The Forum, Rome (46x63cm-18x25in) s.i.d.1877 W/C over
     pencil

MEDNYANSZKY, Laszlo von (1852-1919) Austrian
£620 $1104   (28-Nov-91 CSK167) Kitchen boy (46x58cm-18x23in) s.d.1877
£1490 $2651   (28-Nov-91 D.V7/R) Treck (42x60cm-17x24in) s. (A.S 30000)

MEDSTRAND, Per (1957-) Swedish
£768 $1390   (3-Dec-91 AB.S5106/R) Composition with Grace Kelly (40x77cm-16x30in) s.
     d.1990verso panel (S.KR 8000)
£426 $771   (19-May-92 AB.S5274/R) Composition with crosses (100x70cm-39x28in) s.
     mixed media (S.KR 4500)

MEE, Anne (c.1770-1851) British
£520 $993   (30-Jun-92 SWS2366/R) Portrait of lady wearing turban adorned with coral
     beads and necklace (8x?cm-3x?in) min. oval sold with another min of
     gentleman

MEEGAN, Walter (19th C) British
£895 $1557   (13-Apr-92 SY.J8/R) Street scene by moonlight (50x75cm-20x30in) s.
     (SA.R 4500)
£1000 $1780   (27-Apr-92 PHB246) Twilight street scene with docks (45x60cm-18x24in)
     s.d.95
£1700 $2958   (16-Sep-91 CHAP117/R) Whitby harbour and fishing boats (23x33cm-9x13in)
     s. pair

MEEGEREN, Hans van (1889-1947) Dutch
£1364 $2414   (22-Apr-92 CH.AM27) Portrait of a black oriental (90x60cm-35x24in) s.
     (D.FL 4500)
£432 $756   (18-Feb-92 CH.AM235) A church interior (722x54cm-284x21in) s. pencil W/C
     bodycol. (D.FL 1400)
£1988 $3538   (30-Oct-91 CH.AM338) Reclining nude (62x92cm-24x36in) s. brush ink chl
     col.chk (D.FL 6500)

MEEKER, Joseph R (1827-1889) American
£6857 $12000   (26-Sep-91 CH.NY36/R) Swamp (61x36cm-24x14in) s.d.85
£11050 $20000   (5-Dec-91 SY.NY8/R) Bayou landscape (69x56cm-27x22in) s.d.1877

MEEKS, Eugene (1843-?) American
£520 $998   (29-Jul-92 CSK248) Figures in cottage interior (55x43cm-22x17in) s.i.
£520 $900   (29-Mar-92 MY.F80 f/R) Laughing monk (41x56cm-16x22in) s.

MEER, A van der (?) Dutch
£530 $1017   (7-Jul-92 VN.R143) View of Rotterdam town and harbour (60x80cm-24x31in)
     (D.FL 1700)

MEER, Barend van der (style) (1659-?) Dutch
£1000 $1800   (21-Nov-91 C38/R) Peaches and grapes on partially draped ledge
     (41x35cm-16x14in)

MEER, Barend van der (style) (1659-?) Dutch-cont.
£1813 $3245 (7-May-92 CH.AM6) Mixed fruit, chianti bottle, great tit on upturned basket, marble ledge (56x71cm-22x28in) (D.FL 6000)

MEER, Jan van der (younger) see VERMEER OF HAARLEM, Jan (younger)

MEERE, Charles M (1890-1961) Australian
£4255 $7532 (26-Apr-92 SY.ME246/R) Park, Adelaide (49x59cm-19x23in) s.d.1960 board (A.D 10000)

MEERMANN, Arnold (1829-1908) German
£1718 $2990 (18-Sep-91 N.M617/R) Farmhouse in Werdenberg, Kanton St Gallen (30x31cm-12x12in) s. (DM 5000)

MEERT, Joseph (1905-) American
£1105 $2000 (24-May-92 JRB.C38/R) Sfpring day (46x64cm-18x25in) s.d.39

MEGE, Salvator (19th C) French
£444 $804 (19-May-92 GF.L2742) Girl standing wearing red dress with fan and umbrella (65x46cm-26x18in) s. (S.FR 1200)

MEHEUT, Mathurin (1882-1958) French
£458 $838 (17-May-92 T.B240) *Schlitteurs en Alsace (31x30cm-12x12in) s. gouache (F.FR 4500)*
£814 $1489 (17-May-92 T.B87) *Jeune fille de Penmarch (32x46cm-13x18in) s. gouache (F.FR 8000)*

MEHOFFER, Jozef (1869-1946) Polish
£5677 $10163 (17-Nov-91 REM.W19) Garden in spring (66x54cm-26x21in) s. (P.Z 110000000)
£785 $1358 (8-Sep-91 REM.W21) *Madonna and Child (51x36cm-20x14in) s. W/C (P.Z 15000000)*
£1795 $3195 (3-Nov-91 PSA.W14) *Red umbrella (50x35cm-20x14in) s. W/C (P.Z 35000000)*

MEI, Bernardino (1615-1676) Italian
£104972 $190000 (21-May-92 CH.NY84/R) Allegory of Justice (114x155cm-45x61in) init.i.d.1636

MEICHELT, Heinrich (1805-1880) German
£3072 $5560 (21-May-92 L.K451) River landscape with mountain range beyond. Coastal landscape near Naples (26x38cm-10x15in) s.d.1838 one canvas on panel pair (DM 9000)

MEID, Hans (1883-1957) German
£2797 $4979 (30-Nov-91 VG.B116/R) Courting couple (51x59cm-20x23in) s.d.1913 s.i.d.verso (DM 8000)
£524 $934 (30-Nov-91 VG.B875/R) *Friedrichstrasse, Berlin seen from balcony of Cafe Bauer (16x22cm-6x9in) s.d.1912 chk (DM 1500)*
£717 $1304 (30-May-92 VG.B846/R) *Skaters before ruined tower (41x31cm-16x12in) W/C brush htd white over pencil double-sided (DM 2100)*

MEIDNER, Ludwig (1884-1966) German
£559 $1000 (9-May-92 CE.NY50/R) *Kneeling figure (29x20cm-11x8in) init.i.d.41 wax crayon*
£704 $1275 (6-Dec-91 GB.B6840) *Landscape with young tree (40x47cm-16x19in) mono. chl (DM 2000)*
£1536 $2780 (23-May-92 GB.B6904) *Portrait of elderly woman wearing glasses (68x54cm-27x21in) s.d.1928 indian ink pen over pencil (DM 4500)*
£1718 $3144 (3-Jun-92 L.K316/R) *Two man walking wearing prayer shawl (74x56cm-29x22in) d.1921 st.sig.verso grease chk (DM 5000)*
£6338 $11472 (6-Dec-91 GB.B6839/R) *City scene (44x36cm-17x14in) s.d.1914 pen over chl (DM 18000)*
£10239 $18635 (30-May-92 VG.B187/R) *Apokalyptic scene, stampede from the town (38x57cm-15x22in) s.i.d.1915/1916 indian ink pen over pencil board (DM 30000)*

MEIFFRE, L (?) ?
£1300 $2249 (3-Oct-91 CSK189) The suitor (38x46cm-15x18in) s. panel

MEIFREN Y ROIG, Eliseo (1859-1940) Spanish
£1051 $1975 (17-Dec-91 BRO.B343) Calle de pueblo (17x10cm-7x4in) s. panel (S.P 190000)
£3732 $7017 (17-Dec-91 BRO.B411/R) Cadaques (16x22cm-6x9in) s. panel (S.P 675000)
£4385 $7805 (26-Nov-91 BRO.B412) Marina (25x35cm-10x14in) s. board (S.P 800000)
£4921 $9005 (13-May-92 FER.M140/R) Paseando por los alrededores de la laguna (30x60cm-12x24in) s. (S.P 900000)
£10400 $18927 (26-May-92 DUR.M42/R) La luna reflejandose en la laguna (40x73cm-16x29in) s. (S.P 1900000)
£15869 $28881 (11-Dec-91 FER.M164/R) Olivos (60x73cm-24x29in) s. (S.P 2900000)
£23256 $40000 (17-Oct-91 SY.NY124/R) Boats in village harbour (56x75cm-22x30in) s.
£29774 $53593 (22-Nov-91 PIC.P6/R) Voiliers sur une mer calme (80x130cm-31x51in) s.d.1874 (F.FR 290000)
£30104 $54789 (26-May-92 DUR.M43/R) Mariscadoras (48x65cm-19x26in) s. (S.P 5500000)
£409 $704 (16-Oct-91 FER.M68/R) Arboleda en la llanura (26x33cm-10x13in) s. chl dr (S.P 75000)

MEIFREN Y ROIG, Eliseo (1859-1940) Spanish-cont.
£1797 $3378   (16-Dec-91 ANS.M65/R) *Paisaje con arboles (38x43cm-15x17in) s. chl dr (S.P 325000)*
£2456 $4224   (16-Oct-91 FER.M69/R) *Venecia en la niebla. Plaza de San Marcos (82x94cm-32x37in) s. chl dr htd white (S.P 450000)*

MEIJER, Jan (20th C) Dutch
£1235 $2247   (12-Dec-91 SY.AM284) Untitled (160x134cm-63x53in) s. s.d.1960 verso s.d.stretcher (D.FL 4000)

MEILERTS, Ludmilla (1908-) Australian
£1057 $1882   (26-Nov-91 J.M285/R) Gladioli (74x59cm-29x23in) s.d.49 (A.D 2400)

MEINERS, Claas Hendrik (1819-1894) Dutch
£1529 $2706   (5-Nov-91 SY.AM15/R) Cattle grazing in landscape (38x55cm-15x22in) s. panel (D.FL 5000)

MEINERT, Frederike (19th C) German
£920 $1601   (15-Apr-92 PHL185/R) Mixed flowers and butterflies (50x39cm-20x15in) s.d.1845

MEINZOLT, Georg (1863-1945) German
£877 $1579   (22-Nov-91 SA.A1767/R) Burg Sinn, Spessart (110x171cm-43x67in) s.d.1912 (DM 2500)

MEIREN, Jan Baptist van der (1664-1708) Flemish
£18039 $32290   (15-Nov-91 GK.Z5076/R) Southern harbour scene with shipping and figures. Coastal landscape (27x40cm-11x16in) pair (S.FR 46000)

MEIREN, Jan Baptist van der (attrib) (1664-1708) Flemish
£4500 $8010   (1-Nov-91 C87) Elegant travellers and caravan arriving at Levantine harbour (40x60cm-16x24in)

MEIREN, Nicolas (1660-1700) Belgian
£4706 $8424   (15-Nov-91 GK.Z5076 a/R) Southern harbour bay with ruin (26x40cm-10x16in) (S.FR 12000)

MEIRHANS, Joseph (1890-1981) American
£643 $1100   (12-Mar-92 MFA.C96) Abstract (122x76cm-48x30in) s. panel

MEISEL, Ernst (1838-1895) German
£874 $1495   (18-Mar-92 N.M596/R) Courting couple drinking wine in cellar (65x76cm-26x30in) s. (DM 2500)

MEISSER, Leonhard (1902-) Swiss
£1504 $2752   (4-Jun-92 SY.Z420/R) Evening (38x26cm-15x10in) s.d.55 pavatex (S.FR 4000)

MEISSNER, Adolf Ernst (1837-1902) German
£4000 $7160   (13-Nov-91 CG530/R) Winter landscape witha shepherd and flock (35x60cm-14x24in) s.i.

MEISSNER, Olga (attrib) (1844-1895) German
£550 $957   (18-Sep-91 N.M618) Wooded landscape with figures (42x52cm-17x20in) (DM 1600)

MEISSONIER, Jean Charles (1848-1917) French
£1200 $2040   (22-Oct-91 SWS336/R) Gentleman reading by window (42x30cm-17x12in) s.d.1879
£2975 $5385   (3-Dec-91 AB.S4733/R) Fishermen preparing nets by boats (61x81cm-24x32in) s. (S.KR 31000)
£3429 $6000   (20-Feb-92 SY.NY153/R) Interesting story (51x41cm-20x16in) s.

MEISSONIER, Jean Louis Ernest (1815-1891) French
£1017 $1862   (13-May-92 LC.P21/R) Cheval debout (12x15cm-5x6in) studio st. panel (F.FR 10000)
£564 $959   (25-Oct-91 AT.P109) *Cinq etudes de differents personnages s.d.Septembre 1841 pen (F.FR 5600)*
£576 $1100   (16-Jul-92 SY.NY318/R) *Seated man on a stool (22x17cm-9x7in) init. pencil gouache*

MEISTER, Ernst (19th C) German
£542 $926   (12-Mar-92 RAS.V943) The hunt (42x56cm-17x22in) s.d.1879 (D.KR 6000)

MEISTER, Ferdinand (attrib) (19th C) German
£707 $1237   (3-Apr-92 BM.B679/R) Studio interior with artist and model (27x22cm-11x9in) indis.s. (DM 2000)

MEISTER, Jean Marie (1935-) Swiss
£824 $1409   (21-Mar-92 AT.P68/R) Sans titre (100x100cm-39x39in) s.d.1977 acrylic (F.FR 8000)

MEISTER, Willi (1918-) Swiss
£784 $1333   (23-Oct-91 GD.B499/R) Portrait of young girl (50x90cm-20x35in) s.d.59 (S.FR 2000)

MEISTERMANN, Georg (1911-1990) German

£5769	$10269	(30-Nov-91 VG.B335/R) Kleiner Fries, kreuz und quer (6x30cm-2x12in) mono. (DM 16500)
£5842	$10282	(10-Apr-92 KM.K481/R) Black wing (28x51cm-11x20in) s.i.d.68 canvas on panel on black draped panel (DM 17000)
£6316	$10800	(13-Mar-92 FN.S2560/R) Variation red and black (60x37cm-24x15in) s.i.verso panel (DM 18000)
£7560	$13835	(2-Jun-92 L.K798/R) Onoma (33x30cm-13x12in) mono.i.d.1957verso (DM 22000)
£9123	$16421	(19-Nov-91 L.K944/R) Double dots (44x32cm-17x13in) mono. i.d.1957verso canvas on panel (DM 26000)
£561	*$1011*	*(19-Nov-91 L.K947) Rose (25x38cm-10x15in) mono. mixed media (DM 1600)*
£912	*$1642*	*(19-Nov-91 L.K946/R) Tulips (38x25cm-15x10in) i. mixed media (DM 2600)*

MEIXMORON, Charles de (1839-1912) French

| £1824 | $3301 | (20-May-92 I.N156/R) Le lac du Bourget (43x55cm-17x22in) s. (F.FR 18000) |

MEIXNER, Ludwig (1828-1885) German

| £2407 | $4357 | (20-May-92 GK.Z5078/R) Isar valley with view of Munich (61x48cm-24x19in) s.d.1867 i.verso (S.FR 6500) |

MEJIA Y MARQUEZ, Nicolas (1845-1917) Spanish

| *£1368* | *$2490* | *(26-May-92 DUR.M98/R) Zapatero remendon. Desnudo (35x25cm-14x10in) s.d.9 W/C double-sided (S.P 250000)* |

MELBYE, Anton (1818-1875) Danish

£750	$1334	(28-Apr-92 RAS.K537) Seascape (22x36cm-9x14in) s.indist.d.1878 (D.KR 8500)
£1399	$2518	(19-Nov-91 RAS.K295/R) Seascape with fishingboat, evening (53x67cm-21x26in) s.d.1852 (D.KR 15500)
£2790	$5106	(5-Feb-92 KH.K85/R) The schooner 'America' - winner of America's Cup 1851 (34x53cm-13x21in) s.d.1851 (D.KR 31000)

MELBYE, Wilhelm (1824-1882) Danish

£1146	$2041	(28-Apr-92 RAS.K324/R) Eddystone lighthouse at sunset (26x40cm-10x16in) init.d.62 (D.KR 13000)
£2128	$3766	(26-Apr-92 SY.ME230) Lifeboat alongside foundering ship (54x85cm-21x33in) s.d.1874 (A.D 5000)
£2465	$4141	(28-Aug-91 KH.K142/R) Seascape with sailship off coast, Mediterranean (41x63cm-16x25in) s. (D.KR 28000)
£2481	$4416	(28-Nov-91 BU.S29/R) Sailing ship in evening light (36x61cm-14x24in) s.d.1859 (S.KR 26000)
£2800	$5208	(17-Jun-92 S275/R) Shipping in choppy sea (44x60cm-17x24in) s.d.1880
£2822	$5023	(28-Apr-92 RAS.K152/R) Scene from Venice (48x67cm-19x26in) s. (D.KR 32000)
£4401	$7394	(27-Aug-91 RAS.K29/R) English warships by Iceland (38x64cm-15x25in) s.d.1865 (D.KR 50000)
£6321	$11188	(25-Apr-92 SO.S473/R) Shipwreck (120x179cm-47x70in) s.d.1880 (S.KR 67000)
£9000	$16740	(17-Jun-92 S274/R) Preparing fishing boats (88x148cm-35x58in) s.d.1882

MELCHER, George Henry (1881-1975) American

| £632 | $1200 | (23-Jun-92 MOR.P33) Landscape (64x76cm-25x30in) s. |

MELCHERS, Franz (1868-1944) Dutch

| £606 | $1073 | (22-Apr-92 CH.AM7) Reclining nude (22x36cm-9x14in) s. (D.FL 2000) |
| £3488 | $6000 | (16-Oct-91 CH.NY218/R) Afternoon by the sea, Cannes (99x79cm-39x31in) s.d.14 |

MELCHERS, Gari (1860-1932) American

£1397	$2500	(14-Nov-91 CE.NY389/R) Portrait of Mrs. Mackall (56x46cm-22x18in) s.d.1909
£1486	$2600	(26-Sep-91 CH.NY116/R) Lady in plum (97x71cm-38x28in) s.d.1927
£1839	$3200	(15-Apr-92 SY.NY163/R) Eve holding apple in Garden of Eden (47x31cm-19x12in) s. board
£3466	$6100	(9-Apr-92 FA.PH707) Contemplative state (61x76cm-24x30in) s. board
£50000	$87500	(25-Sep-91 SY.NY62 a/R) Garden party (78x49cm-31x19in) s.

MELCHIOR, Joseph Wilhelm (1810-1883) German

| £1045 | $1902 | (11-Dec-91 N.M524/R) Stable interior with race horses (23x31cm-9x12in) s. (DM 3000) |

MELCHIOR, W (1817-1860) German

| £700 | $1211 | (3-Oct-91 CSK80) Goats on a rocky outcrop, a view of Mount Pilutas beyond (81x107cm-32x42in) s.d.1850 in a painted oval |

MELDOLLA, Andrea see SCHIAVONE, Andrea

MELDRUM, Duncan Max (1875-1955) Australian

£661	$1189	(24-Nov-91 SY.S55) Plains, Naringal, 1923 (23x29cm-9x11in) s. board (A.D 1500)
£8295	$14433	(16-Sep-91 CH.ME145/R) Self-portrait, 1932 (61x70cm-24x28in) s. (A.D 18000)
£17949	$31949	(28-Apr-92 CH.ME126/R) The wattle tree (92x73cm-36x29in) s. st.sig.i.stretcher (A.D 42000)

MELENDEZ, Luis (1716-1780) Italian
£277085 $484899   (20-Feb-92 EP.M11/R) Naturaleza muerta con melocotones, peras, ciruelas y una canastilla de pan sobre una mesa (48x34cm-19x13in) (S.P 50000000)
£381888 $691217   (19-May-92 EP.M9/R) Naturaleza muerta con sandias, barrilete y cajas de dulces (38x50cm-15x20in) s. (S.P 70000000)
£875513 $1558413   (29-Oct-91 EP.M5/R) Bodegon con perdices y cebollas. Bodegon con carne, huevos y tomates (41x62cm-16x24in) one init.d.1778 pair (S.P 160000000)

MELENDEZ, Luis (style) (1716-1780) Italian
£2200 $3916   (30-Oct-91 S67/R) Still life of apples in basket, plums in dish and pears on ledge (46x58cm-18x23in)
£7000 $12740   (11-Dec-91 S148/R) Still life of mixed fruit on ledge (49x37cm-19x15in)

MELIDA Y ALINARI, Don Enrique (1834-1892) Spanish
£998 $1746   (18-Feb-92 DUR.M6/R) Joven caballero con perro lebrero (19x13cm-7x5in) s.d.1876 panel (S.P 180000)

MELIK, Edgar (1904-1976) ?
£571 $1062   (21-Jun-92 LT.P126) Portrait de Cezanne (50x29cm-20x11in) s. oil material panel (F.FR 5600)
£2018 $3471   (20-Oct-91 I.N40/R) Portrait de femme (51x31cm-20x12in) s. board (F.FR 20000)

MELIKOFF, C (20th C) ?
£794 $1469   (10-Jun-92 LD.P146/R) Egyptienne a la gazelle (200x150cm-79x59in) s.d.1936 (F.FR 7800)

MELLAN, Claude (attrib) (1598-1688) French
£2500 $4350   (15-Apr-92 C143 a/R) Portrait of young lady with hand raised to chest (26x21cm-10x8in) i.verso copper oval

MELLE (20th C) Belgian?
£1667 $3017   (21-May-92 SY.AM60/R) Portrait of artist's parents (5x22cm-2x9in) s.d.39 panel (D.FL 5500)
£2160 $3932   (12-Dec-91 SY.AM98/R) Vrouw in landschap Opus I (42x34cm-17x13in) s.d.38 panel (D.FL 7000)

MELLEN, Mary (1817-?) American
£27485 $47000   (11-Mar-92 SY.NY1/R) Shipwreck on beach (33x53cm-13x21in)

MELLERY, Xavier (1845-1921) Belgian
£1800 $3114   (4-Oct-91 C74/R) L'amitie, entrez et vous serez console (80x130cm-31x51in) mono.i. shaped top
£1923 $3500   (11-Dec-91 RO.BA54/R) Paysage anime (39x52cm-15x20in) s. panel
£2667 $4587   (12-Oct-91 KV.L211) Young woman (60x50cm-24x20in) mono. (B.FR 160000)
£1540 $2787   (7-Dec-91 KV.L238/R) The novices (23x29cm-9x11in) mono. ink dr. (B.FR 90000)
£6500 $11115   (18-Mar-92 S49/R) La trinite (68x87cm-27x34in) s.mixed media gold paint three

MELLI, Roberto (1885-1958) Italian
£1487 $2692   (3-Dec-91 F.R214/R) Figura di vecchia (48x62cm-19x24in) faesite (I.L 3200000)

MELLING, Henry (19th C) British
£1800 $3060   (23-Oct-91 S136/R) Four warriors resting. Three warriors and woman (25x36cm-10x14in) s. one i. pen W/C over pencil pair

MELLISH, Thomas (18th C) British
£13000 $22880   (8-Apr-92 S1/R) Two decker and other shipping off Dover (36x57cm-14x22in) s.

MELLON, Campbell (1876-1955) British
£550 $1007   (4-Jun-92 CSK79) Ruined abbey with figures by lake (23x30cm-9x12in) s. board
£650 $1190   (14-May-92 C62/R) S.S. Penton stranded (21x29cm-8x11in) i.verso panel
£650 $1112   (1-Aug-91 CSK89) Gorleston Beach (23x30cm-9x12in) s. panel
£750 $1290   (11-Oct-91 K506) Gorleston beach scene with bathers and pier beyond (23x28cm-9x11in) s.
£820 $1542   (18-Dec-91 C34/R) On the beach, Gorleston (25x35cm-10x14in) s. i.verso
£950 $1786   (18-Dec-91 C35/R) On the sands, Gorleston (23x30cm-9x12in) s.indis.i.verso panel
£1300 $2184   (16-Aug-91 K575) North Norfolk beach scene with figures, cliffs and sailing boat (48x58cm-19x23in) s.
£1400 $2408   (11-Oct-91 K505/R) Gorleston beach scene with bathers and pier beyond (20x25cm-8x10in) s.

MELLOR, Everett W (1878-1965) British
£1900 $3306   (12-Sep-91 CSK168/R) Langdale, Westmorland. A bit of Ullswater (25x37cm-10x15in) s. board

MELLOR, William (1851-1931) British
£511 $900   (8-Apr-92 D.NY54) Rushing forest stream (61x91cm-24x36in) s. i.verso
£636 $1100   (29-Mar-92 MY.F59/R) Washburn Valley, Yorkshire (30x46cm-12x18in) s.

MELLOR, William (1851-1931) British-cont.

£800	$1416	(6-Nov-91 EH1070/R) River landscape with cattle and sheep, Bolton Woods, Yorkshire (38x66cm-15x26in) s.
£1000	$1850	(10-Jun-92 HAR488) Mountain stream, near Capel Curig, North Wales (48x74cm-19x29in) s.
£1120	$2038	(13-Dec-91 CBB75/R) Bolton Abbey (30x46cm-12x18in) s.
£1150	$1990	(4-Sep-91 BT319/R) Figures by rocky stream. Sheep by still river (28x23cm-11x9in) s. oval pair
£1150	$2047	(1-Nov-91 BW369) Rural river scene with sheep grazing in foreground, near Ambleside (20x30cm-8x12in) s.i.verso
£1294	$2302	(25-Nov-91 W.T1900/R) Birkham Crag on the Nidd. View near Knaresborough (20x30cm-8x12in) s. i.verso board (C.D 2600)
£1300	$2314	(30-Apr-92 CSK36/R) On the Lledr, North Wales (51x75cm-20x30in) s.
£1407	$2505	(29-Oct-91 PH.T105/R) Falls on Tummel, Perthshire (74x49cm-29x19in) s. (C.D 2800)
£1800	$3204	(28-Apr-92 PH150) On wharfe, Bolton Abbey, Yorkshire. Posforth Gill, Bolton Woods, Yorks (30x46cm-12x18in) s. i.verso pair
£2000	$3480	(15-Apr-92 PHL179/R) On Scandale, near Ambleside, Westmorland. Thornton Foss, Ingleton (45x29cm-18x11in) s.i.verso pair
£2000	$3700	(10-Jun-92 HAR519/R) On Lledr, North Wales (48x74cm-19x29in)
£2000	$3420	(11-Mar-92 WAL369) On Conway, near Bettws, North Wales - river scene in autumn with sheep (50x75cm-20x30in) i.verso
£2500	$4450	(27-Apr-92 PHB247) On wharf, Bolton Woods, Yorkshire (91x76cm-36x30in) s.i.verso oval
£2700	$4644	(16-Oct-91 PHL288/R) On Wharfe, near Burnsall, Yorkshire (30x45cm-12x18in) s. i.verso
£2800	$5096	(10-Dec-91 HAR728/R) Rydal Lake and Grasmere Lane, Westmorland (28x43cm-11x17in) s. panel pair
£2900	$4988	(16-Oct-91 PHL293/R) View near Knaresborough, Yorkshire (30x45cm-12x18in) s. i.verso
£3000	$5430	(6-Dec-91 TE553/R) Easdale Nab near Grasmere, Westmoreland (51x127cm-20x50in) s. s.i.verso
£3200	$5920	(12-Jun-92 C149/R) On the Burbridge Brook, Derbyshire. View near Parbold, Lancs (25x35cm-10x14in) s.i. pair

MELONI, Altobello (fl,1497-1530) Italian

£28817	$52159	(5-Dec-91 F.M139/R) Adorazione dei Magi (47x34cm-19x13in) panel (I.L 62000000)

MELONI, Altobello (school) (fl.1497-1530) Italian

£8287	$15000	(21-May-92 CH.NY233/R) Standing putto playing lyre (132x80cm-52x31in)

MELONI, Gino (1905-) Italian

£685	$1192	(14-Apr-92 F.M2) Composizione (50x35cm-20x14in) s. canvasboard (I.L 1500000)
£1288	$2305	(14-Nov-91 F.M128/R) Natura morta (35x50cm-14x20in) s. (I.L 2800000)
£1827	$3179	(14-Apr-92 F.M126/R) Immagine (70x82cm-28x32in) s. (I.L 4000000)
£1143	*$2171*	*(23-Jun-92 F.M53/R) Venezia (47x59cm-19x23in) s. mixed media (I.L 2500000)*

MELOTTI, Fausto (1901-1986) Italian

£784	*$1404*	*(15-Nov-91 GK.Z5739) Untitled (35x25cm-14x10in) s.verso W/C (S.FR 2000)*
£823	*$1563*	*(23-Jun-92 F.M56) Natura morta con fruttiera (33x22cm-13x9in) s.d.1929 pastel (I.L 1800000)*
£1006	*$1911*	*(23-Jun-92 F.M52/R) Due alberi (23x15cm-9x6in) s.d.1922 pencil (I.L 2200000)*
£1463	*$2779*	*(23-Jun-92 F.M45/R) Figure sul molo (23x24cm-9x9in) s.d.1931 ink W/C (I.L 3200000)*

MELROSE, Andrew (1836-1901) American

£4396	$8000	(28-May-92 CH.NY47/R) The Palisades (30x45cm-12x18in) s.

MELTZER, Anna Elkan (20th C) American

£947	$1800	(28-Jun-92 LIT.L230) Girl with a pail (89x114cm-35x45in) d.1940

MELVILLE (19th C) British

£646	$1162	(30-Jan-92 RAS.V652/R) 'Elaine' (100x142cm-39x56in) s.d.1874 (D.KR 7200)

MELVILLE, Arthur (1858-1904) British

£4500	$8055	(13-Nov-91 CG596/R) The freanch peasant (61x40cm-24x16in) s.d.1880
£480	*$830*	*(4-Sep-91 BT94/R) The bullfight, Madrid (10x20cm-4x8in) s. W/C*
£6000	*$10680*	*(30-Apr-92 CG831/R) Parisian park with horse drawn carriages (35x54cm-14x21in) i.verso W/C*
£7000	*$12460*	*(1-May-92 PHE43/R) White mules (60x85cm-24x33in) W/C*
£28000	*$50680*	*(4-Dec-91 S341/R) Brig O'Turk (60x85cm-24x33in) s. W/C*

MELVILLE, H S (19th C) British

£1200	$2052	(10-Mar-92 TAY1) Horses, ducks and poultry in farmyard (58x104cm-23x41in) s.d.1876
£1200	$2052	(9-Mar-92 TAY842) Horses, ducks and poultry in farmyard scene (58x104cm-23x41in) s.d.1876

MELZER, Moritz (1877-1966) German?

£614	$1112	(23-May-92 GB.B6913) Peasant couple (100x75cm-39x30in) s.d.1914 paper on canvas (DM 1800)

MELZER, Moritz (1877-1966) German?-cont.
£1706 $3106   (30-May-92 VG.B850/R) Self portrait (50x41cm-20x16in) s. (DM 5000)
£819 $1483   (23-May-92 GB.B6914) Hafen am Lehrter Bahnhof (52x44cm-20x17in) s.d.1919
      i.verso indian ink pen brush board (DM 2400)

MEMLING, Hans (school) (?-1494) Flemish
£1587 $2825   (28-Apr-92 RAS.K191/R) Portrait of young noble lady (27x21cm-11x8in)
      panel (D.KR 18000)

MEMLING, Hans (style) (?-1494) Flemish
£1047 $2000   (16-Jul-92 SY.NY31/R) The Annunciation (38x31cm-15x12in) panel diptych

MENABONI, Athos (1895-?) ?
£367 $660   (23-Nov-91 YFA.M194/R) Cedar waxwing (48x38cm-19x15in) s. W/C

MENAGEOT, Francois Guillaume (1744-1816) French
£30220 $55000   (28-May-92 SY.NY6/R) Le martyre de Saint Sebastien (135x99cm-53x39in) s.

MENARD, Emile Rene (1862-1930) French
£662 $1205   (11-Dec-91 ZZ.F10/R) Mare a la lisiere d'un bois (73x50cm-29x20in) s.
      studio st.verso (F.FR 6500)
£1243 $2250   (22-May-92 S.BM103/R) Sunset, Capri (89x112cm-35x44in) s. pastel linen

MENARD, Rene see MENARD, Emile Rene

MENARDEAU, Maurice (1897-) ?
£820 $1500   (4-Jun-92 GOM.M28/R) Bateaux de peche Venitiens (54x65cm-21x26in) s.
£1124 $2000   (28-Apr-92 PO.BA19) Las parvas (55x46cm-22x18in) s.

MENCIA, A G (19th C) Italian
£859 $1512   (11-Apr-92 AW.H618/R) Young fisher couple by the sea (28x21cm-11x8in) s.
      W/C (DM 2500)

MENDELSON, Marc (1915-) Belgian
£1020 $1743   (21-Mar-92 KV.L210) L'Immobilite bleue (53x67cm-21x26in) s. W/C
      (B.FR 60000)

MENDIVE, Manuel (20th C) Italian
£2303 $4191   (9-Dec-91 CH.R184/R) Flor amarilla (76x102cm-30x40in) s.d.1989
      (I.L 5000000)

MENDJISKY, Maurice (1889-?) Polish
£1575 $2741   (14-Apr-92 ZZ.F17/R) Chemin dans la foret (65x50cm-26x20in) s.d.1919
      (F.FR 15500)

MENDJISKY, Serge (1929-) French
£508 $884   (15-Apr-92 PLF.P92) Paysage aux cypres (38x55cm-15x22in) s.d.73
      (F.FR 5000)
£543 $950   (27-Feb-92 CE.NY7/R) Paysage de Provence (24x35cm-9x14in) s.
£791 $1400   (5-Nov-91 CE.NY50/R) Le passage aux tribunes (46x61cm-18x24in) s.
      init.i.verso
£904 $1600   (5-Nov-91 CE.NY46/R) La petite haie (54x65cm-21x26in) s. init.i.verso
£904 $1600   (5-Nov-91 CE.NY85/R) Paysage (65x81cm-26x32in) s. init.i.verso
£1130 $2000   (5-Nov-91 CE.NY47/R) Vue de Bargemont (81x104cm-32x41in) s. init.i.verso
£1257 $2200   (27-Feb-92 CE.NY49/R) Le petit bois (60x81cm-24x32in) s. init.num.1 verso
£1304 $2322   (29-Nov-91 GAB.G2807/R) La Colle en Provence (38x46cm-15x18in) s. panel
      (S.FR 3300)
£4238 $7290   (20-Oct-91 I.N215/R) Le pont sous la neige (38x61cm-15x24in) s.
      (F.FR 42000)
£4945 $9000   (11-Dec-91 RO.BA57/R) Crepuscule (60x84cm-24x33in) s.
£5438 $9245   (24-Oct-91 CJ.N98/R) Pont de Paris (53x64cm-21x25in) s. (F.FR 54000)
£6263 $11273   (22-Nov-91 PIC.P48/R) Pont Neuf soleil levant (54x73cm-21x29in) s.
      (F.FR 61000)
£730 $1307   (6-May-92 GD.B843/R) Mother with children (36x28cm-14x11in) s. mixed
      media (S.FR 2000)

MENEGHINI, Matteo (1840-1925) Italian
£645 $1174   (10-Dec-91 F.R114) Il mazzo di fiori (50x67cm-20x26in) s. W/C paper on
      board (I.L 1400000)

MENENDEZ PIDAL, Luis (1864-1932) Spanish
£1937 $3312   (17-Mar-92 FER.M150/R) Retrato de su mujer (103x69cm-41x27in) s.
      (S.P 350000)
£7022 $12500   (22-Jan-92 SY.NY543/R) Watching out for Vat (51x71cm-20x28in) s.

MENENDEZ, L (18/19th C) Spanish
£1244 $2339   (17-Dec-91 DUR.M4/R) Bodegon con perdices (65x49cm-26x19in) s.d.1818
      (S.P 225000)

MENEROTH, Paul (19th C) German
£722 $1227   (25-Oct-91 BM.B782/R) Sleeping guard (26x15cm-10x6in) s. i.verso board in
      the manner of Spitzweg (DM 2100)

MENESES OSORIO, Francisco (circle) (1630-1705) Spanish
£800 $1400   (25-Feb-92 PH22) Ascension of the Virgin (30x40cm-12x16in)

MENGHI, Jose Luis (1869-?) Argentinian
£573 $1100   (4-Aug-92 V.BA72) Naturaleza muerta (72x105cm-28x41in)

MENGIN, Charles Auguste (1853-1933) French
£874 $1555   (29-Apr-92 D.V902/R) Reclining female nude (21x28cm-8x11in) indis.s.i.
                          (A.S 18000)

MENGS, Anton Raphael (1728-1779) German
£423 $765   (6-Dec-91 GB.B5552) Glorification of ruler (23x16cm-9x6in) chk (DM 1200)
*£6000 $10920   (11-Dec-91 PH305/R) Danzatrice Greca - Young girl leaning against plinth
                          (29x21cm-11x8in) chk.*

MENGS, Anton Raphael (attrib) (1728-1779) German
£2205 $3924   (28-Apr-92 RAS.K533/R) Allegorical scenes - Summer and Autumn
                          (40x30cm-16x12in) pair (D.KR 25000)
*£1080 $1900   (9-Apr-92 FA.PH654/R) Portrait of gentleman. Portrait of lady
                          (30x25cm-12x10in) pastel pair*
£12000 $23040   (7-Jul-92 C109/R) Portrait of the artist (23x20cm-9x8in) s.d.1750 chk

MENGS, Anton Raphael (circle) (1728-1779) German
£4982 $9218   (8-Jun-92 CH.R768/R) Ritratto di Juan Guillen, Confessore di Don Carlos
                          (37x59cm-15x23in) (I.L 11000000)

MENGS, Anton Raphael (style) (1728-1779) German
£1208 $2163   (7-May-92 CH.AM44/R) Portrait of noblewoman, wearing silk dress and
                          ermine-lined wrap (78x63cm-31x25in) (D.FL 4000)

MENGUY, Bertrand (20th C) Danish
£496 $849   (10-Mar-92 RAS.K243) Composition (198x198cm-78x78in) i. paper on canvas
                          (D.KR 5500)

MENINSKY, Bernard (1891-1950) British
£800 $1416   (6-Nov-91 CB121/R) House in wooded landscape (61x51cm-24x20in) s.
£1900 $3363   (5-Nov-91 PH89) A clearing in the forest (41x51cm-16x20in) s.d.1925
£3500 $6405   (5-Jun-92 C58/R) Still life with green cloth (51x61cm-20x24in)
£4200 $7434   (7-Nov-91 C89/R) Seated nude girl (71x56cm-28x22in) s.d.26
£4500 $8235   (14-May-92 C106/R) Lady in hat, artist's wife (76x63cm-30x25in) s.d.1916
£7200 $12384   (6-Mar-92 C46/R) Spanish siesta (54x67cm-21x26in) s. i.verso
*£650 $1118   (5-Mar-92 CSK133) Landscape with young trees (44x58cm-17x23in) s. W/C
                          pencil*
*£800 $1536   (28-Jul-92 SWS302/R) Portrait of a young lady (54x39cm-21x15in) s. W/C
                          pencil*
£900 $1647   (14-May-92 C24) In Arcady (33x49cm-13x19in) gouache

MENJAUD, Alexandre (attrib) (1773-1832) French
£638 $1155   (23-May-92 G.SB466/R) Raphael peignant la Vierge et l'Enfant
                          (32x24cm-13x9in) rem.sig. paper laid down on canvas (F.FR 6300)

MENKEN, Johann Heinrich (1766-1834) German
£1413 $2473   (3-Apr-92 BM.B529) Hilly river landscape with cattle (84x123cm-33x48in)
                          s.d.1809 (DM 4000)

MENKES, Sigmund (1896-) Polish
£912 $1587   (17-Sep-91 CH.AM521) Tulips in a vase (59x49cm-23x19in) s.indist.d.
                          (D.FL 3000)
£1676 $3000   (13-Nov-91 B.SF2423/R) Portrait of young girl (79x61cm-31x24in) s.
£2123 $3800   (9-May-92 CE.NY86/R) Artist's wife with poppies (56x46cm-22x18in) s.
£3226 $5645   (5-Apr-92 ZZ.F175/R) Nature morte aux fleurs et au masque
                          (82x100cm-32x39in) s. (F.FR 31000)
£3343 $5750   (12-Oct-91 SY.NY143/R) Jeune femme assise (81x66cm-32x26in) s.
£3571 $6250   (28-Feb-92 SY.NY212/R) Porch in summer (109x74cm-43x29in) s.
£5129 $9130   (3-Nov-91 PSA.W16) Portrait in red (45x41cm-18x16in) s. (P.Z 100000000)
£5177 $9732   (21-Dec-91 PSA.W12) Flowers (81x65cm-32x26in) s. (P.Z 100000000)
£10668 $18990   (3-Nov-91 PSA.W15) Still life (51x40cm-20x16in) s. (P.Z 208000000)
£10833 $18957   (29-Sep-91 AG.W10) Still life with guitar (91x64cm-36x25in) s.
                          (P.Z 208000000)
£15530 $29197   (21-Dec-91 PSA.W11) Flowers and a mask (116x81cm-46x32in) s.
                          (P.Z 300000000)

MENN, Barthelemy (1815-1893) Swiss
*£395 $704   (29-Nov-91 GAB.G2140) Eglise de Vandoeuvres (20x14cm-8x6in) s. W/C
                          (S.FR 1000)*

MENNET, Louis (1829-1875) Swiss
£815 $1475   (19-May-92 GF.L2810) Twomaster before coast (21x30cm-8x12in) s. canvas on
                          board (S.FR 2200)

MENOTTI, V A (19th C) Italian
£2473 $4500   (26-May-92 CE.NY165/R) The lesson (50x81cm-20x32in) s.

MENPES, Mortimer L (1860-1938) British
£1100 $1870   (5-Aug-91 WW54/R) Arab street scenes with children (11x8cm-4x3in) s.
                          board pair
£1900 $3249   (11-Mar-92 S67/R) Arab street scenes (11x8cm-4x3in) s. panel pair
£2000 $3560   (28-Nov-91 B182/R) Japanese street scene (15x11cm-6x4in) s. board

MENPES, Mortimer L (1860-1938) British-cont.
£1600 $2800   (23-Sep-91 PHB1/R) Fire fairies (33x37cm-13x15in) s. i. verso W/C pastel

MENS, Isidorus Maria Cornelis van (1890-?) Dutch
£1009 $1786   (5-Nov-91 SY.AM221) Arabs resting (158x128cm-62x50in) s.d.1926
                    (D.FL 3300)

MENSA, Carlos (1936-1982) Spanish
£697 $1268   (13-Dec-91 BM.B848/R) Surrealistic portrait of man in elegant clothes
                    without head (33x24cm-13x9in) s. (DM 2000)

MENSE, Carlo (1886-1965) German
£1123 $2021   (21-Nov-91 L.K331/R) View of Bad Honnef (37x49cm-15x19in) s. W/C
                    (DM 3200)

MENSION, Cornelis Jan (1882-1950) Dutch
£612 $1089   (29-Oct-91 VN.R157) Aapjes bij voerbak (39x59cm-15x23in) s. (D.FL 2000)

MENTA, Edouard (1858-?) French
£3846 $7000   (28-May-92 SY.NY162/R) Le petit cuisinier (65x44cm-26x17in) s.
£7429 $13000   (20-Feb-92 SY.NY164/R) La femme aux perroquets et aux oiseaux
                    (80x65cm-31x26in) s.

MENTELER, Franz Josef (1777-1833) Swiss
£532 $990   (19-Jun-92 ZOF.Z2006/R) Portrait of girl aged 9 (28x25cm-11x10in)
                    i.d.1809verso (S.FR 1400)

MENTOR, Blasco (1918-) Spanish
£1017 $1862   (17-May-92 T.B187) Bouquet (32x40cm-13x16in) s. (F.FR 10000)
£2214 $3786   (22-Mar-92 LT.P98/R) Le Grand saut et Ecuyers (33x46cm-13x18in) s.
                    i.verso (F.FR 21500)
£2266 $3874   (22-Mar-92 LT.P99/R) La Marionnette (46x38cm-18x15in) s. i.verso
                    (F.FR 22000)
£2420 $4139   (22-Mar-92 LT.P100/R) Duo (46x38cm-18x15in) s. i.verso (F.FR 23500)
£4370 $7604   (16-Apr-92 FB.P102/R) Nu allonge sur le divan rouge (60x73cm-24x29in)
                    s.d.60 (F.FR 43000)
£6263 $11273   (19-Nov-91 FB.P61/R) Danseuses au foyer de l'opera (114x148cm-45x58in) s.
                    i.stretcher (F.FR 61000)

MENTOR, Will (20th C) ?
£1714 $3000   (27-Feb-92 CE.NY216/R) There are still places like this
                    (206x145cm-81x57in) s.d.1985 verso

MENYEPCKIN, A (19th C) Russian
£1134 $1973   (17-Sep-91 FN.S2437/R) Mountainous lake landscape with shepherd girl and
                    animals (49x72cm-19x28in) s.d.1878 i.verso (DM 3300)

MENZEL, Adolph (1815-1905) German
£5842 $10165   (17-Sep-91 FN.S2438/R) Kronprinz Friedrich Wilhelm von Preussen seen from
                    behind (25x24cm-10x9in) i.d.1868 canvas on board (DM 17000)
£756 $1399   (12-Jun-92 HN.H587/R) Studies of children (21x12cm-8x5in) mono pencil
                    (DM 2200)
£1224 $2093   (18-Mar-92 N.M295/R) Art observer. Paul Heyse's mother dying. Couple
                    seated. Wedding pencil 4 drawings in 3 passepartouts (DM 3500)
£1502 $2718   (22-May-92 GB.B5969) Study of female robes (21x13cm-8x5in) mono d.1884
                    pencil (DM 4400)
£2730 $4942   (22-May-92 GB.B5970) Study of arm (17x11cm-7x4in) mono.d.1884 pencil
                    (DM 8000)
£2747 $5000   (27-May-92 CH.NY72/R) Man picking fruit and hand studies (12x20cm-5x8in)
                    init. pencil
£3162 $5564   (11-Apr-92 AW.H619/R) Man walking with umbrella under his arm
                    (16x10cm-6x4in) mono. pencil (DM 9200)
£3500 $6195   (14-Feb-92 C72/R) Contemplation (30x20cm-12x8in) s.d.88 pencil
£3933 $7000   (22-Jan-92 SY.NY245/R) Royal coach (8x13cm-3x5in) init.d.70 i.verso
                    graphite
£4096 $7413   (22-May-92 GB.B5966) Study of woman pulling her hair and other studies
                    (13x21cm-5x8in) mono.i.d.1878 chk pencil (DM 12000)
£5119 $9266   (22-May-92 GB.B5965) Portrait of bearded gentleman with hat
                    (17x11cm-7x4in) mono.d.1853 pencil htd white (DM 15000)
£5634 $10197   (6-Dec-91 GB.B5926) Study of grenadiers and head of another
                    (30x12cm-12x5in) chl (DM 16000)
£5842 $10808   (12-Jun-92 HN.H586/R) Woman looking up (21x13cm-8x5in) mono.d.1891
                    graphite (DM 17000)
£6143 $11181   (29-May-92 VG.B1/R) Mark landscape (13x20cm-5x8in) pencil (DM 18000)
£6272 $11415   (12-Dec-91 L.K436/R) Bearded man on ladder with woman beside him
                    (21x13cm-8x5in) mono. pencil (DM 18000)
£10922 $19877   (26-May-92 KF.M391/R) Study for Piazza d'Erbe, Verona (30x23cm-12x9in)
                    mono.i.d.1883 pencil chl (DM 32000)
£11604 $21003   (22-May-92 GB.B5967/R) Schoneberger Ufer, window view, Berlin
                    (11x18cm-4x7in) mono.d.1889 chl (DM 34000)
£12088 $22000   (27-May-92 CH.NY71/R) Man descending stairway with Baroque portal
                    (31x23cm-12x9in) init.d.1884 chk
£58419 $108076   (12-Jun-92 HN.H585/R) Portrait of Karoline Arnold, Freifrau Treusch von
                    Buttlar-Brandenfels (45x34cm-18x13in) mono.d.1848 col.chk (DM 170000)

1224

MENZIO, Francesco (1899-) Italian
£2785 $5235   (19-Dec-91 F.M150/R) Paesaggio lacustre (50x70cm-20x28in) s.
                  (I.L 6000000)
£3357 $6143   (12-May-92 F.R169/R) Natura morta con vaso di fiori (70x50cm-28x20in) s.
                  (I.L 7400000)
£4641 $8725   (19-Dec-91 F.M234/R) Nudo disteso (60x120cm-24x47in) s.d.1955
                  (I.L 10000000)

MENZLER, Wilhelm (1846-?) German
£659 $1200   (26-May-92 CE.NY127/R) Elegant lady in garden. Figures in a garden
                  (32x21cm-13x8in) s. panel double-sided
£1742 $3100   (22-Jan-92 SY.NY271/R) Portrait of elegant young woman (42x27cm-17x11in)
                  s.d.83 panel
£3665 $7000   (16-Jul-92 SY.NY434/R) Tatiana's baby (63x41cm-25x16in) s.

MERCHANT, Henry (fl.1893-1940) British
£674 $1200   (22-Jan-92 SY.NY488/R) Cobbler (81x60cm-32x24in) s.d.1905

MERCIE, Antonin see MERCIE, Marius Jean Antonin

MERCIER, Charles Jean (1832-1909) French
£832 $1457   (5-Apr-92 ZZ.F60/R) Bucherons dans la montagne (29x42cm-11x17in) s. panel
                  (F.FR 8000)

MERCIER, Philippe (1689-1760) French
£1200 $2148   (15-Nov-91 C185/R) Portrait of lady, in satin dress, holding basket of
                  fruit (34x25cm-13x10in)
£2500 $4375   (31-Mar-92 PH17/R) Amorous couple standing at butcher's stall
                  (84x98cm-33x39in)
£2800 $4928   (8-Apr-92 S106/R) Three children in garden (56x67cm-22x26in) indist.s.
£7500 $13425   (15-Nov-91 C38/R) Jester - jeune garcon en costume de folie
                  (76x64cm-30x25in)
£10000 $19200   (7-Jul-92 PH81/R) Portrait of young girl knitting (76x63cm-30x25in) s.
£27933 $50000   (16-Jan-92 CH.NY119/R) Allegory of painting - lady seated at easel
                  attended by putto holding palette (159x153cm-63x60in) s.d.1740

MERCIER, Philippe (attrib) (1689-1760) French
£7143 $12643   (10-Feb-92 GL.P26/R) Jeune mere et son enfant (92x74cm-36x29in)
                  d.1736verso (F.FR 70000)

MERCIER, Philippe (circle) (1689-1760) French
£2000 $3560   (1-Nov-91 C62/R) Three ladies, said to be Madame de la Tour du Pin and
                  daughters, with spaniel (74x60cm-29x24in) with i.stretcher

MERCK, Jacob Franz van der (attrib) (1610-1664) Dutch
£9945 $18000   (22-May-92 SY.NY282/R) Portrait of young woman (71x54cm-28x21in) panel

MERCK, Jacob Franz van der (style) (1610-1664) Dutch
£2160 $3867   (14-Nov-91 CH.AM39) Elegant company at table (48x63cm-19x25in) panel
                  (D.FL 7000)

MERCKAERT, Jules (1872-1924) Belgian
£623 $1183   (24-Jun-92 KM.K1180/R) Field landscape near Worpswede with children by
                  stream (70x90cm-28x35in) s. (DM 1800)

MERCKER, E (1891-1973) German
£1123 $1920   (13-Mar-92 FN.S2867/R) Gute Hoffnungshutte (39x49cm-15x19in) s.i. board
                  (DM 3200)
£1150 $2093   (12-Dec-91 N.M2801/R) Am Hochofen (49x49cm-19x19in) s.i. board (DM 3300)
£1263 $2160   (13-Mar-92 FN.S2866) Wildsee landscape, Black Forest (87x85cm-34x33in)
                  s.i. (DM 3600)

MERCKER, Erich (1891-1973) German
£488 $888   (12-Dec-91 N.M2800/R) Surf (81x110cm-32x43in) s.i. (DM 1400)
£493 $892   (4-Dec-91 DO.H2527/R) Harbour view (38x49cm-15x19in) s.i. board (DM 1400)
£784 $1333   (23-Oct-91 GD.B1175/R) Harbour scene, winter (65x86cm-26x34in) s.i.
                  (S.FR 2000)
£884 $1583   (5-May-92 ZEL.L1437/R) Coastal landscape, morning (44x59cm-17x23in) s.i.
                  board (DM 2600)
£909 $1573   (25-Mar-92 KM.K1308/R) Coastal landscape, Southern Italy (41x51cm-16x20in)
                  s. (DM 2600)
£1399 $2392   (18-Mar-92 N.M597/R) View of Chiemsee with Fraueninsel (65x85cm-26x33in)
                  s.i. panel (DM 4000)
£1443 $2511   (17-Sep-91 FN.S2439/R) Hamburg Harbour, morning (103x120cm-41x47in) s.i.
                  board (DM 4200)
£1512 $2631   (21-Sep-91 SA.A1746/R) View of Capri (108x154cm-43x61in) s.i. (DM 4400)
£8000 $14880   (19-Jun-92 C41/R) Monte Carlo (43x61cm-17x24in) s.i.

MEREDITH, John (?) ?
£1194 $2125   *(26-Nov-91 JOY.T202) Untitled composition (34x42cm-13x17in) s.d.66*
                  col.ink (C.D 2400)

MEREILES DE LIMA, Vitor (1832-1903) Brazilian
£3315 $6000   (18-May-92 CH.NY67/R) Retrato da Menina (65x53cm-26x21in) s.d.1884

MERIAN, Matthaus (elder) (1593-1650) Swiss
£1605 $2873   *(12-Nov-91 SY.AM355/R) Juda and Thamar (16x22cm-6x9in) i.verso pen wash htd.white (D.FL 5200)*

MERIDA (?) ?
£1232 $2241   (26-May-92 DUR.M124/R) Paisaje de la ria de Bilbao (14x24cm-6x9in) s. panel (S.P 225000)

MERIDA, Carlos (1891-1984) Guatemalan
£11050 $20000   (18-May-92 CH.NY175/R) Composition (42x32cm-17x13in) s.d.1977 incised amate paper on composite board
£11111 $20000   (19-Nov-91 CH.NY174/R) Planes (70x50cm-28x20in) s.d.1960 s.i.stretcher
£30556 $55000   (19-Nov-91 CH.NY48/R) Motivo Guatemalteco (97x71cm-38x28in) s.d.1919 s.i.verso
£2500 $4500   (19-Nov-91 CH.NY139/R) Proyecto para mural (24x16cm-9x6in) s. pencil crayon
£5000 $9000   (18-Nov-91 SY.NY116/R) Tres mujeres (28x39cm-11x15in) s.d.27 W/C gouache
£8287 $15000   (19-May-92 SY.NY148/R) Kanek, the God of Fire (55x41cm-22x16in) s.d.1967 gouache amate paper on masonite
£16575 $30000   (19-May-92 SY.NY139/R) Composicion (59x52cm-23x20in) s.d.1964 petroplastic panel
£25000 $45000   (18-Nov-91 SY.NY126/R) Los astrologos (60x45cm-24x18in) s.i.d.1959 s.i.d.stretcher mixed media masonite

MERINO, Daniel (1941-) Spanish
£525 $935   (21-Jan-92 DUR.M65/R) Campesinos (45x54cm-18x21in) s.d.1941 (S.P 95000)
£995 $1871   (16-Dec-91 ANS.M157/R) Libertad (100x81cm-39x32in) s. s.i.d.74verso (S.P 180000)

MERION, C (?) ?
£1800 $3186   (13-Feb-92 CSK208) Meeting of Arab horsemen (98x142cm-39x56in) s.

MERKEL, Georg (1881-1976) Austrian
£497 $884   *(28-Nov-91 D.V202/R) Female figure standing with green cloth (45x29cm-18x11in) s. i.verso pastel (A.S 10000)*

MERKER, Paul (?-1823) German
£772 $1389   (22-Nov-91 SA.A1547/R) Portrait of young man (59x48cm-23x19in) s. (DM 2200)

MERLE, Hughes (1823-1881) French
£2600 $4628   (27-Nov-91 S227/R) Portrait of woman (45x37cm-18x15in)
£3962 $7250   (16-May-92 HG.C50/R) Tarot reading (142x94cm-56x37in)

MERLIN, Daniel (attrib) (1861-1933) French
£824 $1450   (12-Apr-92 LIT.L9) Cats playing (51x61cm-20x24in) s.

MEROUX, A (20th C) French
£653 $1136   (21-Sep-91 SA.A1959/R) Young lady in profile with distant figures (41x33cm-16x13in) s. (DM 1900)
£756 $1315   (21-Sep-91 SA.A1957/R) Young woman on beach (41x34cm-16x13in) s. (DM 2200)

MERRE, Johanna (1867-1940) German
£484 $920   (24-Jun-92 KM.K1181/R) Still life of tulips in glass vase (50x38cm-20x15in) s. (DM 1400)
£623 $1183   (24-Jun-92 KM.K1182/R) Still life of fruit and bunch of summer flowers (65x50cm-26x20in) s. panel (DM 1800)

MERRITT, Anna Lea (1844-1930) British
£800 $1392   (10-Sep-91 HS5) Study of pensive girl (33x43cm-13x17in) bears mono.

MERTE, Oskar (20th C) German
£3000 $5340   (28-Nov-91 B91/R) Heads of four horses (59x83cm-23x33in) s.i.

MERTENS, Julie (attrib) (19th C) ?
£1650 $3003   (10-Dec-91 SWS140/R) The kiss (75x92cm-30x36in) s.i.d.1890

MERTENS, Wouter (17th C) Flemish
£20500 $39360   (8-Jul-92 S187/R) Allegory of Plenty with swags of fruit encircling Bacchus (149x115cm-59x45in) bears sig.d.1661

MERTON, Erling (1898-1967) Norwegian
£833 $1550   (15-Jun-92 B.O108/R) The artist's wife on steps (50x60cm-20x24in) s.d.1945 (N.KR 9500)

MERTON, Owen Heathcote Grierson (1887-1931) New Zealander
£790 $1320   *(21-Aug-91 DS.W99/R) Street and houses Bermuda (24x25cm-9x10in) s.d.1922 W/C (NZ.D 2300)*
£790 $1320   *(21-Aug-91 DS.W114) Sailing ship at wharf (24x17cm-9x7in) s.d.1909 W/C (NZ.D 2300)*
£1418 $2538   *(6-May-92 DS.W22/R) Reculver (55x42cm-22x17in) s.i.d.1909 W/C (NZ.D 4750)*
£1493 $2672   *(6-May-92 DS.W39/R) Coastal trees, Bermuda (32x50cm-13x20in) s.d.22 W/C (NZ.D 5000)*

MERTON, Owen Heathcote Grierson (1887-1931) New Zealander-cont.
£1546 $2582   (21-Aug-91 DS.W98/R) Coastal trees Bermuda (38x50cm-15x20in) s.d.22 W/C
                  (NZ.D 4500)

MERTZ, Emma (1880-1937) Swiss
£1333 $2387   (15-Nov-91 ZOF.Z1804/R) Bundner Maiensass (48x54cm-19x21in) mono. i.verso
                  (S.FR 3400)

MERTZ, Johann Cornelius (1819-1891) Dutch
£515 $891   (7-Sep-91 CH.AM185) The paintress (65x80cm-26x31in) s.d.1849 canvas laid
                  down on panel (D.FL 1700)

MERWART, Paul (1855-1902) Polish
£7576 $13409   (22-Apr-92 CH.AM162/R) An odalisque (160x215cm-63x85in) s.d.1887
                  (D.FL 25000)

MERY, Alfred Emile (1824-1896) French
£510 $913   (5-May-92 ZEL.L1158/R) Monkey and cat (75x50cm-30x20in) s. gouache
                  (DM 1500)

MERZ, Gerhard (20th C) American?
£8380 $15000   (6-May-92 CH.NY222/R) Mountain climber (305x475cm-120x187in) acrylic
                  silkscreen photo-sensitized canvas

MERZ, Mario (1925-) Italian
£5307 $9500   (14-Nov-91 SY.NY222/R) Untitled (101x73cm-40x29in) chl ink
£15636 $27988   (14-Nov-91 F.M93/R) La natura interloquisce sempre con se' stessa
                  (120x150cm-47x59in) s.i.d.1971 tempera pencil collage on fabric
                  (I.L 34000000)
£18436 $33000   (13-Nov-91 CH.NY249/R) Numero Per Pino Cono (92x142cm-36x56in) enamel
                  spray col.chks.others paper mounted board

MESCHERSKY, Arsenii Ivanovich (1834-1902) Russian
£2646 $4709   (28-Apr-92 RAS.K173/R) Coastal landscape with two girls looking out to
                  sea (92x132cm-36x52in) s.d.1875 (D.KR 30000)
£3902 $6790   (19-Sep-91 D.V164/R) Wooded coastal landscape (48x73cm-19x29in) s.
                  (A.S 80000)

MESDAG, Hendrik-Willem (1831-1915) Dutch
£2432 $4231   (17-Sep-91 CH.AM654/R) After the naval review, 15th September 1898, a
                  study (48x78cm-19x31in) (D.FL 8000)
£3364 $5988   (30-Oct-91 CH.AM4/R) Ships on rough seas in stormy weather
                  (24x32cm-9x13in) one s. one init. panel two (D.FL 11000)
£45872 $79817   (14-Apr-92 SY.AM34/R) Return of the fishing fleet (88x68cm-35x27in)
                  s.d.1895 (D.FL 150000)

MESENS, E L T (1903-1971) British
£684 $1239   (7-Dec-91 KV.L238 a) Ceci n'est pas une fleur (12x20cm-5x8in) mono.d.1967
                  col.dr. (B.FR 40000)

MESKER, Theodorus Ludovicus (1853-1894) Dutch
£1162 $2057   (5-Nov-91 SY.AM223/R) Potential client (35x48cm-14x19in) s. (D.FL 3800)

MESMER, Gustav (1865-?) German
£1138 $1957   (16-Oct-91 KM.K1270/R) Ducks in pond landscape, autumn (60x100cm-24x39in)
                  s. (DM 3300)

MESNAGER, Jerome (1961-) French
£813 $1415   (16-Apr-92 FB.P262/R) Sans titre (112x76cm-44x30in) s.d.89 i.verso
                  acrylic panel (F.FR 8000)
£1437 $2587   (19-Nov-91 FB.P257/R) Maternite (140x75cm-55x30in) s.d.89 acrylic fence
                  (F.FR 14000)
£1457 $2549   (5-Apr-92 R.P182) Palissade (210x78cm-83x31in) s. acrylic board
                  (F.FR 14000)
£1030 $1761   (19-Mar-92 CSC.P93/R) La lumiere c'est la vie (92x96cm-36x38in) s.d.88
                  acrylic object canvas wood plank (F.FR 10000)
£1216 $2201   (20-May-92 FB.P16 a) Express vite vite (193x151cm-76x59in) s.d.90 mixed
                  media collage canvas (F.FR 12000)
£1216 $2201   (20-May-92 FB.P15 a) Mesurahr (194x130cm-76x51in) s.d.90 mixed media
                  metal collage canvas (F.FR 12000)
£1545 $2642   (19-Mar-92 CSC.P92/R) Peace and love (131x97cm-52x38in) s.d.80 acrylic
                  object canvas (F.FR 15000)

MESS, George J (?) ?
£747 $1300   (20-Sep-91 DM.D158/R) Indiana landscape (107x122cm-42x48in) s.

MESSAGER, Annette (1943-) French
£804 $1431   (25-Nov-91 WK.M2043/R) Chimeres - no.50 (380x310cm-150x122in) mixed media
                  board on gauze on canvas 4 parts (DM 2300)
£874 $1556   (25-Nov-91 WK.M2044/R) Chimeres - no.53 (260x140cm-102x55in) mixed media
                  board on gauze on canvas 2 parts (DM 2500)

MESSAGIER (1920-) French
£1850 $3533   (30-Jun-92 ZZ.F94/R) L'heure des taupes (112x192cm-44x76in) s. mixed
                  media canvas (F.FR 18000)

MESSAGIER, Jean (1920-) French
£706	$1235	(25-Sep-91 CC.P13) Palais a cueillir (76x104cm-30x41in) d.1976 acrylic paper (F.FR 7000)
£825	$1427	(23-Mar-92 CC.P108) Trois torsions pour mieux voir (65x100cm-26x39in) s.i. acrylic (F.FR 8000)
£1173	$2006	(12-Mar-92 RAS.K651/R) Temple messagerien (45x57cm-18x22in) s.d.1982verso (D.KR 13000)
£1610	$2769	(12-Oct-91 GL.P49/R) Les grands etourneaux (105x170cm-41x67in) s.i.d.octobre 1964 (F.FR 16000)
£1629	$2982	(5-Jun-92 CB.P54) Untitled (32x84cm-13x33in) s. s.d.1954verso frame (F.FR 16000)
£1856	$3210	(29-Mar-92 P.V6/R) Les guerisseurs Philippins (125x192cm-49x76in) s. acrylic (F.FR 18000)
£2213	$3807	(7-Oct-91 RY.P90/R) Le chiens noirs (74x105cm-29x41in) s.i.d.1959verso (F.FR 22000)
£2518	$4481	(28-Oct-91 GL.P163/R) Conversations de fleurs au sujet du 12 mai et du 24 juin (108x180cm-43x71in) s.i. d.1972verso (F.FR 25000)
£2572	$4655	(2-Dec-91 CC.P15/R) Sans titre (57x100cm-22x39in) s.d.1959 (F.FR 25000)
£2621	$4587	(25-Sep-91 CC.P14) Passage d'avril a mai (80x120cm-31x47in) d.1955 (F.FR 26000)
£2736	$4951	(21-May-92 CC.P76/R) Composition (79x148cm-31x58in) s. (F.FR 27000)
£3021	$5378	(28-Oct-91 GL.P164/R) Les piqures de guepes (112x199cm-44x78in) s.i.d.1970 (F.FR 30000)
£3030	$5485	(19-May-92 CH.AM272/R) Noir de Printemps (59x91cm-23x36in) s.i.d.1962 verso (D.FL 10000)
£3049	$5305	(16-Apr-92 FB.P216/R) Chambre no.234 de Raymond Roussel et Charlotte Dufrene au Grand Hotel (198x134cm-78x53in) s.i. d.79verso (F.FR 30000)
£3219	$5537	(8-Oct-91 CC.P30/R) Exposition de ruisseaux (72x120cm-28x47in) s. (F.FR 32000)
£3402	$5886	(29-Mar-92 P.V26/R) Juin equestre (170x105cm-67x41in) s. (F.FR 33000)
£4281	$7963	(15-Jun-92 GL.P40/R) Dermatologie (120x192cm-47x76in) s. acrylic (F.FR 42000)
£10194	$18960	(15-Jun-92 GL.P38/R) Untitled (108x198cm-43x78in) s. (F.FR 100000)
£10288	$18621	(2-Dec-91 CC.P32/R) Rives mobiles (193x165cm-76x65in) s. i.d.mars 57verso (F.FR 100000)
£1811	*$3115*	*(8-Oct-91 CC.P74/R) Moteur a printemps (75x108cm-30x43in) s..i. gouache acrylic (F.FR 18000)*

MESSEG, Aharon (1942-) Israeli
£1170	$2200	(5-Jan-92 GG.TA281/R) Head, bird and fish (73x73cm-29x29in) s.
£1459	$2700	(8-Jun-92 GG.TA200/R) Figures (72x90cm-28x35in) s.
£2444	$4400	(6-Jan-92 GG.TA426/R) Birds (91x115cm-36x45in) twice s.d.1971
£2703	$5000	(8-Jun-92 GG.TA199/R) Vase of flowers (116x129cm-46x51in) s.

MESSEL, Oliver (20th C) British
£450	*$819*	*(12-Dec-91 CSK52) Lady of the Bassa Selim's Harem (35x23cm-14x9in) s. W/C pencil*
£541	*$1000*	*(12-Jun-92 SY.NY71/R) Marriage of Figaro - costume design (53x33cm-21x13in) s. W/C pencil gold paint*

MESSENSEE, Jurgen (1937-) Austrian
£3177	$5655	(31-Oct-91 D.V185/R) Untitled (128x108cm-50x43in) s.d.87verso (A.S 65000)
£679	*$1235*	*(26-May-92 D.V368/R) Untitled (74x55cm-29x22in) s.d.91 mixed media collage (A.S 14000)*
£777	*$1383*	*(28-Apr-92 D.V351/R) Untitled (33x41cm-13x16in) s.d.87 mixed media (A.S 16000)*
£880	*$1566*	*(31-Oct-91 D.V41/R) Schwimmende (47x64cm-19x25in) s.d.69 W/C htd.white (A.S 18000)*

MESSER, Edmund Clarence (1842-?) American
£552	$1000	(21-May-92 S.W2058/R) Blue ridge (46x61cm-18x24in) s.

MESSERLI, Paul Pierre (1899-?) Swiss
£431	$733	(23-Oct-91 GD.B500/R) Vuadens am Greyerzersee (50x64cm-20x25in) s.indis.d. (S.FR 1100)
£706	$1200	(23-Oct-91 GD.B501/R) Townscape (60x74cm-24x29in) s. (S.FR 1800)

MESTRALLET, Paul Louis (1886-?) French
£488	$844	(3-Oct-91 D.V42) Landscape with windmill (22x27cm-9x11in) s.d.1919 panel (A.S 10000)
£503	$900	(6-May-92 CAS.M47/R) Pueblo (27x35cm-11x14in) panel
£670	$1200	(6-May-92 CAS.M46) Puente (35x27cm-14x11in) panel
£732	$1266	(3-Oct-91 D.V43) Wooded landscape (27x35cm-11x14in) s. panel (A.S 15000)

MESTRES Y BORREL, Felix (1872-1933) Spanish
£2189	$3896	(29-Oct-91 BRO.B333/R) Paisaje con pinos (71x50cm-28x20in) s. (S.P 400000)

MET DE BLES, Herri see BLES, Herri met de

METCALF, Conger (20th C) American
£922	*$1650*	*(14-Nov-91 GRO.B172/R) Ragazzo di campagna (94x53cm-37x21in) s. mixed media*

METCALF, Willard Leroy (1858-1925) American
£723	$1250	(29-Mar-92 MY.F96/R) Saint Luke's church (51x46cm-20x18in) s.
£4678	$8000	(12-Mar-92 CH.NY91/R) Sunset at Manchester, Massachusetts, from sandy hollow (12x18cm-5x7in) init.d.77 s.i.d.verso panel
£8772	$15000	(12-Mar-92 CH.NY108/R) North African scene (25x34cm-10x13in)
£12088	$22000	(28-May-92 CH.NY131/R) The poppy field (32x24cm-13x9in)
£12431	$22500	(6-Dec-91 CH.NY142/R) View of the village (21x31cm-8x12in) s.d.77
£35912	$65000	(6-Dec-91 CH.NY153/R) September (65x53cm-26x21in) s.
£38674	$70000	(6-Dec-91 CH.NY161/R) The sunny brook, Chester, Vermont (65x63cm-26x25in) s.d.23
£54945	$100000	(27-May-92 SY.NY76/R) Buds and blossoms (66x74cm-26x29in) s.d.07 i.stretcher

METCALFE, Ethel (?) British
£500	$890	(30-Apr-92 CSK83) The age of innocence (76x63cm-30x25in) after Sir Joshua Reynolds

METEIN-GILLIARD, Valentine (1891-) Swiss
£741	$1341	(19-May-92 GF.L2666/R) Nue assise (73x60cm-29x24in) s. (S.FR 2000)

METEYARD, Thomas B (1865-1928) American
£1519	$2750	(22-May-92 S.BM153/R) Misty day, New England coast (38x56cm-15x22in)

METHFESSEL, Adolf (1836-1909) Swiss
£1788	$3201	(6-May-92 GD.B849/R) Figure on hillside and view of river landscape (100x75cm-39x30in) s.d.1894 (S.FR 4900)
£474	$854	(19-Nov-91 GS.B4519) Figures on wooden bridge near Bremgarten, Bern (27x39cm-11x15in) s. W/C (S.FR 1200)

METHVEN, C V (?) ?
£1021	$1838	(19-Nov-91 GM.B323) Lever de la lune a Londres (92x137cm-36x54in) s. (B.FR 60000)

METSU, Gabriel (1629-1667) Dutch
£14907	$26534	(25-Nov-91 CH.AM86/R) Seated young man asleep (20x21cm-8x8in) chk (D.FL 48000)

METSU, Gabriel (after) (1629-1667) Dutch
£1100	$2090	(23-Jun-92 CG651) Interior with woman at toilet (44x36cm-17x14in) panel
£1200	$2100	(25-Feb-92 PH4/R) The hunter's gift (51x42cm-20x17in)
£1300	$2340	(22-Nov-91 SWS192/R) An interior with a gentleman drinking and a lady sewing (38x31cm-15x12in) panel
£1400	$2548	(10-Dec-91 PH182/R) Hunter's gift (55x44cm-22x17in)

METSU, Gabriel (style) (1629-1667) Dutch
£800	$1464	(12-May-92 SWS745/R) Hunter's gift (56x40cm-22x16in)
£2484	$4247	(18-Mar-92 D.V405/R) Old woman selling fish (49x50cm-19x20in) i. panel (A.S 50000)

METSYS, Cornelis (attrib) (1508-1580) Flemish
£5233	$9000	(10-Oct-91 SY.NY156/R) Mary Magdalene adoring the cross in the wilderness, landscape beyond (47x63cm-19x25in) panel
£13086	$24340	(16-Jun-92 EP.M3/R) San Jeronimo penitente (51x34cm-20x13in) panel (S.P 2400000)

METSYS, Jan (circle) (c.1509-1575) Flemish
£2600	$4732	(10-Dec-91 PH131/R) Peasants bartering (83x114cm-33x45in) panel

METSYS, Jan (school) (c.1509-1575) Flemish
£17453	$30892	(5-Nov-91 BA.S119/R) Lucretia (44x34cm-17x13in) panel (S.KR 185000)

METSYS, Quentin (style) (15/16th C) Flemish
£1000	$1780	(31-Oct-91 B44) Flagellation (65x55cm-26x22in) panel
£1049	$1878	(12-May-92 SY.AM237) The Penitent Magdelene (48x34cm-19x13in) panel (D.FL 3400)
£3744	$6740	(19-Nov-91 JRL.S141/R) Altar frieze, Holy Mary (53x21cm-21x8in) panel (A.D 8500)
£3744	$6740	(19-Nov-91 JRL.S140/R) Altar frieze, Holy Barbara (53x21cm-21x8in) panel (A.D 8500)

METTLING, Louis (1847-1904) French
£612	$1083	(5-Nov-91 SY.AM364) Portrait of lady in white dress (37x24cm-15x9in) s. panel (D.FL 2000)

METZINGER, Jean (1883-1956) French
£5143	$9000	(28-Feb-92 SY.NY49/R) Nature morte (20x25cm-8x10in) s. cradled panel
£6857	$12000	(28-Feb-92 SY.NY20/R) Portrait de femme divisioniste (47x38cm-19x15in) s.
£11190	$20031	(17-Nov-91 GL.P14/R) Nature morte (27x35cm-11x14in) s. (F.FR 110000)
£13000	$22490	(24-Mar-92 C31/R) Composition aux verre, poires et deux de carreau (22x35cm-9x14in) s.
£15819	$28000	(7-Nov-91 SY.NY159/R) Homme assis au chat (32x41cm-13x16in) s.
£18000	$31140	(25-Mar-92 S37/R) Maison dans un paysage (64x49cm-25x19in) s.
£50813	$88415	(19-Apr-92 ZZ.F119/R) Composition cubiste (54x65cm-21x26in) s. (F.FR 500000)

METZINGER, Jean (1883-1956) French-cont.
£56968 $101974   (17-Nov-91 GL.P47/R) Paysage aux deux voiliers (92x60cm-36x24in) s.
                   (F.FR 560000)
£3049 $5305   (19-Apr-92 ZZ.F43/R) Paysage cubiste (24x32cm-9x13in) s. blk.crayon
                   (F.FR 30000)
£5085 $9000   (6-Nov-91 CH.NY121/R) Femme nue (42x31cm-17x12in) s. pencil
£8000 $15280   (30-Jun-92 C145/R) Etude pour La Femme en Bleu (32x24cm-13x9in) s.
                   gouache
£15000 $28650   (30-Jun-92 C134/R) Femme au chapeau (60x48cm-24x19in) s.d.1913 pencil

METZKES, Harald (1929-) ?
£1399 $2490   (30-Nov-91 VG.B888/R) Summer landscape (59x80cm-23x31in) s.d.1975
                   (DM 4000)

METZMACHER, Emile Pierre (19th C) French
£824 $1500   (26-May-92 CE.NY107/R) A glass of cognac (41x33cm-16x13in) s. W/C

MEUBER, F (?) ?
£594 $1052   (25-Apr-92 SO.S475/R) Summer landscape (48x80cm-19x31in) s. (S.KR 6300)

MEUCCI, M (19th C) ?
£1823 $3300   (2-Dec-91 GC.M6) Bouquet de flores (84x60cm-33x24in) s.d.1885
£1823 $3300   (2-Dec-91 GC.M5) Bouquet de flores (84x60cm-33x24in) s.d.1885

MEUCCI, Michelangelo (19th C) Italian
£1800 $3204   (1-Nov-91 S399/R) Still lifes of dead birds. Still life of goldfinch
                   (21x17cm-8x7in) s.i.d.1874 1873 panel oval three one other hand
£2700 $4671   (4-Oct-91 C191/R) Pomegranates and grapes (56x43cm-22x17in) s. oval
£3200 $5472   (18-Mar-92 S184/R) Still life with tulips and lilies (84x59cm-33x23in)
                   s.i.

MEUCCI, Michelangelo (attrib) (19th C) Italian
£1093 $2000   (5-Jun-92 SY.NY146/R) Still lifes of game and fruit (57x41cm-22x16in)
                   painted ovals pair

MEUCCI, Vincenzo (1694-1766) Italian
£400 $696   (13-Apr-92 S175/R) Argus, Mercury and Io (23x34cm-9x13in) pen wash over
                   black chk

MEUGNIER, Jacques (1950-) French
£504 $856   (27-Oct-91 LT.P152/R) Laetitia (46x38cm-18x15in) s. (F.FR 5000)
£504 $856   (27-Oct-91 LT.P165/R) Jeune femme surle banc (38x46cm-15x18in) s.
                   (F.FR 5000)
£595 $1024   (20-Oct-91 LT.P79/R) Petite fille au bouquet (46x38cm-18x15in) s.
                   (F.FR 5900)
£665 $1216   (5-Feb-92 FB.P195) La cueillette de fleurs dans le jardin
                   (46x38cm-18x15in) s. (F.FR 6500)
£1312 $2256   (20-Oct-91 LT.P68/R) Le printemps (60x73cm-24x29in) s. (F.FR 13000)

MEULEN, Adam Frans van der (1632-1690) Flemish
£1387 $2482   (6-May-92 GD.B852/R) Cunstruction d'un fort par Vauban (24x37cm-9x15in)
                   panel (S.FR 3800)
£8114 $14280   (10-Apr-92 AT.P8/R) Bataille dans un paysage (16x22cm-6x9in) s. copper
                   (F.FR 80000)

MEULEN, Adam Frans van der (attrib) (1632-1690) Flemish
£1966 $3500   (22-Jan-92 D.NY35) Louis XIV on battle field (84x109cm-33x43in)
£2484 $4247   (18-Mar-92 D.V256/R) Louis XIV with officers (38x30cm-15x12in)
                   (A.S 50000)
£52000 $94640   (13-Dec-91 C266/R) View of the Chateau de Saint Cloud (84x150cm-33x59in)
£1500 $2880   (6-Jul-92 S154/R) Landscape with traveller and view of riverside town
                   (28x44cm-11x17in) chk wash

MEULEN, Adam Frans van der (studio) (1632-1690) Flemish
£71061 $133594 (18-Dec-91 AT.P42/R) Les Grandes Batailles de Louis XIV six
                   (F.FR 690000)

MEULEN, Steven van der (16th C) Flemish
£38000 $72580   (15-Jul-92 S8/R) Portrait of John Farnham (110x83cm-43x33in) i. panel

MEULEN, Steven van der (style) (16th C) Flemish
£900 $1575   (28-Feb-92 C111) Portrait of gentleman wearing black coat
                   (44x32cm-17x13in) i. panel

MEULEN, van der (17th C) Dutch
£800 $1536   (30-Jul-92 GSP534) Court scene in gardens with fountain (61x74cm-24x29in)

MEULENER, Pieter (1602-1654) Dutch
£10500 $20160   (8-Jul-92 S320/R) Siege of town (84x109cm-33x43in) s.indis.d.165.
£11000 $19250   (1-Apr-92 S90/R) Cavalry battle (71x102cm-28x40in) bears sig.d.1647

MEULENER, Pieter (studio) (1602-1654) Dutch
£4000 $7680   (8-Jul-92 S177/R) Cavalry skirmish (83x119cm-33x47in)

MEURER, Charles A (1865-1955) American
£1341 $2400   (16-Nov-91 WOL.C517/R) In the barnyard (36x61cm-14x24in) s.d.1921

MEURET, Francois (1800-1887) French
£926   *$1676*   *(21-May-92 SY.G37/R) Portrait of lady wearing black velvet gown (10x?cm-4x?in) min. stamped gilt metal frame (S.FR 2500)*

MEURIS (?) French?
£1359 $2514   (8-Jun-92 CH.R627/R) Veduta di Pozzuoli dal Convento dei Cappuccini, alla Solfatara (42x62cm-17x24in) s. tempera (I.L 3000000)

MEURON, Albert de (1823-1897) Swiss
£1581 $2846   (19-Nov-91 GS.B3206) Winter landscape with female figure on woodland path (27x40cm-11x16in) mono. i.stretcher (S.FR 4000)

MEURON, Louis de (1868-1939) Swiss
£9630 $17430   (20-May-92 GK.Z5115/R) Tempesta al Monte Soracte Lazi (118x144cm-46x57in) s.d.1843 (S.FR 26000)

MEURS, Harmen (1891-1964) Dutch
£1394 $2537   (14-Dec-91 BOD.P733/R) Female nude seated on red drape (93x73cm-37x29in) s.d.1936 (DM 4000)
£2321 $4224   (25-May-92 WK.M878/R) Eenzaam (92x73cm-36x29in) s.d.1936 s.i.d.verso st.studio stretcher (DM 6800)
£3436 $6357   (12-Jun-92 HN.H588/R) Interior (116x90cm-46x35in) s.d.1925 s.i.d.verso (DM 10000)
£4545 $8227   (21-May-92 SY.AM31/R) View of Amsterdam Central Station (81x100cm-32x39in) s.d.1929 (D.FL 15000)

MEUSER (1947-) ?
£1676   *$3000*   *(13-Nov-91 CH.NY333/R) Untitled (99x51cm-39x20in) s.d.78verso enamel steel*

MEXICAN SCHOOL, 18th C
£12155 $22000   (19-May-92 SY.NY2/R) Archangels (163x104cm-64x41in)
£110000 $200200   (29-May-92 C341/R) Castas (61x46cm-24x18in) set of thirteen

MEXICAN SCHOOL, 19th C
£2762 $5000   (19-May-92 SY.NY75/R) Retrato de una dama (67x52cm-26x20in)
£2762 $5000   (19-May-92 SY.NY74/R) Hacendado (39x29cm-15x11in)

MEYER (?) ?
£3714 $6500   (20-Feb-92 SY.NY163/R) Jeune femme a l'ombrelle (27x35cm-11x14in) s. panel

MEYER VON BREMEN, Johann Georg see BREMEN, Meyer von

MEYER, Carl Diethelm (1840-1884) German
£1172 $2074   (5-Nov-91 GF.L2543/R) Portrait of young woman in profile (39x31cm-15x12in) s.d.1883 panel (S.FR 3000)

MEYER, Claus (1856-1919) German
£828 $1423   (16-Oct-91 KM.K1271) Medieval figures and nuns leaving church gathering on snow covered yard (143x137cm-56x54in) s.d.1916-1917 (DM 2400)
£839 $1452   (25-Mar-92 KM.K1310/R) Murder of Engelbert I, Archbishop of Cologne (52x80cm-20x31in) s. (DM 2400)
£1000 $1780   (26-Nov-91 PH150/R) Beside the hearth (75x65cm-30x26in) s.
£2496 $4643   (16-Jun-92 F.M202/R) Il documento (49x37cm-19x15in) s. panel (I.L 5500000)

MEYER, Edgar (1853-1925) Austrian
£3000   *$5340*   *(27-Nov-91 S113/R) Procession entering church on Italian coast (134x105cm-53x41in) s.d.84 W/C gouache*

MEYER, Emma Eleonore (1859-1921) Danish
£1977 $3460   (20-Feb-92 D.V430/R) Summer landscape (72x102cm-28x40in) mono.d.91 i.stretcher (A.S 40000)

MEYER, Ernest (1863-1952) American
£1061 $1900   (6-May-92 D.NY47/R) In the apple orchard (56x89cm-22x35in) s.

MEYER, Ernst (1796-1861) Danish
£5722 $9613   (27-Aug-91 RAS.K135/R) Roman street scene with girl having lover's letter read to her (62x70cm-24x28in) i. (D.KR 65000)

MEYER, Felix (1653-1713) Swiss
£704   *$1275*   *(6-Dec-91 GB.B5286/R) Landscape with ruins (27x36cm-11x14in) indian ink pen wash (DM 2000)*

MEYER, Frederick John (attrib) (19th C) British
£1300 $2314   (28-Apr-92 PH16/R) Portrait of young man, seated, wearing waistcoat, stock and coat (30x25cm-12x10in) panel

MEYER, H (?) ?
£2571 $4500   (18-Feb-92 CE.NY9/R) Boxer, Deaf Burke (61x51cm-24x20in)

MEYER, Hendrik de (17/18th C) Dutch
£621 $1106   (25-Nov-91 CH.AM207/R) *View of chateau (27x36cm-11x14in) chk wash*
        (D.FL 2000)

MEYER, Hendrik de (attrib) (17/18th C) Dutch
£3217 $5822   (19-May-92 AB.S4353/R) Cavalry battle (47x64cm-19x25in) indist.sig. panel
        (S.KR 34000)

MEYER, Hendrik de (style) (17/18th C) Dutch
£7500 $14400   (8-Jul-92 S216/R) River landscape with ships and boats before town
        (62x105cm-24x41in) bears sig panel

MEYER, Hendrik de II (1737-1793) Dutch
£5587 $10000   (14-Jan-92 SY.NY113/R) *Extensive landscape with peasants resting before*
        tavern, others beyond (47x64cm-19x25in) s.d.1792 gouache W/C over black
        chk

MEYER, Hendrik de II (attrib) (1737-1793) Dutch
£9500 $18240   (8-Jul-92 S185/R) Wooded landscape with rider and other figures
        (37x45cm-15x18in) panel

MEYER, Hendrik de II (circle) (1737-1793) Dutch
£3600 $6912   (7-Jul-92 PH194/R) Figures boarding ferry moored at riverbank
        (44x62cm-17x24in) bears sig.d.1653 panel

MEYER, Herbert (1882-1960) American
£1412 $2500   (25-Apr-92 YFA.M222/R) *Winter (71x97cm-28x38in) s.*

MEYER, Jeremiah (1735-1789) German
£550 $1007   (2-Jun-92 S683) *Mrs Alexander Stephenson wearing lace scarf and shawl*
        (4x?cm-2x?in) min. i.verso oval gold slide frame
£800 $1408   (9-Apr-92 S144/R) *Portrait of gentleman, wearing scarlet coat and*
        powdered wig (4x?cm-2x?in) min. gold slide frame oval

MEYER, Jeremiah (after) (1735-1789) German
£1700 $3026   (21-Jan-92 SWS1775/R) *Sarah Siddons, gloved hand raised to face*
        (9x?cm-4x?in) min. gilt frame glass verso sepia silhouette

MEYER, Johan (1885-?) Dutch
£856 $1524   (30-Oct-91 CH.AM7) Nevelige Herfstmorgen (44x84cm-17x33in) s. i.verso
        (D.FL 2800)

MEYER, Johann Jakob (1787-1858) Swiss
£22000 $40920   (17-Jun-92 S351/R) *Lac Leman with view of Vevey (41x56cm-16x22in) s. W/C*

MEYER, Johann Jakob (attrib) (1787-1858) Swiss
£4200 $7182   (18-Mar-92 S52/R) Views of Swiss landscapes and towns (6x10cm-2x4in) i.
        pen W/C htd.gum arabic nine

MEYER, Jurgen (1945-) German
£1203 $2201   (2-Jun-92 L.K809) Untitled (45x40cm-18x16in) s.i.d.1988verso (DM 3500)
£1203 $2201   (2-Jun-92 L.K808/R) Untitled (40x45cm-16x18in) s.i.d.1988verso (DM 3500)
£1890 $3459   (2-Jun-92 L.K807/R) Untitled (50x40cm-20x16in) s.i.d.1987/1988verso
        (DM 5500)

MEYER, Louis (1809-1866) Dutch
£749 $1250   (20-Aug-91 RB.HY117/R) Approaching storm (64x76cm-25x30in) s.
£2141 $3810   (30-Oct-91 CH.AM16/R) Dutch steamer off jetty in rough sea and sailors in
        rowing boats (21x32cm-8x13in) s. panel (D.FL 7000)

MEYER, M de (1911-) Belgian
£666 $1239   (16-Jun-92 GM.B567) Pique-Nique sur la plage (40x50cm-16x20in) s. board
        (B.FR 40000)

MEYER, Sal (1877-1965) Dutch
£617 $1123   (11-Dec-91 CH.AM103/R) House along canal, Brugge (27x19cm-11x7in) s.
        panel (D.FL 2000)
£926 $1685   (11-Dec-91 CH.AM86) Still life of flowers in white stoneware vase on
        table (19x14cm-7x6in) s. (D.FL 3000)
£1152 $2084   (21-May-92 SY.AM118/R) Peerdebrug te Brugge (31x23cm-12x9in) s.
        i.d.1928verso panel (D.FL 3800)
£1173 $2135   (11-Dec-91 CH.AM104) House at the edge of forest (30x44cm-12x17in) s.
        (D.FL 3800)
£1235 $2247   (11-Dec-91 CH.AM105) Houses along canal with bridge, Amsterdam
        (31x22cm-12x9in) s. (D.FL 4000)
£1543 $2809   (11-Dec-91 CH.AM102) View on Laten (60x50cm-24x20in) s. (D.FL 5000)
£2727 $4936   (21-May-92 SY.AM72/R) Dorpshoekje blaricum (32x41cm-13x16in) s. panel
        (D.FL 9000)

MEYER-AMDEN, Otto (1885-) Swiss
£2308 $4385   (25-Jun-92 GK.B491) *Grossmunster in Zurich, winter evening (16x9cm-6x4in)*
        W/C (S.FR 6000)
£8269 $15712   (25-Jun-92 GK.B490/R) *Place of pilgrimage with crucifix (31x28cm-12x11in)*
        s.d.1904 W/C (S.FR 21500)

MEYER-BASEL, Carl Theodor (1860-1932) Swiss
£474 $849   (6-May-92 GD.B853) Lake Constance landscape with fisher woman in boat (45x77cm-18x30in) s.d.1894 board (S.FR 1300)
£625 $1106   (5-Nov-91 GF.L2657/R) View of Santis and Churfirsten (45x66cm-18x26in) s.d.1904 (S.FR 1600)
£859 $1503   (27-Sep-91 GRA.B2472/R) View of Lake Constance (26x35cm-10x14in) s. panel (DM 2500)

MEYER-HELLDIEK, Gerd (1891-1987) German
£1237 $2164   (3-Apr-92 BM.B532/R) Portrait of woman before landscape (51x41cm-20x16in) mono.d.1922 (DM 3500)
£469 $830   (5-Nov-91 GF.L2233/R) Composition 61 (15x13cm-6x5in) mono.i.d.1923 indian ink W/C (S.FR 1200)
£625 $1137   (25-May-92 WK.M880/R) Composition (32x24cm-13x9in) mono.d.1923 W/C ove pencil (DM 1830)
£769 $1315   (21-Mar-92 WK.M383/R) Vases (49x39cm-19x15in) mono.d.1924 s.i.d. W/C brush htd white (DM 2200)

MEYER-WIEGAND, Rolf Dieter (1929-) German
£483 $830   (16-Oct-91 KM.K1276) Beach scene with figures (15x23cm-6x9in) s. (DM 1400)

MEYERHEIM, Friedrich Edouard (1808-1879) German
£1472 $2797   (25-Jun-92 D.V448/R) Portrait of Mendelssohn Bartholdy (30x24cm-12x9in) bears sig.i.verso board (A.S 30000)

MEYERHEIM, Friedrich Edouard (attrib) (1808-1879) German
£1045 $1902   (11-Dec-91 N.M526/R) Girl with basket and rake before ripe cornfield (19x14cm-7x6in) rem.sig. panel (DM 3000)

MEYERHEIM, Friedrich Edouard (style) (1808-1879) German
£1742 $3171   (11-Dec-91 N.M527/R) Peasant couple watching children at play (36x44cm-14x17in) mono.i. (DM 5000)

MEYERHEIM, Hermann (1840-1880) German
£3004 $5256   (3-Apr-92 BM.B682/R) View of French riverside town, possibly Strassburg (21x26cm-8x10in) s. (DM 8500)

MEYERHEIM, Hermann (attrib) (1840-1880) German
£1602 $2900   (21-May-92 S.W2920/R) Harbour near Copenhagen (69x89cm-27x35in)

MEYERHEIM, Paul Friedrich (1842-1915) German
£1517 $2609   (13-Oct-91 REM.W18) Still life of fish (61x70cm-24x28in) s. (P.Z 29000000)
£1579 $2842   (22-Nov-91 SA.A1591/R) Goats in field by the edge of the wood (25x34cm-10x13in) mono.d.1861 board (DM 4500)
£2062 $3773   (2-Jun-92 FN.S2665/R) Lions resting in cage (51x80cm-20x31in) s. (DM 6000)
£997 $1854   (20-Jun-92 BM.B866/R) View of Tarast on the street to Fettau with peasant women harvesting (27x37cm-11x15in) s.indis.d.1887 W/C gouache (DM 2900)

MEYERHEIM, Paul Wilhelm (19th C) German
£10381 $19723   (24-Jun-92 KM.K1185/R) Peasant woman with basket in landscape and children behind tree (71x67cm-28x26in) s.d.1879 (DM 30000)

MEYERHEIM, Wilhelm Alexander (1815-1882) German
£1200 $2076   (4-Oct-91 C106/R) Feeding the rabbits (68x94cm-27x37in) s.
£1850 $3293   (27-Apr-92 PHB293/R) Frozen river landscape with children and dog on sled (26x34cm-10x13in) s.d.1854
£8571 $15000   (20-Feb-92 SY.NY222/R) Hay barge (67x97cm-26x38in) s.d.1872

MEYERING, Albert (attrib) (1645-1714) Dutch
£1087 $1935   (25-Nov-91 CH.AM113/R) Classical landscape with figures resting by lake and castle beyond (16x27cm-6x11in) lead pen wash htd.white (D.FL 3500)

MEYEROWITZ, William (1889-?) American
£585 $1000   (22-Mar-92 LIT.L62) Street scene (51x61cm-20x24in) s.
£686 $1200   (19-Feb-92 D.NY59) Shady lane (41x51cm-16x20in) s.
£865 $1600   (10-Jun-92 CE.NY591/R) Cubist still life (61x51cm-24x20in) s.

MEYERS, Isidore (1836-1917) Belgian
£546 $989   (23-May-92 KV.L222) Landscape at sunset (20x37cm-8x15in) s. canvas on panel (B.FR 33000)
£1590 $2831   (30-Oct-91 CH.AM55/R) River landscape with farm along sandy road (50x68cm-20x27in) s. (D.FL 5200)

MEYLAN, Henry (1895-) Swiss
£1186 $2111   (29-Nov-91 GAB.G2809/R) Chevaux de Camargue jouant (65x90cm-26x35in) s.d.1952 panel (S.FR 3000)

MEYNART, Maurice (fl.c.1920-) Belgian?
£795 $1438   (23-May-92 KV.L223) Pond landscape (46x60cm-18x24in) s. (B.FR 48000)

EYS, Marcel (fl.1880-1901) French
.903 $1625   (19-Nov-91 RAS.K63/R) Road through sunny landscape (27x40cm-11x16in) i.d.1904 (D.KR 10000)

EZA, Guillermo (1917-) Mexican
:3889 $7000   (19-Nov-91 CH.NY94/R) Desde la sombra (100x80cm-39x31in) s.i.d.85 s.i.d.verso

EZA, William de (19th C) American
1105 $2000   (4-Dec-91 D.NY61/R) Mother and child (89x61cm-35x24in) s.d.1885 canvas on board

EZIERES, Amelie (19th C) French
:684 $1176   (10-Oct-91 D.V348/R) Portrait of bearded gentleman (8x7cm-3x3in) min.s.d.1856 oval (A.S 14000)

EZZERA, Rosa (1791-1826) Italian
:11317 $20484   (5-Dec-91 SY.MO214/R) Paysage romain (97x133cm-38x52in) s.i.d.1808 (F.FR 110000)

AHLE, Federico (1800-1868) French
.5249 $9500   (19-May-92 SY.NY77/R) Teatro Tacon (47x81cm-19x32in) canvas mounted on masonite

ALA (19th C) Italian
:2400 $4104   (18-Mar-92 S149/R) On the Blue Lagoon, Venice (62x130cm-24x51in) s.

ICH, Jerry (20th C) Australian?
:2137 $3803   (27-Apr-92 J.M345) Interior with red columns (86x183cm-34x72in) s.d.1990 (A.D 5000)

CHAELSON, Hans (1872-?) German
.941 $1712   (13-Dec-91 BM.B779/R) Still life with fruit and candlestick (43x56cm-17x22in) (DM 2700)

CHALLON (attrib) (?) ?
:843 $1500   (30-Oct-91 D.NY51) Hunter in wooded landscape (46x56cm-18x22in)

CHALOVSKI, Piotr (1801-1855) Polish
:713 $1297   (15-Dec-91 REM.W25) French soldier on horseback (25x18cm-10x7in) pen (P.Z 14000000)

CHALSEN, J L (19th C) Danish
:1443 $2568   (25-Nov-91 BU.K4/R) Frederiks Fort and Frederiksted at St. Croix (31x54cm-12x21in) s. pen W/C (D.KR 16000)

CHALSKY, Adolf C (20th C) German
:2131 $3707   (21-Sep-91 SA.A1910/R) View of Dresden with Semperoper and Landtag buildings beyond (40x58cm-16x23in) (DM 6200)

CHAU, Theobald (1676-1765) Flemish
:2134 $3713   (13-Apr-92 AT.P72/R) Scene de cabaret (25x32cm-10x13in) s. panel (F.FR 21000)
.4545 $8182   (19-Nov-91 GS.B3586/R) Figure resting on path in wooded landscape (52x73cm-20x29in) i.d.1777verso panel (S.FR 11500)
:6500 $12480   (10-Jul-92 C159/R) Town on river in winter with men conversing in foreground (23x30cm-9x12in) init. panel
:9935 $16990   (18-Mar-92 D.V113/R) Wooded river landscape with travellers resting (52x73cm-20x29in) s. (A.S 200000)
:10000 $17500   (1-Apr-92 S66/R) Vegetable market near village (67x99cm-26x39in) bears sig.
:10768 $19060   (7-Nov-91 D.V144/R) Riverside cottage with figures seated outside at the end of the day (26x37cm-10x15in) panel (A.S 220000)
:11000 $21120   (10-Jul-92 C111/R) River landscape with peasants on track beside town (34x42cm-13x17in) with sig. panel
:15322 $26813   (24-Feb-92 ARC.P7/R) Scene villageoise (17x25cm-7x10in) s. panel (F.FR 150000)
:21000 $40320   (7-Jul-92 PH6/R) Travellers on country path before village (36x50cm-14x20in) s. panel
:25000 $45500   (11-Dec-91 S92/R) Village scene with peasants going to market (35x48cm-14x19in) bears indist.sig. panel
:36000 $63000   (1-Apr-92 S43/R) River landscape with boats near village (37x62cm-15x24in) panel

CHAU, Theobald (attrib) (1676-1765) Flemish
:3779 $6500   (9-Oct-91 CH.NY174/R) Group of peasants by farmhouse with drover herding cows and pigs, village beyond (44x65cm-17x26in)

CHAU, Theobald (circle) (1676-1765) Flemish
:2200 $3850   (25-Feb-92 PH43/R) Village with merchants loading carts at ferry crossing (33x38cm-13x15in)
:3601 $6842   (26-Jun-92 AT.P68/R) Paysage fluvial anime de pecheurs (100x69cm-39x27in) (F.FR 35000)
:4651 $8000   (9-Oct-91 CH.NY151/R) Travellers on path in wooded landscape (25x36cm-10x14in) panel

MICHAU, Theobald (circle) (1676-1765) Flemish-cont.

£4800	$8544	(29-Oct-91 PH134/R) Travellers on a path in a river landscape (23x35cm-9x14in) panel
£5800	$11136	(9-Jul-92 B168/R) Wooded landscape with fruit sellers and other figures on path (31x43cm-12x17in) panel
£8000	$14560	(13-Dec-91 C120/R) Village kermesse. Waggoner in village (17x22cm-7x9in) copper two

MICHAU, Theobald (style) (1676-1765) Flemish

£850	$1530	(21-Nov-91 CSK135/R) Wooded river landscape with horseman taking directions on road (35x39cm-14x15in)
£880	$1602	(12-Dec-91 B10 f) Cattle drover and other travellers on path with village beyond (16x17cm-6x7in) panel
£1900	$3382	(29-Oct-91 PH11) River landscape with a ferry crossing to a village with a windmill (19x24cm-7x9in) panel
£2400	$4200	(3-Apr-92 C22/R) Wooded river landscape with fishermen selling catch, peasants and cattle (101x70cm-40x28in)
£2700	$5184	(10-Jul-92 C113) Village on river with travellers in foreground (19x24cm-7x9in) panel
£2800	$5040	(22-Nov-91 SWS77/R) River landscape with figures by a village (55x109cm-22x43in)
£3100	$5580	(22-Nov-91 SWS118) River landscapes (17x14cm-7x6in) copper oval pair

MICHAUX, Henri (1899-) Belgian

£2224	$4026	(3-Dec-91 C.A518) Composition (55x75cm-22x30in) mono. acrylic (B.FR 130000)
£2764	$4919	(30-Nov-91 FB.P7/R) Sans titre (24x19cm-9x7in) mono. board (F.FR 27000)
£2884	$4931	(19-Mar-92 CSC.P32/R) Sans titre (44x53cm-17x21in) mono. acrylic paper laid down on canvas (F.FR 28000)
£5081	$8841	(16-Apr-92 FB.P171/R) Sans titre (55x75cm-22x30in) mono. acrylic (F.FR 50000)
£6179	$10566	(17-Mar-92 FB.P54/R) Sans titre (55x74cm-22x29in) mono. acrylic paper (F.FR 60000)
£698	$1200	(12-Oct-91 SY.NY170/R) Femme avec colombe (107x75cm-42x30in) s. init.num.13 verso chl
£864	$1503	(16-Apr-92 FB.P152/R) Sans titre (25x16cm-10x6in) mono. Indian ink (F.FR 8500)
£1842	$3279	(30-Nov-91 FB.P6/R) Visage (42x32cm-17x13in) mono. col.oil crayons (F.FR 18000)
£2060	$3522	(19-Mar-92 CSC.P33) Sans titre (19x28cm-7x11in) gouache (F.FR 20000)
£2149	$3826	(30-Nov-91 FB.P4/R) Sans titre (38x57cm-15x22in) mono. W/C (F.FR 21000)
£2337	$4067	(16-Apr-92 FB.P194/R) Sans titre (25x34cm-10x13in) mono. gouache (F.FR 23000)
£2500	$4300	(12-Oct-91 KV.L214/R) Composition (49x59cm-19x23in) mono. brush chk. (B.FR 150000)
£2648	$4898	(13-Jun-92 AT.P34) Portrait (32x24cm-13x9in) mono. ink wash (F.FR 26000)
£2661	$4737	(30-Nov-91 FB.P1/R) Mouvements (32x24cm-13x9in) mono. Indian ink (F.FR 26000)
£3000	$5160	(17-Oct-91 S6/R) Aqua masques chinois marrons (49x64cm-19x25in) init. W/C pastel
£3422	$6193	(7-Dec-91 KV.L500/R) Composition (75x108cm-30x43in) mono. brush ink (B.FR 200000)
£3862	$6720	(13-Apr-92 GL.P94/R) Sans titre (48x62cm-19x24in) mono. W/C gouache (F.FR 38000)
£4000	$6920	(26-Mar-92 C55/R) Untitled (75x108cm-30x43in) init. ink
£4077	$7584	(15-Jun-92 GL.P77/R) Composition (33x41cm-13x16in) init. acrylic ink canvas laid down on board (F.FR 40000)
£4374	$8005	(14-May-92 BG.P75/R) Composition bleue (56x75cm-22x30in) mono. W/C (F.FR 43000)
£5015	$8927	(30-Nov-91 FB.P2/R) Sans titre (38x57cm-15x22in) mono. W/C (F.FR 49000)
£5498	$10062	(2-Jun-92 L.K811/R) Untitled (74x105cm-29x41in) mono indian ink brush (DM 16000)
£5500	$9515	(26-Mar-92 S9/R) Untitled (70x100cm-28x39in) init. ink
£6606	$11494	(16-Apr-92 FB.P140/R) Sans titre (21x28cm-8x11in) mono. W/C (F.FR 65000)
£7077	$12668	(19-Jan-92 CC.P46/R) Foule (69x98cm-27x39in) mono. Indian ink (F.FR 69000)
£7136	$13272	(15-Jun-92 GL.P8/R) Untitled (74x106cm-29x42in) init. Indian ink (F.FR 70000)
£7332	$13564	(13-Jun-92 AT.P34 b/R) Graphisme (73x100cm-29x39in) inits. Indian ink (F.FR 72000)
£8763	$15160	(23-Mar-92 CC.P32/R) Sans titre (74x107cm-29x42in) mono. indian ink (F.FR 85000)
£9500	$16435	(26-Mar-92 C17/R) Untitled (56x75cm-22x30in) init. ink pastel chl.
£10194	$18960	(15-Jun-92 GL.P6/R) Formes jaunes (48x63cm-19x25in) init. gouache (F.FR 100000)

MICHAUX, John (19/20th C) Belgian

| £1083 | $1885 | (14-Apr-92 GM.B485/R) Mer du Nord (55x74cm-22x29in) s. board (B.FR 65000) |

MICHEL, A (?) ?

| £822 | $1570 | (1-Jul-92 FB.P180 a) Vue de Paris (38x55cm-15x22in) s. (F.FR 8000) |

MICHEL, Georges (1763-1843) French

| £829 | $1500 | (22-May-92 S.BM101/R) Trees (46x56cm-18x22in) board |
| £3709 | $6750 | (27-May-92 CH.NY148/R) Village with stormy skies (61x77cm-24x30in) |

◀CHEL, Georges (1763-1843) French-cont.
`407 $700 (13-Oct-91 H.C30/R) Moulin a Vent (43x51cm-17x20in) chl htd white

◀CHEL, Georges (attrib) (1763-1843) French
`3426 $6065 (7-Nov-91 D.V377/R) Hilly landscape with windmill (46x61cm-18x24in)
(A.S 70000)

◀CHEL, Georges (circle) (1763-1843) French
`800 $1488 (16-Jun-92 PH119) Figures in landscape (33x67cm-13x26in)

CHEL, Jacob (18th C) German
`1590 $2718 (18-Mar-92 D.V307/R) Portrait of Kaiser Karl VII (89x70cm-35x28in)
s.i.d.1715verso (A.S 32000)

◀CHEL, Pierre (1924-) Swiss
`784 $1404 (15-Nov-91 ZOF.Z1805) St Ursanne, le pont (102x70cm-40x28in) s.
i.d.1972verso mixed media panel (S.FR 2000)

◀CHEL, Reinhard (20th C) German?
`524 $907 (25-Mar-92 KM.K1312) Still life of roses, irises and tulips in glass vase
(50x40cm-20x16in) s. panel (DM 1500)

◀CHEL, Robert (1897-1983) German
`1203 $2225 (12-Jun-92 HN.H590/R) Schuhhaus am Joseph (33x32cm-13x13in) st.sig. W/C
indian ink brush htd.white (DM 3500)
`2062 $3814 (12-Jun-92 HN.H593/R) Entwurf fur Reklame-Vorbau im 1. Stock und
Schaufenster-Umbau (22x14cm-9x6in) mono.i.d.1926 collage indian ink
htd.white (DM 6000)
`4895 $8713 (26-Nov-91 KF.M872/R) From X to Y (22x31cm-9x12in) s.i.d.1937 mixed media
board (DM 14000)
`6780 $12000 (7-Nov-91 SY.NY160/R) Hebel (29x23cm-11x9in) s.i.d.1921 col.ink collage
`12969 $23604 (26-May-92 KF.M1076/R) Fishes (59x68cm-23x27in) s.i. mixed media
(DM 38000)
`14685 $26140 (26-Nov-91 KF.M871/R) Stud. macanique II (34x57cm-13x22in)
mono.i.d.1923-24 mixed media collage board panel (DM 42000)
`17747 $32300 (26-May-92 KF.M1077/R) Schloss und Zangenfunktionen (33x39cm-13x15in)
mono.d.1922/23 mixed media (DM 52000)

◀CHEL, S (20th C) Swiss
`588 $1000 (23-Oct-91 GD.B510) Genfersee landscape with village and vineyards
(46x61cm-18x24in) s. (S.FR 1500)

◀CHELANGELO (circle) (1475-1564) Italian
`7000 $12180 (14-Apr-92 C83/R) Two nudes after the central section of the Battle of
Cascina (30x20cm-12x8in) pen vellum
`35000 $60900 (14-Apr-92 C82/R) Studies of arms (20x27cm-8x11in) i. chk

◀CHELET, G (19/20th C) ?
`8721 $15000 (16-Oct-91 CH.NY23/R) Fiesta al Koran (130x197cm-51x78in) s.d.1902 three
panels

◀CHELI, Guglielmo (1866-1926) Italian
`3486 $6310 (3-Dec-91 SY.MI63/R) Soldati in marcia verso la citta (21x33cm-8x13in) s.
panel (I.L 7500000)

◀CHELIN, Jean (1623-1696) French
`7716 $13966 (7-Dec-91 CH.MO53/R) Un repas familial (87x116cm-34x46in) s.d.61
(F.FR 75000)
`12768 $22344 (24-Feb-92 CSC.P25/R) Le couronnement de la rosiere (81x117cm-32x46in) s.
(F.FR 125000)

◀CHETTI, Francesco Paolo (1851-1929) Italian
`837 $1514 (3-Dec-91 SY.MI22) Studio di figura (10x6cm-4x2in) s. panel (I.L 1800000)
`2759 $4939 (14-Nov-91 CH.R49/R) Il bagno (30x46cm-12x18in) s.d.92 canvas on board
(I.L 6000000)
`4767 $8200 (9-Oct-91 RO.BA4/R) L'artista e la sua famiglia (34x16cm-13x6in) s.
`6328 $11454 (18-May-92 SY.MI123/R) Pastorella con gregge (30x45cm-12x18in) s. canvas
on panel (I.L 14000000)
`20349 $35000 (17-Oct-91 SY.NY64/R) Nella Gioia del Sole (91x65cm-36x26in) s.d.1876
`634 $1173 (8-Jun-92 CH.R644) Mareggiata (32x23cm-13x9in) s. pastel (I.L 1400000)
`782 $1399 (14-Nov-91 CH.R31) Paesaggio (28x36cm-11x14in) s.d.1886 pastel
(I.L 1700000)
`782 $1399 (14-Nov-91 CH.R40) Paesaggio (23x32cm-9x13in) s.st.sig. pastel
(I.L 1700000)
`834 $1442 (24-Mar-92 CH.R99) Studio di paesaggio (27x37cm-11x15in) s. pastel
(I.L 1800000)
`1380 $2470 (14-Nov-91 CH.R41) Pastorella con pecore nel paesaggio (20x28cm-8x11in)
s. mixed media (I.L 3000000)
`1500 $2790 (16-Jun-92 PH91/R) Almond blossom (72x54cm-28x21in) s.indis.i.d.84 W/C
bodycol
`1658 $3018 (12-Dec-91 F.M52/R) Testa di contadino abruzzese (51x37cm-20x15in) s. chl
htd.white (I.L 3600000)
`6857 $12000 (20-Feb-92 SY.NY302/R) Portrait of bearded man in straw hat
(53x38cm-21x15in) s. pastel

MICHEUX, Michel-Nicolas (attrib) (1688-1733) French
£5658 $10751 (26-Jun-92 AT.P89/R) Bouquet de fleurs (67x53cm-26x21in) (F.FR 55000)

MICHIE, J (19/20th C) British?
£650 $1131 (12-Sep-91 CSK249/R) Rustic beauty (38x33cm-15x13in) s.d.1858

MICHIE, James Coutts (1861-1919) British
£2600 $4680 (19-Nov-91 PH103/R) St Valentines Day (61x95cm-24x37in) s. s.i.verso

MICHIELI, Andrea dei (c.1539-c.1614) Italian
£750 $1365 (10-Dec-91 C129/R) The Crucifixion. A battle scene with cavalry
(29x20cm-11x8in) red chk. double-sided

MICHIELI, Andrea dei (attrib) (c.1539-c.1614) Italian
£1029 $1862 (5-Dec-91 SY.MO25/R) Homme et deux enfants (18x13cm-7x5in) pen
(F.FR 10000)

MICHIELI, Andrea dei (circle) (c.1539-c.1614) Italian
£7000 $12250 (31-Mar-92 PH83/R) Visit of King Totila to St. Benedict at Monte Casino
(151x293cm-59x115in)

MICHIELI, Andrea dei (style) (c.1539-c.1614) Italian
£4500 $8010 (1-Nov-91 C29/R) Feeding of Five Thousand (68x88cm-27x35in)

MICHONZE, Gregoire (1902-1982) French
£703 $1300 (9-Jun-92 GG.TA397/R) Figures in field (14x29cm-6x11in) s.d.68 board
£712 $1303 (17-May-92 GL.P79) Paysage surrealiste (49x71cm-19x28in) s. canvas on
isorel (F.FR 7000)
£1322 $2420 (17-May-92 GL.P210/R) Les villageoises (20x20cm-8x8in) s.d.1951 panel
(F.FR 13000)
£1714 $3000 (26-Sep-91 SY.I52/R) Lady with green flag (55x33cm-22x13in) s.d.58 board
£2222 $4000 (6-Jan-92 GG.TA425/R) Nudes in countryside (40x60cm-16x24in) s.d.1951
paper on board
£2595 $4800 (9-Jun-92 GG.TA284/R) Rural landscape and figures (61x38cm-24x15in)
s.d.63 paper on canvas
£372 $700 (5-Jan-92 GG.TA75/R) Landscape (21x26cm-8x10in) s.d.1969 pastel W/C
£396 $745 (5-Jan-92 GG.TA74/R) Figures in village (20x25cm-8x10in) s.d.1969 gouache
£532 $1000 (5-Jan-92 GG.TA279/R) Figures (33x50cm-13x20in) s. gouache
£865 $1600 (9-Jun-92 GG.TA396/R) Figures in room (26x21cm-10x8in) s.d.64 gouache

MICKELE, Isaac van (fl.1660-1703) Dutch
£1890 $3289 (18-Sep-91 N.M426/R) Church interior with figures (126x93cm-50x37in) s.
(DM 5500)

MIDDELBOE, Bernhard (19th C) Danish
£3000 $5100 (23-Oct-91 S296/R) Shipping in Table Bay (39x54cm-15x21in) s.i.d.1825 pen
ink W/C htd.bodycol over pencil

MIDDENDORF, Helmut (1953-) German
£1546 $2830 (2-Jun-92 L.K813) Melancholia (100x70cm-39x28in) s.i. acrylic board
(DM 4500)
£3158 $5684 (19-Nov-91 L.K955/R) Male figure before burning town (98x98cm-39x39in)
s.d.86 paper on canvas (DM 9000)
£3911 $7000 (5-May-92 CH.NY156/R) Grosstadt Eingeborene (180x221cm-71x87in)
s.i.d.1982verso linen
£4983 $9119 (2-Jun-92 L.K812/R) German double Hamlet (91x120cm-36x47in) s.i.d.1985
acrylic (DM 14500)
£5587 $10000 (5-May-92 CH.NY129/R) City of the red nights II (253x354cm-100x139in)
s.i.d.1982verso linen diptych
£5587 $10000 (13-Nov-91 CH.NY339/R) Figure with fire (184x257cm-72x101in)
s.i.d.1985verso acrylic
£7429 $13000 (25-Feb-92 SY.NY241/R) Die Strasse I (218x163cm-86x64in) s.i.d.1982verso
acrylic linen
£9123 $16421 (19-Nov-91 L.K953/R) Beneath the umbrella (170x210cm-67x83in) s.i.d.1985
acrylic (DM 26000)
£9825 $17684 (19-Nov-91 L.K952/R) Blue dance (190x230cm-75x91in) s.i.d.1983 tempera
oil (DM 28000)
£762 $1326 (16-Apr-92 FB.P212/R) Grosser traum (29x41cm-11x16in) s.i.d.79 gouache
W/C chk. (F.FR 7500)
£1200 $2064 (17-Oct-91 C102/R) Untitled (59x85cm-23x33in) s.d.80 pastel gouache chl
W/C
£1469 $2614 (26-Nov-91 KF.M878/R) Day and night, head - brush - stars
(62x88cm-24x35in) s.i.d.1980 mixed media (DM 4200)
£1613 $2952 (13-May-92 BU.S124/R) Rumor (47x35cm-19x14in) s.d.1988 W/C (S.KR 17000)
£2303 $4169 (3-Dec-91 AB.S5108/R) 'Im Kopf' (138x110cm-54x43in) s.d.1988 gouache
(S.KR 24000)
£2389 $4348 (30-May-92 VG.B417/R) Studio (99x70cm-39x28in) s.i.d.1983 W/C over pencil
board (DM 7000)

MIDDLE EASTERN SCHOOL, 19th C
£2800 $4760 (23-Oct-91 S39/R) The Mosque at Karbala, Iraq (174x117cm-69x46in)

MIDDLE RHINE SCHOOL, 16th C German
£18000 $34560 (8-Jul-92 S312/R) St Wendelin (64x77cm-25x30in) panel

MIDDLETON, Colin (1910-1983) British

£606	$1126	(15-Jun-92 AD.D44) The Bridge at Rostrevor (30x38cm-12x15in) s.d.1934 (E.P 660)
£1200	$2088	(18-Sep-91 CG160) Untitled composition. Study of hooded girl (76x102cm-30x40in) mono. double-sided
£1200	$2088	(18-Sep-91 CG100) Nude in black stockings (27x36cm-11x14in) s.d.1941
£1400	$2436	(18-Sep-91 CG162) Bogland I. Bogland II (32x32cm-13x13in) s. acrylic board pair
£1600	$2928	(14-May-92 C29/R) Old rigs (35x53cm-14x21in) s. s.i.d.1952 verso
£1800	$3132	(18-Sep-91 CG158) Yellow figure (91x76cm-36x30in) mono. s.i.d.verso board
£2200	$3828	(18-Sep-91 CG101) Innocence (51x51cm-20x20in)
£2243	$3880	(25-Mar-92 A.D176) Hill farm - view of Dicks Farm Carnalridge (51x76cm-20x30in) mono. (E.P 2400)
£2600	$4758	(14-May-92 C149/R) Enigma (51x76cm-20x30in) s.
£3049	$5518	(3-Dec-91 R.T148/R) Bangor, Harbour in Co.Down, Northern Ireland (50x61cm-20x24in) s.i.d.1955verso (C.D 6250)
£4200	$7308	(18-Sep-91 CG159/R) Sunday (90x91cm-35x36in) s.d.72 i.verso collage oil board

MIDDLETON, John (1828-1856) British

£2090	$3992	(16-Jul-92 S151/R) Leith Hill, Surrey (32x50cm-13x20in) d.55 W/C over pencil
£7000	$13370	(14-Jul-92 C27/R) Farm buildings, Tonbridge Wells (33x49cm-13x19in) init.i.d.1847 pencil W/C
£7200	$12672	(9-Apr-92 S79/R) Orchard with farm buildings beyond (33x43cm-13x17in) W/C over pencil

MIDDLETON, Max (1922-) Australian

£1389	$2472	(27-Apr-92 J.M136/R) In the shallows (36x50cm-14x20in) s. canvasboard (A.D 3250)
£2244	$3994	(27-Apr-92 J.M178/R) Harvesting (35x50cm-14x20in) s. canvas on board (A.D 5250)
£2564	$4564	(27-Apr-92 J.M106/R) Ploughing (50x76cm-20x30in) s. (A.D 6000)
£3524	$6273	(26-Nov-91 J.M223/R) Cattle from high country (66x101cm-26x40in) s. (A.D 8000)

MIDDLETON, Sam (1927-) American

£606	$1097	(19-May-92 CH.AM406) Composition (52x77cm-20x30in) s.d.1987 collage mixed media (D.FL 2000)
£909	$1645	(19-May-92 CH.AM412) Composition (52x56cm-20x22in) s.d.1988 collage mixed media (D.FL 3000)
£926	$1685	(11-Dec-91 CH.AM177) Concerto (52x77cm-20x30in) s.d.85 collage mixed media (D.FL 3000)
£3395	$6179	(12-Dec-91 SY.AM234/R) Worry later (91x122cm-36x48in) s.d.62 d.verso gouache paper collage board (D.FL 11000)

MIDELFART, Willi (1904-1975) Norwegian

£487	$887	(9-Dec-91 B.O84/R) Mountain landscape (38x46cm-15x18in) s.d.53 panel (N.KR 5500)
£1935	$3405	(8-Apr-92 GWP.O49/R) Southern landscape with trees and field (80x100cm-31x39in) (N.KR 22000)

MIDWOOD (19th C) British

£1064	$1916	(23-Nov-91 SO.S456/R) Cottage interior with family (70x90cm-28x35in) s. (S.KR 11100)

MIDWOOD, William Henry (19th C) British

£1500	$2580	(4-Mar-92 S112/R) Sailor's farewell (45x37cm-18x15in) arched top
£2460	$4452	(19-May-92 AB.S4354/R) Evening prayer - interior with family (71x91cm-28x36in) s. (S.KR 26000)
£2800	$4788	(19-Mar-92 B40/R) Showing the wedding ring (91x71cm-36x28in) s.i.verso
£3000	$5400	(19-Nov-91 PH101/R) Card Castles (35x45cm-14x18in) s.d.1871 panel
£3400	$5780	(22-Oct-91 RG2443/R) Cottage interior with a young woman in conversation with a sailor (91x69cm-36x27in) s.d.1865
£6000	$10680	(28-Apr-92 PH46/R) Musician (71x91cm-28x36in) s.d.1872
£7000	$12040	(11-Oct-91 C120/R) The centre of attention (70x91cm-28x36in) s.d.1876

MIDY, Charles (19th C) French

£572	$1002	(3-Apr-92 AGS.P171) Le retour de la chasse, scene du Moyen-Age (38x30cm-15x12in) W/C (F.FR 5500)

MIDY, Theophile Adolphe (1821-?) French

£733	$1260	(10-Oct-91 D.V90/R) Portrait of girl in profile (31x24cm-12x9in) mono.i. W/C over pencil oval (A.S 15000)

MIEDUCH, Dan (1947-) American

£1500	$2700	(10-Jan-92 DM.D2001/R) He'd sooner wiat til spring (61x91cm-24x36in) s.d.1979

MIEGHEM, Eugene van (1875-1930) Belgian

£995	$1821	(12-May-92 C.A427) Mother and child (50x35cm-20x14in) s. board (B.FR 60000)
£2446	$4257	(14-Apr-92 SY.AM242) Bateliers (70x106cm-28x42in) s. (D.FL 8000)
£10842	$19083	(7-Apr-92 C.A255/R) Women in a harbour (55x70cm-22x28in) s. (B.FR 650000)
£398	$728	(12-May-92 C.A428) In the church (30x40cm-12x16in) s. dr. (B.FR 24000)

MIEGHEM, Eugene van (1875-1930) Belgian-cont.

£400	$705	(7-Apr-92 C.A256) *Soldiers in the night (29x46cm-11x18in) mono. sanguine* (B.FR 24000)
£400	$705	(7-Apr-92 C.A262) *Young model (29x21cm-11x8in) studio st. sanguine* (B.FR 24000)
£401	$682	(22-Oct-91 C.A1021) *Sewing sacks (18x24cm-7x9in) mono. ink dr.* (B.FR 24000)
£751	$1321	(7-Apr-92 C.A258) *La toilette (35x24cm-14x9in) s. dr. (B.FR 45000)*

MIEL, Jan (1599-1663) Flemish

| £16279 | $28000 | (9-Oct-91 CH.NY164/R) Carnival with figures dancing and playing instruments in piazza (60x77cm-24x30in) |

MIEL, Jan (attrib) (1599-1663) Flemish

| £1220 | $2268 | (16-Jun-92 VN.R166) Allegoric scene with shepherd talking to satyrs in landscape (54x45cm-21x18in) (D.FL 4000) |

MIEL, Jan (circle) (1599-1663) Flemish

£1216	$2225	(12-May-92 SY.AM41/R) Hunter resting after chase with horse and hound (27cm-11ins circular) (D.FL 4000)
£1700	$3043	(13-Nov-91 CG572/R) A goatherd playing pipes with goats and his dog. Picking fleas (20x41cm-8x16in) panel pair
£2039	$3792	(18-Jun-92 SY.MO137/R) La halte des cavaliers (61x77cm-24x30in) (F.FR 20000)
£6173	$11173	(5-Dec-91 SY.MO374/R) Soldats chez l'armurier (44x56cm-17x22in) (F.FR 60000)

MIELDS, Rune (1935-) German

| £1228 | $2211 | (19-Nov-91 L.K956/R) Composition B 29 (90x50cm-35x20in) s.i.d.1970verso (DM 3500) |

MIELICH, Alfons Leopold (1863-1929) Austrian

| £3636 | $6218 | (12-Mar-92 SY.J349/R) Camp at Oasis (45x60cm-18x24in) s. panel (SA.R 18000) |
| £7068 | $13500 | (16-Jul-92 SY.NY436/R) Market scene (134x193cm-53x76in) s. |

MIEREVELT, Michiel Jans van (1567-1641) Dutch

| £1600 | $2800 | (3-Apr-92 C49/R) Portrait of Johan van Oldenbarneveldt, wearing ruff (62x50cm-24x20in) with i. panel |

MIEREVELT, Michiel Jans van (circle) (1567-1641) Dutch

| £950 | $1824 | (9-Jul-92 CSK136/R) Portrait of lady in black dress and ruff (65x55cm-26x22in) i.d.1631 panel |
| £3000 | $5250 | (28-Feb-92 C142) Portrait of woman aged 20, wearing black embroidered dress (75x60cm-30x24in) i.d.1634 panel |

MIEREVELT, Michiel Jans van (studio) (1567-1641) Dutch

| £1300 | $2496 | (10-Jul-92 PH57/R) Portrait of Prince Maurice of Nassau, wearing suit of armour (54x43cm-21x17in) panel |

MIEREVELT, Michiel Jans van (style) (1567-1641) Dutch

£915	$1591	(13-Apr-92 AT.P67) Portrait de gentilhomme (28x23cm-11x9in) panel (F.FR 9000)
£1326	$2400	(19-May-92 CE.NY290/R) Portrait of lady, holding handkerchief and fan (99x71cm-39x28in)
£2600	$4992	(8-Jul-92 S165/R) Portrait of gentleman (61x47cm-24x19in) panel
£3200	$5600	(1-Apr-92 S136/R) Portrait of gentleman (106x74cm-42x29in) i.

MIERIS, Frans van (elder) (1635-1681) Dutch

| £39106 | $70000 | (16-Jan-92 CH.NY77/R) Old woman singing (17x13cm-7x5in) s.d.1677 panel |

MIERIS, Frans van (elder-attrib) (1635-1681) Dutch

| £2000 | $3560 | (30-Oct-91 S36/R) Portrait of lady in white bonnet (15x13cm-6x5in) panel |

MIERIS, Frans van (style) (17/18th C) Dutch

£970	$1727	(28-Apr-92 RAS.K527) Portrait of a man wearing armour (21x15cm-8x6in) (D.KR 11000)
£1300	$2379	(12-May-92 SWS730/R) Duet (24x19cm-9x7in) panel
£1715	$3087	(19-Nov-91 RAS.K434/R) Young girl with grapes and other fruit on balcony (31x25cm-12x10in) panel (D.KR 19000)

MIERIS, Frans van (younger) (1689-1763) Dutch

| £2746 | $4971 | (3-Dec-91 FN.S2332/R) Interior with elegant woman seated at table treated by quack (36x31cm-14x12in) panel (DM 7800) |

MIERIS, Willem van (1662-1747) Dutch

£7407	$13407	(5-Dec-91 SY.MO132/R) Portrait presume du Duc d'Ormond en armure (12x10cm-5x4in) s.d.1705 silver oval (F.FR 72000)
£13260	$24000	(21-May-92 CH.NY4/R) Portrait of gentleman, wearing satin tunic, lace cravat and cloak (14x10cm-6x4in) s.d.1688 panel oval
£45872	$85321	(18-Jun-92 SY.MO42/R) La marchande de volailles et la grappe de raisin (28x24cm-11x9in) one s.d.indist. one s.d.1707 panel pair (F.FR 450000)
£125000	$227500	(13-Dec-91 C36/R) Grocer's shop with woman weighing dried fruit and boy with tin of sweetmeats (39x32cm-15x13in) s.d.1732 panel

MIERIS, Willem van (1662-1747) Dutch-cont.
£2600 $4992   (7-Jul-92 C263/R) Susannah and the Elders. Study of tree and two figures (31x25cm-12x10in) s. chk vellum pair
£4485 $8343   (20-Jun-92 CH.MO202/R) Diane au bain. L'Hiver chassant l'Automne (31x53cm-12x21in) s. chk pair (F.FR 44000)

MIERIS, Willem van (attrib) (1662-1747) Dutch
£1990 $3542   (25-Nov-92 W.T1962) Portrait of gentleman (14x10cm-6x4in) s.d.1688 panel oval (C.D 4000)
£2006 $3591   (14-Nov-91 CH.AM26) Man seted on draped balcony by barrel holding giant roemer (26x22cm-10x9in) s.d.1709 panel after Frans van Mieris I (D.FL 6500)

MIERIS, Willem van (school) (1662-1747) Dutch
£2616 $4500   (9-Oct-91 CH.NY47/R) Elegant figures making music in interior (46x36cm-18x14in) panel

MIERIS, Willem van (style) (1662-1747) Dutch
£900 $1728   (9-Jul-92 CSK182) The young musician (26x22cm-10x9in) panel
£1100 $1958   (31-Oct-91 B66/R) Young lady at window being serenaded by lover (47x37cm-19x15in)
£1400 $2450   (3-Apr-92 C76) Mercenary Love (48x38cm-19x15in) with sig.

MIERIS, van (after) (17/18th C) Dutch
£1717 $3039   (24-Apr-92 CD.P90) Jeune femme se faisant coiffer (40x33cm-16x13in) metal (F.FR 17000)

MIERIS, van (style) (17/18th C) Dutch
£1114 $2017   (20-May-92 CSC.P2) La volaillere a sa fenetre (37x29cm-15x11in) panel (F.FR 11000)

MIESS, Friedrich (1854-?) German
£12000 $21360   (27-Nov-91 S150/R) Children in forest (70x100cm-28x39in) s.

MIGLIARA, Giovanni (1785-1837) Italian
£2081 $3767   (19-May-92 AB.S4355/R) Monastery cellar with monks (38x28cm-15x11in) s. panel (S.KR 22000)

MIGLIARINI, Michele Arcangelo (1785-?) Italian
£3427 $6099   (25-Nov-91 BU.K73/R) Portrait of Augusta Rennenkampff (65x56cm-26x22in) s.d.1809 (D.KR 38000)

MIGLIARO, Vincenzo (1858-1938) Italian
£1143 $2000   (18-Feb-92 CE.NY250/R) Fishing village (23x19cm-9x7in) s. tempera board
£2157 $3667   (23-Oct-91 GD.B1178/R) Market scene with woman selling flowers (18x17cm-7x7in) s. panel (S.FR 5500)
£3171 $5866   (9-Jun-92 F.R174/R) Mascherata (22x17cm-9x7in) s. W/C tempera (I.L 7000000)
£3705 $6410   (24-Mar-92 CH.R138/R) Fantasia araba (19x27cm-7x11in) s.d.1877 W/C tempera (I.L 8000000)

MIGNARD (school) (17/18th C) French
£1646 $3128   (22-Jun-92 PIC.P15) Portrait de jeune enfant en toge rouge (45x38cm-18x15in) (F.FR 16000)

MIGNARD (style) (17/18th C) French
£1200 $2304   (9-Jul-92 B99 p) Portrait of Marie-Catherine de Cuignieres (72x60cm-28x24in) i. oval

MIGNARD, Nicolas (circle) (1606-1668) French
£8000 $15360   (7-Jul-92 PH159/R) Portrait of King Louis XIV of France, in armour. Portrait of Marie Theresa (68x57cm-27x22in) oval pair

MIGNARD, Pierre (17/18th C) French
£5411 $9469   (30-Mar-92 ZZ.F54/R) Saint Francois d'assise (42x34cm-17x13in) painted oval (F.FR 52000)
£1955 $3500   (15-Jan-92 CH.NY67/R) Presumed portrait of artist's daughter, later Comtesse de Feuquiere (12x13cm-5x5in) with i. red white chk

MIGNARD, Pierre (attrib) (17/18th C) French
£4234 $7494   (6-Nov-91 LT.P7272/R) Portrait de la Duchesse de Guise, fille de Gaston d'Orleans (116x89cm-46x35in) (F.FR 42000)
£7000 $13440   (8-Jul-92 S120/R) Godefroy tended by angel (98x130cm-39x51in)

MIGNARD, Pierre (circle) (17/18th C) French
£1461 $2600   (22-Jan-92 SY.NY139/R) Christ Child as Divine sovereign (82x65cm-32x26in)
£1644 $3141   (1-Jul-92 CD.P17) Portrait de jeune femme en robe brune et or et toque rouge oval (F.FR 16000)
£2000 $3840   (10-Jul-92 PH41/R) Portrait of lady, in Italianate landscape (35x27cm-14x11in) panel

MIGNARD, Pierre (school) (17/18th C) French
£1163 $2000   (9-Oct-91 CH.NY93/R) Portrait of Marie-Therese of France, in dress and ermine-lined cloak (72x60cm-28x24in)

MIGNARD, Pierre (studio) (17/18th C) French
£13374 $25412   (22-Jun-92 PIC.P19/R) Portrait en pied de Philippe de Bourbon et
       d'Henriette Anne d'Angleterre (185x130cm-73x51in) (F.FR 130000)

MIGNARD, Pierre (style) (17/18th C) French
£883 $1678   (23-Jun-92 D.V223) Portrait of lady as Caritas (35x30cm-14x12in)
       (A.S 18000)
£1055 $1815   (7-Oct-91 CH.E229/R) Saint Elizabeth with Saint John the Baptist
       (71x57cm-28x22in) (E.P 1150)
£1100 $1958   (31-Oct-91 B131) Portrait of military commander, wearing armour
       (95x84cm-37x33in)
£1200 $2160   (21-Nov-91 C104/R) Madonna and Child (86x71cm-34x28in) panel arched top
£1300 $2340   (21-Nov-91 CSK226) Portrait of child seated blowing bubbles in landscape
       (76x63cm-30x25in) painted oval
£1400 $2450   (28-Feb-92 C16/R) Portrait of a lady, half length, as Minerva
       (81x66cm-32x26in) painted oval
£1468 $2599   (7-Nov-91 D.V365/R) Portrait of lady holding open book (64x44cm-25x17in)
       (A.S 30000)
£2800 $4900   (3-Apr-92 C44/R) Portrait of lady, seated wearing chemise and embroidered
       wrap (90x73cm-35x29in) oval
£2825 $4860   (16-Oct-91 AT.P109/R) Portrait de Louis XIV en marechal de France
       (131x97cm-52x38in) (F.FR 28000)
£3200 $6144   (8-Jul-92 S194/R) Portrait of Mademoiselle Bouthillier seated with
       italianate villa beyond (43x53cm-17x21in) bears i.verso panel oval
£4200 $7476   (30-Oct-91 S157/R) Portrait of lady holding garland of flowers
       (74x59cm-29x23in) oval

MIGNECO, Giuseppe (1908-) Italian
£8222 $14306   (14-Apr-92 F.M176/R) Donna col ventaglio (45x34cm-18x13in) s.d.1962
       s.i.verso (I.L 18000000)
£9526 $17433   (12-May-92 F.R191/R) Spannocchiatrice (42x35cm-17x14in) s.d.1957
       (I.L 21000000)
£16455 $31265   (23-Jun-92 F.M141/R) Pescatore (60x50cm-24x20in) s. (I.L 36000000)
£1116 $2019   (3-Dec-91 F.R126) Mietitrice (29x21cm-11x8in) s.d.1972 W/C paper on
*   canvas (I.L 2400000)*
£1483 $2639   (27-Nov-91 F.M151/R) Maternita (41x34cm-16x13in) s.d.1951 W/C
*   (I.L 3200000)*
£3707 $6599   (26-Nov-91 SY.MI142/R) Personaggio seduto (73x50cm-29x20in) s. gouache
*   paper on canvas (I.L 8000000)*

MIGNON, Abraham (1640-1679) German
£4247 $7263   (12-Mar-92 GK.Z49/R) Still life of fruit, roemer, bread and pipe on table
       (37x48cm-15x19in) panel (S.FR 11000)

MIGNON, Abraham (after) (1640-1679) German
£2879 $4980   (7-Sep-91 CH.AM186/R) Still life with beaker on a claw, fruit, knife a
       tall glass and a giantroemer on a draped ledge (100x75cm-39x30in) s.
       (D.FL 9500)

MIGNON, Abraham (circle) (1640-1679) German
£9784 $18393   (16-Dec-91 AGS.P59/R) Fleurs dans un vase de verre pose sur un
       entablement a godrons (93x74cm-37x29in) (F.FR 95000)

MIGNON, Abraham (style) (1640-1679) German
£1800 $3456   (9-Jul-92 CSK302) Mixed flowers in basket on ledge (74x91cm-29x36in)
£7407 $13259   (14-Nov-91 CH.AM166/R) Giant roemer, fruit, flowers and knife on draped
       ledge in stone niche (52x46cm-20x18in) bears sig. panel (D.FL 24000)
£8500 $14875   (3-Apr-92 C28/R) Mixed flowers in glass vase with snail on stone plinth
       (126x76cm-50x30in) canvas on board

MIGNONI, Fernando (1929-) ?
£829 $1559   (18-Dec-91 DUR.M590/R) Figura (80x105cm-31x41in) s.d.60 (S.P 150000)
£875 $1487   (24-Oct-91 DUR.M1026/R) Torero (80x60cm-31x24in) s.d.59 (S.P 160000)

MIHALOVITS, Miklos (1888-1960) Hungarian
£650 $1151   (13-Feb-92 CSK140/R) The artist's model (70x51cm-28x20in) s.

MIJARES, Jose M (1921-) Cuban
£1520 $2600   (13-Mar-92 WOL.C259/R) Untitled (53x36cm-21x14in) s. paper

MIKHAILOV, Oleg (1934-) Russian
£714 $1327   (17-Jun-92 ARC.P25/R) Un dimanche de fete (70x99cm-28x39in) s. isorel
       (F.FR 7000)

MIKKELSEN, Lauritz (1879-1966) Danish
£502 $904   (30-Jan-92 RAS.V753/R) Interior with several artists (39x43cm-15x17in)
       mono.d.1900 (D.KR 5600)

MIKL, Josef (1929-) Austrian
£582 $1059   (26-May-92 D.V261/R) Untitled (37x26cm-15x10in) s. col.pencil (A.S 12000)
£978 $1740   (31-Oct-91 D.V2/R) Figure in plain (30x34cm-12x13in) s.i.d.50/51 pencil
*   col.pencil paper on board (A.S 20000)*
£1564 $2784   (31-Oct-91 D.V1/R) Figure (46x32cm-18x13in) s. pen indian ink W/C
*   (A.S 32000)*

MIKLOS, Gustave (1888-1967) French
£13211 $22988   (15-Apr-92 PLF.P96/R) Vitesse contraste de forme (93x73cm-37x29in)
s.verso (F.FR 130000)

MIKOLA, Nandor (1911-) Finnish
£506 $890   (12-Apr-92 HOR.H166) Morning (48x70cm-19x28in) s. W/C (F.M 4000)
£518 $912   (12-Apr-92 HOR.H165) Flowers in vase (71x50cm-28x20in) s. W/C (F.M 4100)

MILANESE SCHOOL, 16th C Italian
£2900 $5568   (6-Jul-92 S22/R) Study of a head of a man (20x13cm-8x5in) chk.htd.
£6704 $12000   (14-Jan-92 SY.NY1/R) Study of head of child (13x13cm-5x5in) bears mono.
red chk

MILANESE SCHOOL, 17th C Italian
£1852 $3315   (12-Nov-91 SY.AM204) Virgin and Child (45x34cm-18x13in) panel (D.FL 6000)
£3488 $6000   (10-Oct-91 SY.NY87/R) Biblical scene, possibly Joseph interpreting dreams
while imprisoned (134x96cm-53x38in)

MILANI, Aureliano (1675-1749) Italian
£4000 $7680   (6-Jul-92 S23/R) Man on deathbed, angel by his side and demons tormenting
him (34x48cm-13x19in) chk.

MILANI, Umberto (1912-1969) Italian
£3426 $5961   (14-Apr-92 F.M142/R) Composizione (100x70cm-39x28in) s.d.1963/1964verso
(I.L 7500000)

MILANO (?) ?
£984 $1800   (3-Jun-92 D.NY64) Three card Monte (38x28cm-15x11in) s. board

MILBANKE, Mark (1857-1927) British
£1100 $1969   (5-May-92 H541) Portrait of Jack Lysaght, as young man seated with dog
(127x91cm-50x36in) s.d.1923

MILBOURNE, Henry (1781-1826) British
£880 $1681   (15-Jul-92 S174/R) Dairymaid and cattle in landscape (62x55cm-24x22in) s.

MILBURN, Henry (?) British?
£1100 $1881   (12-Mar-92 CSK163/R) Figures and cattle in wooded river landscape
(25x31cm-10x12in) s. panel

MILDE, Carl Julius (1803-1875) German
£1228 $2211   (22-Nov-91 SA.A1553/R) The girl friends (35x43cm-14x17in) (DM 3500)

MILDE, Karl Friedrich August (1788-?) German
£643 $1125   (20-Feb-92 D.V485/R) Old woman weighing gold (104x93cm-41x37in) after
Rembrandt (A.S 13000)

MILDERT, Johannes van (attrib) (?-1638) Flemish
£619 $1089   (11-Apr-92 AW.H244/R) Figures lamenting Christ (21x33cm-8x13in) pen brush
(DM 1800)

MILES, Edward (1752-1828) British
£550 $946   (4-Mar-92 C81/R) Gentleman, in blue coat, yellow waistcoat, lace cravat
(6x?cm-2x?in) min. gold frame plaited hair verso oval

MILES, J (19th C) British
£3900 $7137   (12-May-92 H359/R) Portrait of prize ewe standing in wooded landscape
with stream (58x71cm-23x28in) i.

MILES, J C (19th C) British
£700 $1253   (15-Nov-91 C182) Portrait of artist, wearing coat and stock, holding
palette and brushes (61x51cm-24x20in) bears i.verso

MILES, J R (20th C?) Australian?
£500 $835   (21-Aug-91 ZZ.B71) Aran Islands, Galway Bay (51x41cm-20x16in) s.
s.i.verso
£623 $1102   (25-Apr-92 SO.S476/R) Fishingboats in rough seas (83x115cm-33x45in) s.
(S.KR 6600)

MILES, Thomas Rose (19th C) British
£500 $890   (29-Oct-91 SWS37) After stormy night, Douglas, Isle of Man
(60x106cm-24x42in) s. s.i.verso
£620 $1104   (31-Oct-91 D105/R) Gorleston Sands (58x107cm-23x42in) s.i.verso
£1200 $2172   (20-May-92 S262/R) Outward bound from Lowestoft (76x64cm-30x25in) s.
s.i.verso
£1600 $2848   (21-Jan-92 PH79) Homeward in morning light (62x108cm-24x43in) s.
s.i.verso
£1900 $3610   (23-Jun-92 PH149/R) Wind and rain off Sheerness (63x108cm-25x43in) s.
s.i.verso
£2000 $3600   (22-Nov-91 C46/R) Fishermen off Kent Coast (61x107cm-24x42in) s.

MILESI, Alessandro (1856-1945) Italian
£3666 $6489   (7-Nov-91 F.M18/R) Mercato a Vittorio Veneto (19x26cm-7x10in) s. i.verso
board painted oval (I.L 8000000)

MILESI, Alessandro (1856-1945) Italian-cont.
£7561 $13383   (7-Nov-91 F.M34/R) Confidenze in giardino (20x30cm-8x12in) s. board
                               (I.L 16500000)

MILET, Yves (1934-) French
£605 $1058   (26-Sep-91 FB.P105) Arbre de feu (100x100cm-39x39in) s.d.84 paper laid
                               down on canvas (F.FR 6000)

MILET-MOREAU, Iphigenie (1780-?) French
£7010 $12128   (27-Mar-92 CN.P55/R) Bouquet de fleurs sur un entablement
                               (40x32cm-16x13in) s. panel (F.FR 68000)

MILGATE, Rodney A (1934-) Australian
£726 $1350   (21-Jun-92 SY.ME11) Family day (181x242cm-71x95in) s.i.d.1978verso
                               (A.D 1800)

MILIADIS, Stelios (19/20th C) Greek
£800 $1360   (23-Oct-91 S185/R) Portrait of German woman wearing white bonnet.
                               Portrait of gentleman (44x35cm-17x14in) s. board double-sided
£1000 $1700   (23-Oct-91 S182/R) Village street (34x27cm-13x11in) s. board
£1300 $2210   (23-Oct-91 S181/R) Sailing boats in cove (26x35cm-10x14in) s. board
£700 $1190   (23-Oct-91 S183) Greek town street (24x33cm-9x13in) W/C over pencil

MILICEVIC, Ksenia (1942-) Yugoslavian
£513 $918   (19-Jan-92 PPB.P166) Grain d'or (61x46cm-24x18in) s.d.90 (F.FR 5000)

MILICH, Adolphe (1884-1964) Polish
£456 $849   (19-Jun-92 G.Z518) Young woman (55x46cm-22x18in) (S.FR 1200)
£913 $1697   (19-Jun-92 G.Z110/R) Deux filles au bord de l'eau (45x55cm-18x22in)
                               s.d.1945 (S.FR 2400)
£996 $1803   (4-Dec-91 G.Z78/R) Nature morte aux fruits (38x56cm-15x22in) s.
                               (S.FR 2500)
£1890 $3250   (16-Oct-91 G.Z110/R) L'olivier (73x60cm-29x24in) s. (S.FR 4800)

MILITZ, Johann Martin (attrib) (1725-1779) Austrian
£1000 $1700   (25-Oct-91 S.W2817/R) Portrait of Maria Theresa (74x74cm-29x29in)

MILLAIS, Raoul (fl.1928-1936) British
£700 $1316   (18-Dec-91 C41/R) Horses grazing, summer in the Cotswolds
                               (30x41cm-12x16in) s. i.stretcher
£3000 $5640   (18-Dec-91 C21/R) Horses startled by fire (41x51cm-16x20in) s.
£450 $756   (27-Aug-91 SWS1744) Figures in park (11x17cm-4x7in) s. W/C col. crayon
                               bodycol.over pencil
£1150 $2162   (18-Dec-91 C20/R) In the paddocks (17x27cm-7x11in) s. pastel

MILLAIS, Sir John Everett (1829-1896) British
£1400 $2478   (6-Nov-91 S225/R) Three figures (11x11cm-4x4in) panel
£11000 $20350   (12-Jun-92 C111/R) Miss Evelyn Otway (123x78cm-48x31in) mono.d.1880
£22000 $37400   (25-Oct-91 C60/R) Portrait of Alice Sophia Caroline Wortley, artist's
                               third daughter (110x85cm-43x33in) mono.d.1887
£537 $966   *(18-Nov-91 HO.ED69) Return of chieftain (12x14cm-5x6in) mono. W/C
                               (C.D 1100)*
£1000 $1850   *(12-Jun-92 C76/R) Portrait study of the Lempriere children
                               (20x28cm-8x11in) init.i.d.1847 pencil*
£1200 $2124   *(6-Nov-91 S321/R) Two studies of Emma Moreland from Edward Gray
                               (18x11cm-7x4in) pencil*

MILLAIS, Sir John Everett (after) (1829-1896) British
£900 $1728   (28-Jul-92 SWS333/R) Ophelia (72x113cm-28x44in)
£1300 $2236   (4-Mar-92 CBB33) Ophelia (81x114cm-32x45in)

MILLAIS, William Henry (1814-1899) British
£560 $1019   (10-Dec-91 SWS463) Fisherman at Frensham (50x61cm-20x24in) s.i.d.1876

MILLAN, Manuel (?) Spanish
£665 $1150   (26-Mar-92 DUR.M958/R) Bodegon (34x52cm-13x20in) s. panel (S.P 120000)

MILLAR, Addison T (1860-1913) American
£559 $1000   (14-Nov-91 CE.NY329) Fisherfolk by shore (30x41cm-12x16in) s.
£865 $1600   (10-Jun-92 CE.NY314/R) Silvermine birches (46x61cm-18x24in) s.d.
£2261 $4250   (18-Dec-91 SY.NY139/R) Summer garden (99x81cm-39x32in) s.
£1236 $2200   (1-Dec-91 DU.E1169) Rug merchant (30x25cm-12x10in) s. pencil

MILLAR, James H C (fl.1884-1903) British
£650 $1131   (12-Sep-91 CSK166/R) In the Highlands (41x61cm-16x24in) s.

MILLAR, William (style) (18th C) British
£1200 $2052   (12-Mar-92 CSK99) Portrait of young lady standing beside flowers in dress
                               with wrap (91x64cm-36x25in)

MILLARD, Frederick (attrib) (1857-?) British
£3300 $5676   (10-Oct-91 L613/R) Love knows no bound, boy picking hollyhock from
                               neighbours garden (91x71cm-36x28in)

MILLARD, P F (?) British?
£450 $788   (17-Feb-92 HS209) *Reclining female nude (34x56cm-13x22in) s. pen pastel*

MILLARES, Manolo (1926-1972) Spanish
£35529 $60399   (22-Oct-91 DUR.M97/R) *Negro, rojo y blanco (48x69cm-19x27in) s. paper* (S.P 6500000)
£80000 $144800   (5-Dec-91 S21/R) *Composition (96x145cm-38x57in) s.d.57 oil string hessian*
£4151 $7097   (17-Mar-92 FER.M98/R) *Eslabones (31x24cm-12x9in) s. ink (S.P 750000)*
£12500 $21500   (17-Oct-91 C17/R) *Untitled (50x70cm-20x28in) s. s.d.61 verso gouache ink W/C*

MILLER, Alfred Jacob (1810-1874) American
£3994 $7150   (14-Nov-91 GRO.B10/R) *Two Baltimore children (112x86cm-44x34in) s.*
£35714 $65000   (28-May-92 CH.NY4/R) *Indian girl swinging (44x35cm-17x14in) init.*

MILLER, Archibald Elliot Haswell (1887-1979) British
£550 $1045   (23-Jun-92 CG618) *Alcantara Bridge, Toledo (53x76cm-21x30in) s.d.1923 W/C*

MILLER, Charles Keith (19th C) British
£550 $957   (14-Apr-92 CSK184) *Ivanhoe racing on Clyde (51x60cm-20x24in) s.i.d.1901 verso card*
£4000 $7640   (17-Jul-92 C155/R) *The barque Orion off the South Shields coast (61x106cm-24x42in) mono.d.1901*
£4000 $7640   (17-Jul-92 C154/R) *The ship Procyon off Newark Castle, Greenock (61x106cm-24x42in) mono.d.1899*

MILLER, George (fl.1827-1853) British
£1421 $2600   (5-Jun-92 SY.NY142/R) *Charley, a springer spaniel (30x34cm-12x13in) s.d.1863 board*

MILLER, Godfrey Clive (1893-1964) Australian
£485 $872   (24-Nov-91 SY.S72) *Nude study (45x60cm-18x24in) init. canvasboard (A.D 1100)*
£749 $1348   (24-Nov-91 SY.S75) *Still life (46x61cm-18x24in) (A.D 1700)*
£8085 $14311   (26-Apr-92 SY.ME474 b/R) *Tree and mountain series, N.T (42x59cm-17x23in) oil ink canvas on board (A.D 19000)*

MILLER, Henry (20th C) American
£683 $1242   (26-May-92 KF.M1081/R) *Surging waves and seagulls over rock (35x25cm-14x10in) s.d.1955 W/C (DM 2000)*
£1189 $2200   (10-Jun-92 CE.NY471) *Kiosk along Seine, Paris (37x52cm-15x20in) s. W/C ink*

MILLER, John (18/19th C) British
£550 $946   (5-Mar-92 CSK119) *Greek church, Venice (45x34cm-18x13in) s. i.verso board*
£700 $1204   (5-Mar-92 CSK118) *San Giorgio, late afternoon (61x91cm-24x36in) s. i.verso*
£900 $1647   (14-May-92 C124/R) *Bell rope, Crete (51x51cm-20x20in) s. i.verso*
£2200 $3982   (20-May-92 B328) *Ornamental poppies near studio (59x70cm-23x28in) s.i.d.1988 verso*

MILLER, Joseph (19th C) German
£2993 $5028   (28-Aug-91 KH.K143/R) *Kitchen interior with children leaving for school (61x52cm-24x20in) s.d.1861 (D.KR 34000)*
£3780 $6577   (18-Sep-91 N.M623/R) *Old peasant couple reading bible in interior (60x50cm-24x20in) s.i.d.1868 (DM 11000)*

MILLER, Ralph Davison (1859-1946) American
£955 $1700   (26-Nov-91 MOR.P88) *Sheep in barn interior (51x76cm-20x30in) s.d.1907*

MILLER, Richard Edward (?) American?
£8571 $15000   (25-Sep-91 SY.NY66/R) *Visit (201x165cm-79x65in) s.*
£11696 $20000   (12-Mar-92 CH.NY104/R) *Mother and child (46x38cm-18x15in) s.*
£52486 $95000   (6-Dec-91 CH.NY139/R) *Cafe society (50x73cm-20x29in) s.*
£230769 $420000   (27-May-92 SY.NY70/R) *Goldfish (100x81cm-39x32in) s.d.1912*

MILLER, Richard Emil (1875-1943) American
£1463 $2750   (18-Dec-91 SY.NY174/R) *Harbour at night (59x73cm-23x29in) s.*

MILLER, William Rickarby (1818-1893) American
£546 $950   (11-Sep-91 D.NY60) *Clock tower (66x51cm-26x20in) s.d.1876 s.d.1868 canvas on masonite*
£2281 $3900   (12-Mar-92 MFA.C108) *River Walk Castle Point (41x36cm-16x14in) s.d.1873*
£608 $1100   (22-May-92 S.BM68 a/R) *Boat ride (36x25cm-14x10in) s.i.d.1855 W/C with tooling*
£3400 $6494   (13-Jul-92 PH92/R) *Morris ... N.Y. (28x41cm-11x16in) s.i.d.1855 pastel arched top pair*
£7143 $13000   (28-May-92 CH.NY23/R) *Jersey City with glimpse of New York (31x50cm-12x20in) s.i.d.1854 W/C gouache*

MILLER-DIFLO, Otto (1878-1949) German
£438 $784   (6-May-92 GD.B861/R) *Birch trees in landscape, late autumn (51x61cm-20x24in) s. i.verso (S.FR 1200)*
£629 $1089   (28-Mar-92 BOD.P989) *River landscape with view of mountain range beyond (13x19cm-5x7in) s. board (DM 1800)*

MILLET, Francis Davis (1846-1912) American
£8791 $16000   (28-May-92 CH.NY93/R) After the festival (51x40cm-20x16in) s.d.1888
£9143 $16000   (20-Feb-92 SY.NY48/R) Turkish soldier (99x74cm-39x29in) s.d.1878

MILLET, Francisque (17/18th C) French
£1629 $3014   (12-Jun-92 ARC.P137/R) Paysage avec cavalier (16x24cm-6x9in) pen W/C
     (F.FR 16000)

MILLET, Francisque (style) (17/18th C) French
£1400 $2688   (9-Jul-92 CSK334/R) Samson and the Lion (47x72cm-19x28in) panel

MILLET, Francois (?-1917) French
£4000 $6920   (4-Oct-91 C55/R) Avant le repas (50x65cm-20x26in) s.indis.d.
£2800 $4956   (14-Feb-92 C23/R) Cattle grazing in meadow (32x43cm-13x17in) s. pastel
     card

MILLET, Frederic (1786-1859) French
£758 $1341   (24-Apr-92 CD.P80/R) Portrait de jeune femme (14x11cm-6x4in) min.s.d.1834
     (F.FR 7500)

MILLET, Jean Francois (1814-1875) French
£1500 $2745   (12-May-92 SWS625/R) Arcadian landscape (40x47cm-16x19in) panel
£3000 $5250   (1-Apr-92 S145/R) Classical landscape with figures near pool
     (30x45cm-12x18in)
£4321 $7821   (5-Dec-91 SY.MO278/R) Paysage arcadien (36x42cm-14x17in) (F.FR 42000)
£16279 $28000   (13-Oct-91 H.C49/R) La fuite en Egypte (33x25cm-13x10in) init. panel
£17582 $32000   (27-May-92 CH.NY175/R) Portrait of Monsieur Fleury (24x19cm-9x7in) canvas
     on panel
£87912 $160000   (28-May-92 SY.NY25/R) Les peupliers (28x18cm-11x7in) s. cradled panel
£1133721 $1950000   (16-Oct-91 CH.NY88/R) Return from the fields (81x100cm-32x39in) st.
£1000 $1710   (18-Mar-92 S95) Sketch for an autumn landscape (11x16cm-4x6in) pencil
£2000 $3560   (27-Nov-91 S191/R) Study for Le Berger et la mer (20x13cm-8x5in) st. chl
£2907 $5000   (17-Oct-91 SY.NY139/R) Standing nudes (28x15cm-11x6in) st.init. chl wash
     double-sided
£3300 $5643   (18-Mar-92 S94/R) Shepherdess on a bench (17x11cm-7x4in) s. ink
£3571 $6500   (28-May-92 SY.NY139/R) Vues d'Auvergne (6x10cm-2x4in) st.init. one i. pen
     four
£3779 $6500   (13-Oct-91 H.C50/R) Le becheur - homme avec une pelle pen
£3866 $7074   (15-May-92 AT.P179/R) Mazeppa (20x31cm-8x12in) black crayon ink brush two
     sheets (F.FR 38000)
£6105 $10500   (13-Oct-91 H.C51/R) Team of horses with plough (23x36cm-9x14in) bears
     st.init. black crayon
£21978 $40000   (27-May-92 CH.NY176/R) Auvergne goat girl (19x18cm-7x7in) init.
     chk.stumping
£220000 $398200   (3-Dec-91 S7/R) L'enfant malade (38x31cm-15x12in) s. black crayon pastel
£520000 $941200   (3-Dec-91 S6/R) Les oies sauvages (60x43cm-24x17in) s. pastel black
     crayon

MILLET, Jean Francois (after) (1814-1879) French
£1500 $2655   (14-Feb-92 C16/R) Le prieure de Vauville (46x55cm-18x22in) bears i.
£850 $1632   (9-Jul-92 B171) Studies for The Gleaners (20x15cm-8x6in) bears i.verso
     pen

MILLET, Jean Francois (circle) (1814-1875) French
£3000 $5250   (3-Apr-92 C127) Wooded classical landscape with philosophers and
     canephoros on path (121x157cm-48x62in)

MILLIKEN, J W (fl.1897-1930) British
£520 $910   (25-Feb-92 CD313) Bruges amrket place with milling figures
     (25x36cm-10x14in) s.

MILLIKEN, Robert W (20th C) British
£492 $880   (14-Nov-91 GRO.B30) Pheasant in landscape (48x36cm-19x14in) s. W/C
£800 $1344   (26-Aug-91 S901/R) The Sunken Butt (63x101cm-25x40in) s.i. W/C

MILLING, Gustav (1876-?) German
£523 $900   (13-Oct-91 REM.W19) Still life (36x41cm-14x16in) s. (P.Z 10000000)

MILLINGER, Josef Stoitzner (1911-1982) Austrian
£890 $1557   (19-Feb-92 D.V219/R) Still life (47x68cm-19x27in) s.d.56 mixed media
     paper on board (A.S 18000)

MILLNER, Karl (1825-1894) German
£3600 $6408   (26-Nov-91 PH20/R) Figures before river in Alpine landscape
     (54x38cm-21x15in) s.
£4811 $8371   (18-Sep-91 N.M624/R) Path from Partenkirchen to Grainau with Waxenstein
     and Zugspitze (97x117cm-38x46in) s.d.1883 (DM 14000)
£6873 $11959   (17-Sep-91 FN.S2444/R) View of Firmianalpe near Salzburg
     (51x87cm-20x34in) s. (DM 20000)
£6969 $12683   (11-Dec-91 WE.MU58/R) Cows watering in mountain lake landscape
     (71x98cm-28x39in) s.i. (DM 20000)
£9059 $16488   (11-Dec-91 WE.MU59/R) Cows grazing in high mountain landscape
     (37x44cm-15x17in) s. i.d.1871 (DM 26000)
£21951 $38195   (19-Sep-91 D.V87/R) View of snowcovered Ortler range (88x128cm-35x50in)
     s.i.d.1862verso (A.S 450000)

MILLNER, Karl (attrib) (1825-1894) German
£474 $849 *(6-May-92 GD.B863/R) Lake landscape with shepherds and cattle grazing (62x84cm-24x33in) gouache (S.FR 1300)*

MILLS, A (19th C) British
£1093 $2000 (3-Jun-92 D.NY65) Coming in from fields (76x127cm-30x50in) s.d.1875

MILLS, H F (?) ?
£793 $1411 (26-Nov-91 J.M905) Fishing boats (56x86cm-22x34in) s. (A.D 1800)

MILLS, Reginald (20th C) British
£500 $905 *(21-May-92 LE150) Winter coaching street scene (38x53cm-15x21in) s. W/C*

MILLS, William (19/20th C) British
£2200 $3828 (12-Sep-91 CSK253/R) Regent Circus (39x31cm-15x12in) s.d.1885 s.i.d.verso
£3000 $5160 (4-Mar-92 S188/R) Regent Circus (38x30cm-15x12in) s.d.1885 s.i.d.verso

MILLSBURY, Albert Nemethy (20th C) American
£629 $1100 (4-Apr-92 E.EDM329/R) Steamboat 'Alexander Hamilton' (61x84cm-24x33in) s.

MILLWARD, Clem (1929-) Australian
£640 $1222 (21-Jul-92 JRL.S160) Dry expanse under claoud (72x119cm-28x47in) s.d.75 board (A.D 1650)
£1008 $1925 (21-Jul-92 JRL.S126) Near Cloncurry (75x90cm-30x35in) s.d.89 (A.D 2600)

MILNE, David Brown (1882-1953) Canadian
£12500 $22125 (6-Nov-91 SY.T41/R) Autumn, forest interior (44x55cm-17x22in) s. (C.D 25000)
£4146 $7463 *(19-Nov-91 FP.M184/R) Indian pipes (24x33cm-9x13in) d.1945 verso W/C (C.D 8500)*
£9453 $16826 *(26-Nov-91 JOY.T6/R) Tree with blue shadow, Boston Corners (27x32cm-11x13in) s.d.20 W/C (C.D 19000)*
£12785 $23269 *(26-May-92 JOY.T100 c) Woman on sofa reading, Mt Riga (39x49cm-15x19in) s.d.1921 W/C drybrush (C.D 28000)*

MILNE, John Maclaughlan (1885-1957) British
£680 $1142 (29-Aug-91 CG89) An east coats fishing village with kelp gatherers on a beach (25x33cm-10x13in) s. board
£800 $1448 (4-Dec-91 S355/R) Coastal village (30x35cm-12x14in) s.
£1500 $2670 (1-Nov-91 PHE58) French farmyard (37x44cm-15x17in) board
£2700 $4806 (1-May-92 PHE71/R) Corrie (51x61cm-20x24in) s.
£2900 $5162 (28-Apr-92 S308/R) View of the sea (46x61cm-18x24in) s.
£3500 $5880 (26-Aug-91 S1047/R) Ferry rock (50x61cm-20x24in) s.
£3600 $6408 (28-Apr-92 S289/R) Preparing the nets (38x55cm-15x22in) s.d.31
£5000 $8400 (26-Aug-91 S1035/R) Sannox Bay, Arran (51x61cm-20x24in) s. canvas board
£5500 $9955 (4-Dec-91 S232/R) Continental street (51x61cm-20x24in) s.d.20
£5500 $9240 (26-Aug-91 S1046/R) Croft in Iona (38x46cm-15x18in) s. board
£5800 $9976 (6-Mar-92 C24/R) White cottages, Aran (43x58cm-17x23in) s.
£6000 $10080 (26-Aug-91 S1034/R) Sheltered cove, St.Tropez (51x61cm-20x24in) s.
£6500 $11310 (11-Sep-91 PHG21/R) Street of the Four Winds, St Tropez (72x90cm-28x35in) s. i. verso
£8500 $14280 (26-Aug-91 S1045/R) Glen Sannox, Arran (51x60cm-20x24in) s. board
£450 $756 *(29-Aug-91 CG15) Cattle grazing by a stream (36x48cm-14x19in) s. W/C*
£3800 $6878 *(4-Dec-91 S233/R) On beach (37x51cm-15x20in) s.indist.d. pastel*

MILNE, Joseph (1861-1911) British
£550 $995 (4-Dec-91 S197) Leven harbour (30x19cm-12x7in) s.i.verso
£1050 $1764 (29-Aug-91 CG71) Street scene, Crail (36x25cm-14x10in) s.i. verso

MILNE, M (1887-1954) British
£520 $910 (3-Apr-92 BW374) Still life study depicting vase of roses (41x33cm-16x13in) s.

MILNE, William Watt (19th C) British
£1000 $1680 (26-Aug-91 S1126/R) On the east coast (51x69cm-20x27in)
£1200 $2076 (24-Mar-92 CG790) Shepherd and sheep by a windmill (51x61cm-20x24in) js.d.1915
£1600 $2768 (24-Mar-92 CG789/R) Driving sheep across a ford (51x61cm-20x24in) s.d.1916
£1700 $3077 (4-Dec-91 S199/R) Feeding swans (45x56cm-18x22in) s.
£1800 $3186 (6-Nov-91 CB141) Changing the fold (28x41cm-11x16in) s. board
£3600 $6048 (26-Aug-91 S1024/R) Crossing a bridge by moonlight (45x61cm-18x24in) s.

MILO, Jean (1906-) Belgian
£501 $852 *(22-Oct-91 C.A258) Gage pour un retour certain (40x31cm-16x12in) s.d.1965 W/C (B.FR 30000)*
£746 $1366 *(12-May-92 C.A218) Promenade (45x60cm-18x24in) s.d.1940 W/C (B.FR 45000)*
£917 $1577 *(12-Oct-91 KV.L216) Une Mises en scene de Maurice Rabinovitch (36x44cm-14x17in) s.d.1983 W/C (B.FR 55000)*

MILON (?) ?
£1061 $1877 (24-Apr-92 CD.P97) Fontaine dans les ruines (24x32cm-9x13in) s.d.1847 (F.FR 10500)

MILONE, Antonio (19th C) Italian
£1309 $2500   (16-Jul-92 SY.NY613/R) Two donkeys and a rooster (22x34cm-9x13in) s. panel
£2759 $4939   (14-Nov-91 CH.R60/R) Pastorella con asinello, pecore e mucca (51x77cm-20x30in) s. (I.L 6000000)
£5094 $8813   (24-Mar-92 CH.R102/R) Pastorella con animali. Il guado (30x40cm-12x16in) s.d.1868 board oval pair (I.L 11000000)
£7358 $13171   (14-Nov-91 CH.R78/R) I due curiosi, il cucito (102x63cm-40x25in) s. (I.L 16000000)

MILONE, Giuseppe (19th C) Italian
£640 $1100   (4-Mar-92 D.NY39) Springtime pasture (30x41cm-12x16in) s.

MILROY, Lisa (20th C) American
£1029 $1800   (27-Feb-92 CE.NY226/R) Untitled (46x61cm-18x24in) s.d.83 stretcher

MILSTEIN, Zvi (1934-) Israeli
£618 $1057   (22-Mar-92 I.N81) Sans titre (63x63cm-25x25in) s. (F.FR 6000)
£766 $1326   (23-Mar-92 AB.L134/R) Marine marchand (73x100cm-29x39in) s. (S.FR 2000)
£1407 $2547   (19-May-92 GF.L2311/R) The female dancer (104x74cm-41x29in) s. mixed media (S.FR 3800)

MILTON, Victor Marais (1872-?) French
£1400 $2492   (27-Nov-91 S235/R) La sieste (34x26cm-13x10in) s. W/C

MILTON-JENSEN, Carl (1855-1928) Danish
£1900 $3382   (27-Nov-91 S54/R) Cattle watering in extensive landscape (100x120cm-39x47in) s.d.1909
£2424 $4411   (27-May-92 D.V638/R) Summer landscape (80x123cm-31x48in) s.d.1883 (A.S 50000)

MILTON-JENSEN, E (19th C) Danish
£1320 $2218   (27-Aug-91 RAS.K418) A day in June (80x123cm-31x48in) s.d.1883 (D.KR 15000)

MIN, Jaap (1914-) Dutch
£1667 $3017   (21-May-92 SY.AM37/R) Het Wiertdijkje, Bergen (80x100cm-31x39in) s. (D.FL 5500)
£1879 $3401   (21-May-92 SY.AM28/R) Cows (50x60cm-20x24in) s. (D.FL 6200)
£1030 $1865   (21-May-92 SY.AM17/R) Landscape in Limburg (56x75cm-22x30in) s.d.1936 gouache (D.FL 3400)

MINARDI, Tommaso (1787-1871) Italian
£1813 $3318   (4-Jun-92 F.M35/R) Madonna con Bambino e San Giovannino (33x26cm-13x10in) s. pencil (I.L 4000000)

MINARIK, Ladislav (1945-) ?
£629 $1120   (25-Nov-91 WK.M2046/R) Adam and Eve greeting modernism (200x260cm-79x102in) d.1984 (DM 1800)
£629 $1120   (25-Nov-91 WK.M2045/R) The bird and the beauty (200x260cm-79x102in) d.1984 (DM 1800)

MINARTZ, Tony (1873-?) French
£780 $1420   (10-Dec-91 SWS50) At the opera (78x68cm-31x27in) s.

MINAUX, Andre (1923-1988) French
£1236 $2113   (18-Mar-92 PIC.P79) Homme allonge (61x125cm-24x49in) s. board (F.FR 12000)
£1339 $2289   (18-Mar-92 PIC.P78/R) Paysage decembre (97x131cm-38x52in) s. s.d.1948verso (F.FR 13000)

MIND, Gottfried (1768-1814) Swiss
£784 $1404   (12-Nov-91 GF.L5101) Cat in window niche (14x11cm-6x4in) W/C indian ink (S.FR 2000)
£927 $1585   (12-Mar-92 GK.Z369/R) Cats (15x16cm-6x6in) pencil (S.FR 2400)
£1725 $3089   (12-Nov-91 GF.L5102/R) Cat and kitten drinking milk (13x17cm-5x7in) W/C (S.FR 4400)

MIND, Gottfried (attrib) (1768-1814) Swiss
£1020 $1825   (12-Nov-91 GF.L5105) Cat and three kittens (20x26cm-8x10in) W/C (S.FR 2600)

MINDERHOUT, Hendrik van (1632-1696) Dutch
£25140 $45000   (17-Jan-92 SY.NY135/R) Aerial view of the Fort Saint Philippe with shipping on the Slijkens (164x231cm-65x91in) s.

MINDERHOUT, Hendrik van (attrib) (1632-1696) Dutch
£8621 $15172   (11-Apr-92 AT.P22/R) Vue d'un port mediterraneen (95x150cm-37x59in) (F.FR 85000)

MINEUR, G (?) ?
£568 $966   (22-Oct-91 C.A826) Village scene (81x116cm-32x46in) s. (B.FR 34000)

MINGORANCE ACIEN, Manuel (1920-) Spanish
£718 $1279   (21-Jan-92 DUR.M110/R) Maternidad (65x46cm-26x18in) s.d.1960 (S.P 130000)

MINGORANCE, Juan E (1906-) Spanish
£798 $1429   (14-Nov-91 ANS.M140/R) Aguas muertas, Tunis s.d.1938 i.d.verso
(S.P 145000)

MINGUZZI, Luciano (1911-) Italian
£741 $1320   (26-Nov-91 SY.MI120) Dalla serie del mostri marini (50x70cm-20x28in) s.i.
gouache indian ink (I.L 1600000)
£768 $1391   (21-May-92 F.M151/R) Due figure sedute (66x49cm-26x19in) s.d.1951
s.i.d.verso gouache (I.L 1700000)

MINNE, George (1866-1941) Belgian
£2667 $4587   (12-Oct-91 KV.L452/R) Christ (47x32cm-19x13in) s.d.1935 chl.
(B.FR 160000)

MINNS, Benjamin Edward (1864-1937) Australian
£641 $1141   (28-Apr-92 CH.ME2) Aboriginal girl, north coast NSW (22x21cm-9x8in)
s.i.d.1930 W/C (A.D 1500)
£806 $1500   (15-Jun-92 MGS.S89) Harbour scene (23x34cm-9x13in) s.d.23 W/C (A.D 2000)
£806 $1500   (15-Jun-92 MGS.S82) Australian farmyard (26x38cm-10x15in) s.d.1935 W/C
(A.D 2000)
£812 $1445   (27-Apr-92 J.M609) The esplanade (26x35cm-10x14in) s. W/C (A.D 1900)
£845 $1411   (19-Aug-91 SY.ME41) Roses in glass vase (34x23cm-13x9in) s.d.1913 W/C
(A.D 1800)
£855 $1521   (27-Apr-92 J.M390) Farmhouse (22x26cm-9x10in) s.d.1919 W/C (A.D 2000)
£969 $1725   (26-Nov-91 J.M156/R) Summer paddocks (21x25cm-8x10in) s.d.1921 W/C
(A.D 2200)
£1000 $1700   (23-Oct-91 S311/R) Lady on wooden bridge in the woods (34x20cm-13x8in)
s.d.91 W/C bodycol
£1624 $2891   (28-Apr-92 CH.ME203/R) Rural scene with stockman resting
(26x38cm-10x15in) s.d.1925 W/C (A.D 3800)
£1938 $3489   (24-Nov-91 SY.S332/R) Sydney harbour (28x38cm-11x15in) s. W/C (A.D 4400)
£2929 $5301   (19-May-92 JRL.S193) Wool wagon (36x53cm-14x21in) s.d.1929 W/C (A.D 7000)
£4222 $7220   (17-Mar-92 JRL.S215/R) Any day any beach (26x36cm-10x14in) s.d.1932 W/C
(A.D 9500)

MINOLI, Paolo (1942-) Italian
£1158 $2062   (26-Nov-91 SY.MI119/R) Interazioni cromatiche (50x50cm-20x20in)
s.i.d.78verso acrylic panel (I.L 2500000)

MINOR, Robert Crannell (1840-1904) American
£597 $1075   (23-Nov-91 YFA.M199/R) Spring landscape (46x61cm-18x24in) s.
£1047 $1800   (14-Oct-91 H.C117/R) Wooded landscape (76x102cm-30x40in) s.

MINOZZI, F (?) Italian
£1029 $1800   (28-Feb-92 SY.NY27/R) Sunset (28x35cm-11x14in) s.d.1909 d.1909 verso
panel

MINTCHINE, Abraham (1898-1931) Russian
£1372 $2387   (14-Apr-92 ZZ.F57/R) Le Moulin de la Galette le 14 Juillet 1926
(16x26cm-6x10in) d.verso board (F.FR 13500)
£1892 $3500   (12-Jun-92 SY.NY21/R) Paysage en Provence (36x46cm-14x18in) s.
£4286 $7500   (26-Sep-91 SY.I50/R) Harbour scene (52x63cm-20x25in) s.
£2979 $5600   (5-Jan-92 GG.TA274/R) Still life with fish (42x56cm-17x22in) s. oil mixed
media paper on canvas

MINTON, John (1917-1957) British
£2000 $3540   (5-Nov-91 PH138) The musicians (22x21cm-9x8in) s.d.1934 board
£540 $956   (5-Nov-91 PH135/R) Portrait of Kevin Maybury (39x28cm-15x11in) s.i.d.1955
pen
£550 $1007   (14-May-92 C142/R) Seated man (38x28cm-15x11in) pen wash
£600 $1080   (30-Jan-92 TL131) View of Stockholm (27x37cm-11x15in) Indian ink wash
£720 $1375   (16-Jul-92 B204/R) Costume design for Duncan from Macbeth
(28x18cm-11x7in) pen
£850 $1488   (27-Sep-91 C13/R) Micheline to Bastia by train (17x16cm-7x6in) pen brush
ink
£850 $1479   (19-Sep-91 CSK124/R) Illustration for Secret River (28x21cm-11x8in) pen
brush wash htd white
£2000 $3460   (2-Oct-91 S151/R) Jovial distress II. The canonisation of the devil
(20x30cm-8x12in) one s. pen ink wash htd.white two
£2000 $3540   (5-Nov-91 PH108/R) Portrait of a boy. Nude (37x27cm-15x11in) pencil
double-sided
£3500 $6195   (8-Nov-91 C207/R) Ruined cottage (27x37cm-11x15in) s.d.1948 i.backboard
pen brush crayon W/C
£3800 $6840   (20-Nov-91 S183/R) Banana trees (36x28cm-14x11in) s.d.1950 pen wash W/C
gouache
£3800 $6726   (8-Nov-91 C206/R) Barge and warehouses (25x38cm-10x15in) s.d.1946
i.backboard brush ink wash W/C bodycol.

MIOTTE, Jean (1926-) French
£5225 $9406   (2-Feb-92 CSC.P99/R) Desir (130x97cm-51x38in) s. acrylic (F.FR 51000)
£9000 $15480   (17-Oct-91 S123/R) Untitled (100x80cm-39x31in) s.d.61 verso

MIR Y TRINXET, Joaquin (1873-1940) Spanish
£22118 $41581   (17-Dec-91 BRO.B354/R) Montserrat (69x80cm-27x31in) s. (S.P 4000000)

MIR Y TRINXET, Joaquin (1873-1940) Spanish-cont.
£27647 $51977   (17-Dec-91 BRO.B417/R) Paisaje con arbol frondoso al contraluz
                     (82x88cm-32x35in) s. (S.P 5000000)
£11074   *$19934*   *(28-Jan-92 EP.M37/R) El estorbo (27x37cm-11x15in) s. mixed media*
                     (S.P 2000000)

MIRA, Alfred S (20th C) American
£4330 $7750   (6-May-92 D.NY30/R) Summer morning (51x61cm-20x24in) s.

MIRADORI, Luigi (17th C) Italian
£14873 $26921   (5-Dec-91 F.M105/R) Vanitas (59x82cm-23x32in) (I.L 32000000)

MIRADORI, Luigi (attrib) (17th C) Italian
£6972 $12619   (5-Dec-91 F.M137/R) Vestizione di un monaco (153x111cm-60x44in)
                     (I.L 15000000)

MIRALDA, Antoni (1942-) Spanish
£1408   *$2423*   *(8-Oct-91 CC.P99/R) Soldats soldes (75x94cm-30x37in) s.i.d.1969 verso*
                     grass plastic panel (F.FR 14000)

MIRALLES DARMANIN, Enrique (1855-1900) Spanish
£656 $1115   (22-Oct-91 DUR.M33/R) Mosqueteros en la taberna (13x17cm-5x7in) init.
                     panel (S.P 120000)
£1374 $2419   (9-Apr-92 ANS.M148/R) La carta (33x22cm-13x9in) s.d.1927 (S.P 250000)

MIRALLES, Enrique (19/20th C) Spanish
£1021 $1838   (19-Nov-91 GM.B276/R) L'Amateur d'Antiquites (60x38cm-24x15in) s.
                     (B.FR 60000)
£1702 $3064   (19-Nov-91 GM.B328/R) Joueurs de Cartes (47x38cm-19x15in) s.
                     (B.FR 100000)
£2043 $3677   (19-Nov-91 GM.B497/R) Interieur d'Antiquaire (100x80cm-39x31in) s.
                     (B.FR 120000)
£2062 $3526   (15-Mar-92 DA.R5/R) Les coulisses du cirque (46x33cm-18x13in) s.
                     (F.FR 20000)
£2984 $5669   (22-Jun-92 AT.P73/R) La chassure rouge (73x50cm-29x20in) s. (F.FR 29000)

MIRALLES, Francisco (1848-1901) Spanish
£10000 $17800   (26-Nov-91 PH68/R) Artist and model (41x32cm-16x13in) s. panel
£12000 $21840   (29-May-92 C379/R) In the boudoir (41x33cm-16x13in) s.d.1875
£16296 $29496   (20-May-92 GK.Z5099/R) At the horse race (31x40cm-12x16in) s.
                     (S.FR 44000)
£18571 $32500   (20-Feb-92 SY.NY68/R) Aires Libres (30x41cm-12x16in) s. panel
£38000 $69160   (29-May-92 C375/R) At the races (41x31cm-16x12in) s. panel
£6686   *$11500*   *(17-Oct-91 SY.NY344/R) Allongee dans l'herbe (27x37cm-11x15in) s.d.1882*
                     W/C

MIRALLES, Francisco (attrib) (1848-1901) Spanish
£6500 $11830   (29-May-92 C378/R) At the races (41x33cm-16x13in)

MIRALLES-DARMANIN, Jose (1851-?) Spanish
£10465 $18000   (17-Oct-91 SY.NY95/R) Spanish fiesta (32x41cm-13x16in) s.d.1876 panel

MIRANDA, R (?) Spanish?
£492 $836   (23-Oct-91 DUR.M452/R) Vista de Palestina (14x31cm-6x12in) s. s.i.verso
                     panel (S.P 90000)

MIRKO (1910-1969) Italian
£1089 $1992   (12-May-92 F.R74) Composizione astratta (68x48cm-27x19in) s. tempera
                     paper sold with W/C by Corrado Cagli (I.L 2400000)

MIRO ARGENTER, Joaquim (1849-1914) Argentinian
£1613 $3000   (16-Jun-92 RO.BA137) Feria Marroqui (36x28cm-14x11in)

MIRO LLEO, Gaspar (1859-1930) Spanish
£1230 $2091   (22-Oct-91 DUR.M40/R) Le Pantheon, Paris (21x15cm-8x6in) s. board
                     (S.P 225000)
£1700 $2941   (4-Oct-91 C122/R) L'Ile de la Cite, Paris (21x27cm-8x11in) s. panel

MIRO, Joachim (19/20th C) Spanish
£665 $1177   (12-Feb-92 ANS.M163/R) El naufragio (15x24cm-6x9in) s. (S.P 120000)
£1364 $2469   (20-May-92 ANS.M145/R) Escena arabe (28x42cm-11x17in) s. (S.P 250000)
£1373 $2513   (17-May-92 T.B189/R) Paris, les Quais (18x24cm-7x9in) s. panel
                     (F.FR 13500)
£3048 $5334   (18-Feb-92 DUR.M30/R) Caravana (32x41cm-13x16in) s.d.1908 canvas laid
                     down on panel (S.P 550000)
£3488 $6000   (17-Oct-91 SY.NY332/R) En el Cairo. Carabana Arabe (32x41cm-13x16in) s.
                     panel pair
£3602 $6304   (18-Feb-92 DUR.M29/R) Carga de la polvora (32x41cm-13x16in) s. panel
                     (S.P 650000)
£3689 $6639   (2-Feb-92 ZZ.F76/R) Paris, les quais et l'institut (25x36cm-10x14in) s.
                     (F.FR 36000)
£19100 $32851   (16-Oct-91 FER.M238/R) Por el sendero se iba adentrando en el bosque
                     (60x80cm-24x31in) s. (S.P 3500000)
£27337 $50027   (13-May-92 FER.M142/R) Mercado en la parte alta de la Rambla de
                     Villanueva (65x54cm-26x21in) s. (S.P 5000000)

MIRO, Joachim (19/20th C) Spanish-cont.

£663	$1246	(3-Jan-92 DUR.M6/R) Caravana de beduinos (38x57cm-15x22in) s. W/C gouache (S.P 120000)
£763	$1313	(7-Oct-91 ANS.M65/R) Escena mora (24x18cm-9x7in) s. W/C (S.P 140000)
£979	$1742	(28-Apr-92 DUR.M521/R) Plaza mora (35x25cm-14x10in) s. W/C (S.P 180000)
£982	$1777	(20-May-92 ANS.M207/R) Escena marroqui (27x44cm-11x17in) s. W/C (S.P 180000)
£998	$1766	(12-Feb-92 ANS.M32/R) Escena mora (36x26cm-14x10in) s. W/C (S.P 180000)

MIRO, Joan (1893-1983) Spanish

£2012	$3461	(12-Oct-91 SY.MO25/R) Projet pour le rideau - Jeux d'Enfants (32x36cm-13x14in) paper (F.FR 20000)
£53672	$95000	(7-Nov-91 SY.NY180/R) Personnage oiseaux (95x60cm-37x24in) s. oil pencil paper on canvas
£54645	$100000	(13-May-92 CH.NY257 a/R) Projet pour une tapisserie (36x27cm-14x11in) paper on canvas
£72000	$130320	(3-Dec-91 C293/R) Femme etoile (28x22cm-11x9in) s. i.d.8/II/78verso
£75000	$143250	(29-Jun-92 C55/R) Chant d'armour des oiseaux (27x41cm-11x16in) s. s.d.17/III/67 verso
£120000	$229200	(29-Jun-92 C58/R) Femme, oiseaux, etoile I (80x54cm-31x21in) s. s.d.11/1/67 verso
£284153	$520000	(12-May-92 CH.NY143/R) Composition a la lune bleu (45x35cm-18x14in) s. s.d.1949 verso
£320000	$579200	(3-Dec-91 S40/R) Peinture 1927 (130x195cm-51x77in) s.d.1927 oil tempera pencil canvas
£2162	$4000	(12-Jun-92 SY.NY191/R) Abstract composition (31x21cm-12x8in) s.i.d.65 crayon
£2200	$4202	(29-Jun-92 CSK152/R) Composition (11x15cm-4x6in) s. s.d.29/X/64 col.crayons
£2400	$4584	(29-Jun-92 CSK144/R) Abstract composition. XXe siecle - Mourlot 274 (29x22cm-11x9in) one s. one s.d.29/X/64 pen lithograph dble-side
£2520	$4360	(4-Oct-91 CSC.P97) Odo a Joan Miro (32x24cm-13x9in) s.d.25/IV/73 i. lead pencil oil pastel (F.FR 25000)
£2541	$4421	(13-Apr-92 GL.P78/R) La melodie acide (14x24cm-6x9in) s. Indian ink (F.FR 25000)
£3200	$5792	(2-Dec-91 CSK144/R) Composition (46x62cm-18x24in) s. indian ink
£3280	$6003	(13-May-92 FER.M184/R) Monigote con espiral y estrella (40x30cm-16x12in) s. col.crayon dr (S.P 600000)
£5200	$9412	(2-Dec-91 CSK143/R) Composition (46x62cm-18x24in) s. indian ink
£5285	$9195	(13-Apr-92 GL.P77/R) Personnage et oiseaux avec un chien (22x16cm-9x6in) s.i.d.14/IV/77 lead pencil (F.FR 52000)
£5292	$9314	(11-Apr-92 AW.H1962/R) Composition en coleurs (30x21cm-12x8in) s.i.d.1977 col.chk (DM 15400)
£6000	$11460	(30-Jun-92 C182/R) Femme nue debout, from La Grande Chaumiere (31x23cm-12x9in) s.d.1937 pencil
£6105	$10500	(12-Oct-91 SY.NY54/R) Untitled (27x21cm-11x8in) s.d.1963 num.VIII s.d.1/X/63 num.IX W/C ink two
£6557	$12000	(13-May-92 CH.NY321/R) Composition no. 1 (47x63cm-19x25in) s. num.1 verso col.wax crayons
£6557	$12000	(13-May-92 CH.NY322/R) Composition no. 3 (47x63cm-19x25in) s. num.3 verso col.wax crayons
£6557	$12000	(13-May-92 CH.NY323/R) Composition no. 5 (47x62cm-19x24in) s. num.5 verso col.wax crayons
£6557	$12000	(13-May-92 CH.NY327/R) Personnage (20x13cm-8x5in) s. pen indian ink over pencil
£6857	$12000	(25-Feb-92 CH.NY98/R) Composition (32x50cm-13x20in) s. col.wax crayons
£7500	$13575	(2-Dec-91 CSK145/R) Composition (22x18cm-9x7in) s. gouache ink
£7500	$14325	(30-Jun-92 C182 a/R) Femme nue assis, from La Grande Chaumiere (31x23cm-12x9in) s.d.1937 pencil
£8000	$13840	(24-Mar-92 C85/R) Composition au point noir (47x71cm-19x28in) init. col.crayons chl
£8796	$15481	(9-Apr-92 ANS.M126/R) Personatni Stls-54 Serie 45 (90x63cm-35x25in) s. etching collage (S.P 1600000)
£9290	$17000	(14-May-92 SY.NY196/R) Composition (28x22cm-11x9in) s.d.69 felt pen
£10286	$18000	(25-Feb-92 CH.NY101/R) Femme et oiseau dans la nuit (49x35cm-19x14in) s. d.num.7/1/72-20/VI/71.II verso brush ink
£10500	$19005	(2-Dec-91 CSK142/R) Elegia per Roma (23x19cm-9x7in) s. two d.80verso ballpoint pen set of three
£11561	$20000	(2-Oct-91 SY.NY61/R) Quelques fleurs pour des amis (41x32cm-16x13in) s. col.crayon wash pair
£12000	$21840	(29-May-92 C435/R) Sin titulo (25x32cm-10x13in) s.d.1949verso brush ink
£12000	$22920	(30-Jun-92 C198/R) Le promeneur (38x28cm-15x11in) s. pastel
£12195	$22195	(11-Dec-91 WE.MU271/R) Composition (22x29cm-9x11in) s.i.d.73 col.chk (DM 35000)
£12969	$23604	(30-May-92 VG.B317/R) Ubu aux Baleares (25x17cm-10x7in) s. col.pencil indian ink brush (DM 38000)
£14000	$24220	(25-Mar-92 S92/R) Composition (44x56cm-17x22in) init.d.31/12/60 W/C blk.crayon wash
£14124	$25000	(7-Nov-91 SY.NY215 b/R) Composition (23x32cm-9x13in) s. indian ink htd white chk
£15000	$28650	(1-Jul-92 S220/R) Composition (65x50cm-26x20in) s. d.70,72verso Indian ink W/C col.crayon
£17141	$32226	(17-Dec-91 BRO.B399/R) Personajes (35x50cm-14x20in) s.d.58 pastel (S.P 3100000)

MIRO, Joan (1893-1983) Spanish-cont.

£18311	$32777	(17-Nov-91 GL.P8/R) Sans titre (62x45cm-24x18in) s.d.28.5.920verso crayon (F.FR 180000)
£18820	$33688	(17-Nov-91 GL.P12/R) Sans titre (63x48cm-25x19in) s.d.19.8.30verso crayon (F.FR 185000)
£26230	$48000	(13-May-92 CH.NY284/R) Untitled (42x64cm-17x25in) s. d.4/1/70 verso gouache W/C brush indian ink
£27322	$50000	(14-May-92 SY.NY192/R) Tete (47cm-19ins circular) W/C ink wash crayon
£28571	$50000	(25-Feb-92 SY.NY63/R) Oiseaux (48x36cm-19x14in) s. oil gouache newsprint on linen
£31000	$59210	(30-Jun-92 C188/R) Homme et femme (65x81cm-26x32in) s. s.d.8/1/63 verso W/C gouache crayon
£40241	$69215	(12-Oct-91 SY.MO24/R) Projets de costumes - Jeux d'Enfants (30x46cm-12x18in) s.i.d.1932 pencil gouache col.crayon board (F.FR 400000)
£78000	$141180	(3-Dec-91 C189/R) Personnage (55x69cm-22x27in) s. gouache wax crayon ink
£80000	$144800	(3-Dec-91 S41/R) Composition (71x108cm-28x43in) s.d.1929 verso chl gouache sandpaper
£81967	$150000	(11-May-92 CH.NY35/R) Maquette pour Programme, Ballets Russes de Monte Carlo, New York (32x25cm-13x10in) s.d.9-33 gouache
£92896	$170000	(12-May-92 CH.NY152/R) Graphisme concret (72x99cm-28x39in) s. gouache white chk brush indian ink
£155769	$295962	(26-Jun-92 GK.B80/R) Femmes devant le soleil (64x48cm-25x19in) s.i.d.1942verso gouache W/C indian ink pen (S.FR 405000)
£169492	$300000	(6-Nov-91 SY.NY33/R) Pastorale (46x61cm-18x24in) s.d.23-10-24 pastel blk.crayon India ink pencil

MIRON SIMA (1902-) Palestinian

| £479 | $900 | (5-Jan-92 GG.TA294/R) Tower and trees (49x65cm-19x26in) s.d.1963-71 |
| £426 | $800 | (5-Jan-92 GG.TA91/R) Still life with fruit and flowers (53x36cm-21x14in) s.indis.d.1946 gouache |

MIROU, Antoine (attrib) (1586-1661) Flemish

| £11000 | $21120 | (10-Jul-92 C114/R) Extensive landscape with Good Samaritan (16x24cm-6x9in) with sig. copper |

MIROU, Antoine (circle) (1586-1661) Flemish

| £7000 | $12460 | (30-Oct-91 S57/R) Woodland scene with stag hunt (13x17cm-5x7in) copper |

MISSINGHAM, Hal (1906-) Australian

| £2766 | $4896 | (26-Apr-92 SY.ME474 k) River landscape (28x40cm-11x16in) s. W/C (A.D 6500) |

MISTI-MIFLIEZ, Ferdinand (fl.1900-1910) French

| £1000 | $1730 | (3-Oct-91 CSK7/R) Portrait of a young girl in a white party dress (119x56cm-47x22in) s.d.1921 pastel |

MITCHELL, Alfred R (1888-1972) American

£1412	$2500	(12-Feb-92 B.SF481/R) Stream and pool (33x41cm-13x16in) s. i.verso board
£2388	$4250	(26-Nov-91 MOR.P91) Dolphin fountain (33x41cm-13x16in) s. board
£8427	$15000	(26-Nov-91 MOR.P51) Dorothea and Amaryllis at our 29th St. House (41x51cm-16x20in) s. board

MITCHELL, Arthur Croft (1872-?) British

| £550 | $1034 | (18-Dec-91 C137) The letter (61x51cm-24x20in) s.i.stretcher |

MITCHELL, Arthur Roy (1886-1977) American

| £1180 | $2100 | (2-Nov-91 IH.NY192/R) Sheriff in pursuit (71x66cm-28x26in) s. |

MITCHELL, Charles Henry (19th C) British

| £400 | $692 | (25-Mar-92 PHI508) Cattle and sheep resting by river (39x69cm-15x27in) s. W/C htd.white |

MITCHELL, Emily (fl.1872-1892) British

| £2166 | $3899 | (19-Nov-91 RAS.K180/R) Girl wearing dress and shawl with flowers (122x66cm-48x26in) s. (D.KR 24000) |

MITCHELL, Ernest Gabriel (1859-?) British

| £500 | $955 | (3-Jul-92 BW374) Harvesting scene with figures to fore (18x25cm-7x10in) s. W/C |

MITCHELL, Flora H (?) British

| £2056 | $3557 | (25-Mar-92 A.D40) Northside of Parnell Square (25x33cm-10x13in) s.i. pen W/C (E.P 2200) |

MITCHELL, George Bertrand (1874-1966) American

| £1130 | $2000 | (13-Feb-92 S.W2825/R) New England Harbour (64x76cm-25x30in) s. |

MITCHELL, Janet (20th C) Canadian

£488	$878	(18-Nov-91 HO.ED142) Untitled landscape (36x51cm-14x20in) board (C.D 1000)
£413	$756	(2-Jun-92 R.T508/R) Summer lakeside view with children boating. Houses with children, nearby (37x55cm-15x22in) s. W/C double-sided (C.D 900)
£413	$756	(2-Jun-92 R.T596) Mist in mountains in autumn. Forest interior (39x56cm-15x22in) s. W/C double-sided (C.D 900)

MITCHELL, Janet (20th C) Canadian-cont.
£537 $966   (18-Nov-91 HO.ED13/R) Untitled - children and snowflakes (28x33cm-11x13in) s.d.58 (C.D 1100)

MITCHELL, Joan (1926-) American
£8380 $15000   (14-Nov-91 SY.NY293/R) Untitled (35x34cm-14x13in) s. canvas on board
£15000 $25800   (17-Oct-91 S22/R) Composition No. 117 (64x54cm-25x21in) s.
£18436 $33000   (6-May-92 CH.NY286/R) Untitled (100x81cm-39x32in) s.verso
£26012 $45000   (3-Oct-91 SY.NY14/R) Untitled (94x91cm-37x36in) s.
£26342 $47680   (21-May-92 CC.P49/R) Canada (100x146cm-39x57in) diptych (F.FR 260000)
£89385 $160000   (12-Nov-91 CH.NY57/R) Grande Vallee no.XII (280x200cm-110x79in) s.
£94972 $170000   (5-May-92 CH.NY42/R) Afternoon (260x160cm-102x63in) s. s.i.verso
£6704 $12000   (7-May-92 SY.NY262/R) Cypresses (49x70cm-19x28in) s. pastel
£9497 $17000   (6-May-92 CH.NY336/R) Untitled (58x78cm-23x31in) s. col.chk

MITCHELL, John Campbell (1862-1922) American
£1500 $2670   (28-Apr-92 S267/R) The road to Appin (38x46cm-15x18in) s. s.i.verso

MITCHELL, William Frederick (1845-1914) British
£400 $720   (27-Jan-92 PH170) H.M.S. Victor Emanuel (20x15cm-8x6in) s.d.1875 num.767 W/C over pencil
£400 $712   (28-Nov-91 PHX417) HMS Nothumberland (28x43cm-11x17in) s.i.d.1902 W/C
£480 $826   (4-Mar-92 DR55) H.M.S. Narcissus in Portsmouth harbour (24x20cm-9x8in) s.d.1874 W/C
£500 $840   (15-Aug-91 B369/R) H.M.S. Alfred (51x74cm-20x29in) s.i.d.1874 i.verso W/C htd white
£580 $986   (5-Aug-91 WW158/R) Shipping in choppy sea (51x74cm-20x29in) s.d.1878 W/C over pencil htd white
£800 $1344   (15-Aug-91 B254/R) Battle of Trafalgar (41x69cm-16x27in) s. W/C htd white
£950 $1596   (15-Aug-91 B379/R) H.M.S. Bacchante with H.M. Yacht Osborne (50x70cm-20x28in) s.d.1883 W/C htd white
£2800 $4704   (15-Aug-91 B380/R) The Victoria and Albert (50x73cm-20x29in) s.d.1880 W/C htd white
£3400 $5712   (15-Aug-91 B378/R) H.M. Yacht Osborne (50x72cm-20x28in) s.i.d.1896 W/C htd white

MITI-ZANETTI, Giuseppe (1859-1929) Italian
£726 $1351   (16-Jun-92 F.M26) Val di Storo (23x32cm-9x13in) s. board (I.L 1600000)
£771 $1435   (16-Jun-92 F.M21) Il naviglio lungo via Senato a Milano (15x20cm-6x8in) s.i. board (I.L 1700000)

MITSUTANI, Kunishiro (1874-1936) Japanese
£2000 $3500   (28-Feb-92 SY.NY19/R) Japanese temple scene (34x50cm-13x20in) s. pencil W/C

MITTERFELLNER, A (1912-1972) German
£2195 $3820   (19-Sep-91 D.V178/R) Forggensee with Sauling near Fussen, Allgau (15x33cm-6x13in) s. panel (A.S 45000)

MITTEY, Joseph (1853-1936) Swiss?
£9000 $15570   (4-Oct-91 C47/R) Studies of golden am amherst pheasants, hummingbirds and other birds (57x70cm-22x28in) s.indis.i.d.1877

MOAL, Jean le (1909-) French
£6484 $11737   (21-May-92 CC.P38/R) Composition (80x80cm-31x31in) s.d.1955 (F.FR 64000)

MODERSOHN, Otto (1865-1943) German
£893 $1555   (17-Sep-91 FN.S2045) Avenue, autumn (60x50cm-24x20in) s.d.1940 board (DM 2600)
£1700 $2992   (8-Apr-92 CSK300/R) Country lane (16x18cm-6x7in) board
£4181 $7610   (13-Dec-91 BM.B534/R) Wumme landscape with two rowing boats (47x45cm-19x18in) board (DM 12000)
£5575 $10146   (13-Dec-91 BM.B533/R) Still life of apples in bowl (47x45cm-19x18in) s. board (DM 16000)
£6272 $11415   (13-Dec-91 BM.B529/R) Flooded fields by the Wumme (65x80cm-26x31in) s.d.39 (DM 18000)
£7560 $13986   (12-Jun-92 HN.H605/R) Bunch of flowers in vase (72x49cm-28x19in) s.d.1933 (DM 22000)
£7560 $13986   (12-Jun-92 HN.H605 b/R) Wooded mountainous landscape, Allgau (69x49cm-27x19in) (DM 22000)
£7666 $13951   (13-Dec-91 BM.B532/R) Bridge near Fischerhude with figures and farmhouse (41x60cm-16x24in) i. board (DM 22000)
£7904 $13436   (25-Oct-91 BM.B596/R) Wumme landscape with flowering trees, spring (50x70cm-20x28in) s.d.25 (DM 23000)
£8247 $15340   (20-Jun-92 BM.B760/R) Peasant woman working in moor with cottage and stable beyond (50x72cm-20x28in) s. panel (DM 24000)
£8481 $14841   (3-Apr-92 BM.B537/R) Cart on path in spring landscape (50x61cm-20x24in) s.d.37 i.verso (DM 24000)
£8834 $15459   (3-Apr-92 BM.B540/R) Woodland clearing in Surheide (63x87cm-25x34in) board on canvas (DM 25000)
£10601 $18551   (3-Apr-92 BM.B538/R) Wumme landscape in thunderstorm atmosphere (61x85cm-24x33in) s.d.36 (DM 30000)
£10601 $18551   (3-Apr-92 BM.B539/R) Farmhouse garden near Fischerhude. Heath landscape (53x72cm-21x28in) pair (DM 30000)

MODERSOHN, Otto (1865-1943) German-cont.

£15464 $26907 (21-Sep-91 SA.A530/R) Children dancing near moorland cottage (28x45cm-11x18in) s. board (DM 45000)
£16725 $30439 (13-Dec-91 BM.B531/R) View of Fischerhude with children (75x95cm-30x37in) s. (DM 48000)
£17526 $32598 (20-Jun-92 BM.B759/R) Ducks on the Wumme in Fischerhude and farmhouse beyond (57x41cm-22x16in) board (DM 51000)
£19795 $36027 (29-May-92 VG.B12/R) Moor landscape, spring (80x64cm-31x25in) s. (DM 58000)
£23704 $42904 (20-May-92 GK.Z5007/R) Summer day (70x110cm-28x43in) s.d.1938 (S.FR 64000)
£24390 $44390 (13-Dec-91 BM.B530/R) Landscape near Fischerhude with farmhouse and peasant woman by canal (85x68cm-33x27in) s. i.verso (DM 70000)
£27304 $49693 (29-May-92 VG.B13/R) Moor landscape with canal and man in boat (85x135cm-33x52in) s. (DM 80000)
£1031 *$1907* *(12-Jun-92 HN.H606/R) Trees and houses by the Wumme (15x24cm-6x9in) chk chl (DM 3000)*
£1053 *$1895* *(21-Nov-91 L.K340/R) Moor landscape with bridge and girl (13x21cm-5x8in) chk (DM 3000)*
£1203 *$2201* *(3-Jun-92 L.K328/R) Moor cottages (28x44cm-11x17in) mono i. chl (DM 3500)*

MODERSOHN-BECKER, Paula (1876-1907) German

£2577 $4381 (25-Oct-91 BM.B597/R) Female nude walking (31x21cm-12x8in) i. chl (DM 7500)
£52632 $90000 (13-Mar-92 FN.S2566/R) Village fair, Weyerberg (53x72cm-21x28in) d.1902 board (DM 150000)
£87719 $150000 (13-Mar-92 FN.S2567/R) Children in the sun (71x47cm-28x19in) board (DM 250000)
£1375 *$2337* *(25-Oct-91 BM.B598/R) Cockerel and hen (20x25cm-8x10in) i. chl (DM 4000)*

MODIGLIANI, Amedeo (1884-1920) Italian

£2682 *$4800* *(9-May-92 CE.NY90/R) Donna seduta (35x25cm-14x10in) pencil*
£9000 *$17190* *(1-Jul-92 S205/R) Nu debout (42x24cm-17x9in) s. pencil*
£9774 *$17690* *(6-Dec-91 GL.P167/R) Portrait de femme au chapeau (31x25cm-12x10in) s. lead pencil (F.FR 95000)*
£14000 *$24220* *(24-Mar-92 C24/R) Nu couche (27x35cm-11x14in) s. pencil paper on panel*
£27155 *$49423* *(25-May-92 CH.R27/R) Les Amoureux (35x25cm-14x10in) s.i. pencil (I.L 60000000)*
£27451 *$47216* *(12-Oct-91 F.L217/R) Le Pelerin - Charles Douglas (42x24cm-17x9in) pencil (S.FR 70000)*
£29661 *$52500* *(7-Nov-91 SY.NY131/R) L'homme a la pipe (48x30cm-19x12in) s.i. pencil*
£47782 *$86962* *(25-May-92 WK.M892/R) Nu assis sur le divan, la belle romaine (59x38cm-23x15in) s. pencil col.indian ink pen sepia panel (DM 140000)*
£54645 *$100000* *(12-May-92 CH.NY120/R) Caryatide (54x42cm-21x17in) s. pen brush ink wash over pencil*

MOELLER, Louis C (1855-1930) American

£4094 $7000 (12-Mar-92 CH.NY55/R) One man's opinion (30x40cm-12x16in) s.i.

MOERENHOUT, Edward (?) Belgian?

£582 $1053 (3-Dec-91 C.A173) Chaloupe au crepuscule (19x26cm-7x10in) s. panel (B.FR 34000)

MOERENHOUT, Joseph Jodocus (1801-1875) Flemish

£525 $950 (5-Dec-91 FA.PH478/R) Figures in landscape by fountain (18x23cm-7x9in) s.d.50 panel
£1101 $1960 (30-Oct-91 CH.AM47) The refreshment (39x49cm-15x19in) s.d.1832 panel (D.FL 3600)
£5505 $9798 (30-Oct-91 CH.AM45/R) The horsefair, Antwerp (88x117cm-35x46in) s.d.1863 (D.FL 18000)

MOERENHOUT, Joseph Jodocus (attrib) (1801-1875) Flemish

£1161 $2124 (12-May-92 C.A219) Fishing village at evening (56x70cm-22x28in) s. (B.FR 70000)

MOERKERCKE, Jan Baptist (?-1689) Flemish

£30581 $56881 (18-Jun-92 SY.MO44/R) Nature morte aux instruments de musique (81x103cm-32x41in) s. (F.FR 300000)

MOESCHLIN, Walter J (1902-1961) Swiss

£706 *$1264* *(15-Nov-91 ZOF.Z1807) Dancer (51x35cm-20x14in) s.d.47 i.verso mixed media (S.FR 1800)*

MOEYAERT, Nicolaes Cornelisz (1592-1655) Dutch

£2439 $4439 (12-Dec-91 L.K109/R) God appearing to Abraham (53x51cm-21x20in) (DM 7000)
£8000 $14240 (1-Nov-91 C123/R) Clearing in forest with boy playing bagpipes and farm animals by ruin (31x46cm-12x18in) panel

MOEYAERT, Nicolaes Cornelisz (attrib) (1592-1655) Dutch

£2222 $3978 (12-Nov-91 SY.AM28/R) Elijah taken by the feet by the Sunnamite woman (61x49cm-24x19in) panel (D.FL 7200)

MOEYAERT, Nicolaes Cornelisz (circle) (1592-1655) Dutch

£2932 $5248 (14-Nov-91 CH.AM41/R) The family of Darius before Alexander (79x111cm-31x44in) panel (D.FL 9500)

MOFFETT, Ross E (1888-1971) American
£2500 $4500   (22-Nov-91 S.BM204/R) Cod fisherman (122x152cm-48x60in) s.
£2730 $4750   (20-Sep-91 DM.D2028/R) The West End, autumn (91x117cm-36x46in) s.

MOGAN, John William (20th C) American
£984 $1800   (6-Jun-92 LAE.L139/R) Wall Street on 4th July (61x61cm-24x24in) s.

MOGEL, Elias (18th C) Austrian
£883 $1678   (23-Jun-92 D.V326/R) Portrait of Judex Curae Nikolaus Palffy von Erdod, Vienna (55x44cm-22x17in) i.verso one of pair (A.S 18000)

MOGFORD OF EXETER, Thomas (1809-1868) British
£3200 $5632   (8-Apr-92 S174/R) Portrait of Malcolm Lewin Esq (90x70cm-35x28in)

MOGFORD, John (1821-1885) British
£5500 $10065   (14-May-92 TL105/R) Entering harbour, Southwold, Suffolk (79x124cm-31x49in) s.d.1879 i.verso canvas on board
£5800 $10614   (7-Feb-92 K504/R) Extensive coastal scene with fisherman resting on rock by fishing boats (86x142cm-34x56in) s.d.1874
£581 $1000   (16-Oct-91 CH.NY252/R) A mountainous lake landscape (26x53cm-10x21in) s.d.1876 W/C htd.white board

MOGGIOLI, Umberto (1886-1919) Italian
£16444 $28613   (14-Apr-92 F.M187/R) Nudo femminile (100x75cm-39x30in) s.d.1917 (I.L 36000000)

MOHOLY-NAGY, Laszlo (1895-1946) Hungarian/American
£45198 $80000   (6-Nov-91 CH.NY286/R) Construction Al 6 (60x50cm-24x20in) s.i.d.33/34 oil aluminum
£629 $1120   (30-Nov-91 VG.B894/R) Self portrait with discus-thrower (8x8cm-3x3in) pencil Hungarian field postcard verso (DM 1800)
£5461 $9939   (26-May-92 KF.M1091/R) Composition (31x24cm-12x9in) mono.i.d.1940 col.chk pencil (DM 16000)

MOHR, Hugo Lous (1889-1970) Norwegian
£561 $960   (13-Mar-92 FN.S2570) Tower of the winds, Athens (65x77cm-26x30in) s. (DM 1600)
£1019 $1854   (14-Dec-91 BU.O78/R) House in mountain landscape (31x38cm-12x15in) init. panel (N.KR 11500)

MOHREN, Jean (1876-?) German
£623 $1183   (24-Jun-92 KM.K1189) Beilstein on the Moselle with Burg Metternich (40x50cm-16x20in) s. (DM 1800)
£761 $1446   (24-Jun-92 KM.K1188/R) View of Cologne with figures (50x40cm-20x16in) s. (DM 2200)

MOHRMANN, J H (19/20th C) British
£1757 $3146   (6-May-92 KH.K137) Steamship 'Bryssel' (50x69cm-20x27in) s.d.1904 (D.KR 20000)

MOHRMANN, John Henry (19/20th C) British
£1800 $3132   (14-Apr-92 CSK177/R) S.S. Bellova off Dover (60x100cm-24x39in) s.d.1894

MOILLIET, Louis (1880-1962) Swiss
£6923 $13154   (25-Jun-92 GK.B506/R) Self portrait (50x35cm-20x14in) s.i.d.1906 (S.FR 18000)
£1314 $2352   (6-May-92 GD.B867/R) Mallorca (23x28cm-9x11in) s.i.d.1926 W/C (S.FR 3600)
£1344 $2419   (19-Nov-91 GS.B3210) Coastal landscape with figures (17x21cm-7x8in) i.verso W/C (S.FR 3400)
£3154 $5992   (25-Jun-92 GK.B507) Mosque (24x32cm-9x13in) W/C (S.FR 8200)

MOILLON, Louise (1609-1696) French
£190000 $345800   (13-Dec-91 C57/R) Peaches and grapes in blue and white Chinese porcelain bowl on ledge (49x64cm-19x25in) s.d.1634 panel
£223124 $392698   (10-Apr-92 AT.P37/R) La marchande de fruits (96x125cm-38x49in) panel (F.FR 2200000)

MOILLON, Louise (style) (1609-1696) French
£2469 $4420   (14-Nov-91 CH.AM43) Mulberries in glass tazza, melon on pewter plate, apricots and dead jay (40x48cm-16x19in) bears sig. canvas on board (D.FL 8000)

MOISES, Julio (1888-?) Spanish
£10385 $17655   (22-Oct-91 DUR.M71/R) Venus delante del espejo (115x147cm-45x58in) s.d.1946 (S.P 1900000)

MOISSET, Maurice (1860-1946) French
£592 $1078   (11-Dec-91 WE.MU113/R) By the edge of the wood (35x42cm-14x17in) (DM 1700)
£1018 $1700   (19-Aug-91 GC.M37/R) Le Chemin de la Commanderie (50x65cm-20x26in) s.

MOISSET, Raymond (1906-) French
£717 $1377   (7-Jul-92 ARC.P87) Tourbillon vegetal (81x100cm-32x39in) s. s.d.1963verso (F.FR 6900)
£416 $798   (7-Jul-92 ARC.P86) Composition (20x47cm-8x19in) s. gouache (F.FR 4000)

MOISSET, Raymond (1906-) French-cont.
£555 $955   (20-Oct-91 I.N209) Le couple (30x39cm-12x15in) s.d.46 gouache (F.FR 5500)

MOITTE, Jean Guillaume (1746-1810) French
£2374 $4250   (14-Jan-92 SY.NY172/R) Design for silver candelabrum, tazza and jars
                  (28x41cm-11x16in) pen wash over black chk
£2514 $4500   (14-Jan-92 SY.NY171/R) Study for three silver urns (15x42cm-6x17in) pen
                  wash over black chk

MOJA, Frederico (1802-1885) Italian
£5859 $10371   (5-Nov-91 GF.L2140/R) Courtyard of Doge's Palace, Venice
                  (43x54cm-17x21in) s.i.indis.d.184. (S.FR 15000)

MOKADI, Moshe (1902-1975) Palestinian
£479 $900   (5-Jan-92 GG.TA270/R) Vase with flowers (35x24cm-14x9in) s. canvas on
                  board
£757 $1400   (8-Jun-92 GG.TA194/R) Landscape, bridge and houses (22x35cm-9x14in) s.
                  board
£757 $1400   (8-Jun-92 GG.TA195/R) Child (15x17cm-6x7in) s. board
£1222 $2200   (6-Jan-92 GG.TA423/R) Landscape (25x35cm-10x14in) s. board
£1459 $2700   (8-Jun-92 GG.TA193/R) Figure (39x29cm-15x11in) s. canvas on board
£2556 $4600   (6-Jan-92 GG.TA421/R) Interior (36x46cm-14x18in) s. canvas on board
£2703 $5000   (9-Jun-92 GG.TA395/R) Figures by tree (43x33cm-17x13in) s. board
£3784 $7000   (8-Jun-92 GG.TA192/R) Figures in field (49x61cm-19x24in) s.
£11351 $21000   (8-Jun-92 GG.TA191/R) Figures (73x92cm-29x36in) s.
£11892 $22000   (8-Jun-92 GG.TA190/R) Woman in room (82x100cm-32x39in) s.
£595 $1100   (8-Jun-92 GG.TA196/R) Untitled (34x46cm-13x18in) s. gouache

MOLA, Pier Francesco (1612-1666) Italian
£15613 $28572   (16-May-92 F.L21/R) Madonna col Bambino e San Giovannino
                  (74x58cm-29x23in) (S.FR 42000)
£33520 $60000   (17-Jan-92 SY.NY88/R) Aaron, High Priest of the Israelites, holding a
                  censer (95x70cm-37x28in)
£1900 $3306   (14-Apr-92 C116/R) The Immaculate Conception (26x19cm-10x7in) chk pen
                  wash corners made up

MOLA, Pier Francesco (after) (1612-1666) Italian
£2107 $3750   (22-Jan-92 SY.NY64/R) Angel appearing to Hagar in desert
                  (42x53cm-17x21in)

MOLA, Pier Francesco (attrib) (1612-1666) Italian
£2235 $3823   (18-Mar-92 D.V27/R) Prophet (72x82cm-28x32in) (A.S 45000)
£821 $1478   (22-Nov-91 AGS.P120) Groupe sur le seuil d'un temple (19x24cm-7x9in) pen
                  (F.FR 8000)

MOLA, Pier Francesco (circle) (1612-1666) Italian
£1500 $2730   (10-Dec-91 PH119/R) Orpheus and Eurydice (25x39cm-10x15in)
£5071 $9229   (26-May-92 FB.P10) Homere lisant (33x25cm-13x10in) (F.FR 50000)
£9790 $17327   (7-Nov-91 D.V25/R) Adoration of the Kings (76x100cm-30x39in) (A.S 200000)

MOLA, Pier Francesco (style) (1612-1666) Italian
£1000 $1750   (3-Apr-92 C92) Moses' spies returning form Promised Land
                  (87x110cm-34x43in)
£1200 $2304   (9-Jul-92 CSK35/R) The finding of Moses (29cm-11ins circular) panel
£1300 $2496   (9-Jul-92 CSK51/R) Saint John the Baptist in the wilderness
                  (64x46cm-25x18in)
£1700 $3060   (22-Nov-91 SWS46/R) The Annunciation to Saint Joachim (74x60cm-29x24in)
£1800 $3150   (28-Feb-92 C124) The rest on the flight into Egypt (62x74cm-24x29in) oval
£1800 $3150   (28-Feb-92 C24/R) Saint John the Baptist preaching to the Multitude
                  (65x49cm-26x19in)
£2600 $4758   (12-May-92 SWS757/R) Preaching of Saint John the Baptist
                  (80x95cm-31x37in)

MOLANUS, Mattheus (?-1645) Dutch
£12237 $21659   (7-Nov-91 D.V138/R) Ambush in wooded landscape with windmill
                  (22x33cm-9x13in) s.d.1637 panel (A.S 250000)

MOLANUS, Mattheus (attrib) (?-1645) German
£1852 $3352   (19-May-92 GF.L2390/R) Village scene with peasants dancing
                  (36x58cm-14x23in) panel (S.FR 5000)

MOLARSKY, Abraham (c.1883-?) Russian/American
£925 $1600   (6-Sep-91 S.BM281/R) Still life with iris (58x51cm-23x20in) s. board

MOLDOVAN, Kurt (1918-) Austrian
£598 $1071   (15-Jan-92 D.V190/R) Group of figure and study of figure
                  (40x30cm-16x12in) s. chl pen indian ink htd.white (A.S 12000)
£777 $1383   (28-Apr-92 D.V323/R) Street scene (32x48cm-13x19in) s.i.d.70 pen brush
                  indian ink (A.S 16000)
£1212 $2206   (26-May-92 D.V185/R) Acrobat and death (29x21cm-11x8in) s.d.56 indian ink
                  (A.S 25000)
£1212 $2206   (26-May-92 D.V186/R) Church (21x24cm-8x9in) s.d.49 pen wash (A.S 25000)
£3151 $5734   (26-May-92 D.V236/R) Station (31x46cm-12x18in) s.i.d.75 W/C (A.S 65000)
£3151 $5734   (26-May-92 D.V237/R) Landscape with palm trees (32x48cm-13x19in) s.i.d.63
                  W/C (A.S 65000)

MOLE, John Henry (1814-1886) British
£400 $712   (28-Nov-91 PHX365) Okehampton Castle (33x53cm-13x21in) i.d.1856 W/C
£500 $890   (29-Oct-91 SWS460) Shepherd with sheep in landscape (45x75cm-18x30in) s. W/C bodycol
£500 $955   (13-Jul-92 PH101) The village spring (25x19cm-10x7in) s.d.1857 W/C bodycol
£600 $1086   (19-May-92 PH64) Autumn glow (44x73cm-17x29in) s. W/C
£600 $1074   (14-Jan-92 SWS36/R) Crossing the moors (30x50cm-12x20in) s.d.1869 W/C bodycol htd.gum arabic
£700 $1204   (4-Mar-92 S269/R) Returning from peat bog (25x17cm-10x7in) s.d.1855 W/C
£715 $1366   (16-Jul-92 S137/R) Young girl carrying basket on the sea shore (20x33cm-8x13in) s.d.1874 W/C over pencil
£1000 $1910   (13-Jul-92 PH95) Figure and donkey on country track (13x22cm-5x9in) s.d.1868 W/C htd white
£1300 $2444   (19-Dec-91 C18/R) At Peter Tavy, South Devon (17x25cm-7x10in) s.d.1874 i.verso pencil W/C htd white
£1400 $2506   (14-Nov-91 S146/R) Oystermouth Castle, Glamorganshire (19x33cm-7x13in) s.d.1869 W/C over pencil htd.bodycol
£2200 $3872   (6-Apr-92 PH48/R) Gleaners returning. At the well (28x22cm-11x9in) s.d.1861 W/C bodycol. pair
£2700 $4941   (3-Jun-92 S266/R) Cliff side path (47x68cm-19x27in) s.d.1860 W/C htd. white
£2800 $4844   (26-Mar-92 RB708) Near Ringwood, Hants (25x38cm-10x15in) s. W/C

MOLENAER, Bartholomeus (?-1650) Dutch
£2400 $4272   (30-Oct-91 S61/R) Peasant family saying grace (37x30cm-15x12in) panel

MOLENAER, Bartholomeus (attrib) (?-1650) Dutch
£2962 $5184   (24-Feb-92 CSC.P40) La partie de cartes (25x21cm-10x8in) panel (F.FR 29000)

MOLENAER, Bartholomeus (style) (?-1650) Dutch
£1368 $2503   (12-May-92 SY.AM30/R) Peasants carousing by cottage (40x52cm-16x20in) indist.s. (D.FL 4500)
£1700 $2975   (27-Feb-92 CSK203) The duet (77x63cm-30x25in)
£12000 $21000   (1-Apr-92 S103/R) Tavern interior (80x70cm-31x28in) panel

MOLENAER, Claes (1540-1589) Flemish
£2568 $4597   (7-May-92 CH.AM77/R) Winter landscape with skaters on frozen waterway by village (49x64cm-19x25in) s. (D.FL 8500)
£3323 $5949   (7-May-92 CH.AM102 a/R) Fishermen in rowing boat on town moat, windmill and bridge beyond (26x37cm-10x15in) init. panel (D.FL 11000)

MOLENAER, Claes (attrib) (1540-1589) French
£1553 $2686   (24-Mar-92 VN.R59/R) Figures and animals on the ice by a town wall (27x34cm-11x13in) panel (D.FL 5000)

MOLENAER, Jan (17th C?) Dutch
£1100 $1958   (29-Oct-91 PH140) Interior of a tavern with a boer being attended by a woman (30x25cm-12x10in) panel
£3680 $6992   (23-Jun-92 D.V230/R) The doctor's visit (32x25cm-13x10in) s. panel (A.S 75000)

MOLENAER, Jan (attrib) (?) Dutch
£846 $1514   (7-May-92 CH.AM45) Portraits of ladies and gentlemen, in costumes with lace collars (7x6cm-3x2in) i. oval five in one display case (D.FL 2800)

MOLENAER, Jan Miense (1610-1668) Dutch
£612 $1089   (29-Oct-91 VN.R159) Tavern interior with figures (32x25cm-13x10in) panel (D.FL 2000)
£3043 $5355   (11-Apr-92 AT.P58/R) La maitresse d'ecole (25x32cm-10x13in) s. panel (F.FR 30000)
£3296 $6196   (18-Dec-91 AT.P152/R) Scene de beuverie a l'interieur d'une auberge (30x29cm-12x11in) s. panel (F.FR 32000)
£3500 $6125   (1-Apr-92 S218/R) Peasants playing games in interior (36x41cm-14x16in) panel
£3779 $6500   (9-Oct-91 CH.NY125/R) Card players in tavern (35x33cm-14x13in) s. panel
£5658 $10751   (26-Jun-92 AT.P97/R) L'arracheur de dents (27cm-11ins circular) s. panel (F.FR 55000)
£7500 $13650   (10-Dec-91 PH49/R) Interior with figures seated around table drinking and smoking (40x37cm-16x15in) indist.s. panel
£9000 $15660   (15-Apr-92 C124/R) Tavern interior with boor carousing with wench and others looking on (36x47cm-14x19in) s. panel
£60000 $109200   (10-Dec-91 PH41/R) Charlatan (106x68cm-42x27in) s.
£145251 $260000   (16-Jan-92 CH.NY127/R) Interior with lady seated at virginal, another lady singing and young girl watching (51x35cm-20x14in) s.d.1634 panel

MOLENAER, Jan Miense (after) (1610-1668) Dutch
£1700 $2890   (22-Oct-91 S248/R) Card players (25x19cm-10x7in) bears sig. panel

MOLENAER, Jan Miense (style) (1610-1668) Dutch
£1500 $2700   (22-Nov-91 SWS191/R) Figures seated at a table in an interior (42x53cm-17x21in) panel

MOLENAER, Klaes (1630-1676) Dutch
£1900 $3382   (29-Oct-91 PH19/R) Figures on a village path before a windmill (35x33cm-14x13in) s. panel
£3400 $5950   (1-Apr-92 S28) Winter landscape with figures beside walls of town (27x35cm-11x14in) panel
£4000 $7680   (7-Jul-92 PH109/R) Peasants leaving riverbank by ferry before Star Inn, with two figures (42x33cm-17x13in) panel
£9259 $16574   (14-Nov-91 CH.AM179/R) Travellers resting near inn by river and swimmers by bridge beyond (89x113cm-35x44in) s. (D.FL 30000)
£9500 $17290   (12-Dec-91 B41/R) River landscape with travellers on path, with sailing barges and windmill beyond (47x62cm-19x24in) panel

MOLENAER, Klaes (attrib) (1630-1676) Dutch
£884 $1600   (22-May-92 SY.NY254/R) Two figures and dog in extensive landscape (27x34cm-11x13in) panel

MOLENAER, Klaes (style) (1630-1676) Dutch
£850 $1556   (12-May-92 SWS813) Dune landscape with fishermen (27x34cm-11x13in) init. panel

MOLFENTER, Hans (1884-?) German
£756 $1315   (17-Sep-91 FN.S2448/R) Tiger in cage (25x37cm-10x15in) s.indis.d. board (DM 2200)
£2577 $4485   (17-Sep-91 FN.S2447/R) Cannstatter Volksfest with monkeys performing (28x23cm-11x9in) mono. canvas on board (DM 7500)
£4124 $7175   (17-Sep-91 FN.S2449) Shipping in harbour (21x26cm-8x10in) s.d.1931 mixed media (DM 12000)

MOLIN, J B du (fl.1670-1695) Dutch?
£2160 $3867   (14-Nov-91 CH.AM75) Portrait of lady standing by column. Portrait of lady standing (?x82cm-?x32in) one s.d.1701 two originally oval (D.FL 7000)

MOLINA CAMPOS, Florencio (1891-1959) Argentinian
£3978 $7400   (16-Jun-92 RO.BA112) Mate y guitarra (33x49cm-13x19in) tempera
£1541 $2650   (9-Oct-91 RO.BA581) Zurciendo recuerdos (21x31cm-8x12in) s. s.i.d.959verso W/C
£1686 $2900   (9-Oct-91 RO.BA582) Matando el tiempo (18x25cm-7x10in) s. W/C
£1744 $3000   (9-Oct-91 RO.BA583) Meta 'Cordiona y Guitarra' (18x25cm-7x10in) s. s.i.d.959verso W/C

MOLINA NUNEZ, Emilio (20th C) Spanish
£763 $1313   (7-Oct-91 ANS.M168/R) Paisaje rural (75x51cm-30x20in) s. (S.P 140000)
£2182 $3950   (20-May-92 ANS.M73/R) Muchacho con gallina (100x81cm-39x32in) s. (S.P 400000)

MOLINA SANCHEZ, Jose Antonio (1918-) Spanish
£982 $1689   (16-Oct-91 FER.M180/R) Abstracto en rosas, verdes y blancos (46x55cm-18x22in) s. (S.P 180000)

MOLINA, Antonio de (fl.1802) Spanish
£2800 $4900   (1-Apr-92 S225/R) Holy Family with Infant Saint John the Baptist and music making angels (173x125cm-68x49in) s.d.1802

MOLINARI, Alexander (1772-1831) German
£1100 $1892   (4-Mar-92 C15/R) Mr. F. M. Magnus (7x?cm-3x?in) min. s.d.1819 gilt-wood frame oval
£1313 $2363   (24-Nov-91 AG.W14) Portrait of Jozef Maksymilian Ossolinski (28x34cm-11x13in) s. pastel (P.Z 26000000)

MOLINARI, Antonio (?-1648) Italian
£7821 $14000   (17-Jan-92 SY.NY154/R) Saint Sebastian (104x96cm-41x38in) within painted oval
£11000 $21120   (7-Jul-92 PH26/R) Feast of Herod with Salome kneeling before Herod (91x179cm-36x70in)
£14525 $26000   (16-Jan-92 CH.NY33/R) Susannah and Elders (125x125cm-49x49in)
£15000 $26250   (1-Apr-92 S10/R) David with head of Goliath before Saul (114x178cm-45x70in)
£58000 $105560   (11-Dec-91 S9/R) Bernice. Sophonisba. Cornelia. Artemisia (91x153cm-36x60in) four
£1350 $2363   (27-Feb-92 CSK94/R) Romans in battle (18x23cm-7x9in) s. d.verso ink wash htd.white

MOLINE, A de (19th C) French
£2520 $4461   (10-Nov-91 ZZ.F34/R) Amazone dans l'allee cavaliere (32x41cm-13x16in) s. (F.FR 25000)

MOLINS, A de (19th C) French
£536 $1007   (16-Dec-91 AGS.P22/R) Depart pour la chasse (11x15cm-4x6in) s. panel (F.FR 5200)

MOLITOR, Martin von (1759-1812) Austrian
£4688 $8297   (5-Nov-91 GF.L2074/R) Biblical scene of Lazarus and the rich man (27x37cm-11x15in) mono. (S.FR 12000)

MOLITOR, Martin von (1759-1812) Austrian-cont.
£8014 $14585   (11-Dec-91 N.M258 a/R) Rocky landscape with cattle watering. River
         landscape with shepherds (56x77cm-22x30in) s.d.1806 and 1808 gouache
         pair (DM 23000)

MOLK, Josef Adam (1714-1794) Austrian
£813 $1415   (13-Apr-92 AT.P82) La Crucifixion (32x23cm-13x9in) s.d.1790verso
         (F.FR 8000)

MOLL, Carl (1861-1945) Austrian
£12413 $22095   (28-Nov-91 D.V65/R) Im Prater (35x35cm-14x14in) mono. panel (A.S 250000)
£24000 $42720   (27-Nov-91 S152/R) View of gardens at Schonbrunn, Vienna
         (34x34cm-13x13in) s. panel

MOLL, Evert (1878-1955) Dutch
£520 $925   (29-Oct-91 VN.R161) Harbour scene with shipping (60x80cm-24x31in) s.
         (D.FL 1700)
£579 $1077   (16-Jun-92 VN.R169/R) Breakwater in the surf (40x60cm-16x24in) s.
         (D.FL 1900)
£581 $1028   (5-Nov-91 SY.AM472) Rotterdam harbour (39x49cm-15x19in) s. (D.FL 1900)
£608 $1058   (17-Sep-91 CH.AM275) A view of a harbour with a fisherman mooring a boat
         (50x70cm-20x28in) s. (D.FL 2000)
£654 $1256   (7-Jul-92 VN.R148) Shipping on the Maas (59x99cm-23x39in) s. (D.FL 2100)
£673 $1198   (29-Oct-91 VN.R160/R) Harbour scene with shipping (59x89cm-23x35in) s.
         (D.FL 2200)
£683 $1182   (24-Mar-92 VN.R61) Shipping in a harbour (79x99cm-31x39in) s. (D.FL 2200)
£683 $1216   (26-Nov-91 VN.R75/R) Shiiping in an inland harbour (58x78cm-23x31in) s.
         (D.FL 2200)
£714 $1236   (24-Mar-92 VN.R63/R) Barge on a river (59x79cm-23x31in) s. (D.FL 2300)
£760 $1322   (17-Sep-91 CH.AM266) A busy day in the harbour, Schiedam
         (60x100cm-24x39in) s. (D.FL 2500)
£909 $1609   (22-Apr-92 CH.AM55) Shipping in a harbour (32x48cm-13x19in) s.
         (D.FL 3000)
£977 $1729   (5-Nov-91 GF.L2758/R) Harbour view with windmill (61x80cm-24x31in) s.
         (S.FR 2500)
£1408 $2549   (3-Dec-91 FN.S2338/R) Dutch canal with bridge and boats. Dutch river
         landscape with town (17x37cm-7x15in) s. panel pair (DM 4000)
£2905 $5055   (14-Apr-92 SY.AM66/R) Still life with flowers and glassware
         (49x68cm-19x27in) s. (D.FL 9500)
£4969 $8596   (24-Mar-92 VN.R62) Shipping in Rotterdam Harbour (75x125cm-30x49in) s.
         (D.FL 16000)

MOLL, Oskar (1875-1947) German
£1754 $3158   (23-Nov-91 N.M229/R) Sailing boats I (72x99cm-28x39in) s.d.1946 paper on
         panel (DM 5000)
£14085 $25493   (6-Dec-91 GB.B6869/R) Interior with rocking chair (70x80cm-28x31in) s.
         (DM 40000)
£15789 $28421   (23-Nov-91 N.M228/R) Portrait of Frau Muller-Oerlinghausen with bunch of
         summer flowers (79x69cm-31x27in) s. (DM 45000)
£699 $1245   (30-Nov-91 VG.B896/R) Im Tiergarten (30x44cm-12x17in) s.d.46 pencil chk
         board (DM 2000)
£1404 $2526   (23-Nov-91 N.M230/R) Riesengebirge landscape (37x29cm-15x11in) s. W/C
         (DM 4000)

MOLLE, Johannes (19th C) ?
£600 $1068   (21-Jan-92 SWS1776/R) Young lady and suitor (13x?cm-5x?in) min. giltwood
         frame

MOLLER, Aenderly (1863-?) German
£1018 $1832   (22-Nov-91 SA.A1757/R) Rose garden before country house (31x57cm-12x22in)
         s.d.1895 canvas on panel (DM 2900)

MOLLER, Andreas (1684-1758) Danish
£2646 $4709   (28-Apr-92 RAS.K192/R) Portrait of Frederik IV's daughter, Pricess
         Charlotte Amalie (76x63cm-30x25in) s.i.d.1740verso (D.KR 30000)

MOLLER, Gunnar (20th C) Danish
£1240 $2257   (25-May-92 RAS.K130/R) Resurrection (125x190cm-49x75in) init.d.85verso
         (D.KR 14000)
£1261 $2169   (4-Mar-92 KH.K166) Light by the fjord (130x90cm-51x35in)
         init.d.87-88verso (D.KR 14000)
£1557 $2709   (18-Sep-91 KH.K158) Coastal zone (134x184cm-53x72in) init.d.84verso
         (D.KR 17500)

MOLLER, I P (19th C) Danish
£632 $1137   (19-Nov-91 RAS.K146/R) Plon Castle in Sachsen (33x44cm-13x17in)
         (D.KR 7000)
£2641 $4437   (27-Aug-91 RAS.K239/R) Fjord landscape with view towards town
         (56x76cm-22x30in) (D.KR 30000)
£2646 $4709   (27-Apr-92 BU.K3/R) View towards Lausanne (50x75cm-20x30in) s. wood panel
         (D.KR 30000)

MOLLER, Olivia Holm (1875-?) Danish
£555 $1009   (10-Dec-91 RAS.K125) Yellow sun, green mountains (80x130cm-31x51in) i.on
         stretcher (D.KR 6200)

MOLLER, Otto (1883-1964) German
£2389 $4348   (30-May-92 VG.B143/R) Wochenmarkt (60x76cm-24x30in) s. (DM 7000)
£1024   *$1863*   *(26-May-92 KF.M1089/R) Water fall (50x37cm-20x15in) W/C over pencil (DM 3000)*

MOLLER, Peter (1948-) Australian
£940 $1674   (28-Apr-92 CH.ME173) Reach for the arts (121x100cm-48x39in) .
     s.i.d.90verso acrylic (A.D 2200)
£769   *$1369*   *(28-Apr-92 CH.ME172) In the gallery ... but ... is it art (121x100cm-48x39in) s. s.i.d.90verso acrylic newspaper canvas (A.D 1800)*
£769   *$1369*   *(28-Apr-92 CH.ME277) Don't blame me, I'm not responsible for this painting (100x100cm-39x39in) s. s.d.90verso acrylic paper on canvas (A.D 1800)*

MOLLER, Rudolf (1881-) German
£962 $1790   (20-Jun-92 BM.B1059/R) Rest on the flight, male and female nude with child in landscape (38x48cm-15x19in) W/C indian ink brush (DM 2800)

MOLLER, Thorvald Christian Benjamin (1842-1925) Danish
£1825 $3284   (22-Nov-91 SA.A1668/R) Sailing ships off the coast (93x131cm-37x52in) s.d.1891 (DM 5200)

MOLLERSWARD, Pekkila (1894-1975) Scandinavian
£414   *$717*   *(28-Mar-92 UA.U495) Vastgotaspangen and Baumbach (24x30cm-9x12in) s.d.1931 W/C (S.KR 4300)*

MOLLES, Anton (fl.1830-1850) Austrian
£1384 $2422   (20-Feb-92 D.V337/R) Roses (36x45cm-14x18in) s. (A.S 28000)

MOLLIS, Anton (1830-?) Austrian
£976 $1776   (11-Dec-91 N.M528/R) Alpine flowers (37x30cm-15x12in) indis.s.d.1873
     (DM 2800)
£1600 $2976   (16-Jun-92 PH39/R) Still life (36x45cm-14x18in) s.
£514   *$884*   *(8-Oct-91 ZEL.L1285/R) Bunch of flowers with lilies, tulips and roses (46x33cm-18x13in) s. gouache (DM 1500)*

MOLNAR, A von (19th C) ?
£500 $950   (24-Jun-92 D.NY59) A sleeping odalisque (61x94cm-24x37in) s.

MOLNAR, Janice S (?) ?
£969 $1725   (26-Nov-91 J.M1178) Study (46x59cm-18x23in) s. (A.D 2200)

MOLNARI, R (?) ?
£756 $1300   (20-Oct-91 HG.C1377) Girl with doll (51x61cm-20x24in) s.

MOLODYKH, Macha (20th C) Russian
£515 $881   (13-Mar-92 ARC.P205/R) Nature morte a la pomme rouge (63x80cm-25x31in) s.
     (F.FR 5000)

MOLS, J H (19/20th C) Belgian
£581 $1011   (14-Apr-92 SY.AM428) Cardplayers (26x36cm-10x14in) s. panel style of
     B.Manfredi (D.FL 1900)

MOLS, N P (1859-1921) Danish
£529 $942   (27-Apr-92 BU.K23/R) Beach landscape with figures and oxcart
     (20x45cm-8x18in) init.d.87 (D.KR 6000)
£542 $926   (12-Mar-92 RAS.V946/R) Dachshund and puppies (48x60cm-19x24in) init.
     (D.KR 6000)

MOLS, Robert (1848-1903) Belgian
£759 $1305   (16-Oct-91 KM.K1282) Still life with peaches (31x26cm-12x10in) s.d.1878
     (DM 2200)
£2813 $4980   (5-Nov-91 SY.AM255/R) Sailing vessels in calm sea (88x108cm-35x43in) s.
     (D.FL 9200)
£4312 $7891   (12-May-92 C.A220/R) The road to Dieppe (52x96cm-20x38in) s.
     (B.FR 260000)
£8563 $15156   (5-Nov-91 SY.AM63/R) View of Duinkerken (44x93cm-17x37in) s. (D.FL 28000)

MOLSTED, Chr (1862-1930) Danish
£3521 $5915   (27-Aug-91 RAS.K41/R) Gammel Strand, morning in the herring season
     (100x132cm-39x52in) s. (D.KR 40000)

MOLTINO, Francis (1818-1874) British
£1350 $2403   (28-Nov-91 B104) Venice (61x91cm-24x36in) s.

MOLTINO, Francis (attrib) (1818-1874) British
£1600 $2768   (1-Oct-91 SWS1708/R) On Grand Canal, Venice (74x126cm-29x50in)

MOLTKE, Harald (1871-1960) Danish
£660 $1142   (2-Sep-91 BU.K14/R) Young girl seated by window (55x45cm-22x18in)
     mono.d.14 (D.KR 7500)
£705 $1256   (27-Apr-92 BU.K15/R) Mother and daughter resting (95x95cm-37x37in)
     mono.d.1917 (D.KR 8000)

MOLTKE, Harald (1871-1960) Danish-cont.
£496 $849   (10-Mar-92 RAS.K97/R) Portrait of mother and daughter (146x115cm-57x45in) s.d.1936 gouache (D.KR 5500)

MOLVIG, John (1923-1970) Australian
£2115 $3806   (24-Nov-91 SY.S519) Cattle grid and carcass (67x93cm-26x37in) s.d.58 board (A.D 4800)
£1250 $2388   (29-Jun-92 AAA.S151) Adam and Eve and the Industrial Revolution (91x108cm-36x43in) s.d.62 mixed media (A.D 3200)

MOLYN, Pieter (1595-1661) Dutch
£1986 $3615   (11-Dec-91 N.M339/R) Peasants and travellers in hilly landscape with wayside cottage (52x49cm-20x19in) mono. panel (DM 5700)
£6395 $11000   (10-Oct-91 SY.NY129/R) Dune landscape with figures on a hillock and trees on the right (31x50cm-12x20in) panel
£1442 $2711   (18-Dec-91 AT.P109/R) Paysans au repos pres de leur ferme (21cm-8ins circular) s.d.1651 W/C crayon (F.FR 14000)
£1553 $2764   (25-Nov-91 CH.AM22/R) Upland landscape with tower on hill (15x21cm-6x8in) chk wash (D.FL 5000)
£2484 $4422   (25-Nov-91 CH.AM21/R) Mountainous wooded landscape with hunting party and ruined castle beyond (15x19cm-6x7in) s.d.1654 chk (D.FL 8000)
£5200 $9048   (13-Apr-92 S298/R) River landscape with small boat by heavily wooded bank (15x19cm-6x7in) s.d.1654 black chk wash

MOLYN, Pieter (attrib) (1595-1661) Dutch
£5556 $10056   (19-May-92 GF.L2047/R) Horse-drawn cart on path and two peasants resting beneath oaktree (88x120cm-35x47in) (S.FR 15000)

MOLYN, Pieter (circle) (1595-1661) Dutch
£1511 $2704   (7-May-92 CH.AM67/R) Manor house by frozen lake with herdsman and cattle in foreground (21cm-8ins circular) panel (D.FL 5000)

MOLYNEUX, Edward (fl.1899-1904) British
£1000 $1790   (5-May-92 H539) Lake and snow-capped mountains beyond (81x127cm-32x50in) s.

MOMMERS, Hendrik (1623-1693) Dutch
£2210 $4000   (22-May-92 SY.NY157/R) Peasant family with market wares in landscape (62x47cm-24x19in) panel
£3520 $6125   (13-Sep-91 C87/R) Extensive landscape with shepherd boy and cattle by tree, farm beyond (49x64cm-19x25in) s. panel
£4200 $7476   (1-Nov-91 C126/R) Woman buying vegetables by ruined classical Portico (47x73cm-19x29in) panel
£5802 $10502   (21-May-92 L.K92/R) Figures driving donkeys and women conversing in river landscape (65x83cm-26x33in) (DM 17000)
£6810 $12121   (28-Apr-92 F.R40/R) Scena di mercato (33x40cm-13x16in) panel (I.L 15000000)
£13812 $25000   (22-May-92 SY.NY145/R) Peasants and animals resting under two trees (71x61cm-28x24in)

MOMMERS, Hendrik (style) (1623-1693) Dutch
£843 $1500   (22-Jan-92 SY.NY187/R) Figures resting with sheep and cattle (62x49cm-24x19in)
£900 $1575   (2-Apr-92 CSK93) Quay with Stevedores and other figures with fish and vegetables (48x71cm-19x28in) panel
£3000 $5400   (21-Nov-91 C29/R) Drover and shepherds by classical ruins in landscape (86x124cm-34x49in)

MOMPER, Frans de (1603-1660) Flemish
£781 $1383   (5-Nov-91 GF.L2373) Rocky river landscape with fortified castle (41x56cm-16x22in) s. (S.FR 2000)
£2300 $4025   (25-Feb-92 PH51/R) Winter landscape with figures near village pond (19x24cm-7x9in) panel
£5587 $10000   (16-Jan-92 CH.NY94/R) Travellers on path in extensive mountainous landscape (62x103cm-24x41in) panel
£20478 $37065   (21-May-92 L.K93/R) Winter landscape with peasants and fagott gatheres before town (42x53cm-17x21in) panel (DM 60000)

MOMPER, Frans de (attrib) (1603-1660) Flemish
£4000 $7280   (10-Dec-91 PH135/R) Milkmaid and cattle before farmhouse (75x93cm-30x37in)

MOMPER, Frans de (circle) (1603-1660) Flemish
£2018 $3471   (16-Oct-91 AT.P56/R) Le jeu de saute-mouton (27x38cm-11x15in) panel (F.FR 20000)

MOMPER, Frans de and VRANCX, Sebastian (17th C) Flemish
£12155 $22000   (22-May-92 SY.NY137/R) Village with two men fixing wheel of cart and townsfolk (62x86cm-24x34in)

MOMPER, Joos de (1564-1635) Flemish
£34263 $60646   (7-Nov-91 D.V119/R) John the Baptist preaching in mountain landscape (49x90cm-19x35in) panel (A.S 700000)
£44693 $80000   (16-Jan-92 CH.NY88/R) Extensive Alpine landscape with story of William Tell (109x165cm-43x65in)

MOMPER, Joos de (1564-1635) Flemish-cont.
£92000 $161000   (1-Apr-92 S25/R) Mountainous coastal landscape with travellers at rest in
                     foreground (46x73cm-18x29in) panel
£257182 $457784   (29-Oct-91 EP.M11/R) Paisaje montanoso con ermitanos (199x277cm-78x109in)
                     (S.P 47000000)
£2531   *$4530*   *(12-Nov-91 SY.AM322/R) Landscape with broken bridge spanning river*
                     (23x36cm-9x14in) d.1610 pen col.wash (D.FL 8200)

MOMPER, Joos de (attrib) (1564-1635) Flemish
£4778 $8648   (21-May-92 L.K95/R) Men on bridge in mountain landscape with fortified
                     castle (33x48cm-13x19in) panel (DM 14000)
£18538 $34851   (18-Dec-91 AT.P33/R) Paysage fluvial (65x81cm-26x32in) wood (F.FR 180000)

MOMPER, Joos de (circle) (1564-1635) Flemish
£17680 $32000   (21-May-92 CH.NY123/R) Extensive mountainous landscape with castle and
                     travellers resting on path (44x63cm-17x25in) panel
£18232 $33000   (21-May-92 CH.NY64/R) Winter landscape with town by frozen waterway
                     (49x65cm-19x26in) panel

MOMPER, Joos de (style) (1564-1635) Flemish
£2500 $4800   (10-Jul-92 C116/R) River landscape with travellers crossing bridge,
                     church beyond (29x41cm-11x16in) panel

MOMPER, Joos de and BRUEGHEL, Jan (younger) (17th C) Flemish
£20346 $37233   (13-May-92 LC.P8/R) Paysage de la vallee du Rhin (43x72cm-17x28in) panel
                     (F.FR 200000)

MOMPER, Joos de and SNAYERS, Peeter (17th C) Flemish
£5000 $8750   (3-Apr-92 C53/R) Ambush in gorge (55x85cm-22x33in) panel

MOMPER, Philips de (elder) (?-1634) Flemish
£40000 $76800   (8-Jul-92 S31/R) Upland landscape with peasants picking fruit
                     (75x105cm-30x41in) panel

MOMPO, Manuel Hernandez see   HERNANDEZ MOMPO, Manuel

MOMPOU, Joseph (1888-1969) Spanish
£8200 $14924   (29-May-92 C427/R) Barcelona, La Rambla (60x72cm-24x28in) s.
                     s.i.d.1944verso

MOMTHOLON, F de (?) ?
£705 $1256   (28-Apr-92 RAS.K586) Summer field of flowers (38x61cm-15x24in) s.
                     (D.KR 8000)

MONACHESI, Sante (1910-1991) Italian
£920 $1646   (14-Nov-91 F.M26/R) Marina con barche (33x50cm-13x20in) s. (I.L 2000000)
£1529 $2722   (29-Nov-91 F.F112) Case (80x60cm-31x24in) s. (I.L 3300000)
£1599 $2782   (14-Apr-92 F.M45/R) Case (50x70cm-20x28in) s. (I.L 3500000)
£1761 $3134   (29-Nov-91 F.F111) Energiagra. Il grande spazio della vita
                     (60x80cm-24x31in) s.d.1965 (I.L 3800000)
£1764 $3315   (19-Dec-91 F.M148/R) Veduta di citta (60x50cm-24x20in) s. (I.L 3800000)
£1827 $3179   (14-Apr-92 F.M4/R) Natura morta (50x61cm-20x24in) s.verso (I.L 4000000)
£1905 $3487   (12-May-92 F.R143) Muri ciechi di Parigi (60x50cm-24x20in) s.
                     (I.L 4200000)
£1918 $3338   (14-Apr-92 F.M88/R) Paesaggio (60x50cm-24x20in) s. (I.L 4200000)
£2092 $3786   (3-Dec-91 F.R223/R) Natura morta realta poetica (50x61cm-20x24in) s.
                     s.i.verso (I.L 4500000)
£3629 $6641   (12-May-92 F.R231/R) Natura morta (50x70cm-20x28in) s.d.1949verso
                     (I.L 8000000)
£6577 $12037   (12-May-92 F.R182/R) Venezia (80x100cm-31x39in) s.d.1970 (I.L 14500000)
£908   *$1616*   *(29-Apr-92 F.F47) Studio di figura con piatto e frutta. Studio di figura*
                     s. chl pair (I.L 2000000)
£1362   *$2424*   *(29-Apr-92 F.F48/R) Studio di figura distesa. Figura femminile eretta.*
                     Figura di profilo s. chl set of three (I.L 3000000)
£2317   *$4124*   *(29-Nov-91 F.F113/R) Vele adriatiche (50x70cm-20x28in) s. s.verso mixed*
                     media (I.L 5000000)

MONALDI, Paolo (18th C) Italian
£10211 $18380   (19-Nov-91 F.R81/R) Pranzo contadino. L'elemosina (64x49cm-25x19in) pair
                     (I.L 22000000)
£185658 $334184   (19-Nov-91 F.R178/R) Danza del saltarello sull'aia. Scena popolare con la
                     moscacieca (245x350cm-96x138in) pair (I.L 400000000)

MONALDI, Paolo (school) (18th C) Italian
£1657 $3000   (21-May-92 CH.NY177/R) Figures outside farmhouse and travellers on path
                     in landscape (46x62cm-18x24in)

MONAMY, Peter (1689-1749) British
£4222 $7938   (18-Dec-91 AT.P191/R) Vaisseaux sur une mer calme (34x43cm-13x17in)
                     (F.FR 41000)
£6000 $10740   (13-Nov-91 S2 a) The Mary Rose repelling attack 1669 (18x24cm-7x9in) s.
£31000 $55490   (13-Nov-91 S2/R) Royal Yacht and other shipping off Gillingham with Upnor
                     Castle (67x154cm-26x61in) s.
£800   *$1432*   *(14-Nov-91 S5) Shipping off the coast (28x38cm-11x15in) bears sig. pen*
                     wash over pencil

MONAMY, Peter (circle) (1689-1749) British
£1400 $2352 (15-Aug-91 B326/R) British Men-o'-War at sea (51x62cm-20x24in) bears sig.
£2600 $4680 (22-Nov-91 C98/R) English two-decker with Royal Yacht under stern
(72x122cm-28x48in)
£4000 $7200 (9-Jan-92 B296) A warship firing a salute (25x31cm-10x12in) pair

MONCALVO see CACCIA, Guglielmo

MONCAYO, Emilio (20th C) ?
£650 $1183 (28-May-92 C23/R) El Chimborazo, Ecuador (69x109cm-27x43in) s. s.i.d.1936
verso

MONCHABLON, Jean Ferdinand (1855-1904) French
£28846 $52500 (28-May-92 SY.NY32/R) Le paturage (91x124cm-36x49in) s.i.d.1888

MONCHOT, L (1850-1920) French
£549 $1000 (13-Dec-91 S.W2869/R) Flirtation in garden (41x30cm-16x12in) s.

MONCIATTI, Maurice (20th C) French?
£458 $819 (17-Nov-91 R.P134) Composition (97x130cm-38x51in) mixed media canvas
(F.FR 4500)
£458 $819 (17-Nov-91 R.P172) Composition (97x130cm-38x51in) mixed media canvas
(F.FR 4500)

MONDINO, Antonio (17th C) Italian
£9945 $18000 (18-May-92 SY.MI219/R) Madonna col Bambino (81x69cm-32x27in)
(I.L 22000000)

MONDO, Domenico (1752-1817) Italian
£3017 $5430 (19-Nov-91 F.R89/R) Maddalena penitente (100x74cm-39x29in) (I.L 6500000)

MONDO, Domenico (circle) (18/19th C) Italian
£7500 $13125 (31-Mar-92 PH111/R) Banishment of Hagar (149x115cm-59x45in) shaped canvas
£10500 $18375 (31-Mar-92 PH110/R) Tobias restoring father's sight (149x115cm-59x45in)
shaped canvas

MONDRIAAN, Frits (1853-1932) Dutch
£730 $1300 (2-May-92 W.W18/R) Barbizon landscape (36x53cm-14x21in) s. W/C

MONDRIAN, Piet (1872-1944) Dutch
£7576 $13712 (21-May-92 SY.AM110/R) Landscape nearby the River Gein (30x50cm-12x20in)
s. canvas on paper (D.FL 25000)
£9259 $16852 (11-Dec-91 CH.AM272/R) View on small stream (31x26cm-12x10in) s.
cardboard (D.FL 30000)
£16667 $30167 (21-May-92 SY.AM109/R) View of the River Gein (30x50cm-12x20in) s. canvas
on board (D.FL 55000)
£46296 $84259 (11-Dec-91 CH.AM232/R) Gein with the isolated tree (64x74cm-25x29in)
cardboard paper on board (D.FL 150000)
£1284153 $2350000 (12-May-92 CH.NY142/R) Cimposition avec rouge, gris, bleu et jaune
(54x53cm-21x21in) init.d.22
£65574 $120000 (13-May-92 SY.NY6/R) Blue chrysanthemum (30x23cm-12x9in) s. W/C gouache

MONDRUS, Martin (20th C) American
£3371 $6000 (26-Nov-91 MOR.P104) Looking west on Venice Blvd., Red Car Yards
(76x91cm-30x36in) s.d.46

MONDZAIN, Simon Francois Stanislas (1890-1979) French
£509 $931 (17-May-92 GL.P171) Une rue de Ghardaia (46x38cm-18x15in) s. (F.FR 5000)
£513 $924 (22-Nov-91 ZZ.F74) Bouquet d'anemones (41x35cm-16x14in) s.d.1962
(F.FR 5000)
£811 $1467 (20-May-92 FB.P19) Nature morte (45x61cm-18x24in) s.d.1953 (F.FR 8000)
£865 $1582 (17-May-92 GL.P166/R) Bouquet (54x63cm-21x25in) s.d.1925 (F.FR 8500)
£1013 $1834 (20-May-92 FB.P2/R) Don Quichotte (72x60cm-28x24in) s.d.1945/66 s.verso
(F.FR 10000)
£1216 $2201 (20-May-92 FB.P18) Anemones (61x50cm-24x20in) s. (F.FR 12000)
£1321 $2299 (16-Apr-92 FB.P32/R) Les toits rouges (81x65cm-32x26in) s.d.19
(F.FR 13000)
£2330 $4218 (20-May-92 FB.P9/R) La Cour d'Afd-El-Tif, Alger (73x60cm-29x24in)
s.d.1925 s.verso (F.FR 23000)
£2634 $4768 (20-May-92 FB.P3/R) Bouquet de fleurs (116x89cm-46x35in) s. (F.FR 26000)
£2736 $4951 (20-May-92 FB.P5/R) La Place du Governement a Alger (80x64cm-31x25in) s.
(F.FR 27000)
£3040 $5502 (20-May-92 FB.P1/R) Baie d'Alger (61x73cm-24x29in) s. (F.FR 30000)
£608 $1100 (20-May-92 FB.P8) Femme a la mandoline (47x31cm-19x12in) s. W/C ink
(F.FR 6000)

MONET, Claude (1840-1926) French
£98361 $180000 (14-May-92 SY.NY260/R) Nympheas (68x54cm-27x21in)
£395480 $700000 (6-Nov-91 SY.NY3/R) Chemin (66x81cm-26x32in) s.d.86
£409836 $750000 (13-May-92 SY.NY51/R) Paysage a Port-Villez (65x81cm-26x32in) s.d.83
£423729 $750000 (5-Nov-91 CH.NY26/R) Le port d'Honfleur (49x65cm-19x26in) s.
£440000 $796400 (3-Dec-91 S22/R) Le Bassin d'Argenteuil (54x74cm-21x29in) s.d.75
£650000 $1241500 (30-Jun-92 S5/R) Les Alpes vues du Cap d'Antibes (67x82cm-26x32in) s.d.88
£1950000 $3724500 (29-Jun-92 C14/R) Charing Cross Bridge, La Tamise (73x100cm-29x39in)
s.d.1903

MONET, Claude (1840-1926) French-cont.
£73446 $130000   (6-Nov-91 CH.NY105/R) Soleil couchant sur la plaine (20x32cm-8x13in) s.
                          pastel paper on board

MONETOV, V (?) Russian
£659 $1160   (11-Apr-92 ZZ.F161/R) Trompe l'oeil - hommage au printemps qui passe
                     (53x36cm-21x14in) s. (F.FR 6500)

MONETTI, Karl (19th C) ?
£916 $1696   (10-Jun-92 ZZ.F33) Elegantes au verre Venitien (64x49cm-25x19in) s.
                     (F.FR 9000)

MONEY, Fred (1882-1956) French
£847 $1500   (6-Nov-91 D.NY73/R) Geraniums (46x54cm-18x21in) s.
£405 $700   (2-Oct-91 D.NY66) Paris sous la neige Bd des Batignolles
                     (46x38cm-18x15in) s.s.i. i.verso mixed media cardboard
£549 $950   (2-Oct-91 D.NY67) Market stalls (51x74cm-20x29in) s. mixed media
                     cardboard
£578 $1000   (2-Oct-91 D.NY65) Neige a Paris (30x41cm-12x16in) s. s.i.verso mixed
                     media masonite

MONFORT, Octavianus (fl.17th C) Italian
£12711 $22626   (28-Apr-92 F.R35/R) Natura morta di pesci e frutta (35x50cm-14x20in)
                           tempera vellum (I.L 28000000)

MONFREID, Georges Daniel de (1856-1929) French
£4800 $8256   (16-Oct-91 S12/R) Nature morte aux oranges (58x82cm-23x32in)
                       init.i.d.1903 board
£8382 $14500   (2-Oct-91 SY.NY24/R) Portrait de la femme de l'artiste a la tasse de the
                         (79x62cm-31x24in) init.d.1906 board

MONGE, Jules (1855-?) French
£1404 $2500   (22-Jan-92 SY.NY402/R) Prise du bois belleau par les troupes Americaines
                       le 29 Juin 1918 (33x46cm-13x18in) s.d.1918

MONGIN, Antoine Pierre (1761-1827) French
£1648 $3098   (18-Dec-91 AT.P110/R) Vue d'une eglise au bord de l'eau et de personnages
                       se promenant (35x52cm-14x20in) gouache (F.FR 16000)

MONGIN, Antoine Pierre (attrib) (1761-1827) French
£8745 $15828   (5-Dec-91 SY.MO303/R) Personnages au pied d'un escalier dans un parc
                         (95x125cm-37x49in) (F.FR 85000)

MONGINOT, Charles (1825-1900) French
£778 $1400   (22-Nov-91 S.BM48/R) Red hot chestnuts - genre scene with monkey and cat
                     (33x25cm-13x10in) s.

MONGRELL Y TORRENT, Jose (1870-?) Spanish
£500 $860   (5-Mar-92 CSK71) Los Caballos Cansados (73x106cm-29x42in) canvas on board
£25698 $46000   (11-Nov-91 GC.M65/R) Labradores del Perello (51x79cm-20x31in) s.
£462 $823   (28-Apr-92 DUR.M22/R) Campesina (19x12cm-7x5in) s. ink dr (S.P 85000)

MONI, Louis de (style) (1698-1771) Dutch
£1094 $1936   (5-Nov-91 GF.L2518) By the window (34x26cm-13x10in) panel (S.FR 2800)
£1100 $1980   (21-Nov-91 C143) Woman selling shrimps to boy (26x21cm-10x8in)
£1124 $2000   (22-Jan-92 SY.NY149/R) Woman cooking fish (30x25cm-12x10in)

MONIES, David (1812-1894) Danish
£615 $1113   (19-May-92 AB.S4356/R) Romantic park landscape with figures by pond
                     (58x75cm-23x30in) s.d.1889 (S.KR 6500)
£697 $1268   (11-Dec-91 N.M529/R) Rendezvous after church by wooden bridge in
                     landscape (48x36cm-19x14in) s.d.1844 (DM 2000)
£877 $1632   (15-Jun-92 B.O110/R) Father and son (28x24cm-11x9in) s.d.1874
                     (N.KR 10000)
£1673 $2810   (28-Aug-91 KH.K146/R) The last 'Oldenborger' - Count Frederik Dannemand
                       (20x17cm-8x7in) s.d.1839 (D.KR 19000)

MONIUSZKO, Jan Czeslaw (1853-1908) Polish
£2617 $4527   (8-Sep-91 REM.W22) Envoys at the Court of John III Sobieski
                       (110x75cm-43x30in) s. (P.Z 50000000)

MONJE, Luis (1925-) Ecuadorian
£5525 $10000   (18-May-92 CH.NY223/R) Selva (170x130cm-67x51in) s.d.1981
£8333 $15000   (19-Nov-91 CH.NY191/R) Selva tropical (127x165cm-50x65in) s.d.1975

MONJO, Hernandez (?) ?
£2600 $4836   (17-Jun-92 S588/R) Harbour scene (75x87cm-30x34in) s.

MONNICKENDAM, Martin (1874-1943) Dutch
£455 $805   (22-Apr-92 CH.AM278) Soleil d'ete (16x23cm-6x9in) s.d.1907 pencil W/C
                     bodycol. (D.FL 1500)

MONNIER, Henri (1805-1877) French
£818 $1497   (3-Feb-92 SD.P168) Le cachot (21x31cm-8x12in) init.i. W/C wash
                     (F.FR 8000)

MONNINGTON, Sir Walter Thomas (1903-1976) British
£500 $855   (1-Aug-91 CSK187) Tree study (76x63cm-30x25in)

MONNINGTON, Sir Walter Thomas (circle) (1903-1976) British
£2800 $5096   (28-May-92 B125/R) Gipsy camp (71x137cm-28x54in)

MONNOT, Maurice Louis (1869-?) French
£1529 $2600   (23-Oct-91 GD.B1181/R) Kitchen still life (55x38cm-22x15in) s.d.1902
                 (S.FR 3900)

MONNOYER, Antoine (1670-1747) French
£7136 $13272 (18-Jun-92 SY.MO249/R) Bouquet de fleurs (56x47cm-22x19in) (F.FR 70000)
£16760 $30000 (17-Jan-92 SY.NY51/R) Tulips, peonies and other flowers in a sculpted urn
                 (135x97cm-53x38in)

MONNOYER, Antoine (attrib) (1670-1747) French
£4800 $8400   (3-Apr-92 C165/R) Mixed flowers in vase (48x38cm-19x15in)

MONNOYER, Jean Baptiste (1636-1699) French
£4400 $8360   (24-Jun-92 LJ228) Still life, flowers in glass vase (39x29cm-15x11in)
£9300 $16461 (7-Nov-91 D.V210/R) Bunch of peonies, carnations and other flowers in
                 vase on stone table (63x77cm-25x30in) (A.S 190000)

MONNOYER, Jean Baptiste (after) (1636-1699) French
£2763 $5250   (24-Jun-92 D.NY60) Still life of flowers in ornate vase (86x71cm-34x28in)

MONNOYER, Jean Baptiste (attrib) (1636-1699) French
£24169 $41088 (21-Oct-91 ARC.P7/R) Bouquet de fleurs dans un vase sur un entablement
                 (74x66cm-29x26in) (F.FR 240000)

MONNOYER, Jean Baptiste (circle) (1636-1699) French
£3058 $5688   (18-Jun-92 SY.MO319/R) Panier de fleurs (38x51cm-15x20in) (F.FR 30000)
£6630 $12000 (22-May-92 SY.NY243/R) Still life of flowers in carved stone urn on ledge
                 (72x93cm-28x37in)
£7303 $13000 (30-Oct-91 D.NY85) Floral still life in gilded urn (102x91cm-40x36in)

MONNOYER, Jean Baptiste (school) (1636-1699) French
£4144 $7500   (21-May-92 CH.NY212/R) Flowers in basket with fruit on stone ledge
                 (49x60cm-19x24in)
£6296 $11396 (19-May-92 GF.L2095/R) Supraporte with flower garlands (36x155cm-14x61in)
                 (S.FR 17000)

MONNOYER, Jean Baptiste (style) (1636-1699) French
£1300 $2496   (9-Jul-92 CSK291/R) Monkey by grapes, melon and other fruit with finch
                 and parrot (66x76cm-26x30in)
£1826 $3250   (22-Jan-92 SY.NY89/R) Floral still life (73x96cm-29x38in)
£2200 $3960   (22-Nov-91 SWS106/R) A still life of flowers on a ledge (68x57cm-27x22in)
£2203 $3899   (7-Nov-91 D.V378/R) Still life of flowers and fruit (76x93cm-30x37in)
                 (A.S 45000)
£2528 $4500   (22-Jan-92 SY.NY97/R) Still life with flowers (47x34cm-19x13in)
£3000 $5760   (8-Jul-92 S298/R) Still life of flowers in basket upon stone ledge
                 (87x114cm-34x45in)
£4000 $7680   (9-Jul-92 CSK290/R) Mixed flowers in basket on ledge (63x76cm-25x30in)
£4711 $8622   (12-May-92 SY.AM1/R) Still life of flowers in sculpted urn
                 (48x64cm-19x25in) (D.FL 15500)
£5000 $8750   (27-Feb-92 CSK175/R) Roses, carnations and tulips and other flowers on
                 dish on ledge (33x41cm-13x16in) panel
£5900 $10207 (4-Sep-91 BT237/R) Still life of flowers in urn (137x112cm-54x44in)
£6050 $10527 (13-Sep-91 C26/R) Mixed flowers in sculpted urn on stone ledge
                 (63x76cm-25x30in)
£6500 $11700 (21-Nov-91 CSK257) Roses, tulips and other flowers in urn on plinth and
                 birds in landscape (112x89cm-44x35in)
£8500 $14875 (23-Sep-91 PHB59) A still life of flowers (67x55cm-26x22in)

MONOGRAMMIST A B (?) ?
£1235 $2198   (27-Apr-92 BU.K57/R) Flowers in vase on table (51x42cm-20x17in) mono.
                 wood panel (D.KR 14000)
£1306 $2272   (18-Sep-91 N.M625/R) Congratulations (100x75cm-39x30in) mono. (DM 3800)

MONOGRAMMIST A H (?) ?
£681 $1233   (19-May-92 AB.S4297/R) Interior with woman standing and man on chair
                 (25x28cm-10x11in) i.d.1785verso panel (S.KR 7200)

MONOGRAMMIST A J (?) ?
£3497 $6049   (28-Mar-92 BOD.P990) Composition (37x26cm-15x10in) mono canvas on board
                 (DM 10000)

MONOGRAMMIST A K (?) ?
£2787 $5073   (11-Dec-91 N.M530/R) Still life of flowers in vase and pomegranates on
                 table (65x100cm-26x39in) mono.d.1913 (DM 8000)

MONOGRAMMIST A L S (?) ?
£859 $1495   (17-Sep-91 FN.S2110/R) Odalisque (63x74cm-25x29in) mono.d.1914 (DM 2500)

MONOGRAMMIST A M N (?) ?
£500 $890   *(28-Nov-91 CSK21/R) Gondolas in St Mark's Basin with Santa Maria della Salute beyond (33x69cm-13x27in) mono.d.1888 pencil W/C*

MONOGRAMMIST A O (19/20th C) ?
£629 $1089   (25-Mar-92 KM.K1318) Still life of flowers (38x26cm-15x10in) mono. panel (DM 1800)

MONOGRAMMIST A R (?) ?
£705 $1256   (28-Apr-92 RAS.K647) Still life of spring flowers and book on table (37x42cm-15x17in) mono.d.77 (D.KR 8000)

MONOGRAMMIST A W J (19th C) ?
£950 $1634   (11-Oct-91 K551/R) The fox hound whisper and her whelps (33x41cm-13x16in) mono.d.1836

MONOGRAMMIST A de V (?) ?
£980 $1755   (15-Nov-91 GK.Z5078) Wooded landscape with two hunters (32x40cm-13x16in) mono. (S.FR 2500)

MONOGRAMMIST C B (?) ?
£4467 $7773   (17-Sep-91 FN.S2627/R) Children playing with sledges in village street (117x114cm-46x45in) mono.indis.d. (DM 13000)

MONOGRAMMIST C K W (?) ?
£1490 $2651   (28-Nov-91 D.V197/R) Gloxinien (80x100cm-31x39in) mono.d.1933 (A.S 30000)

MONOGRAMMIST C M H (?) ?
£1890 $3289   (18-Sep-91 N.M627/R) Police patrouille before Italian verandah (32x43cm-13x17in) mono.d.1835 (DM 5500)

MONOGRAMMIST C R C (?) ?
£880 $1681   *(16-Jul-92 S144) Interiors at Stanton Court, Gloucestershire (24x34cm-9x13in) mono.d.1857 and 1858 W/C over pencil two*
£6600 $12606   *(16-Jul-92 S145/R) Interiors at Elvaston Castle, Derbyshire (34x49cm-13x19in) mono.d.1857 and 1858 W/C over pencil three*

MONOGRAMMIST C S (?) ?
£2062 $3835   (20-Jun-92 BM.B868 a/R) Fun on the ice in Alpine landscape (53x44cm-21x17in) mono (DM 6000)

MONOGRAMMIST C T C (?) ?
£1154 $1996   (25-Mar-92 KM.K1320/R) Still life of fruit hanging on ribbon, dead pigeon and flowering branch (46x37cm-18x15in) mono. (DM 3300)

MONOGRAMMIST C W (?) ?
£4012 $7182   (12-Nov-91 SY.AM27/R) Adoration of the Kings (59x39cm-23x15in) init. (D.FL 13000)

MONOGRAMMIST C W B (?) ?
£6324 $11383   (19-Nov-91 GS.B3589/R) Animals going into Noah's Arc (64x63cm-25x25in) indis.mono.d.17.5 (S.FR 16000)

MONOGRAMMIST E G (19th C) Swiss
£658 $1224   (15-Jun-92 B.O204/R) Flowers and bird (70x55cm-28x22in) mono.d.57 (N.KR 7500)

MONOGRAMMIST E K (19th C) ?
£1259 $2279   (19-May-92 GF.L2611/R) Portrait of girl decorated with flowers (37x34cm-15x13in) mono d.1913 panel (S.FR 3400)

MONOGRAMMIST F H M (?) ?
£640 $1229   *(28-Jul-92 SWS255/R) Children amongst foxgloves (44x34cm-17x13in) mono. W/C paper on canvas*

MONOGRAMMIST F I T (18th C) Dutch
£3182 $5631   (7-Nov-91 D.V280/R) Peasants playing dice in tavern (25x36cm-10x14in) c.1700 mono.copper (A.S 65000)

MONOGRAMMIST F J (?) ?
£488 $844   (3-Oct-91 D.V70/R) Flowers before window (100x100cm-39x39in) mono.d.1930 (A.S 10000)

MONOGRAMMIST F S (?) ?
£1134 $1973   *(17-Sep-91 FN.S2115) Scene beneath viaduct (45x47cm-18x19in) mono.d.1919 gouache W/C (DM 3300)*

MONOGRAMMIST F W H (?) ?
£515 $897   *(18-Sep-91 N.M254/R) Market day in Immenthal (50x35cm-20x14in) mono.i.d.1881 W/C (DM 1500)*

MONOGRAMMIST G D (19th C) German?
£1484 $2627   (5-Nov-91 GF.L2548/R) Staubbachfalle. View of Jungfrau, Berner Oberland (24x32cm-9x13in) mono. board pair (S.FR 3800)

MONOGRAMMIST G I (?) ?
£1890 $3213   (25-Oct-91 BM.B787/R) Gothic church interior with figures
(54x75cm-21x30in) mono. panel (DM 5500)

MONOGRAMMIST H (19th C) ?
£944 $1680   (26-Nov-91 KF.M239) The letter (51x42cm-20x17in) mono.i.d.1873 (DM 2700)

MONOGRAMMIST H B (17th C) Flemish
£17789 $32375   (26-May-92 DUR.M2/R) Llamamiento de Pedro y Andres (51x66cm-20x26in)
mono. copper (S.P 3250000)
£17789 $32375   (26-May-92 DUR.M3/R) En el camino de Emaus (51x66cm-20x26in) copper
(S.P 3250000)
£23262 $42337   (26-May-92 DUR.M1/R) La huida a Egipto (51x66cm-20x26in) mono.d.1640
copper (S.P 4250000)

MONOGRAMMIST H M B (?) ?
£1700 $2958   (12-Sep-91 CSK248/R) Choosing the feather (61x46cm-24x18in) mono.d.92

MONOGRAMMIST H P (19th C) ?
£529 $942   (28-Apr-92 RAS.K368) Farmhouse on outskirts of wood (57x82cm-22x32in)
(D.KR 6000)
£1146 $2041   (28-Apr-92 RAS.K367) Still life of fruit on marble ledge under oaktree
(60x53cm-24x21in) mono. (D.KR 13000)
£1323 $2354   (28-Apr-92 RAS.K369) Jesus and the Woman of Samaria (99x111cm-39x44in)
(D.KR 15000)

MONOGRAMMIST H R (19th C) Swiss?
£3086 $5586   (5-Dec-91 SY.MO86/R) Caprice architectural avec personnages
(17x21cm-7x8in) d.1776 gouache oval (F.FR 30000)

MONOGRAMMIST H V T (?) ?
£3435 $6526   (23-Jun-92 D.V303/R) Noli me tangere (147x116cm-58x46in) c.1600 mono
(A.S 70000)

MONOGRAMMIST H W (20th C) ?
£3285 $5914   *(18-Nov-91 AT.P299/R) Mosquee au vieux Caire (50x35cm-20x14in) mono. W/C*
(F.FR 32000)

MONOGRAMMIST I S (19th C) Swiss
£2800 $4984   (30-Oct-91 S64/R) Peasants in interior beside array of pots and utensils
(46x63cm-18x25in) mono.d.1639 panel
£485 $864   (29-Apr-92 D.V720/R) Portrait of George Washington (8x6cm-3x2in) min. W/C
oval after Gilbert Stuart (A.S 10000)
£1092 $1977   (22-May-92 L.K1099/R) Portrait of Generalfeldmarschall Gebhard Leberecht
Furst Blucher (8x6cm-3x2in) min. brass frame after Friedrich Carl
Groger (DM 3200)

MONOGRAMMIST I V D S (?) ?
£7948 $13592   (18-Mar-92 D.V374/R) Mountain landscape with waterfall, figures and goats
(21x28cm-8x11in) panel (A.S 160000)

MONOGRAMMIST J B (?) ?
£1544 $2779   (22-Nov-91 SA.A1561/R) Rose hedge with butterflies (28x36cm-11x14in)
mono.d.1885 (DM 4400)

MONOGRAMMIST J C (?) ?
£1384 $2630   (24-Jun-92 KM.K932) Still life of roses, anemones and other summer
flowers in glass vase (57x71cm-22x28in) mono (DM 4000)

MONOGRAMMIST J V B (19/20th C) Dutch
£2593 $4693   (19-May-92 GF.L2141/R) Bouquet of flowers (53x40cm-21x16in) mono panel
(S.FR 7000)
£2930 $5186   (5-Nov-91 GF.L2149/R) Bouquet of flowers in glass vase (53x37cm-21x15in)
mono. panel (S.FR 7500)

MONOGRAMMIST K B S (?) ?
£5144 $9311   (5-Dec-91 SY.MO282/R) Nature morte aux fruits et legumes
(35x40cm-14x16in) s.d.1778 three (F.FR 50000)

MONOGRAMMIST L B (?) ?
£748 $1339   (5-May-92 ZEL.L1450/R) Autumn flowers in vase before mirror
(50x110cm-20x43in) d.1092 (DM 2200)

MONOGRAMMIST L C (17th C) ?
£12899 $23090   (17-Jan-92 SY.NY176/R) Still life of flowers in glass vase on table
(25x16cm-10x6in) slate

MONOGRAMMIST L C B (?) ?
£1742 $3171   (12-Dec-91 L.K626) Still life of peach, plum, grapes and berries on stone
ledge (24x30cm-9x12in) mono. copper (DM 5000)

MONOGRAMMIST L K (19th C) German
£632 $1138   (19-Nov-91 GS.B3593) Portrait of boy in uniform with notebook
(18x15cm-7x6in) mono.d.1820 canvas on board (S.FR 1600)

MONOGRAMMIST L S (20th C) ?
£3136 $5707   (12-Dec-91 L.K119/R) The Wedding of Cana (39x30cm-15x12in) mono.
mono.verso (DM 9000)

MONOGRAMMIST L V (?) ?
£510 $867   (23-Oct-91 GD.B521) Wooded landscape (16x18cm-6x7in) mono. board
(S.FR 1300)
£511 $915   (6-May-92 GD.B884/R) Park landscape in autumn sunshine (60x81cm-24x32in)
mono panel (S.FR 1400)

MONOGRAMMIST L W B (?) ?
£1296 $2320   (12-Nov-91 SY.AM18/R) Shipping on estuary (31x35cm-12x14in) init.d.1768
canvas on board (D.FL 4200)

MONOGRAMMIST M (?) ?
*£909 $1636   (19-Nov-91 GS.B3594) Father with son seated and dog in interior
(72x54cm-28x21in) mono. pastel paper on canvas (S.FR 2300)*

MONOGRAMMIST M L (?) ?
£2049 $3689   (2-Feb-92 ZZ.F24/R) Vase de pivoines (93x76cm-37x30in) mono.d.1894
(F.FR 20000)

MONOGRAMMIST M P (?) ?
£2921 $5082   (18-Sep-91 N.M631/R) Roses in basket (35x46cm-14x18in) mono. (DM 8500)

MONOGRAMMIST P B (?) ?
£2641 $4437   (27-Aug-91 RAS.K600) Small girl with doll's pram (61x46cm-24x18in) mono.
(D.KR 30000)

MONOGRAMMIST P G (?) ?
£1961 $3333   (23-Oct-91 GD.B1187) Still life with fruit and jug (40x31cm-16x12in)
mono. panel (S.FR 5000)

MONOGRAMMIST P H (19th C) French
£756 $1315   (18-Sep-91 N.M633) Surburban view in autumn (25x36cm-10x14in) mono.
(DM 2200)

MONOGRAMMIST P Ph (?) ?
£962 $1674   (18-Sep-91 N.M634) Man smoking at table in interior (22x11cm-9x4in) mono.
panel (DM 2800)

MONOGRAMMIST P V B (?) ?
£3833 $6976   (12-Dec-91 L.K120/R) Still life of asters, dahlias and other flowers in
vase (36x27cm-14x11in) mono. (DM 11000)

MONOGRAMMIST R B (?) ?
£680 $1210   (28-Apr-92 D.V119/R) Allegory of spring (84x62cm-33x24in) mono.d.1917
oval (A.S 14000)

MONOGRAMMIST R G H (?) ?
£800 $1344   (16-Aug-91 K580) Children playing in sea (46x53cm-18x21in) mono.

MONOGRAMMIST S J (?) ?
£687 $1196   (21-Sep-91 SA.A1964/R) Harvest scene (35x47cm-14x19in) indis.s. (DM 2000)

MONOGRAMMIST S K (?) ?
£2000 $3820   (16-Jul-92 CSK294/R) Elegant beauty (76x56cm-30x22in) mono.

MONOGRAMMIST S T (?) ?
£511 $915   (6-May-92 GD.B886/R) Mountainous landscape with figures, evening
(30x43cm-12x17in) mono (S.FR 1400)

MONOGRAMMIST T L (?) ?
£528 $956   (7-Dec-91 WK.M468/R) In the garden (51x71cm-20x28in) mono.d.1876
(DM 1500)

MONOGRAMMIST T M (?) ?
£962 $1674   (21-Sep-91 SA.A1766/R) Still life of fruit (20x25cm-8x10in) mono. panel
(DM 2800)

MONOGRAMMIST T M H (?) ?
£3229 $5522   (18-Mar-92 D.V353/R) Fish in basket on stone table (30x36cm-12x14in)
mono. panel (A.S 65000)

MONOGRAMMIST V H (?) ?
£6179 $11617   (18-Dec-91 AT.P177/R) Nature morte a la guirlande de fleurs, aux fruits
et aux oiseaux (89x102cm-35x40in) bears mono.d.1668 (F.FR 60000)

MONOGRAMMIST W E B (?) ?
£510 $913   (5-May-92 ZEL.L1453/R) Scottish highlands, spring (46x61cm-18x24in)
(DM 1500)

MONOGRAMMIST W M (19th C) ?
£1000 $1820   (14-Dec-91 BA.S49) Amsterdam's harbour entrance (80x120cm-31x47in) s.d.85
(S.KR 10500)

MONOGRAMMIST W P (?) ?
£464 $850   (12-May-92 GM.B458) Nu sur un canape jaune mono. pastel (B.FR 28000)

MONOGRAMMIST Y V A (?) ?
£1452 $2513   (2-Sep-91 BU.K59/R) Italian shepherd family on the run in mountains
(64x82cm-25x32in) mono.d.1827 (D.KR 16500)

MONORY, Jacques (1924-) French
£1418 $2567   (20-May-92 FB.P18 a) BR...Moi (92x130cm-36x51in) s.d.64 d.64 verso
(F.FR 14000)
£2572 $4887   (26-Jun-92 FB.P98/R) Fuite N.5 (150x230cm-59x91in) s.i.d.80 acrylic
(F.FR 25000)
£3131 $5542   (24-Apr-92 CN.P206/R) Fruit no.4 (151x232cm-59x91in) acrylic (F.FR 31000)
£5092 $9267   (15-Dec-91 P.V56/R) Peinture a Vendre (119x87cm-47x34in) s.i.d.1988
(F.FR 50000)
£5237 $8902   (27-Oct-91 P.V54/R) Peinture a Vendre (162x130cm-64x51in) s.i.d.1983verso
(F.FR 52000)
£6344 $10785   (27-Oct-91 P.V55/R) D'un oeil bleu (73x92cm-29x36in) s.i.d.1965 acrylic
(F.FR 63000)
£7700 $13937   (20-May-92 FB.P17 a/R) Opera Glace N. 9 - Opera Furia B
(196x230cm-77x91in) s.d.75 verso (F.FR 76000)

MONRAD, A C (18/19th C) ?
£535 $996   (16-Jun-92 RAS.K356/R) The accidental shipwreck of the vessel Foudroye
(35x48cm-14x19in) s.i.d.1808 gouache W/C (D.KR 6000)

MONROY, Paul Lecuit (1858-?) French
£1259 $2253   (5-May-92 ZEL.L1408/R) Mediterranean coastal landscape (46x54cm-18x21in)
s.d.1895 (DM 3700)

MONSTED, Peder (1859-1941) Danish
£529 $942   (28-Apr-92 RAS.K272) Man in boat (46x28cm-18x11in) s.i. (D.KR 6000)
£573 $974   (8-Aug-91 RAS.V965/R) Lake landscape in morning mist (24x28cm-9x11in) s.
(D.KR 6500)
£660 $1109   (27-Aug-91 RAS.K440) Mountainous landscape with flowering trees
(13x20cm-5x8in) init.d.87 (D.KR 7500)
£748 $1257   (27-Aug-91 RAS.K439) Mountain lake with sailboat, Switzerland
(14x19cm-6x7in) s.d.1887 (D.KR 8500)
£767 $1312   (12-Mar-92 RAS.V957/R) Lake with waterlilies (23x28cm-9x11in) s.d.1914
(D.KR 8500)
£836 $1405   (27-Aug-91 RAS.K441) Lake landscape with sailing boat and rowing boat
(16x22cm-6x9in) s.d.1887 (D.KR 9500)
£879 $1573   (6-May-92 KH.K141) River in summer (28x49cm-11x19in) s.d.1905
(D.KR 10000)
£1101 $1916   (14-Apr-92 SY.AM217/R) Irises (54x31cm-21x12in) s.d.1898 canvas laid down
on panel (D.FL 3600)
£1146 $2041   (28-Apr-92 RAS.K659/R) Sunset over the river with two anglers
(32x59cm-13x23in) s.d.1896 (D.KR 13000)
£1226 $2171   (5-Nov-91 BA.S133/R) Quiet summer's day (43x67cm-17x26in) s.d.1880
(S.KR 13000)
£1345 $2422   (30-Jan-92 RAS.V656/R) Coastal landscape from Tyrsbaek (50x71cm-20x28in)
s.d.1920 (D.KR 15000)
£1354 $2315   (12-Mar-92 RAS.V956/R) Lake landscape, summer (54x38cm-21x15in) s.d.1894
(D.KR 15000)
£1408 $2366   (27-Aug-91 RAS.K428) Winter's day with sleigh driving near Leksand
(35x45cm-14x18in) s.d.1927 (D.KR 16000)
£1431 $2605   (12-Dec-91 RAS.V750/R) Danish summer landscape with sheep near Svejbaek
(31x52cm-12x20in) s.d.1913 i.verso (D.KR 16000)
£1496 $2514   (27-Aug-91 RAS.K429) Houses in Italian landscape (33x22cm-13x9in)
s.d.1902 (D.KR 17000)
£1526 $2701   (11-Feb-92 RAS.K139/R) After sunset, figures on roof of house in Capri
(31x55cm-12x22in) s.i.d.1885 (D.KR 17000)
£1542 $2729   (23-Apr-92 RAS.V850/R) View of Vejle fjord from Frydenlund heath
(50x70cm-20x28in) s.i.d.1920 (D.KR 17500)
£1670 $2989   (6-May-92 KH.K142) German river landscape with barge (26x38cm-10x15in)
s.d.09 (D.KR 19000)
£1673 $2893   (2-Sep-91 BU.K54/R) Autumn harvesting scene (40x61cm-16x24in) s.d.1927
(D.KR 19000)
£1762 $3119   (23-Apr-92 RAS.V852/R) Brook running through beach wood (63x42cm-25x17in)
s.d.1908 (D.KR 20000)
£1783 $3066   (15-Oct-91 RAS.K186/R) Two boys skiing near Jonsdals river
(35x50cm-14x20in) s.d.1934 (D.KR 20000)
£1795 $3178   (11-Feb-92 RAS.K129/R) Milking time, Yderholm Kro, west of Koge
(26x33cm-10x13in) s.d.1909 (D.KR 20000)
£1800 $3258   (21-May-92 CSK327/R) Italian peasants on terrace (32x55cm-13x22in)
s.d.1885
£1892 $3425   (19-May-92 AB.S4357/R) Coastal landscape (63x48cm-25x19in) s.i.d.1917
(S.KR 20000)
£1937 $3254   (27-Aug-91 RAS.K575/R) Summer landscape with roses and elderflowers
(38x60cm-15x24in) s.d.1919 (D.KR 22000)
£1940 $3453   (28-Apr-92 RAS.K198/R) Harvesting scene (34x50cm-13x20in) s.i.d.1924
(D.KR 22000)
£1940 $3453   (28-Apr-92 RAS.K257/R) Danish summer landscape with horse and cart on
road (41x62cm-16x24in) s.d.1925 (D.KR 22000)

MONSTED, Peder (1859-1941) Danish-cont.

£2113	$3549	(27-Aug-91 RAS.K577/R) Evening in Stubberup village (33x50cm-13x20in) s.d.1907 (D.KR 24000)
£2211	$3781	(12-Mar-92 RAS.V952/R) Horse and carriage by thatched houses, winter in Herstedoster (51x75cm-20x30in) s.d.1929 (D.KR 24500)
£2562	$4688	(14-May-92 BU.S172/R) Summer day by the bathing place (35x50cm-14x20in) s.d.1936 (S.KR 27000)
£2641	$4437	(27-Aug-91 RAS.K421/R) Young girl on a stone wall in Meran (27x21cm-11x8in) s.d.1913 (D.KR 30000)
£2674	$4599	(15-Oct-91 RAS.K188/R) Summer landscape near Gershoi Church (50x70cm-20x28in) s.i.d.1931 (D.KR 30000)
£2708	$4874	(19-Nov-91 RAS.K109/R) Girl bathing, Sandvig (57x40cm-22x16in) s.i.d.1917 (D.KR 30000)
£2817	$4732	(27-Aug-91 RAS.K105/R) Danish village in summer (37x72cm-15x28in) s.d.1882 (D.KR 32000)
£2988	$5348	(6-May-92 KH.K9/R) Two children outside a farmhouse in summer (61x46cm-24x18in) s.i.d.1928 (D.KR 34000)
£2993	$5028	(27-Aug-91 RAS.K142/R) Heather covered hills near Rebild (81x122cm-32x48in) s.d.1911 (D.KR 34000)
£3246	$5778	(25-Nov-91 BU.K26/R) Alpine landscape with pinetrees (32x61cm-13x24in) s.d.1888 (D.KR 36000)
£3260	$5542	(8-Aug-91 RAS.V967/R) View of thatched houses with girl among heather (52x84cm-20x33in) s.i.d.1912 (D.KR 37000)
£3527	$6279	(28-Apr-92 RAS.K151/R) Wooded landscape with lake in summer (103x95cm-41x37in) s.d.1889 (D.KR 40000)
£3795	$6945	(14-May-92 BU.S170/R) Spring day in Sorup (40x61cm-16x24in) s.d.1936 (S.KR 40000)
£3802	$6806	(16-Nov-91 FAL.M219/R) Winter landscape from Herstedvester (43x60cm-17x24in) s.d.1923 (S.KR 40000)
£4056	$7220	(27-Apr-92 BU.K9/R) Wooded scene flying ducks (64x94cm-25x37in) s.d.1886 (D.KR 46000)
£4405	$7797	(23-Apr-92 RAS.V853/R) Rowingboat on water, snowcovered mountains in background (50x84cm-20x33in) s.d.1914 (D.KR 50000)
£4500	$8010	(27-Nov-91 S50/R) In outskirts of Cairo (40x55cm-16x22in) s.d.1893
£4717	$8349	(5-Nov-91 BA.S131/R) By the farm at Stubberup (33x50cm-13x20in) s.d.1907 (S.KR 50000)
£4828	$8303	(16-Oct-91 KM.K1289/R) Konigsee landscape with figures, spring (86x53cm-34x21in) s.d.1899 (DM 14000)
£5000	$9300	(16-Jun-92 S71/R) Guri and Tikhon in the garden (40x61cm-16x24in) s.d.1931
£5282	$8873	(27-Aug-91 RAS.K112/R) Sunny winter's day at Vestanvik near Leksand, Dalarna (88x130cm-35x51in) s.d.1927 (D.KR 60000)
£5291	$9418	(28-Apr-92 RAS.K63/R) Spring day at Syvendekjop village (70x100cm-28x39in) s.i.d.1927 (D.KR 60000)
£5374	$9727	(3-Dec-91 AB.S4736/R) Wooded landscape with watercourse, summer (59x92cm-23x36in) s.d.1914 (S.KR 60000)
£5415	$9260	(12-Mar-92 RAS.V953/R) Caravane of camels passing pyramids, Egypt (70x110cm-28x43in) s.d.1894 (D.KR 60000)
£5467	$9732	(28-Apr-92 RAS.K97/R) Young girl knitting by farmhouse (55x74cm-22x29in) s.d.1918 (D.KR 62000)
£5467	$9732	(28-Apr-92 RAS.K118/R) Roses in a country garden (62x40cm-24x16in) s.i.d.1929 (D.KR 62000)
£5712	$10224	(6-May-92 KH.K143/R) German canal scene (55x72cm-22x28in) s.d.1914 (D.KR 65000)
£5732	$10203	(28-Apr-92 RAS.K78/R) Loggia with two small Italian girls (110x75cm-43x30in) s.d.1895 (D.KR 65000)
£5866	$10560	(19-Nov-91 RAS.K60/R) Acropolis, seen from the road to the Observatory (90x165cm-35x65in) s.d.1894 (D.KR 65000)
£6173	$10988	(28-Apr-92 RAS.K117/R) Two girls in backyard with roses (62x47cm-24x19in) s.d.1922 (D.KR 70000)
£6349	$11302	(28-Apr-92 RAS.K114/R) Small girl embroidering in doorway of farmhouse (50x70cm-20x28in) s.i.d.1935 (D.KR 72000)
£6602	$11092	(27-Aug-91 RAS.K113/R) Norwegian winter landscape near Lillehammer (68x97cm-27x38in) s.i.d.1918 (D.KR 75000)
£6769	$12184	(19-Nov-91 RAS.K102/R) Village in winter (69x86cm-27x34in) s.d.1925 (D.KR 75000)
£7482	$12570	(27-Aug-91 RAS.K176/R) Summer's day in the wood (75x110cm-30x43in) s.d.1890 (D.KR 85000)
£7590	$13890	(14-May-92 BU.S171/R) Figures with horse and sleigh in Vingnaes (48x70cm-19x28in) s.d.1918 (S.KR 80000)
£7849	$13500	(17-Oct-91 SY.NY279/R) Autumn landscape with stream (53x84cm-21x33in) s.d.1903
£8000	$14480	(22-May-92 C38/R) Way home (71x101cm-28x40in) s.d.1921
£9488	$17362	(14-May-92 BU.S169/R) Landscape with farm and lake (52x84cm-20x33in) s.i.d.1912 (S.KR 100000)
£9884	$17000	(16-Oct-91 CH.NY131/R) River landscape, Summer (90x150cm-35x59in) s.d.1905
£10000	$17300	(4-Oct-91 C116/R) Wooded river landscape (110x110cm-43x43in) s.d.1910
£11429	$20000	(20-Feb-92 SY.NY113/R) Lac Leman (95x67cm-37x26in) s.d.1887
£15000	$27150	(22-May-92 C39/R) Wooded winter landscape with deer (98x68cm-39x27in) s.d.1912
£19340	$34231	(5-Nov-91 BA.S128/R) Winter's day in Norway (83x118cm-33x46in) s.d.1924 (S.KR 205000)
£3263	*$5906*	*(3-Dec-91 AB.S4737/R) Danish winter landscape (29x44cm-11x17in) s.d.1907 gouache cardboard (S.KR 34000)*

ΙONTAGNA, Bartolommeo (style) (1450-1523) Italian
£4800 $9216   (8-Jul-92 S217/R) Madonna and Child before parapet in landscape
     (47x41cm-19x16in) panel

ΙONTAGNE, Louis (1879-1960) French
£713 $1297   (13-Dec-91 ZZ.F25) Le plateau des Angles (38x55cm-15x22in) s. (F.FR 7000)
£1629 $2965   (13-Dec-91 ZZ.F26) La carriere, route d'Aramon (46x62cm-18x24in) s.
     (F.FR 16000)
£1852 $3519   (22-Jun-92 AT.P138/R) Chapelle en Provence (50x65cm-20x26in) s.
     (F.FR 18000)
*£489 $890   (13-Dec-91 ZZ.F30) Devant la cheminee (44x37cm-17x15in) s. W/C htd.chl.
     (F.FR 4800)*
*£815 $1483   (13-Dec-91 ZZ.F23) Le pont de Saint-Benezet (42x59cm-17x23in) s. W/C
     htd.chl. (F.FR 8000)*
*£1629 $2965   (13-Dec-91 ZZ.F31) La corrida a Nimes (44x61cm-17x24in) s. W/C htd.chl.
     (F.FR 16000)*

ΙONTAGUE, A (19th C) British
£681 $1300   (3-Jul-92 S.W3856) Figures in landscape by brook (30x46cm-12x18in) s.
     s.i.verso

ΙONTAGUE, Alfred (fl.1832-1883) British
£519 $950   (3-Jun-92 D.NY66) Path along river (30x46cm-12x18in) s. s.i.verso
£540 $977   (20-May-92 BT252/R) Sunset over estuary (28x43cm-11x17in) s. panel
£1050 $1806   (11-Oct-91 C164/R) View in Rheims (30x46cm-12x18in) s.i.d.1896
£1180 $2100   (22-Jan-92 SY.NY477/R) Rotterdam, Holland (46x36cm-18x14in) s.
£1400 $2394   (17-Mar-92 RG2329) Town riverscene with figures and moored boats
     (25x38cm-10x15in) indist.s.
£1800 $3330   (11-Jun-92 CSK246/R) Figures on bridge in Dutch town. Figures in Dutch
     street (35x26cm-14x10in) s.d.1874 board pair

ΙONTAGUE, Clifford (19th C) British
£900 $1575   (23-Sep-91 PHB48) A continental canal scene with figures
     (61x51cm-24x20in) s.d.1893
£1500 $2655   (6-Nov-91 S35/R) Hawking s. one d.1897 two

ΙONTALANT, I O de (19th C) French?
£874 $1600   (17-May-92 DU.E1091 b) Via Appia (76x41cm-30x16in) s.i.d.1870
£1067 $1900   (22-Jan-92 SY.NY523/R) Figures dancing beneath arbour along coast
     (28x53cm-11x21in) s.d.1861
£14535 $25000   (17-Oct-91 SY.NY137/R) View of Rome with Colosseum (88x152cm-35x60in)
     s.d.1878

ΙONTALBA, Clara (1842-1929) British
£1300 $2444   (19-Dec-91 C138/R) Orange seller by road leading to town (21x31cm-8x12in)
     s. panel

ΙONTANARI, Giuseppe (1889-?) Italian
£8707 $15411   (7-Nov-91 F.M48/R) Sonata a venere (119x150cm-47x59in) s.d.25-26 panel
     (I.L 19000000)

ΙONTANARINI, Luigi (1906-) Italian
£590 $1051   (29-Apr-92 F.F194/R) Autoritratto (10x8cm-4x3in) s.verso panel
     (I.L 1300000)
£817 $1455   (29-Apr-92 F.F169/R) Piazza (70x51cm-28x20in) s. cardboard (I.L 1800000)

ΙONTANIER, Francis (1895-1974) French
£811 $1467   (20-May-92 FB.P201 a) Barque voile violette - barques de peche
     (113x146cm-44x57in) s.d.49 panel (F.FR 8000)

ΙONTAUT, Ernest (1879-1909) ?
*£2018 $3471   (20-Oct-91 PLF.P81/R) L'elegante et son chauffeur noir (53x40cm-21x16in)
     s. W/C crayon (F.FR 20000)*

ΙONTAUT, Gabriel Xavier (1798-1852) French
*£650 $1157   (27-Nov-91 C201/R) Lady in dress with frilled lace collar and fob watch
     on chain (5cm-2ins circular) min.s.d.1820 silver frame with rose-cut
     diamonds*

ΙONTEFORTE, A (19/20th C) Italian
£2200 $4092   (17-Jun-92 S585/R) Views of Naples (18x28cm-7x11in) s. panel pair

ΙONTEFORTE, Eduardo (1849-1933) Italian
£1389 $2404   (24-Mar-92 CH.R132) Donna su un'asinello, col Golfo di Napoli
     (13x17cm-5x7in) s. panel (I.L 3000000)

ΙONTEGA, G (?) ?
£1620 $2900   (5-May-92 SWS390/R) The tavern belles (56x77cm-22x30in) s. pair

ΙONTELATICI, Francesco (1600-1661) Italian
£4500 $7875   (1-Apr-92 S187/R) Judith and Holofernes (167x123cm-66x48in) s.
£35912 $65000   (21-May-92 CH.NY16/R) Allegory of autumn. Allegory of summer
     (98x147cm-39x58in) pair

MONTEMEZZO, Antonio (1841-1898) German
£2062	$3814	(13-Jun-92 WK.M345/R) Peasant woman with grazing cattle in Alpine landscape (101x66cm-40x26in) (DM 6000)
£18000	$33480	(19-Jun-92 C73/R) Le Guardianelle delle Oche (67x132cm-26x52in) s.d.79

MONTENARD, Frederic (1849-1926) French
£1535	$2733	(27-Nov-91 AT.P173/R) Pecheur en Mediterranee (51x81cm-20x32in) s. (F.FR 15000)

MONTENEGRO, Roberto (1881-1968) South American
£40278	$72500	(18-Nov-91 SY.NY33/R) Autorretrato en bola de cristal (77x64cm-30x25in) s.d.53
£1944	*$3500*	*(18-Nov-91 SY.NY147/R) Lex, la Ley (38x56cm-15x22in) s.d.66 graphite W/C gouache gold paint*

MONTEZIN, Pierre Eugene (1874-1946) French
£2000	$3820	(29-Jun-92 CSK22/R) Bouquet aux roses rouges et blanches (33x41cm-13x16in) s.
£3360	$6116	(11-Dec-91 ZZ.F34/R) Bouquet sur une table (116x89cm-46x35in) s. (F.FR 33000)
£7284	$12747	(5-Apr-92 ZZ.F121/R) Petite rue de village (51x62cm-20x24in) st.sig. (F.FR 70000)
£8056	$13696	(27-Oct-91 LT.P61/R) Les moissons (34x60cm-13x24in) (F.FR 80000)
£8197	$14754	(2-Feb-92 ZZ.F130/R) Ferme et paturage a l'oree du bois (61x74cm-24x29in) s. (F.FR 80000)
£9365	$16389	(5-Apr-92 ZZ.F118/R) Fenaison (55x73cm-22x29in) s. (F.FR 90000)
£10000	$19100	(30-Jun-92 C195/R) Bouquet de fleurs et assiette de cerises (59x74cm-23x29in) s.
£10070	$17120	(27-Oct-91 LT.P51/R) Les fenaisons (54x64cm-21x25in) s. (F.FR 100000)
£10656	$19500	(14-May-92 SY.NY309/R) Bouquet de fleurs (115x88cm-45x35in) s.
£13594	$23246	(22-Mar-92 LT.P67/R) Les pommiers en fleurs (60x72cm-24x28in) s. panel (F.FR 132000)
£14000	$24220	(25-Mar-92 S178/R) Bords de Seine - Peupliers (100x81cm-39x32in) s.
£14933	$25536	(22-Mar-92 LT.P59/R) Le train a vapeur aupres de la maison d'Alfred Sisley a Veneux-les-Sablons (73x73cm-29x29in) st.sig. (F.FR 145000)
£832	*$1457*	*(5-Apr-92 ZZ.F157/R) Peupliers dans la vallee (12x27cm-5x11in) s. W/C gouache (F.FR 8000)*
£1310	*$2320*	*(10-Nov-91 ZZ.F192/R) Rue de village (26x20cm-10x8in) s. gouache (F.FR 13000)*
£1643	*$2957*	*(20-Nov-91 CN.P53/R) Charrette sur la route (28x34cm-11x13in) s. gouache (F.FR 16000)*
£1648	*$2818*	*(22-Mar-92 LT.P71/R) Le fenaison en Bordure de Riviere (20x26cm-8x10in) s. gouache (F.FR 16000)*

MONTFORT, Franz van (1889-1980) Belgian
£750	$1433	(29-Jun-92 CSK56/R) Le vase pourpre (55x46cm-22x18in) s.d.1925
£833	$1433	(12-Oct-91 KV.L327) Tete de jeune fille (63x48cm-25x19in) s.d.1938 paper (B.FR 50000)
£833	*$1433*	*(12-Oct-91 KV.L326) Sur la Route vers le Destin (47x62cm-19x24in) s.d.1954 brush (B.FR 50000)*

MONTI, A (?) ?
£900	$1557	(3-Oct-91 CSK248/R) A welcome distraction (58x38cm-23x15in) s.
£900	$1647	(14-May-92 CSK172) The water carriers (61x46cm-24x18in) s.

MONTI, Cesare (1891-1952) Italian
£695	$1237	(26-Nov-91 SY.MI49/R) Il circo (35x120cm-14x47in) s.d.50 (I.L 1500000)

MONTI, Francesco (1646-1712) Italian
£8147	$14827	(28-May-92 F.M124/R) Battaglia (93x134cm-37x53in) (I.L 18000000)
£9884	$17000	(9-Oct-91 CH.NY6/R) Belshazzar's Feast (76x100cm-30x39in)
£11315	$20593	(28-May-92 F.M125/R) La reddizione di una citta orientale (93x134cm-37x53in) (I.L 25000000)
£42000	$74760	(30-Oct-91 S66/R) Cavalry battles (90x149cm-35x59in) pair
£1200	*$2304*	*(6-Jul-92 S28/R) Seated male nude holding a staff (34x21cm-13x8in) chk.wash htd.*

MONTI, Francesco (circle) (1646-1712) Italian
£3557	$6332	(29-Nov-91 GAB.G3086) Antiochus et Stratonice (144x218cm-57x86in) (S.FR 9000)

MONTICELLI (?) Italian
£414	*$750*	*(2-Dec-91 S.SL516/R) View of Naples harbour (43x61cm-17x24in) s. W/C*

MONTICELLI, Adolphe (1824-1886) French
£785	$1500	(3-Jul-92 S.W3070) Columbus before Queen Isabella (15x25cm-6x10in) panel
£1800	$3204	(26-Nov-91 PH214) Le Temple de l'Amour (42x69cm-17x27in) panel
£2446	$4550	(18-Jun-92 SY.MO377/R) Le sonneur de cloches (30x26cm-12x10in) s. panel (F.FR 24000)
£2983	$5250	(9-Apr-92 FA.PH820 a/R) Femmes dans un parc (53x66cm-21x26in) s.
£3393	$6175	(27-May-92 D.V506/R) Still life with fountain (28x36cm-11x14in) (A.S 70000)
£4360	$7500	(9-Oct-91 RO.BA3/R) Fete dans le jardin (39x76cm-15x30in) s. panel
£4862	$8800	(4-Dec-91 NA.BA2/R) Scene oriental (39x42cm-15x17in) s. panel
£5000	$9550	(29-Jun-92 CSK10/R) La Fete Champetre (16x29cm-6x11in) s. panel

MONTICELLI, Adolphe (1824-1886) French-cont.
£5200	$8892	(17-Mar-92 PH119/R) Floral festival (55x102cm-22x40in) s.
£5233	$9000	(16-Oct-91 CH.NY5/R) Une fete (30x46cm-12x18in) s. panel
£6061	$10727	(22-Apr-92 CH.AM191/R) Base-cour, poultry by a basket on a yard (37x48cm-15x19in) s. panel (D.FL 20000)
£6173	$11728	(22-Jun-92 AT.P102/R) La marchande de fleurs (41x24cm-16x9in) s. panel (F.FR 60000)
£6395	$11000	(13-Oct-91 H.C53/R) Dans le jardin (38x64cm-15x25in) s. cradled panel
£6857	$12000	(19-Feb-92 CH.NY14/R) Wedding (57x46cm-22x18in) s. panel
£6977	$12000	(17-Oct-91 SY.NY13/R) Hay-cart (25x39cm-10x15in) s. panel
£7500	$14325	(29-Jun-92 CSK9/R) La Princesse avec ses Habilleuses (33x20cm-13x8in) s. panel
£8138	$14568	(17-Nov-91 FB.P181/R) Scene de parc (18x30cm-7x12in) s. panel (F.FR 80000)
£11405	$20872	(3-Jun-92 PIC.P49/R) Leda et le cygne (49x33cm-19x13in) s. panel (F.FR 112000)
£12000	$20760	(24-Mar-92 C14/R) La reunion des elgantes (29x51cm-11x20in) s. panel
£12844	$22734	(5-Nov-91 SY.AM191/R) Meeting in park (32x46cm-13x18in) s. panel (D.FL 42000)
£21818	$38618	(22-Apr-92 CH.AM170/R) Jeune fille a la fontaine (59x41cm-23x16in) s. panel (D.FL 72000)
£22634	$43004	(22-Jun-92 AT.P103/R) L'offrande (44x64cm-17x25in) s. panel (F.FR 220000)
£290000	$553900	(29-Jun-92 C3/R) Grande nature morte au pichet (44x65cm-17x26in) panel

MONTICELLI, Adolphe (attrib) (1824-1886) French
£632	$1100	(11-Sep-91 D.NY61) Ladies and children in park (23x33cm-9x13in) panel
£656	$1200	(16-May-92 HG.C223/R) Forest gathering (30x41cm-12x16in) s. cradled panel

MONTICELLI, Adolphe (style) (1824-1886) French
£857	$1500	(18-Feb-92 CE.NY264 a/R) Elegant figures in landscape (22x38cm-9x15in) s. panel
£2400	$4344	(21-May-92 CSK229/R) La terrase de Chateau de St. Germain (136x86cm-54x34in)

MONTIGNY, Jenny (1875-1937) Belgian
£3200	$5696	(26-Nov-91 PH95/R) The picnic (61x50cm-24x20in) s.
£15833	$27233	(12-Oct-91 KV.L381/R) Children beside a flowering orchard (37x59cm-15x23in) s. (B.FR 950000)

MONTIGNY, Jules (1847-1899) Belgian
£4254	$7700	(4-Dec-91 NA.BA7/R) Char a chevaux (86x121cm-34x48in) s.d.1892

MONTILLA TINOCO, Carmen (1936-) Venezuelan
£3889	$7000	(19-Nov-91 CH.NY148/R) Iocasta from the series La Selva Interior (162x130cm-64x51in) s.d.1976/77 i.verso

MONTOBIO, Guillaume (1883-1962) Belgian
£620	$1128	(10-Dec-91 SWS202) Meules (35x50cm-14x20in) s.
£1852	$3370	(12-Dec-91 SY.AM42/R) Bord de la Lys (50x65cm-20x26in) s. (D.FL 6000)

MONTOYA, Gustavo (1905-) Mexican
£1221	$2100	(12-Oct-91 SY.NY200/R) Nino en verde con maceta (56x46cm-22x18in) s.
£1453	$2500	(12-Oct-91 SY.NY201/R) Nino con paloma (56x46cm-22x18in) s.
£2027	$3750	(12-Jun-92 SY.NY170/R) Nina con Guitarra (55x45cm-22x18in) s. s.d.1966 verso
£2514	$4500	(13-Nov-91 B.SF2757/R) Girl in pink dress (56x46cm-22x18in) s.

MONTPEZAT, Henri d'Ainecy Comte de (1817-1859) French
£1751	$3291	(16-Dec-91 AGS.P23/R) Promenade en caleche (13x18cm-5x7in) s. panel (F.FR 17000)

MONTREU, J (19th C) Belgian
£741	$1296	(18-Feb-92 CH.AM190) Le boudeur (31x25cm-12x10in) s. panel (D.FL 2400)

MOODY, Fannie (fl.1885-1897) British
£3200	$6144	(28-Jul-92 SWS160/R) A lesson in patience (67x95cm-26x37in) s.i.verso
£800	$1432	(14-Jan-92 B226/R) First come, first served (43x55cm-17x22in) s. pencil pastel

MOONEY, E Hartley (fl.1926-1932) British
£700	$1204	(5-Mar-92 CSK75) Still life of paeonies (48x67cm-19x26in) s. canvas on panel

MOOR, Carel de (1656-1738) Dutch
£3000	$5460	(10-Dec-91 PH33/R) Maidens observing couple sleeping by pool in landscape (21x27cm-8x11in) panel

MOOR, Carel de (after) (1656-1738) Dutch
£1216	$2225	(12-May-92 SY.AM71/R) Portrait of Peter the Great (62x50cm-24x20in) (D.FL 4000)

MOOR, Carel de (attrib) (1656-1738) Dutch
£4972	$9000	(21-May-92 CH.NY85/R) Fishseller holding herring before niche (33x25cm-13x10in) panel

MOOR, Carel de (style) (1656-1738) Dutch
£11000 $19250   (1-Apr-92 S65/R) Still life of military equipment accompanied by two
                          soldiers, landscape (56x80cm-22x31in) panel

MOOR, Karel de (attrib) (1695-?) Dutch
£1300 $2496   (9-Jul-92 CSK179) Boys at grape harvest (36x27cm-14x11in) panel

MOORE OF IPSWICH, John (1820-1902) British
£1500 $2880   (28-Jul-92 SWS359/R) Moonlit coastal scene (28x45cm-11x18in) s. panel
£1700 $3026   (21-Jan-92 PH76) Shipping off coast (16x24cm-6x9in) one s. panel pair

MOORE, Albert Joseph (1841-1893) British
£40000 $68000   (25-Oct-91 C47/R) Roses (98x38cm-39x15in) s. pastel

MOORE, Albert Joseph (style) (1841-1893) British
£950 $1625   (12-Mar-92 CSK278/R) Pensive beauty (74x51cm-29x20in)

MOORE, Barlow (19th C) British
£707 $1237   (3-Apr-92 BM.B684/R) English harbour view in stiff breeze with yacht
                          (50x74cm-20x29in) s. (DM 2000)
*£1400 $2534   (20-May-92 S182/R) The yawl Onyx (54x61cm-21x24in) s.i.d.1888 W/C
                          htd.white*

MOORE, Benson Bond (1882-1974) American
£1786 $3250   (13-Dec-91 S.W2610/R) Georgetown in autumn (41x51cm-16x20in) s.d.1916

MOORE, Claude T S (1853-1901) British
£900 $1548   (11-Oct-91 C78/R) View of Windsor Castle (33x48cm-13x19in) s. s.i.verso
£3500 $6300   (22-Nov-91 C104/R) Views on the Thames at Westminster. Greenwich. The
                          Tower of London (15x20cm-6x8in) s.d.90 s.d.verso set of three
£4000 $7240   (20-May-92 S207/R) Port of Aberdeen (30x45cm-12x18in) s.d.76 i.stretcher

MOORE, Edwin Augustus (1858-1925) American
£1405 $2600   (10-Jun-92 CE.NY192) Cow wading by stream (61x76cm-24x30in) s.d.1893
                          i.d.1893 verso

MOORE, Ernest (1865-?) British
£980 $1686   (16-Oct-91 CSK267) Spring orchard (76x63cm-30x25in) s.verso

MOORE, Frank Montague (1877-1967) British/American
£526 $900   (21-Mar-92 W.W213/R) At anchor, Monterey (51x76cm-20x30in) s.
£684 $1300   (24-Jun-92 B.SF6346/R) Sunset on waves (51x76cm-20x30in) s. board
£1571 $2750   (31-Mar-92 MOR.P77) Moonlight coastal (61x86cm-24x34in) s. board

MOORE, Harry Humphrey (1844-1926) American
£3083 $5889   (1-Jul-92 FB.P128/R) Elegante aux roses (79x61cm-31x24in) s. (F.FR 30000)

MOORE, Henry O M (1898-1986) British
£2400 $4248   (10-Feb-92 B7/R) Reclining figure (17x25cm-7x10in) s. W/C crayon
*£5000 $9050   (2-Dec-91 CSK140/R) The artists hands, pebble in left hand
                          (25x23cm-10x9in) s. ballpoint pen W/C crayon pencil*
*£5085 $9000   (6-Nov-91 CH.NY190/R) Some seated figures. Some linear ones for Paalen
                          (25x18cm-10x7in) s.i.d.50 pen india ink over pencil double-sided*
*£6000 $11460   (1-Jul-92 S228/R) Standing figure, architectural background
                          (26x17cm-10x7in) s.d.79 W/C photomontage chl ink chk*
*£6500 $12415   (1-Jul-92 S227/R) Idea for sculpture - reclining figure (17x25cm-7x10in)
                          s. chl wash over pencil*
£12000 $21720   (3-Dec-91 C193/R) Reclining figure (17x25cm-7x10in) s. chl.pencil wash
*£12429 $22000   (6-Nov-91 CH.NY193/R) Reclining figure (21x29cm-8x11in) s. W/C wax crayon
                          pencil htd.chk over photocopy*

MOORE, Henry R A (1831-1895) British
£560 $1075   (28-Jul-92 SWS317) Wagon on country road (29x39cm-11x15in) s.d.1858-9
*£565 $999   (4-Nov-91 SY.J4/R) The shrimp collector (34x49cm-13x19in) s.d.1856
                          (SA.R 2800)*
*£750 $1305   (11-Sep-91 PHG10) Herring fishing on the Orkney Coast (34x90cm-13x35in)
                          s.d.1879*
£950 $1701   (14-Jan-92 SWS170/R) Moonlight (136x90cm-54x35in) s.d.1878 i.verso
*£1100 $1958   (28-Apr-92 PH76/R) yarmouth jetty, moonlight (39x55cm-15x22in) s.i.d.1876
                          s.i.stretcher*
£1500 $2730   (10-Dec-91 AG339/R) Sunshine and shower (40x63cm-16x25in) s.
*£1600 $2896   (3-Dec-91 RG3263) Extensive moorland landscape with figure riding a horse
                          (97x173cm-38x68in) s.d.1869*
*£1891 $3365   (25-Nov-91 W.T1916/R) Logging in the Swiss Alps (30x55cm-12x22in)
                          s.i.d.1855 (C.D 3800)*
*£2200 $3916   (27-Apr-92 PHB259/R) View of Whitby from Sandsend (30x45cm-12x18in)
                          s.indist.d.*
*£7500 $13275   (8-Nov-91 C224/R) Stringed figures in Lead (12x21cm-5x8in) s.i.d.40 pen
                          W/C blk.crayon col.wax*
*£8239 $15489   (16-Dec-91 AGS.P5/R) Femmes assises (26x18cm-10x7in) s.d.56 crayon
                          (F.FR 80000)*
*£25000 $43250   (25-Mar-92 S74/R) Two reclining figures (25x35cm-10x14in) s.indist.d.46
                          mixed media*

MOORE, John (?) British
£1200 $2076   (25-Mar-92 PHI561) The Kyles of Lochalsh (15x30cm-6x12in) s. board
£1250 $2375   (24-Jun-92 PHI580/R) Shipping at sea on breezy day (20x30cm-8x12in) s.
£4094 $7000   (18-Mar-92 GRO.B14/R) Monroe, Maine (183x366cm-72x144in)
£4800 $8784   (7-Feb-92 K494/R) Views of Cromer along cliff top from east and west
          (25x33cm-10x13in) s.d.1879 pair

MOORE, John Drummond McPherson (1888-1958) Australian
£1538 $2938   (19-Jul-92 SY.ME31/R) The view to Manly (45x55cm-18x22in) s. (A.D 4000)
*£441 $793   (24-Nov-91 SY.S207/R) Jansen's Garden (28x38cm-11x15in) s.d.1933 W/C htd
          bodycol (A.D 1000)*

MOORE, John Henry (19th C) British
*£600 $1074   (16-Jan-92 B200/R) Return of fishing fleet (22x41cm-9x16in) s.d.1866 W/C
          htd white*

MOORE, John Stirling (fl.1887-1916) Australian
£1475 $2566   (16-Sep-91 CH.ME173) Near Delegate (39x59cm-15x23in) s.d.10.04 (A.D 3200)

MOORE, Madena (fl.1880-87) British
£880 $1575   (14-Jan-92 SWS130/R) The little seamstress (45x35cm-18x14in) s.d.1881

MOORE, Percival (1886-1964) British
£5000 $9150   (3-Jun-92 S213/R) Spring (56x76cm-22x30in) s.d.1915

MOORE, Robert (?) ?
£497 $950   (19-Jul-92 JRB.C188/R) Gaff cutters racing (20x30cm-8x12in) s. panel

MOORE, Ronald Lambert (?) British
£540 $999   (9-Jun-92 AG155/R) Bamburgh Castle (51x68cm-20x27in) s.i. W/C

MOORE, Rubens Arthur (fl.1881-1920) British
£620 $1153   (18-Jun-92 CSK245) Malines, France (51x41cm-20x16in) s.

MOORE, William (snr) (1790-1851) British
£560 $1002   (5-May-92 SWS302/R) Portrait of lady with her two daughters at table
          (30x36cm-12x14in) s.d.1838 copper

MOORE-PARK, Carton (1877-1956) British
£1000 $1750   (26-Feb-92 M170/R) Group of flamingos (66x51cm-26x20in) s.d.1898 W/C

MOORMANS, Franz (1832-1893) Dutch
£1332 $2398   (2-Feb-92 ZZ.F34/R) Chez l'ebeniste (27x35cm-11x14in) s. panel
          (F.FR 13000)
£1571 $3000   (3-Jul-92 S.W3077/R) Interior scene - mother , child and toy
          (25x23cm-10x9in) s.d.1872 panel

MOOS, Max von (1903-1979) Swiss
£471 $842   (15-Nov-91 GK.Z5338/R) Untitled (29x22cm-11x9in) s.i.d.1939 tempera paper
          on board (S.FR 1200)
£588 $1053   (15-Nov-91 GK.Z5337) Untitled (30x20cm-12x8in) s.i.d.1939 tempera paper
          (S.FR 1500)
£627 $1123   (15-Nov-91 GK.Z5339/R) Untitled (29x23cm-11x9in) mono. s.i.d.1940 tempera
          paper on board (S.FR 1600)
£730 $1307   (6-May-92 GD.B894/R) Greek impressions (52x38cm-20x15in) mono d.48
          tempera (S.FR 2000)
£7813 $13828   (5-Nov-91 GF.L2795/R) Keimlingsgesicht (50x44cm-20x17in) s.i.d.1969
          tempera oil board (S.FR 20000)
£613 $1061   (23-Mar-92 AB.L62/R) Untitled (59x42cm-23x17in) s.d.49 pen (S.FR 1600)
*£5747 $9943   (23-Mar-92 AB.L78/R) Untitled (37x45cm-15x18in) s. s.verso oil mixed
          media board (S.FR 15000)*
£6641 $11754   (5-Nov-91 GF.L2304/R) Der Dreigesichtige (46x64cm-18x25in)
          s.i.d.1965verso tempera oil oil chk pap.on board (S.FR 17000)
£8429 $14582   (23-Mar-92 AB.L76/R) Untitled (42x57cm-17x22in) s. Indian ink tempera oil
          paper on board (S.FR 22000)

MOOY, Cornelis Pietersz de (?-1693) Dutch
£5500 $9845   (11-Nov-91 S550) Shipping in rising swell (27x33cm-11x13in) s. panel en
          grisaille

MOPOPE, Stephen (1898-?) American
£541 $1000   (14-Jun-92 S.BM36/R) Pipe ceremony (25x20cm-10x8in) s.d.33 tempera

MOR, Antonis (attrib) (1519-1575) Dutch
£813 $1415   (13-Apr-92 AT.P4) Portrait de gentilhomme au colbleu (11cm-4ins circular)
          panel (F.FR 8000)

MOR, Antonis (circle) (1519-1579) Dutch
£11000 $19360   (8-Apr-92 S12/R) Portrait of Mary Tudor, standing with curtains beyond
          (68x44cm-27x17in) panel

MOR, Antonis (school) (1519-1575) Dutch
£2981 $5097   (18-Mar-92 D.V37/R) Portrait of gentleman, possibly Antoine Perrenot de
          Granvella (70x54cm-28x21in) panel (A.S 60000)

MOR, Antonis (studio) (1519-1575) Dutch
£3200 $6144   (10-Jul-92 C143) Portrait of Margaret of Austria, Duchess of Parma
                                  (52x41cm-20x16in) panel

MOR, Antonis (style) (1519-1575) Dutch
£900 $1575   (27-Feb-92 CSK232) Portrait of a gentleman in a ruff, bust length
                                  (42x37cm-17x15in)
£2700 $5184   (8-Jul-92 S244) Portrait of lady beside vase of flowers (46x35cm-18x14in)
                                  copper
£4230 $7571   (7-May-92 CH.AM119/R) Portrait of lady, said to be Lady Jane Dormer,
                                  Duchess of Feria (39x31cm-15x12in) panel (D.FL 14000)

MOR-SUNEGG, Theresa von (1871-1945) Austrian
£748 $1338   (15-Jan-92 D.V6/R) Lake landscape, evening (57x72cm-22x28in) s.d.1915
                                  (A.S 15000)

MORA, Francis Luis (1874-1960) American
£505 $950   (18-Dec-91 SY.NY202 a/R) Our christian era (243x182cm-96x72in)
£599 $1000   (25-Aug-91 LIT.L220) Girl in crinoline (33x23cm-13x9in) s. board
£900 $1674   (16-Jun-92 PH64/R) Mantilla blanca (40x30cm-16x12in) s. i.stretcher
                                  canvas on board
£1514 $2800   (10-Jun-92 CE.NY250/R) Nude with Spanish shawl (40x30cm-16x12in) s. board
£757 $1400   (10-Jun-92 CE.NY472) Copla Sevillana (61x46cm-24x18in) s.d.1914 W/C paper
                                  on board

MORA, Mirka Madeleine (1928-) Australian
£349 $666   (21-Jul-92 JRL.S238/R) Mother and child (75x54cm-30x21in) s.d.63 mixed
                                  media (A.D 900)

MORACH, Otto (1887-1973) Swiss
£3077 $5846   (25-Jun-92 GK.B508) Morning at the seaside (54x65cm-21x26in) (S.FR 8000)
£8365 $15559   (19-Jun-92 ZOF.Z2020/R) Paris street scene (60x73cm-24x29in) i.verso
                                  (S.FR 22000)

MORALES, Armando (1927-) Nicaraguan
£5556 $10000   (19-Nov-91 CH.NY69/R) Still life with two grapefruit and pear
                                  (35x40cm-14x16in) s.d.73 i.stretcher oil wax varnish
£8889 $16000   (19-Nov-91 CH.NY70/R) Tres desnudos y el eclipse (44x35cm-17x14in) s.d.72
                                  oil wax varnish
£9945 $18000   (18-May-92 CH.NY152/R) El Torero. Tauromaquia (24x33cm-9x13in) s.d.89 one
                                  i.verso pair
£11111 $20000   (19-Nov-91 CH.NY180/R) Caballos (28x38cm-11x15in) s.d.49
£11111 $20000   (19-Nov-91 CH.NY84/R) Mujeres con cruce de ferrocarril (70x56cm-28x22in)
                                  s.d.86
£13812 $25000   (19-May-92 SY.NY143/R) Mujer y bicicleta (60x49cm-24x19in) s.d.78 i.verso
                                  board mounted on panel
£22099 $40000   (19-May-92 SY.NY60/R) Woman leaving room II (127x109cm-50x43in) s.d.73
£25000 $45000   (18-Nov-91 SY.NY43/R) Dos figuras (203x162cm-80x64in)
£41436 $75000   (19-May-92 SY.NY68/R) Desnudos (100x81cm-39x32in) s.d.82
£88398 $160000   (18-May-92 CH.NY34/R) Foresta tropical I - Jungla (162x130cm-64x51in)
                                  s.d.85
£8287 $15000   (18-May-92 CH.NY165/R) Nude with circus animals (48x60cm-19x24in) s.d.83
                                  pastel

MORALES, Dario (1944-1988) Colombian
£4444 $8000   (19-Nov-91 CH.NY127/R) Desnudo reclinado (31x37cm-12x15in) st.mono.s.d.81
                                  pencil

MORALES, Divino (circle) (16th C) Spanish
£2319 $3989   (16-Oct-91 FER.M192/R) Cristo llevando la cruz (70x57cm-28x22in)
                                  i.d.1555verso panel (S.P 425000)

MORALES, Eduardo (19/20th C) Cuban
£5139 $9250   (18-Nov-91 SY.NY84/R) Quitrin y Jinete en la campina de Cuba
                                  (34x42cm-13x17in) s.d.1917

MORALES, Juan Antonio and CABALLERO, Jose Luis (20th C) Spanish
£6559 $11151   (22-Oct-91 DUR.M92/R) Cartel original para el estreno de Yerma en 1934
                                  (117x93cm-46x37in) s. panel (S.P 1200000)

MORALES, Luis de (c.1509-1586) Spanish
£30000 $52500   (1-Apr-92 S17/R) Christ carrying cross (80x56cm-31x22in) slate
£125477 $227114   (19-May-92 EP.M3/R) Piedad (57x41cm-22x16in) panel (S.P 23000000)

MORALES, Luis de (attrib) (c.1509-1586) Spanish
£4430 $7973   (28-Jan-92 EP.M9/R) La Virgen con el Nino (43x32cm-17x13in) panel
                                  (S.P 800000)

MORALES, Luis de (circle) (c.1509-1586) Spanish
£1245 $2129   (17-Mar-92 FER.M48/R) Cristo atado a la columna (57x37cm-22x15in) panel
                                  (S.P 225000)
£3058 $5688   (18-Jun-92 SY.MO286/R) Marie Madeleine (49x39cm-19x15in) panel
                                  (F.FR 30000)

MORALES, Luis de (studio) (c.1509-1586) Spanish
£5045 $8678   (15-Oct-91 PPB.P18/R) La morte du Christ (91x71cm-36x28in) panel
        (F.FR 50000)

MORALES, Rodolfo (1925-) Mexican
£3039 $5500   (19-May-92 SY.NY135/R) Untitled (47x34cm-19x13in) s.d.67 canvas mounted
        on board
£3591 $6500   (18-May-92 CH.NY190/R) Dos mundos (80cm-31ins circular) s. s.i.verso
£6630 $12000   (18-May-92 CH.NY189/R) La patria esta primero (80x100cm-31x39in) s.
£6667 $12000   (19-Nov-91 CH.NY139 b/R) Sonrosada (70x100cm-28x39in) s.
£13333 $24000   (19-Nov-91 CH.NY93/R) La espera (79x99cm-31x39in) s.
£20000 $36000   (18-Nov-91 SY.NY72/R) Retorno al pasado (137x175cm-54x69in) s.

MORALT, Willy (1884-1957) German
£5119 $9266   (21-May-92 L.K456/R) Pensive old gentleman on terrace with view of houses
        and church tower (21x30cm-8x12in) s. panel (DM 15000)
£7560 $13155   (17-Sep-91 FN.S2453/R) Figures watching mail coach departing in hilly
        wooded landscape (27x38cm-11x15in) s.i. panel (DM 22000)
£7850 $14208   (21-May-92 L.K457/R) Party walking on way to tavern and view of town
        beyond, possibly Landshut (39x56cm-15x22in) s. (DM 23000)
£8451 $15296   (3-Dec-91 FN.S2339/R) Young woman kneeling before wayside chapel in
        mountain landscape (26x39cm-10x15in) s.i. panel (DM 24000)
£8494 $14525   (12-Mar-92 GK.Z93/R) The Sunday walk (27x38cm-11x15in) s. panel
        (S.FR 22000)
£8711 $15854   (11-Dec-91 N.M537/R) Soldiers checking traveller's papers
        (27x38cm-11x15in) s.i. paper on panel (DM 25000)
£9622 $16742   (17-Sep-91 FN.S2452/R) Hilly landscape with mail coach approaching and
        figures in street (38x55cm-15x22in) s.i. board on panel (DM 28000)
£10801 $19659   (11-Dec-91 N.M536/R) Girl praying before woodland chapel
        (45x38cm-18x15in) s.i. panel (DM 31000)
£1005   *$1789*   *(29-Oct-91 PH.T29/R) Alpine landscape (37x56cm-15x22in) s.d.12 gouache*
        (C.D 2000)
£1812   *$3298*   *(11-Dec-91 WE.MU286) Alpine landscape (37x56cm-15x22in) s.d.1912 gouache*
        (DM 5200)
£2098   *$3587*   *(18-Mar-92 N.M296/R) View of Ebersberg near Munich (31x47cm-12x19in) s.i.*
        i.verso gouache board (DM 6000)

MORAN, E Percy (1862-1935) American
£537 $950   (9-Nov-91 W.W187/R) For the marquise (30x41cm-12x16in) s.
£811 $1500   (10-Jun-92 CE.NY271/R) Lady in plumed hat (35x27cm-14x11in) s.
£1330 $2500   (18-Dec-91 SY.NY124/R) George Washington and Benjamin Franklin
        (71x55cm-28x22in) s.
£1379 $2400   (15-Apr-92 SY.NY47/R) At Fort Ticonderoga - 10th May 1775
        (71x56cm-28x22in) s.
£3856 $7250   (18-Dec-91 SY.NY122/R) In the garden (61x46cm-24x18in) s.

MORAN, Edward (1829-1901) American
£847 $1500   (10-Nov-91 LIT.L89) Seascape (30x46cm-12x18in) s.
£1351 $2500   (10-Jun-92 CE.NY191/R) Sailboats on calm sea (31x41cm-12x16in) s.
£1397 $2500   (6-May-92 D.NY1/R) Entering New York Harbour (46x61cm-18x24in) s.d.1891
        canvas on board
£1695 $3000   (9-Nov-91 W.W171/R) Passing Ambrose lightship (51x41cm-20x16in) s.
£1768 $3200   (4-Dec-91 D.NY5/R) Merchant ship skirting lighthouse point
        (69x56cm-27x22in) s.
£2660 $5000   (18-Dec-91 SY.NY75/R) Fort Hamilton, New York Harbour (23x41cm-9x16in) s.
        board on panel
£3800 $6878   (20-May-92 S170/R) Clipper at sunset (84x85cm-33x33in) s.d.1877
£5143 $9000   (25-Sep-91 SY.NY7/R) Gathering cockles (56x88cm-22x35in) s.d.1883
£9945 $18000   (5-Dec-91 SY.NY13/R) Fish Pond, Orient Bay, Long Island (77x58cm-30x23in)
        s. d.1876verso
£15934 $29000   (27-May-92 SY.NY32/R) Ships at sea (76x127cm-30x50in) s.d.1876
        i.stretcher

MORAN, Edward (attrib) (1829-1901) American
£8287 $15000   (21-May-92 S.W2890/R) Nine New York marine views (41x56cm-16x22in) board

MORAN, Peter (1841-1914) American
£994 $1800   (21-May-92 S.W2930/R) Landscape with watering cows (41x76cm-16x30in) s.

MORAN, Thomas (1837-1926) American
£1536 $2750   (13-Nov-91 B.SF2628/R) Portrait of man in hat (25x20cm-10x8in) s. board
£5747 $10000   (10-Sep-91 BG.M707/R) Long Island landscape with pond and trees
        (23x36cm-9x14in) mono.d.1908
£26374 $48000   (28-May-92 CH.NY75/R) Moonlight in Venice (34x47cm-13x19in) mono.i.d.1898
        panel
£30220 $55000   (28-May-92 CH.NY80/R) Venice (51x76cm-20x30in) mono.i.d.1901
£32967 $60000   (28-May-92 CH.NY123/R) Late afternoon in summer (51x76cm-20x30in)
        mono.i.d.1909
£287293 $520000   (6-Dec-91 CH.NY124/R) In the Teton Range (107x76cm-42x30in) mono.i.d.1899
£1862   *$3500*   *(18-Dec-91 SY.NY42 a/R) Off the Bahamas (20x27cm-8x11in) s.d.1833 W/C*
        gouache
£2857   *$5000*   *(26-Sep-91 CH.NY49/R) Venice (18x23cm-7x9in) s.i.d.1889 W/C pencil*
£32967   *$60000*   *(28-May-92 CH.NY106/R) Moonlight, Devil's Den (32x25cm-13x10in)*
        mono.d.1873 W/C gouache pencil paper on board

MORANA, Jose Manuel (20th C) Spanish
£829 $1559   (18-Dec-91 DUR.M1189/R) Bodegon con figuras (65x81cm-26x32in) s.
                   (S.P 150000)

MORANDI, Giorgio (1890-1964) Italian
£65000	$117650	(3-Dec-91 C251/R) Fiori (23x23cm-9x9in) s.d.1947verso
£99875	$177778	(29-Apr-92 F.F269/R) Fiori (23x23cm-9x9in) s.d.1947verso (I.L 220000000)
£121872	$216932	(29-Nov-91 F.F178/R) Fiori (30x25cm-12x10in) s.d.1953 (I.L 263000000)
£180000	$343800	(29-Jun-92 C59/R) Natura morta (35x31cm-14x12in) s. s.d.1960 verso
£197740	$350000	(5-Nov-91 CH.NY55/R) Natura morta (30x45cm-12x18in) s.
£207254	$377202	(9-Dec-91 CH.R188/R) Paesaggio (48x53cm-19x21in) s.d.1942 (I.L 450000000)
£210000	$401100	(29-Jun-92 C54/R) Natura morta (38x33cm-15x13in) s.
£255795	$445084	(14-Apr-92 F.M239/R) Natura morta (33x49cm-13x19in) s.verso
		(I.L 560000000)
£2716	*$4942*	*(25-May-92 CH.R8/R) Paesaggio (10x12cm-4x5in) s.d.1960 pencil*
		(I.L 6000000)
£4000	*$7000*	*(25-Feb-92 CH.NY55/R) Le conchiglie (13x19cm-5x7in) s.d.1920 pencil*
£4500	*$8595*	*(29-Jun-92 CSK126/R) Edificazioni in un paesaggio (24x33cm-9x13in) s.*
		soft pencil
£4606	*$8382*	*(9-Dec-91 CH.R18/R) Natura morta (6x10cm-2x4in) s. pencil (I.L 10000000)*
£4767	*$8485*	*(29-Apr-92 F.F268/R) Paesaggio (15x20cm-6x8in) s. pencil (I.L 10500000)*
£4767	*$8485*	*(29-Apr-92 F.F265/R) Natura morta (13x17cm-5x7in) s. pencil*
		(I.L 10500000)
£4994	*$8889*	*(29-Apr-92 F.F267/R) Natura morta (24x16cm-9x6in) s. pencil*
		(I.L 11000000)
£4994	*$8889*	*(29-Apr-92 F.F262/R) Natura morta (21x16cm-8x6in) s. (I.L 11000000)*
£4994	*$8889*	*(29-Apr-92 F.F264/R) Paesaggio (16x24cm-6x9in) s. pencil (I.L 11000000)*
£5448	*$9697*	*(29-Apr-92 F.F266/R) Paesaggio (17x23cm-7x9in) s. pencil (I.L 12000000)*
£5675	*$10101*	*(29-Apr-92 F.F263/R) Paesaggio (24x16cm-9x6in) s. pencil (I.L 12500000)*
£5800	*$11078*	*(29-Jun-92 CSK125/R) Natura morta (24x33cm-9x13in) s.d.1961 pencil*
£6129	*$10909*	*(29-Apr-92 F.F261/R) Vaso di fiori (27x19cm-11x7in) s. pencil*
		(I.L 13500000)
£6500	*$11180*	*(16-Oct-91 S95/R) Natura morta (17x24cm-7x9in) s. pencil*

MORANDI, Giovanni Maria (attrib) (1622-1717) Italian
£7200   *$13824*   *(8-Jul-92 PH102/R) Studies for Conversion of St. Paul (32x21cm-13x8in) i.*
                   red black chk

MORANDIS, Gino (1915-) Italian
£695 $1237   (26-Nov-91 SY.MI45/R) Immagine 180 (40x53cm-16x21in) s. panel
                   (I.L 1500000)

MORANO, Wilhelm (1885-?) German
£616 $1060   (11-Oct-91 AW.H2696/R) Mountainside farmstead (53x46cm-21x18in) s.
                   (DM 1800)

MORAS, W (1856-1925) German
£619 $1083   (25-Feb-92 UL.T215) Autumn landscape (60x98cm-24x39in) (N.KR 7000)

MORAS, Walter (1856-1925) German
£900	$1709	(24-Jun-92 KM.K1196/R) Harz landscape with view of town in valley, sunny
		autumn day (80x120cm-31x47in) s. (DM 2600)
£1044	$1910	(12-May-92 GO.G228/R) Winter wood with hunters on bridge
		(75x120cm-30x47in) s. (S.KR 11000)
£1413	$2473	(3-Apr-92 BM.B685/R) Fishing village by the Baltic Sea and sheep grazing
		in heathlands (59x99cm-23x39in) s. (DM 4000)
£1536	$2750	(13-Nov-91 B.SF2321/R) Child with gaggle of geese (39x31cm-15x12in) s.
£2091	$3805	(11-Dec-91 N.M538/R) Farmstead with peasant woman, geese and horse drawn
		cart (43x67cm-17x26in) s. board (DM 6000)
£3242	$5901	(27-May-92 PH.DU127 a/R) Winter in the village (80x120cm-31x47in) s.
		(DM 9500)
£3351	$5830	(18-Sep-91 N.M635/R) Village by pond with geese (55x100cm-22x39in) s.
		(DM 9750)
£391	*$672*	*(10-Oct-91 D.V282/R) Vierwaldstattersee landscape at dusk*
		(29x45cm-11x18in) s. W/C bodycol (A.S 8000)

MORAT, M (19th C) German
£880 $1593   *(4-Dec-91 DO.H2560/R) View of Zell in Wiesental (22x35cm-9x14in) s.i.*
                   gouache (DM 2500)

MORBELLI, Angelo (1853-1919) Italian
£6328 $11454   (18-May-92 SY.MI25) Vecchietta (12x13cm-5x5in) panel (I.L 14000000)
£34491 $64152   (16-Jun-92 F.M285/R) La figlia malata (124x190cm-49x75in) s.
                   (I.L 76000000)

MORCHAIN, Paul-Bernard (1876-?) French
£1665 $2914   (5-Apr-92 ZZ.F68/R) Retour de peche en Bretagne (61x81cm-24x32in) s.
                   (F.FR 16000)

MORCILLO RAYA, Gabriel (1888-1973) Spanish
£15000 $26700   (26-Nov-91 PH61/R) Nude with still life (112x86cm-44x34in) s.
                   s.i.d.1930verso
£16500 $27720   (1-Sep-91 PO.BA18) Fructidores, Bacanal (184x119cm-72x47in) s.

MORCILLO, Gabriel (19th C) Spanish
£6650 $11638   (18-Feb-92 DUR.M26/R) La bola de cristal (73x60cm-29x24in) s.d.1917
      (S.P 1200000)
£7194 $12302   (17-Mar-92 FER.M127/R) Retrato de dama (101x102cm-40x40in) s.d.1916
      (S.P 1300000)
£11628 $20000   (17-Oct-91 SY.NY26/R) Red fez (84x72cm-33x28in) s.d.23

MORDSTEIN, Karl Ludwig (1937-) German
£1136 $2023   (25-Nov-91 WK.M731/R) At the wall (72x56cm-28x22in) mono.d.1976 i.verso
      aquatec pencil panel (DM 3250)

MORDT, Gustav (1826-1856) Norwegian
£571 $982   (7-Oct-91 B.O93/R) Moonlit landscape (14x19cm-6x7in) s. (N.KR 6500)
£4010 $6818   (6-Aug-91 UL.T206/R) Norwegian mountain landscape 1847 (48x63cm-19x25in)
      (N.KR 46000)

MORE, Jacob (1740-1793) British
£20000 $35200   (10-Apr-92 C55/R) The Eruption of Etna with the Pious Brothers of Catania
      (150x204cm-59x80in) s.d.1787

MOREAU, Adrien (1843-1906) French
£1500 $2700   (22-Nov-91 S.BM47/R) Receiving affections - interior genre scene
      (46x38cm-18x15in) s. panel
£3846 $7000   (27-May-92 CH.NY18/R) Summer afternoon by the river (19x21cm-7x8in) s.
      panel

MOREAU, Gustave (1826-1898) French
£290698 $500000   (17-Oct-91 SY.NY30/R) Enamored lion (37x24cm-15x9in) s. W/C gouache

MOREAU, Jean (19th C) French
£968 $1627   (27-Aug-91 RAS.K413/R) Rich children giving money to poor beggar
      (41x33cm-16x13in) s. (D.KR 11000)

MOREAU, Jean Michel (younger) (1741-1814) French
£1222 $2224   (11-Dec-91 LD.P17/R) Bassin dans un parc avec des promeneurs
      (16x36cm-6x14in) s.d. pen ink W/C double-sided (F.FR 12000)
£2900 $5046   (13-Apr-92 S14/R) Two palace interiors, one with flight of steps, other
      with throne room (18x22cm-7x9in) one s.d.1781 pen wash pair

MOREAU, Louis Gabriel (1740-1806) French
£17490 $33230   (26-Jun-92 AT.P33/R) Paysage avec un pecheur au bord d'une riviere
      (70x102cm-28x40in) (F.FR 170000)
£48343 $87500   (22-May-92 SY.NY42/R) Le parc Monceau. Le Cours-la-Reine, Paris
      (8x41cm-3x16in) copper pair

MOREAU, Louis Gabriel (attrib) (1740-1806) French
£1339 $2517   (18-Dec-91 PR.P49) Lavandieres pres du lavoir. Interieur d'etable
      (11x15cm-4x6in) panel pair (F.FR 13000)

MOREAU, P (?) ?
£420 $790   (17-Dec-91 CSK33/R) Lady in boudoir with lovers (10x?cm-4x?in) min. s.
      ormolu frame griffin surmount rec

MOREAU, Paul Charles Chocarne see CHOCARNE-MOREAU, Paul Charles

MOREELSE, Paulus (1571-1638) Dutch
£7500 $13125   (3-Apr-92 C38/R) Officer as civic guard, holding flag (81x65cm-32x26in)
      mono.d.1635 panel
£8840 $16000   (22-May-92 SY.NY267/R) Portrait of young woman (112x79cm-44x31in) bears
      i. panel

MOREELSE, Paulus (attrib) (1571-1638) Dutch
£1850 $3367   (13-Dec-91 C142/R) Portrait of bearded gentleman in black costume and
      ruff (39x31cm-15x12in) panel
£3933 $7000   (22-Jan-92 SY.NY99/R) Portrait of lady (101x84cm-40x33in)

MOREELSE, Paulus (circle) (1571-1638) Dutch
£1200 $2304   (10-Jul-92 PH72/R) Shepherd and shepherdess (83x103cm-33x41in)
£4938 $8840   (14-Nov-91 CH.AM129/R) Portrait of Geertruida Goltstein tot Doorn wearing
      lace collar (70x55cm-28x22in) mono.d.1631 i.coat of arms verso panel
      (D.FL 16000)

MOREELSE, Paulus (style) (1571-1638) Dutch
£785 $1500   (16-Jul-92 SY.NY170/R) Portrait of a child (33x22cm-13x9in) panel
£1771 $3100   (19-Feb-92 D.NY60) Portrait of a lady in a ruff (89x66cm-35x26in) panel
£10000 $17500   (28-Feb-92 C11/R) Shepherdess in straw hat and decollete dress
      (54x42cm-21x17in) panel

MOREL, Casparus Johannes (1798-1861) Dutch
£1500 $2520   (15-Aug-91 B400/R) Dutch merchantman at anchor (41x51cm-16x20in) s.
£5199 $9046   (14-Apr-92 SY.AM83/R) Evening on the river Schelde (65x93cm-26x37in)
      s.d.1858 panel (D.FL 17000)

MOREL, Jan Baptist (17/18th C) Flemish
£29783 $53610   (19-Nov-91 RAS.K38/R) Still life of garland of flowers and butterflies
        (103x160cm-41x63in) indist.s. (D.KR 330000)

MOREL, Jan Evert (1769-1808) Flemish
£1284 $2286   (30-Oct-91 CH.AM11 a) Wooded hilly landscape with herdsman and cow on
        sandy path (26x20cm-10x8in) s. panel (D.FL 4200)
£1661 $2906   (3-Apr-92 BM.B686) Peasants in landscape (23x32cm-9x13in) s. panel
        (DM 4700)
£2000 $3420   (17-Mar-92 PH2) Figures on woodland track. Faggot gatherers in wood
        (20x15cm-8x6in) s. panel pair
£3800 $6764   (26-Nov-91 PH1/R) View of town in river landscape (29x44cm-11x17in) s.
        panel
£5500 $9405   (17-Mar-92 PH31) Figures with sheep on woodland path and river beyond
        (21x15cm-8x6in) s. panel pair

MOREL, Jan Evert II (1835-1905) Dutch
£673 $1171   (14-Apr-92 SY.AM280) Mountainous landscape with figures along river
        (54x63cm-21x25in) s. (D.FL 2200)

MOREL, Jan Evert and SEVERDONCK, Franz van (19th C) Dutch
£1728 $3300   (16-Jul-92 SY.NY485/R) Shepherd tending his flock (33x29cm-13x11in)
        s.i.d.187- panel

MORELLE, John (fl.1884-1886) British
£1500 $2610   (12-Sep-91 CSK219/R) The farmer's daughter (127x102cm-50x40in) s.

MORELLET, Francois (1926-) French
£9500 $16435   (26-Mar-92 S93/R) Trames 1 2 (80x80cm-31x31in) s.d.1959 verso panel
*£1667 $3017   (19-May-92 CH.AM341/R) Superposition (25x25cm-10x10in) s.i.d.1980 verso
        lead acrylic (D.FL 5500)*
*£2026 $3668   (21-May-92 CC.P91/R) Geometrie no.56 (46x38cm-18x15in) s.d.1984verso dr
        branch panel (F.FR 20000)*

MORELLI (?) Italian
£1900 $3363   (14-Feb-92 C158/R) An Oriental (61x49cm-24x19in) s.d.86

MORELLI, Domenico (1826-1901) Italian
£3371 $6000   (22-Jan-92 SY.NY518/R) Lute player (78x48cm-31x19in) s.d.1870
£599 $1090   (10-Dec-91 F.R28) Arabo (25x18cm-10x7in) s.i.d.1880 ink (I.L 1300000)
*£996 $1844   (8-Jun-92 CH.R645) Mopso e Amarilli - Idillio (25x27cm-10x11in) s.i. W/C
        (I.L 2200000)*
*£1585 $2933   (8-Jun-92 CH.R643) Orientale seduto, in meditazione. Orientale in piedi
        s. pen two (I.L 3500000)*

MORELLI, Enzo (1896-?) Italian
£975 $1832   (19-Dec-91 F.M123) Paesaggio (50x60cm-20x24in) s. s.d.1961verso
        (I.L 2100000)
£2269 $4221   (16-Jun-92 F.M309/R) Assisi (29x21cm-11x8in) mono.d.1925 panel
        (I.L 5000000)

MORELLI, Euro (20th C) Italian?
£590 $1051   (29-Apr-92 F.F192/R) Autoritratto (10x8cm-4x3in) masonite (I.L 1300000)

MORELLO, L (18/19th C) Italian
£550 $1018   (11-Jun-92 B166/R) Gossip at fruit sellers (48x66cm-19x26in) s. W/C

MORENI, Mattia (1920-) Italian
£10132 $18441   (9-Dec-91 CH.R149/R) Antibes (100x150cm-39x59in) s.d.1951 s.i.d.verso
        (I.L 22000000)

MORENO TEJADA, J (18/19th C) Spanish
£9302 $16000   (17-Oct-91 SY.NY334/R) Mexican market (43x73cm-17x29in) s.

MORENO Y CARBONERO, Jose see CARBONERO, Jose Moreno

MORENO VILLA, Jose (20th C) Spanish
£8638 $15030   (16-Apr-92 FB.P2/R) Composition cubiste (41x32cm-16x13in) s.i.d.27 panel
        (F.FR 85000)

MORENO, Michel (?) Italian?
£817 $1445   (8-Nov-91 LGB.P146/R) Orchestre (61x54cm-24x21in) s. (F.FR 8100)
£1031 $1763   (11-Mar-92 LGB.P171) Bacchanale (65x54cm-26x21in) s. (F.FR 10000)
£1236 $2323   (18-Dec-91 LGB.P157/R) Concert (65x54cm-26x21in) s. (F.FR 12000)
£1272 $2276   (17-Nov-91 R.P129) Composition (61x50cm-24x20in) (F.FR 12500)
*£665 $1178   (8-Nov-91 LGB.P99/R) Étude pour la Parabole de la vie (28x45cm-11x18in)
        s. gouache (F.FR 6600)*

MORERA Y GALICIA, Jaime (1854-1927) Spanish
£1801 $3188   (12-Feb-92 ANS.M130/R) Paisaje con arboles (29x39cm-11x15in) canvas on
        panel (S.P 325000)
£3558 $6475   (27-May-92 DUR.M380/R) Paisaje (53x89cm-21x35in) s.d.95 (S.P 650000)

MORET, Henry (1856-1913) French

£5900	$10798	(17-May-92 T.B194/R) Sur la Cote en Bretagne Sud (30x36cm-12x14in) (F.FR 58000)
£6148	$11066	(2-Feb-92 ZZ.F122/R) Bord de mer (33x41cm-13x16in) s. (F.FR 60000)
£6967	$12541	(2-Feb-92 ZZ.F97/R) Bateau dans la rade (20x26cm-8x10in) s. (F.FR 68000)
£7076	$12383	(5-Apr-92 ZZ.F110/R) Sieste au bord de la falaise (13x47cm-5x19in) s. (F.FR 68000)
£8571	$15000	(25-Feb-92 CH.NY21/R) Plage de Ragnenez, Finistere (38x61cm-15x24in) s.d.1902
£10682	$19120	(17-Nov-91 GL.P57/R) Paysage Breton (46x55cm-18x22in) s. (F.FR 105000)
£11190	$20031	(17-Nov-91 GL.P59/R) Femma et chien au bord de la mer (55x46cm-22x18in) s. (F.FR 110000)
£12140	$23066	(24-Jun-92 FB.P40/R) Bord de mer a Larmor (56x82cm-22x32in) s.d.91 (F.FR 118000)
£15432	$27932	(4-Dec-91 LD.P82/R) Cote bretonne (50x65cm-20x26in) s.d.1912 (F.FR 150000)
£20576	$37243	(6-Dec-91 GL.P189) Personnages allonges au bord de l'eau (13x46cm-5x18in) s. canvas laid down on board (F.FR 200000)
£24000	$42000	(25-Feb-92 CH.NY14/R) La mer Bretagne (54x64cm-21x25in) s.
£27322	$50000	(14-May-92 SY.NY231/R) Les falaises pres de la mer (47x55cm-19x22in) s.d.96
£28147	$50102	(28-Nov-91 FB.P37/R) Pont-Aven (61x50cm-24x20in) s. (F.FR 275000)
£30837	$54890	(26-Nov-91 J.M8/R) Port Judy, Ile de Groix, Morbilion (58x78cm-23x31in) s.d.1907 i.stretcher (A.D 70000)
£45000	$81450	(3-Dec-91 C224/R) Le Moulin de Riec, Finistere (73x92cm-29x36in) s.d.09
£412	$782	(24-Jun-92 GL.P105) Port-Marly (23x30cm-9x12in) studio st. d.1906verso W/C (F.FR 4000)
£412	$782	(24-Jun-92 GL.P106) La grenouillere, Bougival (20x29cm-8x11in) studio st. d.1906verso W/C (F.FR 4000)
£432	$821	(24-Jun-92 GL.P124) La promenade en barque (16x24cm-6x9in) studio st. W/C (F.FR 4200)
£463	$880	(24-Jun-92 GL.P125) Fete nautique au Bras Migneaux a Poissy (16x24cm-6x9in) studio st. W/C (F.FR 4500)
£514	$977	(24-Jun-92 GL.P133) Village en automne (25x32cm-10x13in) studio st. W/C (F.FR 5000)
£514	$977	(24-Jun-92 GL.P134) Les bancs de sable (23x28cm-9x11in) studio st. W/C (F.FR 5000)
£514	$977	(24-Jun-92 GL.P120) Villebon (26x28cm-10x11in) studio st.d.1906verso W/C (F.FR 5000)
£514	$977	(24-Jun-92 GL.P104/R) Jeune pecheur a l'epuisette (27x23cm-11x9in) studio st. chl dr (F.FR 5000)
£514	$982	(3-Jul-92 GL.P123) L'ecolier (19x17cm-7x7in) ink W/C (F.FR 5000)
£617	$1173	(24-Jun-92 GL.P121) Paysage (37x26cm-15x10in) studio st. W/C (F.FR 6000)
£669	$1271	(24-Jun-92 GL.P135) Basse mer (23x28cm-9x11in) studio st. W/C (F.FR 6500)
£740	$1413	(3-Jul-92 GL.P122) Breton de dos au bord de l'eau (15x16cm-6x6in) chl W/C (F.FR 7200)
£772	$1466	(24-Jun-92 GL.P132/R) Vallee de la Bievre (27x35cm-11x14in) studio st. d.1906verso (F.FR 7500)
£844	$1603	(24-Jun-92 GL.P107/R) La moisson (26x37cm-10x15in) studio st. W/C (F.FR 8200)
£1049	$1994	(24-Jun-92 GL.P123/R) La vallee de la Bievre (33x26cm-13x10in) studio st. d.1906verso W/C (F.FR 10200)
£1049	$1994	(24-Jun-92 GL.P103) La lavandiere (20x31cm-8x12in) studio st. W/C (F.FR 10200)
£1461	$2776	(24-Jun-92 GL.P101/R) La cueillette des fraises, Vallee de la Bievre (38x28cm-15x11in) studio st. d.1906verso W/C (F.FR 14200)
£2778	$5278	(24-Jun-92 GL.P136/R) Maison de la Pointe de Cayenne a Douelan, Finistere, 1895-1908 (26x36cm-10x14in) studio st. W/C (F.FR 27000)
£3154	$5771	(17-May-92 T.B89/R) Mer et cote rocheuse (27x35cm-11x14in) studio st. pastel chl (F.FR 31000)

MORETT, D (20th C) German?

£1138	$1957	(16-Oct-91 KM.K1289 a) Harlingen Harbour (32x63cm-13x25in) s. (DM 3300)

MORETTI (?) Italian

£567	$970	(11-Mar-92 CJ.N279/R) Abstract composition (50x36cm-20x14in) s. Indian ink col. (F.FR 5500)
£1031	$1763	(11-Mar-92 CJ.N271/R) L'embouteillage (73x50cm-29x20in) s. gouache (F.FR 10000)
£1649	$2821	(11-Mar-92 CJ.N282/R) Abstract composition (73x103cm-29x41in) s. Indian ink gouache (F.FR 16000)

MORETTI, Lucien Philippe (20th C) French

£838	$1500	(9-May-92 CE.NY87/R) Jeune fille a sa toilette (27x22cm-11x9in) s.
£8004	$15368	(6-Jul-92 HC.P54) Premiere lecon (38x46cm-15x18in) s. (F.FR 77000)
£435	$774	(29-Nov-91 GAB.G2948/R) Taureau (44x60cm-17x24in) s.d.1958 mixed media (S.FR 1100)
£1109	$1918	(6-Oct-91 E.LA130) Grand-pere et petitfille (50x65cm-20x26in) s. W/C (F.FR 11000)

MORETTI, R (19/20th C) ?

£698	$1200	(15-Oct-91 CE.NY302) Winding the yarn (34x51cm-13x20in) s.i. W/C

MORETTI, Raymond (1931-) French
£420 $747   (29-Nov-91 D.P206) Composition (49x64cm-19x25in) s. gouache varnished
                     (F.FR 4100)

MORETTI, Raymond and COCTEAU, Jean (20th C) French
£464 $793   (11-Mar-92 CJ.N268/R) La tete du Christ (50x36cm-20x14in) s. gouache
                     (F.FR 4500)

MORGAN, Evelyn de (1850-1919) British
£50000 $85000   (25-Oct-91 C56/R) The Crown of Glory (105x54cm-41x21in) s.d.1896
£90000 $153000   (25-Oct-91 C57/R) Clytie (104x44cm-41x17in) init.d.1886-7

MORGAN, Frederick (1856-1927) British
£11000 $19580   (28-Apr-92 PH44/R) Father's welcome (132x89cm-52x35in) s.
£14000 $23800   (25-Oct-91 C4/R) The home of the swans (119x84cm-47x33in) s.
£18000 $31860   (6-Nov-91 S158/R) The dandy chair (89x58cm-35x23in) s. s.i.stretcher
£26000 $49400   (23-Jun-92 PH113/R) Lively haul (76x107cm-30x42in) s.
£46512 $80000   (17-Oct-91 SY.NY111/R) Flower cart (96x71cm-38x28in) s.
£6286   *$11000*   *(19-Feb-92 CH.NY170/R) Gathering flowers (57x38cm-22x15in) s. W/C gouache*
                     htd white gum arabic board

MORGAN, Frederick (attrib) (1856-1927) British
£1200 $2052   (12-Mar-92 CSK273/R) Portrait of young girl standing in coat with fur
                     collar and muff (91x46cm-36x18in)
£1744 $3000   (15-Oct-91 CE.NY96/R) Children playing on the seashore (76x51cm-30x20in)
                     bears sig.

MORGAN, John (1823-1886) British
£917 $1679   (3-Jun-92 R.T160/R) At jam cupboard when mother returns (51x61cm-20x24in)
                     with sig. (C.D 2000)
£2735 $4950   (4-Dec-91 NA.BA21/R) A romp in the hayfield (61x92cm-24x36in) s.

MORGAN, Lynn T (1889-?) American
£925 $1600   (8-Sep-91 LIT.L305) At Plaza, 59th and 5th (76x61cm-30x24in) s.

MORGAN, Mary de Neale (1868-1948) American
£730 $1300   (26-Nov-91 MOR.P110 b) Carmel Valley by sea (13x25cm-5x10in) s. panel
£3390 $6000   (12-Feb-92 B.SF452/R) Carmel coastline (23x81cm-9x32in) s. canvasboard
                     triptych
£421   *$800*   *(24-Jun-92 B.SF6328/R) Mountain landscape (29x39cm-11x15in) s. gouache*
£1447   *$2750*   *(24-Jun-92 B.SF6339/R) Over dunes (39x30cm-15x12in) s. gouache board*

MORGAN, Owen Baxter (fl.1898-1907) British
£1600 $2960   (12-Jun-92 C156) The walled garden (50x60cm-20x24in) s.d.96

MORGAN, Tony (1938-) British
£507 $902   (25-Nov-91 WK.M2047/R) Flying babies (190x212cm-75x83in)
                     s.i.d.1981stretcher (DM 1450)
£559 $996   (25-Nov-91 WK.M2049/R) The bogey man (210x214cm-83x84in)
                     s.i.d.1983stretcher (DM 1600)

MORGAN, Wallace (20th C) American
£421 $750   (2-May-92 IH.NY29/R) Crowd looking at biplane (43x33cm-17x13in) pencil
                     W/C

MORGAN, Walter Jenks (1847-1924) British
£420 $701   (22-Aug-91 CSK24) In the garden at Haddon Hall (30x51cm-12x20in) s. W/C
                     htd white

MORGAN, William (1826-1900) American
£1489 $2800   (18-Dec-91 SY.NY130/R) The visit (61x87cm-24x34in) s.

MORGAN, William F de (1839-1917) British
£3200   *$5472*   *(13-Mar-92 C65/R) Tobias and the Angel at the River Tigris*
                     (46x31cm-18x12in) mono. W/C bodycol

MORGANTINI, Luigi (1867-1938) Italian
£795 $1400   (8-Apr-92 D.NY55) Chores of day (76x127cm-30x50in) s.

MORGENSTERN, Christian (1805-1867) German
£617 $1099   (27-Apr-92 BU.K59/R) Mountainous river landscape (35x53cm-14x21in) init.
                     wood panel (D.KR 7000)

MORGENSTERN, Friedrich Ernst (1853-1919) German
£1117 $2000   (13-Nov-91 B.SF2323/R) Moored sailing boats (41x58cm-16x23in) s.
£1888 $3266   (25-Mar-92 KM.K1327/R) Beach scene with fisherfolk by the North Sea,
                     evening (68x103cm-27x41in) s. (DM 5400)

MORGENSTERN, Friedrich Wilhelm (attrib) (1736-1798) German
£515 $943   (2-Jun-92 FN.S2670) Wooded river landscape with fortified castle and
                     figures (24x30cm-9x12in) canvas on board (DM 1500)

MORGENSTERN, Johann Ludwig Ernst (1738-1819) German
£3550 $6247   (11-Apr-92 AT.P53/R) La salle des gardes. Les veilleurs endormis
                     (11x15cm-4x6in) copper pair (F.FR 35000)

MORGENSTERN, Johann Ludwig Ernst (1738-1819) German-cont.
£5000 $9600   (8-Jul-92 S99/R) Church interior with figures (25x19cm-10x7in) s. copper

MORGENSTERN, Karl Ernst (1847-1928) German
£874 $1512   (28-Mar-92 BOD.P996) Mountainous river landscape with village beyond (65x45cm-26x18in) s.d.1867 (DM 2500)

MORGENSTERNE MUNTHE, G (1875-1927) Dutch
£1112 $2013   (3-Dec-91 C.A187) Harbour scene (65x75cm-26x30in) s.d.1926 (B.FR 65000)

MORGENSTERNE MUNTHE, Gerhard (1875-1927) Dutch
£488 $907   (16-Jun-92 VN.R183) Katwyk fishing boats in the surf (210x143cm-83x56in) (D.FL 1600)
£590 $1021   (24-Mar-92 VN.R66) Fishing boats in the surf (210x143cm-83x56in) (D.FL 1900)
£788 $1395   (22-Apr-92 CH.AM65) A wrecker on a beach (21x16cm-8x6in) s. board (D.FL 2600)
£917 $1633   (30-Oct-91 CH.AM194) Beached bomschuit at sunset (32x41cm-13x16in) s. (D.FL 3000)
£2997 $5305   (5-Nov-91 SY.AM58/R) Fisherwomen on beach (40x55cm-16x22in) s.d.23 (D.FL 9800)
£3211 $5587   (14-Apr-92 SY.AM9/R) Two vessels at sea (51x78cm-20x31in) s.d.1919 (D.FL 10500)

MORGENT, J E E (19th C) ?
£2572 $4655   (3-Dec-91 CN.P31/R) Interieurs d'eglise (28x21cm-11x8in) s. one d.1806 pen W/C pair (F.FR 25000)

MORGENTHALER, Ernst (1887-1962) Swiss
£1024 $1761   (16-Oct-91 G.Z107/R) Stockhorn (44x52cm-17x20in) mono. board (S.FR 2600)
£1176 $2000   (23-Oct-91 GD.B531/R) Wooded river landscape, autumn (37x45cm-15x18in) mono. board (S.FR 3000)
£1880 $3440   (4-Jun-92 SY.Z396/R) Halbinsel Au, Zurichsee (33x44cm-13x17in) mono panel (S.FR 5000)
£2157 $3667   (23-Oct-91 GD.B530/R) Gardener tending garden in early spring (80x100cm-31x39in) mono. (S.FR 5500)
£431 $772   (15-Nov-91 GK.Z5591) Spring landscape (30x42cm-12x17in) mono. grease chk (S.FR 1100)
£435 $783   (19-Nov-91 GS.B3215) Row of houses, possibly Kanton Zurich (23x25cm-9x10in) mono.d.35 W/C (S.FR 1100)
£588 $1053   (15-Nov-91 GK.Z5592) Mountain landscape with shepherdess (29x43cm-11x17in) mono.d.1954 W/C (S.FR 1500)
£923 $1754   (25-Jun-92 GK.B510) Fishes on plate (33x44cm-13x17in) mono.d.1927 board double-sided (S.FR 2400)

MORGNER, Michael (1942-) German?
£594 $1081   (25-May-92 WK.M898/R) Composition with figures (60x89cm-24x35in) s.i.d.1989verso W/C (DM 1740)

MORGNER, Wilhelm (1891-1917) German
£772 $1389   (21-Nov-91 L.K347/R) Study of heads (18x27cm-7x11in) pencil sold with studies of children (DM 2200)
£1224 $2178   (30-Nov-91 VG.B902/R) Figures seated at table (9x16cm-4x6in) s.d.1911 chk (DM 3500)
£1649 $3019   (3-Jun-92 L.K332) Women harvesting hay. Head of bearded man s.d.1911 one mono.d. chl indian ink pen two (DM 4800)

MORIANI, A (?) ?
£518 $932   (23-Nov-91 SO.S461/R) Portrait of man (54x38cm-21x15in) s. W/C (S.KR 5400)

MORIER, David (style) (1705-?) Swiss
£2200 $3916   (30-Apr-92 CG874/R) Portrait of William, Duke of Cumberland in uniform (75x63cm-30x25in) i.

MORIN, A (?) ?
£1515 $2621   (23-Mar-92 B.O157/R) Landscape with goats (65x92cm-26x36in) s. panel (N.KR 17000)

MORIN, Adolphe (1841-?) French
£1579 $2700   (13-Mar-92 FN.S2874/R) Shepherd and flock on path near cottage in evening landscape (38x55cm-15x22in) s. (DM 4500)

MORIN, Louis (1855-?) French
£410 $745   (30-May-92 VG.B859/R) Parrots in jungle (26x20cm-10x8in) mono W/C gouache board on board (DM 1200)

MORISOT, Berthe (1841-1895) French
£54645 $100000   (14-May-92 SY.NY234/R) Venus va demander des armes a Vulcain (114x138cm-45x54in) st.sig.
£4046 $7000   (2-Oct-91 SY.NY11/R) Dans l'Ile du Bois de Boulogne (18x25cm-7x10in) with st.sig. W/C paper on canvas
£5085 $9000   (6-Nov-91 CH.NY113/R) Au bord de la Seine (16x24cm-6x9in) st.init. W/C over pencil paper on paper

MORISOT, Berthe (1841-1895) French-cont.

£15301 $28000   (14-May-92 SY.NY106/R) Nu couche (46x61cm-18x24in) st.sig. pastel ink paper on board

£22599 $40000   (7-Nov-91 SY.NY103/R) Enfant au lit (30x40cm-12x16in) with st.sig. pastel

MORISSET, Francois Henri (1870-?) French

£3198 $5500   (15-Oct-91 CE.NY184/R) By the hearth (54x65cm-21x26in) s.indist.d.

MORITZ, Friedrich Wilhelm (1783-1855) Swiss

£1729 $3165   (4-Jun-92 SY.Z322/R) Simmentaler farmhouse with peasant couple in costume (36x50cm-14x20in) s.d.1817 pencil W/C (S.FR 4600)

MORITZ, Fritz (1922-) German

£552 $949   (16-Oct-91 KM.K1278) Flower market in Amsterdam (50x40cm-20x16in) s. (DM 1600)

MORIZOT, E (19th C) French

£1058 $1884   (28-Apr-92 RAS.K269) River landscape with fishermen (49x64cm-19x25in) s. (D.KR 12000)

MORLAND, George (1763-1804) British

£520 $946   (12-Dec-91 B105) Fishwife on rocky shore with fishermen drinking outside hut (43x54cm-17x21in) s.

£950 $1672   (8-Apr-92 S238/R) Coastal scene with fisherman by boat (13x17cm-5x7in) s. panel

£1600 $2816   (10-Apr-92 C140/R) Travellers on country track with cattle and sheep in hilly landscape (32x39cm-13x15in) s.d.1792

£1600 $2864   (13-Nov-91 S179/R) Study of heads of calves (23x26cm-9x10in) s.

£1748 $2990   (18-Mar-92 N.M439/R) Seascape with shipwreck and figures in storm (27x41cm-11x16in) i.verso panel (DM 5000)

£2000 $3580   (13-Nov-91 S201/R) Landscape with boy fishing (43x35cm-17x14in) s. panel

£2300 $4117   (13-Nov-91 S178/R) The Bell Inn in winter with sportsman (16x21cm-6x8in) s.

£2600 $4576   (8-Apr-92 S199/R) Mare and foal by barn (29x37cm-11x15in) s.d.1792 panel

£3200 $5728   (13-Nov-91 S214/R) Sheep in stable at winter (34x45cm-13x18in) s.d.1799 panel

£4000 $7640   (17-Jul-92 C35/R) Faggot gatherers (35x44cm-14x17in) s.

£4000 $7640   (15-Jul-92 S84/R) The angry boy and tired dog. Young nurse and quiet child (21x16cm-8x6in) canvas on panel pair

£4200 $7518   (13-Nov-91 S205/R) Fishermen unloading catch on beach (19x30cm-7x12in) s.

£5200 $9308   (13-Nov-91 S0/R) Figures on beach on the Isle of Wight (49x64cm-19x25in) s.

£6000 $10680   (28-Apr-92 PH31/R) Two figures in landscape. Young lady seated in landscape (45x35cm-18x14in) s. pair

£14000 $25060   (15-Nov-91 C69/R) Travellers, with horse and dog, approaching ferry boat on lake (101x141cm-40x56in) s.d.1792

£28000 $49280   (8-Apr-92 S6/R) Wreck of Indiaman off Isle of Wight (89x138cm-35x54in)

MORLAND, George (after) (1763-1804) British

£1100 $1958   (31-Oct-91 B197/R) Grooms and horses in stable interior (77x102cm-30x40in)

£1400 $2394   (12-Mar-92 CSK162/R) The stable door (96x127cm-38x50in)

MORLAND, George (attrib) (1763-1804) British

£523 $900   (16-Oct-91 D.NY74) Peasants carrying fagots of wood into town (51x74cm-20x29in) bears sig.d.1795

£562 $1000   (22-Jan-92 D.NY16) White mare in landscape (46x61cm-18x24in) bears sig.

£896 $1594   (25-Nov-91 W.T1909) The Blacksmith's shop (49x64cm-19x25in) (C.D 1800)

£1000 $1790   (13-Nov-91 S183/R) Coast scene with fisherfolk by beached vessel (12x16cm-5x6in) i. panel

£1068 $1902   (28-Apr-92 CH.ME33/R) Fishermen shipwrecked, Isle of Wight (29x37cm-11x15in) indis.s.i.d.1799verso (A.D 2500)

£1176 $2106   (15-Nov-91 GK.Z5079/R) Dogs fighting (42x53cm-17x21in) (S.FR 3000)

£2168 $3750   (6-Sep-91 S.BM125/R) Countryside landscape with shepherds, flock and cattle (102x163cm-40x64in)

£2447 $4332   (7-Nov-91 D.V379/R) Cows watering in river landscape (34x43cm-13x17in) (A.S 50000)

£7000 $12530   (15-Nov-91 C97/R) Portrait of sportsman, identified as Colonel Thornton, lying on ground with two spaniels (150x195cm-59x77in)

MORLAND, George (circle) (1763-1804) British

£700 $1218   (12-Sep-91 CSK198) Mare and foal by barn (30x38cm-12x15in) bears sig.d.

£750 $1335   (31-Oct-91 B199/R) Travellers and donkey resting beside stream, estuary beyond (21x30cm-8x12in) panel

£3000 $5730   (17-Jul-92 C90/R) Two pigs resting in sty. Two sheep by a fence in landscape (26x31cm-10x12in) 1st init. panel pair

MORLAND, George (style) (1763-1804) British

£850 $1454   (18-Mar-92 CSK206) Children feeding donkey and pigs in barn (130x155cm-51x61in) bears sig.

MORLAND, George and IBBETSON, Julius Caesar (18/19th C) British

£7000 $12320   (8-Apr-92 S95/R) Hampstead Heath with distant view of London (45x59cm-18x23in) s.

MORLAND, George and RATHBONE, John (18th C) British
£2400 $4296   (13-Nov-91 S81/R) Rustics on path with distant view of London from Blackheath (21x30cm-8x12in) panel
£4200 $7392   (8-Apr-92 S242/R) River landscape with gypsies resting by fire (43x58cm-17x23in)

MORLAND, Henry Robert (1730-1797) British
£7500 $14325   (14-Jul-92 C30/R) Laundry maid (78x67cm-31x26in) mono. pastel paper on linen three joined sheets

MORLAND, James Smith (?-1921) British
£500 $915   (1-Jun-92 TAY692) Cattle grazing (58x89cm-23x35in) s.d.1885 W/C

MORLEY, Malcolm (1931-) British
£22857 $40000   (25-Feb-92 SY.NY169/R) Love boat (127x203cm-50x80in)
£34286 $60000   (25-Feb-92 SY.NY162/R) Picasso bridge (122x168cm-48x66in) s.d.71
£117318 $210000   (13-Nov-91 SY.NY68/R) Camels and goats (169x254cm-67x100in) s.d.80
£156425 $280000   (6-May-92 SY.NY46/R) Age of catastrophe (152x244cm-60x96in)
£190000 $343900   (5-Dec-91 S34/R) School of Athens (176x247cm-69x97in) s. acrylic canvas
£318436 $570000   (6-May-92 SY.NY43/R) Vermeer, Portrait of the artist in his studio (267x221cm-105x87in) acrylic
£800 $1384   (26-Mar-92 C88/R) Horses and riders (57x77cm-22x30in) s. col.crayon pencil
£1564 $2800   (12-Nov-91 CE.NY111/R) Untitled (91x60cm-36x24in) s. W/C
£4190 $7500   (14-Nov-91 SY.NY358 a/R) Untitled (37x58cm-15x23in) s. W/C
£5587 $10000   (14-Nov-91 SY.NY367/R) Untitled - study for Albatross (32x41cm-13x16in) s. gouache W/C
£14525 $26000   (7-May-92 SY.NY290/R) Indian family (55x76cm-22x30in) W/C
£16760 $30000   (5-May-92 CH.NY139 a/R) Gloria (56x78cm-22x31in) s. s.i.d.1989verso W/C

MORLEY, Robert (1857-1941) British
£1000 $1680   (16-Aug-91 K562) Toadstool and toads in landscape (33x28cm-13x11in) s.
£1100 $1991   (21-May-92 B221) Brockholt Bill, portrait of west highland terrier (38x28cm-15x11in) s.i.d.1920 panel

MORLEY, T W (1859-1925) British
£377 $668   (5-Nov-91 BA.S228/R) Market scene (44x35cm-17x14in) s.d.11 mixed media (S.KR 4000)

MORLOTTI, Ennio (1910-) Italian
£9052 $16474   (26-May-92 SY.MI190/R) Fiori (27x40cm-11x16in) s.d.60verso paper on canvas (I.L 20000000)
£9988 $17778   (29-Apr-92 F.F180/R) Rocce e cielo (30x40cm-12x16in) s. (I.L 22000000)
£9988 $17778   (29-Apr-92 F.F179/R) Rocce a finale (30x40cm-12x16in) s. s.verso (I.L 22000000)
£13619 $24242   (29-Apr-92 F.F256/R) Senza titolo (41x53cm-16x21in) s.d.1964 cardboard (I.L 30000000)
£678 $1227   (21-May-92 F.M37) Cactus (34x37cm-13x15in) s.d.1960 pencil (I.L 1500000)
£1019 $1815   (27-Nov-91 F.M301/R) Testa di bambina (35x24cm-14x9in) s. sanguine (I.L 2200000)
£1842 $3353   (9-Dec-91 CH.R29/R) Girasoli (35x43cm-14x17in) s.d.1973 indian ink (I.L 4000000)
£2410 $4289   (29-Nov-91 F.F96) Senza titolo (30x23cm-12x9in) s. pastel cardboard (I.L 5200000)
£3063 $5758   (19-Dec-91 F.M26/R) Rocce (27x35cm-11x14in) s. pastel wax (I.L 6600000)

MORMILE, G (1839-1890) Italian
£1068 $1902   (27-Apr-92 J.M327) The minstral (74x50cm-29x20in) s.i. board (A.D 2500)

MORMILE, Gaetano (1839-1890) Italian
£994 $1800   (21-May-92 GRO.B49/R) Young girl tending fire in barnyard (33x25cm-13x10in) s.indis.i.d. i.verso panel
£1798 $3200   (22-Jan-92 SY.NY522/R) Serenading outside window (41x33cm-16x13in) s.
£2442 $4200   (15-Oct-91 CE.NY329/R) Donkey's at rest (25x33cm-10x13in) s. panel

MORNER, Axel Otto (1774-1852) Swedish
£3879 $7021   (19-May-92 AB.S4250/R) The Royal Palace, Stockholm with steamboat and sailingboat (53x72cm-21x28in) s. (S.KR 41000)

MORNER, Stellan (1896-1979) Swedish
£658 $1099   (25-Aug-91 BU.M489) After the party (22x27cm-9x11in) s. panel (S.KR 7000)
£1156 $2000   (28-Mar-92 UA.U360/R) House-hunting couple (27x22cm-11x9in) s. panel (S.KR 12000)
£1187 $2066   (13-Apr-92 AB.S177) Interior with woman with two chairs and mirror (23x32cm-9x13in) s. (S.KR 12500)
£1534 $2761   (19-Nov-91 GO.G113) Blue landscape (27x35cm-11x14in) s. tempera panel (S.KR 16000)
£1568 $2808   (16-Nov-91 FAL.M220/R) The Queen and the slave (39x47cm-15x19in) s. (S.KR 16500)
£1987 $3596   (19-May-92 AB.S5282/R) Memory of summer (32x40cm-13x16in) s.d.70 panel (S.KR 21000)
£2863 $5095   (28-Nov-91 BU.S101/R) We are searching from our dream home (46x61cm-18x24in) (S.KR 30000)
£6167 $11286   (11-May-92 NOR.S98/R) Frugal evening meal (46x55cm-18x22in) s. (S.KR 65000)

MORO, Battista Angolo del see ANGOLO DEL MORO, Battista

MORODER, Josef Theodor (1846-1916) Austrian
£6272 $11415   (11-Dec-91 N.M539/R) Tyrolean peasants drinking wine (24x36cm-9x14in) s.
i.verso panel (DM 18000)

MORONI, Giovan Battista (attrib) (1525-1578) Italian
£170000 $297500   (1-Apr-92 S40/R) Portrait of two children (91x114cm-36x45in) panel

MORONI, Giovan Battista (style) (1525-1578) Italian
£1500 $2880   (9-Jul-92 CSK132/R) Portrait of Carthusian Monk at prayer
(41x30cm-16x12in)
£1800 $3276   (10-Dec-91 PH105/R) Portrait of Prospero Alessandri (54x47cm-21x19in)

MOROT, Aime (1850-1913) French
£1571 $2750   (20-Feb-92 SY.NY160/R) Portrait of peasant woman (46x36cm-18x14in)
s.i.d.1876

MOROZ, Georgii (1937-) Russian
£512 $922   (27-Jan-92 ARC.P94/R) Les pivoines (85x104cm-33x41in) s.verso (F.FR 5000)
£1127 $2029   (27-Jan-92 ARC.P95/R) Les iris bleus (76x89cm-30x35in) s.verso
(F.FR 11000)

MOROZOV, Serguei (1954-) Russian
£515 $881   (13-Mar-92 ARC.P188/R) Les bergers (53x63cm-21x25in) s. (F.FR 5000)

MORPHY, Garrett (?-1715) British
£24000 $42960   (13-Nov-91 S26/R) Portrait of Brigadier General William Wolseley standing
wearing armour (129x101cm-51x40in) s.d.1692

MORPHY, Garrett (attrib) (?-1715) British
£3600 $6336   (10-Apr-92 C6/R) Portrait of Nicholas, 2nd Earl of Carlingford on balcony
in landscape (142x105cm-56x41in)
£9000 $15840   (10-Apr-92 C7/R) Portrait of Mry, Countess of Carlingford before wooded
landscape (139x104cm-55x41in) i.d.1691

MORRICE, James Wilson (1865-1924) Canadian
£4250 $7523   (6-Nov-91 SY.T40/R) Canadian cavalry in Flanders (23x33cm-9x13in) panel
(C.D 8500)
£8000 $13600   (22-Oct-91 C46/R) Arab girl (33x24cm-13x9in) s. panel

MORRIS (?) ?
£1947 $3700   (26-Jun-92 WOL.C497) Patience (61x43cm-24x17in) s.

MORRIS, Alfred (19th C) British
£625 $1094   (19-Feb-92 HAR436) Sheep and goats in highland landscape with sailboats
in the distance (124x99cm-49x39in) s.d.1874

MORRIS, Carl (1911-) American
£1056 $1900   (24-Nov-91 JRB.C296) Gray facade (91x122cm-36x48in) s.

MORRIS, Cedric (1889-1982) British
£1350 $2322   (5-Mar-92 CSK173/R) Landscape in Provence (54x60cm-21x24in) s.d.22
£1800 $3096   (5-Mar-92 CSK174/R) Manningtree Wharf (61x71cm-24x28in) s.d.31
s.i.d.verso
£2222 $4022   (19-May-92 GF.L2540/R) Hut on the coast near Bordeaux (54x65cm-21x26in)
s.d.1925 i.verso (S.FR 6000)
£2700 $4914   (12-Dec-91 CSK201/R) Garden Cypress (76x61cm-30x24in) s.d.2.73
£2800 $4956   (7-Nov-91 C19/R) Caldas (75x62cm-30x24in) s.i.d.50
£3000 $5190   (2-Oct-91 S169/R) Wild geese (61x47cm-24x19in) s. board
£3000 $5160   (6-Mar-92 C71/R) Olive trees (53x63cm-21x25in) s.d.26
£4000 $7320   (14-May-92 C210/R) White flowers (68x56cm-27x22in) s.i.d.1934 stretcher
£4000 $6880   (6-Mar-92 C70/R) Newlyn Bridge (60x74cm-24x29in)
£6000 $10980   (13-May-92 S64/R) Arums with poppies and anemones (65x53cm-26x21in)
£6500 $11895   (5-Jun-92 C56/R) Blackbird and flowers (65x109cm-26x43in) s.d.52
£6600 $11418   (2-Oct-91 S206/R) Pilchard boats at Newlyn (56x50cm-22x20in) s.d.19
s.i.verso board
£7500 $13725   (5-Jun-92 C55/R) Rhos Hilly Down (56x69cm-22x27in) s.d.28

MORRIS, Charles (19th C) British
£700 $1295   (11-Jun-92 CSK99/R) The old watermill (27x48cm-11x19in) s.
£950 $1824   (29-Jul-92 CSK186) The old watermill (30x50cm-12x20in) s.

MORRIS, Ebenezer Butler (19th C) British
£604 $1100   (26-May-92 CE.NY157/R) The troubled bride (36x76cm-14x30in) s. s.d.1852
verso

MORRIS, George L K (1905-1975) American
£6857 $12000   (26-Sep-91 CH.NY211/R) Indians hunting no.1 (41x51cm-16x20in) s.d.1934
s.i.d.verso board
£1371 $2400   (26-Sep-91 CH.NY208/R) Study for Suspended Discs (25x20cm-10x8in) s.
gouache pencil
£1437 $2500   (15-Apr-92 SY.NY257/R) Two refrigerators (30x45cm-12x18in) s. collage
gouache

MORRIS, H (19th C) British
£1017 $1750   (7-Mar-92 LAE.L20/R) The gift (38x28cm-15x11in) s.
£1163 $2000   (7-Mar-92 LAE.L21/R) The reading room (38x28cm-15x11in) s.

MORRIS, J (19th C) British
£550 $1056   (29-Jul-92 CSK249) The gillie's son (71x91cm-28x36in) s.
£585 $1035   (25-Apr-92 SO.S478/R) Horse and goats (35x50cm-14x20in) s. (S.KR 6200)

MORRIS, J W (19th C) British
£559 $1000   (13-Nov-91 B.SF2191/R) Guardian of the fold (61x51cm-24x20in) s.d.1881
£789 $1500   (24-Jun-92 D.NY61) Watchful Eye (46x36cm-18x14in) s.
£1200 $2016   (26-Aug-91 S840/R) Sheep in Highlands (61x106cm-24x42in) s.

MORRIS, John (19th C) British
£573 $974   (23-Oct-91 EA.M450) Carriage and distant train in landscape
                 (61x91cm-24x36in) s. (C.D 1100)

MORRIS, John Floyd (20th C) American?
£838 $1500   (14-Nov-91 CE.NY460) Strange parkland (52x170cm-20x67in) s.

MORRIS, John W (?) ?
£550 $1007   (3-Jun-92 R.T156/R) Country gentleman and dog tending flock
                 (61x107cm-24x42in) s. (C.D 1200)

MORRIS, Kathleen (1893-1986) Canadian
£1629 $3014   (9-Jun-92 FB.M41/R) Sheep at Marshall's Bay, Arnprior, Ontario
                 (40x46cm-16x18in) board (C.D 3600)
£2374 $4321   (26-May-92 JOY.T7/R) Street scene, Montreal (26x34cm-10x13in) s. panel
                 (C.D 5200)
£2488 $4428   (26-Nov-91 JOY.T16/R) O'Connor Street, Ottawa, winter (26x35cm-10x14in)
                 s. panel (C.D 5000)

MORRIS, Mary (fl.1919-1950) British
£1700 $3026   (30-Apr-92 CG899) Shower from the north on Arran s.d.1910

MORRIS, Phil (?) British?
£1400 $2562   (5-Feb-92 TM262/R) Christening party (86x152cm-34x60in) s.

MORRIS, Philip Richard (c.1833-1902) British
£1500 $2625   (23-Sep-91 PHB61) The little burglar (112x86cm-44x34in) s.

MORRIS, William (1834-1896) British
£989 $1800   (26-May-92 CE.NY276/R) Young anglers (46x127cm-18x50in) s.d.1883

MORRISH, Sydney S (19th C) British
£800 $1424   (1-May-92 PHE84/R) Still life of dead game and ginger jar
                 (90x70cm-35x28in) s.d.1860
£1400 $2478   (6-Nov-91 S119/R) The anxious mother (70x63cm-28x25in) i.d.1860verso

MORRISON, James (1932-) British
£700 $1246   (28-Apr-92 S313) Hilltops (18x122cm-7x48in) s.d.1961 indist.i.verso board
£720 $1310   (29-May-92 PHG103) Landscape (75x102cm-30x40in) s.d.1977 board

MORRISSEAU, Norval (?) Canadian
£1610 $2914   (2-Dec-91 R.T95/R) Artist and thunderbird (101x75cm-40x30in) s. acrylic
                 (C.D 3300)

MORROCCO, Alberto (1917-) British
£520 $946   (29-May-92 PHG50 d) Benrinnes from Muldearie (38x51cm-15x20in) s. board

MORROCCO, Leon (1942-) Australian?
£470 $837   (27-Apr-92 J.M310) Still life of red pot and watermelon (24x112cm-9x44in)
                 s.d.85 pastel (A.D 1100)
£1068 $1902   (27-Apr-92 J.M83) South Melbourne market (100x150cm-39x59in) s.d.81
                 pastel (A.D 2500)
£2137 $3803   (27-Apr-92 J.M109/R) Summer bounty (76x111cm-30x44in) s.d.89 mixed media
                 (A.D 5000)

MORROW, Gray (20th C) American?
£429 $767   (7-May-92 CH.R316) Dracula contro Frankenstein (62x54cm-24x21in) original
                 poster (I.L 950000)

MORSE, Vernon Jay (1898-1965) American
£1017 $1800   (12-Feb-92 B.SF488/R) Abandoned ferry slip (51x66cm-20x26in) s.d.1927
£791 $1400   (12-Feb-92 B.SF555/R) Suicide Bridge, Pasadena (36x48cm-14x19in) s.d.1934
                 W/C

MORSELLI (?) ?
£965 $1680   (13-Apr-92 AT.P75) L'arracheur de dents (37x46cm-15x18in) s. panel after
                 Gerrit van Honthorst (F.FR 9500)

MORSELLI, G (19th C) Italian
£1634 $3039   (16-Jun-92 F.M80) Cena anticipata. Lettura davanti al camino
                 (46x37cm-18x15in) s.d.1876 panel (I.L 3600000)

MORSING, Ivar (1919-) Swedish
£509 $902   (25-Apr-92 SO.S479/R) Saraceska tower (40x44cm-16x17in) s. panel
                   (S.KR 5400)
£553 $973   (11-Apr-92 FAL.M279/R) 'Picador' (63x45cm-25x18in) s.d.1958 panel
                   (S.KR 5800)
£612 $1089   (28-Oct-91 AB.S150) Table still life (55x54cm-22x21in) s. (S.KR 6500)
£664 $1215   (13-May-92 BU.S126/R) In the studio (55x60cm-22x24in) s. (S.KR 7000)
£816 $1476   (3-Dec-91 AB.S5109/R) Autumn sun - figures (79x69cm-31x27in) s.d.72 panel
                   (S.KR 8500)

MORTEL, Jan (1650-1719) Dutch
£7832 $13862   (7-Nov-91 D.V173/R) Still life of herring, grapes and bottle in basket
                   (36x31cm-14x12in) panel (A.S 160000)

MORTEL, Jan (style) (1650-1719) Dutch
£1884 $3449   (12-May-92 SY.AM136) Bullfinches feeding nest of fledglings
                   (28x19cm-11x7in) panel (D.FL 6200)

MORTELMANS, Frans (1865-c.1936) Belgian
£759 $1305   (16-Oct-91 KM.K1291) Still life of roses in vase (40x30cm-16x12in) s.
                   (DM 2200)
£995 $1821   (12-May-92 C.A224) Still life of fish (41x50cm-16x20in) s. (B.FR 60000)
£5141 $9408   (12-May-92 C.A223/R) Still life of grapes (60x100cm-24x39in) s.
                   (B.FR 310000)
£3276 $5634   (16-Oct-91 KM.K1294/R) Market day in Hessia (10x16cm-4x6in) s. W/C
                   (DM 9500)

MORTENSEN, Richard (1910-) Danish
£8000 $13840   (26-Mar-92 S17/R) Restonica (97x130cm-38x51in) s.d.verso
£11312 $20475   (4-Dec-91 KH.K23/R) Composition (90x65cm-35x26in) s.i.d.41verso
                   (D.KR 125000)
£15837 $28665   (4-Dec-91 KH.K12/R) Notoni (73x92cm-29x36in) init.i.d.1959verso
                   (D.KR 175000)
£28054 $50778   (4-Dec-91 KH.K156/R) Composition, Opus II No.6, 1943 (91x69cm-36x27in)
                   s.d.43 on stretcher (D.KR 310000)
£498 $901   (4-Dec-91 KH.K132) Composition (32x24cm-13x9in) Indian ink (D.KR 5500)

MORTIMER, Lewis (20th C) British
£800 $1392   (19-Sep-91 TL528) Lynmouth. Clovelly 1927 (26x38cm-10x15in) s. W/C pair

MORTON, George (fl.1874-1904) British
£1900 $3382   (1-May-92 PHE9/R) The sisters (33x20cm-13x8in) s.

MORTON, Thomas Corsan (1869-1928) British
£1300 $2184   (29-Aug-91 CG105/R) The old mill, autumn (71x86cm-28x34in) s.d.1888-9

MORTON-JOHNSON (19/20th C) ?
£1107 $1970   (29-Nov-91 GAB.G2814) Femme dans un interieur (73x92cm-29x36in) s.
                   (S.FR 2800)

MORVAN, Jean Jacques (1928-) French
£610 $1061   (13-Apr-92 GL.P156) Ciel et terre (50x150cm-20x59in) s. i.d.1963verso
                   (F.FR 6000)

MORVILLER, Joseph (1800-1870) American
£1934 $3500   (4-Dec-91 D.NY14/R) Morning sun breaking through (46x61cm-18x24in)
                   s.d.1859

MORZENTI, Natale (19th C) Italian
£500 $890   (26-Nov-91 PH243) Standing nude with dog (185x111cm-73x44in) s. oval

MOSBACHER, Alois (1954-) Austrian?
£2444 $4350   (31-Oct-91 D.V170/R) Untitled (100x70cm-39x28in) s.d.1984verso
                   (A.S 50000)
£2622 $4668   (25-Nov-91 WK.M2053/R) Blue picture with dog (195x150cm-77x59in) s.d.1983
                   (DM 7500)
£2908 $5293   (26-May-92 D.V337/R) The hiker, Eiffel tower beyond (170x130cm-67x51in)
                   mono.d.83 (A.S 60000)
£2972 $5290   (25-Nov-91 WK.M2052/R) Kummerkopf (150x195cm-59x77in) s.d.1983 (DM 8500)
£489 $870   (31-Oct-91 D.V206/R) Untitled (72x50cm-28x20in) s. chl (A.S 10000)
£630 $1147   (26-May-92 D.V290/R) Untitled (98x62cm-39x24in) s.d.85 mixed media
                   (A.S 13000)
£648 $1160   (15-Jan-92 D.V276/R) Untitled (65x42cm-26x17in) s.d.82 dispersion acrylic
                   (A.S 13000)

MOSELEY, R S (19th C) British
£550 $995   (5-Dec-91 CSK263) The truants (36x25cm-14x10in) mono.d.79 i.verso

MOSELY, Mrs Henry (19th C) British
£650 $1157   (25-Jan-92 ZZ.B140) Portrait of Mrs Hayes - descendant of Charles Dickens
                   W/C

MOSER, Kolo (1868-1918) Austrian
£745 $1326   (28-Nov-91 D.V46/R) Study (46x15cm-18x6in) chk W/C (A.S 15000)

MOSER, Kolo (1868-1918) Austrian-cont.
£1699 $3024   (28-Apr-92 D.V12/R) Irises (29x24cm-11x9in) s.d.98 W/C pen indian ink
                      (A.S 35000)

MOSER, Mary (style) (1744-1819) British
£1700 $3077   (20-May-92 B101/R) Still life of roses, tulips, dahlias and other flowers
                      (76x63cm-30x25in)

MOSER, Richard (1874-?) Austrian
£1279 $2200   (15-Oct-91 CE.NY393/R) The village stream (25x33cm-10x13in) s.i.d.1915
                      W/C gouache laid paper
£1456 $2592   (29-Apr-92 D.V681/R) Wien, Universitatskirche (47x33cm-19x13in) s.d.1919
                      W/C (A.S 30000)
£2913 $5184   (29-Apr-92 D.V679/R) Das alte Burgtheater am Michaelerplatz
                      (29x36cm-11x14in) s.i.d.1911 W/C (A.S 60000)
£2913 $5184   (29-Apr-92 D.V680/R) Wien, Am Schulhof (39x29cm-15x11in) s.i. W/C
                      (A.S 60000)

MOSER, Wilfried (1914-) Swiss
£945 $1625   (16-Oct-91 G.Z38/R) Composition (21x47cm-8x19in) s.d.1952 board
                      (S.FR 2400)
£974 $1733   (29-Apr-92 G.Z185) Composition (55x39cm-22x15in) s. (S.FR 2600)
£2286 $4000   (28-Feb-92 SY.NY278/R) Marina di Carrara (83x65cm-33x26in) s.d.56
                      s.d.1956 verso s.d.1959 stretcher
£5639 $10320   (4-Jun-92 SY.Z448/R) Metro (106x182cm-42x72in) s.d.63 (S.FR 15000)
£7143 $13071   (4-Jun-92 SY.Z449/R) Motocross (130x162cm-51x64in) s. d.1963-64verso oil
                      collage hessian (S.FR 19000)

MOSES, Anna Mary Robertson (Grandma) (1860-1961) American
£2654 $4750   (13-Nov-91 B.SF2694/R) Where has he gone (21x25cm-8x10in) s. d.1947 verso
                      tempera board
£2654 $4750   (13-Nov-91 B.SF2692/R) Where it was cosy (23x24cm-9x9in) s. d.1947 verso
                      board
£3631 $6500   (13-Nov-91 B.SF2693/R) He'll get there (21x23cm-8x9in) s. d.1947 verso
                      board
£6704 $12000   (13-Nov-91 B.SF2691/R) Old Bridge, Richmond, Vt (28x37cm-11x15in) s.
                      d.1938 verso board
£7429 $13000   (25-Sep-91 SY.NY116/R) Church time (21x28cm-8x11in) s. d.1959 num.1882
                      verso board
£15205 $26000   (11-Mar-92 SY.NY109/R) August (41x61cm-16x24in) s. num.1714 verso tempera
                      masonite

MOSES, Ed (1926-) American
£14706 $25000   (23-Oct-91 B.SF3814/R) Untitled (206x169cm-81x67in) init.d.85-86verso
                      acrylic
£973 $1800   (12-Jun-92 SY.NY310/R) Untitled (63x51cm-25x20in) d.72 graphite masking
                      tape photocopy
£1765 $3000   (23-Oct-91 B.SF3813/R) Untitled (163x132cm-64x52in) mixed media canvas

MOSES, Thomas G (1856-1934) British
£678 $1200   (12-Feb-92 B.SF472/R) Laguna coast (76x102cm-30x40in) s.d.1930

MOSKOWITZ, Robert (1935-) American
£1117 $2000   (9-May-92 CE.NY361/R) Untitled (46x61cm-18x24in) s.d.1962verso graphite
£1955 $3500   (13-Nov-91 CH.NY213/R) Untitled (37x20cm-15x8in) init.d.80
                      col.chks.graphite

MOSLER, Henry (1841-1920) American
£967 $1750   (7-Dec-91 SG.M350) Young girl carrying bowl of milk (30x23cm-12x9in) s.

MOSMAN, William (?-1771) British
£780 $1334   (17-Mar-92 SWS1214) Portrait of a gentleman said to James Gadderar,
                      Bishop of Aberdeen (122x98cm-48x39in)

MOSNER, Ricardo (1948-) Argentina
£908 $1562   (14-Oct-91 AT.P77/R) Gulliver gulp (50x65cm-20x26in) mixed media
                      (F.FR 9000)

MOSNIER, Jean (attrib) (1600-1656) French
£7209 $13553   (18-Dec-91 AT.P175/R) Allegorie de l'Abondance et de la Paix. Allegorie
                      de la Victoire et de la Defaite (85x47cm-33x19in) panel pair
                      (F.FR 70000)

MOSSA, Gustave Adolf (1883-1971) French
£5337 $9500   (22-Jan-92 SY.NY371/R) L'abbe de St. Maurice (46x66cm-18x26in) s.d.1912
                      W/C pen

MOSSCHER, Jacob van (16/17th C) Dutch
£100000 $182000   (13-Dec-91 C4/R) Wooded landscape with angler, horseman on bridge, drover
                      and peasants (86x120cm-34x47in) bears indist.sig. panel

MOSSET, Olivier (1944-) Swiss
£1714 $3000   (27-Feb-92 CE.NY270/R) Little late in day (122x61cm-48x24in) s.d.86 verso
                      acrylic canvas

MOSSET, Olivier (1944-) Swiss-cont.
£2259	$4066	(19-Nov-91 FB.P232/R) Peinture (200x210cm-79x83in) s.d.74verso acrylic (F.FR 22000)
£2577	$4459	(23-Mar-92 CC.P122/R) Peinture (100x100cm-39x39in) s.d.1974verso acrylic (F.FR 25000)
£2669	$4805	(19-Nov-91 FB.P229/R) Cercle noir sur fond blanc (120x120cm-47x47in) s.verso (F.FR 26000)
£2881	$5473	(26-Jun-92 FB.P96/R) Cercle noir sur fond blanc (100x100cm-39x39in) s.d.70verso acrylic (F.FR 28000)
£3021	$5136	(27-Oct-91 P.V94/R) Bandes (200x210cm-79x83in) s.verso acrylic (F.FR 30000)
£3462	$6405	(10-Jun-92 CSC.P151 a/R) Untitled (100x100cm-39x39in) s.verso acrylic canvas (F.FR 34000)
£6173	$11173	(5-Dec-91 BG.P57/R) Composition (140x140cm-55x55in) s.d.77 acrylic diptych (F.FR 60000)

MOSSMER, Raimund (1813-1874) Austrian
£1856	*$3193*	*(10-Oct-91 D.V188/R) Modling near Vienna (15x23cm-6x9in) s.d.1858 W/C (A.S 38000)*

MOSSON, Georges (1851-1933) German
£3697	$6692	(6-Dec-91 GB.B5948) Still life of asters (67x50cm-26x20in) s.d.1923 (DM 10500)

MOST, Ludwig August (attrib) (1807-1883) German
£2857	$5000	(27-Sep-91 S.BM481 a/R) Shore birds among the reeds (99x140cm-39x55in) s.

MOSTAERT, Gillis (16th C) Flemish
£8594	$15211	(5-Nov-91 GF.L2013/R) Mythological scenes (32x41cm-13x16in) copper pair (S.FR 22000)

MOSTAERT, Gillis (attrib) (16th C) Flemish
£2778	$4972	(12-Nov-91 SY.AM232/R) Fishermen in evening landscape with burning town beyond (37x51cm-15x20in) panel (D.FL 9000)

MOSTAERT, Gillis (circle) (16th C) Flemish
£6500	$11375	(3-Apr-92 C151) Village landscape with Cincinnatus (58x74cm-23x29in) panel

MOSTAERT, Gillis (elder-attrib) (1534-1598) Flemish
£2222	$4022	(19-May-92 GF.L2360/R) The Temptation of St Anthony (34x46cm-13x18in) panel (S.FR 6000)

MOSTYN, Tom (1864-1930) British
£620	$1122	(5-Dec-91 CSK225) The summer garden (51x76cm-20x30in)
£750	$1433	(16-Jul-92 B18) Symbolist landscape (102x127cm-40x50in) s.
£780	$1396	(5-May-92 SWS487/R) Dawn on the lake (76x102cm-30x40in) s.
£800	$1368	(12-Mar-92 B117) The garden seat (101x152cm-40x60in) s.
£1000	$1910	(16-Jul-92 B17) A temple upon a hill with lake in foreground (30x40cm-12x16in) s.
£1105	$2000	(5-Dec-91 FA.PH579/R) Old cottage at Stratford on Avon (61x51cm-24x20in) s.
£1150	$2001	(17-Sep-91 PH140) The dream palace (61x106cm-24x42in) s.i. stretcher
£4286	$7500	(20-Feb-92 SY.NY269/R) Never Never Land (176x235cm-69x93in) s.

MOTAU, Julian (1948-1968) South African
£557	*$969*	*(13-Apr-92 SY.J218) Seated female figure (56x52cm-22x20in) s.d.67 chl (SA.R 2800)*

MOTE, George William (1832-1909) British
£1500	$2850	(23-Jun-92 PH174/R) Sheep and cattle in river landscape (60x90cm-24x35in) s.d.1878
£3000	$5130	(12-Mar-92 CSK236) Wooded landscapes with figures beside lake. Children playing beside track (51x61cm-20x24in) one s.d.1889 pair
£4500	$8325	(12-Jun-92 C140/R) Fisherfolk before Chatham Castle (102x127cm-40x50in) s.d.1858

MOTHERWELL, Robert (1915-1991) American
£5119	$9266	(23-May-92 GB.B6938/R) Untitled (43x70cm-17x28in) s. acrylic paper on board (DM 15000)
£7415	$12680	(17-Mar-92 FB.P65/R) Sans titre (23x30cm-9x12in) s.d.1959verso (F.FR 72000)
£9497	$17000	(14-Nov-91 SY.NY313/R) Rough open (51x57cm-20x22in) s.d.75 acrylic paper
£13317	$23038	(6-Oct-91 E.LA108/R) Sans titre (38x51cm-15x20in) s.d.67 acrylic panel (F.FR 132100)
£13966	$25000	(14-Nov-91 SY.NY318/R) Wall painting sketch (30x61cm-12x24in) init.d.73 acrylic canvasboard
£16185	$28000	(3-Oct-91 SY.NY34/R) In Plato's cave VII (112x155cm-44x61in) s.i.d.1973verso acrylic
£17341	$30000	(3-Oct-91 SY.NY41/R) Open series 48 (63x76cm-25x30in) s.i.verso acrylic
£19553	$35000	(7-May-92 SY.NY231/R) Artist - brown figure (95x75cm-37x30in) s.d.48
£22857	$40000	(25-Feb-92 SY.NY121/R) Seville (36x46cm-14x18in) init.d.50 canvasboard
£29330	$52500	(6-May-92 SY.NY3/R) Spanish elegy (23x30cm-9x12in) init.i.d.1959verso canvas board

MOTHERWELL, Robert (1915-1991) American-cont.

£30726 $55000   (12-Nov-91 CH.NY3/R) Spanish Elegy No.17 (23x30cm-9x12in) s.d.1952verso masonite

£33520 $60000   (7-May-92 SY.NY256/R) Sicilian door (183x183cm-72x72in) s.d.72 s.d.1972 verso

£50279 $90000   (14-Nov-91 SY.NY317/R) Summer seaside night (184x214cm-72x84in) init.d.74 s.d.1974 verso acrylic canvas

£167598 $300000   (13-Nov-91 SY.NY24/R) Two figures (137x182cm-54x72in) init.d.58 s.d.1958 verso

£1976 $3300   (25-Aug-91 JRB.C81) Pauillac, 1973 - edition of 53 (76x30cm-30x12in) s. serigraph collage

£5028 $9000   (14-Nov-91 SY.NY275/R) Untitled (35x28cm-14x11in) s.d.45 W/C ink

£11173 $20000   (13-Nov-91 CH.NY126/R) Untitled (36x28cm-14x11in) init.d.59 paper collage ink gouache board

£11173 $20000   (14-Nov-91 SY.NY281/R) Monument for Jackson Pollock (51x61cm-20x24in) s. s.d.1956 verso oil graphite paper on canvas

£41899 $75000   (14-Nov-91 SY.NY310/R) Must it be (114x75cm-45x30in) init.d.72 acrylic paper collage canvasboard

£50279 $90000   (12-Nov-91 CH.NY7/R) The scarlett ring (101x68cm-40x27in) init.d.63 oil chl.paper collage board

MOTTA, Denis (1821-1889) Italian

£852 $1542   (22-May-92 EA.Z137/R) Urnersee landscape (54x73cm-21x29in) s.d.1860 (S.FR 2300)

MOTTET, Johann Daniel (1754-1822) Swiss

£1176 $2106   (15-Nov-91 GK.Z5342) Portrait of Bernhard Friedrich Bitzius (64x53cm-25x21in) s.i.d.1821verso (S.FR 3000)

MOTTET, Yvonne (20th C) French

£743 $1300   (28-Feb-92 SY.NY215/R) Still life with flowers in vase (73x55cm-29x22in) s.

MOTTRAM, Charles Sim (fl.1880-1919) British

£450   *$819*   (11-Dec-91 MMB80) Fishing fleet in calm (28x46cm-11x18in) s.d.91 W/C

£650   *$1112*   (12-Mar-92 CSK18) Misty morning at sea (25x33cm-10x13in) s. W/C

£900   *$1593*   (6-Nov-91 S238/R) Fishing boats off the shore (41x70cm-16x28in) s.d.1902 W/C

MOUALLA, Fikret (1905-1968) Turkish

£1490 $2653   (31-Oct-91 LD.P50/R) Homme assis (33x42cm-13x17in) s.d.05/04/55 gouache (F.FR 14800)

MOUCHERON, Frederic de (1633-1686) Dutch

£2911 $5007   (8-Oct-91 ZEL.L1625 a/R) Wooded landscape with figures on path near waterfall and mountains beyond (37x48cm-15x19in) panel (DM 8500)

£3500 $6720   (10-Jul-92 C125/R) Wooded landscape with travellers on path (48x42cm-19x17in) s. panel

£4500 $8190   (10-Dec-91 PH120/R) Extensive wooded landscape with mule train crossing stream (98x143cm-39x56in)

£7000 $12740   (12-Dec-91 B40/R) Italianate lake landscape with travellers on path (65x79cm-26x31in) s.

£11139 $20051   (19-Nov-91 F.R37/R) Paesaggio con assalto ai viaggiatori (77x109cm-30x43in) s. (I.L 24000000)

MOUCHERON, Frederic de (attrib) (1633-1686) Dutch

£1706 $3089   (22-May-92 GB.B5293) River landscape with bird hunters (56x73cm-22x29in) s. (DM 5000)

£2400 $4080   (23-Oct-91 MMB235/R) Italianate river landscape with peasants and cattle (97x74cm-38x29in)

MOUCHERON, Frederic de (circle) (1633-1686) Dutch

£5153 $9172   (28-Nov-91 BU.S71/R) Landscape with hunting party (127x118cm-50x46in) (S.KR 54000)

MOUCHERON, Frederic de (style) (1633-1686) Dutch

£1500 $2625   (1-Apr-92 S130/R) Hilly southern landscape with figures on path near trees (54x45cm-21x18in) bears sig. panel

MOUCHERON, Isaac de (1667-1744) Dutch

£4200 $7350   (27-Feb-92 CSK162) Elegant company in park by fountain (36x41cm-14x16in) s.

£6485 $11737   (21-May-92 L.K98/R) Italian mountain landscape with cattle and sarcophagus (42x55cm-17x22in) s. (DM 19000)

£1235 $2210   (12-Nov-91 SY.AM278) Italianate landscape with figures and dogs by fountain (23x17cm-9x7in) s. chk wash (D.FL 4000)

£1373 $2513   (15-May-92 AT.P178) Vue d'une ville italienne aux environs de Rome (18x32cm-7x13in) s. pen W/C (F.FR 13500)

£2174 $3870   (25-Nov-91 CH.AM201/R) Terrace of village with figures and boat on pond in mountainous landscape (19x28cm-7x11in) s.d.1739 pen wash htd.white (D.FL 7000)

MOUCHERON, Isaac de (attrib) (1667-1744) Dutch

£550   *$968*   (11-Apr-92 AW.H264) Park with view of landscape with figures (19x16cm-7x6in) chk wash (DM 1600)

MOUCHERON, Isaac de (circle) (1667-1744) Dutch
£1829 $3183   (13-Apr-92 AT.P58/R) Paysage italianaisant (77x103cm-30x41in)
            (F.FR 18000)

MOUCHERON, Isaac de (style) (1667-1744) Dutch
£950 $1663   (27-Feb-92 B109) A Capriccio of Roman ruins with a castle and a river
            valley beyond (31x36cm-12x14in)
£1540 $2680   (13-Sep-91 C158/R) Capriccio of Roman ruins (77x64cm-30x25in) indist.s.
£1600 $3072   (9-Jul-92 CSK235/R) Elegant figures on terrace by fountain in Italianate
            landscape (81x130cm-32x51in)

MOUILLARD, Lucien (1842-1912) French
£491 $913   (16-Jun-92 RAS.K182) Interior with soldiers playing cards
            (46x39cm-18x15in) s.d.1894 (D.KR 5500)

MOUILLOT, Marcel (1889-) French
£1577 $2886   (17-May-92 T.B195) Paquebot devant New York (22x27cm-9x11in) s.
            (F.FR 15500)
£814 $1489   (17-May-92 T.B61) St.Denis - Ile Bourdon (30x40cm-12x16in) s.d.1930 W/C
            (F.FR 8000)

MOULIN, Bertrand (20th C) ?
£572 $1002   (5-Apr-92 R.P159/R) Corridor (100x81cm-39x32in) s. acrylic (F.FR 5500)

MOULIN, Charles Lucien (19th C) French
£4396 $8000   (28-May-92 SY.NY202/R) Baigneuse aux figues (172x71cm-68x28in) init.
£4396 $8000   (28-May-92 SY.NY201/R) Baigneuses (172x71cm-68x28in) s.

MOULINES (?) ?
£924 $1663   (22-Nov-91 ZZ.F75) Vue de Venise (73x60cm-29x24in) s. (F.FR 9000)

MOULINET, Antoine Edouard Joseph (1833-1891) French
£9000 $15390   (17-Mar-92 PH146/R) Birthday surprises (47x71cm-19x28in) s. panel

MOULLIN, Louis (1817-?) French
£8065 $14274   (10-Nov-91 ZZ.F43/R) Inauguration par Napoleon III des travaux de
            construction de la terrassede Chaillot s.d.Mars 1967 (F.FR 80000)
£520 $911   (3-Apr-92 AGS.P167) La place du Mollard a Geneve (22x28cm-9x11in) i. W/C
            htd.gouache (F.FR 5000)

MOULY, Marcel (1920-) French
£1064 $1926   (20-May-92 FB.P206) Cretoise (73x54cm-29x21in) s.d.80 (F.FR 10500)

MOUNCEY, William (1852-1901) British
£800 $1424   (28-Apr-92 S268/R) Tongland, Kirkcudbrightshire (40x51cm-16x20in) s.
            s.i.frame

MOUNT, Shepard Alonzo (1804-1868) American
£4420 $8000   (5-Dec-91 SY.NY14/R) Family homestead (24x38cm-9x15in) s. i.verso panel

MOUREN, Henri-Laurent (1844-1926) French
£578 $988   (17-Mar-92 JRL.S128/R) La Roche Nosay, Barbizon (22x29cm-9x11in) s. board
            (A.D 1300)

MOURIER, Claude (20th C) French
£595 $1041   (29-Sep-91 FE.P212) Paysage (46x54cm-18x21in) s. (F.FR 5900)

MOURLAN, Pierre Joseph Alexandre (1789-1860) French
£800 $1376   (4-Mar-92 C13/R) Gentleman, in dark blue coat, waistcoat, shirt and
            pleated cravat (8x?cm-3x?in) min. gilt beaded frame oval

MOYA LOPEZ (?) Spanish
£997 $1794   (29-Jan-92 FER.M245/R) Mujer recostada entre gasas (60x81cm-24x32in) s.
            (S.P 180000)

MOYA Y CALVO, Victor (1884-?) Spanish
£681 $1172   (7-Oct-91 ANS.M195/R) El pozo (21x34cm-8x13in) s.i. (S.P 125000)

MOYA, Pedro (attrib) (1610-1674) Spanish
£17387 $29732   (18-Mar-92 D.V12/R) Allegory of the face and transitoriness
            (106x165cm-42x65in) (A.S 350000)

MOYNAN, Richard Thomas (1856-1906) British
£3670 $6826   (17-Jun-92 A.D53/R) Study of young boy (53x36cm-21x14in) (E.P 4000)
£4500 $8235   (3-Jun-92 S180) The flower seller (101x61cm-40x24in) s.d.1895
£11009 $20477   (17-Jun-92 A.D92/R) Portrait of artist's daughter, Bridget seated, with
            doll (51x41cm-20x16in) s.d.1891 (E.P 12000)
£16514 $30716   (15-Jun-92 AD.D87/R) The flower seller (102x61cm-40x24in) s.d.1894
            (E.P 18000)
£364 $629   (2-Oct-91 A.D41) Study of young girl in party dress (18x13cm-7x5in) s.
            W/C (E.P 400)

MOYNE, Francois le (16/17th C) French
£12346 $22346   (7-Dec-91 CH.MO61/R) Paysage pittoresque (66x81cm-26x32in) (F.FR 120000)
£226519 $410000   (21-May-92 CH.NY39/R) Bathers (156x121cm-61x48in) indist.s.

MOYNE, Francois le (16/17th C) French-cont.
£920	$1766	(6-Jul-92 S13/R) Studies of two rearing horses among clouds (24x21cm-9x8in) chk
£2200	$4224	(7-Jul-92 C229/R) Seated nude wearing helmet and carrying spear (22x17cm-9x7in) chk wash
£4190	$7500	(14-Jan-92 SY.NY119/R) Study of male nudes (24x34cm-9x13in) black chk htd white chk
£9497	$17000	(14-Jan-92 SY.NY84/R) Study of head of girl (18x16cm-7x6in) bears sig. red chk htd white chk

MOZOS, Pedro (?) Spanish
£821	$1494	(11-Dec-91 FER.M90/R) Capea (24x29cm-9x11in) s. board (S.P 150000)
£2050	$3752	(13-May-92 FER.M152/R) Mujeres cambiando al bebe (47x64cm-19x25in) s. (S.P 375000)
£3007	$5503	(13-May-92 FER.M151/R) Cruce en el camino (84x69cm-33x27in) s. (S.P 550000)
£3597	$6151	(17-Mar-92 FER.M164/R) En la fuente (61x50cm-24x20in) s. (S.P 650000)

MUCHA, Alphonse (1860-1939) Czechoslovakian
£21306	$38990	(3-Jun-92 L.K334/R) Summer (47x60cm-19x24in) s. (DM 62000)
£30000	$53400	(27-Nov-91 S156/R) Life of old slavs (148x114cm-58x45in)
£870	$1549	(27-Nov-91 CB.P8) Les Sentiments, la Musique et le Geste (26x20cm-10x8in) s. W/C Indian ink (F.FR 8500)
£1648	$3000	(28-May-92 SY.NY270/R) Maternite (71x60cm-28x24in) s. col.pencil
£1826	$3250	(22-Jan-92 SY.NY435/R) Portrait study of young woman (17x15cm-7x6in) s. pencil
£7000	$11970	(18-Mar-92 S59/R) Portrait of the artist's daughter, Jarmila with lilies (46x36cm-18x14in) s.d.30 pencil W/C htd.white bodycol.

MUCHE, Georg (1895-?) German
£52448	$93357	(25-Nov-91 WK.M736/R) Composition (97x79cm-38x31in) indis.s.verso (DM 150000)

MUCKLEY, Angelo Fairfax (fl.1886-1896) British
£550	$985	(14-Nov-91 CSK70/R) The letter (23x15cm-9x6in) s.d.1880 W/C bodycol htd.gum arabic

MUCKLEY, William Jabez (1837-1905) British
£2200	$3740	(24-Oct-91 CSK165/R) Eglantine (36x43cm-14x17in) s.d.83 i. verso
£700	$1295	(11-Jun-92 CSK19) Water lilies (36x46cm-14x18in) s.d.82 W/C bodycol htd gum arabic

MUENDEL, George F (1871-1948) American
£983	$1700	(8-Sep-91 LIT.L175) Spring day (76x102cm-30x40in) estate st.
£1170	$2200	(18-Dec-91 SY.NY227/R) View of the pailsades from Upper Manhatten (61x45cm-24x18in) s.d.98

MUENIER, Jules Alexis (1863-1942) French
£1634	$2860	(19-Feb-92 D.P26) Maisons au bord de chemin (51x45cm-20x18in) s. (F.FR 16000)
£4268	$7427	(13-Apr-92 PLF.P86/R) La lecon de clavecin (59x49cm-23x19in) s.i. (F.FR 42000)

MUFF, Orla (20th C) Danish
£492	$895	(10-Dec-91 RAS.K182/R) Composition (137x305cm-54x120in) s.d.62-64 triptych (D.KR 5500)
£1601	$2786	(17-Sep-91 RAS.K133/R) Horse and nude women (160x110cm-63x43in) s. d.1928on stretcher (D.KR 18000)
£1957	$3406	(17-Sep-91 RAS.K134/R) Leda and the swan (180x118cm-71x46in) s. (D.KR 22000)

MUHL, Otto (1924-) Russian
£440	$783	(31-Oct-91 D.V193/R) Untitled (39x30cm-15x12in) s.d.90 mixed media (A.S 9000)

MUHL, Roger (1929-) French
£541	$1000	(12-Jun-92 SY.NY212/R) Montagne Ochre (81x129cm-32x51in) s.
£565	$1000	(6-Nov-91 D.NY101/R) Bergerie (29x60cm-11x24in) s.i.verso
£669	$1210	(4-Dec-91 CSC.P297) Le petit nu (32x30cm-13x12in) s. acrylic (F.FR 6500)
£1230	$2213	(2-Feb-92 ZZ.P215/R) La bergerie (30x60cm-12x24in) s. (F.FR 12000)
£1564	$2800	(9-May-92 CE.NY150/R) Les Alpilles (110x120cm-43x47in) s.
£1744	$3000	(12-Oct-91 SY.NY189/R) Bergerie (50x53cm-20x21in) s.
£1757	$3250	(12-Jun-92 SY.NY216/R) La Mediterranee le soir (129x120cm-51x47in) s.
£2373	$4200	(6-Nov-91 D.NY102/R) Alpilles le matin (100x110cm-39x43in) s.
£3074	$5533	(2-Feb-92 ZZ.P205/R) Paysage des Alpilles a l'Aube (102x110cm-40x43in) s. (F.FR 30000)

MUHLBECK, Joseph (1878-?) German
£989	$1730	(20-Feb-92 D.V325/R) Dachauer Moos landscape (39x53cm-15x21in) s. (A.S 20000)

MUHLENEN, Max von (1903-1971) Swiss
£2549	$4333	(23-Oct-91 GD.B534/R) Pensive girl at table with book (64x81cm-25x32in) s.i.verso pavatex (S.FR 6500)

MUHLENHAUPT, Kurt (1921-) German
£614 $1112   (23-May-92 GB.B6939) The footballer (45x34cm-18x13in) mono.d.77
                s.i.d.verso panel (DM 1800)
£634 $1147   (6-Dec-91 GB.B6874) Berlin SO (40x30cm-16x12in) s.d.1975 i.verso board
                (DM 1800)

MUHLHAN, Adolf (1886-?) German
£989 $1731   (3-Apr-92 BM.B781/R) View of Alster with Hamburg city (40x61cm-16x24in)
                s. (DM 2800)

MUHLIG, Albert Ernst (1862-?) German
£1053 $1800   (13-Mar-92 FN.S2878/R) View of village street (29x38cm-11x15in) s. board
                (DM 3000)
£523   *$951*   *(13-Dec-91 BM.B698/R) View of village street (35x25cm-14x10in) s. gouache*
                (DM 1500)

MUHLIG, Bernard (1829-1910) German
£1150 $2093   (11-Dec-91 N.M540/R) Mother and child in garden before farmhouse, Elbtal
                (17x26cm-7x10in) s. i.stretcher (DM 3300)

MUHLIG, Hugo (1854-1929) German
£1294 $2238   (25-Mar-92 KM.K1328/R) Children on the way to school in landscape
                (36x61cm-14x24in) s.d.1886 canvas on board (DM 3700)
£1375 $2515   (2-Jun-92 FN.S2671/R) Gypsies with horse-drawn cart on tree lined road in
                landscape (41x61cm-16x24in) s.d.1886 (DM 4000)
£6826 $12355   (21-May-92 L.K458/R) Peasant ploughing field and view of village beyond
                (17x28cm-7x11in) s. board (DM 20000)
£8503 $15476   (14-Dec-91 BU.O45/R) Hunters party gathering by open fire
                (60x75cm-24x30in) s. (N.KR 96000)
£9059 $16488   (12-Dec-91 L.K627/R) Grafenberger Wald near Dusseldorf in spring
                (37x60cm-15x24in) s.d.1886 board (DM 26000)
£13993 $25328   (21-May-92 L.K459/R) Autumn landscape with woman harvesting potatoes and
                village beyond (37x53cm-15x21in) s. panel (DM 41000)
£27875 $50732   (12-Dec-91 L.K628/R) Group of figures gathered round fire after the hunt
                in snowy landscape (60x85cm-24x33in) s. canvas on panel (DM 80000)
£3846   *$6577*   *(18-Mar-92 N.M298/R) Beach of La Panne with figures (34x26cm-13x10in)*
                s.d.1909 gouache (DM 11000)

MUHLIG, Meno (1823-1873) German
£1294 $2200   (23-Oct-91 GD.B1200/R) Knight in armour conversing with blacksmith in
                workshop (75x51cm-30x20in) s. canvas on panel (S.FR 3300)
£1387 $2482   (6-May-92 GD.B905/R) Woodland interior with hunter, dog and dead stag
                (76x60cm-30x24in) s. (S.FR 3800)
£1529 $2600   (23-Oct-91 GD.B1199) Gunsmith conversing with nobleman in workshop
                (75x51cm-30x20in) s. canvas over panel (S.FR 3900)
£1730 $3287   (24-Jun-92 KM.K1199/R) Genre scene with peasant children and bird cage
                before barn (43x35cm-17x14in) s. (DM 5000)
£2637 $4536   (8-Oct-91 ZEL.L1627/R) Children collecting wood returning home in wooded
                river landscape (33x44cm-13x17in) (DM 7700)

MUHLSTOCK, Louis (1904-) Canadian
£606 $1061   (25-Sep-91 EA.M511) Forest glade (76x66cm-30x26in) s. (C.D 1200)
£900   *$1593*   *(6-Nov-91 SY.T61) Reclining nude (52x80cm-20x31in) s. chk pastel*
                (C.D 1800)

MUIJSENBERG, Toon van den (1901-1967) Dutch
£1512 $2631   (21-Sep-91 SA.A598/R) The silence of early evening (50x60cm-20x24in)
                s.d.34 (DM 4400)

MUIR, W (19th C) British
£700 $1295   (11-Jun-92 CSK192/R) Cockle gatherers (45x68cm-18x27in) s.d.1882

MUIR-NIMMO, Lorna (?) Australian?
£1318   *$2517*   *(21-Jul-92 JRL.S27/R) Boundary Street, Paddington (48x90cm-19x35in) s.*
                gouache (A.D 3400)

MULARD, Francois Henri (1769-1850) French
£83799 $150000   (17-Jan-92 SY.NY94/R) Portrait of a lady in elegant dress
                (99x81cm-39x32in) s.

MULCAHY, Jeremiah Hodges (?-1889) British
£1500 $2610   (18-Sep-91 CG114/R) Figures initialling rock before large waterfall
                (62x43cm-24x17in) s.d.1852

MULDERS, Camille van (1868-?) Dutch?
£1877 $3416   (27-May-92 PH.DU31/R) Still life of roses (60x42cm-24x17in) s. (DM 5500)

MULDVAD, Emma (19th C) Danish
£1590 $2815   (5-Nov-91 SY.AM295/R) Still life with fruit in basket (61x49cm-24x19in)
                s.d.1885 (D.FL 5200)

MULHAUPT, Frederick J (1871-1938) American
£773 $1400   (22-May-92 S.BM151/R) Stage Fort Park, Half Moon Bay, Gloucester
                (20x25cm-8x10in) s. board
£1806 $3250   (22-Nov-91 S.BM189/R) View of piers, Gloucester (20x25cm-8x10in) s. board

MULHAUPT, Frederick J (1871-1938) American-cont.
£2624 $4750   (2-Dec-91 S.SL303/R) Harbour scene with sailboats near pier at low-tide
       (46x61cm-18x24in) s.
£3757 $6500   (6-Sep-91 S.BM231/R) Gloucester Harbour (20x25cm-8x10in) s. board

MULHERN, Mark (1951-) American?
£503 $900   (12-Nov-91 CE.NY153/R) Sorting it out (198x229cm-78x90in) s.i.d.84verso

MULIER, Pieter (17th C) Dutch
£988 $1759   (29-Nov-91 GAB.G3086 a) Bucheron devant un village (S.FR 2500)
£3800 $6916   (10-Dec-91 PH51/R) Jonah and whale (58x83cm-23x33in)

MULIER, Pieter (attrib) (17th C) Dutch
£1547 $2800   (21-May-92 CH.NY206/R) Shepherd and shepherdess with flock in mountainous
       landscape (52x72cm-20x28in)
£1963 $3729   (23-Jun-92 D.V236/R) The Storm on Lake Genezareth (79x103cm-31x41in)
       (A.S 40000)
£4500 $7875   (27-Feb-92 CSK120) Extensive Italianate landscape with figures by a pool
       (86x163cm-34x64in)

MULIER, Pieter (elder) (1615-1670) Dutch
£18519 $33519   (3-Dec-91 P.P77/R) Marine, bateaux de peche. Marine, bateaux de peche,
       au loin au village (27x37cm-11x15in) mono. panel pair (F.FR 180000)

MULIER, Pieter (elder-attrib) (1615-1670) Dutch
£800 $1424   (29-Oct-91 PH109/R) Man of war in choppy seas (29x24cm-11x9in) panel

MULIER, Pieter (elder-circle) (1615-1670) Dutch
£2000 $3840   (10-Jul-92 C103/R) Dutch East Indiaman running in gale (43x63cm-17x25in)
       with indist.mono. panel

MULIER, Pieter (style) (17th C) Dutch
£750 $1350   (22-Nov-91 SWS199) A boat sailing in a rough sea (42x72cm-17x28in)
£1080 $1934   (12-Nov-91 SY.AM153/R) Christ and the Apostles beset by the storm
       (77x101cm-30x40in) (D.FL 3500)
£1600 $2880   (22-Nov-91 SWS175/R) Shipping in rough seas off a rocky coast
       (48x112cm-19x44in)
£1650 $2871   (13-Sep-91 C171/R) Mediterranean inlet with men caulking ship at sunset
       (51x75cm-20x30in)
£6000 $10500   (3-Apr-92 C133/R) Wooded Italianate landscape with fortified town on
       coast in distance (76x99cm-30x39in)

MULIER, Pieter (younger) (1637-1701) Dutch
£6826 $12355   (21-May-92 L.K99/R) Italian mountain landscape with shepherd and cattle
       by stream (81x109cm-32x43in) (DM 20000)
£13252 $24648   (18-Jun-92 SY.MO32/R) Paysage fluvial (145x122cm-57x48in) (F.FR 130000)
£14403 $26070   (5-Dec-91 SY.MO166/R) Scene pastorale (57x85cm-22x33in) (F.FR 140000)

MULIERE, C (?) ?
£1111 $1978   (27-Apr-92 J.M835) On the canal (45x53cm-18x21in) s. (A.D 2600)

MULKEN, Johannes Josephus van (1796-1879) Dutch
£1223 $2128   (14-Apr-92 SY.AM324/R) Summer landscape with city of Haarlem in distance
       (30x39cm-12x15in) s.d.1853 panel (D.FL 4000)

MULLEN, W (19th C) ?
*£480 $806   (29-Aug-91 CG35) Camels in a mountainous landscape (48x33cm-19x13in)
       init.i.d.Dec 14 1843 W/C*

MULLER (?) ?
£438 $784   (6-May-92 GD.B906/R) Standing nude (28x41cm-11x16in) mono panel
       (S.FR 1200)
£1826 $3196   (23-Sep-91 AAA.S112) Portrait of Dame Nellie Melba (100x73cm-39x29in) s.
       (A.D 4000)

MULLER, Adam August (1811-1844) Danish
£896 $1604   (6-May-92 KH.K139/R) Boy blowing bubbles (26x20cm-10x8in) (D.KR 10200)

MULLER, Albert (1897-1926) Swiss
£2191 $3966   (5-Dec-91 SY.Z87/R) Self portrait. Landscape (57x44cm-22x17in) board
       double-sided (S.FR 5500)
£2353 $4000   (23-Oct-91 GD.B535/R) Village in hilly landscape (34x48cm-13x19in) mono.
       (S.FR 6000)
£4382 $7932   (4-Dec-91 G.Z198/R) Catarina. Flowers in vase (61x62cm-24x24in)
       double-sided (S.FR 11000)
£599 $1067   (29-Apr-92 G.Z94/R) Nude (35x35cm-14x14in) indian ink pen (S.FR 1600)
*£913 $1697   (19-Jun-92 G.Z530) Ticino landscape (23x31cm-9x12in) W/C over pencil
       (S.FR 2400)*

MULLER, Alexander (attrib) (1872-1935) American
£684 $1300   (22-Jun-92 SG.M583) The Truck Garden in Bavaria (86x107cm-34x42in) s.

MULLER, Anton (1853-1897) Austrian
*£1221 $2101   (10-Oct-91 D.V246/R) Der Tiefe Graben, Vienna (46x33cm-18x13in) s. W/C
       (A.S 25000)*

MULLER, August (attrib) (1836-1885) German
£1573 $2800   (22-Jan-92 SY.NY273/R) Mother and child (44x36cm-17x14in)

MULLER, C (?) ?
£1695 $3000   (9-Nov-91 W.W53/R) A Venetian view (61x76cm-24x30in) s.

MULLER, Carl (?) ?
£728 $1296   (29-Apr-92 D.V671/R) Alterhof Neustiftgasse und Ulrichsplatz am Neubau (42x48cm-17x19in) s.d.1904 W/C (A.S 15000)

MULLER, Carl Otto (1901-1968) German
£928 $1624   (27-Sep-91 GRA.B2474/R) Bunch of autumn flowers (61x50cm-24x20in) mono. s.i.d.1943verso board (DM 2700)

MULLER, Charles Louis (1815-1892) French
£1832 $3500   (16-Jul-92 SY.NY389/R) Arab woman with white parrot (96x71cm-38x28in) s.
£3000 $5580   (17-Jun-92 S503/R) L'ecouteuse, une jeune soubrette ecoute a la porte d'un salon (98x72cm-39x28in) s. i.verso
£3552 $6500   (16-May-92 HG.C51/R) Giving daughter into slavery (132x191cm-52x75in) s.i.
£5143 $9000   (20-Feb-92 SY.NY166/R) Au bains de mer (106x76cm-42x30in) s.

MULLER, Emma von (1859-1925) Austrian
£883 $1546   (3-Apr-92 BM.B688/R) Portrait of girl wearing Tyrolean costume (18x14cm-7x6in) s. panel (DM 2500)

MULLER, Erich Martin (1888-1972) German
£1592 $3024   (24-Jun-92 KM.K1200) View of Fraueninsel, Chiemsee (58x69cm-23x27in) s.d.1928 (DM 4600)

MULLER, Friedrich (1749-1825) German
£524 $934   (26-Nov-91 KF.M115/R) Gathering of the gods in clouds with enthroned Pallas Athene (31x47cm-12x19in) pen over chk wash (DM 1500)

MULLER, Fritz (?) German
£455 $786   (28-Mar-92 BOD.P998) Old man reading newspaper (40x30cm-16x12in) s.i. panel (DM 1300)

MULLER, G (20th C) Swiss
£900 $1620   (21-Nov-91 CSK230/R) Portrait of Prince Felipe Prospero (76x61cm-30x24in) s.i.d.55 after Velasquez

MULLER, Gustav (1811-?) Czechoslovakian
£736 $1398   (25-Jun-92 D.V525/R) Still life of flowers (26x21cm-10x8in) s.d.1836 W/C pencil (A.S 15000)

MULLER, Gustav Otto (1827-1922) German
£629 $1100   (27-Sep-91 S.BM590/R) The victory at hand (18x23cm-7x9in) s.d.18 board

MULLER, Heinrich (1885-1960) Swiss
£1523 $2696   (5-Nov-91 GF.L2675/R) Lady with camelias (133x193cm-52x76in) s.d.1922 (S.FR 3900)

MULLER, Johannes (19/20th C) German?
£963 $1676   (14-Sep-91 BU.O298) Mountain district with children 1889 (70x80cm-28x31in) s. (N.KR 11000)
£2303 $4191   (10-Dec-91 UL.T202/R) From Storhove near Faberg, Lillehammer (65x100cm-26x39in) s.d.1889 (N.KR 26000)

MULLER, Leopold Carl (1834-1892) German
£1073 $1867   (19-Sep-91 D.V181/R) Study of rock coastal landscape (41x53cm-16x21in) s. canvas on board (A.S 22000)
£2498 $4496   (21-Nov-91 D.V123/R) Oriental town scene (82x60cm-32x24in) s. (A.S 50000)

MULLER, M (snr) (1841-1899) German
£756 $1315   (19-Sep-91 N.M2792/R) Chamois fleeing landslide (27x20cm-11x8in) s.i.d.95 panel (DM 2200)

MULLER, Maria (19th C?) ?
£874 $1555   (29-Apr-92 D.V854/R) Interior (61x49cm-24x19in) s. (A.S 18000)

MULLER, Moritz (jnr) (20th C) German
£691 $1300   (5-Jan-92 GG.TA266/R) Munchen (68x100cm-27x39in) s.i.d.1923 board

MULLER, Moritz (snr) (1841-1899) German
£750 $1328   (13-Feb-92 CSK97/R) Hound with fox (18x25cm-7x10in) s.i.

MULLER, Moritz Karl Friedrich (1807-1865) German
£3509 $6000   (13-Mar-92 FN.S2882/R) Peasant interior with courting couple seated at table (28x23cm-11x9in) s. (DM 10000)

MULLER, Morten (1828-1911) Norwegian
£1317 $2265   (7-Oct-91 B.O99/R) River landscape with house (28x47cm-11x19in) s.d.93 (N.KR 15000)

MULLER, Morten (1828-1911) Norwegian-cont.
£3518	$6192	(8-Apr-92 GWP.O55/R) Landscape from Nordmarken (28x47cm-11x19in) s.d.1893 i.verso (N.KR 40000)
£4000	$7440	(19-Jun-92 C46/R) Extensive landscape near Oslo (71x105cm-28x41in) s.d.1871
£4222	$7430	(8-Apr-92 GWP.O57/R) Man in rowingboat (83x70cm-33x28in) s.d.1879 (N.KR 48000)
£5200	$9672	(19-Jun-92 C45/R) At the lakeside (84x127cm-33x50in) s.
£5405	$9189	(6-Aug-91 UL.T207/R) Wooded landscape with mill and waterfall (61x81cm-24x32in) (N.KR 62000)
£6023	$10962	(10-Dec-91 UL.T204 a/R) Norwegian fjord landscape with church and figures (66x100cm-26x39in) (N.KR 68000)
£7699	$14705	(21-Jul-92 UL.T197/R) Landscape from Nordmarken 1874 (70x100cm-28x39in) (N.KR 86000)

MULLER, Otto (1874-1930) German
£558	*$1010*	(5-Dec-91 SY.Z182/R) Study for three bodies (41x50cm-16x20in) s.d.1964 chl (S.FR 1400)
£3322	*$5913*	(28-Nov-91 SY.BE40/R) Reclining nude (50x35cm-20x14in) chk (DM 9500)
£79038	*$144639*	(3-Jun-92 L.K336/R) Nude girl seated by water (52x68cm-20x27in) s. W/C chl over pencil (DM 230000)

MULLER, Paul Jakob (1894-1983) Swiss
£438	$784	(6-May-92 GD.B982/R) Clochard (25x35cm-10x14in) s. board (S.FR 1200)
£620	$1111	(6-May-92 GD.B978) Half nude (45x37cm-18x15in) s. panel (S.FR 1700)
£1020	$1733	(23-Oct-91 GD.B570/R) Clochard by roadside (40x32cm-16x13in) s. pavatex (S.FR 2600)

MULLER, Peter Paul (1853-?) German
£1224	$2192	(5-May-92 ZEL.L1458/R) Cattle grazing (34x51cm-13x20in) s.i. board (DM 3600)
£2448	$4185	(18-Mar-92 N.M605/R) Early autumn landscape (80x110cm-31x43in) s. (DM 7000)

MULLER, Richard (1874-1930) Austrian
£1049	$1867	(25-Nov-91 WK.M747/R) The nightmare (76x54cm-30x21in) s.d.1920 (DM 3000)
£13287	$23650	(30-Nov-91 VG.B231/R) The red heart (80x130cm-31x51in) mono.d.1917 (DM 38000)
£928	*$1577*	(26-Oct-91 WK.M469/R) Two reclining female nude (75x103cm-30x41in) s.d.1920 pastel paper on paper (DM 2700)
£1775	*$3230*	(26-May-92 KF.M1098/R) A question I (31x30cm-12x12in) s.d.1971 s.i.verso (DM 5200)
£3671	*$6535*	(30-Nov-91 VG.B230/R) What is fame, what are names (52x44cm-20x17in) s.i.d.1913 pencil chl (DM 10500)

MULLER, Rudolf (1816-1904) Austrian
£5200	$8840	(23-Oct-91 S4/R) The Acropolis, Athen (60x89cm-24x35in) s. W/C over pencil scratching out

MULLER, S (?) ?
£792	$1331	(27-Aug-91 RAS.K423) Interior with young girl at the piano (70x55cm-28x22in) s. (D.KR 9000)

MULLER, T (?) ?
£587	$1056	(19-Nov-91 RAS.K237) Seascape with English ship (60x94cm-24x37in) s.d.48 (D.KR 6500)

MULLER, Thomas (?) ?
£1500	$2715	(20-May-92 S177/R) Steamships in open sea (61x95cm-24x37in) s.d.76

MULLER, William (?) ?
£627	$1067	(23-Oct-91 GD.B547) Nature morte au verre bleu (38x46cm-15x18in) s.d.17 (S.FR 1600)
£912	$1633	(6-May-92 GD.B915/R) Woman wearing white dress (61x56cm-24x22in) s.d.10 panel (S.FR 2500)
£949	$1689	(29-Nov-91 GAB.G2816) Mere et enfant (68x54cm-27x21in) s. (S.FR 2400)

MULLER, William James (1812-1845) British
£2616	$4500	(10-Oct-91 FA.PH693/R) Moor slave carrying tray of fruit (91x71cm-36x28in) s.
£420	*$731*	(9-Sep-91 PH68) Tent of Yurooks, near Xanthus (33x50cm-13x20in) i. W/C
£462	*$882*	(16-Jul-92 S9) Coastal scene with houses and distant fort (32x54cm-13x21in) indis.i. W/C over pencil
£850	*$1522*	(12-Nov-91 C134/R) Two camels at Xanthus (49x34cm-19x13in) init.i.d.Dec.14 1843 pencil W/C htd.white

MULLER-BRIEGHEL, Wilhelm (1860-?) German
£981	$1825	(16-Jun-92 RAS.V764/R) Seascape with sailship (95x148cm-37x58in) s. (D.KR 11000)

MULLER-CASSEL, Adolf Leonhard (1864-?) German
£825	$1402	(26-Oct-91 WK.M47/R) Boulevard in Paris (35x50cm-14x20in) s.d.1900 (DM 2400)

MULLER-CORNELIUS (1864-1946) German
£600 $1068   (28-Nov-91 B66) Cart and figures outside cottage (8x16cm-3x6in) s. board

MULLER-CORNELIUS, L (1864-1946) German
£699 $1196   (19-Mar-92 N.M2804) Mail coach before tavern (9x12cm-4x5in) s. panel
                 (DM 2000)
£769 $1315   (19-Mar-92 N.M2805/R) Hay cart before farmhouse (9x12cm-4x5in) s. panel
                 (DM 2200)
£792 $1331   (27-Aug-91 RAS.K424) Bringing home the hay harvest (10x12cm-4x5in) s.
                 panel (D.KR 9000)

MULLER-CORNELIUS, Ludwig (1864-1946) German
£652 $1174   (19-Nov-91 GO.G237) Alpine landscape with figures and cattle by house
                 (11x16cm-4x6in) s. panel (S.KR 6800)
£976 $1776   (11-Dec-91 N.M543/R) Hay harvest with thunderstorm rising (10x12cm-4x5in)
                 s. panel (DM 2800)
£1031 $1918   (20-Jun-92 BM.B872/R) Mail coach stopping before farmhouse in Alpine
                 landscape (11x16cm-4x6in) s. panel (DM 3000)
£1056 $1912   (3-Dec-91 FN.S2348/R) Peasant with ox-drawn cart before village, autumn
                 (13x18cm-5x7in) s. panel (DM 3000)

MULLER-HUFSCHMID, Willi (1890-1966) German
£699 $1245   (25-Nov-91 WK.M749) Composition (50x36cm-20x14in) indian ink board
                 (DM 2000)

MULLER-KAEMPFF, Paul (1861-1941) German
£1214 $2160   (28-Apr-92 D.V133/R) Landscape in Northern Germany (80x120cm-31x47in) s.
                 (A.S 25000)

MULLER-KRUSEMAN, Johan Caspar (1805-1855) Dutch
£1818 $3218   (22-Apr-92 CH.AM75/R) Still life of flowers in a vase and a peach and
                 grapes on a ledge (42x37cm-17x15in) s. panel (D.FL 6000)

MULLER-KURZWELLY, Konrad Alexander (1855-1914) German
£497 $950   (3-Jul-92 S.W3866) Sunlight in woods (99x71cm-39x28in) s.
£871 $1585   (11-Dec-91 N.M544/R) Wooded river landscape with farmhouse, winter
                 (76x115cm-30x45in) s.d.1906 i.stretcher (DM 2500)
£1012 $1701   (27-Aug-91 RAS.K426) Landscape from Singdal, Lalaa, Sweden
                 (100x150cm-39x59in) s.d.1891 (D.KR 11500)

MULLER-LANDAU, Rolf (1903-1956) Austrian
£993 $1708   (11-Oct-91 AW.H2715/R) Lady reading seated by window (46x9cm-18x4in)
                 s.d.1931 W/C bodycol (DM 2900)

MULLER-LINOW, Bruno (1909-) German
£651 $1119   (11-Oct-91 AW.H2719/R) Apple tree (31x41cm-12x16in) s.d.1978 (DM 1900)
£1375 $2515   (3-Jun-92 L.K337) Beach landscape with sun setting (43x62cm-17x24in)
                 s.d.1950 gouache (DM 4000)

MULLER-MASSDORF, Julius (1863-?) German
£1254 $2283   (12-Dec-91 L.K630) Girl with hat reading (60x50cm-24x20in) s. (DM 3600)

MULLER-SCHWABEN, Fritz (20th C) ?
£865 $1644   (27-Jun-92 FN.L1150/R) Dachau Moor on bright summer's day
                 (70x95cm-28x37in) s. (DM 2500)

MULLEY, Oskar (1891-1949) Austrian
£912 $1560   (13-Mar-92 FN.S2885) South Tyrolean peasant village by foot of mountain
                 range in rising fog (38x31cm-15x12in) s. (DM 2600)
£2424 $4411   (26-May-92 D.V116/R) Hillside farmhouse (28x45cm-11x18in) s. (A.S 50000)
£2727 $4855   (29-Nov-91 ZEL.L1083/R) Summer landscape. Autumn landscape
                 (32x33cm-13x13in) s. paper on board pair (DM 7800)
£2928 $5066   (3-Oct-91 D.V84/R) Mountain lake landscape with village (45x70cm-18x28in)
                 s.d.45 (A.S 60000)
£11307 $19788   (3-Apr-92 BM.B876/R) Alpine summer farmhouse in Garmisch-Partenkirchen
                 (130x109cm-51x43in) s. i.verso (DM 32000)

MULLICAN, Matt (20th C) ?
£4046 $7000   (3-Oct-91 SY.NY156/R) Untitled (183x122cm-72x48in)

MULLINS, George (18th C) British
£5500 $9680   (8-Apr-92 S64) View of Tivoli with Temple of Sibyl and Campagna beyond
                 (106x152cm-42x60in) after Richard Wilson

MULREADY, Augustus E (fl.1863-1905) British
£640 $1133   (4-Nov-91 WW86/R) Left to herself (17x21cm-7x8in) s.i. s.verso panel
£800 $1528   (23-Jul-92 ZZ.B172) Small boy and girl by wall, poster behind
                 (18x15cm-7x6in) s.
£1150 $2197   (23-Jul-92 ZZ.B171) Flower girl seated on stone seat holding flower, with
                 basket flowers (25x18cm-10x7in) s.d.1884
£3000 $5490   (3-Jun-92 S142/R) Uncared for (25x18cm-10x7in) s.d.85
£3200 $5472   (13-Mar-92 C165/R) A penny please (38x28cm-15x11in) s.d.1882 s.i.d.verso
                 panel

MULREADY, W (1786-1863) British
£519 $950   (16-May-92 HG.C145) Young couple asleep (43x53cm-17x21in) s.d.1826

MULREADY, William (1786-1863) British
£2907 $5000   (17-Oct-91 SY.NY303/R) Secret (82x99cm-32x39in) s. mono.d.1855
£5800 $10382   (13-Nov-91 S77/R) Crossing the ford (29x24cm-11x9in)
£7500 $13425   (15-Nov-91 C39/R) Boy's fighting (46x56cm-18x22in) s.d.1817
£440 $840   (16-Jul-92 S30) Fishermen (21x17cm-8x7in) pen
£1009 $1847   (3-Jun-92 R.T145/R) Portrait of two sisters (52x39cm-20x15in) s.d.1847
   W/C graphite paper on canvas arched (C.D 2200)
£4091 $7077   (2-Oct-91 A.D114) Study for Last In (58x71cm-23x28in) s. W/C (E.P 4500)

MULTZ, Andreas Paul (17th C) German
£1900 $3325   (2-Apr-92 CSK123/R) Portrait of Herr Georg Christof Gugel of Hirschbach.
   Portrait of Maria, his wife (28x23cm-11x9in) i.verso one s.d.1679
   copper pair

MULVANY, John George (attrib) (1766-1838) British
£900 $1566   (18-Sep-91 CG112/R) View of Carlingford Castle (48x98cm-19x39in)

MULVANY, Thomas James (1779-1845) British
£2600 $4524   (18-Sep-91 CG111/R) Coast scene, noon - peasants winnowing corn
   (30x46cm-12x18in)

MUNARI, Bruno (1907-?) Italian
£3078 $5601   (26-May-92 SY.MI107/R) Composizione (43x43cm-17x17in) s. panel
   (I.L 6800000)
£741 $1320   (27-Nov-91 F.M45) Ricostruzione teorica di un oggetto immaginario
   (49x49cm-19x19in) s.i.d.1970 collage ink (I.L 1600000)
£2181 $4101   (19-Dec-91 F.M94) Variazione arbitrarie sulla curva di Peano
   (50x50cm-20x20in) s.i.d.1969 collage cardboard (I.L 4700000)
£2228 $4188   (19-Dec-91 F.M38/R) Ricostruzione teorica di un oggetto immaginario
   (70x70cm-28x28in) s.i.d.1970 collage cardboard (I.L 4800000)

MUNARI, Cristoforo (1667-1720) Italian
£25000 $45500   (10-Dec-91 PH13/R) Still life with Chianti bottle, vegetables and copper
   pot in landscape (84x67cm-33x26in)
£30000 $54600   (10-Dec-91 PH12/R) Still life with silver jug, salver, melon, plums and
   bird on branch (84x67cm-33x26in)
£60000 $115200   (8-Jul-92 S82/R) Still life with fruit on salver, books and cups on stone
   ledge (89x75cm-35x30in)

MUNARI, Cristoforo (circle) (1667-1720) Italian
£15084 $27000   (17-Jan-92 SY.NY99 a/R) Still life of grapes, funghi, teacups and lemons
   in a landscape (57x81cm-22x32in)

MUNCASTER, Claude (1903-) British
£520 $874   (15-Aug-91 B286) Calm on Hamble River (31x46cm-12x18in) s. s.i.verso
   board
£950 $1739   (14-May-92 C16/R) Gondolas on Grand Canal, Venice (41x51cm-16x20in) s.
   s.i.d.1961 verso canvasboard

MUNCH, Edvard (1863-1944) Norwegian
£28249 $50000   (7-Nov-91 SY.NY141/R) Portrett av Annie Stenersen (80x65cm-31x26in)
   s.d.1934
£443 $785   (15-Feb-92 BU.O97) Woman knitting, couple embracing (11x16cm-4x6in)
   pencil dr (N.KR 5000)
£1100 $2101   (29-Jun-92 CSK35/R) Fra Kongsgaarden Bygdoy. Portrett studier
   (9x16cm-4x6in) pencil double-sided
£1600 $3056   (29-Jun-92 CSK34/R) Fra Hakloa (16x23cm-6x9in) with i.verso pen wash

MUNCH, Gustav Heinrich (1882-?) German
£481 $880   (2-Jun-92 FN.S2673) Watermill beneath trees, autumn (34x45cm-13x18in)
   s.d.1933 (DM 1400)

MUNCH-KHE, Willi (1885-?) German
£1098 $1965   (15-Nov-91 ZOF.Z1412/R) Portrait of Adolf Dietrich (39x28cm-15x11in)
   s.i.d.34 col.pencil (S.FR 2800)

MUNGER, Gilbert (1837-1903) American
£1500 $2550   (22-Oct-91 C28/R) Seine (23x37cm-9x15in) s. i.verso panel
£2346 $4200   (14-Nov-91 CE.NY82/R) Reflections on lake (30x46cm-12x18in) s. panel

MUNICH SCHOOL, 19th C German
£1961 $3510   (15-Nov-91 GK.Z5080/R) Peasant reading news in blacksmith interior
   (42x52cm-17x20in) pavatex (S.FR 5000)

MUNIER, Emile (1810-1895) French
£5759 $11000   (16-Jul-92 SY.NY381/R) The knitting lesson (52x36cm-20x14in) s.indis.d.
   panel
£6332 $11145   (8-Apr-92 GWP.O54/R) Two young girls with cat and kittens
   (28x22cm-11x9in) s.d.1895 (N.KR 72000)
£42857 $78000   (27-May-92 CH.NY46/R) Mother and child (138x95cm-54x37in) s.d.1892

MUNKACSY, Michel Lieb (1844-1909) Hungarian

£1942	$3456	(29-Apr-92 D.V753/R) Shepherd having meal in landscape (28x39cm-11x15in) s.indis.d.18., panel (A.S 40000)
£2493	$4462	(16-Jan-92 D.V89/R) Portrait of gentleman (67x57cm-26x22in) s. (A.S 50000)
£10989	$19780	(21-Nov-91 D.V126/R) Hungarian Easter customs (111x167cm-44x66in) s.d.865 (A.S 220000)
£13333	$22667	(23-Oct-91 GD.B1201/R) Children feeding dogs (27x41cm-11x16in) s. panel (S.FR 34000)

MUNN, Paul Sandby (1773-1845) British

£420	*$752*	*(12-Nov-91 C92) An angler fishing by a bridge, near Beddgelert, Caernarvon (18x13cm-7x5in) s.i.verso pencil W/C scratching out*

MUNNINGER, Ludwig (20th C) German

£1250	$2100	(16-Aug-91 DM.D2008/R) Winter mountain landscape with figure (102x76cm-40x30in) s.

MUNNINGS (1878-1959) British

£750	$1298	(6-Sep-91 BW428) Scene at horse fair with tents and figures (51x76cm-20x30in) s. board
£900	$1602	(1-Nov-91 BW86) Study of horse in meadow (30x38cm-12x15in) s. board

MUNNINGS, Sir A (1878-1959) British

£750	*$1388*	*(12-Jun-92 K462) Children in rowing boat (36x25cm-14x10in) d.1907 chk*

MUNNINGS, Sir Alfred (1878-1959) British

£2200	$3850	(27-Sep-91 C56/R) Reeds by a river bank, Mendlam, Harleston, Norfolk (36x25cm-14x10in) panel
£2800	$4788	(12-Mar-92 B6/R) Brighworthy Fords, Withypool,Exmoor (40x50cm-16x20in) s.
£4918	$9000	(5-Jun-92 SY.NY303/R) Richmond Park (40x50cm-16x20in) s.
£5200	$9880	(24-Jun-92 LJ229) Paddock, Castle House (49x60cm-19x24in) s. board
£7400	$12654	(11-Mar-92 S14/R) Pierrot (35x25cm-14x10in) s. s.i.stretcher
£7500	$12825	(12-Mar-92 B7/R) Oare (53x61cm-21x24in) s. panel
£10000	$18500	(12-Jun-92 K515/R) Coming home, shrimp leading horses through sunlit evening landscape (48x69cm-19x27in) s.
£10500	$18060	(6-Mar-92 C97/R) Brightworthy Fords, Withypool, Exmoor (49x60cm-19x24in) s. s.i.d.1942verso panel
£14754	$27000	(5-Jun-92 SY.NY319/R) Mrs Robert Rankin and her daughters painted at Broughton Towers (50x61cm-20x24in) board
£16940	$31000	(5-Jun-92 SY.NY282/R) The Duke of Westminster's chestnut mare Angela. Sky study s.i.d.1923 panel double-sided
£17000	$32470	(16-Jul-92 B19/R) Feeding the chickens (33x43cm-13x17in) s.d.1900
£23224	$42500	(5-Jun-92 SY.NY283/R) Ned Osborne up on Grey Tick (25x35cm-10x14in) s. panel
£33000	$60390	(13-May-92 S12 a/R) The white canoe (30x41cm-12x16in) s. board
£35000	$63000	(20-Nov-91 S105/R) Winter morning (63x76cm-25x30in) s.
£38251	$70000	(5-Jun-92 SY.NY295/R) Boy leading a pony (50x61cm-20x24in) s.d.1912
£52000	$95160	(13-May-92 S20/R) In the shade (51x61cm-20x24in) s.d.1911
£54645	$100000	(5-Jun-92 SY.NY290/R) Going out at Epsom (50x61cm-20x24in) panel
£68000	$122400	(20-Nov-91 S102/R) Study no 2 for Cheltenham Race Meeting (30x56cm-12x22in) s. panel
£71038	$130000	(5-Jun-92 SY.NY276/R) The start (29x60cm-11x24in) s. board
£94000	$167320	(30-Apr-92 CG857/R) Tightening the girth (41x51cm-16x20in) s.d.1912
£650	*$1222*	*(18-Dec-91 C40/R) Suffolk horse fair (18x15cm-7x6in) s. pencil*
£850	*$1573*	*(12-Jun-92 K461/R) Stable lad dressed as whip in scarlet on grey mare (25x30cm-10x12in) s.i. pencil*
£2300	*$3979*	*(25-Mar-92 PHI507/R) Man smoking pipe with greyhound beside him (27x21cm-11x8in) W/C over pencil*

MUNOZ ORTIZ, Jose (19th C) Spanish

£831	$1455	(18-Feb-92 DUR.M22/R) Madrid, fines S.XIX (12x21cm-5x8in) s.d.98 panel (S.P 150000)

MUNOZ RUBIO, Ramon (19th C) Spanish

£492	$896	(11-Dec-91 FER.M78/R) Dama con mantilla (47x37cm-19x15in) s. (S.P 90000)

MUNOZ Y CUESTA, Domingo (1850-1912) Spanish

£3764	$6700	(1-Nov-91 PO.BA21) Odalisca (180x94cm-71x37in) s.
£7758	$13577	(18-Feb-92 DUR.M13/R) Feliz encuentro (47x39cm-19x15in) s. (S.P 1400000)

MUNOZ, Bartolome Mongrell (19th C) Spanish

£748	*$1324*	*(12-Feb-92 ANS.M28/R) Bandoleros (11x19cm-4x7in) s. W/C (S.P 135000)*

MUNOZ, Godofredo Ortega (1905-) Spanish

£4324	$8000	(12-Jun-92 SY.NY32/R) Still life with pear (27x30cm-11x12in) s. panel
£30071	$55030	(13-May-92 FER.M176 a/R) Paisaje de tierras rojas (73x93cm-29x37in) s. (S.P 5500000)

MUNOZ, Lucio (1929-) Spanish

£9500	$16435	(26-Mar-92 S47/R) Personaje uacente (100x81cm-39x32in) s.d.1964 verso sculpted board
£17501	$31853	(9-Dec-91 CH.R122/R) Abside 2 (130x97cm-51x38in) s.i.d.1966 panel (I.L 38000000)

MUNOZ, Lucio (1929-) Spanish-cont.
£15000 $27300   *(29-May-92 C457/R) La mandurreja (83x140cm-33x55in) s. s.i.d.1960verso oil composition panel*

MUNOZ-DEGRAIN, Antoine (1843-1927) French
£464 $798   (16-Oct-91 FER.M128/R) Ruinas bajo un cielo de tormenta (16x27cm-6x11in) s. (S.P 85000)
£602 $1095   (11-Dec-91 FER.M95/R) Velero (19x17cm-7x7in) s. paper (S.P 110000)

MUNRO, Hugh (1873-1928) British
£950 $1691   (1-May-92 PHE99/R) The swing (29x24cm-11x9in) s. board
£4054 $7500   (12-Jun-92 SY.NY39/R) In the rose garden (76x63cm-30x25in) s.i.

MUNSCH, Leopold (1826-1888) Austrian
£1253 $2268   (5-Dec-91 D.V83) Goose girl (21x17cm-8x7in) s. (A.S 25000)
£2184 $3888   (29-Apr-92 D.V914/R) Farmyard scene (33x40cm-13x16in) s. (A.S 45000)

MUNSTERHJELM, Ali (1873-1944) Finnish
£1887 $3340   (5-Nov-91 BA.S124/R) Aura river, Abo (45x71cm-18x28in) s. (S.KR 20000)
£1931 $3514   (11-Dec-91 HOR.H74) Summer day by Aura river (48x68cm-19x27in) s. (F.M 15000)
£2188 $3982   (11-Dec-91 HOR.H75) Ice breakers in Sandviken (50x68cm-20x27in) s. (F.M 17000)

MUNSTERHJELM, Hjalmar (1840-1905) Finnish
£632 $1126   (29-Nov-91 GAB.G2816 a) Paysage Scandinave au fjord (74x100cm-29x39in) s. (S.FR 1600)
£7585 $13350   (12-Apr-92 HOR.H172/R) The artist's home in Tulois (23x33cm-9x13in) s.d.1882 (F.M 60000)
£15524 $27633   (1-Dec-91 HOR.H157/R) Evening in the skerries (24x41cm-9x16in) s. (F.M 120000)
£19595 $34488   (12-Apr-92 HOR.H171) The crofter's cottage (35x47cm-14x19in) s. (F.M 155000)

MUNTER, David Heinrich (1816-1879) German
£989 $1731   (3-Apr-92 BM.B547/R) North German landscape with figures and thunderstorm (38x53cm-15x21in) s. (DM 2800)
£1767 $3092   (3-Apr-92 BM.B550/R) Female nudes in field (68x100cm-27x39in) s.d.1930 (DM 5000)

MUNTER, Gabriele (1877-1962) German
£8741 $15559   (28-Nov-91 SY.BE52/R) Still life with flowers (30x43cm-12x17in) mono.i.d.56 paper (DM 25000)
£16041 $29034   (23-May-92 GB.B6952/R) Winter landscape near Elmau (32x44cm-13x17in) s.d.1933 i.d.verso panel (DM 47000)
£26224 $46678   (30-Nov-91 VG.B189/R) Lauensteiner Land. Study of standing child holding rabbit (63x43cm-25x17in) s.d.1927 col.chk.verso double-sided (DM 75000)
£48951 $87133   (29-Nov-91 VG.B31/R) Lilies in landscape (55x46cm-22x18in) s.d.1939 (DM 140000)
£114754 $210000   (13-May-92 CH.NY222/R) Entwurf zum blauen see (48x68cm-19x27in) st.verso board
£2807 $5053   *(23-Nov-91 N.M238/R) Composition (14x11cm-6x4in) mono.d.1953 W/C gouache (DM 8000)*
£7692 $13692   (26-Nov-91 KF.M897/R) Bunch of flowers in vase (61x43cm-24x17in) mono.i.d.1959 oil gouache (DM 22000)
£8191 $14908   (30-May-92 VG.B233/R) Yellow flowers in blue vase (45x38cm-18x15in) mono.i.d.1957 gouache oil indian ink brush (DM 24000)

MUNTHE, Gerhard Peter Franz Vilhelm (1849-1929) Norwegian
£2632 $4895   (18-Jun-92 GWP.O69/R) Village street (36x47cm-14x19in) s.i. (N.KR 30000)
£2708 $4874   (19-Nov-91 RAS.K485/R) Harbour view in winter (102x84cm-40x33in) s.d.1879 (D.KR 30000)
£4074 $7415   (14-Dec-91 BU.O54/R) River landscape (59x89cm-23x35in) s.d.1911 (N.KR 46000)
£4214 $7248   (7-Oct-91 B.O96/R) Spring landscape with brook (54x60cm-21x24in) s.i.d.1924 (N.KR 48000)
£4565 $7853   (7-Oct-91 B.O95/R) Near Mjosa (50x70cm-20x28in) s.i.d.1910 (N.KR 52000)
£14035 $26105   (15-Jun-92 B.O113/R) The artist's home, Levveld (68x100cm-27x39in) s.d.1907 (N.KR 160000)
£535 $925   *(23-Mar-92 B.O94/R) Osterhavet (38x28cm-15x11in) s.i. W/C (N.KR 6000)*
£886 $1612   *(14-Dec-91 BU.O148) Farm in Numedal (22x33cm-9x13in) s. mixed media (N.KR 10000)*
£2456 $4568   *(15-Jun-92 B.O114/R) Kvarberg in Vaage (34x42cm-13x17in) s.i. W/C (N.KR 28000)*

MUNTHE, Ludvig (1841-1896) Norwegian
£1369 $2477   (3-Dec-91 C.A188/R) Winter landscape (52x80cm-20x31in) s. panel (B.FR 80000)
£2144 $3688   (13-Oct-91 REM.W20) Fishing vessels (54x78cm-21x31in) s. (P.Z 41000000)
£3634 $6250   (17-Oct-91 SY.NY282/R) Frozen river at sunset (46x37cm-18x15in) s. panel
£4190 $7500   (6-May-92 D.NY66/R) Daybreak (61x47cm-24x19in) s. board
£4639 $7887   (25-Oct-91 BM.B793/R) Dutch fishing village at sunset with figures on snow covered path (66x54cm-26x21in) s.d.91 panel (DM 13500)

MUNTHE-NORSTEDT, Anna (1854-1936) Swedish
£943 $1670   (5-Nov-91 BA.S126/R) Still life of fruit and flowers (31x40cm-12x16in)
           s.d.1922 (S.KR 10000)

MUNTZ, Laura Adeline see LYALL, Laura Adeline

MUNTZ-ADAMS, Josephine (1861-1950) Australian
£3524 $6273   (26-Nov-91 J.M98) Picnic (45x74cm-18x29in) s. (A.D 8000)

MURA, Angelo della (1867-1922) Italian
£612 $1064   (14-Apr-92 SY.AM139/R) Beached vessels (10x19cm-4x7in) s. panel
           (D.FL 2000)

MURA, Francesco de (1696-1782) Italian
£3500 $6720   (10-Jul-92 C285/R) Putti disporting in landscape (35x48cm-14x19in) with
           i.stretcher oval
£10690 $19349   (5-Dec-91 F.M6/R) Madonna col Bambino (76x62cm-30x24in) (I.L 23000000)
£11767 $21417   (28-May-92 F.M95/R) Adorazione dei pastori (64x75cm-25x30in)
           (I.L 26000000)
£1100 $2002   (11-Dec-91 PH36/R) The Sacrifice of Iphigenia (26x31cm-10x12in) pen chk

MURA, Francesco de (attrib) (1696-1782) Italian
£3488 $6000   (10-Oct-91 SY.NY15/R) A male ecclesiastic Saint in glory
           (74x49cm-29x19in)
£4000 $7280   (10-Dec-91 PH185/R) Virgin (11x9cm-4x4in) copper
£4696 $8500   (22-May-92 SY.NY78/R) Archangel Raphael (124x98cm-49x39in)
£12041 $20831   (25-Mar-92 CH.R97/R) Immacolata (37x24cm-15x9in) copper oval
           (I.L 26000000)

MURA, Francesco de (studio) (1696-1782) Italian
£930 $1683   (3-Dec-91 SY.MI215) Madonna addolorata (69x59cm-27x23in) (I.L 2000000)

MURA, Francesco de (style) (1696-1782) Italian
£950 $1824   (9-Jul-92 CSK44/R) The Holy Family (40x32cm-16x13in)

MURA, Joachim del (19th C) Spanish
£2220 $3818   (16-Oct-91 AT.P40/R) Bouquet de fleurs dans un panier d'osier
           (81x60cm-32x24in) s. (F.FR 22000)

MURANT, Emanuel (1622-1700) Dutch
£4530 $8244   (12-Dec-91 L.K125/R) Village street with pond and tree (37x54cm-15x21in)
           mono. panel (DM 13000)

MURANT, Emanuel (attrib) (1622-1700) Dutch
£2486 $4500   (22-May-92 SY.NY169/R) Horses tethered outside country inn, distant
           landscape beyond (50x71cm-20x28in) panel

MURATON, Euphemie (1840-?) French
£730 $1307   (6-May-92 GD.B919/R) Still life with melon (45x65cm-18x26in) s.
           (S.FR 2000)

MURATORY, L (?) ?
£406 $738   (25-May-92 ARC.P56) Petite fille au chien (116x73cm-46x29in) s.d.1913
           pastel (F.FR 4000)

MURCH, Arthur (1902-1990) Australian
£922 $1604   (16-Sep-91 CH.ME52) Vegetable still life (40x37cm-16x15in) s.d.1928
           (A.D 2000)
£1014 $1764   (16-Sep-91 CH.ME164 a) Towards Tamworth (35x43cm-14x17in) s. canvas on
           board (A.D 2200)
£1016 $1940   (29-Jun-92 AAA.S132 e) Mother and Child (49x39cm-19x15in) s. board
           (A.D 2600)
£1197 $2130   (28-Apr-92 CH.ME132) Mount Linday panorama (60x121cm-24x48in) s.
           s.i.verso board (A.D 2800)
£1282 $2282   (27-Apr-92 J.M131/R) Still life of camelias (43x33cm-17x13in) s.
           canvasboard (A.D 3000)
£1624 $2891   (28-Apr-92 CH.ME243/R) The girl and the goat (40x50cm-16x20in) s.d.80
           canvasboard (A.D 3800)
£1709 $3043   (27-Apr-92 J.M253/R) Aboriginal elder (90x59cm-35x23in) s. board
           (A.D 4000)
£1744 $3331   (21-Jul-92 JRL.S21/R) Family on the beach (40x32cm-16x13in) s. (A.D 4500)

MURER, Augusto (1922-1985) Italian
£590 $1051   (29-Apr-92 F.F197/R) Autoritratto (8x10cm-3x4in) s.d.1975 board
           (I.L 1300000)

MURER, E (1845-1906) French
£1109 $1963   (10-Nov-91 ZZ.F190/R) Femme pres de la riviere (35x27cm-14x11in) s.
           (F.FR 11000)

MURER, Hans (?-1486) German
£7343 $12556   (18-Mar-92 N.M440/R) Noli me tangere (64x77cm-25x30in) panel (DM 21000)

MURGUIA, Ovidio (19th C) Spanish
£546 $939   (16-Oct-91 FER.M61) Penascos en la alta montana (30x42cm-12x17in) s. chl dr (S.P 100000)
£546 $939   (16-Oct-91 FER.M59/R) Casas de Fuenterrabia (42x31cm-17x12in) s. chl pastel dr (S.P 100000)
£928 $1596   (16-Oct-91 FER.M60/R) Casas de Vigo (35x29cm-14x11in) s. chl W/C dr (S.P 170000)

MURI, Auguste (1854-1908) French
£471 $842   (15-Nov-91 GK.Z5081) Shoreland with willow trees (27x40cm-11x16in) s.d.1898 (S.FR 1200)

MURILLO (after) (17th C) Spanish
£710 $1300   (5-Feb-92 D.NY71) Still life of apple resting on book (25x30cm-10x12in)
£1000 $1800   (22-Nov-91 SWS52/R) The Assumption of the Virgin (136x98cm-54x39in)
£1000 $1830   (12-May-92 SWS778/R) Madonna and child (160x106cm-63x42in)
£1100 $1980   (22-Nov-91 SWS26/R) Saint Justa (61x48cm-24x19in)
£1300 $2340   (22-Nov-91 SWS188/R) Two boys eating melon and grapes (139x109cm-55x43in)

MURILLO, Bartolome Esteban (1618-1682) Spanish
£8380 $15000   (13-Nov-91 B.SF2136/R) Vision of Saint Vincent of Ferrara (64x44cm-25x17in) painted with studio
£12205 $22091   (18-May-92 SY.MI291/R) Scena di osteria (196x144cm-77x57in) (I.L 27000000)
£17000 $30940   (13-Dec-91 C277/R) Christ the Man of Sorrows (53x38cm-21x15in)
£20000 $36400   (11-Dec-91 S66/R) Head of boy (66x52cm-26x20in)
£220000 $400400   (29-May-92 C333/R) The Immaculate Conception (167x111cm-66x44in)
£650000 $1183000   (13-Dec-91 C64/R) Laughing boy wearing plumed hat and pointing with right hand (54x40cm-21x16in)
£700000 $1274000   (29-May-92 C332/R) Madonna and Child (103x83cm-41x33in)
£4000 $7280   (29-May-92 C345/R) Shepherd boy (139x91cm-55x36in) i. chk
£22000 $40040   (29-May-92 C344/R) Angel appearing to St Joseph (166x172cm-65x68in) s. chk pen wash

MURILLO, Bartolome Esteban (after) (1618-1682) Spanish
£733 $1400   (3-Jul-92 S.W3851/R) Game of dice
£733 $1400   (3-Jul-92 S.W3852) Boys eating melon
£785 $1500   (3-Jul-92 S.W3854/R) Boys eating fruit with donkey onlooking
£838 $1600   (3-Jul-92 S.W3853) Fruit seller
£900 $1665   (12-Jun-92 TE614) Boy seated with a pitcher (81x66cm-32x26in)
£920 $1638   (29-Oct-91 SWS57) Infant St. John the Baptist and lamb (111x79cm-44x31in)
£1800 $3204   (29-Oct-91 PH146) The Madonna and child surrounded by angels playing musical instruments (145x103cm-57x41in)
£2210 $4000   (21-May-92 CH.NY125/R) Prodigal son as swineherd (28x37cm-11x15in)
£2800 $5376   (9-Jul-92 CSK97) Immaculate Conception (168x127cm-66x50in)
£2800 $4984   (1-Nov-91 C56) Adoration of shepherds (230x160cm-91x63in)

MURILLO, Bartolome Esteban (attrib) (1618-1682) Spanish
£13500 $24570   (13-Dec-91 C250/R) Christ the Man of Sorrows (59x48cm-23x19in)

MURILLO, Bartolome Esteban (circle) (1618-1682) Spanish
£1309 $2500   (16-Jul-92 SY.NY75/R) The Virgin Immaculate (53x43cm-21x17in)

MURILLO, Bartolome Esteban (school) (1618-1682) Spanish
£838 $1500   (13-Nov-91 B.SF2100/R) The game of Morra (95x135cm-37x53in)

MURILLO, Bartolome Esteban (studio) (1618-1682) Spanish
£3665 $7000   (16-Jul-92 SY.NY77/R) St Francis Xavier (57x41cm-22x16in) i.
£6145 $11000   (17-Jan-92 SY.NY181/R) The Martyrdom of Saint Andrew (129x168cm-51x66in)
£55233 $95000   (9-Oct-91 CH.NY40/R) Immaculate Conception (190x145cm-75x57in)

MURILLO, Bartolome Esteban (style) (1618-1682) Spanish
£800 $1536   (9-Jul-92 CSK103/R) Christ the good Shepherd (49x63cm-19x25in)
£846 $1616   (15-Jul-92 CH.S773/R) Elderly woman, wearing bonnet and shawl (49x39cm-19x15in) (A.D 2200)
£1348 $2400   (22-Jan-92 SY.NY98/R) Child giving mother coins by candlelight (114x80cm-45x31in) canvas on board
£6500 $11570   (1-Nov-91 C55/R) Assumption (229x162cm-90x64in)

MURILLO, Gerardo see ATL, Dr

MURPHY, Herman Dudley (1867-1945) American
£889 $1600   (24-Nov-91 JRB.C137/R) Tropical bridge (30x41cm-12x16in) s. board
£1000 $1800   (24-Nov-91 JRB.C96/R) Old San Juan (74x91cm-29x36in) s.mono.
£1124 $2000   (29-Nov-91 MFA.C177/R) Marsh scene (30x41cm-12x16in) s. board
£3135 $5800   (10-Jun-92 CE.NY350 a/R) Monadnock (51x76cm-20x30in) s. mono.verso
£3429 $6000   (26-Sep-91 CH.NY89/R) Mount Monadnock (62x75cm-24x30in) s.
£4167 $7500   (24-Nov-91 JRB.C92/R) The surf (51x69cm-20x27in) mono.

MURPHY, J Francis (1853-1921) American
£601 $1100   (17-May-92 DU.E1036) Landscape with cut trees (28x36cm-11x14in) s. board
£629 $1100   (23-Sep-91 S.SL265) Autumnal landscape (20x25cm-8x10in) s.i. d.1906 verso
£643 $1100   (13-Mar-92 S.BM190/R) October (43x28cm-17x11in) s. panel
£1105 $1900   (13-Oct-91 H.C3/R) Autumn (18x23cm-7x9in) s. panel
£1130 $2000   (13-Feb-92 S.W2850/R) Autumn (23x18cm-9x7in) s.d.1900 board

MURPHY, J Francis (1853-1921) American-cont.
£1462	$2500	(12-Mar-92 CH.NY71/R) The pride of the meadow (28x38cm-11x15in) s. st.studio verso
£1557	$2600	(20-Aug-91 RB.HY161/R) Summer landscape (41x30cm-16x12in) s.d.1904
£1934	$3500	(4-Dec-91 D.NY28/R) Red tree (91x102cm-36x40in) s.d.1912
£2660	$5000	(18-Dec-91 SY.NY92/R) Summer landscape (40x55cm-16x22in) s.d.1905
£2924	$5000	(12-Mar-92 CH.NY106/R) Late afternoon (30x48cm-12x19in) s.d.89
£3509	$6000	(12-Mar-92 CH.NY105/R) Grey afternoon (40x56cm-16x22in) s.d.90

MURRAY, Eben H (?) ?
£1500	$2820	(19-Dec-91 C154/R) The Spirit of Christmas (41x51cm-16x20in) s.indist.d.188.

MURRAY, Elizabeth (1940-) American
£5447	$9750	(13-Nov-91 CH.NY207/R) Madame Cezanne seated in an armchair turning on light (91x91cm-36x36in) s.i.d.72stretcher
£10588	$18000	(23-Oct-91 B.SF3749/R) Madame Cezanne falling out of her chair (89x91cm-35x36in) s.d.72
£13408	$24000	(13-Nov-91 CH.NY214/R) Searchin (148x135cm-58x53in) s.i.d.Dec.1976-Feb.1977verso
£41899	$75000	(13-Nov-91 SY.NY73/R) Small town (335x330cm-132x130in) six parts
£64246	$115000	(14-Nov-91 SY.NY177/R) New York dawn (226x165cm-89x65in) s.d.77 verso
£8380	$15000	(13-Nov-91 CH.NY261/R) Untitled (97x102cm-38x40in) chl.col.chks.

MURRAY, H (fl.1850-60) British
£1628	$2800	(15-Oct-91 CE.NY48) The meet and the scent (28x44cm-11x17in) s. W/C
£1871	$3200	(13-Mar-92 WOL.C444/R) Hunting scene (30x43cm-12x17in) s. W/C pair

MURRAY, Sir David (1849-1933) British
£1500	$2685	(5-May-92 SWS453/R) The approach of autumn (37x45cm-15x18in) s.d.1922 s.i.verso board
£1743	$3190	(3-Jun-92 R.T146/R) Where the world is dark with tempests (152x91cm-60x36in) s.i.d.1876 (C.D 3800)
£580	$1108	(1-Jul-92 B142/R) The ferry crossing (61x91cm-24x36in) s.d.17 W/C
£2000	$3620	(4-Dec-91 S287/R) Shady pool (33x50cm-13x20in) s.d.89 W/C

MURRAY, Thomas (attrib) (1663-1734) British
£1100	$1969	(13-Nov-91 S123/R) Portrait of lady wearing robes with chemise (75x63cm-30x25in) painted oval

MURRAY, William (attrib) (19th C) British
£1600	$3008	(19-Dec-91 C147/R) Hound and two terriers with river landscape beyond (32x37cm-13x15in) indist.s.d.1812

MURTON, Thomas (fl.1800-1804) British
£900	$1575	(25-Feb-92 CSK63/R) Lady Liverpool (24x?cm-9x?in) min.s.d.1800 rec. after George Romney

MUSCHAMP, F Sydney (?-1929) British
£950	$1634	(8-Oct-91 PH128) An old favourite (33x23cm-13x9in) s.
£1100	$1881	(16-Mar-92 LW1752) Girl playing harp (30x20cm-12x8in) s.
£1300	$2379	(5-Feb-92 TM261/R) Piano players (48x74cm-19x29in) s.
£1341	$2400	(11-Nov-91 GC.M51/R) La costura (34x23cm-13x9in) s.52/R
£2000	$3440	(11-Oct-91 C61/R) A clumsy suitor (51x76cm-20x30in) s. canvas laid down on board
£2386	$4151	(13-Apr-92 SY.J251/R) Recital (52x42cm-20x17in) init. (SA.R 12000)
£2800	$4956	(6-Nov-91 S160/R) Making a brew. Young pipe player (43x53cm-17x21in) s. pair
£460	$800	(15-Apr-92 PHL69/R) Dance (42x62cm-17x24in) s. col.wash
£1000	$1790	(12-Nov-91 CHAP273/R) Pity in akin to love (41x61cm-16x24in) s.

MUSGRAVE, Harry (fl.1884-1910) British
£500	$950	(23-Jun-92 CG666) Coastal landscape with herring boat approaching shore (61x91cm-24x36in) s.

MUSIC, Zoran (1909-) Italian
£7658	$14396	(19-Dec-91 F.M126/R) Canale della Giudecca (35x27cm-14x11in) s.d.81 i.d.verso (I.L 16500000)
£9731	$17322	(26-Nov-91 SY.MI143/R) Canale della Giudecca (33x46cm-13x18in) s.d.80 s.i.d.verso (I.L 21000000)
£14527	$25859	(29-Apr-92 F.F251/R) Suite Byzantine (37x46cm-15x18in) s.d.1959 s.i.d.verso (I.L 32000000)
£16000	$28000	(25-Feb-92 SY.NY31/R) Autoritratto (41x33cm-16x13in) s.id.1950 i.d.verso
£17609	$31344	(29-Nov-91 F.F175/R) Cavallini (22x27cm-9x11in) s. s.verso (I.L 38000000)
£17647	$30353	(12-Oct-91 F.L237/R) Chiesa della salute (46x35cm-18x14in) s.d.85 s.d.verso (S.FR 45000)
£18423	$33529	(9-Dec-91 CH.R173/R) Portrait I (64x46cm-25x18in) s.d.1975 s.d.verso acrylic (I.L 40000000)
£21012	$36560	(14-Apr-92 F.M215/R) Ombre sul Carso (73x91cm-29x36in) s.d.1958 s.i.d.verso (I.L 46000000)
£23607	$42020	(29-Apr-92 F.F250/R) Paesaggio italiano (38x62cm-15x24in) s.d.1968 (I.L 52000000)
£25714	$45000	(25-Feb-92 SY.NY32/R) Ida (41x33cm-16x13in) s.d.1942
£27155	$49423	(25-May-92 CH.R78/R) Pierres et buisson (114x145cm-45x57in) s.d.1957 s.i.d.verso (I.L 60000000)

MUSIC, Zoran (1909-) Italian-cont.
£27491	$50309	(3-Jun-92 L.K338/R) Motivo Dalmata (33x41cm-13x16in) s.d.1952 s.i.d.verso (DM 80000)
£34048	$60606	(29-Apr-92 F.F252/R) Paesaggio senese (40x60cm-16x24in) s.d.1950 s.i.d.verso (I.L 75000000)
£38251	$70000	(14-May-92 SY.NY291/R) Cavallini (33x41cm-13x16in) s.d.1951 s.i.d.verso
£48571	$85000	(25-Feb-92 SY.NY33/R) Motiva Dalmata (37x44cm-15x17in) s. s.i.d.1953verso
£60000	$105000	(25-Feb-92 CH.NY93/R) Cavallini (33x41cm-13x16in) s.d.1950
£63584	$110000	(2-Oct-91 NY.NY70/R) Cavallo Azzurro (46x65cm-18x26in) s.d.1950
£105059	$182802	(14-Apr-92 F.M247/R) Motivo dalmata (60x73cm-24x29in) s.d.1950 s.i.d.verso (I.L 230000000)
£487	$887	(9-Dec-91 B.O87/R) By the Adriatic Sea (20x28cm-8x11in) s.d.80 col.pencils (N.KR 5500)
£927	$1650	(26-Nov-91 SY.MI31/R) Cortina s.d.63 indian ink pair (I.L 2000000)
£1622	$2887	(26-Nov-91 SY.MI2/R) Cavallini (12x12cm-5x5in) mono.d.49 pen (I.L 3500000)
£2780	$4949	(26-Nov-91 SY.MI30/R) Paesaggio Roccioso (20x29cm-8x11in) s.d.1978 W/C (I.L 6000000)
£3012	$5361	(26-Nov-91 SY.MI44/R) Paesaggio roccioso (19x27cm-7x11in) s.d.1978 gouache (I.L 6500000)
£3707	$6599	(29-Nov-91 F.F126) Alla Colomba Venezia (35x32cm-14x13in) s. mixed media cardboard (I.L 8000000)
£8042	$14315	(25-Nov-91 WK.M750/R) Composition (50x64cm-20x25in) s.d.1961 mixed media board (DM 23000)
£9268	$16497	(29-Nov-91 F.F161 g) Motivo dalmata (34x26cm-13x10in) s.d.1953 pastel cardboard (I.L 20000000)

MUSIN, Auguste (1852-1920) Belgian
£1369	$2477	(3-Dec-91 C.A190) Marine (28x39cm-11x15in) s. (B.FR 80000)
£1500	$2700	(22-Nov-91 C59/R) Fishing barges in estuary (41x36cm-16x14in) s. panel
£1780	$3400	(16-Jul-92 SY.NY473/R) Claire matinee - calme en Riviere (41x36cm-16x14in) s.i.d.1893
£2527	$4549	(19-Nov-91 RAS.K120/R) Journee pleurieuse, quai de Dortdrecht (54x99cm-21x39in) s. (D.KR 28000)
£3634	$6250	(17-Oct-91 SY.NY244/R) Scheveningue - Holland (68x124cm-27x49in) s.d.1876

MUSIN, Francois Etienne (1820-1888) Belgian
£1468	$2613	(30-Oct-91 CH.AM66) Figures near bomschuiten on beach (11x18cm-4x7in) s. canvas on panel (D.FL 4800)
£1537	$2766	(2-Feb-92 ZZ.F63/R) Voiliers a l'entree du port (27x21cm-11x8in) s. panel (F.FR 15000)
£2000	$3820	(17-Jul-92 C116/R) American frigate hove-to, waiting for her cutter (33x48cm-13x19in) s.
£4500	$8100	(22-Nov-91 C71/R) La Rade de Calais (54x79cm-21x31in) s.
£5963	$10376	(14-Apr-92 SY.AM92/R) Return of the fleet (73x92cm-29x36in) s. (D.FL 19500)
£7000	$12460	(26-Nov-91 PH11/R) Putting into harbour (89x169cm-35x67in) s.

MUSS-ARNOLT, Gustav (1858-1927) American
£686	$1200	(3-Apr-92 S.W2455/R) Chestnut horse in landscape (56x76cm-22x30in) s.d.
£1093	$2000	(3-Jun-92 D.NY67/R) Saratoga Race horse (56x81cm-22x32in) s.d.97
£2119	$3750	(25-Apr-92 YFA.M227/R) Hunting dogs

MUSSAIJASSUL, Halil-Bey (1896-?) Russian
£1115	$2029	(11-Dec-91 N.M547/R) Young woman with lace veil before exotic bushes with blossoms and bird (70x50cm-28x20in) s.d.1931 board (DM 3200)
£1800	$3078	(17-Mar-92 PH91/R) Portrait of lady (71x56cm-28x22in) mono.d.1935 board

MUSSARD, Andreas (fl.1724-1765) British
£680	$1210	(27-Nov-91 C263/R) Portrait of gentleman in coat with gold buttons (5x?cm-2x?in) min.s.d.1750verso gilt-metal frame oval

MUSSCHER, Michiel van (1645-1705) Dutch
£1500	$2625	(3-Apr-92 C67) Portrait of lady, in orange dress, seated by spring (59x47cm-23x19in)
£3086	$5525	(14-Nov-91 CH.AM184/R) Portrait of Jacob Loten standing leaning on pedestel and landscape beyond (46x38cm-18x15in) s. i.stretcher (D.FL 10000)

MUSSCHER, Michiel van (attrib) (1645-1705) Dutch
£1730	$3287	(24-Jun-92 KM.K935/R) Portrait of girl with pearl necklace holding shaft (43x32cm-17x13in) panel (DM 5000)
£2000	$3840	(8-Jul-92 S304/R) Portrait of lady with son in interior (90x74cm-35x29in)

MUSSCHER, Michiel van (style) (1645-1705) Dutch
£2000	$3500	(3-Apr-92 C39/R) Portrait of military commander, wearing breastplate over coat, landscape beyond (108x61cm-43x24in)

MUSSILL, William (c.1800-1860) ?
£800	$1400	(25-Feb-92 C35/R) Bird of Paradise (62x48cm-24x19in) s. W/C bodycol

MUSSINI, Luigi (1813-1888) Italian
£3571	$6500	(26-May-92 CE.NY29/R) Figures in classical courtyard (64x80cm-25x31in) s.

MUSSO, Benedetto (attrib) (?) Italian
£463 $801   (24-Mar-92 CH.R52) Il pittore che dipinge en plein air (9x15cm-4x6in) i.
                     panel (I.L 1000000)

MUSSOLINI, S (19th C) ?
£750 $1283   (16-Mar-92 WHB56) Head of Christ with crown of thorns and wearing purple
                     cloak (74x61cm-29x24in) s.d.1866

MUSTO, Manuel (1893-1940) Argentinian
£5337 $9500   (1-Nov-91 PO.BA50) Otono (79x91cm-31x36in) s.d.37

MUTER, Mela (1886-1967) French
£1469 $2511   (21-Mar-92 WK.M405/R) Gilane endormie (41x33cm-16x13in) s. i.verso panel
                     (DM 4200)
£3097 $5543   (17-Nov-91 REM.W20) Portrait of boy (33x11cm-13x4in) s. board
                     (P.Z 60000000)
£4245 $7981   (21-Dec-91 PSA.W14) Portrait of a woman (55x38cm-22x15in) s.
                     (P.Z 82000000)
£4896 $8567   (29-Sep-91 AG.W11) Landscape (33x43cm-13x17in) s. panel (P.Z 94000000)
£9687 $16952   (29-Sep-91 AG.W12) Avenue. Town by the river (72x62cm-28x24in) s.
                     double-sided (P.Z 186000000)
*£2071 $3893   (21-Dec-91 PSA.W13) Landscape with harbour (51x36cm-20x14in) s. W/C ink
                     (P.Z 40000000)*

MUTSAERS, Gerard (1920-) Australian
£617 $1098   (26-Nov-91 J.M919) Droving sheep along road (90x121cm-35x48in) s.
                     canvasboard (A.D 1400)
£749 $1333   (26-Nov-91 J.M966) Ghost gum (91x121cm-36x48in) s. canvasboard (A.D 1700)

MUTSARDT, Sebastian (?-1694) Dutch
£1080 $1934   (14-Nov-91 CH.AM57) Portrait of Jacob van de Graaff holding letter. His
                     wife Elisabeth (71x58cm-28x23in) pair (D.FL 3500)

MUTTONI, Pietro de/PIETRO DELLA VECCHIA see VECCHIA, Pietro della

MUUKKA, Elias (1853-1938) Finnish
£1737 $3162   (11-Dec-91 HOR.H78) Storm (27x41cm-11x16in) s.d.1884 (F.M 13500)
£2168 $3750   (28-Mar-92 UA.U466/R) Summer landscape (42x68cm-17x27in) s.d.05
                     (S.KR 22500)
£2188 $3982   (11-Dec-91 HOR.H77) Moonlight (36x63cm-14x25in) s.d.1879-1885 (F.M 17000)

MUYDEN, Alfred van (1818-1898) Swiss
£1383 $2490   (19-Nov-91 GS.B3218) Reclining female nude (33x46cm-13x18in) board
                     (S.FR 3500)
*£401 $719   (6-May-92 GD.B921) Roman woman spinning (21x14cm-8x6in) s.d.45 W/C
                     (S.FR 1100)*

MUYDEN, Charles Henri van (1860-1936) Swiss
£3360 $5980   (29-Nov-91 GAB.G2180/R) La petite innocente (60x77cm-24x30in) s.d.96
                     (S.FR 8500)

MUZIANO, Girolamo (attrib) (1528-1592) Italian
£1844 $3300   (17-Jan-92 SY.NY104/R) Saint Jerome in the wilderness (22x17cm-9x7in)
                     copper
*£2800 $5096   (10-Dec-91 C119/R) Study of a seated Saint (27x20cm-11x8in) blk.white
                     chk. squared paper*

MUZZIOLI, Giovanni (1854-1894) Italian
£2979 $5272   (7-Nov-91 F.M97/R) Scena in costume (17x36cm-7x14in) s.i. (I.L 6500000)
£4000 $7080   (14-Feb-92 C102/R) The visit. The seamstresses (13x16cm-5x6in) panel two
                     sold with three by other artists

MY, Hieronymus van der (1687-1761) Dutch
£15432 $27623   (12-Nov-91 SY.AM166/R) Poultry seller. Kitchen maid (29x23cm-11x9in)
                     s.d.1745 panel pair (D.FL 50000)

MYERS, Frank Harmon (1899-1956) American
£474 $900   (24-Jun-92 B.SF6348/R) Rocks and sea (51x61cm-20x24in) s.
£565 $1000   (12-Feb-92 B.SF459/R) Seascape (63x76cm-25x30in) s.
£579 $1100   (24-Jun-92 B.SF6347/R) Big surge (56x71cm-22x28in) s. canvas on board
£678 $1200   (12-Feb-92 B.SF458/R) Pacific surf (63x76cm-25x30in) s.
£3158 $6000   (24-Jun-92 B.SF6350/R) Afternoon bathers (44x55cm-17x22in) s. board

MYERS, Jerome (1867-1941) American
£994 $1700   (21-Mar-92 W.W201/R) New York street vendor (18x23cm-7x9in) s.i.indist.d.
                     paper on masonite
£629 $1100   (26-Sep-91 CH.NY228/R) Woman of 1905 (22x16cm-9x6in) s.d. chl pencil
*£2222 $3800   (12-Mar-92 CH.NY209/R) Ring around the Rosie (41x51cm-16x20in) s.d.1919
                     pastel board*

MYERS, Jerome and STELLA, Joseph (20th C) American
*£3143 $5500   (26-Sep-91 CH.NY248/R) Self-portrait. Sketches of woman's head. Sketch of
                     Parisian postman. Man (28x21cm-11x8in) one bears sig. chl pencil oil
                     four*

MYN, Francis van der (1719-1783) Dutch
£1600 $2800   (25-Feb-92 PH102/R) Portrait of moneylender (76x63cm-30x25in) s.d.1771
£1900 $3648   (7-Jul-92 PH209/R) Money lender (75x62cm-30x24in)
£2000 $3560   (1-Nov-91 S423/R) Portrait of lady (74x61cm-29x24in) oval
£5000 $8950   (13-Nov-91 S37/R) Portrait of lady as shepherdess (73x61cm-29x24in) s.d.1746 painted oval

MYN, Herman van der (1684-1741) Dutch
£4400 $7656   (13-Sep-91 C139/R) Serving woman at table holding broadsheet (25x20cm-10x8in) s. panel
£4500 $8640   (7-Jul-92 PH11/R) Still life of mixed fruit on silver salver on stone ledge (49x40cm-19x16in) s.
£6154 $11754   (15-Jul-92 CH.S744/R) Portrait of lady, seated in silk dress, holding chapelet of flowers, in landscape (90x70cm-35x28in) (A.D 16000)

MYN, Herman van der (attrib) (1684-1741) Dutch
£2762 $5000   (22-May-92 SY.NY206/R) Portrait of Sir Robert Worsley of Appuldercombe, in Isle of Wight (125x100cm-49x39in) i.d.1730
£3529 $6000   (25-Oct-91 S.W2780/R) Esther, Viscountess Chetwynd and child (112x99cm-44x39in) s.d.1723

MYN, Herman van der (circle) (1684-1741) Dutch
£1600 $3056   (17-Jul-92 C57/R) Portrait of young girl holding spindle and young boy with basket of eggs (80x100cm-31x39in)
£11050 $20000   (21-May-92 CH.NY201/R) Mixed flowers in urn, other cut flowers and bird's nest on ledge (86x69cm-34x27in) bears sig.d.

MYN, Robert van der (circle) (1724-?) Dutch
£2500 $4800   (9-Jul-92 CSK294/R) Teal hanging from nail by basket of grapes, apples and other fruit (51x76cm-20x30in)

MYN, van der (style) (18th C) Dutch
£2600 $4550   (27-Feb-92 B165/R) Portrait of a young girl holding a basket of flowers (127x104cm-50x41in)

MYNTTI, Eemu (1890-1943) Finnish
£1358 $2418   (1-Dec-91 HOR.H161) House (38x30cm-15x12in) s. (F.M 10500)
£3105 $5527   (1-Dec-91 HOR.H160) View of Reval (33x41cm-13x16in) s.d.1931 (F.M 24000)
£5183 $9123   (12-Apr-92 HOR.H174/R) Flowers in vase (73x54cm-29x21in) s. (F.M 41000)

MYRBACH-RHEINFELD, Felicien von (1853-1940) Austrian
£748 $1338   (16-Jan-92 D.V142/R) Parade der Kaiserjager, Innsbruck (73x54cm-29x21in) grisaille (A.S 15000)

MYTENS, Daniel (circle) (1590-1648) Dutch
£3600 $6120   (22-Oct-91 S243/R) Portrait of Charles I, wearing tunic with gold and white collar (63x48cm-25x19in)

MYTENS, Jan (1614-1670) Dutch
£9259 $16574   (14-Nov-91 CH.AM130/R) Portrait of Hendrik van der Capellen standing in Italianate landscape (116x94cm-46x37in) s. i. coat of arms verso (D.FL 30000)

MYTENS, Jan (style) (1614-1670) Dutch
£1800 $3294   (12-May-92 SWS633/R) Portrait of young lady as shepherdess (83x62cm-33x24in)

MYTENS, Martin (studio) (17/18th C) Dutch/Swedish
£1685 $3000   (22-Jan-92 SY.NY167/R) Portrait of Francis I of Austria (85x67cm-33x26in)

MYTENS, Martin II (1695-1770) Swedish
£7558 $13000   (9-Oct-91 CH.NY103/R) Portrait of artist, seated before stone ledge, holding folio (127x95cm-50x37in) i. canvas on board

MYTENS, Martin II (attrib) (1695-1770) Swedish
£1987 $3398   (18-Mar-92 D.V185/R) Portrait of lady, possibly Erzherzogin Maria Anna (126x87cm-50x34in) shaped top (A.S 40000)
£2891 $5175   (5-May-92 ZEL.L1441/R) Portrait of Maria Anna Duchess of Lothringen (84x67cm-33x26in) (DM 8500)

MYTENS, Martin II (circle) (1695-1770) Swedish
£981 $1865   (23-Jun-92 D.V329/R) Portrait of Kaiserin Maria Theresia (89x75cm-35x30in) (A.S 20000)
£1093 $1869   (18-Mar-92 D.V305/R) Portrait of Countess Maria Sidonia Palffy (54x43cm-21x17in) i.verso (A.S 22000)
£4471 $7645   (18-Mar-92 D.V186/R) Portrait of Graf Palffy as boy (54x44cm-21x17in) (A.S 90000)

MYTENS, Martin II (school) (1695-1770) Swedish
£894 $1529   (18-Mar-92 D.V330/R) Portrait of nobleman, said to be Kaiser Franz I (91x71cm-36x28in) one of pair (A.S 18000)
£994 $1699   (18-Mar-92 D.V331/R) Portrait of noble lady, said to be Kaiserin Maria Theresia (91x71cm-36x28in) one of pair (A.S 20000)
£4811 $8371   (18-Sep-91 N.M430/R) Portrait of Erzherzog as boy wearing ermine trimmed robe (74x60cm-29x24in) (DM 14000)

MYTENS, Martin II (studio) (1695-1770) Swedish
£1987 $3398   (18-Mar-92 D.V306/R) Portrait of Kaiser Franz Stephan with insignia
                      (117x102cm-46x40in) (A.S 40000)

NAAGER, Franz (1870-1942) German
£621 $1099   (6-Nov-91 N.M1105/R) Venice canal scene (103x74cm-41x29in) s.d.1921
                      s.i.verso board (DM 1800)

NABATOV, Wieceslav (1939-) Russian
£514 $900   (24-Sep-91 ARC.P171/R) Fruits d'automne (72x80cm-28x31in) s. (F.FR 5100)

NACCIARONE, Gustavo (1833-1929) Italian
£500 $890   (26-Nov-91 PH232/R) The death of Pergolesi (63x105cm-25x41in) s.d.1890

NACHTMANN, Franz Xaver (1799-1846) German
£4942 $8500   (15-Oct-91 CE.NY36) The elegant music room (23x29cm-9x11in) s.d.1891
                      gouache W/C paper

NADAL, Carlos (20th C) Spanish
£2600 $4966   (29-Jun-92 CSK111/R) Le port (22x35cm-9x14in) s. board
£2800 $5348   (29-Jun-92 CSK116/R) Vue sur la mer (65x81cm-26x32in) s. s.i.verso
£3800 $7258   (29-Jun-92 CSK114/R) Sainte Adresse (61x73cm-24x29in) s. s.i.verso

NADAR see TOURNACHON, Gaspard Felix

NADELMAN, Elie (1882-1946) American
£2000 $3500   (26-Sep-91 CH.NY294/R) White pipe clay figure of nude and standing woman
                      (23x14cm-9x6in) pencil pair
£3714 $6500   (25-Sep-91 SY.NY83/R) Head study (25x20cm-10x8in) pencil

NADIN, Peter (1954-) American
£559 $1000   (9-May-92 CE.NY189/R) Harbour island Bahamas (36x51cm-14x20in) s.d.1988
                      s.i.d.verso W/C oil col.chk

NADORP, Franz (1794-1876) Italian
£627 $1141   (12-Dec-91 L.K443/R) Travellers on Via Mala on way to Italy
                      (28x19cm-11x7in) i.d.1827 pen wash over pencil (DM 1800)
£836 $1522   (12-Dec-91 L.K444/R) Prinz Franz zu Salm-Salm and other figure by
                      fireplace in Italian tavern (21x29cm-8x11in) s.i.d.1827 pen wash over
                      pencil (DM 2400)

NAES, J L (19th C) Norwegian
£984 $1800   (17-May-92 DU.E1131/R) Boarding the Yoringen (84x137cm-33x54in) s.d.91

NAEYER, C de (19th C) ?
£1250 $2238   (5-May-92 SWS438/R) Still life with chrysanthemums and violin
                      (99x74cm-39x29in) s.d.1890

NAFTEL, Isabel (fl.1862-1891) British
£750 $1358   (20-May-92 B294/R) Still life of pink rose in vase by jug (24x16cm-9x6in)
                      s.d.1874 W/C
£1350 $2417   (14-Jan-92 SWS61/R) Orchard by the sea (26x36cm-10x14in) s.d.1888 W/C
                      bodycol sold with another picture
£2000 $3700   (11-Jun-92 CSK6/R) Portrait of Anna Maria Horton with her son Sidney
                      (71x53cm-28x21in) s.d.1866 pencil W/C htd.bodycol.
£2800 $4788   (12-Mar-92 CSK68/R) Sutton Scotney, Hants (25x36cm-10x14in) s.d.1886
                      pencil W/C htd.white

NAFTEL, Maud (1856-1890) British
£640 $1107   (4-Sep-91 BT75) Border of flowers (20x15cm-8x6in) s.d.1886 W/C
£3100 $5549   (5-May-92 SWS265/R) Poppies (19x14cm-7x6in) s.d.1881 s.i.verso W/C
                      bodycol.

NAFTEL, Paul Jacob (1817-1891) British
£460 $810   (6-Apr-92 PH62) The Black Mount, Argyllshire (23x50cm-9x20in) s.d.1873
                      i.verso W/C bodycol.
£880 $1593   (20-May-92 BT81/R) Les Autelets (36x51cm-14x20in) s.d.1884 i.verso W/C
£1000 $1730   (4-Sep-91 PHK58/R) Digging potatoes, Dungeon Ghyll, Westmorland
                      (34x53cm-13x21in) s.d.1884 s.i.verso W/C gouache
£1800 $3222   (5-May-92 SWS262/R) Landscape with view of Reena Furrugh, County Kerry
                      (45x90cm-18x35in) s.d.1861 W/C gouache

NAGASAKI SCHOOL, 18th C Japanese
£3672 $6500   (7-Nov-91 B.SF1296/R) Flowering spring landscape with birds
                      (152x372cm-60x146in) s. ink colour six-panel folding screen

NAGEL, Peter (1941-) German
£2921 $5345   (2-Jun-92 L.K826/R) Paravent (175x134cm-69x53in) s.d.1970 s.i.d.verso egg
                      tempera acrylic (DM 8500)

NAGEL, Wilhelm (1866-1945) German
£687 $1258   (2-Jun-92 FN.S2680/R) Peasant on cart drawn by cows on tree line road (48x60cm-19x24in) st.studio verso (DM 2000)
£528   *$956*   *(3-Dec-91 FN.S2351/R) Church of Rotteln (64x50cm-25x20in) s. W/C (DM 1500)*
£772   *$1320*   *(13-Mar-92 FN.S2888/R) Rocky Danube landscape (50x65cm-20x26in) s. mixed media (DM 2200)*

NAGELE, Reinhold (1884-?) German
£10997 $20124   (2-Jun-92 FN.S2679/R) Wax figures in boxes coming to life (35x23cm-14x9in) mono.d.1931 glass (DM 32000)
£11579 $19800   (13-Mar-92 FN.S2887/R) Train leaving Murrhardt Station with view of snow covered landscape (47x47cm-19x19in) s.i.d.1942 tempera (DM 33000)

NAGL, Carl (19th C) ?
£1701 $3044   (5-May-92 ZEL.L1463/R) Portrait of young woman wearing veil (94x79cm-37x31in) s.d.1873 oval (DM 5000)

NAGY, Peter (20th C) ?
£670 $1200   (9-May-92 CE.NY200/R) Glioblastoma (92x91cm-36x36in) s.d.1986verso acrylic
£686 $1200   (27-Feb-92 CE.NY254/R) Totally fantastic voyage (91x91cm-36x36in) s.d.86 verso s.d.1986 overlap acrylic

NAGY, Vilmos (1874-?) Hungarian
£650 $1177   (21-May-92 CSK245/R) Elegant lady with greyhound in landscape (80x60cm-31x24in) s.
£650 $1151   (13-Feb-92 CSK170/R) Far away thoughts (58x80cm-23x31in) s.
£1200 $2124   (13-Feb-92 CSK177/R) By the riverside (93x77cm-37x30in) s. panel

NAHA, Raymond (1933-) American
£2000   *$3700*   *(14-Jun-92 S.BM118/R) Night scene - going to Kiva (36x46cm-14x18in) s. casein*

NAHER, Christa (1947-) German
£1031 $1887   (2-Jun-92 L.K824) Woman with dog (80x120cm-31x47in) s.d.1983verso tempera canvas (DM 3000)
£1375   *$2515*   *(2-Jun-92 L.K826/R) Green horses (84x105cm-33x41in) s.d.1985 gouache (DM 4000)*

NAHL, Perham Wilhelm (1869-1935) American
£526 $1000   (24-Jun-92 B.SF6325/R) Manton de Manila (74x61cm-29x24in) s.d.1913
£2895 $5500   (24-Jun-92 B.SF6330/R) Dunes by sea (51x63cm-20x25in) init.

NAIGEON, Jean Claude (1753-1832) French
£54583 $102616   (16-Dec-91 AGS.P61/R) L'atelier du peintre (50x66cm-20x26in) s.d.1789 board (F.FR 530000)

NAIGEON, Jean Guillaume Elzidor (1797-1867) French
£720 $1368   (26-Jun-92 AGS.P47/R) Portrait de fille en robe bleue (30x21cm-12x8in) s. (F.FR 7000)
£3807 $7233   (26-Jun-92 AGS.P48/R) Portrait d'une jeune fille d'Ischia (80x64cm-31x25in) s.d.1829 (F.FR 37000)

NAILOR, Gerald (1917-1952) American
£1676   *$3100*   *(14-Jun-92 S.BM164/R) Yei dancer (33x25cm-13x10in) s. gouache*

NAIRN, James McLachlan (1859-1904) British
£776 $1389   (6-May-92 DS.W56) Coastal scene (28x44cm-11x17in) s.d.96 (NZ.D 2600)

NAIVEU, Matthys (1647-1721) Dutch
£3343 $6119   (12-May-92 SY.AM99/R) Figures gathered round quack in market (52x42cm-20x17in) s. (D.FL 11000)
£3642 $6374   (1-Apr-92 CSC.P6) Vertune et Pomone (64x80cm-25x31in) (F.FR 35000)

NAIVEU, Matthys (circle) (1647-1721) Dutch
£2572 $4655   (5-Dec-91 SY.MO224/R) Vertumne et Pomone (64x80cm-25x31in) bears sig. (F.FR 25000)

NAIWINCX, Herman (1624-1651) Flemish
£6616 $12042   (15-Dec-91 REM.W26) Rocky landscape (74x104cm-29x41in) panel (P.Z 130000000)

NAKAMURA, Kazuo (1926-) Japanese/Canadian
£1477 $2600   (9-Apr-92 FA.PH606/R) Porcelain scholars by gold fish bowl (69x51cm-27x20in)
£3546 $6418   (24-May-92 AT.P96/R) Number structure No.5 (56x66cm-22x26in) s. (F.FR 35000)

NAKIELSKI (19th C) Polish
£903 $1617   (17-Nov-91 REM.W21) At the smithy's (32x38cm-13x15in) s. (P.Z 17500000)

NAKKEN, Willem Carel (1835-1926) Dutch
£459 $812   (5-Nov-91 SY.AM128/R) Hay wagon (39x61cm-15x24in) s. (D.FL 1500)
£2905 $5142   (5-Nov-91 SY.AM40/R) Harvest-time (29x60cm-11x24in) s. panel (D.FL 9500)

NAKKEN, Willem Carel (1835-1926) Dutch-cont.
£1223 $2165   *(5-Nov-91 SY.AM309/R) Harvest (33x54cm-13x21in) s.d.76 W/C (D.FL 4000)*
£3364 $5988   *(30-Oct-91 CH.AM292/R) The harvest (33x54cm-13x21in) s.d.74 W/C (D.FL 11000)*

NAM, Jacques (1881-?) French
£1093 $1912   *(30-Mar-92 ZZ.F88) Jeune tigre couche (65x92cm-26x36in) s. (F.FR 10500)*

NAMATJIRA, Albert (1902-1959) Australian
£1709 $3043   *(28-Apr-92 CH.ME240/R) McDonnell Ranges (26x37cm-10x15in) s. W/C (A.D 4000)*
£1709 $3043   *(28-Apr-92 CH.ME215) Gorge (24x35cm-9x14in) s. W/C (A.D 4000)*
£2765 $4811   *(17-Sep-91 JRL.S392/R) Desert landscape (24x36cm-9x14in) s. W/C (A.D 6000)*
£2778 $4944   *(28-Apr-92 CH.ME193/R) Central Australian landscape with gum trees (38x28cm-15x11in) s. pencil W/C (A.D 6500)*
£3419 $6085   *(27-Apr-92 J.M185/R) Haast's Bluff (25x35cm-10x14in) s. W/C (A.D 8000)*
£4405 $7930   *(24-Nov-91 SY.S408/R) Ghost gum in landscape (25x35cm-10x14in) s. W/C (A.D 10000)*
£4608 $8018   *(16-Sep-91 CH.ME154/R) High Noon at Macdonnell Ranges, 1952 (34x51cm-13x20in) s. W/C (A.D 10000)*
£5128 $9128   *(27-Apr-92 J.M73/R) Central Australian landscape (35x45cm-14x18in) s. W/C (A.D 12000)*
£5286 $9410   *(26-Nov-91 J.M293 a) Central Australia with ghost gum (30x45cm-12x18in) s. W/C (A.D 12000)*
£7234 $12804   *(26-Apr-92 SY.ME439/R) Australian landscape with ghost gum (37x55cm-15x22in) s. W/C (A.D 17000)*

NAMCHEONG (19th C?) Chinese
£2600 $4420   *(23-Oct-91 S351/R) HMS Childers off the coast with junk beyond (44x54cm-17x21in) st.studio verso i.d.stretcher*

NANNEY, Chuck (1958-) French
£1026 $1836   *(19-Jan-92 CC.P33) Mudoney (80x80cm-31x31in) s.d.1989verso collage acrylic canvas (F.FR 10000)*

NANNI, Giovanni (attrib) (1487-1564) Italian
£780 $1357   *(13-Apr-92 S156/R) Studies of birds and heads. Study of archway and entablature (27x18cm-11x7in) pen black chk double-sided*

NANNI, Mario (1922-) Italian
£868 $1510   *(14-Apr-92 F.M117) Nuceli (60x75cm-24x30in) s.d.1960 mixed media masonite (I.L 1900000)*

NANNI, Nino (1888-1969) Italian
£1610 $2881   *(14-Nov-91 CH.R191) Ritratti di Lina Cavalieri, a figura intera (50x32cm-20x13in) s. one i. mixed media pair (I.L 3500000)*

NANNINGA, Jaap (1904-1962) Dutch
£8333 $15167   *(12-Dec-91 SY.AM205/R) Nachthoorn (60x70cm-24x28in) s. (D.FL 27000)*
£1818 $3291   *(19-May-92 CH.AM248/R) Two figures (41x26cm-16x10in) s.d.49 gouache (D.FL 6000)*

NANTEUIL, Charles Gaugiran (1811-?) French
£5233 $9000   *(17-Oct-91 SY.NY147/R) Algerian views - Market place and water trough (27x41cm-11x16in) s. canvas on board pair*

NANTEUIL, G (19th C) French
£3297 $6000   *(26-May-92 CE.NY323/R) Returning from market (33x43cm-13x17in) s.d.1879*

NANTEUIL, Robert (circle) (1623-1678) French
£5329 $9912   *(16-Jun-92 SY.B211/R) Portrait of Henri de la Tour D'Auverne, Viscout of Turenne (131x97cm-52x38in) (B.FR 320000)*

NAPOLETANO, Filippo see ANGELI, Filippo

NARANJO, Eduardo (1944-) Spanish
£6014 $11006   *(13-May-92 FER.M178 a/R) Mujer romantica con cabeza de papel (23x18cm-9x7in) s.d.1977 W/C gouache oil panel (S.P 1100000)*
£15007 $25812   *(16-Oct-91 FER.M253/R) La vuelta del militar (30x22cm-12x9in) s.d.79 mixed media panel (S.P 2750000)*

NARAY, Aurel (1883-?) Hungarian
£605 $1071   *(4-Nov-91 SY.J22/R) Girl with violin (63x52cm-25x20in) s. (SA.R 3000)*

NARDI, Enrico (1864-?) Italian
£450 $837   *(18-Jun-92 B41) View from a terrace, Tivoli (29x64cm-11x25in) s. W/C*
£578 $1000   *(29-Mar-92 MY.F72/R) Italian countess (48x30cm-19x12in) s. W/C board*
£3600 $6372   *(14-Feb-92 C103/R) The return from the fields (74x121cm-29x48in) s. W/C card htd white gum arabic*

NARDI, Francois (1861-1936) French
£1048 $1875   *(5-May-92 ZEL.L1464/R) View of Toulon Harbour, morning (46x64cm-18x25in) s. (DM 3080)*
£3333 $6000   *(24-Nov-91 LIT.L25) View of Venice (51x74cm-20x29in) s.*

NARDI, Francois (1861-1936) French-cont.
£565 $950   (28-Aug-91 MFA.C92/R) Italian peasant women (46x30cm-18x12in) s. W/C

NARDO, Mariotto di (14/15th C) Italian
£31768 $57500   (22-May-92 SY.NY1/R) madonna and Child (90x47cm-35x19in) tempera panel
       arched top

NARDONE, Vincent Joseph (1937-) American
£509 $850   (20-Aug-91 RB.HY287/R) North coast vineyard (28x43cm-11x17in) s.d.89
       mixed media

NARES, Edward Denne (1831-?) Canadian
£647 $1151   (26-Nov-91 JOY.T165/R) Officers at Halifax Garrison (13x20cm-5x8in)
       i.d.1851 W/C (C.D 1300)

NARJOT, Ernest (1826-1898) American
£1034 $1800   (11-Sep-91 D.NY63) Flower seller (56x38cm-22x15in) s.d.1885

NASCHBERGER, Gerhardt (20th C) ?
£699 $1245   (30-Nov-91 VG.B911/R) Untitled (180x230cm-71x91in) s.d.1985 dispersion
       chl cotton (DM 2000)

NASH, Edward (1778-1821) British
£2200 $3872   (9-Apr-92 S182/R) Portrait of officer (8x?cm-3x?in) min. init.d.1802 gold
       frame oval

NASH, Frederick (1782-1856) British
£1540 $2941   (16-Jul-92 S123/R) Beach haze clearing off, Brighton (17x26cm-7x10in) s.
       W/C over pencil gum arabic

NASH, John (1893-1977) British
£27000 $46440   (6-Mar-92 C77/R) Yarmouth Docks (91x63cm-36x25in) s.
£400 $780   (15-Jan-92 CSK3) White anemone (76x44cm-30x17in) s.d.27 pencil W/C
£450 $774   (5-Mar-92 CSK186) Wooded landscape (29x42cm-11x17in) s. W/C pencil
£550 $1001   (12-Dec-91 CSK224) Country road in summer (23x29cm-9x11in) s.d.1965
       pencil W/C double-sided
£2200 $4026   (14-May-92 C185/R) Trees in wood (37x36cm-15x14in) s. pencil pen W/C
       bodycol
£4000 $7080   (7-Nov-91 C18/R) The deserted beach, Audierne (40x56cm-16x22in) s.d.1938
       i.verso pencil W/C

NASH, Joseph (1808-1878) British
£900 $1584   (7-Apr-92 C207/R) Drawing room, Levens, Westmorland (33x48cm-13x19in) s.
       i.verso pencil W/C bodycol
£1000 $1770   (7-Nov-91 PHC650/R) Figures in interior of Canterbury Cathedral
       (55x79cm-22x31in) s.d.1852 W/C bodycol

NASH, Paul (1889-1946) British
£20000 $36600   (13-May-92 S77/R) Farewell (51x61cm-20x24in) s.
£35000 $64050   (13-May-92 S59/R) Wall against the sea (61x89cm-24x35in) s.d.1922
£660 $1109   (16-Aug-91 K485) Sun dogs (25x38cm-10x15in) W/C
£3500 $6020   (6-Mar-92 C82/R) March woods (36x52cm-14x20in) s. W/C pencil
£5000 $9000   (20-Nov-91 S119 a/R) Aldington Woods (39x56cm-15x22in) s.d.1923 pencil
       W/C

NASH, Thomas Saunders (1891-?) British
£500 $870   (19-Sep-91 B38) Christ and Twelve Disciples (24x34cm-9x13in) s.d.1927
       gouache pencil board

NASH, Tom (1931-) British
£900 $1566   (19-Sep-91 CSK182/R) Moses striking rock (63x49cm-25x19in) W/C pencil

NASINI, Giuseppe Niccolo (1657-1736) Italian
£800 $1392   (13-Apr-92 S168) St. Rose of Lima receiving veil from Madonna
       (41x25cm-16x10in) pen wash over black chk
£1400 $2688   (7-Jul-92 C191/R) Madonna and Child appearing to male and female saint
       (39x23cm-15x9in) chk pen wash htd white

NASINI, Giuseppe Niccolo (circle) (1657-1736) Italian
£12967 $22434   (25-Mar-92 CH.R100/R) San Francesco e Santa Teresa donano il Cingolo a un
       santo (76x100cm-30x39in) (I.L 28000000)

NASMYTH, Alexander (1758-1840) British
£720 $1231   (18-Mar-92 CSK246) Hanging out the washing (58x76cm-23x30in) panel
£800 $1408   (8-Apr-92 S241/R) Landscape with thatchers (28x39cm-11x15in) s.verso
       panel
£1520 $2600   (13-Mar-92 WOL.C411 a/R) Thatched cottage beyond a field
       (30x41cm-12x16in) s.
£3500 $6685   (17-Jul-92 C82/R) Figures hanging out washing beside thatched cottage
       (35x48cm-14x19in) s.
£7000 $12460   (30-Apr-92 CG866/R) Duneira, Perthshire, looking west towards Loch Earn
       (38x52cm-15x20in)
£9000 $16110   (13-Nov-91 S70/R) Near Inver, Sutherlandshire (67x87cm-26x34in) s.

NASMYTH, Alexander (circle) (1758-1840) British
£800 $1424   (28-Apr-92 S133/R) River ferry, Perthshire (44x60cm-17x24in)
                 indist.s.i.d.1839verso panel
£980 $1744   (30-Apr-92 CSK60) Wooded landscape with figures by track (23x28cm-9x11in)
                 panel
£3000 $5730   (17-Jul-92 C36/R) Bay hunter with groom by stableyard entrance
                 (63x76cm-25x30in)
£3500 $6230   (28-Apr-92 S122/R) Footbridge. Lochside (43x61cm-17x24in) pair
£5000 $8800   (10-Apr-92 C21/R) The toast (63x76cm-25x30in)

NASMYTH, Charlotte (1804-1884) British
£550 $963   (24-Sep-91 OT450) Figures on a track in a wooded mountainous landscape by
                 stream (32x27cm-13x11in)
£1300 $2314   (28-Apr-92 S127/R) View in North Wales (46x61cm-18x24in) s.d.1857

NASMYTH, James (1808-1890) British
£540 $961   (28-Apr-92 PH94) Helen's Island, Loch Katrine (29x39cm-11x15in) i.verso
                 d.1888 panel

NASMYTH, P (1787-1831) British
£600 $1092   (12-Dec-91 GSP520) Woodland landscape with stream and bridge, two figures
                 on bank (43x58cm-17x23in)

NASMYTH, Patrick (1787-1831) British
£550 $1018   (11-Jun-92 CSK84) Angler in river landscape (17x22cm-7x9in) panel
£550 $995   (4-Dec-91 S124/R) Road through woods (28x38cm-11x15in) s.d.1817 panel
£676 $1210   (14-Nov-91 GRO.B19) Ducks by river (53x79cm-21x31in)
£740 $1265   (17-Mar-92 SWS1215) An undershot mill (39x49cm-15x19in) panel
£1500 $2640   (8-Apr-92 S240/R) Landscape with cottage by path (27x36cm-11x14in) panel
£2400 $4128   (8-Oct-91 PH17) Boats on a river (40x54cm-16x21in) s.d.1818
£8800 $15752   (15-Nov-91 C202/R) View in Hampshire (40x49cm-16x19in) s.d.1826 i.verso
                 panel

NASMYTH, Patrick (attrib) (1787-1831) British
£900 $1548   (8-Oct-91 PH4/R) Figures on a wooded path, landscape beyond
                 (22x30cm-9x12in) panel
£1300 $2210   (24-Oct-91 CSK94/R) Figures on a track by a cottage, a shepherd with
                 sheep beyond (25x30cm-10x12in) sig. panel

NASON, Pieter (1612-1688) Dutch
£2510 $4292   (12-Mar-92 GK.Z34/R) Portrait of gentleman before red drapes
                 (87x69cm-34x27in) (S.FR 6500)
£2949 $5250   (22-Jan-92 D.NY56) Sir John Chardin (86x69cm-34x27in)

NASON, Pieter (style) (1612-1688) Dutch
£1760 $3062   (13-Sep-91 C132/R) Portrait of Charles II, wearing armour and white lace
                 collar (75x61cm-30x24in) oval

NASS, Christian (1888-1931) German
£704 $1275   (3-Dec-91 FN.S1861/R) Renninger See landscape with thunderstorm rising
                 (82x74cm-32x29in) s.d.1919 (DM 2000)

NAST, Thomas (1840-1902) American
£1829 $3200   (26-Sep-91 CH.NY4/R) Capture of Works at Petersburg. General Thomas
                 (74x53cm-29x21in) one s.d.1/64 oil paper wash pen pair
£618 $1100   (2-Nov-91 IH.NY159/R) Ploughing the fields for corruption (18x20cm-7x8in)
                 s. pen
£2171 $3800   (26-Sep-91 CH.NY3/R) Attack on Knoxville. General Sherman
                 (36x51cm-14x20in) one s.d.3/64 wash pen oil pair

NATALI, Renato (1883-?) Italian
£905 $1647   (26-May-92 SY.MI53) Vecchia strada di Liguria (65x27cm-26x11in) s.
                 s.i.verso masonite (I.L 2000000)
£1812 $3352   (9-Jun-92 F.R119) Sera in pineta (35x50cm-14x20in) s. panel (I.L 4000000)
£1852 $3205   (24-Mar-92 CH.R36) Paesaggio marino. Vecchia Livorno. Notturno
                 (20x24cm-8x9in) s. s.i.verso masonite three in one frame (I.L 4000000)
£2138 $3656   (19-Mar-92 F.M47/R) La case del musicista Pietro Mascagni a Livorno
                 (49x35cm-19x14in) s. panel (I.L 4600000)
£3171 $5866   (9-Jun-92 F.R91/R) Caccia in pineta (70x100cm-28x39in) s. (I.L 7000000)

NATIVI, Gualtiero (1921-) Italian
£1634 $2909   (29-Apr-92 F.F213/R) Composizione (70x80cm-28x31in) s. s.d.1988verso
                 (I.L 3600000)

NATKIN, Robert (1930-) American
£559 $1000   (12-Nov-91 CE.NY76/R) Untitled, Bern Series (78x60cm-31x24in) s. acrylic
£647 $1100   (23-Oct-91 B.SF3710/R) Untitled, from the Portico Period
                 (50x41cm-20x16in) s.d.62 acrylic paper
£946 $1750   (12-Jun-92 SY.NY238/R) Untitled (63x72cm-25x28in) acrylic
£1351 $2500   (12-Jun-92 SY.NY237/R) Untitled (228x137cm-90x54in) s.d.1966 acrylic
£1676 $3000   (9-May-92 CE.NY357/R) Untitled (86x86cm-34x34in) s. acrylic
£1714 $3000   (27-Feb-92 CE.NY204/R) Untitled (51x66cm-20x26in) s. s.d.1967 verso
                 acrylic canvas
£2762 $4750   (12-Oct-91 SY.NY350/R) For Madame Fong (221x244cm-87x96in) s. acrylic
                 canvas

NATKIN, Robert (1930-) American-cont.
£2838	$5250	(12-Jun-92 SY.NY235/R) Festival No.2 (152x121cm-60x48in) s. acrylic
£3352	$6000	(9-May-92 CE.NY350/R) Bern series (132x132cm-52x52in) s. acrylic
£5143	$9000	(27-Feb-92 CE.NY205/R) Napolian's tryst (193x218cm-76x86in) s. s.d.1970 stretcher acrylic canvas
£6145	$11000	(12-Nov-91 CE.NY51/R) Intimate light, yellow (168x127cm-66x50in) s. acrylic
£389	$700	(10-Jan-92 DM.D2020/R) Enchanted (61x56cm-24x22in) s.d.1965 W/C
£1210	$2093	(4-Oct-91 CSC.P43) Intimate brighting suite 2 (73x52cm-29x20in) s.d. mixed media (F.FR 12000)

NATOIRE, Charles-Joseph (1700-1777) French
£12000	$23040	(8-Jul-92 S66/R) Allegory of the glory of a prince accompanied by Immortality (116x112cm-46x44in)
£374302	$670000	(16-Jan-92 CH.NY126/R) Hunter and young woman resting in landscape. Hunters on horseback, conversing with two women (101x84cm-40x33in) pair
£1236	$2113	(20-Mar-92 ZZ.F1) Vierge a l'Enfant (23x17cm-9x7in) i. blk.crayon htd.white (F.FR 12000)
£2764	$4919	(29-Nov-91 ARC.P21) Thermes de Titus (31x49cm-12x19in) i. pen wash (F.FR 27000)
£3889	$6923	(29-Nov-91 ARC.P14) Le sacrifice d'Iphigenie (25x37cm-10x15in) s.d.1737 pen pierre noire wash htd.white (F.FR 38000)
£4077	$7584	(20-Jun-92 CH.MO232/R) La Vierge apparaissant a Saint Dominique et Sainte Catherine de Sienne (38x25cm-15x10in) i. chk ink wash (F.FR 40000)
£15400	$27721	(22-Nov-91 AGS.P122/R) Le Lavoir de Marino (31x45cm-12x18in) s.d.20 Juin 176. pierre noire W/C htd.gouache (F.FR 150000)

NATOIRE, Charles-Joseph (attrib) (1700-1777) French
| £1017 | $1862 | (15-May-92 AT.P183/R) L'Ascension de la Vierge (55x42cm-22x17in) sanguine (F.FR 10000) |

NATON, Avraham (20th C) Israeli
| £957 | $1800 | (5-Jan-92 GG.TA289/R) Still life (38x46cm-15x18in) s. |
| £1027 | $1900 | (9-Jun-92 GG.TA399/R) Women in landscape (35x45cm-14x18in) s. gouache |

NATTIER, Jean Marc (1685-1766) French
£24862	$45000	(22-May-92 SY.NY90/R) Portrait of Louis Le Dauphin, Battle of Fontenoy beyond (136x104cm-54x41in) painted with studio
£26000	$49920	(10-Jul-92 C24/R) Portrait of Jean Philippe d'Orleans, Grand Prieur de France (81x65cm-32x26in) painted with studio
£149171	$270000	(22-May-92 SY.NY43/R) Portrait of Madame Royer at ledge, holding mask and fan (81x64cm-32x25in) pastel paper on canvas

NATTIER, Jean Marc (after) (1685-1766) French
| £800 | $1424 | (31-Oct-91 B91) Portrait of Dauphin, wearing armour (61x50cm-24x20in) |

NATTIER, Jean Marc (attrib) (1685-1766) French
| £34530 | $62500 | (22-May-92 SY.NY71/R) Portrait of Madame de Pompadour in guise of Diana (122x97cm-48x38in) s.d. painted with studio |

NATTIER, Jean Marc (studio) (1685-1766) French
| £10173 | $18210 | (15-Nov-91 SD.P14/R) Portrait de Madame Dupin (56x46cm-22x18in) (F.FR 100000) |

NATTIER, Jean Marc (style) (1685-1766) French
| £2584 | $4728 | (12-May-92 SY.AM50/R) Portrait of Louise de Bourbon (67x54cm-26x21in) oval (D.FL 8500) |
| £3743 | $6774 | (3-Dec-91 AB.S4738/R) Allegorical portrait with woman and putti (128x101cm-50x40in) (S.KR 39000) |

NATTRESS, George (fl.1866-1888) British
| £1500 | $2670 | (29-Oct-91 C110/R) Sport at the Mill Pool. Cleve Mill near Goring on Thames s.i.d.1878,1876 pencil W/C htd white two |

NATUR, Jules Maurice le (1851-?) French
| £1512 | $2676 | (10-Nov-91 ZZ.F9/R) L'hirondelle messagere d'amour (22x16cm-9x6in) s.d.1881 (F.FR 15000) |

NAU, Armand (20th C) ?
| £2033 | $3537 | (13-Apr-92 GL.P199) Harmonie no.1 (196x97cm-77x38in) s. oil collage canvas (F.FR 20000) |

NAUDE, Hugo (1869-1941) South African
£566	$967	(12-Mar-92 SY.J393) Seascape (14x21cm-6x8in) s. board (SA.R 2800)
£1337	$2274	(21-Oct-91 SY.J335 a/R) Extensive landscape (20x28cm-8x11in) s. board (SA.R 6500)
£1352	$2352	(13-Apr-92 SY.J316/R) Port Edward (26x36cm-10x14in) s. board (SA.R 6800)
£1392	$2421	(13-Apr-92 SY.J319/R) Jonkershoek, Stellenbosch (17x26cm-7x10in) init. board (SA.R 7000)
£2000	$3400	(22-Oct-91 C63) Cape landscape. Evening light on low hills (25x36cm-10x14in) s. board pair
£2020	$3455	(12-Mar-92 SY.J394/R) Battersea Power Station. Albert Bridge (14x20cm-6x8in) init. board pair (SA.R 10000)
£2323	$3973	(12-Mar-92 SY.J397/R) Hermanus (34x40cm-13x16in) canvasboard (SA.R 11500)

1312

NAUDE, Hugo (1869-1941) South African-cont.
£2621	$4639	(4-Nov-91 SY.J287/R) Wisteria on the artist's studio pergola (44x34cm-17x13in) s. board (SA.R 13000)
£2982	$5189	(13-Apr-92 SY.J317/R) Landscape, Drakensberg (25x30cm-10x12in) s. board (SA.R 15000)
£3629	$6423	(4-Nov-91 SY.J289/R) Valley of Thousand Hills (39x56cm-15x22in) s. canvas on board (SA.R 18000)
£3636	$6218	(12-Mar-92 SY.J391/R) Courtyard with figure and chickens (25x29cm-10x11in) init. board (SA.R 18000)
£4115	$6996	(21-Oct-91 SY.J332/R) Bo-Kapp Street scene (24x29cm-9x11in) s. board (SA.R 20000)
£14113	$24980	(4-Nov-91 SY.J288/R) Washday beside the Hex river (54x72cm-21x28in) s. canvas on board (SA.R 70000)
£806	*$1427*	*(4-Nov-91 SY.J310 b) Worcester Mountains (25x32cm-10x13in) pastel (SA.R 4000)*

NAUER, Adolph (1886-?) Belgian
| £557 | $1015 | (12-Dec-91 N.M2806) Herrenrunde (51x61cm-20x24in) s. (DM 1600) |

NAUJOKS, Heino (1937-) German
| £1469 | $2614 | (26-Nov-91 KF.M905/R) The trumpeter (85x82cm-33x32in) s.i.d.1985verso acrylic (DM 4200) |
| *£1024* | *$1863* | *(26-May-92 KF.M1108/R) Untitled (59x70cm-23x28in) s.d.1968 collage gouache (DM 3000)* |

NAUMAN, Bruce (1941-) American
£4469	$8000	(13-Nov-91 CH.NY266/R) Rats underfoot (57x75cm-22x30in) s.d.1988 col.photos tape paper collage
£8380	$15000	(13-Nov-91 CH.NY265/R) No/on (44x72cm-17x28in) s.d.84 W/C chl.graphite ink
£44693	$80000	(14-Nov-91 SY.NY182/R) Violins, violence, silence (134x154cm-53x61in) s.d.81 lead pencil chl pastel taped paper

NAUMANN, Carl Friedrich (1813-1859) German
| £407 | $737 | (21-May-92 GK.Z1743/R) Portrait of lady wearing pearl earrings and silk dress with white lace (9x7cm-4x3in) min.s. oval gold bronze frame (S.FR 1100) |

NAUR, Albert (1889-1973) Danish
| £805 | $1465 | (10-Dec-91 RAS.K247) Woman in green landscape (124x141cm-49x56in) s.d.57 (D.KR 9000) |

NAVARRA, Pietro (attrib) (17/18th C) Italian
| £6630 | $12000 | (22-May-92 SY.NY308/R) Still life of fruits and glassware on ledge (72x101cm-28x40in) bears mono. |
| £8380 | $15000 | (17-Jan-92 SY.NY140/R) Still life of fruit and game in landscape with roosters and guinea pig (73x98cm-29x39in) |

NAVARRA, Pietro (circle) (17/18th C) Italian
| £4907 | $9323 | (23-Jun-92 D.V49/R) Still life with melon, figs, peaches and grapes (61x75cm-24x30in) (A.S 100000) |

NAVARRO LLORENS, Jose (1867-1923) Spanish
£2454	$4564	(16-Jun-92 EP.M29/R) Pastora con su rebano (47x53cm-19x21in) s. (S.P 450000)
£8748	$16009	(13-May-92 FER.M117/R) Moros (24x35cm-9x14in) s. (S.P 1600000)
£10357	$17814	(7-Oct-91 ANS.M101/R) Portada churrigueresca (32x22cm-13x9in) s. (S.P 1900000)

NAVARRO VIVES, Josep (1931-) Spanish
| £930 | $1656 | (29-Oct-91 BRO.B366) Barca (54x73cm-21x29in) s.d.81 (S.P 170000) |

NAVARRO, Jose (19th C) Spanish
| £32796 | $55753 | (22-Oct-91 DUR.M58/R) Ciudad costera (33x47cm-13x19in) s.d.1901 (S.P 6000000) |

NAVAZIO, Walter de (1887-1921) Argentinian
£1222	$2200	(20-Nov-91 V.BA66) Plenilunio (23x21cm-9x8in) tempera
£1264	$2300	(11-Dec-91 RO.BA235) Paisaje Serrano (30x37cm-12x15in) s.
£4301	$8000	(16-Jun-92 RO.BA71) Primavera (26x35cm-10x14in) panel
£15054	$28000	(16-Jun-92 RO.BA63) Paisaje (80x90cm-31x35in)
£26882	$50000	(16-Jun-92 RO.BA48) Paisaje con desnudo (73x93cm-29x37in)
£29775	$53000	(1-Nov-91 PO.BA42) Jardin gris (72x102cm-28x40in) s.d.1913

NAVEZ, Francois Joseph (1787-1869) Belgian
| £2599 | $4601 | (5-Nov-91 SY.AM342) Doubting Thomas (238x172cm-94x68in) s.d.1823 (D.FL 8500) |

NAVEZ, Leon (1900-1967) Belgian
| £828 | $1498 | (23-May-92 KV.L232) Flowers in blue vase (50x40cm-20x16in) s. (B.FR 50000) |
| £4663 | $8673 | (16-Jun-92 SY.B346/R) An allegory (118x98cm-46x39in) s.d. (B.FR 280000) |

NAVIASKY, Philip (1894-) British
£1000 $1820   (10-Dec-91 HAR781/R) Portrait of lady in green dress (114x86cm-45x34in) s.

NAVONE, Edoardo (19th C) Italian
£1000 $1810   (21-May-92 CSK88/R) Swing (48x23cm-19x9in) s.i. pencil W/C

NAY, Ernst Wilhelm (1902-1968) German
£105000 $190050 (5-Dec-91 C11/R) Gabelungen (100x120cm-39x47in) s.d.53 i.stretcher
£153584 $279522 (29-May-92 VG.B81/R) Magisch 3 (162x140cm-64x55in) s.d.1965 i.stretcher (DM 450000)
£1474 $2653   (19-Nov-91 L.K963/R) Untitled (16x24cm-6x9in) s.i.d.1942 pencil (DM 4200)
£1748 $3112   (30-Nov-91 VG.B315/R) Reclining female nude. Study of female nude standing (27x55cm-11x22in) s.d.1928 brush (DM 5000)
£3780 $6918   (2-Jun-92 L.K829/R) Untitled (49x63cm-19x25in) s.d.1955 indian ink brush (DM 11000)
£5155 $9536   (11-Jun-91 HN.H348) Woman with bird (61x43cm-24x17in) s.d.1947 i.d.verso chl (DM 15000)
£18531 $32986   (25-Nov-91 WK.M758/R) Von Grau umschlossen (42x60cm-17x24in) s.d.1955 s.verso W/C (DM 53000)

NAYLOR, Mrs Hare and FLAXMAN, John (attrib) (18/19th C) British
£5000 $8800   (7-Apr-92 C20/R) Panoramic view of Bologna (30x142cm-12x56in) pencil pen W/C three joined sheets

NEAGLE, John (1796-1865) American
£1117 $2000   (14-Nov-91 CE.NY29/R) Portrait of Joseph C Neal (51x43cm-20x17in) init.i.d.1867

NEAGLE, John (attrib) (1796-1865) American
£615 $1100   (14-Nov-91 CE.NY9/R) Little girl with basket of flowers (56x68cm-22x27in)

NEALE, Edward (19/20th C) British
£3800 $6764   (28-Apr-92 S217/R) Ptarmigan (91x74cm-36x29in) s.d.1869
£850 $1488   (25-Feb-92 C126/R) Blackgame (36x31cm-14x12in) init.d.1871 pencil W/C

NEAPOLITAN SCHOOL (?) Italian
£3867 $7000   (22-May-92 SY.NY168/R) Still life of flowers in bowl on ledge in landscape, with funghi and parrot (64x86cm-25x34in) c.1800
£3867 $7000   (22-May-92 SY.NY208/R) Christ in temple (113x151cm-44x59in) c.1700
£4696 $8500   (22-May-92 SY.NY178/R) Battle scene with soldiers preparing to scale wall (44x61cm-17x24in)
£4942 $8500   (10-Oct-91 SY.NY19/R) Peasants celebrating epiphany night (47x61cm-19x24in) c.1800
£8939 $16000   (17-Jan-92 SY.NY174/R) Still life of roses and other flowers in elaborate gilt urn (65x48cm-26x19in) c.1700
£17000 $30260 (30-Oct-91 S47/R) Figures in river landscape (148x220cm-58x87in) c.1700
£18519 $33519 (5-Dec-91 SY.MO163/R) Vases de fleurs (96x36cm-38x14in) c.1700 pair (F.FR 180000)
£2000 $3560   (28-Nov-91 CSK64 b) Vesuvius erupting by day and by night (36x48cm-14x19in) W/C 13 in one frame
£3200 $5696   (28-Nov-91 CSK64 c) Ruins off the coast. Figures in Naples Harbour (51x71cm-20x28in) bodycol pair
£5405 $9243   (12-Mar-92 GK.Z116/R) Views of Naples (33x46cm-13x18in) i. gouache pair (S.FR 14000)

NEAPOLITAN SCHOOL, 16th C Italian
£19553 $35000 (17-Jan-92 SY.NY102/R) Madonna and Child in glory (133x65cm-52x26in) tempera panel arched top

NEAPOLITAN SCHOOL, 17th C Italian
£1907 $3394   (28-Apr-92 F.R36/R) Vaso di fiori con bambina e cane (47x36cm-19x14in) (I.L 4200000)
£2094 $4000   (16-Jul-92 SY.NY35/R) Madonna and Child (95x72cm-37x28in)
£2321 $4177   (19-Nov-91 F.R104) Vaso di fiori (53x39cm-21x15in) (I.L 5000000)
£2400 $4608   (9-Jul-92 B101/R) Holy Family (114x156cm-45x61in)
£2854 $5309   (18-Jun-92 SY.MO270/R) Scene religieuse (97x135cm-38x53in) (F.FR 28000)
£3394 $6178   (28-May-92 F.M18) Giuditta con la testa di Oloferne (77x62cm-30x24in) (I.L 7500000)
£3400 $5950   (1-Apr-92 S185/R) Saint John the Baptist (98x58cm-39x23in)
£6200 $11904 (9-Jul-92 B139/R) Capriccio view of Mediterranean harbour with merchants on quayside (174x231cm-69x91in)
£7202 $13035 (5-Dec-91 SY.MO280/R) Paysage avec riviere et personne (148x198cm-58x78in) (F.FR 70000)
£7500 $14400 (8-Jul-92 S317) St Jerome (93x111cm-37x44in)
£8114 $14280 (11-Apr-92 AT.P17/R) Putti et ange portant des guirlandes de fleurs (100x71cm-39x28in) circle of Abraham Brueghel (F.FR 80000)
£9274 $16415 (10-Nov-91 ZZ.F76/R) Bouquet de fleurs dans un vase (65x54cm-26x21in) pair (F.FR 92000)
£12000 $21000 (1-Apr-92 S164/R) Maid pouring wine next to dish of water melons (80x103cm-31x41in)
£12800 $22400 (26-Feb-92 MMB312/R) Five skulls (41x51cm-16x20in)
£15000 $27300 (10-Dec-91 PH6/R) Panoramic views of Porto Ferraio, before and after refortification (86x115cm-34x45in) pair

NEAPOLITAN SCHOOL, 17th C Italian-cont.

£17177	$31091	(18-May-92 SY.MI234/R) Natura morta con fiori e frutta (61x74cm-24x29in) (I.L 38000000)
£19871	$33979	(18-Mar-92 D.V10 b/R) Christ and the Apostles in Emmaus (99x119cm-39x47in) (A.S 400000)
£28542	$53089	(18-Jun-92 SY.MO140/R) Natures mortes aux fruits (73x95cm-29x37in) pair (F.FR 280000)
£35912	$65000	(21-May-92 CH.NY80/R) Saint John the Baptist in Wilderness (99x134cm-39x53in)

NEAPOLITAN SCHOOL, 18th C Italian

£2107	$3750	(30-Oct-91 D.NY45) View of Bay of Naples (51x71cm-20x28in) mono
£2138	$3870	(3-Dec-91 SY.MI225/R) Fantasia architettonica con una veduta di porto (49x33cm-19x13in) (I.L 4600000)
£2218	$4036	(28-May-92 F.M4) Scena di porto con rovine antiche (77x51cm-30x20in) (I.L 4900000)
£2712	$4909	(18-May-92 SY.MI221/R) Madonna col Bambino (70x60cm-28x24in) (I.L 6000000)
£3000	$5400	(22-Nov-91 SWS125) St. Jerome (98x72cm-39x28in)
£3198	$5500	(9-Oct-91 CH.NY34/R) Hercules slaying Hydra (66x105cm-26x41in) background painted gold panel
£3254	$5889	(5-Dec-91 F.M19) Paesaggio fluviale con rovine e pastori (67x96cm-26x38in) panel (I.L 7000000)
£4000	$7680	(8-Jul-92 S148/R) Landscape with peasants at table (60x73cm-24x29in)
£4144	$7500	(21-May-92 CH.NY192/R) Portrait of artist, holding palette, brushes and baton (72x57cm-28x22in) i.
£4651	$8000	(10-Oct-91 SY.NY78/R) Still life with flowers and grapes (53x66cm-21x26in)
£5523	$9500	(10-Oct-91 SY.NY132/R) Immacualate conception (62x49cm-24x19in)
£5876	$10636	(18-May-92 SY.MI286/R) Scena di Olimpo (74x50cm-29x20in) (I.L 13000000)
£6972	$12619	(3-Dec-91 SY.MI236/R) Fantasie architettoniche con vedute di porti (49x97cm-19x38in) pair (I.L 15000000)
£7000	$12740	(11-Dec-91 S111/R) Putti with doves and birdcage. Putti beside pool (34x23cm-13x9in) copper shaped pair
£8200	$14596	(30-Oct-91 S182/R) Bay of Naples seen from Posilipo (88x111cm-35x44in)
£9361	$16757	(14-Nov-91 ANS.M82/R) Bodegon de caza (44x57cm-17x22in) (S.P 1700000)
£10225	$18508	(5-Dec-91 F.M58/R) Natura morta con vaso metallico e fiori (43x30cm-17x12in) (I.L 22000000)
£12209	$21000	(10-Oct-91 SY.NY79/R) Capricci with figures among classical ruins (129x93cm-51x37in) pair

NEAPOLITAN SCHOOL, 19/20th C Italian

£4200	*$7182*	*(18-Mar-92 S155/R) View of Naples from the rock of Frisio. View of Naples from Carmine (27x41cm-11x16in) gouache pair*

NEAPOLITAN SCHOOL, 19th C Italian

£506	$905	(14-Nov-91 CH.R94) Mercatino a Porta Capuana (17x21cm-7x8in) panel (I.L 1100000)
£1400	$2422	(4-Oct-91 C160/R) Island of Nisida near Posilipo (26x38cm-10x15in) paper
£3902	$6790	(19-Sep-91 D.V80/R) Family gathered around fire (77x68cm-30x27in) canvas on panel (A.S 80000)
£4500	$8370	(17-Jun-92 S605/R) Views of Bay of Naples (44x64cm-17x25in) gouache pair
£5200	$9672	(16-Jun-92 PH55/R) Figures with cattle in coastal landscapes (51x68cm-20x27in) pair
£6000	$10260	(18-Mar-92 S150/R) View of Naples and Vesuvius (37x61cm-15x24in)
£9756	$16976	(19-Sep-91 D.V17/R) The conquest of Messina in September 1848 (35x59cm-14x23in) (A.S 200000)
£21298	$37485	(10-Apr-92 AT.P69/R) Scenes de la quotidienne (19x14cm-7x6in) paper laid down on board sixteen (F.FR 210000)
£2007	*$3593*	*(6-May-92 GD.B925/R) Napoli dal carmine (46x68cm-18x27in) gouache (S.FR 5500)*
£2007	*$3593*	*(6-May-92 GD.B926/R) S. Lucia (48x66cm-19x26in) gouache (S.FR 5500)*
£2117	*$3789*	*(6-May-92 GD.B927/R) Napoli da Posilipo (49x67cm-19x26in) gouache (S.FR 5800)*
£2296	*$4156*	*(19-May-92 GF.L2211/R) Austrian Navy in Bay of Naples, morning of May 4th, 1821 (45x61cm-18x24in) indis.s.i.d. W/C over indian ink (S.FR 6200)*
£2299	*$4116*	*(6-May-92 GD.B924) Il molo di Napoli (49x66cm-19x26in) gouache (S.FR 6300)*
£2500	*$4375*	*(23-Sep-91 PHB5/R) The Bay of Naples with Vesuvius erupting (51x73cm-20x29in) i. W/C bodycol.*
£2905	*$5055*	*(14-Apr-92 SY.AM63/R) Strolling on quay in Naples, Vesuvius in background (45x65cm-18x26in) gouache (D.FL 9500)*
£4281	*$7450*	*(14-Apr-92 SY.AM420/R) View of Capri. View of Amalfi seen from grotto (55x76cm-22x30in) gouache pair (D.FL 14000)*
£4893	*$9101*	*(19-Jun-92 CN.P46/R) La ville de Naples vue de Capodimonte. La ville de Naples vue de la mer (43x64cm-17x25in) gouache pair (F.FR 48000)*
£5000	*$8850*	*(14-Feb-92 C118/R) Torre del Greco distrutta dall'Eruzione del 1794. Spettacolo notturno bodycol. two*
£6200	*$10726*	*(4-Oct-91 C143/R) Veduta di Napoli da Capodimonte. Veduta di Napoli da mare (47x69cm-19x27in) i. bodycol pair*
£6500	*$11765*	*(22-May-92 C223 d/R) Album of views of Naples and environs, Pompei, Capri, Etna and Catania (11x17cm-4x7in) i. W/C bodycol in album*

NEBBIA, Cesare (1536-1614) Italian
£1676 $3000   (14-Jan-92 SY.NY75/R) Angel (15x12cm-6x5in) pen wash over black chk

NEBEL, Kay Heinrich (1888-1953) German
£1060 $1855   (3-Apr-92 BM.B878/R) Women in garden (50x38cm-20x15in) canvas on board
    (DM 3000)
£1060 $1855   (3-Apr-92 BM.B880) Field landscape, spring (54x44cm-21x17in) (DM 3000)
£1060 $1855   (3-Apr-92 BM.B879/R) Cherry tree in spring (36x24cm-14x9in)
    s.d.1934/44verso panel (DM 3000)
£424 $742   (3-Apr-92 BM.B892) Camelia and bird (36x49cm-14x19in) s.d.1952 W/C indian
    ink pen over pencil (DM 1200)
£530 $928   (3-Apr-92 BM.B893/R) Persian horses (35x35cm-14x14in) W/C (DM 1500)
£601 $1051   (3-Apr-92 BM.B882/R) Cattle watering (35x45cm-14x18in) s.i.d.1929 W/C
    (DM 1700)

NEBEL, Otto (1892-1975) German
£3939 $7130   (19-May-92 CH.AM206/R) Vielgestaltig No.514 (42x27cm-17x11in) s.i.d.1937
    tempera paper (D.FL 13000)
£3953 $7036   (29-Nov-91 GAB.G2816 b) Winterlausser (38x51cm-15x20in) s.d.1969 paper
    (S.FR 10000)
£1193 $2147   (21-Nov-91 L.K354) Aufwuhlend (18x18cm-7x7in) s.d.1948 collage offset
    prints paper on board (DM 3400)
£1615 $3069   (25-Jun-92 GK.B519) Unbeirrbar hoffnungsreich. Hirtengedanken s.i.d.1948
    W/C indian ink two (S.FR 4200)
£1615 $3069   (25-Jun-92 GK.B520) Geschwinde Auflichtung (33x23cm-13x9in) s.d.
    s.i.d.1948 W/C (S.FR 4200)
£1793 $3245   (5-Dec-91 SY.Z145/R) Lyrisches Sinngefuge (23x31cm-9x12in) s.s.i.d.1942
    W/C indian ink (S.FR 4500)

NEDER, Johann Michael (1807-1882) Austrian
£5859 $9961   (24-Oct-91 D.V191/R) In the cowshed (33x46cm-13x18in) s.d.1868 panel
    (A.S 120000)
£9695 $17644   (27-May-92 D.V543/R) Figures making music in pub garden (23x29cm-9x11in)
    s.d.1839 i.d.verso panel (A.S 200000)
£10664 $19409   (27-May-92 D.V544/R) The tired boozers (23x29cm-9x11in) s.d.1839
    i.d.verso panel (A.S 220000)
£733 $1260   (10-Oct-91 D.V108/R) Portrait of seated gentleman with dog
    (40x28cm-16x11in) pencil (A.S 15000)

NEDER, Johann Michael (circle) (1807-1882) Austrian
£1384 $2422   (20-Feb-92 D.V373) Interior with figures (36x46cm-14x18in) (A.S 28000)

NEDERGAARD, Niels (20th C) Scandinavian
£890 $1548   (18-Sep-91 KH.K159) Composition (57x57cm-22x22in) acrylic (D.KR 10000)
£995 $1802   (4-Dec-91 KH.K176/R) Composition (63x42cm-25x17in) s.d.1984 gouache
    (D.KR 11000)

NEEFE, Hermann Joseph (1790-1854) German
£586 $996   (24-Oct-91 D.V195/R) Interior of monastery (49x62cm-19x24in) s.d.1850
    (A.S 12000)

NEEFFS, Pieter (circle) (16/17th C) Flemish
£4133 $7316   (6-Nov-91 LT.P48/R) Inteieur d'eglise avec procession (40x56cm-16x22in)
    trace sig. (F.FR 41000)

NEEFFS, Pieter (elder) (1578-1658) Flemish
£5361 $9274   (27-Mar-92 CD.P2/R) Interieur de la cathedrale d'Anvers. Interieur
    d'eglise (6x9cm-2x4in) mono. copper pair (F.FR 52000)
£9300 $16461   (7-Nov-91 D.V162/R) Interior of Antwerp Cathedral (43x59cm-17x23in) s.
    (A.S 190000)
£12346 $22346   (5-Dec-91 SY.MO272/R) Interieur d'eglise avec personnage
    (74x106cm-29x42in) panel (F.FR 120000)
£15432 $27623   (12-Nov-91 SY.AM77/R) Capriccio of interior of S.Giovanni in Laterano,
    Rome (75x106cm-30x42in) bears sig. panel (D.FL 50000)
£16022 $29000   (22-May-92 SY.NY16/R) Interior of Gothic church (43x63cm-17x25in) s.
    panel
£18000 $31500   (1-Apr-92 S29/R) Gothic church interior (43x59cm-17x23in) s.
£22000 $39160   (30-Oct-91 S6/R) Interior of Antwerp Cathedral (39x51cm-15x20in) panel

NEEFFS, Pieter (elder-circle) (1578-1658) Flemish
£2907 $5000   (10-Oct-91 SY.NY120/R) Church interior (83x103cm-33x41in)
£5618 $9831   (24-Feb-92 CSC.P32/R) Interieur d'eglise avec procession
    (40x56cm-16x22in) trace sig. (F.FR 55000)

NEEFFS, Pieter (elder-style) (1578-1658) Flemish
£2119 $3750   (13-Feb-92 S.W2681/R) Cathedral interior (58x84cm-23x33in)
£2646 $4709   (28-Apr-92 RAS.K343/R) Gothic cathedral interior with figures
    (27x21cm-11x8in) i. panel (D.KR 30000)
£12000 $23040   (8-Jul-92 S237/R) Church interior (31x44cm-12x17in) bears sig. panel

NEEFFS, Pieter (style) (16/17th C) Flemish
£2006 $3591   (12-Nov-91 SY.AM155/R) Church interior (49x63cm-19x25in) i. (D.FL 6500)

NEEFFS, Pieter (younger) (1620-1675) Flemish
£2200 $4004   (10-Dec-91 PH173/R) Interior of church with figures (20x37cm-8x15in)
                     panel
£7407 $13407   (3-Dec-91 CN.P71/R) Interieur d'eglise (31x43cm-12x17in) panel
                     (F.FR 72000)
£7732 $13376   (27-Mar-92 CN.P47/R) Interieur d'eglise (32x42cm-13x17in) panel
                     (F.FR 75000)

NEEFFS, Pieter (younger-studio) (1620-1675) Flemish
£3800 $6840   (21-Nov-91 CSK200/R) Mass celebrated at night in side chapel of church
                     (41x57cm-16x22in) panel

NEEFFS, Pieter (younger-style) (1620-1675) Flemish
£3500 $6125   (3-Apr-92 C60/R) Interior of church with Christening party
                     (31x43cm-12x17in) with sig.

NEEL, Alice (1900-) American
£8000 $14000   (28-Feb-92 SY.NY355/R) Portrait of Edward Weiss (86x114cm-34x45in) s.d.76

NEELMEYER, S (19th C) ?
£1504 $2722   (5-Dec-91 D.V85) Fortified castle in river landscape (29x39cm-11x15in)
                     s.d.1849 (A.S 30000)

NEER, Aert van der (1603-1677) Dutch
£5195 $8832   (26-Oct-91 AL.W4) Landscape (52x81cm-20x32in) (P.Z 100000000)
£11000 $20020   (13-Dec-91 C206/R) River at dusk with fishing boats near village
                     (21x29cm-8x11in) mono.

NEER, Aert van der (attrib) (1603-1677) Dutch
£587 $1056   (19-Nov-91 RAS.K364/R) Moonlit landscape (22x17cm-9x7in) s. panel
                     (D.KR 6500)
£1284 $2350   (1-Jun-92 W.T1382/R) Moonlight at Haarlem (49x61cm-19x24in) mono panel
                     (C.D 2800)
£2405 $4186   (21-Sep-91 SA.A1712/R) Moonlit coastal landscape with Dutch town
                     (51x62cm-20x24in) (DM 7000)
£2982 $5368   (22-Nov-91 SA.A1511/R) Moonlit Dutch river landscape (50x76cm-20x30in)
                     panel (DM 8500)
£4633 $7923   (12-Mar-92 GK.Z79/R) Moonlit river landscape with fishermen and buildings
                     (43x61cm-17x24in) mono. panel (S.FR 12000)
£20000 $38400   (8-Jul-92 S59/R) Village in winter with peasants gathering faggots
                     (97x109cm-38x43in) mono

NEER, Aert van der (circle) (1603-1677) Dutch
£3000 $5250   (27-Feb-92 CSK130/R) Winter landscape with skaters by village
                     (32x49cm-13x19in) panel

NEER, Aert van der (style) (1603-1677) Dutch
£900 $1575   (3-Apr-92 C19) Wooded river landscape at night (32x45cm-13x18in) panel
£900 $1575   (1-Apr-92 S178) Moonlit estuary landscape (19x34cm-7x13in) panel
£931 $1685   (3-Dec-91 AB.S4739/R) Harbour scene with figures in moonlight
                     (19x23cm-7x9in) panel (S.KR 9700)
£1067 $1974   (13-Jun-92 CH.AM180) Gentlemen playing kolf on frozen river in village
                     (29x40cm-11x16in) panel (D.FL 3500)
£2200 $3828   (13-Sep-91 C157/R) Winter landscape with skaters and kolf players by
                     village (32x49cm-13x19in) panel
£2447 $4332   (7-Nov-91 D.V300/R) Moonlit Dutch canal landscape (51x62cm-20x24in)
                     c.1800 (A.S 50000)
£4200 $7350   (2-Apr-92 CSK86/R) Winter landscape with figures on frozen river
                     (43x58cm-17x23in) panel
£5226 $9512   (12-Dec-91 L.K126 a/R) Frozen landscape with ice skaters and village with
                     church (53x70cm-21x28in) panel (DM 15000)

NEER, Eglon Hendrik van der (1634-1703) Dutch
£994 $1800   (22-May-92 SY.NY304/R) Saint John the Baptist in Wilderness
                     (20x26cm-8x10in) indist.s. panel

NEER, Eglon Hendrik van der (circle) (1634-1703) Dutch
£15000 $26700   (1-Nov-91 C99/R) Portrait of young woman, glancing over shoulder
                     (42x34cm-17x13in)

NEERGAARD, Aline (19th C) Scandinavian
£1233 $2097   (8-Aug-91 RAS.V968/R) Still life of flowers in vase on ledge
                     (37x45cm-15x18in) s.d.1836 (D.KR 14000)

NEERGAARD, Hermania (1799-1874) Danish
£2107 $3750   (22-Jan-92 SY.NY430/R) Bird's nest on blossoming cherry bough
                     (18x16cm-7x6in) init.d.1871 panel
£4233 $7534   (28-Apr-92 RAS.K108/R) Garland of flowers (67x158cm-26x62in)
                     s.d.1860verso (D.KR 48000)

NEFKENS, Martinus Jacobus (1866-1941) Dutch
£559 $1000   (13-Nov-91 B.SF2225/R) Along the path (30x24cm-12x9in) s.

NEGRETTI, Jacopo see PALMA, Jacopo

NEGRI, Pietro (attrib) (c.1591-1661) Italian
£4409 $7937   (19-Nov-91 F.R93/R) Scena di seduzione (61x75cm-24x30in) (I.L 9500000)

NEHER, Michael (1798-1876) German
£17483 $31469   (21-Nov-91 D.V87/R) Karlsbrucke in Prag with view of Hradschin
                  (52x43cm-20x17in) s.d.1870 (A.S 350000)

NEHLIG, Victor (1830-1910) American
£1222 $2200   (22-Nov-91 S.BM43/R) House to let (25x20cm-10x8in) s.

NEHRING, Maciej (1901-1977) ?
£356 $648   (15-Dec-91 REM.W27) In a forest (48x39cm-19x15in) s. W/C (P.Z 7000000)

NEILLOT, Louis (1898-1973) French
£758 $1357   (10-May-92 LT.P33) Nu au bras leves, 1948 (46x33cm-18x13in) s.
                  (F.FR 7500)
£1243 $2200   (5-Nov-91 CE.NY88/R) Paysage (38x46cm-15x18in) s.d.71
£1339 $2289   (18-Mar-92 PIC.P82/R) Nature morte aux figues (46x55cm-18x22in) s.d.63
                  (F.FR 13000)
£1545 $2642   (18-Mar-92 PIC.P83) Venteuil au printemps (60x73cm-24x29in) s.
                  (F.FR 15000)
£2357 $4242   (2-Feb-92 ZZ.F148/R) Vue de la Guerne (39x46cm-15x18in) s. i.verso
                  (F.FR 23000)

NEILSON, Raymond Perry Rodgers (1881-1964) American
£678 $1200   (13-Feb-92 S.W2133/R) Chelsea lady and sweetheart roses (76x64cm-30x25in)
                  s.d.1945 i.verso
£9341 $17000   (27-May-92 SY.NY58/R) Before mirror (92x74cm-36x29in) s.

NEKRASSOV, Dimitri (1960-) Russian
£887 $1650   (17-Jun-92 ARC.P198/R) Anton Tchekhov a Yalta (65x46cm-26x18in) s.
                  (F.FR 8700)

NELCK, Annalies (1925-) French
£407 $737   (19-May-92 GF.L2855) Girl with cat (43x33cm-17x13in) s.d.1951 gouache
                  (S.FR 1100)

NELIMARKKA, Eero (1891-1977) Finnish
£1770 $3115   (12-Apr-92 HOR.H180) According to the Bible (78x53cm-31x21in) s.d.1954
                  (F.M 14000)
£1833 $3226   (12-Apr-92 HOR.H178) Snow in wood (82x66cm-32x26in) s.d.1956 (F.M 14500)
£1940 $3454   (1-Dec-91 HOR.H167/R) The last snow (45x46cm-18x18in) s.d.1921
                  (F.M 15000)
£2329 $4145   (1-Dec-91 HOR.H165) Landscape from Alaharma (56x66cm-22x26in) s.d.1945
                  (F.M 18000)
£2535 $4437   (25-Sep-91 HOR.H74) Hazy day (38x67cm-15x26in) s.d.1961 (F.M 18000)
£2587 $4605   (1-Dec-91 HOR.H164/R) Snow melting (46x88cm-18x35in) s.d.1957 (F.M 20000)
£2676 $4737   (6-Nov-91 HOR.H84) Winter's day (50x85cm-20x33in) s.d.1965 (F.M 19000)
£3161 $5563   (12-Apr-92 HOR.H179/R) The country side (45x55cm-18x22in) s.d.1927
                  (F.M 25000)
£5277 $9604   (11-Dec-91 HOR.H79) Town scene (53x70cm-21x28in) s. (F.M 41000)

NELLI, Ottaviano (attrib) (1370-1445) Italian
£40000 $72800   (10-Dec-91 PH56/R) Madonna and child accompanied by scenes of
                  crucifixion, annunciation and four saints (72x61cm-28x24in) panel gold
                  ground

NELLI, Pietro (1672-1740) Italian
£1585 $2933   (8-Jun-92 CH.R770) Ritratto di gentiluomo in abito nero, con una lettera
                  tra le mani (74x61cm-29x24in) (I.L 3500000)

NELLIUS, Martinus (fl.1670-1706) Dutch
£8207 $15018   (12-May-92 SY.AM32/R) Still life of oyster, pear with blackberries and
                  nuts beside roemer on ledge (30x24cm-12x9in) indist.s. panel
                  (D.FL 27000)

NELLIUS, Martinus (after) (fl.1670-1706) Dutch
£756 $1300   (16-Oct-91 D.NY75) Still life of plums and grapes on a silver charger
                  (28x33cm-11x13in) copper

NELSON, Joan (1958-) American
£5028 $9000   (13-Nov-91 CH.NY335/R) Untitled (41x38cm-16x15in) oil wax on masonite
£6145 $11000   (13-Nov-91 CH.NY321/R) Untitled (56x51cm-22x20in) s.d.1988verso oil wax
                  panel
£6704 $12000   (7-May-92 SY.NY213/R) Untitled no.194 (63x51cm-25x20in) s.d.1988
                  num.verso wood
£4571 $8000   (27-Feb-92 CH.NY122/R) Untitled (41x46cm-16x18in) s.d.85verso wax pigment
                  panel
£6145 $11000   (14-Nov-91 SY.NY337 a/R) Untitled - 66 (43x41cm-17x16in) s.d.1985 verso
                  wax pigment masonite
£6145 $11000   (7-May-92 SY.NY210/R) Untitled (102x122cm-40x48in) s.d.1984 verso egg
                  tempera plaster masonite

NEMES, Endre (1909-1985) Hungarian
£912 $1650   (3-Dec-91 AB.S5110/R) Piece of cake (29x38cm-11x15in) s. panel
           (S.KR 9500)
£664   *$1215*   *(13-May-92 BU.S127/R) From Verdun 1914 (40x32cm-16x13in) s.d.1963 mixed
           media collage (S.KR 7000)*

NEO-CLASSICAL SCHOOL, 19th C
£2012 $3461   (11-Oct-91 HC.P8/R) L'Amour endormi (30x40cm-12x16in) (F.FR 20000)

NEOGRADY, Antal (1861-1942) Hungarian
£646 $1157   (5-May-92 ZEL.L1466) Goose girl by stream (60x47cm-24x19in) s. (DM 1900)

NEOGRADY, Laszlo (1900-?) Hungarian
£680 $1218   (5-May-92 ZEL.L1467/R) Woman hanging up washing (49x60cm-19x24in) s.
           (DM 2000)
£750 $1298   (26-Mar-92 CSK5/R) On the coast (76x102cm-30x40in) s.
£750 $1328   (13-Feb-92 CSK90) Winter woodland (58x79cm-23x31in) s.
£753 $1296   (8-Oct-91 ZEL.L1630/R) Girl watching geese in wooded landscape with
           farmhouses (60x80cm-24x31in) s. (DM 2200)
£765 $1400   (17-May-92 DU.E1060/R) Snow scene with mountain and stream
           (61x91cm-24x36in) s.
£814 $1400   (20-Oct-91 HG.C60) Winter forest (61x91cm-24x36in) s.
£1047 $2000   (16-Jul-92 SY.NY458/R) Springtime (61x78cm-24x31in) s.

NEOUSTROEV, Serguei (1927-) Russian
£728 $1275   (5-Apr-92 ARC.P175) Le panier de fleurs (60x79cm-24x31in) s. (F.FR 7000)

NEPO, Ernst (1895-1971) Austrian
£798 $1428   (15-Jan-92 D.V94/R) Self portrait as boy (35x24cm-14x9in) board
           (A.S 16000)
£3972 $7071   (28-Nov-91 D.V152/R) Harvest festival with self portrait
           (86x128cm-34x50in) s.d.1927 (A.S 80000)

NEPOLSKY, Hermann (19/20th C) ?
£659 $1200   (13-Dec-91 S.W1444/R) Floral still life (99x84cm-39x33in) s.

NEPPEL, Heinrich (1874-?) German
£653 $1195   (3-Jun-92 DO.H2359/R) Cattle in lake landscape. Autumnal moor landscape
           with cattle (13x18cm-5x7in) s. board (DM 1900)
£687 $1196   (18-Sep-91 N.M637/R) Cows watering (24x36cm-9x14in) s. board (DM 2000)

NERDRUM, Odd (1944-) Norwegian
£15473 $27078   (25-Feb-92 UL.T222/R) Bidding farewell to the deceased
           (100x120cm-39x47in) (N.KR 175000)
£1667   *$3100*   *(15-Jun-92 B.O117/R) Young woman (57x47cm-22x19in) s.d.1964 pencil
           (N.KR 19000)*
£6023   *$10962*   *(14-Dec-91 BU.O43/R) Self portrait (81x68cm-32x27in) s.d.1981 mixed media
           (N.KR 68000)*

NERLI, Marchese Girolamo Ballatti (1863-1926) Italian
£1432 $2577   (19-Nov-91 JRL.S177/R) Female portrait (76x50cm-30x20in) s. board
           (A.D 3250)
£1542 $2744   (26-Nov-91 J.M197) Fisherman (89x49cm-35x19in) s. (A.D 3500)
£2388 $4275   (6-May-92 DS.W18/R) Amused (33x59cm-13x23in) s. i.verso (NZ.D 8000)
£705   *$1255*   *(26-Nov-91 J.M69) Stone steps (24x16cm-9x6in) s. W/C (A.D 1600)*
£1791   *$3206*   *(6-May-92 DS.W21/R) The old timer (46x36cm-18x14in) s. W/C (NZ.D 6000)*

NERLY, Friedrich (19th C) Italian/Austrian
£3000 $5370   (5-May-92 SWS437/R) The Piazzetta, Venice, by moonlight (61x77cm-24x30in)
           s.
£7266 $13806   (24-Jun-92 KM.K1207/R) Two masked men waiting for ghosts by Canale Grande
           in moonlight (140x130cm-55x51in) s. (DM 21000)
£651   *$1119*   *(11-Oct-91 AW.H1225/R) Ruins in Torcello near Venice (42x26cm-17x10in)
           mono.i.d.1834 pencil (DM 1900)*
£2329   *$4005*   *(11-Oct-91 AW.H1224/R) Piazza Sta Anastasia, Venice with view of church
           entrance (78x56cm-31x22in) s.i.d.1835 W/C gouache over pencil (DM 6800)*
£3873   *$7011*   *(4-Dec-91 DO.H2868/R) Coastal landscape near Terracina (74x104cm-29x41in)
           indian ink brush pen wash htd.white (DM 11000)*

NERLY, Friedrich (elder) (1807-1878) Italian/Austrian
£5212 $8913   (12-Mar-92 GK.Z115/R) Carneval scene in St Mark's Square, Venice
           (41x63cm-16x25in) (S.FR 13500)

NERLY, Friedrich (younger) (1824-1919) Italian
£2337   *$4113*   *(11-Apr-92 AW.H644/R) View of Amalfi, evening (33x49cm-13x19in) s.i. W/C
           gouache (DM 6800)*

NERONI, Bartolomeo (1500-C.1573) Italian
£11315 $20593   (28-May-92 F.M93/R) Sacra Famiglia (55x38cm-22x15in) panel (I.L 25000000)
£1600   *$2912*   *(11-Dec-91 PH248/R) The Procession of St James to execution
           (21x24cm-8x9in) pen wash over chk.*

NERTOBRIGA, F T de (?) ?
£720 $1296   (29-Jan-92 FER.M262) Prision y muerte de la pintura (37x48cm-15x19in) s.
           (S.P 130000)

NERUD, Josef Karl (1900-) German
£687 $1196   (19-Sep-91 N.M2794) Houses on Ibiza (97x56cm-38x22in) s.i. i.verso (DM 2000)

NESBITT, Frances E (1864-1934) British
£540 $934   (4-Sep-91 BT76/R) French street scene (51x36cm-20x14in) s. W/C
£560 $969   (26-Mar-92 ZZ.B875) The harbour, Pittenveen (25x36cm-10x14in) s.i. W/C
£600 $1038   (26-Mar-92 ZZ.B862) Interior view of St Mark's Venice (30x20cm-12x8in) init. W/C
£650 $1157   (29-Oct-91 C83/R) The Steps, Ufford (37x27cm-15x11in) s. i.d.1925verso pencil W/C
£860 $1488   (4-Sep-91 BT77) The Punch and Judy Show (30x23cm-12x9in) s. W/C
£980 $1695   (26-Mar-92 ZZ.B894) Dordrecht market woman selling vegetables (23x33cm-9x13in) i.d.91 W/C

NESBITT, John (1831-1904) British
£450 $806   (13-Nov-91 CG607/R) The Dean Bridge and the waters of Leith, Edinburgh (37x29cm-15x11in) s.d.1871 pencil W/C htd.white

NESBITT, Lowell (1933-) American
£474 $868   (13-May-92 BU.S128/R) Three jump-suits (76x76cm-30x30in) s.d.1974verso (S.KR 5000)
£946 $1750   (12-Jun-92 SY.NY278/R) Spring forest III (177x203cm-70x80in) s.i.d.1984 verso
£1073 $1900   (6-Nov-91 D.NY2/R) Grapes (77x77cm-30x30in) s. i.d.66verso i.stretcher
£1221 $2100   (12-Oct-91 SY.NY233/R) Mangrove shoots (163x198cm-64x78in) s.d.67 verso acrylic canvas
£1599 $2750   (12-Oct-91 SY.NY260/R) Amaryllis (96x76cm-38x30in) s.d.77 verso
£1676 $3000   (9-May-92 CE.NY370/R) Iris (196x196cm-77x77in) s.i.d.65verso acrylic
£1714 $3000   (28-Feb-92 SY.NY339/R) Parrot tulip on white (102x102cm-40x40in) s.d.79 verso
£2098 $3629   (28-Mar-92 BOD.P1001) Studio garden bench (100x100cm-39x39in) s.i.verso (DM 6000)
£2180 $3750   (12-Oct-91 SY.NY259/R) Red lily (159x223cm-63x88in) s.d.69
£4000 $7000   (25-Feb-92 SY.NY174/R) White and yellow Japanese iris on blue (102x183cm-40x72in) s.i.d.79verso

NESCH, Rolf (1893-?) German
£4096 $7454   (30-May-92 VG.B153/R) Flower pot in greenhouse. Landscape composition (39x45cm-15x18in) double-sided (DM 12000)
£420 $717   (21-Mar-92 WK.M408/R) Soaking wet (24x34cm-9x13in) s.i.d.1915 chl (DM 1200)
£447 $759   (26-Oct-91 WK.M478/R) Tod vor Arras beim Durchbruchversuch (33x25cm-13x10in) s.d.1915 i.d.verso chl board (DM 1300)
£2577 $4768   (12-Jun-92 HN.H644/R) Female nudes at the seaside (48x63cm-19x25in) s. chk (DM 7500)
£3387 $5859   (23-Mar-92 B.O97/R) Fish (58x45cm-23x18in) collage copper zinc (N.KR 38000)

NESPOLO, Ugo (1941-) Italian
£1012 $1811   (14-Nov-91 F.M32) Voli and vele (50x50cm-20x20in) s.verso acrylic panel (I.L 2200000)
£1588 $2905   (12-May-92 F.R124/R) La notte (41x61cm-16x24in) s. st.sig.d.verso (I.L 3500000)
£2043 $3636   (29-Apr-92 F.F206/R) Senza titolo (72x50cm-28x20in) s.d.1980verso acrylic panel (I.L 4500000)
£2759 $4939   (14-Nov-91 F.M40) Bozzetti per quadrante di orologio (31x31cm-12x12in) s. s.i.d.1986verso acrylic panel set of three (I.L 6000000)
£3178 $5657   (29-Apr-92 F.F207/R) One strip (100x55cm-39x22in) s. i.verso acrylic panel (I.L 7000000)
£3197 $5564   (14-Apr-92 F.M67/R) Alcatraz n.6 (90x152cm-35x60in) s.i.d.1972verso acrylic panel (I.L 7000000)

NESS, Bjarne (1902-1927) Scandinavian
£4829 $8306   (7-Oct-91 B.O101/R) Gardeners I (60x67cm-24x26in) (N.KR 55000)

NESSI, Marie Lucie (20th C) French
£805 $1400   (15-Sep-91 H.C859/R) Le pin sur la terrase pres de Toulon (81x97cm-32x38in) s.

NESTEROV, Mikhail Vasilievich (1862-1942) Russian
£820 $1460   (28-Nov-91 S409/R) Design for postcard in aid of war widows and orphans, 1915 (20x14cm-8x6in) i. gouache

NESTEROV, Valerian (1923-) Russian
£619 $1058   (13-Mar-92 ARC.P200/R) La promenade en velo (47x133cm-19x52in) s. (F.FR 6000)
£670 $1146   (13-Mar-92 ARC.P199/R) La journee d'ete (90x79cm-35x31in) s. (F.FR 6500)

NETCHITAILO, Dmitri (1940-) Russian
£716 $1275   (25-Nov-91 ARC.P78/R) La fille en rouge (70x49cm-28x19in) s. board (F.FR 7000)
£737 $1312   (25-Nov-91 ARC.P77/R) Le dejeuner (88x120cm-35x47in) s. (F.FR 7200)
£747 $1330   (25-Nov-91 ARC.P81) A midi (66x88cm-26x35in) s. board (F.FR 7300)

NETER, Laurentius de (circle) (1600-?) German
£2000 $3840   (10-Jul-92 PH19/R) Figures seated and standing before table (55x78cm-22x31in) panel

NETHERWOOD, Arthur (?-1930) British
£550 $963   (1-Apr-92 B89/R) *Girl and ducks by stream (75x49cm-30x19in) s.d.1899 i.verso W/C*
£600 $1050   (1-Apr-92 B93/R) *Conway valley from Great Orme's Head (49x74cm-19x29in) s. W/C*
£800 $1400   (31-Mar-92 RJ155) *Cottage and figure by lane with Great Orme in distance (28x48cm-11x19in) s.d.1891 W/C*

NETSCHER, Caspar (1639-1684) Dutch
£2209 $3800   (9-Oct-91 CH.NY48/R) Portrait of lady, seated holding basket of flowers before window, park beyond (54x45cm-21x18in)
£2348 $4250   (7-Dec-91 SG.M300) Europa and bull (71x89cm-28x35in)
£2700 $4914   (11-Dec-91 MMB302/R) Portrait of young girl, standing (33x25cm-13x10in)
£3000 $5760   (7-Jul-92 PH46/R) Portrait of gentleman of Huybert Family, standing against plinth (51x44cm-20x17in) bears d.1653
£5923 $10780   (12-Dec-91 L.K127/R) Portrait of lady seated wearing dress and cloak (52x45cm-20x18in) s. (DM 17000)
£34000 $60520   (1-Nov-91 C111/R) Portrait of girl, in embroidered dress, wrap, picking roses on terrace (48x39cm-19x15in) indist.s.

NETSCHER, Caspar (after) (1639-1684) Dutch
£1419 $2569   (19-May-92 AB.S4358/R) Doctor visiting young lady (32x26cm-13x10in) bears sig. panel (S.KR 15000)

NETSCHER, Caspar (circle) (1639-1684) Dutch
£1700 $3060   (21-Nov-91 C152/R) Courtesan on bed (48x40cm-19x16in)
£2200 $3960   (21-Nov-91 CSK232/R) Portrait of lady seated by plinth with coat of arms (48x39cm-19x15in) i.
£2388 $4250   (30-Oct-91 D.NY68) Four children leaning against window ledge (48x38cm-19x15in)
£2621 $4639   (6-Nov-91 LT.P55) Portrait de jeune femme a la fleur (67x55cm-26x22in) (F.FR 26000)

NETSCHER, Caspar (studio) (1639-1684) Dutch
£2600 $4654   (13-Nov-91 S119/R) Portrait of William III standing wearing armour with battle beyond (52x43cm-20x17in)

NETSCHER, Caspar (style) (1639-1684) Dutch
£1600 $2880   (22-Nov-91 SWS194/R) Elegant figures in an interior (33x27cm-13x11in) panel

NETSCHER, Constantyn (1668-1723) Dutch
£1520 $2781   (12-May-92 SY.AM21/R) Portrait of girl seated in park (50x42cm-20x17in) (D.FL 5000)
£1569 $2808   (15-Nov-91 GK.Z5081 a/R) Girl and boy in elegant interior with view of landscape (52x41cm-20x16in) mono. (S.FR 4000)
£1955 $3538   (5-Dec-91 SY.MO308/R) Portrait de femme dans un paysage (49x39cm-19x15in) (F.FR 19000)
£3180 $5565   (3-Apr-92 BM.B594 a/R) Portrait of noble lady seated on park bench draped with carpet (68x56cm-27x22in) (DM 9000)

NETSCHER, Constantyn (attrib) (1668-1723) Dutch
£3000 $5460   (11-Dec-91 S181/R) Portrait of three children (47x38cm-19x15in)

NETSCHER, Constantyn (circle) (1668-1723) Dutch
£1150 $2093   (12-Dec-91 B63) The moneylender and his wife (30x23cm-12x9in) panel
£1300 $2275   (25-Feb-92 PH77/R) Portrait of lady seated on stone bench holding garland of roses (42x35cm-17x14in)
£2539 $4494   (5-Nov-91 GF.L2057/R) Seated young woman with roses (43x32cm-17x13in) panel (S.FR 6500)

NETSCHER, Constantyn (style) (1668-1723) Dutch
£3200 $5696   (30-Oct-91 S174/R) Portrait of nobleman (79x64cm-31x25in)

NETTLESHIP, John Trivett (1847-1902) British
£700 $1281   (3-Jun-92 S127/R) Found (47x95cm-19x37in) s.d.84
£1500 $2745   (3-Jun-92 S189/R) Indian Blackbuck (112x61cm-44x24in)

NEUBAUER, Egon (1920-) German?
£1638 $2982   (25-May-92 WK.M921/R) *Southern town (30x47cm-12x19in) s.d.1952 W/C over pencil (DM 4800)*

NEUBAUER, M (20th C) Austrian
£450 $797   (13-Feb-92 CSK8/R) *Carriages on the Graben, Vienna (17x28cm-7x11in) s.i. pencil ink W/C*

NEUBAUER, Max (19/20th C) Austrian
£777 $1383   (29-Apr-92 D.V656/R) *Der Platz am Hof mit Radetzkydenkmal (29x34cm-11x13in) mono.i.d.1900 pen indian ink W/C (A.S 16000)*

NEUBERGER, Istvan (1953-) Hungarian
£555 $955   (14-Oct-91 AT.P183) Sans titre (68x103cm-27x41in) s.d.1884 panel
                           (F.FR 5500)
£767 $1319   (14-Oct-91 AT.P184/R) Dans le parc (68x108cm-27x43in) s.d.1984 panel
                           (F.FR 7600)

NEUBERT, Ludwig (1846-1892) German
£528 $956   (3-Dec-91 FN.S2354) Female faggott gatherer on path with puddles by the
                           edge of wood, evening (42x58cm-17x23in) (DM 1500)
£1638 $2965   (21-May-92 L.K460) Moor landscape near Dachau (40x80cm-16x31in) s.
                           (DM 4800)

NEUBOCK, Max (1893-?) Austrian
£698 $1249   (15-Jan-92 D.V143) Steiermark landscape (76x85cm-30x33in) s. (A.S 14000)
£874 $1555   (28-Apr-92 D.V215/R) View of Davos (37x47cm-15x19in) s.i. canvas on board
                           (A.S 18000)

NEUBRAND, Otto (?) German
£687 $1258   (2-Jun-92 FN.S2682) Village street (46x57cm-18x22in) s.d.1938 (DM 2000)

NEUENSCHWANDER, Albert (1902-) Swiss
£1095 $1960   (6-May-92 GD.B928/R) View of Vielbringen in early spring
                           (65x80cm-26x31in) s. (S.FR 3000)

NEUFCHATEL, Nicolas (circle) (1527-1590) Flemish
£2616 $4500   (9-Oct-91 CH.NY144/R) Portrait of Andreas Imhoff, standing holding gloves
                           and sword, by table (101x88cm-40x35in)

NEUGEBAUER, Josef (1810-1895) Austrian
£732 $1266   (3-Oct-91 D.V3/R) Breakfast table (85x115cm-33x45in) s. (A.S 15000)

NEUGEBAUER, Rudolf (1892-?) German
£1579 $2842   (22-Nov-91 SA.A395/R) Female nude seated seen from behind
                           (131x70cm-52x28in) s.d.1912 (DM 4500)

NEUHAUS, Eugen (1879-1963) American
£508 $900   (12-Feb-92 B.SF493/R) Pinnacle rock, Carmel (61x51cm-24x20in)

NEUHUYS, Albert (1844-1914) Dutch
£1512 $2600   (14-Oct-91 H.C63) Hide and seek with mother sewing (30x23cm-12x9in) s.
                           board
£1774 $3086   (14-Apr-92 SY.AM49/R) The letter (14x18cm-6x7in) s.d.80 panel (D.FL 5800)
£424 $751   (22-Apr-92 CH.AM326) Cottage interior with a peasantmother and child by a
                           cradle (13x15cm-5x6in) s. pencil W/C (D.FL 1400)
£581 $1034   (30-Oct-91 CH.AM299) Mother and baby in cottage interior
                           (25x26cm-10x10in) s. W/C htd.white (D.FL 1900)
£1070 $1862   (14-Apr-92 SY.AM1/R) Interior scene with mother and two children
                           (25x17cm-10x7in) s. W/C (D.FL 3500)
£2080 $3618   (14-Apr-92 SY.AM272/R) Portrait of young woman holding fruit-dish
                           (57x42cm-22x17in) s. W/C (D.FL 6800)
£2508 $4363   (14-Apr-92 SY.AM131/R) At the spinning wheel (55x42cm-22x17in) s.d.78 W/C
                           (D.FL 8200)

NEUHUYS, Joseph Hendrikus (1841-1889) Dutch
£734 $1306   (30-Oct-91 CH.AM113) Playing children and geese on farmyard
                           (36x62cm-14x24in) s. (D.FL 2400)

NEUMAN, J H (1819-1898) German
£1552 $2669   (16-Oct-91 KM.K1300) Mountainous landscape with torrent and figures,
                           evening (61x85cm-24x33in) s.indis.d.1878 (DM 4500)

NEUMAN, Johan Heinrich (1819-1898) German
£917 $1633   (30-Oct-91 CH.AM26) Portrait of man holding letter (107x82cm-42x32in) s.
                           (D.FL 3000)

NEUMANN, A (?) ?
£984 $1800   (3-Jun-92 D.NY69/R) Young artist (48x41cm-19x16in) s.

NEUMANN, Abraham (1873-?) Polish
£811 $1500   (8-Jun-92 GG.TA204/R) Walls of Acre (53x64cm-21x25in) s.
£2128 $4000   (5-Jan-92 GG.TA286/R) Thawing snow (111x88cm-44x35in) s.

NEUMANN, Alexander (1831-?) German
£3382 $5750   (25-Oct-91 S.W2779/R) Rachael and Jacob at well (97x119cm-38x47in) s.d.62

NEUMANN, Carl (1833-1891) Danish
£660 $1109   (27-Aug-91 RAS.K443) Seascape with sailingboats at sunset
                           (25x38cm-10x15in) s. (D.KR 7500)
£1077 $1907   (11-Feb-92 RAS.K287/R) Norwegian fjord landscape, early morning
                           (48x63cm-19x25in) init.d.1878 (D.KR 12000)

NEUMANN, Emil (1842-1903) German
£1471 $2529   (19-Oct-91 UA.U321/R) Lapplander near mountain stream, Norway
                           (59x107cm-23x42in) s.d.1882 (S.KR 15500)

NEUMANN, Johan (1860-1940) Danish/German

£628	$1112	(11-Feb-92 RAS.K124) Seascape with boats off Kronborg (73x105cm-29x41in) s. (D.KR 7000)
£856	$1516	(5-Nov-91 SY.AM8/R) Sea battle of Copenhagen, Rheden, 1801 (81x127cm-32x50in) s. (D.FL 2800)
£1670	$2989	(6-May-92 KH.K146/R) Seascape with vessels near Kronborg (79x120cm-31x47in) s. (D.KR 19000)
£1784	$3318	(16-Jun-92 RAS.V838/R) Seascape with vessels at Oresund off Kronborg (90x127cm-35x50in) s. (D.KR 20000)
£2076	$3736	(19-Nov-91 RAS.K297/R) Seascape with sailship off Kronborg (88x112cm-35x44in) s.d.93 (D.KR 23000)

NEUMANN, Max (1949-) German

| *£1329* | *$2365* | *(30-Nov-91 VG.B912/R) 30 Sept 80 (79x60cm-31x24in) s.d.1980 d.verso mixed media paper on canvas (DM 3800)* |
| *£3147* | *$5601* | *(30-Nov-91 VG.B409/R) Better not (150x100cm-59x39in) s.d.1982 Japan aqua canvas (DM 9000)* |

NEUMANN, Robert von (attrib) (1888-1976) American

| £526 | $1000 | (22-Jun-92 SG.M656) Winconsin landscape (66x53cm-26x21in) s. board |

NEUQUELMAN, Lucien (1909-1988) French

£566	$1065	(18-Dec-91 PR.P103) La grille du parc (24x18cm-9x7in) s. (F.FR 5500)
£1717	$3039	(24-Apr-92 CN.P200/R) La baie de Toulon (38x55cm-15x22in) s. panel (F.FR 17000)
£1815	$3212	(10-Nov-91 ZZ.F199/R) Paysage du midi (33x41cm-13x16in) s. (F.FR 18000)
£2815	$5094	(23-May-92 KV.L234/R) Bathers by the Mediterranean (38x55cm-15x22in) s. (B.FR 170000)
£3755	$6684	(29-Nov-91 GAB.G2828/R) Matin sur la Calanque (50x61cm-20x24in) s. i.verso paper laid down on panel (S.FR 9500)
£4200	$7266	(24-Mar-92 C97/R) Beaulieu sur mer (54x66cm-21x26in) s. i.stretcher
£4333	$7453	(12-Oct-91 KV.L473/R) Summer landscape (46x55cm-18x22in) s. (B.FR 260000)
£4348	$7739	(29-Nov-91 GAB.G2817/R) A Douarnenez (48x61cm-19x24in) s. i.verso (S.FR 11000)

NEUREUTHER, Eugen Napoleon (1806-1882) German

| *£619* | *$1076* | *(18-Sep-91 N.M256/R) View of Heidelberg Schloss. View of castle, possibly Harfenburg (27x40cm-11x16in) s.i.d.1824 indis.i.d.verso W/C double-sided (DM 1800)* |

NEUSTATTER, Ludwig (1829-1899) German

| £557 | $1015 | (11-Dec-91 WE.MU232/R) Portrait of Tyrolean peasant (28x21cm-11x8in) s. (DM 1600) |
| £9756 | $17756 | (12-Dec-91 L.K632/R) Young boy trying to snatch jug of beer away from litte girl (35x26cm-14x10in) s.d.1874 panel (DM 28000) |

NEUSTUCK, Maximilian (1756-1834) Swiss

| £1111 | $2011 | (19-May-92 GF.L2589/R) Caught in the act (24x19cm-9x7in) s.d.1810 panel (S.FR 3000) |

NEUVILLE, Alphonse Marie de (1835-1885) French

£438	$784	(6-May-92 GD.B938/R) Interior of Gothic church (23x13cm-9x5in) s.i.d.77 panel (S.FR 1200)
£660	$1187	(20-Nov-91 DUR.M573/R) En el campo de batalla (35x47cm-14x19in) s. (S.P 120000)
£1502	$2674	(29-Nov-91 GAB.G2147) Nature morte aux reine-claudes (54x65cm-21x26in) s. (S.FR 3800)
£3371	$6000	(22-Jan-92 SY.NY381/R) Vedette de dragons (50x40cm-20x16in) s.d.1879
£4094	$7288	(29-Nov-91 ARC.P88/R) Paysage urbain durant la guerre de 1870 s. (F.FR 40000)

NEUVILLE, Alphonse Marie de (attrib) (1835-1885) French

| £628 | $1200 | (16-Jul-92 SY.NY366/R) Cavalier at rest (24x19cm-9x7in) s. panel |

NEUVILLE, B (?) French

| £2998 | $5337 | (28-Apr-92 RAS.K566/R) Still life of prawns, strainer and bottle (43x53cm-17x21in) s. (D.KR 34000) |

NEUVILLE, Bruno (19/20th C) French

| £680 | $1306 | (28-Jul-92 SWS411/R) An unwelcome guest (45x37cm-18x15in) s. |

NEUWIRTH, Arnulf (20th C) Austrian?

| £873 | $1588 | (26-May-92 D.V235/R) The white wall (13x20cm-5x8in) s.d.67 canvas on panel (A.S 18000) |

NEVE, Cornelius de (attrib) (17th C) Flemish

| £7500 | $13200 | (8-Apr-92 S13/R) Portrait of gentleman, possibly Sir Richard Weston, in doublet (72x59cm-28x23in) painted oval |

NEVELSON, Louise (1900-1988) American

£595	*$1100*	*(12-Jun-92 SY.NY256/R) Four women (21x29cm-8x11in) s. pen paper on board*
£2514	*$4500*	*(9-May-92 CE.NY338/R) Series of unknown cosmos IV (61x51cm-24x20in) s. paper painted wood collage board on panel*
£2514	*$4500*	*(9-May-92 CE.NY336/R) Untitled (76x51cm-30x20in) s. col.paper etching silver foil collage board*

NEVINSON, Christopher Richard Wynne (1889-1946) British
£1100 $1991   (20-May-92 BT259/R) Winding stream (28x38cm-11x15in) s. board
£2300 $4117   (15-Jan-92 BT136/R) London in the Blitz (28x38cm-11x15in) s. panel
£3000 $5160   (6-Mar-92 C79/R) The bypass (46x56cm-18x22in) s.
£3800 $6536   (6-Mar-92 C81/R) Battlefields of Britain, opus V Amongst the Clouds
           (40x30cm-16x12in) s. panel
£5700 $9861   (4-Sep-91 BT256/R) French street scene (69x50cm-27x20in) s.
£7000 $11970   (11-Mar-92 S48/R) Bruges (63x76cm-25x30in) s.
£650 $1183   (12-Dec-91 CSK31/R) Seaside town (25x23cm-10x9in) s. pencil W/C
£4000 $7320   (14-May-92 C183/R) Coliseum for Horseguards Parade (28x36cm-11x14in) s.
           pen W/C bodycol
£5500 $9735   (7-Nov-91 C23/R) Ludgate Circus, Fleet Street, London (35x24cm-14x9in)
           s.i.d.30backboard W/C bodycol.blk.crayon

NEWELL, Henry C (fl.1865-1885) American
£1829 $3200   (26-Sep-91 CH.NY5/R) August day on North Shore (35x61cm-14x24in) s.d.75

NEWEY, Harry Foster (1858-1933) British
£400 $728   (10-Dec-91 HAR634/R) Fallen glory - still life with rose petals
           (23x28cm-9x11in) s. W/C

NEWLYN SCHOOL, 20th C British
£3800 $6498   (13-Mar-92 C143/R) Milking time (71x91cm-28x36in) indis.s.d.1906

NEWMAN, Henry Roderick (c.1833-1918) American
£5172 $9000   (15-Apr-92 SY.NY39/R) Cherry blossoms (32x20cm-13x8in) s.d.1898
           init.i.d.99 verso W/C paper on panel
£29240 $50000   (12-Mar-92 CH.NY109/R) Abu Simbel (102x69cm-40x27in) s.i.d.1900 W/C
           pencil paper on linen on panel

NEWMAN, John (1952-) American?
£2235 $4000   (5-May-92 CH.NY150/R) Untitled (74x132cm-29x52in) d.5/28 s.verso graphite
           crayon vellum
£2857 $5000   (27-Feb-92 CH.NY60/R) Drawing for tolled belle (125x64cm-49x25in) s.verso
           graphite col.crayons vellum

NEWMAN, Robert Loftin (1827-1912) American
£550 $1007   (1-Jun-92 W.T1217) Woodland spring (35x61cm-14x24in) s. (C.D 1200)
£1486 $2600   (26-Sep-91 CH.NY220/R) Psyche (26x36cm-10x14in) s.
£1657 $3000   (4-Dec-91 D.NY16 a) Children playing (28x46cm-11x18in) i.verso board

NEWMAN, Thomas (20th C) ?
£782 $1400   (5-May-92 ZEL.L1469/R) Elephant in landscape (76x101cm-30x40in) s.
           (DM 2300)

NEWTON, Algernon (1880-1968) British
£820 $1427   (19-Sep-91 B181/R) Woman riding side-saddle (49x65cm-19x26in) s.
£2000 $3480   (17-Sep-91 PH139/R) Silver birch trees in sunshine (61x91cm-24x36in)
           mono.
£3800 $6536   (15-Oct-91 CSK625/R) London canal scene (51x76cm-20x30in) mono.d.41

NEWTON, Richard (jnr) (20th C) British?
£479 $900   (18-Dec-91 SY.NY401/R) Horses grazing (61x81cm-24x32in) s.

NEWTON, Sir William John (1785-1869) British
£500 $860   (15-Oct-91 SWS1971/R) Noel Lake Esquire wearing a black jacket
           (10x?cm-4x?in) min.s.d.1827 velvet frame rectangular
£600 $1032   (15-Oct-91 SWS1976) A lady with a blue low-cut dress (10x?cm-4x?in)
           min.s.d.1829 rectangular giltwood frame
£749 $1349   (21-Nov-91 D.V189/R) Portrait of two boys and girl in garden landscape
           (38x26cm-15x10in) i.d.1849verso W/C ivory (A.S 15000)

NEY, Lloyd Raymond (1893-1964) American
£1170 $2000   (12-Mar-92 CH.NY250/R) Untitled (28x38cm-11x15in) s.d.41 gouache pencil

NEYMARK, Gustave (1850-?) French
£899 $1600   (22-Jan-92 SY.NY404/R) Bataille de Loos, prise d'une barricade par
           l'armee Anglaise (60x81cm-24x32in) s.

NEYN, Pieter de (1597-1639) Dutch
£4444 $8044   (19-May-92 GF.L2062/R) Two riders with dogs (27x41cm-11x16in) panel
           (S.FR 12000)
£8000 $14560   (13-Dec-91 C191/R) Fishermen selling their catch on beach
           (35x53cm-14x21in) s.d.1638 panel
£9000 $15750   (1-Apr-92 S23/R) Landscape with figures at rest beside cottage
           (39x56cm-15x22in) panel
£13953 $24000   (9-Oct-91 CH.NY170/R) River landscape with ferryboat and two fishermen in
           rowboat, church on river bank (46x68cm-18x27in) bears sig. panel
£15000 $28800   (8-Jul-92 S181/R) Landscape with peasants by farmhouse (33x53cm-13x21in)
           bears init.d.1630 panel
£15897 $27183   (18-Mar-92 D.V79/R) Rest before tavern (32x44cm-13x17in) panel
           (A.S 320000)

NEYTS, Gillis (1623-1687) Flemish
£994 $1769   *(25-Nov-91 CH.AM35/R) Wooded river landscape with travellers by ruined archway (7x11cm-3x4in) s. pen W/C (D.FL 3200)*

NGATANE, Ephraim (1938-) South African
£806 $1427   (4-Nov-91 SY.J138/R) The studio (75x59cm-30x23in) s. acrylic board (SA.R 4000)
£524 $928   *(4-Nov-91 SY.J137) The barber shop (71x52cm-28x20in) s. W/C (SA.R 2600)*

NIBBRIG, Ferdinand Hart (1866-1915) Dutch
£606 $1073   (22-Apr-92 CH.AM12) Still life with a jug and red peppers on a ledge (27x21cm-11x8in) mono.indist.d.89 (D.FL 2000)
£9174 $16239   (5-Nov-91 SY.AM170/R) Philemon and Baucis (99x119cm-39x47in) s. (D.FL 30000)

NIBBS, G (?) British
£650 $1125   (26-Mar-92 CSK27) East Anglian harbour (71x122cm-28x48in) s.

NIBBS, Richard Henry (1816-1893) British
£620 $1042   (27-Aug-91 SWS1504) Dutch waterfront (44x34cm-17x13in) s.d.88
£2000 $3560   (28-Nov-91 PHX538/R) Dutch fishing boats entering estuary at evening (76x112cm-30x44in) s.
£520 $931   *(14-Jan-92 SWS20/R) Going out to unload the catch (30x64cm-12x25in) s.d.86 W/C gouache over pencil*
£720 $1296   *(27-Jan-92 PH159) Fishing boats in port (48x64cm-19x25in) s. W/C*
£1000 $1790   *(5-May-92 SWS108/R) The Palace of Westminster from the Lambeth shore (39x72cm-15x28in) indist.s. W/C over pencil htd bodycol.*

NICE, Don (1932-) American
£1600 $2800   *(27-Feb-92 CE.NY160/R) American predella (96x226cm-38x89in) s.d.1975 num.1 W/C graphite*

NICHOLAS, Hilda Rix (19/20th C) Australian
£3404 $6026   (26-Apr-92 SY.ME453/R) Snowy river ranges (64x79cm-25x31in) s. s.i.verso (A.D 8000)

NICHOLL, Andrew (1804-1886) British
£440 $814   *(11-Jun-92 B40/R) North East end of Loch Awe with figures in rowing boat (32x47cm-13x19in) s. W/C*
£660 $1181   *(5-May-92 SWS168/R) Windsor Castle from head of the river (33x51cm-13x20in) s. W/C bodycol. scratching out*
£900 $1719   *(14-Jul-92 C157/R) Elie house in Mutural, Colombo, Ceylon (35x52cm-14x20in) s. pencil W/C*
£1466 $2800   *(15-Jul-92 D.NY69) Figures on mountain road. Cows on path with castle in distance (33x51cm-13x20in) s. W/C pair*
£2000 $3400   *(23-Oct-91 S246/R) Gateway of Ptolemy III, Karnak, Egypt (41x65cm-16x26in) s. W/C over pencil scratching out*
£2400 $4080   *(23-Oct-91 S295/R) Landscape with the Trois Mamelles, Mauritius (23x34cm-9x13in) W/C htd bodycol over pencil scratching out*
£2749 $5250   *(15-Jul-92 D.NY68/R) Wildflowers at river's edge (33x48cm-13x19in) W/C*

NICHOLLS, Bertram (1883-?) British
£780 $1388   (1-May-92 PHE69) Umbrian landscape (43x61cm-17x24in) s.
£560 $997   *(30-Apr-92 T299) Portugese landscape (41x56cm-16x22in) s.d.1934 W/C*

NICHOLLS, Burr H (1848-1915) American
£599 $1000   (23-Aug-91 DOU.M17) Canal scene with green door (51x38cm-20x15in)
£838 $1500   (13-Nov-91 B.SF2618/R) On canal (51x36cm-20x14in) s.

NICHOLLS, Charles Wynne (1831-1903) British
£2200 $3762   (12-Mar-92 CSK268) The water bearer (91x71cm-36x28in) s. s.i.verso

NICHOLLS, Michael (20th C) Australian?
£978 $1672   (17-Mar-92 JRL.S243) Fall of Icarus (210x191cm-83x75in) s.d.1988 verso (A.D 2200)

NICHOLS, Ben (20th C) German
£825 $1435   (17-Sep-91 FN.S2052) Irregularity - Unreality - Contradiction (40x50cm-16x20in) s.d.1941 s.i.d.verso board (DM 2400)

NICHOLS, Dale (1904-) American
£2286 $4000   (26-Nov-91 CH.NY163/R) Man on Wyoming Island (61x76cm-24x30in) s.d.1970 init.i.d.1970 verso
£367 $660   *(23-Nov-91 YFA.M210/R) Squirrels in tree (28x20cm-11x8in) s. W/C*

NICHOLS, Henry Hobart (1869-1962) American
£1000 $1910   (16-Jul-92 B40/R) Boats in harbour by moonlight (45x56cm-18x22in) s. board
£1299 $2300   (10-Nov-91 LIT.L67) Autumn gold (64x76cm-25x30in) s.
£1437 $2500   (20-Sep-91 DM.D2176/R) Landscape (76x91cm-30x36in)
£3143 $5500   (26-Sep-91 CH.NY77/R) Culvert, Bronxville (64x77cm-25x30in) s.
£3143 $5500   (26-Sep-91 CH.NY78/R) Across valley (64x76cm-25x30in) s.

NICHOLS, Joseph (attrib) (18th C) British

£7800 $13728   (10-Apr-92 C56/R) The Thames at Westminster Bridge with the Abbey and Westminster Hall (63x101cm-25x40in)

£30000 $53400   (30-Apr-92 CG869/R) Views of River Thames from Somerset House, towards St.Paul's Cathedral and towards Westminster Bridg (76x127cm-30x50in) pair

NICHOLS, Joseph (circle) (18th C) British

£14000 $25060   (15-Nov-91 C52/R) View of Thames at Westminster Bridge, with Westminster Abbey, Palace of Westminster and St. John's (79x135cm-31x53in)

NICHOLS, Joseph (style) (18th C) British

£4500 $7920   (10-Apr-92 C58/R) View of the Thames at Westminster Bridge (57x91cm-22x36in)

NICHOLSON, Ben (1894-1982) British

£25000 $45250   (3-Dec-91 C287/R) Pistaccio (23x33cm-9x13in) s.i.d.June 1961 thinned oil carved relief board

£54645 $100000   (13-May-92 CH.NY300/R) Sept 63 - prato (67x102cm-26x40in) s.verso oil pencil cut masonite

£84746 $150000   (5-Nov-91 CH.NY9/R) Still life (31x41cm-12x16in) bears copy sig.d.49 verso canvasboard mounted on board

£765027 $1400000   (12-May-92 CH.NY147/R) November, 1956 - Pistoia (122x214cm-48x84in) s.d.56 verso i.stretcher masonite

£2200 $3894   (5-Nov-91 PH82/R) Goulet fragment (25x24cm-10x9in) s.i.d.1957 pen col.crayons wash

£3400 $6018   (5-Nov-91 PH83/R) St.Ives (32x51cm-13x20in) s.i.d.Aug.27verso pencil

£5500 $9955   (3-Dec-91 C192/R) Ronco 29 (36x30cm-14x12in) s.d.Aug.58 i.verso pencil W/C paper laid board

£6500 $12415   (30-Jun-92 C204/R) June 1981 (58x49cm-23x19in) oil pen wash paper on artist's board

£8000 $15280   (1-Jul-92 S223/R) Still life with goblets (36x35cm-14x14in) s.d.1968 i.verso W/C col.chk ink pencil

£8200 $15170   (11-Jun-92 C30/R) One Plain, One Curly Goblet (29x20cm-11x8in) s.i.verso pencil wash paper on board

£12000 $22920   (1-Jul-92 S224/R) Goblets on yellow ground (32x38cm-13x15in) s.i.d.52 backboard oil pencil board laid down

£12000 $20760   (25-Mar-92 S82/R) Three forms, two blacks (42x25cm-17x10in) s.i.d.1968verso pencil gouache wax crayon

£15000 $28650   (16-Jul-92 B171/R) Megalith 1961 (41x48cm-16x19in) s.i.d.verso oil gouache pencil board

£17486 $32000   (13-May-92 CH.NY316/R) may 53 - Tring (25x17cm-10x7in) s.d.53 verso oil pencil paper on masonite

£18000 $34380   (30-Jun-92 C189/R) Two forms 1940-42 (23x23cm-9x9in) s.i.d.1940-42 verso gouache incised card

£24000 $43440   (4-Dec-91 S182/R) Still life (56x60cm-22x24in) s.d.1946 verso oil pencil

£27000 $48870   (4-Dec-91 S179/R) Still life (61x39cm-24x15in) s.i.d.1955 verso oil pencil canvasboard

£36723 $65000   (5-Nov-91 CH.NY17/R) Still life (19x18cm-7x7in) init. s.i.d.47 verso tempera pencil board

£50000 $90500   (2-Dec-91 C33/R) 1938 - Composition (48x66cm-19x26in) s.d.1938verso gouache board

£170000 $307700   (3-Dec-91 S42/R) 1933 - collage with Spanish postcard (50x75cm-20x30in) s.d.1933 overlap oil pencil paper fabric canvas

NICHOLSON, Edward H (1901-1966) American

£684 $1300   (23-Jun-92 MOR.P120 b) Reclining nude (41x56cm-16x22in)

NICHOLSON, Francis (1753-1844) British

£550 $995   (19-May-92 SWS277) The Dropping Well at Knaresborough (44x60cm-17x24in)

£540 $918   (22-Oct-91 SWS49) Launceston Castle, Cornwall (20x29cm-8x11in) W/C over pencil

£1800 $3204   (30-Apr-92 CG801/R) View of Scarborough from beach (29x41cm-11x16in) ink W/C

NICHOLSON, George W (1832-1912) American

£610 $1050   (10-Oct-91 FA.PH738) Encampment (41x30cm-16x12in) s. panel

£811 $1500   (10-Jun-92 CE.NY196) Peasants in village with Bay of Naples in distance (82x66cm-32x26in) s. panel

£914 $1600   (3-Apr-92 S.W2464/R) Fisherfolk along shore, unloading day's catch (61x107cm-24x42in) s.

£1149 $2000   (15-Apr-92 SY.NY77/R) Outskirts of Arabian village (51x91cm-20x36in) s.

£1250 $2100   (28-Aug-91 MFA.C85/R) Boating on lake (30x51cm-12x20in) s. panel

£1257 $2250   (13-Nov-91 B.SF2779/R) Coastal village (58x41cm-23x16in) s. board

£442 $800   (24-May-92 JRB.C144/R) Landscape with figures (25x36cm-10x14in) s. W/C

NICHOLSON, John Millar (19th C) British

£540 $977   (6-Dec-91 CBS216) Landscape at Baldwin with cottages (66x112cm-26x44in) s.d.1880

£850 $1539   (6-Dec-91 CBS244) Design for decorating the Victoria Hall, Douglas (38x66cm-15x26in) init. W/C

NICHOLSON, Kate (20th C) ?

£500 $890   (28-Nov-91 L232) Still life with bottles, pears and fruit (56x61cm-22x24in)

NICHOLSON, Sir William (1872-1949) British
£580 $1003   (4-Sep-91 BT74/R) A Musketeer (25x20cm-10x8in) s.i.d.97 ink W/C

NICHOLSON, Winifred (1893-1981) British
£650 $1131   (17-Sep-91 PH126/R) Rustle of dried grasse (76x30cm-30x12in) s.i.d.1967 stretcher
£3200 $5664   (5-Nov-91 PH133/R) Little snapdragons (48x35cm-19x14in) s.i.d.1937 board
£4400 $7524   (11-Mar-92 S154/R) Forest at Feoch (68x76cm-27x30in)
£4500 $7785   (2-Oct-91 S147/R) Midsummer magnolia (63x63cm-25x25in) s.i.d.1970verso oil gilt
£5500 $9515   (2-Oct-91 S148/R) Sowthistle (61x41cm-24x16in) board
£6000 $10260   (11-Mar-92 S144/R) Vases from Brittany (55x55cm-22x22in) s.i.d.1975 verso board
£7500 $13725   (13-May-92 S61/R) Lily (61x51cm-24x20in) s.i.d.1934 verso
£9500 $16815   (5-Nov-91 PH48/R) Flower table no.4 (76x61cm-30x24in)
£12500 $22875   (5-Jun-92 C104/R) Summer flowers in glass vase (76x43cm-30x17in) s.i.verso paper laid on panel
£16000 $28320   (5-Nov-91 PH49/R) Candlemas I (61x61cm-24x24in) s.i.d.1951verso board

NICKELE, Isaak van (?-1703) Dutch
£3918 $6777   (27-Mar-92 CN.P45/R) Interieur d'eglise (19x17cm-7x7in) panel (F.FR 38000)

NICKELE, Isaak van (attrib) (?-1703) Dutch
£2484 $4247   (18-Mar-92 D.V351/R) Church interior (37x42cm-15x17in) i.d.1615 panel (A.S 50000)

NICOL, Erskine (1825-1904) British
£872 $1500   (15-Oct-91 CE.NY64/R) A seaman in stormy weather (47x37cm-19x15in) s.d.1870
£1309 $2500   (3-Jul-92 S.W3110/R) Notice to quit (51x38cm-20x15in) s.
£1800 $3096   (11-Oct-91 C30/R) A willing pupil (68x52cm-27x20in) s.d.1878 canvas laid down on board
£1832 $3500   (16-Jul-92 SY.NY562/R) The bashful suitor (40x63cm-16x25in) s.
£1900 $3192   (26-Aug-91 S872/R) Come out o' that (27x23cm-11x9in) s.i.d.1858 label stretcher
£1966 $3500   (22-Jan-92 SY.NY501/R) Crow to pluck (33x41cm-13x16in) s.d.1856 s.indist.i.verso
£3600 $6444   (5-May-92 SWS422/R) The loose button (34x26cm-13x10in) s.d.1855 panel
£4000 $7120   (28-Apr-92 S164/R) His favourite brew (49x39cm-19x15in) s.d.1869
£6800 $11628   (13-Mar-92 C169/R) The Ryans and Dwyers, calumniated men (33x43cm-13x17in) s.d.56 s.i.verso

NICOLAES, K (?) ?
£1314 $2352   (6-May-92 GD.B940/R) Still life of flowers on stone socle (50x40cm-20x16in) s. panel (S.FR 3600)

NICOLAI, Paul (1876-1948) ?
£1643 $2957   (18-Nov-91 AT.P360/R) Le marche d'Aumale (80x100cm-31x39in) s. (F.FR 16000)

NICOLAIEV, Boris (1925-) Russian
£510 $948   (17-Jun-92 ARC.P17/R) Bouquet de branchages (71x90cm-28x35in) s. (F.FR 5000)
£765 $1422   (17-Jun-92 ARC.P18/R) Nature morte de printemps (75x90cm-30x35in) s. (F.FR 7500)

NICOLAUS, Martin (1870-1945) German
£634 $1147   (3-Dec-91 FN.S2356/R) Barensee near Stuttgart with two girls bathing (56x55cm-22x22in) s. (DM 1800)
£686 $1200   (18-Feb-92 CE.NY184) Afternoon reverie (72x93cm-28x37in) s.

NICOLAY, A (?) ?
£1017 $1821   (17-Nov-91 FB.P134) Nature morte aux fleurs (25x34cm-10x13in) s. (F.FR 10000)

NICOLAYSEN, Lyder Wentzel (1821-1898) Norwegian
£1426 $2467   (23-Mar-92 B.O98/R) Evening landscape by the coast (78x122cm-31x48in) s.d.79 s.i.verso (N.KR 16000)

NICOLINA, A (19th C) Italian
£1099 $2000   (26-May-92 CE.NY167/R) At thw tavern (80x63cm-31x25in) s.

NICOLL, Archibald Frank (1886-1953) New Zealander
£1194 $2137   (6-May-92 DS.W12) Cotton wool clouds (39x49cm-15x19in) s. (NZ.D 4000)

NICOLLE, Victor Jean (1754-1826) French
£600 $1044   (13-Apr-92 S224) Bay of Naples (12x17cm-5x7in) pen over black chk
£728 $1275   (3-Apr-92 AGS.P172/R) Vue de la Fontaine et de la Place Navone a Rome (7cm-3ins circular) i. W/C pen (F.FR 7000)
£823 $1490   (5-Dec-91 SY.MO96) Vue d'une eglise et vue de l'eglise de san Andrea a Rome (6x9cm-2x4in) pen wash W/C pair (F.FR 8000)
£916 $1696   (12-Jun-92 ARC.P144) La fontaine des trois cascades (12cm-5ins circular) s.d.1784 W/C pen (F.FR 9000)

NICOLLE, Victor Jean (1754-1826) French-cont.
£1114	$2017	(22-May-92 BL.P16/R) Oratoire romain. Scene de rue a Rome (17x12cm-7x5in) pen wash pair (F.FR 11000)
£2029	$3551	(3-Apr-92 AGS.P173/R) Vue de l'Eglise Saint Gregoire, Rome. Vue de la Eglise Saint Andre, Rome (6x9cm-2x4in) i. W/C traces pen two (F.FR 19500)
£2081	$3642	(3-Apr-92 AGS.P174/R) Deux vues de Rome (7x9cm-3x4in) i. W/C pen two (F.FR 20000)
£3831	$6780	(6-Nov-91 LT.P56) Vue de l'Arc de Constantin au pied du Capitole de Rome (15cm-6ins circular) s. pen W/C traces crayon (F.FR 38000)
£6790	$12290	(5-Dec-91 SY.MO87/R) Vue de l'arc de Septime severe (20x30cm-8x12in) s. pen W/C (F.FR 66000)
£8500	$16320	(6-Jul-92 S108/R) Views of the Isola Tiberina in Rome (20x31cm-8x12in) pen wash pair
£8800	$16896	(6-Jul-92 S109/R) A palazzo, Rome. The Temple of Vesta, Rome (19x31cm-7x12in) pen wash pair
£9174	$17064	(20-Jun-92 CH.MO241/R) L'Amphitheatre de Flavius a Rome (23x34cm-9x13in) s. chk ink wash W/C (F.FR 90000)
£9500	$18240	(6-Jul-92 S111/R) The Colosseum. The Isola Tiberina (19x31cm-7x12in) pen wash pair

NIE OU (1948-) Chinese
| £6575 | $11243 | (22-Mar-92 SY.TA33/R) When snow falls (53x58cm-21x23in) s. (T.D 286000) |
| £629 | $1100 | (30-Mar-92 CH.HK375/R) Playing flute on boat (68x68cm-27x27in) s.d.1987 ink W/C scroll (HK.D 8500) |

NIE, Eric de (1944-) Dutch
| £727 | $1316 | (21-May-92 SY.AM352) The sketch (150x200cm-59x79in) s.d.1975 s.i.d.stretcher acrylic (D.FL 2400) |

NIEDERBERGER, Louis (1821-1895) Swiss
| £1542 | $2775 | (19-Nov-91 GS.B3226) Nikolaus von der Flute as hermit (75x51cm-30x20in) s.i.d.1887 (S.FR 3900) |

NIEDERBUHL, Roland (1896-1958) German
| £1443 | $2511 | (17-Sep-91 FN.S2463/R) Kaiserberg Hohenstauffen (105x136cm-41x54in) s.d.1939/40 (DM 4200) |

NIEDERHAUSERN, Auguste de see NIEDERHAUSERN-RODO

NIEDERHAUSERN, Francois Louis Fritz de (1828-1888) Swiss
| £632 | $1126 | (29-Nov-91 GAB.G2149) Petit patre dans un paysage (73x54cm-29x21in) s. (S.FR 1600) |
| £917 | $1596 | (14-Apr-92 SY.AM119/R) View of the River Nile (46x115cm-18x45in) s.d.1871 (D.FL 3000) |

NIEDMANN, August Heinrich (1826-1910) German
| £2372 | $4246 | (6-May-92 GD.B942/R) Hunter courting peasant servant in Alpine landscape, evening (87x68cm-34x27in) s.d.1896 (S.FR 6500) |

NIEHAUS, Kaspar (1889-1974) Dutch
| £912 | $1587 | (17-Sep-91 CH.AM85/R) Nude figures and animals in a landscape (90x91cm-35x36in) canvas laid down on board (D.FL 3000) |

NIELSEN, Amaldus Clarin (1838-1932) Norwegian
£1056	$1775	(28-Aug-91 KH.K151/R) Moonlit landscape, Lindenaes (15x28cm-6x11in) s.d.1895 (D.KR 12000)
£1316	$2447	(15-Jun-92 B.O119/R) Coastal landscape (31x54cm-12x21in) s.d.1922 (N.KR 15000)
£1401	$2438	(14-Sep-91 BU.O301) Sunset by the sea (18x26cm-7x10in) s. panel (N.KR 16000)
£4960	$9027	(9-Dec-91 B.O90/R) Landscape at night (71x110cm-28x43in) s.d.1866 (N.KR 56000)
£9284	$16247	(25-Feb-92 UL.T223/R) Norwegian mountain landscape (75x110cm-30x43in) (N.KR 105000)

NIELSEN, Arthur (1883-1946) Danish
| £1939 | $3529 | (26-May-92 D.V19/R) Still life of flowers and fruit (76x250cm-30x98in) s. (A.S 40000) |

NIELSEN, Carl (1848-1908) Scandinavian
| £526 | $979 | (15-Jun-92 B.O121/R) Landscape from Fjaeland (32x48cm-13x19in) s.indist.d. panel (N.KR 6000) |
| £567 | $963 | (6-Aug-91 UL.T214) Wanderer in the mountains (35x55cm-14x22in) d.1877 (N.KR 6500) |

NIELSEN, Eivind (1864-1939) Norwegian
| £526 | $979 | (15-Jun-92 B.O122/R) Day by the sea (33x41cm-13x16in) s. canvas on cardboard (N.KR 6000) |

NIELSEN, Jais (1885-1961) Danish
| £489 | $851 | (17-Sep-91 RAS.K660) Madonna and Child (68x45cm-27x18in) s.d.19 glass (D.KR 5500) |
| £626 | $1140 | (10-Dec-91 RAS.K141) Landscape with women (89x80cm-35x31in) s.d.14 (D.KR 7000) |

NIELSEN, Jais (1885-1961) Danish-cont.
£681 $1192   (1-Apr-92 KH.K188) Town scene with view of mill (87x69cm-34x27in)
       mono.d.18 (D.KR 7500)
£1016 $1768   (16-Apr-92 FB.P31/R) Nature morte (76x73cm-30x29in) s.d.14 (F.FR 10000)
£1272 $2225   (1-Apr-92 KH.K32/R) Nature morte (60x57cm-24x22in) s.d.22 (D.KR 14000)
£2888 $4939   (12-Mar-92 RAS.K728/R) Frederik VII presenting deed of gift to Countess
       Danner (65x65cm-26x26in) s.s.d.1918 on stretcher (D.KR 32000)
£500   *$874*   *(1-Apr-92 KH.K169) Cubist landscape (34x26cm-13x10in) s.d.19 W/C*
       (D.KR 5500)

NIELSEN, Johan (1835-1912) Norwegian
£753 $1370   (9-Dec-91 B.O91/R) Fjord landscape (36x27cm-14x11in) s.d.71 (N.KR 8500)

NIELSEN, John David (1938-) Norwegian
£753 $1370   (9-Dec-91 B.O92/R) Houses (53x61cm-21x24in) init. i.d.1986-88verso
       (N.KR 8500)

NIELSEN, Kay (1868-?) Danish
£535 $920   (16-Oct-91 KH.K224) Attacking woman (125x133cm-49x52in) (D.KR 6000)
£1769   *$3096*   *(5-Apr-92 CSC.P24) L'Histoire de la Tzarine Violette (29x26cm-11x10in)*
       Indian ink W/C (F.FR 17000)

NIELSEN, Kehnet (20th C) Danish
£812 $1389   (10-Mar-92 RAS.K165) Nature (160x130cm-63x51in) s.verso (D.KR 9000)
£1264 $2161   (10-Mar-92 RAS.K164/R) Cathedral II (190x160cm-75x63in) s.verso
       (D.KR 14000)

NIELSEN, Knud (1916-) Danish
£667 $1161   (17-Sep-91 RAS.K70) Bird and man (65x50cm-26x20in) s. (D.KR 7500)
£850 $1547   (10-Dec-91 RAS.K87) Yellow composition (100x81cm-39x32in) s.d.57verso
       (D.KR 9500)
£890 $1548   (18-Sep-91 KH.K160) Composition (81x65cm-32x26in) s.d.48 double-sided
       (D.KR 10000)
£1719 $3112   (4-Dec-91 KH.K168/R) The jugglers dance (130x97cm-51x38in) s.d.74
       (D.KR 19000)

NIELSON, Reinholdt (?) ?
£700 $1281   (5-Feb-92 CSK245) Deer in autumn wood (84x114cm-33x45in) s.

NIEMANN, Edmund John (1813-1876) British
£840 $1554   (12-Jun-92 C152/R) View of Ludlow (25x25cm-10x10in) s.d.1853 panel oval
£900 $1530   (24-Oct-91 CSK111/R) Richmond, Yorkshire from Reeth Moors
       (33x51cm-13x20in) s.i.d.75
£950 $1644   (25-Mar-92 B124/R) River landscape (51x76cm-20x30in) s.
£1100 $2035   (11-Jun-92 CSK104/R) The Thames from the Bells of Ouzeley
       (45x61cm-18x24in) s.i.
£1300 $2379   (15-May-92 TE400) View of Richmond, Yorkshire from Reeth Moors
       (33x51cm-13x20in) s.d. i.verso
£1700 $3026   (27-Nov-91 WAL198/R) Vicarage, Aber N. Wales - view up rocky gorge,
       fisherman by torrent (44x54cm-17x21in) s.i.d.69
£1800 $3078   (16-Mar-92 LW1722/R) View across Thames to Windsor with footpath and
       trees in foreground (76x127cm-30x50in) s.
£1854 $3300   (22-Jan-92 SY.NY496/R) Richmond, Yorkshire (76x127cm-30x50in) s.
£2700 $5157   (29-Jun-92 PHB171/R) Highlands (77x128cm-30x50in) s.d.66
£5300 $9699   (3-Jun-92 S71/R) Richmond, Yorks, Easby Abbey in distance
       (53x46cm-21x18in) s.i.d.67

NIEMANN, Edmund John (jnr) (19th C) British
£552 $1000   (5-Dec-91 FA.PH479 a) View of the River Swale (51x76cm-20x30in) s.
£1571 $3000   (16-Jul-92 SY.NY515/R) View from Epsom, Surrey (50x76cm-20x30in) s.

NIEMANN, Edward H (fl.1863-1867) British
£488 $883   (3-Dec-91 R.T131/R) Figure on sunlit road by river with bridge
       (35x51cm-14x20in) s. (C.D 1000)
£600 $1068   (28-Apr-92 PH135/R) Richmond Castle on River Swale (30x46cm-12x18in) s.
£650 $1118   (3-Mar-92 SWS1631) Figure on a path with a castle (49x75cm-19x30in) s.
£1000 $1720   (4-Mar-92 S38/R) Broad river valley (76x127cm-30x50in) s.
£1900 $3401   (14-Jan-92 SWS142/R) View down valley (30x50cm-12x20in) s.
£2078 $3637   (18-Feb-92 DUR.M59/R) Vista del puente de Barley (51x77cm-20x30in) s.
       (S.P 375000)
£2500 $4300   (4-Mar-92 S21/R) Views of Richmond, Yorkshire (51x77cm-20x30in) s. pair

NIEMEYER-HOLSTEIN, Otto (1896-) German
£596 $1074   (22-Nov-91 SA.A429/R) Summer flowers (30x40cm-12x16in) mono.d.1933 board
       (DM 1700)
£614 $1112   (23-May-92 GB.B6963) Female nude seated (69x45cm-27x18in) mono.d.68/69
       mono.i.d.verso panel (DM 1800)
£614 $1118   (30-May-92 VG.B875/R) Flowers (31x24cm-12x9in) mono s.i.d.1961 board
       (DM 1800)
£842 $1516   (22-Nov-91 SA.A431/R) Still life of flowers (28x36cm-11x14in) mono. board
       (DM 2400)
£2405 $4186   (21-Sep-91 SA.A575/R) Still life of flowers (45x55cm-18x22in) s.d.29
       (DM 7000)
£1031   *$1753*   *(25-Oct-91 BM.B1084/R) Ticino church (62x47cm-24x19in) mono.i.d.1925*
       pastel (DM 3000)

NIERMAN, Leonardo (1932-) Mexican
£734 $1300   (9-Nov-91 W.W74/R) Biblical fire (79x58cm-31x23in) s. i.verso masonite

NIESIOLOWSKI, Tymon (1882-1966) Polish
£1398 $2628   (22-Dec-91 AG.W7) Harlequin (72x59cm-28x23in) (P.Z 27000000)
£1702 $3013   (26-Apr-92 SY.ME235/R) Young nude on yellow chair (72x50cm-28x20in) mono.
         (A.D 4000)

NIESTLE, Henry (1876-1966) Swiss
£3476 $6187   (28-Nov-91 D.V5/R) Morning sun (76x89cm-30x35in) mono.i.d.1914verso
         (A.S 70000)

NIETO, Rodolfo (1936-1988) Mexican
£5556 $10000   (18-Nov-91 SY.NY141/R) Mexico (116x89cm-46x35in) s.

NIETSCHE, Paul (20th C) British?
£463 $843   (11-Dec-91 A.D116 a) Coumeenoele (30x46cm-12x18in) s. s.i.d.1933verso
         board (E.P 500)

NIEULANDT, Willem van (16/17th C) Flemish
£2600 $4992   (7-Jul-92 PH167/R) David with head of Goliath (43x72cm-17x28in) panel
£7452 $12742   (18-Mar-92 D.V112/R) Phantastic view of Rome with scene of Flight into
         Egypt (36x48cm-14x19in) copper (A.S 150000)
£9119 $16687   (12-May-92 SY.AM4/R) Peasant couple with cattle by farm (54x74cm-21x29in)
         s.d.1630 panel (D.FL 30000)
£19337 $35000   (22-May-92 SY.NY100/R) View of Roamn Forum with shpeherds grazing flocks
         (41x69cm-16x27in) s. copper

NIEULANDT, Willem van (circle) (16/17th C) Flemish
£780 $1498   (9-Jul-92 CSK26/R) Christ bearing the Cross (18x13cm-7x5in) panel

NIEUWAEL, Jan van (circle) (fl.1620-1661) Dutch
£2863 $5095   (28-Nov-91 BU.S72/R) Shepherdess watering cow (116x85cm-46x33in)
         (S.KR 30000)

NIEUWENHOVEN, Willem van (1879-?) Dutch
£497 $884   (26-Nov-91 VN.R80) Old man smoking a pipe (39x29cm-15x11in) s. panel
         (D.FL 1600)
£994 $1769   (26-Nov-91 VN.R79) Coppersmith at work (29x23cm-11x9in) s. (D.FL 3200)

NIEUWENHUIS, Cesar Domela (1900-?) Dutch
£2930 $5186   (5-Nov-91 GF.L2224/R) Composition (60x46cm-24x18in) mixed media
         (S.FR 7500)

NIEWEG, Jaap (1877-1955) Dutch
£547 $952   (17-Sep-91 CH.AM167 a) A still life with flowers in a glass vase
         (45x35cm-18x14in) mono.d.1944 (D.FL 1800)
£727 $1316   (21-May-92 SY.AM106) Still life (70x95cm-28x37in) s.d.1930 (D.FL 2400)
£788 $1426   (21-May-92 SY.AM126/R) The terrace of Hotel Huis ter Duin, Noordwyk
         (40x60cm-16x24in) mono.d.30 (D.FL 2600)

NIGG, Joseph (1782-1863) Austrian
£20619 $35876   (21-Sep-91 SA.A1778/R) Still life of flowers (35x26cm-14x10in) s. gouache
         bodycol board (DM 60000)

NIGHTINGALE, Basil (1864-1940) British
£750 $1328   (6-Nov-91 RBB879) Three hunters close to barn (61x91cm-24x36in) s.d.1905
£1200 $2076   (26-Mar-92 LE212) Captain Bay, Middleton Doveraille, winner of 137 races
         (61x91cm-24x36in) s.d.1893
£400 $684   (20-Mar-92 CBB255) Mr Harnetts Gigante by San Martin - study of racehorse
         W/C pencil htd white
£500 $865   (4-Sep-91 PHK54/R) A water jumper (36x54cm-14x21in) s.i.d.1905 W/C black
         chk htd white
£850 $1539   (5-Dec-91 LE503) A good start (23x30cm-9x12in) s. W/C
£850 $1462   (3-Mar-92 SWS1701) A white squall (53x69cm-21x27in) s.i.d.1917 W/C over
         blk.chk.
£900 $1584   (6-Apr-92 PH136) In full cry (43x71cm-17x28in) s.d.1922 W/C over black
         chk htd white

NIGHTINGALE, Frederick C (19th C) British
£420 $802   (16-Jul-92 CSK8) Canal San Giorgio, Venice (24x54cm-9x21in) init.d.1876
         s.i.num.4 verso pencil W/C htd wht

NIGNET, Georges (20th C) French
£894 $1600   (6-May-92 D.NY122/R) Quai sur bateau (61x91cm-24x36in) s.
£904 $1600   (6-Nov-91 D.NY88/R) Boulevard d'Orleans (61x91cm-24x36in) s.
£904 $1600   (6-Nov-91 D.NY89/R) La rivere de Loire (76x102cm-30x40in) s.
£1006 $1800   (6-May-92 D.NY119/R) French Riviera (61x91cm-24x36in) s.
£1117 $2000   (6-May-92 D.NY120/R) Le marche de fleurs (61x91cm-24x36in) s.
£1117 $2000   (6-May-92 D.NY121/R) Bateau sur la Marne (61x91cm-24x36in) s.
£1307 $2300   (9-Apr-92 FA.PH576) Portofino (76x102cm-30x40in) s.
£1469 $2600   (6-Nov-91 D.NY100/R) Les quai du Seine (76x102cm-30x40in) s.

NIGRO, Mario (1917-) Italian
£1675	$3048	(26-May-92 SY.MI105/R) Il prato sul monte (40x40cm-16x16in) s.i.verso acrylic (I.L 3700000)
£1842	$3353	(9-Dec-91 CH.R74/R) Senza titolo (50x40cm-20x16in) s. (I.L 4000000)
£5097	$9073	(26-Nov-91 SY.MI168/R) Giallo (61x50cm-24x20in) s. s.i.d.1963verso (I.L 11000000)
£6961	$13087	(19-Dec-91 F.M190/R) Spazio totale (65x54cm-26x21in) s.verso mixed media canvas (I.L 15000000)

NIJLAND, Dirk (1881-?) Dutch
| £2469 | $4494 | (12-Dec-91 SY.AM31/R) Landscape (45x60cm-18x24in) mono.d.10 (D.FL 8000) |

NIJMEGEN, Dionys van (1705-1789) Dutch
| £2528 | $4500 | (22-Jan-92 D.NY62) Putti in niche with portrait relief surrounded by garland of flowers (81x155cm-32x61in) |

NIJMEGEN, Gerard van (1735-1808) Dutch
| £767 | $1395 | (12-Dec-91 L.K448/R) Southern landscape with classical figures i.d.1773 pen sepia wash (DM 2200) |

NIJS, Alex (20th C) Dutch?
| £550 | $974 | (5-Nov-91 SY.AM389) Hot news (56x44cm-22x17in) s. (D.FL 1800) |

NIKEL, Lea (1918-) Israeli
£1064	$2000	(5-Jan-92 GG.TA288/R) Untitled (50x40cm-20x16in) s. s.d.1969verso
£2333	$4200	(6-Jan-92 GG.TA427/R) Untitled (55x46cm-22x18in) s. s.d.1970verso
£3143	$5500	(26-Sep-91 SY.I117/R) Composition in red (61x46cm-24x18in) s. d.1958verso
£4571	$8000	(26-Sep-91 SY.I116/R) Studio interior (72x59cm-28x23in) s. s.d.1951verso
£486	$900	(8-Jun-92 GG.TA64/R) Untitled (35x27cm-14x11in) s.d.74 W/C pencil

NIKODEM, Artur (1870-1940) Austrian
| £5958 | $10606 | (28-Nov-91 D.V102/R) Portrait of woman (57x54cm-22x21in) s.d.26 canvas on board (A.S 120000) |
| £1359 | $2419 | (28-Apr-92 D.V210/R) Rovereto (34x35cm-13x14in) s.i.d.27 pen (A.S 28000) |

NIKOLAKI, Z P (?) ?
| £1000 | $1900 | (26-Jun-92 WOL.C461/R) After the ball (102x76cm-40x30in) s. |

NIKUTOWSKI, Erich (1872-1921) German
| £629 | $1089 | (25-Mar-92 KM.K1341) View of village in the Eifel (25x35cm-10x14in) s. (DM 1800) |

NILSEN, Ulf Roger (1950-) Norwegian
| £483 | $831 | (7-Oct-91 B.O102/R) Untitled (190x306cm-75x120in) init. triptych (N.KR 5500) |

NILSON, Johann Esaias (1721-1788) German
£1186	$2111	(29-Nov-91 GAB.G2987 a) Les quatre saisons (32x52cm-13x20in) s.d.1745-46 pen three (S.FR 3000)
£1747	$3004	(11-Oct-91 AW.H996/R) Design for cartouche with river gods (27x31cm-11x12in) s.d.1745 pen ochre wash (DM 5100)
£2514	$4500	(15-Jan-92 CH.NY171/R) Design for frontispiece - Faith seated under awning, garden beyond (18x26cm-7x10in) s.d.1757 black chk pen wash htd white

NILSON, Johann Esaias (attrib) (1721-1788) German
| £722 | $1270 | (11-Apr-92 AW.H369/R) Hunting scene (28x21cm-11x8in) indian ink sepia pen brush (DM 2100) |

NILSON, Karl Gustaf (1942-) Swedish
| £720 | $1303 | (3-Dec-91 AB.S5112/R) The river (70x70cm-28x28in) s.d.1988 (S.KR 7500) |
| £1008 | $1824 | (3-Dec-91 AB.S5113/R) 'Partitur' (70x70cm-28x28in) s.d.1988 (S.KR 10500) |

NILSON, Severin (1846-1918) Swedish
£854	$1563	(12-May-92 GO.G104) Coastal landscape with headland (31x47cm-12x19in) s. panel (S.KR 9000)
£1201	$2114	(11-Apr-92 FAL.M285/R) Coastal landscape (33x77cm-13x30in) s. (S.KR 12600)
£1423	$2604	(12-May-92 GO.G105) Landscape from Tronninge, Halland (40x70cm-16x28in) s. (S.KR 15000)
£1440	$2606	(3-Dec-91 AB.S4645/R) Autumn landscape with houses and woman on road (32x26cm-13x10in) s. panel (S.KR 15000)
£1460	$2598	(28-Oct-91 AB.S158) Field in summer (67x89cm-26x35in) s. (S.KR 15500)
£1466	$2654	(19-May-92 AB.S4252/R) Summer landscape with corn stooks (40x70cm-16x28in) s. (S.KR 15500)
£1745	$3070	(11-Apr-92 FAL.M286/R) Winter landscape with trees and belfry (32x23cm-13x9in) s. panel (S.KR 18300)
£1994	$3470	(13-Apr-92 AB.S181) Lake landscape with trees, evening sun (67x99cm-26x39in) s.d.1910 (S.KR 21000)
£2087	$3820	(14-May-92 BU.S48/R) Girl in birch grove (69x45cm-27x18in) panel (S.KR 22000)
£2170	$3841	(5-Nov-91 BA.S137 a/R) Poultry feeding by farmhouse (52x69cm-20x27in) s. (S.KR 23000)
£2286	$4160	(14-Dec-91 BA.S54) Cottage interior with old woman (68x51cm-27x20in) s. (S.KR 24000)

NILSON, Severin (1846-1918) Swedish-cont.

£2354	$4190	(28-Oct-91 AB.S157) Farmers on the way to church near coast (58x86cm-23x34in) s. (S.KR 25000)
£2460	$4452	(19-May-92 AB.S4251/R) Swedish lake landscape with red building in summer (28x63cm-11x25in) s. panel (S.KR 26000)
£2554	$4623	(19-May-92 AB.S4912/R) Summer landscape with red cottage by lake (28x40cm-11x16in) s. panel (S.KR 27000)
£2562	$4688	(12-May-92 GO.G107) Moonlit landscape, Kolmarden (90x70cm-35x28in) s. (S.KR 27000)
£2687	$4864	(3-Dec-91 AB.S4644/R) River landscape in autumn (68x99cm-27x39in) s. (S.KR 28000)
£3500	$6299	(23-Nov-91 SO.S466/R) Hunter with gun in wood (97x54cm-38x21in) s. (S.KR 36500)

NILSSON, Axel (1887-1981) Swedish

£1789	$3185	(28-Oct-91 AB.S155/R) Still life with azalea (40x32cm-16x13in) s. (S.KR 19000)
£1898	$3472	(13-May-92 BU.S130/R) Still life of fruit (38x46cm-15x18in) s. panel (S.KR 20000)
£1987	$3596	(19-May-92 AB.S5285/R) Still life of potted plants on table (39x27cm-15x11in) s. (S.KR 21000)
£2372	$4341	(13-May-92 BU.S131/R) Tulips and apples on table (54x45cm-21x18in) s.d.1935 (S.KR 25000)
£16556	$29967	(19-May-92 AB.S5284/R) View through open window towards Skeppsbron and Strommen, Stockholm (60x83cm-24x33in) s.d.43 (S.KR 175000)

NILSSON, Bert Johnny (1934-) Swedish

£667	$1174	(11-Apr-92 FAL.M288/R) Woman with fly I (73x60cm-29x24in) s. (S.KR 7000)
£667	$1174	(11-Apr-92 FAL.M289/R) Woman with fly II (73x60cm-29x24in) s. (S.KR 7000)
£724	$1275	(11-Apr-92 FAL.M290/R) Woman with fly III (73x60cm-29x24in) s. (S.KR 7600)
£2176	$3939	(19-May-92 AB.S5286/R) 'The 4th way' (129x161cm-51x63in) s.d.1982 (S.KR 23000)

NILSSON, Lars (1956-) Swedish

| £474 | $868 | (13-May-92 BU.S134/R) Malmo Exchange (28x76cm-11x30in) s.verso panel diptych (S.KR 5000) |
| *£1145* | *$2038* | *(27-Nov-91 BU.S68/R) Female face (94x94cm-37x37in) s.d.1987verso mixed media (S.KR 12000)* |

NILSSON, Nils (1901-1949) Swedish

£759	$1389	(12-May-92 GO.G110) Avenue of trees (54x41cm-21x16in) init. (S.KR 8000)
£806	$1476	(12-May-92 GO.G109) Roof tops (55x52cm-22x20in) init. (S.KR 8500)
£868	$1536	(10-Nov-91 BU.M95) Portrait with flowers (73x60cm-29x24in) st.sig.verso (S.KR 9200)
£1139	$2083	(13-May-92 BU.S135/R) View from Hovshallar, with figures (60x75cm-24x30in) init. (S.KR 12000)
£4554	$8334	(11-May-92 NOR.S79/R) Interior (97x127cm-38x50in) init. (S.KR 48000)
£623	*$1122*	*(19-Nov-91 GO.G281) Ladies on the stairs (53x43cm-21x17in) s. gouache (S.KR 6500)*

NILSSON, Olof (1868-1956) Swedish

| £678 | $1207 | (28-Oct-91 AB.S156) Summer evening near Torne marsh (46x60cm-18x24in) s.d.1945 (S.KR 7200) |
| £755 | $1336 | (5-Nov-91 BA.S135/R) Mountain landscape, Kebenekajse area (83x64cm-33x25in) s.d.1933 (S.KR 8000) |

NILSSON, Vera (1888-1979) Swedish

£1044	$1910	(13-May-92 BU.S137/R) Portrait of a darkhaired man (52x38cm-20x15in) init. (S.KR 11000)
£1813	$3227	(28-Nov-91 BU.S102/R) Palm trees, Spain (57x60cm-22x24in) s. (S.KR 19000)
£3036	$5556	(13-May-92 BU.S136/R) The small path (80x65cm-31x26in) init. (S.KR 32000)
£3626	$6454	(28-Nov-91 BU.S103/R) Katarina by bouquet of violets (32x45cm-13x18in) init. (S.KR 38000)
£8065	$14758	(11-May-92 NOR.S95/R) Small girl writing (40x31cm-16x12in) s. (S.KR 85000)

NIMMO, John Jules (1830-?) French

£450	*$788*	*(25-Feb-92 CSK47) A lady in blue dress wearing a purple coat (16x?cm-6x?in) min.s.d.1879verso oval after Mme.Vigee-Lebrun*
£520	*$910*	*(25-Feb-92 CSK51) La Cruche cassee (16x?cm-6x?in) min.s.d.1879 oval after Jean Baptiste Greuze*
£720	*$1260*	*(25-Feb-92 CSK50/R) Diane au bain (9x?cm-4x?in) min.s.d.1879verso rec.after Francois Boucher*

NIN Y TUDO, Jose (1840-1908) Spanish

| £1107 | $1993 | (29-Jan-92 FER.M242/R) Perfil de joven (37x27cm-15x11in) s. (S.P 200000) |

NINERZE-RUIZ, E (19/20th C) Spanish

| £955 | $1700 | (22-Jan-92 SY.NY536/R) Portrait of young woman holding eggs (74x59cm-29x23in) s.d.1925 |

NINNES, Bernard (19th C?) British

| £500 | $875 | (27-Feb-92 L302) Still life of vase of roses (61x51cm-24x20in) s. |

NIQUILLE, Armand (1912-) Swiss
£1569 $2667   (23-Oct-91 GD.B551/R) L'humilie (55x46cm-22x18in) s.d.43 i.d.verso tempera (S.FR 4000)

NISBET, Noel Laura (1887-1956) British
£4800 $8256   (11-Oct-91 C172/R) The Seven Deadly Sins (88x173cm-35x68in)
£500 $925   *(11-Jun-92 CSK24) Idle moments (36x25cm-14x10in) s. paneil W/C*

NISHIZAWA, Luis (1926-) Mexican
£2368 $4500   (25-Jun-92 BG.M64/R) Latin American float scene with figures (122x76cm-48x30in) s.d.52 canvasboard

NISS, Thorvald (1842-1905) Danish
£484 $813   (27-Aug-91 RAS.K444) Man collecting firewood (52x40cm-20x16in) mono. (D.KR 5500)
£579 $996   (15-Oct-91 RAS.K191) Autumn day in the wood (79x123cm-31x48in) s.d.1891 (D.KR 6500)
£634 $1096   (2-Sep-91 BU.K55/R) Landscape with large trees (80x69cm-31x27in) s.d.1899 (D.KR 7200)
£716 $1302   (12-Dec-91 RAS.V753) Coastal landscape with pier and steamship (51x76cm-20x30in) s.d.1888 (D.KR 8000)
£880 $1479   (27-Aug-91 RAS.K431/R) Boy skating on frozen lake (48x72cm-19x28in) mono. (D.KR 10000)
£898 $1589   (11-Feb-92 RAS.K233/R) Landscape with cows at daybreak (67x85cm-26x33in) mono.d.1884 (D.KR 10000)
£1058 $1884   (28-Apr-92 RAS.K120/R) Wooded landscape with brook (126x111cm-50x44in) s.d.1890 (D.KR 12000)
£2377 $3993   (27-Aug-91 RAS.K594/R) From a country garden - peonies and lilacs (82x52cm-32x20in) s.d.1895 (D.KR 27000)
£2822 $5023   (28-Apr-92 RAS.K62/R) At the back of the farmhouse, summer (85x125cm-33x49in) mono. (D.KR 32000)

NISSL, Rudolf (1870-1955) Austrian
£1045 $1902   (11-Dec-91 N.M551/R) Female nude standing before patterned drape (73x57cm-29x22in) s. d.1916verso i.stretcher (DM 3000)
£1049 $1815   (25-Mar-92 KM.K1343/R) Pandora (45x35cm-18x14in) s. (DM 3000)
£1166 $2099   (30-Jan-92 RAS.V659/R) Still life of dinner service (70x100cm-28x39in) s. (D.KR 13000)
£1738 $3093   (28-Nov-91 D.V195/R) Still life (78x64cm-31x25in) s. (A.S 35000)
£1963 $3729   (25-Jun-92 D.V478/R) Pandora (45x35cm-18x14in) s. (A.S 40000)

NITSCH, Hermann (1938-) Austrian
£872 $1561   (19-Jan-92 CC.P22) Sans titre (68x99cm-27x39in) s.d.1987verso paper (F.FR 8500)
£8725 $15880   (26-May-92 D.V204/R) Golgotha (105x122cm-41x48in) s.i.d.1956 (A.S 180000)
£526 $947   *(23-Nov-91 N.M245/R) Neunzehnte Malaktion (21x32cm-8x13in) s.d.1986 oil dispersion board (DM 1500)*
£1515 $2742   *(19-May-92 CH.AM279/R) Composition in red (68x99cm-27x39in) s.i.d.1987 verso bodycol. (D.FL 5000)*
£2243 $4015   *(15-Jan-92 D.V246/R) Untitled (52x65cm-20x26in) s.d.1983 blood canvas (A.S 45000)*
£2564 $4590   *(19-Jan-92 CC.P21/R) Relique d'action (55x55cm-22x22in) s. dried blood tissue (F.FR 25000)*
£3151 $5734   *(26-May-92 D.V331/R) Schuttbild (104x80cm-41x31in) s.d.1983 chk dispersion hessian (A.S 65000)*
£4211 $7579   *(19-Nov-91 L.K974/R) Frammento della pittura dell'O.M Theater (200x50cm-79x20in) i.d.1985verso red paint hessian on panel (DM 12000)*

NITTIS, Giuseppe de (1846-1884) Italian
£5978 $10701   (14-Nov-91 CH.R164) Foresta di Fontainebleau (21x31cm-8x12in) s.d.73 canvas on board (I.L 13000000)
£27888 $47688   (19-Mar-92 F.M89/R) Paesaggio toscano (12x30cm-5x12in) s. paper on panel (I.L 60000000)
£69719 $119219   (19-Mar-92 F.M86/R) Leontine (20x17cm-8x7in) s. board (I.L 150000000)
£87209 $150000   (16-Oct-91 CH.NY206/R) Place des Pyramides (33x24cm-13x9in) s. panel
£306763 $524564   (19-Mar-92 F.M84/R) Il pasto delle anitre (25x60cm-10x24in) s.d.1874 panel (I.L 660000000)
£915 $1657   *(3-Dec-91 FN.S1861 a/R) Paris boulevard, evening (30x23cm-12x9in) s. chl htd.white (DM 2600)*
£1859 $3179   *(19-Mar-92 F.M53) Studi di teste di donne. Studi di figure sedute (10x17cm-4x7in) st.studio st.studio verso pencil double-sided (I.L 4000000)*
£6275 $10730   *(19-Mar-92 F.M52/R) Testina di Jacques (37x27cm-15x11in) st.studio i. W/C (I.L 13500000)*

NITTIS, Giuseppe de (circle) (1846-1884) Italian
£1702 $3046   (14-Nov-91 CH.R91) Paesaggio fluviale (12x32cm-5x13in) i. panel (I.L 3700000)

NIVARD, Charles Francois (1739-1821) French
£4587 $8532   (18-Jun-92 SY.MO322/R) Orientaux pres de ruines antiques (47x56cm-19x22in) s. (F.FR 45000)

NIVELLE, Jean (20th C) French?
£819 $1458   (27-Nov-91 CB.P37/R) L'eternelle chanson (117x156cm-46x61in) s.d.1948
           gouache (F.FR 8000)

NIVERT, Georgette (20th C) French
£557 $1015   (11-Dec-91 WE.MU311) Female nude (33x55cm-13x22in) s. board (DM 1600)

NIXON, John (1760-1818) British
£1800 $3222   (14-Nov-91 S142/R) Dublin, busy street (48x68cm-19x27in) s.d.1790 W/C
           over pencil

NIXON, Kay (1895-1988) British
£550 $995   (2-Dec-91 B66/R) Taken by surprise (36x53cm-14x21in) s. chl W/C gouache

NIZOVAIA, Sofia (1918-) Russian
£409 $729   (25-Nov-91 ARC.P151/R) La nouvelle robe (42x60cm-17x24in) s. W/C
           (F.FR 4000)
£450 $802   (25-Nov-91 ARC.P149/R) Les tricoteuses (65x68cm-26x27in) s. W/C
           (F.FR 4400)
£461 $820   (25-Nov-91 ARC.P153/R) Les jeunes musiciens (70x75cm-28x30in) s. pastel
           (F.FR 4500)

NOAILLY, A (?) ?
£1673 $2893   (2-Sep-91 BU.K70/R) Rococo interior with figures playing chess
           (62x85cm-24x33in) s. (D.KR 19000)
£2205 $3924   (28-Apr-92 RAS.K147/R) Romantic scene with young couples in rococo
           interior (60x86cm-24x34in) s. (D.KR 25000)

NOAILLY, Francisque (?) French?
£1751 $3291   (16-Dec-91 BG.P111) Le port d'Alger (100x81cm-39x32in) s. (F.FR 17000)

NOAKOWSKI, Stanislaw (1867-1928) Polish
£419 $724   (8-Sep-91 REM.W23) Castle interior (36x55cm-14x22in) s. gouache
           (P.Z 8000000)

NOBLE, James (1919-1989) British
£520 $926   (30-Apr-92 CSK23) Roses in vase on ledge (52x41cm-20x16in) s.
£850 $1496   (7-Apr-92 EH3) Still life study of roses in glass (38x28cm-15x11in) s.

NOBLE, Jill (?) ?
£940 $1674   (27-Apr-92 J.M316) The very slow train (85x110cm-33x43in) s.d.87
           (A.D 2200)

NOBLE, John Sargeant (1848-1896) British
£800 $1376   (15-Oct-91 CSK617/R) There's many a slip twixt cup and lip
           (45x81cm-18x32in) s.d.1874
£900 $1629   (4-Dec-91 S173/R) Mallard (21x36cm-8x14in) s.
£1450 $2509   (4-Sep-91 PHK126/R) In charge (33x44cm-13x17in) s. s.i.verso panel
£1700 $3196   (19-Dec-91 C153/R) On the Moors (53x43cm-21x17in) s.

NOBLE, Richard Pratchett (fl.1830-1861) British
£900 $1584   (6-Apr-92 PH68/R) By a cottage at Claygate, Surrey (26x37cm-10x15in) W/C
           htd white

NOBLE, Robert (1857-1917) British
£2100 $3570   (21-Oct-91 H269) Portrait of Staffordshire bull terrier (48x41cm-19x16in)
           init.
£5200 $9412   (4-Dec-91 S206/R) By riverside (91x167cm-36x66in) s.

NOBLE, Thomas Satterwhite (1835-1907) American
£2069 $3600   (15-Apr-92 SY.NY776/R) Library (46x61cm-18x24in) i.verso board

NOCKEN, Wilhelm Theodor (1830-1905) German
£687 $1196   (18-Sep-91 N.M640/R) Mountain lake with rocky banks (49x67cm-19x26in) s.
           (DM 2000)
£767 $1395   (11-Dec-91 N.M552/R) Sunlit mountain lake landscape, possibly
           Vierwaldstatter See (56x81cm-22x32in) i. (DM 2200)

NOCRET, Jean (circle) (1617-1672) French
£3043 $5355   (11-Apr-92 AT.P79/R) Portrait presume d'une fille de Louis XIV
           (56x46cm-22x18in) (F.FR 30000)

NOCRET, Jean Charles (1648-1691) French
£12860 $23277   (5-Dec-91 SY.MO149/R) Portrait de Monsieur, Philippe d'Orleans, en Mars
           (140x200cm-55x79in) (F.FR 125000)

NOE, Luis Felipe (1933-) Argentinian
£3333 $6000   (19-Nov-91 CH.NY153/R) Cuadro del Agnostico (96x129cm-38x51in) s.
           s.i.d.1963verso acrylic silver gold collage

NOEL, Alexandre Jean (1752-1834) French
£3500 $6370   (10-Dec-91 C219/R) Peasants in a storm (34x46cm-13x18in) s. bodycol
£7209 $13553   (16-Dec-91 AGS.P62/R) Paysage avec des lavandieres et des pecheurs au
           pied d'une cascade.Marine au clair de lune (48x68cm-19x27in) s.d.1794
           gouache pair (F.FR 70000)

NOEL, Alexandre Jean (1752-1834) French-cont.

| £7821 | $14000 | (14-Jan-92 SY.NY68/R) Peasants on river bank, with houses and boat in background (35x46cm-14x18in) s. gouache |
| £11732 | $21000 | (14-Jan-92 SY.NY67/R) Ships on stormy sea, with figures on shore (40x56cm-16x22in) gouache |

NOEL, Georges (20th C) French

£821	$1478	(19-Nov-91 FB.P125/R) Sans titre (30x35cm-12x14in) s. d.58verso board laid down on panel (F.FR 8000)
£1126	$2004	(29-Nov-91 D.P209) Composition rouge (33x49cm-13x19in) s.d.56 paper laid down on canvas (F.FR 11000)
£2881	$5214	(6-Dec-91 GL.P274/R) Composition (63x90cm-25x35in) s. d.1961verso paper laid down on canvas (F.FR 28000)
£4527	$7787	(12-Oct-91 GL.P50/R) Going North (76x56cm-30x22in) s.i.1987 i.verso oil sable (F.FR 45000)
£6379	$11545	(2-Dec-91 CC.P28/R) Palimpseste (97x130cm-38x51in) s.d.1961 mono.i.verso oil resin sable (F.FR 62000)

NOEL, John Bates (19/20th C) British

| £523 | $900 | (16-Oct-91 NY77) Rushing Mountain river (51x76cm-20x30in) init.d.1909 |
| £1150 | $1990 | (4-Sep-91 PHK79) Peat stacks, Arthog Moor, near Barmouth (48x75cm-19x30in) s.d.1893 s.i.d.verso |

NOEL, Jules (1815-1881) French

£771	$1326	(4-Mar-92 AT.P176) La corvette mixte - La Cassinni (36x33cm-14x13in) s. canvas laid down on board (F.FR 7500)
£872	$1500	(14-Oct-91 H.C54/R) French village scene (36x25cm-14x10in) s. panel
£1569	$2667	(23-Oct-91 GD.B1204/R) Sunday school (38x27cm-15x11in) s.indis.i. (S.FR 4000)
£1896	$3356	(5-Nov-91 SY.AM60/R) Moored sailing vessels (25x36cm-10x14in) s.d.1877 (D.FL 6200)
£4104	$7306	(25-Nov-91 W.T1990/R) French fishing boats in harbour (37x55cm-15x22in) s. (C.D 8250)
£7200	$12312	(20-Mar-92 C21 a/R) French vessels moored outside town (39x55cm-15x22in) s.
£8235	$14000	(25-Oct-91 S.W2777/R) Harbour scene (38x53cm-15x21in) s.
£12358	$21133	(18-Mar-92 PIC.P85) Les elegantes au bord de la mer (33x46cm-13x18in) s.d.1869 panel (F.FR 120000)
£30550	$55906	(3-Jun-92 PIC.P37/R) Crinolines sur la plage a Fecamp (74x110cm-29x43in) s.d.1871 (F.FR 300000)
£1368	$2476	(22-May-92 LD.P4) Scene maritime. Scene orientale (24x33cm-9x13in) s.d.1846 pencil gouache wash pair (F.FR 13500)

NOEL, Jules (attrib) (1815-1881) French

| £750 | $1358 | (21-May-92 CSK158) Boats beached on stormy coast (27x38cm-11x15in) s. board |

NOEL, T B (19/20th C) ?

| £460 | $833 | (18-May-92 HS267) Harvesters in extensive landscape (25x34cm-10x13in) s.d.08 W/C |

NOELSMITH, T (fl.1889-1900) British

| £500 | $960 | (29-Jul-92 CSK51) Surrey cottage (27x38cm-11x15in) s.i. pencil W/C htd.white |

NOELSMITH, Thomas (fl.1889-1900) British

| £750 | $1433 | (1-Jul-92 B81/R) Pevensey Church (37x63cm-15x25in) s.i. W/C |

NOERR, Julius (1827-1897) German

| £4600 | $7958 | (4-Oct-91 C76 e/R) The hawking party (35x70cm-14x28in) s.d.1875 |
| £7904 | $13753 | (18-Sep-91 N.M641/R) Fisher family resting on the banks of lake Chiemsee (24x45cm-9x18in) s. panel (DM 23000) |

NOGALES, Jose (1860-?) Spanish

| £2737 | $4981 | (26-May-92 DUR.M89/R) Bodegon (54x65cm-21x26in) s. (S.P 500000) |

NOGARET, Henri (20th C) French?

| £605 | $1058 | (25-Sep-91 CC.P15) Untitled (31x35cm-12x14in) d.1984 panel (F.FR 6000) |

NOGARI, Giuseppe (1699-1763) Italian

£1963	$3729	(23-Jun-92 D.V35/R) Portrait of artist drawing, possibly self portrait (55x44cm-22x17in) one of pair (A.S 40000)
£3435	$6526	(23-Jun-92 D.V34/R) Portrait of woman threading rosary beads (55x44cm-22x17in) one of pair (A.S 70000)
£8445	$14441	(20-Mar-92 ZZ.F20) Vieille femme tenant un verre de vin (59x45cm-23x18in) (F.FR 82000)

NOGARI, Giuseppe (circle) (1699-1763) Italian

| £1524 | $2652 | (13-Apr-92 AT.P40) Allegorie de l'Hiver (73x57cm-29x22in) trace sig. (F.FR 15000) |

NOGARI, Giuseppe (style) (1699-1763) Italian

| £1183 | $2140 | (19-May-92 AB.S4359/R) Young girl with vegetables (53x43cm-21x17in) (S.KR 12500) |

NOGARI, Giuseppe (style) (1699-1763) Italian-cont.
£2700 $4806   (29-Oct-91 PH123) Portrait of a peasant woman holding a pair of spectacles (63x49cm-25x19in)

NOGUCHI, Isamu (1904-) American
£2260 $4000   (7-Nov-91 SY.NY37/R) The Bells - design for the decor, the Dance of the Ghouls (40x28cm-16x11in) gouache pencil board

NOGUES (?) ?
£493 $897   (27-May-92 DUR.M386/R) Pescadores catalanes (60x70cm-24x28in) bears sig. (S.P 90000)

NOIRE (?) French
£832 $1597   (7-Jul-92 ARC.P89) Bord de mer (31x48cm-12x19in) s. (F.FR 8000)

NOIRE, Maxime (19th C) French
£669 $1258   (18-Dec-91 PR.P104) Village oriental (41x32cm-16x13in) s. (F.FR 6500)
£712 $1275   (17-Nov-91 FB.P87) Bou saada (35x65cm-14x26in) s. (F.FR 7000)

NOIROT, Emile (1853-1924) French
£640 $1088   (23-Oct-91 MMB263) Haystacks and poultry (33x51cm-13x20in) s.i.d.1889
£1373 $2333   (23-Oct-91 GD.B1205/R) Rue de Roanne with flags (45x32cm-18x13in) s.indis.d. (S.FR 3500)
£1818 $3218   (22-Apr-92 ZZ.F129) Les filets bleus a Concarneau (50x61cm-20x24in) s.d.1908 i.verso (F.FR 18000)

NOIZEUX, Henri (1871-?) French
£407 $707   (13-Apr-92 AT.P160) La Casbah d'Alger (32x24cm-13x9in) s. W/C (F.FR 4000)

NOLAN, Sidney (1917-) Australian
£470 $851   (2-Dec-91 AAA.S87 m) Wildflowers (29x23cm-11x9in) s.verso paper (A.D 1100)
£524 $917   (30-Mar-92 AAA.S140) Waterfall (26x31cm-10x12in) glass (A.D 1200)
£638 $1130   (26-Apr-92 SY.ME391) Yachts and foreshore (91x122cm-36x48in) s. s.i.d.1986 verso acrylic board (A.D 1500)
£793 $1427   (24-Nov-91 SY.S97) Jack Jesus (30x25cm-12x10in) init.i.d.1956 verso paper (A.D 1800)
£809 $1431   (26-Apr-92 SY.ME329) Yacht and city (91x122cm-36x48in) s. s.i.d.1986 verso acrylic board (A.D 1900)
£876 $1524   (16-Sep-91 CH.ME10/R) Military camp (24x29cm-9x11in) on glass (A.D 1900)
£936 $1657   (26-Apr-92 SY.ME44) Lincoln, U.S.A (51x63cm-20x25in) s. s.i. paper (A.D 2200)
£1057 $1903   (24-Nov-91 SY.S44) Convict and landscape (51x62cm-20x24in) s. paper on board (A.D 2400)
£1057 $1903   (24-Nov-91 SY.S23) Roses (62x51cm-24x20in) i.d.1962 verso paper (A.D 2400)
£1145 $2062   (24-Nov-91 SY.S3/R) Profile (30x25cm-12x10in) init.d.27-7-56 verso paper (A.D 2600)
£1174 $1960   (19-Aug-91 SY.ME99) Elephants (50x61cm-20x24in) s. paper on board (A.D 2500)
£1447 $2561   (26-Apr-92 SY.ME416) Sir Charles Hotham, Governor of Victoria (24x29cm-9x11in) init.d.1949 verso (A.D 4500)
£1850 $3330   (24-Nov-91 SY.S537/R) Leda and swan (121x151cm-48x59in) board (A.D 4200)
£1915 $3389   (26-Apr-92 SY.ME239/R) Bottle-brush (71x58cm-28x23in) s.verso board (A.D 4500)
£1923 $3423   (27-Apr-92 J.M13) Elephant - African series (52x62cm-20x24in) s. paper on board (A.D 4500)
£7042 $11761   (19-Aug-91 SY.ME295/R) Antarctic camp (120x120cm-47x47in) s.d.1964 board (A.D 15000)
£20513 $36513   (28-Apr-92 CH.ME151/R) Kelly and drought (91x121cm-36x48in) init.d.57 i.verso ripolin board (A.D 48000)
£21368 $38034   (28-Apr-92 CH.ME123/R) Wimmera landscape (121x150cm-48x59in) s. s.i.d.1966verso board (A.D 50000)
£385 $685   (27-Apr-92 J.M411) Figurative study and bird (55x34cm-22x13in) s.d.83 mixed media (A.D 900)
£430 $821   (29-Jun-92 AAA.S135) Bird in flight (29x24cm-11x9in) s. ripolin (A.D 1100)
£461 $802   (16-Sep-91 CH.ME1/R) Simpson and donkey (25x19cm-10x7in) i.verso ripolin board (A.D 1000)
£553 $962   (16-Sep-91 CH.ME128) Gallipoli (25x29cm-10x11in) i. mixed media board (A.D 1200)
£578 $988   (17-Mar-92 JRL.S229) Italian church (20x30cm-8x12in) s. ripolin (A.D 1300)
£939 $1568   (19-Aug-91 SY.ME16/R) Bourke and Wills (51x75cm-20x30in) s. mixed media (A.D 2000)
£939 $1568   (19-Aug-91 SY.ME55) Ned Kelly with rifle (63x51cm-25x20in) s. ripolin paper (A.D 2000)
£978 $1672   (17-Mar-92 JRL.S189/R) Greek medieval city (30x20cm-12x8in) s. ripolin (A.D 2200)
£1200 $2052   (17-Mar-92 JRL.S195/R) Umbrian valley (20x30cm-8x12in) s. ripolin (A.D 2700)
£1221 $2038   (19-Aug-91 SY.ME57) Central Australian landscape (51x75cm-20x30in) s. ripolin paper (A.D 2600)
£14085 $23521   (19-Aug-91 SY.ME290/R) Landscape - Central Australia (90x120cm-35x47in) s.d.20-2-50 ripolin board (A.D 30000)

NOLAND, Kenneth (1924-) American

£6704	$12000	(13-Nov-91 CH.NY161/R) Revelet (15x256cm-6x101in) s.i.d.1969 acrylic
£8380	$15000	(6-May-92 CH.NY327/R) Via Toss (42x175cm-17x69in) s.d.1968 verso acrylic canvas
£9497	$17000	(13-Nov-91 CH.NY206/R) Watch for Dawn (168x114cm-66x45in) s.i.d.1986verso acrylic
£11429	$20000	(25-Feb-92 SY.NY196/R) Beauty spot (14x259cm-6x102in) s.i.d.1969 acrylic
£16760	$30000	(13-Nov-91 CH.NY154/R) Winged (163x163cm-64x64in) s.d.1964verso acrylic
£17877	$32000	(13-Nov-91 CH.NY160/R) Capella (114x114cm-45x45in) i.verso acrylic
£18156	$32500	(7-May-92 SY.NY259 a/R) Keen transit (244x60cm-96x24in) s.d.1967 verso acrylic canvas
£26289	$45479	(29-Mar-92 P.V36/R) Florida (216x177cm-85x70in) s.d.1983verso acrylic (F.FR 255000)
£3800	*$6536*	*(17-Oct-91 S82/R) Handmade papers - horizontal stripes series III-23 (126x83cm-50x33in) s.d.78 six layers paper pulp*

NOLAU, Francois Joseph (1804-1883) French

£1249	*$2185*	*(3-Apr-92 AGS.P175/R) Rideau de Scene avec vue sur le Louvre et les Tuileries (45x47cm-18x19in) s. W/C wash htd.white gouache (F.FR 12000)*

NOLDE, Emil (1867-1956) German

£136519	$248464	(29-May-92 VG.B29/R) Sculpture of negro with vase of poppies (65x83cm-26x33in) s.d.1920 (DM 400000)
£283276	$515563	(29-May-92 VG.B27/R) Girl and lilies (59x37cm-23x15in) s. i.stretcher (DM 830000)
£594406	$1058042	(29-Nov-91 VG.B24/R) Little girl in flowering garden (60x70cm-24x28in) s.d.1908 s.i.stretcher (DM 1700000)
£6215	$11000	(6-Nov-91 CH.NY126/R) Zwei kostumierte Figuren (34x23cm-13x9in) s. W/C paper on paper
£6500	$11765	(2-Dec-91 CSK41/R) Weidende Kuhe (45x60cm-18x24in) s. brush ink
£10169	$18000	(6-Nov-91 CH.NY143/R) Buddhakopf vor roten Blumen (29x23cm-11x9in) s. W/C
£15120	$27973	(12-Jun-92 HN.H647/R) Junk before red evening sky (16x24cm-6x9in) s. W/C indian ink brush (DM 44000)
£15358	$27952	(26-May-92 KF.M1120/R) On the ice (21x26cm-8x10in) s. W/C over pencil (DM 45000)
£16376	$29805	(13-Dec-91 BM.B850/R) Farmhouse (14x9cm-6x4in) s. W/C (DM 47000)
£17065	$31058	(29-May-92 VG.B19/R) Female dancer (25x20cm-10x8in) s.i. W/C (DM 50000)
£17065	$31058	(30-May-92 VG.B218/R) Head of woman (31x22cm-12x9in) s. W/C indian ink (DM 50000)
£20000	$38000	(26-Jun-92 GK.B91/R) Cows grazing in landscape (33x45cm-13x18in) s. W/C indian ink (S.FR 52000)
£22184	$40375	(29-May-92 VG.B30/R) Madonna and tulips (35x47cm-14x19in) s. W/C (DM 65000)
£27491	$50859	(12-Jun-92 HN.H648/R) Portrait of woman (46x31cm-18x12in) s. W/C (DM 80000)
£27491	$50859	(12-Jun-92 HN.H646/R) Boats in yellow seascape (28x40cm-11x16in) s. W/C (DM 80000)
£27972	$49790	(28-Nov-91 SY.BE48/R) Sailing boat on stormy sea (22x27cm-9x11in) s. W/C bodycol (DM 80000)
£29210	$49656	(25-Oct-91 BM.B1085/R) Moor landscape with houses by stream (34x45cm-13x18in) s. W/C (DM 85000)
£30717	$55904	(29-May-92 VG.B28/R) Flowers (34x47cm-14x19in) s. W/C (DM 90000)
£32765	$59631	(29-May-92 VG.B20/R) Two tugboats in Hamburg Harbour (31x45cm-12x18in) s. W/C (DM 96000)
£39519	$72320	(3-Jun-92 L.K346/R) Poppies (27x22cm-11x9in) s. W/C (DM 115000)
£41237	$76289	(12-Jun-92 HN.H645/R) Tischrunde (21x26cm-8x10in) s. W/C indian ink brush (DM 120000)
£45455	$80909	(29-Nov-91 VG.B19/R) Two women in landscape (34x45cm-13x18in) s. W/C (DM 130000)
£49828	$91186	(3-Jun-92 L.K345/R) Branch of orchids (15x19cm-6x7in) s.i. W/C (DM 145000)
£51195	$93174	(27-May-92 PH.DU65/R) Cyclamen and chrysanthemums (35x47cm-14x19in) s. W/C (DM 150000)
£51546	$94330	(3-Jun-92 L.K344/R) Flowering magnolia (48x34cm-19x13in) s. W/C (DM 150000)
£57045	$104392	(3-Jun-92 L.K343/R) Zinnias and sunflowers (38x26cm-15x10in) s. W/C (DM 166000)
£59441	$105804	(26-Nov-91 KF.M919/R) Summer flowers (47x35cm-19x14in) s. W/C (DM 170000)
£73427	$130699	(29-Nov-91 VG.B23/R) Poppies (33x46cm-13x18in) s. W/C (DM 210000)
£75085	$136655	(29-May-92 VG.B26/R) Sunflowers (33x46cm-13x18in) s. W/C (DM 220000)
£80420	$143147	(29-Nov-91 VG.B20/R) Sailing boats at sunset (23x26cm-9x10in) s. W/C (DM 230000)
£85664	$152483	(29-Nov-91 VG.B35/R) Flowers in blue vase (34x47cm-13x19in) s. W/C (DM 245000)
£87432	$160000	(12-May-92 CH.NY125/R) Grosser roter Mohn (35x47cm-14x19in) s. W/C Japan paper
£97902	$174266	(29-Nov-91 VG.B33/R) Sunflowers (36x44cm-14x17in) s. W/C (DM 280000)

NOLLEKENS, Josef Frans (circle) (1702-1748) Flemish

£1700	$2975	(31-Mar-92 PH1/R) Elegant figures seated at foot of grand stairway in formal garden (76x64cm-30x25in)

NOME, Francois de (1593-c.1640) French

£18525	$32048	(25-Mar-92 CH.R93/R) Veduta fantastica di piazza con edifici monumentali e statua equestre (37x50cm-15x20in) (I.L 40000000)

NOME, Francois de (1593-c.1640) French-cont.
£22346 $40000   (17-Jan-92 SY.NY101/R) The desctruction of Sodom (51x75cm-20x30in)
       s.indist.d.1624

NOMELLINI, Plinio (1866-1943) Italian
£11346 $21103   (16-Jun-92 F.M295/R) Sulla spiaggia (27x46cm-11x18in) s. (I.L 25000000)

NONELL Y MONTURIOL, Isidro (1873-1911) Spanish
£5539 $9582   (24-Mar-92 EP.M8/R) Figura de perfil (32x24cm-13x9in) s.d.1909 sanguine
       W/C (S.P 1000000)

NONETTI, A (19/20th C) Italian
£920 $1600   (13-Sep-91 S.W2352/R) Italian port scene (51x76cm-20x30in) s.

NONN, Carl (1876-1949) German
£690 $1186   (16-Oct-91 KM.K1305) Snow covered Eifel landscape with cottage
       (42x26cm-17x10in) s.i.verso (DM 2000)
£1522 $2893   (24-Jun-92 KM.K1210/R) Monschau in the Eifel (81x66cm-32x26in) s.
       (DM 4400)

NONNOTTE, Donat (1708-1785) French
£5355 $10068   (18-Dec-91 AT.P204/R) Portrait d'un lettre (88x69cm-35x27in) s.d.1750
       (F.FR 52000)

NONNOTTE, Donat (studio) (1708-1785) French
£1512 $2676   (6-Nov-91 LT.P62/R) Dame de qualite en buste (66x53cm-26x21in)
       (F.FR 15000)

NONO, Luigi (1850-1918) Italian
£17212 $31842   (9-Jun-92 F.R152/R) Sottomarina (24x49cm-9x19in) s.d.1881 (I.L 38000000)

NOOMS, Reinier (1623-1667) Dutch
£13500 $24570   (13-Dec-91 C170/R) Mediterranean estuary with Dutch galleys and
       man-of-war (38x56cm-15x22in) s.

NOOMS, Reinier (style) (1623-1667) Dutch
£850 $1513   (31-Oct-91 B104) Dutch Men-o'-War and whalers off coastline
       (46x60cm-18x24in) bears sig. panel

NOORDIJK, Willem Frederik (1887-?) Dutch
£745 $1282   (7-Mar-92 CH.AM241/R) Laren in winter (50x70cm-20x28in) s. s.i.stretcher
       (D.FL 2400)

NOORT, Adam van (circle) (16/17th C) Flemish
£5523 $9500   (9-Oct-91 CH.NY181/R) Adoration of shepherds (97x126cm-38x50in) panel

NOORT, Adam van (style) (16/17th C) Flemish
£785 $1406   (7-May-92 CH.AM56) Christ on road to Emmaus (58x116cm-23x46in) panel
       (D.FL 2600)

NOORT, Adrianus Cornelis van (1914-) Dutch
£459 $839   (1-Jun-92 W.T1374/R) Woman on beach chair (30x40cm-12x16in) s. panel
       (C.D 1000)
£519 $924   (2-May-92 W.W31/R) Beach scene with child in white (23x28cm-9x11in) s.
       panel
£562 $1000   (2-May-92 W.W27/R) Figures on beach (28x38cm-11x15in) s. panel
£702 $1200   (21-Mar-92 W.W105/R) Clamdiggers (23x28cm-9x11in) s. panel
£734 $1343   (1-Jun-92 W.T1373/R) Under the blue umbrella (30x45cm-12x18in) s. panel
       (C.D 1600)
£741 $1296   (25-Feb-92 VN.R212/R) People on a beach (29x39cm-11x15in) s. panel
       (D.FL 2400)
£820 $1500   (16-May-92 HG.C233) Children on beach (51x69cm-20x27in) s. panel
£1404 $2400   (21-Mar-92 W.W116/R) Picnic by shore (48x69cm-19x27in) s. panel

NOORT, Jan van (style) (16-18th C) Dutch
£750 $1440   (10-Jul-92 C296) Portrait of young girl, wearing red costume and cap
       (39x28cm-15x11in)

NOORT, Lambert van (circle) (c.1520-1571) Dutch
£1500 $2670   (29-Oct-91 PH65/R) The Lamentation (77x104cm-30x41in) panel

NOORTIG, Jan (17th C) Dutch
£4282 $7750   (22-May-92 SY.NY162/R) Peasants playing jump rope (46x52cm-18x20in)
       s.d.1655 panel

NOOTEBOOM, Jacobus Hendricus Johannes (1811-1878) Dutch
£525 $918   (18-Feb-92 CH.AM328) Peasants resting near entrance to castle in wooded
       landscape (38x45cm-15x18in) s. (D.FL 1700)
£1529 $2722   (30-Oct-91 CH.AM267) Swiss hilly river landscape with peasant women near
       torrent at dawn (61x83cm-24x33in) s. (D.FL 5000)
£2160 $3781   (18-Feb-92 CH.AM323/R) Wooded hilly landscape with sailing vessels on
       river (17x23cm-7x9in) s.d.1842 panel two (D.FL 7000)

NORBERTO (1923-) Italian
£1905 $3487   (12-May-92 F.R165/R) Paesino sotto la neve (40x30cm-16x12in) s.
st.sig.l.verso panel (I.L 4200000)

NORBLIN DE LA GOURDAINE, Jean Pierre (1745-1830) French
£950 $1700   (15-Jan-92 CH.NY120/R) Paris and Helen (16x17cm-6x7in) s.d.1822 black
lead wash htd white
£2354 $4048   (13-Oct-91 REM.W21) Oriental rider (32x23cm-13x9in) s. W/C (P.Z 45000000)

NORBLIN DE LA GOURDAINE, Stefan (1892-1952) Polish
£480 $874   (11-Dec-91 CSK47/R) A Cossack on a spotted horse (20x23cm-8x9in)
s.i.d.1922 pen W/C bodycol.htd.varnish

NORDALM, Federico (1949-) Nicaraguan
£3889 $7000   (19-Nov-91 CH.NY209/R) Naturaleza muerta con cajas y latas
(85x93cm-33x37in) s.d.1990 s.d.verso
£4696 $8500   (18-May-92 CH.NY226/R) Naturaleza muerta con naranjas (85x91cm-33x36in)
s.d.1991 canvas on composite board

NORDAU, Maxa (20th C) French
£520 $998   (6-Jul-92 HC.P86/R) La pionniere (50x25cm-20x10in) s. (F.FR 5000)
£851 $1600   (5-Jan-92 GG.TA287) Still life (61x46cm-24x18in) s.
£1081 $2000   (8-Jun-92 GG.TA205/R) Landscape (49x60cm-19x24in) s.

NORDBERG, Olle (1905-1986) Swedish
£472 $835   (25-Apr-92 SO.S490/R) Hunter (25x12cm-10x5in) s. panel (S.KR 5000)
£547 $968   (25-Apr-92 SO.S489/R) Horse in enclosed pasture (32x40cm-13x16in) s.d.63
panel (S.KR 5800)
£565 $1006   (28-Oct-91 AB.S163) Girl and her attendants (20x37cm-8x15in) s.d.58
(S.KR 6000)
£570 $991   (13-Apr-92 AB.S184) Quiet moment - interior with organ (37x45cm-15x18in)
s.d.76 panel (S.KR 6000)
£623 $1122   (19-Nov-91 GO.G116) Seated girl and cyclist in landscape (22x27cm-9x11in)
s.d.45 panel (S.KR 6500)
£800 $1425   (28-Oct-91 AB.S162) Saturday afternoon in crofter's cottage
(30x40cm-12x16in) s.d.58 panel (S.KR 8500)
£826 $1438   (13-Apr-92 AB.S185) Garden scene with chickens (45x54cm-18x21in) s.d.67
panel (S.KR 8700)
£963 $1667   (28-Mar-92 UA.U363) Talking to the elders (46x55cm-18x22in) s.d.56 panel
(S.KR 10000)
£1130 $2011   (28-Oct-91 AB.S159/R) The engagement present - interior with figures
(37x45cm-15x18in) s.d.60 panel (S.KR 12000)
£1177 $2095   (28-Oct-91 AB.S160) Couple seated on sofa in parlour (45x37cm-18x15in)
s.d.57 panel (S.KR 12500)
£6831 $12501   (13-May-92 BU.S138/R) Summer dream (91x117cm-36x46in) s. (S.KR 72000)
£8111 $14437   (28-Nov-91 BU.S104/R) Jansson's memory (162x130cm-64x51in) s.
(S.KR 85000)

NORDEL, Sigismund (19/20th C) ?
£520 $952   (14-May-92 TL4/R) Die weinprobe (25x30cm-10x12in) s.d.1903 panel

NORDELL, Carl J (1885-?) American
£1955 $3500   (13-Nov-91 B.SF2683/R) Still life with jug and teapot (61x81cm-24x32in)
s.

NORDENBERG, Bengt (1822-1902) Swedish
£568 $977   (8-Mar-92 BU.M347) Portrait of man in black costume (58x47cm-23x19in)
s.d.1848 (S.KR 5900)
£3774 $6755   (7-May-92 RAS.S5/R) The first steps (41x56cm-16x22in) s.d.1868
(S.KR 40000)
£5676 $10274   (19-May-92 AB.S4914/R) Young goat herders (58x48cm-23x19in) s.d.1878
(S.KR 60000)
£6149 $11131   (19-May-92 AB.S4253/R) Stjarngossarna - young boys holding a large star
(70x100cm-28x39in) s.d.1895 (S.KR 65000)
£7569 $13699   (19-May-92 AB.S4913/R) One Sunday morning on Ronneby river
(70x94cm-28x37in) s.d.85 (S.KR 80000)
£9962 $18231   (12-May-92 GO.G113/R) Returned from bearhunt, peasants celebrating by the
porch (55x78cm-22x31in) s.d.1873 (S.KR 105000)
£11036 $19976   (3-Dec-91 AB.S4646/R) Summer landscape with children on woody hill
(63x81cm-25x32in) s.d.1885 (S.KR 115000)

NORDENBERG, Hendrick (1857-1928) Swedish
£1091 $1997   (12-May-92 GO.G114) Cellar interior with old woman (60x48cm-24x19in) s.
(S.KR 11500)
£1617 $2700   (25-Aug-91 BU.M13) Interior with girl playing with kitten
(45x37cm-18x15in) s.d.91 panel (S.KR 17200)

NORDFELDT, Bror Julius Olsson (1878-1955) American
£770 $1378   (16-Nov-91 FAL.M230/R) Old man with stick (93x40cm-37x16in) mono.
(S.KR 8100)
£1632 $3100   (26-Jun-92 WOL.C474) Still life of vase and sheaves of wheat
(64x48cm-25x19in) s.
£4454 $7750   (15-Apr-92 SY.NY154/R) Minnesota landscape (76x102cm-30x40in) s.d.35
i.stretcher

NORDGREN, Anna (1847-1916) Swedish
£896 $1586   (5-Nov-91 BA.S138/R) 'Dometorp, Vastergotland' (40x56cm-16x22in) s. (S.KR 9500)
£1438 $2589   (19-Nov-91 GO.G282) Young girl eating her meal in her room (50x60cm-20x24in) s. W/C htd white (S.KR 15000)

NORDGREN, Axel (1828-1888) Swedish
£800 $1448   (21-May-92 CSK119) Hunters stalking reindeer (61x102cm-24x40in) s.d.1872
£1408 $2366   (27-Aug-91 RAS.K147/R) Coastal landscape with rocks and man by his boat (51x73cm-20x29in) s.d.1861 (D.KR 16000)
£1734 $3000   (28-Mar-92 UA.U364/R) Moonlit water course with solitary fisherman (63x87cm-25x34in) s.d.1862 (S.KR 18000)
£1898 $3472   (14-May-92 BU.S49/R) Bohuslan landscape with fishermen (51x75cm-20x30in) s.d.1861 (S.KR 20000)
£1932 $3438   (29-Oct-91 UL.T208/R) Evening landscape 1864 (50x83cm-20x33in) (N.KR 22000)

NORDLIEN, Olaf (1864-1919) Norwegian
£537 $1026   (21-Jul-92 UL.T201) Wooded landscape (47x86cm-19x34in) (N.KR 6000)

NORDSTROM, Gerhard (1925-) Scandinavian
£485 $868   (16-Nov-91 FAL.M231/R) Southern landscape (65x75cm-26x30in) s.d.52 (S.KR 5100)

NORDSTROM, Karl (1845-1923) Swedish
£2236 $4070   (10-Dec-91 RAS.K202/R) Town wall outside Visby (55x46cm-22x18in) mono.i.on stretcher (D.KR 25000)
£3795 $6945   (11-May-92 NOR.S8/R) Winter landscape (97x83cm-38x33in) s.d.1888 (S.KR 40000)
£5218 $9549   (11-May-92 NOR.S12/R) Landscape, Koon, Kyrkosund (128x188cm-50x74in) s.d.1909 (S.KR 55000)
£963 $1667   (28-Mar-92 UA.U366/R) Rainclouds by the coast (70x98cm-28x39in) s. col chk (S.KR 10000)

NORDSTROM, Lars Gunnar (1924-) Scandinavian
£4678 $8233   (12-Apr-92 HOR.H181/R) Red composition (122x122cm-48x48in) s.d.1954 (F.M 37000)

NORIE, Orlando (1832-1901) British
£400 $732   (14-May-92 B277/R) Troop of Hussars receiving refreshment at farmstead (32x47cm-13x19in) s. W/C
£1000 $1850   (12-Jun-92 C12) Field Battery of Royal Regiment of Artillery en route to Pirbright (45x73cm-18x29in) s. pencil W/C htd.white

NORLIND, Ernst (1877-1952) Swedish
£520 $894   (8-Mar-92 BU.M470) Stork (68x60cm-27x24in) s.d.48 panel (S.KR 5400)
£1430 $2517   (11-Apr-92 FAL.M299/R) Stork on the marshes (70x80cm-28x31in) s.d.43 panel (S.KR 15000)
£2281 $4084   (16-Nov-91 FAL.M236/R) Farm in twilight (100x107cm-39x42in) s.d.29 panel (S.KR 24000)

NORMANN, Adelsteen (1848-1918) Norwegian
£802 $1388   (23-Mar-92 B.O99/R) Morning by the sea (43x36cm-17x14in) s. canvas on panel (N.KR 9000)
£1103 $1985   (19-Nov-91 GO.G239) Fjord landscape with boats (35x45cm-14x18in) s. (S.KR 11500)
£1134 $1973   (18-Sep-91 N.M642) Alpine valley with travellers on road (26x36cm-10x14in) s. board on panel (DM 3300)
£1336 $2552   (1-Jul-92 FB.P116/R) Fjord de Norvege (32x48cm-13x19in) s. (F.FR 13000)
£1714 $3000   (18-Feb-92 CE.NY168) Furies (95x76cm-37x30in) s.
£2458 $4228   (7-Oct-91 B.O107/R) Coastal landscape with boats (32x48cm-13x19in) s. (N.KR 28000)
£2622 $4537   (25-Mar-92 KM.K1344/R) Norwegian fjord landscape with shipping, early spring (74x100cm-29x39in) s. (DM 7500)
£2685 $4832   (19-Nov-91 GO.G240) Near Raftsund, Lofoten, autumn (70x100cm-28x39in) s. (S.KR 28000)
£2759 $4745   (16-Oct-91 KM.K1306/R) Norwegian fjord landscape with shipping (104x156cm-41x61in) s. (DM 8000)
£3339 $6011   (19-Nov-91 RAS.K57/R) Norwegian fjordlandscape (63x96cm-25x38in) s. (D.KR 37000)
£3340 $5945   (28-Nov-91 BU.S30/R) Norwegian fjord landscape (75x113cm-30x44in) s. (S.KR 35000)
£3947 $7342   (18-Jun-92 GWP.O72/R) Fjord landscape (104x156cm-41x61in) s. (N.KR 45000)
£4917 $8457   (10-Oct-91 BU.O77/R) Sunset near the coast (94x81cm-37x32in) s. (N.KR 56000)
£5795 $9967   (10-Oct-91 BU.O20/R) Fjord landscape (72x99cm-28x39in) s. (N.KR 66000)
£10526 $19579   (18-Jun-92 GWP.O73/R) Fjord landscape (103x156cm-41x61in) s.d.81 (N.KR 120000)

NORMANN, E Pastor (19/20th C) Scandinavian
£1200 $2124   (13-Feb-92 CSK198) Young girl in summer meadow (72x48cm-28x19in) s.

NORMANN, Emil Wilhelm (1798-1881) Danish
£529 $936   (23-Apr-92 RAS.V859/R) Seascape with sailship, evening init.d.1844 (D.KR 6000)

NORMANN, Emil Wilhelm (1798-1881) Danish-cont.
| £2070 | $3665 | (23-Apr-92 RAS.V857/R) Sailship and figures by quay (27x38cm-11x15in) init.d.1839 (D.KR 23500) |
| £2775 | $4912 | (23-Apr-92 RAS.V858/R) Seascape with sailship, Elben (27x44cm-11x17in) s.d.1848verso (D.KR 31500) |

NORMIL, Andre (1934-?) Haitian
| £994 | $1800 | (21-May-92 S.W2905/R) Adam and Eve (51x76cm-20x30in) s. |

NORREGAARD, Asta (1853-1933) Norwegian
| £8619 | $15170 | (8-Apr-92 GWP.O61/R) Children learning how to make flower chains (55x68cm-22x27in) s.d.1879 (N.KR 98000) |

NORRIS, Bessie (1878-1939) British
| £500 | $890 | (28-Nov-91 B166/R) The chickweed man (41x37cm-16x15in) s.i.verso pencil W/C |

NORRIS, William (1857-?) British
| £720 | $1274 | (6-Nov-91 S259) Harvest (28x38cm-11x15in) s.d.1890 pastel |

NORRMAN, Herman (1864-1906) Swedish
| £584 | $1039 | (28-Oct-91 AB.S168) Peasant family in farmyard, Halland (32x41cm-13x16in) i.verso (S.KR 6200) |

NORSELIUS, Erik (1874-1956) Swedish
| £613 | $1085 | (5-Nov-91 BA.S140/R) Fishergirl from Brittany (117x88cm-46x35in) s.d.1913 (S.KR 6500) |

NORSTEDT, Reinhold (1843-1911) Swedish
| £1140 | $1983 | (13-Apr-92 AB.S191) 'Skepparstugan' - summer landscape, Vingaker (30x39cm-12x15in) s.d.1906 (S.KR 12000) |

NORTH EUROPEAN SCHOOL, 16th C
| £2087 | $3820 | (14-May-92 BU.S152/R) Mary Magdalene with ointment pot (48x28cm-19x11in) panel (S.KR 22000) |

NORTH EUROPEAN SCHOOL, 17th C
| £56000 | $95200 | (23-Oct-91 S23/R) Portrait of Turkish lady (188x104cm-74x41in) |

NORTH GERMAN SCHOOL, 17th C
| £2944 | $5594 | (23-Jun-92 D.V337/R) Portrait of Helena von Munchhausen (83x65cm-33x26in) i.verso (A.S 60000) |

NORTH GERMAN SCHOOL, 18th C
| £2800 | $4984 | (1-Nov-91 S356/R) Musical party in interior (35x44cm-14x17in) copper |

NORTH ITALIAN SCHOOL (?) Italian
£2300	$4416	(9-Jul-92 B105/R) Finding of Moses (74x96cm-29x38in) c.1700
£2600	$4550	(28-Feb-92 C32) Portrait of boy wearing white shirt with lace collar (118x88cm-46x35in)
£2900	$5220	(22-Nov-91 SWS58/R) A Bacchante (65x56cm-26x22in) c.1700 panel
£3043	$5355	(11-Apr-92 AT.P12/R) Le repos pendant la fuite en Egypte (62x110cm-24x43in) c.1700 (F.FR 30000)
£3200	$5856	(12-May-92 SWS720) Bacchanal (113x167cm-44x66in) panel c.1700
£3300	$6039	(12-May-92 SWS648/R) Saint Sebastian tended by Saint Irene and angels (142x195cm-56x77in)
£3600	$6300	(1-Apr-92 S87/R) Summer and autumn (73x93cm-29x37in) pair c.1700
£4000	$7000	(3-Apr-92 C93/R) Portrait of noblewoman, wearing high ruff and tiara (65x50cm-26x20in) c.1600
£5071	$8925	(11-Apr-92 AT.P23/R) L'avare et son chat (84x67cm-33x26in) c.1600 (F.FR 50000)
£6000	$10500	(1-Apr-92 S73/R) Portrait of young man in red coat (144x102cm-57x40in) i.stretcher c.1700
£7985	$14292	(14-Nov-91 ANS.M88 a/R) Escena de caceria (88x50cm-35x20in) c.1700 (S.P 1450000)
£8033	$15102	(16-Dec-91 AGS.P45/R) Nature morte au col vert, becasse perdreau rouge (67x895cm-26x352in) c.1700 (F.FR 78000)
£9500	$18240	(9-Jul-92 B110/R) Christ before Pilate (6x9cm-2x4in) card c.1700

NORTH ITALIAN SCHOOL, 15th C
| £2577 | $4485 | (18-Sep-91 N.M439/R) Ecce Homo (35x23cm-14x9in) panel (DM 7500) |

NORTH ITALIAN SCHOOL, 16th C
£2800	$5376	(10-Jul-92 C254/R) Virgin and Saint Joseph, head and shoulders (26x30cm-10x12in) paper on panel
£4360	$7500	(10-Oct-91 SY.NY32/R) Saint Catherine of Alexandria (26x16cm-10x6in) panel
£5092	$9267	(11-Dec-91 LD.P46/R) Saint Jean Baptiste (95x31cm-37x12in) panel (F.FR 50000)
£6500	$11375	(25-Feb-92 PH59) Building of the Tower of Babel with Nimrod and some of his followers (48x64cm-19x25in) panel
£16734	$29452	(11-Apr-92 AT.P6/R) Vierge a l'Enfant (56x45cm-22x18in) panel (F.FR 165000)
£20000	$36400	(13-Dec-91 C84/R) The Lamentation (66x51cm-26x20in) panel arched top

NORTH ITALIAN SCHOOL, 16th C-cont.

£2000	$3840	(7-Jul-92 C16/R) St Andrew (29x15cm-11x6in) i. chk pen wash htd white pricked for transfer

NORTH ITALIAN SCHOOL, 17th C

£2018	$3471	(16-Oct-91 AT.P27/R) Un paysan tenant son cheval (120x91cm-47x36in) i. (F.FR 20000)
£2200	$4224	(9-Jul-92 B108/R) Christ appearing to ten female saints (100x133cm-39x52in)
£3400	$6222	(12-May-92 SWS623/R) Saint Catherine of Alexandria (47x37cm-19x15in)
£3687	$6600	(14-Nov-91 GRO.B2/R) Holy family with saints (30x23cm-12x9in)
£3779	$6500	(10-Oct-91 SY.NY141/R) Jacob wrestling with the angel (117x95cm-46x37in)
£3800	$6802	(11-Nov-91 S478/R) Portrait of cardinal (73x61cm-29x24in)
£3800	$6916	(11-Dec-91 S164/R) Portrait of nobleman, wearing robe and insignia of Order Golden Fleece (99x77cm-39x30in)
£4200	$7476	(30-Oct-91 S87/R) Landscape with figures and waggon on the outskirts of village (51x74cm-20x29in)
£5600	$9800	(1-Apr-92 S226/R) Susannah and Elders (147x118cm-58x46in)
£6000	$11520	(8-Jul-92 S95/R) Assumption of the Virgin (20x30cm-8x12in) copper oval
£7063	$12926	(16-May-92 F.L54/R) Paesaggi con figure (74x102cm-29x40in) pair (S.FR 19000)
£7182	$13000	(22-May-92 SY.NY306/R) Garden of Eden with God the Father drawing rib from Adam (123x172cm-48x68in)
£12170	$22150	(26-May-92 FB.P5/R) Le Festin d'Herode (90x137cm-35x54in) rem.sig. (F.FR 120000)
£13000	$22620	(15-Apr-92 C175/R) Allegories of air and earth (32x42cm-13x17in) slate pair
£4200	$7308	(13-Apr-92 S154/R) Descent from Cross (29x18cm-11x7in) bears i. pen wash

NORTH ITALIAN SCHOOL, 18th C

£2907	$5000	(10-Oct-91 SY.NY72/R) Extensive landscape with peasants eating by a river (147x153cm-58x60in)
£3000	$5760	(8-Jul-92 S157/R) Adoration of the Shepherds (119x68cm-47x27in) arched top
£3182	$5631	(7-Nov-91 D.V51/R) Boar hunting (83x101cm-33x40in) (A.S 65000)
£3500	$6300	(22-Nov-91 SWS212/R) Capriccio landscape with figures beside a fort at the edge of a river (47x61cm-19x24in)
£3933	$7000	(22-Jan-92 SY.NY200/R) Capriccio of ruins with figures (69x110cm-27x43in) i.
£4070	$7000	(9-Oct-91 CH.NY168/R) Figures on path among classical ruins in mountainous river landscape (81x145cm-32x57in)
£4200	$7350	(1-Apr-92 S101/R) Mountainous landscapes with figures near water (67x105cm-26x41in) pair
£4775	$8500	(22-Jan-92 SY.NY219/R) Harbour scenes (87x116cm-34x46in) pair
£5000	$8750	(1-Apr-92 S228/R) Flight into Egypt (91x71cm-36x28in)
£6379	$11545	(5-Dec-91 SY.MO312/R) Scene pastorale (31x42cm-12x17in) pair (F.FR 62000)
£7263	$13000	(17-Jan-92 SY.NY118/R) Soldiers plundering a convent (85x116cm-33x46in)
£15686	$28078	(15-Nov-91 GK.Z5067/R) Landscape with ruins and shepherds with donkeys on path (177x132cm-70x52in) (S.FR 40000)
£23000	$40250	(1-Apr-92 S39/R) Portrait of young gentleman (148x111cm-58x44in) octagonal
£23715	$42688	(19-Nov-91 GS.B3606/R) Capricci of harbours (72x96cm-28x38in) pair (S.FR 60000)

NORTH ITALIAN SCHOOL, 19th C

£5839	$10453	(6-May-92 GD.B948/R) Jesus being taken prisoner (52x72cm-20x28in) (S.FR 16000)

NORTH, C (19th C) British?

£900	$1647	(13-May-92 WI1108) Extensive seascape dawn, fishermen unloading catch from beached boats (60x91cm-24x36in) s.d.1886

NORTH, John William (1842-1924) British

£2800	$5012	(13-Nov-91 CG504/R) Beyond the blue hills (65x93cm-26x37in) init.d.1892 W/C htd.bodycol.
£2800	$4900	(23-Sep-91 PHB11) In the Orchard (63x45cm-25x18in) s. W/C
£11000	$20680	(19-Dec-91 C9/R) The House of Roses, Tripoli (65x93cm-26x37in) init. pencil W/C htd white scratching out

NORTHCOTE, James (1746-1831) British

£847	$1500	(9-Nov-91 W.W163/R) Under the willow (41x61cm-16x24in) s.d.1887 i.verso
£23000	$40480	(8-Apr-92 S49/R) Portrait of artist, seated in profile (90x74cm-35x29in) s. i.verso
£26000	$46540	(15-Nov-91 C83/R) Standard poodle, in coastal landscape (102x127cm-40x50in) s.d.1806

NORTHCOTE, James (attrib) (1746-1831) British

£800	$1376	(3-Mar-92 SWS1619) A favourite Shropshire terrier bitch in a landscape (77x70cm-30x28in)
£4360	$7500	(10-Oct-91 SY.NY193/R) Portrait of a young girl as a cleaner (73x61cm-29x24in)

NORTHERN DUTCH SCHOOL, 16th C

£2315	$4144	(14-Nov-91 CH.AM54) Portrait of woman aged 43 wearing lace bonnet (59x45cm-23x18in) i.d.1574 painted oval (D.FL 7500)

NORTHERN FRENCH SCHOOL, 16th C
£12237 $21659   (7-Nov-91 D.V192/R) Triumph of Truth, Confrerie du Puy (112x79cm-44x31in)
                     panel (A.S 250000)

NORTON, Benjamin Cam (1835-1900) British
£620 $1097   (12-Feb-92 B78) Watering cattle (23x30cm-9x12in) s.d.1884

NORTON, Rosaleen (1917-) Australian
£655 $1146   (30-Mar-92 AAA.S144 l) Bells (65x47cm-26x19in) s. W/C (A.D 1500)

NORTON, W E (1843-1916) American
£620 $1060   (11-Mar-92 WAL335/R) View from Church buildings, Creechurch Lane, with
                  figures loading cart (50x39cm-20x15in) i.verso

NORTON, William Edward (1843-1916) American
£1600 $2976   (18-Jun-92 CSK187) Fisherfolk on beach (30x46cm-12x18in) s.
£3380 $6050   (14-Nov-91 GRO.B61/R) Last load (46x61cm-18x24in) s.
£4375 $7700   (9-Apr-92 FA.PH808) Delivering a passenger (51x76cm-20x30in) s.

NORWELL, Graham Noble (1901-1967) Canadian
£500 $885   (6-Nov-91 SY.T152) Landscape with farm (49x60cm-19x24in) s. (C.D 1000)
£1400 $2548   (28-May-92 C42/R) Laurentian winter (69x79cm-27x31in) s.

NORWID, Cyprian Kamil (1824-1883) Polish
£1221 $2223   (15-Dec-91 REM.W28) A cardinal's bust (18x11cm-7x4in) s. pen
                  (P.Z 24000000)

NOSKE, Hugo (1886-1960) Austrian
£586 $1013   (3-Oct-91 D.V106/R) Venice (100x150cm-39x59in) s.d.1930 i.verso
                  (A.S 12000)

NOTER, David de (1825-?) Belgian
£2356 $4500   (16-Jul-92 SY.NY476/R) Still life with game, fruit and pie
                  (32x24cm-13x9in) s. panel
£3058 $5321   (14-Apr-92 SY.AM54/R) Still life with flowers and peaches
                  (35x27cm-14x11in) s. (D.FL 10000)
£4000 $6840   (17-Mar-92 PH18/R) Still life in interior (33x25cm-13x10in) s. panel
£4500 $8010   (29-Nov-91 C14/R) Preparing the meal (71x58cm-28x23in) s.indist.d.1859
                  panel
£4842 $8134   (27-Aug-91 RAS.K206/R) Still life of grapes, oranges, currants, flowers
                  and butterfly (32x38cm-13x15in) s.d.1867 panel (D.KR 55000)
£5714 $10000   (20-Feb-92 SY.NY198/R) Un bon livre (80x64cm-31x25in) s. panel
£6728 $11976   (30-Oct-91 CH.AM56/R) Still life of flowers, fruit, red pepper and fish
                  on forest floor (82x66cm-32x26in) s. (D.FL 22000)
£9000 $16020   (29-Nov-91 C13/R) Back from market (66x55cm-26x22in) s.d.46 panel
£10989 $20000   (28-May-92 SY.NY79/R) Les lettres d'amour (61x53cm-24x21in) s.d.1843
                  panel
£12000 $21360   (29-Nov-91 C12/R) Fruits of the garden (81x26cm-32x10in) s. panel

NOTER, David de and GOUPIL, Jules Adolphe (19th C) Belgian/French
£6500 $12090   (17-Jun-92 S287/R) Lady's obedient dog (79x65cm-31x26in) s.

NOTER, Jean Baptiste Andre de (1787-1855) Belgian
£3980 $7284   (12-May-92 C.A72/R) L'eglise Notre-Dame de l'autre cote de la Dyle a
                  Malines (26x32cm-10x13in) mono.d.1823 panel (B.FR 240000)
£2046 $3847   (18-Dec-91 GM.B4136/R) Vue de la porte Sainte-Catherine a Malines
                  (23x32cm-9x13in) s. W/C (B.FR 120000)

NOTERMAN, Zacharias (1820-1890) German
£1613 $2855   (10-Nov-91 ZZ.F16/R) La lecture de la lettre (29x41cm-11x16in) s. panel
                  (F.FR 16000)
£2049 $3689   (2-Feb-92 ZZ.F32/R) Le singe declamant (38x45cm-15x18in) s. panel
                  (F.FR 20000)
£2442 $4370   (17-Nov-91 FB.P88/R) Le singe qui boit (26x19cm-10x7in) s. panel
                  (F.FR 24000)

NOTT, Raymond (19/20th C) American
£632 $1200   (24-Jun-92 B.SF6411/R) Seaside town (47x61cm-19x24in) s. pastel

NOTTE, Emilio (1891-1982) Italian
£2317 $4124   (26-Nov-91 SY.MI92/R) Composizione (77x52cm-30x20in) s.d.1971 panel
                  (I.L 5000000)

NOTZ, Johannes (1802-1862) Swiss
£879 $1600   (26-May-92 CE.NY6/R) Portrait of lady. Portrait of gentleman
                  (44x27cm-17x11in) s.d.1836 chk.pencil chl. pair

NOURSE, Elizabeth (1860-1938) American
£497 $900   (7-Dec-91 LAE.L83/R) Interior scene with mother and children
                  (56x41cm-22x16in) s. W/C

NOUVEAU, Henri (1901-1959) Rumanian
£762 $1326   (16-Apr-92 FB.P20/R) Frohlicher torso (29x20cm-11x8in) s.d.1931 i.verso
                  mixed media (F.FR 7500)

NOUVEAU, Henri (1901-1959) Rumanian-cont.

£1186	$2051	(27-Mar-92 PPB.P55/R) Composition (39x26cm-15x10in) mono.d.1955 gouache (F.FR 11500)
£1332	$2398	(27-Jan-92 GL.P27) Composition (45x32cm-18x13in) init.d.52 gouache board (F.FR 13000)
£2263	$4300	(24-Jun-92 GL.P171/R) Composition (27x31cm-11x12in) inits.d.1933 gouache (F.FR 22000)

NOVELLI, Gastone (1925-) Italian

£1358	$2471	(26-May-92 SY.MI10/R) Composizione (48x33cm-19x13in) s.d.57 mixed media (I.L 3000000)
£1810	$3295	(26-May-92 SY.MI88/R) Composizione (45x56cm-18x22in) s.d.58 mixed media (I.L 4000000)
£15353	$27329	(30-Nov-91 FB.P45/R) Tender as a rose (49x60cm-19x24in) s. i.d.60verso mixed media collage canvas (F.FR 150000)
£16444	$28613	(14-Apr-92 F.M225/R) Omaggio a Leautaud (70x90cm-28x35in) s.i.d.1963verso mixed media canvas (I.L 36000000)

NOVELLI, Pietro Antonio (1729-1804) Italian

£512	$927	(22-May-92 GB.B5648/R) Studies of heads (30x20cm-12x8in) pen (DM 1500)
£512	$927	(22-May-92 GB.B5646/R) St Anna teaching Mary (14x11cm-6x4in) i. pen wash (DM 1500)
£580	$1009	(13-Apr-92 S28/R) Caricature of quack astrologer (32x22cm-13x9in) i. pen wash
£2700	$5184	(8-Jul-92 PH106/R) View of regatta on Grand Canal, 2 April 1791 (36x50cm-14x20in) i. pen wash
£4273	$7819	(15-May-92 AT.P182) Les deux sybilles Cibele et Cerere (18x32cm-7x13in) pen htd white (F.FR 42000)

NOVERRE (1933-) German

£938	$1659	(5-Nov-91 GF.L2744/R) Vase with summer flowers (98x72cm-39x28in) s.d.1990 (S.FR 2400)

NOVIKOV, Nikolai (1922-) Russian

£614	$1093	(25-Nov-91 ARC.P116/R) Visite du Marechal Boudionii (22x29cm-9x11in) s. board (F.FR 6000)
£617	$1117	(6-Dec-91 ARC.P15/R) Promenade au soleil (71x50cm-28x20in) s. board (F.FR 6000)
£665	$1184	(25-Nov-91 ARC.P113/R) Le bai de soleil (80x90cm-31x35in) s. (F.FR 6500)
£696	$1239	(25-Nov-91 ARC.P114/R) Sur la passerelle (69x49cm-27x19in) s. board (F.FR 6800)
£716	$1275	(25-Nov-91 ARC.P117/R) Le coucher de soleil (23x24cm-9x9in) s. board (F.FR 7000)
£864	$1503	(13-Apr-92 ARC.P177/R) Coucher de soleil (35x49cm-14x19in) s. board (F.FR 8500)
£965	$1680	(13-Apr-92 ARC.P176/R) Vacances a la campagne (90x70cm-35x28in) s. (F.FR 9500)
£977	$1769	(6-Dec-91 ARC.P12/R) La lettre (80x57cm-31x22in) s. (F.FR 9500)
£1016	$1768	(13-Apr-92 ARC.P178/R) La terrasse de l'hotel (35x50cm-14x20in) s. board (F.FR 10000)
£1382	$2460	(25-Nov-91 ARC.P115/R) A l'Ecole militaire (35x50cm-14x20in) s. board (F.FR 13500)

NOVO, Stefano (1862-?) Italian

£1117	$2000	(11-Nov-91 GC.M40/R) Ponte di barche (16x25cm-6x10in) s.d.1920 board
£1500	$2565	(19-Mar-92 B91/R) A pretty young girl (39x34cm-15x13in) s. panel
£1512	$2600	(15-Oct-91 CE.NY373/R) An outdoor market in Venice (25x33cm-10x13in) s. panel
£2038	$3771	(8-Jun-92 CH.R542/R) L'attacca manifesti (62x36cm-24x14in) s.d.1895 (I.L 4500000)
£2691	$4790	(30-Oct-91 CH.AM85/R) The flower and fruit seller (65x46cm-26x18in) s. (D.FL 8800)
£2907	$5000	(16-Oct-91 CH.NY189 a/R) A flower vendor. Produce vendor (41x20cm-16x8in) both s.d.1899 panel pair
£4857	$8500	(18-Feb-92 CE.NY152/R) Feeding cat (53x75cm-21x30in) s.d.1900 canvas on masonite

NOWAK, Eduard (1921-) German

£515	$897	(21-Sep-91 SA.A1813/R) Shepherds and flock in moor landscape, autumn (81x100cm-32x39in) s. (DM 1500)

NOWAK, Ernst (1853-1919) Austrian

£1065	$1811	(25-Oct-91 BM.B795/R) Young woman holding rake standing in garden, autumn (50x63cm-20x25in) s.d.1903 (DM 3100)
£1955	$3500	(13-Nov-91 B.SF2310/R) Cardinal with glass of wine (47x38cm-19x15in) s.
£2400	$4104	(18-Mar-92 S67/R) The prospect of a good meal (37x30cm-15x12in) s. panel
£2613	$4756	(11-Dec-91 WE.MU193/R) Cellar master having snack (48x38cm-19x15in) s. (DM 7500)
£6000	$10680	(27-Nov-91 S140/R) Selene visiting sleeping Endymion (129x179cm-51x70in) s.

NOWAK, Franz (19/20th C) Austrian

£474	$854	(19-Nov-91 GS.B3603) Still life of fruit and decanter with red wine on table (8x10cm-3x4in) s. board (S.FR 1200)

NOWAK, Otto (1874-1945) Austrian
£1374 $2610   *(25-Jun-92 D.V523/R) Couple before church, Steiermark. Couple on village street, Otztal (26x18cm-10x7in) s. i.verso W/C pair (A.S 28000)*

NOWAK, Wilhelm (1886-?) Austrian
£894 $1591   (29-Nov-91 D.V63/R) Hay harvest (25x40cm-10x16in) s.d.75 board (A.S 18000)
£1818 $3236   (30-Nov-91 VG.B268/R) Lake landscape (60x86cm-24x34in) s.d.1936 (DM 5200)

NOWLAN, Carlotta (fl.1885-1911) British
£680 $1299   *(30-Jun-92 SWS2329/R) Portrait of lady wearing blue bonnet tied beneath chin (8x?cm-3x?in) min.s.d.1905 gilt frame*

NOWLAN, Frank (19th C) British
£550 $1007   *(3-Jun-92 S296) Faithful friends (23x17cm-9x7in) s. W/C arched top*

NOYER, Philippe (1917-) French
£1117 $2000   (9-May-92 CE.NY162/R) Dejeuner dans le jardin (65x50cm-26x20in) s.d.45
£1537 $2766   (2-Feb-92 CSC.P36) Jeune fille au canotier (80x80cm-31x31in) s. (F.FR 15000)
£503 $900   *(15-Nov-91 DM.D2005/R) Boy with parakeet (48x64cm-19x25in) s.d.1955 W/C*

NOYES, George L (19/20th C) Canadian
£819 $1400   (13-Mar-92 S.BM254/R) Indian genre scene (13x20cm-5x8in) s. panel
£1222 $2200   (24-Nov-91 JRB.C149/R) Spirit of the woods (51x41cm-20x16in) s.d.1919 i.verso
£2660 $5000   (18-Dec-91 SY.NY168/R) An April morning, Millis, Massachusetts (30x40cm-12x16in) s.d.16 verso canvas board
£2926 $5500   (18-Dec-91 SY.NY223/R) Winter stretch, Medfield, Mass (34x38cm-13x15in) s. canvasboard

NOZAL, Alexandre (1852-1929) French
£2551 $4566   (5-May-92 ZEL.L1477/R) River landscape, spring (72x100cm-28x39in) s. (DM 7500)
£3023 $5441   (2-Feb-92 ZZ.F95/R) Paysage aux meules (38x55cm-15x22in) s. (F.FR 29500)

NOZKOWSKI, Tom (1944-) American
£838 $1500   (9-May-92 CE.NY351/R) Untitled (41x51cm-16x20in) s.i.d.1987verso canvasboard

NUDERSCHER, Frank (1880-1959) American
£2180 $3750   (7-Mar-92 LAE.L177/R) View of Eads Bridge with Courthouse, St Louis (48x61cm-19x24in) s.

NUNAMAKER, Kenneth R (1890-1957) American
£4396 $8000   (28-May-92 CH.NY192/R) The icy river (56x61cm-22x24in) s.

NUNEN, David van (1952-) Australian
£513 $913   (27-Apr-92 J.M822) Camp Cove (61x61cm-24x24in) s. (A.D 1200)
£556 $989   (27-Apr-92 J.M1110) Berry's Bay (61x61cm-24x24in) s.d.89 (A.D 1300)

NUNEZ DE CELIS, Francisco (1919-) Spanish
£526 $932   (12-Feb-92 ANS.M69/R) Picos de Europa (23x32cm-9x13in) s. s.i.d.verso tablex (S.P 95000)
£602 $1151   (2-Jul-92 ANS.M90/R) Paisaje con alpinistas (110x85cm-43x33in) s. (S.P 110000)
£984 $1673   (23-Oct-91 DUR.M534/R) Montanas (50x61cm-20x24in) s. panel (S.P 180000)
£1524 $2697   (12-Feb-92 ANS.M122/R) Castillo de Loarre (58x80cm-23x31in) s. (S.P 275000)
£2488 $4678   (16-Dec-91 ANS.M118/R) Arenas de San Pedro (101x81cm-40x32in) s. s.d.1945verso (S.P 450000)

NUNEZ LOSADA, Francisco (1890-) Spanish
£2765 $5198   (16-Dec-91 ANS.M97/R) Jaras y encinas, Picos de Europa (80x100cm-31x39in) s. i.verso (S.P 500000)
£3041 $5717   (16-Dec-91 ANS.M115/R) Paisaje (51x56cm-20x22in) s. board (S.P 550000)
£4956 $8871   (14-Nov-91 ANS.M81/R) Nieblas en el monte (70x81cm-28x32in) s. (S.P 900000)
£7188 $13514   (16-Dec-91 ANS.M101/R) Hoz del Duraton, Segovia (90x116cm-35x46in) s. s.i.verso (S.P 1300000)
£8313 $14713   (12-Feb-92 ANS.M93/R) Islallana, Logrono (100x110cm-39x43in) s. (S.P 1500000)

NUREMBERG SCHOOL, 18th C German
£3200 $5568   *(14-Apr-92 C185) Wooded landscapes with travellers by castle during storm. With rainbow (17x22cm-7x9in) bodycol vellum pair*

NURY, Amede (1856-?) French
£816 $1461   (5-May-92 ZEL.L1478/R) Sunset in Mediterranean landscape (38x60cm-15x24in) s.d.1894 (DM 2400)

NUSSBAUM, Jacob (1873-1936) German
£815 $1475   (19-May-92 GF.L2562/R) Peasant women in field (60x80cm-24x31in) s.d.1909 (S.FR 2200)

NUVOLONE, Carlo Francesco (1608-1665) Italian
£4000 $6960   (15-Apr-92 C168/R) The Holy Family (103x89cm-41x35in)
£9215 $16679   (21-May-92 L.K116/R) Christ Child sleeping surrounded by angels with
     symbols of suffering (155x120cm-61x47in) (DM 27000)

NUVOLONE, Carlo Francesco (style) (1608-1665) Italian
£5000 $8750   (28-Feb-92 C7/R) Putto holding wreath. Two putti cavorting
     (85x54cm-33x21in) two

NUVOLONE, Giuseppe (circle) (1619-1703) Italian
£2640 $4594   (13-Sep-91 C41/R) Charity (96x127cm-38x50in)

NUVOLONE, Giuseppe (style) (1619-1703) Italian
£1800 $3276   (13-Dec-91 C232/R) Madonna and Child with Saint Anne (64x51cm-25x20in)

NUYEN, Wijbrand Johannes Josephus (1813-1839) Dutch
£3670 $6532   (30-Oct-91 CH.AM202 a/R) River landscape with peasants in rowing boats
     conversing by mansion (65x55cm-26x22in) s. (D.FL 12000)
£450 $836   (16-Jun-92 SY.B295) Figures on a frozen river (23x17cm-9x7in) s. W/C
     (B.FR 27000)
£2273 $4023   (22-Apr-92 CH.AM271/R) Moored shipping in a harbour, Normandy, at low
     tide (21x31cm-8x12in) s. ink W/C htd.white (D.FL 7500)

NUYEN, Wijbrand Johannes Josephus (attrib) (1813-1839) Dutch
£606 $1073   (22-Apr-92 CH.AM138) A view in a town (30x21cm-12x8in) panel (D.FL 2000)

NUYSSEN, Abraham Janssens van see JANSSENS, Abraham

NUZZI, Mario (1603-1673) Italian
£8178 $14967   (16-May-92 F.L14/R) Natura morta con vaso di fiori (64x54cm-25x21in)
     (S.FR 22000)

NUZZI, Mario (attrib) (1603-1673) Italian
£6200 $11036   (1-Nov-91 C19/R) Mixed flowers in gilt vase on stone pedestal
     (49x37cm-19x15in) oval
£11329 $19372   (20-Mar-92 ZZ.F41) Natures mortes aux fleurs (70x53cm-28x21in) pair
     (F.FR 110000)

NUZZI, Mario (circle) (1603-1673) Italian
£6600 $11484   (13-Sep-91 C130/R) Mixed flwoers in gilt vase, Dianthus in pot with
     convolvulus and grapes on vine (30x45cm-12x18in)

NUZZI, Mario (style) (1603-1673) Italian
£1800 $3456   (9-Jul-92 CSK293/R) Tulips, peonies and other spring flowers on ledge
     (74x90cm-29x35in)
£2762 $4750   (10-Oct-91 SY.NY67/R) Still life of flowers encircling a sculptured urn,
     resting on a ledge (71x56cm-28x22in)

NYBLOM, Lennart (1872-1947) Swedish
£569 $979   (19-Oct-91 UA.U396) Landscape in evening light (62x82cm-24x32in) s.
     (S.KR 6000)
£664 $1142   (19-Oct-91 UA.U395/R) Spring haze (71x92cm-28x36in) s.d.1907 (S.KR 7000)
£2277 $4167   (14-May-92 BU.S50/R) View of Florence (124x124cm-49x49in) s.d.1928 panel
     (S.KR 24000)

NYBOE, Friis (1869-1929) Danish
£668 $1150   (15-Oct-91 RAS.K77/R) Evening in the studio (150x200cm-59x79in) s.d.1914
     (D.KR 7500)
£1832 $3500   (16-Jul-92 SY.NY464/R) In the studio (152x200cm-60x79in) s.d.1914
£1938 $3431   (23-Apr-92 RAS.V861/R) Lamplit interior with figures around table
     (173x204cm-68x80in) s.d.07 (D.KR 22000)

NYBORG, Peter (20th C) Danish
£489 $851   (18-Sep-91 KH.K161) Black banner (65x81cm-26x32in) s.d.61verso
     (D.KR 5500)
£1252 $2279   (10-Dec-91 RAS.K96) Composition (165x110cm-65x43in) s.d.88verso
     (D.KR 14000)
£451 $772   (10-Mar-92 RAS.K81) 'Aldebaran I' (72x101cm-28x40in) s.d.86 W/C gouache
     (D.KR 5000)

NYE, Edgar (1879-1943) American
£625 $1200   (31-Jul-92 E.EDM55/R) Landscape (61x51cm-24x20in) s. masonite

NYL-FROSCH, Marie (1857-1914) German
£663 $1246   (3-Jan-92 DUR.M34/R) Rosas (54x32cm-21x13in) s.d.90 (S.P 120000)
£1368 $2490   (26-May-92 DUR.M115/R) Rosas (54x32cm-21x13in) s.d.90 (S.P 250000)
£1492 $2700   (24-May-92 LIT.L118) Still life of fruit, flowers, insects, pocket watch
     and glass of wine (66x53cm-26x21in) s.

NYMAN, Bjorn (1934-) Swedish
£993 $1798   (19-May-92 AB.S5290/R) Still life II (24x28cm-9x11in) s.d.1977 panel
     (S.KR 10500)

NYMAN, Olle (1909-) Swedish

£473	$856	(19-May-92 AB.S5292/R) Steamboat in the skerries (31x24cm-12x9in) s.d.46 panel (S.KR 5000)
£787	$1424	(3-Dec-91 AB.S5117/R) Buildings and trees (13x15cm-5x6in) s. panel (S.KR 8200)
£1171	$2119	(3-Dec-91 AB.S5116/R) Fishing harbour (32x39cm-13x15in) s. panel (S.KR 12200)
£1440	$2606	(3-Dec-91 AB.S5115/R) Reading at night - the artist's mother (72x90cm-28x35in) s.d.49 (S.KR 15000)

NYSTROM, H C (?) ?

£848	$1502	(22-Apr-92 CH.AM213) A brd's nest on a forest floor (17x22cm-7x9in) s. cardboard oval (D.FL 2800)

NYSTROM, Jenny (1854-1946) Swedish

£1045	$1818	(13-Apr-92 AB.S193) Still life of spring flowers in vase (27x21cm-11x8in) s.d.1940 (S.KR 11000)
£3605	$6598	(14-May-92 AB.S51/R) Young lady wearing Old Scandinavian costume (61x50cm-24x20in) s. (S.KR 38000)
£5943	$10520	(5-Nov-91 BA.S142/R) Small girl with bouquet of flowers (34x25cm-13x10in) s.d.1942 (S.KR 63000)
£380	$661	(13-Apr-92 AB.S396) Wanderer and country girl with goat (23x14cm-9x6in) s. Indian ink wash (S.KR 4000)
£386	$687	(28-Oct-91 AB.S373) Dagger in tree - from Volsungarnes Saga (23x14cm-9x6in) init. Indian ink htd white (S.KR 4100)
£386	$687	(28-Oct-91 AB.S372) Gunnar and Brynhild - from Volsungarnes Saga (23x14cm-9x6in) init. Indian ink htd white (S.KR 4100)
£451	$811	(23-Nov-91 SO.S484/R) Sleeping on the sofa (7x17cm-3x7in) s. Indian ink wash htd white (S.KR 4700)
£472	$835	(5-Nov-91 BA.S234/R) Romance (23x13cm-9x5in) init. Indian ink wash (S.KR 5000)
£476	$867	(14-Dec-91 BA.S159) Silly boy (18x11cm-7x4in) init. Indian ink wash (S.KR 5000)
£481	$828	(8-Mar-92 BU.M63) Remembrance in Sweden (33x28cm-13x11in) mono. W/C htd white (S.KR 5000)
£519	$918	(5-Nov-91 BA.S235/R) Boys by runic stone (16x22cm-6x9in) s. Indian ink wash (S.KR 5500)
£537	$955	(28-Oct-91 AB.S376) The comforter (20x12cm-8x5in) s. Indian ink W/C (S.KR 5700)
£565	$1006	(28-Oct-91 AB.S375) The King and the girl of the sea (26x17cm-10x7in) init. Indian ink htd white (S.KR 6000)
£566	$1002	(5-Nov-91 BA.S233/R) On the road to Blakulla (16x21cm-6x8in) init. Indian ink (S.KR 6000)
£569	$1042	(12-May-92 GO.G275) Interior with Carolean and country folk (20x12cm-8x5in) s. wash (S.KR 6000)
£584	$1039	(28-Oct-91 AB.S374) Two children keeping guard (25x17cm-10x7in) init. Indian ink htd white (S.KR 6200)
£767	$1381	(23-Nov-91 SO.S485/R) The magi on the way to Bethlehem (15x24cm-6x9in) s. W/C (S.KR 8000)
£997	$1735	(13-Apr-92 AB.S394) Three girls (11x17cm-4x7in) s. W/C (S.KR 10500)
£1132	$2004	(5-Nov-91 BA.S231/R) The kiss (27x19cm-11x7in) s. W/C (S.KR 12000)
£1462	$2588	(5-Nov-91 BA.S232/R) Small boy writing letter (34x23cm-13x9in) init. Indian ink wash (S.KR 15500)
£1887	$3340	(5-Nov-91 BA.S230/R) Christmas morning with Father Christmas' helper (16x23cm-6x9in) s. W/C htd white (S.KR 20000)
£2100	$3801	(22-May-92 C74/R) Jultomten (30x27cm-12x11in) init.i. with i.verso pencil pen W/C htd white
£3113	$5510	(5-Nov-91 BA.S229/R) Christmas Day early service (34x28cm-13x11in) s. mixed media (S.KR 33000)
£3935	$7122	(3-Dec-91 AB.S4647/R) Children playing with cats on sofabench (34x25cm-13x10in) s. W/C (S.KR 41000)
£5314	$9672	(14-Dec-91 BU.O48/R) Young girl skater with muff (37x23cm-15x9in) s.d.1898 mixed media (N.KR 60000)
£9488	$17362	(14-May-92 BU.S99/R) Young lady resting under parasol (37x26cm-15x10in) s.d.1884 W/C (S.KR 100000)

OAKES, John Wright (1820-1887) British

£1400	$2492	(31-Oct-91 D107/R) Peel Castle, Isle of Man (56x64cm-22x25in) s.d.76

OAKES, Minnie F (19th C) American

£1170	$2000	(13-Mar-92 S.BM290/R) Still life with pink and white azaleas (61x46cm-24x18in) s.d.89

OAKLEY, Octavius (1800-1867) British

£540	$967	(5-May-92 SWS27) Julia and Louisa Bacon, daughters of Henry Bacon of Redlands, Surrey (41x31cm-16x12in) s.d.1839 W/C over pencil htd white
£800	$1464	(3-Jun-92 S239/R) A coy beauty (50x35cm-20x14in) s.d.1858 W/C htd.bodycol.
£850	$1462	(4-Mar-92 S272/R) In straw hat (28x24cm-11x9in) s. W/C htd white oval
£1100	$2101	(16-Jul-92 CSK93/R) Gypsy mother (53x40cm-21x16in) s.i.d.1847 verso pencil W/C htd white

OATES, Bennett (1928-) British
£1100	$1969	(5-May-92 SWS497/R) Summer flowers (52x44cm-20x17in) s. board
£1500	$2685	(5-May-92 SWS498/R) Still life study of petunias and berries in vase (60x50cm-24x20in) s. board

OBACH, Kaspar (1807-1865) Swiss
£444	$808	(26-May-92 KF.M402) View near Koengen (13x18cm-5x7in) W/C (DM 1300)
£1775	$3230	(26-May-92 KF.M400/R) Rondellplatz and Verfassungssaule, Karlsruhe (24x34cm-9x13in) s. pen W/C board (DM 5200)

OBERHUBER, Oswald (1931-) Austrian
£5817	$10587	(26-May-92 D.V333/R) Elephants (250x438cm-98x172in) s.d.85 (A.S 120000)
£388	$706	(26-May-92 D.V351/R) O.T. man with cloud above his head (43x29cm-17x11in) s.d.82 col.pencil (A.S 8000)
£388	$691	(28-Apr-92 D.V370/R) Untitled (42x56cm-17x22in) s.d.86 pencil col.pencil (A.S 8000)
£391	$696	(31-Oct-91 D.V157/R) Untitled (42x56cm-17x22in) s.d.86 pencil col.pencil (A.S 8000)
£436	$794	(26-May-92 D.V354/R) Untitled (44x60cm-17x24in) s.d.84 pencil col.pencil (A.S 9000)
£437	$778	(28-Apr-92 D.V368/R) Untitled (44x59cm-17x23in) s.d.83 pencil col.pencil (A.S 9000)
£440	$783	(31-Oct-91 D.V158/R) Untitled (42x56cm-17x22in) s.d.82 pencil col.pencil (A.S 9000)
£449	$803	(15-Jan-92 D.V266/R) Untitled (41x55cm-16x22in) s.d.86 pencil col.pencil (A.S 9000)
£449	$803	(15-Jan-92 D.V265/R) Untitled (36x48cm-14x19in) s.d.85 pencil col.pencil (A.S 9000)
£485	$864	(28-Apr-92 D.V369/R) Untitled (41x54cm-16x21in) s.d.86 pencil col.pencil (A.S 10000)
£544	$952	(19-Feb-92 D.V244/R) Untitled (55x42cm-22x17in) s.d.88 pencil col.pencil (A.S 11000)
£582	$1059	(26-May-92 D.V188/R) Untitled (50x35cm-20x14in) s.d.1951 chl (A.S 12000)
£733	$1305	(31-Oct-91 D.V126/R) Untitled (50x35cm-20x14in) s.d.1953 chk pen indian ink (A.S 15000)
£969	$1764	(26-May-92 D.V350/R) Untitled (50x60cm-20x24in) s.d.88 mixed media canvas (A.S 20000)
£1454	$2647	(26-May-92 D.V199/R) Untitled (49x34cm-19x13in) s.d.50 mixed media (A.S 30000)

OBERMAN, Anthony (1781-1845) Dutch
£4175	$7264	(13-Apr-92 SY.J248/R) Still life with fruit in basket and bird (49x43cm-19x17in) s. board (SA.R 21000)
£1000	$1920	(8-Jul-92 PH86/R) Man seated against tree holding reins of two horses (24x31cm-9x12in) s.d.1823 W/C pen

OBERMUELLNER, Adolf (1833-1898) Austrian
£989	$1730	(20-Feb-92 D.V470/R) Lake landscape with glacier (37x48cm-15x19in) i.verso (A.S 20000)
£1003	$1815	(5-Dec-91 D.V88) Achensee landscape (34x43cm-13x17in) s.d.1872 (A.S 20000)
£1953	$3320	(24-Oct-91 D.V91/R) View of village in Vorarlberg (46x57cm-18x22in) s. (A.S 40000)

OBERSTEINER, Ludwig (1857-?) Austrian
£1374	$2500	(26-May-92 CE.NY194/R) Feeding time (15x11cm-6x4in) s.i.panel

OBERTEUFFER, George (1878-?) American
£2235	$4000	(14-Nov-91 CE.NY297/R) Rear view of cathedral Paris, possibly Notre Dame (80x95cm-31x37in) s.

OBIDOS, Josefa de see AYALA, Josefa de

OBIN, Philome (1892-1986) Haitian
£1806	$3250	(18-Nov-91 SY.NY185/R) Women washing clothes (38x51cm-15x20in) s.i. board laid down on masonite
£3488	$6000	(12-Oct-91 SY.NY217/R) I ere section du Bas-du-Limbe (61x76cm-24x30in) 61x76
£3779	$6500	(12-Oct-91 SY.NY218/R) Des paysans revenant de leur champ (51x61cm-20x24in) s.i. masonite
£5278	$9500	(19-Nov-91 CH.NY227/R) Quelques deguisees du carnaval (38x47cm-15x19in) s.i.d.1947 board
£7182	$13000	(19-May-92 SY.NY190/R) Carnaval de 1954 - Rue du Pont du Cap-Haitien (61x76cm-24x30in) s.d.56 masonite

OBIN, Seneque (1893-1977) Haitian
£2333	$4200	(19-Nov-91 CH.NY224/R) Nature morte (35x34cm-14x13in) s. masonite
£2917	$5250	(18-Nov-91 SY.NY184/R) A table (51x61cm-20x24in) s.i. masonite

OBOZNENKO, Dimitri (1930-) Russian
£1217	$2215	(27-May-92 GL.P61/R) Pierrot (75x68cm-30x27in) s. (F.FR 12000)
£2243	$4171	(17-Jun-92 ARC.P137/R) Soiree Parisienne (40x45cm-16x18in) s. board (F.FR 22000)

OBREGON, Alejandro (1920-) Spanish
£8889 $16000 (18-Nov-91 SY.NY182/R) Condor (84x48cm-33x19in) s. s.i.verso
£12707 $23000 (19-May-92 SY.NY112/R) Flores (73x55cm-29x22in) s.
£1934 $3500 *(19-May-92 SY.NY202/R) Composicion (55x75cm-22x30in) s. ink wash paper laid down on board*

O'BRIEN, Dermod (1865-1945) British
£467 $808 (25-Mar-92 A.D22) Above the Shannon (25x36cm-10x14in) i.verso board (E.P 500)

O'BRIEN, Justin Maurice (1917-) Australian
£1221 $2038 (19-Aug-91 SY.ME210) Still life (55x40cm-22x16in) s.d.1936 canvasboard (A.D 2600)
£1290 $2245 (16-Sep-91 CH.ME110/R) Head of Christ (35x28cm-14x11in) s. ink wash (A.D 2800)
£3200 $5696 (28-Nov-91 C88/R) Portrait (55x38cm-22x15in) s.d.1942 board
£11268 $18817 (19-Aug-91 SY.ME249/R) Boy with blue hen, 1953 (75x60cm-30x24in) s. (A.D 24000)
£11521 $20046 (16-Sep-91 CH.ME139/R) St. George's Day, Skyros (91x57cm-36x22in) s. canvas on board (A.D 25000)
£11966 $21299 (28-Apr-92 CH.ME167/R) The minstrels (76x54cm-30x21in) s. board (A.D 28000)
£13146 $21953 (19-Aug-91 SY.ME219/R) Butterfly catchers (49x59cm-19x23in) s. (A.D 28000)
£16170 $28621 (26-Apr-92 SY.ME466/R) Still life (50x61cm-20x24in) s. (A.D 38000)
£427 $774 *(2-Dec-91 CH.ME241) Male nude (27x37cm-11x15in) s.d.60 red chk (A.D 1000)*
£3965 $7137 *(24-Nov-91 SY.S261/R) View from room (46x33cm-18x13in) s. i.verso ink W/C (A.D 9000)*
£7269 $13084 *(24-Nov-91 SY.S433/R) Marriage at Cana (44x55cm-17x22in) s. i.verso ink W/C (A.D 16500)*

O'BRIEN, Kitty Wilmer (1910-1982) British
£682 $1180 (2-Oct-91 A.D196) Boathaven, Old Head, Louisburgh, Co. Mayo (46x61cm-18x24in) board (E.P 750)
£509 $927 *(11-Dec-91 A.D158) Leenane, The Killary, Mayo (25x61cm-10x24in) s. gouache (E.P 550)*

O'BRIEN, Lucius Richard (1832-1899) Canadian
£697 $1240 *(26-Nov-91 JOY.T247) Coasters in Portland Harbour (19x14cm-7x6in) s.d.78 W/C (C.D 1400)*
£729 $1225 *(28-Aug-91 EA.M764 a) Summer along the St Lawrence (20x36cm-8x14in) s.d.'89 W/C (C.D 1400)*
£1125 $1991 *(6-Nov-91 SY.T100/R) Ship at dock (32x23cm-13x9in) s.d.1883 W/C (C.D 2250)*
£1750 $3098 *(6-Nov-91 SY.T23/R) Meadow (32x54cm-13x21in) s.d.1891 W/C (C.D 3500)*
£1875 $3319 *(6-Nov-91 SY.T6/R) Napanee, Ontario (22x34cm-9x13in) s.d.74 W/C (C.D 3750)*
£2000 $3540 *(6-Nov-91 SY.T99/R) Sailboats in marsh (32x54cm-13x21in) s.d.1898 W/C (C.D 4000)*

OBROVSKY, Jacub (1882-1949) Czechoslovakian
£3684 $6632 (23-Nov-91 N.M366/R) Breakfast is served - female nude and maid (124x158cm-49x62in) (DM 10500)

OCHOA, Florencio (?) Spanish
£553 $1040 (18-Dec-91 DUR.M754/R) Sevilla (50x61cm-20x24in) s. (S.P 100000)
£720 $1246 (24-Mar-92 DUR.M563/R) Torre del Oro (65x81cm-26x32in) s. (S.P 130000)

OCHTERVELT, Jacob (1635-1682) Dutch
£6363 $11263 (7-Nov-91 D.V112/R) The adorning of the bride (86x80cm-34x31in) (A.S 130000)

OCHTMAN, Leonard (1854-1935) American
£893 $1500 (28-Aug-91 MFA.C145/R) Autumn landscape (41x56cm-16x22in) s.
£1676 $3000 (6-May-92 D.NY52/R) Spring at Greyledge, Coscob (61x76cm-24x30in) s.d.1903 s.i.stretcher
£541 $1000 *(10-Jun-92 CE.NY386) Evening sunset (30x23cm-12x9in) s. W/C paper on board*

OCKENHOLT, Erik (20th C) Danish?
£542 $926 *(10-Mar-92 RAS.K13) Composition (136x180cm-54x71in) s.d.88verso oil acrylic collage (D.KR 6000)*
£722 $1235 *(10-Mar-92 RAS.K11) Neuf femmes dans paysage (138x150cm-54x59in) s.d.88verso oil collage (D.KR 8000)*

O'CONNOR, James Arthur (1792-1841) British
£1500 $2640 (10-Apr-92 C149/R) Shepherd and flock crossing stone bridge beside ruined tower in landscape (27x36cm-11x14in) init. panel
£1600 $2816 (10-Apr-92 C148/R) Shepherd and dog on wooded path with hilly landscape beyond (26x31cm-10x12in)
£1900 $3344 (10-Apr-92 C157/R) Countrywoman on wooded path with rocky seascape beyond (25x30cm-10x12in) s.d.1838 board
£1944 $3539 (11-Dec-91 A.D75 a) Wagon and driver in wooded landscape (13x20cm-5x8in) inits. board (E.P 2100)

O'CONNOR, James Arthur (1792-1841) British-cont.

£2300	$4048	(10-Apr-92 C156/R) Countryman on wooded path beside river with figure in rowing boat (20x30cm-8x12in) init.d.1840
£2800	$4928	(10-Apr-92 C159/R) Countrywoman and dog on forest path beside rocky waterfall (35x44cm-14x17in) s.d.1839
£3000	$5730	(15-Jul-92 S54/R) Napoleon's Tomb, St Helena (42x58cm-17x23in)
£3200	$5632	(10-Apr-92 C158/R) Figure on path in wooded lake landscape (23x28cm-9x11in) init.d.1839 board
£3400	$5984	(10-Apr-92 C151/R) Figure on wooded path in mountainous lake landscape (25x35cm-10x14in) init.indis.d.18..
£3600	$6336	(10-Apr-92 C152/R) Figure on path in mountainous wooded landscape (46x61cm-18x24in) init.d.1838
£4074	$7415	(11-Dec-91 A.D150/R) Landscape with figures (25x20cm-10x8in) s. panel (E.P 4400)
£4100	$7380	(22-Nov-92 SWS268/R) Wooded landscape with a traveller and his dog on a country road (43x54cm-17x21in)
£4400	$7744	(10-Apr-92 C154/R) Irish glen with figures in rocky wooded landscape (64x76cm-25x30in) s.d.1836
£4800	$8448	(10-Apr-92 C153/R) Countryman and dog on wooded path in mountainous landscape (35x46cm-14x18in) init.d.1839
£5500	$9790	(21-Jan-92 PH11/R) Figures on path in extensive landscape, castle on hill beyond (30x38cm-12x15in) s.d.1826 board
£6500	$11440	(8-Apr-92 S70/R) Irish landscape with figures on path (34x44cm-13x17in) s.d.1837 indist.i.verso
£7600	$13376	(10-Apr-92 C150/R) Shepherd and figures on woodland path in rocky mountainous landscape (43x55cm-17x22in) s.
£8200	$14432	(8-Apr-92 S69/R) Irish river landscape with fisherman (34x44cm-13x17in) s.d.1837
£17757	$30720	(25-Mar-92 A.D98/R) A recollection of the river Bray (64x76cm-25x30in) s.d.1834 (E.P 19000)
£909	*$1573*	*(2-Oct-91 A.D119) Coastal and river landscapes (20x30cm-8x12in) one s.d.1815 monochrome wash pair (E.P 1000)*
£1468	*$2730*	*(17-Jun-92 A.D170) Wicklow landscapes (20x30cm-8x12in) one s.d.1815 monochrome wash pair (E.P 1600)*

O'CONNOR, James Arthur (attrib) (1792-1841) British

£540	$1004	(16-Jun-92 SWS242/R) Irish landscape with figures resting by cliff (14x19cm-6x7in) bears sig.d. panel

O'CONNOR, Victor G (1918-) Australian

£511	$904	(26-Apr-92 SY.ME7) Bar fiddler (24x11cm-9x4in) s. canvas on board (A.D 1200)

O'CONOR, Roderick (1860-1940) Irish

£1400	$2492	(29-Oct-91 SWS89/R) Rose in green jug (66x55cm-26x22in) s.d.24 painted with another artist
£2062	$3526	(15-Mar-92 DA.R6/R) Portrait de jeune fille en buste (37x32cm-15x13in) studio st.verso board (F.FR 20000)
£9091	$15727	(2-Oct-91 A.D79/R) Rocky coastal landscape (25x36cm-10x14in) s.d.1898 board (E.P 10000)
£15000	$28650	(16-Jul-92 B16/R) Blue sea and rocks, Brittany (56x66cm-22x26in)
£19000	$34200	(20-Nov-91 S121/R) Head of Breton boy with cap (30x35cm-12x14in) st.studio verso board
£24415	$44680	(17-May-92 T.B197/R) Jeune bretonne de Pont-Aven (75x100cm-30x39in) studio st. (F.FR 240000)
£1385	*$2631*	*(25-Jun-92 GK.B532) Bretonne assise dans un paysage (23x28cm-9x11in) st.studio W/C bodycol over pencil (S.FR 3600)*

ODAZZI, Giovanni (1663-1731) Italian

£2734	$4840	(5-Nov-91 GF.L2065/R) Ecstasy of St Theresa (47x38cm-19x15in) (S.FR 7000)

ODAZZI, Giovanni (attrib) (1663-1731) Italian

£7200	$12816	(1-Nov-91 C20/R) Mystic marriage of Saint Catherine (52cm-20ins circular)

ODDIE, Walter M (1808-1865) American

£1149	$2000	(15-Apr-92 SY.NY8/R) Fishing on gentle river (63x76cm-25x30in) s.d.1858 painted oval

ODEGAARD, Hans (1876-1943) Norwegian

£1949	$3547	(14-Dec-91 BU.O1/R) Woman and man in landscape (39x60cm-15x24in) s. (N.KR 22000)

ODELMARK, F W (1849-1937) Swedish

£1144	$2013	(11-Apr-92 FAL.M302/R) Farmyard scene with woman and chickens (50x75cm-20x30in) s. (S.KR 12000)
£443	*$762*	*(8-Mar-92 BU.M146) Woman by window, Vencie (44x27cm-17x11in) s.indis.d.1892 W/C (S.KR 4600)*

ODELMARK, Frans Wilhelm (1849-1937) Swedish

£760	$1322	(13-Apr-92 AB.S194) Maroccan town scene with figures (50x36cm-20x14in) s. (S.KR 8000)
£867	$1500	(28-Mar-92 UA.U368) The farm (53x70cm-21x28in) s.i. (S.KR 9000)
£993	$1798	(19-May-92 AB.S4258/R) Cellar interior with monk plucking chicken (43x35cm-17x14in) s.d.1900 (S.KR 10500)
£1342	$2416	(19-Nov-91 GO.G121) Monastery kitchen (68x53cm-27x21in) s. (S.KR 14000)

ODELMARK, Frans Wilhelm (1849-1937) Swedish-cont.

£1344	$2432	(3-Dec-91 AB.S4649/R) Maroccan town scene with figures (40x26cm-16x10in) s. (S.KR 14000)
£1423	$2604	(17-May-92 BU.M363) Girl feeding chickens (90x66cm-35x26in) s. (S.KR 15000)
£1887	$3340	(5-Nov-91 BA.S144/R) Italian woman by well (95x67cm-37x26in) s. (S.KR 20000)
£1987	$3596	(19-May-92 AB.S4257/R) Italian street scene with figures near Doge's Palace, Venice (50x38cm-20x15in) s.d.1900 panel (S.KR 21000)
£2087	$3820	(12-May-92 GO.G117/R) On a balcony in Cairo (90x70cm-35x28in) s. (S.KR 22000)
£373	*$683*	*(6-Feb-92 B.O189) Camel rider (44x30cm-17x12in) s. W/C (N.KR 4200)*
£456	*$817*	*(16-Nov-91 FAL.M241/R) Lade with red umbrella near Falsterbohus (35x18cm-14x7in) s. W/C (S.KR 4800)*
£1008	*$1824*	*(3-Dec-91 AB.S4648/R) Farmyard in Seville with figures and donkey (62x42cm-24x17in) s. W/C (S.KR 10500)*
£1046	*$1872*	*(16-Nov-91 FAL.M240/R) Palace yard, Alhambra (57x39cm-22x15in) s. W/C (S.KR 11000)*
£1053	*$1811*	*(19-Oct-91 UA.U328) The old inn (59x40cm-23x16in) s.d.1897 W/C (S.KR 11100)*

ODENBACH, Marcel (1953-) French?

£1200	$2064	(17-Oct-91 C107) Energie Krise (105x287cm-41x113in) s.d.1988 pencil gouache chl collage

ODIN, Blanche (1865-?) French

£420	*$752*	*(5-May-92 SWS138/R) Carnations (24x29cm-9x11in) s. W/C*
£550	*$1007*	*(4-Jun-92 CSK93/R) Sunflowers in blue vase (95x59cm-37x23in) s. W/C*

ODJIG, Daphne (1928-) Canadian

£976	$1766	(2-Dec-91 R.T96/R) Spiritual harmony (56x61cm-22x24in) s.i.d.1983verso acrylic (C.D 2000)

OECONOMO, Aristide (1821-1887) Austrian

£2498	$4496	(21-Nov-91 D.V65/R) Faust and Mephisto in the Ratskeller (48x37cm-19x15in) s. (A.S 50000)
£4246	$7642	(21-Nov-91 D.V134/R) Portrait of gentleman (99x84cm-39x33in) s.d.1840 (A.S 85000)

OEDER, Georg (1846-1931) German

£855	$1548	(3-Dec-91 C.A193) Geese in landscape (27x34cm-11x13in) s. panel (B.FR 50000)
£1706	$3106	(27-May-92 PH.DU15/R) At the edge of the forest (47x37cm-19x15in) s. panel (DM 5000)

OEDER, Georg and HUNTEN, Emil (19th C) German

£8000	$14240	(27-Nov-91 S127/R) Taking tumble in hunting field (115x187cm-45x74in) s.

OEHLEN, Albert (20th C) ?

£8000	$14000	(27-Feb-92 CH.NY70/R) Loves body (199x199cm-78x78in) s.d.85 oil plastic canvas
£10056	$18000	(5-May-92 CH.NY153/R) Untitled (240x200cm-94x79in)
£3158	*$5684*	*(19-Nov-91 L.K977/R) Schachtelhalme (60x49cm-24x19in) distemper cotton (DM 9000)*
£4983	*$9119*	*(2-Jun-92 L.K835/R) Acker ohne Wiederkehr (140x150cm-55x59in) latex oil spray paint canvas (DM 14500)*
£10615	*$19000*	*(5-May-92 CH.NY126/R) Rock n'Roll Beerdigung (189x241cm-74x95in) s.d.85 oil lacquer brass plaque canvas*

OEHLER, Christian (1909-) German

£756	$1384	(2-Jun-92 FN.S2379/R) Mountain valley with tree lined stream (48x64cm-19x25in) s. (DM 2200)

OEHMICHEN, Hugo (1843-1933) German

£699	$1210	(25-Mar-92 KM.K1350/R) Portrait of girl (37x27cm-15x11in) s. paper (DM 2000)
£1207	$2076	(16-Oct-91 KM.K1310) Peasant woman with toddler in interior (28x21cm-11x8in) s. canvas on panel (DM 3500)
£5495	$10000	(28-May-92 SY.NY39 a/R) Sewing lesson (61x51cm-24x20in) s.
£6993	$12098	(25-Mar-92 KM.K1349/R) Young boy holding apples standing in larder (50x40cm-20x16in) s. (DM 20000)
£7666	$13951	(12-Dec-91 L.K636/R) Two young boys looking through hole in fence (50x39cm-20x15in) s. (DM 22000)
£10140	$17542	(25-Mar-92 KM.K1347/R) Grandmother and granddaughter doing homework in interior (64x54cm-25x21in) (DM 29000)
£10490	$17937	(18-Mar-92 N.M609/R) Grandmother telling stories (83x67cm-33x26in) s.d.1819 (DM 30000)

OELBKE, W (fl.1814-1846) German

£1831	$3314	(3-Dec-91 FN.S2360/R) Old woman reading hand of Neapolitan girls by well in landscape (60x53cm-24x21in) s.i.d.1845 (DM 5200)

OELENHAINZ, Friedrich (1745-1804) German

£1590	$2718	(18-Mar-92 D.V329/R) Portrait of Viennese Hofapotheker Wenzel Cerny (69x55cm-27x22in) (A.S 32000)

OELENHAINZ, Friedrich (attrib) (1745-1804) German
£1242 $2124   (18-Mar-92 D.V309/R) Portrait of Furst Karl Josef Anton Auersperg, Herzog
von Gottschee (57x46cm-22x18in) i.verso (A.S 25000)

OELTJEN, Jan (1880-?) German
£1220 $2220   (13-Dec-91 BM.B537/R) Wooded landscape (84x111cm-33x44in) s.d.1930
(DM 3500)

OELZE, Richard (1900-1980) German
£3072 $5590   (30-May-92 VG.B333/R) Elefantenvogel (16x17cm-6x7in) s.d.1948 pencil
(DM 9000)
£6294 $11203   (30-Nov-91 VG.B328/R) Composition (49x63cm-19x25in) s. (DM 18000)

OEPTS, Willem Anthonie (1904-1988) Dutch
£4321 $7864   (11-Dec-91 CH.AM437 a) Figures near coach (23x33cm-9x13in) s.d.56
(D.FL 14000)
£5758 $10421   (19-May-92 CH.AM239/R) Landscape (33x41cm-13x16in) s.d.62 (D.FL 19000)
£6173 $11235   (12-Dec-91 SY.AM40/R) Village square (50x65cm-20x26in) s.d.65
(D.FL 20000)
£7407 $13481   (11-Dec-91 CH.AM437/R) View on village square (24x41cm-9x16in) s.d.63
(D.FL 24000)

OERDER, Frans (1866-1944) Dutch
£806 $1427   (4-Nov-91 SY.J262/R) The skapu player (48x19cm-19x7in) s. (SA.R 4000)
£854 $1588   (16-Jun-92 VN.R186/R) Still life of waterlilies (48x58cm-19x23in) s.
(D.FL 2800)
£917 $1596   (14-Apr-92 SY.AM64) Still life with asters, flowers and peaches
(48x58cm-19x23in) s. (D.FL 3000)
£1371 $2427   (4-Nov-91 SY.J310 d) Boy playing morobaraba (22x14cm-9x6in) s.d.98
(SA.R 6800)
£1455 $2575   (22-Apr-92 CH.AM11/R) Still life with nasturtium in a blue vase on a
draped table (71x91cm-28x36in) s. (D.FL 4800)
£1512 $2676   (4-Nov-91 SY.J310) Farmhouse between trees (36x57cm-14x22in) s.
(SA.R 7500)
£1529 $2706   (5-Nov-91 SY.AM316) View of Katwijk Beach, Scheveningen in distance
(33x54cm-13x21in) s. (D.FL 5000)
£3579 $6227   (13-Apr-92 SY.J294/R) Bayonet with groom, Lane-Corporal Childs, Pretoria
(65x81cm-26x32in) s.d.1901 (SA.R 18000)
£5645 $9992   (4-Nov-91 SY.J309) Derdepoort, Pretoria (54x90cm-21x35in) s.d.96
(SA.R 28000)
£605 $1071   (4-Nov-91 SY.J261/R) Calendulas in bowl (23x29cm-9x11in) s. W/C
(SA.R 3000)

OESCH, Albert Sebastian (1893-1920) Swiss
£3008 $5504   (4-Jun-92 SY.Z373/R) Mimi Pinson in interior (43x31cm-17x12in) mono.d.19
board (S.FR 8000)
£474 $849   (6-May-92 GD.B957) The allotment (23x30cm-9x12in) s.i.d.1912 pastel
(S.FR 1300)
£478 $865   (4-Dec-91 G.Z992) Southern landscape (40x32cm-16x13in) s. pastel
(S.FR 1200)

OESER, Friedrich Ludwig (1751-1792) German
£580 $1050   (21-May-92 L.K312) Arcadian landscape with gods (19x28cm-7x11in) pen wash
(DM 1700)

OESTERLEY, Carl August Heinrich Ferdinand (1839-1930) German
£544 $974   (5-May-92 ZEL.L1480) Portrait of blonde girl with apple (49x40cm-19x16in)
s.d.1886 canvas on board (DM 1600)

OFEK, Avraham (1935-1990) Israeli
£691 $1300   (5-Jan-92 GG.TA147/R) Figures, lizard and bull (55x61cm-22x24in) s.

OFFERMANS, Tony Lodewyk George (1854-1911) Dutch
£1239 $2267   (1-Jun-92 W.T1381) Pause for a smoke (65x46cm-26x18in) s. (C.D 2700)

OFFORD, John J (19th C) British
£950 $1758   (11-Jun-92 CSK142/R) The timer wagon (61x36cm-24x14in) s.

OFSTI, Einar (19/20th C) Norwegian
£482 $838   (14-Sep-91 BU.O368) After the storm (70x51cm-28x20in) s. panel
(N.KR 5500)

OFVERSTROM, Hugo (1900-1973) Swedish
£474 $816   (15-Oct-91 GO.G1181) Fishingboats by jetty (44x57cm-17x22in) s.
(S.KR 5000)
£534 $940   (7-Apr-92 GO.G1121) Fishingboats in harbour (64x80cm-25x31in) s. panel
(S.KR 5600)
£569 $979   (15-Oct-91 GO.G1178) Fishing village with beach huts and fishingboats
(65x98cm-26x39in) s. (S.KR 6000)
£601 $1057   (7-Apr-92 GO.G1123) Fishingboats and boathouses (65x81cm-26x32in) s.
(S.KR 6300)
£684 $1190   (13-Apr-92 AB.S296) Fishing village on the west coast (64x99cm-25x39in)
s. (S.KR 7200)
£767 $1381   (23-Nov-91 SO.S661/R) Boathouses and fishingboats in harbour
(64x96cm-25x38in) s. (S.KR 8000)

OFVERSTROM, Hugo (1900-1973) Swedish-cont.
£887 $1560   (7-Apr-92 GO.G1122) Fishingboats at sea (64x94cm-25x37in) s. (S.KR 9300)

OGDEN, Jane (19th C) British
£1000   *$1830   (3-Jun-92 S300/R) Bluebells and primroses with bird's nest
                        (27x37cm-11x15in) s.d.1866 W/C*

OGER, Ferdinand (1872-1929) French
£471 $800   (23-Oct-91 GD.B1207/R) Donkey with young (65x54cm-26x21in) s. (S.FR 1200)

OGGIONO, Marco (style) (1470-1530) Italian
£12155 $22000   (22-May-92 SY.NY283/R) Madonna and Child (37x28cm-15x11in) panel

OGILVIE, William Abernethy (1901-1989) Canadian
£415 $750   (2-Dec-91 R.T269/R) Field in winter (33x39cm-13x15in) s.d.75 i.verso W/C
                    ink (C.D 850)
£995 $1771   (26-Nov-91 JOY.T36/R) First snow, Beaver Valley (36x53cm-14x21in) s.d.84
                    W/C (C.D 2000)

OGILVY, Charles (19th C) ?
£785 $1500   (3-Jul-92 S.W3871) Ship, Rathfern (51x76cm-20x30in) s.d.1874

O'GORMAN, Juan (1905-1982) Mexican
£22222 $40000   (18-Nov-91 SY.NY47/R) La Ciudad Podrida (22x57cm-9x22in) s. sheet metal
£166667 $300000   (19-Nov-91 CH.NY26/R) Los mitos paganos (122x91cm-48x36in) s.d.1944
                          tempera panel
£3333 $6000   (19-Nov-91 CH.NY131/R) Boceto para El Proyecto de monumento a Venus
                      (36x22cm-14x9in) s.i.d.1966 pencil paper on board
£5556 $10000   (19-Nov-91 CH.NY132/R) Los compadres (43x53cm-17x21in) s.i. gouache W/C
                       paper on board
£11050 $20000   (19-May-92 SY.NY28/R) Boceto para el mosaico - Mexico Antiguo
                        (79x108cm-31x43in) s. W/C gouache
£11050 $20000   (19-May-92 SY.NY29/R) Boceto para el mosaico - Nueva Espana
                        (80x108cm-31x43in) s.d.1952 W/C gouache
£15556 $28000   (18-Nov-91 SY.NY31/R) Mesa revuelta (22x20cm-9x8in) s.i.d.1947 tempera
                        collage board

O'GORMAN, Juan (attrib) (1905-1982) Mexican
£497 $850   (21-Mar-92 W.W98/R) Composition (20x20cm-8x8in) s. graphite

OGUISS, Takanari (1901-1986) Japanese
£40241 $69215   (11-Oct-91 HC.P37/R) Savarin, vue d'une ville (73x60cm-29x24in) s.
                        (F.FR 400000)
£1976 $3518   (29-Nov-91 GAB.G3191/R) Le tabac (21x15cm-8x6in) s. W/C (S.FR 5000)
£3299 $5707   (23-Mar-92 GL.P135/R) Ruelle parisienne (32x24cm-13x9in) W/C (F.FR 32000)
£3388 $6099   (19-Nov-91 FB.P70/R) Le campement (24x33cm-9x13in) s.d.44 W/C
                      (F.FR 33000)
£4150 $7387   (29-Nov-91 GAB.G3192/R) Restaurant Cogneaux (24x21cm-9x8in) s.d.nov.1935
                      W/C (S.FR 10500)
£4379 $8101   (12-Jun-92 AT.P32/R) Impasse hautes formes (24x31cm-9x12in) s.d.1968 W/C
                      (F.FR 43000)

O'HARA, Helen (fl.1881-1908) British
£389 $708   (11-Dec-91 A.D191) Stormy coastal landscape (23x36cm-9x14in) mono. W/C
                    (E.P 420)
£1000 $1760   (6-Apr-92 PH97) Children gathering flowers on country lane
                      (27x36cm-11x14in) mono. W/C
£1300 $2262   (18-Sep-91 CG59/R) Blue tits (26x37cm-10x15in) mono. W/C

O'HIGGINS, Pablo (1905-) Mexican
£3056 $5500   (19-Nov-91 CH.NY188/R) Paisaje Rocalloso (53x74cm-21x29in) s.

OHLIGSCHLAGER, Josef (20th C) German
£634 $1147   (3-Dec-91 FN.S2361/R) Lower Rhine landscape with sailing boats and view
                    of village (60x80cm-24x31in) s.i. (DM 1800)

OHLSEN, Theodor (1855-?) German
£2273 $3886   (18-Mar-92 N.M611/R) View of Jerusalem. The Wailing Wall
                      (50x40cm-20x16in) s. canvas on panel pair (DM 6500)

OHLSON, Doug (1936-) American
£571 $1000   (27-Feb-92 CE.NY209/R) Cherry (193x198cm-76x78in) acrylic

OHMANN, Friedrich (1858-1927) Austrian
£728 $1296   (29-Apr-92 D.V549/R) Study of Makartplatz in Salzburg (38x72cm-15x28in)
                    s.d.907 pen indian ink wash (A.S 15000)

OHRSTROM, Alma (1897-1987) Swedish
£1335 $2349   (11-Apr-92 FAL.M435/R) Where I played as a child (88x99cm-35x39in)
                      s.verso (S.KR 14000)
£2044 $3658   (16-Nov-91 FAL.M379/R) 'Mor fargar mattrasor' (74x82cm-29x32in) mono.d.76
                      (S.KR 21500)

OINONEN, Mikko (1883-1956) Finnish
£1811 $3224   (1-Dec-91 HOR.H175) The red roof (55x65cm-22x26in) s.d.1956 (F.M 14000)

OINONEN, Mikko (1883-1956) Finnish-cont.
£1940 $3454   (1-Dec-91 HOR.H174) From Myllynkulma (65x81cm-26x32in) s.d.1945
                 (F.M 15000)

OJA, Onni (1909-) Finnish
£952 $1733   (11-Dec-91 HOR.H87) Rian (33x46cm-13x18in) s. (F.M 7400)
£1811 $3224   (1-Dec-91 HOR.H179) Evening in September (27x41cm-11x16in) s.d.1985
                 (F.M 14000)
£2212 $3894   (12-Apr-92 HOR.H185) Spring brook (40x80cm-16x31in) s. (F.M 17500)

OKADA, Kenzo (1902-) Japanese/American
£12291 $22000   (6-May-92 CH.NY366/R) Grove (161x129cm-63x51in) s.
£32857 $57500   (25-Feb-92 SY.NY116/R) No 8 (147x142cm-58x56in) s.

OKASHY, Avshalom (1916-1980) Israeli
£649 $1200   (9-Jun-92 GG.TA422/R) Oriental woman (62x47cm-24x19in) s.
£1027 $1900   (9-Jun-92 GG.TA423/R) Figures in room (51x61cm-20x24in) s.d.1955
£432 $800   (9-Jun-92 GG.TA425/R) Figures in acre (48x66cm-19x26in) s. gouache
£649 $1200   (9-Jun-92 GG.TA424/R) Acre (48x65cm-19x26in) s. gouache

O'KEEFFE, Georgia (1887-1986) American
£55249 $100000   (5-Dec-91 SY.NY86/R) Blue morning glory (30x25cm-12x10in) i.d.1936verso
£109890 $200000   (27-May-92 SY.NY102/R) Calla lilies (39x30cm-15x12in) board
£315934 $575000   (27-May-92 SY.NY114/R) Lake George reflections (147x86cm-58x34in) init.
                 d.1921 or 1922 verso

O'KELLY, Aloysius (1853-?) Irish
£2542 $4500   (6-Nov-91 D.NY28/R) Young Breton maiden holding flower (61x42cm-24x17in)
                 s.
£2804 $4850   (25-Mar-92 A.D60) Portrait of Breton girl holding a daffodil
                 (61x41cm-24x16in) s. (E.P 3000)
£3249 $5750   (6-Nov-91 D.NY29/R) By the hearth (61x74cm-24x29in) s.
£8939 $16000   (6-May-92 D.NY79/R) Reflections at Concarneau (43x56cm-17x22in) s.
£12963 $23593   (11-Dec-91 A.D75/R) Breton woman cleaning pans (64x53cm-25x21in) s.d.1909
                 (E.P 14000)

OLDE, Hans (1855-1917) German
£848 $1484   (3-Apr-92 BM.B918/R) Female nude seated in wicker chair (65x52cm-26x20in)
                 s. (DM 2400)

OLDENBURG, Claes (1929-) American
£670 $1200   (9-May-92 CE.NY314/R) Untitled (55x37cm-22x15in) init.i.d.84 frottage
                 crayon col.chk newsprint
£4190 $7500   (14-Nov-91 SY.NY355/R) Sketch for feasible monument in form of ashtray
                 with cigarette-ends (23x30cm-9x12in) init.d.72 W/C pencil
£5202 $9000   (3-Oct-91 SY.NY66/R) Two purses from a Los Angeles billboard
                 (36x42cm-14x17in) init.d.63 W/C crayon
£5202 $9000   (3-Oct-91 SY.NY73/R) Ironing board (60x46cm-24x18in) init.i.d.63
                 chk.crayon W/C
£11173 $20000   (14-Nov-91 SY.NY384/R) Study for stake hitch (47x36cm-19x14in) init.d.83
                 chl W/C

OLDEWELT, Ferdinand Gustaaf Willem (1857-1935) Dutch
£1070 $1862   (14-Apr-92 SY.AM59) Street scene (62x50cm-24x20in) s.d.1903 (D.FL 3500)

OLEFFE, Auguste (1867-1932) Belgian
£22388 $40970   (12-May-92 C.A229/R) Matin de fete (143x127cm-56x50in) s.d.1919
                 (B.FR 1350000)

OLIBECK, Jacobus (17th C) Dutch
£3520 $6125   (13-Sep-91 C1/R) Dutch galley frigate running, other shipping off rocky
                 promontory (47x64cm-19x25in) s.

OLINSKY, Ivan G (1878-1962) British
£1250 $2200   (12-Apr-92 LIT.L58) Portrait of young woman (61x48cm-24x19in) s.
                 i.stretcher
£1657 $3000   (7-Dec-91 LAE.L81/R) Girl in folk blouse (91x76cm-36x30in) s.
£10140 $18150   (14-Nov-91 GRO.B117/R) Golden statuette (91x76cm-36x30in) s. canvas on
                 masonite
£462 $800   (25-Mar-92 D.NY48) Bather (30x20cm-12x8in) s.d.1902 W/C cardboard

OLIPHANT, Francis Wilson (attrib) (1818-1859) British
£820 $1500   (3-Jun-92 D.NY72) Off market (51x69cm-20x27in) init.

OLIS, Jan (1610-1676) Dutch
£1237 $2153   (17-Sep-91 FN.S2467/R) Dutch interior with figures playing cards before
                 fireplace (5x23cm-2x9in) s.d.1657 panel (DM 3600)

OLITSKI, Jules (1922-) American/Russian
£3352 $6000   (12-Nov-91 CE.NY50/R) Divine hostage - 4 (165x122cm-65x48in)
                 s.d.1973verso acrylic
£4749 $8500   (6-May-92 CH.NY300/R) First love-22 (236x130cm-93x51in) s.d.1972 verso
                 acrylic canvas
£5587 $10000   (6-May-92 CH.NY297/R) Untitled (142x42cm-56x17in) s.verso acrylic canvas

OLITSKI, Jules (1922-) American/Russian-cont.
£5587 $10000   (7-May-92 SY.NY268/R) First love-2 (185x140cm-73x55in) s.d.1972 verso
   acrylic canvas
£19553 $35000   (7-May-92 SY.NY259/R) Wand (203x146cm-80x57in) s.d.1965 verso acrylic
   canvas

OLIVA, Eugenio (19/20th C) Spanish
£774 $1455   (18-Dec-91 DUR.M598/R) Casa de campo (17x28cm-7x11in) s. panel
   (S.P 140000)

OLIVE, Ceferi (1907-) Spanish
£383 $697   (27-May-92 DUR.M372/R) Puerto (27x38cm-11x15in) s.d.1960 W/C (S.P 70000)
£818 $1406   (7-Oct-91 ANS.M70/R) El corral (37x45cm-15x18in) s.d.1954 W/C
   (S.P 150000)
£932 $1659   (26-Nov-91 BRO.B335) Paisaje con rio (46x61cm-18x24in) s.d.1955 W/C
   (S.P 170000)
£981 $1688   (7-Oct-91 ANS.M74/R) Puerto pesquero (46x60cm-18x24in) s.d.1955 W/C
   (S.P 180000)
£1308 $2250   (7-Oct-91 ANS.M73/R) Junto a la catedral (47x63cm-19x25in) s.d.1954 W/C
   (S.P 240000)

OLIVE, Jacint (1896-1967) French?
£1751 $3117   (29-Oct-91 BRO.B323) El Baleares (73x92cm-29x36in) s. s.i.d.1943verso
   (S.P 320000)

OLIVE, Jean Baptiste (1848-1936) French
£979 $1820   (17-Jun-92 I.N75/R) Entree de port (25x35cm-10x14in) s. panel (F.FR 9600)
£4141 $7330   (24-Apr-92 CN.P185/R) Menton (31x41cm-12x16in) s.d.1892 panel
   (F.FR 41000)
£5658 $10751   (22-Jun-92 AT.P98/R) Peches dans une coupe et grappes retombant d'une
   piece d'orfevrerie (74x61cm-29x24in) s. (F.FR 55000)
£6422 $11945   (21-Jun-92 LT.P59/R) Grands voiliers au port (33x46cm-13x18in) s.
   (F.FR 63000)
£12322 $22795   (10-Jun-92 ZZ.F32/R) Maisons en bord de mer (46x61cm-18x24in) s.
   (F.FR 121000)

OLIVEIRA, Nathan (1928-) American
£35714 $62500   (25-Feb-92 SY.NY156 a/R) Seated man (107x102cm-42x40in) s.d.60
£471 $800   (23-Oct-91 B.SF3720/R) Cat I (30x23cm-12x9in) s. gouache chl pencil
£2000 $3500   (25-Feb-92 SY.NY160/R) Head (30x23cm-12x9in) s.d.59 W/C pencil
£2647 $4500   (23-Oct-91 B.SF3723/R) Nude (38x48cm-15x19in) s.d.76 W/C
£10588 $18000   (23-Oct-91 B.SF3722/R) Standing man (76x61cm-30x24in) s.d.58 oil collage
   canvas

OLIVER, A (?) ?
£980 $1676   (2-Aug-91 BW401) Winter woodland scene with pheasants (46x81cm-18x32in)
   s.

OLIVER, Alfred (?) ?
£1500 $2775   (12-Jun-92 C240/R) Lovers in a garden (61x40cm-24x16in) s.

OLIVER, Archer James (1774-1842) British
£1235 $2100   (25-Oct-91 S.W2791/R) Portrait of Miss Hardinge (76x64cm-30x25in) i.verso

OLIVER, Emma Sophie (1819-1885) British
£550 $1051   (13-Jul-92 PH68/R) The Doge's Palace and the Campanile, Venice
   (14x25cm-6x10in) s.d.1860 W/C htd white

OLIVER, Isaac (c.1550-1617) British
£5500 $9680   (9-Apr-92 S135/R) Portrait of lady, called Mrs Holland, with upswept hair
   (5x?cm-2x?in) min. mono. gilt frame scroll surmount oval

OLIVER, Thomas William (1877-?) British?
£902 $1633   (5-Dec-91 D.V90) Pond landscape (25x35cm-10x14in) s.indis.i. panel
   (A.S 18000)

OLIVER, William (early 19th C) (1805-1853) British
£612 $1090   (22-Jan-92 SY.NY487/R) Snowball time (61x51cm-24x20in) s.
£1826 $3250   (22-Jan-92 SY.NY462/R) Young woman in classical dress (76x51cm-30x20in)
   s.
£3700 $6327   (13-Mar-92 C101/R) View on the river Inn near Swartz, Tyrol
   (46x75cm-18x30in) s.d.1849

OLIVER, William (late 19th C) (fl.1865-1897) British
£800 $1392   (12-Sep-91 CSK235/R) Learning to talk (36x28cm-14x11in) s.d.1879
£1400 $2394   (18-Mar-92 CSK203/R) Young beauty (74x56cm-29x22in) s. panel
£1400 $2562   (3-Jun-92 S152/R) Say yes or no (51x61cm-20x24in) s.d.1880

OLIVETTI, Luigi (16th C) Italian
£549 $1000   (26-May-92 CE.NY174/R) Boy fishing off a rock (54x36cm-21x14in) s.i. W/C
   paperboard
£632 $1100   (13-Sep-91 S.W2037) Maiden spinning yarn (53x36cm-21x14in) s. W/C
£686 $1200   (18-Feb-92 CE.NY302) Spinning yarn by terrace (53x37cm-21x15in)
   s.d.MCMXIII W/C
£714 $1300   (26-May-92 CE.NY308/R) Spinning thread (51x36cm-20x14in) s.i. W/C board

OLIVETTI, Luigi (16th C) Italian-cont.
£1371 $2400   *(18-Feb-92 CE.NY296) Water carrier by arched doorway (55x37cm-22x15in) s.d.MCMXIII W/C*

OLIVIER, Ferdinand (1873-?) French
£1925 $3484   (20-May-92 I.N158/R) Vue de l'etang de Berre (83x105cm-33x41in) s. board (F.FR 19000)

OLIVIER, Herbert Arnould (1861-1952) British
£1000 $1830   (3-Jun-92 S186/R) A bond of friendship (61x50cm-24x20in) indis.s. on stretcher

OLIVIER, Michel Barthelemy (1712-1784) French
£28729 $52000   (21-May-92 CH.NY40/R) Fetes galantes (42x33cm-17x13in) s. pair
£4273 $7819   *(15-May-92 AT.P184/R) Jeune femme a la palette (19x15cm-7x6in) sanguine (F.FR 42000)*

OLIVIER, Olivier O (20th C) French
£407 $745   *(14-May-92 BG.P49) Femme a l'eventail (45x36cm-18x14in) s. col.crayon dr (F.FR 4000)*

OLIVIERI (?) Italian
£768 $1391   (18-May-92 SY.MI14/R) Veduta di Palazzo Ducale (46x60cm-18x24in) s.d.1917 (I.L 1700000)

OLIVOE, F (?) ?
£4000 $7240   (21-May-92 CSK269/R) Young beauty reclining on bed (69x105cm-27x41in) s.

OLJDUKENREZ, Taveusz (19th C) ?
£1411 $2511   (28-Apr-92 RAS.K660/R) Crown prince Rubrecht of Austria leading autumn manouvre (36x58cm-14x23in) i. panel (D.KR 16000)

OLLEROS Y QUINTANA, Blas (1851-1919) Italian
£4286 $7500   (20-Feb-92 SY.NY324/R) At beach (23x44cm-9x17in) s.i. panel

OLLERS, Edvin (1888-1959) Swedish
£512 $938   (12-May-92 GO.G119) Gullholmen fishing village (33x41cm-13x16in) s.d.1951 (S.KR 5400)
£770 $1324   (8-Mar-92 BU.M19) Southern landscape (64x80cm-25x31in) s.d.1942 (S.KR 8000)

OLLEY, Margaret Hannah (1923-) Australian
£661 $1189   (24-Nov-91 SY.S4) Prancing horse and lute player (14x31cm-6x12in) s.d.1945 board (A.D 1500)
£766 $1356   (26-Apr-92 SY.ME92) Still life with jug and oranges (45x64cm-18x25in) s. board (A.D 1800)
£855 $1521   (27-Apr-92 J.M133) Girl with flowers (121x95cm-48x37in) s.d.70 board (A.D 2000)
£1957 $3465   (26-Apr-92 SY.ME48/R) Still life with capsicum and flowers (41x53cm-16x21in) s. board (A.D 4600)
£5286 $9515   (24-Nov-91 SY.S324/R) Lemons (75x100cm-30x39in) s.d.1964 board (A.D 12000)

OLLILA, Yrjo (1887-1932) Finnish
£1408 $2465   (25-Sep-91 HOR.H75) Lady in blue (55x38cm-22x15in) s.d.1921 (F.M 10000)
£1423 $2533   (1-Dec-91 HOR.H181) Lady wearing blue (60x50cm-24x20in) s.d.1919 (F.M 11000)

OLMO, Gregorio del (20th C) Spanish?
£7108 $13007   (13-May-92 FER.M153/R) Nina cosiendo (100x81cm-39x32in) s. (S.P 1300000)
£415 $710   *(17-Mar-92 FER.M29/R) Desnudo femenino en el sofa (36x51cm-14x20in) s.d.30-3-48 ink dr (S.P 75000)*

OLOFSSON, Pierre (1921-) ?
£617 $1129   *(11-May-92 NOR.S102/R) Composition (4x17cm-2x7in) s. gouache (S.KR 6500)*
£1431 $2548   *(27-Nov-91 BU.S52/R) 'Kontrapunkt II- rudelltema II' (10x137cm-4x54in) s. wax Indian ink gouache paper (S.KR 15000)*

OLPINSKI, Kazimierz (1878-?) Polish
£1047 $1811   (8-Sep-91 REM.W24) Man with violin (74x155cm-29x61in) (P.Z 20000000)
£1570 $2716   (8-Sep-91 REM.W25) Portrait of a woman (48x40cm-19x16in) s. (P.Z 30000000)

OLRICK, Henrik Benedikt (1830-1890) Danish
£1940 $3453   (28-Apr-92 RAS.K142/R) Nun in her cell, morning (60x45cm-24x18in) s.d.1863 (D.KR 22000)

OLRIK, Balder (20th C) Danish
£1264 $2161   (10-Mar-92 RAS.K15) Gateway to Hel's (140x120cm-55x47in) s.d.86verso acrylic (D.KR 14000)
£2523 $4339   (4-Mar-92 KH.K122 d/R) Intruder (165x125cm-65x49in) s.d.89verso (D.KR 28000)

OLSEN, Alfred (1854-1932) Danish
£671 $1221   (12-Dec-91 RAS.V756/R) Seascape with vessels (61x94cm-24x37in) s.
                     (D.KR 7500)

OLSEN, Carl (1818-1878) Danish
£1144 $1923   (27-Aug-91 RAS.K245/R) Seascape with 'Grete of Dragor' (55x84cm-22x33in)
                     s.d.1862 (D.KR 13000)
£1173 $2112   (19-Nov-91 RAS.K148/R) Ships portrait 'Larsens Plads' (55x85cm-22x33in)
                     s.d.1853 (D.KR 13000)
£2200 $3982   (20-May-92 S121/R) British brig off Kronborg (52x82cm-20x32in) s.i.d.1872
£2921 $5345   (3-Jun-92 DO.H2032/R) Three master before chalk cliffs, possibly Isle of
                     Moen (54x82cm-21x32in) s.d.1861 (DM 8500)

OLSEN, Chr Benjamin (1873-1935) Danish
£830 $1420   (12-Mar-92 RAS.V874/R) Seascape with the steamer E.M.Dalgas and sailship
                     (74x101cm-29x40in) s.d.1923 (D.KR 9200)
£1070 $1840   (15-Oct-91 RAS.K194) Seascape with sailship in Sundet (46x65cm-18x26in)
                     s. (D.KR 12000)

OLSEN, Gudmund (20th C) Scandinavian
£856 $1472   (4-Mar-92 KH.K174) Nature morte (94x64cm-37x25in) s.d.1948 (D.KR 9500)
£1057 $1914   (20-May-92 KH.K151) Nature morte, Opus V (100x81cm-39x32in) s.d.1955verso
                     (D.KR 12000)

OLSEN, John (1928-) Australian
£2423 $4313   (26-Nov-91 J.M172/R) Opium bed (80x120cm-31x47in) s.i. paper (A.D 5500)
£7479 $13312   (28-Apr-92 CH.ME1/R) Figure and still life (65x55cm-26x22in) s.d.51
                     (A.D 17500)
£9390 $15681   (19-Aug-91 SY.ME306 a) Landscape leisurely humming (166x151cm-65x59in)
                     s.d.1982 (A.D 20000)
£10213 $18077   (26-Apr-92 SY.ME308/R) Self portrait by sea (151x135cm-59x53in) s.i.
                     (A.D 24000)
£12207 $20385   (19-Aug-91 SY.ME213/R) Life upon Golden River (136x182cm-54x72in) s.d.90
                     (A.D 26000)
£415 $722   *(17-Sep-91 JRL.S338/R) Cottles Bridge landscape (42x54cm-17x21in) s.d.70*
                     W/C (A.D 900)
£441 $793   *(24-Nov-91 SY.S144) Design for tapestry - London (47x67cm-19x26in)*
                     s.i.d.1966 mixed media collage (A.D 1000)
£513 $913   *(27-Apr-92 J.M326) Spider monkey No.1 (56x76cm-22x30in) s. crayon*
                     (A.D 1200)
£598 $1065   *(27-Apr-92 J.M1097) Giraffe (59x41cm-23x16in) s.d.70 crayon (A.D 1400)*
£769 $1369   *(27-Apr-92 J.M463) Dogs (76x56cm-30x22in) s. W/C (A.D 1800)*
£769 $1369   *(27-Apr-92 J.M82 a) Spider monkeys, No.6 (41x58cm-16x23in) s.i. mixed*
                     media (A.D 1800)
£793 $1411   *(26-Nov-91 J.M641) Musk rat (46x102cm-18x40in) s. mixed media (A.D 1800)*
£855 $1521   *(27-Apr-92 J.M1154) Frog (75x56cm-30x22in) s.d.90 mixed media (A.D 2000)*
£876 $1524   *(17-Sep-91 JRL.S479) Animals drinking (56x76cm-22x30in) s. W/C (A.D 1900)*
£1026 $1826   *(27-Apr-92 J.M80) Mouse and gorgonzola cheese (56x76cm-22x30in) s.i.d.87*
                     mixed media (A.D 2400)
£1154 $2054   *(27-Apr-92 J.M309) Cormorant nest, Lake Eyre (90x16cm-35x6in) s.d.77 W/C*
                     gouache (A.D 2700)
£1282 $2282   *(27-Apr-92 J.M49) Cat (76x56cm-30x22in) s. mixed media (A.D 3000)*
£1282 $2282   *(28-Apr-92 CH.ME21/R) Underwater (55x75cm-22x30in) init. W/C crayon*
                     (A.D 3000)
£1826 $3196   *(23-Sep-91 AAA.S148) Landscape (62x97cm-24x38in) s. mixed media*
                     (A.D 4000)
£2137 $3803   *(27-Apr-92 J.M77/R) Chats at Coopers Creek (95x99cm-37x39in) s.i. W/C*
                     (A.D 5000)
£2159 $3885   *(24-Nov-91 SY.S528/R) Dog in landscape (82x98cm-32x39in) s. mixed media*
                     diptych (A.D 4900)
£2203 $3921   *(26-Nov-91 J.M41 a/R) Rock pool (88x79cm-35x31in) s. mixed media*
                     (A.D 5000)
£2765 $4811   *(17-Sep-91 JRL.S415) Elephants (100x125cm-39x49in) s. mixed media*
                     (A.D 6000)
£2817 $4704   *(19-Aug-91 SY.ME354) Blue pond (95x99cm-37x39in) s.d.90 mixed media*
                     (A.D 6000)
£2991 $5325   *(27-Apr-92 J.M90/R) Inside Africa (130x90cm-51x35in) s.i.d.90 W/C gouache*
                     (A.D 7000)
£3084 $5551   *(24-Nov-91 SY.S443) Giraffes at Kenya (100x95cm-39x37in) s.i.d.90 mixed*
                     media (A.D 7000)

OLSEN, William Skotte (20th C) Danish
£578 $1006   (17-Sep-91 RAS.K176) Nocturne with galloping horse (95x132cm-37x52in)
                     init.d.73 (D.KR 6500)
£623 $1084   (17-Sep-91 RAS.K195/R) Guitar player (85x85cm-33x33in) init.d.70
                     (D.KR 7000)
£756 $1316   (17-Sep-91 RAS.K179) Composition with figures (60x70cm-24x28in) init.d.68
                     (D.KR 8500)
£979 $1703   (17-Sep-91 RAS.K196/R) Composition with faces and red towers
                     (85x85cm-33x33in) init.d.72 (D.KR 11000)

⁑ SOMMER, Charles Clos (1883-1966) Swiss
⁷⁶ $2000   *(23-Oct-91 GD.B560/R) Portrait of boy in profile (21x17cm-8x7in) s. mixed*
                     media (S.FR 3000)

OLSOMMER, Charles Clos (1883-1966) Swiss-cont.

£1304	$2322	(29-Nov-91 GAB.G2822) *Paysage du Haut-Valais (29x45cm-11x18in) s. pastel W/C (S.FR 3300)*
£2174	$3870	(29-Nov-91 GAB.G2820/R) *Mere et enfant (35x29cm-14x11in) st.s. W/C Indian ink gold sheet (S.FR 5500)*
£5490	$9333	(23-Oct-91 GD.B558/R) *Wallis woman praying (38x31cm-15x12in) s. W/C (S.FR 14000)*

OLSON, Anders (1880-1955) Swedish

£713	$1276	(16-Nov-91 FAL.M271/R) View of Triangeln, Malmo (61x50cm-24x20in) s.d.1945 (S.KR 7500)

OLSON, Axel (1899-1986) Swedish

£655	$1133	(28-Mar-92 UA.U388/R) Surrealistic beach scene (13x19cm-5x7in) s. (S.KR 6800)
£1518	$2778	(12-May-92 GO.G122/R) Death on beach (31x42cm-12x17in) s.d.40 (S.KR 16000)
£1708	$3125	(12-May-92 GO.G124/R) Harbour in pink (27x35cm-11x14in) s. (S.KR 18000)
£1892	$3425	(19-May-92 AB.S5295/R) Utopia (32x41cm-13x16in) s. d.1985verso (S.KR 20000)
£1919	$3474	(3-Dec-91 AB.S5118/R) Epilog (41x50cm-16x20in) s.d.1940 (S.KR 20000)
£2063	$3735	(3-Dec-91 AB.S5119/R) Calm - sailingboats and figures (26x69cm-10x27in) s. (S.KR 21500)
£2207	$3995	(3-Dec-91 AB.S5127/R) The white horse (32x40cm-13x16in) s.d.42 panel (S.KR 23000)
£2467	$4514	(13-May-92 BU.S141/R) Girl against the window (41x33cm-16x13in) s. (S.KR 26000)
£3795	$6945	(12-May-92 GO.G121/R) The stone quarry, Haverdal (45x60cm-18x24in) s.i. (S.KR 40000)
£4447	$8048	(19-May-92 AB.S5293/R) Plough and harrow, man in landscape (59x72cm-23x28in) s.d.39 (S.KR 47000)
£720	$1303	(3-Dec-91 AB.S5120/R) *Landscape with mill building (19x28cm-7x11in) s.d.29 W/C (S.KR 7500)*
£883	$1598	(3-Dec-91 AB.S5121/R) *Surrealistic composition (16x11cm-6x4in) s.d.35 gouache (S.KR 9200)*

OLSON, Bengt (1930-) Swedish

£1230	$2226	(19-May-92 AB.S5296/R) Untitled composition (81x65cm-32x26in) s.i.d.83 (S.KR 13000)
£1246	$2167	(17-Sep-91 RAS.K165/R) Composition (78x78cm-31x31in) s. (D.KR 14000)
£2467	$4514	(12-May-92 GO.G125) Composition (97x130cm-38x51in) s. (S.KR 26000)

OLSON, Erik (1901-1986) Swedish

£1349	$2333	(28-Mar-92 UA.U389/R) 'Siesta' (25x26cm-10x10in) s.d.1947 cardboard (S.KR 14000)
£1551	$2590	(25-Aug-91 BU.M236) Landscape, Sondrum (22x30cm-9x12in) s.d.1945 panel (S.KR 16500)
£1601	$2786	(17-Sep-91 RAS.K112/R) Stone breakers (35x45cm-14x18in) s.d.1945 (D.KR 18000)
£1608	$2911	(19-May-92 AB.S5299/R) Harvest (27x42cm-11x17in) s.d.44 panel (S.KR 17000)
£1613	$2952	(13-May-92 BU.S143/R) Corn field (30x39cm-12x15in) s.d.1942 panel (S.KR 17000)
£2271	$4110	(19-May-92 AB.S5298/R) Landscape with hay stacks (50x61cm-20x24in) s.d.43-44 panel (S.KR 24000)
£2288	$4027	(11-Apr-92 FAL.M325/R) Stone-quarry (35x45cm-14x18in) s.d.45 (S.KR 24000)
£3795	$6945	(13-May-92 BU.S142/R) Antonius' dream (51x32cm-20x13in) s.d.1923 (S.KR 40000)
£4194	$7382	(11-Apr-92 FAL.M324/R) Goldfish (71x70cm-28x28in) s.d.1932 (S.KR 44000)
£384	$695	(3-Dec-91 AB.S5126/R) *Harvesting time (20x28cm-8x11in) s.d.1952 crayon chl (S.KR 4000)*

OLSSON, Emil (1890-1964) Scandinavian

£760	$1361	(16-Nov-91 FAL.M275/R) Autumn landscape (49x61cm-19x24in) s.d.1931 (S.KR 8000)

OLSSON, Julius (1864-1942) British

£507	$882	(17-Sep-91 JRL.S251) Waves (59x75cm-23x30in) s. board (A.D 1100)
£850	$1556	(14-May-92 CSK259) The Needles from the Channel (51x61cm-20x24in) s.
£1100	$1925	(27-Sep-91 C59/R) Coastline at Sunbreak (44x61cm-17x24in) s.
£1400	$2562	(14-May-92 C60/R) Evening waves (43x58cm-17x23in) s.
£1600	$2736	(17-Mar-92 ACA618) Breaking waves, moonlit seascape (56x76cm-22x30in) s.
£2400	$4128	(10-Oct-91 L149) Gentle swell with distant shipping approaching the coast (76x102cm-30x40in) s.

OLSSON, Wilgot (1906-1990) Swedish

£671	$1208	(19-Nov-91 GO.G129) Woman wearing red hat (80x65cm-31x26in) s. (S.KR 7000)

OLSSON-HAGALUND, Olle (1904-1972) Swedish

£1349	$2333	(28-Mar-92 UA.U390/R) Landscape in Bohuslan (38x46cm-15x18in) s. panel (S.KR 14000)
£3947	$7342	(15-Jun-92 B.O123/R) The sea-side road (43x50cm-17x20in) s. panel (N.KR 45000)

OLSSON-HAGALUND, Olle (1904-1972) Swedish-cont.
£10911 $19967   (13-May-92 BU.S144/R) Street scene, Hagalund by the barber's corner
     (64x77cm-25x30in) s. (S.KR 115000)
£14313 $25477   (28-Nov-91 BU.S105/R) Ballet dancer with red hair (73x50cm-29x20in) s.
     (S.KR 150000)
£24125 $43666   (19-May-92 AB.S5300/R) The chappel (92x103cm-36x41in) s. (S.KR 255000)
*£2941 $5382   (13-May-92 BU.S145/R) Couple in Paris (36x28cm-14x11in) s. crayon
     (S.KR 31000)*

OLSZANSKI, A (19th C) ?
£500 $840   (29-Aug-91 CG111) A winter hunt (30x51cm-12x20in) s.d.1888

OLSZEWSKI, Eugeniusz Zygfryd (1924-) German
£518 $937   (4-Dec-91 G.Z994/R) La montagna di Gridone (39x48cm-15x19in) mono.
     s.verso (S.FR 1300)
£518 $937   (4-Dec-91 G.Z993/R) Chiesa nel Ticino (49x49cm-19x19in) mono. s.verso
     (S.FR 1300)

OLTMANNS, W (?) ?
£801 $1459   (13-Dec-91 BM.B786) Bunch of summer flowers and pot plant. Study of
     landscape (67x59cm-26x23in) s. board double-sided (DM 2300)

O'LYNCH OF TOWN, Karl (1869-1942) German
£906 $1649   (12-Dec-91 N.M2795/R) Rowing boat by pier (41x56cm-16x22in) s. board
     (DM 2600)

O'MALLEY, Michael Augustine Power (1878-1946) Irish
£702 $1200   (12-Mar-92 MFA.C181) Cottages by mountains (61x76cm-24x30in) s.

O'MALLEY, Tony (1913-) British
£734 $1365   (15-Jun-92 AD.D86) Evening sky and flight (38x48cm-15x19in) s. paper
     (E.P 800)

OMAN, Valentin (1935-) Austrian
*£388 $706   (26-May-92 D.V295/R) Female nudes (43x30cm-17x12in) s.d.83 pen brush
     col.indian ink (A.S 8000)
£533 $970   (26-May-92 D.V296/R) Untitled (71x37cm-28x15in) s.d.82 mixed media
     unfolded box on board (A.S 11000)*

O'MEARA, Frank (1853-1888) British
£10000 $17400   (18-Sep-91 CG154/R) Mill by bridge (46x56cm-18x22in) s.i.stretcher

OMICCIOLI, Giovanni (1901-1975) Italian
£503 $955   (23-Jun-92 F.M8/R) Passoscuro (33x48cm-13x19in) s. tempera paper
     (I.L 1100000)
£640 $1216   (23-Jun-92 F.M54/R) Passoscuro n.122 (35x50cm-14x20in) s. i.verso tempera
     paper (I.L 1400000)
£685 $1192   (14-Apr-92 F.M89/R) Pesci (27x36cm-11x14in) s.d.1955 panel (I.L 1500000)
£874 $1556   (25-Nov-91 WK.M776/R) Landscape (36x51cm-14x20in) s. i.verso board
     (DM 2500)
£1390 $2475   (29-Nov-91 F.F168/R) Paesaggio (50x60cm-20x24in) s. s.verso (I.L 3000000)
£1946 $3464   (29-Nov-91 F.F167/R) Paesaggio (50x78cm-20x31in) s.d.1952 (I.L 4200000)
£2088 $3926   (19-Dec-91 F.M117/R) Donna in riva al mare (50x75cm-20x30in) s.
     (I.L 4500000)
£2785 $5235   (19-Dec-91 F.M136/R) Impianto di betonaggio (45x55cm-18x22in) s.
     canvasboard (I.L 6000000)
£4416 $7992   (3-Dec-91 F.R164/R) Scalo ferroviario a Camigliatello (44x52cm-17x20in)
     s. (I.L 9500000)
£5801 $10906   (19-Dec-91 F.M170/R) Il 4 Novembre a Ustica (48x70cm-19x28in) s.
     i.d.1957verso (I.L 12500000)

OMMEGANCK, Balthasar Paul (1755-1826) Flemish
£1563 $2766   (5-Nov-91 GF.L2516/R) Shepherd couple with flock crossing river
     (40x52cm-16x20in) panel (S.FR 4000)
£2234 $3887   (18-Sep-91 N.M643/R) Peasant couple with sheep in stable
     (55x74cm-22x29in) s.d.1810 panel (DM 6500)
£3136 $5707   (11-Dec-91 N.M344/R) Shepherdess and mule drivers in landscape with
     classical builing beyond (46x61cm-18x24in) s. panel (DM 9000)

OMMEGANCK, Balthasar Paul (attrib) (1755-1826) Flemish
£1400 $2534   (21-May-92 CSK112/R) Sheep in landscape, drover beyond (27x36cm-11x14in)
     with sig.d.1807 panel

OMMEGANCK, Balthasar Paul (style) (1755-1826) Flemish
£1092 $1977   (21-May-92 L.K122) Rural scene before farmhouse (25x35cm-10x14in) panel
     (DM 3200)

ONATE, L (19th C) Spanish
£547 $1001   (13-May-92 FER.M45/R) La boda (22x12cm-9x5in) s. panel (S.P 100000)

ONDERDONK, Julian (1882-1922) American
£2286 $4000   (26-Sep-91 CH.NY106/R) Summer evening (15x23cm-6x9in) s. s.i.d.1909 verso
     board
     $4000   (26-Sep-91 CH.NY105/R) Spring blossoms (40x61cm-16x24in) s.

O'NEILL Y ROSINOL, Juan (1828-1907) Spanish
£930 $1767   (23-Jun-92 DUR.M35/R) Paisaje de Mallorca (9x17cm-4x7in) s.d.1884 panel
           (S.P 170000)
£1247 $2207   (12-Feb-92 ANS.M77/R) Paisaje de Mallorca (9x18cm-4x7in) s.d.1894 board (S.P 225000)

O'NEILL, Daniel (1920-1974) British
£2000 $3480   (18-Sep-91 CG139/R) Young actress (56x46cm-22x18in) s.
£2273 $3932   (2-Oct-91 A.D36) Cornfield (51x69cm-20x27in) s. board (E.P 2500)
£2593 $4719   (11-Dec-91 A.D189) Moonlit landscape (41x51cm-16x20in) s. board
           (E.P 2800)
£2617 $4527   (25-Mar-92 A.D144) Head of a girl (51x41cm-20x16in) s. board (E.P 2800)
£2778 $5056   (11-Dec-91 A.D182/R) Winter river landscape with figures and boats
           (51x76cm-20x30in) s. board (E.P 3000)
£2800 $4900   (27-Sep-91 C151/R) Young man in a romantic costume (58x39cm-23x15in) s.
           board
£3500 $6090   (18-Sep-91 CG140/R) Single figure (47x41cm-19x16in) s. i.verso board
£3800 $6650   (27-Sep-91 C149/R) An old house (40x51cm-16x20in) s. i. verso board
£4000 $7000   (27-Sep-91 C135/R) Orpheus (61x51cm-24x20in) s. i. verso canvas laid down
           on panel
£4167 $7292   (17-Feb-92 AD.D62) Waiting for bus (38x48cm-15x19in) s. card (E.P 4500)
£4500 $7830   (18-Sep-91 CG141/R) Hat (46x51cm-18x20in) s. board

O'NEILL, George Bernard (1827-1917) British
£3800 $6802   (13-Nov-91 CG517/R) Toll the bell (48x62cm-19x24in) s.
£9500 $17385   (3-Jun-92 S140/R) The love letter (61x51cm-24x20in) s.
£14000 $24080   (4-Mar-92 S108/R) Story (52x40cm-20x16in) s.d.1900 s.verso panel

O'NEILL, George Bernard and HARDY, Frederick Daniel (19/20th C) British
£1500 $2820   (19-Dec-91 C191/R) Returning home (18x16cm-7x6in) s.i.d.verso panel

O'NEILL, Henry Nelson (1817-1880) British
£780 $1490   (29-Jun-92 PHB166) Vigil (61x51cm-24x20in) s.
£6000 $10800   (19-Nov-91 PH58/R) The pink domino (36x30cm-14x12in) s.d.1857 oval

O'NEILL, Raymond Edgar (1893-1962) American
£9714 $17000   (26-Sep-91 CH.NY206/R) On trial (124x99cm-49x39in) s.i.d.1935 masonite

O'NEILL, Rose (1875-1944) American
£393 $700   (2-Nov-91 IH.NY83/R) Nanny and children (33x53cm-13x21in) s. pen

ONGAMIA, Umberto (19th C) Italian
£1100 $1947   (7-Nov-91 F.M56) Riva degli Schiavoni, Venezia (27x58cm-11x23in) s. W/C
           board (I.L 2400000)

ONKEN, Karl (1846-1934) German
£874 $1555   (29-Apr-92 D.V900/R) Wine tasting in Spitz an der Donau (21x32cm-8x13in)
           s. panel (A.S 18000)
£3600 $6156   (18-Mar-92 S82/R) View of Tivoli near Rome (49x63cm-19x25in) s.

ONKEN-PALME, Marie (1871-1951) Austrian
£1366 $2377   (19-Sep-91 D.V189/R) From Latsch, old church, Vintschgau
           (40x31cm-16x12in) s. i.verso board (A.S 28000)

ONLEY, Toni (1928-) Canadian
£585 $1054   (18-Nov-91 HO.ED144/R) White rock (41x51cm-16x20in) board (C.D 1200)
£1106 $1935   (17-Feb-92 HO.ED144/R) Small island (51x61cm-20x24in) s. i.d.1980verso
           board (C.D 2300)
£417 $708   (23-Oct-91 MA.V44) Galiano Island W/C (C.D 800)
£417 $708   (23-Oct-91 MA.V43) Shoreline serigraph (C.D 800)
£529 $925   (17-Feb-92 HO.ED46/R) Red Deer River, Alberta II/IV (27x36cm-11x14in)
           s.i.d.1977 W/C (C.D 1100)

ONNES, Harm Henrick Kamerlingh (1893-1985) Dutch
£606 $1097   (19-May-92 CH.AM35 a) Couple in a cafe (40x30cm-16x12in) init.d.62 board
           (D.FL 2000)
£606 $1097   (19-May-92 CH.AM35) Onderonsje (30x40cm-12x16in) init.d.72 board
           (D.FL 2000)
£667 $1207   (19-May-92 CH.AM58) Queue up (32x36cm-13x14in) init.d.61 board
           (D.FL 2200)
£988 $1728   (25-Feb-92 VN.R133) Still life (40x45cm-16x18in) W/C (D.FL 3200)

ONSAGER, Soren (1878-1946) Norwegian
£891 $1542   (23-Mar-92 B.O100/R) Landscape from Son (63x74cm-25x29in) mono.
           (N.KR 10000)
£1405 $2416   (7-Oct-91 B.O110/R) Day in November (57x80cm-22x31in) indist.s.
           (N.KR 16000)

ONSLOW, Edouard Amable (19th C) French
£1872 $3219   (15-Oct-91 RAS.K198/R) Quack doctor on outskirts of town
           (60x80cm-24x31in) s. (D.KR 21000)

ONSLOW-FORD, Gordon (1912-) British
£9200 $16284   (5-Nov-91 PH41/R) Surrealist composition (76x101cm-30x40in) s.d.5-40

OORSCHOT, Dorus van (1910-) Dutch
£578 $1005   (17-Sep-91 CH.AM258) A view of a kitchen in a farm (50x70cm-20x28in) s.
                 (D.FL 1900)
£669 $1164   (17-Sep-91 CH.AM257) Peasants at work in a farmyard by a stream
                 (60x80cm-24x31in) s. (D.FL 2200)

OOST, Jacques van (elder-attrib) (1601-1671) Belgian
£1226 $2145   (21-Feb-92 LC.P24 b/R) Portrait d'un clerc (60x48cm-24x19in) i.verso
                 (F.FR 12000)

OOST, Jacques van (elder-circle) (1601-1671) Belgian
£4696 $8500   (21-May-92 CH.NY197/R) Adoration of shepherds (84x121cm-33x48in)

OOSTEN, Izaack van (1613-1661) Flemish
£6250 $11063   (5-Nov-91 GF.L2038/R) River landscape (93x134cm-37x53in) (S.FR 16000)
£9935 $16990   (18-Mar-92 D.V116/R) Wooded river landscape and farmhouses
                 (18x24cm-7x9in) copper on panel (A.S 200000)
£25680 $45967   (7-May-92 CH.AM97/R) Travellers halting outside Swan Inn in village
                 (52x78cm-20x31in) panel (D.FL 85000)

OOSTEN, Izaack van (attrib) (1613-1661) Flemish
£3575 $6256   (24-Feb-92 CSC.P49/R) Cavaliers dans un paysage (50x66cm-20x26in) metal
                 (F.FR 35000)

OOSTEN, Izaack van (circle) (1613-1661) Flemish
£3734 $6422   (16-Oct-91 AT.P72/R) Promeneurs dans un paysage de montagnes
                 (29x52cm-11x20in) panel pair (F.FR 37000)

OOSTSANEN, Jacob Cornelisz van (attrib) (1477-1533) Dutch
£6704 $12000   (17-Jan-92 SY.NY189/R) Portrait of Edward I, Count of East Friesland
                 (70x56cm-28x22in) panel

OPDENHOFF, George Willem (1807-1873) Dutch
£1250 $2100   (28-Aug-91 MFA.C177/R) Ships in port (25x38cm-10x15in) s. panel
£1617 $2862   (26-Apr-92 SY.ME195) Fishermen and boats at low tide (39x49cm-15x19in) s.
                 board (A.D 3800)
£3086 $5401   (18-Feb-92 CH.AM39) Shipping in rough seas, a lighthouse in the distance,
                 in sunset (60x82cm-24x32in) s. (D.FL 10000)
£3714 $6500   (18-Feb-92 CE.NY114/R) Shipping in estuary (25x38cm-10x15in) s. panel

OPFER, Gustav (1876-?) German
£2035 $3500   (15-Oct-91 CE.NY462/R) Spring blossoms (66x48cm-26x19in) s.

OPHEY, Walter (1882-1930) German
£4211 $7579   (21-Nov-91 L.K364/R) Landscape near Malmedy (49x59cm-19x23in) s. board
                 (DM 12000)
£772 $1389   (23-Nov-91 N.M619) Avenue (38x47cm-15x19in) s. chl sold with 5 etchings
                 of landscapes (DM 2200)
£807 $1453   (21-Nov-91 L.K365) Church tower, Sauerland (25x30cm-10x12in) s. chk
                 (DM 2300)
£962 $1761   (3-Jun-92 L.K354) Park landscape with canal and bridge (33x42cm-13x17in)
                 st.sig col.chk (DM 2800)
£1237 $2264   (3-Jun-92 L.K355) Hofgarten in Dusseldorf (38x47cm-15x19in) s. i.verso
                 pastel (DM 3600)
£1306 $2390   (3-Jun-92 L.K353/R) House in hilly landscape (32x43cm-13x17in) s.d.1924
                 col.chk (DM 3800)
£1333 $2400   (21-Nov-91 L.K367/R) Black sun (32x41cm-13x16in) st.sig. i.d.1921verso
                 pastel chk (DM 3800)
£2105 $3789   (21-Nov-91 L.K369/R) View of Camberg (38x47cm-15x19in) s. col.chk
                 (DM 6000)

OPIE, John (1761-1807) British
£6000 $10560   (8-Apr-92 S38/R) Portrait of Hon. Caroline Sackville (74x61cm-29x24in)

OPIE, John (circle) (1761-1807) British
£2791 $4800   (9-Oct-91 CH.NY137/R) Portrait of young boy, seated, wearing coat,
                 breeches and shirt (62x51cm-24x20in)

OPIE, Julian (1958-) British
£2543 $4654   (14-May-92 BG.P40/R) Le Bon francais painted metal diptych (F.FR 25000)

OPISSO SALA, Ricardo (1880-1960) Spanish
£602 $1071   (29-Oct-91 BRO.B268) Sardanas (30x23cm-12x9in) s. Indian ink dr
                 (S.P 110000)
£2214 $3785   (17-Mar-92 FER.M158/R) Arabe y su familia sobre el burro (33x24cm-13x9in)
                 s.d.1927 W/C (S.P 400000)

OPITZ, Ferdinand (20th C) ?
£534 $950   (28-Apr-92 D.V161/R) Nude (38x29cm-15x11in) mono ochre (A.S 11000)

OPITZ, Georg Emanuel (1775-1841) German
°171371 $303327 (7-Nov-91 AT.P77/R) La promenade dans les jardins du Palais Royal
                 (180x255cm-71x100in) s.d.1815 (F.FR 1700000)

OPITZ, Johann Adolph (1763-1825) German
£1993 $3508   (11-Apr-92 AW.H370/R) Quodlibet (38x50cm-15x20in) s.i.d.1783 pen W/C
                paper on panel (DM 5800)

OPPEL, Lisel (1897-1960) German
£1413 $2473   (3-Apr-92 BM.B558/R) Portrait of young woman before window
                (64x55cm-25x22in) s.d.35 board on board (DM 4000)
£1590 $2783   (3-Apr-92 BM.B557/R) By the stream (55x64cm-22x25in) mono board on board
                (DM 4500)

OPPENHEIM, Dennis (1938-) American
£1337 $2421   (6-Dec-91 GL.P277/R) Study for objects dream of flying terminated by
                collision (97x127cm-38x50in) s.i. gouache pastel (F.FR 13000)
£1423 $2476   (16-Apr-92 FB.P240/R) Study for functioning face, ceramic, urinal,
                plumbing metal slugs... (192x126cm-76x50in) s.i.d.1990 mixed media
                (F.FR 14000)
£1500 $2580   (17-Oct-91 C106/R) Study for spinning dancers from series Power
                (97x128cm-38x50in) s.i.d.1989 W/C col.crayon chl pastel
£1953 $3730   (30-Jun-92 ZZ.F1/R) Study for the radiator (127x97cm-50x38in) s.d.1983
                mixed media (F.FR 19000)
£2500 $4300   (17-Oct-91 C121/R) Study for crystal recorder (127x194cm-50x76in)
                s.i.d.1982 chl col.crayon pastel two sheets
£2680 $4637   (23-Mar-92 CC.P55/R) Virus (126x193cm-50x76in) s.d.1989 gouache W/C
                crayon (F.FR 26000)

OPPENHEIM, Meret (1913-1986) Swiss
£1569 $2667   (23-Oct-91 GD.B561/R) Composition (19x20cm-7x8in) s.d.1970 collage brush
                technique (S.FR 4000)

OPPENHEIMER, Charles (1875-1961) British
£550 $979   (28-Apr-92 S196/R) Old bridge in Galloway (51x76cm-20x30in) s.
                i.stretcher
£3600 $6300   (26-Feb-92 MMB301/R) Arched bridge and village (51x76cm-20x30in) s.
£420 $727   (24-Mar-92 CG703) The Old Bridge, Dumfries (22x29cm-9x11in) s. W/C
£1100 $1848   (26-Aug-91 S1095/R) Santa Maria della Salute, Venice (35x40cm-14x16in)
                s.d.1912 W/C over chl

OPPENHEIMER, Max (1885-1954) German
£883 $1546   (3-Apr-92 BM.B919/R) Portrait of lady (78x63cm-31x25in) s. (DM 2500)
£2979 $5303   (28-Nov-91 D.V14/R) The concert, Wiener Philharmoniker (49x61cm-19x24in)
                s. pencil pen Indian ink (A.S 60000)

OPPENOORTH, Willem (1847-1905) Dutch
£979 $1732   (5-Nov-91 SY.AM200) 'Avond aan den vijver te lent (47x30cm-19x12in) s.
                panel (D.FL 3200)
£1152 $2038   (22-Apr-92 CH.AM47) Cows in a meadow by windmill. Goats in a swampy
                greenland (24x35cm-9x14in) s. panel pair (D.FL 3800)
£1543 $2701   (18-Feb-92 CH.AM46/R) Potato-lifters in the field (71x101cm-28x40in) s.
                i.stretcher (D.FL 5000)
£515 $912   (22-Apr-92 CH.AM318) Het Eiland Marken (23x34cm-9x13in) s.i. W/C
                htd.white (D.FL 1700)

OPPENORT, Gilles (1672-1742) French
£2088 $3862   (12-Jun-92 ARC.P150) Fontaine (24x19cm-9x7in) i. sanguine (F.FR 20500)

OPPER, Frederick B (1857-1937) American
£534 $950   (2-May-92 IH.NY126/R) Happy Hooligan boards a boat for America
                (71x53cm-28x21in) s. pen ink W/C

OPPI, Ubaldo (1889-1942) Italian
£1131 $1945   (4-Mar-92 AT.P75) Les baigneuses (36x47cm-14x19in) s. dr wash
                (F.FR 11000)

OPPI, Ubaldo (attrib) (1889-1942) Italian
£2483 $4419   (28-Nov-91 D.V100/R) Study of women bathing at the seaside
                (36x47cm-14x19in) (A.S 50000)

OPPLER, Ernst (1869-?) German
£2218 $3925   (4-Nov-91 SY.J234/R) Rainy day on the beach (22x31cm-9x12in) s. board
                (SA.R 11000)
£4498 $8547   (27-Jun-92 FN.L1153/R) Autumnal beach scene (38x61cm-15x24in) s.d.12
                (DM 13000)
£5245 $9336   (30-Nov-91 VG.B120/R) Unter den Linden, Victoriaecke, parade
                (49x65cm-19x26in) s. i.stretcher (DM 15000)

OPRANDI, Giorgio (20th C) Italian
£1208 $2187   (3-Dec-91 SY.MI29/R) La Kasbah (33x41cm-13x16in) s. cardboard
                (I.L 2600000)

OPSOMER, Isidore (1878-1967) Flemish
£500 $915   (5-Feb-92 ZZ.B203) Still life of dead mallards (60x80cm-24x31in) s.
£4010 $6817   (22-Oct-91 C.A262/R) Sailing boat (60x86cm-24x34in) s. (B.FR 240000)

ORANT, Marthe (1874-1953) French
£1399 $2420   (28-Mar-92 BOD.P1004) Portrait of woman seated before easel
                          (100x72cm-39x28in) s. paper on panel (DM 4000)
£1831 $3278   (13-Nov-91 CD.P16/R) Jardin public (38x46cm-15x18in) s. board
                          (F.FR 18000)

ORBAN, Desiderius (1884-1986) Hungarian
£507 $882   (16-Sep-91 CH.ME9) Church in Hungary (37x45cm-15x18in) s. (A.D 1100)
£578 $988   (17-Mar-92 JRL.S71) Landscape (38x51cm-15x20in) s.d. board (A.D 1300)
£622 $1064   (17-Mar-92 JRL.S24) Cathedral (68x58cm-27x23in) s. (A.D 1400)
£684 $1217   (27-Apr-92 J.M290 a) Road through the hills (45x60cm-18x24in) s.
                          (A.D 1600)
£837 $1515   (19-May-92 JRL.S216) River scene (52x63cm-20x25in) s. board (A.D 2000)
£933 $1596   (17-Mar-92 JRL.S179) Village scene (79x59cm-31x23in) s. (A.D 2100)
£422 $722   (17-Mar-92 JRL.S273) Paris scene (34x51cm-13x20in) s. pastel (A.D 950)
£1021 $1808   (26-Apr-92 SY.ME6) Winter (63x48cm-25x19in) s. s.i.verso pastel
                          (A.D 2400)
£3084 $5489   (26-Nov-91 J.M255) Still life (61x47cm-24x19in) s. pastel (A.D 7000)

ORBO, Karl (1890-1958) Swedish
£753 $1341   (28-Oct-91 AB.S276) On the way to church, woman dressed in Sunday best
                          (72x59cm-28x23in) s.d.31 (S.KR 8000)

ORCAJO, Angel (1934-) Spanish
£824 $1484   (19-Nov-91 DUR.M121/R) El sueno (109x134cm-43x53in) s.d.1960 (S.P 150000)

ORDWAY, Alfred (1819-1897) American
£1105 $2000   (22-May-92 S.BM56/R) Early summer, Echo Lake, late afternoon
                          (61x102cm-24x40in) mono.d.71

O'REILLY, Captain Montague (19/20th C) British
£917 $1624   (5-Nov-91 SY.AM367) H.M.S. Bellorophon by English harbour
                          (82x108cm-32x43in) (D.FL 3000)

ORIANI, Pippo (1909-1972) Italian
£1358 $2471   (26-May-92 SY.MI87) Le collier aux perles noires (49x69cm-19x27in) s.
                          masonite (I.L 3000000)
£2270 $4040   (29-Apr-92 F.F233/R) Pulcinella (60x50cm-24x20in) s. (I.L 5000000)
£2942 $5354   (26-May-92 SY.MI45/R) Aeropaesaggio (70x100cm-28x39in) s.
                          s.i.d.1934-35verso (I.L 6500000)
£510 $907   (29-Nov-91 F.F58/R) Maschera (33x42cm-13x17in) s. encaustic board
                          (I.L 1100000)
£772 $1374   (29-Apr-92 F.F232/R) Arlecchino con chitarra (45x32cm-18x13in) s.
                          encaustic dr cardboard (I.I 1700000)
£1518 $2716   (14-Nov-91 F.M17/R) Chit... e oottiglia (50x60cm-20x24in) s. mixed media
                          collage panel (I.L 3300000)
£3178 $5657   (29-Apr-92 F.F234/R) Senza titolo (60x80cm-24x31in) s. oil mixed media
                          canvas (I.L 7000000)
£3939 $7011   (29-Nov-91 F.F59/R) Senza titolo (60x80cm-24x31in) s. oil mixed media
                          canvas (I.L 8500000)

ORIENTAL SCHOOL, 18th C
£3049 $5305   (13-Apr-92 AT.P173/R) Les femmes du harem (24x27cm-9x11in) copper
                          (F.FR 30000)

ORIENTAL SCHOOL, 19th C
£4593 $8405   (2-Jun-92 AT.P197/R) Constantinople. Le Bosphore (21x41cm-8x16in) one
                          d.1887 panel pair (F.FR 45100)

ORIZONTE see BLOEMEN, Jan Frans van

ORLANDO, Felipe (1911-) Cuban
£1143 $2000   (3-Apr-92 S.W2004/R) Lamp (89x58cm-35x23in) s.i.d.7-7-50 verso

ORLEY, Barend van (circle) (c.1492-1542) Flemish
£6969 $12683   (11-Dec-91 N.M314/R) Madonna with Child before grotto and view of
                          mountainous river landscape (52x36cm-20x14in) panel (DM 20000)

ORLEY, Barend van (studio) (c.1492-1542) Flemish
£9302 $16000   (10-Oct-91 SY.NY136/R) The Resurrection (46x30cm-18x12in) panel shaped
                          top

ORLEY, Barend van (style) (c.1492-1542) Flemish
£3600 $6300   (31-Mar-92 PH54/R) Christ on Road to Calvary (42x33cm-17x13in) panel
£5800 $10440   (21-Nov-91 C109/R) St Bernard of Clairvaux and the Miracle of Lactation
                          (27x37cm-11x15in) panel

ORLEY, Richard van (1663-1732) Flemish
£2793 $5000   (15-Jan-92 CH.NY155/R) Susanna and Elders (20x15cm-8x6in) s.d.1713 black
                          chk bodycol htd wht gold vellum

ORLEY, Richard van (circle) (1663-1732) Flemish
£1500 $2730   (11-Dec-91 PH14) Lady accompanied by oriental attendants in a garden
                          (34x25cm-13x10in) gouache

ORLIK, Emil (1870-1932) Czechoslovakian

£5245	$9336	(26-Nov-91 KF.M929/R) Bunch of roses (56x68cm-22x27in) s. (DM 15000)
£6993	$12448	(30-Nov-91 VG.B247/R) Still life of fishes (48x60cm-19x24in) s. (DM 20000)
£7343	$13070	(30-Nov-91 VG.B28) Cypress near Kalamotta (73x50cm-29x20in) s. s.i.verso (DM 21000)
£8392	$14937	(30-Nov-91 VG.B256/R) Autumn flowers in alabaster vase (54x65cm-21x26in) s. paper on board (DM 24000)
£9556	$17392	(30-May-92 VG.B145/R) Still life of flowers (99x80cm-39x31in) s.d.1918 (DM 28000)
£375	$680	(23-May-92 GB.B6976) American woman with glasses and red scarf underneath hat (29x23cm-11x9in) s. winelist verso chk (DM 1100)
£736	$1398	(25-Jun-92 D.V663/R) Luigi Pirandello (13x11cm-5x4in) s.i.d.29 chk (A.S 15000)
£751	$1367	(25-May-92 WK.M946/R) Self portrait (20x13cm-8x5in) s.d.1926 indian ink pen over pencil (DM 2200)
£769	$1369	(30-Nov-91 VG.B918/R) Geisha (34x15cm-13x6in) mono. W/C pen board (DM 2200)
£825	$1452	(11-Apr-92 AW.H2066/R) Lady with pearl necklace and hat in profile (21x13cm-8x5in) s. W/C col.chk (DM 2400)
£1263	$2274	(21-Nov-91 L.K370/R) After the bath (56x47cm-22x19in) s.d.08 col.chk board wash (DM 3600)
£3497	$6224	(30-Nov-91 VG.B263/R) Cafe du Dome (13x20cm-5x8in) s.i. W/C over pen (DM 10000)
£17065	$31058	(30-May-92 VG.B142/R) Still life of flowers in blue vase (176x166cm-69x65in) s.d.1914 oil over chk (DM 50000)

ORLOFF, Alexander (1899-?) Polish

£559	$973	(14-Apr-92 ZZ.F43/R) Composition en rose et bleu (81x60cm-32x24in) (F.FR 5500)

ORLOFF, J Y (19th C) Russian

£612	$1096	(5-May-92 ZEL.L1485/R) Wolves attacking sledge in winter landscape (15x31cm-6x12in) s. i.verso one of pair (DM 1800)
£612	$1096	(5-May-92 ZEL.L1484/R) Wolves attacking sledge in winter landscape (15x31cm-6x12in) s. i.verso one of pair (DM 1800)

ORLOV, Oleg (1937-) Russian

£612	$1138	(17-Jun-92 ARC.P13/R) Jeune ballerine (35x27cm-14x11in) s. (F.FR 6000)
£866	$1612	(17-Jun-92 ARC.P15/R) Apres le spectacle (38x46cm-15x18in) s. (F.FR 8500)
£2128	$3851	(20-May-92 ARC.P161/R) Sur le balcon (46x55cm-18x22in) s. (F.FR 21000)

ORLOVSKI, Hans (1894-?) German

£1296	$2359	(11-Dec-91 CH.AM39/R) Young girl seated (110x66cm-43x26in) s. board (D.FL 4200)

ORLOWSKI, Vladimir (1842-1914) Russian

£3265	$6072	(20-Jun-92 BM.B877/R) Peasant women harvesting in river landscape (56x104cm-22x41in) s. (DM 9500)
£6593	$12000	(28-May-92 SY.NY262/R) Country scenes (98x57cm-39x22in) s. canvas on panel mounted as screen four

ORME, Daniel (c.1766-c.1802) British

£638	$1219	(16-Jul-92 S62) Duke of Devonshire's new Russian car driver (13x9cm-5x4in) s.i.d.1829 W/C over pencil

ORMEA, Willem and WILLAERTS, Isaac (17th C) Dutch

£5093	$9116	(12-Nov-91 SY.AM16/R) Fishermen bringing catch ashore (39x53cm-15x21in) init. panel (D.FL 16500)

ORNY, Ludwig (1920-) German

£632	$1137	(23-Nov-91 N.M621) Still life of fruit, glasses and bottles (35x60cm-14x24in) s. (DM 1800)

OROZCO, Jose Clemente (1883-1949) Mexican

£8840	$16000	(18-May-92 CH.NY127/R) Estado mayor de bufones (30x37cm-12x15in) s. canvas on masonite
£12222	$22000	(19-Nov-91 CH.NY53/R) Torso (46x37cm-18x15in) s. canvas on board
£116667	$210000	(18-Nov-91 SY.NY26/R) Autorretrato (74x61cm-29x24in) s.d.1938
£3315	$6000	(18-May-92 CH.NY129/R) La pareja (37x29cm-15x11in) s. brush ink
£6111	$11000	(18-Nov-91 SY.NY94/R) Untitled (23x32cm-9x13in) s. ink wash
£22099	$40000	(18-May-92 CH.NY7/R) Parnaso Mexica con Catrinas de Pulque (35x49cm-14x19in) s. gouache
£36111	$65000	(19-Nov-91 CH.NY1/R) La Cortina Roja (23x33cm-9x13in) s. W/C pencil

ORPEN, Bea (1913-1980) British

£545	$944	(2-Oct-91 A.D15) Boats at Crook Point (25x36cm-10x14in) s.d.1953 W/C (E.P 600)
£591	$1022	(2-Oct-91 A.D135) Tahiti (48x33cm-19x13in) s. gouache (E.P 650)

ORPEN, Sir William (1878-1931) British

£30000	$52200	(19-Sep-91 B15/R) Major A.N. Lee, D.S.O., O.B.E., T.D., in hut office at Beaumerie-sur-Mer France (76x63cm-30x25in) s.i.d.1918 sold with book
£125000	$215000	(6-Mar-92 C19/R) In Dublin Bay (105x83cm-41x33in) s.

ORPEN, Sir William (1878-1931) British-cont.

£370	$648	(17-Feb-92 AD.D27) Sketch of young child (20x28cm-8x11in) pencil (E.P 400)
£748	$1293	(25-Mar-92 A.D128) Mary (25x18cm-10x7in) conte chk.pencil (E.P 800)
£850	$1479	(17-Sep-91 PH63/R) Portrait of Grace Gifford (21x21cm-8x8in) s. blk.crayon
£1050	$1922	(14-May-92 C171/R) Song of Orps, Alone in Paris at Midnight (24x18cm-9x7in) i.d.1919 ink wash
£1111	$1944	(17-Feb-92 AD.D66) Young Arabian girl (33x25cm-13x10in) s. W/C (E.P 1200)
£4000	$6880	(6-Mar-92 C9/R) The white swan, Grace and Kit (28x23cm-11x9in) i. pastel crayon

ORPHOOT, Burnett Napier Henderson (1880-?) British

£550	$985	(5-May-92 SWS251/R) Paris street scene (53x36cm-21x14in) s. indist.i.verso W/C

ORRENTE, Pedro (1570-1644) Spanish

£1938	$3488	(29-Jan-92 FER.M119/R) Natividad (87x129cm-34x51in) (S.P 350000)
£60011	$108620	(19-May-92 EP.M6/R) Jacob y Raquel en el pozo (112x184cm-44x72in) (S.P 11000000)

ORROCK, James (1829-1913) British

£420	$756	(30-Jan-92 TL205) Near Brighton, extensive downland landscape (29x44cm-11x17in) s. W/C bodycol.
£452	$805	(29-Oct-91 PH.T127/R) Old mill in Essex (48x74cm-19x29in) indist.s. W/C (C.D 900)
£700	$1253	(5-May-92 SWS213) Windmill in Sussex (19x48cm-7x19in) s.d.1894 W/C pencil gum arabic scratching out
£720	$1382	(28-Jul-92 SWS223/R) Angler in rowing boat in river landscape (49x75cm-19x30in) s.d.1890 W/C over pencil
£750	$1335	(1-Nov-91 MAI285) Ford Bridge near Floddenfield s.i.d.1903 W/C
£1600	$2688	(26-Aug-91 S795/R) Linlithgow (34x51cm-13x20in) s.i.d.1892 W/C over pencil htd scratching out

ORSI, Lelio (1511-1587) Italian

£10000	$18200	(10-Dec-91 C113/R) Fighting horses (23x36cm-9x14in) ink

ORTEGA, Jose (20th C) Spanish

£1390	$2475	(29-Nov-91 F.F128/R) Ginestre (52x65cm-20x26in) s.d.1973 s.i.d.verso tempera paper on canvas (I.L 3000000)

ORTEGO Y VEREDA, Francisco Javier (1833-1881) Spanish

£1772	$3047	(7-Oct-91 ANS.M155/R) El pesame (46x37cm-18x15in) s.d.1875 panel (S.P 325000)

ORTH, Benjamin (1803-1875) German

£692	$1315	(27-Jun-92 FN.L1154) Portrait of elegant young lady in lace trimmed dress (78x63cm-31x25in) s.d.1850 oval (DM 2000)

ORTH, Willy (1889-?) German?

£1512	$2570	(26-Oct-91 WK.M501/R) Still life of flowers (95x69cm-37x27in) s.d.1916 (DM 4400)
£1546	$2861	(13-Jun-92 WK.M349/R) Dachau street scene (72x92cm-28x36in) (DM 4500)

ORTIZ DE ZARATE, Manuel (1886-1946) French

£1160	$1996	(20-Oct-91 I.N141) Interieur (341x27cm-134x11in) s. canvas laid down on board (F.FR 11500)
£1515	$2742	(19-May-92 CH.AM7) Still life with fruit and roses (84x82cm-33x32in) s. (D.FL 5000)
£1769	$3096	(5-Apr-92 ZZ.F149/R) Fleurs et coupe de fruits (46x55cm-18x22in) s. (F.FR 17000)

ORTIZ MONASTERIO, Luis (1906-) Mexican

£3889	$7000	(19-Nov-91 CH.NY192/R) Vendedores de flores (54x77cm-21x30in) s.d.31 gouache W/C pencil paper on board

ORTIZ, Manuel Angeles (1895-1984) Spanish

£2324	$4252	(13-May-92 FER.M178/R) Albaicin (45x54cm-18x21in) s. panel (S.P 425000)
£4907	$9128	(16-Jun-92 EP.M47/R) Paisaje Granadino (81x100cm-32x39in) s.d.1963 i.d.verso (S.P 900000)
£1935	$3638	(16-Dec-91 ANS.M68/R) Sol radiante (52x34cm-20x13in) s. W/C (S.P 350000)

ORTIZ-ECHAGUE, Antonio (1883-1942) Mexican

£8500	$15470	(29-May-92 C394/R) In the park (94x82cm-37x32in) s.

ORTLIEB, Friedrich (1839-1909) German

£3436	$6289	(2-Jun-92 FN.S2688/R) Mother and child offering alm to old man in peasant interior (67x80cm-26x31in) s.i. (DM 10000)
£5143	$9000	(20-Feb-92 SY.NY224/R) Right note (76x101cm-30x40in) s.i.

ORTOLANO see BENVENUTI, Giambattista

ORTMANN, Theo (1902-1941) German/Dutch

£1080	$1966	(12-Dec-91 SY.AM115/R) Untitled (39x30cm-15x12in) mono. tempera canvas (D.FL 3500)

)RTMANS, Francois-Auguste (1827-1884) French
£1400 $2492   (26-Nov-91 PH45/R) Figure and cattle by pool in wooded landscape
    (46x37cm-18x15in) s. panel

)RTVAD, Erik (20th C) ?
£984 $1791   (10-Dec-91 RAS.K97) Composition (68x84cm-27x33in) s.d.1962verso
    (D.KR 11000)
£1957 $3406   (18-Sep-91 KH.K98/R) Composition. Figure composition (76x94cm-30x37in)
    s.d.1963 double-sided (D.KR 22000)
£400 $697   (18-Sep-91 KH.K51/R) Composition (29x39cm-11x15in) W/C (D.KR 4500)
£450 $775   (4-Mar-92 KH.K180) Composition (29x45cm-11x18in) i.d.41 W/C (D.KR 5000)

)'RYAN, Fergus (1911-1989) British
£500 $865   (2-Oct-91 A.D78) Dublin Georgian Square with figures (28x38cm-11x15in) s.
    board (E.P 550)
£602 $1095   (11-Dec-91 A.D63) Roundstone from Gregduff (33x64cm-13x25in) s. board
    (E.P 650)
£648 $1134   (17-Feb-92 AD.D30) King River, Co. Wicklow (41x48cm-16x19in) s. board
    (E.P 700)
£826 $1536   (17-Jun-92 A.D7/R) Denmark Street, Dublin (30x41cm-12x16in) s. board
    (E.P 900)
£1100 $1914   (18-Sep-91 CG177/R) Plaza Aratanzas, Majorca (35x46cm-14x18in) s.
    s.i.verso board
£1101 $2048   (17-Jun-92 A.D90) Marsh's Library and St. Patrick's, Dublin
    (56x69cm-22x27in) s. board (E.P 1200)
£1121 $1940   (25-Mar-92 A.D131) The Liffey at Kippure (51x61cm-20x24in) s. board
    (E.P 1200)
£1273 $2202   (2-Oct-91 A.D185) Spring shower (38x48cm-15x19in) s. board (E.P 1400)
£1759 $3202   (11-Dec-91 A.D175) The canal at Baggot Street (66x76cm-26x30in) s.
    (E.P 1900)
£2243 $3880   (25-Mar-92 A.D83/R) Charlemont Bridge, Dublin (48x74cm-19x29in) s. board
    (E.P 2400)
£417 $729   (17-Feb-92 AD.D13) Chrysanthemums (20x33cm-8x13in) s. W/C (E.P 450)

)S, Jan van (1744-1808) Dutch
£6955 $11893   (18-Mar-92 D.V121/R) Seascape with sailing ships (26x30cm-10x12in) panel
    (A.S 140000)
£150000 $273000   (10-Dec-91 PH74/R) Still life of fruit and flowers on marble ledge, with
    butterflies and insects (59x49cm-23x19in) s. panel

)S, Jan van (attrib) (1744-1808) Dutch
*£732 $1273   (19-Sep-91 D.V265/R) Flowering branch and raspberries (21x33cm-8x13in)
    W/C (A.S 15000)*

)S, Jan van (circle) (1744-1808) Dutch
£1600 $3072   (9-Jul-92 B159/R) Fishing boats in swell with Men-o'-War in distance
    (46x69cm-18x27in) panel
£2200 $3696   (15-Aug-91 B413/R) Fishing boats in swell with men-o'-war in distance
    (46x69cm-18x27in) panel
£2752 $4872   (5-Nov-91 SY.AM166) Hilly landscape with horse-cart, figures with cattle
    in distance (44x64cm-17x25in) bears sig. panel (D.FL 9000)
£2907 $5000   (9-Oct-91 CH.NY72/R) Ferryboat and fishermen in estuary (41x54cm-16x21in)
    bears indist.sig.

)S, Jan van (style) (1744-1808) Dutch
£1200 $2196   (12-May-92 SWS687/R) Still life of fruit, nuts and flowers on marble
    ledge (24x20cm-9x8in) copper
£1600 $2848   (29-Oct-91 PH107) Still life of flowers and fruit on a stone ledge
    (75x61cm-30x24in) panel
£1800 $3438   (21-Jul-92 PH244) Peasants crossing river in ferry (27x40cm-11x16in)
    panel
£4938 $8938   (5-Dec-91 SY.MO223/R) Bouquet de fleurs (22x18cm-9x7in) bears sig. panel
    (F.FR 48000)
£13953 $24000   (10-Oct-91 SY.NY165/R) Still lifes of flowers in vases with landscapes
    beyond (80x61cm-31x24in) panel pair
£18023 $31000   (10-Oct-91 SY.NY155/R) Still life of vase of flowers and birdnest with
    fledglings on a ledge (68x50cm-27x20in) bears traces of sig. panel

)S, Maria Margrita van (1780-1862) Dutch
£767 $1381   (19-Nov-91 RAS.K366) Basket of fruit on wooded bank (28x43cm-11x17in)
    s.indist.d.71 panel (D.KR 8500)

)S, Maria Margrita van (attrib) (1780-1862) Dutch
£740 $1288   (11-Sep-91 PHL108/R) Still life of mixed fruit on stone ledge
    (20x25cm-8x10in) copper

)S, Pieter Frederik van (1808-1860) Dutch
£1284 $2235   (14-Apr-92 SY.AM42) Fair on market-square (24x22cm-9x9in) s.d.1826
    (D.FL 4200)

)S, Pieter Gerardus van (1776-1839) Dutch
£800 $1400   (27-Feb-92 CSK143) Two cavalrymen at a gallop (27x32cm-11x13in) s. panel
£2593 $4693   (22-May-92 EA.Z150) Landscape with shepherds and cattle (55x65cm-22x26in)
    s.d.1818 (S.FR 7000)

OS, Toon van (1866-?) Belgian
£575 $1000   (15-Apr-92 B.SF3501/R) Still life with flowers on marble ledge (41x30cm-16x12in) s. panel

OS, van (style) (18th C) Dutch
£2200 $4224   (9-Jul-92 B99 r) Still life of mixed flowers in terracotta urn, bird's nest, fruit (95x76cm-37x30in)

OS-DELHEZ, Hendrik van (1880-1976) Dutch
£612 $1089   (30-Oct-91 CH.AM44) Tuilerieen, Paris (30x40cm-12x16in) s. s.i.verso (D.FL 2000)
£917 $1633   (30-Oct-91 CH.AM42/R) View of Place du Tetre, Paris with figures seated on sunlit pavement (40x51cm-16x20in) s. s.verso (D.FL 3000)

OSBERT, Alphonse (1857-1939) French
£4077 $7584   (18-Jun-92 SY.MO382/R) La danse (73x36cm-29x14in) s. s.d.1908verso (F.FR 40000)

OSBORN, Emily Mary (1834-?) British
£550 $1056   (29-Jul-92 CSK194) Where the weary are at rest (30x25cm-12x10in) i.verso
£850 $1479   (12-Sep-91 CSK245/R) A pleasure hour (76x63cm-30x25in) s. s.i.verso

OSBORNE, W (19th C) British
£980 $1686   (10-Oct-91 L168) Pond before farmstead (46x58cm-18x23in) s.

OSBORNE, Walter (1859-1903) British
£15455 $26736   (2-Oct-91 A.D61/R) Miss Mollie - daughter of J. G. Nutting Esq (91x66cm-36x26in) s. (E.P 17000)
£25926 $47185   (11-Dec-91 A.D89/R) Breton courtyard (48x28cm-19x11in) s.d.1893 (E.P 28000)
£30841 $53355   (25-Mar-92 A.D87/R) Potato gathering (30x38cm-12x15in) s.d.1888 board (E.P 33000)
£1028 $1779   (25-Mar-92 A.D88) Study of a young boy (18x10cm-7x4in) s. pencil (E.P 1100)

OSBORNE, Walter (attrib) (1859-1903) British
£1000 $1850   (9-Jun-92 LW1796/R) Barges on Thames (46x36cm-18x14in)
£1450 $2683   (9-Jun-92 LW1795/R) Cheyne Walk - summer, with figures on pavements, Thames beyond (36x43cm-14x17in) i.stretcher

OSBORNE, William (1823-1901) British
£4486 $7761   (25-Mar-92 A.D146) Critics in the studio (71x81cm-28x32in) (E.P 4800)
£6168 $10671   (25-Mar-92 A.D61/R) Horse and two terriers (51x64cm-20x25in) mono. (E.P 6600)
£10500 $18480   (10-Apr-92 C81/R) Portrait of Thomas Conolly seated on grey hunter in wooded landscape (112x133cm-44x52in)
£16000 $28160   (10-Apr-92 C82/R) Portrait of Mrs Thomas Conolly seated on chestnut hunter in landscape (112x133cm-44x52in)

OSCAR (?) ?
£929 $1700   (3-Jun-92 D.NY73) Portrait of boy with toy ship. Portrait of girl with basket of roses (46x36cm-18x14in) s. pair

OSCARSSON, Bernhard (1894-1971) Swedish
£584 $1039   (28-Oct-91 AB.S182) Mountain landscape, Harjedalen (49x64cm-19x25in) s.d.1956 (S.KR 6200)

OSGOOD, Charles (attrib) (1809-1890) American
£1081 $2000   (10-Jun-92 CE.NY12/R) Portrait of boy (122x92cm-48x36in)
£1189 $2200   (10-Jun-92 CE.NY11) Portrait of girl (122x92cm-48x36in)

O'SHEA, John (1876-1956) American
£2429 $4250   (31-Mar-92 MOR.P49) Landscape, birches (61x76cm-24x30in) s.

OSIPOW, Paul (1937-) Finnish
£2708 $4630   (10-Mar-92 RAS.K78/R) Karhun Elefantii (167x260cm-66x102in) s.d.1983verso (D.KR 30000)

OSMENT, Philip (20th C) British
£400 $720   (9-Jan-92 B149/R) Sailing vessels off a lighthouse (34x77cm-13x30in) s. W/C

OSOSKI, Gerald Judah (1903-) British
£600 $1044   (19-Sep-91 CSK112) Fair, Hampstead Heath (35x53cm-14x21in) s.d.1930 pen W/C

OSSENBEECK, Jan van (1624-1674) Dutch
£2963 $5363   (19-May-92 GF.L2031/R) Annunciation to the Shepherds (117x149cm-46x59in) s.d.1644 (S.FR 8000)

OSSLUND, Helmer (1866-1938) Swedish
£522 $955   (12-May-92 GO.G132) Cloudy landscape (17x24cm-7x9in) s. panel (S.KR 5500)
£1038 $1837   (5-Nov-91 BA.S148/R) Rowanberries by river's edge (29x41cm-11x16in) laid down (S.KR 11000)

OSSLUND, Helmer (1866-1938) Swedish-cont.
£1092 $1900 (13-Apr-92 AB.S206) Northern river landscape (42x35cm-17x14in) s.
(S.KR 11500)
£1132 $2004 (5-Nov-91 BA.S150/R) River landscape (36x83cm-14x33in) s. (S.KR 12000)
£1151 $2071 (23-Nov-91 SO.S567/R) Northern landscape (23x33cm-9x13in) s. (S.KR 12000)
£1509 $2672 (5-Nov-91 BA.S149/R) Coastal landscape, Scotland (34x26cm-13x10in) s.
(S.KR 16000)
£1614 $2809 (13-Apr-92 AB.S205/R) On the way to Stora Sjofallet, early spring
(46x52cm-18x20in) s. (S.KR 17000)
£1708 $3125 (13-May-92 BU.S147/R) Fax river by Tvar river (40x64cm-16x25in) s.
cardboard (S.KR 18000)
£2072 $3687 (28-Oct-91 AB.S186) Spring day by Torna Marsh (40x74cm-16x29in) s.
(S.KR 22000)
£3226 $5903 (14-May-92 BU.S53/R) Fax river one summer's evening (66x72cm-26x28in) s.
(S.KR 34000)
£4080 $7466 (12-May-92 GO.G131/R) Northern river landscape in autumn
(35x68cm-14x27in) s. panel (S.KR 43000)
£807 $1405 (13-Apr-92 AB.S399) Autumn in Angermanland (42x30cm-17x12in) s. W/C
(S.KR 8500)
£3585 $6417 (7-May-92 RAS.S72/R) Reindeer in the mountains (42x92cm-17x36in) s. mixed
media panel (S.KR 38000)

OSSOLA, Giancarlo (1935-) Italian
£868 $1510 (14-Apr-92 F.M61) Interno esterno (40x50cm-16x20in) s.d.1985 s.i.d.verso
(I.L 1900000)

OSSORIO, Alfonso (1916-) American
£2616 $4500 (12-Oct-91 SY.NY286/R) maxie (79x57cm-31x22in) init.d.68 mixed media
panel
£2907 $5000 (12-Oct-91 SY.NY283/R) Adam (122x122cm-48x48in) init.d.68 mixed media
sculpture panel

OSSWALD, Eugen (1879-?) German
£619 $1132 (2-Jun-92 FN.S2692) Horse market (29x35cm-11x14in) s.d.1922 board
(DM 1800)

OSSWALD, Fritz (1878-?) Swiss
£478 $870 (25-May-92 WK.M956/R) Piz Roseg (70x77cm-28x30in) s.s.st.studio i. panel
(DM 1400)
£488 $878 (29-Jan-92 N.M813/R) Seiseralm with Langkofel (70x77cm-28x30in) s.
i.verso panel (DM 1400)
£523 $951 (12-Dec-91 N.M2810/R) Snow covered mountains near Davos (40x53cm-16x21in)
s. i.verso canvas on panel (DM 1500)
£687 $1258 (2-Jun-92 FN.S2382) Tree lined stream in snow covered winter landscape,
morning (95x85cm-37x33in) s.i.d.1909 (DM 2000)
£895 $1557 (13-Apr-92 SY.J269/R) Wimpfen am berg (68x75cm-27x30in) s. (SA.R 4500)
£912 $1642 (23-Nov-91 N.M247/R) Main railway station, Munich (70x78cm-28x31in)
s.d.1910 (DM 2600)

OSSWALD-TOPPI, Margherita (1897-1971) Italian
£1316 $2408 (4-Jun-92 SY.Z430/R) Still life of flowers (67x81cm-26x32in) s.
(S.FR 3500)
£3725 $6333 (23-Oct-91 GD.B564/R) The Temptation (75x110cm-30x43in) s. board
(S.FR 9500)

OST, Alfred (20th C) Belgian?
£616 $1115 (7-Dec-91 KV.L250) Carter with horse (27x36cm-11x14in) s.d.43 W/C pen
(B.FR 36000)
£629 $1139 (23-May-92 KV.L236) Flemish proverb (37x35cm-15x14in) mono.d.1923 wash
(B.FR 38000)
£646 $1104 (21-Mar-92 KV.L217) Young horse in a field (39x48cm-15x19in) mono. chl.
(B.FR 38000)
£993 $1798 (23-May-92 KV.L235) Children at play (60x39cm-24x15in) mono.d.20 W/C
(B.FR 60000)
£2379 $4068 (21-Mar-92 KV.L464/R) Family circle (53x68cm-21x27in) mono. W/C
(B.FR 140000)
£2908 $5264 (7-Dec-91 KV.L392/R) Choux de Bruxelles (46x61cm-18x24in) mono. W/C
(B.FR 170000)

OSTADE, Adriaen van (1610-1684) Dutch
£3436 $5979 (17-Sep-91 FN.S2469/R) Peasant interior with open fireplace and figures
(35x30cm-14x12in) s. panel (DM 10000)
£6977 $12000 (10-Oct-91 SY.NY88/R) Barn interior with two peasants and a pig's carcass
(45x35cm-18x14in) mono. panel
£8500 $16320 (10-Jul-92 C167/R) Peasants drinking and smoking in barn (28x24cm-11x9in)
s.d.1640 panel
£17132 $30323 (7-Nov-91 D.V104/R) Old man in doorway of farmhouse (27x22cm-11x9in)
panel (A.S 350000)
£12000 $23040 (7-Jul-92 C83/R) Peasant bowling (8x7cm-3x3in) mono chk pen W/C
£14000 $26880 (6-Jul-92 S77/R) Study of bearded man wearing a hat (9x8cm-4x3in) init.
chk.

OSTADE, Adriaen van (after) (1610-1684) Dutch
£1100 $1870 (22-Oct-91 S224) Ale drinker (25x20cm-10x8in)
£1500 $2880 (10-Jul-92 PH48/R) School room (39x33cm-15x13in)

OSTADE, Adriaen van (circle) (1610-1684) Dutch
£5908 $10517   (28-Apr-92 RAS.K52/R) Inn scene with peasants drinking (39x53cm-15x21in)
                        panel (D.KR 67000)
*£1164 $2003   (11-Oct-91 AW.H846/R) Village school (18x17cm-7x7in) indian ink pen W/C
                        (DM 3400)*

OSTADE, Adriaen van (style) (1610-1684) Dutch
£800 $1400   (27-Feb-92 CSK195/R) Elderly couple courting at a casement
                        (51x38cm-20x15in)
£1100 $1925   (27-Feb-92 B108) Family saying Grace around a table in a cottage interior
                        (28x33cm-11x13in) panel
£1250 $2188   (25-Feb-92 PH6/R) Interior of inn with boers seated around table smoking
                        (45x39cm-18x15in) panel
£1320 $2297   (13-Sep-91 C9/R) Boor carousing with serving girl (33x27cm-13x11in) panel
£1338 $2422   (3-Dec-91 FN.S2368/R) Interior of Dutch tavern with figures
                        (32x30cm-13x12in) panel (DM 3800)
£1500 $2880   (10-Jul-92 C161/R) Three peasants playing cards in interior
                        (28x23cm-11x9in) with sig.d.1661 panel
£1520 $2781   (12-May-92 SY.AM102) Peasants carousing in tavern (44x60cm-17x24in) panel
                        (D.FL 5000)
£1870 $3254   (13-Sep-91 C114/R) Three boors at casement (35x27cm-14x11in) with
                        indist.i. num.28 verso panel
£2623 $4696   (12-Nov-91 SY.AM144/R) Figures in peasant kitchen (26cm-10ins circular)
                        bears sig.d.1640 panel (D.FL 8500)
£4943 $9294   (18-Dec-91 AT.P154/R) Interieur de taverne (49x40cm-19x16in) (F.FR 48000)

OSTADE, Isaac van (1621-1649) Dutch
£13000 $23660   (13-Dec-91 C164/R) Peasants in barn (30x25cm-12x10in) s. panel
£13580 $24309   (12-Nov-91 SY.AM227/R) Boors playing cards at table in barn
                        (53x40cm-21x16in) s.indis.d.16.4 panel (D.FL 44000)
*£932 $1658   (25-Nov-91 CH.AM82/R) Woman and peasant on chair. Fragmentary study
                        (8x6cm-3x2in) chk pen wash double-sided (D.FL 3000)*
*£12963 $23204   (12-Nov-91 SY.AM297/R) Boors carousing (22x34cm-9x13in) pen wash over chk
                        (D.FL 42000)*
*£21229 $38000   (15-Jan-92 CH.NY145/R) Tavern with peasants dancing, piper standing on
                        barrel (15x31cm-6x12in) init. black lead pen wash*

OSTADE, Isaac van (after) (1621-1649) Dutch
£4163 $7744   (16-Jun-92 SY.B273/R) Farmhouse interior with peasants playing cards
                        (48x64cm-19x25in) panel (B.FR 250000)

OSTADE, Isaac van (attrib) (1621-1649) Dutch
£1536 $2750   (13-Nov-91 B.SF2115/R) Peasants on road near cottage with church ruins
                        beyond (33x43cm-13x17in) cradled panel
£3951 $7231   (12-May-92 SY.AM63/R) Peasants butchering pig (36x27cm-14x11in) panel
                        oval (D.FL 13000)
*£2163 $4066   (18-Dec-91 AT.P105/R) Depecage d'un animal dans la rue (27x30cm-11x12in)
                        pen wash (F.FR 21000)*

OSTADE, Isaac van (school) (1621-1649) Dutch
£6955 $11893   (18-Mar-92 D.V104/R) White horse in stable interior (26x37cm-10x15in)
                        panel (A.S 140000)

OSTADE, Isaac van (style) (1621-1649) Dutch
£2000 $3500   (25-Feb-92 PH19/R) Horsemen and mounts taking refreshments before inn in
                        village street (59x81cm-23x32in)
£2100 $3780   (22-Nov-91 SWS68) A peasant in a barn interior (18cm-7ins circular)
                        indist.s. panel

OSTADE, Isaac van and DUSART, Cornelis (17th C) Dutch
*£1863 $3317   (25-Nov-91 CH.AM81/R) Study of man seated in chair (7x6cm-3x2in) lead pen
                        wash (D.FL 6000)*

OSTENDORFER, Michael (attrib) (c.1490-1559) German
£8000 $15360   (7-Jul-92 C95/R) Portrait of man wearing hat (28x20cm-11x8in) init. chk

OSTERLIN, Anders (1926-) Swedish
£591 $1040   (11-Apr-92 FAL.M438/R) Composition in dark red (24x29cm-9x11in) s. panel
                        (S.KR 6200)
£672 $1216   (3-Dec-91 AB.S5188/R) Landscape (54x65cm-21x26in) s.d.1961 (S.KR 7000)
£757 $1370   (19-May-92 AB.S5357/R) Composition in red and blue (81x65cm-32x26in) s.
                        (S.KR 8000)
£823 $1490   (19-May-92 AB.S5358/R) Composition in red and green (81x73cm-32x29in) s.
                        (S.KR 8700)
£823 $1490   (19-May-92 AB.S5359/R) Composition in blue and green (81x73cm-32x29in) s.
                        (S.KR 8700)
£1248 $2258   (3-Dec-91 AB.S5187/R) Unreal composition (37x45cm-15x18in) s.d.51 panel
                        (S.KR 13000)
£1898 $3472   (13-May-92 BU.S226/R) Object and mark (54x73cm-21x29in) s.d.1958
                        (S.KR 20000)

OSTERLIND, Allan (1855-1938) Swedish
*£536 $916   (22-Mar-92 LT.P15) Les Anadlouses (49x23cm-19x9in) s. col.crayons
                        (F.FR 5200)*

OSTERLIND, Allan (1855-1938) Swedish-cont.
£592 $1037   (26-Feb-92 CK.P61) La creuse aux environs de Gargilesse (52x71cm-20x28in)
                   s.d.1950 W/C (F.FR 5800)

OSTERLIND, Anders (1887-1960) French
£838 $1466   (26-Feb-92 CK.P62) Village au bord de l'oued (60x72cm-24x28in) s.d.1950
                   hardboard (F.FR 8200)
£864 $1503   (15-Apr-92 PLF.P95) Honfleur (60x73cm-24x29in) s.d.1922 (F.FR 8500)
£3909 $7076   (4-Dec-91 LD.P79/R) Le village (82x75cm-32x30in) s. (F.FR 38000)

OSTERLUND, Herman (1873-1964) Swedish
£808 $1446   (16-Nov-91 FAL.M383/R) The Canal near Hovratten (44x61cm-17x24in)
                   s.d.1920 (S.KR 8500)
£903 $1616   (16-Nov-91 FAL.M382/R) Landscape from Rovarkulan (68x92cm-27x36in) s.d.96
                   (S.KR 9500)
£2186 $3913   (16-Nov-91 FAL.M381/R) Luxembourg garden, Paris (45x60cm-18x24in)
                   s.d.1905 (S.KR 23000)

OSTERMAN, Bernhard (1870-1938) ?
£519 $918   (5-Nov-91 BA.S151/R) Dark haired girl wearing white dress
                   (40x32cm-16x13in) (S.KR 5500)
£527 $949   (23-Nov-91 SO.S666/R) Introducing Gustav IV Adolf, probably Prince
                   Wilhelm (125x75cm-49x30in) s. mixed media (S.KR 5500)

OSTERMANN, August (20th C) German
£836 $1522   (11-Dec-91 WE.MU48/R) Harvest time in Kranzberg (55x70cm-22x28in) s.
                   i.verso board (DM 2400)

OSTERSETZER, Carl (19/20th C) German
£600 $1038   (3-Oct-91 CSK215) A young peasant girl (15x10cm-6x4in) panel
£1994 $3569   (16-Jan-92 D.V107/R) Interior of peasant kitchen (46x67cm-18x26in) s.
                   canvas on panel (A.S 40000)

OSTHAUS, Edmund H (1858-1928) American
£760 $1300   (13-Mar-92 WOL.C457 b/R) Two pointers (76x102cm-30x40in) s.
£1868 $3250   (13-Sep-91 S.W2870/R) Autumn view - dawn over rapids (66x137cm-26x54in)
                   s.
£5464 $10000   (5-Jun-92 SY.NY312/R) On the scent (60x76cm-24x30in) s.
£5814 $10000   (14-Oct-91 H.C127/R) Five puppies with quail (36x61cm-14x24in) s.
£11475 $21000   (5-Jun-92 SY.NY312 a/R) German short-haired pointer puppies playing with
                   a bee (55x91cm-22x36in) s.d.1893
£13812 $25000   (5-Dec-91 SY.NY36/R) Retrieving (72x55cm-28x22in) s.d.1891
£16575 $30000   (5-Dec-91 SY.NY35/R) At the rendezvous (49x126cm-19x50in) s.
£19337 $35000   (6-Dec-91 CH.NY90/R) Hunting dogs (102x183cm-40x72in) s.d.1890
£1130 $2000   (9-Nov-91 W.W234/R) The brood of young grouse (48x38cm-19x15in) s. W/C
£1913 $3500   (5-Jun-92 SY.NY309/R) Following the scent (26x36cm-10x14in) s. W/C
£3488 $6000   (14-Oct-91 H.C128/R) On the scent (43x61cm-17x24in) s. W/C
£3825 $7000   (5-Jun-92 SY.NY308/R) An akward moment (44x39cm-17x15in) s. W/C
£4094 $7000   (12-Mar-92 CH.NY127/R) Hunting dogs (38x50cm-15x20in) s.d.98 W/C gouache
                   pencil on board
£5464 $10000   (5-Jun-92 SY.NY179 a/R) Three on point (55x75cm-22x30in) s. W/C board

OSTROVA, Lydia (1914-) Russian
£706 $1235   (24-Sep-91 ARC.P176/R) Le conte enchante (98x80cm-39x31in) s. (F.FR 7000)

O'SULLIVAN, Daniel (?) ?
£578 $1000   (25-Mar-92 D.NY49) Towards Blue Mountain Lake (61x46cm-24x18in) s.d.73

O'SULLIVAN, Sean (1906-) British
£537 $940   (17-Feb-92 AD.D33) Winter near Goatstown (15x23cm-6x9in) s. board
                   (E.P 580)

OTERO ABELEDO LAXEIRO, Jose (1908-) Spanish
£989 $1781   (19-Nov-91 DUR.M29/R) Maternidad (69x50cm-27x20in) s.d.91 ink dr
                   (S.P 180000)
£1227 $2222   (20-May-92 ANS.M54/R) Gaiteiro (29x27cm-11x11in) s.i. chl dr (S.P 225000)
£2153 $3703   (7-Oct-91 ANS.M59/R) Figuras (50x35cm-20x14in) s.d.90 W/C (S.P 395000)
£3819 $6912   (20-May-92 ANS.M53/R) El gaitero (49x34cm-19x13in) s.d.1965 chl dr
                   (S.P 700000)
£4373 $7434   (24-Oct-91 DUR.M1047/R) Joven (64x50cm-25x20in) s.d.1945 W/C (S.P 800000)

OTERO, Alejandro (1921-) Venezuelan
£16667 $30000   (19-Nov-91 CH.NY166/R) Tablon 55 (200x55cm-79x22in) s.i.d. i.d.73verso
                   duco wood formica

OTHONIEL, Jean Michel (1964-) French
£928 $1605   (23-Mar-92 CC.P110) Sans titre (98x59cm-39x23in) metal plaque (F.FR 9000)

OTIS, Bass (1784-1861) American
£2158 $4100   (26-Jun-92 WOL.C420/R) Portrait of mother and child (114x89cm-45x35in)
                   s.d.1838 panel

OTIS, George Demont (1877-1962) American
£1286 $2250   (31-Mar-92 MOR.P20) Landscape, foothills (23x30cm-9x12in) s. board
£1316 $2500   (24-Jun-92 B.SF6305/R) Settlement (41x51cm-16x20in) s.

OTIS, George Demont (1877-1962) American-cont.
£1421 $2600 (6-Jun-92 LAE.L100/R) California bungalow, Douglas Shively Ranch, South
Mountain, Santa Paula (41x51cm-16x20in) s. board
£2299 $4000 (15-Apr-92 SY.NY223/R) Desert bloom (50x61cm-20x24in) s.d.31 s.i.d.1928
verso panel
£3955 $7000 (12-Feb-92 B.SF463/R) North of Muir Beach - Pacific shores
(71x91cm-28x36in) s.
£5650 $10000 (12-Feb-92 B.SF475/R) View through Aspen (76x102cm-30x40in) s.

OTTA, M H J (19/20th C) ?
£1410 $2537 (24-Nov-91 SY.S256/R) Three seamen (45x75cm-18x30in) s.d.06 (A.D 3200)

OTTE, Friedrich Wilhelm (1795-1861) German
£916 $1584 (7-Sep-91 AL.W5) Sailing boats (36x58cm-14x23in) s. (P.Z 17500000)

OTTE, William Louis (1871-1957) American
£3107 $5500 (12-Feb-92 B.SF448/R) West wind (36x56cm-14x22in) s.d.1928 verso board

OTTENFELD, Rudolf Ritter von (1856-1913) Italian
£8200 $14596 (29-Oct-91 HB578/R) Turkish horseman and girl at well (56x43cm-22x17in)
s.i.d.1885

OTTERSTEDT, C (19th C) ?
£1223 $2275 (19-Jun-92 ARC.P15) Jete de fleurs (83x72cm-33x28in) s. (F.FR 12000)

OTTESEN, O D (1816-1892) Danish
£767 $1381 (19-Nov-91 RAS.K396/R) Waterlilies (43x64cm-17x25in) s. (D.KR 8500)
£1173 $2112 (19-Nov-91 RAS.K477/R) Still life of flowers (20x18cm-8x7in) s.i. after
van Huysom (D.KR 13000)
£2780 $5004 (30-Jan-92 RAS.V661/R) Wild flowers and butterfly (29x19cm-11x7in)
s.d.1851 (D.KR 31000)
£3587 $6457 (30-Jan-92 RAS.V660/R) Grotto at Kullen with wild flowers
(92x77cm-36x30in) s.d.1886 (D.KR 40000)
£5106 $8833 (2-Sep-91 BU.K63/R) Alpine flowers by waterfall (79x52cm-31x20in)
s.d.1876 (D.KR 58000)
£5282 $8873 (27-Aug-91 RAS.K145/R) Wooded bank with wild spring flowers and beach
leaves (55x65cm-22x26in) s.d.1863 panel (D.KR 60000)
£7042 $11831 (27-Aug-91 RAS.K186/R) Still life of roses in vase on marble table
(76x59cm-30x23in) s.d.1882 (D.KR 80000)

OTTESEN, Otto Didrik (1816-1892) Danish
£989 $1730 (20-Feb-92 D.V494/R) Spring flowers (24x31cm-9x12in) mono. (A.S 20000)
£1700 $3009 (14-Feb-92 C74/R) Bird's nest amongst wild roses, strawberries, vibernum
and cow parsley (27x20cm-11x8in) s.d.1847 panel
£2857 $5000 (19-Feb-92 CH.NY82/R) Still life with strawberries (21x26cm-8x10in)
s.d.1857 panel
£4000 $7240 (22-May-92 C2/R) Pink rose (20x27cm-8x11in) s. panel
£4396 $8000 (28-May-92 SY.NY268/R) Bouquet of spring flowers on ledge
(27x39cm-11x15in) s.d.1869

OTTEWELL, Benjamin John (fl.1885-1930) British
*£450 $833 (11-Jun-92 CSK55/R) Sheep grazing by a river bank (30x48cm-12x19in)
s.d.1905 pencil W/C*

OTTINI, Pasquale (1580-1630) Italian
£11213 $20856 (18-Jun-92 SY.MO285/R) Christ en croix (45x22cm-18x9in) slate arched top
(F.FR 110000)

OTTINI, Pasquale (circle) (1580-1630) Italian
£1100 $1914 (15-Apr-92 C154/R) The Entombment (38x32cm-15x13in) slate

OTTMANN, Henri (1877-1927) French
£520 $911 (3-Apr-92 CB.P52) Bouquet de fleurs (36x28cm-14x11in) s. (F.FR 5000)
£1013 $1834 (22-May-92 LD.P18/R) La Seine a Saint-Cloud (54x65cm-21x26in) s.
(F.FR 10000)
£1110 $1909 (20-Oct-91 I.N183/R) Bord de riviere (38x56cm-15x22in) s. (F.FR 11000)
£3049 $5305 (19-Apr-92 ZZ.F120/R) Bouquet de fleurs (65x54cm-26x21in) s. (F.FR 30000)
£3354 $5835 (19-Apr-92 ZZ.F105/R) Le port de Nantes le matin (54x65cm-21x26in)
s.d.1919 (F.FR 33000)
£3529 $6318 (15-Nov-91 GK.Z5243/R) Still life of oysters (65x81cm-26x32in) s.
(S.FR 9000)

OTTO, Alfred (1873-1953) German
£1250 $2263 (4-Dec-91 DO.H2872/R) Norwegian coastal landscape mono. (DM 3550)

OTTO, Johanna (1839-1914) German?
£1483 $2595 (20-Feb-92 D.V462/R) Hunting still life (148x129cm-58x51in) s.
(A.S 30000)

OUBORG, Piet (1893-?) Dutch
£1543 $2809 (12-Dec-91 SY.AM308/R) Masker (34x44cm-13x17in) (D.FL 5000)
£4012 $7302 (12-Dec-91 SY.AM196/R) Blad (27x34cm-11x13in) init.d.1948 s.d.verso
(D.FL 13000)
£10303 $18648 (21-May-92 SY.AM276/R) Abstract (39x50cm-15x20in) s.d.1947verso
(D.FL 34000)

OUBORG, Piet (1893-?) Dutch-cont.
£10494 $19099   (12-Dec-91 SY.AM201/R) Composities laatste phase (51x66cm-20x26in) s. (D.FL 34000)
£424 $768   (21-May-92 SY.AM195/R) Surrealistische tekening (30x23cm-12x9in) d.1932-34 W/C ink (D.FL 1400)
£455 $823   (21-May-92 SY.AM250/R) Op blauw (23x15cm-9x6in) W/C ink (D.FL 1500)
£525 $955   (12-Dec-91 SY.AM252/R) In de kamer (18x22cm-7x9in) gouache (D.FL 1700)
£1235 $2247   (12-Dec-91 SY.AM194/R) Teken op geblokte ondergrond (29x19cm-11x7in) gouache black chk newspaper (D.FL 4000)
£3395 $6179   (12-Dec-91 SY.AM197/R) Jachtende ster (65x50cm-26x20in) gouache (D.FL 11000)

OUBRE, Hayward L (20th C) American
£2099 $3800   (24-May-92 JRB.C64/R) Cotton picker (84x36cm-33x14in) s.d.49
£3315 $6000   (24-May-92 JRB.C65/R) Pensive family (97x61cm-38x24in) s.d.49 i.verso

OUDENROEGE, Johannes Dircksz (1622-1653) Dutch
£2160 $3867   (14-Nov-91 CH.AM24/R) Old woman seated by spinning wheel in interior warming hands over brazier (40x34cm-16x13in) indis.s. panel (D.FL 7000)
£3000 $5340   (1-Nov-91 C105/R) Blacksmith's forge at night (29x23cm-11x9in) panel

OUDERRA, Pierre van der (1841-1915) Belgian
£2600 $4628   (28-Nov-91 CSK124/R) Mount of Olives, Jerusalem (56x86cm-22x34in) s.

OUDINOT, Achille (1820-1891) Flemish
£571 $1000   (1-Mar-92 LIT.L309) Village by sea (53x74cm-21x29in) s.
£5278 $9500   (22-Nov-91 S.BM28/R) By banks of river (130x97cm-51x38in) s.d.1878

OUDOT, Roland (1897-1981) French
£659 $1192   (18-May-92 AT.P136) L'homme a la pipe (81x60cm-32x24in) s. (F.FR 6500)
£1243 $2200   (5-Nov-91 CE.NY53/R) Les baigneuses (22x33cm-9x13in) s.
£1243 $2200   (5-Nov-91 CE.NY56/R) Les nymphes (22x33cm-9x13in) s.
£1423 $2533   (29-Nov-91 GAB.G2824/R) Ancien moulin a Noirmoutier (24x35cm-9x14in) s. (S.FR 3600)
£1439 $2604   (18-May-92 AT.P135) Paysage nuageux (53x72cm-21x28in) s. (F.FR 14200)
£1665 $2914   (5-Apr-92 ZZ.F126/R) Grands chenes pres de la Grange (46x61cm-18x24in) s. (F.FR 16000)
£1873 $3278   (5-Apr-92 ZZ.F156/R) Les nymphes (22x33cm-9x13in) s. (F.FR 18000)
£1930 $3300   (13-Mar-92 FN.S2577/R) Le marchand d'alcarasas (81x54cm-32x21in) s. i.verso (DM 5500)
£1930 $3300   (13-Mar-92 FN.S2578/R) L'Arlesienne a l'Eventail (73x50cm-29x20in) s. i.verso (DM 5500)
£2049 $3689   (2-Feb-92 ZZ.F158/R) Le bain de minuit (23x33cm-9x13in) s. (F.FR 20000)
£2100 $3781   (27-Jan-92 GL.P78) Chapelle dans la campagne (65x81cm-26x32in) s.d.1929 (F.FR 20500)
£2165 $3724   (16-Oct-91 G.Z89/R) La plage (47x61cm-19x24in) s. (S.FR 5500)
£2373 $4200   (5-Nov-91 CE.NY10/R) Nature morte aux fleurs et fruits (58x91cm-23x36in) s.
£2417 $4302   (28-Oct-91 GL.P221/R) Village breton au bord de la mer (50x73cm-20x29in) s. (F.FR 24000)
£2429 $4250   (28-Feb-92 SY.NY117/R) Landscape with trees and church (65x92cm-26x36in) s.
£2470 $4371   (10-Nov-91 ZZ.F196/R) Chalutier sortant du port (38x46cm-15x18in) s. (F.FR 24500)
£2601 $4553   (5-Apr-92 ZZ.F135/R) Petite eglise dans la vallee (65x81cm-26x32in) s.d.1929 (F.FR 25000)
£3276 $5799   (10-Nov-91 ZZ.F244/R) Fruits et fleurs devant un paysage (38x46cm-15x18in) s. (F.FR 32500)
£4868 $8860   (25-May-92 D.P178/R) Jeune femme a la source (97x130cm-38x51in) s. (F.FR 48000)
£6148 $11066   (2-Feb-92 ZZ.F165/R) Panier de fleurs et de fruits dans un paysage (58x92cm-23x36in) s. (F.FR 60000)

OUDRY (style) (?) French
£4094 $7288   (25-Nov-91 GL.P8/R) Scene de chasse (260x322cm-102x127in) (F.FR 40000)

OUDRY, Jacques-Charles (1720-1778) French
£3024 $5353   (10-Nov-91 ZZ.F81/R) Nature morte aux fruits sur un entablement de pierre (23x33cm-9x13in) s. (F.FR 30000)
£3262 $6067   (19-Jun-92 CN.P21/R) Nature morte au canard (18x25cm-7x10in) sanguine (F.FR 32000)

OUDRY, Jacques-Charles (attrib) (1720-1778) French
£4036 $6942   (16-Oct-91 AT.P117/R) Natures mortes aux frutis et legumes dans des paysages (24cm-9ins circular) paper pasted on board pair (F.FR 40000)
£4895 $8664   (7-Nov-91 D.V205/R) Caged leopard with two dogs barking (131x180cm-52x71in) (A.S 100000)

OUDRY, Jacques-Charles (circle) (1720-1778) French
£1650 $2888   (3-Apr-92 C27/R) Pair of dead Feral pigeons hanging from nail (65x53cm-26x21in)
£3800 $6650   (25-Feb-92 PH63/R) Wild boar hunt in hilly landscape (92x127cm-36x50in)

OUDRY, Jean Baptiste (1686-1755) French
£8745	$16615	(26-Jun-92 AGS.P52/R) Nature morte d'oiseaux au papillon (32x23cm-13x9in) s. (F.FR 85000)
£51724	$91034	(10-Apr-92 AT.P44/R) Portrait d'un gentilhomme (147x114cm-58x45in) s.d.1720 (F.FR 510000)
£5587	*$10000*	*(14-Jan-92 SY.NY122/R) Still life of wading birds and fish by seashore (32x42cm-13x17in) bears i. black white chk*
£7500	*$14400*	*(8-Jul-92 PH89/R) Fox guarding kill. Study of hound stalking pheasant (18x13cm-7x5in) s.d.1750 pastel pair*

OUDRY, Jean Baptiste (after) (1686-1755) French
| £3041 | $5717 | (17-Dec-91 BRO.B402) El acoso al lobo (161x191cm-63x75in) s. (S.P 550000) |

OUDRY, Jean Baptiste (attrib) (1686-1755) French
| £3913 | $7357 | (18-Dec-91 AT.P197/R) Nature morte aux peches, aux poires et aux prunes (32x40cm-13x16in) traces sig. (F.FR 38000) |
| £1017 | *$1862* | *(15-May-92 AT.P185/R) Vue d'un parc (25x19cm-10x7in) black crayon htd white (F.FR 10000)* |

OUDRY, Jean Baptiste (circle) (1686-1755) French
£1744	$3000	(9-Oct-91 CH.NY27/R) Ducks in stream beneath tree by ruins (267x81cm-105x32in)
£43210	$78210	(5-Dec-91 SY.MO171/R) Sanglier dans un paysage (127x156cm-50x61in) (F.FR 420000)
£1540	*$2772*	*(21-Nov-91 BL.P17) Le singe sculpteur (26cm-10ins circular) gouache (F.FR 15000)*

OUDRY, Jean Baptiste (studio) (1686-1755) French
| £9073 | $16058 | (10-Nov-91 ZZ.F65/R) Blanche, chienne de la meute de Louis XV (113x146cm-44x57in) (F.FR 90000) |

OULESS, P J (1817-1885) British
| £1000 | $1820 | (11-Dec-91 LJ212) Wreck on stormy foreshore (27x40cm-11x16in) s. metal |

OULTON, Therese (20th C) ?
| £2793 | $5000 | (6-May-92 CH.NY339/R) Incognita IV-V (76x112cm-30x44in) s.d.85 verso diptych |

OUNKOVSKII, Andrei (1928-) Russian
| £557 | $1009 | (20-May-92 ARC.P188/R) Au port (35x50cm-14x20in) s. board (F.FR 5500) |

OUSSIK, Serguei (1958-) Russian
£461	*$830*	*(27-Jan-92 ARC.P67) Vue de St Petersbourg (26x32cm-10x13in) s. pastel (F.FR 4500)*
£461	*$830*	*(27-Jan-92 ARC.P65/R) Lumiere du soir (24x58cm-9x23in) s. pastel (F.FR 4500)*
£512	*$922*	*(27-Jan-92 ARC.P63/R) L'eglise d'Alexandre Nievski (48x47cm-19x19in) s. pastel (F.FR 5000)*
£564	*$1014*	*(27-Jan-92 ARC.P66) Vue de Petropavlovka (48x50cm-19x20in) s. pastel (F.FR 5500)*

OUTCAULT, Richard F (1863-1923) American
| £2247 | $4000 | (2-May-92 IH.NY44/R) Ballerina examines flowers as messenger waits (38x58cm-15x23in) s. ink wash |

OUTHWAITE, Ida Rentoul (20th C) Australian
£489	*$836*	*(16-Mar-92 MGS.S179) Webb (24x30cm-9x12in) s.d.09 ink (A.D 1100)*
£641	*$1141*	*(27-Apr-92 J.M849) Fairy dream (24x29cm-9x11in) s. ink (A.D 1500)*
£940	*$1674*	*(27-Apr-92 J.M346) Spring in the Botanic Gardens, Melbourne (30x40cm-12x16in) s.i. ink (A.D 2200)*
£1923	*$3423*	*(27-Apr-92 J.M100) The secret (38x25cm-15x10in) init. W/C (A.D 4500)*

OUVRIE, Justin (1806-1879) French
£3147	$5444	(25-May-92 KM.K1357/R) View of Chartres with shipping and figures (21x27cm-8x11in) s. panel (DM 9000)
£3200	$5760	(29-Jan-92 RBB895/R) View of Bruges from the river with figures and boats by bridge (43x69cm-17x27in) s.d.1855
£3561	$6373	(13-Nov-91 PIC.P77/R) Coteaux dominant la Seine (24x33cm-9x13in) s.d.1863 panel (F.FR 35000)
£2043	*$3575*	*(24-Feb-92 ARC.P17/R) Le port fluvial (25x42cm-10x17in) s.d.1859 W/C gouache (F.FR 20000)*

OUWATER, Isaak (1750-1793) Dutch
| £11500 | $21965 | (21-Jul-92 PH253/R) Figures skating on frozen canal, before City gate (34x38cm-13x15in) s. |
| £36000 | $69120 | (8-Jul-92 S50/R) Amsterdam, view along Nieuwezyds Voorburgwal with back of Royal Palace (46x57cm-18x22in) s.d.1782 |

OUWATER, Isaak (attrib) (1750-1793) Dutch
| £5525 | $10000 | (21-May-92 CH.NY155/R) Diachonie orphanage on Amstel, Amsterdam (40x52cm-16x20in) panel |

OUWATER, Isaak (circle) (1750-1793) Dutch
| £1100 | $1936 | (6-Apr-92 WW83/R) Figures conversing outside gabled house (223x31cm-88x12in) |

OUWATER, Isaak (circle) (1750-1793) Dutch-cont.
| £1500 | $2625 | (2-Apr-92 CSK78/R) Dutch town street with figures and cart (37x53cm-15x21in) |

OVADYAHU, Samuel (1892-1963) Israeli
£649	$1200	(9-Jun-92 GG.TA410/R) Figures in city (26x22cm-10x9in) s. board
£745	$1400	(5-Jan-92 GG.TA303/R) Landscape (27x36cm-11x14in) s. board
£757	$1400	(9-Jun-92 GG.TA417/R) Street (43x53cm-17x21in) s. paper
£865	$1600	(8-Jun-92 GG.TA214/R) Landscape (36x57cm-14x22in) s. board
£904	$1700	(5-Jan-92 GG.TA302/R) Seascape (31x36cm-12x14in) s.
£1297	$2400	(9-Jun-92 GG.TA415/R) Vase of flowers (46x34cm-18x13in) s. board
£1297	$2400	(9-Jun-92 GG.TA413/R) Trees by lake (32x41cm-13x16in) s.
£1514	$2800	(8-Jun-92 GG.TA213/R) Trees in landscape (52x63cm-20x25in) s.
£1568	$2900	(9-Jun-92 GG.TA414/R) Landscape (47x55cm-19x22in) s. board
£2486	$4600	(9-Jun-92 GG.TA411/R) Portrait of Bialik (65x46cm-26x18in) board
£3459	$6400	(9-Jun-92 GG.TA412/R) Sand-diggers (72x60cm-28x24in) s.
£3892	$7200	(9-Jun-92 GG.TA406/R) Ha'ari synagogue in Safed (60x69cm-24x27in) s.
£3892	$7200	(9-Jun-92 GG.TA408/R) View of Jaffa (54x65cm-21x26in) s.
£486	$900	(9-Jun-92 GG.TA416/R) Minaret against sea (35x42cm-14x17in) s. W/C
£541	$1000	(9-Jun-92 GG.TA409/R) Nude (98x58cm-39x23in) s.d.1912 chl pastel
£2486	$4600	(9-Jun-92 GG.TA407/R) Carriage in rain (63x53cm-25x21in) oil gouache

OVENS, Jurgen (1623-1678) German
| £64246 | $115000 | (17-Jan-92 SY.NY29/R) Portrait of a family, said to be Colonel John Hutchinson and family (132x170cm-52x67in) s.d.1659 |

OVERBECK, A V (20th C) ?
| £586 | $1013 | (3-Oct-91 D.V59/R) Girl with goats in hilly landscape (28x30cm-11x12in) s. canvas on board (A.S 12000) |

OVERBECK, Fritz (1869-1909) German
| £24735 | $43286 | (3-Apr-92 BM.B559/R) Eichenhof (89x152cm-35x60in) s.d.99 (DM 70000) |

OVERBEEK, Gijsbertus Johannes van (1882-1947) Dutch
£436	$837	(7-Jul-92 VN.R158) Haulage trucks on a quay (58x99cm-23x39in) s. (D.FL 1400)
£590	$1021	(24-Mar-92 VN.R72/R) Horse and cart on a quay (60x80cm-24x31in) s. (D.FL 1900)
£592	$1136	(7-Jul-92 VN.R159) Haulage trucks on a Rotterdam quay (58x99cm-23x39in) s. (D.FL 1900)
£683	$1182	(24-Mar-92 VN.R71) Rotterdam town with tugs at the quayside (32x40cm-13x16in) s. (D.FL 2200)
£1273	$2253	(22-Apr-92 CH.AM29/R) Busy streetscene in the Korte Hoogstraat, Rotterdam (60x80cm-24x31in) s. (D.FL 4200)
£1543	$2701	(18-Feb-92 CH.AM57/R) Horse-drawn cart on a quay, Rotterdam, in winter (60x80cm-24x31in) s. (D.FL 5000)

OVERMAN, Gerard (1855-1906) Dutch
| £973 | $1692 | (17-Sep-91 CH.AM678) A young girl seated in a painter's studio feeding cats (65x45cm-26x18in) indist.s. (D.FL 3200) |

OVERSCHIE, Pieter van (17th C) Flemish
| £4938 | $8840 | (12-Nov-91 SY.AM39/R) Still life of birds and fish arranged on ledge (64x84cm-25x33in) s. panel (D.FL 16000) |

OVIEDO, Ramon (1927-) Dominican
£2210	$4000	(18-May-92 CH.NY224/R) Escena en Rojo (76x101cm-30x40in) s. s.i.verso mixed media canvas
£3315	$6000	(19-May-92 SY.NY208 a/R) Colombinos (102x127cm-40x50in) s. s.i.verso mixed media canvas
£3611	$6500	(18-Nov-91 SY.NY187/R) Prisa para que (102x127cm-40x50in) s. s.i.verso oil collage canvas

OVTCHINNIKOV, Alexandre (1929-) Russian
| £1041 | $1821 | (30-Mar-92 ZZ.F208/R) La folie printaniere (120x140cm-47x55in) s. (F.FR 10000) |

OWEN, Jurgen (style) (17th C) Danish?
| £794 | $1413 | (28-Apr-92 RAS.K628) Alchemist in his study (98x83cm-39x33in) (D.KR 9000) |

OWEN, Robert Emmett (19/20th C) American
£492	$900	(9-Feb-92 LIT.L218) Fall lake scene (51x46cm-20x18in) s.
£702	$1250	(29-Nov-91 MFA.C112/R) Winter snow scene (33x41cm-13x16in) s.
£1093	$2000	(9-Feb-92 LIT.L216) House in Redding (64x86cm-25x34in) s.
£1170	$2000	(13-Mar-92 S.BM238) Red barn, winter sunset (41x51cm-16x20in) s.
£1170	$2000	(12-Mar-92 MFA.C235) Landscape (76x64cm-30x25in) s.
£1271	$2300	(7-Dec-91 LAE.L30/R) Autumn landscape (76x91cm-30x36in) s.
£1412	$2500	(25-Apr-92 YFA.M235/R) Farm road in winter (51x61cm-20x24in) s. s.i.verso
£2022	$3700	(9-Feb-92 LIT.L164) Snowscape with barns (76x102cm-30x40in) s.
£2486	$4500	(4-Dec-91 D.NY85/R) Winter sun casting shadows, Litchfield, Connecticut (64x76cm-25x30in) s. i.verso

OWEN, Samuel (1768-1857) British
| £680 | $1217 | (5-May-92 SWS49/R) Indiaman laying to for a pilot (14x22cm-6x9in) s. indist.d. W/C over pencil scratching out |

OWEN, Samuel (1768-1857) British-cont.
£1650 $3152   (16-Jul-92 S73) Sea battle between the English and French. Shipping off
                  the coast (8x12cm-3x5in) s. W/C over pencil pair
£3100 $5549   (14-Nov-91 S117/R) Shipping off Dover (12x23cm-5x9in) s.d.28 W/C over
                  pencil htd.bodycol

OWEN, William (attrib) (1769-1825) British
£800 $1528   (15-Jul-92 S151) Portrait of lady with her child (90x75cm-35x30in)
£3200 $5632   (10-Apr-92 C113/R) Portrait of boy with cricket bat and girl seated
                  holding bird's nest (157x102cm-62x40in)

OXHOLM, Charlotte (1846-1922) German
£1162 $2103   (4-Dec-91 DO.H2873/R) Interior with woman sewing by light of lamp
                  (40x34cm-16x13in) s.d.1889 board (DM 3300)

OYENS, David (1842-1902) Flemish
£1216 $2116   (17-Sep-91 CH.AM541/R) The painter's model (50x35cm-20x14in) s. panel
                  (D.FL 4000)

OYSTON, George (fl.1890's) British
£440 $757   (3-Mar-92 SWS1783) Corner of the common (35x53cm-14x21in) s.d.1918 W/C
                  over pencil

OZANNE, Nicolas Marie (1728-1811) French
£924 $1663   (22-Nov-91 AGS.P124/R) Le Port de Brest (13x22cm-5x9in) pen wash W/C
                  (F.FR 9000)
£1190 $2105   (10-Nov-91 ZZ.F51/R) Le lancement d'un vaisseau de guerre
                  (22x33cm-9x13in) pen W/C (F.FR 11800)

OZANNE, Pierre (1737-1813) French
£458 $838   (15-May-92 AT.P187) Vue de Carthagene prise de la mer (10x15cm-4x6in) pen
                  wash (F.FR 4500)
£763 $1396   (15-May-92 AT.P186) Vue de Buenos Aires (10x16cm-4x6in) pen wash
                  (F.FR 7500)
£870 $1549   (29-Nov-91 ARC.P89/R) Vue de Pic de Teneriffe (39x52cm-15x20in) s.i.
                  pierre noire white chk. (F.FR 8500)

OZENFANT, Amedee (1886-1966) French
£9143 $16000   (25-Feb-92 SY.NY68/R) Trois yachts (46x60cm-18x24in) s.
£610 $1061   (19-Apr-92 ZZ.F34) Femme a sa coiffure (31x28cm-12x11in) st.sig. crayon
                  dr. (F.FR 6000)
£800 $1528   (29-Jun-92 CSK83/R) Etude pour les verres (27x22cm-11x9in) s.i.d.1917 pen
                  pencil
£10500 $18165   (25-Mar-92 S41/R) Composition puriste (27x35cm-11x14in) s.d.XXV pencil
                  crayon gouache card

OZOLS, Vilis (1929-) Latvian
£526 $900   (13-Mar-92 S.BM305/R) Klusa daba, table top still life (56x64cm-22x25in)
                  s. i.verso masonite

P L (17th C) ?
£620 $1178   (23-Jun-92 PH195) Poodle. West highland terrier (49x39cm-19x15in) mono
                  pair

P V P (?) ?
£687 $1196   (18-Sep-91 N.M429/R) Rabbit feeding (16x14cm-6x6in) mono. panel oval
                  (DM 2000)

PAALEN, Wolfgang (1905-1959) Austrian
£4980 $8665   (16-Apr-92 FB.P42/R) Composition (55x38cm-22x15in) mon. (F.FR 49000)
£19052 $34865   (12-May-92 F.R248/R) La balance - reve interprete - vue gothique
                  (99x73cm-39x29in) mono.d.1937verso (I.L 42000000)

PACCHIA, Girolamo del (studio) (1477-1533) Italian
£22000 $40040   (10-Dec-91 PH39/R) nativity (87cm-34ins circular) panel

PACE, Michelangelo see CAMPIDOGLIO, Michele di

PACENZA, Onofrio (1904-1971) Argentinian
£889 $1600   (20-Nov-91 V.BA68) Paisaje jujeno (35x47cm-14x19in) d.1947
£2905 $5200   (6-May-92 V.BA71/R) Callejon de Quilmes (62x71cm-24x28in)
£4583 $8250   (20-Nov-91 V.BA69/R) Junto al muelle (59x89cm-23x35in)

PACHECO, Fernando Castro (20th C) South American
£474 $900   (26-Jun-92 WOL.C106) Portrait of woman draped with a cloth
                  (61x48cm-24x19in) s.d.55

PACHER, Ferdinand (1852-1911) German
£2787 $5073   (11-Dec-91 N.M554/R) Women in peasant interior looking at material
                  (30x38cm-12x15in) s. panel (DM 8000)

PACKH, Leopold (19th C) ?
£757 $1370   (19-May-92 AB.S4364/R) Woman with pigeons (79x63cm-31x25in) s.d.1855
(S.KR 8000)

PACZKA FERENCZ, Franz (1856-1925) Hungarian
£430 $770   (14-Nov-91 GRO.B63/R) Peasant women in farmyard (13x23cm-5x9in) s.i.
panel

PACZKA WAGNER, Cornelia (1864-?) German
£909 $1573   (25-Mar-92 KM.K1358/R) View from balcony over mountain landscape, June
morning (92x76cm-36x30in) s. (DM 2600)

PADDAY, Charles Murray (1868-1954) British
£1300 $2262   (14-Apr-92 CSK163/R) Fishing boats off Trouville (35x25cm-14x10in) s.
i.verso

PADERLIK, Arnost (1919-) Czechoslovakian?
£497 $884   (29-Nov-91 D.V146/R) Still life with owl (45x60cm-18x24in) s.d.79
(A.S 10000)

PADILLA, Eugenio Lucas see LUCAS Y PADILLA, Eugenio

PADUA SCHOOL, 15th C Italian
£16268 $29445   (3-Dec-91 SY.MI247/R) Madonna col Bambino, S.Giovannino e S.Gerolamo
(44x31cm-17x12in) tempera on panel (I.L 35000000)

PADUA, Paul Matthias (1903-1981) Austrian
£1568 $2854   (13-Dec-91 BM.B851/R) Interior with lady's desk and chair
(68x54cm-27x21in) s.i.d.1928 (DM 4500)
£3158 $5684   (23-Nov-91 N.M248/R) Picking fruit (40x31cm-16x12in) s. panel (DM 9000)
£3952 $7232   (3-Jun-92 L.K356/R) Portrait of child (80x62cm-31x24in) s.d.1934 panel
(DM 11500)
£5263 $9474   (21-Nov-91 L.K371/R) Portrait of lady (65x48cm-26x19in) s.d.50 panel
(DM 15000)
£10309 $17938   (17-Sep-91 FN.S2471/R) Seated peasant couple courting in interior
(85x55cm-33x22in) s.d.1942 board (DM 30000)
*£1024 $1863   (25-May-92 WK.M958/R) Bunch of flowers (34x27cm-13x11in) s.d.1962 W/C
htd.white (DM 3000)*

PADVA, Yefime (1915-) Russian
£512 $922   (27-Jan-92 ARC.P177/R) Neige et givre (70x60cm-28x24in) s. (F.FR 5000)

PAEDE, Paul (1868-1929) German
£767 $1395   (11-Dec-91 WE.MU220/R) Female nude (43x35cm-17x14in) (DM 2200)
£1131 $1979   (3-Apr-92 BM.B922/R) Female nudes bathing and dancing in landscape
(21x14cm-8x6in) s. panel (DM 3200)
£1568 $2854   (12-Dec-91 L.K646) Two nude ladies by pond (52x62cm-20x24in) s. (DM 4500)
£2405 $4186   (17-Sep-91 FN.S2472/R) Nude girl standing in interior with teddy bear
seated on divan (75x66cm-30x26in) s.d.1921 (DM 7000)
£2662 $4845   (26-May-92 KF.M403/R) Female nude seen from behind before mirror
(27x19cm-11x7in) s. panel (DM 7800)

PAEFFGEN, C O (20th C) German
£14737 $26526   (19-Nov-91 L.K981/R) Sul letto di Dolore (110x170cm-43x67in) s.d.1971
acrylic (DM 42000)

PAEFFGEN, Claes Otto (20th C) German
*£378 $699   (11-Jun-92 HN.H360/R) Two politicians conversing (15x10cm-6x4in)
mono.d.1987 indian ink brush (DM 1100)*

PAEP, Thomas (1628-1670) Flemish
£13000 $22750   (1-Apr-92 S141/R) Still life of oysters, figs, prawns and lemons on dish
with grapes, pipes and roemer on draped ledge (48x36cm-19x14in) s.
panel

PAERELS, Willem (1878-1962) Belgian
£545 $987   (21-May-92 SY.AM85/R) Entree de parc (40x50cm-16x20in) s. i.verso
(D.FL 1800)
£818 $1481   (21-May-92 SY.AM101/R) Portrait of Rient van Santen (39x26cm-15x10in)
s.i. panel (D.FL 2700)
£1671 $2840   (22-Oct-91 C.A265/R) The port (70x74cm-28x29in) s. (B.FR 100000)
£2121 $3839   (21-May-92 SY.AM90/R) Herinnering aan Lombeek (40x50cm-16x20in) s.
s.i.d.1903verso cardboard (D.FL 7000)
£2315 $4213   (11-Dec-91 CH.AM290) Still life with jug, plate with apples and vase with
flowers on table (80x60cm-31x24in) s.d.28 board (D.FL 7500)
£4012 $7302   (11-Dec-91 CH.AM284/R) Vue de Collioure (105x137cm-41x54in) s.
(D.FL 13000)
£5681 $9657   (22-Oct-91 C.A264/R) Snow (100x80cm-39x31in) s. (B.FR 340000)

PAESCHKE, Paul (1875-1943) German
*£1365 $2471   (23-May-92 GB.B6998/R) Kurfurstendamm in Berlin (40x29cm-16x11in) s.
pastel (DM 4000)*

PAEZ, Jose de (18th C) Mexican
£6667 $12000   (19-Nov-91 CH.NY219/R) San Ignacio (42x33cm-17x13in) s.i. copper

PAGANI, Gregorio (circle) (1558-1605) Italian
£6288 $11067   (11-Apr-92 AT.P11/R) Job sur son fumier (173x231cm-68x91in) (F.FR 62000)

PAGANI, Vincenzo (attrib) (1490-1568) Italian
£1346 $2571   (15-Jul-92 CH.S777) God the Father (33x27cm-13x11in) panel arched top
     (A.D 3500)

PAGANO, Michele (1697-1732) Italian
£3304 $5947   (19-Nov-91 JRL.S113/R) Landscape with peasants and animals
     (76x127cm-30x50in) (A.D 7500)
£3405 $6061   (28-Apr-92 F.R80/R) Veduta costiera con veliero e figure (15x22cm-6x9in)
     copper (I.L 7500000)
£3524 $6344   (19-Nov-91 JRL.S125/R) Landscape with figures by lake (76x127cm-30x50in)
     (A.D 8000)

PAGE, Edward A (1853-?) American
£562 $1000   (26-Jan-92 JRB.C37) Dock with barrels (36x56cm-14x22in) s.d.1920

PAGE, Evelyn (1899-?) New Zealander
£1235 $2235   (4-Dec-91 DS.W32) The deserted cottage (33x53cm-13x21in) s. (NZ.D 4000)
£1375 $2296   (21-Aug-91 DS.W190) Storm clouds, Karamea s. (NZ.D 4000)
£1890 $3156   (21-Aug-91 DS.W22) Deserted cottage (33x53cm-13x21in) s. (NZ.D 5500)
£2836 $5076   (6-May-92 DS.W9/R) Thames Valley from Richmond (40x50cm-16x20in)
     s.i.d.verso (NZ.D 9500)

PAGE, H Maurice (19th C) British
£520 $952   (5-Feb-92 B125/R) Twilight winter landscape with blacksmith's in
     foreground (36x67cm-14x26in) s.

PAGE, Marie Danforth (1869-1940) American
£8772 $15000   (13-Mar-92 S.BM279/R) Her littlest one (91x74cm-36x29in) s.d.1915

PAGE, Robert (fl.1881-1890) British
£3000 $5160   (11-Oct-91 C1/R) 'Which hand will you have' (51x41cm-20x16in)
     s.i.d.1883verso

PAGE, Walter Gilman (1862-1934) American
£718 $1300   (5-Dec-91 GRO.B447/R) Still life of book, candle, box and glasses
     (25x38cm-10x15in) s.i.verso

PAGE, William (1811-1885) American
£950 $1615   (23-Oct-91 S127/R) *View of Corinth and the Acrocorinth (14x23cm-6x9in)*
     W/C over pencil
£1000 $1700   (23-Oct-91 S128/R) *Temple of Zeus, Nemea (20x27cm-8x11in) W/C over pencil*
     sold with another picture
£1600 $2720   (23-Oct-91 S129/R) *Greeks seated at the Temple of Zeus, Nemea*
     (27x38cm-11x15in) W/C over pencil
£1900 $3230   (23-Oct-91 S141/R) *Greek warrior (25x20cm-10x8in) W/C over pencil*
£12000 $20400   (23-Oct-91 S193/R) *Temple of Jupiter Olympus, Acropolis and Parthenon*
     (63x97cm-25x38in) W/C over pencil
£12500 $21250   (23-Oct-91 S194/R) *Temple of Jupiter Olympus, Athens (66x101cm-26x40in)*
     s. i.verso W/C over pencil

PAGE, William (attrib) (1811-1885) American
£550 $935   (23-Oct-91 S13/R) *Study of helmet found at Olympia (26x37cm-10x15in) i.*
     W/C over pencil

PAGES, Jules (?) American
£1038 $1900   (7-Jun-92 LIT.L172) Standing nude (56x30cm-22x12in) s.

PAGES, Jules Francois (1833-1910) American
£787 $1400   (26-Nov-91 MOR.P50) Still life - copper pan with fresh vegetables, wine
     and crock (25x36cm-10x14in) s.d.02

PAGET, Sidney (1861-1908) British
£400 $760   (23-Jun-92 CG610) *Mountainous lake scene with angler by stream and*
     figures resting on road (48x73cm-19x29in) s. W/C

PAGGI, Giovanni Battista (1554-1627) Italian
£842 $1440   (13-Mar-92 FN.S1972/R) *Flora seated (25x20cm-10x8in) s. sepia wash*
     (DM 2400)

PAGLIACCI, Aldo (20th C) Italian
£904 $1600   (5-Nov-91 CE.NY220/R) Donne nude (56x43cm-22x17in) s.d.57

PAGLIEI, Gioacchino (?-1896) Italian
£960 $1700   (13-Feb-92 S.W2865/R) Life study of standing male nude (99x69cm-39x27in)
     s.d.1880

PAICE, George (fl.1878-1910) British
£1250 $2213   (6-Nov-91 S101/R) Peter. Robbie (35x45cm-14x18in) s.i.d.08 pair
£1300 $2496   (28-Jul-92 SWS133/R) Pastime, Pasionate and Jock-two hounds and terrier
     in landscape (29x55cm-11x22in) s.i.d.21
£1503 $2750   (5-Jun-92 SY.NY216/R) Royal Scots Greys Steeplechase (33x43cm-13x17in) s.
     set of four

PAIK, Nam June (20th C) American?
£711 $1238   (16-Apr-92 FB.P249/R) Sans titre (51x62cm-20x24in) s. crayon (F.FR 7000)

PAIL, Edouard (1851-?) French
£2088 $3800   (11-Dec-91 RO.BA56/R) Paysage (60x74cm-24x29in) s.

PAILES, Isaac (1895-1978) French
£565 $1080   (3-Jul-92 GL.P125) Bouquet (46x38cm-18x15in) (F.FR 5500)
£1221 $2234   (17-May-92 GL.P235/R) Les jongleurs (116x81cm-46x32in) s. d.1966 verso
       (F.FR 12000)
£1389 $2500   (6-Jan-92 GG.TA431/R) Figure at the entrance to the village
       (65x91cm-26x36in) s.

PAILHES, Fred (20th C) ?
£401 $719   (6-May-92 GD.B967/R) Beach scene with women bathing in surf
       (50x60cm-20x24in) s.d.26 W/C gouache htd.white (S.FR 1100)

PAILLET, Fernand (1850-1918) French
£748 $1338   (16-Jan-92 D.V10/R) Persian cat (53x71cm-21x28in) s.verso (A.S 15000)

PAILLOU, Peter (fl.1745-1780) British
£1100 $1969   (14-Nov-91 S20/R) Cardinal birds. Blue birds of America (54x38cm-21x15in)
       i.verso W/C bodycol. pencil two
£1200 $2148   (14-Nov-91 S21/R) Green and yellow birds. Birds from the East Indies
       (55x38cm-22x15in) i. i.verso bodycol. W/C two
£2200 $3938   (14-Nov-91 S18/R) Tar Tar hens s.d.1755 i.verso W/C bodycol pair

PAILLOU, Peter (jnr) (18/19th C) British
£1700 $2992   (9-Apr-92 S185/R) Portrait of officer, wearing scarlet uniform
       (6x?cm-2x?in) min. s.d.1790 gilt frame woven hair verso oval

PAILOS, Manuel (1918-) Uruguayan?
£538 $1000   (17-Jun-92 CAS.M14) Constructivo (34x28cm-13x11in) board
£1613 $3000   (17-Jun-92 CAS.M15/R) Constructivo (33x27cm-13x11in) ink W/C

PAIN, Robert Tucker (fl.1863-1877) British
£1236 $2250   (13-Dec-91 S.W2647/R) Junction of Machno and Conway, Near pandy Mill,
       North Wales (74x89cm-29x35in) s.d.1864 s.verso

PAJETTA, Pietro (1845-1911) Italian
£2944 $5447   (8-Jun-92 CH.R545/R) Mucca e pastorella (30x46cm-12x18in) s.
       (I.L 6500000)
£7261 $13506   (16-Jun-92 F.M271/R) Schiarita dopo il temporale (18x39cm-7x15in)
       s.d.1886 panel (I.L 16000000)

PAJOU, Augustin (1730-1809) French
£800 $1456   (11-Dec-91 PH280/R) Moses striking the rock (32x48cm-13x19in) s.i.verso
       chk.htd.white

PAJOU, Jacques Augustin Catherine (1766-1828) French
£36772 $64351   (24-Feb-92 ARC.P12/R) La mort de Getta dans les bras de sa mere par ordre
       de Caracalla son frere (125x179cm-49x70in) s.d.1788 (F.FR 360000)

PAKOUN, Filaret (1912-) Russian
£507 $917   (20-May-92 ARC.P159) Le fleuve bleu (32x46cm-13x18in) s. board
       (F.FR 5000)
£665 $1184   (25-Nov-91 ARC.P98) Le moine (48x41cm-19x16in) s. board (F.FR 6500)
£870 $1549   (25-Nov-91 ARC.P95/R) Les bouleaux (31x47cm-12x19in) s. board (F.FR 8500)
£874 $1583   (6-Dec-91 ARC.P162/R) En hiver (33x47cm-13x19in) s. board (F.FR 8500)
£912 $1650   (20-May-92 ARC.P157/R) Le printemps (33x48cm-13x19in) s. board
       (F.FR 9000)
£977 $1769   (6-Dec-91 ARC.P164/R) Les lilas (32x47cm-13x19in) s. board (F.FR 9500)
£1132 $2048   (6-Dec-91 ARC.P161/R) Les fuaties (35x46cm-14x18in) s. board (F.FR 11000)
£2263 $4097   (6-Dec-91 ARC.P166) Les crepuscules (80x125cm-31x49in) s. (F.FR 22000)
£2693 $4686   (13-Apr-92 ARC.P139/R) Au bord du fleuve (60x80cm-24x31in) s. board
       (F.FR 26500)
£2947 $5128   (13-Apr-92 ARC.P138/R) Farniente (59x80cm-23x31in) s. board (F.FR 29000)
£3086 $5586   (6-Dec-91 ARC.P163/R) L'amour maternal (89x116cm-35x46in) s. (F.FR 30000)
£3242 $5868   (20-May-92 ARC.P156/R) Les inseparables (78x70cm-31x28in) s. (F.FR 32000)
£3343 $6052   (20-May-92 ARC.P160/R) La plage au crepuscule (80x99cm-31x39in) s.
       (F.FR 33000)
£3354 $5835   (13-Apr-92 ARC.P137/R) Jour de soleil (70x79cm-28x31in) s. (F.FR 33000)
£3378 $6012   (25-Nov-91 ARC.P97/R) L'aniversaire de Catherine (77x97cm-30x38in) s.
       (F.FR 33000)
£3455 $6012   (13-Apr-92 ARC.P140/R) Avant l'orage (90x161cm-35x63in) s. (F.FR 34000)
£3889 $6923   (25-Nov-91 ARC.P94/R) Les deux soeurs (99x94cm-39x37in) s. (F.FR 38000)
£5144 $9311   (6-Dec-91 ARC.P160/R) Sur la plage (99x99cm-39x39in) s. (F.FR 50000)

PAL, Fried (1914-) Hungarian
£492 $900   (17-May-92 DU.E1098 a) Ballet dancer adjusting slipper (61x91cm-24x36in)
       s.
£497 $900   (7-Dec-91 SG.M216) Carmen (61x76cm-24x30in) s. i.verso
£514 $900   (1-Mar-92 LIT.L46) Ballerina (61x76cm-24x30in) s.
£537 $950   (9-Nov-91 W.W79/R) Nanette (61x76cm-24x30in) s. i.verso
£819 $1400   (13-Mar-92 WOL.C512) The rodeo (64x74cm-25x29in) s.

PAL, Fried (1914-) Hungarian-cont.
£1287　$2200　(13-Mar-92 WOL.C516/R) Cowboy roping steer (61x76cm-24x30in) s.

PALACIOS (20th C) Spanish
£1217　$2215　(25-May-92 AT.P145/R) Portrait aux boucles d'oreille (34x24cm-13x9in)
　　　　　s.d.1930 gouache (F.FR 12000)
£1318　$2400　(25-May-92 AT.P147/R) Portrait au bonnet rose (33x24cm-13x9in) s. gouache
　　　　　(F.FR 13000)

PALACIOS, Alirio (1944-) Venezuelan
£6630　$12000　(18-May-92 CH.NY104/R) Jinete y caballo (140x164cm-55x65in) s.d.89 mixed
　　　　　media paper on canvas
£10000　$18000　(19-Nov-91 CH.NY181/R) From the series Magical Horses (182x188cm-72x74in)
　　　　　s.d.89 mixed media paper on canvas

PALACIOS, Joaquin Vaquero (1900-) Spanish
£885　$1663　(17-Dec-91 DUR.M103/R) Paisaje (18x28cm-7x11in) s. panel (S.P 160000)
£2999　$5578　(16-Jun-92 EP.M45/R) Paisaje (53x72cm-21x28in) s. (S.P 550000)
£16420　$29885　(26-May-92 DUR.M59/R) Surcos (130x194cm-51x76in) s. s.i.d.1959verso
　　　　　(S.P 3000000)

PALADE BONNAL, Felicie (19th C) French
£3779　$6500　(16-Oct-91 CH.NY51/R) Jeune Bretonne au Rouet (93x74cm-37x29in) s.

PALADINO, Mimmo (1948-) Italian
£5938　$10332　(14-Apr-92 F.M191/R) Il salto tra i rovi (70x120cm-28x47in)
　　　　　s.i.d.1979verso tempera (I.L 13000000)
£26257　$47000　(5-May-92 CH.NY132/R) Poeta all'Ombra (70x50cm-28x20in) s.d.1982verso
　　　　　i.stretcher oil gold paint linen
£1848　$3326　(19-Nov-91 FB.P269/R) Personnage dans un paysage (28x33cm-11x13in) W/C
　　　　　(F.FR 18000)
£2741　$4769　(14-Apr-92 F.M68/R) Senza titolo (31x43cm-12x17in) s. collage mixed media
　　　　　cardboard (I.L 6000000)
£2793　$5000　(6-May-92 CH.NY223/R) Untitled (30x40cm-12x16in) s.d.1984 W/C pen
　　　　　graphite silver leaf collage
£2857　$5000　(27-Feb-92 CE.NY241/R) Untitled (49x69cm-19x27in) s.d.1982 verso col.chk
　　　　　oil
£2857　$5000　(27-Feb-92 CE.NY239/R) Untitled (49x69cm-19x27in) s.d.1982 verso col.chk
　　　　　oil
£3178　$5657　(29-Apr-92 F.F272) Senza titolo (50x70cm-20x28in) s. collage cardboard
　　　　　(I.L 7000000)
£3352　$6000　(12-Nov-91 CE.NY114/R) Untitled (49x69cm-19x27in) s.d.1982verso col.chk
　　　　　gesso silver ink
£4568　$7948　(14-Apr-92 F.M173/R) Senza titolo (82x59cm-32x23in) s.d.1980verso oil
　　　　　mixed media cardboard (I.L 10000000)
£22839　$39740　(14-Apr-92 F.M217/R) Senza titolo (70x105cm-28x41in) s.d.1981verso
　　　　　collage oil canvas triptych (I.L 50000000)

PALAMEDES, Anthonie (1601-1673) Dutch
£2793　$5000　(17-Jan-92 SY.NY33/R) An elegant couple in an interior (13x16cm-5x6in) s.
　　　　　panel
£4144　$7500　(22-May-92 SY.NY158/R) Portrait of old woman, age 79 (79x66cm-31x26in)
　　　　　s.i.
£5986　$10835　(3-Dec-91 FN.S2370/R) Fancy dress ball with elegant figures in hall
　　　　　(84x114cm-33x45in) panel (DM 17000)

PALAMEDES, Anthonie (attrib) (1601-1673) Dutch
£1057　$1871　(23-Apr-92 RAS.V865/R) Interior with three women, man and dog
　　　　　(40x30cm-16x12in) s. (D.KR 12000)
£2048　$3706　(22-May-92 GB.B5326) Dutch party celebrating (60x41cm-24x16in) s. panel
　　　　　(DM 6000)
£2225　$4250　(16-Jul-92 SY.NY145/R) Guard room interior (59x83cm-23x33in) panel

PALAMEDES, Anthonie (studio) (1601-1673) Dutch
£3226　$5710　(6-Nov-91 LT.P66/R) Reunion galante. Soldats pillant une maison
　　　　　(25x33cm-10x13in) panel oval pair (F.FR 32000)

PALAMEDES, Anthonie (style) (1601-1673) Dutch
£1200　$2160　(21-Nov-91 C45) Ladies at cards and young gentlemen drinking nearby
　　　　　(24x30cm-9x12in) panel
£1400　$2492　(31-Oct-91 B136 c) Officers and women merrymaking in interior
　　　　　(39x55cm-15x22in) panel
£2732　$4672　(18-Mar-92 D.V407/R) Elegant party in interior (25x33cm-10x13in) panel
　　　　　oval one of pair (A.S 55000)
£2732　$4672　(18-Mar-92 D.V408/R) Soldiers looting house (25x33cm-10x13in) panel oval
　　　　　one of pair (A.S 55000)
£3000　$5460　(13-Dec-91 C161) Elegant figures making music in interior
　　　　　(55x79cm-22x31in) panel
£4200　$7350　(27-Feb-92 B94/R) Elegant company merrymaking at a table in a palace
　　　　　garden (53x76cm-21x30in) panel

PALAMEDES, Palamedesz (17th C) Dutch
£2400　$4200　(1-Apr-92 S200/R) Cavalry Melee (23x28cm-9x11in) s.d. copper
£7558　$13000　(10-Oct-91 SY.NY171/R) Military skirmish on a bridge (46x61cm-18x24in)
　　　　　panel

PALAMEDES, Palamedesz (17th C) Dutch-cont.
£10299 $19361   (18-Dec-91 AT.P41/R) Choc de cavalerie dans un paysage italianisant
      (81x123cm-32x48in) (F.FR 100000)
£25000 $43750   (1-Apr-92 S44/R) Cavalry engagement by river (35x51cm-14x20in) s.d.1633
      panel

PALAMEDES, Palamedesz (attrib) (17th C) Dutch
£5200 $8840   (22-Oct-91 S271/R) Military encampment with mounted soldiers in
      foreground (39x71cm-15x28in) panel

PALAMEDES, Palamedesz (style) (17th C) Dutch
£800 $1456   (12-Dec-91 B54) Cavalry skirmish (18x41cm-7x16in) panel

PALAMEDES, Palamedesz I (1607-1638) Dutch
£5263 $9000   (13-Mar-92 FN.S2898/R) Skirmish (24x31cm-9x12in) copper (DM 15000)

PALAMEDES, Palamedesz I (after) (1607-1638) Dutch
£2879 $5211   (3-Dec-91 AB.S4741/R) The cavalry (77x100cm-30x39in) indist.s.
      (S.KR 30000)

PALAMEDES, Palamedesz I (circle) (1607-1638) Dutch
£3500 $6370   (13-Dec-91 C200/R) Cavalry encampment (41x72cm-16x28in) panel

PALANGE, H Houyez (17th C) ?
£9296 $16825   (4-Dec-91 CH.R122/R) Allegoria con Pegaso, Atena, Omero, Apelle
      (90x114cm-35x45in) s.d.1639 (I.L 20000000)

PALANTI, Giuseppe (1881-1946) Italian
£1099 $2000   (26-May-92 CE.NY303/R) Laghetto a Madonna di Campiglio (33x54cm-13x21in)
      s.i. panel

PALAZUELO, Pablo (1916-) Spanish
£5982 $10647   (28-Apr-92 EP.M16/R) Untitled (50x63cm-20x25in) s.d.64 gouache
      (S.P 1100000)

PALDI, Israel (1892-1979) Israeli
£479 $900   (5-Jan-92 GG.TA312/R) Creatures (100x120cm-39x47in) s.
£811 $1500   (9-Jun-92 GG.TA426/R) Beach (24x30cm-9x12in) s. board
£865 $1600   (9-Jun-92 GG.TA427/R) Women with urns (48x37cm-19x15in) s. board
£957 $1800   (5-Jan-92 GG.TA308/R) The border between Jaffa and Tel Aviv
      (37x52cm-15x20in) s.i.d.1929-30 paper on canvas

PALENCIA, Benjamin (1894-1980) Spanish
£4362 $8113   (16-Jun-92 EP.M43/R) La era (35x50cm-14x20in) s. paper laid down on board
      (S.P 800000)
£11996 $22312   (16-Jun-92 EP.M44/R) Paisaje cantabro (37x45cm-15x18in) s.d.1946
      (S.P 2200000)
£38272 $70038   (13-May-92 FER.M163/R) Pasajes (61x50cm-24x20in) s.d.47 (S.P 7000000)
£547 $1001   (13-May-92 FER.M15 a/R) Personajes de teatro (31x22cm-12x9in)
      s.d.1976,1977 wax crayon dr double-sided (S.P 100000)
£655 $1126   (16-Oct-91 FER.M57/R) La nina 'monitos' (42x28cm-17x11in) s.d.1961 chl dr
      (S.P 120000)
£711 $1295   (11-Dec-91 FER.M44/R) Marina (21x15cm-8x6in) s.d.66 col.pen dr
      (S.P 130000)
£1363 $2344   (7-Oct-91 ANS.M51/R) Alfareras de Mota del Cuervo (38x54cm-15x21in)
      s.d.1965 ink dr (S.P 250000)
£1374 $2473   (19-Nov-91 DUR.M31/R) Arboleda (49x34cm-19x13in) s. W/C (S.P 250000)
£2729 $4693   (16-Oct-91 FER.M251/R) La feria de ganado (43x58cm-17x23in) s.d.59 wax
      crayon dr (S.P 500000)
£3543 $6094   (7-Oct-91 ANS.M117/R) Paisaje manchego (53x74cm-21x29in) s. W/C
      (S.P 650000)
£5467 $10005   (13-May-92 FER.M162/R) Mujer en un interior (60x45cm-24x18in) s.d.48
      gouache (S.P 1000000)

PALEOLOGU, Jean de (1855-?) Rumanian
£474 $854   (19-Nov-91 GS.B3614) Portrait of lady wearing big hat (31x23cm-12x9in) i.
      col.pencil (S.FR 1200)

PALERMO, Blinky (1943-1977) German
£4190 $7500   (13-Nov-91 SY.NY120/R) Untitled (74x49cm-29x19in) felt tip pen paper folded
      and collaged
£6145 $11000   (13-Nov-91 SY.NY114/R) Untitled plan for mural (30x33cm-12x13in)
      s.i.d.69/70 ink felt tip marker pencil two
£12291 $22000   (13-Nov-91 SY.NY102/R) Untitled (34x28cm-13x11in) s.d.66verso W/C gouache
      pencil newsprint collage

PALIGO, D (?) Italian
£1900 $3382   (28-Nov-91 CSK204/R) The Hall of the Illiad in the Pitti Palace, Florence
      (41x56cm-16x22in) s.

PALIZZI, Filippo (1818-1899) Italian
£2944 $5447   (8-Jun-92 CH.R654/R) Ritratto del cugino del Duca di Fondi
      (53x40cm-21x16in) (I.L 6500000)
£5500 $9790   (27-Nov-91 S324/R) Dog on cliff (32x46cm-13x18in) s.d.1849
£13000 $24180   (17-Jun-92 S581/R) In stable (54x73cm-21x29in) s.d.1848

PALIZZI, Filippo (1818-1899) Italian-cont.
£20422	$37985	(16-Jun-92 F.M210/R) Caprone e capra (26x40cm-10x16in) s.d.1856
		(I.L 45000000)
£31000	$53010	(18-Mar-92 S159/R) The hunter and his dog (34x47cm-13x19in) s.d.1846
£102254	$174855	(19-Mar-92 F.M92/R) Ritorno dai campi (83x118cm-33x46in) s.d.1862
		(I.L 220000000)

PALIZZI, Filippo (attrib) (1818-1899) Italian
£2759	$4939	(14-Nov-91 CH.R90/R) Testa di cagnolino (16x22cm-6x9in) oval board
		(I.L 6000000)
£8651	$14793	(22-Mar-92 LT.P30/R) Le petite patre (43x35cm-17x14in) s.d.1854
		(F.FR 84000)

PALIZZI, Filippo (circle) (1818-1899) Italian
| £4369 | $7820 | (14-Nov-91 CH.R43) Natura morta di fiori (38x48cm-15x19in) i. |
| | | (I.L 9500000) |

PALIZZI, Filippo (style) (1818-1899) Italian
| £1200 | $2076 | (3-Oct-91 CSK261) Donkeys in a barn (30x51cm-12x20in) |

PALIZZI, Giuseppe (1812-1888) Italian
£2809	$5000	(28-Apr-92 PO.BA1) Gallinas en el corral (55x66cm-22x26in) s.d. oval
£4077	$7542	(9-Jun-92 F.R154/R) Pastore e capretta sul ciglio (20x23cm-8x9in) mono
		panel (I.L 9000000)
£4631	$8012	(24-Mar-92 CH.R105/R) Pastorello col gregge (32x23cm-13x9in) s. panel
		(I.L 10000000)
£5618	$10000	(28-Apr-92 PO.BA2) Ovejas junto al establo (56x69cm-22x27in) s.d. oval
£10465	$18000	(17-Oct-91 SY.NY14/R) View of Roman ruins (56x46cm-22x18in)
£12967	$22434	(24-Mar-92 CH.R100/R) Mucche al pascolo, Fontainbleau (38x55cm-15x22in)
		s. (I.L 28000000)

PALIZZI, Giuseppe (attrib) (1812-1888) Italian
| £3488 | $6000 | (16-Oct-91 CH.NY179/R) A shepherd and his flock (47x77cm-19x30in) s. |

PALIZZI, Nicola (1820-1870) Italian
£2718	$5028	(8-Jun-92 CH.R668/R) Paesaggio fluviale con capanno (21x31cm-8x12in) s.
		(I.L 6000000)
£14494	$26815	(9-Jun-92 F.R179/R) Festa militare ai Campi Flegrei (35x67cm-14x26in) s.
		paper (I.L 32000000)

PALLARES Y ALLUSTANTE, Joaquin (1853-1935) Spanish
£1493	$2807	(16-Dec-91 ANS.M123/R) El Piropo (31x21cm-12x8in) s. panel (S.P 270000)
£2473	$4500	(26-May-92 CE.NY357/R) Elegant ladies crossing the Boulevards of Paris
		(24x33cm-9x13in) s. panel pair
£2791	$4800	(15-Oct-91 CE.NY441/R) Elegant ladies crossing the boulevards of Paris
		(24x33cm-9x13in) s. panel two
£4070	$7000	(17-Oct-91 SY.NY367/R) La Place de la Concorde (28x40cm-11x16in) s.
£4070	$7000	(17-Oct-91 SY.NY368/R) L'Avenue de Champs Elysees (32x45cm-13x18in) s.
£8210	$14943	(26-May-92 DUR.M38/R) La Puerta del Sol-Madrid (52x63cm-20x25in) s.
		(S.P 1500000)

PALLMANN, Gotz (1908-1966) German
| £1000 | $1710 | (17-Mar-92 PH43) Figures resting beside woodland path (31x36cm-12x14in) |
| | | s. board |

PALLUT, Pierre (1918-) French
| £2014 | $3585 | (28-Oct-91 GL.P182/R) Composition (83x105cm-33x41in) s. (F.FR 20000) |

PALM, Anna (1854-1924) Swedish
£2400	$4104	(11-Mar-92 WIN699) Waterside view with ships and buildings
		(23x48cm-9x19in) s.i.
£899	*$1627*	*(19-May-92 AB.S4261/R) View towards Riddarholmen, Stockholm*
		(12x16cm-5x6in) s. W/C (S.KR 9500)
£943	*$1670*	*(5-Nov-91 BA.S239/R) Blekinge fishing (20x37cm-8x15in) s. W/C*
		(S.KR 10000)
£967	*$1730*	*(6-May-92 KH.K263/R) Children tabogganing (14x22cm-6x9in) s.i.d.1885 W/C*
		(D.KR 11000)
£1041	*$1884*	*(19-May-92 AB.S4260/R) Summer landscape from Stockholm (8x18cm-3x7in) s.*
		W/C (S.KR 11000)
£1100	*$1957*	*(1-Dec-91 HOR.H14) Borgholms Palace (20x37cm-8x15in) s. W/C (F.M 8500)*
£1300	*$2327*	*(5-May-92 SWS148/R) Stockholm (9x26cm-4x10in) s.i. W/C gouache over*
		pencil
£1488	*$2692*	*(3-Dec-91 AB.S4650/R) Quay scene with sailship and vessels at anchor*
		(13x24cm-5x9in) s. W/C (S.KR 15500)
£1918	*$3452*	*(19-May-92 GO.G284) Hunting scene with horse and dog (37x54cm-15x21in) s.*
		W/C htd white (S.KR 20000)
£2264	*$4053*	*(7-May-92 RAS.S4/R) Le Harve harbour with figures (20x34cm-8x13in) s. W/C*
		(S.KR 24000)
£2600	*$4836*	*(17-Jun-92 S328/R) View of Royal Palace, Stockholm (22x48cm-9x19in) s.i.*
		W/C
£4057	*$7180*	*(5-Nov-91 BA.S236 b/R) View of Riddarhuset with figures (25x45cm-10x18in)*
		s.i.d.1892 W/C (S.KR 43000)
£4103	*$7303*	*(28-Nov-91 BU.S54/R) Stockholm's river (22x60cm-9x24in) s. W/C*
		(S.KR 43000)

PALM, Gustaf Wilhelm (1810-1890) Swedish
£3784 $6850   (19-May-92 AB.S4262/R) Figures at Piazza della Signoria, Florence
                            (47x61cm-19x24in) s.d.1879 (S.KR 40000)
£4057 $7180   (5-Nov-91 BA.S152/R) Giuseppe Garibaldi resting with horses
                            (66x84cm-26x33in) mono.d.1849 (S.KR 43000)

PALM, Gustaf Wilhelm (after) (1810-1890) Swedish
£949 $1736   (17-May-92 BU.M319) The Grand Canal, Venice (75x105cm-30x41in)
                            (S.KR 10000)

PALM, Gustaf Wilhelm (attrib) (1810-1890) Swedish
£648 $1141   (11-Apr-92 FAL.M332/R) Southern lake landscape with sheep and two
                            shepherds (25x41cm-10x16in) (S.KR 6800)

PALM, Torsten (1875-1934) Swedish
£678 $1207   (28-Oct-91 AB.S187) Morbylandadalen - landscape from Oland
                            (37x45cm-15x18in) s. panel (S.KR 7200)

PALMA, Jacopo (16/17th C) Italian
£8230 $14897   (5-Dec-91 SY.MO339/R) Le Christ mort soutenu par un ange
                            (52x35cm-20x14in) panel (F.FR 80000)
£410 $741   (22-May-92 GB.B5327) Madonna enthroned on clowds adored by five saints
                            (14x8cm-6x3in) pen (DM 1200)

PALMA, Jacopo (attrib) (16/17th C) Italian
£6977 $12000   (10-Oct-91 SY.NY117/R) Vision of a Saint (74x61cm-29x24in)
£2058 $3724   (5-Dec-91 SY.MO6/R) Etude d'homme vu de dos (26x12cm-10x5in)
                            blk.chk. htd.white chk. (F.FR 20000)

PALMA, Jacopo (il Giovane) (1544-1628) Italian
£1535 $2733   (29-Nov-91 ARC.P10/R) Homme se tournant vers la gauche (22x16cm-9x6in)
                            pen wash htd.white (F.FR 15000)
£1600 $2912   (10-Dec-91 C130/R) The Visition (12x17cm-5x7in) ink wash
£1800 $3456   (7-Jul-92 C21/R) The Entombment (16x18cm-6x7in) chk
£1800 $3456   (7-Jul-92 C141 a/R) Bearded man and old man in profile (20x16cm-8x6in)
                            pen made up areas
£2000 $3480   (14-Apr-92 C104/R) St Francis receiving the stigmata (29x20cm-11x8in) i.
                            chk pen wash htd.white
£3058 $5688   (20-Jun-92 CH.MO208/R) Un prisonnier, les mains derriere le dos
                            (22x15cm-9x6in) chk ink wash htd white (F.FR 30000)
£3500 $6090   (14-Apr-92 C103/R) St Paul preaching (29x20cm-11x8in) d.1628 chk pen wash
                            htd.white
£3800 $7296   (7-Jul-92 C141/R) The transfiguration (29x21cm-11x8in) i. chk pen wash
                            htd.white
£5500 $10560   (7-Jul-92 C20/R) Study of head of bearded old man and another head,
                            possibly self portrait (25x17cm-10x7in) chk pen wash
£6000 $11520   (7-Jul-92 C140/R) St Christopher (27x20cm-11x8in) chk pen wash htd.white

PALMA, Jacopo (il Giovane-attrib) (1544-1628) Italian
£7000 $12250   (1-Apr-92 S15/R) Portrait of bearded man (68x51cm-27x20in)
£1200 $2196   (15-May-92 TE278) Standing female figure (13x8cm-5x3in) pen red chk

PALMA, Jacopo (il Giovane-circle) (1544-1628) Italian
£2800 $4872   (15-Apr-92 C165/R) Madonna and Child in glory with Sts Sebastian and John
                            the Evangelist (67x40cm-26x16in) grisalle pen oil paper on canvas
                            bozzetto
£6395 $11000   (9-Oct-91 CH.NY150/R) Portrait of Venetian senator, seated wearing ermine
                            trimmed cloak, sash (120x99cm-47x39in) indist.i.

PALMA, Jacopo (il Vecchio-after) (1480-1528) Italian
£3340 $5945   (28-Nov-91 BU.S73/R) Christ the Saviour (91x70cm-36x28in) (S.KR 35000)

PALMA, Jacopo (il Vecchio-studio) (1480-1528) Italian
£67039 $120000   (16-Jan-92 CH.NY100/R) Sacrifice of Noah. Drunkenness of Noah
                            (66x152cm-26x60in) pair

PALMA, Jacopo (style) (16/17th C) Italian
£800 $1456   (10-Dec-91 PH113/R) Portrait of bearded gentleman, seated with book
                            (72x62cm-28x24in) panel
£1100 $1925   (25-Feb-92 PH50) The Mystic Marriage of St Catherine attended by St Lucy
                            and Longinus (44x62cm-17x24in)
£1500 $2700   (21-Nov-91 C128/R) Saint baptising children. Supplicant before king
                            (12x34cm-5x13in) canvas on board pair
£2000 $3500   (28-Feb-92 C83) Venus and Adonis (46x41cm-18x16in)
£3000 $5250   (27-Feb-92 CSK52) The Holy Family (38x46cm-15x18in) panel
£3625 $6489   (7-May-92 CH.AM15/R) Holy Family (47x63cm-19x25in) panel (D.FL 12000)

PALMAROLI Y GONZALEZ, Vicente (1834-1896) Spanish
£2880 $5500   (16-Jul-92 SY.NY575/R) A good book (34x26cm-13x10in) s. panel
£3071 $5466   (25-Nov-91 GL.P1/R) Portrait de femme (54x45cm-21x18in) s. panel
                            (F.FR 30000)
£12298 $20907   (22-Oct-91 DUR.M17/R) Vaya corte de pelo (79x53cm-31x21in) s.
                            (S.P 2250000)
£17442 $30000   (16-Oct-91 CH.NY169/R) By the seashore (52x79cm-20x31in) s. panel

PALMAROLI Y GONZALEZ, Vicente (1834-1896) Spanish-cont.
£38462 $70000 (28-May-92 SY.NY97/R) Summer's afternoon at beach (59x99cm-23x39in) s.
cradled panel

PALMEIRO, Jose (1903-1984) Spanish
£605 $1064 (9-Apr-92 ANS.M168/R) Bodegon (27x28cm-11x11in) s. panel (S.P 110000)
£608 $1142 (3-Jan-92 DUR.M37/R) Florero (46x38cm-18x15in) s. board (S.P 110000)
£900 $1539 (12-Mar-92 B106/R) Environs de Cannes (65x81cm-26x32in) s.i.verso
£900 $1539 (12-Mar-92 B107/R) Le Port de Nice (61x81cm-24x32in) s.i.d.1965verso
£1108 $1962 (12-Feb-92 ANS.M141/R) Paisaje (60x73cm-24x29in) s. (S.P 200000)
£1209 $2129 (9-Apr-92 ANS.M152/R) Paisaje (60x73cm-24x29in) s. (S.P 220000)
£1231 $2241 (11-Dec-91 FER.M197/R) Pueblo (50x40cm-20x16in) s. (S.P 225000)
£1319 $2322 (9-Apr-92 ANS.M143/R) Florero (80x52cm-31x20in) s. (S.P 240000)
£1626 $2829 (19-Apr-92 ZZ.F140/R) Bouquet champetre (73x54cm-29x21in) s.i.
(F.FR 16000)
£1795 $3375 (3-Jan-92 DUR.M3/R) La nina de azul (72x60cm-28x24in) s. (S.P 325000)
£1873 $3278 (5-Apr-92 ZZ.F155/R) Vase de fleurs (73x58cm-29x23in) s. panel
(F.FR 18000)
£3284 $5977 (26-May-92 DUR.M58/R) El Sena por Bougival (46x51cm-18x20in) s.d.60
(S.P 600000)
£4130 $7393 (14-Nov-91 ANS.M83/R) Paisaje (57x76cm-22x30in) s.d.63 tablex
(S.P 750000)
£6076 $11422 (3-Jan-92 DUR.M1/R) Bodegon (100x72cm-39x28in) s.d.62 (S.P 1100000)
*£550 $968 (9-Apr-92 ANS.M66/R) Desnudo femenino (46x60cm-18x24in) s.d.32 chl dr
(S.P 100000)*
*£831 $1471 (12-Feb-92 ANS.M45/R) Desnudo femenino (46x60cm-18x24in) s.d.32 chl dr
(S.P 150000)*
*£1101 $1971 (14-Nov-91 ANS.M114/R) Desnudo femenino (46x60cm-18x24in) s.d.32 chl dr
(S.P 200000)*

PALMER, Harry Sutton (1854-1933) British
£420 $748 (27-Apr-92 PHB244) Hens on river bank (23x35cm-9x14in) s.d.82 W/C
*£800 $1416 (6-Nov-91 S246/R) Looking towards the Isle of Wight (34x51cm-13x20in) s.
W/C*
*£800 $1424 (29-Oct-91 C118/R) Windsor Castle. Arundel Castle (17x22cm-7x9in)
s.i.verso pencil W/C pair*
£900 $1530 (22-Oct-91 SWS181/R) Cader Idris (38x63cm-15x25in) s.d.1875 W/C
£950 $1739 (3-Jun-92 S225/R) In the mountains (34x50cm-13x20in) s. W/C
£1050 $1817 (6-Sep-91 T207) River landscape (38x56cm-15x22in) s. W/C
£1100 $1903 (4-Sep-91 BT95/R) By Loch Katrine (36x53cm-14x21in) s. W/C
*£1100 $1958 (28-Apr-92 S136/R) Slopes of Ben Dearg in Ross-shire (34x52cm-13x20in) s.
W/C*
*£1200 $2064 (4-Mar-92 S285/R) Still life with bird's nest. Still life with apples,
blackberries, nuts (20x28cm-8x11in) one s. one mono.d.68 W/C htd white
pair*
£1600 $2752 (4-Mar-92 S221/R) Lake District (56x79cm-22x31in) s. W/C
£2100 $3717 (6-Nov-91 S251/R) Stratford-on-Avon (36x52cm-14x20in) s. W/C
£2200 $3916 (27-Nov-91 B206) Loch Katrine (36x53cm-14x21in) s. W/C
£2400 $4128 (4-Mar-92 S217/R) Richmond Bridge, Surrey (22x36cm-9x14in) s. W/C
£2700 $5157 (13-Jul-92 PH118/R) On the Thames (49x75cm-19x30in) s. W/C
£3000 $5160 (4-Mar-92 S239/R) On Wye (40x60cm-16x24in) s.d.81 W/C

PALMER, Herbert Sidney (1881-1970) Canadian
£505 $923 (2-Jun-92 R.T477/R) Overlooking Horseshoe Lake, Haliburton, Ontario
(26x34cm-10x13in) s. millboard (C.D 1700)
£746 $1328 (26-Nov-91 JOY.T235/R) Backwater on Opeonga (26x33cm-10x13in) s.
canvasboard (C.D 1500)
£776 $1413 (26-May-92 JOY.T16/R) Farm on hillside, autumn (21x26cm-8x10in) s. canvas
on board (C.D 1700)
£850 $1505 (6-Nov-91 SY.T68) Northern landscape, late summer (25x33cm-10x13in) s.
board (C.D 1700)
£995 $1771 (26-Nov-91 JOY.T28/R) Country lane, with grazing sheep (40x50cm-16x20in)
s. (C.D 2000)
£1294 $2302 (25-Nov-91 W.T1600/R) Northern farm with old stump fence
(27x33cm-11x13in) s.i. board (C.D 2600)
£1375 $2434 (6-Nov-91 SY.T223/R) Gravel bank (26x33cm-10x13in) s. board (C.D 2750)
£4110 $7479 (26-May-92 JOY.T195/R) Mill at Barrow Bay (125x150cm-49x59in) s.
(C.D 9000)

PALMER, J E (19th C) American?
£659 $1200 (15-Dec-91 LIT.L274) Swinging in the orchard (20x33cm-8x13in)
s.d.1875verso

PALMER, Lynwood (1868-1941) British
£10000 $17700 (6-Nov-91 S166/R) Portrait of lady on hunter (102x127cm-40x50in) s.d.1917

PALMER, Pauline (1867-1938) American
£562 $1000 (26-Jan-92 LIT.L141) Young girl with doll (71x56cm-28x22in) s. board
£1573 $2800 (3-May-92 LIT.L92) Still life with flowers, pheasant, candlestick and
figurine (64x76cm-25x30in) s.
£1744 $3000 (13-Oct-91 H.C1/R) Flower girl on garden path (102x76cm-40x30in) s.
canvas on board
£1878 $3400 (7-Dec-91 LAE.L40/R) Gordon and Priscilla Pike, 1929 (117x86cm-46x34in)
s.d.1929

PALMER, R (?) ?
£580 $1050   (24-May-92 LIT.L201) Steamer Ligonier (97x132cm-38x52in) s.

PALMER, Samuel (1805-1881) British
£11500 $20585   (12-Nov-91 C138/R) Sheep in the shade (37x53cm-15x21in) s. pencil W/C htd.white
£20000 $35800   (14-Nov-91 S163/R) Cypresses at the Villa d'Este, Tivoli (51x71cm-20x28in) W/C over pencil htd.bodycol
£30000 $52800   (9-Apr-92 S115/R) Poet (19x42cm-7x17in) s. i.verso W/C over pencil bodycol gum arabic
£100000 $179000   (14-Nov-91 S126/R) Old England's Sunday evening (30x70cm-12x28in) s. W/C bodycol

PALMER, Sutton (1854-1935) British
£1800 $3258   (6-Dec-91 CBS242) Wooded river landscape with cattle watering (38x61cm-15x24in) s. W/C

PALMER, Walter L (1854-1932) American
£5587 $10000   (13-Nov-91 B.SF2638/R) Harvest time (73x90cm-29x35in) s.d.1881 board
£7821 $14000   (13-Nov-91 B.SF2637/R) Moonlit stream in winter (43x66cm-17x26in) s.
£8571 $15000   (26-Sep-91 CH.NY72/R) Afternoon idle (24x41cm-9x16in) s.d.82
£11050 $20000   (6-Dec-91 CH.NY141/R) Twilight at the World's Columbian Exposition (41x57cm-16x22in) s.
£13408 $24000   (6-May-92 D.NY15/R) Weighted boughs (61x86cm-24x34in) s.
£16575 $30000   (6-Dec-91 CH.NY156/R) Ice in the glen (76x101cm-30x40in) s.
£1802 $3100   (20-Oct-91 HG.C1) Autumn scene with pumpkin (36x43cm-14x17in) s.d.1884 W/C
£3509 $6000   (12-Mar-92 CH.NY191/R) Cottage in the snow (46x61cm-18x24in) s. gouache pencil paper on board

PALMERO, Alfredo (19/20th C) Spanish
£1368 $2490   (26-May-92 DUR.M143/R) Romeria del Rocio, Sevilla (80x65cm-31x26in) s. (S.P 250000)
£1662 $2875   (24-Mar-92 DUR.M51/R) Capea en Chinchon (46x55cm-18x22in) s. (S.P 300000)
£2050 $3485   (23-Oct-91 DUR.M500/R) Capea en Chinchon (46x55cm-18x22in) s. (S.P 375000)

PALMERO, Maestro (20th C) Spanish
£2728 $4937   (20-May-92 ANS.M75/R) Caballos (88x115cm-35x45in) s. (S.P 500000)

PALMEZZANO, Marco (style) (1458-1539) Italian
£1250 $2188   (28-Feb-92 C17) The Angel of the Annunciation (143x52cm-56x20in) panel

PALMIER, Charles (1863-1911) German
£859 $1572   (2-Jun-92 FN.S2693/R) Dachau moorlandscape (44x62cm-17x24in) s. board (DM 2500)
£5000 $9550   (29-Jun-92 CSK28/R) Altes rathaus, Marienplatz, Munich (150x99cm-59x39in)

PALMIERI, Pietro (18/19th C) Italian
£1132 $2004   (5-Nov-91 BA.S241/R) Veduta di Normandie (31x45cm-12x18in) s. W/C (S.KR 12000)
£1415 $2505   (5-Nov-91 BA.S240/R) Gathering by the well (31x45cm-12x18in) s. W/C (S.KR 15000)
£1899 $3419   (21-Nov-91 BL.P18) Scene champetre avec chevaux (42x45cm-17x18in) s. ink wash two (F.FR 18500)

PALMIERI, Pietro Giacomo (?-c.1819) Italian
£1900 $3306   (14-Apr-92 C142/R) Women drawing water from well and couple conversing by ruins (33x46cm-13x18in) s. chk W/C

PALNAY, R (19/20th C) ?
£1499 $2697   (21-Nov-91 D.V116/R) King of the gypsies (45x34cm-18x13in) s. panel (A.S 30000)
£1748 $3147   (21-Nov-91 D.V117/R) Gypsies resting (45x34cm-18x13in) s. panel (A.S 35000)

PALTRONIERI, Pietro (1673-1741) Italian
£40892 $74833   (16-May-92 F.L38/R) Architetture fantastiche (86x165cm-34x65in) set of four (S.FR 110000)

PALTRONIERI, Pietro (attrib) (1673-1741) Italian
£5801 $10500   (22-May-92 SY.NY288/R) Architectural capriccio of ruins with figures (155x100cm-61x39in) tempera canvas irregular shape

PALTRONIERI, Pietro (circle) (1673-1741) Italian
£2732 $4672   (18-Mar-92 D.V18/R) Italian palace architecture (101x76cm-40x30in) (A.S 55000)
£6484 $11217   (25-Mar-92 CH.R7/R) Capriccio architettonico con figure (156x175cm-61x69in) tempera (I.L 14000000)

PALUMBO, Onofrio (17th C) Italian
£10652 $18428   (25-Mar-92 CH.R109/R) Maddalena penitente (102x85cm-40x33in) (I.L 23000000)

PAMBOUJIAN, Gerard (1941-) French
£806	$1427	(10-Nov-91 ZZ.F262/R) Les gardiano dans les arenes d'Arles (54x65cm-21x26in) s. i.verso (F.FR 8000)
£989	$1701	(20-Oct-91 I.N46) Bouquet de fleurs (46x33cm-18x13in) s. (F.FR 9800)
£2546	$4659	(7-Jun-92 LT.P65/R) Les demoiselles d'Arles (73x60cm-29x24in) s. (F.FR 25000)
£2935	$5019	(22-Mar-92 LT.P97/R) Aurore dans le parc en Arles (65x54cm-26x21in) s. (F.FR 28500)
£3640	$6516	(10-May-92 LT.P71/R) Les filles d'Arles (73x60cm-29x24in) s. (F.FR 36000)
£3811	$6516	(22-Mar-92 LT.P89/R) La terrasse des deux magots (117x90cm-46x35in) s. (F.FR 37000)

PAN TIANSHOU (1897-1971) Chinese
£1271	*$2250*	*(7-Nov-91 B.SF1226/R) Eagle (135x49cm-53x19in) s.d.1953 ink colour scroll*
£8876	*$15533*	*(30-Mar-92 CH.HK125/R) Three eagles on rock (80x80cm-31x31in) s.i.d.1953 ink W/C silk hanging scroll (HK.D 120000)*
£8876	*$15533*	*(30-Mar-92 CH.HK227/R) Bird standing on rock (68x45cm-27x18in) s.d.1965 ink W/C hanging scroll (HK.D 120000)*

PANAMERENKO (20th C) Belgian
| *£2632* | *$4737* | *(19-Nov-91 L.K989/R) Saltoarte (36x29cm-14x11in) collage pencil W/C cut out letters board (DM 7500)* |

PANCOAST, Morris Hall (1877-?) American
£556	$1000	(22-Nov-91 S.BM138/R) Winter scene (36x46cm-14x18in) s.
£608	$1100	(24-May-92 JRB.C109/R) Warm day in January (36x36cm-14x14in) s. board
£1271	$2300	(22-May-92 S.BM154/R) On the beach (18x25cm-7x10in) s. canvasboard
£5263	$9000	(13-Mar-92 S.BM244/R) Winter scene (64x76cm-25x30in) s.

PANEK, Jean Luc (1958-) ?
| £604 | $1076 | (30-Oct-91 QWA.P196/R) Minos (81x130cm-32x51in) s. (F.FR 6000) |
| £604 | $1076 | (30-Oct-91 QWA.P198) Le repos de name (118x76cm-46x30in) s. wood (F.FR 6000) |

PANERAI, Gino (19/20th C) Italian
| *£442* | *$800* | *(21-May-92 GRO.B69) Piazza della Signoria, Florence (20x13cm-8x5in) s.i. W/C* |

PANERAI, Ruggero (1862-1923) Italian
£1326	$2400	(22-May-92 S.BM94/R) Street scene (18x10cm-7x4in) s. board
£1852	$3205	(24-Mar-92 CH.R46) Sulla spiaggia a Senigaglia (21x14cm-8x6in) s.d.1883 panel (I.L 4000000)
£1852	$3205	(24-Mar-92 CH.R37) Busto di contadina (23x30cm-9x12in) s. board (I.L 4000000)
£8153	$15083	(8-Jun-92 CH.R560/R) Il sensale di matrimonio (50x80cm-20x31in) s. (I.L 18000000)
£16000	$28480	(29-Nov-91 C117/R) In the paddock (20x34cm-8x13in) s. panel
£20341	$36818	(18-May-92 SY.MI127/R) Veduta di Piazza Cavour (19x31cm-7x12in) s. panel (I.L 45000000)

PANERAI, Ruggero (attrib) (1862-1923) Italian
| £2500 | $4325 | (3-Oct-91 CSK260/R) A shepherdess and sheep on a country track (48x64cm-19x25in) with sig. |

PANINI, Giovanni Paolo (1691-1765) Italian
£32000	$61440	(10-Jul-92 C274/R) Capriccio of classical ruins with peasants (99x75cm-39x30in)
£32000	$61440	(10-Jul-92 C275/R) Capriccio of classical ruins with soldiers and women conversing (99x75cm-39x30in)
£33520	$60000	(16-Jan-92 CH.NY1/R) Cappricci of classical ruins, including Colosseum and Pyramid of Caius Cestius (51x41cm-20x16in) pair
£51127	$92540	(4-Dec-91 CH.R119/R) Capriccio con rovine die tempio antico con figure e donna presso fonte (50x64cm-20x25in) (I.L 110000000)
£110000	$211200	(10-Jul-92 C29/R) Capricci of classical palaces (60x74cm-24x29in) one s.i. pair
£111732	$200000	(16-Jan-92 CH.NY120/R) Imaginary Mediterranean harbour with colonnade and figures on shore (102x127cm-40x50in) bears sig. init. with studio
£223048	$408178	(16-May-92 F.L33/R) Capriccio con rovine romane e la statua di Marco Aurelio (133x96cm-52x38in) (S.FR 600000)

PANINI, Giovanni Paolo (after) (1691-1765) Italian
| £3488 | $6000 | (9-Oct-91 CH.NY140/R) Capriccio of ruins with sibyl prophesying (51x69cm-20x27in) |

PANINI, Giovanni Paolo (attrib) (1691-1765) Italian
| *£3000* | *$5760* | *(6-Jul-92 S116/R) View of the Forum, the columns of the Temple of Castor and Pollux (46x24cm-18x9in) chk.wash htd.white* |

PANINI, Giovanni Paolo (circle) (1691-1765) Italian
£3000	$5700	(23-Jun-92 CG660/R) Harbour capriccio with sailing boats and figures on quayside (49x65cm-19x26in)
£5097	$9480	(18-Jun-92 SY.MO148/R) Personnages devant des ruines (60x46cm-24x18in) (F.FR 50000)
£11115	$19229	(25-Mar-92 CH.R89/R) Capriccio di rovine antiche con i resti di un tempio classico e Colosseo (62x98cm-24x39in) (I.L 24000000)

PANINI, Giovanni Paolo (circle) (1691-1765) Italian-cont.
£17877 $32000 (16-Jan-92 CH.NY39/R) Capricci of Roman ruins with figures
(67x51cm-26x20in) pair
£55233 $95000 (9-Oct-91 CH.NY5/R) Capriccio of ruins with Colosseum, Arch of
Constantine, Trajan's Column and figures (79x110cm-31x43in) canvas on
board

PANINI, Giovanni Paolo (studio) (1691-1765) Italian
£24862 $45000 (21-May-92 CH.NY253/R) Imaginary Mediterranean harbour with colonnade and
figures on shore (88x116cm-35x46in)
£36313 $65000 (16-Jan-92 CH.NY66/R) Capriccio of Roman ruins including equestrian
statue of Marcus Aurelius and figures conversing (109x148cm-43x58in)
£82873 $150000 (22-May-92 SY.NY33/R) Capriccio with Trajan's column, Colosseum, Arch of
Constantine, Hercules and Borghese vase, temple (122x111cm-48x44in)

PANINI, Giovanni Paolo (style) (1691-1765) Italian
£850 $1530 (21-Nov-91 CSK147) Figures amongst classical ruins (30x38cm-12x15in)
£1100 $1980 (21-Nov-91 C91/R) Banquet by ionic colonnade (22x27cm-9x11in) paper on
canvas
£1210 $2105 (13-Sep-91 C96/R) Capriccio of Roman ruins with pyramid of Cestus and
Banditti (49x68cm-19x27in)
£1440 $2750 (16-Jul-92 SY.NY270/R) Figures among classical ruins. (73x58cm-29x23in)
canvas on masonite pair
£2439 $4512 (13-Jun-92 CH.AM183/R) Christ and the Woman of Samaria (92x116cm-36x46in)
(D.FL 8000)
£2600 $4992 (10-Jul-92 C276/R) Capriccio of classical ruins with shepherds resting by
fountain (60x45cm-24x18in)
£2600 $4992 (10-Jul-92 C277/R) Capriccio of classical ruins with peasants resting by
fountain (60x45cm-24x18in)
£3200 $5760 (21-Nov-91 CSK148/R) Capriccios of Roman classical ruins
(52x77cm-20x30in) pair
£3500 $6720 (8-Jul-92 S150/R) Capriccio of classical ruins (71x91cm-28x36in)
£3800 $6650 (1-Apr-92 S166/R) Capriccio of Roman ruins (89x111cm-35x44in)
£4000 $7000 (3-Apr-92 C51/R) Capriccio of Roman ruins (55x31cm-22x12in)
£4200 $7476 (30-Oct-91 S198/R) Landscape with soldiers conversing beside classical
ruins (101x126cm-40x50in)
£4260 $7497 (11-Apr-92 AT.P26/R) Personnages dans des ruines (73x44cm-29x17in)
(F.FR 42000)
£4648 $8413 (5-Dec-91 F.M24/R) Capriccio architettonico con l'arco di Giano, piramide
Cestia e figure (74x110cm-29x43in) (I.L 10000000)
£5771 $10446 (19-May-92 AB.S4365/R) Mythological landscape with figures
(97x74cm-38x29in) (S.KR 61000)
£9174 $17064 (18-Jun-92 SY.MO150/R) Caprices Veniticns (148x97cm-58x38in) pair
(F.FR 90000)
£21000 $36750 (1-Apr-92 S69/R) Capriccio of Roman ruins (90x96cm-35x38in)

PANITZSCH, Robert (1879-?) German/Danish
£500 $890 (28-Nov-91 CSK203/R) Drawing room interior (65x81cm-26x32in) s.d.27
£634 $1096 (2-Sep-91 BU.K52/R) Interior (66x81cm-26x32in) s.d.1922 (D.KR 7200)
£856 $1490 (14-Apr-92 SY.AM178/R) Harbour scene (124x98cm-49x39in) s.d.42
(D.FL 2800)
£1500 $2790 (17-Jun-92 S318/R) Portrait of artist's daughter reading by window
(75x95cm-30x37in) s.
£2000 $3720 (17-Jun-92 S316/R) Lady in interior (62x79cm-24x31in) s.

PANKIEWICZ, Jozef (1866-1943) Polish
£880 $1655 (21-Dec-91 HO.P3) St Joseph's Church, Cracow (24x25cm-9x10in) s.
(P.Z 17000000)
£1414 $2545 (24-Nov-91 AG.W15) In the greenery (39x40cm-15x16in) s. (P.Z 28000000)
£3624 $6813 (21-Dec-91 PSA.W15) View from Samara (54x65cm-21x26in) s. (P.Z 70000000)

PANKOK, Bernhard (1872-1943) German
£859 $1495 (17-Sep-91 FN.S2057/R) Portrait of hunter wearing Bavarian costume seated
with dog (94x65cm-37x26in) s.d.1940 (DM 2500)
£1404 $2526 (22-Nov-91 SA.A1781/R) Painter seated before easel (81x54cm-32x21in)
s.d.1893 (DM 4000)

PANKOK, Otto (1893-1966) ?
£2234 $4088 (3-Jun-92 L.K357/R) Cornfield (95x122cm-37x48in) mono chl (DM 6500)

PANN, Abel (1883-1963) Israeli/Latvian
£2447 $4600 (5-Jan-92 GG.TA314/R) Two heads (32x25cm-13x10in) s. pastel

PANNART, Mathias (1935-) German
£515 $907 (11-Apr-92 AW.H2100/R) Korinthen (45x72cm-18x28in) s. mixed media
(DM 1500)

PANNO, Laura (20th C) Italian
£1600 $3040 (23-Jun-92 F.M41/R) Alfabeto del corpo (25x36cm-10x14in) canvas on panel
and metal wire (I.L 3500000)
£2057 $3908 (23-Jun-92 F.M117/R) Cerere (50cm-20ins circular) s.d.1990 s.i.d.verso
canvas wire netting (I.L 4500000)

PANOZZI, Americo (1887-?) Argentinian
£3141 $6000 (30-Jun-92 PO.BA19) Paisaje con lago (80x93cm-31x37in) s.

PANSING, Fred (19th C) American
£838 $1500   (14-Nov-91 CE.NY201) Harbour scene (13x25cm-5x10in) s. W/C paperboard

PANTAZIS, Pericles (1849-1884) Greek
£47000 $87420   (17-Jun-92 S586/R) Boy with watermelon (152x93cm-60x37in) s.

PANTOJA DE LA CRUZ (attrib) (1551-1608) Spanish
£23464 $42000   (16-Jan-92 CH.NY15/R) Portrait of young lady, standing, holding
                      handkerchief, by chair with dog (173x124cm-68x49in)

PANTON, Lawrence Arthur Colley (1894-1954) Canadian
£547 $974   (26-Nov-91 JOY.T248/R) Georgian Bay, No. 3 (22x27cm-9x11in) s. board
                      (C.D 1100)
£688 $1259   (1-Jun-92 W.T1120 a/R) Grey day, Lake Rosseau (28x35cm-11x14in) s.
                      i.verso board (C.D 1500)

PANZA, Giovanni (19th C) Italian
£2616 $4500   (15-Oct-91 CE.NY426/R) A marketplace (61x71cm-24x28in) s.

PANZA, Giovanni (attrib) (19th C) Italian
£1019 $1763   (24-Mar-92 CH.R106) Maternita (40x30cm-16x12in) s. panel (I.L 2200000)

PAOLETTI, Antonio (1834-1912) Italian
£950 $1767   (17-Jun-92 S551/R) Lady and dog by gondola (24x34cm-9x13in) s.i. panel
£1400 $2604   (17-Jun-92 S552/R) Venetian flower sellers (24x37cm-9x15in) s.
£4000 $7240   (22-May-92 C262/R) Pesce fresco (24x44cm-9x17in) s.i.
£4000 $6840   (18-Mar-92 S170/R) Selling oranges on the Riva Degli Schiavoni, Venice
                      (33x23cm-13x9in) s.i. panel
£4500 $8010   (26-Nov-91 PH65/R) Fishing on the Lagoon, Venice (43x59cm-17x23in) s.i.
£5000 $9300   (17-Jun-92 S553/R) Collecting pomegranates (54x79cm-21x31in) s.i.
£6000 $10860   (22-May-92 C233/R) Fruit seller, Venice (56x81cm-22x32in) s.i.
£6000 $11160   (19-Jun-92 C56/R) The Antiques Stall (20x37cm-8x15in) s. panel
£14000 $24920   (27-Nov-91 S332/R) Young greengrocer (33x53cm-13x21in) s.i. panel
£17000 $30770   (22-May-92 C261/R) Young critics (81x56cm-32x22in) s.

PAOLETTI, Rodolfo (1866-1940) Italian
£1300 $2340   (21-Nov-91 CSK235) Portrait of the artist (74x58cm-29x23in) i.verso after
                      Sir Anthony van Dyke

PAOLETTI, Sylvius D (1864-1921) Italian
£2300 $3979   (4-Oct-91 C183/R) The fishergirl (55x41cm-22x16in) s.i.
£8721 $15000   (16-Oct-91 CH.NY199/R) The sewing song (65x96cm-26x38in) s.i.

PAOLILLO, Luigi (1864-?) Italian
£2528 $4500   (28-Apr-92 PO.BA3) Noche de luna, marina (36x64cm-14x25in) s.
£3933 $7000   (1-Nov-91 PO.BA5) Venecia y paisaje costero (37x27cm-15x11in) s. pair

PAOLINI, Giulio (1940-) Italian
£4840 $8277   (19-Mar-92 CSC.P103/R) Faillit Imago (210x310cm-83x122in) dr.collage nine
                      in same mount (F.FR 47000)
£1728 $3006   (16-Apr-92 FB.P234/R) Sans titre (22x20cm-9x8in) s.d.1980verso collage
                      (F.FR 17000)
£5337 $10034   (19-Dec-91 F.M191/R) Studio per Fuori l'autore (44x34cm-17x13in) s.verso
                      mixed media collage (I.L 11500000)
£10862 $19769   (26-May-92 SY.MI176/R) Senza titolo (95x95cm-37x37in) s.d.1967 mixed
                      media canvas (I.L 24000000)
£16760 $30000   (13-Nov-91 SY.NY130/R) Et.Quid.Amabo.Nisi.Quod.Aenigma,Est
                      (67x434cm-26x171in) silver paint pencil cotton
£27593 $49391   (14-Nov-91 F.M109/R) Diapason (100x150cm-39x59in) s.d.1979/1980 pencil
                      collage canvas frieze (I.L 60000000)

PAOLINI, Pietro (1603-1681) Italian
£93923 $170000   (21-May-92 CH.NY19/R) Concert (100x133cm-39x52in) mono.

PAOLINI, Pietro (circle) (1603-1681) Italian
£1963 $3750   (16-Jul-92 SY.NY61/R) Vertuminus and Pomona (63x86cm-25x34in)

PAOLO DI GIOVANNI FEI (14/15th C) Italian
£127072 $230000   (21-May-92 CH.NY20/R) Madonna of Humility (70x42cm-28x17in) tempera gold
                      ground panel arched top

PAOLOZZI, Eduardo (1924-) British
£950 $1653   (19-Sep-91 TL424) Collage (52x62cm-20x24in) s.d.1951 pen W/C
£2200 $3894   (8-Nov-91 C231/R) Composition (51x62cm-20x24in) s.d.June 1951 W/C brush
                      ink paper collage

PAP, Emil (1884-?) Hungarian
£550 $952   (3-Oct-91 CSK197) A lady being served tea in an interior
                      (102x76cm-40x30in) s.
£752 $1361   (5-Dec-91 D.V91) Getting ready (100x75cm-39x30in) s. (A.S 15000)

PAPADOPOULOS, Panos (19/20th C) Greek
£600 $1020   (23-Oct-91 S176) Two master off the coast (30x50cm-12x20in) s.d.1905

PAPALUCA, L (?) Italian

£2600	$4706	(20-May-92 S142/R) Heartsease, R.Y.S. (44x68cm-17x27in) s.i. gouache pair
£850	$1479	(14-Apr-92 CSK67/R) R.T.Y.C. Sunbeam in full sail (44x65cm-17x26in) s.i. bodycol
£1600	$2896	(20-May-92 S150/R) Heartsease, R.Y.S (46x68cm-18x27in) s.i. gouache

PAPALUCA, L (attrib) (?) Italian

| £900 | $1629 | (20-May-92 S127/R) The ship Mount Stewart (43x61cm-17x24in) W/C bodycol |

PAPART, Max (1911-) French

£1141	$2042	(16-Nov-91 FAL.M282/R) Lemons on an orange plate (19x34cm-7x13in) s. d.1954verso (S.KR 12000)
£1545	$2642	(19-Mar-92 CSC.P60) Personnage au ballon violet (40x32cm-16x13in) s. mixed media collage (F.FR 15000)
£1561	$2732	(5-Apr-92 ZZ.F240/R) Paysage au clair de lune (33x41cm-13x16in) s. (F.FR 15000)
£2060	$3522	(19-Mar-92 CSC.P20/R) Solaire II (65x54cm-26x21in) s. i.d.69verso (F.FR 20000)
£2337	$4067	(14-Apr-92 CSC.P62/R) Metaphysique (80x80cm-31x31in) s. (F.FR 23000)
£3137	$5333	(23-Oct-91 GD.B1213/R) Le muguet, still life with playing cards, dices and flowers (54x64cm-21x25in) s.d.56 s.i.verso (S.FR 8000)
£3330	$5728	(20-Oct-91 I.N211/R) Le modele (72x91cm-28x36in) s.d.56 i.verso (F.FR 33000)
£395	$700	(5-Nov-91 CE.NY175/R) Portrait d'homme (27x21cm-11x8in) s.i.d.LXXX felt-tip pen
£403	$706	(25-Sep-91 CC.P16) Portrait de prevert (63x50cm-25x20in) crayons (F.FR 4000)
£436	$789	(20-May-92 FB.P215/R) Le peintre et son modele (50x63cm-20x25in) s.d.55 indian ink htd white (F.FR 4300)
£454	$785	(4-Oct-91 CSC.P70) La fete (22x18cm-9x7in) s. collage (F.FR 4500)
£509	$932	(3-Jun-92 CSC.P128) Composition (14x18cm-6x7in) s.d.LXXXI oil collage (F.FR 5000)
£509	$932	(3-Jun-92 CSC.P126) Composition (13x16cm-5x6in) s.d.LXXXI oil collage (F.FR 5000)
£515	$881	(18-Mar-92 LT.P86) Maitre d'ecole (13x34cm-5x13in) s.i.d.III/IX/LXIX col.crayons collage (F.FR 5000)
£553	$985	(29-Nov-91 GAB.G2826 a) Le coq parisien (50x66cm-20x26in) s.d.65 pastel gouache collage (S.FR 1400)
£559	$973	(14-Apr-92 CSC.P77/R) Les joueurs de cartes (20x29cm-8x11in) s.d.51 Indian ink wash (F.FR 5500)
£608	$1100	(20-May-92 FB.P215 a) Honeysuckle Rose (49x61cm-19x24in) s. mixed media collage (F.FR 6000)
£638	$1155	(4-Dec-91 CSC.P304) Le cycliste (38x25cm-15x10in) s. W/C colages (F.FR 6200)
£824	$1409	(18-Mar-92 LT.P88/R) Le chat serieux (25x52cm-10x20in) s.d.LXXXVI collage mixed media (F.FR 8000)
£870	$1549	(1-Dec-91 I.N7) Sans titre (33x24cm-13x9in) s. gouache collage (F.FR 8500)
£971	$1700	(27-Feb-92 CE.NY119/R) Thing of beauty is joy forever (49x64cm-19x25in) s. acrylic paper collage
£972	$1731	(29-Nov-91 D.P211) Blue man (33x24cm-13x9in) s. d.1983-90verso mixed media panel (F.FR 9500)
£1018	$1864	(3-Jun-92 CSC.P65/R) Personnage (65x50cm-26x20in) s. s.d.1965 verso oil collage isorel (F.FR 10000)
£1029	$1800	(27-Feb-92 CE.NY121/R) Along seashore (49x64cm-19x25in) s. acrylic paper collage
£1243	$2200	(5-Nov-91 CE.NY116/R) Personnage (31x19cm-12x7in) s. gouache collage ink lithography
£1434	$2582	(2-Feb-92 CSC.P114) Composition au violon (54x35cm-21x14in) s.d.57 mixed media (F.FR 14000)
£1629	$2982	(3-Jun-92 CSC.P120/R) Couple illegitime (38x46cm-15x18in) s. s.d.LXII verso oil collage canvas (F.FR 16000)
£1636	$2994	(5-Feb-92 FB.P204/R) Femme au violon (65x51cm-26x20in) s.d.3.57 ink collage (F.FR 16000)
£1728	$3006	(15-Apr-92 PLF.P97/R) Portrait d'homme (65x50cm-26x20in) s.d.LXI ink dr paper laid down on canvas (F.FR 17000)
£2033	$3537	(14-Apr-92 CSC.P63) Portrait au yeux bleus (29x22cm-11x9in) s. mixed media collage (F.FR 20000)
£2033	$3537	(14-Apr-92 CSC.P57/R) Dame au faisan (50x64cm-20x25in) s.d.LXIII mixed media collage board (F.FR 20000)
£2500	$4325	(26-Mar-92 C59/R) L'Homme (65x50cm-26x20in) s. paper collage W/C pencil crayon

PAPAS, John (?) ?

| £653 | $1090 | (21-Aug-91 DS.W92) Valleys End '81 (161x119cm-63x47in) s. acrylic (NZ.D 1900) |

PAPAZOFF, Georges (1894-1972) Bulgarian

£616	$1109	(20-Nov-91 CN.P207) Portrait d'homme (73x60cm-29x24in) (F.FR 6000)
£873	$1571	(20-Nov-91 CN.P206) Le couple (24x35cm-9x14in) s. (F.FR 8500)
£1129	$2033	(20-Nov-91 CN.P205/R) Impression d'une cathedrale (54x30cm-21x12in) s. i.d.1939verso (F.FR 11000)
£1437	$2587	(20-Nov-91 CN.P203/R) Sans titre (54x73cm-21x29in) s. (F.FR 14000)
£1643	$2957	(20-Nov-91 CN.P202/R) Personnage fantastique (54x46cm-21x18in) s. (F.FR 16000)

PAPAZOFF, Georges (1894-1972) Bulgarian-cont.
£1953 $3359   (4-Mar-92 AT.P179) Branchages fond bleu (41x24cm-16x9in) s. (F.FR 19000)
£2567 $4620   (20-Nov-91 CN.P204/R) Cavalier fantastique (33x40cm-13x16in) s.
         (F.FR 25000)
£2800 $5348   (29-Jun-92 CSK139/R) Porteur 2 (47x27cm-19x11in) s.

PAPE, Eric (1870-1938) American
£936 $1600   (13-Mar-92 S.BM210 a/R) View along the Nile (20x38cm-8x15in) s.
£1287 $2200   (12-Mar-92 MFA.C199) Vegetables and pottery (58x51cm-23x20in) s.
£1519 $2750   (21-May-92 S.W2679/R) Still life of fruits, vegetables, vessels and plate
         (24x20cm-9x8in) s.d.1936
£1547 $2800   (22-May-92 S.BM91/R) The last soldier (94x64cm-37x25in) s. canvasboard
£2072 $3750   (22-May-92 S.BM173/R) Portrait of young woman with umbrella
         (150x117cm-59x46in)

PAPE, Friedrich Eduard (1817-1905) German
£1000 $1860   (16-Jun-92 PH13/R) Village in the Alps (40x60cm-16x24in) s. board
£12044 $21558   (6-May-92 GD.B986/R) Lake Constance landscape with view of Untersee and
         Insel Reichenau (72x112cm-28x44in) s.d.80 (S.FR 33000)

PAPE, William (1859-1920) German
£3299 $5740   (21-Sep-91 SA.A1950/R) Interior of jam factory Longwy with workers
         (36x82cm-14x32in) s.d.1918 i.verso (DM 9600)

PAPENDRECHT, Jan Hoynck van (1858-1933) Dutch
£545 $965   (22-Apr-92 CH.AM255) Portrait of Wachtmeester van Turnhout
         (49x34cm-19x13in) init.d.13 oct 85 pencil ink W/C (D.FL 1800)

PAPETY, Dominique Louis (1815-1849) French
£1011 $1800   (22-Jan-92 SY.NY336/R) Head of woman, said to be Madame de Moitessier
         (37x31cm-15x12in)

PAPKO, Valentin (1939-) Russian
£509 $932   (3-Jun-92 ARC.P25/R) La promenade (64x52cm-25x20in) s.verso (F.FR 5000)

PAPPERITZ, Fritz Georg (1846-1918) German
£2000 $3620   (22-May-92 C170/R) Young girl (82x58cm-32x23in) s.

PARADIES, Herman Cornelis Adolf (1883-1966) Dutch
£428 $762   (29-Oct-91 VN.R217/R) View of Rotterdam (50x69cm-20x27in) W/C (D.FL 1400)
£436 $837   (7-Jul-92 VN.R161) Shipping in a Rotterdam canal (48x70cm-19x28in) s.
         crayon (D.FL 1400)
£667 $1180   (22-Apr-92 CH.AM252) View of a quay, Dordrecht (50x70cm-20x28in) s. ink
         W/C htd.white (D.FL 2200)
£734 $1306   (30-Oct-91 CH.AM294/R) View of Oude Korn, Delfhaven, Rotterdam with
         shipping on canal (49x70cm-19x28in) s. pencil W/C bodycol (D.FL 2400)
£887 $1579   (29-Oct-91 VN.R219/R) View of harbour town (46x66cm-18x26in) s. W/C
         (D.FL 2900)
£1223 $2177   (30-Oct-91 CH.AM308) View of the Spui, Rotterdam with the Vlasmarktsluis
         (50x70cm-20x28in) s. W/C (D.FL 4000)

PARADIS, Normand (1956-) Canadian
£507 $917   (24-May-92 AT.P94) Figure (80x40cm-31x16in) s. (F.FR 5000)
£1013 $1834   (24-May-92 AT.P93/R) Figure (200x58cm-79x23in) s. (F.FR 10000)

PARADISE, Philip Herschel (1905-) American
£1836 $3250   (12-Feb-92 B.SF624/R) Morning in village (46x71cm-18x28in) s. W/C

PARCELL, Malcolm S (1896-?) American
£632 $1200   (26-Jun-92 WOL.C452/R) Hal-dressed woman seated in chair (23x18cm-9x7in)
         s. board

PARDINAS, Alejandro (19/20th C) Cuban
£553 $1040   (16-Dec-91 ANS.M164/R) Anciana (76x51cm-30x20in) s. (S.P 100000)

PARDO, Gennaro (1865-1927) Italian
£2989 $5351   (14-Nov-91 CH.R52) Napoli vecchia, Vicoletto S. Liborio (41x31cm-16x12in)
         s. panel (I.L 6500000)

PAREDES, Vicenta de (1857-?) Spanish
£821 $1494   (11-Dec-91 FER.M96/R) La llegada al Nuevo Mundo (49x65cm-19x26in) s.
         (S.P 150000)
£2200 $3762   (17-Mar-92 PH220/R) The winning hand (46x55cm-18x22in) s.
£4360 $7500   (17-Oct-91 SY.NY358/R) Tales from the Front (43x69cm-17x27in) s.
£7758 $13577   (18-Feb-92 DUR.M10/R) El bautizo (37x54cm-15x21in) s. (S.P 1400000)
£12791 $22000   (17-Oct-91 SY.NY349/R) Hunting party (63x113cm-25x44in) s.

PARESCE, Renato (1886-1937) Italian
£11340 $20753   (12-May-92 F.R238/R) La sposa del marinaio (64x54cm-25x21in) s.d.1934
         (I.L 25000000)

PARET Y ALCAZAR, Luis (1746-1799) Spanish
£10442 $18796   (19-Nov-91 DUR.M67/R) Retrato de la Reina Maria Luisa de Parma
         (250x180cm-98x71in) (S.P 1900000)

PARET Y ALCAZAR, Luis (1746-1799) Spanish-cont.
£20897 $38869   (20-Jun-92 CH.MO258/R) Ecce Agnus Dei - projet de decoration pour un compartiment de coupole (49x42cm-19x17in) s.d.1785 pencil ink wash (F.FR 205000)
£33926 $60389   (29-Oct-91 EP.M1/R) Una cebra (48x35cm-19x14in) s.i.d.M.DCC.LXXIV pen W/C (S.P 6200000)

PARET Y ALCAZAR, Luis (attrib) (1746-1799) Spanish
£66872 $121039   (5-Dec-91 SY.MO179/R) Vue de Rome avec Saint-Jean-de-Latran a droite (86x148cm-34x58in) (F.FR 650000)

PARFONRY, Paul (?-1920) French
£671 $1208   (19-Nov-91 GO.G241) Interior (75x47cm-30x19in) s.d.1910 (S.KR 7000)

PARIETTI, Antime (20th C) Italian
£510 $867   (23-Oct-91 GD.B1218/R) Interior still life with bowl of fruit and bottle of wine with glass (70x50cm-28x20in) s.d.1963 (S.FR 1300)

PARIS, Alfred Jean Marie (1846-1908) French
£2571 $4500   (18-Feb-92 CE.NY129/R) Return home (108x81cm-43x32in) s.d.1885

PARIS, H (19th C) ?
£1769 $3096   (30-Mar-92 ZZ.F87/R) Moutonas dans un pre (38x48cm-15x19in) s. (F.FR 17000)

PARIS, Joseph (1784-1871) French
£646 $1150   (26-Jan-92 LIT.L165) Animals in landscape (28x36cm-11x14in) s.

PARIS, Walter (19th C) British
£559 $1000   (14-Nov-91 CE.NY158) Cabin on lake (25x36cm-10x14in) s.d.1894 W/C board

PARISOD, C (20th C) ?
£593 $1055   (29-Nov-91 GAB.G2827/R) Paysage du Leman (28x47cm-11x19in) s. (S.FR 1500)

PARK, David (1911-1960) American
£2927 $5298   (3-Dec-91 R.T73/R) Standing white figure (92x61cm-36x24in) s. (C.D 6000)
£3073 $5500   (13-Nov-91 CH.NY141/R) Standing couple (42x35cm-17x14in) s.i.d.verso graphite
£5294 $9000   (23-Oct-91 B.SF3706/R) Seated man (46x38cm-18x15in) gouache

PARK, Henry (1816-1871) British
£850 $1556   (5-Feb-92 TM264/R) Sheep and lambs in landscape scene (18x28cm-7x11in) s.d.1864 verso
£1203 $2093   (21-Sep-91 SA.A1338/R) Cows watering in lake landscape (51x77cm-20x30in) s.d.1862 (DM 3500)

PARK, John Anthony (1880-1962) British
£550 $952   (3-Oct-91 DLY222/R) Figures at St. Ives (15x20cm-6x8in) s. board
£596 $1038   (13-Apr-92 SY.J258/R) Lane with cart (32x39cm-13x15in) s. board (SA.R 3000)
£600 $1074   (5-May-92 SWS478/R) St.Ives Harbour (49x59cm-19x23in) s.
£720 $1318   (4-Jun-92 CSK66) St Ives Harbour (34x43cm-13x17in) s. panel
£750 $1313   (27-Feb-92 L30/R) Looking towards the Sloop Inn, St Ives, Cornwall (48x58cm-19x23in) board
£780 $1427   (6-Feb-92 DLY54/R) Busy quay (30x41cm-12x16in) s. board
£800 $1392   (19-Sep-91 B124/R) Cornish fishing village (44x54cm-17x21in) s. panel
£900 $1647   (14-May-92 C65/R) On Thames (51x61cm-20x24in) s. panel
£900 $1575   (27-Feb-92 L200 h) Waves breaking in Cornish cove (15x23cm-6x9in) s.
£950 $1663   (27-Sep-91 C63/R) Fish street, St Ives (40x30cm-16x12in) s. board
£1000 $1830   (6-Feb-92 DLY281/R) High tide in harbour s.d.12 board
£1150 $2093   (12-Dec-91 CSK128/R) The Down-Along, Newquay (51x41cm-20x16in) s.
£1150 $2105   (4-Jun-92 DLY63/R) Fishing boats, St Ives (33x41cm-13x16in) s. board
£2100 $3675   (27-Feb-92 L180/R) Off to the fishing, Concarneau (25x33cm-10x13in) s.
£2500 $4300   (10-Oct-91 L295/R) Fishing boats setting off, St Ives Harbour. Fishermen unloading boats (13x15cm-5x6in) one s. board pair
£2600 $4758   (4-Jun-92 DLY353/R) Summer in St Ives (48x58cm-19x23in) s. board
£3200 $5536   (2-Oct-91 S8/R) Summer breezes (76x61cm-30x24in) s.d.05

PARK, Stuart (1862-1933) British
£650 $1092   (26-Aug-91 S1014/R) Three fish (23x43cm-9x17in) s.d.1886 canvas laid down on board
£700 $1218   (11-Sep-91 PHG55) Pansies (47x37cm-19x15in) s.
£800 $1424   (1-May-92 PHE10) Still life of red and white geraniums (75x96cm-30x38in) s.
£900 $1629   (5-Dec-91 CG216) Red and white roses in glass vase (61x51cm-24x20in) s.
£1000 $1680   (26-Aug-91 S1016/R) Still life of flowers in white vase (39cm-15ins circular) s.
£1100 $1958   (1-Nov-91 PHE10) Still life of crimson and cream roses (36x36cm-14x14in) s. panel
£1300 $2184   (26-Aug-91 S1012/R) Roses (38x63cm-15x25in) s.
£1500 $2520   (26-Aug-91 S1011/R) Still life of flowers in vase (51x41cm-20x16in) s.
£1500 $2670   (30-Apr-92 CG945) Red and white roses on ledge (57x92cm-22x36in) s.
£1600 $2848   (28-Apr-92 S274/R) Orchids (63x38cm-25x15in) s.
£1800 $3222   (13-Nov-91 CG626/R) Pink orchids (51x51cm-20x20in) s.
£1800 $3024   (26-Aug-91 S1019/R) Pink roses (45x76cm-18x30in) s.

PARK, Stuart (1862-1933) British-cont.
£2000	$3620	(4-Dec-91 S335/R) Pink roses (51x51cm-20x20in) s.
£2600	$4368	(26-Aug-91 S1017/R) Still life of red and white roses (53x90cm-21x35in) s. oval
£3000	$5340	(28-Apr-92 S283/R) Pink and white begonias (72x57cm-28x22in) s. oval
£5000	$8400	(26-Aug-91 S1018/R) White azaleas (39x48cm-15x19in) s. oval
£7500	$12600	(26-Aug-91 S1009/R) White azaleas (63x81cm-25x32in) s.

PARKER, Agnes Miller (19/20th C) American
£2069	$3600	(15-Apr-92 SY.NY170/R) School projects (61x45cm-24x18in) s.d.1927 s.indist.i.verso

PARKER, Alan (1965-) British
£1000	$1830	(3-Feb-92 B114/R) Green jacket (109x127cm-43x50in) s.verso
£1000	$1830	(3-Feb-92 B115) Pact (61x66cm-24x26in) board
£400	*$732*	*(3-Feb-92 B116) Bull terrier (38x46cm-15x18in) gouache collage cotton paper*

PARKER, Bill (1922-) American
£554	$970	(25-Sep-91 CC.P18) Composition (130x97cm-51x38in) d.1980 (F.FR 5500)
£655	$1147	(25-Sep-91 CC.P17) Composition (130x97cm-51x38in) (F.FR 6500)
£1221	$2185	(17-Nov-91 R.P239) Composition abstraite (80x60cm-31x24in) s. (F.FR 12000)

PARKER, Charles S (1860-1930) American
£1350	$2417	(5-May-92 SWS338/R) Waiting (45x37cm-18x15in) s.indist.d.

PARKER, Colin Ross (1941-) Australian
£617	$1098	(26-Nov-91 J.M167) Laneway at Sofala (60x90cm-24x35in) s. board (A.D 1400)

PARKER, Cushman (1882-1940) American
£1545	$2750	(2-May-92 IH.NY94/R) Family at breakfast (61x76cm-24x30in) s.

PARKER, Henry H (1858-1930) British
£750	$1335	(30-Apr-92 CSK21/R) The Mole, Dorking, Surrey (32x47cm-13x19in) s. i.verso
£1200	$2064	(4-Mar-92 S66/R) Walking home (40x61cm-16x24in) s.
£1450	$2610	(30-Jan-92 TL90) Tranquil river landscape with cattle watering (34x49cm-13x19in) s.i.verso
£1453	$2500	(15-Oct-91 CE.NY404/R) Clearing the meadow (619x2cm-244x1in) s.
£1800	$3096	(4-Mar-92 S67/R) Sleeping waters (40x61cm-16x24in) s. s.i.verso
£1923	$3500	(26-May-92 CE.NY228/R) Sleeping waters on the banks of the Thames (50x76cm-20x30in) s.i.
£2100	$3738	(21-Jan-92 PH97/R) Sleeping waters (41x61cm-16x24in) s. s.i.verso
£2459	$4500	(17-May-92 DU.E1088/R) Haystacks near the Thames (51x76cm-20x30in) s.
£2600	$4472	(4-Mar-92 S68/R) Playing with billy goat (76x63cm-30x25in) s.
£2600	$4472	(11-Oct-91 C101/R) The Thames at Pangbourne (30x46cm-12x18in) s. s.i.verso
£2800	$4900	(23-Sep-91 PHB38/R) Streatley on Thames (76x127cm-30x50in) s. i. verso
£3000	$5550	(12-Jun-92 C142/R) Cattle by wooded river (61x107cm-24x42in) s.
£3665	$7000	(16-Jul-92 SY.NY505/R) When the day's works is done (61x91cm-24x36in) s.
£3714	$6500	(18-Feb-92 CE.NY71/R) Near Great Marlow, on Thames (42x70cm-17x28in) s. s.i.verso
£3766	$6816	(19-May-92 JRL.S180/R) Harvesting in south coast (59x90cm-23x35in) s. (A.D 9000)
£4396	$8000	(13-Dec-91 DM.D1998/R) Cows watering near Goring on the Thames (61x91cm-24x36in) s. s.verso
£4500	$7830	(14-Apr-92 ZZ.B37) Harvesting on the banks of the Thames (49x75cm-19x30in) s. s.i.verso
£4800	$8208	(12-Mar-92 CSK196/R) Homewards, Albingdon Surrey (61x91cm-24x36in) s. s.i.verso
£5000	$9000	(19-Nov-91 PH43/R) Near Great Marlow on the Thames (61x91cm-24x36in) s. s.i.verso
£5400	$9342	(4-Sep-91 PHK86/R) Cornfield, Stratford on Avon (50x75cm-20x30in) s. i.verso
£5800	$10788	(18-Jun-92 B100/R) A Surrey cornfield, near Reigate (59x90cm-23x35in) s.i.
£6500	$11180	(11-Oct-91 C98/R) Norfolk village (66x102cm-26x40in) s. s.i.verso
£6800	$12172	(5-May-92 SWS427/R) Harvest time, Godalming, Surrey (49x75cm-19x30in) s. s.i.verso
£6800	$12444	(14-May-92 TL116) Thames at Streetley (58x89cm-23x35in) s. i.verso
£7800	$13416	(4-Mar-92 S59/R) Evening - backwater on Thames, Henley (61x91cm-24x36in) s. s.i.verso
£9000	$15300	(24-Oct-91 CSK91/R) Harvest time on the south coast, near Worthing (51x76cm-20x30in) s. i. verso
£700	*$1211*	*(6-Sep-91 T222) Midgham, Berks (36x53cm-14x21in) s. W/C*
£1250	*$2150*	*(11-Oct-91 K427/R) Pyrford near Woking (36x53cm-14x21in) s. i.verso W/C*

PARKER, Henry Perle (1795-1873) British
£700	$1330	(23-Jun-92 PH142/R) Children fishing (29x38cm-11x15in) s.
£1579	$2937	(15-Jun-92 B.O124/R) Shipwrecked smugglers (59x45cm-23x18in) s.i.d.1879verso (N.KR 18000)
£3000	$5040	(13-Aug-91 AG270/R) The smugglers (50x38cm-20x15in) s.d.1826 panel

PARKER, Henry Perle (1795-1873) British-cont.
£3200 $5856   (15-May-92 TE404/R) Smuggler looking out (76x64cm-30x25in) s.d.1837
                  s.i.d.verso

PARKER, Henry Perle (circle) (1795-1873) British
£1500 $2670   (28-Nov-91 B97/R) The fisher's courtship (76x63cm-30x25in) i.d.1858verso

PARKER, Lawton S (1868-1954) American
£11842 $22500   (23-Jun-92 MOR.P40) Reclining nude in landscape (64x79cm-25x31in) s.
£449 $800   (26-Nov-91 MOR.P23) Flowers in interior (15x13cm-6x5in) s. pencil mixed
                  media
£571 $1000   (31-Mar-92 MOR.P17) Figure in interior (23x18cm-9x7in) s. mixed media

PARKHOMENKO, Avenir (1921-1988) Russian
£520 $911   (5-Apr-92 ARC.P90/R) Le peintre au chevalet (23x17cm-9x7in) s.verso
                  canvas laid down on board (F.FR 5000)
£655 $1147   (24-Sep-91 ARC.P185/R) Reunion politique (32x41cm-13x16in) s. verso
                  (F.FR 6600)
£665 $1164   (24-Sep-91 ARC.P181/R) Le jeune pianiste (27x41cm-11x16in) s. verso board
                  (F.FR 6600)
£706 $1235   (24-Sep-91 ARC.P182/R) Scene de plage en Crimee (29x30cm-11x12in) s.
                  verso (F.FR 7000)
£756 $1323   (24-Sep-91 ARC.P184/R) Sous le parasol (33x15cm-13x6in) s. verso
                  (F.FR 7500)
£756 $1323   (24-Sep-91 ARC.P183/R) Canards sur l'etang (20x22cm-8x9in) s. verso
                  (F.FR 7500)

PARKMAN, Alfred Edward (1852-?) British
£560 $997   (29-Nov-91 T256) The Mumbles, Swansea (28x53cm-11x21in) s.d.1914

PARKS, Ti (20th C) Australian
£1210 $2250   (21-Jun-92 SY.ME48) Number 3 (241x167cm-95x66in) d.1969/70 s.i.verso
                  acrylic (A.D 3000)

PARKYN, J Herbert (1864-?) British
£2200 $3938   (13-Nov-91 CG627/R) In summer (79x63cm-31x25in) s. i.verso

PARMA SCHOOL (?) Italian
£19553 $35000   (17-Jan-92 SY.NY130/R) Madonna and Child with the infant Saint John the
                  Baptist (102x92cm-40x36in) c.1600

PARMA SCHOOL, 16th C Italian
£15000 $28800   (7-Jul-92 PH72/R) St. Jerome in wilderness accompanied by multitude of
                  birds and animals (29x40cm-11x16in) gold leaf oil copper

PARMA SCHOOL, 17th C Italian
£3938 $6774   (11-Oct-91 AW.H796/R) Venus, Juno and Minerva (22x16cm-9x6in) mono. chk
                  htd.white oval (DM 11500)

PARMIGIANINO see ROCCA, Michele

PARMIGIANO, il see MAZZOLA, Francesco

PARMINTER, Vye (19/20th C) British?
£2500 $4300   (8-Oct-91 PH116) La coupe de cornitie (76x114cm-30x45in) s.i.stretcher
                  after P.0.J.Coomans

PARODI, Antonio (19/20th C) Argentinian
£769 $1400   (11-Dec-91 RO.BA454) Apacible (41x50cm-16x20in) s. panel

PARPETTE, Philippe (1738-1793) French
£4500 $7875   (31-Mar-92 PH45/R) Still life of vase mixed flowers on stone ledge,
                  beside grapes, peaches (81x80cm-32x31in) s.d.1771

PARRA (19/20th C) Spanish
£415 $748   (29-Jan-92 FER.M234/R) Platanera (57x37cm-22x15in) s. (S.P 75000)
£664 $1247   (17-Dec-91 DUR.M81/R) Bodegon con langosta (40x48cm-16x19in) s.
                  (S.P 120000)
£719 $1351   (17-Dec-91 DUR.M80/R) Bodegon con espejo y frutas (40x58cm-16x23in)
                  (S.P 130000)

PARRA, Gines (1895-1960) Spanish
£815 $1508   (9-Jun-92 F.R63) Nudo di donna (87x200cm-34x79in) s. (I.L 1800000)
£1118 $1945   (15-Apr-92 PLF.P99) La coupe de fruits (30x17cm-12x7in) s. panel
                  (F.FR 11000)
£1230 $2251   (13-May-92 FER.M173/R) Ceramica (46x55cm-18x22in) s. studio st.verso
                  (S.P 225000)
£1663 $2909   (19-Feb-92 DUR.M804/R) Desnudo (39x30cm-15x12in) s. board (S.P 300000)
£1909 $3456   (20-May-92 ANS.M106/R) Bodegon de cesta con frutas (35x46cm-14x18in)
                  s.d.1946 (S.P 350000)
£2033 $3537   (15-Apr-92 PLF.P98/R) Nature morte aux citrons (41x61cm-16x24in) s.
                  s.d.54verso (F.FR 20000)
£2237 $4049   (20-May-92 ANS.M104/R) Nature morte (45x60cm-18x24in) s. s.i.d.1937verso
                  (S.P 410000)
£2237 $4049   (20-May-92 ANS.M105/R) Bodegon de peces (61x50cm-24x20in) s. (S.P 410000)

PARRA, Gines (1895-1960) Spanish-cont.
£2350	$4418	(17-Dec-91 DUR.M40/R) Frutero (26x40cm-10x16in) s. (S.P 425000)
£2488	$4678	(16-Dec-91 ANS.M119/R) Paisaje (60x74cm-24x29in) s.d.1948 (S.P 450000)
£2494	$4364	(18-Feb-92 DUR.M39/R) Plato azul (33x41cm-13x16in) s. (S.P 450000)
£2599	$4938	(23-Jun-92 DUR.M22/R) Homenaje a Juan Gris (35x61cm-14x24in) s. s.i.d.1954verso (S.P 475000)
£3557	$6473	(11-Dec-91 FER.M187/R) Arboleda en invierno (54x66cm-21x26in) s. i.d.55verso (S.P 650000)
£736	*$1333*	*(20-May-92 ANS.M204/R) Bodegon de los porrones (55x45cm-22x18in) s. W/C (S.P 135000)*

PARRA, Jose Felipe (19th C) Spanish
£1368	$2490	(11-Dec-91 FER.M156/R) Bodegon de perdiz (50x36cm-20x14in) s. (S.P 250000)

PARRIS, Edmond Thomas (1793-1873) British
£2600	$4628	(21-Jan-92 SWS976/R) Young sculptors (61x130cm-24x51in) s.d.1838 canvas on board semi-circular
£3000	$5640	(19-Dec-91 C120/R) On the Severn, North Wales (71x84cm-28x33in) s.d.1857 s.i.verso

PARRISH, Maxfield (1870-1966) American
£30409	$52000	(12-Mar-92 CH.NY107/R) Little Sugar River, evening (39x51cm-15x20in) s. panel
£65714	$115000	(25-Sep-91 SY.NY48/R) Dinkey-bird (53x39cm-21x15in) s.d.1904 paper

PARRISH, Stephen (1846-1938) American
£1657	$3000	(22-May-92 S.BM118/R) On Annisquam river (51x76cm-20x30in) s. i.d.1919verso

PARROCEL, Charles (1688-1752) French
£2800	*$4872*	*(13-May-92 S81/R) Three galley slaves (35x24cm-14x9in) red chk*
£9500	*$18240*	*(7-Jul-92 C56 a/R) Head of man with moustache wearing hat. Study of figures duelling (27x19cm-11x7in) chk double-sided*

PARROCEL, Etienne (1696-1776) French
£409	*$729*	*(29-Nov-91 ARC.P22) La mort d'Hippolyte (31x41cm-12x16in) pierre noire htd.white (F.FR 4000)*
£468	*$856*	*(15-May-92 AT.P191) Apparition de la Vierge et l'enfant jesus a trois femmes est enfant (15x10cm-6x4in) wash black crayon (F.FR 4600)*
£611	*$1130*	*(12-Jun-92 ARC.P155) Les Saintes femmes, Saint Jean et Saint Pierre au tombeau du Christ (21x35cm-8x14in) black chk htd white (F.FR 6000)*
£3568	$6636	(20-Jun-92 CH.MO272/R) Un ange assis tenant un baton (37x36cm-15x14in) black white chk (F.FR 35000)
£9000	$16380	(10-Dec-91 C196/R) The Virgin and Child (54x41cm-21x16in) blk.white chk.

PARROCEL, Joseph (1646-1704) French
£3259	$5931	(11-Dec-91 LD.P41/R) Cavaliers franchissant un guet (41x56cm-16x22in) (F.FR 32000)
£6116	$11376	(18-Jun-92 SY.MO92/R) Militaires dans un paysage (40x55cm-16x22in) s. (F.FR 60000)
£1733	*$3223*	*(20-Jun-92 CH.MO224/R) Un convoi militaire (16x27cm-6x11in) ink wash (F.FR 17000)*
£2200	$4004	(10-Dec-91 C193/R) Landscape with bird catchers (20x33cm-8x13in) s. blk.chk.ink wash

PARROCEL, Joseph (style) (1646-1704) French
£1300	$2275	(25-Feb-92 PH86/R) Cavalry skirmish (44x36cm-17x14in)
£1700	$2856	(13-Aug-91 AG249/R) Christian troops repulsing attack by Turkish cavalry (96x187cm-38x74in)

PARROCEL, Joseph Francois (1704-1781) French
£514	*$931*	*(5-Dec-91 SY.MO46/R) Deux tetes de guerriers d'apres l'antique (27x39cm-11x15in) bears sig. blk.chk.htd.white chk. (F.FR 5000)*

PARROCEL, Joseph Francois (attrib) (1704-1781) French
£900	$1638	(10-Dec-91 C205/R) A standing nude holding a sickle. A standing man turned to the left (35x23cm-14x9in) blk.white chk.

PARROCEL, Pierre (1670-1739) French
£6116	$11376	(18-Jun-92 SY.MO166/R) Scene d'interieur (32x40cm-13x16in) (F.FR 60000)

PARROTT, William (1813-1869) British
£4200	$7896	(19-Dec-91 C117/R) Windsor Castle from the Thames (30x48cm-12x19in) s.

PARROTT, William (circle) (1813-1869) British
£2400	$4368	(12-Dec-91 B96/R) View of Thames at Putney with fishermen on riverbank (38x57cm-15x22in)

PARROW, Karin (1900-1986) Swedish
£959	$1726	(19-Nov-91 GO.G134) Trees (34x42cm-13x17in) s. (S.KR 10000)
£959	$1726	(19-Nov-91 GO.G133) Interior with red chair (66x48cm-26x19in) s.d.1951 (S.KR 10000)
£1103	$1985	(19-Nov-91 GO.G135) Harbour view (46x61cm-18x24in) s. (S.KR 11500)

PARRY, Joseph (1744-1826) British
£19000 $36290   (21-Jul-92 PH257/R) View of Irwell Bank, seat of Joseph Clegg on River Irwell (71x90cm-28x35in) s.i.d.1816

PARSHALL, Dewitt (1864-1956) American
£678 $1200   (12-Feb-92 B.SF571/R) Moonlight Grand Canyon (41x51cm-16x20in) s. board

PARSONS, A W (19/20th C) British
£420 $769   (5-Jun-92 BW167) Landscape with figures burning stubble to fore (41x56cm-16x22in) s. W/C

PARSONS, Alfred William (1847-1920) British
£580 $1038   (14-Jan-92 SWS247/R) Thorn bush in landscape (24x34cm-9x13in) s. indis.i.verso canvas board
£600 $1146   (29-Jun-92 PHB172/R) Wooden bridge (40x76cm-16x30in) s.
£2000 $3580   (5-May-92 SWS367/R) Apple blossoms (39x19cm-15x7in) s.d.1884 s.i.verso
£6200 $10602   (12-Mar-92 CSK235/R) Apple picking (142x183cm-56x72in) s.

PARSONS, Arthur Wilde (1854-1931) British
£8500 $15300   (19-Nov-91 PH40/R) Pool of London (76x102cm-30x40in) s.d.1910
£450 $801   (27-Apr-92 PHB243) Inspecting lobster pots at dawn (30x45cm-12x18in) s.d.1912 W/C bodycol
£620 $1085   (23-Sep-91 PHB16) Timber ships on the float, Bristol (27x37cm-11x15in) s.d.1925 pencil W/C
£1550 $2775   (6-May-92 MMB203) Canons Marsh, Bristol (30x46cm-12x18in) s.d.1909 W/C
£4700 $8977   (29-Jun-92 PHB161/R) Autumn morning on Avon (60x99cm-24x39in) s.d.1913 W/C

PARSONS, Beatrice (1870-1955) British
£480 $869   (20-May-92 B217/R) Boboli Gardens, Florence (29x17cm-11x7in) s. W/C
£640 $1088   (22-Oct-91 SWS209/R) Spring garden (16x24cm-6x9in) s. W/C
£800 $1376   (5-Mar-92 D65/R) Oxhey Court, Hertfordshire, home of artist (25x18cm-10x7in) s. W/C bodycol
£900 $1647   (3-Jun-92 S258/R) A sundial (35x26cm-14x10in) s. W/C
£1300 $2288   (6-Apr-92 PH96/R) In the Professor's garden, Bordighera (35x25cm-14x10in) s. W/C htd white pair
£1309 $2500   (3-Jul-92 S.W3125/R) Formal garden (25x36cm-10x14in) s. W/C
£1311 $2400   (3-Jun-92 D.NY75/R) Springtime flowers (25x33cm-10x13in) s. W/C
£1400 $2534   (20-May-92 B365/R) Crocuses, Rose Hill, Falmouth (29x39cm-11x15in) s. W/C
£1500 $2580   (5-Mar-92 D66/R) Wild garden, St. John's College Oxford (30x23cm-12x9in) s. W/C bodycol

PARSONS, Betty (1900-1982) American
£559 $1000   (12-Nov-91 CE.NY6/R) Magic (125x102cm-49x40in) s.d.57 s.i.d.verso

PARSONS, J F (19th C) British
£1083 $1949   (19-Nov-91 RAS.K235/R) Young girl wearing classical dress (75x48cm-30x19in) s.d.1896 pastel (D.KR 12000)

PARTHENIS, Constantine (1878-1967) Greek
£25000 $42750   (18-Mar-92 S187/R) Female nude in a landscape, the cypress tree (30x48cm-12x19in)

PARTON, Arthur (1842-1914) American
£774 $1300   (28-Aug-91 MFA.C266/R) Landscape (46x66cm-18x26in) s.
£1064 $2000   (18-Dec-91 SY.NY24/R) Landscape with sheep in a meadow (30x50cm-12x20in) s.d.1866
£1092 $1900   (15-Apr-92 SY.NY56/R) Cows grazing by stream (30x51cm-12x20in) s.
£1228 $2100   (12-Mar-92 MFA.C81) View of mystic (46x61cm-18x24in)
£1341 $2400   (14-Nov-91 CE.NY74/R) Afternoon on lake (20x33cm-8x13in) s.d.1868
£1352 $2420   (14-Nov-91 GRO.B42/R) landscape with cattle (56x91cm-22x36in) s.d.1878
£1659 $2970   (14-Nov-91 GRO.B43/R) Landscape with castle (61x107cm-24x42in) s.

PARTON, Ernest (1845-1933) British
£1341 $2428   (3-Dec-91 R.T141/R) The Derwent Valley. Studland Bay, Dorset (43x30cm-17x12in) s. i.verso two (C.D 2750)
£2047 $3500   (12-Mar-92 CH.NY83/R) The lily pond (25x35cm-10x14in) s. canvasboard

PARTOS, Paul (20th C) Australian?
£7660 $13557   (26-Apr-92 SY.ME459/R) Calendar day (197x213cm-78x84in) s.i.d.84 verso (A.D 18000)

PARTRIDGE, Ellen (fl.1844-93) British
£500 $865   (4-Sep-91 BT352) Cottages near Glasbury, Radnorshire (30x51cm-12x20in) s.d.1881 s.i.verso

PARTRIDGE, J C (19th C) British
£600 $1056   (8-Apr-92 S206/R) Dark bay hunter in stable (34x44cm-13x17in) s.d.1884
£1000 $1750   (1-Apr-92 RBB733) Shamrock (48x66cm-19x26in)
£1000 $1750   (1-Apr-92 RBB732/R) Paleface (48x66cm-19x26in)

PARTRIDGE, John (1790-1872) British
£800 $1368   (12-Mar-92 CSK125/R) Portrait of Mrs Howard in dress with fur wrap and feathered hat (94x72cm-37x28in) i.verso

PARTRIDGE, John (attrib) (1790-1872) British
£1571 $3000   (16-Jul-92 SY.NY303/R) Portrait of lady (94x71cm-37x28in)
£6200 $11036   (28-Apr-92 PH20/R) Rape of Lock (63x73cm-25x29in) i.verso panel

PARTRIDGE, William H (1858-?) American
£899 $1600   (3-May-92 LIT.L14) French farmhouse, Vernet, France (76x91cm-30x36in) s.
      i.verso

PARTURIER, Marcel (1901-) French
£557 $991   (29-Apr-92 D.P151) Port de Honfleur (22x27cm-9x11in) s. panel (F.FR 5500)
£557 $1009   (23-May-92 G.SB474/R) La Pointe du Raz (33x24cm-13x9in) studio st. panel
      (F.FR 5500)

PASCAL, Paul (1832-1903) French
£458 $819   *(17-Nov-91 FB.P25) Caravane passant devant les pyramides*
      (30x46cm-12x18in) s.d.1903 gouache W/C (F.FR 4500)
£659 $1200   *(26-May-92 CE.NY292/R) An Arab caravan (45x64cm-18x25in) s.d.1900 gouache*
      W/C paperboard
£977 $1857   *(26-Jun-92 CSC.P23) Paysage orientaliste (23x16cm-9x6in) s.d.1874 gouache*
      (F.FR 9500)
£1078 $1940   *(18-Nov-91 AT.P302) Cavaliers au campement. Halte devant le marabout*
      (20x28cm-8x11in) s. gouache (F.FR 10500)

PASCAL, Paul (1867-?) French
£782 $1400   *(6-May-92 CAS.M58/R) Atardecer (27x19cm-11x7in) paper*
£782 $1400   *(6-May-92 CAS.M57) Amanecer (27x19cm-11x7in) paper*
£756 $1300   *(15-Oct-91 CE.NY314/R) A view of the Pyramids (44x63cm-17x25in) s.*
      gouache

PASCALI, Pino (1935-1968) Italian
£1856 $3490   *(19-Dec-91 F.M25/R) Plastica dei liquida profondita - colore*
      (50x70cm-20x28in) s.d.1962 ink acrylic (I.L 4000000)

PASCH, Lorens (after) (18th C) Swedish
£1080 $1934   (12-Nov-91 SY.AM105/R) Portrait of Queen Louisa Eleanora in Coronation
      robes (60x50cm-24x20in) (D.FL 3500)

PASCH, Lorens (younger) (1733-1805) Swedish
£4223 $7643   (3-Dec-91 AB.S4651/R) Portrait of Johan Henrik Weylandt (59x49cm-23x19in)
      s.d.1781 oval (S.KR 44000)

PASCH, Lorens (younger-style) (1733-1805) Swedish
£3500 $6336   (19-May-92 AB.S4263/R) Symbols of summer and winter (135x70cm-53x28in)
      pair (S.KR 37000)

PASCH, Ulrika (attrib) (1735-1796) Swedish
£587 $1062   (19-May-92 AB.S4264/R) Portrait of Queen Sofia Magdalena (18x14cm-7x6in)
      panel (S.KR 6200)

PASCHKE, Ed (1939-) American
£12291 $22000   (6-May-92 CH.NY385/R) Transactionale (87x178cm-34x70in) s.d.81 linen
£13714 $24000   (27-Feb-92 CH.NY126/R) Joeski (173x203cm-68x80in) s.d.86 s.i.d.verso
      s.i.d.stretcher linen
£17877 $32000   (13-Nov-91 CH.NY200/R) Coupe faim (107x203cm-42x80in) s.i.d.1985
£1392 $2408   *(23-Mar-92 CC.P98/R) Cha Cha (80x64cm-31x25in) s.d.1975 i. lead pencil*
      (F.FR 13500)

PASCHUKOWA, Natasha (1950-) Russian
£488 $844   (3-Oct-91 D.V313/R) Wahrsagen (50x50cm-20x20in) s. s.d.1990verso
      (A.S 10000)

PASCIN, Jules (1885-1930) American
£62147 $110000   (7-Nov-91 SY.NY153 a/R) Femme couchante (35x43cm-14x17in) s. panel
£378 $700   *(12-Jun-92 SY.NY58/R) At the dance (11x16cm-4x6in) s.i. ink board*
£403 $714   *(8-Nov-91 LGB.P103/R) Deux nus (12x17cm-5x7in) studio st. pen W/C*
      (F.FR 4000)
£416 $798   *(6-Jul-92 HC.P23) Femmes a la lecture (10x10cm-4x4in) studio st. dr*
      (F.FR 4000)
£423 $753   *(25-Nov-91 W.T1775/R) Figure sketch (14x11cm-6x4in) s. W/C (C.D 850)*
£432 $824   *(3-Jul-92 GL.P127/R) Etude pour une discussion (16x20cm-6x8in) st.sig.*
      Indian ink W/C (F.FR 4200)
£486 $900   *(8-Jun-92 GG.TA224/R) Cuba, figures (12x19cm-5x7in) st. pencil W/C*
£515 $881   *(18-Mar-92 LT.P22) Personnages autour d'une table (20x26cm-8x10in)*
      st.sig.studio st. crayon (F.FR 5000)
£559 $973   *(14-Apr-92 ZZ.F4/R) Pecheurs sur le port (21x16cm-8x6in) studio st.*
      st.sig. blk.crayon W/C (F.FR 5500)
£578 $1000   *(6-Sep-91 S.BM301/R) Three figures lying down (20x28cm-8x11in) graphite*
      on laid paper
£581 $1000   *(12-Oct-91 SY.NY87/R) Figure studies (40x53cm-16x21in) s. crabon transfer*
      double-sided
£610 $1117   *(17-May-92 GL.P138/R) Les deux commeres (21x25cm-8x10in) st.sig. d.1906*
      W/C indian ink (F.FR 6000)
£612 $1138   *(17-Jun-92 I.N129) Personnages (18x22cm-7x9in) st.sig. pen dr W/C*
      (F.FR 6000)

ASCIN, Jules (1885-1930) American-cont.

£630	$1096	(14-Apr-92 ZZ.F6) Musiciens au parc (16x20cm-6x8in) studio st. st.sig. W/C (F.FR 6200)
£649	$1200	(8-Jun-92 GG.TA223/R) Carriages and horse riders. Woman (18x26cm-7x10in) st. pen double-sided
£649	$1200	(12-Jun-92 SY.NY52/R) Reclining nude (33x43cm-13x17in) i. chl
£661	$1149	(13-Apr-92 GL.P46) L'orateur (19x16cm-7x6in) st.sig.studio st. W/C Indian ink (F.FR 6500)
£661	$1149	(14-Apr-92 ZZ.F5) Conversation pres du chariot, Cuba (10x22cm-4x9in) studio st. st.sig. W/C (F.FR 6500)
£665	$1130	(24-Oct-91 D.P120/R) Scene de Floride (16x20cm-6x8in) s. W/C (F.FR 6600)
£700	$1239	(23-Apr-92 CSK92) Trois figures (18x21cm-7x8in) studio st. pencil wash
£734	$1300	(5-Nov-91 CE.NY70/R) Femme allongee (31x25cm-12x10in) st.sig. W/C pencil chl
£757	$1400	(12-Jun-92 SY.NY54/R) En attendant l'autobus (11x23cm-4x9in) st.sig. i.d.1917verso W/C
£802	$1379	(4-Mar-92 AT.P76) Personnages a La Havane (18x25cm-7x10in) s. pen wash (F.FR 7800)
£838	$1500	(9-May-92 CE.NY107/R) Two women. Studies of women (15x11cm-6x4in) W/C gouache pen double-sided
£857	$1500	(28-Feb-92 SY.NY36/R) Femme orientale. Circus figure (21x8cm-8x3in) st.sig. pencil W/C indian ink pair
£857	$1500	(28-Feb-92 SY.NY16/R) Jeune femme a la fenetre (15x13cm-6x5in) s. pen wash double-sided
£865	$1582	(17-May-92 GL.P139) Personnages a Cuba (20x25cm-8x10in) studio st. crayon (F.FR 8500)
£865	$1582	(17-May-92 GL.P137) Paysans a Cuba (16x23cm-6x9in) studio st. wash ink (F.FR 8500)
£900	$1548	(16-Oct-91 S56/R) Recontre un dimanche (21x27cm-8x11in) st.sig. brush ink wash
£1016	$1768	(16-Apr-92 FB.P92/R) Femme assise (27x20cm-11x8in) st.sig.studio st. crayon htd.W/C (F.FR 10000)
£1016	$1768	(13-Apr-92 GL.P45/R) Scene de maison close (11x18cm-4x7in) st.sig.studio st. d.1914 W/C lead pencil (F.FR 10000)
£1016	$1768	(13-Apr-92 GL.P43) Scene de cafe (12x17cm-5x7in) st.sig.studio st. W/C lead pencil (F.FR 10000)
£1126	$2039	(23-May-92 GB.B7012/R) Five women getting dressed (16x18cm-6x7in) s. indian ink pen wash col.pencil (DM 3300)
£1169	$2034	(16-Apr-92 FB.P118/R) L'aperitif (22x30cm-9x12in) studio st. ink htd.W/C (F.FR 11500)
£1338	$2422	(4-Dec-91 DO.H3348/R) Girl seated on bench (40x34cm-16x13in) s. W/C (DM 3800)
£1366	$2472	(3-Dec-91 R.T39/R) Reunion (18x23cm-7x9in) st.studio i.d.1923 graphite (C.D 2800)
£1429	$2500	(28-Feb-92 SY.NY11/R) Three female nudes (22x27cm-9x11in) st.sig. pen Indian ink W/C
£1429	$2500	(28-Feb-92 SY.NY33/R) Two women on sofa (48x62cm-19x24in) st.sig. i.verso pencil
£1453	$2600	(9-May-92 CE.NY89/R) Femme assise (29x36cm-11x14in) s. pencil
£1462	$2529	(4-Oct-91 CSC.P3) Trois filles (21x16cm-8x6in) st.sig. studio st. Indian ink (F.FR 14500)
£1596	$3000	(5-Jan-92 GG.TA315/R) Women (23x14cm-9x6in) st.sig. W/C pencil
£1599	$2750	(12-Oct-91 SY.NY86/R) Femme nue (20x25cm-8x10in) st.sig. estate st.i.d.1912 indian ink W/C
£2393	$4355	(12-Dec-91 CSC.P369/R) Femme endormie (49x35cm-19x14in) s.studio st. drawing (F.FR 23500)
£2857	$5000	(26-Sep-91 SY.I105/R) Figures at play (22x29cm-9x11in) st.sig. W/C chl
£3200	$5504	(16-Oct-91 S55/R) Le quadrille. Les lavandieres one s. pen W/C crayon pencil paper on card two
£3390	$6000	(5-Nov-91 CE.NY173/R) Au cafe (19x31cm-7x12in) s. W/C pen
£3500	$6020	(16-Oct-91 S54/R) Scene de cafe (16x20cm-6x8in) pen W/C
£3564	$6487	(13-Dec-91 ZZ.F60) Nu feminin (60x47cm-24x19in) studio st.griffe gouache crayon paper on canvas (F.FR 35000)
£8230	$15638	(24-Jun-92 GL.P146/R) Scenes curieuses (47x63cm-19x25in) st.sig. studio st. pen W/C wash (F.FR 80000)
£9000	$16290	(3-Dec-91 C112/R) L'attente (50x36cm-20x14in) s. pencil
£13714	$24000	(26-Sep-91 SY.I53/R) Seated girl. Townscape (40x29cm-16x11in) bears sig. oil over pencil gouache double-sided
£31000	$56110	(4-Dec-91 S175/R) La blonde Marcelle (74x59cm-29x23in) s. oil pencil canvas

ASCOE, E Willie (19th C) British

£880	$1531	(17-Sep-91 H368/R) Portrait of 'Carbineer' in stable interior (71x91cm-28x36in) s.d.1862

ASCUAL RODES, Ivo (1883-1949) Spanish

£1438	$2703	(17-Dec-91 BRO.B425) Cami de la Moixina (42x59cm-17x23in) s. s.i.verso (S.P 260000)

ASCUTTI, Antonio (19th C) Austrian

£695	$1202	(24-Mar-92 CH.R43) Ritratto del Dr Voltolin (19x15cm-7x6in) s.i. panel (I.L 1500000)
£4273	$7648	(17-Nov-91 FB.P103/R) Le salon de musique (14x19cm-6x7in) s.d.1876 panel (F.FR 42000)

PASINELLI, Lorenzo (1629-1700) Italian
£8754 $14969   (20-Mar-92 ZZ.F30) Le massacre des innocents (37x52cm-15x20in) copper
                   (F.FR 85000)

PASINELLI, Lorenzo (attrib) (1629-1700) Italian
£1309 $2500   (16-Jul-92 SY.NY190/R) Cleopatra (75x59cm-30x23in)
£5000 $8700   (15-Apr-92 C186/R) Woman wearing turban (61x51cm-24x20in)

PASINELLI, Lorenzo (school) (1629-1700) Italian
£2414 $4344   (19-Nov-91 F.R88) Sibilla (92x72cm-36x28in) octagonal (I.L 5200000)

PASINI, Alberto (1826-1899) Italian
£3187 $5800   (15-Dec-91 LIT.L280) The halt (23x41cm-9x16in) s.d.1857
£4651 $8000   (16-Oct-91 CH.NY176/R) Porto Custodia della Madonna (36x28cm-14x11in)
                   s.i.d.1879
£9665 $17688   (16-May-92 F.L113/R) Cavalcata araba (38x56cm-15x22in) s. (S.FR 26000)
£9984 $18570   (16-Jun-92 F.M217/R) Carovana orientale (25x19cm-10x7in) s.d.1867 panel
                   (I.L 22000000)
£17844 $32654   (16-May-92 F.L114/R) Mercato (27x35cm-11x14in) s.d.1873 (S.FR 48000)
£19477 $36032   (9-Jun-92 F.R153/R) Accampamento di nomadi (26x46cm-10x18in) s.d.1866
                   panel (I.L 43000000)
£40698 $70000   (17-Oct-91 SY.NY43/R) Market day, Constantinople (36x28cm-14x11in)
                   s.d.1887

PASINI, Alberto (attrib) (1826-1899) Italian
£1695 $3000   (13-Feb-92 S.W2699/R) Street scene (36x28cm-14x11in) bears sig. panel

PASINI, R (?) Italian
£949 $1718   (18-May-92 SY.MI99) Mercatino in un cortile (33x48cm-13x19in) s.
                   (I.L 2100000)

PASMORE, Daniel (19th C) British
£1517 $2700   (22-Jan-92 SY.NY465/R) Hurdy-gurdy player (41x30cm-16x12in) s.d.1857
£1685 $3000   (22-Jan-92 SY.NY464/R) Trinket box (53x65cm-21x26in) s.i.d.1847

PASMORE, Daniel (attrib) (19th C) British
£1103 $1898   (16-Oct-91 KM.K1313/R) Children blowing bubbles before house
                   (53x43cm-21x17in) (DM 3200)

PASMORE, Daniel (jnr) (19th C) British
£905 $1610   (29-Oct-91 PH.T125/R) What the eyes do not see (42x54cm-17x21in) s.d.1871
                   (C.D 1800)

PASMORE, Daniel (snr) (19th C) British
£3600 $6228   (25-Mar-92 PHI573/R) In the wheelwright's shop (63x76cm-25x30in) s.d.1851

PASMORE, Victor (1908-) British
£4000 $6920   (2-Oct-91 S81/R) From a window, Chiswick (30x35cm-12x14in) init. board

PASQUIER, Nathalie du (20th C) French?
£1006 $1730   (13-Oct-91 SY.MO10/R) Projet de motif pour tissu (23x23cm-9x9in)
                   s.d.fevrier 82 wash (F.FR 10000)

PASSANTINO, George (?) ?
£601 $1100   (5-Feb-92 D.NY73) Portofino (56x69cm-22x27in) s. s.i.verso

PASSAROTTI, Bartolomeo (1529-1592) Italian
£1200 $2088   (13-Apr-92 S82) Studies of Knees. Sketch of part of male figure
                   (39x25cm-15x10in) pen double-sided
£4600 $8004   (13-Apr-92 S3/R) Lamentation (36x27cm-14x11in) pen wash

PASSAROTTI, Bartolomeo (circle) (1529-1592) Italian
£4000 $7280   (13-Dec-91 C242/R) Saint Francis of Assisi (54x47cm-21x19in) panel
£28000 $53760   (10-Jul-92 C59/R) Portrait of youth, wearing burgundy doublet
                   (75x56cm-30x22in)

PASSAUER, Ludwig von (fl.1835-1842) German
£1232 $2231   (3-Dec-91 FN.S2374/R) Sunday school in church interior with parents
                   watching (47x42cm-19x17in) s.d.1835 (DM 3500)

PASSE, Chrispijn van de (elder) (c.1564-1637) Dutch
£6832 $12161   (25-Nov-91 CH.AM45/R) Study of girl's head (10x9cm-4x4in) chk wash
                   (D.FL 22000)

PASSERI, Giuseppe (1654-1714) Italian
£6687 $12104   (5-Dec-91 SY.MO338/R) Deposition (44x35cm-17x14in) (F.FR 65000)
£600 $1044   (14-Apr-92 C117/R) St Jerome appearing to two monastic saints
                   (16x10cm-6x4in) i. chk pen wash htd.white
£2081 $3642   (3-Apr-92 AGS.P181) La trinite (19cm-7ins circular) pen htd.white gouache
                   (F.FR 20000)
£2800 $5376   (6-Jul-92 S138/R) Scene from Roman history (21x24cm-8x9in) pen wash over
                   chk.

ASSERI, Giuseppe (attrib) (1654-1714) Italian
£1742 $3100   (22-Jan-92 SY.NY41/R) Martyrdom of Saint Andrew (48x30cm-19x12in) shaped canvas

ASSET, Gerard (20th C) French
£571 $1000   (19-Feb-92 D.NY61) Route dans la Plaine (61x76cm-24x30in) s. i.verso
£636 $1100   (2-Oct-91 D.NY73) Voile sur la Seine (41x33cm-16x13in) s. s.i.verso

ASSEY, C H (fl.1870-1885) British
£617 $1098   (26-Nov-91 J.M784) Harvest time (73x125cm-29x49in) s.d.1877 (A.D 1400)

ASSEY, Charles H (fl.1870-1885) British
£1200 $2136   (21-Jan-92 PH90) Gathering harvest (76x128cm-30x50in) s.

ASSINI, Paul Robert (1881-1956) Austrian
£393 $746   (25-Jun-92 D.V613/R) Vienna, Laaerberg, Oppenheimgasse - Flossler (42x62cm-17x24in) s.d.1956 W/C (A.S 8000)

ASSMORE, John Richard (1904-1984) Australian
£2553 $4519   (26-Apr-92 SY.ME276/R) Untitled (34x33cm-13x13in) init. board (A.D 6000)
£3419 $6085   (28-Apr-92 CH.ME183) Rose landscape, Millers Point (40x50cm-16x20in) board (A.D 8000)
£8811 $15859   (24-Nov-91 SY.S340/R) Argument (28x40cm-11x16in) init. cardboard (A.D 20000)
£1101 $1982   (19-Nov-91 JRL.S236/R) Untitled (54x81cm-21x32in) init.d.1956 gouache newspaper (A.D 2500)

ASSOT, Nicolas (16th C) French
£16575 $30000   (22-May-92 SY.NY59/R) Elaborate church interior with religious procession in background (124x160cm-49x63in) s.

ASTEGA, Luigi (1858-1927) Italian
£2198 $4000   (26-May-92 CE.NY135/R) The watercarrier (53x40cm-21x16in) s.
£6000 $10620   (14-Feb-92 C100/R) A helping hand (76x50cm-30x20in) s.d.1884

ASTERNAK, Leonid Ossipowitsch (1862-1945) Russian
£1695 $3000   (6-Nov-91 D.NY70/R) Portrait of Judith Spat (58x46cm-23x18in) s. pastel

ASTINA, Ed (19th C) Italian
£1500 $2670   (28-Nov-91 PHX539/R) Coastal landscape with figures at shrine with Isle of Capri beyond (76x102cm-30x40in) s.i.d.1857
£4651 $8000   (10-Oct-91 FA.PH925/R) Namad amidst architectural ruins (99x135cm-39x53in) i. s.verso

ASTOR, Hanns (1917-) German
£1404 $2526   (19-Nov-91 L.K991) Untitled (40x50cm-16x20in) s.d.1971 plaster sand glue indian ink oil panel (DM 4000)

ASTORIS, Federico (1837-1884) Italian
£3265 $5680   (18-Sep-91 N.M644/R) Antique dealer with broken Chinese vase (53x29cm-21x11in) s.d.1876 panel (DM 9500)

ASTOUR, Louis (1876-1948) French
£585 $1007   (20-Oct-91 I.N27) Le chemin des Lauriers a Toulon (12x20cm-5x8in) s.d.1917 board (F.FR 5800)
£605 $1041   (20-Oct-91 I.N28) Brumes a Cannes (13x21cm-5x8in) s. d.1932verso board (F.FR 6000)
£957 $1675   (5-Apr-92 ZZ.F170/R) Paysage de Haute Provence (39x56cm-15x22in) s. (F.FR 9200)

ASUCELLI, E (19th C) ?
£798 $1428   (16-Jan-92 D.V103/R) View of Sorrent (63x140cm-25x55in) s.i.d.1885 (A.S 16000)

ATCH, Thomas (1720-1782) British
£16500 $31515   (21-Jul-92 PH258/R) Numerous figures, some hauling in fishing nets, in Mediterranean Bay (73x98cm-29x39in)
£25000 $47750   (17-Jul-92 C26/R) View of the River Arno, Florence with the Ponte Santa Trinita (77x133cm-30x52in)

ATEK, Ludwig (1837-?) Austrian
£859 $1495   (21-Sep-91 SA.A1779/R) Painter before easel beside window (39x42cm-15x17in) s. (DM 2500)

ATEL, Antoine Pierre (younger) (1648-1707) French
£6559 $11282   (16-Oct-91 AT.P95/R) Bergers dans un paysage de la avec un temple antique en ruine (89x102cm-35x40in) (F.FR 65000)
£3352 $6000   (15-Jan-92 CH.NY71/R) Mountainous landscape with waterfall. Landscape with ruined temple (17x26cm-7x10in) s. bodycol vellum pair

ATEL, Antoine Pierre (younger-style) (1648-1707) French
£2200 $4004   (13-Dec-91 C211) Capriccio of classical ruins by pool with man drinking at fountain (40x35cm-16x14in)
£6000 $10980   (12-May-92 SWS711/R) Capriccio landscape with figures beneath ruins (107x154cm-42x61in)

PATEL, Pierre (elder) (1605-1676) French
£17000 $30940   (10-Dec-91 PH23/R) Figures and cattle amongst ruins of ancient temple in wooded landscape (115x71cm-45x28in) oval

PATEL, Pierre (elder-circle) (1605-1676) French
£8500 $14875   (28-Feb-92 C147/R) Ruins of a Roman Town (72x91cm-28x36in) indist.s.d.1659

PATEL, Pierre (style) (17th C) French
£1400 $2688   (9-Jul-92 CSK237/R) Shepherds and sheep by ruin (57x71cm-22x28in)

PATEL, Pierre (younger-attrib) (1648-1707) French
£4767 $8389   (10-Apr-92 AGS.P18) Paysage avec la fuite en Egypte (49x74cm-19x29in) (F.FR 47000)
£1013 $1834   (20-May-92 CSC.P11) Paysage avec personnages dans des ruines antiques (17x24cm-7x9in) gouache on wood (F.FR 10000)

PATELLIERE, Amedee de la (1890-1932) French
£825 $1427   (23-Mar-92 GL.P204/R) Femme endormie (81x65cm-32x26in) s. (F.FR 8000)
£1082 $1873   (23-Mar-92 GL.P206) Portrait de femme (81x65cm-32x26in) s. (F.FR 10500)
£1636 $2994   (5-Feb-92 FB.P209) Buste de femme brune (54x72cm-21x28in) s. (F.FR 16000)
£2661 $4737   (27-Nov-91 AT.P178) Baigneuses (24x33cm-9x13in) init. (F.FR 26000)
£2680 $4637   (23-Mar-92 GL.P201/R) Le bouquet dans la mansarde (81x65cm-32x26in) s.d.1926 (F.FR 26000)
£3093 $5351   (23-Mar-92 GL.P203) Bouquet de lilas dans un verre (46x38cm-18x15in) s. (F.FR 30000)
£3093 $5351   (23-Mar-92 GL.P202/R) Baigneuse sortant de l'eau (65x54cm-26x21in) s. (F.FR 30000)
£3259 $5963   (3-Jun-92 HC.P32) Scene pastorale (50x61cm-20x24in) s. (F.FR 32000)
£5155 $8918   (23-Mar-92 GL.P200/R) La femme endormie (50x60cm-20x24in) s.d.1925 (F.FR 50000)
£433 $749   (23-Mar-92 GL.P101) Vaches a l'etable (44x60cm-17x24in) s.d.1920 lead pencil stumping (F.FR 4200)

PATENIER, Joachim (circle) (1485-1524) Flemish
£11000 $19250   (1-Apr-92 S5/R) Saint Anthony Abbot in rocky landscape (22cm-9ins circular) panel
£30726 $55000   (16-Jan-92 CH.NY46/R) Rest on Flight into Egypt (56x71cm-22x28in) panel

PATENIER, Joachim (style) (1485-1524) Flemish
£16616 $29743   (7-May-92 CH.AM126/R) Flight into Egypt (31x22cm-12x9in) panel (D.FL 55000)

PATER, Jean Baptiste (1695-1736) French
£20597 $38723   (18-Dec-91 AT.P61/R) Scene galante dans un parc (32x41cm-13x16in) (F.FR 200000)
£290055 $525000   (22-May-92 SY.NY40/R) Elegant figures bathing at fountain and stream (52x65cm-20x26in) pair

PATER, Jean Baptiste (studio) (1695-1736) French
£1700 $2975   (31-Mar-92 PH44/R) Amorous couples resting on grassy bank (27x26cm-11x10in) panel

PATER, Jean Baptiste (style) (1695-1736) French
£4651 $8000   (10-Oct-91 SY.NY51/R) Militiamen at rest. Preparing to march (24x31cm-9x12in) copper pair
£8200 $15006   (12-May-92 SWS703/R) Fete champetre (65x81cm-26x32in)

PATERSON, Caroline (fl.1880's) British
£1400 $2506   (5-May-92 SWS253/R) In a peaceful country garden (19x26cm-7x10in) s. W/C scratching out
£2571 $4500   (20-Feb-92 SY.NY260/R) Doctor (36x30cm-14x12in) s. W/C gouache

PATERSON, Emily Murray (1855-1934) British
£500 $870   (9-Sep-91 PH222) Flowers in a jug (61x45cm-24x18in) s. W/C htd.white
£850 $1471   (24-Mar-92 CG725) The salute, Venice (49x69cm-19x27in) s. i.verso W/C htd.bodycol.

PATERSON, Esther (?) Australian?
£577 $1027   (28-Apr-92 CH.ME255) Flemington Park, Melbourne (24x30cm-9x12in) s. board (A.D 1350)
£598 $1065   (28-Apr-92 CH.ME255 a) Albert Park Lake, Melbourne (22x29cm-9x11in) s. canvas on board (A.D 1400)
£404 $716   (26-Apr-92 SY.ME12/R) Milking time (18x27cm-7x11in) s. gouache (A.D 950)

PATERSON, James (1854-1932) British
£976 $1756   (19-Nov-91 FP.M91/R) Moniaive (63x74cm-25x29in) s. (C.D 2000)
£460 $791   (11-Oct-91 PHE16) Mountain mist (36x24cm-14x9in) s.
£1700 $3077   (4-Dec-91 S363/R) Cockington. Anstys Cove (24x17cm-9x7in) s.i. W/C pair

PATERSON, John Ford (1851-1912) Australian
£1762 $3137   (26-Nov-91 J.M182/R) Afternoon promenade, St Kilda (23x34cm-9x13in) s.d.1909 canvasboard (A.D 4000)

PATERSON, T (fl.early 1900's) British
£500 $865   (4-Oct-91 BW381) Little in girls in sand dunes (36x48cm-14x19in) s. W/C

PATERSON, Viola (20th C) British
£476 $852   (5-May-92 ZEL.L1489/R) Bunch of peonies in vase on draped table
               (61x77cm-24x30in) s.d.1952 (DM 1400)

PATINI, Teofilo (1840-1906) Italian
£3705 $6410   (24-Mar-92 CH.R114) Piccolo gregge (17x34cm-7x13in) s. (I.L 8000000)

PATINO, Virgilio (1947-) Colombian
£3867 $7000   (18-May-92 CH.NY222/R) Paisaje del Valle del Cauca (150x100cm-59x39in)
               s.d.1990

PATON, Donald A see THOMPSON, Edward H

PATON, Frank (1856-1909) British
£800 $1392   (12-Sep-91 CSK195) 'Sportsman', dark bay gelding in loose box
               (43x53cm-17x21in) s.i.d.1886
£1500 $2610   (19-Sep-91 TL390) Retrievber and retrieved (27x22cm-11x9in) s.d.1886
£3500 $5985   (13-Mar-92 C135/R) Smooth haired fox terrier with ball (61x51cm-24x20in)
               s.d.1904
£5000 $8900   (28-Apr-92 PH60/R) Poacher (51x61cm-20x24in) s.d.1892
£8500 $15130   (30-Apr-92 CG851/R) Happy family (20x25cm-8x10in) s.d.1890 panel
£500 $860   (4-Mar-92 DR98/R) Midge, poodle seated on cushion (25x33cm-10x13in)
               s.i.d.1908 W/C
£660 $1181   (14-Jan-92 SWS67/R) Retriever and partridge (23x32cm-9x13in) s.d.1895 W/C
               gouache
£684 $1176   (10-Oct-91 D.V310/R) Rabbits grazing in landscape, spring
               (45x75cm-18x30in) s.d.1904 W/C (A.S 14000)

PATON, Richard (1717-1791) British
£3500 $6300   (22-Nov-91 C106/R) Commodore Wager's night enggement with the Spanish
               (135x175cm-53x69in) i.d.1735

PATON, Sir Joseph Noel (1821-1900) British
£650 $1203   (11-Jun-92 CSK248/R) Death is the door of life (28x18cm-11x7in)
               mono.d.1866 board

PATON, Waller Hugh (1828-1895) British
£1000 $1790   (13-Nov-91 CG610/R) Entrance to Quiraing, Isle of Skye (36x53cm-14x21in)
               s.d.1872
£1200 $2016   (26-Aug-91 S804/R) Stron Criese from King's House, Glencoe, Argyll
               (32x47cm-13x19in) s.d.1879 board
£1500 $2610   (11-Sep-91 PHG12/R) At Luss, Loch Lomond (59x92cm-23x36in) s.d.1882
               arched top
£398 $708   (25-Nov-91 W.T1789) Scottish coastal scene (22x32cm-9x13in) s. W/C
               (C.D 800)
£650 $1092   (26-Aug-91 S786/R) Ben Rioth, Arrochar (23x33cm-9x13in) s.d.1857 W/C
£700 $1246   (28-Apr-92 S137/R) Near Seafield, Fife (33x51cm-13x20in) s.d.1872 W/C
£900 $1512   (26-Aug-91 S785/R) Duilater (34x52cm-13x20in) s.d.1876 W/C
£1000 $1810   (4-Dec-91 S142/R) Invermoriston (24x35cm-9x14in) s.i.d.1887 W/C htd
               bodycol
£1600 $2688   (26-Aug-91 S784) Carr Bridge (24x35cm-9x14in) s.i.d.1887 W/C htd bodycol.
               arched top
£1600 $2688   (26-Aug-91 S781/R) Moulinearn (34x52cm-13x20in) s.i.d.1877 W/C

PATOUX, Emile (1893-1985) Belgian
£3200 $6112   (29-Jun-92 CSK96/R) Coin de plage, La Panne (44x49cm-17x19in) s.i.d.25

PATRICK, J (19th C) British
£900 $1611   (13-Nov-91 B117/R) Portrait of Mary Greswolde Wilson aged three seated
               holding doll (90x72cm-35x28in) s.i.d.1823

PATRICK, James McIntosh (1907-) British
£5500 $9790   (28-Apr-92 S328/R) Ponies grazing in parkland (63x76cm-25x30in) s.
£6800 $12104   (1-May-92 PHE91/R) The croft, Tor-A-Bhan, Lochiel (34x44cm-13x17in) s.
               board
£8000 $14240   (30-Apr-92 CG918/R) Haystacks (51x61cm-20x24in) s.
£8200 $13776   (26-Aug-91 S1150/R) Farm in winter (41x51cm-16x20in) s.
£10000 $16800   (26-Aug-91 S1153/R) Harvest in Perthshire (46x56cm-18x22in) s.
£10000 $17800   (1-May-92 PHE25/R) The carse of Gowrie from Dron (64x76cm-25x30in) s.
£11000 $19690   (13-Nov-91 CG653/R) Pictur Den, Angus, autumn (63x72cm-25x28in) s.
£11000 $19140   (19-Sep-91 B78/R) Oak trees in May, Carse of Gowrie (54x63cm-21x25in) s.
£11500 $20470   (1-May-92 PHE101/R) Carmichael's farm, Longforgan (63x76cm-25x30in) s.
£13000 $23270   (13-Nov-91 CG655/R) The Brook, Carse of Gowrie (51x61cm-20x24in) s.d.47
£24000 $40320   (26-Aug-91 S1152/R) Den of Fowlis (63x76cm-25x30in) s.
£500 $895   (13-Nov-91 CG654) Easdale, Argyllshire (18x27cm-7x11in) s. W/C cotton
£650 $1157   (28-Apr-92 S330/R) Street scene (23x33cm-9x13in) s.d.31 W/C ink
£1000 $1680   (26-Aug-91 S1151) The Volturno, Capua (32x39cm-13x15in) s.d.46 gouache
£1800 $3204   (28-Apr-92 S318/R) Evening, Yorkshire. Farm buildings. Bridge
               (20x28cm-8x11in) s.d.41,42 set of three
£2000 $3560   (1-May-92 PHE72) Farm buildings above the loch (53x74cm-21x29in) s. W/C
£2400 $4272   (30-Apr-92 CG810/R) Tullybaccart Farm, Angus (54x75cm-21x30in) s. W/C htd
               white

PATRICK, James McIntosh (1907-) British-cont.
£4500 $8055   *(13-Nov-91 CG656/R) The drinking place, Loch Spout, Rossie Priory, Perthshire (60x80cm-24x31in) s. W/C*

PATROIS, Isidore (1815-1884) French
£900 $1674   (16-Jun-92 SWS239/R) Figures in interior (83x75cm-33x30in) s.d.69

PATRONI, Jacobi (?) Italian?
£2809 $5000   (22-Jan-92 D.NY95) Portrait of Benedict XIV Prospero Lambertini (94x69cm-37x27in) i.verso

PATRU, Emile (20th C) French?
£1333 $2267   (23-Oct-91 GD.B577/R) Wooded river landscape (54x65cm-21x26in) s.d.1902 (S.FR 3400)

PATTEIN, Cesar (19/20th C) French
£2857 $5000   (21-Feb-92 BG.M255/R) Faggot gatherers (61x79cm-24x31in) s.d.1908
£4429 $7750   (20-Feb-92 SY.NY130/R) Children fishing (79x117cm-31x46in) s.d.1894

PATTEN, Alfred Fowler (1829-1888) British
£4500 $8550   (24-Jun-92 DR184/R) Reclining Odalisque (49x54cm-19x21in) s.d.1858 verso

PATTEN, William (jnr) (?-1843) British
£700 $1204   *(4-Mar-92 C79/R) Cleric, seated in red chair, wearing spectacles (8x?cm-3x?in) min. init.verso gilt frame oval lock hair pearl*

PATTEN, William Vandyke (fl.1844-1871) British
£600 $1062   *(22-Apr-92 CSK25/R) Children playing Blind Man's Bluff (16x?cm-6x?in) min. rec.*
£700 $1246   *(29-Apr-92 RBB762/R) Portrait of girl carrying basket of flowers (36x25cm-14x10in) s.d.1844 W/C*

PATTERSON, Ambrose McCarthy (1877-1967) American
£4701 $8368   (28-Apr-92 CH.ME87/R) Le pardon, Bretagne (49x61cm-19x24in) s. canvas on panel (A.D 11000)

PATTERSON, Charles Robert (1878-?) American
£939 $1700   (21-May-92 GRO.B108/R) Naval ships at sea (76x127cm-30x50in) s.

PATTERSON, Margaret Jordan (1867-1950) American
£497 $850   *(21-Mar-92 W.W185/R) San Luis Obispo, Lisbon, Portugal (43x30cm-17x12in) s.d.1909 gouache*
£538 $1000   *(21-Jun-92 JRB.C59/R) Harbour reflections (48x41cm-19x16in) s. gouache*

PATTYN, J (?) ?
£800 $1488   (18-Jun-92 CSK216) Rest in the inn (130x109cm-51x43in) s. panel

PATY, Leon du and POILPOT, Theophile (19th C) French
£3714 $6500   (20-Feb-92 SY.NY118/R) Le Siege de Paris en 1871 (47x151cm-19x59in) s. four framed as six

PAU DE SAINT MARTIN, Alexandre (18th C) French
£1816 $3124   *(16-Oct-91 AT.P132/R) Vue d'une eglise dans la campagne (54x70cm-21x28in) s.d.1796 (F.FR 18000)*

PAU, Emil (?) ?
£720 $1296   (29-Jan-92 FER.M246/R) Joven tocando la mandolina (79x59cm-31x23in) s. (S.P 130000)

PAUELSEN, Erik (1749-1790) Danish
£1056 $1775   (28-Aug-91 KH.K153/R) Portrait of young girl wearing white dress (76x60cm-30x24in) s.d.1789 oval (D.KR 12000)
£1264 $2274   (19-Nov-91 RAS.K390/R) Portrait of young girl wearing blue dress (75x58cm-30x23in) oval (D.KR 14000)
£1333 $2400   (22-Nov-91 SA.A1543/R) Portrait of Graf Godske von Moltke (55x43cm-22x17in) i.stretcher (DM 3800)
£2465 $4141   (27-Aug-91 RAS.K203/R) Portrait of young lady wearing pink dress (76x63cm-30x25in) (D.KR 28000)

PAUELSEN, Erik (attrib) (1749-1790) Danish
£810 $1482   (5-Feb-92 KH.K93/R) Portrait of lady in blue dress holding flowers (78x62cm-31x24in) (D.KR 9000)

PAUL, John (19th C) British
£700 $1295   (11-Jun-92 CSK85/R) Elegant figures promenading in formal gardens (50x61cm-20x24in)
£700 $1281   (14-May-92 TL53/R) Bay horse in stable (56x71cm-22x28in) s.d.1860
£824 $1500   (26-May-92 CE.NY22/R) Bay stallion in a stall (49x61cm-19x24in) s.d.1872
£900 $1665   (11-Jun-92 CSK80/R) Northumberland House, Charing Cross (50x60cm-20x24in)
£920 $1766   (28-Jul-92 SWS115/R) Huntsman on a bay horse (59x75cm-23x30in) s.d.1876
£1100 $1914   (12-Sep-91 CSK186) Thames with view of St.Paul's and Blackfriars Bridge (72x91cm-28x36in)
£1300 $2405   (11-Jun-92 CSK82/R) Westminster Hall (63x72cm-25x28in)
£1300 $2288   (8-Apr-92 S234/R) View of Thames at London Bridge (62x92cm-24x36in)

PAUL, John (19th C) British-cont.
£1450 $2683   (12-Jun-92 K518/R) Horse portrait Johnny Ray in stable (56x74cm-22x29in) s.
£3591 $6500   (22-May-92 SY.NY218/R) Hampton Court Bridge, Middlesex (76x127cm-30x50in)
£31768 $57500   (22-May-92 SY.NY54/R) View of old Northumberland House, Charing Cross (123x187cm-48x74in)

PAUL, Joseph (1804-1887) British
£520 $952   (14-May-92 CSK257) Wooded river landscape with cattle watering (61x51cm-24x20in)
£800 $1368   (17-Mar-92 SWS1209/R) Moonlit river landscape (75x62cm-30x24in)
£1200 $2100   (27-Feb-92 B198/R) Wooded landscape with figures resting on a log (75x105cm-30x41in)
£3200 $5728   (15-Nov-91 C125/R) Extensive wooded landscape with figures and cottages, windmill beyond (87x113cm-34x44in)

PAUL, Joseph (attrib) (1804-1887) British
£3000 $5220   (12-Sep-91 CSK139/R) East Anglian river landscape with figures ploughing, windmill beyond (76x127cm-30x50in)

PAULI, Fritz (1891-1968) Swiss
£365 $653   (6-May-92 GD.B993/R) *Mother with child (40x31cm-16x12in) s.d.46 W/C over pencil (S.FR 1000)*

PAULI, Fritz Eduard (1891-1968) Swiss
£1102 $1896   (16-Oct-91 G.Z109/R) Golino (50x70cm-20x28in) s. (S.FR 2800)

PAULI, Georg (1855-1935) Swedish
£565 $1006   (28-Oct-91 AB.S190) Summer landscape with trees by shore (32x45cm-13x18in) s. (S.KR 6000)
£566 $1018   (23-Nov-91 SO.S570/R) Town scene (30x40cm-12x16in) s. panel (S.KR 5900)
£674 $1167   (28-Mar-92 UA.U392) Women sunbathing (43x38cm-17x15in) s. panel (S.KR 7000)
£3679 $6586   (7-May-92 RAS.S40/R) Boys swimming in Venetian Canal (48x34cm-19x13in) s.i.d.1881 panel (S.KR 39000)
£18921 $34248   (19-May-92 AB.S4265/R) Mid summer wake (170x240cm-67x94in) s.d.1903 (S.KR 200000)
£29245 $52349   (7-May-92 RAS.S12/R) From a Roman bath (100x150cm-39x59in) s.d.82 (S.KR 310000)

PAULI, Richard (1855-1892) American
£1029 $1800   (19-Feb-92 D.NY62) Saturated landscape (38x61cm-15x24in) s. panel

PAULMAN, Joseph (?) ?
£850 $1522   (5-May-92 SWS371/R) The young anglers (29x40cm-11x16in) s.
£900 $1611   (5-May-92 SWS372/R) Burning leaves (29x39cm-11x15in) s.
£1420 $2457   (25-Mar-92 PHI555/R) Driving the sheep (40x61cm-16x24in) s. pair
£1800 $3222   (5-May-92 SWS352/R) Geese by pond. Driving geese (29x39cm-11x15in) s. pair

PAULSEN, Julius (1860-1940) Danish
£528 $887   (27-Aug-91 RAS.K448) Model study (35x29cm-14x11in) s. (D.KR 6000)
£529 $942   (28-Apr-92 RAS.K637) The model resting (21x26cm-8x10in) s. (D.KR 6000)
£546 $944   (2-Sep-91 BU.K17/R) View from Tisvildeleije (29x36cm-11x14in) init. panel (D.KR 6200)
£718 $1271   (11-Feb-92 RAS.K22) View from the coast at Tisvildeleije (29x46cm-11x18in) init. panel (D.KR 8000)
£766 $1364   (25-Nov-91 BU.K2/R) In the light of the oil lamp (12x14cm-5x6in) (D.KR 8500)
£879 $1573   (6-May-92 KH.K152/R) Mother and child (80x60cm-31x24in) s.d.1920 (D.KR 10000)
£880 $1479   (28-Aug-91 KH.K158) Landscape with road through fields (60x73cm-24x29in) s.d.1915 (D.KR 10000)
£923 $1652   (6-May-92 KH.K151) Seascape (49x61cm-19x24in) init. (D.KR 10500)
£990 $1812   (5-Feb-92 KH.K95) Landscape, sunrise (26x32cm-10x13in) init.d.06 (D.KR 11000)
£1408 $2366   (28-Aug-91 KH.K157/R) Odalisc (34x24cm-13x9in) s. (D.KR 16000)
£1986 $3574   (19-Nov-91 RAS.K251/R) Model resting of sofa (50x61cm-20x24in) s. (D.KR 22000)
£2962 $5243   (11-Feb-92 RAS.K21/R) After the rain, Horneby (60x85cm-24x33in) s.d.94 (D.KR 33000)
£4401 $7394   (28-Aug-91 KH.K155/R) Evening toilette (61x50cm-24x20in) s.d.1919 (D.KR 50000)

PAULSEN, N Chr (19th C) Danish
£2730 $4750   (20-Sep-91 DM.D2174/R) Naval gun battle involving two fleets (71x114cm-28x45in) s.

PAULUCCI, Enrico (1901-) Italian
£1558 $2727   (28-Feb-92 SY.NY275/R) Scogli (60x70cm-24x28in) s. s.d.1957 num.22 verso
£1814 $3320   (12-May-92 F.R181/R) Vele (50x40cm-20x16in) s. s.i.verso (I.L 4000000)
£2949 $5396   (12-May-92 F.R193/R) Vigneti di Langa (50x60cm-20x24in) s.d.1954 s.i.verso (I.L 6500000)

PAULUS, Pierre (1881-1959) Belgian
£834 $1468   (7-Apr-92 C.A194) Rocky coast (60x70cm-24x28in) s. (B.FR 50000)
£2804 $4794   (21-Mar-92 KV.L387/R) Still life of flowers (36x44cm-14x17in) s.d.18
                          board (B.FR 165000)

PAUNILA, Marjukka (1949-) Finnish
£822 $1446   (12-Apr-92 HOR.H186) Pink still life (100x110cm-39x43in) s.d.1988
                          (F.M 6500)

PAUSINGER, Clemens von (1855-1936) German
£383   *$700*   *(3-Jun-92 D.NY76) Portrait of Maria Jeritza in black cloak*
                          (94x69cm-37x27in) s.d.1937 pastel
£3800   *$6764*   *(27-Nov-91 S130/R) Tambourine girl (70x54cm-28x21in) s.d.91 pastel panel*

PAUSINGER, Franz von (1839-1915) German
£1297 $2347   (22-May-92 GB.B5995) Cattle in woods (31x39cm-12x15in) s. (DM 3800)
£1499 $2697   (21-Nov-91 D.V42/R) Stag (116x87cm-46x34in) s. (A.S 30000)
£3393 $6175   (27-May-92 D.V554/R) Chamois in high mountain landscape covered in snow
                          (124x94cm-49x37in) s. oil tempera paper on canvas (A.S 70000)
£388   *$691*   *(29-Apr-92 D.V518) Stag (84x67cm-33x26in) s. chl paper on canvas*
                          (A.S 8000)

PAUTSCH, Fryderyk (1877-1950) Polish
£1342 $2402   (17-Nov-91 REM.W22) Wild boar at bay (63x89cm-25x35in) s. (P.Z 26000000)
£3468 $6521   (21-Dec-91 PSA.W16) Still life (45x37cm-18x15in) s. (P.Z 67000000)

PAUW, Gabriel de (1924-) Belgian
£816 $1395   (21-Mar-92 KV.L95) Still life with coffee pot (80x100cm-31x39in) s.
                          (B.FR 48000)

PAUW, Jef de (1888-1930) Belgian
£600 $1032   (12-Oct-91 KV.L82) Meadow in the snow (24x19cm-9x7in) rem.sig. board
                          (B.FR 36000)
£753 $1363   (7-Dec-91 KV.L107) Hof Den Hese in Luiseekdam (30x44cm-12x17in) s. panel
                          (B.FR 44000)
£1500 $2580   (12-Oct-91 KV.L80) Granary in landscape (39x49cm-15x19in) s. (B.FR 90000)
£2669 $4697   (7-Apr-92 C.A418) Winter landscape (100x120cm-39x47in) s. (B.FR 160000)

PAUW, Rene de (1887-1946) Belgian
£564 $1032   (12-May-92 C.A75/R) Interior scene (80x70cm-31x28in) s. panel
                          (B.FR 34000)

PAUWELS, Ferdinand (1830-1904) Belgian
£2749 $4784   (18-Sep-91 N.M645/R) 17th century scene with thief fleeing from palace
                          guards (53x29cm-21x11in) s.d.1876 panel (DM 8000)

PAVAN, Angelo (1893-1945) Italian
£1180 $2195   (16-Jun-92 F.M102) Barche a vela nella laguna. Barche nella laguna
                          (23x30cm-9x12in) panel pair (I.L 2600000)

PAVELIC, Myfanwy Spencer (1916-) Canadian
£548   *$1003*   *(14-May-92 SY.T59) Nude (39x33cm-15x13in) s. s.d.1980 verso pastel*
                          (C.D 1200)

PAVIL, Elie Anatole (1873-1948) French
£589 $1026   (14-Apr-92 ZZ.F33/R) La Seine au Bas Meudon (32x46cm-13x18in) traces sig.
                          (F.FR 5800)
£768 $1383   (2-Feb-92 ZZ.F81/R) Paris, le place de la Republique (22x27cm-9x11in) s.
                          panel (F.FR 7500)
£917 $1679   (1-Jun-92 W.T1441) Moroccan travellers (27x34cm-11x13in) s. panel
                          (C.D 2000)
£1257 $2400   (16-Jul-92 SY.NY407/R) Au bord de la Seine (38x55cm-15x22in) s.
£1286 $2443   (26-Jun-92 CSC.P106) Paysage fluvial (55x38cm-22x15in) s. (F.FR 12500)
£2000 $3480   (19-Sep-91 CSK133/R) Canal de l'Ourcq (60x81cm-24x32in) s.
£3262 $6067   (21-Jun-92 LT.P76/R) Animation sur le Parvis de Notre-Dame
                          (73x92cm-29x36in) s. (F.FR 32000)
£4115 $7819   (22-Jun-92 AT.P78/R) Les quais a Paris, 908 s. (F.FR 40000)

PAVILLON, Isidore Pean du (1790-1856) French
£995 $1900   (16-Jul-92 SY.NY369/R) Portrait of an officer (91x73cm-36x29in) s.d.1839

PAVLOVSKI, Serafime (1903-) Russian
£764 $1398   (3-Jun-92 ARC.P44/R) Artek et Adelary (50x79cm-20x31in) s.d.65 board
                          (F.FR 7500)
£927 $1696   (3-Jun-92 ARC.P39/R) Nu (50x69cm-20x27in) s.verso (F.FR 9100)
£1018 $1864   (3-Jun-92 ARC.P41/R) Nu et vase (100x79cm-39x31in) s.d.1968 (F.FR 10000)
£2648 $4845   (3-Jun-92 ARC.P40/R) Legumes sur fond rouge (59x74cm-23x29in) s.
                          (F.FR 26000)

PAVY, Philippe (19th C) French
£500 $905   (19-May-92 SWS297) The connoisseur (4x19cm-2x7in) s.d.1879 panel
£2800 $4956   (14-Feb-92 C86/R) Nubian warrior (46x21cm-18x8in) s.d.1882

PAWLA, Frederick Alexander (1877-?) American
£523 $900   (7-Mar-92 LAE.L64) Sailing ship (76x86cm-30x34in) s.

PAWLE, John (1915-) British
£550 $946   (5-Mar-92 CSK131/R) Pavilion onto Mediterranean (46x51cm-18x20in) s.
   s.i.d.verso masonite

PAWLEY, James (fl.1845-1869) British
£6686 $11500   (17-Oct-91 SY.NY307/R) Pet cockatoo (77x94cm-30x37in) s.

PAWLISZAK, Waclaw (1866-1904) Polish
£732 $1259   (13-Oct-91 REM.W22) Study of female nude (39x21cm-15x8in) s. board
   (P.Z 14000000)

PAXSON, Edgar S (1852-1919) American
£5556 $9500   (11-Mar-92 SY.NY37/R) Golden West (45x102cm-18x40in) s.d.1910 board
£9341 $17000   (27-May-92 SY.NY44/R) War party (100x70cm-39x28in) s.d.-2-1901-

PAXTON, William McGregor (1869-1941) American
£2485 $4250   (18-Mar-92 GRO.B68/R) Portrait of Frederic E. Snow (97x81cm-38x32in) s.
£16484 $30000   (28-May-92 CH.NY173/R) The red mules (51x61cm-20x24in) masonite

PAY, Michel (19th C) French
£785 $1500   (16-Jul-92 SY.NY393/R) Scene sur le Lac Smere de Poshkur
   (137x113cm-54x44in) s.d.1874

PAYAG (attrib) (17th C) Indian
£24000   *$43920*   *(15-May-92 TE274/R) Hunting scene - Prince Dara Shikoii and Crown Prince
   shooting blue bulls (15x25cm-6x10in) gold coloured paint*

PAYER, Julius J P (1841-1915) Austrian
£1000 $1810   (19-May-92 GF.L2722) Polar bear hunt (67x100cm-26x39in) s. (S.FR 2700)

PAYNE, C J (19th C) British
£700   *$1337*   *(20-Jul-92 WW132) H.M.S. Encounter (22x37cm-9x15in) s.d.39 W/C*

PAYNE, Charles Johnson (1884-1967) British
£1450 $2523   (15-Apr-92 PHL104/R) Caricature sketches Scotch, including Gordons,
   H.L.I., Scottish Trifles (41x31cm-16x12in) s.i. gouache

PAYNE, David (19th C) British
£700 $1218   (12-Sep-91 CSK171/R) Rest on village track (41x61cm-16x24in) s.
£800 $1464   (5-Jun-92 BW430/R) Landscape with figures, horse and cart to fore, cows
   in distance (51x61cm-20x24in) s. board
£580   *$1009*   *(15-Apr-92 PHL33) Trompe l'oeil of drawing, Illustrated London News,
   Punch, Correspondence (55x46cm-22x18in) s.d.1877 pen wash*
£1000   *$1920*   *(10-Jul-92 CSK56/R) Trompe l'oeil of ink drawing, London News and Punch
   magazine, envelopes (53x46cm-21x18in) s.d.1877 pencil pen W/C*

PAYNE, Edgar (1882-1947) American
£681 $1300   (19-Jul-92 JRB.C229/R) Mountain landscape (23x30cm-9x12in) s. canvasboard
£1124 $2000   (26-Nov-91 MOR.P37) Clouds over Sierra Lake (30x38cm-12x15in) s.
£1124 $2000   (26-Nov-91 MOR.P66 a) Sierra landscape (30x36cm-12x14in) s. canvasboard
£1374 $2500   (13-Dec-91 DM.D2014/R) California mountain landscape (23x33cm-9x13in) s.
£1404 $2500   (26-Nov-91 MOR.P101) Boats at dock (30x23cm-12x9in) s.
£1579 $3000   (24-Jun-92 B.SF6419/R) Deep in Sierras (25x36cm-10x14in) s. canvasboard
£2105 $4000   (23-Jun-92 MOR.P62) Boats in harbour (30x41cm-12x16in) s.
£2401 $4250   (12-Feb-92 B.SF557/R) Sunny Sierra (28x38cm-11x15in) s. canvas on board
£2429 $4250   (31-Mar-92 MOR.P80 b) Sierra landscape (30x41cm-12x16in) s. canvas on
   board
£2632 $5000   (23-Jun-92 MOR.P50) Square rigger (30x25cm-12x10in) s. board
£2809 $5000   (26-Nov-91 MOR.P101 a) Landscape, California vista (30x41cm-12x16in) s.
£3107 $5500   (12-Feb-92 B.SF479/R) Adriatic fishing boats (25x30cm-10x12in) s. canvas
   on board
£3714 $6500   (31-Mar-92 MOR.P67) Laguna Canyon (30x41cm-12x16in) s. canvas on board
£3714 $6500   (31-Mar-92 MOR.P45) Boats in harbour (33x38cm-13x15in) s. canvas on board
£4000 $7000   (25-Sep-91 SY.NY38/R) Mount Ritter (51x61cm-20x24in) s. i.stretcher
£4000 $7000   (31-Mar-92 MOR.P68 a) Landscape (41x51cm-16x20in) s. canvas laid down
£4737 $9000   (23-Jun-92 MOR.P48) Adriatic fishing boats (51x61cm-20x24in) s.
£4737 $9000   (24-Jun-92 B.SF6394/R) Reflected sails, Chioggia (61x51cm-24x20in) s.
£5143 $9000   (26-Sep-91 CH.NY69/R) Day's end at harbour (74x74cm-29x29in) s.
£6486 $12000   (10-Jun-92 CE.NY348 a/R) Blue hills (46x103cm-18x41in) s.
£6780 $12000   (12-Feb-92 B.SF425/R) Palisade glacier (56x66cm-22x26in) s.
£7310 $12500   (11-Mar-92 SY.NY28/R) Snowcapped mountains (51x61cm-20x24in) s.
£7429 $13000   (31-Mar-92 MOR.P44) Landscape, foothills (41x51cm-16x20in) s. canvas laid
   down
£8571 $15000   (31-Mar-92 MOR.P43 a) Adriatic ships (61x71cm-24x28in) s. indis.i.verso
£8772 $15000   (11-Mar-92 SY.NY30/R) Mountain lake (63x77cm-25x30in) s.
£10169 $18000   (12-Feb-92 B.SF485/R) Tuna boats (46x48cm-18x19in) s.
£14054 $26000   (10-Jun-92 CE.NY351 a/R) Hills of Altadena (91x114cm-36x45in) s.
£38136 $67500   (12-Feb-92 B.SF535/R) Sierra Divide (61x71cm-24x28in) s.d.1921
£506   *$900*   *(26-Nov-91 MOR.P90 b) Boats of Sotto Marino (33x36cm-13x14in) s. mixed
   media*
£2368   *$4500*   *(23-Jun-92 MOR.P439) California oaks (33x51cm-13x20in) s. gouache*

PAYNE, Elsie Palmer (1884-1971) American
£508 $900   (12-Feb-92 B.SF618/R) California houses and trees (30x41cm-12x16in) s.
   canvasboard

PAYNE, Elsie Palmer (1884-1971) American-cont.
£368 $700   (24-Jun-92 B.SF6488/R) Lateen sails (30x38cm-12x15in) s. gouache
£452 $800   (12-Feb-92 B.SF621/R) House in Spuyten Dayvil, New York, no.2
                (51x41cm-20x16in) s. gouache board
£537 $950   (12-Feb-92 B.SF620/R) Italian memory (46x56cm-18x22in) s. W/C
£537 $950   (12-Feb-92 B.SF617/R) Old Chinatown, Los Angeles (33x36cm-13x14in) s.
                gouache
£565 $1000   (12-Feb-92 B.SF619/R) Macarthur Park, Los Angeles (43x38cm-17x15in) s.
                W/C
£579 $1100   (24-Jun-92 B.SF6493/R) House in Spuyten Duyvil, New York
                (30x36cm-12x14in) s. gouache
£734 $1300   (12-Feb-92 B.SF623/R) Lake Louise (30x38cm-12x15in) s. gouache
£737 $1400   (24-Jun-92 B.SF6487/R) Italian village. La Ville Close, Concarneau
                (32x37cm-13x15in) s. gouache pair
£895 $1700   (24-Jun-92 B.SF6494/R) California house no.2 (28x36cm-11x14in) s. gouache
£1316 $2500   (24-Jun-92 B.SF6498/R) Lake Louise, Canada. Mountain lake. Green Valley,
                Sierras (30x36cm-12x14in) s. gouache three
£2260 $4000   (12-Feb-92 B.SF616/R) Hillside homes (47x53cm-19x21in) s. gouache

PAYNE, Frances Mallalieu (fl.1900-1930) Australian
£2128 $3766   (26-Apr-92 SY.ME72) Sand baby (42x49cm-17x19in) s.d.28 s.i.verso board
                (A.D 5000)

PAYNE, Henry A (1868-1940) British
£800 $1376   (15-Oct-91 CSK627) Two soldiers from the West Kent Imperial Yoemanry
                training in Mote Park,1905 (42x55cm-17x22in) s.i.d.05

PAYNE, Sydenham (19th C) British
£750 $1373   (6-Feb-92 PHF176/R) Folkestone Harbour, with figures on quayside and
                shipping (32x47cm-13x19in) s.d.1882 i.verso

PAYNE, William (1760-1830) British
£480 $830   (4-Sep-91 BT105/R) Waiting for the ferry (13x15cm-5x6in) W/C
£500 $855   (12-Mar-92 CSK35/R) Prospect of Great Haldon near Exeter, Lawrence Tower
                on hillside beyond (69x107cm-27x42in) s. W/C
£700 $1253   (5-May-92 SWS25/R) Dover Castle (13x20cm-5x8in) W/C over pencil
£1000 $1910   (14-Jul-92 C18/R) Figures resting by cove (26x34cm-10x13in) s. pencil pen
                W/C
£1100 $1969   (5-May-92 SWS26/R) Oystermouth Castle, Swansea Bay (13x20cm-5x8in) s. ink
                W/C over pencil
£1200 $2148   (14-Nov-91 S87) View on the Rhone, France. View across the Bay of Naples,
                Italy (26x39cm-10x15in) s.i.d.1819 W/C over pencil pair
£1600 $2800   (1-Apr-92 B45/R) Weymouth on the road from Dorchester (23x34cm-9x13in)
                W/C
£2000 $3580   (14-Nov-91 S86/R) View on river near Plymouth, Devon (30x40cm-12x16in) s.
                s.i.verso pen W/C over pencil

PAYTON, Joseph (19th C) British
£720 $1261   (18-Feb-92 DUR.M71/R) Una bella melodia (25x26cm-10x10in) s.d.98 panel
                (S.P 130000)

PAYZANT, Charles (1898-1980) American
£489 $850   (14-Sep-91 LAE.L313/R) Fisherman (43x58cm-17x23in) s. W/C

PAZOTTI (19/20th C) ?
£811 $1467   (18-May-92 AT.P139) Voilier sur le grand canal (54x81cm-21x32in) s.
                (F.FR 8000)

PEACOCK, George Edward (1806-?) Australian
£2600 $4420   (22-Oct-91 C103/R) View of Craigend, Darlinghurst, Port Jackson
                (26x30cm-10x12in)
£2766 $4896   (26-Apr-92 SY.ME413/R) Red Bluff (24x34cm-9x13in) s.d.1860 board
                (A.D 6500)
£8000 $13600 (22-Oct-91 C104/R) Sydney (24x33cm-9x13in) init.i.d.1848 stretcher
£68545 $114469 (19-Aug-91 SY.ME346/R) Port Jackson, New South Wales showing Observatory
                (34x74cm-13x29in) bears sig.d.1845 verso canvas on board (A.D 146000)

PEACOCK, Ralph (1868-1946) British
£1400 $2436   (10-Sep-91 RG2156) Portrait of Lady Monica Salmon (46x36cm-18x14in) s.
                i.verso

PEAKE, Robert (attrib) (16/17th C) British
£1550 $2790   (22-Nov-91 SWS257) Portrait of young girl wearing a bronze-coloured dress
                (73x55cm-29x22in) panel

PEAKE, Robert (elder-circle) (?-1626) British
£3867 $7000   (22-May-92 SY.NY276/R) Portrait of nobleman, said to be a king of England
                (110x85cm-43x33in) panel

PEALE, Charles Willson (1741-1827) American
£5814 $10000 (10-Oct-91 FA.PH933/R) Portrait of Mrs. Joseph Daffin (89x69cm-35x27in)
                s.

PEALE, Harriet Cany (1800-1869) American
£1829 $3200   (26-Sep-91 CH.NY16/R) Portrait of girl with bonnet (76x63cm-30x25in)
     s.d.1854 painted oval

PEALE, James (elder) (1749-1831) American
£26316 $45000   (11-Mar-92 SY.NY11/R) Still life with fruit (51x67cm-20x26in)
     indist.i.verso

PEALE, Rubens (1784-1865) American
£2793 $5250   (18-Dec-91 SY.NY3/R) Still life (24x35cm-9x14in) s.

PEALE, Sarah Miriam (1800-1885) American
£8000 $13600   (23-Oct-91 S266/R) Still life with fruit in bowl (32x40cm-13x16in)
     s.d.1829 panel

PEAN, Rene (1875-?) French
£2766 $4896   (26-Apr-92 SY.ME217/R) Young lady admiring prints (44x54cm-17x21in) s.
     pastel paper on canvas (A.D 6500)

PEARCE, Charles Sprague (1851-1914) American
£10447 $18700   (14-Nov-91 GRO.B118/R) Reading music (30x46cm-12x18in) s.i. canvas on
     board

PEARLSTEIN, Philip (1924-) American
£3488 $6000   (12-Oct-91 SY.NY256/R) Female nude lying down (66x76cm-26x30in) s.d.63
£556 $950   (13-Mar-92 WOL.C73 a) Seated female with hand in hair (46x38cm-18x15in)
     s.d.70 pencil
£2857 $5000   (27-Feb-92 CE.NY176/R) Two female models in hammock and office chair
     (75x104cm-30x41in) s.d.75 brush sepia ink

PEARS, Charles (1873-1958) British
£520 $874   (15-Aug-91 B316/R) H.M.S. Anson leaving Gib (36x62cm-14x24in) s.i. paper
     on board
£636 $1107   (13-Apr-92 SY.J260/R) Off Isle of Wight (70x90cm-28x35in) s. (SA.R 3200)
£1150 $2070   (9-Jan-92 B310/R) Thames sailing barges, Grey Twilight (71x91cm-28x36in)
     s.

PEARSON, Cornelius (1805-1891) British
£400 $680   (8-Aug-91 B192) Cattle watering at the edge of a Loch (16x48cm-6x19in)
     s.d.1863 W/C scratching out
£420 $739   (7-Apr-92 C205) Prospect of Leeds Castle (14x23cm-6x9in) i.num.3 verso
     pencil W/C
£900 $1530   (22-Oct-91 SWS87/R) Sailbarge on river. Two men in rowing boat
     (25x47cm-10x19in) s.d.1860 W/C over pencil white pair

PEARSON, Cornelius and WAINEWRIGHT, Thomas Francis (19th C) British
£475 $879   (9-Jun-92 FB.M210/R) Cattle watering near river bend (21x40cm-8x16in)
     s.i.d.1876 W/C (C.D 1050)
£550 $1018   (11-Jun-92 CSK8/R) Sheep resting by a river (20x41cm-8x16in) s.d.1878
     pencil W/C htd. white

PEARSON, J (19th C) British
£1011 $1780   (12-Apr-92 HOR.H24) Among mountains (45x80cm-18x31in) s.d.1879 (F.M 8000)

PEARSON, Marguerite S (1898-1978) American
£778 $1400   (24-Nov-91 JRB.C179/R) Chrysanthemums (46x61cm-18x24in) s. board
£1436 $2600   (24-May-92 LIT.L106) Espresso (91x76cm-36x30in) s.
£2901 $5250   (21-May-92 GRO.B126/R) Fireside task (64x76cm-25x30in) s.

PEART, John (1945-) Australian
£1938 $3489   (24-Nov-91 SY.S486/R) Summer (122x99cm-48x39in) s.d.12/2/66 board
     (A.D 4400)
£2203 $3965   (24-Nov-91 SY.S397) Cool Corner II, 1968 (171x171cm-67x67in) acrylic
     canvas (A.D 5000)
£4637 $8625   (21-Jun-92 SY.ME60/R) Neelima (240x600cm-94x236in) s.i.d.1985verso
     acrylic four panels (A.D 11500)

PEASE, Ray (1908-) American
£500 $950   (26-Jun-92 WOL.C130) Sunday afternoon (41x36cm-16x14in) s. board

PEAT, Thomas (18th C) British
£1500 $2670   (27-Nov-91 C243/R) Portrait of Lady Charlotte Barbara Ferrars
     (8x?cm-3x?in) min.s. gold frame oval mono.hair verso

PECCHIO, Domenico (attrib) (1712-1759) Italian
£3925 $7458   (23-Jun-92 D.V21/R) View of lagoon with church, boats and figures
     (55x68cm-22x27in) (A.S 80000)

PECHAUBES, Eugene (1890-1967) French
£963 $1742   (22-May-92 LD.P9) Prix de l'Arc de Triomphe gagne par Oroso
     (33x55cm-13x22in) (F.FR 9500)
£1013 $1834   (22-May-92 LD.P8/R) Longchamp 1946, Prix du Jockey-Club gagne par Prince
     Chevalier (33x55cm-13x22in) s. (F.FR 10000)
£1114 $2017   (22-May-92 LD.P10) Longchamp 1954, Le Grand Criterium gagne par
     Beau-Prince (33x55cm-13x22in) s. (F.FR 11000)

PECHAUBES, Eugene (1890-1967) French-cont.

£1114	$2017	(22-May-92 LD.P11) 1957, Prix de L'Arc de Triomphe gagne par Oroso (33x55cm-13x22in) s. (F.FR 11000)
£1131	$1900	(1-Sep-91 PO.BA6) Militar a caballo (26x21cm-10x8in) s.
£1667	$2950	(22-Apr-92 CH.AM182/R) Le Grand Steeple Chase,Cannes 1931 (33x92cm-13x36in) s.d.1931 i. (D.FL 5500)
£1722	$3118	(22-May-92 LD.P13) Longchamp 1955, Le Grand Criterium gagne par Apollonia (33x55cm-13x22in) s.i. (F.FR 17000)
£1824	$3301	(22-May-92 LD.P12) Chantilly 1956, Prix de Diane gagne par Apollonio (33x55cm-13x22in) s.i. (F.FR 18000)
£1824	$3301	(22-May-92 LD.P14) Chantilly 1956, Prix du Jockey Club gagne par Philius (33x55cm-13x22in) s.i. (F.FR 18000)
£437	$765	(30-Mar-92 ZZ.F126) Les joueurs de Polo (48x64cm-19x25in) s.d.1926 crayon htd.W/C (F.FR 4200)

PECHSTEIN, Max (1881-1955) German

£9449	$16252	(16-Oct-91 G.Z147/R) Female nude standing by stove (29x22cm-11x9in) s.d.1905 tempera board (S.FR 24000)
£11888	$21161	(28-Nov-91 SY.BE12/R) Street in Paris (24x32cm-9x13in) mono.d.08 s.i.verso tempera over pencil (DM 34000)
£16434	$29252	(30-Nov-91 VG.B184/R) Fruit bowl (60x70cm-24x28in) mono.d.1930 s.i.verso (DM 47000)
£24000	$45840	(1-Jul-92 S136/R) Blumenstilleben en balustervase (97x69cm-38x27in) inits.d.1924
£33217	$59126	(28-Nov-91 SY.BE21/R) Hollyhocks in Chinese bronze vase Ku (81x71cm-32x28in) mono.d.1918 (DM 95000)
£40462	$70000	(2-Oct-91 SY.NY51/R) Madchen mit buch (99x75cm-39x30in) init. s.i.verso
£56993	$101448	(28-Nov-91 SY.BE13/R) Oranges (51x55cm-20x22in) mono.d.09 i.verso (DM 163000)
£61433	$111809	(29-May-92 VG.B33/R) Keitelkahne (70x80cm-28x31in) mono.d.1919 hessian (DM 180000)
£62937	$112028	(30-Nov-91 VG.B182/R) Baltic sea landscape with dunes (80x99cm-31x39in) s.d.34 s.i.d.verso (DM 180000)
£70370	$127370	(20-May-92 GK.Z5011/R) Monastery of San Gimignano (69x78cm-27x31in) mono.d.1914 (S.FR 190000)
£98592	$178451	(6-Dec-91 GB.B6941/R) Mouth of the Lupow (74x118cm-29x46in) s.d.1927 s.i.verso (DM 280000)
£170000	$324700	(29-Jun-92 C42/R) Meererzahlung (120x90cm-47x35in) mono.d.1920 s.d.verso
£1754	*$3158*	*(22-Nov-91 SA.A426/R) Hilly coastal landscape with boats (35x55cm-14x22in) s.d.1924 indian ink brush (DM 5000)*
£2098	*$3734*	*(30-Nov-91 VG.B165/R) Composition with figures (28x28cm-11x11in) mono.d.1912 mono.d.verso pen wash htd.white (DM 6000)*
£2560	*$4633*	*(23-May-92 GB.B7015/R) Peasants reaping (27x37cm-11x15in) s.d.1927 indian ink pen chk (DM 7500)*
£2749	*$4674*	*(25-Oct-91 BM.B1088/R) Still life of African sculpture (41x30cm-16x12in) mono.d.1912 W/C indian ink (DM 8000)*
£3468	*$6000*	*(2-Oct-91 SY.NY53/R) Reusen vor gehoft (23x30cm-9x12in) s.d.1927 col.crayon*
£4930	*$8923*	*(6-Dec-91 GB.B6942/R) Female nude seated (49x32cm-19x13in) mono.d.1914 carpenter's pencil (DM 14000)*
£5245	*$9336*	*(28-Nov-91 SY.BE29/R) Old age and youth (43x34cm-17x13in) mono.d.1918 chk chl wash (DM 15000)*
£5769	*$10962*	*(25-Jun-92 GK.B538/R) Beladen der Keitelkahne (51x37cm-20x15in) mono.d.1909 indian ink brush W/C (S.FR 15000)*
£6529	*$12079*	*(12-Jun-92 HN.H685/R) Still life with chrysanthemums and fan (37x51cm-15x20in) s.d.1917 W/C pencil (DM 19000)*
£12000	*$21720*	*(3-Dec-91 C151/R) Bluhende Obstbaume (50x62cm-20x24in) s.d.1928 W/C gouache wax crayon*
£12238	*$21783*	*(26-Nov-91 KF.M939/R) Rocky coastal landscape, Italy (24x33cm-9x13in) mono.d.1919 chk indian ink W/C (DM 35000)*
£12287	*$22362*	*(30-May-92 VG.B220/R) Fishing on high sea (25x34cm-10x13in) mono.d.1920 W/C pencil (DM 36000)*
£12587	*$22406*	*(30-Nov-91 VG.B183/R) Fisherman's house in Rowe (48x62cm-19x24in) s.d.1919 W/C over pencil paper on board (DM 36000)*
£15385	*$27385*	*(28-Nov-91 SY.BE64/R) Viaduct outside of Collioure (64x50cm-25x20in) s.d.1931 i.verso gouache over pencil (DM 44000)*
£22599	*$40000*	*(6-Nov-91 CH.NY135/R) Fruhling I (49x64cm-19x25in) s.i.d.1922 W/C over pencil*
£40956	*$74539*	*(29-May-92 VG.B34/R) Girl resting (44x60cm-17x24in) s.d.1921 W/C over pencil (DM 120000)*

PECHSTEIN, Max (attrib) (1881-1955) German

| *£492* | *$900* | *(16-May-92 HG.C126) Country landscape with church (23x30cm-9x12in) bears sig. W/C* |

PECRUS, Charles (1826-1907) French

£728	$1275	(5-Apr-92 CSC.P96) Conversation (21x16cm-8x6in) s. panel (F.FR 7000)
£1831	$3278	(17-Nov-91 FB.P157/R) Le the (24x18cm-9x7in) s.d.1855 or 56 panel (F.FR 18000)
£3597	$6871	(1-Jul-92 FB.P51/R) Gentilhomme en costume Louis XIII assis en train de peindre devant son chevalet (24x18cm-9x7in) s. panel (F.FR 35000)
£5046	$8629	(22-Mar-92 LT.P31/R) L'arrivee des visiteurs au chateau (61x46cm-24x18in) s. (F.FR 49000)
£5233	$9000	(17-Oct-91 SY.NY223/R) La plage a Trouville (27x45cm-11x18in) s.i. panel

PECRUS, Charles (1826-1907) French-cont.
£10989 $20000   (27-May-92 CH.NY62/R) Scene du Plage, Trouville (27x46cm-11x18in)
s.d.1875 panel

PECZARSKI, Feliks (1804-1862) Polish
£916 $1667   (15-Dec-91 REM.W29) Portrait of a man (24x19cm-9x7in) (P.Z 18000000)

PEDDIE, James Dick (fl.1885-1918) British
£700 $1176   (26-Aug-91 S1098/R) View from room in Rue de Varennes, Paris
(35x26cm-14x10in) s.i.d.1890verso board

PEDEMONTE, Adan (1896-1976) Argentinian
£781 $1500   (4-Aug-92 V.BA75) Naturaleza muerta (70x83cm-28x33in) tempera
£1146 $2200   (4-Aug-92 V.BA76) Paisaje serrano (90x110cm-35x43in)

PEDERSEN, Carl-Henning (1913-) Danish
£1802 $3099   (4-Mar-92 KH.K183) Red birds (45x125cm-18x49in) init. (D.KR 20000)
£2798 $4784   (12-Mar-92 RAS.K621/R) Sailing in heaven and trees (81x104cm-32x41in)
s.i.d.1952verso (D.KR 31000)
£11013 $19934   (20-May-92 KH.K56/R) The eyes of the summer (124x104cm-49x41in)
s.i.d.1990verso (D.KR 125000)
£13939 $25230   (21-May-92 SY.AM280/R) La dame et la ligorne avec l'oiseau jaune
(205x160cm-81x63in) s.i.d.1985verso (D.FL 46000)
£16975 $30895   (12-Dec-91 SY.AM199/R) Birds (70x100cm-28x39in) init.d.1943 verso
(D.FL 55000)
£34234 $58883   (4-Mar-92 KH.K122 h/R) Mother and children - Blue universe
(206x290cm-81x114in) s.i.d.1987verso (D.KR 380000)
£623 $1084   (17-Sep-91 RAS.K211/R) Blue horse (22x29cm-9x11in) init.d.46 Indian ink
W/C (D.KR 7000)
£623 $1084   (17-Sep-91 RAS.K209) Sunshine over town with figures (18x23cm-7x9in)
init. W/C (D.KR 7000)
£712 $1238   (17-Sep-91 RAS.K214/R) Crying man with hat (22x29cm-9x11in) init.d.46
Indian ink W/C (D.KR 8000)
£712 $1238   (17-Sep-91 RAS.K213/R) Woman with crown (22x29cm-9x11in) init.d.46 Indian
ink W/C (D.KR 8000)
£886 $1612   (25-May-92 RAS.K127/R) Bird (21x28cm-8x11in) init.d.39 crayon
(D.KR 10000)
£905 $1638   (4-Dec-91 KH.K179/R) Composition, Barbizon (46x35cm-18x14in) init.d.1977
W/C Indian ink (D.KR 10000)
£934 $1625   (17-Sep-91 RAS.K212/R) Woman with crown, blue bird and rabbit
(22x29cm-9x11in) init.d.46 Indian ink W/C (D.KR 10500)
£995 $1802   (4-Dec-91 KH.K3/R) Sunset (35x52cm-14x20in) init.d.1958 crayon
(D.KR 11000)
£1068 $1858   (17-Sep-91 RAS.K222/R) Figures (22x30cm-9x12in) init.d.45 pencil crayon
(D.KR 12000)
£1431 $2605   (10-Dec-91 RAS.K64/R) Riding on a bird (29x39cm-11x15in) init.d.41 crayon
(D.KR 16000)
£1512 $2632   (17-Sep-91 RAS.K208/R) Floating and nude figures with bird
(42x30cm-17x12in) init. Indian ink W/C (D.KR 17000)
£1690 $2941   (17-Sep-91 RAS.K215 a/R) Birds and figures in landscape (20x30cm-8x12in)
init.i. Indian ink gouache W/C (D.KR 19000)
£1991 $3604   (4-Dec-91 KH.K56/R) Birds (17x22cm-7x9in) crayon (D.KR 22000)

PEDERSEN, Finn (1944-) Danish
£546 $989   (23-May-92 KV.L244) Composition (57x39cm-22x15in) s.d.90 acrylic
(B.FR 33000)
£757 $1370   (19-May-92 AB.S5302/R) Composition (81x65cm-32x26in) s. (S.KR 8000)
£1483 $2639   (26-Nov-91 SY.MI32/R) Composizione (60x73cm-24x29in) s.d.77 s.d.verso
(I.L 3200000)

PEDERSEN, Holger Topp (1868-1938) Danish
£572 $990   (2-Sep-91 BU.K28/R) Beached boats near Agger (30x53cm-12x21in) s.d.93
(D.KR 6500)

PEDERSEN, Hugo Vilfred (1870-?) Danish
£856 $1490   (14-Apr-92 SY.AM47/R) Mountainous landscape (89x125cm-35x49in) s.
(D.FL 2800)
£893 $1555   (18-Sep-91 N.M646/R) Fireworks over Benares (110x82cm-43x32in) s.
(DM 2600)
£2646 $4709   (28-Apr-92 RAS.K67/R) View from Agra with figures and camels by temple
(190x270cm-75x106in) s.i. (D.KR 30000)

PEDERSEN, Ole (1856-1898) Danish
£529 $942   (27-Apr-92 BU.K10/R) Two women in field after harvest (55x78cm-22x31in)
(D.KR 6000)

PEDERSEN, Viggo (1854-1926) Danish
£539 $953   (11-Feb-92 RAS.K130) Landscape after sunset (30x40cm-12x16in) s.d.1872
(D.KR 6000)
£600 $1068   (30-Oct-91 ZZ.B112) View of a woodland (72x100cm-28x39in) s.d.1910
£624 $1161   (16-Jun-92 RAS.K210) Summer landscape with cattle grazing by fjord
(66x95cm-26x37in) s. (D.KR 7000)
£632 $1137   (19-Nov-91 RAS.K256) Road through Arild, August (45x65cm-18x26in) s.
(D.KR 7000)

PEDERSEN, Viggo (1854-1926) Danish-cont.
£851	$1541	(19-May-92 AB.S4367/R) Summer landscape with cliffs (45x66cm-18x26in) s.i.d.1913 (S.KR 9000)
£1232	$2070	(27-Aug-91 RAS.K510/R) Autumn landscape with young girls resting in shadow of large trees (86x155cm-34x61in) s.d.1879 (D.KR 14000)
£1426	$2453	(15-Oct-91 RAS.K203/R) Summer's day with thatched house, fence being mended (67x95cm-26x37in) s.d.1881 (D.KR 16000)
£1761	$2958	(28-Aug-91 KH.K159/R) Interior with the artist's wife reading (54x44cm-21x17in) s. (D.KR 20000)
£1923	$3500	(12-Dec-91 RAS.V760/R) Winter's day in a small town (39x57cm-15x22in) s. (D.KR 21500)

PEDERSEN, Vilhelm (1820-1859) Danish
£599	$1036	(2-Sep-91 BU.K27/R) Seascape with sailingvessel (24x34cm-9x13in) s.d.1849 (D.KR 6800)

PEDERSOLI, P (19th C) Italian
£580	$992	(17-Mar-92 PH200) Woman spinning yarn (36x30cm-14x12in) s.d.89

PEDONE, Antonio (1899-1973) Argentinian
£1075	$2000	(16-Jun-92 RO.BA107) Paisaje (26x33cm-10x13in)
£1075	$2000	(16-Jun-92 RO.BA106) Otono (30x34cm-12x13in)

PEDRA, Victor (20th C) Spanish?
£1091	*$2028*	*(16-Jun-92 EP.M53/R) Mujeres en el campo de golf (50x68cm-20x27in) s. mixed media (S.P 200000)*

PEDRETTI, Turo (1896-1964) Swiss
£3759	$6880	(4-Jun-92 SY.Z604/R) Garden table with straw hat (104x84cm-41x33in) s.d.56 s.i.d.verso (S.FR 10000)
£6015	$11008	(4-Jun-92 SY.Z608/R) Birthday table (75x75cm-30x30in) s.d.61 s.i.d.verso (S.FR 16000)
£1128	*$2064*	*(4-Jun-92 SY.Z575/R) Lago Viola di Campo (32x40cm-13x16in) mono.d.61 s.i.verso (S.FR 3000)*

PEDRINI, Filippo (1763-1856) Italian
£12996	$23393	(19-Nov-91 F.R161/R) Sofonisba riceve il veleno da Massinissa (153x246cm-60x97in) (I.L 28000000)

PEDRINI, Giovanni/RICCI, Gian Pietro see GIANPIETRINO

PEDRO EL MUDO (style) (?-1648) Spanish
£1200	$2304	(10-Jul-92 C220) Saints Margaret and Barbara (32x25cm-13x10in) panel

PEDULLI, Federigo (1860-?) Italian
£1397	*$2500*	*(13-Nov-91 B.SF2249/R) Il Cortile del Bargello a Firenze (76x53cm-30x21in) s. W/C board*

PEEL, James (1811-1906) British
£524	$1000	(16-Jul-92 SY.NY518/R) Witley, Surrey (61x101cm-24x40in) s.i.
£553	$996	(19-Nov-91 GS.B3615/R) Mountain landscape with cattle (25x38cm-10x15in) s. (S.FR 1400)
£650	$1183	(10-Dec-91 SWS122/R) The valley farm (38x59cm-15x23in) s.d.86
£900	$1611	(14-Jan-92 SWS138/R) Faggot gatherers by old mill (49x75cm-19x30in)
£1100	$2046	(18-Jun-92 B152 a) Figure on riverside path. Cattle watering (38x64cm-15x25in) s. pair
£1309	$2500	(16-Jul-92 SY.NY539/R) Travellers on country path (91x76cm-36x30in) s.
£1650	$2954	(14-Jan-92 SWS157/R) Cattle watering and resting in landscape (39x64cm-15x25in) mono.d.1859

PEEL, James (attrib) (1811-1906) British
£4000	$7080	(6-Nov-91 S64/R) Travelling companions (47x73cm-19x29in)

PEEL, Paul (1861-1892) Canadian
£1370	$2507	(14-May-92 SY.T129/R) Portrait of bearded gentleman (18x13cm-7x5in) s. canvas on board (C.D 3000)
£4000	$7080	(6-Nov-91 SY.T162/R) Woodland glade (32x39cm-13x15in) s.d.1890 canvas on board (C.D 8000)
£6000	$10620	(6-Nov-91 SY.T121/R) Lady Ross examining passion flower (74x56cm-29x22in) (C.D 12000)
£10959	$20055	(14-May-92 SY.T47/R) Portrait of Gloria Roberts (77x56cm-30x22in) s.d.1889 (C.D 24000)

PEELE, James (1847-1905) Australian
£601	$1004	(21-Aug-91 DS.W193 c) Untitled s.d.1891 (NZ.D 1750)
£687	$1148	(21-Aug-91 DS.W193 b) Mitre Peak, Milford s.d.1891 (NZ.D 2000)
£722	$1205	(21-Aug-91 DS.W153) Lake and mountain scene (49x89cm-19x35in) s.d.1900 (NZ.D 2100)
£978	$1672	(17-Mar-92 JRL.S201) Seascape with mountains (31x60cm-12x24in) s.d.1901 (A.D 2200)
£1443	$2410	(21-Aug-91 DS.W31/R) Stream in bush (34x43cm-13x17in) s.d.1873 (NZ.D 4200)
£4185	$7449	(26-Nov-91 J.M27/R) Alpine landscape (90x70cm-35x28in) s.d.1894 (A.D 9500)

EELLAERT, J (19th C) Belgian
£1835 $3193   (14-Apr-92 SY.AM89/R) Landscape with cattle and men in rowing-boat
                          (82x146cm-32x57in) s.i. (D.FL 6000)

EELOR, Harold (1856-1940) American
£1130 $2000   (12-Feb-92 B.SF494/R) Mission San Xavier del Bac, Tucson, Arizona
                          (71x102cm-28x40in) s. board

EERBOOM, Alfons (1882-1958) German
£1404 $2526   (22-Nov-91 SA.A1805/R) Interior (40x50cm-16x20in) s. i.verso (DM 4000)

EERDT, Ernst te (1852-1932) German
£1229 $2224   (21-May-92 L.K468/R) Lower Rhine landscape with view of farmhouses
                          amongst trees (30x39cm-12x15in) s. panel (DM 3600)
£1843 $3336   (21-May-92 L.K469) Still life of tomatoes on pewter plate with knife
                          (33x50cm-13x20in) s. panel (DM 5400)

EERLESS, Tom (19/20th C) Australian
£525   *$950*   *(4-Dec-91 DS.W66) Milford Sound (76x56cm-30x22in) s. W/C (NZ.D 1700)*
£864   *$1564*   *(4-Dec-91 DS.W67) Caswell Sound, Otago N.Z (55x75cm-22x30in) s.i. W/C*
                          (NZ.D 2800)

EETERS, Bonaventura (17/18th C) Flemish
£8000 $14240   (30-Oct-91 S121/R) Shipwreck (58x90cm-23x35in) mono. panel

EETERS, Bonaventura (circle) (17/18th C) Flemish
£843 $1500   (30-Oct-91 D.NY76) View of Mediterranian port (41x69cm-16x27in) canvas on
                          masonite

EETERS, Bonaventura (style) (17/18th C) Flemish
£880 $1531   (13-Sep-91 C25/R) View of Levantine coast with figures by classical
                          gateway and shipping (37x49cm-15x19in)

EETERS, Clara (circle) (1594-1657) Flemish
£1927 $3391   (11-Apr-92 AT.P39/R) Nature morte de volatiles (51x73cm-20x29in) panel
                          (F.FR 19000)

EETERS, Gillis (attrib) (1612-1653) Flemish
£4012 $7182   (12-Nov-91 SY.AM120/R) Shepherd with cattle and hermit beneath ruin
                          beyond (40x53cm-16x21in) panel (D.FL 13000)

EETERS, Jacob (style) (17th C) Flemish
£10000 $17800   (1-Nov-91 S383/R) Architectural capriccio of Levantine port with Arabs
                          and other figures (153x107cm-60x42in)

EETERS, Jacobus (1637-1695) Flemish
£5274 $9282   (11-Apr-92 AT.P52/R) Preparatifs de fete dans la cour d'un palais
                          (59x84cm-23x33in) traces sig. (F.FR 52000)

EETERS, Jan (1624-1680) Flemish
£7500 $13650   (10-Dec-91 PH17/R) Small craft in heavy seas (47x63cm-19x25in) init.
                          panel
£11050 $20000   (21-May-92 CH.NY46/R) Stormy seascape with shipping in distress and boat
                          foundering against rocky coastline (114x186cm-45x73in) init.

EETERS, Jan (attrib) (1624-1680) Flemish
£1600 $3072   (8-Jul-92 S178) Dutch shipping rough seas (35x45cm-14x18in) indis.s.
                          panel
£9700 $17266   (28-Apr-92 RAS.K27/R) Harbour scene with merchantmen returning home
                          (75x118cm-30x46in) (D.KR 110000)

EETERS, Jozef (1895-1960) Belgian
£667 $1174   (7-Apr-92 C.A555) Arrival of the fishermen (60x78cm-24x31in) s.
                          (B.FR 40000)

EGOT-OGIER, Jean Bertrand (1877-1915) French
£1119 $2048   (17-May-92 T.B200) Bord de mer (29x39cm-11x15in) s. (F.FR 11000)
£2060 $3522   (18-Mar-92 PIC.P87/R) Jeune bretonne sur la berge (36x49cm-14x19in)
                          st.sig. board (F.FR 20000)
£4273 $7819   (17-May-92 T.B201/R) Pardon de la Pietie au Pouldu (38x26cm-15x10in) s.
                          panel (F.FR 42000)
£1933   *$3537*   *(17-May-92 T.B64) La Gavotte bretonne (47x63cm-19x25in) s.d.1913 W/C*
                          (F.FR 19000)

EGURIER, Auguste (1856-1936) French
£559 $973   (15-Apr-92 CB.P29) Les martigues-le port des pecheurs (22x33cm-9x13in) s.
                          board (F.FR 5500)
£781   *$1343*   *(4-Mar-92 AT.P77) Saint Tropez (31x24cm-12x9in) s. pastel (F.FR 7600)*

EHRSON, Karl Axel (1921-) Swedish
£1152 $2084   (3-Dec-91 AB.S5132/R) Composition (46x33cm-18x13in) s. (S.KR 12000)
£1892 $3425   (19-May-92 AB.S5303/R) Neginia Excisa (34x26cm-13x10in) s. panel
                          (S.KR 20000)
£2657 $4861   (13-May-92 BU.S149/R) Thirteen-eyes and blue avicula (65x40cm-26x16in)
                          s.d.1969 (S.KR 28000)

PEHRSON, Karl Axel (1921-) Swedish-cont.

£2685	$4832	(19-Nov-91 GO.G142/R) 'Stora fallet, Attotio' (38x58cm-15x23in) s. acrylic (S.KR 28000)
£515	$906	(7-Apr-92 GO.G1165/R) Studie I (40x28cm-16x11in) s.d.48 pastel (S.KR 5400)
£631	$1123	(28-Oct-91 AB.S384) Studie II (23x30cm-9x12in) s.d.1947 W/C (S.KR 6700)

PEIFFER-WATENPHUL, Max (1896-1976) German

£10000	$18100	(3-Dec-91 C246/R) Venedig, Ca'di Desdeomona (78x61cm-31x24in) init.i.d.48
£11228	$20211	(21-Nov-91 L.K378/R) Still life on white (78x100cm-31x39in) canvas on panel (DM 32000)
£756	$1384	(3-Jun-92 L.K362/R) Townscape (25x15cm-10x6in) s.i.d.191 W/C over pencil (DM 2200)
£1481	$2681	(20-May-92 GK.Z5005/R) Cefalu (27x46cm-11x18in) i.d.1939 W/C (S.FR 4000
£2799	$5094	(26-May-92 KF.M1141/R) View of Canale Grande, Venice (43x30cm-17x12in) mono.i.d.1949 W/C (DM 8200)
£3147	$5601	(30-Nov-91 VG.B281/R) Rhodos, Temple in Lindos (28x40cm-11x16in) mono.d1964 W/C over pencil (DM 9000)
£3497	$6224	(26-Nov-91 KF.M946/R) Umbrian landscape (28x48cm-11x19in) s.i.D.1940 W/C (DM 10000)

PEINADO, Joaquin (1898-1975) Spanish

£3827	$7004	(13-May-92 FER.M166/R) Bahia de San Francisco (47x55cm-19x22in) s.d.71 (S.P 700000)
£385	$677	(9-Apr-92 ANS.M79/R) La recogida del heno (26x20cm-10x8in) s.d.62 W/C (S.P 70000)
£385	$677	(9-Apr-92 ANS.M78/R) Casona (23x31cm-9x12in) s. W/C (S.P 70000)
£463	$797	(7-Oct-91 ANS.M48/R) El estudio (32x24cm-13x9in) s.d.67 pencil dr (S.P 85000)
£465	$850	(13-May-92 FER.M97/R) La merienda (28x36cm-11x14in) s.d.62 W/C (S.P 85000)
£664	$1247	(16-Dec-91 ANS.M218/R) La recogida del heno (26x20cm-10x8in) s.d.21-8-62 W/C (S.P 120000)
£734	$1365	(17-Jun-92 I.N131) Vue d'un port (20x26cm-8x10in) studio st.d.73 W/C pencil (F.FR 7200)
£831	$1471	(12-Feb-92 ANS.M44/R) La Lampara (29x23cm-11x9in) s.d.63 W/C dr (S.P 150000)
£1090	$1875	(7-Oct-91 ANS.M52/R) La recogida del heno (26x20cm-10x8in) s.d.21-8-62 W/C (S.P 200000)
£1472	$2531	(7-Oct-91 ANS.M84/R) La estacion (43x33cm-17x13in) s. gouache (S.P 270000)

PEINER, Werner (1897-1981) German

| £2448 | $4234 | (25-Mar-92 KM.K1362/R) View of Spanish mountain town in evening glow (70x99cm-28x39in) s. mixed media canvas on board (DM 7000) |

PEIRANO (17th C) Italian

| £14365 | $26000 | (22-May-92 SY.NY259/R) Still life of flowers on stone ledge (72x86cm-28x34in) s. |

PEIRCE, Waldo (1884-1970) American

£536	$900	(14-Aug-91 B.P57/R) The Roman Forum (25x30cm-10x12in) s.d.24 Feb 12
£1310	$2200	(14-Aug-91 B.P56/R) The back yard (41x66cm-16x26in) s.i.d.18 April 49
£517	$900	(15-Apr-92 SY.NY212/R) Big pine (45x60cm-18x24in) s.i.d.1941 W/C

PEIRE, Luc (1916-) Belgian

£2089	$3551	(22-Oct-91 C.A271) Horizon (30x61cm-12x24in) mono.d.1955 panel (B.FR 125000)
£2980	$5394	(23-May-92 KV.L462/R) Don Ruiz (73x50cm-29x20in) s.verso (B.FR 180000)
£4177	$7101	(22-Oct-91 C.A267/R) San Miguel (85x116cm-33x46in) s.d.1962 verso (B.FR 250000)

PEISER, Kurt (1887-1962) Belgian

£510	$872	(21-Mar-92 KV.L223) In the cafe (33x24cm-13x9in) s. board (B.FR 30000)
£662	$1199	(23-May-92 KV.L249) On the quay (30x40cm-12x16in) s. canvas on panel (B.FR 40000)
£748	$1279	(21-Mar-92 KV.L226) On the beach (9x14cm-4x6in) s.d.1924 board (B.FR 44000)
£767	$1342	(24-Sep-91 GM.B578/R) La causerie (47x36cm-19x14in) s. (B.FR 46000)
£2318	$4195	(23-May-92 KV.L247) Beached boat (103x51cm-41x20in) s. (B.FR 140000)
£828	$1498	(23-May-92 KV.L248) The family (68x50cm-27x20in) chk. (B.FR 50000)
£1359	$2325	(21-Mar-92 KV.L222/R) In the cafe (73x52cm-29x20in) s. gouache pastel (B.FR 80000)

PEITHNER VON LICHTENFELS, Eduard (1833-1913) Austrian

£1504	$2722	(5-Dec-91 D.V100) South Tyrolean landscape (32x25cm-13x10in) s.d.1897 board (A.S 30000)
£1368	$2353	(10-Oct-91 D.V203/R) Path along the Danube near Durnstein (34x48cm-13x19in) s.d.1888 pen indian ink W/C (A.S 28000)
£1368	$2353	(10-Oct-91 D.V204/R) Church and graveyard of Durnstein (48x36cm-19x14in) s.i. pen indian ink W/C (A.S 28000)

PELAEZ, Amelia (1897-1968) Cuban

| £10497 | $19000 | (19-May-92 SY.NY192/R) Naturaleza muerta (61x65cm-24x26in) canvas mounted on panel |

PELAEZ, Amelia (1897-1968) Cuban-cont.
£14444 $26000   (18-Nov-91 SY.NY36/R) Nocturno (74x97cm-29x38in) s.d.1947

PELAYO, Orlando (1920-1990) Spanish
£818 $1406   (7-Oct-91 ANS.M185/R) Untitled (21x27cm-8x11in) s. paper (S.P 150000)
£818 $1406   (7-Oct-91 ANS.M186/R) Untitled (21x27cm-8x11in) s. paper (S.P 150000)
£1369 $2492   (25-May-92 ZZ.F84) Retrato (35x35cm-14x14in) s. (F.FR 13500)
£1443 $2497   (27-Mar-92 PPB.P60/R) Caravane (20x71cm-8x28in) s. (F.FR 14000)
£1546 $2675   (27-Mar-92 PPB.P61) Port d'Oran (26x34cm-10x13in) s. (F.FR 15000)
£5198 $9461   (11-Dec-91 FER.M195/R) Grande Vitesse (75x81cm-30x32in) s.d.1988
        (S.P 950000)
£6364 $10883   (17-Mar-92 FER.M173/R) La dama de Alcala (81x100cm-32x39in) s.
        s.i.d.1989verso (S.P 1150000)
£1417 $2438   (7-Oct-91 ANS.M183/R) Picador (23x29cm-9x11in) s. mixed media
        (S.P 260000)

PELGROM, Jacobus (1811-1861) Dutch
£2385 $4246   (30-Oct-91 CH.AM217) Quack in front of the inn In de Kroon
        (63x74cm-25x29in) s.d.1858 (D.FL 7800)

PELHAM, Thomas Kent (19th C) British
£650 $1203   (11-Jun-92 CSK204/R) At the spring (38x27cm-15x11in) s.
£1200 $2232   (18-Jun-92 B57) Spanish fruitseller. Fishergirl of Sebastien
        (29x19cm-11x7in) init. pair
£1400 $2604   (18-Jun-92 CSK237) Italian maid. At the well (38x28cm-15x11in) s. pair

PELLAN, Alfred (1906-1990) Canadian
£438 $784   (6-May-92 GD.B999/R) Descent from the Cross (23x33cm-9x13in) s. board
        (S.FR 1200)
£3980 $7085   (26-Nov-91 JOY.T77/R) Untitled composition (12x17cm-5x7in) s. col.ink
        wash (C.D 8000)
£4338 $7938   (14-May-92 SY.T189/R) Femmes au profil (20x18cm-8x7in) s. col.ink paper
        on panel (C.D 9500)

PELLEGRINI, Alfred Heinrich (1881-1958) Swiss
£1394 $2524   (5-Dec-91 SY.Z116/R) Female bathing (22x18cm-9x7in) mono. s.i.verso board
        oval (S.FR 3500)
£1504 $2752   (4-Jun-92 SY.Z576/R) Hyacinths II (50x38cm-20x15in) mono board
        (S.FR 4000)
£1880 $3440   (4-Jun-92 SY.Z597/R) Violets and apricot blossoms (44x36cm-17x14in)
        mono.d.1935 (S.FR 5000)
£1880 $3440   (4-Jun-92 SY.Z599/R) Bouquet of flowers with tulips (45x39cm-18x15in)
        mono.d.31 (S.FR 5000)
£2148 $3803   (5-Nov-91 GF.L2280/R) Portrait of Annemarie Nadolny. Study
        (58x71cm-23x28in) mono.d.1938 i.stretcher double-sided (S.FR 5500)
£2632 $4816   (4-Jun-92 SY.Z600/R) Autumnal still life with fruit and dead pheasant
        (50x73cm-20x29in) mono.d.51 pavatex (S.FR 7000)
£2632 $4816   (4-Jun-92 SY.Z606/R) Female nude (98x77cm-39x30in) s. cotton (S.FR 7000)
£3195 $5848   (4-Jun-92 SY.Z570/R) At 12 o'clock in the night after thunderstorm in
        Lappland (27x36cm-11x14in) mono.d.24 s.i.d.verso canvas on panel
        (S.FR 8500)
£3759 $6880   (4-Jun-92 SY.Z567/R) The wild horse (28x35cm-11x14in) mono.d.16 panel
        (S.FR 10000)
£4887 $8944   (4-Jun-92 SY.Z571/R) After the snowstorm (47x62cm-19x24in) s.d.52 pavatex
        (S.FR 13000)
£5639 $10320   (4-Jun-92 SY.Z593/R) Zeus coming to Joe (125x180cm-49x71in) s.d.1953
        (S.FR 15000)
£6203 $11352   (4-Jun-92 SY.Z566/R) Self portrait. Wrestling (70x100cm-28x39in) bears
        mono.d.13 board double-sided (S.FR 16500)
£8271 $15135   (4-Jun-92 SY.Z586/R) Table with flowers (67x52cm-26x20in) mono.d.33
        canvas on board (S.FR 22000)
£10526 $19263   (4-Jun-92 SY.Z568/R) Stream in winter (71x53cm-28x21in) s.d.1917 panel
        (S.FR 28000)
£12218 $22359   (4-Jun-92 SY.Z577/R) Die vier Weltteile, Europa (300x185cm-118x73in)
        s.d.21 (S.FR 32500)
£12218 $22359   (4-Jun-92 SY.Z580/R) Die vier Weltteile, Amerika (300x185cm-118x73in)
        mono.d.27 (S.FR 32500)
£12218 $22359   (4-Jun-92 SY.Z578/R) Die vier Weltteile, Asien (300x185cm-118x73in)
        s.d.27 (S.FR 32500)
£12218 $22359   (4-Jun-92 SY.Z579/R) Die vier Weltteile, Afrika (300x185cm-118x73in)
        s.d.26 (S.FR 32500)
£13158 $24079   (4-Jun-92 SY.Z591/R) Spring flowers with snowdrops and anemones
        (39x50cm-15x20in) mono.d.31 board (S.FR 35000)
£608 $1088   (15-Nov-91 ZOF.Z1834/R) Das dummste Madchen ... (30x22cm-12x9in) s.d.1908
        W/C (S.FR 1550)
£677 $1238   (4-Jun-92 SY.Z585/R) Allegory in blue (23x29cm-9x11in) mono.d.08 pencil
        gouache (S.FR 1800)
£677 $1238   (4-Jun-92 SY.Z607/R) Female nude with long hair seen from behind
        (38x29cm-15x11in) mono.d.20 pencil (S.FR 1800)
£940 $1720   (4-Jun-92 SY.Z558/R) Study of roses (40x55cm-16x22in) s.i.d.99 W/C pencil
        (S.FR 2500)
£1692 $3096   (4-Jun-92 SY.Z592/R) Still life with grapes (35x47cm-14x19in) mono.d.57
        dispersion board (S.FR 4500)

PELLEGRINI, Giacomo Antonio (18th C) Austrian
£8763 $15160   (27-Mar-92 CN.P56/R) Portrait de femme en habit de cour
                     (130x105cm-51x41in) s.i. (F.FR 85000)

PELLEGRINI, Giovanni Antonio (1675-1741) Italian
£15385 $29385   (15-Jul-92 CH.S761/R) Allegory of Age and Prudence - old man and girl
                     (71x54cm-28x21in) (A.D 40000)
£70000 $134400   (10-Jul-92 C56/R) Saint Mary Magdalen in penitence (119x94cm-47x37in)

PELLEGRINI, Giovanni Antonio (attrib) (1675-1741) Italian
£1963 $3729   (23-Jun-92 D.V181/R) The Holy Family with angel (131x137cm-52x54in)
                     (A.S 40000)
£2800 $4900   (3-Apr-92 C81/R) Triumph of Art over Envy (34x27cm-13x11in) painted arch

PELLEGRINI, Giovanni Antonio (circle) (1675-1741) Italian
£1200 $2100   (28-Feb-92 C5/R) Eve (52x42cm-20x17in)
£3000 $5460   (10-Dec-91 PH168 a) Allegory of arts (36x44cm-14x17in)

PELLEGRINI, Giovanni Antonio (style) (1675-1741) Italian
£1300 $2275   (25-Feb-92 PH54/R) Bacchus carrying ewer attended by fawn and putti
                     (50x34cm-20x13in)
£2600 $4550   (28-Feb-92 C21/R) The Continence of Scipio (76x60cm-30x24in)

PELLEGRINI, Riccardo (1863-1934) Italian
£2000 $3420   (17-Mar-92 PH208/R) Game of boules (32x24cm-13x9in) s. panel
£2207 $3951   (14-Nov-91 CH.R203) Fumatori di Narghile. Sentinelle nel deserto
                     (11x20cm-4x8in) s.d.1893 panel pair (I.L 4800000)
£2793 $5000   (6-May-92 CAS.M53/R) Moro (23x31cm-9x12in) panel
£6395 $11000   (17-Oct-91 SY.NY378/R) Ritorno all' ovile (35x49cm-14x19in) s. board
£6395 $11000   (17-Oct-91 SY.NY377/R) Ritorno delle oche (35x49cm-14x19in) s.
£916   *$1622*   *(7-Nov-91 F.M61/R) Scena all'osteria (34x23cm-13x9in) s.i.d.1911 W/C*
                     tempera (I.L 2000000)

PELLERIER, Maurice (1875-?) French
£573   *$1048*   *(3-Feb-92 SD.P173) Paris, Inondation Quai des Grands Augustins*
                     (34x49cm-13x19in) s.d.30 janvier 1910 W/C (F.FR 5600)

PELLETIER, Pierre-Jacques (1869-1931) French
£2791 $4800   (15-Oct-91 CE.NY273/R) Washerwoman by a riverbank (64x91cm-25x36in) s.
£907   *$1606*   *(10-Nov-91 ZZ.F105/R) Bord de Seine (52x72cm-20x28in) s. pastel*
                     (F.FR 9000)

PELLICCIOTTI, Tito (1872-1943) Italian
£632 $1126   (29-Nov-91 GAB.G2151/R) A l'etable (13x17cm-5x7in) s. panel (S.FR 1600)
£998 $1857   (16-Jan-92 F.M103) Vecchio pescatore. Popolana (27x16cm-11x6in) s. one
                     i.verso panel pair (I.L 2200000)
£3254 $5564   (19-Mar-92 F.M111/R) Interno di stalla con asinelli, pecore e galline
                     (54x89cm-21x35in) s. (I.L 7000000)
£3718 $6358   (19-Mar-92 F.M113/R) Festa di paese (31x53cm-12x21in) s. (I.L 8000000)
£4857 $8500   (20-Feb-92 SY.NY280/R) Young music makers (34x40cm-13x16in) s.

PELLICER, Rafael (1906-1963) Spanish
£606 $1084   (14-Nov-91 ANS.M102/R) El moro (46x38cm-18x15in) s. (S.P 110000)

PELOUSE, Leon Germain (1838-1891) French
£1040 $1809   (14-Apr-92 SY.AM460) Woman in landscape (24x33cm-9x13in) s. board
                     (D.FL 3400)
£1127 $2039   (4-Dec-91 DO.H2876/R) Village street (28x40cm-11x16in) s. (DM 3200)
£1185 $2145   (19-May-92 GF.L2507/R) Old watermill (54x65cm-21x26in) s. (S.FR 3200)
£1336 $2298   (4-Mar-92 AT.P182) Les chenes a Rochefort en Terre (55x38cm-22x15in) s.
                     (F.FR 13000)
£3670 $6532   (30-Oct-91 CH.AM245/R) Wooded landscape with mother and child on shady
                     path carrying faggots (55x76cm-22x30in) s. (D.FL 12000)
£5025 $8945   (29-Oct-91 PH.T158/R) Figure in landscape (64x90cm-25x35in) s.
                     (C.D 10000)

PELS, Albert (1910-) American
£541 $1000   (10-Jun-92 CE.NY509/R) Rush hour (51x76cm-20x30in) s. panel
£640 $1100   (7-Mar-92 LAE.L147/R) Coney Island bather (61x46cm-24x18in) s.
                     d.1938verso
£782 $1400   (14-Nov-91 CE.NY354/R) Waiting room train station (30x41cm-12x16in) s.
£1117 $2000   (14-Nov-91 CE.NY376) Three black musicians (48x68cm-19x27in) s. panel

PELTON, Agnes (1881-?) American
£737   *$1400*   *(26-Jun-92 WOL.C125/R) Iris (51x36cm-20x14in) s. W/C*
£1453   *$2600*   *(14-Nov-91 CE.NY306/R) Gladiolas (89x74cm-35x29in) s. W/C*

PELUSO (19th C) Italian
£1890 $3289   (18-Sep-91 N.M647/R) Cavalier and servant girl before barrel in wine
                     cellar (60x45cm-24x18in) s. (DM 5500)

PELUSO, Francesco (1836-?) Italian
£872 $1500   (9-Oct-91 RO.BA575) Explicaciones amables (27x39cm-11x15in) s.
£1399 $2420   (25-Mar-92 KM.K1364) Figures wearing rococo costumes in park landscape
                     (106x66cm-42x26in) s. (DM 4000)

PENA Y MUNOZ, Maximino (1863-1940) Spanish
£1642 $2989   (26-May-92 DUR.M79/R) Pensando (53x73cm-21x29in) s. pastel (S.P 300000)
£3597 $6151   (17-Mar-92 FER.M137/R) Madre e hija (76x61cm-30x24in) s. pastel
     (S.P 650000)

PENA, Jose Encarnacion (1902-) American
£865 $1600   (14-Jun-92 S.BM241/R) Los Matachines (30x43cm-12x17in) s. gouache

PENA, Tonita (1895-1949) American
£973 $1800   (14-Jun-92 S.BM217/R) Eagle dancers (23x30cm-9x12in) s. gouache
£1027 $1900   (14-Jun-92 S.BM159/R) Corn dancers with drummer (28x41cm-11x16in) s.
     gouache

PENAGOS ZALABARDO, Rafael de (1889-1954) Spanish
£464 $798   (16-Oct-91 FER.M154/R) Dama leyendo el periodico, portada de la novela de
     Lola Mendez (51x32cm-20x13in) s.d.1925 gouache (S.P 85000)

PENCK, A R (1939-) German
£3352 $6000   (6-May-92 CH.NY231/R) Untitled (52x84cm-20x33in) s. acrylic paper
£5237 $8902   (27-Oct-91 P.V104/R) Sans titre (150x200cm-59x79in) s. acrylic board
     (F.FR 52000)
£7716 $14043   (12-Dec-91 SY.AM300/R) M.L. 4 (50x70cm-20x28in) (D.FL 25000)
£19553 $35000   (5-May-92 CH.NY157/R) Das rote Flugzeug (150x150cm-59x59in) i.
     s.i.d.1977stretcher
£23000 $43930   (2-Jul-92 C66/R) Untitled (102x121cm-40x48in) s.d.82 acrylic canvas
£27000 $48870   (5-Dec-91 C54/R) Deutschland nach der Mauer (100x200cm-39x79in) s.
     dispersion
£33520 $60000   (7-May-92 SY.NY127/R) Konzept - first draft (175x119cm-69x47in) masonite
£36000 $65160   (5-Dec-91 C44/R) Important meeting, number 1 (250x330cm-98x130in) acrylic
£50279 $90000   (5-May-92 CH.NY152/R) Standart 3 (150x150cm-59x59in)
£69832 $125000   (13-Nov-91 SY.NY5/R) Untitled (285x285cm-112x112in)
£950 $1644   (26-Mar-92 S105/R) Untitled (42x29cm-17x11in) s.d.60 chl
£1124 $2000   (29-Apr-92 G.Z99/R) Untitled (42x29cm-17x11in) s.d.1962 chl (S.FR 3000)
£1228 $2211   (19-Nov-91 L.K995/R) Dresden breweries (42x59cm-17x23in) mono.d.1966
     pencil collage (DM 3500)
£1229 $2236   (30-May-92 VG.B894/R) The hand in the green woman (42x60cm-17x24in) s.
     col.felt tip pen (DM 3600)
£1536 $2795   (30-May-92 VG.B895/R) Composition with red nude (42x59cm-17x23in) s.
     col.felt tip pen (DM 4500)
£1570 $2857   (30-May-92 VG.B896/R) Discussion (42x59cm-17x23in) s. col.felt tip pen
     (DM 4600)
£1843 $3354   (30-May-92 VG.B897/R) Head of woman and female nude (42x59cm-17x23in) s.
     col.felt tip pen (DM 5400)
£3333 $6033   (19-May-92 CH.AM276/R) Cosmic II (98x68cm-39x27in) s. gouache
     (D.FL 11000)
£3497 $6224   (25-Nov-91 WK.M795/R) Composition (41x51cm-16x20in) s. W/C (DM 10000)
£8591 $14948   (21-Sep-91 SA.A620/R) Untitled (54x83cm-21x33in) s. mixed media
     (DM 25000)

PENCZ, Georg (1500-1550) German
£20000 $36400   (11-Dec-91 S42/R) Lucretia (82x68cm-32x27in) s.d. panel

PENCZ, Georg (circle) (1500-1550) German
£780 $1498   (8-Jul-92 PH276/R) Seated nude woman holding blazing object with putto
     standing next to her (16x10cm-6x4in) pen wash over graphite htd white

PENDER, Jack (1918-) British
£500 $890   (28-Nov-91 L192) Stop Gap - punt and wave forms (51x69cm-20x27in)
     s.d.1959 board
£800 $1400   (27-Sep-91 C106 a/R) High and Dry (51x76cm-20x30in) s. board
£1200 $2196   (14-May-92 C139/R) Clinker punt (61x122cm-24x48in) s. s.i.d.1967 verso
     board

PENDL, Erwin (1875-?) Austrian
£679 $1235   (27-May-92 D.V664/R) Linienkapelle auf der Lerchenfelder Linie
     (21x33cm-8x13in) s. W/C (A.S 14000)
£777 $1383   (29-Apr-92 D.V666/R) City Hall of Vienna, winter (28x18cm-11x7in) s. W/C
     (A.S 16000)
£1499 $2697   (21-Nov-91 D.V190/R) Hochzeitsbrunnen am Hohen Markt (40x22cm-16x9in)
     s.d.1912 W/C shaped top (A.S 30000)

PENE DU BOIS, Guy (1884-1958) American
£958 $1600   (20-Aug-91 RB.HY214/R) Portrait of young woman (28x20cm-11x8in) s.d.36
     paper
£4286 $7500   (26-Sep-91 CH.NY172/R) Portrait of Patrick Henry Bruce (101x81cm-40x32in)
     s.
£13105 $23196   (7-Nov-91 AT.P68/R) Sunburned nude (139x114cm-55x45in) s.d.34
     (F.FR 130000)
£60000 $105000   (26-Sep-91 CH.NY249/R) Sin twisters (51x38cm-20x15in) s.d. panel
£800 $1400   (26-Sep-91 CH.NY235/R) Garden (26x21cm-10x8in) s.d. pencil
£1277 $2400   (18-Dec-91 SY.NY352/R) Nude (38x34cm-15x13in) s. gouache
£2571 $4500   (26-Sep-91 CH.NY230/R) Patience (39x34cm-15x13in) s.d. W/C ink
£3714 $6500   (26-Sep-91 CH.NY234/R) Seated woman. Nude study (54x36cm-21x14in) s.
     pencil pen double-sided

PENE DU BOIS, Guy (1884-1958) American-cont.
£10989 $20000   (28-May-92 CH.NY216/R) Ladies of fashion, Fourteenth Street
(39x33cm-15x13in) s. chl.pen W/C gouache board

PENE DU BOIS, Yvonne (1913-) American
£492 $900   (6-Jun-92 LAE.L125/R) Fisherman (33x56cm-13x22in) s.d.

PENE, Varlene (1916-1990) Russian
£662 $1211   (3-Jun-92 ARC.P180/R) Le balcon (58x68cm-23x27in) s. (F.FR 6500)
£2016 $3528   (24-Sep-91 ARC.P225/R) Vue de la terrasse (80x70cm-31x28in) s. verso
(F.FR 20000)

PENFIELD, Edward (1866-1925) American
£2431 $4400   (24-May-92 LIT.L92) Boy and girl in tulip fields, Holland
(53x76cm-21x30in) s. board
£899 $1600   (2-May-92 IH.NY165/R) Horses walking along Spanish road (20x30cm-8x12in)
mono W/C
£1966 $3500   (2-Nov-91 IH.NY186/R) Knight on horseback (41x43cm-16x17in) s. ink W/C

PENFOLD, Frank C (19th C) American
£525 $950   (21-May-92 S.W2435/R) Gathering marsh hay (66x74cm-26x29in) s.

PENKOAT (1945-) French
£815 $1491   (3-Jun-92 CSC.P152) Composition (106x75cm-42x30in) s. acrylic collage
board (F.FR 8000)

PENKOAT, Pierre (1945-) French
£833 $1508   (4-Dec-91 CSC.P310) Composition (147x65cm-58x26in) s. oil collage panel
(F.FR 8100)

PENLEY, E A (fl.1853-1872) British
£440 $788   (12-Nov-91 OT710/R) Cadir Idris from across lake with mill and figures
before (35x74cm-14x29in) s.d. W/C

PENN, Salome (20th C) ?
£1518 $2702   (29-Apr-92 D.P152/R) The yellow flowers (90x65cm-35x26in) s.d.85
(F.FR 15000)

PENNACCHI, Gerolamo da (style) (1497-1544) Italian
£4070 $7000   (9-Oct-91 CH.NY184/R) Adoration of shepherds (72x86cm-28x34in)

PENNASILICO, Giuseppe (1861-1940) Italian
£2069 $3704   (14-Nov-91 CH.R189) Modella nuda in posa (24x31cm-9x12in) s. panel
(I.L 4500000)
£2179 $3900   (11-Nov-91 GC.M73) Ninos con paraguas rojos (104x70cm-41x28in) s. pastel

PENNE, Olivier de (1831-1897) French
£1093 $2000   (5-Jun-92 SY.NY194/R) Apres la chasse (32x24cm-13x9in) s. panel
£2235 $4000   (13-Nov-91 B.SF2195/R) Beagles after the hunt (46x37cm-18x15in) s.indist.
cradled panel
£2600 $4420   (26-Oct-91 TA.B1) Hounds by a boundary post in a wooded landscape
(38x35cm-15x10in) s. board
£2989 $5410   (22-May-92 BL.P83/R) Les retrievers (55x46cm-22x18in) s. panel
(F.FR 29500)
£3409 $6000   (9-Apr-92 FA.PH579/R) Hounds at rest (41x28cm-16x11in) s. panel
£400 $768   (29-Jul-92 CSK2) The meet (11x17cm-4x7in) s. pencil W/C htd. white
£1000 $1920   (28-Jul-92 SWS55/R) Two pointers in landscape (23x33cm-9x13in) s. W/C
over pencil
£1155 $2090   (4-Dec-91 NA.BA47) Chiens (16x25cm-6x10in) s. W/C sepia

PENNELL, Harry (19th C) British
£1000 $1710   (19-Mar-92 B131) Groomsbridge. The Old cottage (61x41cm-24x16in) s.
i.verso pair
£1000 $1730   (24-Mar-92 PHC398) View in Aber Valley (92x71cm-36x28in) s. i.verso

PENNELL, Joseph (1860-1926) American
£638 $1200   (18-Dec-91 SY.NY146/R) The Canongate Edinburgh (35x25cm-14x10in)
indis.s.i.d.1882 gouache India ink pencil
£1163 $2000   (13-Oct-91 H.C9/R) Long night - New York harbour (25x33cm-10x13in) s. W/C
£1163 $2000   (13-Oct-91 H.C10/R) White afternoon - view of New York harbour with
Statue of Liberty (23x30cm-9x12in) s. W/C

PENNEY, James and LEVINE, David (20th C) American
£1086 $1900   (26-Sep-91 CH.NY265/R) Dressmakers. Beach scene (41x61cm-16x24in) one
s.d. pastel one oil masonite pair

PENNI, Luca (1500-1556) Italian
£12000 $21840   (10-Dec-91 C190/R) Diana and Callisto (40x29cm-16x11in) i. blk.chk.ink
wash htd.white

PENNY, Edward (attrib) (1714-1791) British
£3500 $6510   (16-Jun-92 SWS271/R) Gentleman said to be Mr Prattinton of Bewdley aged
68 standing (42x28cm-17x11in) i.

PENNY, Edwin (?) British?
£680 $1210   (27-Apr-92 PHB226) Two young magpies on branch (50x36cm-20x14in) s. W/C bodycol
£850 $1513   (27-Apr-92 PHB225/R) Magpies on fence (51x36cm-20x14in) s. W/C bodycol
£3500 $6125   (25-Feb-92 C108/R) Hobby (36x50cm-14x20in) s. W/C bodycol
£3800 $6650   (25-Feb-92 C136/R) Grouse among heather (51x37cm-20x15in) s. pencil W/C htd white
£3800 $6650   (25-Feb-92 C137/R) Partridges at edge of field (51x37cm-20x15in) s. pencil W/C htd white
£4800 $8400   (25-Feb-92 C138/R) Cock pheasant (50x71cm-20x28in) s. W/C bodycol

PENNY, F James (fl.1849-1919) British
£500 $900   (22-Nov-91 C16/R) Single ship action between USS Chesapeake and HMS Shannon, 1813 (22x29cm-9x11in) init.i.d.1813 pencil W/C htd.white

PENNY, William D (1834-1924) British
£2400 $4248   (14-Feb-92 DA842) Hull Whale and Sea Co. 'Diana' stranded off Greenland in pack ice (76x48cm-30x19in) s.d.1889

PENSIONANTE DEL SARACENI (after) (17th C) Italian
£28000 $49840   (1-Nov-91 C52/R) Denial of Saint Peter (101x119cm-40x47in)

PENSTONE, Edward (fl.1871-1896) British
£1550 $2837   (3-Jun-92 S292/R) Reverie (22x17cm-9x7in) s. W/C

PENTECHIN, Ivan (1927-) Russian
£540 $1005   (17-Jun-92 ARC.P204/R) Les lilas au soleil (65x85cm-26x33in) s. (F.FR 5300)

PEOLI, Juan Jorge (19th C) Spanish
£3488 $6000   (16-Oct-91 CH.NY166/R) A family surveying a Dam, Cuba (90x126cm-35x50in) s.

PEPINO, Anton Josef (1863-1921) Austrian
£485 $864   (29-Apr-92 D.V912/R) Italian vegetable market (11x20cm-4x8in) s. panel (A.S 10000)

PEPLOE, Samuel John (1871-1935) British
£20000 $34800   (11-Sep-91 PHG65/R) Still life with three carnations (46x55cm-18x22in) s.

PEPLOE, Samuel John (1871-1935) British-cont.
£30000 $53400   (1-May-92 PHE65/R) Still life of roses in vase. Still life of fruit, rose
                             and tea caddy (56x51cm-22x20in) s. double-sided
£35000 $62650   (13-Nov-91 CG661/R) Pink roses in a Japanese Vase with oranges and a fan
                             on a draped table (51x41cm-20x16in) s.

PEPPER, Beverly (1924-) American
£2206 $3750   (23-Oct-91 B.SF3716/R) Street people (100x85cm-39x33in) s. s.i.d.verso

PEPPER, Charles Hovey (1864-?) American
£676   *$1210*   *(14-Nov-91 GRO.B174/R) Landscape with tree (48x30cm-19x12in) s. gouache*

PEPPER, George Douglas (1903-1962) Canadian
£1700 $3009   (6-Nov-91 SY.T15/R) Winter sunlight in lumber town (30x36cm-12x14in) s.
                             board (C.D 3400)

PEQUEUX, Guy (1942-) French
£661   *$1184*   *(17-Nov-91 R.P114/R) Les montagnes rouges (100x100cm-39x39in) s. mixed*
                             media canvas (F.FR 6500)

PERAHIM, Jules (20th C) French
£712 $1303   (14-May-92 BG.P89) Composition (81x116cm-32x46in) s. (F.FR 7000)

PERAIRE, Paul Emmanuel (1829-1893) French
£1407 $2547   (19-May-92 GF.L2514/R) River landscape with rowing boat (35x68cm-14x27in)
                             s. (S.FR 3800)
£1923 $3327   (25-Mar-92 KM.K1365/R) River landscape with shipping, Northern France
                             (29x55cm-11x22in) s. (DM 5500)
£2240 $3853   (20-Oct-91 I.N93/R) Nogent-sur-Marne (31x61cm-12x24in) s. (F.FR 22200)
£3010 $5750   (16-Jul-92 SY.NY346/R) Sur la Riviere (43x85cm-17x33in) s.d.1879

PERAKOS, A (?) Greek
£800 $1360   (23-Oct-91 S149/R) The Parthenon (58x88cm-23x35in) s.

PERBOYRE, Paul Emile Leon (19/20th C) French
£553 $996   (22-Nov-91 EA.Z135) The roll call (19x24cm-7x9in) s.i. panel (S.FR 1400)
£730 $1300   (22-Jan-92 SY.NY393/R) Les Morocains dans les combles (46x55cm-18x22in)
                             s.
£787 $1400   (22-Jan-92 SY.NY418/R) Les Allemands rejetes par la cavalerie Francaise
                             hors des faubourgs de St. Quentin (46x55cm-18x22in) s.d.1918
£787 $1400   (22-Jan-92 SY.NY416/R) Otages delivres dans un village aux environs de
                             Munster - Alsace (46x55cm-18x22in) s.
£787 $1400   (22-Jan-92 SY.NY415/R) Prise d' une batterie Allemande (54x65cm-21x26in)
                             s.d.1919
£899 $1600   (22-Jan-92 SY.NY403/R) Convoi de prisonniers en Picardie
                             (46x55cm-18x22in) s.d.1917
£899 $1600   (1-Nov-91 PO.BA14) Soldado a caballo (33x24cm-13x9in) s. panel
£899 $1600   (22-Jan-92 SY.NY417/R) Artillerie Allemande suprise par des cuirassiers
                             Francais (50x61cm-20x24in) s.d.1914
£1011 $1800   (22-Jan-92 SY.NY419/R) Artillerie Allemande prise dans le village
                             d'Estrees (53x65cm-21x26in) s.d. panel
£1067 $1900   (22-Jan-92 SY.NY394/R) Combat de cavalerie dans Balschwiller
                             (55x65cm-22x26in) s. d.1916 stretcher
£1067 $1900   (22-Jan-92 SY.NY392/R) Artillerie de 75 en batterie (46x55cm-18x22in)
                             s.indist.d.
£1292 $2300   (22-Jan-92 SY.NY401/R) La cavalerie Anglaise s'emparant de Morlan-Court
                             (46x55cm-18x22in) s.d.1919
£1404 $2500   (22-Jan-92 SY.NY395/R) La sortie de la tranchee 2eme vague
                             (46x55cm-18x22in) s.d.1917
£2473 $4500   (28-May-92 SY.NY169/R) Les cuirassiers (31x23cm-12x9in) s. panel
£3327 $5888   (10-Nov-91 ZZ.F129/R) Amazone et cavalier (38x46cm-15x18in) s.
                             (F.FR 33000)

PERCEVAL, John (1923-) Australian
£1233 $2220   (24-Nov-91 SY.S96) Crouching angel (69x43cm-27x17in) s.d.1960 paper on
                             board (A.D 2800)
£2128 $3766   (26-Apr-92 SY.ME323) Woman knitting (70x54cm-28x21in) s. i.verso canvas
                             on board (A.D 5000)
£2863 $5097   (26-Nov-91 J.M131 a) Vegetable patch (59x75cm-23x30in) s. (A.D 6500)
£3846 $6846   (28-Apr-92 CH.ME248/R) Snow falling on Two Chums Mine (74x96cm-29x38in)
                             s. s.i.d.86verso (A.D 9000)
£7048 $12687   (24-Nov-91 SY.S447/R) Forest (100x80cm-39x31in) s.d.60 canvas on board
                             (A.D 16000)
£7981 $13329   (19-Aug-91 SY.ME292/R) Crab eunuch (74x100cm-29x39in) s.d.89 i.verso
                             (A.D 17000)
£17512 $30470   (16-Sep-91 CH.ME152/R) Marguerites (62x77cm-24x30in) s.d.40 (A.D 38000)
£385   *$685*   *(28-Apr-92 CH.ME62) Portrait of lady at exhibition (29x32cm-11x13in)*
                             s.i.d.66 ink after John Brack (A.D 900)
£385   *$685*   *(28-Apr-92 CH.ME44) Hermia Boyd sewing (37x29cm-15x11in) s. pencil*
                             (A.D 900)
£485   *$863*   *(26-Nov-91 J.M1205) Milking time (36x48cm-14x19in) s. pencil (A.D 1100)*
£513   *$913*   *(27-Apr-92 J.M1203) Children eating in playground (26x21cm-10x8in) s.d.44*
                             pencil dr (A.D 1200)

PERCEVAL, Matthew (1945-) Australian
£524 $917   (30-Mar-92 AAA.S136) Spring blossom (75x61cm-30x24in) s. (A.D 1200)
£594 $1039   (23-Sep-91 AAA.S150 b) Yellow boat and seagull (51x61cm-20x24in) s.
     (A.D 1300)
£639 $1119   (23-Sep-91 AAA.S119) Illawarra Bush (76x62cm-30x24in) s. (A.D 1400)
£684 $1238   (2-Dec-91 AAA.S132) Still life of springs bounty (76x66cm-30x26in) s.
     (A.D 1600)
£685 $1199   (23-Sep-91 AAA.S136) Spring blossom (60x75cm-24x30in) s. (A.D 1500)
£705 $1276   (2-Dec-91 AAA.S60) Black boy in rainforest (76x66cm-30x26in) s.
     (A.D 1650)

PERCIER, Charles (1764-1838) French
£2793 $5000   (14-Jan-92 SY.NY174) *Capriccio of classical sculpture (51x41cm-20x16in)*
     pen wash

PERCIER, Charles (circle) (1764-1838) French
£1700 $2890   (23-Oct-91 S116/R) *Obelisk. Column (54x41cm-21x16in) i.verso pen wash*
     over pencil two

PERCIER, Charles and FONTAINE, Pierre Francois L (attrib) (18th C) French
£916 $1675   (15-May-92 AT.P192) *Vue d'une place italienne (27x37cm-11x15in) pen W/C*
     (F.FR 9000)

PERCIVAL, Phyllis M (20th C) Canadian
£594 $1086   (14-May-92 SY.T197/R) Lunenberg harbour (60x75cm-24x30in) s. (C.D 1300)

PERCY, Arthur (1886-1976) Swedish
£950 $1652   (13-Apr-92 AB.S212) Oland landscape, cloudy day (64x45cm-25x18in)
     s.d.1969 (S.KR 10000)
£1708 $3125   (13-May-92 BU.S148/R) Wild flowers (46x32cm-18x13in) s. panel
     (S.KR 18000)
£2687 $4864   (3-Dec-91 AB.S5133/R) Girl with oranges in interior (57x47cm-22x19in) s.
     (S.KR 28000)
£4698 $8456   (23-Nov-91 SO.S574/R) Still life of flowers in vases (99x60cm-39x24in)
     s.d.1968 (S.KR 49000)

PERCY, Hudson J (19th C) British
£520 $889   (18-Mar-92 CSK95) Young gentleman standing with golden retreiver and
     landscape beyond (36x28cm-14x11in) s.d.1843 pencil W/C htd.white

PERCY, Sidney Richard (1821-1886) British
£1418 $2567   (20-May-92 I.N167/R) Lac en Grande-Bretagne, circa 1870 (46x92cm-18x36in)
     s. panel (F.FR 14000)
£1585 $2662   (28-Aug-91 KH.K163/R) Highland landscape with cattle by mountain lake
     (61x100cm-24x39in) s. (D.KR 18000)
£1800 $3132   (11-Sep-91 MMB354/R) Lyn Llydaw (58x79cm-23x31in) s.d.1882
£2200 $4136   (19-Dec-91 C108/R) The Lledyr Valley, North Wales (27x46cm-11x18in)
     s.d.1867
£2400 $4104   (13-Mar-92 C105/R) Countryfolk, cattle and sheep in lake landscape
     (61x102cm-24x40in) s.
£2752 $5037   (1-Jun-92 W.T1317 a) Rydal Water with cattle and anglers (24x46cm-9x18in)
     s. (C.D 6000)
£2800 $4816   (11-Oct-91 C44/R) Milkmaid crossing ford, with sheep and cattle beyond
     (54x89cm-21x35in) s.d.1857
£3000 $5340   (28-Nov-91 B188 b) Highland lock scene with cattle watering
     (23x38cm-9x15in) s.d.1872
£4300 $8170   (24-Jun-92 MMB329/R) The Valley of the Conwy near Bettws-y-Coed, N.Wales
     (36x58cm-14x23in) s.d.1873
£4500 $8550   (23-Jun-92 PH111/R) Winter on the Stour (41x66cm-16x26in) s.
£5000 $9550   (20-Jul-92 WW18/R) Cattle fording river (25x38cm-10x15in) s.
£7200 $12960   (19-Nov-91 PH41/R) Fisherfolk and punts on river (50x76cm-20x30in)
     s.d.1850
£8257 $15110   (3-Jun-92 R.T153/R) Young travellers and pony resting in extensive
     Highland landscape with flock and cattle (61x96cm-24x38in) s.d.1877
     (C.D 18000)
£8721 $15000   (16-Oct-91 CH.NY246/R) Llambries Lake, North Wales (64x96cm-25x38in)
     s.d.1856
£10000 $18000   (19-Nov-91 PH42/R) Stepping stones (66x97cm-26x38in) s.d.68
£10989 $20000   (28-May-92 SY.NY278/R) No. 1 Road to Rhaiads Dam near Maentwrog, North
     Wales (91x146cm-36x57in) s.d.1862 s.i.stretcher

PERCY, Sidney Richard (attrib) (1821-1886) British
£3000 $5220   (12-Sep-91 CSK160/R) Blea Tarn, Westmorland (24x38cm-9x15in) bears sig.

PEREBOOM, Frans (1897-1969) Belgian
£510 $872   (21-Mar-92 KV.L227) Polare landscape (23x30cm-9x12in) s. panel
     (B.FR 30000)

PEREDA, Antonio de (attrib) (1599-1669) Spanish
£1600 $2848   (29-Oct-91 PH26) St. Jerome (119x89cm-47x35in)

PEREGO, Eugenio (1845-1923) Italian
£2419 $4500   (17-Jun-92 CAS.M51) Joven Compositora (82x60cm-32x24in)
£665 $1150   (29-Mar-92 MY.F73/R) The repast (43x28cm-17x11in) s. W/C board

PEREHUDOFF, William (20th C) Canadian?
£2752 $5037   (2-Jun-92 R.T578/R) AC - 78 - 25 (136x143cm-54x56in) s.verso acrylic
                  canvas (C.D 6000)

PERESI, Francesco (18th C) Italian
£1650 $2888   (1-Apr-92 S169) Archangel Michael (23x15cm-9x6in) mono. copper

PERETTI, Jean Michel (?) ?
£515 $968   (18-Dec-91 LGB.P164) Nature morte pain et poterie (24x33cm-9x13in) board
                  (F.FR 5000)

PEREYRA, Vicente I (1893-?) Argentinian
£843 $1500   (1-Nov-91 PO.BA51) Paisaje (70x99cm-28x39in) s.

PEREZ DE VILLAAMIL, Genaro (1807-1854) Spanish
£2200 $3850   (3-Apr-92 C134) Spanish landscape with travellers conversing on path,
                  hilltop fort (65x88cm-26x35in) s.
£12038 $21910   (11-Dec-91 FER.M136/R) Interior de la catedral de Burgos
                  (55x44cm-22x17in) s.d.1837 (S.P 2200000)
£13000 $23660   (29-May-92 C350/R) Bull fight. Casa del Rey D. Pedro en Alcala de Henares
                  one s.i.d.1852verso one s.i.verso metal pair
£26813 $47726   (29-Oct-91 EP.M6/R) Paisajes con figuras (63x78cm-25x31in) one s. one
                  s.d.1827 pair (S.P 4900000)
£655 $1126   (16-Oct-91 FER.M66/R) Veleros y vapor siguiendo el curso del rio
                  (24x35cm-9x14in) s.d.1834 chl dr (S.P 120000)
£711 $1295   (11-Dec-91 FER.M39/R) Mercado de la Paja de Madrid (22x27cm-9x11in) s.
                  pencil dr (S.P 130000)
£819 $1408   (16-Oct-91 FER.M65/R) Aldea de los Alpes (29x45cm-11x18in) s. chl dr
                  (S.P 150000)
£928 $1596   (16-Oct-91 FER.M67/R) Cruzando el puente en una aldea de los Alpes
                  (29x47cm-11x19in) s. chl dr (S.P 170000)

PEREZ VILLALTA, Guillermo (20th C) Spanish
£2828 $5033   (28-Apr-92 EP.M30/R) Untitled (105x74cm-41x29in) init.d.1988 board
                  (S.P 520000)

PEREZ, Alonzo (fl.1893-1914) Spanish
£734 $1306   (30-Oct-91 CH.AM86) The suitor (27x21cm-11x8in) s. panel (D.FL 2400)
£6105 $10500   (17-Oct-91 SY.NY370/R) Intermission at opera (40x32cm-16x13in) s. panel

PEREZ, Bartolomeo (attrib) (1634-1693) Spanish
£5658 $10242   (5-Dec-91 SY.MO343/R) Bouquet de fleurs (65x46cm-26x18in) (F.FR 55000)

PEREZ, Bartolomeo (circle) (1634-1693) Spanish
£7800 $14196   (11-Dec-91 S130/R) Still life of flowers in sculpted vase upon ledge
                  (83x58cm-33x23in)

PEREZ-VILLAGROSA, Mariano Alonso see ALONSO-PEREZ, Mariano

PERFALL, Erich Freiherr von (1882-1961) German
£830 $1578   (24-Jun-92 KM.K1215) Sunrise in Lower Rhine landscape (41x50cm-16x20in)
                  s. (DM 2400)

PERGER, Anton Chevalier de (1809-1876) Austrian
£1306 $2272   (17-Sep-91 FN.S2475/R) Capitulation of Leipzig during Thirty Year War
                  (95x80cm-37x31in) s.d.1844 (DM 3800)

PERICOLI, Tullio (1936-) Italian
£1827 $3179   (14-Apr-92 F.M48) Cosa c'e sulle pietre corrose (100x70cm-39x28in)
                  s.i.verso mixed media collage canvas on panel (I.L 4000000)

PERICONI, D F (20th C) American
£520 $900   (29-Mar-92 MY.F141/R) Vanity (74x41cm-29x16in) s.

PERIGAL, Arthur (jnr) (1816-1884) British
£1500 $2880   (28-Jul-92 SWS326/R) Cattle and angler in wooded river landscape
                  (39x59cm-15x23in) s.d.1864 arched
£2100 $3801   (5-Dec-91 CG299/R) Ben Eiach, Glen Torridon (71x160cm-28x63in) s.d.1865
                  indis.i.verso
£5800 $9744   (26-Aug-91 S779/R) Old bridge in Glenlivet, Banffshire - destroyed by
                  floods in 1829 (66x100cm-26x39in) s.d.1853 s.i.label stretcher

PERILLI, Achille (1927-) Italian
£1901 $3460   (25-May-92 CH.R57/R) Replica uno (30x40cm-12x16in) s.d.68 s.i.d.verso
                  thinned oil (I.L 4200000)
£2043 $3636   (29-Apr-92 F.F271/R) Composizione (40x49cm-16x19in) s.d.1971
                  (I.L 4500000)
£2514 $4777   (23-Jun-92 F.M104/R) Il falso Senufo (60x60cm-24x24in) s.d.1988
                  s.i.d.1988verso acrylic (I.L 5500000)
£4866 $8661   (26-Nov-91 SY.MI135/R) Opera per la dissimulazione (65x81cm-26x32in)
                  s.d.88 s.i.d.verso acrylic (I.L 10500000)
£5097 $9073   (26-Nov-91 SY.MI177/R) Il privilegio dell'oscurita (81x100cm-32x39in)
                  s.d.83 s.i.d.verso acrylic (I.L 11000000)
£815 $1483   (26-May-92 SY.MI72/R) Composizione (25x43cm-10x17in) s.d.84 W/C
                  (I.L 1800000)

PERILLI, Achille (1927-) Italian-cont.

£1126	$2050	(25-May-92 WK.M994/R) La voglia di vivere (60x40cm-24x16in) s.d.1964 s.d.verso mixed media canvas (DM 3300)
£1187	$2042	(7-Oct-91 RY.P96/R) Festoso in diagonale (67x76cm-26x30in) gouache (F.FR 11800)
£1399	$2490	(25-Nov-91 WK.M800/R) L'incanto della pelle (35x50cm-14x20in) s.d.1963 s.d.verso mixed media canvas (DM 4000)
£2177	$3985	(12-Mar-92 F.R204/R) Comics code (40x60cm-16x24in) s.d.1970 s.d.verso mixed media (I.L 4800000)
£3394	$6178	(26-May-92 SY.MI207/R) La parodia della forma (100x81cm-39x32in) s.d.69 s.i.d.verso mixed media canvas (I.L 7500000)
£4634	$8248	(26-Nov-91 SY.MI163/R) Il fallo solare (100x81cm-39x32in) s.d.71 s.i.d.verso oil mixed media canvas (I.L 10000000)
£11315	$20593	(26-May-92 SY.MI226/R) La diversita degli spiriti (150x150cm-59x59in) s.d.61 s.i.d.verso oil mixed media canvas (I.L 25000000)

PERILLO, Gregory (1932-) American?

£575	$1000	(15-Apr-92 SY.NY221/R) Blackfoot brave (61x76cm-24x30in) s.
£829	$1500	(7-Dec-91 LAE.L38/R) In enemy territory (76x76cm-30x30in) s.d.85

PERIN-SALBREUX, Lie Louis (1753-1817) French

£1399	$2533	(22-May-92 L.K1106/R) Portrait of Furstin Amalia Gallitzin and daughter in park landscape (7cm-3ins circular) min.d.1809 (DM 4100)
£2037	$3687	(21-May-92 SY.G22) Portrait of lady seated reading book (6cm-2ins circular) min.s. stamped gilt metal mount (S.FR 5500)
£6296	$11396	(21-May-92 SY.G26/R) Portrait of Monsieur de Desaugiers (7cm-3ins circular) min. ormulu frame (S.FR 17000)

PERIS BRELL, J (19th C) Spanish

£5000	$8900	(27-Nov-91 S331/R) Matador. Picador. Toreador (68x48cm-27x19in) two s.d.86 one s.d.1887 three

PERIS, J (19th C) Spanish

£850	$1479	(11-Sep-91 PHG38) The Toreador (67x47cm-26x19in) s.i.d.1887
£1300	$2262	(11-Sep-91 PHG45/R) The picador (54x34cm-21x13in) s.d.86 other i. pair

PERKINS, Christopher (1891-1968) British

£537	$962	(6-May-92 DS.W47/R) Trinity Bridge (59x89cm-23x35in) init. i.verso (NZ.D 1800)
£412	$689	(21-Aug-91 DS.W11) Aboriginal man (28x20cm-11x8in) init. chl (NZ.D 1200)

PERKINS, Granville (1830-1895) American

£1064	$2000	(18-Dec-91 SY.NY16/R) Seascape. Woodland landscape with waterfall (55x45cm-22x18in) s.d.1894 pair
£2595	$4800	(10-Jun-92 CE.NY218/R) Sailing on rough seas (30x45cm-12x18in) s.d.1891
£489	$850	(15-Apr-92 SY.NY26/R) Stormy coast (28x70cm-11x28in) s.d.1890 W/C gouache board

PERKINS, Mary Smyth (1875-1931) American

£4396	$8000	(28-May-92 CH.NY186/R) Summer day, Lake Solitude (76x91cm-30x36in)
£7692	$14000	(28-May-92 CH.NY185/R) Boys bathing in the canal, New Hope (76x91cm-30x36in) s.d.07

PERKO, Anton (1833-1905) Austrian

£586	$1008	(10-Oct-91 D.V213/R) Sailing ship in rough sea (31x48cm-12x19in) s. W/C (A.S 12000)

PERLASCA, Martino (1860-1899) Swiss

£5495	$10000	(27-May-92 CH.NY73/R) Still life of assorted flowers (113x85cm-44x33in) s.

PERLBERG, Friedrich (1848-1921) German

£920	$1638	(28-Nov-91 CSK11/R) Evening in Cairo (66x97cm-26x38in) s.i. pencil W/C bodycol
£950	$1691	(28-Nov-91 CSK12/R) Jerusalem from the Mount of Olives (53x71cm-21x28in) s.i. pencil W/C htd.white

PERLBERG, Georg (1807-1884) German

£9756	$17756	(12-Dec-91 L.K648/R) View from window of Nurnberger Burg over the town (41x33cm-16x13in) s.d.1861 (DM 28000)

PERLIN, Bernard (1918-) American

£747	$1300	(15-Apr-92 SY.NY262/R) Gas station (33x56cm-13x22in) s.d.1945 tempera paper
£760	$1300	(13-Mar-92 S.BM314/R) Under the Queensboro Bridge (46x48cm-18x19in) s. tempera board
£2128	$4000	(18-Dec-91 SY.NY428/R) Divorce (62x45cm-24x18in) s. tempera board
£12155	$22000	(6-Dec-91 CH.NY219/R) Autumn leaves (101x76cm-40x30in) s.d.1947 tempera board

PERMAN, Louise E (?-1921) British

£1600	$2848	(28-Apr-92 S310/R) Still life of roses (61x51cm-24x20in) s. oval

PERMEKE, Constant (1886-1951) Belgian

£1852	$3370	(11-Dec-91 CH.AM309) Winter landscape (49x70cm-19x28in) s. (D.FL 6000)

PERMEKE, Constant (1886-1951) Belgian-cont.
£6173 $11235   (11-Dec-91 CH.AM265/R) Fishing boat in Oostende Harbour (56x73cm-22x29in)
                            s. (D.FL 20000)
£9259 $16852   (12-Dec-91 SY.AM39/R) Landscape (64x90cm-25x35in) s. (D.FL 30000)
£10606 $19197   (19-May-92 CH.AM187/R) Haystack and farm in landscape (60x80cm-24x31in)
                            s. (D.FL 35000)
£18349 $32294   (7-Apr-92 C.A197/R) Snowy landscape (65x75cm-26x30in) s. (B.FR 1100000)
£1212 $2194   (21-May-92 SY.AM99/R) Farmhouses (48x58cm-19x23in) s. chl (D.FL 4000)
£1698 $3090   (12-Dec-91 SY.AM104/R) Landscape with trees (61x78cm-24x31in) s. chl
                            (D.FL 5500)
£6623 $11987   (23-May-92 KV.L484/R) Seated woman (100x70cm-39x28in) s. pastel
                            (B.FR 400000)
£6954 $12586   (23-May-92 KV.L423/R) Standing nude (121x84cm-48x33in) s. chl. chk.
                            (B.FR 420000)

PERMEKE, Paul (1918-1990) Belgian
£530 $960   (7-Dec-91 KV.L255) Snowy landscape with blue light (40x50cm-16x20in) s.
                            panel (B.FR 31000)
£1504 $2556   (22-Oct-91 C.A870) Landscape (80x100cm-31x39in) s. (B.FR 90000)

PERNES, Leo (19/20th C) ?
£759 $1351   (29-Apr-92 D.P154/R) Pardon a Notre Dame de la joie, Pemarch
                            (65x81cm-26x32in) s. (F.FR 7500)

PERNET, Jean Henry Alexandre (1763-?) French
£530 $980   (12-Jun-92 ARC.P157) Caprice d'architecture (23x19cm-9x7in) pen indian
                            ink oval (F.FR 5200)
£1629 $3014   (12-Jun-92 ARC.P156) Marines (21cm-8ins circular) pen wash htd white
                            (F.FR 16000)
£3189 $5773   (3-Dec-91 CN.P29/R) Temple en ruine avec personages. Temple en ruine et
                            personnages devant une fontaine (28x43cm-11x17in) pen W/C pair
                            (F.FR 31000)

PERNET, Jean Henry Alexandre (attrib) (1763-?) French
£2400 $4368   (10-Dec-91 C224/R) A path through a wood with a grotto decorated with
                            Frescoes (34x49cm-13x19in) i. blk.chk.W/C

PERNHARDT, Marcus (1828-1871) Austrian
£4449 $7785   (20-Feb-92 D.V394/R) Waterfall in mountain landscape (47x35cm-19x14in) i.
                            panel (A.S 90000)

PERRACHON, Andre (1827-1909) French
£2535 $4462   (6-Apr-92 GGL.L4/R) Bouquet de roses (54x65cm-21x26in) s. (F.FR 25000)
£9500 $16910   (27-Nov-91 S243/R) Still life of vase summer flowers (115x87cm-45x34in)
                            s.d.1857

PERRACHON, Andre (attrib) (1827-1909) French
£1011 $1800   (30-Oct-91 D.NY14) Still life of flowers, grapes, butterfly and bird's
                            nest on marble ledge (33x36cm-13x14in) gouache

PERRATT, Marthe (19/20th C) French
£1053 $1800   (12-Mar-92 MFA.C125) Mothers' helpers (46x38cm-18x15in) s.

PERRAULT, Leon (1832-1908) French
£1099 $2000   (26-May-92 CE.NY315/R) Young woman holding feather fan (112x86cm-44x34in)
                            s.d.1889
£5714 $10000   (19-Feb-92 CH.NY61/R) Battling boys (96x129cm-38x51in) s.d.1889

PERREGAUX, Suzanne (19th C) Swiss
£720 $1267   (9-Apr-92 S177/R) Portrait of gentleman, wearing black coat and waistcoat
                            and jabot (7cm-3ins circular) min. gilt mount lacquer frame

PERRET, Aime (1847-1927) French
£1429 $2500   (18-Feb-92 CE.NY37/R) La Sieste des Faneuses (51x61cm-20x24in) s.d.1925
£3198 $5500   (16-Oct-91 CH.NY79/R) A day of labour (81x66cm-32x26in) s.
£3962 $7250   (3-Feb-92 S.SL363/R) Field labour (81x66cm-32x26in) s.

PERRET, Cles (19th C) French
£1124 $2000   (1-Nov-91 PO.BA15) Retrato de Napoleon Bonaparte (160x90cm-63x35in)

PERRET, Henri-Francois (1820-?) French
£2218 $3925   (10-Nov-91 ZZ.F126/R) Paysage anime de pecheurs (60x73cm-24x29in) s.
                            panel (F.FR 22000)

PERRETT, John Douglas (1859-1937) New Zealander
£1375 $2296   (21-Aug-91 DS.W59) Mitre and Lion Peaks, Harrison's Cove, Milford Sound
                            (89x166cm-35x65in) s. (NZ.D 4000)

PERRIER, Alexandre (1862-1936) Swiss
£2314 $3933   (23-Oct-91 GD.B579/R) Spring in Cologny with flowering trees by Lac Leman
                            (60x92cm-24x36in) mono. (S.FR 5900)

PERRIER, Emilio Sanchez see SANCHEZ-PERRIER, Emilio

PERRIER, Francois (1584-1650) French
£18000 $32760   (13-Dec-91 C55/R) Bacchanalian revel by classical sarcophagus (87x107cm-34x42in)

PERRIN, Jean Charles Nicaise (1754-1831) French
£10000 $17800   (27-Nov-91 S179/R) La generosite de Scipio (81x99cm-32x39in) indist.i.verso

PERRINE, Dearing van (1869-1955) American
£1086 $1900   (22-Feb-92 YFA.M153/R) Sunset near Hudson (28x36cm-11x14in) s. board

PERRON, Charles Clement Francis (1893-1958) French
£620 $1110   (14-Jan-92 SWS241) Le pain de seigle (18x23cm-7x9in) s. i.stretcher
£916 $1602   (5-Apr-92 ZZ.F114/R) Nu en buste (21x15cm-8x6in) s. panel (F.FR 8800)

PERRON, Louis Paul (1919-) Canadian
£585 $1054   (19-Nov-91 FP.M157) Retour a la maison (48x63cm-19x25in) s. pastel (C.D 1200)

PERRONEAU, Jean Baptiste (1715-1783) French
£55444 $98135   (7-Nov-91 AT.P75/R) Portrait de Madame Miron (64x53cm-25x21in) s.d.1771 (F.FR 550000)
£2364 $4515   (3-Jul-92 SD.P97) Portrait d'homme en buste (58x48cm-23x19in) pastel (F.FR 23000)

PERRY, Adelaide (1891-1973) Australian
£879 $1590   (19-May-92 JRL.S181/R) Still life with fruits (49x59cm-19x23in) s.d.1928 (A.D 2100)
£2423 $4361   (24-Nov-91 SY.S300/R) Rushcutters Bay (44x34cm-17x13in) s.d.1927 s.i.verso plywood (A.D 5500)

PERRY, Enoch Wood (1831-1915) American
£4094 $7000   (11-Mar-92 SY.NY19/R) Reading paper. Tending fire (18x23cm-7x9in) s.d.77 pair

PERRY, Lilla Cabot (1848-1933) American
£722 $1300   (22-Nov-91 S.BM130/R) Mauve hills (25x36cm-10x14in) s.

PERRY, W (19th C) British
£1500 $2700   (19-Nov-91 PH129/R) Who is coming (92x67cm-36x26in) s.d.68

PERSEUS, Edward (1841-1890) Swedish
£943 $1670   (5-Nov-91 BA.S153/R) Two sisters (115x82cm-45x32in) s. (S.KR 10000)

PERSOGLIA, Franz von (attrib) (1852-1912) Austrian
£643 $1125   (20-Feb-92 D.V370) Lake landscape (46x72cm-18x28in) (A.S 13000)

PERSSON, Folke (1905-1964) Swedish
£623 $1122   (19-Nov-91 GO.G138) Landscape from Styrso (49x57cm-19x22in) s. (S.KR 6500)
£626 $1146   (12-May-92 GO.G135) Gothenburg harbour in winter (55x46cm-22x18in) s. (S.KR 6600)

PERSSON, P A (1862-1914) Swedish
£570 $1021   (16-Nov-91 FAL.M286/R) Lake landscape (27x38cm-11x15in) s. (S.KR 6000)
£953 $1678   (11-Apr-92 FAL.M337/R) Ducks on cliff (34x46cm-13x18in) s. (S.KR 10000)

PERSSON, Peter Adolf (1862-1914) Swedish
£1536 $2779   (3-Dec-91 AB.S4652/R) Wooded landscape with cromlech by water (96x148cm-38x58in) s. (S.KR 16000)

PERSSON, Ragnar (1905-) Swedish
£1132 $2004   (25-Apr-92 SO.S570/R) Harvesters (21x26cm-8x10in) mono. (S.KR 12000)
£1235 $2148   (13-Apr-92 AB.S213) French street scene, Paris (33x24cm-13x9in) s. (S.KR 13000)
£1419 $2569   (19-May-92 AB.S5304/R) At the bus stop (27x34cm-11x13in) s. panel (S.KR 15000)
£1536 $2779   (3-Dec-91 AB.S5136/R) Parisian street scene (29x20cm-11x8in) s. (S.KR 16000)
£1698 $3006   (25-Apr-92 SO.S569/R) By the window (36x44cm-14x17in) mono. panel (S.KR 18000)
£1708 $3125   (12-May-92 GO.G137) Portrait of girl (51x38cm-20x15in) init. (S.KR 18000)
£1823 $3300   (3-Dec-91 AB.S5134/R) Market day (28x37cm-11x15in) s. panel (S.KR 19000)
£2015 $3648   (3-Dec-91 AB.S5135/R) Interior with couple (33x41cm-13x16in) s. panel (S.KR 21000)
£2397 $4314   (19-Nov-91 GO.G143) Figures by horse and cart (38x44cm-15x17in) init. s.verso panel (S.KR 25000)
£2657 $4861   (13-May-92 BU.S151/R) In the waiting room (32x41cm-13x16in) init. s.verso panel (S.KR 28000)
£7590 $13890   (11-May-92 NOR.S87/R) Bride and groom (66x90cm-26x35in) init. s.d.1960verso (S.KR 80000)
£14395 $25335   (11-Apr-92 FAL.M335/R) Interior with three women seated at table (89x115cm-35x45in) s.d.48/49 (S.KR 151000)

PERUVIAN SCHOOL, 18th C
£8840 $16000   (19-May-92 SY.NY71/R) Virgen de Copacabana (135x153cm-53x60in)

PERUZZINI, Antonio Francesco (circle) (1668-?) Italian
£6932 $12893   (19-Jun-92 CN.P48/R) Paysage anime de personnages (94x133cm-37x52in)
                   (F.FR 68000)

PERUZZINI, Giovanni (1629-1694) Italian
£5431 $9885   (28-May-92 F.M122/R) Paesaggio con cacciatori e viandanti
                  (103x130cm-41x51in) (I.L 12000000)

PERUZZINI, Giovanni (attrib) (1629-1694) Italian
£700 $1274   (10-Dec-91 C24) *The martyrdom of Saints Cosmas and Damian*
                 (38x28cm-15x11in) i. blk.chk.ink wash

PESCE, Pietro (17th C) Italian
£5926 $10726   (19-May-92 GF.L2016/R) Candlelit tavern interior (42x50cm-17x20in) s.
                   (S.FR 16000)

PESCHERET, Leon (1892-1961) American
£550 $925   (14-Aug-91 B.P71/R) *Martha's vineyard (15x18cm-6x7in) s. W/C*

PESCHKA, Anton (1885-1940) Austrian
£2234 $3977   (28-Nov-91 D.V118/R) Photographer in landscape (55x68cm-22x27in) s.d.1932
                  (A.S 45000)
£631 $1123   (28-Apr-92 D.V237) *Hoarfrost near the Wurzenhof at Wolfsgraben,*
                 Tullnerbach, Wienerwald (34x48cm-13x19in) s.i.d.1927 mixed media
                 (A.S 13000)

PESCI, Girolamo (attrib) (1684-1759) Italian
£8591 $14948   (18-Sep-91 N.M441/R) Biblical scene with Moses, Aaron and the Israelites
                   collecting manna (50x98cm-20x39in) (DM 25000)

PESICOVA, Jaroslava (1935-) Czechoslovakian
£1490 $2651   (29-Nov-91 D.V152/R) Bohemian memories (145x165cm-57x65in) s.d.90
                  (A.S 30000)

PESKE, Geza (1859-1934) Hungarian
£642 $1175   (3-Jun-92 R.T129/R) Feeding geese (26x32cm-10x13in) s. (C.D 1400)

PESKE, Jean (1870-1949) French
£1433 $2551   (27-Nov-91 AT.P180) Bord de mer mediterraneen (27x46cm-11x18in) s. panel
                  (F.FR 14000)
£2064 $3510   (24-Oct-91 D.P141) Nature morte aux cepes (54x65cm-21x26in) s.
                  (F.FR 20500)
£4370 $7604   (19-Apr-92 ZZ.F103/R) La pointe de Gouron et la plage du Lavandou
                  (42x55cm-17x22in) s. (F.FR 43000)

PESNE, Antoine (attrib) (1683-1757) French
£2081 $3642   (30-Mar-92 ZZ.F62) Portrait d'une Dame de quality en Cleopatre
                  (116x92cm-46x36in) (F.FR 20000)

PESNE, Antoine (circle) (1683-1757) French
£1657 $3000   (21-May-92 CH.NY213/R) Elegant lady having fortune told, surrounded by
                  attendants (95x130cm-37x51in) 214/R
£3164 $5885   (16-Jun-92 SY.B247/R) Portrait of Johan Roeleman von Quadt
                  (75x60cm-30x24in) i.verso (B.FR 190000)

PESNE, Antoine (style) (1683-1757) French
£859 $1495   (18-Sep-91 N.M442/R) Johanna Elisabeth Furstin zu Anthalt-Zerbst
                 (78x66cm-31x26in) i.verso (DM 2500)
£1484 $2627   (5-Nov-91 GF.L2409/R) Portrait of young nobleman (81x65cm-32x26in)
                  (S.FR 3800)
£1650 $2871   (13-Sep-91 C18/R) Ceres with putto and shepherd (60x46cm-24x18in)

PESSONEAUX, L (?) ?
£4200 $7140   (23-Oct-91 S86/R) Town by the sea, Italy (74x106cm-29x42in) s.

PETER, Axel (1863-1942) Swedish
£800 $1425   (28-Oct-91 AB.S195) View from Skeppsholmen, Stockholm (94x149cm-37x59in)
                 s.d.1886 (S.KR 8500)

PETER, Emanuel (1799-1873) Austrian
£874 $1555   (29-Apr-92 D.V721/R) *Portrait of young lady and clouds beyond*
                 (9x7cm-4x3in) min.s. W/C oval in leather case (A.S 18000)
£1400 $2562   (2-Jun-92 S715) *Lady wearing white gown. Gentleman wearing black coat*
                 (8x?cm-3x?in) min.s.d.1851 oval pair framed
£1942 $3456   (29-Apr-92 D.V722/R) *Portrait of young lady before drapes (10x8cm-4x3in)*
                 min.s.d.835 W/C oval (A.S 40000)

PETER, Johann Wenzel (1742-1829) German
£1224 $2166   (7-Nov-91 D.V315/R) Portrait of Archbishop Cardinal Migazzi of Vienna
                  standing by table (138x99cm-54x39in) s. (A.S 25000)
£75000 $144000   (8-Jul-92 S62/R) Adam and Eve surrounded by all the animals of Paradise
                     in landscape (200x254cm-79x100in) indis.s.d.17..

ETER, Johann Wenzel (attrib) (1745-1829) German
£8000 $15360   (10-Jul-92 C298/R) Peacock, turkey and rabbit by classical column
                     (103x127cm-41x50in)

ETER, Johann Wenzel (circle) (1745-1829) German
£10500 $20160   (10-Jul-92 C299/R) Poultry in landscape (112x133cm-44x52in)

ETER, Wenceslaus see PETER, Johann Wenzel

ETERELLE, Adolphe (1874-1947) French
£611 $1130   (11-Jun-92 ARC.P11/R) Charrette en charge (41x33cm-16x13in) s.
                     (F.FR 6000)
£866 $1601   (11-Jun-92 ARC.P12) La danse en foret (F.FR 8500)

ETERS, A (?) ?
£488 $888   (12-Dec-91 N.M2814/R) Farmhouse by pond (50x81cm-20x32in) s. (DM 1400)

ETERS, Anna (1843-1926) German
£1831 $3314   (3-Dec-91 FN.S2378) Flower bed in garden (26x19cm-10x7in) s. (DM 5200)
£4296 $7474   (17-Sep-91 FN.S2477/R) Roses in vase on white drape (50x38cm-20x15in) s.
                     (DM 12500)
£5498 $9567   (17-Sep-91 FN.S2476) Spring flowers in pot and willow basket on grass
                     floor (50x73cm-20x29in) s. oval board on panel (DM 16000)
£5965 $10200   (13-Mar-92 FN.S2902/R) Still life of fruit with basket on wooden table
                     (66x57cm-26x22in) s. oval (DM 17000)
£7509 $13666   (27-May-92 PH.DU32/R) Peonies (40x50cm-16x20in) s. (DM 22000)
£8286 $14500   (20-Feb-92 SY.NY208/R) Still life with flowers and lace (60x50cm-24x20in)
                     s.
£14334 $26089   (27-May-92 PH.DU33/R) Still life of summer flowers and raspberries. Still
                     life of winter flowers and fir branches (66x57cm-26x22in) s. oval pair
                     (DM 42000)

ETERS, Carl W (1897-1988) American
£1143 $2000   (23-Sep-91 S.SL78) New England town (51x61cm-20x24in) s.

ETERS, Hela (1885-?) German
£3436 $6392   (20-Jun-92 BM.B1064/R) Young woman reading seated in armchair in garden
                     (84x96cm-33x38in) s.d.1914 (DM 10000)

ETERS, Matthew William (?-1814) British
£1676 $3000   (13-Nov-91 B.SF2213/R) Portrait of young lady holding bouquet of flowers
                     (86x63cm-34x25in)

ETERS, Pieter Francis (1818-1903) Dutch
£5282 $9560   (3-Dec-91 FN.S2379/R) Lake Thun landscape (81x105cm-32x41in) s.d.1902
                     (DM 15000)
£489 $840   (10-Oct-91 D.V217/R) Rainy landscape with Hopfenau near Fuss
                     (42x63cm-17x25in) s.i. W/C (A.S 10000)
£550 $957   (17-Sep-91 FN.S2479) Schloss Langenburg in Hohenlohe (30x23cm-12x9in)
                     s.i. W/C over pencil (DM 1600)
£1031 $1887   (2-Jun-92 FN.S2698/R) Lake Constance and view of Lindau (22x38cm-9x15in)
                     s.d.1849 W/C (DM 3000)
£1333 $2280   (13-Mar-92 FN.S2903/R) Cottage with figures near Interlaken
                     (22x33cm-9x13in) s.i.d.1859 W/C (DM 3800)

ETERS, Pieter Francis (attrib) (1818-1903) Dutch
£584 $1069   (2-Jun-92 FN.S2697/R) Neckar landscape near Mettingen (43x29cm-17x11in)
                     s.i. W/C (DM 1700)

ETERS, Pietronella (1848-1924) German
£1443 $2511   (17-Sep-91 FN.S2478) Still life with field flowers in jug before basket
                     on cupboard (40x33cm-16x13in) s. board (DM 4200)
£1930 $3300   (13-Mar-92 FN.S2904/R) Girl feeding chickens before Alpine stable
                     (38x23cm-15x9in) s. canvas on board (DM 5500)

ETERS, Udo (1884-1964) German
£1767 $3092   (3-Apr-92 BM.B561/R) Early spring (50x71cm-20x28in) s. i.verso board
                     (DM 5000)

ETERS, Wilhelm (1817-1903) German
£697 $1186   (6-Aug-91 UL.T217/R) Canal view, Netherland (28x39cm-11x15in) (N.KR 8000)
£1053 $1958   (18-Jun-92 GWP.O220) Avenue of trees (70x54cm-28x21in) s. (N.KR 12000)
£1063 $1934   (9-Dec-91 B.O94/R) Against the Romans (175x76cm-69x30in) s.i.d.1879
                     (N.KR 12000)
£1754 $3263   (18-Jun-92 GWP.O75/R) Mountain farm (71x50cm-28x20in) s.d.90 (N.KR 20000)

ETERSEN, Anna (1845-1910) Danish
£650 $1209   (16-Jun-92 PH69) Interior of St Genevieve, Paris (79x65cm-31x26in) init.
£968 $1627   (28-Aug-91 KH.K164/R) During the service - scene from Jylland
                     (66x86cm-26x34in) init.d.90 (D.KR 11000)

ETERSEN, Edvard (1841-1911) Danish
£1761 $3046   (2-Sep-91 BU.K34/R) Landscape, Stadsgraven near Norrevold
                     (50x83cm-20x33in) init. (D.KR 20000)

PETERSEN, Eilif (1852-1928) Norwegian
£3012	$5481	(9-Dec-91 B.O96/R) Landscape from Dachau (55x68cm-22x27in) s.d.75 (N.KR 34000)
£3543	$6448	(14-Dec-91 BU.O58/R) Summer landscape (38x55cm-15x22in) s.d.93 i.verso (N.KR 40000)
£10097	$17366	(10-Oct-91 BU.O28/R) Mountain farm (80x70cm-31x28in) s.d.21 (N.KR 115000)

PETERSEN, Eilif (attrib) (1852-1928) Norwegian
£1493	$2657	(2-Nov-91 BU.O52) Portrait of man (125x100cm-49x39in) s.verso (N.KR 17000)

PETERSEN, Emmanuel Aage (1894-1948) Danish
£535	$920	(15-Oct-91 RAS.K206) Coastal landscape, Greenland (70x100cm-28x39in) s. (D.KR 6000)
£970	$1727	(28-Apr-92 RAS.K502) Seascape with sailship (60x80cm-24x31in) init.d.1921 (D.KR 11000)
£1235	$2198	(28-Apr-92 RAS.K593/R) Hunter and polar bear in snowy landscape (66x100cm-26x39in) s. (D.KR 14000)

PETERSEN, Hans Ritter von (1850-1914) German
£853	$1553	(26-May-92 KF.M404/R) Thaw (92x108cm-36x43in) s. (DM 2500)

PETERSEN, Heinrich Andreas (19th C) ?
£5682	$10000	(9-Apr-92 FA.PH630) Ship champion (5x79cm-2x31in) 630

PETERSEN, Jakob (1774-1854) Danish
£2646	$4709	(28-Apr-92 RAS.K10/R) Ships portrait 'Brig Tyne Side' (76x53cm-30x21in) s.i.d.1847 W/C gouache (D.KR 30000)
£2888	$5199	(19-Nov-91 RAS.K44/R) The brig 'immanuel of Copenhagen' (48x67cm-19x26in) s.d.1845 pen W/C (D.KR 32000)

PETERSEN, L (19th C) ?
£2113	$3549	(27-Aug-91 RAS.K242/R) On the road to the Autumn party. At the Autumn party, Southern Sweden (45x55cm-18x22in) s.d.1842 pair (D.KR 24000)
£508	$946	(16-Jun-92 RAS.K342) 'Schiff Triton von Sonderburg' (52x65cm-20x26in) s. W/C (D.KR 5700)

PETERSEN, Lorenz (1803-1870) German
£2460	$4404	(6-May-92 KH.K164/R) Seascape with two sailship (25x35cm-10x14in) s.d.1864 (D.KR 28000)
£5634	$10197	(4-Dec-91 DO.H2532/R) Hamburg ship Howard I on voyage to America (68x96cm-27x38in) s.i.d.1846 (DM 16000)

PETERSEN, Olaf (20th C) Norwegian
£949	$1699	(6-May-92 GD.B1008/R) Fjord landscape with shipping and fishing village (36x57cm-14x22in) s. panel (S.FR 2600)

PETERSEN, Robert Storm (1882-1949) Danish
£636	$1113	(1-Jul-92 KH.K218) Clown (18x17cm-7x7in) init. W/C (D.KR 7000)
£1248	$2146	(16-Oct-91 KH.K215/R) Pawnbroker (29x22cm-11x9in) s. W/C (D.KR 14000)
£2763	$4752	(16-Oct-91 KH.K216/R) 'Gullasch' (24x20cm-9x8in) s. W/C (D.KR 31000)

PETERSEN, Roland (1926-) American
£2647	$4500	(23-Oct-91 B.SF3736/R) 17 yard 6 inches (72x98cm-28x39in) s.d.63 oil synthetic resin canvas
£4412	$7500	(23-Oct-91 B.SF3737/R) Autumn picnic (154x178cm-61x70in) s.d.61 oil synthetic resin canvas

PETERSEN, Sophus (1837-1904) Danish
£539	$953	(11-Feb-92 RAS.K133) Still life of grapes, melon and tomato (25x40cm-10x16in) s.d.1885 (D.KR 6000)
£993	$1798	(19-May-92 AB.S4366/R) Still life of grapes, pommegranets and apples (29x23cm-11x9in) s.d.1871 (S.KR 10500)
£1764	$3139	(28-Apr-92 RAS.K167/R) Oysters and wine (67x57cm-26x22in) s.d.1884 (D.KR 20000)

PETERSEN, Vilhelm (1812-1888) Danish
£572	$961	(27-Aug-91 RAS.K463) Coastal landscape, Nykoping (19x32cm-7x13in) mono.d.78 (D.KR 6500)
£1070	$1991	(16-Jun-92 RAS.K218) North Sjaelland coastal landscape with beached boats (17x27cm-7x11in) mono.d.1862 (D.KR 12000)
£1320	$2218	(27-Aug-91 RAS.K464) View of Stockholm's Canal (23x31cm-9x12in) sketch (D.KR 15000)

PETERSON, Jane (1876-1965) American
£525	$950	(22-May-92 S.BM193/R) Pansies on a teal bowl (46x64cm-18x25in)
£698	$1200	(7-Mar-92 LAE.L180/R) Maine Coast, Prouts Neck (41x51cm-16x20in) s.
£1111	$1900	(21-Mar-92 W.W210/R) Breeze through palms (51x61cm-20x24in) s.
£1215	$2200	(22-May-92 S.BM195/R) Pansies (46x46cm-18x18in) s.
£1279	$2200	(20-Oct-91 HG.C38) Lady in garden (28x28cm-11x11in) masonite
£1337	$2300	(7-Mar-92 LAE.L179/R) Stage Fort Beach (46x46cm-18x18in) s. i.verso board
£1488	$2500	(28-Aug-91 MFA.C75 k/R) Madrid street scene (61x46cm-24x18in) s.
£1657	$2850	(7-Mar-92 LAE.L96/R) Harbour scene (61x46cm-24x18in) s.
£1862	$3500	(18-Dec-91 SY.NY257/R) June flowers (45x45cm-18x18in) s. canvasboard
£2047	$3500	(13-Mar-92 S.BM302/R) 7 pansies (61x76cm-24x30in) s. i.verso

ETERSON, Jane (1876-1965) American-cont.
2198	$4000	(27-May-92 SY.NY81/R) Venetian canal (44x44cm-17x17in) s. board
2924	$5000	(11-Mar-92 SY.NY65/R) Gladiolus (76x61cm-30x24in) s.
3429	$6000	(26-Sep-91 CH.NY60/R) Neighbourhood gathering (45x30cm-18x12in) s.
4050	$7250	(6-May-92 D.NY44 a) View of cathedral town (60x45cm-24x18in) s.
4386	$7500	(11-Mar-92 SY.NY66/R) Red roses in vase (76x63cm-30x25in) s. canvasboard
8287	$15000	(4-Dec-91 D.NY95/R) market day at Rialto, Venice (46x46cm-18x18in) s. i.verso board
11111	$19000	(11-Mar-92 SY.NY60/R) Clock tower, Venice (46x46cm-18x18in) s. s.i.verso
405	$700	(6-Sep-91 S.BM2667/R) Gate Napolians' Garden, Italy (46x46cm-18x18in) s. i. verso W/C gouache graphite
522	$950	(15-Dec-91 LIT.L263) Purple morning glories (58x43cm-23x17in) s. gouache W/C
565	$1000	(10-Nov-91 LIT.L140) Wisteria vine (64x48cm-25x19in) s. W/C
689	$1240	(23-Nov-91 YFA.M221/R) Ststue by garden pond (61x46cm-24x18in) s. gouache
833	$1600	(31-Jul-92 E.EDM38/R) Poppies in a vase (61x38cm-24x15in) s. pastel
847	$1500	(10-Nov-91 LIT.L50) Palm trees (38x48cm-15x19in) s. W/C
1250	$2100	(28-Aug-91 MFA.C121/R) Beach scene (20x28cm-8x11in) s. gouache
2924	$5000	(11-Mar-92 SY.NY62/R) Brittany street scene (61x46cm-24x18in) s. gouache W/C
3509	$6000	(11-Mar-92 SY.NY61/R) San Maggiore, Venice (46x61cm-18x24in) s. gouache chl
4571	$8000	(26-Sep-91 CH.NY164/R) Garden pool (46x61cm-18x24in) s. gouache W/C chl
9942	$17000	(12-Mar-92 CH.NY180/R) The Market Grasse, Paris (46x30cm-18x12in) s. gouache chl paper on board

ETHER, Abraham (1756-1812) British
730	$1270	(14-Apr-92 ACA830) Moonlit landscape with figures on path (36x46cm-14x18in) i.
850	$1624	(15-Jul-92 S204 a) Moonlit river landscape with castle by a bridge (48x67cm-19x26in)
944	$1700	(22-Nov-91 S.BM17/R) Herder with horse, cattle and sheep on riverbank (41x53cm-16x21in) s.
26000	$49660	(15-Jul-92 S56/R) Landscape with figure resting by lake, ruined abbey beyond (118x150cm-46x59in) s.

ETHER, Henry (19th C) British
2600	$4576	(8-Apr-92 S97/R) Boats moored by shore (63x75cm-25x30in) s.i.
2800	$5180	(12-Jun-92 C145/R) River landscape with figures by moonlight (44x59cm-17x23in) s.

ETHER, Sebastian (1790-1844) British
900	$1611	(15-Nov-91 DA900/R) Moonlight scene with ruins and figures (58x48cm-23x19in) mono.

ETHER, Sebastian (style) (1790-1844) British
1100	$1925	(27-Feb-92 B211) Moonlit view of Greenwich with shipping on the Thames and fishermen (56x74cm-22x29in) panel

ETILLION, Jules (1845-1899) French
1532	$2681	(23-Feb-92 I.N91/R) Entree de village (26x36cm-10x14in) s.i.d.1887 panel (F.FR 15000)

ETIT, Alfred (?-1895) French
12000	$21360	(26-Nov-91 PH43/R) Summer flowers (160x200cm-63x79in) s.

ETIT, C (?) ?
2096	$3500	(20-Aug-91 RB.HY118/R) Repast of the children (56x46cm-22x18in) s.d.1878 board

ETIT, Charles (19th C) French?
870	$1504	(24-Mar-92 VN.R74/R) Angler in polder landscape (77x103cm-30x41in) s. (D.FL 2800)
3500	$6230	(27-Nov-91 S8) Evening meal (56x45cm-22x18in) s.d.1878 board

ETIT, E (19/20th C) French
600	$1050	(24-Sep-91 GM.B673) Chiens de Chasse (38x47cm-15x19in) s. (B.FR 36000)

ETIT, Eugene (1839-1886) French
1056	$1912	(3-Dec-91 FN.S2380) Still life of poppies, marguerites and other flowers in vase on table (40x60cm-16x24in) s. panel (DM 3000)
1148	$2100	(17-May-92 DU.E1067) Pointing setters (46x56cm-18x22in) s.
1978	$3600	(26-May-92 CE.NY84/R) Flowers in a basket (71x99cm-28x39in) s. canvas on board
3968	$7063	(28-Apr-92 RAS.K130/R) Pink roses and white lilies in vase on table (130x99cm-51x39in) s.d.72 (D.KR 45000)

ETIT, Pierre Joseph (18/19th C) French
5000	$8750	(3-Apr-92 C1/R) Roman capriccio with Basilica of Maxentius and Temple of Vesta (44x59cm-17x23in) s.d.1786 panel

ETIT-GERARD, Pierre (1852-?) French
566	$1065	(16-Dec-91 BG.P110) La revue militaire (114x147cm-45x58in) s. (F.FR 5500)

PETIT-RADEL, Louis Charles Francois (1740-1818) French
£1672 $3026   *(22-May-92 LD.P52) Lavandieres dans un temple en ruine (62x82cm-24x32in)*
                      s.d.1782 ink wash (F.FR 16500)

PETITBOIS, Agathon du (19th C) French?
£14632 $25166   (16-Oct-91 AT.P139/R) Vue imaginaire d'un paysage a l'italienne
                      (114x162cm-45x64in) s.d.1822 (F.FR 145000)

PETITE, H le (?) ?
£1650 $2954   (12-Nov-91 OT753/R) Stray kitten (49x74cm-19x29in) s.

PETITI, Filiberto (1845-1924) Italian
£1449 $2681   (8-Jun-92 CH.R608) Paesaggio fluviale con pastore e pecore
                      (60x50cm-24x20in) s. board (I.L 3200000)
£3090 $5500   (22-Jan-92 SY.NY525/R) Wooded landscape with figures boating on river
                      (57x100cm-22x39in) s.d.1876

PETITJEAN, Edmond (1844-1925) French
£1803 $3300   (16-May-92 HG.C214/R) Country landscape with cottage and river
                      (51x76cm-20x30in) s.d.1889
£1988 $3697   (19-Jun-92 CN.P71/R) Le Havre (46x73cm-18x29in) s.d.1887 (F.FR 19500)
£2088 $3800   (26-May-92 CE.NY321/R) Sunlit cottages by a pond (55x45cm-22x18in) s.
£3297 $6000   (27-May-92 CH.NY194/R) Street in Normandy village (42x61cm-17x24in) s.
£3429 $6000   (19-Feb-92 CH.NY31/R) French river village (48x44cm-19x17in) s.d.1888
£3494 $6010   (4-Mar-92 AT.P185/R) Les lavandieres (45x63cm-18x25in) s. (F.FR 34000)
£3807 $6890   (4-Dec-91 CB.P110) Village en Vendee (46x65cm-18x26in) s. (F.FR 37000)
£4070 $7000   (16-Oct-91 CH.NY72/R) French river village with a washerwoman
                      (46x65cm-18x26in) s.
£5544 $9814   (10-Nov-91 ZZ.F113/R) Apres-midi sous la treille (46x65cm-18x26in) s.
                      (F.FR 55000)
£5658 $10751   (24-Jun-92 GL.P152/R) Bateaux dans un port (48x67cm-19x26in) s.
                      (F.FR 55000)
£7377 $13279   (2-Feb-92 ZZ.F59/R) Le Port (40x54cm-16x21in) s. canvas laid down on
                      panel (F.FR 72000)
£7863 $13917   (10-Nov-91 ZZ.F140/R) Le port anime (46x66cm-18x26in) s. (F.FR 78000)

PETITJEAN, Hippolyte (1854-1929) French
£1073 $1900   (5-Nov-91 CE.NY3/R) Paysage (14x23cm-6x9in) mono. board
£1744 $3000   (12-Oct-91 SY.NY26/R) La maison sur mer (24x36cm-9x14in) atelier st.
                      board
£2053 $3696   (19-Nov-91 FB.P50/R) Vue de Douzy (21x29cm-8x11in) bears studio st. W/C
                      (F.FR 20000)

PETITOT, Jean (snr) (1607-1691) French
£900 $1611   (11-Nov-91 PH87/R) Portrait of gentleman wearing armour and lace cravat
                      (3x?cm-1x?in) min.enamel gilt metal frame oval

PETLEY, Roy (1950-) British
£580 $1009   (19-Sep-91 CSK59) Gorleston Beach lighthouse (30x46cm-12x18in) s. board
£900 $1575   (27-Sep-91 C16/R) Sandy Pier (23x33cm-9x13in) s. board
£900 $1575   (27-Sep-91 C15/R) Bank Holiday, Hyde Park (49x75cm-19x30in) s. board
£1100 $2013   (4-Jun-92 CSK140) Day at beach (30x44cm-12x17in) s. board
£1200 $2196   (4-Jun-92 CSK142) Boats on river (41x61cm-16x24in) s. masonite
£1800 $3294   (4-Jun-92 CSK139/R) Summer's day on Cromer Beach (40x60cm-16x24in) s.
                      board
£3800 $6954   (14-May-92 C66/R) Balloon seller (51x76cm-20x30in) s. board
£480 $850   (7-Nov-91 CSK29) Norfolk cottages in the snow (35x51cm-14x20in) s.d.89
                      W/C

PETO, John F (1854-1907) American
£1397 $2500   (13-Nov-91 B.SF2603/R) Still life with papers tacked on wall
                      (56x41cm-22x16in)
£8571 $15000   (25-Sep-91 SY.NY15/R) Still life with mug, pipe and book (13x18cm-5x7in)
                      s. i.d.1899 verso panel
£26901 $46000   (12-Mar-92 CH.NY63/R) Still life with candle, pipe and books
                      (25x19cm-10x7in) s. board

PETRELLA DA BOLOGNA, Vittorio (1886-1951) Italian
£453 $838   (8-Jun-92 CH.R527) Ballo di carnevale (29x37cm-11x15in) s. canvas laid
                      down on board (I.L 1000000)

PETRIDES, Konrad (1863-1943) Austrian
£395 $692   (20-Feb-92 D.V525/R) The black lake, Hohe Tatra (33x44cm-13x17in)
                      s.i.d.1898 verso mixed media (A.S 8000)

PETRINI, Giuseppe Antonio (circle) (1677-1758) Italian
£1391 $2379   (18-Mar-92 D.V235/R) St Peter (69x60cm-27x24in) (A.S 28000)

PETROCELLI, Achille (1861-?) Italian
£950 $1634   (15-Oct-91 CSK615/R) A lute player (31x24cm-12x9in) s.

PETROCELLI, Vincenzo Pasquale Angelo (1823-1896) Italian
£500 $855   (17-Mar-92 PH247) Swordsman seated in landscape (55x40cm-22x16in) s.
                      panel

ETROS (1928-) Greek
2514 $4777   (23-Jun-92 F.M118/R) Il mondo di Talete (80x60cm-31x24in) s.
         s.i.d.1990verso (I.L 5500000)

ETROV-VODKIN, Kuzma (1878-1939) Russian
6000 $10860   (22-May-92 C110/R) Samarkhand scene (51x63cm-20x25in) init.d.1921
44000 $78320   (28-Nov-91 S428/R) Mother of God of Notre Dame Cathedral
         (81x66cm-32x26in) init.d.1925
3000 $5580   *(16-Jun-92 S78/R) Archangel on red horse, design for calendar*
         (36x29cm-14x11in) init.i.verso W/C over pencil htd.white

ETROVITS, Ladislaus Eugen (1839-1907) Austrian
684    $1176   *(10-Oct-91 D.V276/R) Treelined road, Goisern (38x28cm-15x11in) s.d.1903*
         W/C (A.S 14000)

ETRUOLO, Salvatore (1857-1946) Italian
900    $1602   *(28-Nov-91 CSK64 a) Figures in market square (23x38cm-9x15in)*
         W/C htd.bodycol
950    $1644   *(3-Oct-91 CSK25/R) On the Neapolitan Coast, near Sorrento*
         (53x43cm-21x17in) s.d.1930 pencil W/C htd.white

ETTENKOFEN, August von (1822-1889) Austrian
1367 $2324   (24-Oct-91 D.V161/R) Czikos dancing in tanya (21x31cm-8x12in) panel
         (A.S 28000)
1977 $3460   (20-Feb-92 D.V507/R) Woman seated with spinning wheel (21x14cm-8x6in)
         i.verso board (A.S 40000)
534    $950   *(29-Apr-92 D.V537/R) Street scene with figures (15x9cm-6x4in) pencil*
         (A.S 11000)
583    $1037   *(29-Apr-92 D.V542/R) Figures conversing on draw bridge (18x11cm-7x4in)*
         pencil (A.S 12000)
977    $1681   (10-Oct-91 D.V102/R) Landscape (44x32cm-17x13in) chl (A.S 20000)
1456 $2592   *(29-Apr-92 D.V502/R) Ox-drawn cart with figures in town (23x16cm-9x6in)*
         mono pencil (A.S 30000)
2062 $3588   *(17-Sep-91 FN.S2482) Hungarian market scene with animals and figures*
         (17x22cm-7x9in) s. W/C (DM 6000)

ETTER, Franz Xaver (1791-1866) Austrian
759    $1305   (16-Oct-91 KM.K1318) Still life of peach, grapes and nut (16x25cm-6x10in)
         s. (DM 2200)
2424 $4411   (27-May-92 D.V512/R) Still life of fruit (17x24cm-7x9in) s. (A.S 50000)

ETTER, Franz Xaver (style) (1791-1866) Austrian
1461 $2600   (22-Jan-92 SY.NY95/R) Still life with flowers (48x38cm-19x15in)

ETTIBONE, Robert (20th C) American
532    $1000   (17-Dec-91 BG.M678/R) Girl with ball (23x15cm-9x6in) acrylic

ETTIE, John (1839-1893) British
600    $1068   (21-Jan-92 PH29) Portrait of gentleman (85x62cm-33x24in) s.d.1875
         s.indist.i.stretcher

ETTINGER, J F (20th C) British
850    $1454   (1-Aug-91 CSK33) Ladies seated in dunes on summer's day (25x35cm-10x14in)
         s.d.1916 canvas laid down on board

ETTITT, Charles (19th C) British
500    $860   (16-Oct-91 CSK258) Buttermere from near Sour Milk Ghyll (24x38cm-9x15in)
         s.d.1864 s.i.d.1864 verso
550    $1001   (10-Dec-91 AG323) Helvellyn from Thirlmere, Cumberland (49x74cm-19x29in)
         mono.d.1882 i.verso
800    $1368   (18-Mar-92 B159) Highland loch view (37x60cm-15x24in) s.d.1860
850    $1454   (18-Mar-92 B160) On the plateau of Coed Mawr looking towards Llyn Ogwen,
         early winter (29x36cm-11x14in) s.d.1860 i.verso
900    $1575   (24-Sep-91 SWO1) Lyn Craenant, North Wales (38x61cm-15x24in) s.d.1861
900    $1647   (3-Jun-92 S50/R) Windsor Castle from Romney Island (35x53cm-14x21in)
         mono.d.1876
2200 $4136   (19-Dec-91 C109/R) Llyn Crafnant-Moel Siabad in distance, North Wales
         (38x61cm-15x24in) s.d.1861 s.i.d.verso

ETTITT, Joseph Paul (?-1882) British
4800 $8544   (27-Apr-92 PHB301/R) Vale of Neath, South Wales (61x91cm-24x36in)
         s.i.d.1861
6000 $11100   (12-Jun-92 C159 a/R) The Vale of Neath, S. Wales (61x91cm-24x36in)
         s.d.1861

ETTITT, Joseph Paul (circle) (?-1882) British
850    $1479   (19-Sep-91 TL379) Lake landscape, N Wales (50x74cm-20x29in)

ETTORUTI, Emilio (1892-1971) Argentinian
4945 $9000   (11-Dec-91 RO.BA23/R) Paisaje Cordobes (16x21cm-6x8in)
5495 $10000   (11-Dec-91 RO.BA22/R) Sierras de Cordoba (19x24cm-7x9in) s.d.1912
14365 $26000   (18-May-92 CH.NY70/R) Avenida Arbolada (48x29cm-19x11in) s.d. s.i.d.verso
         panel
16279 $28000   (9-Oct-91 RO.BA15/R) Lago di Como (50x40cm-20x16in) s.d.917
16484 $30000   (11-Dec-91 RO.BA21/R) Paisaje (66x100cm-26x39in) s.d.1912

PETTORUTI, Emilio (1892-1971) Argentinian-cont.
£19337	$35000	(18-May-92 CH.NY28/R) Caida de hojas (81x54cm-32x21in) s.d.
£25000	$45000	(19-Nov-91 CH.NY57/R) Ragazza (23x27cm-9x11in) s.d.1922verso board
£25000	$45000	(19-Nov-91 CH.NY30/R) El mantel a cuadros (60x80cm-24x31in) s.d.938 s.i.d.verso
£27624	$50000	(19-May-92 SY.NY17/R) Naturaleza muerta (25x34cm-10x13in) s.d.18 canvas laid down on board
£33333	$60000	(18-Nov-91 SY.NY18/R) Vino rubi (50x65cm-20x26in) s.d.945 s.i.d.verso
£43011	$80000	(16-Jun-92 RO.BA14) L'oiseau blanc (81x31cm-32x12in)
£46512	$80000	(9-Oct-91 RO.BA14/R) La casa del poeta (73x54cm-29x21in) s.d.1935
£53763	$100000	(16-Jun-92 RO.BA11) Pureza (100x75cm-39x30in)
£66298	$120000	(18-May-92 CH.NY26/R) Midi en hiver - Farfala (146x114cm-57x45in) s.d.1964
£68681	$125000	(11-Dec-91 RO.BA24) El Mantel Blanco (54x73cm-21x29in) s.d.49 s.i.d.1949verso
£133333	$240000	(19-Nov-91 CH.NY27/R) El Cantor (81x60cm-32x24in) s.d.934 s.i.d.verso canvas on canvas

PETTY, George (20th C) American
£4213	$7500	(2-Nov-91 IH.NY23/R) Woman ice-skater (46x30cm-18x12in) gouache col.pencil

PETUEL, R (1870-?) German
£515	$897	(19-Sep-91 N.M2798/R) Peonies in vase (67x51cm-26x20in) s. i.verso board (DM 1500)

PETZHOLDT, Fritz (1805-1838) Danish
£2636	$4719	(6-May-92 KH.K170/R) From the Roman Campagna (23x27cm-9x11in) (D.KR 30000)

PETZL, Ferdinand (1819-1899) German
£4811	$8804	(2-Jun-92 FN.S2700/R) View of Esslingen on the Neckar with figures, evening (28x35cm-11x14in) s. i.verso (DM 14000)

PEUGNIEZ, Pauline (1890-?) French
£1854	$3485	(18-Dec-91 PR.P105) La chapelle dans les vergers (81x100cm-32x39in) s.i.d.1921 (F.FR 18000)

PEURSEN, A van (19th C) Dutch?
£2749	$4784	(18-Sep-91 N.M648/R) Dutch landscape with traveller on path through dunes (48x55cm-19x22in) s.d.1851 (DM 8000)

PEVERELLI, Cesare (1922-) Italian
£1019	$1815	(26-Nov-91 SY.MI4/R) Composizione (50x70cm-20x28in) s.d.1953 (I.L 2200000)
£1462	$2543	(14-Apr-92 F.M13/R) Composizione a fondo blu (116x89cm-46x35in) s. (I.L 3200000)

PEVSNER, Antoine (1886-1962) Russian
£75000	$143250	(30-Jun-92 S41/R) Formes abstraites (82x61cm-32x24in) mono. oil wax
£515	$892	(23-Mar-92 GL.P111) Profil, face et sphere (23x29cm-9x11in) s.d.1923 lead pencil (F.FR 5000)
£670	$1159	(23-Mar-92 GL.P112) Profil dans une sphere (37x26cm-15x10in) s.d.1920 lead pencil dr. (F.FR 6500)
£1028	$1768	(4-Mar-92 AT.P79) Rythme (26x20cm-10x8in) s.d.24 crayon (F.FR 10000)
£1031	$1784	(23-Mar-92 GL.P110/R) Tete (44x38cm-17x15in) s.d.17 lead pencil dr. (F.FR 10000)
£1749	$3166	(6-Dec-91 GL.P170 b) Composition (27x17cm-11x7in) s.d.1924 lead pencil stumping (F.FR 17000)
£2846	$4951	(16-Apr-92 FB.P4/R) Femme (39x26cm-15x10in) s.d.1924 lead pencil (F.FR 28000)
£3000	$5160	(16-Oct-91 S65/R) Tete de femme (29x21cm-11x8in) s.d.1924 pencil
£3200	$5504	(16-Oct-91 S66/R) Portrait de femme encadre (29x21cm-11x8in) s.d.1924 pencil
£3799	$6838	(19-Nov-91 FB.P114/R) Femme (28x21cm-11x8in) s.d.1925 lead pencil (F.FR 37000)
£6982	$12567	(19-Nov-91 FB.P172/R) Femme (28x21cm-11x8in) s.d.1924 lead pencil (F.FR 68000)
£7000	$12670	(4-Dec-91 S148/R) Projet de sculpture (39x24cm-15x9in) s.d.37 pencil
£31421	$57500	(13-May-92 SY.NY214/R) Fond vert (35x28cm-14x11in) s.d.1923 absorbed chemical painting

PEYRAUD, Frank Charles (1858-1948) American
£1143	$2000	(21-Feb-92 BG.M266/R) Summer landscape (76x86cm-30x34in) s.

PEYRE, Marie Joseph (attrib) (1730-1788) French
£412	$745	(6-Dec-91 ARC.P220/R) Detail d'architecture (24x18cm-9x7in) i. pierre noire (F.FR 4000)

PEYRISSAC, Jean (1895-) French
£1057	$1798	(24-Oct-91 D.P121/R) Composition (31x22cm-12x9in) s. W/C gouache (F.FR 10500)

YROL-BONHEUR, Juliette (1830-1891) French
4121 $7500   (26-May-92 CE.NY200/R) Cows grazing on cliffs by the sea
                       (67x101cm-26x40in) s.

YRONNET, Dominique Paul (1872-1943) French
81000 $140130   (25-Mar-92 S190/R) La source (60x81cm-24x32in) s. st.sig.verso

ZANT, Aymar (1846-?) French
673    $1198   (29-Oct-91 VN.R232) Landscape with cattle (46x66cm-18x26in) s.
                       (D.FL 2200)

ZOUS, Jean (1815-1885) French
456    $849   (19-Jun-92 ZOF.Z612/R) Paysage avec vaches et moutons (14x20cm-6x8in) s.
                       panel (S.FR 1200)

ZUELA, A (19th C) ?
774   *$1455*   *(17-Dec-91 DUR.M51/R) Pueblo pesquero (54x37cm-21x15in) s. W/C*
                       (S.P 140000)
1244   *$2339*   *(17-Dec-91 DUR.M50/R) Pescadores (53x37cm-21x15in) s.d.87 W/C*
                       (S.P 225000)

ZZO, Lucio del (1933-) Italian
916    $1675   (14-May-92 BG.P90) Pyramide avec eclair (108x54cm-43x21in) s.d.1968verso
                       panel (F.FR 9000)
834   *$1485*   *(29-Nov-91 F.F66) Mensola (10x8cm-4x3in) s.d.1964 mixed media panel*
                       (I.L 1800000)
1297   *$2310*   *(29-Nov-91 F.F65/R) Dimensione (38x28cm-15x11in) s.d.1987 mixed media*
                       collage (I.L 2800000)
3405   *$6061*   *(29-Apr-92 F.F81/R) Senza titolo (101x81cm-40x32in) s. oil mixed media*
                       panel (I.L 7500000)

AFF, Jean (1945-) Swiss
1141 $2122   (19-Jun-92 ZOF.Z2041/R) Yantra no 95 (130x130cm-51x51in) s.i.d.73verso
                       acrylic (S.FR 3000)
1294   *$2316*   *(15-Nov-91 ZOF.Z1839) Yantra no 103 (110x110cm-43x43in) d.1974 s.i.verso*
                       acrylic (S.FR 3300)

AHLER, Karl Georg (1926-) German
2632 $4737   (19-Nov-91 L.K1002/R) Stutt-rot (50x70cm-20x28in) s.i.d.1966/67 (DM 7500)
4266 $7765   (30-May-92 VG.B377/R) Concord IV Jangsoo (100x107cm-39x42in)
                       s.i.d.1965/66 (DM 12500)
4467 $8265   (11-Jun-92 HN.H367/R) Jet no III (110x100cm-43x39in) s.i.d.1965 acrylic
                       (DM 13000)
5155 $9536   (11-Jun-92 HN.H368/R) Clipper W (80x70cm-31x28in) s.i.d.1967 acrylic
                       (DM 15000)
6143 $11181   (30-May-92 VG.B378/R) Doppeltex IV (110x100cm-43x39in) s.i.d.1965
                       (DM 18000)
9825 $17684   (19-Nov-91 L.K1001/R) Metro R B G (110x100cm-43x39in) s.i.d.1967verso
                       (DM 28000)
962   *$1761*   *(2-Jun-92 L.K873) Untitled (50x65cm-20x26in) s.d.1962 poster paint indian*
                       ink col.chk board (DM 2800)

EIFFER, Gordon (1899-1983) Canadian
1000 $1770   (6-Nov-91 SY.T31/R) Winter view of Quebec City from St. Lawrence River
                       (44x61cm-17x24in) s. board (C.D 2000)

EILER, Maximilian (circle) (18th C) German
6500 $12480   (10-Jul-92 C216/R) Fruit, flowers and dead game (59x99cm-23x39in) canvas
                       on board pair

LUG, Christiane Sybille (1936-1972) Canadian
2250 $3983   (6-Nov-91 SY.T197/R) Railroad yard at Liquor Control Building, Toronto
                       (62x76cm-24x30in) s.d.1961 sold with book (C.D 4500)

LUG, Johan Baptist (1785-1866) German
48110 $83711   (17-Sep-91 FN.S2483/R) Battle of Ostrach in 1799 with Erzherzog Karl von
                       Osterreich (57x77cm-22x30in) s. (DM 140000)

LUG, Johan Baptist (circle) (1785-1866) German
880    $1593   (3-Dec-91 FN.S2381/R) Coach with horses and figures resting before well
                       beneath tree (21x16cm-8x6in) (DM 2500)

UND, Alois (1876-1946) Austrian
687    $1271   (13-Jun-92 WK.M352/R) Garmisch during the Olympic Games (50x80cm-20x31in)
                       s.i.d.1936 (DM 2000)

UND, Roger (1943-) Swiss
510   *$867*   *(23-Oct-91 GD.B2223) Composition in red and blue (84x38cm-33x15in) s.d.74*
                       gouache collage (S.FR 1300)
843   *$1458*   *(23-Mar-92 AB.L211/R) Portrait Marcel Proust (105x72cm-41x28in) s.d.75/76*
                       mixed media over collage (S.FR 2200)

YFFER, Niklaus (1836-1908) Swiss
1778 $3218   (19-May-92 GF.L2635/R) Lake Geneva with castle Nyon (35x56cm-14x22in) s.
                       (S.FR 4800)

PHELAN, Charles T (1840-?) American
£579 $1100 (26-Jun-92 WOL.C343/R) Pastoral landscape with sheep (61x94cm-24x37in) s.

PHELPS, Richard and BAMFYLDE, Copleston Warre (18th C) British
£65000 $117000 (30-Jan-92 TL54/R) Portrait of Col.John Bampfylde on horseback with groom
and dogs (390x360cm-154x142in) s.d.1746

PHELPS, William Preston (1848-1923) American
£552 $1000 (24-May-92 JRB.C101/R) Tending the cows (46x61cm-18x24in) s.
£743 $1300 (28-Sep-91 YFA.M193) Girls gathering firewood (61x41cm-24x16in) s.
£833 $1500 (22-Nov-91 S.BM143/R) Autumn woodlands, Chesham, New Hampshire
(61x91cm-24x36in) s.
£1167 $2100 (22-Nov-91 S.BM62 c/R) Twilight chores - farmyard scene (56x99cm-22x39in)
s.
£1381 $2500 (24-May-92 JRB.C100/R) Cows taking water (43x58cm-17x23in) s.

PHILIPP, Michael (elder) (fl.1659-1687) German
*£1900 $3648 (7-Jul-92 C105/R) Mercury abduting Psyche (51x30cm-20x12in) s.d.1652 chk
pen wash htd.white*
*£2400 $4608 (7-Jul-92 C104/R) Mercury abducting Psyche (54x32cm-21x13in) s.d.1652 chk
pen wash htd white*

PHILIPP, Robert (1895-1981) American
£702 $1250 (29-Nov-91 MFA.C52 a/R) Cocktail time (28x36cm-11x14in) s.
£778 $1400 (24-Nov-91 JRB.C195/R) Letty (64x76cm-25x30in) s.
£814 $1400 (13-Oct-91 LIT.L178) Still life with flowers, Paris, 1929
(51x61cm-20x24in) s.
£1117 $2000 (14-Nov-91 CE.NY375/R) Still life with flowers in vase on ledge
(91x76cm-36x30in) s.
£1117 $2100 (18-Dec-91 SY.NY284/R) Rochelle in red kimono (76x63cm-30x25in)
s.i.d.1966 verso
£1955 $3500 (6-May-92 D.NY34/R) Cafe conversation (30x41cm-12x16in) s. s.i.verso
£2235 $4000 (14-Nov-91 CE.NY359/R) At theatre (46x38cm-18x15in) s.
£3005 $5500 (16-May-92 HG.C92/R) Two women in cafe (61x76cm-24x30in) init.
£1397 $2500 (13-Nov-91 B.SF2833/R) Reclining nude (56x71cm-22x28in) s. pastel

PHILIPPEAU, Karel Frans (1825-1897) Dutch
£4070 $7000 (15-Oct-91 CE.NY136/R) Offering grapes (30x41cm-12x16in) s.d.67 panel

PHILIPPI, Peter (1866-1958) German
£687 $1271 (12-Jun-92 HN.H695/R) Portrait of elderly man reading letter
(21x22cm-8x9in) s. board (DM 2000)
£687 $1271 (12-Jun-92 HN.H696/R) Portrait of man wearing glasses (19x17cm-7x7in)
s.d.1924 (DM 2000)

PHILIPPOTEAUX, Henri Felix Emmanuel (1815-1884) French
£1118 $1945 (13-Apr-92 AT.P207) La kasbah (70x40cm-28x16in) s. (F.FR 11000)

PHILIPPOTEAUX, Paul Dominique (1846-?) American
£1440 $2750 (17-Jul-92 DM.D2246/R) Exotic dancers (51x61cm-20x24in) s.

PHILIPS, F A (19th C) American?
£1049 $1794 (18-Mar-92 N.M613/R) Child with Punch (20x25cm-8x10in) s.d.1878 (DM 3000)

PHILIPSEN, Sally (1879-1936) Danish
£535 $920 (15-Oct-91 RAS.K212) Coastal landscape (93x116cm-37x46in) s.d.1908
(D.KR 6000)

PHILIPSEN, Theodor (1840-1920) Danish
£501 $897 (6-May-92 KH.K195) Study of a sheep (23x24cm-9x9in) mono. (D.KR 5700)
£517 $962 (16-Jun-92 RAS.K220) Red cow (30x23cm-12x9in) mono. (D.KR 5800)
£632 $1137 (19-Nov-91 RAS.K132) Study of cows (26x30cm-10x12in) mono. (D.KR 7000)
£1146 $2041 (28-Apr-92 RAS.K282) Fjord landscape with road along water
(58x87cm-23x34in) mono.d.1903 (D.KR 13000)
£1345 $2422 (30-Jan-92 RAS.V667/R) From the large watering place at Saltholmen
(100x135cm-39x53in) (D.KR 15000)
£1408 $2366 (27-Aug-91 RAS.K144/R) Landscape from the heights behind Banjole
(60x84cm-24x33in) mono.d.1904 (D.KR 16000)
£1789 $3256 (12-Dec-91 RAS.V763/R) Landscape with cattle, Gronneogard
(105x160cm-41x63in) mono.d.1869 (D.KR 20000)
£2250 $4118 (5-Feb-92 KH.K102/R) Young cattle at Saltholmen (80x123cm-31x48in)
(D.KR 25000)
£2734 $4866 (28-Apr-92 RAS.K230/R) Hay harvest (75x108cm-30x43in) mono.d.1914
(D.KR 31000)
£2817 $4732 (27-Aug-91 RAS.K143/R) Landscape with cattle (30x51cm-12x20in)
mono.d.1880 (D.KR 32000)
*£1056 $1775 (28-Aug-91 KH.K275) Cows in stable (17x21cm-7x8in) mono.i.d.1899 pen
(D.KR 12000)*

PHILIPSON, Robin (1916-) British
£2200 $3696 (26-Aug-91 S1157/R) Combat (30x40cm-12x16in) s. board
£3000 $5310 (10-Feb-92 B74/R) Compotier of fruit (71x65cm-28x26in) s.verso
£3500 $6195 (8-Nov-91 C301/R) Crowing cock (67x79cm-26x31in) s.
£4000 $7120 (28-Apr-92 S326/R) Cockfight, Rose Window, fighting cocks
(30x41cm-12x16in) s. board

PHILIPSON, Robin (1916-) British-cont.
£750	$1335	(30-Apr-92 CG836) Crowing cock (28x22cm-11x9in) s. W/C
£800	$1456	(29-May-92 PHG25) Sleeping figures (18x28cm-7x11in) W/C
£1000	$1820	(29-May-92 PHG116) Men observed (22x27cm-9x11in) oil pastel
£1100	$2002	(29-May-92 PHG53) Crow and ram (80x80cm-31x31in) s. W/C
£1300	$2184	(26-Aug-91 S1154/R) Humankind (29x29cm-11x11in) s.backboard mixed media leather on board
£1450	$2639	(29-May-92 PHG18/R) Sea approach to Anstruther (56x77cm-22x30in) s.d.59 W/C pastel
£1600	$2688	(26-Aug-91 S1156/R) Blue figures (17x17cm-7x7in) s. s.i.label backboard W/C

PHILLIP, John (1817-1867) British
£780	$1413	(3-Dec-91 R.T134/R) Spanish beauty with tambourine (61x46cm-24x18in) s.d.1857 (C.D 1600)
£1800	$3132	(11-Sep-91 PHL127/R) Figures in cottage interior (30x40cm-12x16in) s.d.1852 panel

PHILLIP, John (circle) (1817-1867) British
£1100	$1969	(14-Nov-91 CSK294) The fortune teller (91x71cm-36x28in) mono.

PHILLIP, John (style) (1817-1867) British
£900	$1557	(24-Mar-92 PHC413) Tambourine player (77x62cm-30x24in) bears mono.

PHILLIPS, Ammi (attrib) (1787-1865) American
£2630	$4734	(29-Jan-92 FER.M116/R) Nina de las cerezas (55x46cm-22x18in) d.1850verso (S.P 475000)

PHILLIPS, Bert G (1868-1956) American
£3590	$6750	(18-Dec-91 SY.NY380/R) Dear hunter, Taos (17x21cm-7x8in) s. s.i.d.1927 verso board
£9341	$17000	(28-May-92 CH.NY119/R) The scout (30x30cm-12x12in) s.i. board

PHILLIPS, Charles (1708-1747) British
£800	$1528	(17-Jul-92 C64) Portrait of Rev M Hill seated at a table (75x61cm-30x24in) i.
£1000	$1800	(22-Nov-91 CBB100/R) Portrait study (51x41cm-20x16in) s.d.
£12155	$22000	(21-May-92 CH.NY134/R) Portrait of Matthew Lynch of Drumcong House. Portrait of wife, seated (38x31cm-15x12in) pair

PHILLIPS, Charles (attrib) (1708-1747) British
£900	$1539	(12-Mar-92 CSK109/R) Portrait of nobleman standing in Garter Robes holding coronet (33x25cm-13x10in) panel

PHILLIPS, Charles (circle) (1708-1747) British
£2308	$4408	(15-Jul-92 CH.S778/R) Players from Commedia dell'Arte in wood (52x44cm-20x17in) canvas on panel (A.D 6000)

PHILLIPS, Coles (1880-1927) American
£5056	$9000	(2-Nov-91 IH.NY185/R) Girl walking between heads of old woman and doctor (53x46cm-21x18in) s. W/C gouache

PHILLIPS, F A (19th C) British?
£1900	$3344	(8-Apr-92 CSK257) Card players (46x60cm-18x24in) s.d.59 i.verso after Theodor Rombouts

PHILLIPS, Gordon (1927-) American
£1462	$2500	(12-Mar-92 CH.NY130/R) Snowed last night (71x61cm-28x24in) s.d.78
£4420	$8000	(6-Dec-91 CH.NY115/R) Talk of the Southern Trails (61x76cm-24x30in) s.
£4670	$8500	(28-May-92 CH.NY126/R) Chores (61x106cm-24x42in) s.i.d.71
£9392	$17000	(5-Dec-91 SY.NY52/R) A welcome sight (58x81cm-23x32in) s.d.66 i.verso board

PHILLIPS, Peter (1939-) British
£8939	$16000	(13-Nov-91 CH.NY107/R) Wall machine (183x152cm-72x60in) oil newsprint collage canvas

PHILLIPS, S George (20th C) American
£857	$1500	(22-Feb-92 YFA.M156/R) Riverside in spring (91x64cm-36x25in) s.

PHILLIPS, S H (20th C) ?
£500	$850	(7-Aug-91 CSK453) The powder boat (20x28cm-8x11in) s.d.1919 i.d.verso panel

PHILLIPS, Thomas (1770-1845) British
£3591	$6500	(22-May-92 SY.NY276 a/R) Portrait of George O'Brien Wyndham, 3rd Earl of Egremont (137x120cm-54x47in) i.verso

PHILLIPS, Thomas (attrib) (1770-1845) British
£2209	$3800	(9-Oct-91 CH.NY58/R) Portrait of gentleman, said to be Lord Lyndhurst (76x63cm-30x25in)
£5200	$9932	(15-Jul-92 S80/R) William Blake and other portrait studies (60x50cm-24x20in)

PHILLIPS, Tom (1937-) British
£1300 $2405   (11-Jun-92 C85/R) XXI Terminal Greys III (122x20cm-48x8in) s.d.LXXIX
           overlap
£800 $1504   (18-Dec-91 C185) Johann Sebastian Bach (22x32cm-9x13in) s.i.d.MCMVLXXIV
           pencil W/C bodycol

PHILLIPS, Walter Joseph (1884-1963) American
£2740 $5014   (14-May-92 SY.T49/R) Mount Cathedral from Lake O'Hara (41x51cm-16x20in)
           gouache panel (C.D 6000)

PHILLIPS, William Francis (20th C) British
£460 $791   (15-Oct-91 B106) Seven Dials Mystery by Agatha Christie (37x25cm-15x10in)
           init. gouache

PHILP, James George (1816-1885) British
£1250 $2350   (19-Dec-91 C55/R) Fishing boats in stormy conditions (43x73cm-17x29in)
           s.d.1860 pencil W/C htd white

PHILPOT, Glyn (1884-1937) British
£3800 $6726   (7-Nov-91 C54/R) Early painting (19x24cm-7x9in) init. canvasboard
£92000 $162840   (7-Nov-91 C52/R) Penelope (136x92cm-54x36in)
£1200 $2052   (11-Mar-92 S58/R) Oedipus and sphinx (42x26cm-17x10in) init. pencil pen
           wash htd white
£8500 $15045   (7-Nov-91 C55/R) Bistro, Havre (36x23cm-14x9in) init. pencil W/C bodycol.

PHIPPS, Edmund (fl.1884-1915) British
£420 $735   (1-Apr-92 B158) On the Alt (38x76cm-15x30in) s.d.1894 W/C

PIACENZA, Carlo (1814-1887) Italian
£1375 $2433   (7-Nov-91 F.M39) Sentiero con contadino (20x36cm-8x14in) s. board
           (I.L 3000000)

PIANCA, Giuseppe Antonio (18th C) Italian
£1267 $2306   (28-May-92 F.M2) Maddalena (74x99cm-29x39in) (I.L 2800000)

PIANE, Giovanni Maria delle (1660-1745) Italian
£5000 $9100   (10-Dec-91 PH46/R) Portrait of lady (66x50cm-26x20in)

PIATOWSKI, Henryk (1853-1932) Polish
£509 $926   (15-Dec-91 REM.W30) Roman couple (78x79cm-31x31in) s. (P.Z 10000000)

PIATTELLA, Oscar (20th C) ?
£2051 $3672   (19-Jan-92 CC.P70/R) Muro Azzurro-Viola (110x133cm-43x52in) s.d.1959verso
           (F.FR 20000)

PIATTI, Antonio (1875-1962) Italian
£1023 $1851   (3-Dec-91 SY.MI5) Le lavandaie (40x29cm-16x11in) s.d.1920 cardboard
           (I.L 2200000)
£1301 $2356   (3-Dec-91 SY.MI2/R) Le sartine (35x26cm-14x10in) s.d.1923 cardboard
           (I.L 2800000)
£1627 $2944   (3-Dec-91 SY.MI87) Donne in un campo di fiori (27x34cm-11x13in) s.d.1923
           cardboard (I.L 3500000)
£4648 $8413   (3-Dec-91 SY.MI6/R) Bozzetti per la lettura del Decamerone
           (38x38cm-15x15in) s.d.1923 set of three (I.L 10000000)

PIAUBERT, Jean (1900-?) French
£2060 $3522   (22-Mar-92 I.N69/R) Aerienne (50x65cm-20x26in) s. board laid down on
           canvas (F.FR 20000)
£3568 $6636   (15-Jun-92 GL.P51/R) Abyssale (195x130cm-77x51in) s. (F.FR 35000)

PIAZZA, Calisto (1505-1561) Italian
£61453 $110000   (16-Jan-92 CH.NY124/R) Coronation of Virgin (262x135cm-103x53in) i. panel

PIAZZETTA, Giambattista (1682-1754) Italian
£17173 $30912   (19-Nov-91 F.R54/R) San Nicola da Tolentino. San Carlo Borromeo
           (31x23cm-12x9in) oval pair (I.L 37000000)
£7263 $13000   (14-Jan-92 SY.NY103/R) Study of young boy holding recorder
           (39x31cm-15x12in) black chk htd white chk
£22346 $40000   (14-Jan-92 SY.NY101/R) Study of Bravo. Study of kneeling figure holding
           stick (39x27cm-15x11in) black chk htd white chk double-sided
£67039 $120000   (14-Jan-92 SY.NY100/R) Study of girl with flowers in hair
           (39x27cm-15x11in) black chk htd white chk

PIAZZETTA, Giambattista (circle) (1682-1754) Italian
£7000 $12740   (13-Dec-91 C275/R) Saint Joseph with the sleeping Christ Child
           (54x42cm-21x17in)
£1000 $1920   (8-Jul-92 PH84/R) Study of back of nude woman, lying on side
           (30x43cm-12x17in) red chk htd white
£2000 $3480   (14-Apr-92 C138/R) Seated faun (54x40cm-21x16in) chk

PIAZZETTA, Giambattista (style) (1682-1754) Italian
£4000 $7200   (22-Nov-91 SWS15/R) Study of a young peasant girl and boy. Study of two
           peasant boyswith a bird cage (57x44cm-22x17in) pair
£1500 $2610   (13-Apr-92 S206/R) Study of reclining male nude (40x56cm-16x22in) red chk
           htd white

PIAZZONI, Gottardo (1872-?) Italian

£508	$900	(12-Feb-92 B.SF421/R) Summer, Kenfield, California, 1914 (22x26cm-9x10in) s. board
£734	$1300	(12-Feb-92 B.SF422/R) Boathouse (14x22cm-6x9in) s. s.d.02 verso board

PICABIA (1879-1953) French

£7003	$11975	(18-Mar-92 ARC.P11 a/R) Paysage, bord de riviere (16x27cm-6x11in) s.d.1904 (F.FR 68000)

PICABIA, Francis (1879-1953) French

£2043	$3575	(24-Feb-92 ARC.P29/R) Paysage et port mediterraneen (21x27cm-8x11in) s.d.1902 board (F.FR 20000)
£2043	$3575	(24-Feb-92 ARC.P28/R) Venise - Le redempteur et la Giudecca (25x33cm-10x13in) s.d.1900 panel (F.FR 20000)
£3049	$5305	(13-Apr-92 BG.P113) Les oliviers au bord de l'eau (23x31cm-9x12in) s. panel (F.FR 30000)
£3226	$5645	(5-Apr-92 ZZ.F107/R) Vue de Venise (26x34cm-10x13in) s.d.1902 panel (F.FR 31000)
£3330	$5827	(5-Apr-92 ZZ.F105/R) Barques de peche dans la baie (21x27cm-8x11in) s. panel (F.FR 32000)
£3488	$6000	(12-Oct-91 SY.NY20/R) Femme nue debout (29x18cm-11x7in) s. board
£3911	$7000	(9-May-92 CE.NY38/R) Peniches sur la riviere (23x32cm-9x13in) s.d.1902 panel
£4330	$7491	(23-Mar-92 GL.P176/R) Chapelle a Saint-Paul-de-Vence (41x33cm-16x13in) board (F.FR 42000)
£5000	$9550	(29-Jun-92 CSK95/R) Roses au vase blanc (45x37cm-18x15in) s. board
£5490	$9827	(15-Nov-91 GK.Z5248/R) Village view with farmhouse amongst trees (41x29cm-16x11in) s. (S.FR 14000)
£5587	$10000	(9-May-92 CE.NY39/R) Antibes (27x34cm-11x13in) s. canvasboard
£7320	$12663	(23-Mar-92 GL.P175/R) Jeudi (46x38cm-18x15in) s.d.1951 (F.FR 71000)
£7560	$13835	(3-Jun-92 L.K363/R) Les barques, Martigues (27x41cm-11x16in) s.d.1905 i.d.stretcher (DM 22000)
£7863	$13917	(10-Nov-91 ZZ.F180/R) Plage et rochers a Douarnenez (33x41cm-13x16in) s.d.1901 (F.FR 78000)
£13986	$24895	(30-Nov-91 VG.B181/R) Cassis (50x61cm-20x24in) s.d.1910 i.d.stretcher (DM 40000)
£15275	$28259	(12-Jun-92 AT.P17/R) Les Martigues (38x46cm-15x18in) s.d.1903 (F.FR 150000)
£19000	$32680	(16-Oct-91 S32/R) Bords du Loing (50x61cm-20x24in) s.
£19774	$35000	(6-Nov-91 CH.NY267/R) Le Sully a Nemours, effet de soleil (73x60cm-29x24in) s.d.1908 s.i.d.stretcher
£27000	$49140	(29-May-92 C420/R) Le chapeau jaune (61x50cm-24x20in) s.
£405	$734	(20-May-92 FB.P216) Femme de dos (27x21cm-11x8in) ink wash (F.FR 4000)
£1486	$2600	(28-Feb-92 SY.NY7 a/R) Portrait of woman (28x20cm-11x8in) init. graphite
£1810	$3295	(26-May-92 SY.MI97/R) Ritratto di donna (22x15cm-9x6in) s. chl pencil (I.L 4000000)
£2300	$3979	(25-Mar-92 S166/R) Portrait de jeune femme. Nu de dos s. pencil W/C wash two
£3714	$6500	(25-Feb-92 CH.NY62/R) Ou sont les ames des betes (26x22cm-10x9in) s. W/C pencil
£5295	$9637	(15-Dec-91 P.V16/R) Transparence, papillon (32x24cm-13x9in) s. W/C ink (F.FR 52000)
£6495	$11236	(23-Mar-92 GL.P146/R) Papillon (32x24cm-13x9in) s. W/C ink (F.FR 63000)
£7716	$14660	(24-Jun-92 GL.P181/R) Composition (53x44cm-21x17in) s. gouache board (F.FR 75000)
£8755	$15584	(29-Oct-91 BRO.B356/R) La dame au chien (61x48cm-24x19in) s. W/C (S.P 1600000)
£58000	$104980	(3-Dec-91 C179/R) Femmes espagnols (101x86cm-40x34in) gouache board

PICARD, Louis (1861-?) French

£4000	$7120	(27-Nov-91 S262/R) Soir au bord de la mer (59x91cm-23x36in) s.

PICART LE DOUX, Charles (1881-1959) French

£550	$979	(26-Nov-91 PH194) Still life with flowers in glass vase (46x38cm-18x15in) s.
£1917	$3298	(15-Oct-91 PPB.P61/R) Nu assis sur le sofa (55x46cm-22x18in) s. (F.FR 19000)

PICART, Bernard (1673-1733) French

£400	$728	(10-Dec-91 C83) A bacchanal (73x11cm-29x4in) red chk.ink wash oval
£989	$1730	(3-Apr-92 AGS.P182) L'enseignement d'un docteur. Scene de combat nocturne (8x17cm-3x7in) s.d.1702 pen wash htd.white two in same mount (F.FR 9500)
£994	$1769	(25-Nov-91 CH.AM40/R) Inca wedding (15x21cm-6x8in) s.d.1723 pen wash (D.FL 3200)

PICART, Jean Michel (style) (1600-1682) Flemish

£6076	$11423	(18-Dec-91 AT.P157/R) Vase de fleurs sur un entablement (71x53cm-28x21in) (F.FR 59000)

PICART, O (19th C) French

£994	$1700	(21-Mar-92 W.W26/R) Puss and family (58x41cm-23x16in) s.

PICASSO, Pablo (1881-1973) Spanish

£3528	$6104	(4-Oct-91 CSC.P99/R) Tete de taureau (22x15cm-9x6in) s.i.d.17.10.60 oil pastel (F.FR 35000)
£60000	$114600	(30-Jun-92 S44/R) Verre et radis (19x27cm-7x11in) s. d.44verso
£79096	$140000	(6-Nov-91 CH.NY302/R) Nature morte, fruit et pichet (16x24cm-6x9in) s.d.38
£174863	$320000	(11-May-92 CH.NY60/R) Nature morte au crane de mouton (50x61cm-20x24in) s.d.6.10.39
£174863	$320000	(12-May-92 CH.NY153/R) Tete d'homme (65x54cm-26x21in) s.d.9.7.69 panel
£191257	$350000	(14-May-92 SY.NY288/R) Tete de femme (41x24cm-16x9in) d.39 d.verso
£204918	$375000	(13-May-92 SY.NY94/R) Tete de mousquetaire (90x71cm-35x28in) d.72verso
£237288	$420000	(6-Nov-91 SY.NY57/R) Tete de femme aux boucles d'oreille (51x34cm-20x13in) s. paper laid down on canvas
£255885	$455476	(28-Nov-91 FB.P1/R) Esquisse pour les demoiselles d'Avignon (18x20cm-7x8in) (F.FR 2500000)
£296610	$525000	(6-Nov-91 SY.NY61/R) Compotier, bouteille et verre (46x57cm-18x22in)
£300000	$543000	(2-Dec-91 C37/R) Juan-les-Pins (38x46cm-15x18in) s.i.d.13 Aout 37
£338983	$600000	(6-Nov-91 SY.NY62/R) L'enlevement des sabines (73x60cm-29x24in) s.d.3.11.62 IIverso
£451977	$800000	(5-Nov-91 CH.NY52/R) Femme assise a la galette des rois (92x73cm-36x29in) i.d.65verso
£557830	$992938	(28-Nov-91 FB.P2/R) Guitare (54x65cm-21x26in) s. oil sable (F.FR 5450000)
£1912568	$3500000	(11-May-92 CH.NY52/R) Compotier et guitare (97x130cm-38x51in) s.d.13.2.32
£432	$821	(24-Jun-92 GL.P188) Visage aux cornes (9x7cm-4x3in) chl terracotta (F.FR 4200)
£1173	$2135	(11-Dec-91 CH.AM350) Bulls head (7x11cm-3x4in) s.d.63 felttip pen (D.FL 3800)
£1237	$2140	(23-Mar-92 GL.P121) Petite fille aux bras leves (8x4cm-3x2in) crayon board (F.FR 12000)
£1392	$2408	(23-Mar-92 GL.P122/R) Portrait de Francoise Gilot et de Claude dans son landau (21x24cm-8x9in) col.crayons cut card (F.FR 13500)
£1495	$2586	(23-Mar-92 GL.P123) Petite fille conduisant une charrette (21x7cm-8x3in) col.crayons card (F.FR 14500)
£1495	$2586	(23-Mar-92 GL.P125) Petit garcon conduisant une charrette (21x7cm-8x3in) col.crayons card (F.FR 14500)
£1598	$2764	(23-Mar-92 GL.P124/R) Paloma et son jouet (11x7cm-4x3in) col.crayons cut card (F.FR 15500)
£1840	$3368	(5-Feb-92 FB.P211) Portrait d'homme au chapeau (27x23cm-11x9in) col.crayon (F.FR 18000)
£1856	$3210	(23-Mar-92 GL.P120/R) La poule et l'escargot (9x9cm-4x4in) col.crayons cut board (F.FR 18000)
£2263	$4300	(24-Jun-92 GL.P189) Portrait de femme (8x6cm-3x2in) s. chl dr on pebble (F.FR 22000)
£2661	$4737	(27-Nov-91 AT.P52) Portrait du Pere Fredi (19x11cm-7x4in) blk.crayon (F.FR 26000)
£4802	$8500	(6-Nov-91 CH.NY116/R) Le vieillard (21x13cm-8x5in) pen graph paper on board
£5030	$8652	(12-Oct-91 SY.MO6/R) Etudes - nature mortes, personnages et paysages (20x26cm-8x10in) pencil thin plywood on card six one mount (F.FR 50000)
£5464	$10000	(14-May-92 SY.NY182/R) Les chevaux (23x32cm-9x13in) brush ink brown envelope on paper
£5800	$10498	(2-Dec-91 CSK141/R) Tete de taureau (31x23cm-12x9in) s.i.d.53 pencil
£6000	$10380	(25-Mar-92 S97/R) Faun (16x16cm-6x6in) s.d.7.7.60 wax crayons
£6557	$12000	(14-May-92 SY.NY147/R) La fille de l'artiste, Maya (34x20cm-13x8in) d.42 pencil graph paper
£6866	$12428	(6-Dec-91 GB.B6967/R) Colombe volant (21x22cm-8x9in) s. ochre (DM 19500)
£7000	$12110	(25-Mar-92 S96/R) Oeuf de Pacques (42x25cm-17x10in) s.d.31.3.61
£7975	$14595	(3-Feb-92 SD.P178/R) Nativite (21x13cm-8x5in) pen (F.FR 78000)
£8500	$15385	(2-Dec-91 CSK135/R) Tete de faune (33x25cm-13x10in) s.i.d.66 col.crayon
£8857	$15500	(25-Feb-92 SY.NY56/R) Tete d'homme (22x18cm-9x7in) s.d.68 pen
£9000	$15570	(25-Mar-92 S98/R) Femme au balcon (66x50cm-26x20in) s. wax crayons over lithograph
£9290	$17000	(11-May-92 CH.NY64/R) Tete masquee (29x24cm-11x9in) s.d.17.11.67 black felt-tip pen
£9500	$16340	(16-Oct-91 S76/R) Tete d'homme (16x12cm-6x5in) s.d.70 d.verso col.crayon felt-tip pencil card
£9500	$16435	(24-Mar-92 C106/R) Guitare et compotier (14x10cm-6x4in) s. W/C
£9836	$18000	(14-May-92 SY.NY195/R) Buste de femme. Tete de femme (29x22cm-11x9in) s.i.d.71 felt pen crayon board on canvas pair
£10000	$19100	(1-Jul-92 S207/R) Nu allonge (20x27cm-8x11in) s.d.41 ink card
£10500	$18165	(24-Mar-92 C80/R) Deux combattants (22x31cm-9x12in) s.d.69 red felt-tip pen
£11000	$21010	(30-Jun-92 C207/R) Tete de Mousquetaire (23x16cm-9x6in) s.d.20.6.69 W/C pen cardboard
£11000	$18920	(16-Oct-91 S77/R) Profils (19x14cm-7x6in) s.d.70 s.d.verso felt-tip pen pencil card
£11299	$20000	(6-Nov-91 CH.NY164/R) Pour Kertesz (27x21cm-11x8in) s.i.d.47 pen ink
£11992	$20627	(7-Oct-91 ANS.M85 a/R) Ser or no ser (29x40cm-11x16in) chl dr (S.P 2200000)
£12000	$20760	(24-Mar-92 C107/R) Le gueridon devant la fenetre (12x16cm-5x6in) s.d.1922 W/C ink
£12000	$21720	(4-Dec-91 S127/R) Nu debout (17x11cm-7x4in) s. pen
£12000	$21720	(3-Dec-91 C105/R) Deux garcons (38x47cm-15x19in) pencil paper laid down on board

PICASSO, Pablo (1881-1973) Spanish-cont.

£12994	$23000	(7-Nov-91 SY.NY129/R) Baigneuse au bord d'un Ruisseau et un Viellard (25x16cm-10x6in) s. pencil
£13078	$22495	(12-Oct-91 SY.MO32/R) La muse (42x25cm-17x10in) d.45 verso pencil two sheets (F.FR 130000)
£13115	$24000	(11-May-92 CH.NY76/R) Achille (27x21cm-11x8in) d.num.28.10.62.III pencil
£13115	$24000	(11-May-92 CH.NY87/R) Etude pour Dejeuner sur l'herbe XVI (27x43cm-11x17in) d.num.14.6.62.XVI pencil
£13559	$24000	(6-Nov-91 CH.NY119/R) Le fils du peintre Ricardo Canals (21x13cm-8x5in) s.i. pen
£15000	$28650	(1-Jul-92 S165/R) Etudes pour le cheval et pour les costumes des managers - Parade (27x20cm-11x8in) i. ink htd gouache
£15301	$28000	(13-May-92 CH.NY324/R) Deux tetes d'hommes. Nu couche et trois tetes de face (18x25cm-7x10in) s.d.11/10/68 black felt-tip pen board dbl-sided
£15301	$28000	(11-May-92 CH.NY49/R) La corrida (27x21cm-11x8in) s.d.1.10.59 s.d.10.11.59 felt pen brush pair
£15789	$28421	(21-Nov-91 L.K390/R) Le rameur (31x42cm-12x17in) s.d.1971 pencil board double-sided (DM 45000)
£15819	$28000	(7-Nov-91 SY.NY126/R) Seduction (30x21cm-12x8in) s. brush ink
£16000	$30560	(30-Jun-92 C208/R) Bouquet de fleurs (41x29cm-16x11in) s.i.d.17.7.57 pastel paper on board
£16393	$30000	(11-May-92 CH.NY45/R) Deux tetes de Dora Maar (12x18cm-5x7in) s. pencil
£16393	$30000	(11-May-92 CH.NY66/R) Etude pour Dejeuner sur l'herbe II (27x35cm-11x14in) d.num.16.6.62.II pencil
£18000	$32580	(3-Dec-91 C184/R) La danse (27x21cm-11x8in) d.29.4.56 pallpoint pen
£18579	$34000	(11-May-92 CH.NY75/R) Cavalier (21x27cm-8x11in) d.num.1.11.62.VI pencil
£18644	$33000	(7-Nov-91 SY.NY214/R) Colombe (51x66cm-20x26in) s. pencil
£19429	$34000	(25-Feb-92 SY.NY62/R) Les cravates (67x25cm-26x10in) s. col.crayon collage
£20339	$36000	(7-Nov-91 SY.NY132/R) Femme nue drapee (31x22cm-12x9in) s. pen
£22599	$40000	(7-Nov-91 SY.NY127/R) Homme debout accoude (30x20cm-12x8in) pencil
£24000	$45840	(30-Jun-92 C125/R) Jeune fille au doigt. Autoportrait et etudes de nu (15x25cm-6x10in) s. wash pen double-sided
£24644	$45591	(12-Jun-92 AT.P9/R) Femme dans un fauteuil (17x11cm-7x4in) s. crayon dr (F.FR 242000)
£25000	$45500	(29-May-92 C412/R) Picador (31x24cm-12x9in) s.d.19 pencil
£26923	$51154	(26-Jun-92 GK.B92/R) Bacchus et jeune femme nue (24x32cm-9x13in) s.d.1954 indian ink pen brush (S.FR 70000)
£28000	$53480	(1-Jul-92 S209/R) Tete d'homme barbu. Tete d'homme en profil (29x21cm-11x8in) s.d.3/6/72 W/C gouache double-sided
£30000	$54300	(3-Dec-91 C106/R) Au cafe (12x21cm-5x8in) s. chl.col.crayons
£32787	$60000	(11-May-92 CH.NY88/R) Etude pour Dejeuner sur l'herbe II (24x32cm-9x13in) d.num.1.8.62.II col.wax crayons pencil
£34286	$60000	(25-Feb-92 SY.NY38/R) Femme nue assise (35x25cm-14x10in) s.d.25 pen indian ink
£35000	$63350	(4-Dec-91 S126/R) Jeune homme et enfants (19x13cm-7x5in) s.i. pencil W/C
£35282	$61038	(4-Oct-91 CSC.P100/R) Scene classique et tete d'homme (39x50cm-15x20in) s.d.5 decembre MCMXXXIII crayon Indian ink (F.FR 350000)
£35519	$65000	(11-May-92 CH.NY65/R) Etude pour Dejeuner sur l'herbe I (24x32cm-9x13in) d.num.I.8.62.I col.pencils
£35519	$65000	(14-May-92 SY.NY159/R) Les trois graces (36x27cm-14x11in) s. indian ink
£36082	$62784	(21-Sep-91 SA.A591/R) Mousquetaire et nu depot (22x17cm-9x7in) s.d.71 s.d.verso pen brush indian ink (DM 105000)
£38251	$70000	(11-May-92 CH.NY74/R) Femme nue allongee (24x32cm-9x13in) d.num.24.12.61.I pencil htd white wax crayon
£39548	$70000	(6-Nov-91 SY.NY182/R) Trois tete d'hommes. Femme, fleur et oiseaux (49x60cm-19x24in) s.i.d.67 brush wash pen india ink double-sided
£40000	$76400	(30-Jun-92 C111/R) Chambre d'hotel (19x20cm-7x8in) col.crayons chl
£40000	$76400	(30-Jun-92 S38/R) Quatre nus au harem (22x31cm-9x12in) d.27-5-20 chalk
£42000	$76020	(4-Dec-91 S192/R) Dans l'atelier (26x35cm-10x14in) s.d.24.12.53 pen brush indian ink paper on card
£43716	$80000	(13-May-92 SY.NY37/R) Jeunne femme et homme age (13x9cm-5x4in) s. col.crayons over pen
£43716	$80000	(11-May-92 CH.NY7/R) Tete de femme, coffret et pomme (23x32cm-9x13in) s. pencil
£46000	$87860	(1-Jul-92 S211/R) Projet pour un livre (35x27cm-14x11in) two s.d.17.9.61 wax crayons ten
£46448	$85000	(11-May-92 CH.NY1/R) Femme nue debout (24x16cm-9x6in) s. brush indian ink
£54645	$100000	(13-May-92 CH.NY295/R) Le peintre (23x17cm-9x7in) s.d.23.5.70 d.23.5.70 verso pen298/R
£55000	$105050	(30-Jun-92 S46/R) Femme debout les bras ecartes (30x20cm-12x8in) d.5.7.38 pen Indian ink over chl
£55769	$105962	(26-Jun-92 GK.B93/R) Homme et femme nu dans un interieur (33x69cm-13x27in) s.i.d.1971 pencil (S.FR 145000)
£60606	$109697	(19-May-92 CH.AM192/R) Minotaure et nu (34x50cm-13x20in) s.d. pen (D.FL 200000)
£65574	$120000	(11-May-92 CH.NY27/R) Arlequin tenant une bouteille et femme (21x12cm-8x5in) s.d.1915 verso gouache W/C over pencil
£65856	$119200	(24-May-92 GL.P22/R) Tete d'homme. Etude (44x33cm-17x13in) s.d.39 gouache Indian ink double-sided (F.FR 650000)
£79096	$140000	(6-Nov-91 SY.NY47/R) Femme assise aux 4 Gats (31x28cm-12x11in) s.i. chl.pastel laid paper
£81967	$150000	(11-May-92 CH.NY21/R) Compotier, bouteille, pain sur la table (62x47cm-24x19in) s.verso chl graphite

1436

PICASSO, Pablo (1881-1973) Spanish-cont.
£84507	$145352	(12-Oct-91 SY.MO10/R) Le minotaure (33x44cm-13x17in) s.d.XXXIII pen indian ink paper on card (F.FR 840000)
£118644	$210000	(6-Nov-91 CH.NY178/R) Figures (49x61cm-19x24in) s.d.67 d.verso gouache W/C pen brush india ink
£120219	$220000	(11-May-92 CH.NY31/R) Pierrot (28x19cm-11x7in) s.d.1918 pencil
£120219	$220000	(13-May-92 CH.NY283/R) Composition (26x33cm-10x13in) s.d.XXXIV pen brush indian ink W/C
£123457	$234568	(24-Jun-92 FB.P45/R) Nature morte a la guitare (46x65cm-18x26in) s. pastel (F.FR 1200000)
£130785	$224950	(12-Oct-91 SY.MO31/R) Portrait de Francoise (31x24cm-12x9in) s.d.43 s.verso gouache brush pen indian ink (F.FR 1300000)
£141243	$250000	(5-Nov-91 CH.NY47/R) Nu debout (60x47cm-24x19in) s. chl
£142077	$260000	(11-May-92 CH.NY33/R) Guitare sur un gueridon (28x22cm-11x9in) s.d.12-1-21 gouache over pencil paper on board
£180000	$343800	(29-Jun-92 C17/R) Arlequin a cheval (22x12cm-9x5in) s.verso W/C pen paper on Japan paper
£190000	$362900	(30-Jun-92 S23/R) Le repas du pauvre (24x33cm-9x13in) s. W/C
£196721	$360000	(11-May-92 CH.NY30/R) Verre et bouteille de Bass (24x19cm-9x7in) s.collage gouache indian ink pencil paper board
£218579	$400000	(13-May-92 SY.NY9/R) Study of head for nude with drapery (31x24cm-12x9in) gouache W/C paper on canvas
£256831	$470000	(13-May-92 SY.NY71/R) Bouteille de bass, verre, paquet de table, pipe et as de trefle (24x26cm-9x10in) oil sawdust board
£341530	$625000	(13-May-92 SY.NY10/R) Study for nude with drapery (32x23cm-13x9in) s. gouache paper on canvas
£367232	$650000	(6-Nov-91 SY.NY25/R) Tete de femme (49x36cm-19x14in) s. gouache crayon pencil paper laid on panel
£382514	$700000	(11-May-92 CH.NY24/R) Bouteille de bass et guitare (47x63cm-19x25in) s.verso pastel chl ink
£409836	$750000	(13-May-92 SY.NY7/R) Etude pour l'acteur et deux profils de Fernande (47x32cm-19x13in) s. pencil
£480874	$880000	(11-May-92 CH.NY42/R) Homme a la sucette (67x44cm-26x17in) s.d.23.7.38 chl
£737705	$1350000	(12-May-92 CH.NY124/R) Femme au voile (107x72cm-42x28in) s. sanguine

PICAULT, C E (19/20th C) French
£650	$1157	(28-Nov-91 B77/R) Wooded river landscape (38x56cm-15x22in) s. panel

PICCINNI, Antonio (1846-1920) Italian
£1487	$2692	(3-Dec-91 SY.MI82/R) Barca in secca (35x21cm-14x8in) s. (I.L 3200000)

PICHETTE, James (1920-) French
£655	$1165	(28-Oct-91 GL.P235) Composition (46x54cm-18x21in) s.d.1958 (F.FR 6500)
£410	$738	(2-Feb-92 CSC.P102) Compositon rouge (18x14cm-7x6in) s.d.70 gouache (F.FR 4000)
£813	$1415	(13-Apr-92 GL.P177/R) Dans un sens interrogatif (67x102cm-26x40in) s.i.d.1968 gouache paper laid down on canvas (F.FR 8000)
£1321	$2299	(14-Apr-92 CSC.P54) Composition (41x31cm-16x12in) s.d.50 gouache (F.FR 13000)

PICHLER, Walter (1936-) Austrian
£2444	$4350	(31-Oct-91 D.V129/R) Untitled (30x42cm-12x17in) s.d.1977 pencil pen indian ink wash (A.S 50000)
£3910	$6960	(31-Oct-91 D.V128/R) Turmchen (29x42cm-11x17in) s.i.d.1980 pencil W/C (A.S 80000)

PICHOT GIRONES, Ramon Antonio (1872-1925) Spanish
£3297	$6000	(27-May-92 CH.NY230/R) Lady in her dressing room (40x32cm-16x13in) s. board

PICHOT, Ramon (1925-) Spanish
£740	$1317	(26-Nov-91 BRO.B352) Figura agitanada (90x71cm-35x28in) s. (S.P 135000)
£1400	$2408	(5-Mar-92 CSK183/R) Verano (81x65cm-32x26in) s. i.verso
£1915	$3486	(11-Dec-91 FER.M166/R) Tipos populares (24x20cm-9x8in) (S.P 350000)
£3557	$6189	(16-Apr-92 FB.P83/R) Ricon de Estudio (46x55cm-18x22in) s. i.verso (F.FR 35000)

PICK, Anton (1840-?) Austrian
£700	$1211	(25-Mar-92 PHI571) Figures before chalets at the lake's edge in continental lake landscape (47x67cm-19x26in) s.

PICK, Anton (attrib) (1840-?) Austrian
£528	$956	(3-Dec-91 FN.S2382) Woman collecting brushwood by stream in mountain landscape, evening (41x66cm-16x26in) i. (DM 1500)
£528	$956	(3-Dec-91 FN.S2383) Peasant woman with child by stream in mountain landscape, evening (41x66cm-16x26in) s.i. (DM 1500)

PICKARD, Louise (c.1865-1928) British
£900	$1602	(28-Nov-91 L367/R) The Thames - view from Chelsea (89x127cm-35x50in) s.

PICKENOY, Nicolaes Elias see ELIAS, Nicolaes

PICKERING, Henry (attrib) (18th C) British
£6500 $11635   (13-Nov-91 S38/R) Portrait of lady standing in landscape wearing riding habit (124x100cm-49x39in)

PICKERING, Joseph Langsdale (1845-1912) British
£600 $1020   (24-Oct-91 CSK134/R) A mare and foal in a field by a stream (36x53cm-14x21in) s.d.1873

PICKERSGILL, Frederick Richard (1820-1900) British
£720 $1238   (8-Oct-91 PH130) Perseus rescuing Andromeda (77x63cm-30x25in)
£4286 $7500   (19-Feb-92 CH.NY179/R) Three Graces (56x91cm-22x36in)
£12088 $22000   (28-May-92 SY.NY63/R) Flight of Pagan Deities (112x196cm-44x77in) init.d.1856

PICKERSGILL, Henry William (1782-1875) British
£2800 $5180   (11-Jun-92 CSK71) Portrait of brother and sister in landscape (151x119cm-59x47in)

PICKERSGILL, Henry William (attrib) (1782-1875) British
£1344 $2500   (19-Jun-92 S.BM170) Portrait of gentleman in black coat and stock with yellow waistcoat (76x64cm-30x25in)
£3974 $6796   (18-Mar-92 D.V259/R) Portrait of General John Nowater wearing uniform before landscape (127x101cm-50x40in) (A.S 80000)

PICKNELL, William Lamb (1854-1897) American
£2762 $5000   (4-Dec-91 D.NY4/R) Along river's edge (51x91cm-20x36in) s.
£4111 $7852   (1-Jul-92 FB.P130) Le cavalier en hiver (28x24cm-11x9in) s.d.1889 (F.FR 40000)
£15363 $27500   (14-Nov-91 GRO.B96/R) Watering trough (91x76cm-36x30in) s.

PICO, Jose (1904-) Spanish
£929 $1701   (13-May-92 FER.M155/R) Balcones (100x81cm-39x32in) s.d.85 s.i.d.verso (S.P 170000)

PICOLO Y LOPEZ, Manuel (1850-1892) Spanish
£602 $1096   (26-May-92 DUR.M125/R) La vanguardia del ejercito (16x22cm-6x9in) s. W/C (S.P 110000)

PICOT, Jean Claude (?) ?
£881 $1568   (26-Nov-91 J.M1092) La promenade a Caboury (43x58cm-17x23in) s. (A.D 2000)
£881 $1568   (26-Nov-91 J.M31) Le Pont d'Austerlitz (43x52cm-17x20in) s. (A.D 2000)

PICOTTE, Michel (1947-) Canadian
£811 $1467   (24-May-92 AT.P77) Peint en vert (52x62cm-20x24in) s. acrylic (F.FR 8000)
£1013 $1834   (24-May-92 AT.P76) Stratte Kabaslitique (92x92cm-36x36in) s. mixed media canvas (F.FR 10000)

PICOU, Henri Pierre (1824-1895) French
£1796 $3250   (6-Dec-91 E.EDM729/R) Portrait of semi-draped woman weighing cupid against butterfly in scale (74x51cm-29x20in) s.
£2035 $3642   (17-Nov-91 FB.P122/R) Cupidon tenant une pomme (55x46cm-22x18in) s.d.1891 (F.FR 20000)
£66735 $120123   (18-Nov-91 AT.P367/R) La partie d'echecs (191x283cm-75x111in) s. (F.FR 650000)

PIDGEON, Henry Clark (1807-1880) British
£400 $732   (4-Jun-92 DLY287/R) Canal barge (30x53cm-12x21in) W/C
£400 $732   (4-Jun-92 DLY286/R) Twickenham Ferry (30x51cm-12x20in) s.d.1853 W/C
£450 $806   (5-May-92 SWS210/R) Bringing in the harvest (35x53cm-14x21in) s.d.1862 W/C bodycol.scratching out

PIEDMONTESE SCHOOL, 18th C Italian
£2324 $4206   (3-Dec-91 SY.MI234) Ritratto di gentiluomo (99x972cm-39x383in) oval (I.L 5000000)
£4416 $8391   (23-Jun-92 D.V156/R) Scholar in his study (140x108cm-55x43in) (A.S 90000)
£5578 $10095   (3-Dec-91 SY.MI232/R) Il trionfo di Nettuno (59x119cm-23x47in) panel gold ground (I.L 12000000)
£6200 $11036   (30-Oct-91 S156/R) Portrait of lady (128x102cm-50x40in)

PIELER, Franz Xaver (1879-1952) Austrian
£500 $930   (16-Jun-92 PH8) Still life with vase of mixed flowers on stone ledge (30x24cm-12x9in) s. board
£1203 $2093   (18-Sep-91 N.M651/R) Bunch of flowers on table and grasshopper (39x31cm-15x12in) s. panel (DM 3500)
£1236 $2163   (20-Feb-92 D.V386/R) Still life of flowers (50x40cm-20x16in) s. panel (A.S 25000)
£1453 $2500   (15-Oct-91 CE.NY219/R) Flowers with butterflies and ladybugs on marble ledges (28x22cm-11x9in) s. two
£1546 $2691   (18-Sep-91 N.M650/R) Bunch of summer flowers in vase on table and butterfly (41x33cm-16x13in) s. panel (DM 4500)
£1832 $3500   (16-Jul-92 SY.NY426/R) Still life of flowers and bird's nest (80x58cm-31x23in) s.
£2062 $3588   (18-Sep-91 N.M649/R) Bunch of summer flowers in vase on marble ledge (80x57cm-31x22in) s. panel (DM 6000)

PIELER, Franz Xaver (1879-1952) Austrian-cont.
£2737 $4926   (22-Nov-91 SA.A1643/R) Still life of flowers (30x39cm-12x15in) s. panel (DM 7800)

PIELMANN, Edmund Georg (1923-1985) German
£741 $1341   (22-May-92 EA.Z82) Venice (93x75cm-37x30in) s. (S.FR 2000)

PIEMONT, Nicolas (1644-1709) Dutch
£12000 $23040   (8-Jul-92 S107/R) Anglers by waterfall in italianate landscape (101x82cm-40x32in) s.

PIEMONT, Nicolas (attrib) (1644-1709) Dutch
£1011 $1800   (22-Jan-92 D.NY60) Cowherd beside waterfall (122x86cm-48x34in)

PIENE, Otto (1928-) German
£1890 $3459   (2-Jun-92 L.K877/R) Mutation (66x47cm-26x19in) s.i.d.1977 fire gouache (DM 5500)
£1890 $3459   (2-Jun-92 L.K876/R) Scirocco (96x66cm-38x26in) s.i.d.1975 fire gouache (DM 5500)
£2797 $4979   (25-Nov-91 WK.M810/R) Purple heart (73x102cm-29x40in) s.i.d.1983 mixed media fire gouache board (DM 8000)
£3147 $5601   (30-Nov-91 VG.B353/R) Orange becomes green (68x47cm-27x19in) s.i.d.1966 fire gouache velvet board (DM 9000)

PIENKOWSKI, Ignacy (1877-1948) Polish
£509 $926   (15-Dec-91 REM.W31) In a park (45x36cm-18x14in) s. board (P.Z 10000000)
£2381 $4477   (21-Dec-91 PSA.W17) Nude (96x67cm-38x26in) s. board (P.Z 46000000)

PIEPER, Christian (1843-?) German
£544 $952   (19-Feb-92 D.V76) Winter in Venice (26x27cm-10x11in) canvas on panel (A.S 11000)

PIER FRANCESCO (15th C) Italian
£34000 $60520   (1-Nov-91 C23/R) Madonna and Child with infant Saint John the Baptist and adoring angel (71x55cm-28x22in) canvas on panel

PIERCE, Charles Franklin (1844-1920) American
£1287 $2200   (13-Mar-92 S.BM179/R) Enjoying spirng's warmth, pasture view with sheep (38x53cm-15x21in) s.i.

PIERCE, H Winthrop (1850-?) American
£782 $1400   (14-Nov-91 CE.NY174/R) Bundling wheat (68x56cm-27x22in) s.d.1884

PIERCE, Lucy Valentine (1887-1974) American
£565 $1000   (12-Feb-92 B.SF602/R) Portrait of Ina Story (76x63cm-30x25in) s.

PIERNEEF, Jacob Hendrik (1886-1957) South African
£2187 $3805   (13-Apr-92 SY.J335/R) Aloes (65x53cm-26x21in) s.d.30 board (SA.R 11000)
£2823 $4996   (4-Nov-91 SY.J281/R) Willow trees on river bank (29x39cm-11x15in) s.d.28 board (SA.R 14000)
£2823 $4996   (4-Nov-91 SY.J279/R) Free State thunderstorm (29x33cm-11x13in) s. board (SA.R 14000)
£3226 $5710   (4-Nov-91 SY.J280/R) Landscape Great Karoo (31x46cm-12x18in) s.d.1931 board (SA.R 16000)
£3226 $5710   (4-Nov-91 SY.J277/R) Karoo landscape (27x31cm-11x12in) s.d.24 board (SA.R 16000)
£3232 $5527   (12-Mar-92 SY.J410/R) Farm buildings, Cape (29x39cm-11x15in) s. board (SA.R 16000)
£3579 $6227   (13-Apr-92 SY.J332/R) Farm, Derdepoort (19x29cm-7x11in) s. board (SA.R 18000)
£3831 $6780   (4-Nov-91 SY.J274/R) Clump of trees in landscape (37x50cm-15x20in) sd.1923 (SA.R 19000)
£4175 $7264   (13-Apr-92 SY.J330/R) Wooded landscape, Lowveld (49x65cm-19x26in) s. (SA.R 21000)
£4435 $7851   (4-Nov-91 SY.J276/R) Cottage in mountain landscape (30x46cm-12x18in) s.d.29 board (SA.R 22000)
£4938 $8395   (21-Oct-91 SY.J344/R) Tall trees in mountain landscape (30x45cm-12x18in) s.d.25 board (SA.R 24000)
£5567 $9686   (13-Apr-92 SY.J328/R) Roodeplaat Dam (35x51cm-14x20in) studio st. board (SA.R 28000)
£5964 $10378   (13-Apr-92 SY.J334/R) Evening in valley (38x51cm-15x20in) s.d.1921 (SA.R 30000)
£6362 $11070   (13-Apr-92 SY.J333/R) Old harbour, Hermanus (44x60cm-17x24in) s.d.49 board (SA.R 32000)
£7157 $12453   (13-Apr-92 SY.J326/R) Premier mine (65x53cm-26x21in) s.d.32 i.verso board (SA.R 36000)
£7661 $13560   (4-Nov-91 SY.J278/R) Bushveld landscape with trees (40x52cm-16x20in) s.d.47 (SA.R 38000)
£8350 $14529   (13-Apr-92 SY.J331/R) Extensive mountain landscape with storm clouds (40x55cm-16x22in) s.d.52 (SA.R 42000)
£9073 $16058   (4-Nov-91 SY.J272/R) Cape farmhouse and outbuildings (35x54cm-14x21in) s.d.1922 casein (SA.R 45000)
£11928 $20755   (13-Apr-92 SY.J329/R) Inheemse Bome, Shwingwedsi (45x61cm-18x24in) s.d.55 i.verso (SA.R 60000)

PIERNEEF, Jacob Hendrik (1886-1957) South African-cont.

£13105	$23196	(4-Nov-91 SY.J275/R) Street in Tulbagh (46x61cm-18x24in) s. board (SA.R 65000)
£14911	$25944	(13-Apr-92 SY.J325/R) Landscape, Northern Transvaal (50x65cm-20x26in) s. (SA.R 75000)
£22863	$39781	(13-Apr-92 SY.J324/R) Extensive landscape with summer clouds (60x75cm-24x30in) s.d.48 (SA.R 115000)
£30242	$53528	(4-Nov-91 SY.J273/R) Hardekool Bome, Bosveld, N.TVL (61x81cm-24x32in) s.d.1944 (SA.R 150000)
£497	$865	(13-Apr-92 SY.J322) Wilgerboom Naby Sabie (19x27cm-7x11in) s.d.19 W/C (SA.R 2500)
£517	$899	(13-Apr-92 SY.J127) De wild (26x37cm-10x15in) s.i. pencil W/C (SA.R 2600)
£755	$1315	(13-Apr-92 SY.J335 a) Pontdrif, Limpopo (37x52cm-15x20in) s.i.d.1956 pencil (SA.R 3800)
£895	$1557	(13-Apr-92 SY.J321/R) Wildevyeboom, Hectorspruit (35x51cm-14x20in) s.i.d.1944 pencil (SA.R 4500)
£926	$1574	(21-Oct-91 SY.J343) Battersea Bridge, London (23x34cm-9x13in) s.i.d.1934 pencil wash (SA.R 4500)
£1070	$1819	(21-Oct-91 SY.J345) Swaziland (22x29cm-9x11in) s.i. pencil wash (SA.R 5200)
£1111	$1900	(12-Mar-92 SY.J411) Mountain landscape (41x54cm-16x21in) s.d.1917 gouache (SA.R 5500)
£1292	$2249	(13-Apr-92 SY.J323) Limpopo (37x52cm-15x20in) s.i.d.1956 pencil W/C (SA.R 6500)
£1411	$2498	(4-Nov-91 SY.J271/R) Cottage in the Karoo (29x47cm-11x19in) s.d.1920 W/C (SA.R 7000)
£1613	$2855	(4-Nov-91 SY.J270/R) Karoo Farm (30x47cm-12x19in) s. W/C (SA.R 8000)

PIERO DI COSIMO (style) (1462-1521) Italian

£1900	$3420	(21-Nov-91 CSK71) Madonna (34x25cm-13x10in) panel

PIERON, Henry (19th C) French

£1000	$1810	(21-May-92 CSK128/R) View Prayon pres Liege, Belgique (84x60cm-33x24in) s.d.1874 s.i.d.1874 verso panel

PIEROTTI, Giuseppe (attrib) (19th C) Italian

£486	$850	(23-Sep-91 S.SL255) Sleeping putto (64x48cm-25x19in) s.

PIERRAKOS, Alkis (1920-) ?

£685	$1200	(26-Sep-91 FB.P126) Fenetre (85x65cm-33x26in) s.d.77 i.verso (F.FR 6800)

PIERRAT, Nicolas-Constant (1829-1910) French

£1150	$2036	(4-Nov-91 WW95) Still life of vase of flowers (65x54cm-26x21in) s.
£3706	$6634	(15-Nov-91 ZOF.Z1416/R) Still life with vegetables, cheese and apples (90x132cm-35x52in) s. (S.FR 9450)

PIERRE, Jean Baptiste Marie (1713-1789) French

£412	$713	(27-Mar-92 CD.P1) Jeunes filles dans un paysage (18x26cm-7x10in) wash (F.FR 4000)

PIERRE, Jean Baptiste Marie (circle) (1713-1789) French

£11602	$21000	(22-May-92 SY.NY149/R) Mercury and Argus (160x131cm-63x52in)

PIERRE, Jean Baptiste Marie (style) (1713-1789) French

£3000	$5400	(21-Nov-91 C154/R) Reclining nudes with cupids (32x40cm-13x16in) pair

PIERRI, Orlando (1913-1992) Argentinian

£521	$1000	(4-Aug-92 V.BA77) Paisaje (48x76cm-19x30in)
£917	$1650	(20-Nov-91 V.BA71) El viejito (33x22cm-13x9in) d.1948
£950	$1700	(6-May-92 V.BA75) El bosque (50x70cm-20x28in)

PIERRON, Charles (19/20th C) ?

£713	$1304	(2-Jun-92 AT.P176) Dans les jardins derriere la mosquee (19x28cm-7x11in) s. W/C (F.FR 7000)

PIET, Fernand (1869-1942) French

£515	$881	(11-Mar-92 CSC.P71/R) Avant la danse (14x17cm-6x7in) W/C (F.FR 5000)
£567	$970	(11-Mar-92 CSC.P33/R) Trois Mignonnes au Cabaret (14x20cm-6x8in) W/C (F.FR 5500)

PIETERCELIE, Alfred (1879-1955) Belgian

£917	$1577	(12-Oct-91 KV.L236) Yellow chrysanthemums (60x70cm-24x28in) s.d.1924 (B.FR 55000)

PIETERS, Evert (1856-1932) Dutch

£1040	$1851	(30-Oct-91 CH.AM127/R) Faggot gatherers loading cart at sunset (36x26cm-14x10in) panel (D.FL 3400)
£1070	$1894	(5-Nov-91 SY.AM147/R) Coastal view in South of France (49x60cm-19x24in) s.d.1921 (D.FL 3500)
£1520	$2600	(13-Mar-92 S.BM167/R) Interior scene (61x48cm-24x19in) s.
£1529	$2661	(14-Apr-92 SY.AM136) Sunset s.d.28 (D.FL 5000)
£2857	$5000	(20-Feb-92 SY.NY204/R) Awaiting ferry (41x60cm-16x24in) s.
£3041	$5200	(13-Mar-92 WOL.C504/R) Coastal scene (56x64cm-22x25in) s.
£4478	$7970	(25-Nov-91 W.T1963/R) Young mother and children (107x87cm-42x34in) s. (C.D 9000)

PIETERS, Evert (1856-1932) Dutch-cont.
£8000	$14000	(20-Feb-92 SY.NY202/R) Toy horse (78x92cm-31x36in) s.
£8046	$14000	(13-Sep-91 S.W2780/R) Afternoon meal (91x79cm-36x31in) s.
£8140	$14000	(16-Oct-91 CH.NY225/R) The contented family (79x93cm-31x37in) s.
£8242	$15000	(28-May-92 SY.NY237/R) Clamming at Scheveningen (80x129cm-31x51in) s.
£8869	$15697	(5-Nov-91 SY.AM299/R) In conservatory (74x62cm-29x24in) s. (D.FL 29000)
£9174	$16239	(5-Nov-91 SY.AM97/R) Artist's wife standing on balcony overlooking Manhattan (108x87cm-43x34in) s.d.1919 (D.FL 30000)
£12791	$22000	(16-Oct-91 CH.NY226/R) Children in a field (62x51cm-24x20in) s.
£14835	$27000	(28-May-92 SY.NY115/R) In garden (95x82cm-37x32in) s.
£612	*$1083*	*(5-Nov-91 SY.AM326) On beach (43x59cm-17x23in) W/C (D.FL 2000)*

PIETERSZ, Pieter II (circle) (1578-1631) Flemish
£950	$1663	(25-Feb-92 PH107/R) Portrait of lady wearing lace bonnet and ruff collar (30x24cm-12x9in) panel

PIETRI, Pietro Antonio de (1663-1716) Italian
£4800	$8352	(15-Apr-92 C162/R) The Nativity. The Madonna and Child with midwives (27x23cm-11x9in) one i.verso painted ovals paper on canvas two
£1173	*$2100*	*(14-Jan-92 SY.NY141/R) Allegory of Papal Rome, portrait in cartouche above (27x20cm-11x8in) pen wash over red chk*

PIETRO, Giovanni di (?) Italian
£8840	$16000	(21-May-92 CH.NY17/R) Subject from Sienese History (27x33cm-11x13in) tempera panel

PIETROCOLA, Floriano (1809-?) Italian
£947	*$1620*	*(13-Mar-92 FN.S2906) Portrait of Neapoletan woman (54x43cm-21x17in) s.d.1880 oval (DM 2700)*

PIETRONI, Antonio (?) ?
£1178	$2179	(8-Jun-92 CH.R599) Ritorno - S.Marino (48x60cm-19x24in) s.d.1930 panel (I.L 2600000)

PIFFARD, Harold (fl.1895-1899) British
£500	$870	(15-Apr-92 PHL176) Tyrolean (63x51cm-25x20in)
£1200	$2196	(3-Jun-92 S177/R) The tamboureen girl (76x63cm-30x25in) s.
£1550	$2697	(15-Apr-92 PHL175/R) New bonnet (63x50cm-25x20in) s.i.
£3400	$6222	(3-Jun-92 S176/R) Spring blossom (76x63cm-30x25in) s.

PIGAL, Edme Jean (1798-1872) French
£773	$1400	(22-May-92 S.BM34/R) War stories - in the service of Napoleon III (33x25cm-13x10in) s. panel

PIGALLE, Jean Baptiste (attrib) (1714-1785) French
£2235	*$4000*	*(15-Jan-92 CH.NY86/R) Putti with bows and arrows. Putti with garlands and wreaths (13x32cm-5x13in) with i. black white chk pair*

PIGHLEIN, Elimar Ulrich Bruno (1848-1894) German
£1404	$2526	(22-Nov-91 SA.A1778/R) Girl seated on red sofa (95x80cm-37x31in) s.i. (DM 4000)

PIGNATELLI, Ercole (1935-) Italian
£463	$825	(26-Nov-91 SY.MI53/R) Paesggio meridionale (70x50cm-28x20in) s.d.64 s.init.d.verso (I.L 1000000)

PIGNOLAT, Pierre (attrib) (1838-1913) Swiss
£912	$1633	(6-May-92 GD.B1010) Wooded landscape with figures (26x45cm-10x18in) board (S.FR 2500)

PIGNON, Edouard (1905-) French
£790	$1430	(20-May-92 FB.P217) La Catalane (62x47cm-24x19in) s.d.1945 paper (F.FR 7800)
£3931	$6801	(6-Oct-91 BG.P156/R) La Pleureuse (81x60cm-32x24in) s.d.1946 (F.FR 39000)
£4913	$8745	(1-Dec-91 I.N54/R) Cueillette de asmin (38x55cm-15x22in) s.d.1955 (F.FR 48000)
£8247	$14268	(29-Mar-92 P.V63/R) Colline de Sanary (114x146cm-45x57in) s.d.1957 (F.FR 80000)
£10286	$18000	(25-Feb-92 SY.NY91/R) Nature morte (73x60cm-29x24in) s.d.44
£11975	$21794	(9-Dec-91 CH.R150/R) Sans titre (195x130cm-77x51in) s.d.1970 (I.L 26000000)
£21494	$38260	(1-Dec-91 I.N52/R) Bataille multicolore (114x195cm-45x77in) s.d.1954 i.stretcher (F.FR 210000)
£737	*$1326*	*(21-Nov-91 L.K400/R) Chevre (15x21cm-6x8in) s.d.57 pen wash (DM 2100)*
£965	*$1680*	*(13-Apr-92 GL.P71) Tete de guerrier (56x76cm-22x30in) s.d.1968 gouache paper laid down on canvas (F.FR 9500)*
£1007	*$1712*	*(24-Oct-91 D.P122) Barques de peche au port (46x61cm-18x24in) s.i.d.1er Janvier 58 W/C (F.FR 10000)*
£1309	*$2226*	*(27-Oct-91 LT.P97/R) La sortie de la gare (34x49cm-13x19in) s.d.1929 gouache (F.FR 13000)*
£1340	*$2319*	*(23-Mar-92 GL.P150/R) Maternites (20x26cm-8x10in) s.d.1941 W/C Indian ink (F.FR 13000)*
£1931	*$3360*	*(13-Apr-92 GL.P72/R) Nues au parasol (57x78cm-22x31in) s.d.1983 gouache (F.FR 19000)*

PIGNON, Edouard (1905-) French-cont.

£2039	$3792	(15-Jun-92 GL.P22/R) *Femme assise (62x47cm-24x19in) s.d.1945 gouache (F.FR 20000)*
£2051	$3672	(19-Jan-92 CC.P78) *Composition (58x78cm-23x31in) s.d.1962 W/C gouache pastel (F.FR 20000)*
£2303	$4099	(1-Dec-91 I.N53/R) *Ostende (25x42cm-10x17in) s.d.1946 (F.FR 22500)*
£2317	$4124	(26-Nov-91 SY.MI34/R) *Nu blanc au parasol blanc (58x77cm-23x30in) s.d.71 s.init.d.verso gouache paper on canvas (I.L 5000000)*
£2371	$4102	(29-Mar-92 P.V52/R) *Nu rose (55x76cm-22x30in) s.d.1980 gouache (F.FR 23000)*
£2559	$4555	(1-Dec-91 I.N50/R) *Battage a Filacciano (58x78cm-23x31in) s.d.1960 W/C (F.FR 25000)*
£2577	$4459	(23-Mar-92 CC.P22) *Sans titre (58x78cm-23x31in) s.d. W/C (F.FR 25000)*
£2716	$4672	(8-Oct-91 CC.P27/R) *Baigneuses (56x76cm-22x30in) s.d.1978 W/C (F.FR 27000)*
£2887	$4936	(11-Mar-92 LGB.P128/R) *Ostende, le pecheur (48x64cm-19x25in) s.d.1948 W/C (F.FR 28000)*
£2968	$5284	(1-Dec-91 I.N55/R) *Cueillette de jasmin (50x65cm-20x26in) s.d.1955 gouache laid down on canvas (F.FR 29000)*
£3018	$5191	(12-Oct-91 GL.P19/R) *Les troncs d'arbres (47x62cm-19x24in) s.d.1961 W/C (F.FR 30000)*
£3071	$5466	(1-Dec-91 I.N49/R) *Tete d'homme (55x74cm-22x29in) s.d.1968 W/C paper laid down on canvas (F.FR 30000)*
£3080	$5544	(19-Nov-91 FB.P191/R) *Ostende (56x37cm-22x15in) s.d.47 W/C (F.FR 30000)*
£3244	$5547	(22-Mar-92 I.N60/R) *Batage (50x64cm-20x25in) s.d.1960 gouache W/C (F.FR 31500)*
£3292	$5959	(6-Dec-91 GL.P159/R) *Les batisseurs (45x60cm-18x24in) s.d.1953 gouache W/C Indian ink (F.FR 32000)*

PIGNONI, Simone (attrib) (1614-1698) Italian

£1100	$2002	(11-Dec-91 PH191/R) *Putti dancing with basket of fruit held above their heads (28x24cm-11x9in) chk.*

PIGNONI, Simone (style) (1614-1698) Italian

£1500	$2700	(21-Nov-91 CSK103) Judith (87x74cm-34x29in)

PIGOTT, Marjorie (1904-1990) Canadian

£675	$1195	(6-Nov-91 SY.T183) *Wildflowers (55x61cm-22x24in) s. W/C (C.D 1350)*

PIGOTT, W H (c.1810-1901) British

£3200	$5920	(12-Jun-92 K504/R) Rural landscape with shire horse ploughing match (64x140cm-25x55in) s.d.1896

PIGOTT, Walter Henry (c.1810-1901) British

£2000	$3700	(12-Jun-92 C209/R) Welsh mountaineers (129x86cm-51x34in) s.d.1876
£3000	$5160	(16-Oct-91 PHL342/R) Figure fishing and cattle grazing by river before Haddon Hall (74x125cm-29x49in) s.d.95

PIGUENIT, William Charles (1836-1914) Australian

£2600	$4420	(22-Oct-91 C109/R) Australian landscape (48x69cm-19x27in) s.d.1893
£3111	$5320	(17-Mar-92 JRL.S200/R) Mountain range (59x90cm-23x35in) s. (A.D 7000)
£4405	$7930	(19-Nov-91 JRL.S270/R) Early morning at Southport (40x60cm-16x24in) s.d.1903 (A.D 10000)
£4500	$7650	(22-Oct-91 C97/R) Sydney harbour (25x39cm-10x15in) s.d.1883 board
£21368	$38034	(27-Apr-92 J.M107/R) Sunset after the shower (45x75cm-18x30in) s. (A.D 50000)

PIGUET, Rodolphe (1840-1915) Swiss

£553	$996	(19-Nov-91 GS.B3231) *View of monastery of Romainmotier in spring landscape (32x46cm-13x18in) s. pastel (S.FR 1400)*

PIKE, John (1911-) American

£575	$1000	(13-Sep-91 S.W2345/R) *Passing patrol (48x69cm-19x27in) s. W/C*

PIKE, Sidney (fl.1880-1901) British

£632	$1113	(12-Apr-92 HOR.H26) Mother and child (36x23cm-14x9in) s.i.d.1884 (F.M 5000)
£650	$1118	(11-Oct-91 K499/R) Sheep resting and grazing in sun lit orchard (20x28cm-8x11in) s.d.1895
£850	$1658	(15-Jan-92 CSK163) Cattle in meadow (25x46cm-10x18in) s.

PIKE, William H (1846-1908) British

£4200	$7308	(17-Sep-91 ZZ.B687/R) Polperro, busy harbour scene with figures unloading cargo (102x150cm-40x59in) with indist.sig.d.1888
£1300	$2262	(17-Sep-91 ZZ.B688) *Charlestown, Cornwall, busy harbour scene with figures unloading cargo (53x91cm-21x36in) s.d.1883 W/C*

PILLATI, Henryk (1832-1894) Polish

£671	$1201	(17-Nov-91 REM.W23) Old woman and boy (13x11cm-5x4in) s. panel (P.Z 13000000)

PILLE, Jacques (20th C) ?

£1076	$1948	(23-May-92 KV.L253) Figure with amulet (78x71cm-31x28in) s.d.1990 (B.FR 65000)

PILLEAU, Henry (1815-1899) British
£1800 $3060   *(23-Oct-91 S245) Panoramic view of Jerusalem (8x31cm-3x12in) mono W/C over pencil*

PILLEMENT (studio) (18th C) French
£3327 $5888   (6-Nov-91 LT.P76/R) Scene de naufrage (54x80cm-21x31in) bears sig. (F.FR 33000)

PILLEMENT, Jean (1728-1808) French
£3477 $5946   (18-Mar-92 D.V68/R) Shepherds resting in wooded landscape (55x65cm-22x26in) oval (A.S 70000)
£3893 $7008   (29-Jan-92 LC.P16/R) Cavalier au premier plan d'un paysage montagneux et boise (23x33cm-9x13in) s.d.1788 (F.FR 38000)
£4162 $7284   (30-Mar-92 ZZ.F59/R) Scene de peche au Portugal (21x27cm-8x11in) (F.FR 40000)
£8313 $14547   (18-Feb-92 DUR.M45/R) Marina (53x78cm-21x31in) s.d.1785 (S.P 1500000)
£10000 $17400   (15-Apr-92 C143/R) Wooded hilly landscape with peasants, goat and sheep on track near ruins (54x76cm-21x30in) paper on canvas
£19553 $35000   (16-Jan-92 CH.NY30/R) View of Tagus, Portugal, with fisherfolk resting on rocks by moored boat (47x68cm-19x27in) bears sig.d.1790
£22380 $40956   (13-May-92 LC.P9/R) Paysage de riviere au Portugal (39x58cm-15x23in) s.d. (F.FR 220000)
£24742 $42804   (26-Mar-92 PIC.P6/R) Lavandieres dans un paysage de cascades. Bord de mer au Portugal (48x65cm-19x26in) one s.d.1794 one bears sig.d.1793 pair (F.FR 240000)
£1900 $3306   *(13-Apr-92 S262/R) Landscapes- two peasants by stream, with watermill. Man and dog by tree and pond (29x41cm-11x16in) s.d.1772 black chk card pair*
£8380 $15000   *(15-Jan-92 CH.NY111/R) Coastal landscape with figures looking at sunset (39x58cm-15x23in) s. pastel*

PILLEMENT, Jean (attrib) (1728-1808) French
£3500 $6125   (27-Feb-92 CSK154) Shipwrecked figures on a rocky coast (53x77cm-21x30in) bears sig.

PILLEMENT, Jean (circle) (1728-1808) French
£1404 $2500   (22-Jan-92 SY.NY211/R) Figures by waterfall (46x74cm-18x29in)
£7821 $14000   (17-Jan-92 SY.NY145/R) Chinese musicians in stylized gardens (162x51cm-64x20in) three mounted as a screen
£11050 $20000   (22-May-92 SY.NY171/R) Extensive mountainous landscape with herdsman driving flock (71x95cm-28x37in)

PILLEMENT, Jean (style) (1728-1808) French
£4000 $7000   (28-Nov-92 C30) Wooded landscapes with shepherd and shepherdess (104x81cm-41x32in) pair
£1742 $3100   *(22-Jan-92 SY.NY21/R) Views of waterfall and distant town (16x22cm-6x9in) gouache vellum on board pair*

PILLET, Edgar (1912-) French
£449 $800   (29-Apr-92 G.Z130/R) Egypt (94x66cm-37x26in) s. fiberglass (S.FR 1200)
£569 $1042   (13-May-92 BU.S153/R) Abstract composition (96x93cm-38x37in) s. (S.KR 6000)
£570 $1061   (19-Jun-92 G.Z564) Evasion (64x80cm-25x31in) s. i.verso (S.FR 1500)
£2037 $3727   (5-Jun-92 CB.P57) Fuego (56x86cm-22x34in) s.d.51 panel (F.FR 20000)
£4995 $9291   (15-Jun-92 GL.P48/R) Interferences (84x158cm-33x62in) s. s.i.d.1952verso (F.FR 49000)
£5731 $10202   (29-Nov-91 GAB.G2832/R) Suie noir desir (81x157cm-32x62in) s.d.56 i.verso (S.FR 14500)
£5912 $10997   (15-Jun-92 GL.P52/R) Aquatique (130x162cm-51x64in) s. i.d.1959verso (F.FR 58000)

PILNY, Otto (1866-?) Swiss
£1297 $2360   (27-May-92 PH.DU35/R) Portrait of an Oriental before a carpet (113x56cm-44x22in) s.i.d.1893 (DM 3800)
£1333 $2413   (19-May-92 GF.L2180/R) Slave market (80x120cm-31x47in) s. (S.FR 3600)
£2778 $5028   (19-May-92 GF.L2181/R) The story teller (110x160cm-43x63in) s. (S.FR 7500)
£5505 $9798   (30-Oct-91 CH.AM93/R) Sweet oriental dance (120x181cm-47x71in) s.d.96 (D.FL 18000)
£5929 $10553   (29-Nov-91 GAB.G2154) Bonheur du crepuscule a l'Oasis au pied des Pyramides (128x98cm-50x39in) s.d.1904 (S.FR 15000)

PILON, E Agathe (19th C) French
£6116 $11376   (18-Jun-92 SY.MO349/R) Branche de fleurs sur un entablement de marbre (24x32cm-9x13in) s. (F.FR 60000)

PILOT, Robert Wakeham (1898-1967) Canadian
£459 $839   (2-Jun-92 R.T476/R) November, near Mt Tremblant, P.Q (21x27cm-8x11in) s.d.1950 verso panel (C.D 1000)
£878 $1580   (19-Nov-91 FP.M40/R) Quebec village nestled on St. Lawrence (18x24cm-7x9in) s. d.1939 verso board (C.D 1800)
£1005 $1828   (26-May-92 JOY.T59) Venise (17x14cm-7x6in) init. panel (C.D 2200)
£1250 $2213   (6-Nov-91 SY.T32/R) After-glow, Levis, P.Q (20x27cm-8x11in) s. s.d.1958 verso panel (C.D 2500)

PILOT, Robert Wakeham (1898-1967) Canadian-cont.

£1341	$2415	(19-Nov-91 FP.M175/R) On beach, Metis, P.Q (32x42cm-13x17in) s. d.1954 verso board (C.D 2750)
£2110	$3861	(2-Jun-92 R.T513/R) Old city wall, Quebec (20x26cm-8x10in) s.i. panel (C.D 4600)
£2800	$4760	(23-Oct-91 S281/R) View of Staff College, Quebec (37x47cm-15x19in) s.
£6341	$11478	(2-Dec-91 R.T224/R) Place d'Armes, Quebec City (71x56cm-28x22in) s. (C.D 13000)
£6393	$11635	(26-May-92 JOY.T122/R) Winter near St. Sauveur, P.Q (45x60cm-18x24in) s.d.59 (C.D 14000)
£7306	$13297	(26-May-92 JOY.T83/R) Place d'Armes, Quebec (55x70cm-22x28in) s.d.49 (C.D 16000)
£7306	$13370	(14-May-92 SY.T45/R) Pommier en fleurs (39x49cm-15x19in) s. i.verso (C.D 16000)
£7813	$13281	(23-Oct-91 EA.M507/R) Winter in Laurentians (46x61cm-18x24in) s.d.41 (C.D 15000)
£9000	$15930	(6-Nov-91 SY.T138/R) Seigneur's Mill (56x70cm-22x28in) s. (C.D 18000)
£9132	$16621	(26-May-92 JOY.T99/R) Prince of Wales Terrace, Montreal (40x50cm-16x20in) s. (C.D 20000)
£13699	$25068	(14-May-92 SY.T71/R) Smelt fishers, Quebec (47x60cm-19x24in) s. s.d.1956 stretcher (C.D 30000)
£20500	$36285	(6-Nov-91 SY.T33/R) Prince of Wales Terrace, Montreal (52x70cm-20x28in) s. (C.D 41000)
£365	$665	(26-May-92 JOY.T276) Artist at easel (32x20cm-13x8in) init.d.1919 col.crayons (C.D 800)

PILOTY, Karl Theodor von (1826-1886) German

£30523	$52500	(17-Oct-91 SY.NY88/R) Henry VIII and Anne Boleyn (118x176cm-46x69in) s.

PILSBURY, Wilmot (1840-1908) British

£900	$1719	(2-Jul-92 D122/R) Figure outside cottage door at dawn (23x33cm-9x13in) s.d.1886 W/C bodycol
£920	$1610	(1-Apr-92 B91) Cottage in wooded landscape (18x29cm-7x11in) s.d.1899 W/C
£1500	$2745	(3-Jun-92 S244/R) Evington Brook (26x37cm-10x15in) s.d.1888 W/C

PILTZ, Otto (1846-1910) German

£2962	$5390	(11-Dec-91 N.M557/R) Young Dachau woman visiting knitting old peasant woman seated outside (47x56cm-19x22in) s. (DM 8500)
£4225	$7648	(3-Dec-91 FN.S2385/R) Alpine peasant interior with woman sewing at table and suitor (84x89cm-33x35in) s. (DM 12000)

PIMENTEL, Vincente (1948-) ?

£566	$969	(18-Mar-92 LT.P125) Composition (130x106cm-51x42in) s. mixed media canvas (F.FR 5500)
£662	$1211	(3-Jun-92 CSC.P141) Serie - Ballade dans l'imaginaire (112x43cm-44x17in) s.verso mixed media canvas (F.FR 6500)
£768	$1383	(2-Feb-92 CSC.P155) Composition (96x73cm-38x29in) s.d.1990 mixed media (F.FR 7500)

PINAL, Fernand (1881-1958) French

£1577	$2822	(17-Nov-91 FB.P205) Reverie au piano (101x90cm-40x35in) s. i.verso (F.FR 15500)

PINAZO, Ignacio (?) ?

£1093	$2001	(13-May-92 FER.M79/R) La boya (38x27cm-15x11in) (S.P 200000)

PINCAS, Julius see PASCIN, Jules

PINCAS, Moreno (1939-) Bulgarian

£3586	$6455	(27-Jan-92 GL.P82/R) Les couturieres (130x162cm-51x64in) s.d.1986-87 (F.FR 35000)

PINCEMIN, Jean-Pierre (1944-) French

£5030	$8652	(12-Oct-91 GL.P96/R) Sans titre (269x199cm-106x78in) open canvas (F.FR 50000)
£5097	$9480	(15-Jun-92 GL.P85/R) Untitled (247x183cm-97x72in) (F.FR 50000)
£6173	$11728	(26-Jun-92 FB.P93/R) Untitled (120x120cm-47x47in) s.d.1978verso (F.FR 60000)
£6286	$11000	(27-Feb-92 CH.NY46/R) Untitled (220x170cm-87x67in)
£22936	$42661	(15-Jun-92 GL.P57/R) Untitled (172x220cm-68x87in) (F.FR 225000)
£1037	$1804	(16-Apr-92 FB.P254/R) Sans titre (101x78cm-40x31in) s.d.85verso mixed media paper laid down canvas (F.FR 10200)

PINCHART, Emile Auguste (1842-1924) French

£547	$980	(6-May-92 GD.B1013/R) Beduin with camel resting, Tunis (35x27cm-14x11in) s.i. (S.FR 1500)
£706	$1200	(23-Oct-91 GD.B1231/R) Portrait of girl resting head on arm (54x44cm-21x17in) s. (S.FR 1800)
£730	$1307	(6-May-92 GD.B1012) Tea on the terrace (55x46cm-22x18in) s.verso (S.FR 2000)
£1863	$3224	(24-Mar-92 VN.R75/R) Elegant lady by steps (26x42cm-10x17in) s. (D.FL 6000)

PINCHON, Joseph Parphyre (1871-?) French
£756 $1338   (5-Nov-91 ZZ.F115/R) Buffet sur la terrasse dans un arc. L'Adoration des rois mages (65x50cm-26x20in) s. double-sided (F.FR 7500)

PINCHON, Robert Antoine (1886-1943) French
£25915 $45091   (19-Apr-92 ZZ.F100/R) Journee d'ete a Saint-Adrien (55x73cm-22x29in) s. (F.FR 255000)
£38191 $64161   (16-Aug-91 ZZ.F107/R) Rouen, le bassin du jardin des plantes (65x81cm-26x32in) s. (F.FR 380000)
£60976 $106098   (19-Apr-92 ZZ.F66/R) Le petit train, cote Sainte-Catherine (54x73cm-21x29in) s. (F.FR 600000)
£3354 $5835   (19-Apr-92 ZZ.F39/R) Travaux des champs (23x30cm-9x12in) s.d.1916 pastel (F.FR 33000)

PINCHON, Robert Henri (?) French
£4379 $8101   (12-Jun-92 ARC.P6) Port de Bretagne (48x64cm-19x25in) s. panel (F.FR 43000)

PINDER, Douglas H (?) British
£500 $865   (3-Oct-91 DLY252/R) Polperro (56x76cm-22x30in) s. W/C

PINE, Robert Edge (1742-1788) British
£534 $950   (30-Oct-91 D.NY30) Portrait of gentleman (56x46cm-22x18in) s.d.1742/3 pastel paper on canvas

PINE, Robert Edge (circle) (1742-1788) British
£2000 $3580   (15-Nov-91 C138/R) Portrait of choir boy (75x61cm-30x24in)

PINELLI, Achille (19th C) Italian
£1500 $2790   (17-Jun-92 S540/R) Players and drinkers in tavern at Monte Porsio (16x23cm-6x9in) s.i.d.1831 W/C

PINELLI, Bartolomeo (1781-1835) Italian
£2200 $4004   (11-Dec-91 PH95/R) La Communione Che va Dagli Ammalati (30x40cm-12x16in) s.d.1821 W/C chk pen
£2446 $4550   (20-Jun-92 CH.MO205/R) Deux danseurs Napolitains (40x62cm-16x24in) i. ink (F.FR 24000)
£2600 $4732   (10-Dec-91 C42/R) The grape harvest on the Palatine (26x36cm-10x14in) s.i.d.1821 pencil inkW/C

PINELLI, Bartolomeo (attrib) (1781-1835) Italian
£367 $631   (7-Oct-91 CH.E260/R) Bandits with girl on path (15x17cm-6x7in) pencil W/C (E.P 400)
£461 $838   (10-Dec-91 F.R56/R) Donne presso una fontana (19x24cm-7x9in) W/C (I.L 1000000)

PINELLI, Bartolomeo (style) (1781-1835) Italian
£3951 $7151   (4-Dec-91 CH.R52/R) Allegoria pastorale con Diana, amorino ed un pastore in paesaggio (27x35cm-11x14in) copper (I.L 8500000)

PINELO YANEZ, Jose (19/20th C) Spanish
£1374 $2500   (11-Dec-91 RO.BA283) Patio de las Danzas Rl.Alcazar (58x39cm-23x15in) s.d.1911

PINGGERA, H (1900-) Italian
£3200 $5472   (18-Mar-92 S71/R) In a Babylonian court (96x141cm-38x56in) indist.s.
£13143 $23000   (20-Feb-92 SY.NY231/R) Romans of Decadence (106x158cm-42x62in) s.

PINGGERA, Heinz (1900-) Italian
£488 $849   (19-Sep-91 D.V253/R) View of Prague from Karlskirche (33x23cm-13x9in) s.d. W/C spray technique (A.S 10000)

PINGRET, Edouard Henri Theophile (1788-1875) French
£496 $849   (12-Mar-92 RAS.V963) Young couple seated on clifftop (56x76cm-22x30in) s. (D.KR 5500)
£1235 $2346   (22-Jun-92 AT.P82) Jeune femme au chapeau de paille (39x32cm-15x13in) s. paper on canvas (F.FR 12000)
£6141 $10931   (27-Nov-91 PLF.P26/R) Jeune femme dans un salon avec vue sur un parc (80x63cm-31x25in) s.d.1821 (F.FR 60000)

PINHEIRO, O (?) ?
£581 $1028   (5-Nov-91 SY.AM201) Market in Portugal (46x55cm-18x22in) s. (D.FL 1900)

PINKAS, Hippolyt Sobeslav (1827-1901) Czechoslovakian
£2600 $4836   (17-Jun-92 S386/R) Scenes of jaguar, lions and tigers hunting prey (151x108cm-59x43in) s.d.1891 three

PINKOW, Bruno (19th C) German
£1000 $1770   (13-Feb-92 CSK183/R) Brother and sister (62x77cm-24x30in) s. panel

PINO, Marco da (1525-1588) Italian
£12000 $21360   (1-Nov-91 C25/R) Penitent Magdalen (87x73cm-34x29in) with i.verso panel

PINOLE Y RODRIGUEZ, Nicanor (1878-?) Spanish
£553 $984   (21-Jan-92 DUR.M115/R) Anochecer (28x35cm-11x14in) s. W/C (S.P 100000)

ꞌINOLE Y RODRIGUEZ, Nicanor (1878-?) Spanish-cont.
£982 $1689   *(16-Oct-91 FER.M123/R) Paisaje asturiano (23x35cm-9x14in) s. W/C (S.P 180000)*
£1374 $2473   *(19-Nov-91 DÜR.M77/R) Paisaje asturiano (25x30cm-10x12in) pastel (S.P 250000)*

ꞌINOS, Juan (1862-1910) Spanish
£1514 $2711   *(14-Nov-91 ANS.M107/R) Arreglando la guadana (40x60cm-16x24in) s. (S.P 275000)*

ꞌINOT, Albert (1875-1962) Belgian
£962 $1674   *(17-Sep-91 FN.S2492/R) Still life of asters in blue vase (50x70cm-20x28in) s. (DM 2800)*

ꞌINS, Yaacov (1917-) ?
£691 $1300   *(5-Jan-92 GG.TA306/R) Figure in the alleys of Jerusalem (50x35cm-20x14in) s.d.1950*

ꞌINTO, Biagio (20th C) American
£511 $900   *(9-Apr-92 FA.PH663) Sailboats (38x30cm-15x12in) s.*

ꞌINTO, Octavio (1890-1941) Argentinian
£1293 $2250   *(19-Sep-91 V.BA73) Paisaje, Mallorca (40x40cm-16x16in)*

ꞌINTURICCHIO, Bernardino (circle) (1454-1513) Italian
£4500 $8640   *(7-Jul-92 C116/R) Heads of bearded man and woman (18x14cm-7x6in) i.verso wash vellum*

ꞌINWELL, George John (1842-1875) British
£1500 $2685   *(11-Nov-91 PH159/R) Rest from the croquet game (19x15cm-7x6in) W/C htd.white*

ꞌIOLA, Domenico (17/18th C) Italian
£67039 $120000   *(17-Jan-92 SY.NY38/R) An allegory with a classically dressed female holding a torch with two putti (154x118cm-61x46in)*
£680 $1306   *(8-Jul-92 PH38/R) St Michael vanquishing Devil (27x20cm-11x8in) i. pen wash over black chk*
£1500 $2610   *(14-Apr-92 C119/R) Madonna and Child with cherubim (28x20cm-11x8in) i. chk wash*
£1527 $2826   *(12-Jun-92 ARC.P165/R) Le Christ entrant a Jerusalem - les Rameaux (43x29cm-17x11in) pen wash (F.FR 15000)*
£2500 $4800   *(8-Jul-92 PH150/R) Design for wall decoration with medallion enclosing crucifixion scene (34x22cm-13x9in) pen wash over black chk*

ꞌIOLA, Domenico (attrib) (17/18th C) Italian
£15821 $28636   *(18-May-92 SY.MI235/R) Gioco di putti e fauni (138x202cm-54x80in) (I.L 35000000)*

ꞌIOLA, Domenico (circle) (17/18th C) Italian
£4800 $8640   *(21-Nov-91 CSK255/R) Putti with garlands of flowers (60x178cm-24x70in)*
£9200 $16100   *(2-Apr-92 CSK49/R) Venus and Cupid by fountain (60x47cm-24x19in)*

ꞌIOLA, Domenico (elder-attrib) (1627-1703) Italian
£3500 $6720   *(10-Jul-92 C261/R) Personification of Charity (63x48cm-25x19in) canvas on board oval*

ꞌIOLA, Domenico (style) (17/18th C) Italian
£4000 $7680   *(8-Jul-92 S143/R) Putti with fruit (97x72cm-38x28in)*

ꞌIOLA, Paolo Gerolamo (1666-1724) Italian
£540 $961   *(1-Nov-91 S402/R) Peasants resting under tree (10x26cm-4x10in) pen wash over black chk htd white*

ꞌIOMBO, Sebastiano del (circle) (1485-1547) Italian
£2039 $3792   *(18-Jun-92 SY.MO104) Portrait de Clement VII (56x46cm-22x18in) panel (F.FR 20000)*

ꞌIOT, Adolphe (1850-1910) French
£3198 $5500   *(17-Oct-91 SY.NY186/R) L'innocence (36x28cm-14x11in) s.*
£4070 $7000   *(16-Oct-91 CH.NY34/R) Sweet innocence (82x66cm-32x26in) s.*
£4645 $8500   *(17-May-92 DU.E1117/R) Portrait of lady in love (66x51cm-26x20in) s.*
£6593 $12000   *(28-May-92 SY.NY62/R) La jeune femme a la rose (102x69cm-40x27in)*
£9890 $18000   *(28-May-92 SY.NY71/R) Reading lesson (86x66cm-34x26in) s. canvas on masonite*
£686 $1200   *(18-Feb-92 CE.NY218/R) Young beauty (41x31cm-16x12in) s.*

ꞌIOTROWSKI, Antoni (1853-1924) Polish
£1700 $3026   *(26-Nov-91 PH121/R) Matinee sur le Danube (41x88cm-16x35in) s.i.d.1880*
£2093 $3622   *(8-Sep-91 REM.W26) Battle scene (68x98cm-27x39in) s.board (P.Z 40000000)*

ꞌIOTROWSKI, Korwin Mieczyslaw (1869-1930) Polish
£1047 $1811   *(8-Sep-91 REM.W27) Mansion in autumn (50x70cm-20x28in) s. (P.Z 20000000)*

ꞌIPAL, Viktor (1887-1971) Austrian
£1887 $3358   *(28-Nov-91 D.V229/R) Winter in Grinzing (48x61cm-19x24in) s. (A.S 38000)*

PIPAL, Viktor (1887-1971) Austrian-cont.
£4469 $7954   (28-Nov-91 D.V230/R) Kahlenberger Dorf in winter (48x60cm-19x24in) s.
                  (A.S 90000)

PIPER, John (1903-1992) British
£1100 $2013   (4-Jun-92 CSK158/R) Study for Marsh landscape, France (15x20cm-6x8in)
                  s.panel
£4545 $8091   (29-Nov-91 GAB.G2950/R) Mascarade (100x161cm-39x63in) s. (S.FR 11500)
£180000 $329400 (13-May-92 S57 a/R) Paintings 1935 (25x51cm-10x20in) s.i.d.1935 verso
                  canvas on board
£400 $716   (14-Jan-92 PH95/R) Design for Oundle School windows (46x70cm-18x28in) s.
                  i.verso pencil
£500 $855   (19-Mar-92 T185) The cathedral (36x28cm-14x11in) s.i. W/C
£550 $941   (1-Aug-91 CSK91) Derelict cottage at Bupton, Wiltshire (23x26cm-9x10in)
                  s.i. ink pencil W/C
£600 $1146   (16-Jul-92 B197) Notre Dame, Paris (31x16cm-12x6in) s. W/C pen collage
£650 $1118   (5-Mar-92 CSK2/R) Back cloth design for 'What the Old Man says is always
                  right' (21x52cm-8x20in) init. W/C brush ink
£650 $1190   (14-May-92 C86/R) Appian way (22x31cm-9x12in) s.i. W/C bodycol col.chk
                  wax crayon
£700 $1239   (8-Nov-91 C213/R) Landscape with a church (10x15cm-4x6in) pencil W/C
                  bodycol.
£907 $1606   (4-Nov-91 SY.J238/R) Tower and balustrade (36x24cm-14x9in) s. pen collage
                  (SA.R 4500)
£942 $1800   (3-Jul-92 S.W3855) Gloriana (20x33cm-8x13in) s.d.1953 W/C gouache
£1000 $1790   (14-Jan-92 PH101/R) Red Wahrf Bay, Anglesey (28x38cm-11x15in) s. i.verso
                  pen col.crayon W/C bodycol
£1200 $2052   (11-Mar-92 S165) Sketch after Rembrandt (16x21cm-6x8in) init.i. gouache
                  chinese ink over pencil htd wht
£1600 $2848   (27-Apr-92 PHB213) Arlingham-on-Severn (53x38cm-21x15in) s. i.verso
                  pencil ink W/C
£1650 $3020   (14-May-92 C85/R) Monument Folly, Farley Down, Farley (37x49cm-15x19in)
                  s.d.1945 pen col.crayon W/C
£1800 $3204   (27-Apr-92 PHB214/R) Bolton Castle, Wensleydale (23x36cm-9x14in) s.d.1942
                  ink col.wash
£1800 $3330   (9-Jun-92 ZZ.B4) Ruined church in Pembroke (30x43cm-12x17in) s.d.1948 W/C
£1800 $3078   (11-Mar-92 S122/R) Espira (57x75cm-22x30in) s. W/C gouache pastel
£1800 $3078   (11-Mar-92 S167/R) Santa Maria, Venice (38x26cm-15x10in) s. W/C wax
                  resist pastel htd white
£2000 $3500   (27-Sep-91 C150/R) Moreton Corbet, Shropshire (37x56cm-15x22in) s. i.d.6
                  III 74 W/C bodycol.gouache brush ink
£2000 $3540   (8-Nov-91 C214/R) Sandringham Castle (18x53cm-7x21in) s. pencil
                  col.crayon W/C bodycol.
£2000 $3660   (14-May-92 C88/R) Venice (16x53cm-6x21in) s.d.1960 pencil col.crayon W/C
                  bodycol
£2000 $3480   (19-Sep-91 B59/R) Weymouth (37x46cm-15x18in) s.d.1934 gouache
£2300 $4255   (9-Jun-92 ZZ.B5) Ruins in South Wales (43x79cm-17x31in) s.d.1942 W/C
£2400 $4200   (27-Sep-91 C148/R) Brittany Foreshore (37x53cm-15x21in) s. i. verso W/C
                  col.chk. brush pen wash
£2616 $4500   (12-Oct-91 SY.NY154/R) Garn fawr (36x51cm-14x20in) s. d.1983 verso
                  gouache W/C Indian ink
£2700 $5157   (14-Jul-92 DR398) View of Watergate, Fawley Court (48x36cm-19x14in) W/C
                  mixed media
£2800 $4956   (8-Nov-91 C215/R) Dymchurch Sands (35x53cm-14x21in) s. W/C bodycol.wax
                  crayon
£3000 $5310   (8-Nov-91 C212/R) Sheffield (33x41cm-13x16in) pen W/C bodycol.blk.crayon
£3200 $5664   (8-Nov-91 C210/R) Rebuilding Sheffield (34x53cm-13x21in) s.i. W/C pen
                  gouache col.chks.
£3300 $6303   (20-Jul-92 WW183/R) Stackpole Quay IV (37x55cm-15x22in) s. W/C gouache
                  pastel
£3800 $7258   (14-Jul-92 DR397/R) View off Folly, Fawley Court (51x38cm-20x15in)
                  s.i.d.1940 W/C mixed media

PIPPAL, Hans Robert (1915-) Austrian
£976 $1689   (3-Oct-91 D.V307/R) Vienna, Volksgarten (23x26cm-9x10in) s.d.1953 panel
                  (A.S 20000)
£2979 $5303   (28-Nov-91 D.V252/R) Sieveringer Strasse, Vienna (43x50cm-17x20in) s.
                  canvas on panel (A.S 60000)
£442 $839   (25-Jun-92 D.V581/R) Stockholm (46x61cm-18x24in) s.d.50 pastel chk
                  (A.S 9000)
£976 $1689   (3-Oct-91 D.V306/R) Vienna, Theater in der Josefstadt (33x41cm-13x16in)
                  s.i. W/C htd.white (A.S 20000)
£1212 $2206   (26-May-92 D.V240/R) Venice (33x39cm-13x15in) s.d.1977 pencil W/C
                  (A.S 25000)
£1551 $2823   (26-May-92 D.V239/R) Heldenplatz, Vienna (24x28cm-9x11in) s.i. W/C
                  (A.S 32000)
£2234 $3977   (28-Nov-91 D.V250/R) Kohlmarkt, Vienna (23x28cm-9x11in) s. W/C
                  (A.S 45000)
£2483 $4419   (28-Nov-91 D.V251/R) Prater, Vienna (31x39cm-12x15in) s. W/C (A.S 50000)

PIPPEL, Otto (1878-1960) German
£687 $1271   (13-Jun-92 WK.M353/R) Lago di Federa, Dolomites (48x60cm-19x24in) s.
                  i.stretcher (DM 2000)
£893 $1555   (18-Sep-91 N.M654/R) Hochkalter landscape (81x70cm-32x28in) s.
                  i.stretcher (DM 2600)

PIPPEL, Otto (1878-1960) German-cont.

£997	$1694	(26-Oct-91 WK.M536/R) Landscape with view of mountains (22x28cm-9x11in) s. board (DM 2900)
£1020	$1827	(5-May-92 ZEL.L1492/R) Lake landscape with boats, possibly Lake Garda (50x60cm-20x24in) s. canvas on panel (DM 3000)
£1306	$2272	(17-Sep-91 FN.S2494/R) Hunting party on horses in wooded landscape (60x80cm-24x31in) s. i.verso (DM 3800)
£1375	$2392	(18-Sep-91 N.M656/R) Wooded Alpine valley (81x101cm-32x40in) s. (DM 4000)
£1468	$2656	(21-May-92 L.K471 a) Hunt riding through forest (85x85cm-33x33in) s. panel (DM 4300)
£1469	$2511	(18-Mar-92 N.M614/R) Lady receiving gentleman before palace at night (70x60cm-28x24in) s. (DM 4200)
£1742	$3171	(11-Dec-91 N.M560/R) View from Zwieselalm to Gosau lakes (115x95cm-45x37in) s. i.stretcher (DM 5000)
£1853	$3169	(18-Mar-92 N.M615) Church interior with worshippers (50x62cm-20x24in) s. (DM 5300)
£2091	$3805	(11-Dec-91 N.M562/R) Bay of Sorrent (58x77cm-23x30in) s. i.verso (DM 6000)
£2817	$5099	(3-Dec-91 FN.S2387) South Tyrolean mountain landscape with farmhouses beneath rainbow (49x61cm-19x24in) s. (DM 8000)
£2921	$5082	(18-Sep-91 N.M655/R) Elegant party having candle light dinner (47x42cm-19x17in) s. i.stretcher (DM 8500)
£2962	$5390	(11-Dec-91 N.M561/R) Edge of woods in winter sun. Study of tree (100x90cm-39x35in) s. double-sided (DM 8500)
£3521	$6373	(3-Dec-91 FN.S2386/R) Interior with paintings and elegant figures dining by candlelight (52x62cm-20x24in) s. i.verso (DM 10000)
£3754	$6833	(27-May-92 PH.DU67/R) Hunting lodge by a lake (95x106cm-37x42in) s.i.d.22 (DM 11000)
£3780	$6577	(17-Sep-91 FN.S2493/R) View of Tegernsee with Wallberg and cattle grazing (96x116cm-38x46in) s. panel (DM 11000)
£4124	$7175	(21-Sep-91 SA.A1805/R) Wooded Dachstein landscape (100x110cm-39x43in) s. (DM 12000)
£4124	$7546	(2-Jun-92 FN.S2704/R) Peasant family loading ox-drawn hay cart, Planegg near Munich (72x81cm-28x32in) s.i. (DM 12000)
£4355	$7927	(11-Dec-91 N.M559/R) Morning view of Grand Canal, Venice (50x62cm-20x24in) indis.s. i.verso i.stretcher panel (DM 12500)
£4467	$7773	(21-Sep-91 SA.A529/R) The opera performance (66x76cm-26x30in) s. (DM 13000)
£4800	$8688	(2-Dec-91 CSK32/R) Der Dom in Passau (94x82cm-37x32in) s.d.1918 s.i.d.verso
£4811	$8371	(21-Sep-91 SA.A1806/R) View from Zwieselalm to Dachstein mountains (116x100cm-46x39in) s. i.verso (DM 14000)
£7500	$13575	(2-Dec-91 CSK31/R) Promenadenspaziergang unter Baumen (71x82cm-28x32in) s.

PIPPICH, Carl (1862-1932) Austrian

£976	$1698	(19-Sep-91 D.V195/R) Summer afternoon in Wachau (29x39cm-11x15in) mono.d.98 i.verso board (A.S 20000)

PIRA, Gioacchino la (19th C) Italian

£2600	$4446	(18-Mar-92 S154/R) View of Naples. View of Amalfi (30x46cm-12x18in) s. gouache pair
£8290	$15088	(12-Dec-91 F.M81/R) Veduta della baia di Napoli con L'isola di Nisida (44x64cm-17x25in) s..i. gouache (I.L 18000000)

PIRA, la (19th C) Italian

£979	$1732	(5-Nov-91 SY.AM95) 'Foro a Pompei (30x44cm-12x17in) s.d. gouache (D.FL 3200)
£1100	$1881	(17-Mar-92 PH223/R) Vesuvius erupting. Naples and the Bay (30x47cm-12x19in) s.d.1822 gouache pair
£1832	$3500	(16-Jul-92 SY.NY590/R) Fisherman at sunset (45x64cm-18x25in) s.i. gouache paper on board
£1986	$3574	(19-Nov-91 RAS.K526) Bay of Naples. View of a bay (32x46cm-13x18in) one s. gouache pair (D.KR 22000)
£2061	$3647	(22-Apr-92 CH.AM292/R) La grotta di Possuoli (63x43cm-25x17in) s.i. chk.bodycol. (D.FL 6800)

PIRA, la   see also LAPIRA

PIRAK, Lars (1933-) Scandinavian

£1132	$2004	(25-Apr-92 SO.S574/R) Lapplander with reindeer (67x89cm-26x35in) s. (S.KR 12000)

PIRANDELLO, Fausto (1899-) Italian

£18145	$33205	(12-May-92 F.R186/R) Bagnanti (34x52cm-13x20in) s.d.1940 panel (I.L 40000000)
£18564	$34900	(19-Dec-91 F.M175/R) Natura morta (70x50cm-28x20in) s. board (I.L 40000000)
£1382	$2515	(9-Dec-91 CH.R8/R) Bagnanti (27x37cm-11x15in) s.d.1947 pastel wax (I.L 3000000)
£1588	$2905	(12-May-92 F.R67/R) Il lavoro nei campi (28x22cm-11x9in) s. pastel tempera (I.L 3500000)
£2324	$4206	(3-Dec-91 F.R77/R) Figura femminile (39x23cm-15x9in) s. pastel paper on cardboard (I.L 5000000)

PIRANDELLO, Fausto (1899-) Italian-cont.
£10674 $20067   (19-Dec-91 F.M207/R) Motivo continuo (71x102cm-28x40in) mixed media collage board (I.L 23000000)

PIRANESI, Giovan Battista (1720-1778) Italian
£497 $950   (3-Jul-92 S.W3727/R) Study of dog (8x5cm-3x2in) sepia ink

PIREZ, Alvaro see ALVARO DI PIERO

PIRKHERT, Alfred V (1887-1971) Yugoslavian
£989 $1730   (19-Feb-92 D.V20/R) Forest nymph (104x82cm-41x32in) s.d.1915 (A.S 20000)

PIRKNER, F (?) ?
£503 $894   (29-Oct-91 PH.T38) Rapids (48x79cm-19x31in) s. (C.D 1000)

PIROLI (?) ?
£1375 $2392   (18-Sep-91 N.M259/R) View of Florence (26x49cm-10x19in) indis.s. W/C pen htd.white (DM 4000)

PIRON, Leo (1899-1962) Belgian
£1333 $2293   (12-Oct-91 KV.L237/R) Snowy landscape in Etikhove (27x35cm-11x14in) s.d.1941 (B.FR 80000)

PIRSCH, Adolf (1858-1929) Austrian
£1483 $2595   (19-Feb-92 D.V123/R) Female in landscape (100x124cm-39x49in) s.d.1923 (A.S 30000)

PISA, Alberto (1864-1931) Italian
£2038 $3771   (8-Jun-92 CH.R571/R) Passeggiata alle cascine (22x38cm-9x15in) s. canvas laid down on board (I.L 4500000)
£700 $1302   (18-Jun-92 B15/R) The Pool, Villa D'Este, Tivoli (36x26cm-14x10in) s.i. W/C
£960 $1718   (5-May-92 SWS151/R) The village fair (35x45cm-14x18in) s.

PISANI, L (?) Italian
£2200 $4224   (28-Jul-92 SWS401/R) Music (71x55cm-28x22in) s.i.verso oval

PISANI, Louis (?) Italian?
£800 $1440   (21-Nov-91 CSK220) Self portrait (63x46cm-25x18in) i.verso after Andrea del Sarto
£1100 $2112   (9-Jul-92 CSK27) The Madonna della Grotte (69x51cm-27x20in) i.verso after Leonardo da Vinci oval

PISANI, T (?) ?
£1600 $2720   (23-Oct-91 S171) Corfu (22x44cm-9x17in) s. W/C over pencil pair

PISCHINGER, Carl (1823-1886) Austrian
£1579 $2842   (22-Nov-91 SA.A1693/R) The two guard soldiers (37x44cm-15x17in) mono. (DM 4500)

PISIS, Filippo de (1896-1956) Italian
£550 $1006   (2-Jun-92 FN.S2391) Seagulls and view of bay with lighthouse (48x63cm-19x25in) i.d.1956verso panel (DM 1600)
£8751 $15926   (9-Dec-91 CH.R109/R) Nevio (45x30cm-18x12in) s.i.d.1939 panel (I.L 19000000)
£11315 $20593   (25-May-92 CH.R33/R) Natura morta con ventaglio (27x22cm-11x9in) s.i.d.1946 i.d.verso panel (I.L 25000000)
£13438 $23920   (26-Nov-91 SY.MI191/R) Fiori (27x55cm-11x22in) s. (I.L 29000000)
£13619 $24242   (29-Apr-92 F.F258/R) Paesaggio a Brughiero (39x50cm-15x20in) s.d.1949 canvas on board (I.L 30000000)
£14500 $26390   (11-Dec-91 MMB306/R) Apples and grapes (41x53cm-16x21in) s.i. board
£15530 $27023   (14-Apr-92 F.M183/R) Natura morta marina con grande foglia (51x71cm-20x28in) s.d.1952 masonite (I.L 34000000)
£15541 $29528   (23-Jun-92 F.M142/R) Strada di Ferrara (52x45cm-20x18in) s.d.1926 (I.L 34000000)
£15755 $28044   (29-Nov-91 F.F161 a) Parigi (54x21cm-21x8in) s.d.1939 panel (I.L 34000000)
£16444 $28613   (14-Apr-92 F.M204/R) Fiori in un interno (50x40cm-20x16in) s.d.1930 board (I.L 36000000)
£20000 $34000   (23-Oct-91 GD.B922/R) Still life of flowers (55x37cm-22x15in) s.d.20 (S.FR 51000)
£21940 $41687   (23-Jun-92 F.M181/R) Veduta di Milano (50x34cm-20x13in) s.d.1942 (I.L 48000000)
£22630 $41186   (26-May-92 SY.MI209/R) Natura morta aerea (117x90cm-46x35in) s.d.31 (I.L 50000000)
£25487 $45366   (29-Nov-91 F.F177/R) Vaso di fiori (55x38cm-22x15in) s.d.1931 (I.L 55000000)
£27634 $50294   (9-Dec-91 CH.R169/R) Vaso con fiori (70x61cm-28x24in) s.d.1940 canvas on panel (I.L 60000000)
£29509 $52525   (29-Apr-92 F.F295/R) Cortile di Villa Patrizi (70x50cm-28x20in) s.d.1943 (I.L 65000000)
£31996 $60793   (23-Jun-92 F.M216/R) Natura morta con funghi, castagne e bicchieri (50x66cm-20x26in) s.d.1933 board (I.L 70000000)
£34258 $59609   (14-Apr-92 F.M220/R) Natura morta con la ruggine (60x80cm-24x31in) s.d.1950 i.d.verso (I.L 75000000)

PISIS, Filippo de (1896-1956) Italian-cont.

£39496	$70303	(29-Apr-92 F.F296/R) La bottega dell'antiquario (64x50cm-25x20in) (I.L 87000000)
£40230	$69598	(28-Mar-92 F.L82/R) Parigi (92x65cm-36x26in) s.d.1934 (S.FR 105000)
£71373	$122761	(12-Oct-91 F.L214/R) La tavola apparecchiata (65x92cm-26x36in) s.d.33 (S.FR 182000)
£817	$1455	(29-Apr-92 F.F109/R) Nudo disteso. Due studi di nudo (31x48cm-12x19in) d.1942 chl pencil verso double-sided (I.L 1800000)
£875	$1593	(9-Dec-91 CH.R11/R) Giovane (41x27cm-16x11in) s. pencil (I.L 1900000)
£921	$1676	(9-Dec-91 CH.R5/R) Studi (35x25cm-14x10in) s.d.1924 s.verso pencil (I.L 2000000)
£1085	$1964	(21-May-92 F.M92) Figure maschile in piedi (30x21cm-12x8in) s. pastel (I.L 2400000)
£1297	$2310	(27-Nov-91 F.M198) Paesaggio con ponte (12x17cm-5x7in) s. W/C (I.L 2800000)
£1390	$2475	(29-Nov-91 F.F93) Figura (22x16cm-9x6in) s.d.1940 pastel htd.white cardboard (I.L 3000000)

PISSARRO, Camille (1830-1903) French

£70621	$125000	(7-Nov-91 SY.NY115/R) Vue des bassins Duquesne et Berrigny a Dieppe (22x27cm-9x11in) s.d.1902
£180000	$343800	(30-Jun-92 S13/R) Bouquet de fleurs, roses roses (65x54cm-26x21in) st.mono.
£251762	$427996	(21-Oct-91 ARC.P30/R) Hiver, soleil couchant, Eragny (81x60cm-32x24in) s.d.98 (F.FR 2500000)
£254237	$450000	(6-Nov-91 SY.NY13 a/R) Vue de la ferme d'Osny (46x54cm-18x21in) s.d.1883
£273224	$500000	(12-May-92 CH.NY104/R) Moulin a Knocke, Belgique (54x65cm-21x26in) s.d.94
£440000	$796400	(2-Dec-91 C13/R) Le jardin de Kew, Alice de la Grande Serre (54x65cm-21x26in) s.d.1892
£451977	$800000	(6-Nov-91 SY.NY16/R) Le moisson (32x41cm-13x16in) s.d.83
£508475	$900000	(5-Nov-91 CH.NY30/R) Paysannes assisses, causant (60x73cm-24x29in) s.d.81
£546448	$1000000	(13-May-92 SY.NY48/R) Jardin de Kew, l'alle des rhododendrons (54x65cm-21x26in) s.d.1892
£792350	$1450000	(13-May-92 SY.NY43/R) Le parc aux charrettes, Pontoise (65x54cm-26x21in) s.d.1878
£928962	$1700000	(12-May-92 CH.NY111/R) Le Pont-Neuf, apres-midi de pluie (80x63cm-31x25in) s.d.1901
£1700000	$3077000	(2-Dec-91 C10/R) Le Gelee blanche, femme cassant du bois (126x128cm-50x50in) s.d.1890 i.stretcher
£3502825	$6200000	(5-Nov-91 CH.NY36/R) Le printemps. L'ete. L'automne. L'hiver (55x130cm-22x51in) s. one d.1872 set of four
£532	$973	(3-Feb-92 SD.P182) Etude de jambes (22x10cm-9x4in) bears studio st.d.1852 blk.crayon (F.FR 5200)
£1628	$2914	(13-Nov-91 PIC.P79/R) Pecheurs (18x30cm-7x12in) bistre ink dr (F.FR 16000)
£1739	$3096	(29-Nov-91 GAB.G3198/R) Rue de Paris (27x18cm-11x7in) mono. lead pencil (S.FR 4400)
£1955	$3500	(13-Nov-91 B.SF2393/R) Rouen, rue de Arpente (16x16cm-6x6in) s.i. ink
£2136	$3824	(13-Nov-91 PIC.P78/R) Portrait de femme (15x12cm-6x5in) init. chl dr (F.FR 21000)
£2312	$4000	(25-Mar-92 D.NY54) Seaman. Figures in the garden (10x15cm-4x6in) st.init. pencil two
£2312	$4000	(25-Mar-92 D.NY56) Three paysannes. Woman in a landscape st.init. pencil two
£2457	$4250	(25-Mar-92 D.NY55) Deux femmes. Woman and Harvesters st.init. pencil second double-sided two
£2747	$4917	(13-Nov-91 PIC.P85/R) Deux paysannes (24x23cm-9x9in) init. crayon chl ink dr (F.FR 27000)
£4811	$8804	(3-Jun-92 L.K376/R) Femme et deux enfants sur un banc (17x22cm-7x9in) s. W/C (DM 14000)
£7429	$13000	(25-Feb-92 SY.NY9/R) Paysage a la campagne (23x32cm-9x13in) st.init. pencil htd. conte crayon chk
£14000	$24080	(16-Oct-91 S3/R) Paysage d'Osny (22x29cm-9x11in) s.i. W/C pencil
£17000	$29410	(25-Mar-92 S2/R) Au marche (24x19cm-9x7in) st.init. col.chks. paper laid down on paper
£19774	$35000	(7-Nov-91 SY.NY117/R) Paysage (29x23cm-11x9in) i.d. W/C over pencil
£21858	$40000	(13-May-92 SY.NY56/R) Meule a Eragny sur Epte (23x29cm-9x11in) s.i. W/C chl paper on board
£23224	$42500	(13-May-92 SY.NY40/R) Femmes cousant (22x17cm-9x7in) st.init. pen over pencil
£24011	$42500	(7-Nov-91 SY.NY116/R) Paysage (24x31cm-9x12in) s. pastel paper on board
£24590	$45000	(13-May-92 SY.NY38/R) Paysanne sur un sentier (8x13cm-3x5in) W/C gouache pencil
£24590	$45000	(13-May-92 SY.NY39/R) La lumiere de la lampe (22x17cm-9x7in) st.init. pen over pencil
£207650	$380000	(12-May-92 CH.NY113/R) Au bord de l'eau (35x25cm-14x10in) s.d.81 gouache pencil silk on cardboard

PISSARRO, Camille (style) (1830-1903) French

| £3148 | $5698 | (19-May-92 GF.L2510/R) Thunderstorm rising in river landscape. La Varenne, St Hilaire (34x62cm-13x24in) bears sig.d.1873 (S.FR 8500) |

PISSARRO, Claude (1935-) French

| £2105 | $4000 | (24-Jun-92 D.NY65) La Ferme de Fresney (61x74cm-24x29in) s. s.i.verso |
| £2105 | $4000 | (24-Jun-92 D.NY64) Le verger barny (46x56cm-18x22in) s. i.verso |

PISSARRO, Claude (1935-) French-cont.

£2162	$4000	(12-Jun-92 SY.NY136/R) L'Avenue de la Gare a Rennes (45x54cm-18x21in) s.
£2407	$4357	(20-May-92 GK.Z5029/R) L'Embarcadere (33x40cm-13x16in) s. (S.FR 6500)
£2459	$4500	(5-Feb-92 D.NY76) Verger pres de Conde (51x61cm-20x24in) s. s.i.verso
£2571	$4500	(28-Feb-92 SY.NY128/R) Michelle a Amelie (51x61cm-20x24in) s. s.i.verso
£2571	$4500	(28-Feb-92 SY.NY132/R) Le jardin d'Amelie (50x61cm-20x24in) s. s.i.num.51 verso
£2571	$4500	(27-Feb-92 CE.NY113/R) Roses et seringa (50x61cm-20x24in) s.
£2793	$5000	(6-May-92 D.NY109/R) L'Avenue Melior a Rennes (47x55cm-19x22in) s. s.i.verso
£2890	$5000	(25-Mar-92 D.NY51) Le Petit Lac (46x56cm-18x22in) s. i.verso
£3073	$5500	(9-May-92 CE.NY16/R) Granville, l'entree du port, a la maree (46x55cm-18x22in) s. s.i.verso
£3143	$5500	(27-Feb-92 CE.NY35/R) Varangeville (50x61cm-20x24in) s.
£3198	$5500	(12-Oct-91 SY.NY29/R) Les deux clochers (33x41cm-13x16in) s. s.i.verso
£3352	$6000	(9-May-92 CE.NY57/R) Le presbytere de Listrou (50x61cm-20x24in) s. s.i.verso
£3352	$6000	(9-May-92 CE.NY12/R) Les bords de l'Etang Perrey (50x61cm-20x24in) s. s.i.verso
£3468	$6000	(25-Mar-92 D.NY52) La Ferme des Moulines (53x66cm-21x26in) s. i.verso
£3613	$6250	(2-Oct-91 D.NY79) La Maison de la Compagne (51x61cm-20x24in) s. s.i.verso
£3814	$6750	(6-Nov-91 D.NY77/R) La villa du haut de Septeuil (60x73cm-24x29in) s.i.verso
£3902	$6750	(2-Oct-91 D.NY76) La plaine du cher blere (46x56cm-18x22in) s. s.verso
£3955	$7000	(5-Nov-91 CE.NY130/R) Le presbytere de Listrou (50x61cm-20x24in) s. s.i.verso
£4000	$7000	(23-Sep-91 S.SL252) La femme en rouge (46x53cm-18x21in)
£4802	$8500	(5-Nov-91 CE.NY68/R) Etude pour Les Trois Clochers (51x64cm-20x25in) s. s.i.verso
£5028	$9000	(9-May-92 CE.NY153/R) La Promenade a Nice (46x52cm-18x20in) s. s.i.verso
£5307	$9500	(9-May-92 CE.NY79/R) Etude pour Les Trois Clochers (51x64cm-20x25in) s. s.i.verso
£578	$1000	(25-Mar-92 D.NY50) Village in snow (36x48cm-14x19in) s. pastel
£800	$1400	(19-Feb-92 D.NY67) Jardin du Bord de Cher (36x48cm-14x19in) s. i.verso pastel
£1029	$1800	(19-Feb-92 D.NY69) Le toit rouge (33x41cm-13x16in) s. i.verso
£1098	$1900	(25-Mar-92 D.NY53) Les Maison Roses (33x48cm-13x19in) s. i.verso pastel
£1111	$2011	(20-May-92 GK.Z5033/R) Wooded landscape with peasant woman and child (23x35cm-9x14in) s. pastel (S.FR 3000)
£1130	$2000	(5-Nov-91 CE.NY38/R) Petits vachers gardant les jeunisses au champs (25x38cm-10x15in) s. s.i.verso col.chk
£1222	$2212	(20-May-92 GK.Z5034/R) Le moulin de la Martinee sur les bords de la Vere (27x35cm-11x14in) s. pastel (S.FR 3300)
£1229	$2200	(9-May-92 CE.NY61/R) Le tournant du Petit-Mesnil (25x37cm-10x15in) s. i.verso pastel
£1257	$2200	(28-Feb-92 SY.NY133/R) Verger a la fillotiere (25x37cm-10x15in) s. pastel
£1429	$2500	(27-Feb-92 CE.NY90/R) Les pommiers de la Menendiere (36x49cm-14x19in) s. col.chk
£1469	$2600	(5-Nov-91 CE.NY31/R) Le Moulin de Bouche l'Huisre au Mans (36x50cm-14x20in) s. i.verso pastel
£1486	$2600	(27-Feb-92 CE.NY43/R) L'Esplanade des Invalides, Paris (37x50cm-15x20in) s. col.chk
£1788	$3200	(9-May-92 CE.NY64/R) Voiliers (36x49cm-14x19in) s. s.verso col.chk
£1850	$3200	(2-Oct-91 D.NY78) Le Port de Collioure (23x33cm-9x13in) s. s.i.verso pastel
£1908	$3300	(2-Oct-91 D.NY77) La Seine a Vethery (23x33cm-9x13in) s. s.verso pastel
£1946	$3600	(12-Jun-92 SY.NY147/R) Paris - La Cathedral Notre Dame (36x50cm-14x20in) s. pastel
£1955	$3500	(6-May-92 D.NY116/R) Le chemin du Chateau de Jambrille aux environes de Themezico (35x48cm-14x19in) s. i.verso pastel
£1955	$3500	(6-May-92 D.NY4/R) La Seine a Paris (35x49cm-14x19in) s. s.i.verso pastel
£2123	$3800	(9-May-92 CE.NY148/R) Le bouquet a la chope (51x37cm-20x15in) s. i.verso col.pastel
£2143	$3750	(28-Feb-92 SY.NY135/R) L'Avenue des Bains a Bagnoles de L'Orne (36x49cm-14x19in) s. pastel
£2260	$4000	(5-Nov-91 CE.NY39/R) Femme dans la campagne (80x60cm-31x24in) s. oil col.wax crayons
£2514	$4500	(9-May-92 CE.NY66/R) Le vieux pont a Fresnay-sur-Sarthe (39x51cm-15x20in) s. s.i.verso col.chk
£2793	$5000	(6-May-92 D.NY115/R) Boulevard Saint Germain (28x37cm-11x15in) s. s.verso pastel
£3249	$5750	(6-Nov-91 D.NY80/R) Bord de Riviere (35x48cm-14x19in) s. s.verso pastel

PISSARRO, Lucien (1863-1944) British

£4000	$7080	(7-Nov-91 C90/R) Girl by a trellis (43x33cm-17x13in) mono.d.1929 board
£5000	$8600	(6-Mar-92 C57/R) Mist on the hills, fishpond, Devon (15x23cm-6x9in) mono.d.1918 i.verso panel
£19000	$33630	(7-Nov-91 C80/R) Rabbit hill, Brough (53x65cm-21x26in) mono.d.1914 i.stretcher
£47000	$86010	(13-May-92 S31/R) Vue du Lavandou avec mer bleue (60x73cm-24x29in) mono.d.1923
£820	$1468	(14-Jan-92 PH18) Duton Hill (12x18cm-5x7in) mono.i. pencil col.crayons
£1200	$2100	(27-Sep-91 C4/R) Landscape with village and downs (10x12cm-4x5in) mono.d.1026 pencil W/C

PISSARRO, Lucien (1863-1944) British-cont.
£1300	$2301	(7-Nov-91 C82/R) Rye (12x16cm-5x6in) mono.i.indist.d.1912 pencil col.crayons
£4200	$7434	(7-Nov-91 C81/R) Landscape, L'aillery (16x24cm-6x9in) mono.i.d. pencil W/C

PISSARRO, Ludovic Rodo (1878-1952) French
£525	$898	(22-Mar-92 LT.P1) Au theatre (32x31cm-13x12in) init.st.mono. W/C ink (F.FR 5100)

PISSARRO, Orovida (1893-1968) British
£1850	$3478	(18-Dec-91 C24/R) The stable lantern (127x102cm-50x40in) s.d.1957 s.i.stretcher

PISSARRO, Paul Emile (1884-1972) French
£971	$1700	(28-Feb-92 SY.NY210/R) Neige au bord de la Lievre (55x46cm-22x18in) s.
£1130	$2000	(6-Nov-91 D.NY67/R) Le pain de sucre a travers les arbres (65x54cm-26x21in) s. i.verso i.stretcher
£1356	$2400	(5-Nov-91 CE.NY51/R) Les moissons a Cley (46x61cm-18x24in) s. i.stretcher
£1622	$3000	(12-Jun-92 SY.NY137/R) Le lac (49x61cm-19x24in) s.
£1857	$3250	(28-Feb-92 SY.NY204/R) Arbres verts et arbres a contre jour (54x65cm-21x26in) s.
£2429	$4250	(28-Feb-92 SY.NY219/R) La maison du bateau (53x65cm-21x26in) s. masonite
£2520	$4461	(10-Nov-91 ZZ.F246/R) Bord de riviere (66x92cm-26x36in) s. (F.FR 25000)
£366	$681	(16-Jun-92 SY.B373) Village in mountain landscape (30x22cm-12x9in) s. W/C (B.FR 22000)
£511	$894	(23-Feb-92 I.N100) Paysage a la chaumiere (24x31cm-9x12in) s. W/C (F.FR 5000)
£556	$1000	(10-Jan-92 DM.D2037/R) Landscape (23x30cm-9x12in) s. W/C gouache
£556	$1000	(10-Jan-92 DM.D2038/R) Wheat field (23x30cm-9x12in) s. W/C gouache
£632	$1100	(11-Sep-91 D.NY65 a) Stone smoke house (23x30cm-9x12in) s. W/C crayon
£1857	$3250	(28-Feb-92 SY.NY206/R) Farm. La Colline au bord de l'Orne (46x55cm-18x22in) one s. W/C chl one s. oil canvas pair

PISSIS, Amaro (1810-1850) French?
£1056	$1900	(18-Nov-91 SY.NY81/R) Prancha de Botanica, Dracoena Brasiliensis (29x21cm-11x8in) W/C oil
£1222	$2200	(18-Nov-91 SY.NY82/R) Entree de la Baie de Rio de Janeiro (22x29cm-9x11in) black wash htd white
£1222	$2200	(18-Nov-91 SY.NY80/R) Botafogo (21x28cm-8x11in) wash

PISTILLI, Enrico (1854-?) Italian
£679	$1257	(9-Jun-92 F.R81) Natura morta di frutta (75x99cm-30x39in) s.d.1919 (I.L 1500000)

PISTOLETTO, Michelangelo (1933-) Italian
£5345	$9675	(3-Dec-91 F.R218/R) Io sono una catena (104x73cm-41x29in) s.d.1977/80 mixed media (I.L 11500000)

PISTORIUS, Max (1894-1960) Austrian
£499	$892	(15-Jan-92 D.V105/R) Sunlit woodland path (68x55cm-27x22in) s.d.55 (A.S 10000)

PITA, Gerardo (1950-) ?
£1594	$2806	(9-Apr-92 ANS.M70/R) Flores secas (45x54cm-18x21in) s.d.1989 pencil dr (S.P 290000)
£1594	$2806	(9-Apr-92 ANS.M69/R) Pareja de coliflores (32x45cm-13x18in) s.d.1988 pencil dr (S.P 290000)

PITCHER, Neville Sotheby (20th C) British
£1000	$1800	(22-Nov-91 C94/R) Lochinvar with rowing boat coming alongside (63x76cm-25x30in) s.d.1952

PITCHFORTH, Roland Vivian (1895-1982) British
£440	$774	(6-Apr-92 WW144) Boating on river Thames (46x58cm-18x23in) s. W/C
£550	$1007	(4-Jun-92 CSK30/R) Malta (43x58cm-17x23in) s. W/C
£1200	$2184	(12-Dec-91 CSK243/R) Malta (43x58cm-17x23in) s. W/C

PITLOO, Antonio Sminck (1791-1837) Dutch
£11000	$20460	(17-Jun-92 S558/R) View of Vesuvius from Posilippo. View from Monte Nuovo, Naples (19x27cm-7x11in) s. panel pair
£14067	$24477	(14-Apr-92 SY.AM168/R) Italian landscape with figures near cave (33x25cm-13x10in) s.d.1830 panel (D.FL 46000)
£15596	$27138	(14-Apr-92 SY.AM81/R) Hilly landscape with shepherds and cattle by lake (43x59cm-17x23in) s. (D.FL 51000)
£5046	$8780	(14-Apr-92 SY.AM305/R) Fisherfolk on Neapolitan quay (15x21cm-6x8in) s. W/C (D.FL 16500)

PITOCCHI, Matteo de (attrib) (17th C) Italian
£3477	$5946	(18-Mar-92 D.V25/R) Allegory of birth (79x93cm-31x37in) (A.S 70000)

PITT, Charles (19/20th C) British
£730	$1307	(6-May-92 GD.B1016/R) Street scene in medieval village (45x34cm-18x13in) s. (S.FR 2000)

PITT, William (19th C) British

£500	$870	(19-Sep-91 TL397) Tranquil river landscape with figure on track (40x76cm-16x30in) s.d.79
£700	$1281	(3-Jun-92 S20/R) Carew Castle, S.Wales (31x26cm-12x10in) mono.d.1873
£900	$1548	(11-Oct-91 C79/R) Dinant on the Meuse, Belgium (61x91cm-24x36in)
£970	$1649	(7-Aug-91 WAW334) Wivenhoe on the Colne, Essex (34x59cm-13x23in) mono.d.77 i.verso

PITTARA, Carlo (1836-1890) Italian

£10892	$20259	(16-Jun-92 F.M237/R) Pascolo alpino (153x88cm-60x35in) s. (I.L 24000000)
£1733	*$3223*	*(18-Jun-92 SY.MO514/R) La Place Pigalle et le Moulin Rouge (36x57cm-14x22in) s. W/C gouache (F.FR 17000)*

PITTMAN, Hobson (1898-?) American

£909	$1600	(9-Apr-92 FA.PH821) Still life with fruit (61x46cm-24x18in) s. paper
£663	*$1200*	*(5-Dec-91 FA.PH584 a) Stormy summer evening (64x48cm-25x19in) s. pastel*
£847	*$1500*	*(22-Apr-92 D.NY77) Floral still life of carnations in pitcher (64x48cm-25x19in) s.d.70 pastel pencil*
£939	*$1700*	*(5-Dec-91 FA.PH584) Room interior (41x56cm-16x22in) s. W/C*

PITTMAN, Osmund (1874-1958) British

£657	$1176	(6-May-92 DS.W10) Acharague, south of Loch Shiel, Scotland (29x39cm-11x15in) s. i.verso (NZ.D 2200)

PITTO, Giacomo (?) ?

£802	$1419	(25-Apr-92 SO.S575/R) Market scene (56x76cm-22x30in) s.d.1931 (S.KR 8500)
£815	$1467	(23-Nov-91 SO.S583/R) Market scene (47x68cm-19x27in) s. (S.KR 8500)
£1100	$1903	(3-Oct-91 CSK246) A market beauty (51x71cm-20x28in) s.
£2000	$3460	(3-Oct-91 CSK262/R) In the market (48x69cm-19x27in) s.

PITTONI, Giovanni Battista (16-18th C) Italian

£11732	$21000	(17-Jan-92 SY.NY74/R) The vision of Saint Joseph (45x31cm-18x12in)
£120000	$218400	(11-Dec-91 S75/R) Sacrifice of Polyxena (74x54cm-29x21in)

PITTONI, Giovanni Battista (younger-attrib) (c.1687-1767) Italian

£2484	$4247	(18-Mar-92 D.V202/R) Alexander the Great cutting through the Gordian Knot (25x40cm-10x16in) (A.S 50000)

PITZNER, M (?) ?

£767	$1395	(12-Dec-91 N.M2818/R) Hunter with girl girl and geese (13x9cm-5x4in) s.i. panel (DM 2200)

PIXIS, Theodor (1831-1907) German

£4878	$8878	(12-Dec-91 L.K654/R) Classical scene with Gudrun carrying laundry received by Konigin Gerlinde (117x78cm-46x31in) s.d.1860 (DM 14000)
£756	*$1315*	*(18-Sep-91 N.M260/R) View of Florence (17x31cm-7x12in) s.d.1903 W/C htd.white (DM 2200)*

PIZARRO, Cecilio (19th C) Spanish

£2217	$3879	(18-Feb-92 DUR.M9/R) Toledo, Catedral (34x24cm-13x9in) s.d.1848 tinplate (S.P 400000)
£2217	$3879	(18-Feb-92 DUR.M8/R) Sevilla, la Catedral y la Giralda (34x24cm-13x9in) s.d.1848 tinplate (S.P 400000)

PIZZICANNELLA, Piero (1955-) Italian

£1508	$2866	(23-Jun-92 F.M76/R) Senza titolo (75x54cm-30x21in) s.d.1982 paper (I.L 3300000)
£1532	$2879	(19-Dec-91 F.M89/R) Composizione (86x56cm-34x22in) s.verso cardboard (I.L 3300000)
£1998	$3556	(29-Apr-92 F.F229/R) Senza titolo (68x48cm-27x19in) s.d.1990 cardboard (I.L 4400000)

PLA Y GALLARDO, Cecilio (1860-?) Spanish

£1200	$2172	(20-May-92 ANS.M69/R) Retrato de joven (39x29cm-15x11in) s. canvas on panel (S.P 220000)
£1636	$3043	(16-Jun-92 EP.M22/R) Nino en la playa (31x44cm-12x17in) (S.P 300000)
£2083	$3500	(1-Sep-91 PO.BA17) Vista de Espino, Portugal (26x36cm-10x14in) s. panel
£3280	$6003	(13-May-92 FER.M132/R) Ninos en la playa (17x23cm-7x9in) s. board (S.P 600000)
£3544	$6592	(16-Jun-92 EP.M23/R) Fiesta de la Cruz Roja (19x24cm-7x9in) (S.P 650000)
£8500	$15470	(29-May-92 C369/R) Figures on beach (15x23cm-6x9in) s.i.st.studio verso board
£8571	$15000	(20-Feb-92 SY.NY325/R) Playa (23x28cm-9x11in) s. board
£9302	$16000	(17-Oct-91 SY.NY362 b/R) Watching boats from beach (15x25cm-6x10in) s.d.1916 panel
£10515	$17980	(17-Mar-92 FER.M134/R) Besando el relicario (85x115cm-33x45in) s. (S.P 1900000)
£11000	$20020	(29-May-92 C370/R) Figures on beach (15x23cm-6x9in) s. st.studio verso board
£14000	$25480	(29-May-92 C368/R) Figures on beach (23x28cm-9x11in) s. st.studio verso canvas on board
£382	*$657*	*(16-Oct-91 FER.M2/R) Retratos y apuntes de Portugal s. pencil dr six in one frame (S.P 70000)*
£415	*$710*	*(17-Mar-92 FER.M4/R) Preparandose para la pesca (15x21cm-6x8in) s. pencil dr (S.P 75000)*

PLA Y GALLARDO, Cecilio (1860-?) Spanish-cont.
£518	$892	(16-Oct-91 FER.M3/R) Apuntes costumbristas de Portugal s. pencil dr six in one frame (S.P 95000)
£1245	$2129	(17-Mar-92 FER.M133/R) Reflejos (16x26cm-6x10in) s. W/C (S.P 225000)
£2156	$4054	(16-Dec-91 ANS.M213/R) Dama en interior (42x31cm-17x12in) s. W/C (S.P 390000)

PLA Y GARCIA, Alberto (?) Spanish
£711	$1208	(23-Oct-91 DUR.M504/R) Moras (88x48cm-35x19in) s. (S.P 130000)

PLA Y RUBIO, Alberto (1867-?) Spanish
£955	$1728	(20-May-92 ANS.M126/R) Moros y cristianos (30x20cm-12x8in) s. panel (S.P 175000)

PLA, Salvador (?) ?
£1231	$2339	(23-Jun-92 DUR.M24/R) Bodegon de caza (73x48cm-29x19in) s. (S.P 225000)

PLAGEMANN, Carl (1805-1868) Swedish
£767	$1381	(19-Nov-91 GO.G131) Cloister interior with nun (73x61cm-29x24in) s. (S.KR 8000)

PLANAS DORIA, Francisco (1879-1955) Spanish
£547	$996	(27-May-92 DUR.M968/R) Rincon de ciudad (48x69cm-19x27in) s. tablex (S.P 100000)

PLANELLS, Angel (1902-1989) Spanish
£719	$1351	(17-Dec-91 BRO.B372) Pintura surrealista (46x55cm-18x22in) s.d.83 (S.P 130000)

PLANK, Josef (1815-1901) Austrian
£1246	$2231	(15-Jan-92 D.V101/R) Female nude on the beach (104x80cm-41x31in) s. (A.S 25000)

PLANQUETTE, Felix (1873-?) French
£1011	$1800	(1-Dec-91 DU.E1142/R) End of day (38x56cm-15x22in) s.

PLANSON, Andre (1898-1981) French
£618	$1162	(18-Dec-91 PR.P106) Le calvaire du village (40x60cm-16x24in) s.d.41 panel (F.FR 6000)
£1848	$3326	(20-Nov-91 CN.P209/R) Nu a la serviette jaune (46x38cm-18x15in) s.d.53 (F.FR 18000)
£2218	$3925	(10-Nov-91 ZZ.F149/R) Paysage de Provence (55x82cm-22x32in) s. (F.FR 22000)
£2472	$4252	(20-Oct-91 I.N187/R) Bord de riviere et pecheurs (46x33cm-18x13in) s.d. board (F.FR 24500)
£3093	$5351	(27-Mar-92 PPB.P62/R) La baigneuse (54x46cm-21x18in) s. (F.FR 30000)
£3455	$6012	(16-Apr-92 FB.P96/R) Les peniches (65x81cm-26x32in) s.d.1956 (F.FR 34000)
£4137	$7240	(21-Feb-92 LC.P48/R) Village de Provence (81x65cm-32x26in) s. (F.FR 40500)
£411	$739	(20-Nov-91 CN.P59) Miremon de Quercy (46x60cm-18x24in) s.d.1940 W/C gouache (F.FR 4000)
£1395	$2400	(12-Oct-91 SY.NY83/R) Reclining nude (51x66cm-20x26in) s. W/C (F.FR 17500)
£1789	$3275	(3-Feb-92 SD.P183/R) Modele accoudee (53x67cm-21x26in) s.d.47 W/C gouache (F.FR 17500)

PLANTEY, M (19/20th C) French
£1098	$1900	(2-Oct-91 D.NY80) Reclining nude (23x28cm-9x11in) s.init.i.verso

PLAS, Pieter (1810-1853) Dutch
£2736	$4760	(17-Sep-91 CH.AM492/R) Summer - peasant couple and dog near forest. Winter - faggot gatherers pushing sledge (37x31cm-15x12in) both s.d.1837 panel (D.FL 9000)

PLASENCIA, Casto (1846-1890) Spanish
£985	$1793	(11-Dec-91 FER.M138/R) La ajorca de oro, leyenda de Becquer (33x47cm-13x19in) s. i.verso (S.P 180000)

PLASKETT, Joe (1918-) Canadian
£868	$1579	(26-May-92 JOY.T185/R) Flowers and figure with shadows (64x96cm-25x38in) s.d.83 (C.D 1900)
£495	$841	(23-Oct-91 MA.V85) Transition at Skedans (71x84cm-28x33in) s.d. pastel (C.D 950)

PLASSAN, Antoine-Emile (1817-1903) French
£680	$1210	(1-May-92 PHE53 a) In the fields (9x15cm-4x6in) s.
£1538	$2800	(26-May-92 CE.NY249/R) Une Ferme a Anvers (21x33cm-8x13in) s.i. panel
£1923	$3500	(28-May-92 SY.NY211/R) Family news (48x63cm-19x25in) s.d.73 cradled panel

PLATHNER, Hermann (1831-1902) German
£2473	$4500	(26-May-92 CE.NY132/R) Hungry visitors (36x29cm-14x11in) s.d.1863
£5923	$10780	(12-Dec-91 L.K655/R) Peasant interior with family at table looking at grandfather's portrait (62x75cm-24x30in) s.d.1869 (DM 17000)

PLATT, Charles Adams (1861-1933) American
£1955	$3500	(14-Nov-91 CE.NY57/R) Inlet (56x91cm-22x36in) init.

PLATTEEL, Jean (1839-1867) Belgian
£580 $1032   (29-Oct-91 SWS44) Scene from life of Duke of Orange (32x42cm-13x17in)
     s.d.1849 panel

PLATTENBERG, Mathieu van (1608-1660) Flemish
£4074 $7374   (19-May-92 GF.L2083/R) Stormy seascape (72x98cm-28x39in) (S.FR 11000)
£4360 $7500   (10-Oct-91 SY.NY76/R) Ships floundering on a stormy sea
     (89x137cm-35x54in)

PLATTENBERG, Mathieu van (attrib) (1608-1660) Flemish
£2600 $4992   (8-Jul-92 S289/R) Dutch vessels in stormy sea off rocky coast
     (70x122cm-28x48in)

PLATTENSTEINER, Christian von (1806-1858) Austrian
£702 $1270   (5-Dec-91 D.V102) Wooded landscape (21x18cm-8x7in) paper on board
     (A.S 14000)

PLATTENSTEINER, Christian von (attrib) (1806-1858) Austrian
£1496 $2677   (16-Jan-92 D.V135/R) Konigssee landscape (30x22cm-12x9in) board
     (A.S 30000)

PLATTNER, Karl (1919-1987) Austrian
£17171 $32282   (19-Dec-91 F.M197/R) Due figure (142x105cm-56x41in) s.d.1966/67
     (I.L 37000000)

PLATUNOVA, Aleksandra Georgevna (1896-1955) Russian
£1609 $2784   (28-Mar-92 F.L66/R) Festa a Kazan (18x24cm-7x9in) tempera cardboard
     (S.FR 4200)
£1418   *$2452*   *(28-Mar-92 F.L57/R) Progetto per manifesto (27x22cm-11x9in) s.d.1924*
     pencil W/C (S.FR 3700)
£2874   *$4971*   *(28-Mar-92 F.L56/R) Progetto per manifesto. Study (29x21cm-11x8in) pencil*
     W/C double-sided (S.FR 7500)

PLATZER, Johann Georg (1704-1761) Austrian
£3147 $5381   (18-Mar-92 N.M446/R) Sleeping singer and cavalier (11x15cm-4x6in) metal
     (DM 9000)
£24390 $44390   (11-Dec-91 N.M345/R) Classical scene with Narcissus falling in love with
     his own image (32x47cm-13x19in) copper (DM 70000)
£152420 $286550   (18-Dec-91 AT.P57/R) Alexandre devant le grand - pretre (67x94cm-26x37in)
     s. copper (F.FR 1480000)

PLATZODER, Ludwig (1898-) German
£871 $1585   (11-Dec-91 N.M563/R) Still life of candle, books and bowl
     (38x50cm-15x20in) s. panel (DM 2500)
£1224 $2093   (18-Mar-92 N.M616) Still life with jug, apples in bowl, glass and books
     (39x33cm-15x13in) s.d.1968 panel (DM 3500)

PLAYER, William H (fl.1858-1884) British
£1676 $3000   (13-Nov-91 B.SF2181/R) Bonchurch, Isle of Wight (40x60cm-16x24in)
     s.d.1852

PLEISSNER, Ogden M (1905-1983) American
£9890 $18000   (28-May-92 CH.NY262/R) Late afternoon, Brittany (61x91cm-24x36in) s.
£1379   *$2400*   *(15-Apr-92 SY.NY236/R) Upsalquitch River, New Brunswick (25x39cm-10x15in)*
     s. W/C pencil
£1379   *$2400*   *(15-Apr-92 SY.NY237/R) Moisie River, Quebec (25x39cm-10x15in) s. W/C*
£1729   *$3250*   *(18-Dec-91 SY.NY229/R) La neige (34x44cm-13x17in) s. W/C*
£1862   *$3500*   *(18-Dec-91 SY.NY368/R) Vannes (17x25cm-7x10in) s. i.verso W/C*
£2021   *$3800*   *(18-Dec-91 SY.NY405/R) Farm in Normandy (31x57cm-12x22in) s. W/C*
£2128   *$4000*   *(18-Dec-91 SY.NY325/R) Netting the salmon (16x25cm-6x10in) i.verso W/C*
     gouache pencil
£2527   *$4750*   *(18-Dec-91 SY.NY365/R) The card players - Luxembourg Gardens*
     (43x27cm-17x11in) s. W/C
£5495   *$10000*   *(27-May-92 SY.NY123/R) Coast of Normandie (47x72cm-19x28in) s. W/C*
£8000   *$14000*   *(26-Sep-91 CH.NY148/R) Fosse au fer (40x58cm-16x23in) s. W/C*
£10440   *$19000*   *(28-May-92 CH.NY261/R) St George's Bay, Bermuda (37x52cm-15x20in) s. W/C*
     pencil

PLERSCH, Jan Bogumil (1732-1817) Polish
£611   *$1112*   *(15-Dec-91 REM.W32) Design for a ceiling (33x23cm-13x9in) pencil W/C*
     (P.Z 12000000)

PLEUER, Hermann (1863-1911) German
£3088 $5280   (13-Mar-92 FN.S2910/R) View of Stuttgart seen from Westbahnhof
     (42x53cm-17x21in) canvas on board (DM 8800)
£8247 $14351   (17-Sep-91 FN.S2496/R) Steam train leaving Stuttgart station
     (51x70cm-20x28in) (DM 24000)
£8421 $14400   (13-Mar-92 FN.S2911/R) View of Stuttgart Bahnhof (41x53cm-16x21in)
     s.d.1906 canvas on board (DM 24000)

PLEUER, Hermann (attrib) (1863-1911) German
£584 $1016   (17-Sep-91 FN.S2496 a/R) Young woman seated on bed reading by candlelight
     (29x21cm-11x8in) mono. canvas on board (DM 1700)

PLEYSIER, Ary (1809-1879) Dutch
£2281 $4105   (22-Nov-91 SA.A1666/R) Coastal scene with shipping (44x68cm-17x27in) s. panel (DM 6500)

PLIMER, Andrew (1763-1837) British
£440 $840   (30-Jun-92 SWS2364/R) Portrait of lady wearing lace trimmed cap (7x?cm-3x?in) min. oval
£900 $1584   (9-Apr-92 S159/R) Portrait of gentleman, with powdered hair, wearing petrol coloured coat (6x?cm-2x?in) min. gold frame blue glass verso hair lock oval
£3000 $5280   (9-Apr-92 S164/R) Portrait of lady, left hand to cheek, wearing white dress, bandeau hair (8x?cm-3x?in) min. gold frame paste-set border oval

PLOCKHORST, Bernhard (1825-1907) German
£599 $1031   (8-Oct-91 ZEL.L1653/R) Portrait of Agnes Schoder (39x31cm-15x12in) mono.d.1850 board (DM 1750)

PLOLL, Victor (?) ?
£756 $1300   (15-Oct-91 CE.NY86/R) Conversation at the well (26x16cm-10x6in) s. panel

PLOMTEUX, Leopold (1920-) Belgian
£1159 $2098   (23-May-92 KV.L256) Vue de Mexico (60x50cm-24x20in) s. (B.FR 70000)
£993 $1798   (23-May-92 KV.L257) Composition (48x65cm-19x26in) s.d.1944 W/C (B.FR 60000)

PLOTNOV, Andrei (1916-) Russian
£711 $1238   (13-Apr-92 ARC.P7/R) Dans les dunes (25x35cm-10x14in) s. (F.FR 7000)
£762 $1326   (13-Apr-92 ARC.P8/R) A bicyclette (26x47cm-10x19in) s. (F.FR 7500)
£1220 $2122   (13-Apr-92 ARC.P9/R) Un bouquet pour maman (35x25cm-14x10in) s. board (F.FR 12000)

PLUCKEBAUM, Meta (1876-?) German
£759 $1305   (16-Oct-91 KM.K1320/R) Cat watching bee (51x41cm-20x16in) s. panel (DM 2200)

PLUM, Poul August (1815-1876) Danish
£529 $942   (28-Apr-92 RAS.K283) A juggler family (62x53cm-24x21in) (D.KR 6000)

PLUMOT, Andre (1829-1906) Belgian
£513 $929   (3-Dec-91 C.A246) Cattle in landscape (28x36cm-11x14in) s. panel (B.FR 30000)
£684 $1239   (3-Dec-91 C.A245) Returning to the stable (19x35cm-7x14in) s. panel (B.FR 40000)
£719 $1301   (3-Dec-91 C.A230) Study of goats (27x42cm-11x17in) mono. board (B.FR 42000)
£1407 $2547   (23-May-92 KV.L258) Cow herders in a wood (20x32cm-8x13in) s. (B.FR 85000)

PLUYM, Carel van der (attrib) (1625-1677) Dutch
£1080 $1934   (12-Nov-91 SY.AM257/R) Bearded man (14x12cm-6x5in) brush ink (D.FL 3500)

PLUYM, Carel van der (circle) (1625-1677) Dutch
£7800 $14976   (7-Jul-92 PH212/R) Cobbler in workshop (123x108cm-48x43in)

PO, Giacomo del (attrib) (1652-1726) Italian
£2600 $4628   (30-Oct-91 S98) Amphitrite (52x39cm-20x15in)

POBOGENSKY, Wjatscheslaw (1943-) Russian
£1102 $1896   (16-Oct-91 G.Z152/R) Reclining female nude (80x120cm-31x47in) s.d.1989 acrylic (S.FR 2800)

POCCETTI, Bernardino (attrib) (1542-1612) Italian
£1453 $2600   (14-Jan-92 SY.NY131) Study of seated woman (18x17cm-7x7in) black chk htd white

POCCETTI, Bernardino (studio) (1542-1612) Italian
£1100 $2112   (7-Jul-92 C28/R) The seven founders supervising construction of monastery of Monte Senario (25x40cm-10x16in) chk pen wash htd white lunette

POCCI, Franz Graf von (1807-1876) German
£1028 $1850   (19-Nov-91 GS.B3622/R) Wooded river landscape, evening (26x33cm-10x13in) mono. paper on canvas (S.FR 2600)

POCK, H (?) ?
£524 $907   (25-Mar-92 KM.K1368) Hay harvest, Upper Bavaria (20x25cm-8x10in) s. board (DM 1500)

POCOCK, Isaac (1782-1835) British
£1600 $3056   (15-Jul-92 S141/R) Portrait of Nicholas Pocock, the artist (74x62cm-29x24in) s. pair

POCOCK, Lilian J (fl.1908-1928) British
£500 $890   (30-Apr-92 CG840/R) The Red Cross (23x23cm-9x9in) s. s.i.verso W/C

POCOCK, Nicholas (1740-1821) British
£1400 $2548   (12-Dec-91 B106/R) Action between H.M.S.Brunswick and the Men-o-War Vengeur and Achille,1794 (44x60cm-17x24in)
£7500 $13425   (13-Nov-91 S8/R) Capture of the French frigate Piedmontaise (83x118cm-33x46in) s.d.1809
£400   *$680*   *(24-Oct-91 CSK63) At the foothills of the Mountains, Llanberis (41x58cm-16x23in) s.i.d.1796 pencil W/C*
£520   *$931*   *(5-May-92 SWS24/R) View from the Priory Walk, Brecon (57x78cm-22x31in) s.i.d.1806verso W/C over pencil*
£900   *$1539*   *(11-Mar-92 WIN701/R) Rustic landscape with figures and cattle (41x56cm-16x22in) s.d.1796 W/C pair*
£1400   *$2506*   *(12-Nov-91 C93/R) Llanberis Lake from the foot of Carn Glo, with labourers unloading slate (41x26cm-16x10in) s.i.d.1798 pencil W/C*

POCOCK, Nicholas (attrib) (1740-1821) British
£760 $1376   (3-Dec-91 LW2021) Marine scape with de-masted Englsih Men-O'-War

PODCHERNIKOFF, Alexis M (1886-1931) American
£500 $950   (24-Jun-92 B.SF6277/R) Golden sunset (25x30cm-10x12in) s. canvas on board
£500 $950   (24-Jun-92 B.SF6273/R) Pastoral landscape (56x72cm-22x28in) s.
£500 $950   (23-Jun-92 MOR.P13) Figure in landscape (20x25cm-8x10in) s.
£526 $1000   (23-Jun-92 MOR.P131) Old Spanish adobe, Santa Barbara (30x41cm-12x16in) s.
£571 $1000   (31-Mar-92 MOR.P97) Moonlight landscape (51x41cm-20x16in) s.
£678 $1200   (12-Feb-92 B.SF420/R) Little rabbit hunter (36x46cm-14x18in) s. board
£895 $1700   (24-Jun-92 B.SF6276/R) Figure and cattle beside pond (25x30cm-10x12in) s. canvas on board
£899 $1600   (26-Nov-91 MOR.P129) Figures in landscape (76x51cm-30x20in) s.
£1124 $2000   (26-Nov-91 MOR.P128) California nocturne (76x51cm-30x20in) s.
£1412 $2500   (12-Feb-92 B.SF401/R) Afternoon glow (102x76cm-40x30in) s. s.d.1918 verso
£1974 $3750   (24-Jun-92 B.SF6449/R) Morning light, Santa Inez Mountains (66x117cm-26x46in) s.

PODKOWINSKI, Wladyslaw (1866-1895) Polish
£2799 $5095   (15-Dec-91 REM.W33) Children in country landscape (40x44cm-16x17in) (P.Z 55000000)
£407   *$741*   *(15-Dec-91 REM.W34) Grand pianos (23x29cm-9x11in) s. pen (P.Z 8000000)*
£2864   *$5013*   *(29-Sep-91 AG.W13) By the fireplace (35x28cm-14x11in) s.ink gouache board (P.Z 55000000)*

PODLIASKI, Galina (1951-) Russian
£524 $917   (24-Sep-91 ARC.P222/R) Un coin de la cuisine (74x54cm-29x21in) s. (F.FR 5200)

POEL, Egbert van der (1621-1664) Dutch
£1079 $2051   (23-Jun-92 D.V289/R) Fire raging in village at night (33x48cm-13x19in) panel (A.S 22000)
£1381 $2500   (22-May-92 SY.NY294/R) Cottage ablaze at night with villagers attempting to extinguish fire (44x55cm-17x22in) panel
£2749 $4784   (18-Sep-91 N.M443/R) Fire raging at night with peasants fleeing (38x49cm-15x19in) s. (DM 8000)
£2791 $4800   (9-Oct-91 CH.NY124/R) Peasants extinguishing cottage fire (35x27cm-14x11in) bears sig. panel
£3800 $6840   (21-Nov-91 C88/R) Studies of travellers, man in sledge and woman on horseback (12x25cm-5x10in) indis.s.d.62 panel
£7000 $12740   (13-Dec-91 C208/R) Explosion of the Powder Magazine at Delft, 1654 (30x46cm-12x18in) s. panel

POEL, Egbert van der (attrib) (1621-1664) Dutch
£1109 $1963   (6-Nov-91 LT.P46) Villageois combattant l'incendie d'une maison (44x55cm-17x22in) panel (F.FR 11000)

POELENBURGH, Cornelis van (1586-1667) Dutch
£1923 $3288   (18-Mar-92 N.M447/R) Mary and angels on clouds above landscape with classical ruins (36x30cm-14x12in) copper (DM 5500)
£2037 $3687   (19-May-92 GF.L2388/R) Nymphs and fauns in landscape with ruins (36x47cm-14x19in) mono (S.FR 5500)
£12963 $23204   (14-Nov-91 CH.AM181/R) Christ on the Cross with St Mary Magdalen, St John and the Madonna (33x25cm-13x10in) init. panel shaped top (D.FL 42000)
£1000   *$1820*   *(11-Dec-91 PH51) Figures strolling near ruins of Colosseum (26x37cm-10x15in) pen wash chk sold with another W/C*

POELENBURGH, Cornelis van (attrib) (1586-1667) Dutch
£4500 $8640   (10-Jul-92 C145/R) Portrait of girl (11cm-4ins circular) copper

POELENBURGH, Cornelis van (circle) (1586-1667) Dutch
£3867 $7000   (19-May-92 CE.NY320) Diana and nymphs bathing after hunt amongst classical ruins (66x81cm-26x32in) canvas on board

POELENBURGH, Cornelis van (style) (1586-1667) Dutch
£769 $1315   (18-Mar-92 N.M448) Satyrs and nymphs by lake shore (36x53cm-14x21in) indis.i. panel (DM 2200)
£785 $1500   (16-Jul-92 SY.NY175/R) Bathers in landscape (57x67cm-22x26in)
£800 $1440   (21-Nov-91 CSK97) Diana and nymphs bathing at woodland pool (35x42cm-14x17in)

POELENBURGH, Cornelis van (style) (1586-1667) Dutch-cont.
£1850 $3386   (12-May-92 SWS627/R) Diana and handmaidens with Jupiter and other gods beyond (40x53cm-16x21in)
£5500 $9570   (13-Sep-91 C12/R) Diana and Actaeon (30x39cm-12x15in) panel

POELENBURGH, Cornelis van and KEIRINCX, Alexander (17th C) Dutch/Flemish
£2800 $4984   (29-Oct-91 PH18/R) A wooded landscape with nymphs bathing (39x66cm-15x26in) bears init.C.P panel

POERSON, Charles (1609-1667) French
£9000 $16380   (13-Dec-91 C221/R) Virgin and Child in landscape (59x51cm-23x20in)

POERSON, Charles (attrib) (1609-1667) French
£4634 $8713   (18-Dec-91 AT.P183/R) Allegorie de Flore et Zephyr (41x56cm-16x22in) painted octagonal (F.FR 45000)

POGGENBEEK, Geo (1853-1903) Dutch
£727 $1287   (22-Apr-92 CH.AM58) Extensive polderlandscape with farmers working in the field (12x32cm-5x13in) studio st. canvas laid down on panel (D.FL 2400)

POGGI, C (?) Italian
£680 $1231   (19-May-92 SWS175) Italian peasant woman (84x66cm-33x26in) s. oval

POGGI, Raphael (fl.1863-1879) French
£10194 $18960   (18-Jun-92 SY.MO89/R) Offrandes a la Divinite (49x64cm-19x25in) s.d.1873 panel (F.FR 100000)
£10194 $18960   (18-Jun-92 SY.MO88/R) Scene Pompeienne (49x64cm-19x25in) s.d.1873 panel (F.FR 100000)

POGGIANTI, C (19th C) Italian?
£1013 $1844   (10-Dec-91 F.R134) Paese sul mare (30x20cm-12x8in) s. (I.L 2200000)

POHL, Carl Robert (1891-?) German
£1038 $1972   (27-Jun-92 FN.L1157/R) Still life of wild roses and bird's nest (31x40cm-12x16in) s.i. W/C (DM 3000)

POHL, Frans van (19th C) Dutch
£612 $1064   (14-Apr-92 SY.AM25) Feeding the ducks (60x100cm-24x39in) s.d.1894 (D.FL 2000)

POHLE, Heinrich Jacob (fl.1729-1747) ?
£2100 $3612   (4-Mar-92 C24/R) King Frederik V of Denmark and mother Queen Sophia Magdalene (5x?cm-2x?in) min. one i.d.1740 verso gilt card rec pair

POHLE, Hermann (1831-1901) German
£519 $986   (24-Jun-92 KM.K1219) Wooded mountain landscape with traveller on path along stream, autumn (40x31cm-16x12in) s. (DM 1500)
£621 $1068   (16-Oct-91 KM.K1323) Hunter with dog on woodland path (38x33cm-15x13in) s. (DM 1800)
£3497 $6294   (21-Nov-91 D.V7/R) Torrent in mountain landscape (110x154cm-43x61in) s.d.60 (A.S 70000)

POHLE, Hermann (attrib) (1831-1901) German
£552 $949   (16-Oct-91 KM.K1324) Woodland with doe by stream (13x24cm-5x9in) mono.d.95 paper (DM 1600)

POHLE, Hermann Emil (jnr) (1863-1914) German
£741 $1298   (19-Feb-92 D.V65/R) Bathers (64x50cm-25x20in) s.d.98 (A.S 15000)

POHLE, Leon (1841-1908) German
£13538 $24368   (19-Nov-91 RAS.K56/R) Family saying grace (100x160cm-39x63in) s.d.1876 (D.KR 150000)

POILPOT, Theophile and PATY, Leon du (19th C) French
£3714 $6500   (20-Feb-92 SY.NY118/R) Le Siege de Paris en 1871 (47x151cm-19x59in) s. four framed as six

POKITONOV, Ivan (1851-1924) Russian
£3429 $6000   (18-Feb-92 CE.NY111/R) Hunter in winter landscape (16x27cm-6x11in) s.d.88 panel
£4286 $7500   (18-Feb-92 CE.NY195/R) Hunter in marshy landscape (16x27cm-6x11in) s.d.1898 panel

POKORNY, Richard (20th C) Austrian
£388 $691   (29-Apr-92 D.V675/R) Mariahilfer Strasse, Vienna (25x33cm-10x13in) s. W/C (A.S 8000)
£489 $840   (10-Oct-91 D.V272/R) View of Rauchfangkehrerkirche (24x35cm-9x14in) s. W/C (A.S 10000)
£537 $924   (10-Oct-91 D.V268/R) Stallburggasse, Vienna (32x26cm-13x10in) s. W/C (A.S 11000)
£537 $924   (10-Oct-91 D.V238/R) View of Rothenburg ob der Tauber (38x33cm-15x13in) s.d.1968 W/C (A.S 11000)
£635 $1092   (10-Oct-91 D.V267/R) Hofapotheke and tower of Michaelerkirche (32x23cm-13x9in) s. W/C (A.S 13000)

POKORNY, Richard (20th C) Austrian-cont.
£780 $1358   (19-Sep-91 D.V270/R) Hof in Wien, market day (27x45cm-11x18in) s.i. W/C
     (A.S 16000)
£890 $1557   (20-Feb-92 D.V524/R) Kahlenberger Dorf near Vienna (24x35cm-9x14in) s.
     W/C (A.S 18000)
£1068 $1901   (29-Apr-92 D.V676/R) Stefansplatz with Haashaus (44x30cm-17x12in) s. W/C
     (A.S 22000)
£1246 $2231   (16-Jan-92 D.V163/R) Hauptplatz in Perchtoldsdorf (31x26cm-12x10in) s.
     W/C (A.S 25000)

POL, Albertus Gerhard Hulshoff (1883-1957) Dutch
£547 $952   (17-Sep-91 CH.AM493/R) A river impression (62x88cm-24x35in) s. i.
     stretcher (D.FL 1800)

POLANSKY, Rudolf (1951-) Austrian
£582 $1059   (26-May-92 D.V345/R) Untitled (90x90cm-35x35in) s.d.85 mixed media
     acrylic oil canvas (A.S 12000)
£1369 $2436   (31-Oct-91 D.V233/R) Folienkombinationsbild (123x73cm-48x29in) s.d.91
     mixed media collage canvas (A.S 28000)

POLEDNE, Franz (1873-?) Austrian
£1221 $2101   (10-Oct-91 D.V243/R) Interior of Schloss Hetzendorf near Vienna
     (22x33cm-9x13in) s. W/C bodycol (A.S 25000)
£1221 $2101   (10-Oct-91 D.V244/R) Rittersaal of Schloss Tratzberg, Tyrol
     (22x33cm-9x13in) s.i. W/C (A.S 25000)

POLELONEMA, Otis (1902-) American
£1730 $3200   (14-Jun-92 S.BM112/R) Corn dancers (53x33cm-21x13in) s. gouache

POLEO, Hector (1918-) Venezuelan
£16575 $30000   (18-May-92 CH.NY81/R) La rose (60x73cm-24x29in) s.d.1966 i.stretcher

POLESE, Tobia (1855-?) Italian
£1300 $2314   (26-Nov-91 PH274) Mediterranean coastal scene (60x77cm-24x30in) s. pair

POLI, Gherardo and Giuseppe (18th C) Italian
£42761 $77397   (3-Dec-91 SY.MI264/R) Vedute di porto con una moltitudine di figure
     (96x152cm-38x60in) pair (I.L 92000000)

POLI, Jacques (20th C) French
£978 $1673   (19-Mar-92 CSC.P104/R) Sphere rose (116x89cm-46x35in) s.i.d.3-4-1970verso
     waxed canvas (F.FR 9500)

POLIAKOFF, Nicolas (20th C) Russian
£890 $1548   (18-Sep-91 KH.K163/R) Modele (55x43cm-22x17in) s.d.1931 pastel
     (D.KR 10000)

POLIAKOFF, Serge (1906-1969) Russian
£8642 $15728   (11-Dec-91 CH.AM325/R) Composition mur tempera (38x46cm-15x18in) init.
     (D.FL 28000)
£19553 $35000   (14-Nov-91 SY.NY285/R) Untitled (65x49cm-26x19in) s.i. tempera paper
£19697 $35652   (19-May-92 CH.AM261/R) Composition Rouge Blanc Bleu (46x65cm-18x26in) s.
     paper on canvas (D.FL 65000)
£21000 $36330   (26-Mar-92 C13/R) Composition abstraite noire, bleue, grise
     (73x60cm-29x24in) s.
£30000 $57300   (2-Jul-92 S18/R) Untitled (81x65cm-32x26in) s.
£36000 $65160   (5-Dec-91 C5/R) Composition (130x97cm-51x38in) s. wood
£37143 $65000   (25-Feb-92 SY.NY135/R) Untitled (83x102cm-33x40in) s. s.d.1969verso
£40123 $73025   (12-Dec-91 SY.AM207/R) Composition (100x81cm-39x32in) s.d.1969
     (D.FL 130000)
£40527 $73354   (24-May-92 GL.P31/R) Composition en rouge, bleu, noir et blanc
     (92x73cm-36x29in) s. (F.FR 400000)
£44580 $80689   (24-May-92 GL.P30/R) Composition polychrome a la forme blanche
     (59x80cm-23x31in) s. (F.FR 440000)
£59794 $103443   (29-Mar-92 P.V45/R) Composition (116x89cm-46x35in) s. (F.FR 580000)
£92000 $158240   (17-Oct-91 S18/R) Composition (67x56cm-26x22in) s. d.1953 verso
£102389 $186348   (25-May-92 WK.M1029/R) Composition verte (130x97cm-51x38in) s.d.1964
     (DM 300000)
£136052 $231289   (27-Oct-91 P.V28/R) Composition (162x130cm-64x51in) s.d.1969
     (F.FR 1351000)
£7000 $12110   (26-Mar-92 C15/R) Composition polychrome (33x42cm-13x17in) i.verso
     gouache paper mounted on board
£8333 $14500   (14-Apr-92 CSC.P51/R) Formes emboitees (49x64cm-19x25in) s. gouache
     craft-paper (F.FR 82000)
£8500 $14705   (26-Mar-92 C12/R) Composition bleue (45x61cm-18x24in) s. gouache paper
     mounted on card
£9877 $17975   (11-Dec-91 CH.AM326/R) Abstract composition (48x64cm-19x25in) s. gouache
     paper on canvas (D.FL 32000)
£9877 $17975   (11-Dec-91 CH.AM327/R) Composition jaune, vert, rouge, noir
     (63x48cm-25x19in) s. gouache paper on canvas (D.FL 32000)
£10288 $18621   (2-Dec-91 CC.P11/R) Composition (32x41cm-13x16in) s. gouache
     (F.FR 100000)
£10526 $18000   (13-Mar-92 FN.S2583/R) Composition (63x46cm-25x18in) s. gouache
     (DM 30000)

OLIAKOFF, Serge (1906-1969) Russian-cont.
£11000	$21010	(2-Jul-92 S4/R) Composition (45x58cm-18x23in) s. gouache paper laid down on board
£11723	$21804	(15-Jun-92 GL.P25/R) Untitled (45x60cm-18x24in) s. gouache (F.FR 115000)
£12121	$21939	(21-May-92 SY.AM261/R) Composition (64x48cm-25x19in) s. gouache paper on card (D.FL 40000)
£12424	$22488	(21-May-92 SY.AM262/R) Composition (66x50cm-26x20in) s. s.verso gouache (D.FL 41000)
£13109	$23333	(29-Apr-92 G.Z58/R) Composition jaune et orange (60x45cm-24x18in) s. gouache (S.FR 35000)
£13846	$26308	(26-Jun-92 GK.B130/R) Composition, lie de vin vert rose (48x63cm-19x25in) s. gouache (S.FR 36000)
£14334	$26089	(26-May-92 KF.M1155/R) Composition (48x63cm-19x25in) s. gouache (DM 42000)

OLICASTRO, Enrique (1898-1971) Argentinian
£559	$1000	(6-May-92 V.BA82) Paisaje (21x30cm-8x12in) tempera
£718	$1250	(19-Sep-91 V.BA77) Quebrada de Humahuaca (27x37cm-11x15in)
£3407	$6200	(11-Dec-91 RO.BA37/R) Maizal (50x75cm-20x30in) s.d.60
£5108	$9500	(16-Jun-92 RO.BA67) En el circo (49x37cm-19x15in)

OLIDORO DA CARAVAGGIO (1492-1543) Italian
£791	$1400	(13-Feb-92 S.W1838/R) Soldiers of Ciro (13x18cm-5x7in) bears sig. sepia ink

OLINI, A (19/20th C) Italian?
£1178	$2250	(3-Jul-92 S.W3069/R) On Grand Canal, Venice (41x61cm-16x24in) s.d.1889

OLKE, Sigmar (1941-) German
£10000	$17300	(26-Mar-92 C114/R) Untitled (98x74cm-39x29in) s.d.86 acrylic synthetic resin paper
£2000	$3460	(26-Mar-92 C113/R) Ist der ofen aus (29x21cm-11x8in) s.i.d.66 brush ink
£6936	$12000	(3-Oct-91 SY.NY131/R) Untitled (61x46cm-24x18in) s.d.65 gouache
£15363	$27500	(13-Nov-91 SY.NY124/R) Untitled (85x61cm-33x24in) init.d.66 ink
£15642	$28000	(6-May-92 CH.NY215/R) Untitled (69x99cm-27x39in) s.d.82 spray enamel acrylic
£19553	$35000	(6-May-92 CH.NY240/R) Untitled (99x70cm-39x28in) s.d.83 gouache W/C gold paint tempera
£21000	$36120	(17-Oct-91 C129/R) Untitled (75x100cm-30x39in) s.d.86 ink acrylic cardboard on canvas
£55866	$100000	(7-May-92 SY.NY130/R) Bildnis Helmut Klinker (135x98cm-53x39in) dispersion canvas
£78212	$140000	(5-May-92 CH.NY7/R) Loop Prayer Book Maximilian (249x249cm-98x98in) s.d.86verso resin pigment dispersion canvas
£94972	$170000	(5-May-92 CH.NY22/R) Medallion (150x180cm-59x71in) resin acrylic fabric

OLLACK, H (20th C) British
£500	$950	(23-Jun-92 PH175) Sunny lake landscape (101x127cm-40x50in) s.

OLLAIUOLO, Antonio (circle) (1433-1498) Italian
£750	$1440	(7-Jul-92 C114/R) Nude with staff, possibly Paris (15x6cm-6x2in) i. chk pen wash

OLLAIUOLO, Piero (attrib) (1443-1496) Italian
£632	$1080	(13-Mar-92 FN.S2913) St Sebastian (70x50cm-28x20in) (DM 1800)

OLLAK, August (1838-?) Austrian
£2500	$4325	(4-Oct-91 C108/R) Chrysanthemums in basket (75x125cm-30x49in) s.d.1900

OLLAK, Leopold (1816-1880) Austrian
£2000	$3820	(29-Jun-92 PHB179/R) Portrait of Italian girl (55x47cm-22x19in) s.i.d.1861 oval
£6300	$11970	(24-Jun-92 DR185/R) Portrait of young harem girl, with dove carrying message (170x96cm-67x38in) s.i.d.1852

OLLARD, James (1797-1859) British
£2000	$3820	(15-Jul-92 S104/R) The Royal Mail's leaving from the General Post Office (35x43cm-14x17in) s.d.1828
£4800	$9168	(15-Jul-92 S103/R) The Royal Day Mail at Snaresbrook (35x44cm-14x17in) s.d.1848
£7200	$12816	(29-Oct-91 HB559/R) Mr Sam Montagu angling at South Stoneham (18x23cm-7x9in) s.d.1838 panel
£8200	$14596	(29-Oct-91 HB560/R) Pike fishing at Harleyford-on-Thames (28x38cm-11x15in) s.indis.d.
£21000	$40110	(15-Jul-92 S102/R) Hyde Park Corner (30x51cm-12x20in) s.

OLLARD, James and HERRING, John Frederick (snr-attrib) (19th C) British
£4749	$8500	(13-Nov-91 B.SF2268/R) Horses and poultry in farmyard (76x127cm-30x50in) s.

OLLENTINE, Alfred (19th C) British
£588	$1012	(19-Oct-91 UA.U339) The Grand Canal, Venice (30x25cm-12x10in) s. (S.KR 6200)
£600	$1152	(29-Jul-92 CSK251) The Grand Canal, Venice (25x27cm-10x11in) s.i.
£700	$1197	(12-Mar-92 CSK308) The Grand Canal, Venice (25x25cm-10x10in) s. s.i.

POLLENTINE, Alfred (19th C) British-cont.
£1130	$2000	(13-Feb-92 S.W2833/R) Grand Canal, Venice (51x76cm-20x30in) s.
£1350	$2322	(4-Mar-92 CBB5/R) San Petri De Castello Venice (42x61cm-17x24in) s.i.verso
£1500	$2580	(4-Mar-92 S145/R) Venice (29x49cm-11x19in) s.d.82 canvas on board
£1600	$2752	(11-Oct-91 C145/R) The Dogana, Venice (51x76cm-20x30in) s. s.i.verso
£1600	$2960	(11-Jun-92 CSK242/R) Venetian canals and gondoliers (40x30cm-16x12in) s.
£1700	$3043	(11-Nov-91 HS351/R) The Dogana. The Grand Canal, Venice (29x50cm-11x20in) s.d.1883 i.verso pair
£1800	$3078	(12-Mar-92 CSK307/R) Scuola di San Marco in the Campo San Giovanne e Paolo, Venice (41x61cm-16x24in) s.d.87 s.i.verso
£2600	$4472	(11-Oct-91 C165/R) The Columns of St.Mark's, Venice (51x41cm-20x16in) s.d.87 s.i.verso
£3000	$5190	(24-Mar-92 PHC442/R) Dogana, Venice (76x51cm-30x20in) s. s.i.verso pair
£4000	$7120	(28-Apr-92 PH70/R) Mediterranean harbour town (77x127cm-30x50in) s.d.74
£4400	$7788	(6-Nov-91 S23/R) St Mark's Square, Venice (76x127cm-30x50in) s.d.79
£4800	$8256	(11-Oct-91 C71/R) The Dogana. Santa Maria della Salute, Venice (30x61cm-12x24in) s. s.i.verso pair
£6000	$10320	(4-Mar-92 S144/R) Grand Canal, Venice. Dogana, Venice (31x51cm-12x20in) s.d.83 s.i.verso pair

POLLENTINE, Alfred (style) (19th C) British
| £800 | $1464 | (14-May-92 CSK163) The Grand Canal, Venice (46x56cm-18x22in) board |

POLLENTINE, V (19th C) ?
| £879 | $1600 | (13-Dec-91 S.W2880) Ducal Palace, Venice (41x61cm-16x24in) s.d.85 |

POLLET, Victor Florence (1811-1882) French
| *£1486* | *$2600* | *(18-Feb-92 CE.NY186/R) Repos (26x34cm-10x13in) s.d.1875 W/C gouache h white gum arabic* |

POLLITT, Albert (fl.1889-1920) British
£500	*$900*	*(27-Jan-92 PH80) Autumnal river (38x58cm-15x23in) s.d.1900 W/C over pencil*
£660	*$1155*	*(17-Feb-92 HS197/R) River landscape in North Wales with figures and flock of sheep on path (42x60cm-17x24in) s.d.1902 W/C*
£1400	*$2674*	*(30-Jun-92 RJ196) Beach scene with fishermen unloading catch s.d.1909 W/C*

POLLITT, Mary E (20th C) British
| £2800 | $4704 | (26-Aug-91 S1145/R) Still life of sweet peas in vase (42x51cm-17x20in) s. board |

POLLOCK, Jackson (1912-1956) American
£13966	*$25000*	*(14-Nov-91 SY.NY279/R) Untitled (25x19cm-10x7in) ink gouache*
£83799	*$150000*	*(12-Nov-91 CH.NY13/R) Silver and black (22x32cm-9x13in) s.d.1950verso oil enamel silver paint canvas*
£167598	*$300000*	*(13-Nov-91 SY.NY17/R) Untitled (48x63cm-19x25in) s. brush spatter inks*

POLO, Bernabe (17th C) Spanish
| £17000 | $30940 | (29-May-92 C338/R) The Triumphal Entry of Alessandro Farnese into Brussels (119x197cm-47x78in) s. |

POLO, Roberto (20th C) ?
| £9143 | $16000 | (28-Feb-92 SY.NY322) untitled (127x183cm-50x72in) s.d.2/68 verso |

POLOVTSOFF, Helene (20th C) ?
| £650 | $1118 | (5-Mar-92 CSK181) Busy garden square (60x72cm-24x28in) s. |

POLSON, Evelyn see PAGE, Evelyn

POLSTERER, Hilde (1903-) Austrian?
| £727 | $1323 | (26-May-92 D.V162/R) Still life with triangle (76x56cm-30x22in) s. panel (A.S 15000) |

POMA, Silvio (1840-1932) Italian
£1673	$2861	(19-Mar-92 F.M33/R) Cortile rustico (32x47cm-13x19in) s. (I.L 3600000)
£2778	$5028	(22-May-92 EA.Z92/R) Lago Maggiore landscape (53x45cm-21x18in) s. (S.FR 7500)
£4648	$7948	(19-Mar-92 F.M95/R) Pascolo montano (85x130cm-33x51in) s. (I.L 10000000)
£14000	$24920	(29-Nov-91 C106/R) Lake Como (65x121cm-26x48in) s.
£22000	$39160	(29-Nov-91 C105/R) Lake Como (65x121cm-26x48in) s.i.

POMARDI, Simone (1760-1830) Italian
| *£3200* | *$5472* | *(18-Mar-92 S151/R) View of the Piazza dei Miracoli, Pisa (46x73cm-18x29in) s.i. ink W/C htd.gum arabic* |
| *£14053* | *$25998* | *(12-Jun-92 ARC.P166/R) Promeneurs parmi des monuments antiques dans le parc de la ville Borghese a Rome (54x75cm-21x30in) one s.d.1796 W/C gouache pair (F.FR 138000)* |

POMARENKO, Oleg (1948-) Russian
| £1075 | $1913 | (25-Nov-91 ARC.P8/R) Le bain du soir (60x70cm-24x28in) s. (F.FR 10500) |
| £1126 | $2004 | (25-Nov-91 ARC.P6/R) Les baigneuses (49x79cm-19x31in) s. board (F.FR 11000) |

POMASSL, Franz (1903-1982) Austrian
£598 $1071   (15-Jan-92 D.V122/R) Train in landscape (45x60cm-18x24in) s. board
                       (A.S 12000)

POMI, Alessandro (1890-) Italian
£552 $988   (14-Nov-91 CH.R224) Marinaio che guarda il mare (33x23cm-13x9in) s. panel
                       (I.L 1200000)

POMMAYRAC, Pierre Paul de (1807-1880) French
£465 $822   (24-Apr-92 CD.P83) Portrait de jeune femme (12x9cm-5x4in) min.s.d.1859
                       gilt frame oval (F.FR 4600)

POMMEREUL, Elisabeth (1959-) French
£404 $694   (14-Oct-91 AT.P153/R) Songes (100x73cm-39x29in) s. i.d.1991verso acrylic
                       chl.cloth Arches paper (F.FR 4000)

POMODORO, Gio (1930-) Italian
£678 $1227   (21-May-92 F.M142/R) Folla (13x38cm-5x15in) s.i.d.1992 gouache collage
                       (I.L 1500000)
£678 $1227   (21-May-92 F.M302/R) Studi per superfici in tensione (22x32cm-9x13in)
                       s.i.d.1962 W/C indian ink (I.L 1500000)

POMPA, Gaetano (1928-) Italian
£3856 $7056   (12-May-92 F.R188/R) Il guerriero (50x70cm-20x28in) s.d.1982
                       (I.L 8500000)

POMPE, Gerrit (17th C) Dutch
£5500 $10560   (8-Jul-92 S96/R) English and other shipping in choppy sea
                       (37x48cm-15x19in) s.d.1691 panel

POMPE, Gerrit (attrib) (17th) Dutch
£1600 $2928   (12-May-92 SWS816/R) Dutch man o' war and other shipping in light breeze
                       (23x31cm-9x12in) indist.init. panel

PONA, J F (19th C) British?
£448 $801   (6-May-92 DS.W3) Bamborough Castle, Northumberland (25x45cm-10x18in)
                       indis.s. i.verso W/C (NZ.D 1500)

PONC, Juan (1927-1984) Spanish
£1384 $2366   (17-Mar-92 FER.M169/R) Paisatge benefic (27x22cm-11x9in) (S.P 250000)
£8294 $15593   (17-Dec-91 BRO.B365/R) Jarron con flores (105x57cm-41x22in) s.d.56
                       (S.P 1500000)
£987 $1756   (26-Nov-91 BRO.B366) Figura y cruces (21x15cm-8x6in) s.d.46verso gouache
                       Indian ink (S.P 180000)
£1313 $2338   (29-Oct-91 BRO.B357) Luna y figuras (45x32cm-18x13in) s.d.59 mixed media
                       (S.P 240000)
£1800 $3239   (28-Jan-92 EP.M67/R) Figuras (49x49cm-19x19in) s.d.70 ink (S.P 325000)
£3318 $6237   (17-Dec-91 BRO.B332/R) Figura y signos (50x65cm-20x26in) s.d.47verso
                       mixed media (S.P 600000)
£4976 $9356   (17-Dec-91 BRO.B390) Simultaneismo (50x65cm-20x26in) s.d.47verso mixed
                       media (S.P 900000)
£13680 $24350   (29-Oct-91 BRO.B320/R) Vision nocturna (65x46cm-26x18in) s. s.d.47verso
                       oil gouache paper on canvas (S.P 2500000)

PONCE DE LEON, Fidelio (1896-1957) Cuban
£3889 $7000   (19-Nov-91 CH.NY205/R) Retrato de mujer (59x48cm-23x19in) s. board
£6077 $11000   (19-May-92 SY.NY187/R) Untitled (65x53cm-26x21in) s.
£52778 $95000   (18-Nov-91 SY.NY37/R) Five women (84x112cm-33x44in) s.d.41

PONCE, Antonio (17th C) Spanish
£32000 $58240   (29-May-92 C323/R) Swags of mixed flowers with butterflies
                       (53x106cm-21x42in) indis.s. pair
£45000 $81900   (29-May-92 C322/R) Apples, grapes and pomegranates in basket
                       (43x61cm-17x24in) s.

PONCELET, Thierry (19/20th C) ?
£550 $985   (14-Jan-92 B183) An old head on young shoulders (71x49cm-28x19in) s.
£750 $1358   (2-Dec-91 B114) Portrait of lady in green dress (85x70cm-33x28in) s.

POND, Arthur (attrib) (1705-1758) British
£800 $1456   (10-Dec-91 SWS184/R) Portrait of Mrs Hume wearing white bonnet decorated
                       with ribbon (74x62cm-29x24in) painted oval

POND, Dana (19/20th C) ?
£597 $1075   (23-Nov-91 YFA.M226/R) Industrial landscape (64x76cm-25x30in)

PONGA, Giuseppe (1856-1925) Italian
£2231 $4038   (3-Dec-91 SY.MI127) Veduta del duomo di Milano dal laghetto
                       (46x54cm-18x21in) panel (I.L 4800000)

PONGRATZ, Peter (1940-) German
£978 $1740   (31-Oct-91 D.V86/R) Portrait in profile (73x54cm-29x21in) s.i.d.74 oil
                       tempera (A.S 20000)
£440 $783   (31-Oct-91 D.V84/R) Untitled (43x48cm-17x19in) s.i.d.74 mixed media
                       collage (A.S 9000)

PONGRATZ, Peter (1940-) German-cont.
£489 $870   (31-Oct-91 D.V85/R) *Sechs ozeanische Wichtl (31x48cm-12x19in) s.d.76 mixed media (A.S 10000)*

PONS, Louis (20th C) ?
£924 $1663   (19-Nov-91 FB.P268/R) *24 positions de replis (67x51cm-26x20in) s.i.d.1963 indian ink (F.FR 9000)*

PONS-ARNAU, Francisco (1886-1955) Spanish
£1396 $2667   (2-Jul-92 ANS.M83/R) Retrato de dama con mantilla (47x30cm-19x12in) s. panel (S.P 255000)

PONT-AVEN SCHOOL (?) French
£5301 $10179   (7-Jul-92 ARC.P91 a/R) Douleur et Espoir (46x29cm-18x11in) i. (F.FR 51000)

PONTE see BASSANO

PONTE, Gerolamo da see BASSANO, Gerolamo

PONTECORVO, Raimondo (19th C) Italian
£1243 $2200   (6-Nov-91 D.NY34/R) *The looking glass (72x51cm-28x20in) s. W/C*

PONTHUS-CINIER, Antoine (1812-1885) French
£1844 $3320   (2-Feb-92 ZZ.F3/R) L'arrivee du bac (43x59cm-17x23in) s. (F.FR 18000)
£2372 $4221   (29-Nov-91 GAB.G2156) Paysage aux danseurs (65x81cm-26x32in) s. (S.FR 6000)
£3195 $5623   (6-Apr-92 GGL.L8/R) Vue de Privas (54x81cm-21x32in) s. (F.FR 31500)

PONTI, Gio (?-1979) Italian
£417 $742   (27-Nov-91 F.M77) *Disegno per ceramica (30x20cm-12x8in) s. pastel (I.L 900000)*

PONTI, Pino (1905-) Italian
£471 $809   (12-Oct-91 F.L209/R) Ritratto (16x12cm-6x5in) s.d.1941 board (S.FR 1200)
£510 $877   (12-Oct-91 F.L208/R) Ritratto (16x12cm-6x5in) s.d.1941 board (S.FR 1300)

PONTOY, Henri Jean (1888-?) French
£1951 $3511   (18-Nov-91 AT.P372) Aux abords du ksar (45x55cm-18x22in) s. (F.FR 19000)
£2134 $3713   (13-Apr-92 AT.P201/R) Les lavandieres (69x86cm-27x34in) s. (F.FR 21000)
£2541 $4421   (13-Apr-92 AT.P202/R) Le souk a Goulimine (73x60cm-29x24in) s. (F.FR 25000)
£610 $1061   (13-Apr-92 AT.P161) *L'oued Moulouya entre Taza et Oujdah (47x59cm-19x23in) s. gouache (F.FR 6000)*
£1931 $3360   (13-Apr-92 AT.P162/R) *Kasbah et oued dans le sud marocain (42x52cm-17x20in) s. gouache (F.FR 19000)*

POOLE, James (1804-1886) British
£1200 $2184   (12-Dec-91 B99/R) Highland wooded river landscape with figures beside waterfall (60x93cm-24x37in) s.
£2000 $3580   (11-Nov-91 S596/R) Drover with cattle by river (65x90cm-26x35in) s.
£2100 $3759   (5-May-92 SWS346/R) Loch Lomond (75x112cm-30x44in) s.

POOLE, Paul Falconer (1807-1879) British
£1600 $2960   (11-Jun-92 CSK145) The harvesters (49x74cm-19x29in) s.d.1860
£2201 $3697   (27-Aug-91 RAS.K167/R) Woman and two children in meadow (60x52cm-24x20in) s. (D.KR 25000)
£3000 $5400   (19-Nov-91 PH126/R) Making hay (29x36cm-11x14in) s. panel
£3200 $5472   (13-Mar-92 C90/R) Escape of Glaucus and Ione with the blind girl Nydia from Pompei (109x154cm-43x61in) mono.d.1860

POOLEY, Thomas (1646-1723) Irish
£1900 $3401   (13-Nov-91 S145/R) Portrait of Robert Percival (76x63cm-30x25in) i.d.1657

POONS, Larry (1937-) American
£6145 $11000   (7-May-92 SY.NY267/R) 72nd Street dead (193x254cm-76x100in) s.d.1973 acrylic canvas

POORE, Henry Rankin (1959-1940) American
£1011 $1850   (9-Feb-92 LIT.L204) Horse pasture (25x51cm-10x20in) s. board

POORTEN, Jacobus Johannes van (1841-1914) German
£1399 $2420   (25-Mar-92 KM.K1373) Stag by stream in woodland (86x140cm-34x55in) s. (DM 4000)
£1818 $3145   (25-Mar-92 KM.K1372/R) Stag and deer in woodland clearing (82x130cm-32x51in) s. (DM 5200)

POORTER, Willem de (1608-1648) Dutch
£3229 $5522   (18-Mar-92 D.V280/R) Salomon and the queen of Sheba (42x50cm-17x20in) panel (A.S 65000)
£7000 $12460   (29-Oct-91 PH55/R) Young woman seated beside a table gazing into a mirror (25x22cm-10x9in) panel

POOT, Rik (1924-) Belgian
£445 $805   (7-Dec-91 KV.L259/R) Reclining nude (31x45cm-12x18in) s. ink dr.
     (B.FR 26000)

POPE, Alexander (1849-1924) American
£988 $1700   (20-Oct-91 HG.C31) Stallion (76x102cm-30x40in) s.
£2586 $4500   (15-Sep-91 JRB.C98/R) Hunting dog with pheasant (61x51cm-24x20in) s.

POPE, Alexander (1763-1835) British
£1320 $2521   (16-Jul-92 S66/R) Portrait of the Stoughton sisters. Rev.Anthony
     Stoughton with daughter (27x36cm-11x14in) pencil W/C pair

POPE, G (19/20th C) British
£760 $1315   (4-Oct-91 BW409) Interior scene with figures (107x135cm-42x53in) s.

POPHILLAT (20th C) French
£776 $1359   (23-Feb-92 LT.P103) Fleurs sur fond de paysage Mediterraneen
     (38x46cm-15x18in) s. (F.FR 7600)

POPOVA, Liubov (1889-1929) Russian
£950 $1634   (5-Mar-92 D116/R) Study of female nude (20x13cm-8x5in) pencil

POPOVITCH, Ljuba see   LJUBA

POPP, Johann Baptist (1812-?) German
£1224 $2093   (18-Mar-92 N.M618/R) Village with timber framed houses (46x60cm-18x24in)
     s. (DM 3500)

PORAY, Stanislaus (1888-1948) American
£534 $950   (26-Nov-91 MOR.P107) Still life - fruit, brass and glass
     (74x91cm-29x36in) s.d.26
£579 $1100   (23-Jun-92 MOR.P39) The jade vase (51x61cm-20x24in) s.
£743 $1300   (31-Mar-92 MOR.P65) Nocturnal, CA mission (53x69cm-21x27in) s.

PORCAR, Joan B (1888-1974) Spanish
£4976 $9356   (17-Dec-91 BRO.B334/R) Marina (66x81cm-26x32in) s. (S.P 900000)

PORCAR, Juan Bautista (?) Spanish
£711 $1295   (11-Dec-91 FER.M9/R) Aldeana de espaldas (42x30cm-17x12in) s. sanguine
     (S.P 130000)

PORCELLIS, Jan (16/17th C) Dutch
£4115 $7449   (3-Dec-91 CN.P73/R) Marine, grisaille (21x33cm-8x13in) panel (F.FR 40000)
£4630 $8796   (26-Jun-92 AT.P79/R) Barque au large de la cote (23x30cm-9x12in) mono.
     panel (F.FR 45000)
£14590 $26699   (12-May-92 SY.AM130/R) Shipping in estuary (28x35cm-11x14in) (D.FL 48000)

PORCELLIS, Jan (attrib) (16/17th C) Dutch
£1650 $2871   (13-Sep-91 C101/R) Large flute on starboard reach in storm
     (36x67cm-14x26in) init. panel

PORCELLIS, Jan (style) (16/17th C) Dutch
£6500 $11375   (28-Feb-92 C66/R) An estuary at low tide (29x66cm-11x26in) with sig.
     panel

PORCELLIS, Jan I (1584-1632) Dutch
£7407 $13259   (14-Nov-91 CH.AM183/R) Travellers about to board wijdschip watched by
     fisherman ashore (30x46cm-12x18in) init.d. 1624 panel oval (D.FL 24000)

PORCELLIS, Jan I (style) (1584-1632) Dutch
£1389 $2486   (12-Nov-91 SY.AM68/R) Ship on stormy sea (21x29cm-8x11in) panel
     (D.FL 4500)

PORCELLIS, Julius (attrib) (1610-1645) Dutch
£4471 $7645   (18-Mar-92 D.V363/R) Fishing boats in light breeze (24x30cm-9x12in) mono.
     (A.S 90000)

PORCELLIS, Julius (circle) (1610-1645) Dutch
£2500 $4800   (8-Jul-92 S98/R) Fishing boats in choppy sea (25x35cm-10x14in) indis.s.
     panel

PORCHERON, Lucien (1876-1957) French?
£514 $977   (22-Jun-92 RY.P80/R) Vue de Cabri (58x76cm-23x30in) s. (F.FR 5000)
£514 $977   (22-Jun-92 RY.P14) Sous bois (74x55cm-29x22in) s. (F.FR 5000)
£669 $1271   (22-Jun-92 RY.P7/R) Vue de Saint Tropez (44x55cm-17x22in) s. (F.FR 6500)
£772 $1466   (22-Jun-92 RY.P122 b) Tempete (65x81cm-26x32in) s. (F.FR 7500)

POREAU, Oswald (1877-1955) Belgian
£938 $1763   (17-Dec-91 GM.B883/R) Nature morte aux roses (52x44cm-20x17in) s. wood
     (B.FR 55000)
£995 $1821   (12-May-92 GM.B383) Le Bief (80x100cm-31x39in) s.d.1930 (B.FR 60000)
£1327 $2428   (12-May-92 GM.B378/R) Le passage du Harwick (85x100cm-33x39in) s.d.1920
     (B.FR 80000)

PORGES, Clara (1879-?) Swiss
£1647 $2800   (23-Oct-91 GD.B586) Sunrise over mountain lake (44x59cm-17x23in) s. (S.FR 4200)
£647 $1158   (15-Nov-91 ZOF.Z1844/R) Silsersee landscape (50x40cm-20x16in) s. W/C (S.FR 1650)
£1369 $2546   (19-Jun-92 ZOF.Z2048/R) Engadin mountain landscape (56x78cm-22x31in) s. W/C (S.FR 3600)

PORPORA, Paolo (?-1673) Italian
£17442 $30000   (10-Oct-91 SY.NY80/R) Still life of fish in a landscape (51x69cm-20x27in)

PORT, D M (?) ?
£700 $1246   (1-Nov-91 MAI582) Dutch sailing barges returning to harbour s.

PORTA, Baccio della see BARTOLOMMEO, Fra

PORTA-MISSE, Josep Maria (1927-) Spanish
£1368 $2435   (29-Oct-91 BRO.B345/R) Composicion (65x80cm-26x31in) s. mixed media (S.P 250000)
£2212 $4158   (17-Dec-91 BRO.B352/R) Insinuacion (130x97cm-51x38in) s. mixed media panel (S.P 400000)

PORTAELS, Jean Francois (1818-1895) Belgian
£3525 $6274   (31-Oct-91 LD.P210/R) Portrait de Paul Deroulede (102x79cm-40x31in) s.d.1877 panel (F.FR 35000)

PORTE, Roland de la see ROLAND DE LA PORTE, Henri Horace

PORTENAART, Jeanne (1911-) Belgian
£917 $1577   (12-Oct-91 KV.L239) Le beau et la bete (55x65cm-22x26in) s. s.i.d.1959 verso panel (B.FR 55000)
£3167 $5447   (12-Oct-91 KV.L476/R) L'Ange (80x100cm-31x39in) s. panel (B.FR 190000)

PORTER, Charles E (1847-1923) American
£601 $1100   (6-Jun-92 LAE.L60/R) Forest interior (53x43cm-21x17in) s.d.1890

PORTER, Fairfield (1907-1976) American
£9890 $18000   (27-May-92 SY.NY119/R) Wild flowers (36x63cm-14x25in) s.d.55
£14917 $27000   (5-Dec-91 SY.NY105/R) Autumn I (48x46cm-19x18in) s.d.67 s.i.stretcher
£2857 $5000   (26-Sep-91 CH.NY157/R) Along country road. Autumn landscape (39x51cm-15x20in) s.d.63 W/C pencil double-sided

PORTER, John J (19th C) American
£9341 $17000   (28-May-92 CH.NY17/R) Mail call, the steamboat Wyandotte (76x117cm-30x46in) s.d.1859

PORTER, Katherine (1941-) American
£407 $700   (12-Oct-91 SY.NY353) Untitled (41x31cm-16x12in) W/C
£703 $1300   (12-Jun-92 SY.NY324/R) Untitled (41x48cm-16x19in) gouache graphite colour pencil
£1117 $2000   (12-Nov-91 CE.NY133/R) Winter dance (51x51cm-20x20in) gouache col.chk graphite

PORTIELJE, Edward Antoon (1861-1949) Belgian
£1056 $1827   (24-Mar-92 VN.R76/R) Woman sewing in an interior (23x18cm-9x7in) s. panel (D.FL 3400)
£3149 $5700   (2-Dec-91 S.SL288/R) Interior with two women seated around table, near window (46x38cm-18x15in) s.
£3648 $6677   (12-May-92 C.A258/R) The model ship (50x65cm-20x26in) s. (B.FR 220000)
£3868 $6886   (21-Jan-92 DUR.M58/R) Maternidad (46x38cm-18x15in) s. panel (S.P 700000)
£4545 $8045   (22-Apr-92 CH.AM146/R) A spinster in love (50x42cm-20x17in) s. (D.FL 15000)
£4619 $8361   (3-Dec-91 C.A248/R) The first visit (50x65cm-20x26in) s. (B.FR 270000)
£5307 $9711   (12-May-92 C.A256/R) Visiting the young mother (51x67cm-20x26in) s. (B.FR 320000)
£5500 $10230   (17-Jun-92 S311/R) Farm girls having coffee (64x89cm-25x35in) s.d.1913
£5638 $10318   (12-May-92 C.A257/R) Time for tea (51x66cm-20x26in) s. (B.FR 340000)
£5944 $10283   (25-Mar-92 KM.K1374/R) Washerwomen in interior and view of sea through open door (46x37cm-18x15in) s. (DM 17000)
£6568 $11954   (26-May-92 DUR.M45/R) El tramposo (103x143cm-41x56in) s. (S.P 1200000)
£7699 $13935   (3-Dec-91 C.A247/R) Time for tea (66x92cm-26x36in) s.d.1914 (B.FR 450000)

PORTIELJE, Gerard (1856-1929) Belgian
£1061 $1900   (13-Nov-91 B.SF2237/R) The musician (22x15cm-9x6in) s. panel
£1990 $3642   (12-May-92 C.A262/R) A cunning fox (22x16cm-9x6in) s.d.1894 panel (B.FR 120000)
£2813 $5008   (30-Oct-91 CH.AM63/R) A good vintage (28x37cm-11x15in) s. panel (D.FL 9200)
£3317 $6070   (12-May-92 C.A260/R) The helpful coachman (26x19cm-10x7in) s. panel (B.FR 200000)
£4975 $9104   (12-May-92 C.A261/R) The schoolmaster (32x25cm-13x10in) s. panel (B.FR 300000)
£7678 $13896   (3-Dec-91 AB.S4745/R) Interior with men drinking wine (53x70cm-21x28in) s. (S.KR 80000)

PORTIELJE, Gerard (1856-1929) Belgian-cont.
£8800 $15664   (27-Nov-91 S39/R) Not wisely but too well (43x62cm-17x24in) s.d.1879
                    st.verso panel

PORTIELJE, Jon Frederik Pieter (1829-1895) Dutch
£2647 $4500   (11-Aug-91 LIT.L52) Portrait of woman (61x48cm-24x19in) s. panel
£6857 $12000   (20-Feb-92 SY.NY44/R) Oriental beauty (72x56cm-28x22in) s.
£9121 $16692   (12-May-92 C.A263/R) The necklace (113x86cm-44x34in) s. (B.FR 550000)

PORTIELJE, Jon Frederik Pieter (circle) (1829-1895) Dutch
£750 $1343   (13-Nov-91 B89) Young woman in fez (76x64cm-30x25in)

PORTINARI, Candido (1903-1962) Brazilian
£4420 $8000   (18-May-92 CH.NY213/R) Retrato de Roberto Cantalupo (46x38cm-18x15in)
                  s.d. i.d.1933 stretcher
£10000 $18000   (19-Nov-91 CH.NY75/R) Incendio (17x21cm-7x8in) s.d.960 panel
£11050 $20000   (18-May-92 CH.NY214/R) Retrato de Sofia Cantalupo (46x38cm-18x15in) s.
                    i.d.1933 stretcher
£11050 $20000   (18-May-92 CH.NY115/R) Portrait of Maria Sermolino (73x60cm-29x24in)
                    s.d.1940
£26519 $48000   (18-May-92 CH.NY22/R) Moca (41x30cm-16x12in) s.d.1940 linen on board
£1657   *$3000*   *(18-May-92 CH.NY126/R) Estudio del Ultimo Baluarte (26x36cm-10x14in) s.i.*
                    pen brush indian ink pencil paper on board

PORTINARI, Candido and FOUJITA, Tsuguharu (20th C) Brazilian/Japanese
£4571   *$8000*   *(25-Feb-92 CH.NY58/R) Composition (47x58cm-19x23in) s.d.1932 collage W/C*
                    gouache pencil paper board

PORTOCARRERO, Rene (1912-1986) Cuban
£690 $1200   (13-Sep-91 S.W2794) Lovers (25x23cm-10x9in) s. tempera scratchboard oval
£785 $1500   (30-Jun-92 PO.BA15) Vaso con flores (64x50cm-25x20in) s.d.83
£1309 $2500   (30-Jun-92 PO.BA14) Naturaleza muerta con silla y frutas
                  (100x80cm-39x31in) s.
£8287 $15000   (18-May-92 CH.NY184/R) Ciudad (46x61cm-18x24in) s.d.1956
£10497 $19000   (19-May-92 SY.NY188/R) Catedral (100x74cm-39x29in) s.
£71823 $130000   (19-May-92 SY.NY45/R) Paisaje (104x78cm-41x31in) s.i.d.1944verso board
£678   *$1200*   *(6-Nov-91 D.NY10) Woman seated in chair (59x39cm-23x15in) pastel*
£1111   *$2000*   *(18-Nov-91 SY.NY149/R) Composicion geometrica (37x28cm-15x11in)*
                    s.i.d.1953 tempera ink board
£1934   *$3500*   *(19-May-92 SY.NY177/R) Mujer en Azul (49x33cm-19x13in) s. pastel*
£3333   *$6000*   *(18-Nov-91 SY.NY110/R) Dos figuras (47x57cm-19x22in) s. pen*
£3591   *$6500*   *(19-May-92 SY.NY179/R) Cabeza (40x28cm-16x11in) s. gouache ink board laid*
                    down on canvas
£3867   *$7000*   *(19-May-92 SY.NY206/R) Mujer sentada (70x55cm-28x22in) s.d.1945 gouache*
                    board

PORTUGUESE SCHOOL (?) Portuguese
£6200 $10850   (2-Apr-92 CSK56/R) Saint Francis Xavier, Missionary, in Goa
                    (117x96cm-46x38in)

POSCHINGER, Richard von (1839-1915) German
£1483 $2624   (6-Nov-91 N.M1117/R) Lake Starnberg with fishing boat (25x34cm-10x13in)
                  paper on board (DM 4300)

POSI, Paolo (1708-1776) Italian
£2600   *$4524*   *(14-Apr-92 C136/R) Project for tomb of Pope Benedict XIV in St Peter's,*
                    Rome (34x47cm-13x19in) s.i. chk pen wash

POSILLIPO SCHOOL (?) Italian
£5435   *$10055*   *(9-Jun-92 F.R56/R) Veduta di Napoli (22x33cm-9x13in) mono (I.L 12000000)*

POSSART, Felix (1837-1928) German
£1429 $2600   (13-Dec-91 S.W2854/R) Rest on Flight into Egypt (122x173cm-48x68in) s.

POSSENTI, Antonio (1933-) Italian
£635 $1162   (12-May-92 F.R140) Natura morta con bacio appassionato (29x19cm-11x7in)
                  s. canvasboard (I.L 1400000)
£930 $1683   (3-Dec-91 F.R184) Natura morta (40x30cm-16x12in) s. board on canvas
                  (I.L 2000000)
£1297 $2310   (29-Nov-91 F.F157) Bambina (40x30cm-16x12in) s. canvas on panel
                  (I.L 2800000)
£1498 $2667   (29-Apr-92 F.F97/R) Uccelli nel nido (40x50cm-16x20in) s. canvas on panel
                  (I.L 3300000)
£1627 $2944   (3-Dec-91 F.R172/R) Paesaggio con figure (40x30cm-16x12in) s.
                  (I.L 3500000)
£2043 $3636   (29-Apr-92 F.F99/R) Autoritratto con Franceschino (50x60cm-20x24in) s.
                  s.i.verso masonite (I.L 4500000)

POST, Frans (1612-1680) Dutch
£42000 $76440   (11-Dec-91 S54/R) Extensive Brazilian landscape, with natives on sugar
                    plantation (26x35cm-10x14in) s.
£240223 $430000   (16-Jan-92 CH.NY93/R) Brazilian landscape with procession emerging form
                      ruined cathedral of See of Olinda (61x83cm-24x33in) indist.s.

POST, Frans (attrib) (1612-1680) Dutch
£4074 $7374   (19-May-92 GF.L2386/R) Brasilian landscape with water buffalo and
    shepherd (28x38cm-11x15in) bears sig.d.1650 panel (S.FR 11000)

POST, George (1906-) American
£368   *$700*   *(23-Jun-92 MOR.P87) Fishermen mending nets (46x61cm-18x24in) s. W/C*

POST, William Merritt (1856-1935) American
£811 $1500   (10-Jun-92 CE.NY299) Fall landscape with stream (35x51cm-14x20in) s.
£1657 $2850   (7-Mar-92 LAE.L166/R) Sunset on the marshes (30x41cm-12x16in) s.

POSTEL, Jules (1867-1955) Belgian
£533 $933   (24-Sep-91 GM.B559) Pont a Bruges (76x97cm-30x38in) s. (B.FR 32000)

POSTIGLIONE, Luca (1876-1936) Italian
£6678 $12154   (12-Dec-91 F.M42/R) Scena conviviale con Pulcinella (44x60cm-17x24in) s.
    canvas on board (I.L 14500000)
£9262 $16024   (24-Mar-92 CH.R142/R) Giovane donna che spolvera (94x43cm-37x17in) s.
    (I.L 20000000)

POT, Hendrick Gerritsz (attrib) (1585-1657) Dutch
£2266 $4056   (7-May-92 CH.AM73/R) Portrait of young woman dressed as shepherdess
    (50x40cm-20x16in) panel (D.FL 7500)
£3406 $6165   (19-May-92 AB.S4368/R) Portraits of shepherd and shepherdess
    (30x26cm-12x10in) panel pair (S.KR 36000)

POT, Hendrick Gerritsz (style) (1585-1657) Dutch
£2115 $3785   (7-May-92 CH.AM48/R) Interior with gentlemen playing backgammon greeting
    newcomer (45x74cm-18x29in) mono.indist.d. panel (D.FL 7000)
£2500 $4800   (8-Jul-92 S238/R) Portrait of lady wearing black and holding gloves
    (31x22cm-12x9in) panel

POTHAST, Bernard (1882-1966) British
£2800 $4844   (4-Oct-91 C72/R) Awaiting his return (31x25cm-12x10in) s.
£2985 $5313   (25-Nov-91 W.T1876/R) Home joys (29x40cm-11x16in) s. (C.D 6000)
£3571 $6179   (24-Mar-92 VN.R77/R) Woman and her two children by a window
    (64x54cm-25x21in) s. (D.FL 11500)
£4299 $7952   (9-Jun-92 FB.M106/R) Family circle (51x61cm-20x24in) s. (C.D 9500)
£4300 $7697   (14-Jan-92 SWS211/R) Cup of milk (31x25cm-12x10in) s.
£4587 $8394   (1-Jun-92 W.T1242/R) The knitting lesson (48x58cm-19x23in) s. (C.D 10000)
£4598 $8000   (10-Sep-91 BG.M646/R) Sewing lesson (48x58cm-19x23in) s.
£4645 $8500   (17-May-92 DU.E1121/R) Feeding the baby (76x64cm-30x25in) s.
£4651 $8000   (17-Oct-91 SY.NY245/R) Reading lesson (56x46cm-22x18in) s.
£5789 $11000   (26-Jun-92 WOL.C477/R) Playing with baby (71x66cm-28x26in) s.
£7000 $13020   (19-Jun-92 C7/R) Motherly love (66x54cm-26x21in) s.
£8000 $14880   (17-Jun-92 S315/R) Feeding baby (48x58cm-19x23in) s.
£8242 $15000   (27-May-92 CH.NY251/R) The happy family (80x101cm-31x40in) s.
£8800 $15048   (20-Mar-92 C3/R) The reading lesson (56x46cm-22x18in) s.
£13930 $24796   (25-Nov-91 W.T1875/R) Young mother and children (72x81cm-28x32in) s.
    (C.D 28000)

POTRONAT, L (1889-?) French
£700 $1274   (12-Dec-91 CSK75) Farmhouse in Provence with coastline beyond
    (46x54cm-18x21in) s.
£750 $1365   (12-Dec-91 CSK74) Cote d'Azur, Haut var comps (46x54cm-18x21in) s.
    i.verso

POTSCH, Igo (1884-?) Austrian
£781 $1351   (3-Oct-91 D.V158/R) Landscape (60x65cm-24x26in) s. (A.S 16000)
£1212 $2206   (26-May-92 D.V130/R) Still life with apples, flowers and blue glass
    (60x75cm-24x30in) s.d.24 panel (A.S 25000)

POTT, Constance Mary (1862-c.1930) British
£550   *$979*   *(29-Oct-91 C76) London, Tivoli Corner, Bank of England and the new Bank*
    Buildings (34x54cm-13x21in) s.d.1890 pencil W/C htd white

POTT, Laslett John (1837-1898) British
£700 $1246   (28-Nov-91 B59/R) On the bridge (34x46cm-13x18in) init.

POTTER, Adolphe (1835-1911) Swiss
£511 $915   (6-May-92 GD.B1021) Sailing boat near rocky coast in stiff breeze
    (60x100cm-24x39in) s. (S.FR 1400)

POTTER, Beatrix (1866-1943) British
£7000   *$12460*   *(27-Nov-91 WAL195/R) Rabbit wearing coat, wading in snow and other rabbit*
    fallen off toboggan (9x11cm-4x4in) init.d.94 pencil W/C card in
    autograph album

POTTER, Mary (1900-) British
£550 $1007   (4-Jun-92 CSK156) Tree (71x51cm-28x20in) s.d.78 verso
£650 $1118   (5-Mar-92 CSK28/R) Magnolia blossom (61x50cm-24x20in) s.
£800 $1360   (23-Oct-91 MMB269) Magnolias in vase (61x51cm-24x20in) s.
£1800 $3186   (8-Nov-91 C229/R) Council houses (69x60cm-27x24in)
£1900 $3268   (5-Mar-92 D67/R) Fine afternoon (28x33cm-11x13in) i.verso

POTTER, Mary (1900-) British-cont.
£2200 $4202   (16-Jul-92 B32/R) Small landscape with telegraph pole (24x19cm-9x7in) board

POTTER, P (after) (17th C) Dutch
£1300 $2483   (14-Jul-92 DR401/R) Cattle and sheep in landscape with cowherd in foreground (23x37cm-9x15in) panel

POTTER, Paulus (attrib) (1625-1654) Dutch
£1900 $3344   (10-Apr-92 K476/R) Dutch wooded landscape with cattle and sheep resting, buildings beyond (46x53cm-18x21in)

POTTER, Paulus (style) (1625-1654) Dutch
£1400 $2450   (27-Feb-92 CSK159/R) Cattle and goats in a wooded landscape (47x57cm-19x22in)
£1563 $2766   (5-Nov-91 GF.L2353/R) Shepherd with cattle in river landscape (46x56cm-18x22in) bears sig. (S.FR 4000)

POTTER, Pieter Symonsz (1597-1652) Dutch
£8951 $16022   (14-Nov-91 CH.AM197/R) Officer inspecting looted goods with soldiers and prisoners in mansion (46x69cm-18x27in) panel (D.FL 29000)

POTTER, Pieter Symonsz (school) (1597-1652) Dutch
£1242 $2124   (18-Mar-92 D.V293/R) Possibly artist's self portrait (36x47cm-14x19in) panel (A.S 25000)

POTTHAST, Edward Henry (1857-1927) American
£2339 $4000   (12-Mar-92 MFA.C214 a) Landscape (30x41cm-12x16in) s. board
£3073 $5500   (14-Nov-91 GRO.B94 a/R) House through trees (41x51cm-16x20in) s.
£3626 $6200   (13-Mar-92 WOL.C458/R) Kneeling female nude (89x71cm-35x28in) s.
£6077 $11000   (6-Dec-91 CH.NY149/R) Golden sunset (30x40cm-12x16in) s. board
£9341 $17000   (28-May-92 CH.NY171/R) The Maine Coast (61x76cm-24x30in) s.
£10440 $19000   (27-May-92 SY.NY68/R) Bathers in cove (23x30cm-9x12in) s. panel
£11053 $21000   (26-Jun-92 WOL.C481/R) Woodland dance (61x76cm-24x30in) s.
£17582 $32000   (28-May-92 CH.NY153/R) Wading at the shore (31x20cm-12x8in) s. board
£23077 $42000   (28-May-92 CH.NY157/R) Brighton Beach (40x30cm-16x12in) s. panel
£49451 $90000   (28-May-92 CH.NY145/R) At the seashore (30x41cm-12x16in) s. canvas on board
£4670 $8500   (28-May-92 CH.NY146/R) Woman with a parasol (16x22cm-6x9in) s.d.91 pencil gouache

POTTNER, Emil (1872-?) German
£1053 $1895   (22-Nov-91 SA.A399/R) The chamber maid (43x43cm-17x17in) s. board (DM 3000)

POTUZNIK, Heribert (1910-1984) Austrian
£748 $1338   (15-Jan-92 D.V234/R) Thunderstorm over Mariathal, Weinviertel (48x69cm-19x27in) s.i.d.62 W/C gouache (A.S 15000)
£883 $1678   (25-Jun-92 D.V569/R) Untitled (52x73cm-20x29in) s.d.1976 mixed media (A.S 18000)

POUGNY, Jean (1894-1956) French
£4098 $7377   (2-Feb-92 ZZ.F166/R) L'omnibus (23x34cm-9x13in) s. (F.FR 40000)
£1053 $1895   (23-Nov-91 N.M262/R) Reclining female nude (33x39cm-13x15in) st.studio mixed media (DM 3000)
£1426 $2637   (10-Jun-92 LD.P120) Bord de mer a Antibes (11x28cm-4x11in) studio st. gouache (F.FR 14000)

POULAIN, Michel Marie (1906-) French
£650 $1112   (12-Mar-92 B79/R) Small Hill village (85x87cm-33x34in) s.d.1945 panel

POULLIARD (19th C) French
£624 $1093   (5-Apr-92 ZZ.F36/R) Couple d'amoureux pres du champ de ble (46x38cm-18x15in) s. (F.FR 6000)
£624 $1093   (5-Apr-92 ZZ.F34/R) Couple d'amoureux pres du champ de ble (46x38cm-18x15in) s. (F.FR 6000)

POULTON, James (attrib) (19th C) British
£1300 $2353   (18-May-92 HS452) Still life of mixed fruit and foliage in basket (68x80cm-27x31in)

POURBUS, Frans (circle) (16/17th C) Flemish
£750 $1313   (25-Feb-92 PH104) Portrait of bearded gentleman wearing lace ruff (41x30cm-16x12in) panel

POURBUS, Frans (elder-circle) (1545-1581) Flemish
£8800 $15400   (1-Apr-92 S72/R) Portrait of gentleman (101x71cm-40x28in)

POURBUS, Frans (style) (16/17th C) Flemish
£1200 $2184   (13-Dec-91 C127) Portrait of lady in widow's weeds (73x60cm-29x24in)
£1650 $2871   (13-Sep-91 C71/R) Portraits of gentleman and lady (16x12cm-6x5in) copper oval pair
£1676 $3000   (13-Jan-92 CE.NY193) Portrait of a gentleman (47x40cm-19x16in) i.d.1581
£2265 $4190   (8-Jun-92 CH.R745/R) Ritratto di condottiero, con l'Ordine del Toson d'oro (80x60cm-31x24in) in oval (I.L 5000000)

POURBUS, Frans (younger) (1570-1622) Flemish
£687 $1196   (17-Sep-91 FN.S2498) Portrait of ruling princess wearing ermine dress and
                 crown (14x10cm-6x4in) copper (DM 2000)
£1786 $3000   (1-Sep-91 PO.BA10) Busto de mujer (60x47cm-24x19in)
£7637 $13900   (11-Dec-91 LD.P54/R) Portrait d'un homme de cour en buste, de trois-quart
                 (76x62cm-30x24in) d.1601 panel (F.FR 75000)

POURBUS, Frans (younger-attrib) (1570-1622) Flemish
£24839 $42474   (18-Mar-92 D.V10 a/R) Portrait of lady, probably Eleonora de Medici
                 (151x116cm-59x46in) (A.S 500000)

POURBUS, Frans (younger-circle) (1570-1622) Flemish
£1953 $3730   (1-Jul-92 CD.P15) Portrait de Marie de Brisay (48x41cm-19x16in)
                 (F.FR 19000)

POURBUS, Peeter Jansz (circle) (1510-1584) Flemish
£7407 $13259   (12-Nov-91 SY.AM48/R) St Michael with rebel angels. Battle of Milvian
                 Bridge. Last Jugdement.Wounded archer found by sheph (146x46cm-57x18in)
                 panel set of four (D.FL 24000)

POURBUS, Peeter Jansz (style) (1510-1584) Flemish
£1500 $2880   (10-Jul-92 C149 a) Two gentlemen kneeling, ruins beyond (88x26cm-35x10in)
                 i. panel transferred canvas wings triptych pair
£1998 $3717   (16-Jun-92 SY.B248/R) The Annunciation (36x25cm-14x10in) panel
                 (B.FR 120000)

POUSSIN (after) (?) French
£1600 $2896   (18-May-92 HS416/R) Italian lakeland scene with travellers. River scene
                 with figures on bridge (33x45cm-13x18in) pair

POUSSIN, Gaspard see DUGHET, Gaspard

POUSSIN, Nicolas (1594-1665) French
*£38000 $69160   (11-Dec-91 PH298/R) Mythological subject - Jupiter and Eurynome
                   (21x38cm-8x15in) pen wash over chk*

POUSSIN, Nicolas (after) (1594-1665) French
£1600 $2800   (28-Feb-92 C137) The dance of the four seasons to the music of time
                 (82x105cm-32x41in)
£3000 $5400   (21-Nov-91 CSK96/R) Venus and the shepherds (16x21cm-6x8in) panel

POUSSIN, Nicolas (attrib) (1594-1665) French
*£377 $648   (11-Oct-91 AW.H850/R) Male nude seated on stone seen from behind
                 (13x8cm-5x3in) pen brush over ochre (DM 1100)*

POUSSIN, Nicolas (circle) (1594-1665) French
£5658 $10751   (26-Jun-92 AT.P82/R) Sainte Famille entouree de putti dans un paysage
                 (59x71cm-23x28in) (F.FR 55000)
£12791 $22000   (9-Oct-91 CH.NY20/R) Christ and woman of Samaria (94x122cm-37x48in)

POUSSIN, Nicolas (style) (1594-1665) French
£1009 $1736   (15-Oct-91 PPB.P11) Vierge a l'Enfant (68x49cm-27x19in) (F.FR 10000)
£1514 $2603   (15-Oct-91 PPB.P9) La mort de Germanicus (76x113cm-30x44in) (F.FR 15000)
£3436 $6289   (2-Jun-92 FN.S2706/R) Classical scene with young woman baptisting in
                 wooded landscape (112x154cm-44x61in) (DM 10000)
£4564 $8032   (11-Apr-92 AT.P87/R) Le repas chez Simon ou la Penitence
                 (66x82cm-26x32in) (F.FR 45000)

POUSTOCHKINE, Basil (1893-1973) Russian
£504 $896   (31-Oct-91 LD.P145) Village au bord de l'eau (21x28cm-8x11in) s. canvas
                 laid down on panel (F.FR 5000)

POUWELSEN, Willem (19th C) Dutch
£7034 $12450   (5-Nov-91 SY.AM86/R) Figures on markt, Middelburg (62x80cm-24x31in)
                 s.d.1858 (D.FL 23000)

POWDITCH, Peter (1942-) Australian
*£661 $1189   (24-Nov-91 SY.S11) Sun torso 153 (95x64cm-37x25in) s.i.d.1973-77 verso
                 enamel board (A.D 1500)*
*£661 $1176   (26-Nov-91 J.M180/R) Sun torso 118 (121x90cm-48x35in) s.verso synthetic
                 oil board (A.D 1500)*

POWELL, A W (?) ?
*£842 $1440   (13-Mar-92 FN.S2915/R) View of Venice with S.Marco (37x61cm-15x24in) s.
                 W/C (DM 2400)*

POWELL, Alfred (fl.1870-1901) British
*£1550 $2682   (4-Sep-91 BT137/R) Hazy morning on the Thames, Mapledurham
                 (48x71cm-19x28in) s. s.i.label backpanel W/C*

POWELL, Charles Martin (?-1824) British
£3500 $6335   (20-May-92 S69/R) Shipping scene (18x25cm-7x10in) s.indis.d. panel
£3500 $6335   (20-May-92 S80/R) Fishing boats off the Dutch coast (48x63cm-19x25in) s.
£3500 $5880   (15-Aug-91 B412) Shipping off Tenerife Island (34x54cm-13x21in) s. panel

POWELL, Charles Martin (style) (?-1824) British
£1000 $1740   (19-Sep-91 TL374) Man o War and other shipping off harbour entrance
     (19x25cm-7x10in) 379

POWELL, E M S (?) British
£500 $865   (26-Mar-92 ZZ.B804) Castle Street Farnham with figures and horse-drawn
     cart (28x38cm-11x15in) W/C

POWELL, Joseph Rubens (fl.1835-1871) British
£2100 $3759   (11-Nov-91 S599) Cupid disarmed (27x27cm-11x11in) panel

POWELL, Leonard Marlborough (fl.1883-1916) British
£950 $1701   (13-Nov-91 CG501/R) A view of Edinburgh from Carlton Hill looking down
     Princes street (39x49cm-15x19in) s.d.1906 W/C htd.white

POWELL, Lucien Whiting (1846-1930) American
£678 $1200   (9-Nov-91 W.W186/R) Bay of Naples (46x76cm-18x30in) s.
£3041 $5200   (12-Mar-92 MFA.C207) Grand Canyon (61x91cm-24x36in) s.
£565 $1000   (9-Nov-91 W.W225) Woodland waterfall (66x48cm-26x19in) s. W/C

POWELL, W E (?) ?
£440 $814   (9-Jun-92 AG206) Studies of dragonflies (26x13cm-10x5in) s. W/C

POWELL, William E (19th C) British
£1100 $1925   (25-Feb-92 C155/R) Ptarmigan in autumn plumage (32x44cm-13x17in) s.d.25
     i.verso pencil W/C htd white
£1250 $2225   (21-Jan-92 SWS1357) Mallard flushed. Mallard pitching (34x24cm-13x9in) s.
     W/C bodycol over pencil pair

POWER, Harold Septimus (1878-1951) New Zealander
£598 $1065   (27-Apr-92 J.M329) Fitting the bridle (43x42cm-17x17in) s. (A.D 1400)
£749 $1333   (26-Nov-91 J.M1061) Farm cottages France (38x31cm-15x12in) s. canvas on
     board (A.D 1700)
£786 $1376   (30-Mar-92 AAA.S80 k) Portrait of lady s. (A.D 1800)
£1277 $2260   (26-Apr-92 SY.ME31/R) Jock (29x39cm-11x15in) s. bears i.d.1910 verso
     (A.D 3000)
£1282 $2282   (27-Apr-92 J.M332) Near Bayswater (40x60cm-16x24in) s. (A.D 3000)
£1762 $3137   (26-Nov-91 J.M191) Horses in windswept landscape (54x74cm-21x29in) s.
     canvas on board (A.D 4000)
£2043 $3615   (26-Apr-92 SY.ME288/R) Spaniels (35x41cm-14x16in) s. canvasboard
     (A.D 4800)
£2137 $3803   (27-Apr-92 J.M156) Country laneway (49x59cm-19x23in) s. (A.D 5000)
£2203 $3921   (26-Nov-91 J.M107/R) Green pastures (75x62cm-30x24in) s. (A.D 5000)
£2643 $4705   (26-Nov-91 J.M288/R) Hunt (34x44cm-13x17in) s.d.1911 (A.D 6000)
£3965 $7137   (24-Nov-91 SY.S465/R) Workers (49x78cm-19x31in) s.d.1908 (A.D 9000)
£3965 $7057   (26-Nov-91 J.M226/R) Roses (50x60cm-20x24in) s. (A.D 9000)
£4060 $7226   (27-Apr-92 J.M108/R) Cocker spaniels (65x53cm-26x21in) s. (A.D 9500)
£6667 $11400   (17-Mar-92 JRL.S183/R) Portrait of young woman with two spaniels
     (92x92cm-36x36in) s. (A.D 15000)
£8370 $14899   (26-Nov-91 J.M94/R) Ready for work (103x116cm-41x46in) s.d.1943
     (A.D 19000)
£9692 $17251   (26-Nov-91 J.M215) Ploughing (62x74cm-24x29in) s. (A.D 22000)
£1233 $2220   (24-Nov-91 SY.S403/R) Cows in summer landscape (24x35cm-9x14in) s. W/C
     (A.D 2800)
£1454 $2617   (24-Nov-91 SY.S90/R) Shoeing horses (24x35cm-9x14in) s. W/C (A.D 3300)
£1542 $2744   (26-Nov-91 J.M51) Unloading cart (49x53cm-19x21in) s. W/C (A.D 3500)
£1972 $3293   (19-Aug-91 SY.ME18) Hillside landscape with grazing sheep
     (50x66cm-20x26in) s. W/C (A.D 4200)
£3687 $6415   (16-Sep-91 CH.ME123/R) Hay cart (48x61cm-19x24in) s. W/C (A.D 8000)

POWER, John Wardell (c.1942) Australian
£5589 $9726   (15-Apr-92 CB.P10/R) Composition animee (66x51cm-26x20in) mono.verso
     (F.FR 55000)

POWNALL, George Hyde (20th C) Australian?
£1150 $2047   (28-Nov-91 B143) Piccadilly Circus (15x23cm-6x9in) s.i.verso board

POWNALL, Leonard A (fl.1897-1913) British
£600 $1032   (4-Mar-92 S270/R) Connemara lass (29x24cm-11x9in) s.d.1911 W/C htd white

POY DALMAU, Emilio (1876-1933) Spanish
£989 $1781   (19-Nov-91 DUR.M131/R) Conduciendo el ganado (23x44cm-9x17in) s. panel
     (S.P 180000)
£1503 $2555   (22-Oct-91 DUR.M68/R) El zapatero (91x75cm-36x30in) s. (S.P 275000)
£1797 $3378   (18-Dec-91 DUR.M631/R) La tabernera (53x77cm-21x30in) s. (S.P 325000)
£3010 $5477   (11-Dec-91 FER.M148/R) La puerta del Retiro en la Plaza de la
     Independencia (40x56cm-16x22in) s.d.1907 (S.P 550000)
£3816 $6563   (7-Oct-91 ANS.M103/R) El memorialista (50x70cm-20x28in) s.
     s.i.d.1922verso (S.P 700000)
£4646 $7898   (22-Oct-91 DUR.M67/R) Lavanderas (50x76cm-20x30in) s. (S.P 850000)

POYNTER, Sir Edward John (1836-1919) British
£400 $692   (1-Oct-91 SWS1870) Reclining female nude (28x48cm-11x19in) init.d.1901
     black chk htd white

POYNTER, Sir Edward John (1836-1919) British-cont.
£900 $1602   *(29-Oct-91 C3/R) Study of woman standing in classical drapery*
       (35x25cm-14x10in) studio st. black and white chk
£1100 $1881   *(13-Mar-92 C76/R) Study for the Cave of the Storm Nymphs*
       (29x46cm-11x18in) init.d.1901 chk

POZNANSKI, Wieslaw (1904-) Polish
£1353 $2327   (20-Oct-91 UNI.W6) Archers (100x71cm-39x28in) s. (P.Z 26000000)

POZO, Julian del (?) Spanish?
£820 $1394   (23-Oct-91 DUR.M505/R) Paisaje (65x100cm-26x39in) s. (S.P 150000)

POZZA, Giovanni Battista (17th C) Italian
£800 $1456   *(10-Dec-91 C153) A nude lying on his back, study of his feet*
       (27x42cm-11x17in) i.verso red chk.htd.white

POZZATI, Concetto (1935-) Italian
£2270 $4040   (29-Apr-92 F.F59/R) Fiori (58x78cm-23x31in) s.d.1988 chl (I.L 5000000)
£2951 $5253   *(29-Apr-92 F.F221/R) Zia Virginia (70x80cm-28x31in) s. i.d.1977verso*
       mixed media canvas on panel (I.L 6500000)

POZZI, Ennio (1893-) Italian
£545 $970   (29-Apr-92 F.F190/R) Autoritratto (10x8cm-4x3in) panel (I.L 1200000)

POZZI, Stefano (1707-1768) Italian
£400 $696   *(13-Apr-92 S227) Male nude standing sideways with staff in hand. Monk*
       (36x24cm-14x9in) bears i. black chk htd white double-sided
£900 $1728   *(7-Jul-92 C195/R) The Immaculate Conception (38x19cm-15x7in) i. chk*
£1800 $3456   *(7-Jul-92 C194/R) Holy Family and deacon martyr with angel supporting*
       cross (41x29cm-16x11in) chk htd white

POZZO, Andrea (attrib) (18th C) Spanish
£6500 $11830   (10-Dec-91 PH72/R) Apotheosis of Saint Bernardino (134x98cm-53x39in)

POZZO, Ugo (20th C) Italian
£768 $1391   (21-May-92 F.M9) Donna e profumi (44x30cm-17x12in) s. tempera cardboard
       (I.L 1700000)
£814 $1473   (21-May-92 F.M275/R) Automobile e grattacieli (49x34cm-19x13in) s.
       s.sig.verso tempera (I.L 1800000)
£904 $1636   (21-May-92 F.M34/R) Profilo femminile (39x33cm-15x13in) s. st.sig.verso
       tempera cardboard (I.L 2000000)
£914 $1737   (23-Jun-92 F.M64) Le amiche (33x33cm-13x13in) s. tempera (I.L 2000000)
£994 $1800   (21-May-92 F.M94) Piroscafo (36x27cm-14x11in) s. tempera cardboard
       (I.L 2200000)
£1019 $1815   (27-Nov-91 F.M228) L'automobile (42x30cm-17x12in) s. tempera pair
       (I.L 2200000)
£1518 $2716   (14-Nov-91 F.M15/R) Il sorpasso (41x30cm-16x12in) s. thinned oil board
       (I.L 3300000)
£417 $742   *(27-Nov-91 F.M111) Ritratto di Macario (24x17cm-9x7in) collage*
       (I.L 900000)
£814 $1473   *(21-May-92 F.M120/R) Automobili da corsa (28x22cm-11x9in) s. W/C*
       (I.L 1800000)
£1066 $1897   *(27-Nov-91 F.M253/R) Sarabanda (18x20cm-7x8in) s. pencil (I.L 2300000)*

POZZOSERRATO see   TOEPUT, Lodewyk

PRAAG, Alexander Salomon van (1812-1865) Dutch
£1284 $2273   (5-Nov-91 SY.AM11/R) Figures on quay (18x22cm-7x9in) s. panel (D.FL 4200)

PRACHENSKY, Markus (20th C) Austrian
£2048 $3727   (26-May-92 KF.M1165/R) Solitude (70x50cm-28x20in) d.1964 acrylic paper
       (DM 6000)
£4500 $7785   (26-Mar-92 C31/R) Untitled (79x77cm-31x30in)
£2560 $4659   *(26-May-92 KF.M1166/R) Untitled (99x64cm-39x25in) s.d.1965 gouache*
       acrylic board (DM 7500)

PRADA, Carlo (1884-1960) Italian
£511 $960   (19-Dec-91 F.M31/R) Case di S.Margherita (60x50cm-24x20in) s.d.1959
       (I.L 1100000)
£1013 $1844   (12-Dec-91 F.M27) Lago Maggiore (26x37cm-10x15in) i.verso board
       (I.L 2200000)

PRADALIER, Cecile (1939-) French
£908 $1562   (14-Oct-91 AT.P60) Vignes (146x114cm-57x45in) s. paper laid down on
       canvas (F.FR 9000)

PRADES, Alfred F de (fl.1844-1883) British
£1500 $2670   (21-Jan-92 PH66/R) Portrait of Lieutenant-Colonel Frederick Swinfen on
       bay charger (62x46cm-24x18in) s.d.1861 board
£1800 $3168   (10-Apr-92 C163/R) Changing horses in French country town. Coach and four
       at dusk (23x43cm-9x17in) panel pair
£2732 $5000   (16-May-92 HG.C127/R) Coaching scenes - snow storm and rain storm
       (38x61cm-15x24in) s. pair
£4372 $8000   (5-Jun-92 SY.NY15/R) Two gentlemen driving a pony and trap
       (27x40cm-11x16in) s. board

PRADIER, J J (1792-1852) French
£494 $938   (24-Jun-92 CSC.P5) La bacchante endormie (15x21cm-6x8in) pen wash htd W/C
           (F.FR 4800)

PRADIER, Jean Jacques (1792-1852) French
£562 $1000   (22-Jan-92 SY.NY298/R) Draped female nude with harp (27x18cm-11x7in)
           init. chk

PRADILLA Y ORTIZ, Francisco (1848-1921) Spanish
£2381 $4000   (1-Sep-91 PO.BA14) Paisaje fluvial (21x35cm-8x14in) s.
£3177 $5909   (16-Jun-92 F.M246/R) Le paludi Pontine (24x38cm-9x15in) s.d.1847 i.verso
           board (I.L 7000000)
£6691 $12245   (16-May-92 F.L124/R) Lavoro all'aria aperta (49x29cm-19x11in) s. panel
           (S.FR 18000)
£9724 $17600   (4-Dec-91 NA.BA19/R) La Ribera de Vigo, al Atardecer (24x38cm-9x15in) s.
           panel
£12209 $21000   (17-Oct-91 SY.NY361/R) Un rapto (45x62cm-18x24in) s.i.
£1094 $1980   (4-Dec-91 NA.BA18) Ferrarina (29x46cm-11x18in) s.d.1897 W/C

PRADILLA Y ORTIZ, Francisco (attrib) (1848-1921) Spanish
£420 $743   (13-Feb-92 CSK70/R) Spanish beauty (34x25cm-13x10in) pencil W/C

PRADILLA, Francisco (?) Spanish
£464 $798   (16-Oct-91 FER.M7/R) Arboles de Albano (46x31cm-18x12in) s.i. chl dr
           (S.P 85000)

PRAGUE SCHOOL (?) Czechoslovakian
£2100 $3780   (22-Nov-91 SWS44/R) The Holy Family (87x57cm-34x22in) c.1600

PRAGUE SCHOOL, 17th C Czechoslovakian
£3043 $5355   (11-Apr-92 AT.P33/R) La Circoncision (190x140cm-75x55in) (F.FR 30000)

PRAM-HENNINGSEN, C (1846-1892) Danish
£668 $1150   (15-Oct-91 RAS.K214/R) Small girl getting dressed (60x48cm-24x19in) s.
           (D.KR 7500)

PRAMPOLINI, Enrico (1894-1956) Italian
£6173 $11173   (6-Dec-91 GL.P169) Sans titre (31x39cm-12x15in) s. hardboard (F.FR 60000)
£34491 $61738   (14-Nov-91 F.M110/R) Sur le motif (81x100cm-32x39in) s.d.1954 oil sand
           canvas jute (I.L 75000000)
£1208 $2187   (3-Dec-91 F.R129) L'asino e le stelle (11x11cm-4x4in) s. indian ink sold
           with dr.by Franco Gentilini (I.L 2600000)
£4981 $8617   (28-Mar-92 F.L74/R) Progetto per la Mostra del Minerale, Roma
           (30x48cm-12x19in) s.d.1936 pastel collage (S.FR 13000)
£5364 $9280   (28-Mar-92 F.L84/R) Progetto per architettura polimaterica
           (23x34cm-9x13in) s.d.1941 pastel board (S.FR 14000)

PRASCH, Wenzel Ignaz see BRASCH, Wenzel Ignaz

PRASSINOS, Mario (1916-1985) Turkish
£1084 $1908   (7-Apr-92 C.A199/R) Eygalieres (57x77cm-22x30in) s.d.1952 paper on canvas
           (B.FR 65000)
£2049 $3689   (2-Feb-92 CSC.P78/R) Oiseaux-avions (46x55cm-18x22in) s. i.d.1954verso
           (F.FR 20000)
£4913 $8745   (27-Nov-91 BL.P211/R) Roches blanches (89x116cm-35x46in) s. d.56verso
           (F.FR 48000)
£1057 $1882   (28-Oct-91 GL.P177) Sans titre (99x149cm-39x59in) s.d.15 mars 76 indian
           ink (F.FR 10500)
£1460 $2599   (28-Oct-91 GL.P177 b) Sans titre (48x128cm-19x50in) s.d.17 avril 63
           indian ink oil (F.FR 14500)

PRAT, Juan Abello (1922-) Spanish
£1368 $2599   (23-Jun-92 DUR.M483/R) El Montseny nevat (73x93cm-29x37in) s.
           s.i.d.75verso (S.P 250000)
£1642 $2922   (29-Oct-91 BRO.B305) Saimons sur Seine (65x81cm-26x32in) s.
           s.i.d.1983verso (S.P 300000)
£1644 $2927   (26-Nov-91 BRO.B355) Flores (92x73cm-36x29in) s.d.52 s.i.d.verso
           (S.P 300000)
£1970 $3506   (29-Oct-91 BRO.B350) Paisage, Camps (81x100cm-32x39in) s. s.d.1991verso
           (S.P 360000)
£547 $974   (29-Oct-91 BRO.B272) Leccion de patinaje (50x64cm-20x25in) s. pastel
           (S.P 100000)

PRATELLA, Attilio (1856-1932) Italian
£1220 $2220   (13-Dec-91 BM.B704/R) Coastal landscape near Naples (22x31cm-9x12in) s.
           panel (DM 3500)
£1815 $3376   (16-Jun-92 F.M231/R) Costiera amalfitana (13x18cm-5x7in) s. panel
           (I.L 4000000)
£2944 $5447   (9-Jun-92 F.R159/R) Inverno (23x13cm-9x5in) s. tile (I.L 6500000)
£3254 $5889   (3-Dec-91 SY.MI80/R) Bozzetto di strada con figure (14x17cm-6x7in) s.d.30
           panel (I.L 7000000)
£4068 $7364   (18-May-92 SY.MI44/R) Marina (30x54cm-12x21in) s. (I.L 9000000)
£4077 $7542   (9-Jun-92 F.R155/R) Casciaro dipinge en plein air (14x17cm-6x7in) s.
           panel (I.L 9000000)

PRATELLA, Attilio (1856-1932) Italian-cont.
| £4529 | $8380 | (8-Jun-92 CH.R664/R) Il porto di Napoli (23x35cm-9x14in) s. panel (I.L 10000000) |

£5000	$8650	(4-Oct-91 C195/R) Fishing boats in the Bay of Naples (32x47cm-13x19in) s.
£6780	$12273	(18-May-92 SY.MI125/R) Marina (22x35cm-9x14in) s. panel (I.L 15000000)
£7267	$12500	(17-Oct-91 SY.NY371/R) Bay of Naples (25x38cm-10x15in) s. board
£9493	$17182	(18-May-92 SY.MI126/R) Veduta di citta (22x35cm-9x14in) s. panel (I.L 21000000)
£10191	$18854	(9-Jun-92 F.R143/R) Paesaggio invernale (34x23cm-13x9in) s. panel (I.L 22500000)
£11777	$21787	(9-Jun-92 F.R180/R) Marina flegrea (13x27cm-5x11in) s.d.91 panel (I.L 26000000)
£20000	$35000	(20-Feb-92 SY.NY88/R) Bay of Naples (51x70cm-20x28in) s.
£1860	*$3200*	*(15-Oct-91 CE.NY350) Fisherman by a harbour (28x22cm-11x9in) s. W/C board*

PRATELLA, Attilio (style) (1856-1932) Italian
| £1400 | $2394 | (17-Mar-92 PH210/R) Fishing in the Bay of Naples (61x91cm-24x36in) indis.s. |

PRATELLA, Fausto (1888-1964) Italian
£544	$1006	(8-Jun-92 CH.R639) Marina con barche (31x45cm-12x18in) s. tempera (I.L 1200000)
£2000	$3720	(17-Jun-92 S556/R) Beach at Capri. Terrace, Capri (25x31cm-10x12in) s. panel pair
£2055	$3926	(1-Jul-92 FB.P102/R) Capri (54x65cm-21x26in) s.d.1932 canvas laid down on board (F.FR 20000)
£5519	$9878	(14-Nov-91 CH.R32) Marina grande di Capri (66x101cm-26x40in) s.d.1929 (I.L 12000000)

PRATERE, Edmond Joseph de (1826-1888) Belgian
| £2487 | $4750 | (16-Jul-92 SY.NY472/R) Cows by a ruin (55x71cm-22x28in) s. |

PRATT, Douglas Fieldew (1900-1972) Australian
| £581 | $1110 | (21-Jul-92 JRL.S61) Woolloomooloo Bay, Sydney (50x75cm-20x30in) s.d.68 (A.D 1500) |
| £598 | $1065 | (27-Apr-92 J.M1123) Guardians of the valley (58x73cm-23x29in) s.d.68 (A.D 1400) |

PRATT, Henry Cheever (1803-1880) American
| £5495 | $10000 | (28-May-92 CH.NY11/R) The Ohio River near Marietta (61x101cm-24x40in) s.d.1855 |

PRATT, Hilton L (circle) (19th C) British
| £1073 | $1942 | (3-Dec-91 R.T145/R) Fighting cock by barn window. Fighting cock by hay bin (31x23cm-12x9in) init. board pair (C.D 2200) |

PRATT, William (1855-?) British
£741	$1341	(4-Dec-91 DS.W33) Carradale (44x59cm-17x23in) s.d.1926 i.verso (NZ.D 2400)
£1692	$3011	(25-Nov-91 W.T1928/R) Sunday morning (63x79cm-25x31in) s.d.84 (C.D 3400)
£2198	$4000	(28-May-92 SY.NY290/R) Little gardener (36x25cm-14x10in) s.d.1896
£2300	$4094	(28-Apr-92 S213/R) Homeward at eventide (82x66cm-32x26in) s.d.1903
£2800	$4704	(26-Aug-91 S972/R) Fishing harbour (41x51cm-16x20in) s.
£4800	$8064	(26-Aug-91 S974/R) Thistledown (61x46cm-24x18in) s.d.1913

PRAX, Valentine (1899-1981) French
£1119	$2048	(17-May-92 GL.P63) L'offrande (43x51cm-17x20in) s. (F.FR 11000)
£1143	$2000	(27-Feb-92 CE.NY74/R) Femme devant une fenetre (60x49cm-24x19in) s. oil over pencil paper on board
£1543	$2932	(24-Jun-92 FB.P23/R) Femme nue debout dans un interieur (48x33cm-19x13in) s. (F.FR 15000)
£3262	$6067	(19-Jun-92 ARC.P43/R) Les jeux (50x61cm-20x24in) s. (F.FR 32000)
£3561	$6516	(17-May-92 GL.P62) Bouquet (73x50cm-29x20in) s.d.1939 (F.FR 35000)
£4183	$7779	(19-Jun-92 G.Z32/R) Le musicien (73x54cm-29x21in) s. (S.FR 11000)
£5512	$9480	(16-Oct-91 G.Z84/R) Scene au restaurant (76x111cm-30x44in) s.d.1925 (S.FR 14000)
£7216	$12485	(23-Mar-92 GL.P165/R) Jeune femme au gueridon (100x81cm-39x32in) s. i.verso (F.FR 70000)
£8485	$15358	(19-May-92 CH.AM237/R) Portrait of a family (116x89cm-46x35in) s. (D.FL 28000)
£9073	$16058	(10-Nov-91 ZZ.F187/R) Le dejeuner sur l'herbe (114x146cm-45x57in) s.d.1926 (F.FR 90000)
£15768	$28856	(17-May-92 GL.P234/R) Les fiancailles (115x81cm-45x32in) s. (F.FR 155000)

PREAUX, Raymond (1916-) French
| £1495 | $2586 | (29-Mar-92 FE.P305) Nature morte (F.FR 14500) |

PREECE, Glen Robert (?) Australian?
£504	$962	(21-Jul-92 JRL.S125) Paper woman (59x48cm-23x19in) s. board (A.D 1300)
£543	$1036	(21-Jul-92 JRL.S146) Summer by the bridge (75x100cm-30x39in) s. (A.D 1400)
£659	$1259	(21-Jul-92 JRL.S134) Lennox Bridge, Parramatta (70x74cm-28x29in) s.board (A.D 1700)
£756	$1444	(21-Jul-92 JRL.S148) The Saturday cricketers (50x70cm-20x28in) s. (A.D 1950)

PREECE, Patricia (1900-) British
£540 $940   (17-Sep-91 PH46/R) Still life of roses in a pot (41x36cm-16x14in) s.

PREEN, Hugo von (1854-?) Austrian
£537 $913   (24-Oct-91 D.V243/R) Passau street scene (32x20cm-13x8in) s. pastel
                 (A.S 11000)
£777 $1383   (29-Apr-92 D.V689/R) Farmhouse in wooded landscape, autumn
                 (27x39cm-11x15in) s. pastel (A.S 16000)
£780 $1358   (19-Sep-91 D.V268/R) Marienhohe, hilly landscape (26x41cm-10x16in)
                 mono.i.d.35 pastel (A.S 16000)
£976 $1698   (19-Sep-91 D.V274/R) Farmhouse in Osternberg (28x41cm-11x16in) s. pastel
                 (A.S 20000)

PREGARTBAUER, Louis (1899-1971) Austrian
£1842 $3352   (26-May-92 D.V87/R) In the forest (26x21cm-10x8in) mono.d.27 s.d.verso
                 (A.S 38000)
£388 $691   (28-Apr-92 D.V285/R) Prater (47x43cm-19x17in) mono.d.1931 s.verso chk
                 pencil (A.S 8000)

PREISS, Fritz see PREISS, Ferdinand

PREISS, Helmut (1940-) Austrian
£989 $1730   (19-Feb-92 D.V211/R) Kap Hoorn (53x72cm-21x28in) s.d.82 mixed media panel
                 (A.S 20000)

PREISSLER, Johann Daniel (1666-1737) German
£1268 $2294   (6-Dec-91 GB.B5581/R) Male nude (42x28cm-17x11in) s.i.d.1695 ochre
                 htd.chk (DM 3600)

PRELL, Walter (1857-?) German
£2326 $4000   (17-Oct-91 SY.NY274/R) Soir de Novembre (128x192cm-50x76in) s.
£2348 $4250   (21-May-92 S.W2900/R) Horses in pasture, early morning, autumn
                 (130x193cm-51x76in) s. s.i.stretcher

PRELLER, Alexis (1911-1975) South African
£1210 $2141   (4-Nov-91 SY.J323/R) Mother Earth (29x35cm-11x14in) (SA.R 6000)
£3226 $5710   (4-Nov-91 SY.J324/R) Seychelles girl with flower (44x39cm-17x15in) s.d.39
                 (SA.R 16000)
£4435 $7851   (4-Nov-91 SY.J322/R) Three women (30x25cm-12x10in) s.d.50 panel
                 (SA.R 22000)
£605 $1071   (4-Nov-91 SY.J308) Untitled pencil 1 sketch by Guna Massyn 8 in one
                 frame (SA.R 3000)

PRELLER, Friedrich Johann Christian Ernst (1804-1878) German
£565 $1000   (13-Feb-92 S.W2353) Fleets along the shore (30x53cm-12x21in) s.
£819 $1483   (22-May-92 GB.B6002/R) Roman campagna, thunderstorm rising. View of
                 Wartburg (29x41cm-11x16in) i.verso pen wash pencil double-sided
                 (DM 2400)
£1937 $3505   (4-Dec-91 DO.H2885/R) Rocky coast with shipwreck and sailor in surf
                 (68x58cm-27x23in) mono.i.d.1856 indian ink brush pen over pencil
                 (DM 5500)

PRELOG, Drago J (1939-) Yugoslavian
£485 $882   (26-May-92 D.V209/R) Untitled (64x48cm-25x19in) s.d.1961 pencil
                 col.pencil wash (A.S 10000)

PREM, Heimrad (1934-1978) German
£2469 $4494   (11-Dec-91 CH.AM405/R) The bathing room (85x70cm-33x28in) s.d.76
                 (D.FL 8000)
£3439 $6224   (4-Dec-91 KH.K90/R) Der gelbe Ranstrich (65x65cm-26x26in) s.d.65
                 (D.KR 38000)
£3915 $6811   (17-Sep-91 RAS.K14/R) Figures (60x58cm-24x23in) s.d.61 (D.KR 44000)
£6940 $12075   (17-Sep-91 RAS.K19/R) Figure (80x60cm-31x24in) s.d.1961 (D.KR 78000)
£13287 $23650   (26-Nov-91 KF.M969/R) Composition (81x110cm-32x43in) s.i.d.1960
                 (DM 38000)
£1211 $2313   (4-Jul-92 BOD.P628) Composition (37x51cm-15x20in) s.verso mixed media
                 (DM 3500)
£1423 $2477   (17-Sep-91 RAS.K15/R) Two figures (61x42cm-24x17in) s.d.77 gouache W/C
                 (D.KR 16000)
£1629 $2948   (4-Dec-91 KH.K120/R) Composition (42x58cm-17x23in) s.d.66 acrylic W/C
                 pencil (D.KR 18000)

PRENDERGAST, Maurice (1861-1924) American
£1800 $3060   (9-Aug-91 T286) Two women in the park (20x15cm-8x6in) s. W/C
£19231 $35000   (28-May-92 CH.NY144/R) Low tide, Afternoon, Treport (32x23cm-13x9in)
                 s.d.92 W/C pencil
£38462 $70000   (27-May-92 SY.NY82/R) Little Bridge, Venice (39x49cm-15x19in) s. W/C
                 pencil
£38674 $70000   (5-Dec-91 SY.NY76/R) The cove (36x51cm-14x20in) s. W/C pencil
£419890 $760000   (5-Dec-91 SY.NY69/R) Franklin Park, Boston (32x49cm-13x19in) s. W/C

PRENDERGAST, Maurice (after) (1861-1924) American
£947 $1800   (24-Jun-92 D.NY67) After the rain, Piazza San Marco (30x23cm-12x9in)
                 bears sig.i.d.1899 gouache

PRENDERGAST, Maurice (attrib) (1861-1924) American
£1279 $2200   *(20-Oct-91 HG.C1501) Figures outside archway (28x33cm-11x13in) s. W/C*

PRENTICE, Levi Wells (1851-1935) American
£719 $1200   (20-Aug-91 RB.HY65/R) W. Seneca, Near Buffalo, N.Y. (23x30cm-9x12in) one s. pair
£4396 $8000   (27-May-92 SY.NY1/R) Still life with strawberries (13x25cm-5x10in) s.
£7821 $14000   (6-May-92 D.NY21/R) Basket of apples beneath tree (41x30cm-16x12in) s.d.1891 s.verso
£9890 $18000   (27-May-92 SY.NY2/R) Still life with Bass ale and oysters (41x51cm-16x20in) s.
£13714 $24000   (26-Sep-91 CH.NY22/R) Apple harvest (38x48cm-15x19in) init. s.verso
£16571 $29000   (25-Sep-91 SY.NY4/R) Tea, cake and strawberries (41x51cm-16x20in) s.

PRESAS, Leopoldo (1915-) Argentinian
£659 $1200   (11-Dec-91 RO.BA253) Figuras (31x29cm-12x11in) s.
£698 $1200   (9-Oct-91 RO.BA594) Maniqui (34x26cm-13x10in) s.
£1056   *$1900*   *(20-Nov-91 V.BA79) Naturaleza muerta (30x38cm-12x15in) mixed media*

PRESNOV, Andrei (1935-) Russian
£611   *$1112*   *(11-Dec-91 ZZ.F1/R) Lenine sur la Place Rouge (26x47cm-10x19in) s.verso W/C (F.FR 6000)*

PRESNOV, Andrei and KRIKOUNOV, Youri (20th C) Russian
£509 $927   (11-Dec-91 ZZ.F4/R) La prise du Reichstag (114x152cm-45x60in) s.verso (F.FR 5000)
£1833 $3336   (11-Dec-91 ZZ.F5/R) Lenine et le Comite Central (130x181cm-51x71in) s.verso (F.FR 18000)

PRESSMANE, Joseph (1904-1967) French
£595 $1100   (8-Jun-92 GG.TA230/R) Woman standing (35x14cm-14x6in) s. board
£1526 $2792   (17-May-92 GL.P175/R) Femme dans un paysage (41x27cm-16x11in) s. (F.FR 15000)
£2486 $4600   (8-Jun-92 GG.TA228/R) Portrait of man in white shirt (40x32cm-16x13in) s.
£3429 $6000   (26-Sep-91 SY.I92/R) Village (52x64cm-20x25in) s.d.1921
£6286 $11000   (26-Sep-91 SY.I58/R) Village (73x54cm-29x21in) s.d.64
£7568 $14000   (9-Jun-92 GG.TA431/R) Concert in kibbutz (40x55cm-16x22in) s.d.1926
£8511 $16000   (5-Jan-92 GG.TA325/R) City by river and boats (49x65cm-19x26in) s.d.1952 s.verso
£1714   *$3000*   *(26-Sep-91 SY.I59/R) House under trees (54x38cm-21x15in) s.d.59 oil pencil card on canvas*

PRESTON, J (19th C) ?
£909 $1573   (25-Mar-92 KM.K1376 a/R) Mountainous landscape (41x61cm-16x24in) s.d.1870 (DM 2600)

PRESTON, Margaret Rose (1883-?) Australian
£3991 $6664   (19-Aug-91 SY.ME263/R) Cottage kitchen (89x89cm-35x35in) indist.init. (A.D 8500)
£28169 $47042   (19-Aug-91 SY.ME310/R) Thunbergia (44x44cm-17x17in) s.indist.d. (A.D 60000)
£4681   *$8285*   *(26-Apr-92 SY.ME440/R) Dry river bed, N.T (30x35cm-12x14in) s.d.1953 i.verso stencil mixed media board (A.D 11000)*
£4681   *$8285*   *(26-Apr-92 SY.ME475/R) Fungi on log (37x47cm-15x19in) s.d.1953 stencil mixed media board (A.D 11000)*
£5164   *$8624*   *(19-Aug-91 SY.ME222/R) Still life with daisies in basket (43x58cm-17x23in) s. W/C pencil (A.D 11000)*

PRESTON, May Wilson (1873-1949) American
£936 $1600   (12-Mar-92 CH.NY215/R) Three children with kite (23x29cm-9x11in) s. board
£393   *$700*   *(2-Nov-91 IH.NY82/R) Three dancing couples (23x33cm-9x13in) s.d.1913 W/C*

PRETE, Juan del (1897-1987) Argentinian
£1628 $2800   (9-Oct-91 RO.BA215) Figuras (60x50cm-24x20in) s.d.44
£2688 $5000   (16-Jun-92 RO.BA47) Barco azul (50x35cm-20x14in)
£4494 $8000   (1-Nov-91 PO.BA58) Bodegon (70x43cm-28x17in) s.d.43 board
£838   *$1500*   *(6-May-92 V.BA34) Composicion (70x40cm-28x16in) collage*

PRETI, Mattia (1613-1699) Italian
£138122 $250000   (21-May-92 CH.NY14/R) Triumph of Love (169x366cm-67x144in)
£279834 $506500   (22-May-92 SY.NY63/R) Boethius and Philosophy (185x254cm-73x100in)
£400000 $728000   (11-Dec-91 S27/R) Belisarius receiving alms (152x198cm-60x78in) i.
£845   *$1530*   *(6-Dec-91 GB.B5328) Soldiers resting (20x31cm-8x12in) chk (DM 2400)*

PRETI, Mattia (after) (1613-1699) Italian
£5500 $10010   (10-Dec-91 PH157/R) Card players (112x140cm-44x55in)

PRETI, Mattia (attrib) (1613-1699) Italian
£3929 $6954   (10-Feb-92 GL.P8/R) Loth et ses filles (73x56cm-29x22in) (F.FR 38500)
£2400   *$4608*   *(8-Jul-92 PH234/R) Two studies of Lamentation (33x22cm-13x9in) i. red chk*

PRETI, Mattia (style) (1613-1699) Italian
£1100 $2112   (9-Jul-92 CSK98) Saints Lawrence and Roch with Madonna interceding with Trinity (42x35cm-17x14in)
£2000 $3560   (30-Oct-91 S160/R) St Nicholas of Bari (114x71cm-45x28in)

PRETI, Mattia (style) (1613-1699) Italian-cont.
£3680 $6330   (15-Oct-91 CH.R66/R) San Giovanni Battista (112x79cm-44x31in)
          (I.L 8000000)

PREUDHOMME, Jean (1732-1795) Swiss
£1596 $3001   (16-Dec-91 AGS.P64/R) Portrait de gentilhomme en veste verte, en buste
          (64x51cm-25x20in) s.d.1776 painted oval (F.FR 15500)

PREUSS, Emil (19th C) German
£500 $915   (15-May-92 TE411/R) Young woman at casement window, holding rose
          (89x53cm-35x21in) s.

PREUSS, Rudolf (1879-?) Austrian
£420 $718   (17-Mar-92 PH68) Goldenes Dachl, Innsbruck (18x21cm-7x8in) s.i.d.35 W/C
          htd.white
£1214 $2160   (29-Apr-92 D.V667/R) View over the rooftops of Vienna (28x17cm-11x7in)
          s.d. W/C (A.S 25000)

PREUSSER, Robert Ormerod (20th C) ?
£995 $1900   (19-Jul-92 JRB.C112/R) Seismic pattern (38x56cm-15x22in) s. canvasboard
£2632 $4500   (13-Mar-92 S.BM334/R) Colour action (61x71cm-24x28in) s.d.41verso

PREUX, E (19th C) Belgian?
£500 $905   (21-May-92 CSK217) Le bouton de rose (99x59cm-39x23in) s.d.1879 after
          Anton Joseph Wiertz

PREVERT, Jacques (20th C) French
£1016 $1768   (16-Apr-92 FB.P18/R) Sans titre (26x41cm-10x16in) s.i.d.Aout 69 collage
          (F.FR 10000)

PREVIATI, Gaetano (1852-1920) Italian
£1766 $3197   (3-Dec-91 SY.MI62) Scena di storia medioevale (19x32cm-7x13in) s.
          cardboard (I.L 3800000)
£13747 $24333   (7-Nov-91 F.M53/R) Idillio (55x79cm-22x31in) s. (I.L 30000000)

PREVITALI, Andrea (attrib) (1470-1528) Italian
£60000 $109200   (11-Dec-91 S21/R) Saint Jerome (33x40cm-13x16in) panel

PREVITALI, Andrea (school) (1470-1528) Italian
£11047 $19000   (9-Oct-91 CH.NY131/R) Holy Family with Saint Catherine (37x46cm-15x18in)
          panel

PREVON, Eugene (20th C) French
£2577 $4485   (17-Sep-91 FN.S2500/R) Sitting room interior with girl holding doll
          seated by piano (49x60cm-19x24in) s. (DM 7500)

PREVOST (elder-attrib) (18th C) French
£12921 $23000   (30-Oct-91 D.NY43/R) Fleurs dans un vase (48x38cm-19x15in) bears
          indis.init.

PREVOST, Alexandre Celeste (19th C) French
£1076 $1948   (23-May-92 KV.L264) Scene de Harem (39x99cm-15x39in) s.d.1889 pastel
          (B.FR 65000)

PREVOST, Jean Louis and VALLAYER-COSTER, Anne (circle) (18th C) French
£3704 $6704   (19-May-92 GF.L2109/R) Still life of roses and lily of the valley
          (38x32cm-15x13in) panel (S.FR 10000)

PREVOT-VALERI, Andre (1890-) French
£500 $860   (5-Mar-92 CSK49) Sunlit river landscape (54x71cm-21x28in) s.
£520 $952   (5-Feb-92 ZZ.B164) River landscape (38x46cm-15x18in) s.
£1081 $2000   (12-Jun-92 SY.NY27/R) Summer landscape with stream (46x55cm-18x22in) s.

PREWITT, William (fl.1735-1750) British
£1300 $2236   (4-Mar-92 C55/R) Gentleman, in mole-coloured coat, waistcoat, lace cravat
          and wig (4x?cm-2x?in) min. s.verso enamel gilt mount wood frame oval

PREYER, Emilie (1849-1930) German
£10500 $17955   (20-Mar-92 C13/R) Peaches, plums and grapes on draped table
          (17x23cm-7x9in) s.
£14067 $24477   (14-Apr-92 SY.AM216/R) Still life with fruit on table (17x23cm-7x9in) s.
          (D.FL 46000)
£16000 $28000   (20-Feb-92 SY.NY12/R) Still life with walnut and fruit (22x27cm-9x11in)
          s.d.1871
£17500 $32550   (17-Jun-92 S379/R) Still life of fruit and glass of champagne
          (24x34cm-9x13in) s.
£22093 $38000   (16-Oct-91 CH.NY103/R) Still life with assorted flowers, fruits nuts and
          a glass of champagneon a marble ledge (31x39cm-12x15in) s.

REYER, Johann Wilhelm (attrib) (1803-1889) German
£1718 $2921   (25-Oct-91 BM.B805/R) Still life of fruit and glass of champagne on table
          (33x27cm-13x11in) (DM 5000)

REYER, Paul (1847-1931) German
£2498 $4496   (21-Nov-91 D.V161/R) A cup of milk (27x24cm-11x9in) s.d.1874 (A.S 50000)

PREZIOSI, Amadeo (1816-1882) Italian
£1300	$2210	(23-Oct-91 S10) Turk smoking hookah (23x18cm-9x7in) W/C over pencil
£1400	$2422	(4-Oct-91 C140/R) Fishermen on the Bosphorous (24x32cm-9x13in) s.d.1855 pencil W/C htd white
£1500	$2715	(22-May-92 C205/R) Turk smoking pipe (27x20cm-11x8in) s.d.1843 pencil W/C htd white
£3000	$5100	(23-Oct-91 S218/R) Turkish ladies above the Bosphorus at Rumeli Hissar (33x53cm-13x21in) s.d.1880 W/C over pencil
£3000	$5370	(11-Nov-91 S565/R) Turkish band (52x43cm-20x17in) s. W/C over pencil oval
£3400	$5780	(23-Oct-91 S216/R) Shipping at entrance to Golden Horn, Constantinople (34x53cm-13x21in) s.d.1880 W/C over pencil
£3500	$6335	(22-May-92 C215/R) Constantinople from Eyub (41x52cm-16x20in) s.d.1863 pencil W/C
£4000	$6800	(23-Oct-91 S233/R) Turkish lady playing the lute (37x26cm-15x10in) s. W/C over pencil bodycol
£4200	$7434	(14-Feb-92 C92/R) Turkish warriors (52x44cm-20x17in) s.d.1854 pencil W/C htd white oval
£4200	$7140	(23-Oct-91 S36/R) The Golden Horn, Constantinople (56x76cm-22x30in) s.d.1852 W/C over pencil
£4400	$7480	(23-Oct-91 S37/R) In the bazaar, Constantinople (53x69cm-21x27in) s.d.1862 pen ink W/C htd.gouache
£12000	$20400	(23-Oct-91 S224/R) The Fourth Court on the Topkapi Saray (51x71cm-20x28in) s.d.1853 W/C over pencil
£18000	$30600	(23-Oct-91 S223/R) In the bazaar, Constantinople (53x74cm-21x29in) s.d.1851 W/C over pencil htd bodycol gum arabic

PREZIOSI, Amadeo (style) (1816-1882) Italian
£3000	$5100	(23-Oct-91 S215/R) Crowded mosque (52x69cm-20x27in) s. pen W/C

PREZZI, Wilma Maria (1915-1964) American
£1170	$2000	(13-Mar-92 S.BM303/R) Still lifes (64x76cm-25x30in) s.

PRICE, C S (1874-1950) American
£2011	$3500	(15-Sep-91 JRB.C232/R) Two birds (64x76cm-25x30in) s.

PRICE, Clayton Sumner (1874-1950) American
£621	$1100	(12-Feb-92 B.SF595/R) Horse (20x28cm-8x11in) s. pencil

PRICE, Frank Corbyn (1862-?) British
£480	$816	(22-Oct-91 SWS200/R) Moorland and down (34x54cm-13x21in) s. i.verso W/C

PRICE, Garrett (19/20th C) American
£1124	$2000	(2-Nov-91 IH.NY127/R) Woman at telephone, cat with kittens (33x23cm-13x9in) s. pastel W/C

PRICE, J W (19th C) British
£520	$926	(29-Apr-92 B120) Welsh mill at Dolgelly, N.Wales (61x94cm-24x37in) s. s.i.d.1879stretcher

PRICE, James (19/20th C) British
£900	$1584	(9-Apr-92 S105) Figures in farmyard (37x53cm-15x21in) W/C over pencil

PRICE, Jane R (?-1941) Australian
£1322	$2352	(26-Nov-91 J.M206/R) Figures in summer paddock (29x38cm-11x15in) s. (A.D 3000)

PRICE, Julius Mendes (1857-1924) British
£890	$1593	(6-May-92 MMB392) Young lacemaker by a harbour wall (51x41cm-20x16in) s.

PRICEKINE, Nikolai (1928-) Russian
£591	$1100	(17-Jun-92 ARC.P50/R) Bouquet sur un drap rouge (73x64cm-29x25in) s. (F.FR 5800)
£693	$1289	(17-Jun-92 ARC.P51/R) Un canal de Venise (58x39cm-23x15in) s. isorel (F.FR 6800)

PRIDEAUX, Edmund (1693-1745) British
£1100	$2101	(16-Jul-92 S6/R) Padstow, Cornwall, with Prideaux Place beyond (23x34cm-9x13in) gouache vellum

PRIECHENFRIED, Alois (1867-1953) German
£4070	$7000	(13-Oct-91 H.C57/R) Going to church in Czechoslovakia (56x69cm-22x27in) s.
£5479	$9425	(8-Oct-91 ZEL.L1666/R) Interior of monastery library with figure seated at table (79x64cm-31x25in) s. (DM 16000)

PRIEST, Alfred (1874-1929) British
£1850	$3534	(14-Jul-92 DR388) Portrait of Mr R Mackenzie and Miss M Mackenzie seated on cushion (138x102cm-54x40in) s.d.1907

PRIEST, Thomas (18th C) British
£2200	$3938	(13-Nov-91 S189/R) Capriccio view of Chelsea Hospital on the Thames (49x73cm-19x29in) canvas on panel

PRIESTMAN, Bertram (1868-1951) British
£550	$957	(17-Sep-91 PH19) Cattle grazing near a stream (25x34cm-10x13in) init.i.d.32 card
£1200	$2184	(11-Dec-91 PHL58/R) The village ferry (40x60cm-16x24in) s.d.1919
£1200	$2064	(16-Oct-91 PHL278/R) Cattle by river (58x115cm-23x45in) s.d.1903
£1300	$2275	(27-Sep-91 C67 a/R) Summer (38x59cm-15x23in) s.d.04
£2800	$4900	(23-Sep-91 PHB64/R) The river meadow (81x122cm-32x48in) s.d.1901
£4200	$7518	(14-Jan-92 SWS282/R) On the Maas, Holland (111x131cm-44x52in) s.d.39

PRIKING, Franz (1927-1979) French
£1676	$3000	(9-May-92 CE.NY76/R) Paysage (55x65cm-22x26in)
£2235	$4000	(9-May-92 CE.NY82/R) Nature morte (55x46cm-22x18in) s.d.51
£3905	$7459	(3-Jul-92 GL.P137/R) Le cheval bleu (54x65cm-21x26in) s. (F.FR 38000)
£4107	$7392	(19-Nov-91 FB.P60/R) Nature morte (53x65cm-21x26in) s. (F.FR 40000)
£7187	$12936	(19-Nov-91 FB.P98/R) Nature morte a l'Aiguiere (104x145cm-41x57in) s. (F.FR 70000)
£7645	$14220	(21-Jun-92 LT.P75 b) Portrait d'une jeune femme (116x89cm-46x35in) s.d.56 (F.FR 75000)
£971	$1778	(5-Feb-92 FB.P216/R) Bouquet de fleurs (31x49cm-12x19in) s. W/C (F.FR 9500)

PRIM, Josep M (1907-1973) ?
£548	$976	(26-Nov-91 BRO.B376) Paisaje de la costa (73x92cm-29x36in) s. (S.P 100000)

PRIMATICCIO, Francesco (1504-1570) French
£31000	$59520	(6-Jul-92 S20/R) Fortitude (21x15cm-8x6in) i. pen chk.wash

PRIMAVESI, Georg (1776-1855) German
£1232	$2231	(4-Dec-91 DO.H2886/R) Stream in rocky landscape (13x18cm-5x7in) panel (DM 3500)

PRINA, Andre Julien (1886-1941) French?
£803	$1437	(6-May-92 GD.B1026/R) Nature morte aux pommes et aux citrons (18x24cm-7x9in) s. (S.FR 2200)
£7843	$14039	(15-Nov-91 GK.Z5252/R) Lake Geneva landscape (36x43cm-14x17in) (S.FR 20000)

PRINA, Carla (20th C) ?
£510	$913	(15-Nov-91 GK.Z5751) Untitled (33x43cm-13x17in) s.d.1950 wood (S.FR 1300)

PRINCE, Richard (1949-) American?
£3352	$6000	(6-May-92 CH.NY201/R) All I've heard (61x45cm-24x18in) s.d.1989 verso silkscreen acrylic canvas

PRINCE, William Meade (1893-1951) American
£843	$1500	(2-Nov-91 IH.NY177/R) Self portrait of artist seated at easel (51x41cm-20x16in) s.
£1264	$2250	(2-May-92 IH.NY54/R) Hun toppling Statue of Liberty (76x53cm-30x21in) s.

PRINCESS MARIE (?) ?
£397	$706	(28-Apr-92 RAS.K691) Nature morte with doves (55x72cm-22x28in) s. W/C (D.KR 4500)

PRINCESS VICTORIA MELITA (?) ?
£500	$860	(3-Mar-92 SWS1577) Cornflowers (29x49cm-11x19in) init.

PRINET, Rene-Xavier (1861-1946) French
£963	$1742	(20-May-92 FB.P260) Coin de salon (55x46cm-22x18in) s. (F.FR 9500)

PRINGLE, James (19th C) British
£4800	$8592	(15-Nov-91 C67/R) Extensive landscape with figures on road, boating lake and houses beyond (63x77cm-25x30in) s.d.1812

PRINS, Benjamin (1860-1934) Dutch
£673	$1198	(30-Oct-91 CH.AM5) Muurbloempje (21x27cm-8x11in) s. s.i.verso (D.FL 2200)
£2294	$4060	(5-Nov-91 SY.AM21/R) Ijdel (100x79cm-39x31in) s. (D.FL 7500)

PRINS, Johannes Huibert (1757-1806) Dutch
£5556	$9944	(12-Nov-91 SY.AM23/R) River landscapes (18x25cm-7x10in) s. copper pair (D.FL 18000)
£621	$1106	(25-Nov-91 CH.AM218) Ruined farmhouse in wooded landscape with couple conversing by well (25x30cm-10x12in) pencil W/C (D.FL 2000)
£2099	$3757	(12-Nov-91 SY.AM256/R) Street scene with figures by bridge over canal (31x21cm-12x8in) s. W/C over chk (D.FL 6800)

PRINS, Johannes Huibert (attrib) (1757-1806) Dutch
£1481	$2652	(12-Nov-91 SY.AM361/R) View of Delft from the north (11x18cm-4x7in) W/C over pen (D.FL 4800)

PRINS, Pierre (1838-1913) French
£1337	$2541	(26-Jun-92 AGS.P19/R) Eglise de village (58x74cm-23x29in) s. (F.FR 13000)
£619	$1058	(11-Mar-92 LGB.P131/R) Les deux chaumieres (30x46cm-12x18in) s. pastel (F.FR 6000)

PRINSEP, Lilian (19th C) French
£730 $1300   (22-Jan-92 SY.NY354/R) Bouquet of summer flowers in basket (32x42cm-13x17in) s.d.91

PRINSEP, Valentine Cameron (1838-1904) British
£7800 $14040   (19-Nov-91 PH55/R) Newmarket Heath, the morning of the sale (107x183cm-42x72in) s.d.1874
£11628 $20000   (17-Oct-91 SY.NY108/R) Among brambles (95x74cm-37x29in)
£28000 $47600   (25-Oct-91 C53/R) The Lady of the Tootni-Nameh or The Legend of the Parrot (91x116cm-36x46in) s.indis.i.stretcher

PRINSEP, William (19th C) British
£8000 $13600   (25-Oct-91 C10/R) Government House and the Maidan, Calcutta (38x91cm-15x36in) mono.indis.d.18..
£400 $716   (12-Nov-91 C111) Gourhatee, Assam (25x35cm-10x14in) init.d.1849 pencil W/C
£3100 $5332   (4-Mar-92 DR45/R) Canton, street behind factories, kolao or cook's shop (23x29cm-9x11in) s.d.1839 W/C

PRINZ, Christian August (1819-1867) Norwegian
£877 $1632   (18-Jun-92 GWP.O76/R) Still life of flowers (19x25cm-7x10in) s.d.1851 i.verso panel (N.KR 10000)
£1768 $3095   (25-Feb-92 UL.T226/R) Still life, Paris 1852 (31x39cm-12x15in) (N.KR 20000)
£3333 $6200   (15-Jun-92 B.O125/R) Rabbits (55x45cm-22x18in) s.d.1857 (N.KR 38000)

PRIOR, William Matthew (1806-1873) American
£5556 $10000   (11-Jan-92 S.BM194/R) Portrait of Charles Franklin Peel (61x51cm-24x20in)

PRITCHARD, G Thompson (1878-?) American
£947 $1800   (24-Jun-92 B.SF6406/R) Ship at sea (63x76cm-25x30in) s.
£1184 $2250   (24-Jun-92 B.SF6405/R) Boats at dock (63x76cm-25x30in) s.

PRITCHARD, Thomas (fl.1866-1877) British
£471 $800   (23-Oct-91 GD.B590/R) A sketch at Zermatt (36x54cm-14x21in) s.d.1870 W/C (S.FR 1200)

PRITCHETT, Edward (fl.1828-1864) British
£775 $1341   (4-Sep-91 BT289/R) Embarking on Gondola on Grand Canal, Venice (18x25cm-7x10in) board
£2500 $4450   (27-Apr-92 PHB245/R) Venetian scene (45x65cm-18x26in) i.verso
£3000 $5220   (15-Apr-92 HAR484/R) Venetian canal scene (25x33cm-10x13in) s. pair
£4500 $8235   (3-Jun-92 S9/R) The Doge's Palace from Santa Maria. The Doge's Palace (25x35cm-10x14in) one signed pair
£6014 $10464   (21-Sep-91 SA.A1752/R) Piazzetta with Doge's Palace and St Mark's Column, Venice (45x65cm-18x26in) s. (DM 17500)
£11000 $19470   (6-Nov-91 S28/R) The Grand Canal, Venice (45x66cm-18x26in) s.d.1838
£12791 $22000   (17-Oct-91 SY.NY290/R) View of St. Mark's Square (63x99cm-25x39in) s.
£16000 $29600   (12-Jun-92 C180/R) The Bacino, Venice (63x99cm-25x39in)

PRITCHETT, Edward (attrib) (fl.1828-1864) British
£5500 $9845   (5-May-92 SWS411/R) Looking towards the Piazzetta, Santa Maria della Salute and Grand Canal, Venice (51x79cm-20x31in)

PRITCHETT, Edward (circle) (fl.1828-1864) British
£2800 $5180   (11-Jun-92 CSK243/R) The Bacino di San Marco (54x85cm-21x33in) pair

PRITCHETT, Samuel (19th C) British
£3017 $5250   (13-Sep-91 S.W2874/R) Venetian view (61x91cm-24x36in) s.

PRIVAT-LIVEMONT (1852-?) Belgian
£2088 $3800   (26-May-92 CE.NY340/R) The toast. After dinner coffee (34x26cm-13x10in) s. panel

PRIVATO, Cosimo (1889-?) Italian
£635 $1182   (16-Jun-92 F.M64) Giornata autunnale a Venezia (60x40cm-24x16in) s.d.1957 (I.L 1400000)
£1301 $2356   (3-Dec-91 SY.MI55) Giochiamo alla scuola (39x48cm-15x19in) s. cardboard (I.L 2800000)

PROBST, Carl (1854-1924) Austrian
£2234 $3887   (18-Sep-91 N.M657/R) Old man feeding bird before cage (34x24cm-13x9in) s.d.1886 panel (DM 6500)

PROBST, Thorwald (1886-1948) American
£686 $1200   (31-Mar-92 MOR.P120) Landscape (41x51cm-16x20in) s. board

PROCACCINI, Camillo (1546-1629) Italian
£4281 $7963   (20-Jun-92 CH.MO207/R) Tete de vieillard (16x13cm-6x5in) red black chk (F.FR 42000)
£41000 $75030   (15-May-92 TE302/R) Head of Goliath (25x20cm-10x8in) black red chk

PROCACCINI, Camillo (attrib) (1546-1629) Italian
£2235 $4000   (14-Jan-92 SY.NY22/R) Study of head of old man, looking down (32x22cm-13x9in) bears i. red chk

PROCACCINI, Giulio Cesare (1570-1625) Italian
£10675 $19216 (19-Nov-91 F.R84/R) Salome riceve la testa del Battista. Martirio di San
 Bartolomeo (153x120cm-60x47in) pair painted with studio (I.L 23000000)
£46000 $80040 (15-Apr-92 C169/R) The Holy Family (101x89cm-40x35in) panel
£190000 $364800 (8-Jul-92 S89/R) Judith and Holofernes (143x109cm-56x43in) bears i.verso
£3500 $6090 (14-Apr-92 C102/R) Madonna and Child with Infant St John the Baptist
 (10x12cm-4x5in) chk wash htd.white hexagonal squared
£12000 $23040 (7-Jul-92 C166/R) Holy Family. Mucius Scaevola (17x12cm-7x5in) i. chk
 double-sided

PROCACCINI, Giulio Cesare (style) (1570-1625) Italian
£3000 $5250 (3-Apr-92 C148/R) Mystic marriage of Saint Catherine (71x79cm-28x31in)

PROCHAZKA, Antonin (1882-1945) Czechoslovakian
£20000 $36200 (3-Dec-91 C244/R) The violinist (66x36cm-26x14in) s. d.1917stretcher oil
 sand

PROCHAZKA, Iaro (1886-1947) Czechoslovakian
£674 $1200 (22-Jan-92 SY.NY436/R) St. Nicolas Church, Mala Strana, Prague
 (69x51cm-27x20in) s. board

PROCHKINE, Vladimir (1931-) Russian
£564 $1014 (27-Jan-92 ARC.P39/R) Le yacht club (54x65cm-21x26in) s. (F.FR 5500)
£707 $1273 (27-Jan-92 ARC.P41/R) Les voiles blanches (55x78cm-22x31in) s.verso
 (F.FR 6900)

PROCKTOR, Patrick (20th C) British
£1200 $2064 (5-Mar-92 CSK176/R) Ballyconeely (41x34cm-16x13in) s.d.68 W/C
£1800 $3186 (8-Nov-91 C260/R) Portrait of Joe Orton (22x32cm-9x13in) s.i. pen

PROCTER, Burt (1901-1980) American
£1184 $2250 (24-Jun-92 B.SF6440/R) Two riders (41x71cm-16x28in) s.

PROCTER, Dod (1892-1972) British
£2700 $4698 (19-Sep-91 CSK139/R) West Indian girl smiling (31x26cm-12x10in) s. panel
£2800 $4956 (7-Nov-91 C92/R) Poppies and foxgloves in a bowl (53x68cm-21x27in) s.

PROCTER, Ernest (1886-1935) British
£1650 $3020 (14-May-92 TL139/R) Fishing boats, Newlyn. Schooner in harbour, Newlyn
 (33x25cm-13x10in) s.d.1914 W/C bodycol pair

PROCTOR, Alethea Mary (1879-1966) Australian
£460 $833   (19-May-92 JRL.S251) Shuttlecock (13x13cm-5x5in) s. W/C (A.D 1100)
£556 $1006   (2-Dec-91 CH.ME249/R) Calico (25x36cm-10x14in) s.i.d.64 chl pencil
           (A.D 1300)
£3404 $6026   (26-Apr-92 SY.ME425/R) Woman and child (17x47cm-7x19in) s. W/C silk fan
           shape (A.D 8000)

PROCTOR, Thea (fl.1907-1920) British
£3800 $6460   (23-Oct-91 S323/R) Woman sewing (42x46cm-17x18in) s. W/C over pencil

PROKOFIEFF, Dimitrij (?-1944) Russian
£1031 $1918   (20-Jun-92 BM.B953/R) Birch wood with pond (58x74cm-23x29in) s. canvas on
           board (DM 3000)

PROL, Rick (20th C) American
£743 $1300   (27-Feb-92 CE.NY249/R) Quantos Anos (128x107cm-50x42in) init.

PRONSATO, Domingo (1881-1971) Argentinian
£538 $1000   (16-Jun-92 RO.BA104) Paisaje del Sur (17x22cm-7x9in) panel
£538 $1000   (16-Jun-92 RO.BA105) Arroyito San Bernardo (24x32cm-9x13in)
£625 $1200   (4-Aug-92 V.BA81) Paisaje (27x30cm-11x12in)

PROOST, Alfons (1880-1957) Belgian
£1632 $3035   (16-Jun-92 SY.B307/R) A fair (58x78cm-23x31in) s. (B.FR 98000)
£7519 $12782   (22-Oct-91 C.A273/R) Woman in a sunny garden (90x60cm-35x24in) s.d.1920
           (B.FR 450000)

PROOST, Frans (1866-1941) Belgian
£1198 $2168   (3-Dec-91 C.A250/R) Agreeable conversation (53x48cm-21x19in) s.
           (B.FR 70000)

PROOYEN, A J van (1834-1898) Dutch
£489 $871   (29-Oct-91 VN.R238) Landscape with cattle (15x24cm-6x9in) panel
           (D.FL 1600)

PROOYEN, Albert Jurardus van (1834-1898) Dutch
£988 $1728   (18-Feb-92 CH.AM21/R) Peasantwomen conversing in a farmyard
           (90x70cm-35x28in) s.d.1867 (D.FL 3200)

PROSCHWITZKY, Frank (fl.1883-1889) ?
£1366 $2500   (5-Jun-92 SY.NY209/R) The Persian cat (50x40cm-20x16in) s.d.1886

PROSDOCINI, Alberto (1852-?) Italian
£400 $708   (13-Feb-92 CSK72) Fishing vessels on Riva degli Schiavoni
           (23x34cm-9x13in) s. W/C
£420 $802   (20-Jul-92 WW117) Winged lion of St. Marks, Venice (60x23cm-24x9in) s.
           W/C over pencil
£480 $830   (3-Oct-91 CSK35/R) Townsfolk beside the Colleoni Monument, Venice
           (30x15cm-12x6in) s. pencil W/C
£494 $850   (15-Oct-91 CE.NY336/R) A Venetian canal with a gondola (45x25cm-18x10in)
           s. W/C paperboard
£1413 $2473   (3-Apr-92 BM.B693/R) Canale Grande, evening (50x79cm-20x31in) s. W/C
           (DM 4000)
£1800 $3186   (13-Feb-92 CSK56/R) Fishing craft in Lagoon, Venice (16x29cm-6x11in) s.
           pencil W/C one htd white pair
£2000 $3720   (16-Jun-92 PH92/R) Venice at dusk (53x82cm-21x32in) s. W/C

PROSI, Henri (1936-) French
£664 $1215   (13-May-92 BU.S154/R) Series obuques (120x80cm-47x31in) s.d.1989 verso
           mixed media collage on oil (S.KR 7000)

PROSSALENDIS, Emilios (19/20th C) Greek?
£5800 $9860   (23-Oct-91 S175/R) Fishing boats off the coast, Corfu (36x60cm-14x24in)
           s.

PROST, Maurice (1894-?) French
£1925 $3369   (3-Apr-92 CB.P31/R) Tetes de tigre (43x66cm-17x26in) s. W/C gouache
           htd.oil varnished paper (F.FR 18500)

PROUD, Geoffrey (1946-) Australian
£437 $764   (30-Mar-92 AAA.S177) Sydney harbour (126x140cm-50x55in) s.d.1983 pastel
           (A.D 1000)

PROUT, John Skinner (1806-1876) British
£513 $913   (27-Apr-92 J.M1220) Landscape (24x39cm-9x15in) s.d.1845 W/C (A.D 1200)
£520 $926   (28-Nov-91 PHX424) Continental landscape with valley town and figures
           near track (38x56cm-15x22in) s. W/C htd.white
£520 $915   (6-Apr-92 PH47/R) Fishermen's cottages - east coast (15x21cm-6x8in) s.
           W/C htd white
£700 $1253   (12-Nov-91 C120/R) Ratisbon Cathedral (51x39cm-20x15in) s.d.1858 pencil
           W/C htd.white
£700 $1190   (22-Oct-91 C99/R) Tasmanian landscape (29x40cm-11x16in) s.d.1845 W/C htd
           white
£950 $1815   (21-Jul-92 PH241/R) Figures before cathedral (35x25cm-14x10in) s.d.1859
           W/C bodycol

PROUT, John Skinner (1806-1876) British-cont.
£1100 $2101   (14-Jul-92 C134/R) Screen in Chartres Cathedral (72x54cm-28x21in) s.d.1862 pencil W/C htd white
£1357 $2591   (21-Jul-92 JRL.S239) Hobart Hills (17x24cm-7x9in) s.d.1846 W/C (A.D 3500)

PROUT, Samuel (1783-1852) British
£1200 $2292   (15-Jul-92 S185/R) The convict ship (23x37cm-9x15in) i.verso
£400 $704   (6-Apr-92 PH14) Fisherman's cottage (20x28cm-8x11in) s. W/C pencil
£400 $716   (5-May-92 SWS98) Rustics by the Market Cross, Chagford, Devon (20x28cm-8x11in) s. W/C over pencil
£400 $692   (23-Mar-92 HS103) A view at Wintzburgh (31x23cm-12x9in)
£410 $725   (9-Nov-91 W.W89/R) Figures amongst ruins near a cathedral (30x20cm-12x8in) W/C gouache
£445 $850   (3-Jul-92 S.W2787) Cathedral interior (43x30cm-17x12in) s.d.1836 W/C
£473 $841   (25-Nov-91 W.T1817) Bridge of Prague (30x22cm-12x9in) init. W/C over pencil (C.D 950)
£480 $845   (7-Apr-92 C166/R) Doge's Palace, Venice (27x37cm-11x15in) i. pencil pen wash htd white
£480 $917   (13-Jul-92 PH19) Off the Devon Coast (20x31cm-8x12in) s. W/C
£500 $955   (13-Jul-92 PH13) Fisherman's cottage near Totnes (20x28cm-8x11in) s. W/C
£550 $968   (7-Apr-92 C167/R) Bridge of Saints, Prague (35x53cm-14x21in) i. pencil htd white
£900 $1584   (7-Apr-92 C162/R) Loading coach at Trois Piliers, Beauvais (23x33cm-9x13in) pencil W/C
£950 $1815   (14-Jul-92 C133/R) Wurzburg (31x22cm-12x9in) pencil pen W/C
£1000 $1760   (6-Apr-92 PH19/R) Ruins - Old Delhi (10x17cm-4x7in) W/C over pencil
£1000 $1910   (14-Jul-92 C135/R) Figures at prayer in Continental cathedral (42x27cm-17x11in) s.pencil pen W/C htd white
£1100 $1925   (1-Apr-92 B16/R) Venetian canal with figures in boats (54x42cm-21x17in) pen ink W/C htd.white
£1200 $2196   (14-May-92 B250/R) Padua (71x53cm-28x21in) pen W/C
£1400 $2464   (7-Apr-92 C142/R) Canonica, Venice (43x32cm-17x13in) s.i.d.1807 pencil W/C
£1400 $2674   (13-Jul-92 PH23/R) Fishing boats off Hastings (26x20cm-10x8in) mono W/C
£1500 $2640   (9-Apr-92 S104) Strasbourg, France (27x20cm-11x8in) s. pen W/C htd bodycol
£8500 $16235   (14-Jul-92 C137/R) Figures on river banks at St. Etienne, Caen (54x72cm-21x28in) pencil W/C

PROUT, Samuel Gillespie (1822-1911) British
£880 $1540   (1-Apr-92 B44) Continental street. Port (32x23cm-13x9in) s. W/C pair

PROUVE, Victor (1858-1943) French
£429 $786   (3-Feb-92 SD.P188) Le serpent d'Airain (45x60cm-18x24in) s.d.1876 chl.stumping (F.FR 4200)
£955 $1700   (22-Jan-92 SY.NY299/R) Study for Sardanapalus (76x50cm-30x20in) s.i. num.118 white chk chl

PROVENCE SCHOOL, 17th C French
£2236 $3890   (13-Apr-92 AT.P119/R) Le repos de la Sainte Famille (101x82cm-40x32in) (F.FR 22000)

PROVOST, Jan (style) (15/16th C) Flemish
£1800 $3150   (27-Feb-92 CSK18) Christ in the Garden of Gethsemene (77x63cm-30x25in)

PROWSE, Ruth (1883-1967) South African
£1955 $3323   (21-Oct-91 SY.J331/R) Union celebrations, Church Street, Cape Town (32x26cm-13x10in) mono.d.1910 canvas on board (SA.R 9500)

PRUCHA, Gustav (1875-?) Austrian
£857 $1500   (18-Feb-92 CE.NY178/R) Winter hunt (81x107cm-32x42in) s.
£1057 $1871   (23-Apr-92 RAS.V873/R) Summer landscape with couple flirting, woman and horses by well (65x92cm-26x36in) s. (D.KR 12000)
£1276 $2194   (16-Oct-91 KM.K1326/R) Music making Hungarians on horse-drawn cart in snow covered landscape (70x100cm-28x39in) s. (DM 3700)
£1800 $3204   (28-Nov-91 CSK160/R) Wedding party in winter landscape (70x100cm-28x39in) s.
£2057 $3600   (18-Feb-92 CE.NY42/R) Troika in winter (74x102cm-29x40in) s.

PRUCKENDORFER, Hans (1518-?) German
£10453 $19024   (11-Dec-91 N.M347/R) Holy Family in carpenter's workshop (49x35cm-19x14in) panel (DM 30000)

PRUDHOMME (?) ?
£1198 $2168   (3-Dec-91 C.A252) Marine (25x35cm-10x14in) s. panel (B.FR 70000)

PRUDHON (school) (18/19th C) French?
£3232 $5721   (24-Apr-92 CD.P87) Venuse et l'Amour (41x50cm-16x20in) (F.FR 32000)

PRUDHON, Pierre Paul (1758-1823) French
£356779 $663609   (20-Jun-92 CH.MO92/R) Portrait de Louise de Gueheneuc, Duchesse de Montebello (55x47cm-22x19in) s. (F.FR 3500000)
£5500 $10560   (7-Jul-92 C72/R) L'entrevue des empereurs, Napoleon after the Battle of Austerlitz (26x21cm-10x8in) chk

PRUDHON, Pierre Paul (1758-1823) French-cont.

£6918	$12659	(15-May-92 AT.P194/R) Tete d'enfant endormi (18x22cm-7x9in) black crayon htd white (F.FR 68000)
£8147	$14827	(11-Dec-91 LD.P24/R) Homme debout marchant, les bras leves, la tete tournee vers la droite (58x42cm-23x17in) pierre noire htd.white (F.FR 80000)
£14000	$26880	(7-Jul-92 C71/R) Woman dancing playing tambour (45x23cm-18x9in) chl chk

PRUDHON, Pierre Paul (circle) (1758-1823) French

£942	$1800	(16-Jul-92 SY.NY212/R) The bather (36x29cm-14x11in) panel
£1221	$2075	(24-Oct-91 D.V120/R) Head of boy, said to be Napoleon (31x27cm-12x11in) (A.S 25000)
£3315	$6000	(21-May-92 CH.NY224/R) Portrait of lady, said to be Caroline Murat, seated beside table with book (63x76cm-25x30in)

PRUNA, Pedro (1904-1977) Spanish

£1714	$3000	(27-Feb-92 CE.NY63/R) Les baigneuses (21x27cm-8x11in) s. paper on board
£1829	$3200	(27-Feb-92 CE.NY67/R) Jeune mere (33x21cm-13x8in) s.d.24 board
£2765	$5198	(17-Dec-91 BRO.B340) Anunciacion (162x129cm-64x51in) s. (S.P 500000)
£13306	$23685	(28-Nov-91 FB.P28 a/R) Femme nue assise (65x63cm-26x25in) s.d.26 (F.FR 130000)
£16588	$31186	(17-Dec-91 BRO.B350/R) Figuras de circo (92x73cm-36x29in) s.d.58 (S.P 3000000)
£857	$1500	(28-Feb-92 SY.NY80/R) Les matelots - costume design for sailor (27x21cm-11x8in) s.d.1926 W/C gouache pencil paper on board
£912	$1650	(18-May-92 AT.P204) Marchande de fruits (30x23cm-12x9in) s. W/C gouache (F.FR 9000)
£1051	$1975	(17-Dec-91 BRO.B367) Figuras (66x46cm-26x18in) s.d.47 mixed media (S.P 190000)
£1107	$1903	(12-Oct-91 SY.MO9/R) Hermaphrodite (23x19cm-9x7in) s.i.verso oil pencil canvas (F.FR 11000)
£1243	$2336	(3-Jan-92 DUR.M13/R) Circo (40x32cm-16x13in) s. W/C (S.P 225000)
£1308	$2249	(12-Oct-91 SY.MO8/R) Les Trois Graces (18x13cm-7x5in) s.d.1925 pen indian ink W/C gouache (F.FR 13000)
£3283	$5844	(29-Oct-91 BRO.B358) Figura femenina (58x45cm-23x18in) s.d.27 chl pastel (S.P 600000)

PRUSSE, K (19th C) German

£1065	$1811	(25-Oct-91 BM.B806/R) Interior with set coffee table (82x64cm-32x25in) s. panel (DM 3100)

PRYDE, James (1869-1941) British

£1600	$2768	(2-Oct-91 S37/R) The decoy (37x25cm-15x10in)

PRYN, Harald (1891-?) Danish

£491	$913	(16-Jun-92 RAS.K223) Old barrel organ man in village (67x97cm-26x38in) s.i. (D.KR 5500)
£539	$953	(11-Feb-92 RAS.K137) Winter in Malov (70x100cm-28x39in) s.i.d.42 (D.KR 6000)
£539	$953	(11-Feb-92 RAS.K136) View towards Bloustrod Church (68x100cm-27x39in) s.i. (D.KR 6000)
£542	$975	(19-Nov-91 RAS.K262/R) Winter in Frederiksdal wood (70x96cm-28x38in) s.i. (D.KR 6000)
£624	$1073	(15-Oct-91 RAS.K215) Winter landscape from Bagsvaerd Lake (70x100cm-28x39in) s.i. (D.KR 7000)
£624	$1073	(15-Oct-91 RAS.K216) Winter landscape (101x133cm-40x52in) s.d.1923 (D.KR 7000)
£646	$1157	(16-Nov-91 FAL.M291/R) Beechwood with flowering wood anemones (71x97cm-28x38in) s.i. (S.KR 6800)
£673	$1192	(11-Feb-92 RAS.K141) Winter landscape (70x100cm-28x39in) s. (D.KR 7500)
£718	$1271	(11-Feb-92 RAS.K135) Winter's day (103x140cm-41x55in) s.i. (D.KR 8000)
£760	$1361	(16-Nov-91 FAL.M290/R) Winter landscape with running brook (71x100cm-28x39in) s. (S.KR 8000)
£824	$1500	(26-May-92 CE.NY225/R) Snowy path (102x137cm-40x54in) s.i.

PSEUDO GHERARDI (16th C) Italian?

£600	$1152	(6-Jul-92 S139/R) Adoration of the Shepherds (13x19cm-5x7in) i. pen htd.white

PSEUDO GUARDI (18th C) Italian

£14000	$26880	(7-Jul-92 PH149/R) Still life of vase of flowers and wicker basket on stone ledge, fruit on ground (67x79cm-26x31in)

PSEUDO PACCHIA (16th C) Italian?

£1200	$2088	(13-Apr-92 S255) Marcus Curtius leaping into abyss (29x22cm-11x9in) pen

PTSCHELNIKOWA, Olga (20th C) ?

£493	$892	(6-Dec-91 GB.B7007) Abstract figure standing (33x20cm-13x8in) indian ink pen col.chk (DM 1400)

PU HUA (1830-1911) Chinese

£11095	$19416	(30-Mar-92 CH.HK202/R) Flowers of four seasons (141x38cm-56x15in) s.i. one d.1900 ink W/C hanging scrolls four (HK.D 150000)

PU RU (1896-1963) Chinese

£452	$800	(7-Nov-91 B.SF1215) Withered trees in late autumn (96x31cm-38x12in) s. ink colour scroll
£847	$1500	(7-Nov-91 B.SF1255/R) Landscape with figures (121x32cm-48x13in) s. ink colour scroll
£1775	$3107	(30-Mar-92 CH.HK406/R) Scholar in landscape (107x50cm-42x20in) s.i. ink W/C hanging scroll (HK.D 24000)
£2959	$5178	(30-Mar-92 CH.HK396/R) Zhong Kui (19x51cm-7x20in) s.i. i.verso ink W/C folding fan (HK.D 40000)
£3328	$5825	(30-Mar-92 CH.HK103/R) Guanyin under pine tree (85x35cm-33x14in) s.d.1936 ink W/C scroll (HK.D 45000)
£3328	$5825	(30-Mar-92 CH.HK209/R) Roses, bamboo and butterflies (97x49cm-38x19in) s.i. ink W/C hanging scroll (HK.D 45000)
£5547	$9708	(30-Mar-92 CH.HK214/R) Peach blossom spring (107x45cm-42x18in) s.i. ink W/C hanging scroll (HK.D 75000)
£7396	$12944	(30-Mar-92 CH.HK212/R) Landscapes and figures (38x31cm-15x12in) s.i. ink W/C album eight leaves (HK.D 100000)
£8136	$14238	(30-Mar-92 CH.HK105/R) Landscape in autumn (134x48cm-53x19in) s.i. ink W/C hanging scroll (HK.D 110000)
£10355	$18121	(30-Mar-92 CH.HK213/R) Landscapes (25x17cm-10x7in) s.i. ink W/C album twelve leaves (HK.D 140000)
£11834	$20710	(30-Mar-92 CH.HK104/R) Temple deep in mountains (121x36cm-48x14in) s.i.d.1936 ink W/C silk scroll (HK.D 160000)
£11834	$20710	(30-Mar-92 CH.HK287/R) Landscape (7x189cm-3x74in) s.i. ink W/C handscroll (HK.D 160000)
£16272	$28476	(30-Mar-92 CH.HK210/R) Walking in snowy mountains (124x61cm-49x24in) s.i.d.1941 ink W/C hanging scroll (HK.D 220000)
£22929	$40126	(30-Mar-92 CH.HK211/R) Zhong Kui and sister (181x96cm-71x38in) i. ink hanging scroll (HK.D 310000)

PUCCINI, Mario (1869-1920) Italian

£4077	$7542	(8-Jun-92 CH.R566/R) Ritratto della sorellastra Carlotta (42x23cm-17x9in) s.d.87 (I.L 9000000)
£21647	$39397	(12-Dec-91 F.M77/R) Barche nel porto di Livorno (72x48cm-28x19in) s. board (I.L 47000000)

PUCHINGER, Erwin (1876-1944) Austrian

£593	$1038	(19-Feb-92 D.V75) Still life of cactus (42x38cm-17x15in) s. (A.S 12000)
£439	$760	(3-Oct-91 D.V161/R) Landscape (68x102cm-27x40in) s.indis.i.d.1927 W/C paper on board (A.S 9000)

PUEYRREDON, Prilidiano (1823-1870) Argentinian

£1548	$2600	(1-Sep-91 PO.BA24) Retrato de Victorina Correa de Costa de Arguibel (115x85cm-45x33in)

PUGA, Antonio (attrib) (17th C) Italian?

£13260	$24000	(21-May-92 CH.NY21/R) Penitent Magdalene (90x132cm-35x52in)

PUGET, Pierre (attrib) (1620-1694) French

£12000	$21840	(13-Dec-91 C213/R) Mediterranen coasts with shipping off ports (53x44cm-21x17in) pair

PUGH, Clifton Ernest (1924-1990) Australian

£2553	$4519	(26-Apr-92 SY.ME272/R) Flood debri (67x90cm-26x35in) s.d.63 i.verso board (A.D 6000)
£2643	$4705	(26-Nov-91 J.M178/R) Sand birds (91x136cm-36x54in) s.d.64 board (A.D 6000)
£2817	$4704	(19-Aug-91 SY.ME352/R) Landscape (178x90cm-70x35in) s.d.1977 board (A.D 6000)
£3052	$5096	(19-Aug-91 SY.ME339/R) Memories of Chappell (64x89cm-25x35in) s.i.d.1962 board (A.D 6500)
£3226	$5613	(16-Sep-91 CH.ME41/R) Eros Suite No 3 (90x120cm-35x47in) s.d.74 (A.D 7000)
£3419	$6085	(27-Apr-92 J.M295/R) Eros Suite No.1 (91x121cm-36x48in) s.d.74 board (A.D 8000)
£3756	$6272	(19-Aug-91 SY.ME316/R) Vixen (67x90cm-26x35in) s. board (A.D 8000)
£3846	$6846	(27-Apr-92 J.M111/R) Tibooburna (67x90cm-26x35in) s.d.67 board (A.D 9000)
£5128	$9128	(27-Apr-92 J.M210/R) Crucifixion on the Salts Plains III (90x105cm-35x41in) s.d.60/61 board (A.D 12000)
£5530	$9622	(16-Sep-91 CH.ME146) Pelicans at Coopers Creek (105x192cm-41x76in) s. (A.D 12000)
£6912	$12028	(16-Sep-91 CH.ME56) Governor General Viscount de L'isle in Robes of Order of Garter (136x90cm-54x35in) s.d.63 board (A.D 15000)
£7834	$13631	(16-Sep-91 CH.ME93/R) Two crows at Stonehenge (68x91cm-27x36in) s.d.1957 masonite (A.D 17000)
£8000	$14240	(28-Nov-91 C67/R) Rape of Europa (122x170cm-48x67in) s.d.59 i.verso masonite
£9362	$16570	(26-Apr-92 SY.ME313/R) Apostle birds (90x121cm-35x48in) s.d.69 board (A.D 22000)
£15420	$27450	(26-Nov-91 J.M220/R) Saturday afternoon, Bondi (165x207cm-65x81in) i.d.89 (A.D 35000)
£769	$1369	(27-Apr-92 J.M228) Beach series 8 am, 10 am, 6 pm (71x55cm-28x22in) s.d.74 gouache tryptich (A.D 1800)
£940	$1674	(27-Apr-92 J.M570) Outback panorama (54x73cm-21x29in) s.d.79 gouache (A.D 2200)

PUGH, Clifton Ernest (1924-1990) Australian-cont.
£1429	$2486	(17-Sep-91 JRL.S328) Point Arkwright (55x74cm-22x29in) s.d.13.1.89 mixed media paper on board (A.D 3100)
£2200	$3916	(28-Nov-91 C65/R) Sheep in landscape (58x84cm-23x33in) s.i.d.1974 gouache
£7981	$13329	(19-Aug-91 SY.ME340/R) Blackbirds (90x120cm-35x47in) s.d.73 mixed media board (A.D 17000)

PUGH, Herbert (?-1788) British
£5600	$10024	(15-Nov-91 C56/R) View of Tatton park from river (64x91cm-25x36in)

PUGIN, Augustus Welby Northmore (1812-1852) British
£800	$1376	(8-Oct-91 PH10) Melrose Abbey (43x61cm-17x24in) i.verso panel

PUHONNY, Ivo (1876-?) German
£2199	$4025	(2-Jun-92 FN.S2708/R) View of Stuttgart (57x106cm-22x42in) s.d.1907 board (DM 6400)

PUIG DENGOLAS, V (?) ?
£2983	$5400	(2-Dec-91 GC.M28 a/R) Acantilados (46x55cm-18x22in) s.

PUIG PERUCHO, Bonaventura (1886-1977) Spanish
£1096	$1951	(26-Nov-91 BRO.B323) Viladrau (76x62cm-30x24in) s. s.i.d.1954verso (S.P 200000)

PUIG-RODA, Gabriel (1865-1919) Spanish
£6593	$12000	(28-May-92 SY.NY319/R) Mujer Sentada, Cosiendo (70x55cm-28x22in) s.d.1902 W/C
£7418	$13500	(28-May-92 SY.NY324/R) Proposition (51x76cm-20x30in) s.d.93 W/C
£9000	$16020	(26-Nov-91 PH60/R) Two women at prayer (52x75cm-20x30in) s.i.d.93 W/C
£9884	$17000	(17-Oct-91 SY.NY340/R) La artista pintando en su estudio (77x55cm-30x22in) s.d.1909 W/C

PUIGAUDEAU, Fernand du (1866-1930) French
£3049	$5305	(16-Apr-92 FB.P117/R) La chapelle des Muriers et l'Eglise du Bourg de Bats (46x56cm-18x22in) s. (F.FR 30000)
£5800	$10034	(25-Mar-92 S174/R) Le Manoir du Kervadu - Au Croisic (50x61cm-20x24in) s.
£8000	$14000	(28-Feb-92 SY.NY25/R) Le port du Croisic (46x61cm-18x24in) s.
£8286	$14500	(28-Feb-92 SY.NY26/R) La Grande Briere (50x65cm-20x26in) s.
£14000	$26740	(30-Jun-92 C117/R) Voiliers sur la mer, le soir (73x100cm-29x39in) s.
£787	$1400	(2-May-92 W.W28/R) Parisian street scene (33x28cm-13x11in) s. chl pastel
£4476	$8191	(17-May-92 T.B267) La Fete des Bonnets a Saint-Pol de Leon (42x63cm-17x25in) studio st. pencil col.crayon (F.FR 44000)
£5295	$9796	(12-Jun-92 AT.P1/R) Jeunes bretonnes avant la procession (23x31cm-9x12in) s. W/C gouache (F.FR 52000)

PUIGDENGOLAS BARELLA, Jose (1906-1987) Spanish
£1315	$2341	(26-Nov-91 BRO.B362) Goleta en un puerto (24x31cm-9x12in) s. (S.P 240000)
£1382	$2459	(21-Jan-92 DUR.M119/R) Retrato de Adela (38x30cm-15x12in) s. s.i.verso panel (S.P 250000)
£2322	$4366	(17-Dec-91 BRO.B370) Flores (46x55cm-18x22in) s. s.i.d.1940verso (S.P 420000)
£4009	$7537	(17-Dec-91 BRO.B344) Cala Pola, Tossa (46x55cm-18x22in) s. s.i.verso (S.P 725000)
£6087	$10410	(17-Mar-92 FER.M152/R) Bodegon de rosas amarillas (90x75cm-35x30in) s. (S.P 1100000)
£11059	$20791	(17-Dec-91 BRO.B424/R) Vista de Cadaques (73x92cm-29x36in) s. (S.P 2000000)

PUJOL DE GUASTAVINO, Clement (1850-1905) French
£1223	$2128	(14-Apr-92 SY.AM312/R) Forest creek (52x71cm-20x28in) s. (D.FL 4000)

PUJOL, Josep (1905-1987) Spanish
£766	$1364	(29-Oct-91 BRO.B372) Pueblo de montana (27x41cm-11x16in) s.d.1935 (S.P 140000)

PUJOL, Paul (19th C) French
£6180	$11000	(22-Jan-92 SY.NY378/R) Le palais du justice (188x137cm-74x54in) s.

PULIGO, Domenico (1492-1527) Italian
£55000	$100100	(13-Dec-91 C81/R) Portrait of gentleman in grey cloak and hat, holding pair of gloves (96x73cm-38x29in) panel

PULIGO, Domenico (style) (1492-1527) Italian
£1208	$2163	(7-May-92 CH.AM23/R) Madonna and Child (88x62cm-35x24in) panel (D.FL 4000)

PULLER, John Anthony (19th C) British
£5200	$9984	(28-Jul-92 SWS337) Penny for the guy. Maypole dance (13x16cm-5x6in) s. board pair

PULLICINO, Alberto (attrib) (18th C) Maltese?
£6173	$11173	(5-Dec-91 SY.MO299/R) Vue de Malte (56x63cm-22x25in) (F.FR 60000)
£24691	$44691	(5-Dec-91 SY.MO159/R) Vues de Malte (52x104cm-20x41in) pair (F.FR 240000)

PULVIRENTI, Rosario (1899-?) Italian
£453 $838   (9-Jun-92 F.R40) Paesaggio fluviale (73x93cm-29x37in) s. (I.L 1000000)

PULZONE, Scipione (style) (1550-1598) Italian
£900 $1575   (2-Apr-92 CSK6) Pieta (33x28cm-13x11in)
£1400 $2520   (21-Nov-91 CSK211) Portrait of lady thought to be Isabella d'Este
                     (60x52cm-24x20in) i.verso

PUNI, Ivan see POUGNY, Jean

PUPINI, Biagio (16th C) Italian
£700 $1344   (8-Jul-92 PH27/R) Mary leading Magdalen to Christ (27x39cm-11x15in) pen
                     wash htd white
£1500 $2730   (10-Dec-91 C110/R) Scholars admiring a classical statue (23x39cm-9x15in)
                     blk.chk.ink htd.white
£1900 $3458   (11-Dec-91 PH203/R) Mary leading the Magdalen to Christ (26x38cm-10x15in)
                     pen wash htd.white
£3500 $6720   (7-Jul-92 C123/R) Satyr sacrifice (22x43cm-9x17in) chk pen wash htd

PUPINI, Biagio (circle) (16th C) Italian
£1600 $2848   (29-Oct-91 PH23/R) The Adoration of the Magi (45x59cm-18x23in) canvas
                     transferred from panel

PURDY, Donald (20th C) American
£686 $1200   (27-Feb-92 CE.NY143/R) Red umbrella (61x76cm-24x30in) s.d.88 masonite
£751 $1300   (2-Oct-91 D.NY81) Circus tent (51x61cm-20x24in) s. masonite
£867 $1500   (25-Mar-92 D.NY59) On the beach (51x61cm-20x24in) s. i.verso masonite
£2312 $4000   (25-Mar-92 D.NY60) Umbrellas on the beach (61x76cm-24x30in) s.d.88 board

PURIFICATO, Domenico (1915-1984) Italian
£1761 $3134   (29-Nov-91 F.F100/R) Uccellino sul ramo (30x20cm-12x8in) s. (I.L 3800000)
£1952 $3533   (3-Dec-91 F.R209/R) Volto femminile (21x20cm-8x8in) s. s.i.verso canvas
                     on board (I.L 4200000)
£3718 $6730   (3-Dec-91 F.R187/R) Spettatori alla riva, Omaggio a Carpaccio
                     (40x60cm-16x24in) s. (I.L 8000000)
£4873 $9161   (19-Dec-91 F.M57/R) Natura morta con cesto di frutta (50x60cm-20x24in) s.
                     (I.L 10500000)
£1361 $2490   (12-May-92 F.R65/R) Martedi grasso (50x34cm-20x13in) s. tempera W/C paper
                     on canvas (I.L 3000000)

PURO, Veikko (1884-1959) Finnish
£453 $806   (1-Dec-91 HOR.H183) Summer's day, coastal cliffs (45x55cm-18x22in)
                     s.d.1936 (F.M 3500)
£507 $887   (25-Sep-91 HOR.H78) Winter (37x41cm-15x16in) s.d.1917 (F.M 3600)
£1011 $1780   (12-Apr-92 HOR.H187) Abo in winter (56x45cm-22x18in) s.d.1944 (F.M 8000)

PURRMANN, Hans (1880-1966) German
£692 $1245   (19-Nov-91 GS.B3627) Southern landscape with village nestling in hills
                     (51x76cm-20x30in) s. (S.FR 1750)
£692 $1245   (19-Nov-91 GS.B3628) Southern landscape with view of hillside village
                     (51x76cm-20x30in) s. (S.FR 1750)
£2048 $3727   (30-May-92 VG.B269/R) Portrait study of young woman (46x56cm-18x22in)
                     panel (DM 6000)
£7167 $13044   (30-May-92 VG.B270/R) Lake Constance landscape (73x60cm-29x24in)
                     st.studio verso (DM 21000)
£20280 $36098   (25-Nov-91 WK.M831/R) Wooded landscape with house, Langenargen
                     (46x37cm-18x15in) s. (DM 58000)
£25175 $44811   (28-Nov-91 SY.BE63/R) Vase of flowers (89x72cm-35x28in) s. (DM 72000)
£51546 $94330   (3-Jun-92 L.K385/R) Anemones in vase (55x46cm-22x18in) s.d.1953/54
                     (DM 150000)
£58419 $106907   (3-Jun-92 L.K386/R) Landscape near Castagnola (38x45cm-15x18in) s.
                     (DM 170000)
£1020 $1825   (12-Nov-91 GF.L5350) View of Schwetzingen Schlosspark (26x40cm-10x16in)
                     mono.i.d.05 W/C (S.FR 2600)
£3704 $6704   (20-May-92 GK.Z5002/R) Wooded landscape (36x26cm-14x10in) s. W/C
                     (S.FR 10000)
£3937 $6772   (16-Oct-91 G.Z11/R) Still life of fruit (45x59cm-18x23in) s. W/C
                     (S.FR 10000)
£4371 $7780   (30-Nov-91 VG.B271/R) Bunch of spring flowers in glass vase. Study of jug
                     (37x42cm-15x17in) s. W/C pencil double-sided (DM 12500)
£4437 $8075   (30-May-92 VG.B267/R) Park landscape near Vollombrosa (23x33cm-9x13in)
                     s.i. W/C over pencil (DM 13000)

PURSER, William (19th C) British
£950 $1672   (7-Apr-92 C177/R) Shipping on calm sea (16x12cm-6x5in) s. W/C

PURTSCHER, Alfons (1885-1962) Austrian
£1443 $2511   (21-Sep-91 SA.A1835/R) Cows in shade of trees (61x81cm-24x32in) s.d.1908
                     s.i.verso (DM 4200)

PURVIS, Tom (20th C) British
£700 $1218   (19-Sep-91 CSK107/R) East Coast, bathers (102x63cm-40x25in) s. gouache
                     bodycol board

PUSHMAN, Hovsep (1877-1966) American
£14835 $27000   (28-May-92 CH.NY179/R) An Oriental theme (71x61cm-28x24in) s. oil gold leaf masonite

PUTCHINOFF, Matvei Ivanovitch (1716-1797) Russian
£3345 $5787   (2-Sep-91 BU.K66/R) Cupid and Venus (138x161cm-54x63in) (D.KR 38000)

PUTEANI, Friedrich von (1849-1917) German
£1195 $2174   (27-May-92 PH.DU134) Rider and dogs in landscape (70x55cm-28x22in) s. (DM 3500)
£4000 $7120   (28-Nov-91 CSK165/R) Military encampment (76x114cm-30x45in) s.d.1884

PUTHUFF, Hanson Duvall (1875-1972) American
£514 $900   (31-Mar-92 MOR.P38) Landscape (20x25cm-8x10in) s. canvas on board
£1053 $1800   (13-Mar-92 WOL.C447) Desert mountain (30x41cm-12x16in) s.i.verso board
£1554 $2750   (12-Feb-92 B.SF515/R) Foothills in spring (18x23cm-7x9in) s. board
£1554 $2750   (12-Feb-92 B.SF519/R) Tree study (30x41cm-12x16in) s. canvasboard
£1977 $3500   (12-Feb-92 B.SF508/R) Malibu Lake (24x30cm-9x12in) s. board
£2401 $4250   (12-Feb-92 B.SF509/R) Foothills in autumn (20x25cm-8x10in) s. canvas on board
£3390 $6000   (12-Feb-92 B.SF507/R) Grand Canyon (25x30cm-10x12in) s. canvas on board
£3933 $7000   (26-Nov-91 MOR.P100 b) Landscape - autumnal bloom (61x76cm-24x30in) s.

PUTTER, Pieter de (circle) (1600-1659) Dutch
£2800 $4900   (28-Feb-92 C154/R) Cod, skate, plaice and other fish on shore (137x185cm-54x73in) indist.s.

PUTTNER, Walther (attrib) (1872-1953) German
£800 $1416   (13-Feb-92 CSK84) Still life of mixed flowers in vase on ledge (60x46cm-24x18in) bears sig.

PUTZ, Leo (1869-1940) German
£12281 $22105   (23-Nov-91 N.M263/R) View across the Amper to Dachau (43x55cm-17x22in) s. (DM 35000)
£16904 $29413   (17-Sep-91 RAS.K146/R) Reclining nude woman (115x125cm-45x49in) (D.KR 190000)
£17747 $32300   (26-May-92 KF.M1175/R) Autumn flowers in vase (65x57cm-26x22in) s. (DM 52000)
£38908 $70812   (25-May-92 WK.M1043/R) Morning sun (80x70cm-31x28in) s. s.i.stretcher (DM 114000)
£45455 $80909   (25-Nov-91 WK.M835/R) Male nude reclining in wood (99x110cm-39x43in) s. (DM 130000)
£109215 $198771   (25-May-92 WK.M1041/R) Garden table still life with tea pot (85x100cm-33x39in) s.d.1908 (DM 320000)
£139860 $248951   (25-Nov-91 WK.M834/R) Pauline on sofa (127x120cm-50x47in) s.d.1908 (DM 400000)

PUTZHOFEN-HAMBUCHEN, Paul (19/20th C) German
£495 $866   (3-Apr-92 BM.B694/R) Townscape (62x82cm-24x32in) s. (DM 1400)
£931 $1601   (16-Oct-91 KM.K1328) View of Blens near Heimbach, autumn (70x90cm-28x35in) s. (DM 2700)
£1209 $2200   (11-Dec-91 RO.BA278) Paysage (69x91cm-27x36in) s.

PUVIS DE CHAVANNES, Pierre (1824-1898) French
£24390 $44390   (12-Dec-91 L.K657/R) Perseus freeing Andromeda (140x106cm-55x42in) s. (DM 70000)
£464   *$803*   *(27-Mar-92 PPB.P4) La Charite (26x22cm-10x9in) s. blk.crayon pen (F.FR 4500)*
£2035   *$3723*   *(15-May-92 AT.P196/R) Une etude de femme assise (32x24cm-13x9in) s. black chk htd white chk (F.FR 20000)*

PUVIS DE CHAVANNES, Pierre (attrib) (1824-1898) French
£560   *$1036*   *(12-Jun-92 ARC.P167) Tete d'homme (36x29cm-14x11in) i.verso black crayon (F.FR 5500)*

PUY, Jean (1876-1959) French
£1490 $2563   (4-Mar-92 AT.P191) Nu devant une fenetre (37x37cm-15x15in) panel (F.FR 14500)
£1718 $2990   (21-Sep-91 SA.A590/R) Bridge across river by edge of town (40x50cm-16x20in) s. (DM 5000)
£2026 $3668   (19-May-92 FB.P13) L'invitation au voyage (28x35cm-11x14in) s. paper (F.FR 20000)
£2252 $4008   (27-Nov-91 AT.P187) Modele allonge (60x81cm-24x32in) s. (F.FR 22000)
£2533 $4585   (19-May-92 FB.P2/R) Trois femmes au piano (32x29cm-13x11in) s. board (F.FR 25000)
£2533 $4585   (19-May-92 FB.P29) Nature morte au homard et a la soupiere (37x46cm-15x18in) s.d.1914 panel (F.FR 25000)
£2533 $4585   (19-May-92 FB.P15) Bord de mer en Bretagne (32x53cm-13x21in) s.d.1900 (F.FR 25000)
£2736 $4951   (19-May-92 FB.P5/R) Nu dans l'atelier (30x20cm-12x8in) s. (F.FR 27000)
£2857 $5000   (27-Feb-92 CE.NY20/R) Gros temps a Saint Tropez (51x73cm-20x29in) s. paper on canvas
£3040 $5502   (19-May-92 FB.P14) Scene de revolution (46x90cm-18x35in) st.sig. (F.FR 30000)

PUY, Jean (1876-1959) French-cont.

£3040	$5502	(19-May-92 FB.P16) Femme nue assise de dos (91x73cm-36x29in) s. s.d.1907verso (F.FR 30000)
£3040	$5502	(19-May-92 FB.P25) Saint Alban, Le Casino (53x65cm-21x26in) s. (F.FR 30000)
£3107	$5500	(5-Nov-91 CE.NY7/R) Nature morte aux fruits (28x35cm-11x14in) s. panel
£3567	$6171	(29-Mar-92 FE.P48) Nature morte a la soupiere (50x61cm-20x24in) board (F.FR 34600)
£3647	$6602	(19-May-92 FB.P17) Nature morte aux oranges et aux citrons (49x64cm-19x25in) s.d.1912 (F.FR 36000)
£3647	$6602	(19-May-92 FB.P31/R) Paysage de Saint Alban (61x81cm-24x32in) s.d.1908 (F.FR 36000)
£4053	$7335	(19-May-92 FB.P19/R) Sortie de Messe en Bretagne (60x73cm-24x29in) s. (F.FR 40000)
£4053	$7335	(19-May-92 FB.P7/R) Le Chatellus a Saint Alban (64x81cm-25x32in) s.d.1901 (F.FR 40000)
£4053	$7335	(19-May-92 FB.P8/R) Roses et marguerites (60x73cm-24x29in) s. (F.FR 40000)
£4053	$7335	(19-May-92 FB.P9/R) La Comparaison - Les Trois Graces (92x73cm-36x29in) s. (F.FR 40000)
£4255	$7702	(19-May-92 FB.P22/R) Au theatre (33x46cm-13x18in) s.d.1902 (F.FR 42000)
£4559	$8252	(19-May-92 FB.P12/R) Bateau a voile (46x55cm-18x22in) s.d.1914 (F.FR 45000)
£4559	$8252	(19-May-92 FB.P33/R) Femme allongee (46x61cm-18x24in) s. (F.FR 45000)
£5066	$9169	(19-May-92 FB.P4/R) Au bord de l'eau en Bretagne (40x64cm-16x25in) s.d.1900 (F.FR 50000)
£5066	$9169	(19-May-92 FB.P23/R) Le peintre dans son atelier (72x92cm-28x36in) s. (F.FR 50000)
£5268	$9536	(19-May-92 FB.P20/R) Femme assise aux bas noirs (45x53cm-18x21in) s. (F.FR 52000)
£5572	$10086	(19-May-92 FB.P3/R) Interieur aux fleurs (72x90cm-28x35in) st.sig. (F.FR 55000)
£6282	$11370	(19-May-92 FB.P10/R) Arbres devant la mer, Cavaliere (92x73cm-36x29in) s. (F.FR 62000)
£6282	$11370	(19-May-92 FB.P32/R) Nature morte au compotier et aux grappes de raisins (45x55cm-18x22in) s. (F.FR 62000)
£9119	$16505	(19-May-92 FB.P24/R) Madame Puy au jardin (100x80cm-39x31in) s.d.1913 (F.FR 90000)
£9119	$16505	(19-May-92 FB.P1/R) Femme lisant dans la foret (56x72cm-22x28in) s. (F.FR 90000)
£12941	$23165	(15-Nov-91 GK.Z5253/R) View of Mont Blanc (55x41cm-22x16in) s. (S.FR 33000)
£909	*$1618*	*(29-Nov-91 GAB.G2835/R) Nu assis (62x46cm-24x18in) gouache (S.FR 2300)*
£1028	*$1829*	*(29-Nov-91 GAB.G2834/R) Baigneuse (62x46cm-24x18in) gouache (S.FR 2600)*

PUYET, Jose (?) Spanish

£459	$839	(1-Jun-92 W.T1481) Spanish beauty (80x63cm-31x25in) s. (C.D 1000)
£1869	$3290	(9-Apr-92 ANS.M140/R) Pintandose los labios (61x50cm-24x20in) s. (S.P 340000)
£3827	$7004	(13-May-92 FER.M129/R) En el hogar, Pareja degustando las viandas (97x130cm-38x51in) s. s.i.d.1876verso (S.P 700000)

PUYL, Louis Francois Gerard van der (1750-1824) Dutch

| £1011 | $1800 | (22-Jan-92 D.NY54) Portrait of young officer said to be Andre Henri Alexandre (61x61cm-24x24in) i.verso |

PUYTLINCK, Christoffel (?1638-?) Dutch

| £2160 | $3867 | (14-Nov-91 CH.AM186/R) Dead partridge and pigeon with bunch of turnips on rock in landscape (45x39cm-18x15in) s. (D.FL 7000) |
| £5587 | $10000 | (16-Jan-92 CH.NY40/R) Dog attacking fowl, whilst cat waits to pounce from above - urn, fruit and basket on ledge (113x88cm-44x35in) s. |

PYCKE, Francois (1890-1970) Belgian

| £1167 | $2007 | (12-Oct-91 KV.L241) Reclining nude by a window (34x44cm-13x17in) s. panel (B.FR 70000) |

PYK, Madeleine (1934-) Swedish

£541	$942	(13-Apr-92 AB.S218) Granella's house, Southern scene (46x36cm-18x14in) s. (S.KR 5700)
£816	$1476	(3-Dec-91 AB.S5137/R) Sun God (123x99cm-48x39in) s.d.66 (S.KR 8500)
£901	$1649	(13-May-92 BU.S156/R) The helicopter (47x34cm-19x13in) s. (S.KR 9500)
£993	$1798	(19-May-92 AB.S5306/R) Composition with figures (74x66cm-29x26in) s.d.63 (S.KR 10500)
£1007	$1812	(19-Nov-91 GO.G147) Ostra Skagga (60x50cm-24x20in) s. (S.KR 10500)
£1056	$1911	(3-Dec-91 AB.S5138/R) Tiger (66x58cm-26x23in) s. (S.KR 11000)
£1139	$2083	(13-May-92 BU.S155/R) Wailing wall (67x85cm-26x33in) s. (S.KR 12000)
£2004	$3567	(27-Nov-91 BU.S70/R) Family of tennis players (93x83cm-37x33in) s.d.1988 (S.KR 21000)

PYKE, Guelda (20th C) Australian

| £769 | $1392 | (2-Dec-91 AAA.S297) Visit to the zoo (51x69cm-20x27in) s. (A.D 1800) |

PYLE, Howard (1853-1911) American

| £4678 | $8000 | (11-Mar-92 SY.NY107 a/R) Paul Revere's ride (44x30cm-17x12in) init.d.85 indist.i. board en grisaille |

PYLE, Howard (1853-1911) American-cont.
£5618	$10000	(2-May-92 IH.NY88/R) Man entering doorway, other man rising from sleep (69x46cm-27x18in) s.
£6742	$12000	(2-Nov-91 IH.NY113/R) Day dreams (46x28cm-18x11in) s. panel
£7303	*$13000*	*(2-May-92 IH.NY89/R) Boy at desk receiving instruction (33x38cm-13x15in) s. gouache grisaille*

PYNACKER, Adam (1622-1673) Dutch
£4444	$8044	(19-May-92 GF.L2379/R) Southern mountain landscape with waterfalls (58x51cm-23x20in) copper (S.FR 12000)
£10299	$19361	(18-Dec-91 AT.P50/R) Berger et son troupeau au paturage (49x68cm-19x27in) canvas laid down on wood (F.FR 100000)

PYNACKER, Adam (attrib) (1622-1673) Dutch
£5973	$11230	(18-Dec-91 AT.P164/R) Paysage fluvial (90x86cm-35x34in) bears sig. (F.FR 58000)
£8000	$13920	(15-Apr-92 C115/R) Italianate landscape at sunset with cattle drovers on path above river (38x46cm-15x18in) panel

PYNACKER, Adam (style) (1622-1673) Dutch
£3600	$6408	(30-Oct-91 S148/R) River landscape with figures in boat (99x116cm-39x46in)

PYNAS, Jacob (1585-1648) Dutch
£5664	$10649	(18-Dec-91 AT.P145/R) Saint Francois recevant les stigmates (51x93cm-20x37in) s.d.1635 panel (F.FR 55000)

PYNAS, Jacob (circle) (1585-1648) Dutch
£3200	$6144	(7-Jul-92 PH128/R) Flight into Egypt (46x57cm-18x22in)

PYNE, George (1800-1884) British
£550	*$1007*	*(15-May-92 TE332) Peckwater Quadrangle, Oxford (18x28cm-7x11in) s.d.1849 W/C*
£550	*$968*	*(7-Apr-92 C202/R) Trinity College, Cambridge (21x29cm-8x11in) s.d.1850 i.verso pencil W/C*
£600	*$1098*	*(15-May-92 TE333) Peckwater Quadrangle, Oxford (18x25cm-7x10in) s.d.1850 W/C*
£750	*$1373*	*(15-May-92 TE334/R) Christchurch, Oxford (18x25cm-7x10in) s.d.1849 W/C*
£1100	*$1936*	*(9-Apr-92 S88/R) Old school and Parish church, Harrow-on-the-Hill, from High Street (20x28cm-8x11in) W/C over pencil htd bodycol gum arabic*
£1600	*$2816*	*(9-Apr-92 S89/R) Old school, Harrow, from church walk. Old school from playground (21x27cm-8x11in) W/C over pencil htd bodycol gum arabic pair*

PYNE, H (?) ?
£850	$1556	(15-May-92 MAI618) Continental street scene, possibly Bruges

PYNE, J B (1800-1870) British
£498	$886	(25-Nov-91 W.T1891) Mediterranean riverside with figure (51x89cm-20x35in) s. (C.D 1000)
£520	$874	(27-Aug-91 EH794) Figures walking across a city bridge with buildings in background (36x51cm-14x20in) s.d.1845
£925	$1647	(26-Nov-91 J.M472) Herding flock (34x60cm-13x24in) s. (A.D 2100)

PYNE, James Baker (1800-1870) British
£800	$1536	(29-Jul-92 PHC412/R) Continental lake landscape (57cm-22ins circular) s.d.1850
£800	$1376	(8-Oct-91 PH11) Water carrier on mountainous steps (27x43cm-11x17in) s.d.1860 panel
£900	$1548	(11-Oct-91 C80/R) Sorting the catch (30x46cm-12x18in) s.
£1050	$1900	(20-May-92 D.NY98) View on the Machus (41x30cm-16x12in) s.d.1848
£1381	$2500	(21-May-92 S.W2915/R) Fishing vessels in port (61x91cm-24x36in) s.d.1885
£1600	$2832	(6-Nov-91 S24/R) Temple near Naples (63x88cm-25x35in) s.i.d.1853 canvas on board
£2000	$3560	(21-Jan-92 PH82) View of Lake Maggiore (40x57cm-16x22in) indist.s.num.d.
£2500	$4300	(4-Mar-92 S29/R) Borrowdale (66x91cm-26x36in) s.d.1849
£2800	$5264	(19-Dec-91 C137/R) On the Margin of Fair Zurich's Waters (53x83cm-21x33in) s.d.1865
£3000	$5340	(28-Apr-92 PH65/R) Laying monster tubes from new river, foggy morning (43x60cm-17x24in) s.d.1855 num.432
£7000	$12040	(11-Oct-91 C117/R) Capriccio view of the Port of Genoa from New Terrace (61x91cm-24x36in) s.d.1861 s.i.stretcher
£9012	$15500	(17-Oct-91 SY.NY291/R) Windsor. Rochester (61x92cm-24x36in) pair
£10000	$17000	(25-Oct-91 C72/R) The Lake of Zurich (76x137cm-30x54in) s.i.d.1865
£13000	$22880	(8-Apr-92 S98/R) Menai straits from Cheyny Rocks above Beaumaris (47x79cm-19x31in) s.d.1848
£620	*$1079*	*(9-Sep-91 PH131) View of Richmond, Yorks (51x73cm-20x29in) s. W/C over pencil*
£2400	*$4224*	*(9-Apr-92 S97/R) Castello di Canero, Lake Maggiore (30x49cm-12x19in) s.d.1852 W/C over pencil htd bodycol*

PYNE, James Baker (attrib) (1800-1870) British
£2179	$3987	(3-Jun-92 R.T163/R) Travellers at camp overlooking extensive landscape (51x42cm-20x17in) i. oval (C.D 4750)

PYNE, Thomas (1843-1935) British
£1700 $2907   (16-Mar-92 LW1724/R) Landscape with figures harvesting wheat (69x97cm-27x38in) s.d.1889
£400 $720   (27-Jan-92 PH187 a) At Streatley Weir on Thames (23x33cm-9x13in) s. W/C

PYNE, William Henry (1769-1843) British
£420 $756   (30-Jan-92 TL198/R) Towpath with lock gates and barges (24x34cm-9x13in) s.d.1900 W/C
£780 $1404   (30-Jan-92 TL170/R) A sheep fair (30x40cm-12x16in) s. W/C

PYNE, William Henry (style) (1769-1843) British
£1100 $1870   (23-Oct-91 S12/R) The Temple of Minerva, Cape Sounium (21x6cm-8x2in) panel

QI BAISHI (1863-1957) Chinese
£4438 $7766   (30-Mar-92 CH.HK146/R) Flowers and birds (34x34cm-13x13in) s. ink W/C two scrolls (HK.D 60000)
£4438 $7766   (30-Mar-92 CH.HK144/R) Insects around tall rock (136x41cm-54x16in) s. ink W/C hanging scroll (HK.D 60000)
£5547 $9708   (30-Mar-92 CH.HK265/R) Insects and flower (27x34cm-11x13in) s.i. ink W/C scroll (HK.D 75000)
£5917 $10355   (30-Mar-92 CH.HK272/R) Shrimp (95x36cm-37x14in) s.d.1950 ink hanging scroll (HK.D 80000)
£5917 $10355   (30-Mar-92 CH.HK276/R) Morning glories (30x100cm-12x39in) s. ink W/C scroll (HK.D 80000)
£5917 $10355   (30-Mar-92 CH.HK267/R) Loquats (81x34cm-32x13in) s. ink W/C hanging scroll (HK.D 80000)
£7396 $12944   (30-Mar-92 CH.HK145/R) Calligraphy in seal script - zhuan shu (137x34cm-54x13in) s.d.1943 ink hanging scroll (HK.D 100000)
£7396 $12944   (30-Mar-92 CH.HK147/R) Peaches and insect (69x34cm-27x13in) s. ink W/C hanging scroll (HK.D 100000)
£11834 $20710   (30-Mar-92 CH.HK148/R) Flowers and bees (104x34cm-41x13in) s. ink W/C hanging scroll (HK.D 160000)
£11834 $20710   (30-Mar-92 CH.HK269/R) Cock and chicks (105x35cm-41x14in) s.d.1948 ink W/C hanging scroll (HK.D 160000)
£14793 $25888   (30-Mar-92 CH.HK273/R) Studying music and appreciating antiques (97x37cm-38x15in) i.d.1933 ink W/C hanging scroll (HK.D 200000)
£16272 $28476   (30-Mar-92 CH.HK271/R) Liu Hai holding toad (119x33cm-47x13in) s.i. ink W/C hanging scroll (HK.D 220000)
£17012 $29771   (30-Mar-92 CH.HK270/R) Eagle standing on top of pine tree (134x61cm-53x24in) s.d.1929 ink W/C hanging scroll (HK.D 230000)
£23669 $41420   (30-Mar-92 CH.HK143/R) Crane (172x49cm-68x19in) s.i.d.1928 ink W/C hanging scroll (HK.D 320000)
£23669 $41420   (30-Mar-92 CH.HK149/R) Three longevities (111x52cm-44x20in) s.i.d.1928 ink W/C hanging scroll (HK.D 320000)

QI BAISHI and ZHENG XIAOXU (19/20th C) Chinese
£2825 $5000   (7-Nov-91 B.SF1229/R) Wisteria and calligraphy (?x53cm-?x21in) s.i.d.1925 ink colour fan double-sided

QI GONG (1912-) Chinese
£1109 $1942   (30-Mar-92 CH.HK371/R) Landscape after Yuan master (118x46cm-46x18in) s.i.d.1947 ink W/C hanging scroll (HK.D 15000)

QIAN SONGYAN (1895-1985) Chinese
£1183 $2071   (30-Mar-92 CH.HK401/R) Coconut tree (50x34cm-20x13in) s.i. ink W/C hanging scroll (HK.D 16000)
£2589 $4530   (30-Mar-92 CH.HK255/R) Peach blossom landscape (56x34cm-22x13in) s.d.1964 ink W/C hanging scroll (HK.D 35000)

QUADAL, Martin Ferdinand (1736-1811) Austrian
£1348 $2400   (22-Jan-92 D.NY99) Fox and fowl (79x99cm-31x39in)
£1750 $3360   (10-Jul-92 PH29) Two cats observing fish on plate upon table (63x74cm-25x29in)
£2937 $5198   (7-Nov-91 D.V85/R) Still life of fishes and two cats (63x75cm-25x30in) s. (A.S 60000)
£10500 $19110   (13-Dec-91 C181/R) Tea service on tray with candle (39x50cm-15x20in) s.d.1779

QUADT, Jan (fl.1674-1696) Dutch
£8200 $14596   (1-Nov-91 C109/R) Artist, seated at table, drawing statue of cupid, musical instruments on wall beyond (41x33cm-16x13in) s.

QUAEDVLIEG, Carel Max Gerlach Anton (1823-1874) Dutch
£5000 $8650   (4-Oct-91 C64/R) The meet (23x34cm-9x13in) s. panel
£19000 $35340   (19-Jun-92 C36/R) Threshing corn in Roman campagna. Workmen on Via Appia (52x103cm-20x41in) s. pair

QUAEDVLIEG, Carel Max Gerlach Anton (attrib) (1823-1874) Dutch
£2022 $3600   (22-Jan-92 SY.NY278/R) Roman landscapes (13x26cm-5x10in) pair

QUAGLIA, Carlo (1907-1970) Italian
£1859 $3365   (3-Dec-91 F.R158/R) Dioscuri (67x48cm-26x19in) s. s.i.d.1961verso
        masonite (I.L 4000000)
£2324 $4206   (3-Dec-91 F.R221) Paesaggio romano (45x61cm-18x24in) s. s.i.d.1959
        masonite (I.L 5000000)
£2780 $4949   (26-Nov-91 SY.MI80/R) Foro Romano (44x60cm-17x24in) s. s.init.verso
        masonite (I.L 6000000)

QUAGLIO, Domenico (1787-1837) German
£44674 $77732   (18-Sep-91 N.M658/R) Nonnenberg and Festung. St Maximus Kapelle and
        graveyard, Salzburg (46x54cm-18x21in) one s.d.1819 panel pair
        (DM 130000)

QUAGLIO, Domenico (circle) (1787-1837) German
£3200 $5440   (22-Oct-91 S262/R) Rome from Tiber with Castel San Angelo
        (21x29cm-8x11in) indist.s. board

QUAGLIO, Franz (1844-1920) German
£1099 $2000   (26-May-92 CE.NY93/R) Haywagon (12x16cm-5x6in) s. panel
£1568 $2854   (11-Dec-91 N.M564/R) Encampment with horses (21x27cm-8x11in) s.d.1889
        panel (DM 4500)
£1761 $3187   (7-Dec-91 WK.M473/R) Christkindlmark, Munich (46x57cm-18x22in) s.d.1873
        (DM 5000)
£2198 $4000   (26-May-92 CE.NY112/R) A haircut. Mealtime for everyone (14x17cm-6x7in)
        s.d.1900 panel pair

QUAGLIO, Lorenzo (18/19th C) German
£962 $1674   (18-Sep-91 N.M262/R) Young Munich woman (22x18cm-9x7in) i.verso
        mono.d.1830verso W/C pencil htd.white (DM 2800)
£962 $1674   (18-Sep-91 N.M263) Munich woman in costume (22x18cm-9x7in) mono.d.1830
        pencil (DM 2800)
£3846 $6577   (18-Mar-92 N.M299/R) Hohenschwangau with Tyrolean mountain range. Fir
        trees (24x33cm-9x13in) s.i.d.1855/56 i.d.verso double-sided (DM 11000)

QUAGLIO, Simon (1795-1870) German
£6000 $10680   (29-Nov-91 C34/R) The Schrannenplatz, Munich (20x26cm-8x10in) init.
        s.i.d.1835verso pencil W/C card

QUARENGHI, Giacomo (1744-1817) Italian
£2600 $4732   (10-Dec-91 C183/R) The elevation of the Church of the Cemetery of Kazan
        (20x30cm-8x12in) blk.lead pen W/C
£3000 $5760   (6-Jul-92 S48/R) Design for the Empress's Pavilion in the English Garden
        at Peterhof (29x47cm-11x19in) pen W/C
£16760 $30000   (14-Jan-92 SY.NY178/R) Plan for English garden at Peterhof, on outskirts
        of St. Petersburg (68x48cm-27x19in) i. pen W/C

QUARTARARO, Riccardo (fl.1485-1501) Italian
£22346 $40000   (17-Jan-92 SY.NY11/R) The Archangel Michael triumphant over Satan
        (91x65cm-36x26in) panel

QUARTREMAIN, W W (fl.1906-1908) British
£440 $757   (18-Oct-91 CBB250) On the Avon (23x36cm-9x14in) s.
£1175 $1962   (23-Aug-91 CBB250/R) Anne Hathaway's Cottage near Stratford-upon-Avon
        (28x20cm-11x8in) s.d.1920 W/C

QUARTREMAIN, William Wells (fl.1906-1908) British
£800 $1440   (22-Nov-91 CBB265) Study of carved four poster bed in Anne Hathaways
        cottage, nr Stratford (23x36cm-9x14in) s. W/C
£940 $1805   (28-Jul-92 MCB1) Large timber framed house (25x18cm-10x7in) s.d.1904 W/C
£1000 $1780   (24-Jan-92 CBB250/R) Wimpstone Bridge, nr Stratford-upon-Avon
        (18x25cm-7x10in) s. W/C
£1250 $2250   (22-Nov-91 CBB250) River and Holy Trinity Church, Stratford-upon-Avon
        (30x41cm-12x16in) s. W/C
£1600 $2816   (6-Apr-92 PH117/R) Hall's Croft, Old Town, Stratford-on-Avon
        (23x37cm-9x15in) s.d.1927 W/C
£2000 $3460   (4-Sep-91 PHK74/R) The Guild Chapel and Alms House viewed from Stratford
        Grammar School (32x27cm-13x11in) s. W/C htd white
£2400 $4368   (13-Dec-91 CBB250/R) Wintry approach to Holy Trinity Chruch, Stratford
        upon Avon (33x28cm-13x11in) s.

QUAST, Pieter (1606-1647) Dutch
£1543 $2762   (14-Nov-91 CH.AM148/R) Deathbed scene (38x49cm-15x19in) s. panel
        (D.FL 5000)
£1271 $2238   (11-Apr-92 AW.H279/R) Ecce homo (23x28cm-9x11in) s.d.1641 pencil wash
        (DM 3700)
£13966 $25000   (14-Jan-92 SY.NY136/R) Mocking of Spaniard (22x30cm-9x12in) s.d.1642
        black chk vellum

QUAST, Pieter (attrib) (1606-1647) Dutch
£1987 $3398   (18-Mar-92 D.V291/R) Cavalier smoking (22x14cm-9x6in) mono. panel
        (A.S 40000)
£3568 $6636   (20-Jun-92 CH.MO23/R) Une reunion de fumeurs (25x34cm-10x13in) panel
        (F.FR 35000)

QUELLINUS, Erasmus (17th C) Flemish
£9128 $16065   (10-Apr-92 AT.P57/R) Sainte Cecile entouree d'anges dans un paysge de
                              riviere (27x37cm-11x15in) copper (F.FR 90000)
£10000 $17400   (15-Apr-92 C110/R) Jephthah greeted by his daughter (50x73cm-20x29in)
                              indis.s. panel
£29000 $55680   (8-Jul-92 S40/R) Madonna and Child enthroned with St Joseph and male and
                              female saints (147x212cm-58x83in)

QUELLINUS, Erasmus (circle) (17th C) Flemish
£3651 $6426   (11-Apr-92 AT.P46/R) Salomon recevant la reine de Saba (56x82cm-22x32in)
                              (F.FR 36000)

QUELLINUS, Erasmus (style) (17th C) Flemish
£750 $1373   (12-May-92 SWS807) Two putti playing by swag of fruit (36x29cm-14x11in)
                              panel

QUELLINUS, Erasmus II (1607-1678) Flemish
£19553 $35000   (16-Jan-92 CH.NY57/R) Madonna and Child (122x96cm-48x38in)
£28000 $50960   (13-Dec-91 C31/R) The Triumph of Hope (74x74cm-29x29in) panel

QUELLINUS, Jan Erasmus (1634-1715) Flemish
£5200 $9516   (12-May-92 SWS701/R) Daughters of Cecrops with Erichthonius
                              (146x131cm-57x52in)

QUENTIN, Bernard (1923-) French
£824 $1409   (18-Mar-92 LT.P132) Ciel (93x69cm-37x27in) s. acrylic tissue laid down on
                              board (F.FR 8000)
£927 $1585   (18-Mar-92 LT.P130/R) Incandescence (96x69cm-38x27in) s.d.89 acrylic
                              tissue laid down on board (F.FR 9000)
£1013 $1834   (20-May-92 FB.P20 a) Composition (181x133cm-71x52in) s.d.1969 wood
                              (F.FR 10000)
£1016 $1768   (13-Apr-92 GL.P179/R) Composition a la lettre M (67x116cm-26x46in)
                              s.d.1963 wood (F.FR 10000)
£1018 $1864   (3-Jun-92 CSC.P153/R) Bataille (52x92cm-20x36in) s.d.58 oil panel
                              (F.FR 10000)
£1030 $1761   (19-Mar-92 CSC.P59) Foule (37x37cm-15x15in) s.d.60 acrylic (F.FR 10000)
£1511 $2568   (24-Oct-91 CSC.P40) E - mc 2 (87x68cm-34x27in) s.d.63 acrylic panel
                              (F.FR 15000)
£2064 $3510   (24-Oct-91 CSC.P41) Ecriture (68x88cm-27x35in) s.d.62 acrylic board laid
                              down on panel (F.FR 20500)
£2459 $4426   (2-Feb-92 CSC.P159/R) Foule (80x60cm-31x24in) s.d.60 board (F.FR 24000)
£491 $884   (19-Nov-91 L.K1018) Milano (29x42cm-11x17in) s.i.d.1962 indian ink felt
                              tip ball point pen (DM 1400)
£508 $884   (13-Apr-92 GL.P191) Presence (49x74cm-19x29in) s.d.1988 ink serigraph
                              (F.FR 5000)
£721 $1233   (22-Mar-92 I.N15) Ocean (76x106cm-30x42in) s.d.1988 mixed media canvas
                              (F.FR 7000)
£1133 $1937   (21-Mar-92 AT.P8/R) Bataille (54x75cm-21x30in) s.d.1955 mixed media paper
                              laid down on panel (F.FR 11000)
£1133 $1937   (21-Mar-92 AT.P9) Moquette - Moi (72x92cm-28x36in) s.d.1961 mixed media
                              paper laid down on panel (F.FR 11000)
£1722 $3118   (20-May-92 FB.P19 a/R) Ecriture (152x230cm-60x91in) s. mixed media canvas
                              (F.FR 17000)
£3071 $5466   (1-Dec-91 I.N32/R) Talisman (95x115cm-37x45in) s.d.1989 mixed media panel
                              (F.FR 30000)

QUERENA, Luigi (1820-c.1890) Italian
£5345 $9675   (3-Dec-91 SY.MI100/R) Veduta di Palazzo Ducale e Piazza San Marco
                              (23x55cm-9x22in) s.d.1871 (I.L 11500000)

QUERFURT, August (1696-1761) German
£687 $1168   (25-Oct-91 BM.B664 a/R) Travellers with horse-drawn cart before hut
                              (46x37cm-18x15in) (DM 2000)
£1105 $2000   (21-May-92 CH.NY118/R) Bandits watched by two horsemen, one dismounted,
                              on coastal path (15x18cm-6x7in) copper
£3500 $6125   (1-Apr-92 S199/R) Military encampment (28x38cm-11x15in) panel
£4161 $7364   (7-Nov-91 D.V350/R) Two riders before farmhouse (28x34cm-11x13in) one of
                              pair (A.S 85000)
£4199 $7600   (22-May-92 SY.NY188/R) Couple on horseback falconing (68x50cm-27x20in)
                              panel

QUERFURT, August (attrib) (1696-1761) German
£1739 $2973   (18-Mar-92 D.V322/R) Skirmish (33x42cm-13x17in) (A.S 35000)
£5866 $10617   (19-May-92 AB.S4369/R) Italianate landscape with figures by well
                              (28x21cm-11x8in) panel (S.KR 62000)

QUERFURT, August (circle) (1696-1761) German
£800 $1432   (11-Nov-91 S489/R) Cavalry charge (55x42cm-22x17in)

QUERFURT, August (style) (1696-1761) German
£1100 $2112   (9-Jul-92 CSK205/R) Military engagement (43x58cm-17x23in) canvas laid
                              down on panel
£1590 $2718   (18-Mar-92 D.V323/R) Cavalier and lady with two riders (16x22cm-6x9in)
                              panel (A.S 32000)

QUERFURT, August (style) (1696-1761) German-cont.
£1662	$2974	(7-May-92 CH.AM12/R) Cavalry tending wounded infantry on battlefield (56x71cm-22x28in) (D.FL 5500)
£7000	$12250	(28-Feb-92 C20/R) Elegant hunting party resting after luncheon beneath outcrop (44x33cm-17x13in) copper

QUERNER, Curt (1904-1976) German
£634	$1147	(6-Dec-91 GB.B7013) Farmstead in Kardorf, early spring (19x48cm-7x19in) i.d.1966verso panel (DM 1800)
£1433	$2595	(23-May-92 GB.B7133) Self portrait (30x23cm-12x9in) s.i.d.71 panel (DM 4200)
£421	*$758*	*(23-Nov-91 N.M635) Female nude standing seen from the side (72x26cm-28x10in) mono.d.1962 W/C (DM 1200)*
£785	*$1421*	*(23-May-92 GB.B7136) Young peasant woman working (41x36cm-16x14in) mono.d.1967 i.verso (DM 2300)*

QUERO, Jose Hernandez (20th C) Spanish
£712	$1295	(26-May-92 DUR.M135/R) Paisaje en amarillo (60x74cm-24x29in) s. (S.P 130000)

QUERRIEN, Guillaine (20th C) French?
£708	*$1238*	*(5-Apr-92 R.P81) Allons voir plus loin (80x120cm-31x47in) s. mixed media (F.FR 6800)*

QUESADAS, Augusto Manuel (19th C) Spanish
£1384	$2366	(17-Mar-92 FER.M123/R) Bodegon con guitarra y violin (91x121cm-36x48in) s.d.1874 (S.P 250000)

QUESNE, Fernand le (1856-?) French
£909	$1609	(26-Apr-92 FE.P54) Femme espagnole (61x102cm-24x40in) s. (F.FR 9000)

QUETGLAS, Matias (1946-) Spanish
£2589	$4454	(7-Oct-91 ANS.M116/R) La contemplacion (55x46cm-22x18in) s.d.1987 s.i.verso panel (S.P 475000)

QUICK (?) ?
£1061	*$1920*	*(19-May-92 CH.AM303/R) When people don't know what you're about....... (91x122cm-36x48in) s.d.87 acrylic collage on canvas (D.FL 3500)*

QUIGLEY, Daniel (18th C) British
£5200	$8996	(25-Mar-92 PHI567/R) The Goldolphin Arabian, chestnut horse standing in stable yard (96x128cm-38x50in) s.i.

QUIGNON, Fernand Just (1854-1941) French
£505	$868	(20-Oct-91 E.LA30) Pluie a Wissant (21x27cm-8x11in) s. panel (F.FR 5000)
£505	$868	(20-Oct-91 E.LA35) Les foins fauches pres de Nesles (21x27cm-8x11in) s. panel (F.FR 5000)
£505	$868	(20-Oct-91 E.LA49) Wisant - bord de mer (18x27cm-7x11in) s. board (F.FR 5000)
£525	$903	(20-Oct-91 E.LA6) Bles murs au soleil (33x41cm-13x16in) s. panel (F.FR 5200)
£555	$955	(20-Oct-91 E.LA17/R) Orage pers de Nesles (26x35cm-10x14in) s.d.1930 panel (F.FR 5500)
£585	$1007	(20-Oct-91 E.LA32) Nesles - la ferme Vermont (26x40cm-10x16in) s. d.1894 panel (F.FR 5800)
£656	$1128	(20-Oct-91 E.LA23) Nesles - carriere et foret (38x46cm-15x18in) s. panel (F.FR 6500)
£686	$1180	(20-Oct-91 E.LA10) Paysage d'Auvergne (61x46cm-24x18in) s. (F.FR 6800)
£706	$1215	(20-Oct-91 E.LA37/R) Nesles - la chaumiere de l'artiste au printemps (45x61cm-18x24in) s. (F.FR 7000)
£706	$1215	(20-Oct-91 E.LA19) Mais a Valmondois (26x40cm-10x16in) s. d.1887verso panel (F.FR 7000)
£928	$1597	(20-Oct-91 E.LA25/R) Vue de Montargis (46x38cm-18x15in) s. panel (F.FR 9200)
£3532	$6075	(20-Oct-91 E.LA11/R) Epicerie a Pont-Aven (63x70cm-25x28in) s. (F.FR 35000)
£5600	$9633	(20-Oct-91 E.LA22/R) La Durolle a Thiers (76x115cm-30x45in) s. (F.FR 55500)
£10293	$17703	(20-Oct-91 E.LA29/R) Les Moyettes (155x238cm-61x94in) s. (F.FR 102000)

QUILLIARD, Pierre Antoine (attrib) (1701-1733) French
£2937	$5198	(7-Nov-91 D.V200/R) Fete champetre in palatial gardens (30x40cm-12x16in) copper one of pair after Antoine Watteau (A.S 60000)
£2937	$5198	(7-Nov-91 D.V201/R) Fete champetre with couple dancing (30x40cm-12x16in) copper one of pair after Nicolas Lancret (A.S 60000)

QUILLIARD, Pierre Antoine (circle) (1701-1733) French
£3601	$6517	(5-Dec-91 SY.MO292/R) Danse dans un parc (54x40cm-21x16in) oval (F.FR 35000)

QUILP (style) (?) ?
£1400	$2562	(3-Jun-92 SWS322/R) Fighting cocks (56x43cm-22x17in) board pair

UINAUX, Joseph (1822-1895) Belgian
559    $1000   (13-Nov-91 B.SF2222/R) Paysage en l'Ile de France (29x41cm-11x16in) s. panel
2000 $3620   (22-May-92 C186/R) Cattle watering by stream (64x89cm-25x35in) s.d.1855

UINCKART, G (17th C) ?
500    $860   (3-Mar-92 SWS1622) Portrait of Adolf von Willick (75x59cm-30x23in) s.d.1649 panel painted oval

UINET, Mig (1908-) Belgian
535    $909   (22-Oct-91 C.A887) Composition (60x40cm-24x16in) s. gouache (B.FR 32000)

UINN, James Peter (1870-1951) Australian
563    $941   (19-Aug-91 SY.ME66) French basque, Les Aldudes Basses Pyrenees, France (61x40cm-24x16in) s. i.verso (A.D 1200)
881    $1568   (26-Nov-91 J.M446) Young veiled lady (59x38cm-23x15in) s. (A.D 2000)
7930 $14273   (24-Nov-91 SY.S353/R) Daffodils (101x67cm-40x26in) s. s.i.verso (A.D 18000)

UINN, Tom (20th C) British?
1500 $2610   (19-Sep-91 B130) Portrait head of young girl (25x18cm-10x7in) s. paper

UINQUELA MARTIN, Benito (1890-1977) Argentinian
2688 $5000   (16-Jun-92 RO.BA56) Manana gris (23x30cm-9x12in)
3226 $6000   (16-Jun-92 RO.BA24) Iglesia de San Javier (40x27cm-16x11in)
3448 $6000   (19-Sep-91 V.BA83) Regreso de la barcas (50x60cm-20x24in)
4121 $7500   (11-Dec-91 RO.BA225) Crepusculo (50x60cm-20x24in) s. s.i.d.1961verso
4301 $8000   (16-Jun-92 RO.BA69) Rincon boquense (50x60cm-20x24in)
4419 $7600   (9-Oct-91 RO.BA577 b) Proas iluminadas (50x60cm-20x24in) s.
4888 $8700   (1-Nov-91 PO.BA45) Botes en la isla Maciel (37x55cm-15x22in) s.d.1918 board
5233 $9000   (9-Oct-91 RO.BA208/R) Rincon de la boca (61x70cm-24x28in) s.
6183 $11500   (16-Jun-92 RO.BA57) Rincon boquense (60x70cm-24x28in) s.
6395 $11000   (9-Oct-91 RO.BA389) Dia de sol en la boca (60x70cm-24x28in) s.
6897 $12000   (19-Sep-91 V.BA82/R) Salida de un velero (50x60cm-20x24in) d.1957
7031 $13500   (4-Aug-92 V.BA85/R) Rincon de la Boca (60x70cm-24x28in)
7222 $13000   (19-Nov-91 CH.NY52/R) A la Orilla del Rio (60x80cm-24x31in) s.
12088 $22000   (11-Dec-91 RO.BA7/R) Creciente en la boca (90x100cm-35x39in) s. s.i.d.1953verso
13736 $25000   (11-Dec-91 RO.BA6/R) Puente del Arroyo Maciel (90x100cm-35x39in) s.
13978 $26000   (16-Jun-92 RO.BA55) Estibadores (180x120cm-71x47in)
16124 $28700   (1-Nov-91 PO.BA46) Otono rosado (89x98cm-35x39in) s.
19186 $33000   (9-Oct-91 RO.BA32) Despues de la Lluvia (122x122cm-48x48in) s. s.i.d.1952verso

UINSA, Giovanni (?) Italian
22000 $40040   (29-May-92 C325/R) Strawberries in bowl, flowers in vase and pigeons in basket on ledge (69x87cm-27x34in)

UINSAC, Paul Francois (1858-?) French
553    $985   (29-Nov-91 GAB.G2158) Femme a la cruche (82x51cm-32x20in) s. (S.FR 1400)
7136 $13272   (18-Jun-92 SY.MO380/R) Jeune femme au cafe (40x31cm-16x12in) s. panel (F.FR 70000)

UINTON (?) ?
815    $1517   (17-Jun-92 I.N104/R) Vaches dans un paysage (44x55cm-17x22in) s. (F.FR 8000)

UINTON, Alfred Robert (1853-?) British
1742 $3100   (22-Jan-92 SY.NY504/R) Vale of Evesham from Bredon Hill, Worcestershire (60x100cm-24x39in) s. W/C

UINTON, Clement (1851-?) French
949    $1708   (22-Nov-91 EA.Z115/R) Ploughing team returning home (50x65cm-20x26in) s. (S.FR 2400)
1061 $1877   (22-Apr-92 CH.AM178/R) Peasant resting on a tree-trunk by a horse-drawn timber-wagon (50x65cm-20x26in) s. (D.FL 3500)

UIROS, Cesareo Bernaldo (1881-1968) Argentinian
3090 $5500   (28-Apr-92 PO.BA30) Dorado (65x50cm-26x20in) s. board
3846 $7000   (11-Dec-91 RO.BA48/R) Paisaje del Parana (24x35cm-9x14in) s.
5814 $10000   (9-Oct-91 RO.BA24/R) Orden y Justicia (94x76cm-37x30in) s.
9066 $16500   (11-Dec-91 RO.BA44) El puesto (72x75cm-28x30in) s.
9948 $19000   (30-Jun-92 PO.BA18) El rancho (68x69cm-27x27in) s. board
10440 $19000   (11-Dec-91 RO.BA224) Entrada al parque (42x35cm-17x14in) s.
10753 $20000   (16-Jun-92 RO.BA2) Arrieros (55x46cm-22x18in)
11538 $21000   (11-Dec-91 RO.BA41/R) Paisaje (49x54cm-19x21in) s.
12366 $23000   (16-Jun-92 RO.BA40) Claro de luna (35x49cm-14x19in)
13736 $25000   (11-Dec-91 RO.BA42/R) Hacia su destino (73x81cm-29x32in) s. panel
15517 $27000   (19-Sep-91 V.BA84) Engarce en oro, Mallorca (63x74cm-25x29in)
16279 $28000   (9-Oct-91 RO.BA22/R) Camino de cielo (80x91cm-31x36in) s.
17857 $32500   (11-Dec-91 RO.BA47/R) La Chacra (61x76cm-24x30in) s.
18817 $35000   (16-Jun-92 RO.BA17) Los matreros (70x80cm-28x31in)
20330 $37000   (11-Dec-91 RO.BA45/R) Vista de parque (81x92cm-32x36in) s.
20330 $37000   (11-Dec-91 RO.BA40/R) Alto en el camino (76x85cm-30x33in) s.

QUIROS, Cesareo Bernaldo (1881-1968) Argentinian-cont.

£20879	$38000	(11-Dec-91 RO.BA43/R) Sargento federal (75x60cm-30x24in) s.
£23837	$41000	(9-Oct-91 RO.BA23/R) Tapera de los Robles (100x122cm-39x48in) s.
£26882	$50000	(16-Jun-92 RO.BA1) Montonero (81x73cm-32x29in) panel
£39535	$68000	(9-Oct-91 RO.BA21/R) Quijote entre los gauchos (123x136cm-48x54in) s.
£68063	$130000	(30-Jun-92 PO.BA17) Playa salada, Mallorca (121x143cm-48x56in) s. panel
£69892	$130000	(16-Jun-92 RO.BA8) Amaneciendo (98x100cm-39x39in)

QUIZET, Alphonse (1885-1955) French

£1200	$2172	(2-Dec-91 CSK119/R) Les peniches (20x25cm-8x10in) s. board
£1400	$2534	(2-Dec-91 CSK121/R) Montmartre (17x28cm-7x11in) s. board
£2000	$3620	(2-Dec-91 CSK120/R) Place du Tertre, Paris (25x20cm-10x8in) s. panel
£2026	$3668	(20-May-92 I.N171/R) La petite France a Strasbourg (57x50cm-22x20in) s. board (F.FR 20000)
£2567	$4620	(19-Nov-91 FB.P12/R) Les quais (38x45cm-15x18in) s. hardboard (F.FR 25000)
£3364	$6257	(17-Jun-92 I.N153/R) Canal a Paris (38x46cm-15x18in) s. isorel (F.FR 33000)
£3502	$5988	(18-Mar-92 PIC.P91/R) Paysage de Romainville (92x73cm-36x29in) s. (F.FR 34000)
£3811	$7164	(16-Dec-91 BG.P106/R) Paysage fluvial (60x73cm-24x29in) s. panel (F.FR 37000)
£3913	$6692	(18-Mar-92 PIC.P90/R) Les affiches a Montmartre, sous la neige (92x73cm-36x29in) s. (F.FR 38000)
£4000	$7240	(2-Dec-91 CSK118/R) La Maison Berlioz, Paris (38x46cm-15x18in) s.i.d.1912verso board
£4086	$7150	(21-Feb-92 LC.P42/R) La voie ferree (54x65cm-21x26in) s. panel (F.FR 40000)
£4611	$8299	(2-Feb-92 ZZ.F159/R) Bord de canal (60x73cm-24x29in) s. board laid down on panel (F.FR 45000)

QUOST, Ernest (1844-1931) French

| £919 | $1609 | (19-Feb-92 D.P28) Le jardin du Luxembourg (63x70cm-25x28in) bears studio st. (F.FR 9000) |
| *£624* | *$1073* | *(7-Oct-91 CSC.P134) Bouquet de fleurs (47x60cm-19x24in) studio st. pastel (F.FR 6200)* |

R F (19th C) ?

| £1400 | $2408 | (4-Mar-92 DR159/R) Beach scene with fisherfolk and village beyond (20x30cm-8x12in) init.d.55 panel |

RAAB, Georg (1821-1885) Austrian

| *£1730* | *$3028* | *(21-Feb-92 D.V779/R) Kronprinz Rudolf von Osterreich (60x46cm-24x18in) s.d.1872verso W/C bodycol (A.S 35000)* |

RAADSIG, P (1806-1882) Danish

| £542 | $975 | (19-Nov-91 RAS.K122/R) Italian family resting by roadside altar (62x51cm-24x20in) s. (D.KR 6000) |

RAADSIG, Peter (1806-1882) Danish

£528	$887	(27-Aug-91 RAS.K433/R) Horse and sleigh in wooded winter landscape (77x110cm-30x43in) s.d.1868 (D.KR 6000)
£704	$1183	(27-Aug-91 RAS.K468) Italian shepherd family by ruin (37x32cm-15x13in) init. (D.KR 8000)
£980	$1686	(15-Oct-91 RAS.K231) Italian street scene (44x29cm-17x11in) init.i.d.1843 (D.KR 11000)
£1323	$2354	(28-Apr-92 RAS.K554/R) Poor people receiving alms in a village kitchen (52x63cm-20x25in) s.d.1880 (D.KR 15000)
£2289	$3845	(27-Aug-91 RAS.K15/R) Fishermen returning home, North Sjaelland coast (86x125cm-34x49in) s.d.1875 (D.KR 26000)

RAAPHORST, Cornelis (1875-1954) Dutch

£917	$1596	(14-Apr-92 SY.AM290) Playing kittens (38x48cm-15x19in) s. (D.FL 3000)
£979	$1703	(14-Apr-92 SY.AM213) Two kittens (29x39cm-11x15in) s. (D.FL 3200)
£1064	$1830	(12-Oct-91 CH.AM187) Three is a crowd (30x40cm-12x16in) s. (D.FL 3500)
£1284	$2273	(5-Nov-91 SY.AM182) Playful kittens (23x29cm-9x11in) s. (D.FL 4200)
£1529	$2661	(14-Apr-92 SY.AM230) Five playful kittens on table (48x58cm-19x23in) s. (D.FL 5000)
£1835	$3193	(14-Apr-92 SY.AM198/R) The letter (29x39cm-11x15in) s. (D.FL 6000)
£1835	$3193	(14-Apr-92 SY.AM12/R) Dinner time (40x50cm-16x20in) s. (D.FL 6000)
£1970	$3486	(22-Apr-92 CH.AM72/R) Who's first (24x30cm-9x12in) s. (D.FL 6500)
£1976	$3438	(17-Sep-91 CH.AM686/R) Curious cats (47x67cm-19x26in) s. canvas laid down on cardboard (D.FL 6500)
£2000	$3560	(28-Nov-91 CSK113) The young students (180x264cm-71x104in) s.
£2141	$3810	(30-Oct-91 CH.AM188) Kittens playing near box on Persian rug (60x80cm-24x31in) s. (D.FL 7000)
£2200	$3916	(28-Nov-91 CSK112) By the fireside (69x89cm-27x35in) s.
£2360	$4201	(26-Nov-91 VN.R91/R) Three kittens at play (63x53cm-25x21in) s. (D.FL 7600)
£2446	$4355	(30-Oct-91 CH.AM187/R) Playful kittens (60x80cm-24x31in) s. (D.FL 8000)
£2469	$4321	(18-Feb-92 CH.AM299/R) Playful kittens (60x80cm-24x31in) s. (D.FL 8000)

RAAPHORST, Cornelis (1875-1954) Dutch-cont.
£2752 $4789 (14-Apr-92 SY.AM169/R) Young scholars s. (D.FL 9000)
£3647 $6347 (17-Sep-91 CH.AM534) Quarelling kittens (51x70cm-20x28in) s. (D.FL 12000)
£5116 $8800 (16-Oct-91 CH.NY237/R) Playful kittens (50x61cm-20x24in) s.

RABAN, Zeev (1890-1970) Israeli
£426 $800 (5-Jan-92 GG.TA349/R) Fortress and eagles (2x16cm-1x6in) s. W/C ink

RABENDING, Fritz (1862-1929) Austrian
£389 $700 (24-Nov-91 JRB.C76/R) Morning on the Sarca (53x48cm-21x19in) s. W/C board

RABES, Max (1868-1944) Austrian
£1774 $3157 (30-Oct-91 CH.AM90/R) Abend bei Assuan, Egypt (120x77cm-47x30in) s.
s.i.stretcher (D.FL 5800)
£2000 $3560 (26-Nov-91 PH137/R) Figures with camels in North African river landscape
(38x65cm-15x26in) s.
£2189 $3985 (26-May-92 DUR.M5/R) Paisaje de Charlottenburg (129x208cm-51x82in) s.
(S.P 400000)

RABUS, Carl (1898-1974) German
£1911 $3478 (26-May-92 KF.M1179/R) Fallen asleep (79x59cm-31x23in) (DM 5600)

RACITI, Mario (1934-) Italian
£388 $676 (14-Apr-92 F.M51) Composizione (40x30cm-16x12in) st.sig.verso mixed media
canvas (I.L 850000)
£1483 $2639 (26-Nov-91 SY.MI40) Tunnel (70x50cm-28x20in) s.d.65 s.init.d.verso mixed
media canvas (I.L 3200000)

RACKHAM, Arthur (1867-1939) British
£2800 $4984 (29-Oct-91 C18/R) Christmas Night (23x20cm-9x8in) s. s.i.verso pencil ink
W/C
£10000 $17100 (13-Mar-92 C58/R) Almost fairy time (21x18cm-8x7in) s.d.1908 pencil pen
ink W/C

RACOFF, Rotislaw (20th C) Russian
£575 $1035 (19-Nov-91 GO.G242) Ancienne Maison, Ille St. Louis (35x28cm-14x11in) s.
acrylic panel (S.KR 6000)

RADCLYFFE, Charles Walter (1817-1903) British
£440 $774 (6-Apr-92 WW173) Field of stocked corn at Edgebaston (27x49cm-11x19in)
init.d.1864 W/C over pencil

RADEMAKER, Abraham (1675-1735) Dutch
£559 $1000 (15-Jan-92 CH.NY156/R) Ruins of Kathuyser Church, near Delft
(12x21cm-5x8in) with i. pen W/C htd white
£1382 $2460 (29-Nov-91 ARC.P5/R) Paysage fluvial aux abords d'un village
(16x22cm-6x9in) s. gouache (F.FR 13500)
£1842 $3279 (29-Nov-91 ARC.P6/R) Paysage fluvial avec un chateau (18x25cm-7x10in) i.
gouache (F.FR 18000)
£2484 $4422 (25-Nov-91 CH.AM200/R) View of walled city by estuary (13x20cm-5x8in) s.
bodycol W/C (D.FL 8000)

RADEMAKER, Hermanus Everhardus (1820-1885) Dutch
£1774 $3157 (30-Oct-91 CH.AM39/R) Wooded landscape with herdsman and flock on sandy
track along mansion (79x100cm-31x39in) s.d.1846 (D.FL 5800)
£1818 $3218 (22-Apr-92 CH.AM107) Wooded hilly landscape with travellers on path
(36x50cm-14x20in) init.d.1852 panel (D.FL 6000)

RADERSCHEIDT, Anton (1892-1970) German
£842 $1516 (21-Nov-91 L.K410) Portrait of lady en face (81x59cm-32x23in) s.d.1957
board (DM 2400)
£928 $1633 (10-Apr-92 KM.K514) Biarritz (81x60cm-32x24in) mono.d.59 i.verso
(DM 2700)
£1031 $1887 (3-Jun-92 L.K393) Street cafe (65x50cm-26x20in) s.d.1956 egg tempera
board (DM 3000)
£1031 $1887 (3-Jun-92 L.K391/R) Street scene, Dusseldorf city (65x50cm-26x20in)
s.d.55 tempera board (DM 3000)
£1053 $1895 (21-Nov-91 L.K412/R) Frigate in harbour (38x56cm-15x22in) s.d.1933 W/C
tempera (DM 3000)
£1228 $2211 (21-Nov-91 L.K416/R) Cologne, St Aposteln (50x65cm-20x26in) tempera board
(DM 3500)
£1237 $2264 (3-Jun-92 L.K392/R) Street scene with Cologne Cathedral (65x50cm-26x20in)
s.d.1954 tempera board (DM 3600)
£1333 $2400 (21-Nov-91 L.K409/R) Juanita, abstract composition (81x60cm-32x24in)
d.1955/58 i.verso (DM 3800)
£1375 $2515 (3-Jun-92 L.K390/R) Self portrait, Anton despairing in Bern
(59x42cm-23x17in) s.d.1949 tempera (DM 4000)
£1754 $3158 (21-Nov-91 L.K415/R) Women (80x65cm-31x26in) mono.d.1957 oil tempera
board (DM 5000)
£1787 $3270 (3-Jun-92 L.K395/R) Horses grazing (65x50cm-26x20in) s.d.1956 tempera
board (DM 5200)
£4124 $7629 (12-Jun-92 HN.H736/R) Still life of roses (28x22cm-11x9in) s. board
(DM 12000)
£4211 $7579 (21-Nov-91 L.K408/R) Two cats on armchair (65x46cm-26x18in) s.d.48
(DM 12000)

RADERSCHEIDT, Anton (1892-1970) German-cont.
£1389 $2486   (15-Nov-91 KM.K598/R) Horses grazing (61x47cm-24x19in) s.d.57 gouache
                  (DM 4000)
£1546 $2830   (3-Jun-92 L.K389/R) Self portrait (50x34cm-20x13in) mono.d.1947 gouache
                  (DM 4500)

RADICE, Mario (1900-) Italian
£9282 $17450   (19-Dec-91 F.M221/R) Composizione (100x100cm-39x39in) s. (I.L 20000000)
£30630 $57584   (19-Dec-91 F.M182/R) Composition (175x95cm-69x37in) s. (I.L 66000000)
£2101 $3656   (14-Apr-92 F.M253/R) Composizione C.A.N.P. (19x22cm-7x9in) s.i.d.1958
                  st.sig.verso pastel tempera board (I.L 4600000)

RADIMOV, Pavel Alexandrovitch (c.1887-1967) Russian
£1613 $2823   (24-Sep-91 ARC.P188/R) Le conte du soir (71x90cm-28x35in) s. (F.FR 16000)

RADINSKY, Vaclav (1867-?) ?
£736 $1398   (25-Jun-92 D.V640/R) Sheep returning home in the evening
                  (47x68cm-19x27in) s. board (A.S 15000)
£1311 $2400   (4-Jun-92 GOM.M34/R) Atardecer Otonal (68x80cm-27x31in) s. board
£1927 $3391   (10-Apr-92 AGS.P34) Bord de riviere (66x92cm-26x36in) s. (F.FR 19000)

RADZIWILL, Franz (1895-1983) German
£2807 $5053   (21-Nov-91 L.K418/R) View of Varel (38x46cm-15x18in) s.d.1927 W/C
                  (DM 8000)
£11945 $21741   (30-May-92 VG.B249/R) Der Goldlack (42x32cm-17x13in) mono i.verso canvas
                  on panel (DM 35000)
£30717 $55904   (30-May-92 VG.B248/R) Bird on window (71x53cm-28x21in) s.d.1938 canvas on
                  panel (DM 90000)
£40070 $72927   (13-Dec-91 BM.B539/R) Sender Norddeich (80x100cm-31x39in) s.d.1933
                  i.verso (DM 115000)
£64685 $115140 (29-Nov-91 VG.B55/R) Self portrait (64x53cm-25x21in) s. canvas on panel
                  (DM 185000)
£76923 $136923 (29-Nov-91 VG.B56/R) Immer schneller fliegen (78x99cm-31x39in) s.d.1938
                  canvas on panel (DM 220000)
£410 $741   (23-May-92 GB.B7138) Woman seated at table seen from behind
                  (57x37cm-22x15in) s.d.1924 chk (DM 1200)
£683 $1242   (30-May-92 VG.B906/R) Head of bearded man (15x10cm-6x4in) s.i.verso W/C
                  ink postcard (DM 2000)
£687 $1278   (20-Jun-92 BM.B770/R) Landscape with celestial body (16x23cm-6x9in) mono
                  pencil col.pencil (DM 2000)
£3413 $6212   (30-May-92 VG.B247/R) Still life with jug (36x49cm-14x19in) mono W/C over
                  pencil (DM 10000)
£3889 $7039   (20-May-92 GK.Z5009/R) Fishermen's cottages on shore (38x49cm-15x19in)
                  mono d.1922 W/C (S.FR 10500)
£9556 $17392   (25-May-92 WK.M1043 a/R) Landscape with houses (43x55cm-17x22in) mono
                  gouache canvas (DM 28000)

RAE, Barbara (20th C) British
£1200 $2016   (26-Aug-91 S1161/R) Beach gleaming (110x80cm-43x31in) s.d.85 acrylic
                  collage board

RAE, Iso (fl.1880-1920) Australian
£470 $837   (28-Apr-92 CH.ME147) Etaples (45x29cm-18x11in) s.i.d.1917 pastel
                  (A.D 1100)

RAEBURN, Agnes (?-1955) British
£450 $864   (29-Jul-92 PHC297) Roses in a blue vase (49x40cm-19x16in) s. W/C
£750 $1260   (26-Aug-91 S1143/R) Pink roses (58x45cm-23x18in) s. W/C

RAEBURN, Sir Henry (1756-1823) British
£1700 $3145   (10-Jun-92 HAR511/R) Portrait of Colonel Alex Creighton (74x61cm-29x24in)
£2443 $4250   (16-Sep-91 B.SF2009/R) Portrait of John Alexander Ogilvie
                  (74x60cm-29x24in)
£3181 $5535   (13-Apr-92 SY.J249/R) Portrait of Master Knox (74x60cm-29x24in)
                  (SA.R 16000)
£3867 $7000   (20-May-92 D.NY14) Portrait of the Honorable Harry Erskine, Lord Advocate
                  of Scotland (76x64cm-30x25in)

RAEBURN, Sir Henry (attrib) (1756-1823) British
£2500 $4400   (8-Apr-92 S43/R) Portrait of Archibald Skirving (46x35cm-18x14in)

RAEBURN, Sir Henry (circle) (1756-1823) British
£1200 $2112   (8-Apr-92 CSK259) Portrait of gentleman, in jacket and cravat, view of
                  castle beyond (76x63cm-30x25in)

RAEBURN, Sir Henry (style) (1756-1823) British
£700 $1225   (23-Sep-91 PHB51) A portrait of a young boy (59x49cm-23x19in)
£2800 $4984   (1-Nov-91 S432/R) Portrait of Admiral Richard Thomas of Stonehouse
                  (75x62cm-30x24in)

RAEL (20th C) Swiss
£877 $1579   (23-Nov-91 N.M264) Vergluhen (45x45cm-18x18in) s.d.1962 (DM 2500)

RAETZER, Hellmuth (1838-1909) German
£2498 $4496   (21-Nov-91 D.V6/R) Shepherd with goats in mountain lake landscape (108x180cm-43x71in) s.i. (A.S 50000)

RAFFAELLI, Jean Francois (1850-1924) French
£6857 $12000   (19-Feb-92 CH.NY35/R) House along river (43x56cm-17x22in) s. panel
£10465 $18000   (16-Oct-91 CH.NY11/R) A house along the river (43x56cm-17x22in) s. panel
£17442 $30000   (16-Oct-91 CH.NY10/R) Menton (67x88cm-26x35in) s.
£760 $1375   (20-May-92 I.N172) La marchande de quatre saisons (30x24cm-12x9in) s. W/C pen (F.FR 7500)
£1903 $3616   (28-Jun-92 FE.P22) Marchande de fleurs (30x24cm-12x9in) s. W/C pen (F.FR 18500)
£2727 $4827   (26-Apr-92 FE.P69) French cancan (20x31cm-8x12in) dr W/C (F.FR 27000)

RAFFALT, Ignaz (1800-1857) Austrian
£1220 $2122   (19-Sep-91 D.V226/R) Thunderstorm over mountain landscape (17x21cm-7x8in) s. panel (A.S 25000)
£1595 $2855   (16-Jan-92 D.V139/R) Harbour scene (22x32cm-9x13in) s. panel (A.S 32000)
£1953 $3320   (24-Oct-91 D.V28/R) Puszta landscape (34x60cm-13x24in) mono. (A.S 40000)
£5498 $9567   (18-Sep-91 N.M660/R) Rest before tavern in mountain valley (32x42cm-13x17in) s.d.1840 panel (DM 16000)
£8725 $15880   (27-May-92 D.V635/R) Village scene (45x62cm-18x24in) s. panel (A.S 180000)

RAFFALT, Johann Gualbert (1836-1865) Austrian
£2248 $4046   (21-Nov-91 D.V71/R) Puszta landscape with evening glow (37x95cm-15x37in) (A.S 45000)

RAFFIN, Andre (1927-) French
£1835 $3413   (17-Jun-92 I.N201/R) Les voiliers, Honfleur (60x92cm-24x36in) s.d.1978 (F.FR 18000)

RAFFY LE PERSAN, Jean (1920-) French
£541 $947   (5-Apr-92 ZZ.F279/R) Paysage hivernal (22x27cm-9x11in) s. panel (F.FR 5200)
£2542 $4500   (5-Nov-91 CE.NY57/R) Montmartre (73x92cm-29x36in) s.d.52

RAGER, Deodatus (18th C) ?
£600 $1032   (16-Oct-91 FER.M44/R) Escena campestre (40x61cm-16x24in) s.d.1799 pencil W/C dr (S.P 110000)

RAGGI, Giovanni (1712-1792) Italian
£33520 $60000   (17-Jan-92 SY.NY76/R) Saint Grata showing her father Lupus the flowers of Saint Alexander (248x156cm-98x61in)
£378 $665   (11-Apr-92 AW.H380/R) Two female figures on cloud with putti (32x24cm-13x9in) sepia pen brush over chk (DM 1100)

RAGGIO, Giuseppe (1823-1916) Italian
£2200 $3806   (4-Oct-91 C187/R) Buffalo herders at rest (61x50cm-24x20in) s.d.1868
£6686 $11500   (10-Oct-91 FA.PH927/R) Rounding up team (66x142cm-26x56in) s.i.d.78

RAGIONE, Raffaele (1851-1925) Italian
£12230 $22625   (9-Jun-92 F.R175/R) Fanciulle al parco (31x40cm-12x16in) s. (I.L 27000000)
£18857 $33000   (20-Feb-92 SY.NY322/R) Au parc Monceau (32x41cm-13x16in) s.

RAGLESS, Maxwell Richard (1901-1981) Australian
£548 $959   (23-Sep-91 AAA.S75) River Onkaparinga (36x61cm-14x24in) s. (A.D 1200)
£641 $1141   (27-Apr-92 J.M121) Summer midday (76x102cm-30x40in) s.d.1935 (A.D 1500)
£655 $1146   (30-Mar-92 AAA.S105/R) Second valley (51x70cm-20x28in) s. board (A.D 1500)

RAGOT, Jules (19th C) French
£741 $1296   (18-Feb-92 CH.AM192) Still life of flowers in basket on draped table (64x44cm-25x17in) s. (D.FL 2400)
£1186 $2111   (29-Nov-91 GAB.G2159) Portrait d'une dame de la belle societe en 1890 (155x100cm-61x39in) s.d.90 (S.FR 3000)
£1414 $2503   (22-Apr-92 ZZ.F136/R) Nature morte aux fruits (65x55cm-26x22in) s.d.96 (F.FR 14000)

RAGUENET, Jean Baptiste Nicolas (1715-1793) French
£38000 $69160   (13-Dec-91 C58/R) Ile Saint-Louis, Paris, with Hotel de Bretonvilliers, from Quai Saint Bernard (46x84cm-18x33in) s.d.1753

RAHL, Carl (1812-1865) Austrian
£826 $1479   (14-Nov-91 ANS.M73/R) Joven napolitana (100x71cm-39x28in) s.d.1844 (S.P 150000)
£994 $1699   (18-Mar-92 D.V238/R) St Sebastian leading Sts Mark and Marcellianus to the marter (31x44cm-12x17in) paper on canvas (A.S 20000)

RAHN, Johann Caspar (1769-1840) Swiss
£2820 $5160   (4-Jun-92 SY.Z309/R) View of Bad Pfafers with view towards Taminatal (39x53cm-15x21in) s.d.1826 (S.FR 7500)

RAHON, Alice (1916-1987) French
£21667 $39000   (18-Nov-91 SY.NY127/R) Scene de chasse (65x65cm-26x26in) s.i.d.42verso

RAIBOLINI, Giacomo see FRANCIA, Giacomo

RAILLARD, Theophil (1819-1894) Swiss?
£614 $1112   (21-May-92 L.K319/R) Teplitz in Bohemia with castle of the Dukes of Clary
                            and Aldringen (16x25cm-6x10in) s. W/C (DM 1800)

RAIMONDI, Aldo (1902-) Italian
£731 $1272   (14-Apr-92 F.M3) Case di montagna (40x50cm-16x20in) s.d.1945 panel
                            (I.L 1600000)
£1429 $2600   (11-Dec-91 RO.BA59/R) Galline (50x70cm-20x28in) s.d.1948 W/C

RAINER (19/20th C) ?
£755 $1336   (5-Nov-91 BA.S154/R) Bowls of cherries (28x36cm-11x14in) s.d.1914
                            (S.KR 8000)

RAINER, Arnulf (1929-) Austrian
£2000 $3440   (17-Oct-91 C92/R) Untitled (60x37cm-24x15in) s. oil on photograph
£2200 $3784   (17-Oct-91 C91/R) Totenmaske (50x61cm-20x24in) init. oil on photograph
£29084 $52933   (26-May-92 D.V338/R) Untitled (73x102cm-29x40in) mono board (A.S 600000)
£874 $1495   (21-Mar-92 WK.M506/R) Self portrait (24x18cm-9x7in) s.i.d.1971/72 oil chk
                            (DM 2500)
£1536 $2780   (23-May-92 GB.B7139) Death mask Toulet (22x20cm-9x8in) s. gouache over
                            offset print double-sided (DM 4500)
£1818 $3236   (26-Nov-91 KF.M971/R) Fendi Ubermalung (24x16cm-9x6in) s. mixed media
                            paper on board (DM 5200)
£2749 $5031   (2-Jun-92 L.K887) Untitled (33x25cm-13x10in) s. oil over photograph on
                            metal panel (DM 8000)
£2996 $5333   (29-Apr-92 G.Z146/R) Christ (41x30cm-16x12in) s.i.d.1967 chl (S.FR 8000)
£3158 $5684   (19-Nov-91 L.K1019/R) Singing (47x60cm-19x24in) s.i. oil W/C over photo
                            (DM 9000)
£3200 $5504   (17-Oct-91 C90) Die Mittagsseligen (36x53cm-14x21in) s.num.3/96 chl
                            pastel lithograph
£4369 $7951   (30-May-92 VG.B398/R) Angelica Kaufmann (42x29cm-17x11in) s. col.chk
                            gouache over photo of litho (DM 12800)
£6469 $11514   (25-Nov-91 WK.M840 a/R) Miro uberzeichnet (19x22cm-7x9in) s. mixed media
                            over etching (DM 18500)
£6485 $11802   (26-May-92 KF.M1181/R) Tree (44x30cm-17x12in) s.i.d.1967 mixed media
                            (DM 19000)
£14815 $26963   (12-Dec-91 SY.AM241/R) Untitled (50x70cm-20x28in) s.d.51 wax crayon W/C
                            (D.FL 48000)
£25256 $45966   (26-May-92 KF.M1180/R) Restecke (73x51cm-29x20in) s.d.1978 oil mixed
                            media board (DM 74000)
£27972 $49790   (30-Nov-91 VG.B369/R) Hagen, black warrior, over Giacometti drawing
                            (82x62cm-32x24in) s.i.d.1961/62 W/C col.oil chk (DM 80000)

RAINER, Arnulf and ETIENNE, Loftus (20th C) Austrian
£4196 $7469   (26-Nov-91 KF.M974/R) Untitled (69x54cm-27x21in) s.d.1985 mixed media
                            collage (DM 12000)

RAINER, Arnulf and ROTH, Dieter (20th C) Austrian
£6119 $10892   (26-Nov-91 KF.M975/R) Untitled (44x62cm-17x24in) s.i.d.1976 mixed media
                            board (DM 17500)

RAINEY, William (1852-1936) British
£1400 $2632   (19-Dec-91 C20/R) Game of cards in Dutch lodging house (69x56cm-27x22in)
                            s.d.1894 pencil W/C bodycol.

RAITTILA, Tapani (1921-) Finnish
£1294 $2303   (1-Dec-91 HOR.H184) From Skatudden (41x31cm-16x12in) s. (F.M 10000)
£453 $806   (1-Dec-91 HOR.H185) Cows (46x31cm-18x12in) s. W/C (F.M 3500)

RAJADELL, Jorge (1952-) Argentinian
£10753 $20000   (16-Jun-92 RO.BA54) Felis Tigris (100x150cm-39x59in) acrylic

RAKOCZI, Basil (20th C) British?
£480 $850   (23-Apr-92 B92) Figure with sunflower (66x51cm-26x20in) s. gouache

RAKSSANYI, Dezso (1879-?) Hungarian
£2500 $4525   (21-May-92 CSK192/R) Spring personified (159x159cm-63x63in) s.

RALEIGH, Charles Sidney (1830-1925) American
£5525 $10000   (24-May-92 JRB.C2/R) 'The Ethel A' (66x91cm-26x36in) s.d.1890

RALEIGH, Henry Patrick (1880-1944) American
£393 $700   (26-Jan-92 JRB.C148) Afternoon tea (28x43cm-11x17in) s.d.28 graphite

RALLI, Theodore Jacques (1852-1909) Greek
£8000 $14240   (26-Nov-91 PH37/R) The temptress (38x46cm-15x18in) s.d.82 s.i.verso
                            canvas on board
£26000 $44460   (18-Mar-92 S189/R) Portrait of a Greek woman, Helen from Megara
                            (21x15cm-8x6in) s.i. panel
£2800 $4788   (18-Mar-92 S188/R) Young beauty (24x16cm-9x6in) s. W/C

RAMAH, Henri (1887-1947) Belgian
£2549 $4359   (21-Mar-92 KV.L465/R) Nu rose (75x49cm-30x19in) paper (B.FR 150000)

RAMBERG, H (19th C) German?
£1394 $2537   (12-Dec-91 L.K659) Sick child seated on grandfather's lap and mother
            offering medicine (75x61cm-30x24in) s. (DM 4000)

RAMENGHI, Bartolomeo (16th C) Italian
£9884 $17000   (10-Oct-91 SY.NY42/R) The Madonna and child with Saints Sebastian and
            Francis (65x46cm-26x18in) panel

RAMENGHI, Giovan Battista (attrib) (1521-1601) Italian
£5556 $9944   (12-Nov-91 SY.AM2/R) Madonna and Child with St John (55x48cm-22x19in)
            panel (D.FL 18000)

RAMIREZ, Felipe (17th C) Spanish
£20000 $36400   (29-May-92 C315/R) Christ the Man of Sorrows (165x109cm-65x43in) s.d.1631

RAMIREZ, Joaquin (19/20th C) ?
£6500 $11050   (22-Oct-91 C7/R) Funeral in Mexico (47x66cm-19x26in) s.i.d.1900

RAMIREZ-IBANEZ, Manuel (1856-1925) Spanish
£6572 $12552   (2-Jul-92 ANS.M114/R) Nina en la plaza de San Marcos (52x36cm-20x14in) s.
            (S.P 1200000)

RAMIS, Julio (1910-) Spanish
£1505 $2739   *(11-Dec-91 FER.M189/R) Arboleda (16x24cm-6x9in) s. wax crayon gouache*
            (S.P 275000)
£3001 $5162   *(16-Oct-91 FER.M267/R) Maternidad en el parque (28x35cm-11x14in) s. mixed*
            media (S.P 550000)

RAMO, Joachim (1928-) Spanish
£523 $900   *(7-Oct-91 RY.P102/R) Sans titre (97x130cm-38x51in) mixed media canvas*
            (F.FR 5200)

RAMON, A A (20th C) American
£579 $1100   (24-Jun-92 B.SF6400/R) Laguna (30x46cm-12x18in) s.d.22.29 canvasboard

RAMOS (?) ?
£546 $939   (16-Oct-91 FER.M134/R) Paseando junto a los chopos (60x100cm-24x39in) s.
            (S.P 100000)

RAMOS ARTAL, Manuel (19th C) Spanish
£664 $1247   (18-Dec-91 DUR.M1176) Caja junto al lago (20x40cm-8x16in) s.d.1900 panel
            (S.P 120000)
£719 $1351   (18-Dec-91 DUR.M1177/R) Lavanderas junto al rio (20x40cm-8x16in) s.d.1900
            panel (S.P 130000)
£720 $1282   (30-Apr-92 CSK11) Spring time. In a villa garden (20x11cm-8x4in) s. panel
            pair
£1230 $2251   (13-May-92 FER.M118/R) Paisaje con rio al amanecer (30x50cm-12x20in)
            s.d.1886 (S.P 225000)
£1367 $2501   (13-May-92 FER.M119/R) Paisaje crepuscular con rio (30x50cm-12x20in)
            s.d.1887 (S.P 250000)

RAMOS, Domingo (20th C) South American
£3500 $5950   (22-Oct-91 C9/R) Cuban landscape (50x65cm-20x26in) s.d.1945 canvas on
            board
£6354 $11500   (19-May-92 SY.NY123/R) Paisaje tropical (46x56cm-18x22in) s.d.1954
£9444 $17000   (19-Nov-91 CH.NY190/R) Bahia de cabana (96x122cm-38x48in) s.d.1953
            i.verso i.stretcher

RAMOS, Francisco (?) ?
£984 $1801   (13-May-92 FER.M62/R) Acampada gitana. Escalinata (16x9cm-6x4in) s. panel
            pair (S.P 180000)

RAMOS, Maximo (1880-?) Spanish?
£436 $750   *(7-Oct-91 ANS.M47/R) Galanteo (18x16cm-7x6in) s. pencil dr (S.P 80000)*
£885 $1663   *(18-Dec-91 DUR.M749) Bello sueno (30x46cm-12x18in) s. W/C (S.P 160000)*

RAMOS, Mel (1935-) American
£2793 $5000   (12-Nov-91 CE.NY61/R) Leta and the scissor-tailed flycatcher
            (127x254cm-50x100in) s.i.d.1969verso canvas on panel diptych
£18286 $32000   (27-Feb-92 CH.NY27/R) Peek-a-Boo, red head (70x51cm-28x20in)
            s.i.d.1964verso
£41899 $75000   (13-Nov-91 CH.NY169/R) Life savers (178x155cm-70x61in) s.i.d.1965verso

RAMPAZO, Luciano (1936-) French
£950 $1700   (6-May-92 D.NY108/R) Porte St Denis (77x102cm-30x40in) s. i.stretcher
£1073 $1900   (6-Nov-91 D.NY92/R) La Madeleine (66x89cm-26x35in) s.

RAMPL, Oswald (1911-) Austrian
£494 $865   (19-Feb-92 D.V178) Going near Elmau with Kaiser range (39x48cm-15x19in)
            s.d.1951 panel (A.S 10000)

RAMSAY, Allan (1713-1784) British
£3077	$5877	(15-Jul-92 CH.S759/R) Portrait of Mrs. Campbell, nee Susan Erskine of Menzie (76x63cm-30x25in) s.i.d.1748 painted oval (A.D 8000)
£4500	$8055	(15-Nov-91 C26/R) Portrait of Martha Baker, wearing dress, cap and shawl (77x64cm-30x25in) s.i.d.1739 painted cartouche
£7500	$13425	(13-Nov-91 CG561/R) A portrait of Mary Campbell of Lochlane (76x63cm-30x25in) s.d.1736 i.stretcher painted oval
£11000	$19690	(13-Nov-91 S43/R) Portrait of Brigadier General Sir John Mordaunt wearing furlined coat (76x63cm-30x25in) s.d.1746 i.d.verso painted oval
£28000	$53480	(15-Jul-92 S22/R) Portrait of lady, probably Lady Sarah Bunbury (92x71cm-36x28in)

RAMSAY, Allan (circle) (1713-1784) British
£820	$1402	(12-Mar-92 CSK111/R) Portrait of young lady in dress with lace collar and choker (46x36cm-18x14in)
£850	$1513	(21-Jan-92 PH45/R) Portrait of lady, wearing dress and choker (60x51cm-24x20in) feigned oval
£2000	$3560	(21-Jan-92 PH46/R) Portrait of lady, wearing satin dress and cloak (76x63cm-30x25in)
£2528	$4500	(22-Jan-92 SY.NY230/R) Portrait of Mrs Neville Walter (75x62cm-30x24in)

RAMSAY, Allan (style) (1713-1784) British
£1000	$1790	(14-Jan-92 SWS116) Portrait of officer wearing uniform (73x61cm-29x24in)

RAMSAY, Allan (fl.1880-1903) British
£700	$1281	(12-May-92 LV238) Evening glow, near Glamis (61x46cm-24x18in) s.
£1300	$2184	(26-Aug-91 S796/R) Autumn evening in Glenesk (30x45cm-12x18in) s.d.1897 s.i.d.verso

RAMSAY, Dennis (20th C) British
£793	$1411	(26-Nov-91 J.M9/R) Magnolia in antique Chinese vase (58x44cm-23x17in) s. oil tempera board (A.D 1800)
£1709	$3043	(27-Apr-92 J.M267) Still life with fruit (59x75cm-23x30in) s. oil tempera board (A.D 4000)
£2533	$4509	(26-Nov-91 J.M269/R) Still life with fruit (59x75cm-23x30in) s. oil tempera board (A.D 5750)

RAMSAY, James (1786-1854) British
£1500	$2685	(14-Nov-91 CSK330/R) The old campaigner (193x160cm-76x63in) s.

RAMSEY, Milne (1847-1915) American
£1124	$2000	(26-Jan-92 JRB.C60/R) Study in yellow (46x56cm-18x22in) s.d.88
£1389	$2500	(22-Nov-91 S.BM89/R) Still life with orange, almonds and vases. Sketch of cottage (61x51cm-24x20in) s.i.d. double-sided
£3571	$6500	(28-May-92 CH.NY49/R) Study in yellow (48x56cm-19x22in) s.d.88

RANCILLAC, Bernard (1931-) French
£4893	$9101	(15-Jun-92 GL.P55/R) Untitled - woman smoking (80x80cm-31x31in) s.d.1989verso (F.FR 48000)
£5658	$10751	(26-Jun-92 FB.P83/R) La poursuite (116x80cm-46x31in) s. (F.FR 55000)

RANDOLPH, Lee F (1880-?) American
£960	$1700	(12-Feb-92 B.SF431/R) Lighthouse point (14x18cm-6x7in) s. i.verso canvasboard

RANFT, Richard (1862-1931) Swiss
£857	$1500	(28-Feb-92 SY.NY102/R) Picnic by chateau (60x72cm-24x28in) s.d.1929

RANFTL, Johann Matthias (1805-1854) Austrian
£7429	$13000	(20-Feb-92 SY.NY219/R) Playing with puppies (34x28cm-13x11in) s.d.1848 panel
£1221	*$2101*	*(10-Oct-91 D.V206/R) Guerilla fighters in costume on guard, Banat (12x18cm-5x7in) s. W/C gouache (A.S 25000)*

RANGER, Henry Ward (1858-1916) American
£497	$900	(7-Dec-91 LAE.L108/R) Farm landscape (30x43cm-12x17in) s.
£549	$950	(8-Sep-91 LIT.L215) Road by lake (30x41cm-12x16in) s.d.1908 board
£885	$1700	(31-Jul-92 E.EDM80/R) Becalmed sailboat (46x64cm-18x25in) s.
£1618	$2800	(8-Sep-91 LIT.L92) Landscape (71x91cm-28x36in) s.d. estate st.verso

RANK, Georg (1855-1938) Austrian
£388	*$691*	*(28-Apr-92 D.V41/R) Dance (29x39cm-11x15in) chl ochre chk (A.S 8000)*

RANKEN, William Bruce Ellis (1881-1941) British
£3800	$7144	(18-Dec-91 C169/R) Pygmalion (110x85cm-43x33in) indis.s.

RANKIN, David (1946-) Australian
£685	$1275	(21-Jun-92 SY.ME33/R) Tanzan good luck (102x152cm-40x60in) s.i.d.1971verso acrylic (A.D 1700)
£892	$1490	(19-Aug-91 SY.ME67) River flats (66x101cm-26x40in) s.d.1988 i.verso (A.D 1900)
£1408	$2352	(19-Aug-91 SY.ME137) Tallerook (101x151cm-40x59in) s.d.73 i.verso (A.D 3000)
£1617	$2862	(26-Apr-92 SY.ME460) Untitled landscape (151x167cm-59x66in) s. (A.D 3800)

RANKIN, David (1946-) Australian-cont.
£1694	$3150	(21-Jun-92 SY.ME97/R) The end of the escarpment (259x136cm-102x54in) s.d.1987 s.i.d.verso (A.D 4200)
£1709	$3043	(27-Apr-92 J.M274) Wanda Sand Hills II (152x167cm-60x66in) s.d.84 (A.D 4000)
£1735	$3037	(23-Sep-91 AAA.S167) Small sandy ridge (91x123cm-36x48in) s.d.90 (A.D 3800)
£1762	$3137	(26-Nov-91 J.M198/R) Three fish beach (106x213cm-42x84in) s.d.86 (A.D 4000)
£1787	$3163	(26-Apr-92 SY.ME393) Ribbon fish - Moonie Moonie II (210x128cm-83x50in) s.d.1983 (A.D 4200)
£1935	$3600	(21-Jun-92 SY.ME120) Port hacking (180x360cm-71x142in) s.d.1982 (A.D 4800)
£2113	$3528	(19-Aug-91 SY.ME336) Longridge and scrub (102x183cm-40x72in) s.d.1989 i.verso (A.D 4500)
£2304	$4009	(16-Sep-91 CH.ME53) Walking across, 1975 (169x169cm-67x67in) s.i.d.verso (A.D 5000)
£3521	$5880	(19-Aug-91 SY.ME353/R) Bundeena (152x167cm-60x66in) s.d.84 (A.D 7500)

RANNEY, William T (1813-1857) American
| £29762 | $50000 | (28-Aug-91 MFA.C163/R) Wounded trooper (41x61cm-16x24in) |

RANSY, Jean (1910-) Belgian
| £4010 | $6817 | (22-Oct-91 C.A891) Still life (80x130cm-31x51in) s.d.1964 (B.FR 240000) |

RANTTILA, Martti (1897-1964) Finnish
| £970 | $1727 | (1-Dec-91 HOR.H186) Lamb by the brook (37x48cm-15x19in) s.d.1944 (F.M 7500) |

RANUCCI, Lucio (20th C) Italian
| £2549 | $4537 | (26-Nov-91 SY.MI94/R) Bric a brac des oignons (60x60cm-24x24in) s.d.1991 s.init.d.verso (I.L 5500000) |

RANZONI, Daniele (attrib) (1843-1889) Italian
| £1840 | $3293 | (14-Nov-91 CH.R204) Busto di giovane signora (50x41cm-20x16in) i.d.1881 (I.L 4000000) |

RANZONI, Hans (19/20th C) Austrian
| £1250 | $2225 | (21-Jan-92 ACA522) Viennese scene (25x36cm-10x14in) s.d.1922 board |

RAOUX, Albert (19th C) French
| £917 | $1633 | (30-Oct-91 CH.AM252) Still life of bunch of flowers around stone with Jean van Huysum (25x37cm-10x15in) s.d.1864 panel (D.FL 3000) |

RAOUX, Jean (1677-1734) French
| £7832 | $13862 | (7-Nov-91 D.V194/R) Eliezer and Rebecca by the fountain (85x101cm-33x40in) (A.S 160000) |

RAOUX, Jean (attrib) (1677-1734) French
| £3125 | $5531 | (5-Nov-91 GF.L2089/R) Family making music (70x92cm-28x36in) (S.FR 8000) |

RAOUX, Jean (circle) (1677-1734) French
| £900 | $1638 | (26-May-92 PH160) Portrait of lady, wearing velvet hat and pearls and white robe (65x49cm-26x19in) |

RAOUX, Jean (style) (1677-1734) French
| £2809 | $5000 | (22-Jan-92 SY.NY160/R) Young girl with bird (46x34cm-18x13in) |

RAPACKI, Jozef (1871-1929) Polish
| £827 | $1496 | (7-Dec-91 AL.W6) Cowslips (66x83cm-26x33in) s. board (P.Z 16500000) |
| £1361 | $2354 | (8-Sep-91 REM.W28) Birch tree (95x66cm-37x26in) s. board (P.Z 26000000) |

RAPHAEL (after) (1483-1520) Italian
£680	$1190	(2-Apr-92 CSK55) Portrait of artist (58x45cm-23x18in)
£750	$1350	(21-Nov-91 CSK214) Portrait of Pope Julius II (15x11cm-6x4in) board oval
£750	$1313	(27-Feb-92 B70) The Transfiguration (49x32cm-19x13in) panel
£785	$1500	(16-Jul-92 SY.NY202/R) The visitation (22x16cm-9x6in) copper
£800	$1400	(27-Feb-92 CSK56/R) Pope Leo X with Cardinals Giulio de Medici and Luigo de' Rossi (60x45cm-24x18in) panel
£800	$1424	(29-Oct-91 PH118) The Madonna del Passeggio (106x94cm-42x37in)
£800	$1400	(27-Feb-92 CSK5) Madonna and Child with the infant Saint John (22x80cm-9x31in)
£800	$1400	(27-Feb-92 B54) The Madonna della Sedia (21x21cm-8x8in)
£803	$1437	(6-May-92 GD.B650) Madonna and Child with saints (34x29cm-13x11in) (S.FR 2200)
£900	$1575	(27-Feb-92 CSK42) The Madonna della Cardellino (36x26cm-14x10in)
£900	$1719	(21-Jul-92 PH246) Madonna (46x35cm-18x14in)
£900	$1620	(22-Nov-91 SWS213) The Madonna della Sedia (42x34cm-17x13in)
£918	$1661	(19-May-92 AB.S4370/R) Madonna and Child (112x94cm-44x37in) (S.KR 9700)
£919	$1700	(10-Jun-92 GRO.B416) Madonna di Foligno (170x114cm-67x45in) s.i.verso
£950	$1729	(26-May-92 PH153/R) Madonna del Granduca (83x56cm-33x22in) canvas on board
£950	$1663	(2-Apr-92 CSK14/R) Saint Cecilia (103x75cm-41x30in)
£1047	$1800	(16-Oct-91 D.NY81) Madonna del Granduca (84x56cm-33x22in)

RAPHAEL (after) (1483-1520) Italian-cont.

£1050	$2006	(14-Jul-92 DR344/R) Madonna with infant Christ and St. John (152x76cm-60x30in)
£1067	$1900	(22-Jan-92 SY.NY39/R) Madonna and Child with St. Elizabeth and St. John (47x38cm-19x15in)
£1180	$2100	(22-Jan-92 SY.NY33/R) Sistine Madonna (159x117cm-63x46in)
£1200	$2196	(12-May-92 SWS612/R) Madonna and child with St. Elizabeth and infant St. John Baptist, landscape (43x32cm-17x13in)
£1300	$2353	(3-Dec-91 RG3247) Madonna and child with St John (74cm-29ins circular)
£1300	$2275	(27-Feb-92 B25) The Holy Family of Francis I (208x136cm-82x54in)
£1312	$2256	(16-Oct-91 AT.P91/R) Sainte famille avec Sainte Anne, Saint Jean Baptiste enfant et deux anges (75x63cm-30x25in) (F.FR 13000)
£1396	$2400	(8-Mar-92 BU.M231) Madonna and Child with St.John (72cm-28ins circular) s.verso (S.KR 14500)
£1500	$2880	(9-Jul-92 CSK34/R) The Madonna della Sedia
£1600	$2800	(27-Feb-92 CSK28/R) The Holy Family with Saint Elizabeth and the infant Saint John (138x107cm-54x42in)
£1702	$3250	(16-Jul-92 SY.NY187/R) Holy Family with St John the Baptist (98x71cm-39x28in)
£1761	$2958	(27-Aug-91 RAS.K274/R) Mary and Anne with Jesus and Johannes (138x105cm-54x41in) (D.KR 20000)
£1800	$3456	(9-Jul-92 CSK48/R) The Tempi Madonna (80x56cm-31x22in) after Raphael
£1950	$3393	(11-Sep-91 PHL93/R) Virgin and Child with St. John (107x76cm-42x30in)
£1958	$3465	(7-Nov-91 D.V237/R) Madonna in landscape (114x88cm-45x35in) panel (A.S 40000)
£2000	$3840	(9-Jul-92 CSK109/R) The Impanata Madonna (155x123cm-61x48in)
£2011	$3600	(16-Nov-91 WOL.C3600) Madonna and Child (71cm-28ins circular)
£2077	$3800	(5-Feb-92 D.NY78) Madonna della Sedia (76x76cm-30x30in) circular
£2200	$3850	(28-Feb-92 C152) The Madonna and Child (82x61cm-32x24in) panel
£2500	$4775	(16-Jul-92 CSK230) Madonna and child with infant St. John (74x74cm-29x29in) indist.i.verso
£2500	$4375	(25-Feb-92 PH52/R) Sacra conversazione, St Cecilia, Mary Magdalen and others (105x68cm-41x27in) panel
£2795	$4807	(7-Mar-92 CH.AM245) Madonna della Sedia (74x73cm-29x29in) panel in tondo (D.FL 9000)
£2881	$5214	(5-Dec-91 SY.MO336/R) La Transfiguration du Christ (32x23cm-13x9in) copper (F.FR 28000)
£3000	$5400	(22-Nov-91 SWS86/R) The Madonna della sedia (72cm-28ins circular)
£3600	$6552	(26-May-92 PH165) Madonna della Sedia (75x75cm-30x30in)
£3839	$6948	(3-Dec-91 AB.S4746/R) Saint Cecilia (190x114cm-75x45in) shaped (S.KR 40000)
£4400	$8052	(12-May-92 SWS776/R) Madonna della Sedia (74cm-29ins circular) i.d.1843 verso panel
£4420	$8000	(22-May-92 SY.NY127/R) Holy Family (46x36cm-18x14in) panel
£4500	$7695	(18-Mar-92 S174/R) Madonna della Sedia (71cm-28ins circular)
£4968	$8495	(18-Mar-92 D.V33/R) Madonna della Seggiola (46cm-18ins circular) (A.S 100000)
£6500	$11570	(27-Nov-91 S386/R) Madonna della Sedia (71cm-28ins circular)
£9392	$17000	(22-May-92 SY.NY222/R) Madonna dell'Impannata (155x121cm-61x48in) panel
£23529	$42118	(15-Nov-91 GK.Z5088/R) Middle piece of praedella (18x19cm-7x7in) panel (S.FR 60000)
£820	*$1566*	*(14-Jul-92 DR347) Madonna with infant Christ and St. John (76x51cm-30x20in) pastel*

RAPHAEL (school) (1483-1520) Italian

£11583	$19807	(12-Mar-92 GK.Z26/R) Ecce homo (18x19cm-7x7in) panel (S.FR 30000)

RAPHAEL (style) (1483-1520) Italian

£1700	*$2958*	*(13-Apr-92 S69/R) Resurrection (37x46cm-15x18in) pen wash htd white octagonal*
£3500	*$6720*	*(7-Jul-92 C256/R) Head of bearded man (45x35cm-18x14in) chk bodycol*

RAPHAEL, Joseph (1872-1950) American

£1271	$2250	(12-Feb-92 B.SF499/R) Painting in Bruges (27x35cm-11x14in) init. i.verso board
£6316	$12000	(24-Jun-92 B.SF6316/R) Oriental still life (76x91cm-30x36in) s.d.40 verso board
£20950	$37500	(13-Nov-91 B.SF2622/R) La fete du Bourgmestre Captain N.W. van den Broek of Laren, N. Holland (204x226cm-80x89in)

RAPHAEL, William (1833-1914) Prussian/Canadian

£1256	$2298	(14-May-92 SY.T167/R) In mirror (32x24cm-13x9in) s.d.1870 board (C.D 2750)
£1707	$3073	(19-Nov-91 FP.M170/R) Berry picker (48x33cm-19x13in) s. (C.D 3500)
£4110	$7521	(14-May-92 SY.T165/R) Afternoon in woods (61x107cm-24x42in) s.d.1870 (C.D 9000)

RAPIN, Aime (1869-?) Swiss

£1481	*$2681*	*(19-May-92 GF.L2326/R) Young shepherdess lighting fire (40x53cm-16x21in) s. pastel board (S.FR 4000)*
£2037	*$3687*	*(19-May-92 GF.L2324/R) Portrait of young girl (46x34cm-18x13in) s.d.1904 pastel board (S.FR 5500)*

RAPOUS, Michele Antonio (1733-1819) Italian
£9044 $17274   (3-Jul-92 SD.P102/R) Nature morte de fruits. Lapins dans un paysage
                        (73x99cm-29x39in) pair (F.FR 88000)

RAPOUS, Michele Antonio (attrib) (1733-1819) Italian
£6104 $10926   (13-Nov-91 PIC.P123/R) Bouquet de fleurs dans un vase, raisins et fruits
                        devant un plat renverse (81x64cm-32x25in) (F.FR 60000)

RAPP, Alex (1869-1927) Finnish
£489 $890   (11-Dec-91 HOR.H97) Sailing (23x43cm-9x17in) s. (F.M 3800)

RAPP, Johann Rudolf (1827-1903) Swiss
£2107 $3750   (22-Jan-92 SY.NY283/R) Coastal seascape. Alpine vista (35x43cm-14x17in)
                        one s.i. one s.i. s.verso canvas board pair

RAQUIN (?) ?
£1815 $3139   (4-Oct-91 CSC.P60/R) Soleil couchant (54x65cm-21x26in) s. (F.FR 18000)
£2357 $4242   (2-Feb-92 CSC.P39/R) Bateau amarre (54x65cm-21x26in) s. (F.FR 23000)
£2823 $4883   (4-Oct-91 CSC.P57/R) Bord de mer (80x80cm-31x31in) s. (F.FR 28000)
£2869 $5164   (2-Feb-92 CSC.P40) Bord de riviere (54x65cm-21x26in) s. (F.FR 28000)

RAQUIN, Iris Michelle (1933-) French
£728 $1275   (5-Apr-92 ZZ.F250/R) Vase de fleurs (92x65cm-36x26in) s. (F.FR 7000)
£2810 $4917   (5-Apr-92 ZZ.F235/R) Vol de Mouettes sur l'etang (81x81cm-32x32in) s.
                        (F.FR 27000)
£3528 $6245   (10-Nov-91 ZZ.F259/R) Fleurs et roseaux sur la Lagune (73x100cm-29x39in)
                        s. (F.FR 35000)

RASCHEN, Henry (1854-1937) German/American
£3911 $7000   (13-Nov-91 B.SF2711/R) Mountain glow, Apache (62x91cm-24x36in) s.

RASELL, Robert (fl.1868-1880) British
£1400 $2506   (5-May-92 SWS312/R) Study of bull terrier seated on chair
                        (65x52cm-26x20in) s.

RASENBERGER, Gernot (17th C) German
£702 $1263   (22-Nov-91 SA.A1659/R) Frozen river landscape with figures
                        (30x60cm-12x24in) s.i. (DM 2000)
£772 $1389   (22-Nov-91 SA.A1808/R) Street scene with view of restaurant Nussbaum,
                        Berlin (50x40cm-20x16in) s.i. (DM 2200)
£1053 $1895   (22-Nov-91 SA.A1812/R) Berlin, Brandenburger Tor, summer evening
                        (60x80cm-24x31in) s.i. (DM 3000)

RASETTI, Georges (19th C) French
£814 $1489   (17-May-92 T.B205/R) Course cycliste sur route (70x72cm-28x28in) s. board
                        (F.FR 8000)

RASKIN, Joseph (1897-1981) American
£599 $1000   (20-Aug-91 RB.HY90/R) Cape Cod Village (61x76cm-24x30in) s. st.verso

RASKO, Maxmilian Aurel Reinitz (1883-1961) American
£914 $1600   (3-Apr-92 S.W2437/R) Portrait of Emma Kessler (203x117cm-80x46in) s.d.27

RASMUSSEN, Carl (1841-1893) Danish
£539 $953   (11-Feb-92 RAS.K144) Evening at Godthabsfjord, Greenland
                        (25x50cm-10x20in) init.d.1871 (D.KR 6000)

RASMUSSEN, Georg Anton (1842-1914) Norwegian
£589 $1055   (16-Nov-91 FAL.M295/R) Woman in landscape (27x20cm-11x8in) s. panel
                        (S.KR 6200)
£627 $1123   (16-Nov-91 FAL.M294/R) Children in landscape (27x20cm-11x8in) s. panel
                        (S.KR 6600)
£833 $1550   (15-Jun-92 B.O126 a/R) Landscape from Sognefjord (40x60cm-16x24in)
                        s.d.1910 (N.KR 9500)
£862 $1483   (16-Oct-91 KM.K1330/R) Fjord landscape (25x38cm-10x15in) canvas on panel
                        (DM 2500)
£1133 $1927   (6-Aug-91 UL.T220/R) Fjord landscape (23x33cm-9x13in) panel (N.KR 13000)
£1829 $3200   (18-Feb-92 CE.NY189/R) Fjord (75x104cm-30x41in) s.
£1953 $3320   (24-Oct-91 D.V77/R) Fjord landscape (20x32cm-8x13in) s. (A.S 40000)
£2923 $5320   (10-Dec-91 UL.T212/R) Fjord landscape from Vestlandet (60x90cm-24x35in)
                        (N.KR 33000)
£3000 $5130   (18-Mar-92 S19/R) Figures on a beach in a Fjord (67x49cm-26x19in)
                        s.d.1883
£5500 $10230   (17-Jun-92 S331/R) Crossing fjord in boat (75x124cm-30x49in) s.d.1887
£5596 $10072   (19-Nov-91 RAS.K119/R) Norwegian fjord landscape (78x126cm-31x50in) s.
                        (D.KR 62000)

RASMUSSEN, I E C (1841-1893) Danish
£1145 $2027   (23-Apr-92 RAS.V879/R) Seascape with sailship near coastal cliffs
                        (50x68cm-20x27in) s. (D.KR 13000)
£2291 $4055   (23-Apr-92 RAS.V878/R) Boy resting, watching cows and sailship near
                        Svendborgsund (87x143cm-34x56in) s.d.1876 (D.KR 26000)
£3568 $6637   (16-Jun-92 RAS.V855/R) Coastal landscape with fishermen and children
                        playing (52x80cm-20x31in) s.d.1876 (D.KR 40000)

RASMUSSEN, N P (19/20th C) Danish
£661 $1170   (23-Apr-92 RAS.V880/R) Two birds by water wheel (26x38cm-10x15in)
                     mono.d.1906 (D.KR 7500)

RASMUSSEN, Niels Peter (1847-1918) Danish
£728 $1296   (29-Apr-92 D.V880/R) Ducks on woodland pond (31x45cm-12x18in) i.d.1918
                     (A.S 15000)

RASMUSSEN, Peter Augustave (1927-) British
£500 $890   (28-Nov-91 L26) Tobogganing - young girl in the snow (61x43cm-24x17in) s.
                     pastel

RASPAL, Antoine (attrib) (1738-1811) French
£1226 $2145   (24-Feb-92 CSC.P58) Gentilhomme tenant une rose (65x54cm-26x21in)
                     (F.FR 12000)

RASPAUD, Eric (20th C) French?
£509 $910   (17-Nov-91 R.P180) Les indiens sont parmi nous (116x79cm-46x31in) s.
                     acrylic jeans (F.FR 5000)

RASSENFOSSE, Armand (1862-1934) Belgian
£612 $1083   (5-Nov-91 SY.AM368) 'Type de Walonne' (30x23cm-12x9in) s.d.1922 black red
                     chk (D.FL 2000)
£795 $1438   (23-May-92 KV.L271/R) Young girl putting on her bonnet (28x22cm-11x9in)
                     mono. pastel (B.FR 48000)

RATHBONE, John (1750-1807) British
£680 $1163   (17-Mar-92 SWS1199/R) Angler beside a lake (22x29cm-9x11in) s. panel
£920 $1757   (15-Jul-92 S198/R) River landscape with figures under a bridge
                     (44x60cm-17x24in)
£950 $1710   (19-Nov-91 PH110/R) Drover with horse and cart on country path
                     (17x25cm-7x10in) panel
£2949 $5250   (22-Jan-92 SY.NY115/R) Landscape near Matlock, Derbyshire
                     (71x91cm-28x36in)
£4000 $7160   (13-Nov-91 S198/R) Landscapes with cattle (34x43cm-13x17in) pair

RATHBONE, John (style) (1750-1807) British
£750 $1320   (8-Apr-92 CSK296/R) Wooded landscape with artist sketching by watermill,
                     drover beyond (71x86cm-28x34in)

RATHBONE, John and MORLAND, George (18th C) British
£2400 $4296   (13-Nov-91 S81/R) Rustics on path with distant view of London from
                     Blackheath (21x30cm-8x12in) panel
£4200 $7392   (8-Apr-92 S242/R) River landscape with gypsies resting by fire
                     (43x58cm-17x23in)

RATHSMAN, Siri (1895-1974) Swedish
£480 $869   (3-Dec-91 AB.S5142/R) Fisherman (39x78cm-15x31in) s.d.1955 (S.KR 5000)
£759 $1389   (13-May-92 BU.S159/R) Victory 1942 (54x65cm-21x26in) s. (S.KR 8000)
£1233 $2257   (13-May-92 BU.S158/R) Woman and seagull on beach (110x80cm-43x31in)
                     (S.KR 13000)
£1919 $3474   (3-Dec-91 AB.S5141/R) Composition (97x130cm-38x51in) s. d.1931verso
                     (S.KR 20000)

RATTERMAN, Walter G (1887-1944) American
£710 $1300   (3-Jun-92 D.NY78) Portrait of artist's sister, Pearl Margaret
                     (102x86cm-40x34in) s.d.1925 s.i.d.1925 verso

RATTNER, Abraham (1893-1978) American
£1149 $2000   (14-Sep-91 LAE.L309/R) Seine River, Paris (66x81cm-26x32in) s.

RATTRAY, Alexander Wellwood (1849-1902) American
£500 $840   (26-Aug-91 S1088/R) 'Let the swan on still Mary's loch, float double swan
                     and shadow' (30x51cm-12x20in) s.

RATY, Albert (1889-1970) Belgian
£917 $1604   (24-Sep-91 GM.B670/R) Vue de Vallee (60x70cm-24x28in) s. (B.FR 55000)
£2000 $3500   (24-Sep-91 GM.B643/R) Our graide (55x65cm-22x26in) s. (B.FR 120000)

RAU, Emil (1858-1937) German
£880 $1593   (7-Dec-91 WK.M474/R) Der Tegernseer (29x23cm-11x9in) s. canvas on board
                     (DM 2500)
£1895 $3240   (13-Mar-92 FN.S2918/R) Girl seated at table in garden (81x63cm-32x25in)
                     s.d.1894 (DM 5400)
£4286 $7500   (20-Feb-92 SY.NY217/R) Green hat (56x46cm-22x18in) s.d.87
£5842 $10165   (18-Sep-91 N.M661/R) Upper Bavarian females playing zither in peasant
                     interior (87x67cm-34x26in) s. (DM 17000)
£6857 $12000   (19-Feb-92 CH.NY74/R) Hiking in Alps (110x90cm-43x35in) s.
£7429 $13000   (20-Feb-92 SY.NY218/R) Tyrolean family (90x110cm-35x43in) s.
£8721 $15000   (16-Oct-91 CH.NY112/R) The courtship (79x96cm-31x38in) s.d.80

RAU, Emil (attrib) (1858-?) German
£596 $1020   (13-Mar-92 FN.S2919/R) Peasant wearing Tyrolean costume on path in
                     mountain landscape (93x73cm-37x29in) s. pastel (DM 1700)

RAUBER, Wilhelm Carl (1849-1926) German
£2062　　$3588　　(18-Sep-91 N.M659/R) Fox hunt (55x80cm-22x31in) s. (DM 6000)

RAUCH, Johann Nepomuk (1804-1847) Austrian
£3198　　$5500　　(16-Oct-91 CH.NY95/R) Figures with a horse, cows and goats near a well
　　　　　　　　　with a city beyond (34x45cm-13x18in) s.d.1836 panel

RAUCH, Johann Nepomuk (attrib) (1804-1847) Austrian
£979　　$1694　　(25-Mar-92 KM.K1380) Italian shepherd couple and animals resting by
　　　　　　　　wayside memorial, evening (24x33cm-9x13in) indis.s. (DM 2800)

RAUDET, C (18th C) ?
£1600　　$2720　　(23-Oct-91 S80/R) Classical figures amidst ruins (61x46cm-24x18in)
　　　　　　　　s.d.1797 s.verso gouache

RAUMAN, A (19th C) German
£603　　$1073　　(29-Oct-91 PH.T33/R) Admiring needlepoint (43x33cm-17x13in) s. (C.D 1200)

RAUMANN, Joseph (1908-) Hungarian
£605　　$1041　　(20-Oct-91 LT.P33) Sur la Plage de Deauville (33x41cm-13x16in) s. panel
　　　　　　　　(F.FR 6000)
£871　　$1568　　(2-Feb-92 ZZ.F228/R) Fleuve traversant la ville (22x33cm-9x13in) s. panel
　　　　　　　　(F.FR 8500)

RAUPP, Karl (1837-1918) German
£1306　　$2272　　(18-Sep-91 N.M664) Boats houses on banks of lake Chiemsee
　　　　　　　　(33x60cm-13x24in) rem.sig. board (DM 3800)
£1468　　$2656　　(22-May-92 GB.B6012) Sailing boat on lake (12x18cm-5x7in) s. panel
　　　　　　　　(DM 4300)
£1478　　$2571　　(18-Sep-91 N.M663/R) Chiemsee landscape (36x60cm-14x24in) mono.indis.d.
　　　　　　　　board (DM 4300)
£2424　　$4411　　(27-May-92 D.V570/R) Chiemsee landscape (36x18cm-14x7in) si.d.94 panel
　　　　　　　　(A.S 50000)
£3436　　$5979　　(18-Sep-91 N.M662/R) Lake Chiemsee landscape (29x58cm-11x23in) s.d.1914
　　　　　　　　canvas on board (DM 10000)
£411　　$707　　(8-Oct-91 ZEL.L1292/R) Praying nun at river bank (20x24cm-8x9in) col.chk
　　　　　　　　(DM 1200)
£411　　$707　　(8-Oct-91 ZEL.L1291/R) Portrait of ferryman (23x19cm-9x7in) pen gouache
　　　　　　　　(DM 1200)
£497　　$854　　(8-Oct-91 ZEL.L1294/R) Study of boy wearing short leather pants
　　　　　　　　(26x21cm-10x8in) i. W/C over pencil (DM 1450)

RAUPP, Karl (attrib) (1837-1918) German
£2577　　$4716　　(2-Jun-92 FN.S2710/R) Women with spinning wheel in interior
　　　　　　　　(160x119cm-63x47in) i. grisaille (DM 7500)

RAURICH Y PETRE, Nicolas (1871-1945) Spanish
£1216　　$2287　　(17-Dec-91 BRO.B416) Anochecer (50x35cm-20x14in) s. (S.P 220000)

RAUSCHENBERG, Robert (1925-) American
£1081　　$2000　　(12-Jun-92 SY.NY258/R) Untitled (27x22cm-11x9in) s.d.1958 on paper cup
　　　　　　　　lid on board
£1489　　$2636　　(26-Apr-92 SY.ME227) Light - from Seven Character Series
　　　　　　　　(108x77cm-43x30in) s.d.1982 mixed media card on board (A.D 3500)
£4749　　$8500　　(6-May-92 CH.NY316/R) April's Fool V (34x25cm-13x10in) s.d.86 solvent
　　　　　　　　transfer
£10056　　$18000　　(13-Nov-91 CH.NY187/R) Untitled (58x39cm-23x15in) s.d.79 paper collage
　　　　　　　　solvent transfer
£14525　　$26000　　(6-May-92 CH.NY379/R) Half acre (151x102cm-59x40in) s.d.79 solvent
　　　　　　　　transfer fabric collage
£15180　　$27780　　(12-May-92 GO.G231/R) Lighthouse keeping (120x210cm-47x83in) s. mixed
　　　　　　　　media metal (S.KR 160000)
£25714　　$45000　　(25-Feb-92 SY.NY165/R) Close-out (57x76cm-22x30in) s.i.d.69 graphite
　　　　　　　　transfer dr. gouache
£44693　　$80000　　(5-May-92 CH.NY29/R) Untitled (23x23cm-9x9in) s.i.d.1960verso metal paper
　　　　　　　　collage oil canvas
£55866　　$100000　　(14-Nov-91 SY.NY347/R) Allegory - lesson I (105x75cm-41x30in) s.d.69
　　　　　　　　solvent transfer pencil W/C
£61453　　$110000　　(14-Nov-91 SY.NY365/R) Omen (72x85cm-28x33in) s.d.1965 verso pencil W/C
　　　　　　　　transfer collage

RAVEEL, Roger (1921-) Belgian
£1869　　$3196　　(21-Mar-92 KV.L433/R) The window (50x72cm-20x28in) s.d.75 acrylic paper
　　　　　　　　(B.FR 110000)
£9410　　$17032　　(7-Dec-91 KV.L501/R) The orator (195x145cm-77x57in) s.d.83 (B.FR 550000)
£911　　$1648　　(23-May-92 KV.L273) Man seen from the back (29x20cm-11x8in) s.d.87
　　　　　　　　acrylic pencil (B.FR 55000)
£1159　　$2098　　(23-May-92 KV.L272) Man with square (35x25cm-14x10in) s.d.1990-91 acrylic
　　　　　　　　pastel (B.FR 70000)
£4333　　$7453　　(12-Oct-91 KV.L244/R) A drawing and a picture (65x80cm-26x31in) s.d.1977
　　　　　　　　mixed media (B.FR 260000)

RAVEL, Daniel (1915-) French
£564　　$1010　　(19-Jan-92 CC.P80) Le soleil frappe (54x65cm-21x26in) s. i.verso
　　　　　　　　(F.FR 5500)

RAVEL, Daniel (1915-) French-cont.
£974 $1744   (19-Jan-92 CC.P81) Sonate verte (54x65cm-21x26in) s. i.verso (F.FR 9500)

RAVEL, Edouard-John E (1847-1920) Swiss
£657 $1176   (6-May-92 GD.B1037/R) Estavayer (64x50cm-25x20in) s.verso (S.FR 1800)
£1569 $2667   (23-Oct-91 GD.B595/R) Seated black daxhound Dolly (56x70cm-22x28in)
        s.i.d.1900 (S.FR 4000)

RAVEN, Samuel (1775-1847) British
£600 $1050   (1-Apr-92 ZZ.B91) Three Staffordshire Bull Terriers with master
        (17x22cm-7x9in) init. panel

RAVEN, Samuel (attrib) (1775-1847) British
£650 $1164   (14-Jan-92 B130) A bitch and puppies in an interior (17x23cm-7x9in) panel

RAVENSBERG, Ludwig Christian (1871-1958) Norwegian
£915   *$1556*   *(6-Aug-91 UL.T221/R) View of Christiania from Hammersborg 1892*
        (27x40cm-11x16in) W/C (N.KR 10500)

RAVENSWAAY, Jan van (1789-1869) Dutch
£917 $1596   (14-Apr-92 SY.AM338/R) Herd with cattle (52x68cm-20x27in) mono.
        (D.FL 3000)

RAVESTEYN, Dirck de Quade van (circle) (fl.1589-1619) Dutch
£2963 $5363   (19-May-92 GF.L2401/R) Venus and Amor (13x20cm-5x8in) copper (S.FR 8000)

RAVESTEYN, Jan Anthonisz van (1570-1657) Dutch
£4972 $9000   (21-May-92 CH.NY162/R) Portrait of gentleman, wearing grey costume, with
        ruff and sash (63x50cm-25x20in) panel
£20284 $35700   (10-Apr-92 AT.P13/R) Portrait d'un echevin (143x119cm-56x47in)
        mono.d.1635 i. (F.FR 200000)
£86592 $155000   (17-Jan-92 SY.NY28/R) Portrait of Joannes de Ruyter (121x79cm-48x31in)
        s.i.d.1632 panel

RAVESTEYN, Jan Anthonisz van (attrib) (1570-1657) Dutch
£1568 $2854   (11-Dec-91 N.M348/R) Portrait of lady wearing lace cap (60x49cm-24x19in)
        panel (DM 4500)
£3096 $5666   (3-Jun-92 R.T179/R) Portrait of bearded gentleman in lace collar
        (76x63cm-30x25in) (C.D 6750)

RAVESTEYN, Jan Anthonisz van (style) (1570-1657) Dutch
£1100 $2112   (9-Jul-92 CSK140/R) Portrait of soldier wearing armour (46x34cm-18x13in)
        panel
£1210 $2141   (4-Nov-91 SY.J206/R) Portrait of lady (20x15cm-8x6in) panel (SA.R 6000)
£1685 $3000   (22-Jan-92 SY.NY106/R) Portrait of two children (61x65cm-24x26in)
        indist.d. panel

RAVESTEYN, Nicolas van II (1661-1750) Dutch
£4839 $8468   (25-Sep-91 CSC.P5/R) Portrait d'enfant tenant un chien sur fond de
        paysage (111x86cm-44x34in) s.d.1690 (F.FR 48000)

RAVIER, Auguste Francois (1814-1895) French
£929 $1700   (6-Jun-92 LAE.L47/R) Landscape (20x25cm-8x10in) s. board
£1500 $2565   (17-Mar-92 PH153) Wooded landscape (24x31cm-9x12in) indis.s. paper on
        board
£1927 $3391   (10-Apr-92 AGS.P35) Paysage au crepuscule (15x22cm-6x9in) s. W/C
        (F.FR 19000)
£2000 $3420   (17-Mar-92 PH152) Wooded landscape (32x41cm-13x16in) s. canvas on board
£4578 $8194   (17-Nov-91 FB.P82/R) Paysage. Vue d'une cirque (31x40cm-12x16in) s.
        double-sided (F.FR 45000)
£1221   *$2234*   *(15-May-92 AT.P198) Vue d'un pont dans la campagne (28x43cm-11x17in) s.*
        W/C oval (F.FR 12000)

RAVILIOUS, Eric (1908-1942) British
£3200   *$5536*   *(2-Oct-91 S78/R) Country church (25x37cm-10x15in) s.i. pencil W/C sold*
        with another W/C by Bliss

RAVN, Johannes (1922-) Swedish
£472 $835   (25-Apr-92 SO.S578/R) Family of ducks swimming (63x91cm-25x36in) s.d.50
        (S.KR 5000)
£504 $902   (16-Nov-91 FAL.M296/R) Cranes in boggy landscape (65x92cm-26x36in) s.d.50
        (S.KR 5300)
£522 $909   (13-Apr-92 AB.S221) Autumn lake landscape with pair of swans
        (48x59cm-19x23in) s.d.49 (S.KR 5500)

RAY, Charles (1871-1918) French
£673 $1198   (30-Oct-91 CH.AM98) Moored boats in the river Seine, Paris
        (16x22cm-6x9in) s.d.1904 panel (D.FL 2200)

RAYA-SORKINE (1936-) French
£1232 $2218   (19-Nov-91 FB.P6/R) Les feux de la St Jean a Brignogan (54x65cm-21x26in)
        s. i.d.Juillet 1973verso (F.FR 12000)
£1232 $2218   (19-Nov-91 FB.P80/R) Fleurs (81x54cm-32x21in) s.d.67 d.66verso
        (F.FR 12000)
£1322 $2420   (17-May-92 GL.P114) Ecoute Israel (65x54cm-26x21in) s. (F.FR 13000)

RAYA-SORKINE (1936-) French-cont.
£5136	$8731	(27-Oct-91 LT.P60/R) Les amoureux aux fruits (60x73cm-24x29in) s. (F.FR 51000)
£811	$1467	(20-May-92 FB.P246/R) Le musicien (65x50cm-26x20in) s.d.70 oil gouache (F.FR 8000)

RAYNAL (?) ?
£1721	$3184	(9-Jun-92 F.R122/R) Passeggiata al Pincio (26x38cm-10x15in) s.d.66 gouache (I.L 3800000)
£2000	$3560	(29-Nov-91 C103/R) Castel Gandolfo. Porto di Napoli con il Maschio Angioino (27x39cm-11x15in) one s.i.d.66 one s.d.67 pencil bodycol.pair

RAYNAUD, Jean Pierre (1939-) French
£4273	$7819	(14-May-92 BG.P36/R) Signalisation, petits cailloux (55x45cm-22x18in) s.d.1967verso mixed media (F.FR 42000)

RAYNER, Louise (1832-1924) British
£8000	$13760	(11-Oct-91 C138/R) Market day, Chippenham (25x61cm-10x24in) s.
£1257	$2200	(18-Feb-92 CE.NY121/R) Cobblestone street (41x29cm-16x11in) s. W/C chl htd white
£2000	$3560	(29-Oct-91 C106/R) Port of Leith, Edinburgh (27x37cm-11x15in) s. pencil W/C bodycol.
£2200	$3916	(29-Oct-91 C104/R) All Saints Pavement, York (31x26cm-12x10in) s. i.verso W/C bodycol.
£2600	$4628	(29-Oct-91 C103/R) Magdalen Bridge, Cambridge (31x23cm-12x9in) s. i.verso pencil W/C bodycol.
£3800	$6536	(4-Mar-92 S196/R) Hastings (51x34cm-20x13in) s. W/C htd white
£4000	$7120	(29-Oct-91 C105/R) Foss Gate, York (46x29cm-18x11in) s. pencil W/C bodycol.
£4200	$7182	(13-Mar-92 C24/R) Old houses, Shrewsbury (22x35cm-9x14in) s. pencil W/C bodycol
£4200	$7476	(29-Oct-91 C101/R) Canterbury Cathedral (28x43cm-11x17in) s. W/C bodycol.
£6000	$10740	(13-Nov-91 CG505/R) The West Bow, Edinburgh (57x41cm-22x16in) s. W/C htd.bodycol.
£6000	$10620	(6-Nov-91 S315/R) Old Hastings (37x54cm-15x21in) s. W/C htd.bodycol

RAYNER, Louise (circle) (1832-1924) British
£1000	$1780	(28-Apr-92 S170/R) John Knox's House, Edinburgh (30x41cm-12x16in) W/C

RAYSSE, Martial (1936-) French
£821	$1478	(19-Nov-91 FB.P143/R) Composition (119x60cm-47x24in) s.d.59verso (F.FR 8000)
£108000	$195480	(5-Dec-91 S27/R) Conversation printaniere (228x127cm-90x50in) oil assemblage canvas
£1222	$2236	(3-Jun-92 CSC.P228) Untitled (7x49cm-3x19in) s. indian ink (F.FR 12000)
£2000	$3440	(17-Oct-91 C62/R) Variation sur un palmier 2 ordinateur IBM et MR 65 (66x50cm-26x20in) i. gouache ink paper collage
£48000	$83040	(26-Mar-92 S61/R) Brigitte Bardot I (163x97cm-64x38in) s.d.65 verso acrylic flocage card on canvas

RAZDROGUINE, Igor (1923-) Russian
£820	$1475	(27-Jan-92 ARC.P229/R) Le traineau Tchukcha (121x151cm-48x59in) s. (F.FR 8000)

RE, Marco del (20th C) French
£1509	$2596	(12-Oct-91 GL.P86/R) Profile della storia (134x53cm-53x21in) s.i.d.1989 wash chl. (F.FR 15000)

READ, F (19th C) British?
£460	$791	(4-Mar-92 C87/R) Young girl, holding pink rose in folds of white dress, hat with feather (6x?cm-2x?in) min. mono.verso gold frame plaited hair oval

READ, Richard II (c.1796-?) Australian
£2996	$5392	(24-Nov-91 SY.S415/R) Fortune teller (35x50cm-14x20in) i.verso W/C htd bodycol (A.D 6800)

READ, Roderic (1956-) British
£850	$1556	(3-Feb-92 B132 a) Coach interior (105x117cm-41x46in)

READ, Samuel (1816-1883) British
£640	$1158	(19-May-92 SWS391) The Coro, Cathedral of Toledo (56x81cm-22x32in) s.d.1864 s.i.verso W/C over pencil htd.bodycol

READ, Thomas Buchanan (1822-1872) American
£4971	$8500	(12-Mar-92 CH.NY13/R) Mill Creek Valley, Cincinnati (76x127cm-30x50in) s.

READY, William James Durant (1823-1873) British
£580	$1032	(27-Apr-92 PHB289) View at Gorleston, Suffolk (12x22cm-5x9in) s. i.verso panel

REALFONSO, Tommaso (18th C) Italian
£10056	$18000	(17-Jan-92 SY.NY139/R) Still life of a basket with knitting and other objects on a ledge (39x65cm-15x26in) s.

REALFONSO, Tommaso (18th C) Italian-cont.
£13966 $25000   (17-Jan-92 SY.NY82/R) Still life with flowers in elaborate silver and
gold urns (92x93cm-36x37in) mono.

REAM, C P (1837-1917) American
£497 $950   (17-Jul-92 DM.D2254/R) Still life with grapes (20x25cm-8x10in) s.

REAM, Carducius Plantagenet (1837-1917) American
£838 $1500   (14-Nov-91 CE.NY100) Peaches (46x60cm-18x24in) s.
£894 $1600   (14-Nov-91 CE.NY102) Grapes (24x35cm-9x14in) s. board
£1453 $2600   (14-Nov-91 CE.NY115/R) Mixed fruit. New bonnet (69x56cm-27x22in) s. pair
£1788 $3200   (6-May-92 D.NY20/R) Still life of peaches spilling from basket
(46x61cm-18x24in) s.

REAM, Carducius Plantagenet (attrib) (1837-1917) American
£1160 $2100   (2-Dec-91 S.SL296/R) Still life of fruit on table (33x48cm-13x19in) mono.
board

REAM, Morston C (1840-1898) American
£1709 $2905   (24-Oct-91 D.V41/R) Still life (44x60cm-17x24in) s. (A.S 35000)

REAULT, Patrick (?) French?
£515 $892   (29-Mar-92 FE.P130) Bouquet de fleurs (100x81cm-39x32in) (F.FR 5000)

REBANE, Erikx (1922-) Russian
£520 $911   (5-Apr-92 ARC.P26/R) La reuinion scolaire (47x45cm-19x18in) s.d.52 board
(F.FR 5000)
£928 $1587   (13-Mar-92 ARC.P130/R) La fete des marins (56x43cm-22x17in) s.d.1956
(F.FR 9000)

REBAY, Hilla (20th C) French
£3714 $6500   (28-Feb-92 SY.NY258/R) Composition no.9 (61x70cm-24x28in) st.init. panel
*£857 $1500   (28-Feb-92 SY.NY255/R) Composition no.12 (27x37cm-11x15in) s. W/C indian
ink collage*

REBEYROLLE, Paul (1926-) French
£1223 $2275   (15-Jun-92 GL.P71/R) Le poulet (41x72cm-16x28in) s.d.1950 panel
(F.FR 12000)
£1235 $2346   (24-Jun-92 GL.P247) Nature morte au saumon (32x100cm-13x39in) panel with
studies of faces verso (F.FR 12000)
£2000 $3480   (19-Sep-91 B118/R) Landscape (95x98cm-37x39in) s.d.1953 panel
£3505 $6064   (29-Mar-92 P.V56/R) Untitled (50x100cm-20x39in) s. (F.FR 34000)
£3913 $6692   (19-Mar-92 CSC.P43/R) Suicide (80x120cm-31x47in) s.d.1982 paper laid down
on canvas (F.FR 38000)
£24698 $42727   (6-Oct-91 BG.P96/R) L'atelier de la Ruche (260x200cm-102x79in) s.d.1952
(F.FR 245000)
*£8130 $14146   (14-Apr-92 CSC.P64/R) L'aquarelle no.1 (100x100cm-39x39in) s.d.67 i.verso
mixed media canvas (F.FR 80000)*
*£8445 $14441   (17-Mar-92 FB.P93/R) La fuite terminee (244x195cm-96x77in) mixed media
collage canvas (F.FR 82000)*

REBIERRE, Marc (1934-) ?
£2349 $4111   (23-Feb-92 FE.P178) Nature morte et fillette (46x55cm-18x22in) s.
(F.FR 23000)

REBOLO, Marc (1955-) French
£1953 $3730   (30-Jun-92 ZZ.F37/R) Ronces (195x165cm-77x65in) s.verso oil varnish
powdered marble (F.FR 19000)

REBOUSSIN, Roger (1881-) French?
£1509 $2640   (30-Mar-92 ZZ.F138) Cerf au brame (44x66cm-17x26in) s.d.1930 (F.FR 14500)

REBRY, Gaston (?) ?
£746 $1328   (26-Nov-91 JOY.T241/R) Winter solitude (60x75cm-24x30in) s. (C.D 1500)

RECALCATI, Antonio (1938-) Italian
£602 $1072   (26-Nov-91 SY.MI110) Composizione (100x80cm-39x31in) (I.L 1300000)
£1205 $2145   (26-Nov-91 SY.MI3/R) Studio per l'Attesa (80x120cm-31x47in)
s.init.d.59verso (I.L 2600000)
£2085 $3712   (26-Nov-91 SY.MI39/R) Composizione (69x80cm-27x31in) s. (I.L 4500000)

RECCO, Elena (attrib) (17th C) Italian
£4825 $8686   (21-Nov-91 BL.P45/R) Nature morte aux poissons (92x131cm-36x52in)
(F.FR 47000)

RECCO, Giovan Battista (1630-1675) Italian
£28817 $52159   (4-Dec-91 CH.R40/R) Natura morta con aragosta, granceola, granchi su una
coppa e uova (59x76cm-23x30in) (I.L 62000000)

RECCO, Giuseppe (1634-1695) Italian
£6356 $11313   (28-Apr-92 F.R94/R) Natura morta di pesci (41x67cm-16x26in)
(I.L 14000000)
£6704 $12000   (17-Jan-92 SY.NY185/R) Still life of fish and lobsters (51x71cm-20x28in)

RECCO, Giuseppe (circle) (1634-1695) Italian
£6630 $12000   (22-May-92 SY.NY198/R) Kitchen still life (105x129cm-41x51in)
£6977 $12000   (9-Oct-91 CH.NY39/R) Mixed flowers in blue and white porcelain vase on
               ledge (68x51cm-27x20in)
£9814 $18646   (23-Jun-92 D.V192/R) Still life with apples and turkey (69x95cm-27x37in)
               (A.S 200000)

RECCO, Nicola Maria (18th C) Italian
£6500 $12480   (7-Jul-92 PH15/R) Still lilfe with fish on rocky ledge with earthenware
               bowl (72x97cm-28x38in)
£18000 $32760   (11-Dec-91 S82/R) Still life of fish with copper vessel upon sea-shore
               (107x166cm-42x65in)

REDER, Christian (1656-1729) German
£4200 $8064   (8-Jul-92 S174/R) Cavalry battles between Christians and Turks
               (21x31cm-8x12in) pair

REDER, Christian (style) (1656-1729) German
£4600 $8188   (30-Oct-91 S106/R) Cavalry skirmish. Soldiers after battle
               (25x44cm-10x17in) panel pair
£7200 $13824   (8-Jul-92 S180/R) Cavalry melees (33x43cm-13x17in) canvas on board pair

REDER, Giovanni (attrib) (1693-1749) Italian
£10490 $17937   (18-Mar-92 N.M449/R) Market scene in Piazza Navona, Rome
               (97x133cm-38x52in) (DM 30000)

REDER-BROILI, Franz (1854-1918) German
£1038 $1900   (17-May-92 DU.E1091 c) Landscape with duck hunter (91x58cm-36x23in) s.i.
£1045 $1902   (11-Dec-91 N.M565/R) Dachauer Moos at dusk (21x30cm-8x12in) s. i.verso
               board (DM 3000)
£2273 $3886   (18-Mar-92 N.M622/R) Bay of Naples at sunset (70x122cm-28x48in) s.
               (DM 6500)
£6186 $10515   (25-Oct-91 BM.B809/R) View of Rome at sunrise (67x100cm-26x39in) s.
               (DM 18000)

REDFERN, June (20th C) ?
£550 $974   (23-Apr-92 B38) The ferry (183x167cm-72x66in) s.i.d.1990verso

REDFIELD, Edward (1869-1965) American
£5525 $10000   (7-Dec-91 LAE.L82/R) The shepherd (81x53cm-32x21in) s.d.93
£8430 $14500   (10-Oct-91 FA.PH929/R) Winter landscape at sunset (66x81cm-26x32in)
               s.d.05
£26243 $47500   (5-Dec-91 SY.NY65/R) The brook (80x65cm-31x26in) s.
£34341 $62500   (27-May-92 SY.NY85/R) Washington's birthday, New Hope (81x102cm-32x40in)
               s. s.i.stretcher
£35714 $65000   (28-May-92 CH.NY190/R) Road to the village (81x101cm-32x40in) s.d.1908

REDGATE, Arthur W (19/20th C) British
£1200 $2292   (15-Jul-92 WI419/R) Washing the sheep (34x52cm-13x20in) s.
£1700 $3196   (19-Dec-91 C128/R) The Trent at King's Mills (51x76cm-20x30in) s.
               indist.i.verso
£1800 $3294   (5-Feb-92 B51) Unloading catch, fishermen in coastal scene
               (91x152cm-36x60in) s.

REDGRAVE, Richard (1804-1888) British
£4000 $7160   *(14-Nov-91 S129/R) Pont de la Concorde, Paris (10x30cm-4x12in) s. W/C*
               over pencil

REDIG, Laurent Herman (1822-1861) Dutch
£9714 $17000   (19-Feb-92 CH.NY128/R) Cold winter's day (98x139cm-39x55in) s.d.1860

REDKO, Kliment Nikolaevich (1897-1956) Russian
£805   *$1384*   *(12-Oct-91 SY.MO184/R) Portrait of Boris Kochno (51x37cm-20x15in)*
               s.d.1927 col.crayon paper on card (F.FR 8000)

REDMOND, Granville (1871-1935) American
£1271 $2250   (12-Feb-92 B.SF430/R) Tiburon and Belvedere Island (11x16cm-4x6in) s.
               board
£2143 $3750   (31-Mar-92 MOR.P32) Coastal (30x23cm-12x9in) s. canvas on board
£3090 $5500   (26-Nov-91 MOR.P16 a) Landscape, country road (15x20cm-6x8in) s.
£5714 $10000   (31-Mar-92 MOR.P25) Moonlight landscape (30x23cm-12x9in) s. canvas on
               board
£8571 $15000   (26-Sep-91 CH.NY108/R) California sunset (46x81cm-18x32in) s.

REDMOND, Thomas (c.1745-1785) British
£580   *$1061*   *(15-May-92 TE261/R) Lady wearing ermine trimmed turquoise dress*
               (8x?cm-3x?in) min. gold suspension frame glazed hair v. oval

REDMORE, Henry (1820-1887) British
£1900 $3401   (5-May-92 SWS323/R) A choppy sea (35x52cm-14x20in) s.
£1923 $3500   (26-May-92 CE.NY58/R) Off Dover (33x55cm-13x22in) s.d.1876
£4100 $7462   (11-Dec-91 PHL121/R) Figures by a grounded ship with other vessels in
               calm seas beyond (21x36cm-8x14in) s. i.verso
£4800 $8496   (6-Nov-91 S12/R) Shipping in estuary (30x45cm-12x18in) s.d.1864

REDMORE, Henry (1820-1887) British-cont.

£6000	$10800	(22-Nov-91 C43/R) Shipping at entrance of Hull Harbour (20x33cm-8x13in) s.d.1885 panel
£6200	$10974	(6-Nov-91 S10/R) The entrance to Whitby Harbour (59x91cm-23x36in) s.d.1884
£6200	$11346	(6-Feb-92 DLY80/R) Shipping off Dover. Frigate at anchor and other shipping off Dutch coast (30x51cm-12x20in) init.d.1866 pair
£7000	$12600	(22-Nov-91 C44/R) Fishing boats and other vessels on the Scheldt near Rotterdam (31x46cm-12x18in) s.d.1852
£7500	$13500	(22-Nov-91 C45/R) Dismasted in storm off Kent Coast (61x91cm-24x36in) s.
£7600	$13680	(22-Nov-91 C42/R) Shipping in the Humber off Burlington Quay, Hull (46x76cm-18x30in) s.d.1873
£8500	$14280	(15-Aug-91 B412 a) Shipping in calm (43x61cm-17x24in) s.d.1862
£12000	$21480	(12-Nov-91 CHAP305/R) Shipping off Flamborough. Shipping outside Bridlington Harbour (46x76cm-18x30in) s.indist.d. pair

REDON, Georges (19/20th C) French

£1500	$2595	(3-Oct-91 CSK106) The bell tower, Notre Dame, Paris (53x74cm-21x29in) s.
£774	$1300	(14-Aug-91 B.P123/R) The flirt (25x15cm-10x6in) s. pastel chl. demi-lune
£2345	$4361	(18-Jun-92 CB.P30/R) Nu allonge (11x17cm-4x7in) mono. dr (F.FR 23000)

REDON, Odilon (1840-1916) French

£9040	$16000	(6-Nov-91 CH.NY250/R) Petit village (14x18cm-6x7in) init. paper on board
£20000	$38200	(1-Jul-92 S112/R) Le centaure au violoncelle (35x27cm-14x11in) s.
£20000	$34400	(16-Oct-91 S17/R) La chute d'Icare (20x25cm-8x10in) init. paper on board
£169492	$300000	(6-Nov-91 SY.NY23/R) Le char d'Apollon (75x47cm-30x19in) panel
£310734	$550000	(5-Nov-91 CH.NY39/R) Vase de fleurs (65x50cm-26x20in) s.
£4046	$7000	(2-Oct-91 SY.NY19/R) Prophet (21x18cm-8x7in) s. wash pencil
£4808	$9135	(25-Jun-92 GK.B631/R) Etude de nu (25x15cm-10x6in) mono indian ink brush pen over pencil (S.FR 12500)
£19126	$35000	(13-May-92 CH.NY205/R) Tete flotante (35x28cm-14x11in) s. chl
£75000	$143250	(30-Jun-92 S17/R) Vase de fleurs (35x29cm-14x11in) s. pastel
£101852	$185370	(11-Dec-91 CH.AM253/R) Tete suspendue, coiffee, par une chaine (46x38cm-18x15in) s. chk (D.FL 330000)
£173780	$302378	(15-Apr-92 CB.P22/R) Personnage au bouquet de fleurs (43x29cm-17x11in) s. pastel (F.FR 1710000)

REDONDELA, Agustin (1923-) Spanish

£2460	$4502	(13-May-92 FER.M159/R) Paisaje castellano (46x56cm-18x22in) s.d.69 (S.P 450000)
£3322	$5980	(28-Jan-92 EP.M63/R) Paisaje con figuras (46x55cm-18x22in) s.d.69 (S.P 600000)
£4430	$7973	(28-Jan-92 EP.M55/R) Paisaje (46x55cm-18x22in) s.d.69 (S.P 800000)
£4707	$8472	(28-Jan-92 EP.M56/R) Nocturno en Chillaron, Guadalajara (64x81cm-25x32in) s.d.59 (S.P 850000)
£496	$887	(14-Nov-91 ANS.M50/R) Paisaje de Almunia de Tajuna (16x24cm-6x9in) s.i. W/C (S.P 90000)
£1244	$2339	(17-Dec-91 DUR.M114/R) Paisaje con sierra (35x35cm-14x14in) s. gouache (S.P 225000)
£2319	$3989	(16-Oct-91 FER.M246/R) Atardecer en el puerto (49x69cm-19x27in) s. W/C (S.P 425000)

REDOUTE, P J (1759-1840) French

£735	$1250	(22-Oct-91 GM.B668) Developpement de la fleur s. W/C (B.FR 44000)

REDOUTE, Pierre Joseph (1759-1840) French

£518	$892	(16-Oct-91 FER.M108/R) Rosas (27x21cm-11x8in) s. W/C (S.P 95000)

REDPATH, Anne (1895-1965) British

£2500	$4450	(28-Apr-92 S279/R) Altar in San Roque (76x76cm-30x30in) s. i.verso board
£8000	$13760	(6-Mar-92 C109/R) Storm at Cambrils (50x60cm-20x24in) s. panel
£8000	$13920	(11-Sep-91 PHG69/R) Red and white roses (65x55cm-26x22in) s. board
£10000	$16800	(26-Aug-91 S1142/R) Canary Island village (71x91cm-28x36in) s. board
£10000	$16800	(26-Aug-91 S1140/R) Still life with dried flowers (63x91cm-25x36in)
£1000	$1830	(14-May-92 C28/R) Two houses, Concarneau (24x36cm-9x14in) s. brush ink crayon W/C
£1900	$3401	(13-Nov-91 CG682) Cottages, Skye (42x52cm-17x20in) s. W/C htd.bodycol.
£2600	$4628	(30-Apr-92 CG830/R) The Old Harbour, Bastia (25x34cm-10x13in) s. chl W/C htd white
£2800	$4984	(30-Apr-92 CG829/R) Tulips and Irises (55x64cm-22x25in) s. W/C
£3000	$5040	(26-Aug-91 S1159/R) Crofters cottages (31x41cm-12x16in) s. W/C gouache over black chk

REDPATH, Barbara (20th C) British

£700	$1218	(11-Sep-91 PHG66/R) Autumn table (95x125cm-37x49in) s. board

REDTWITZ, A (19th C) German

£501	$907	(5-Dec-91 D.V105) Still life of fruit with water jug (73x100cm-29x39in) s. (A.S 10000)

REDWITH, A (?) ?

£762	$1387	(14-Dec-91 BA.S104 b) Still life of fruit and bottle of wine (73x100cm-29x39in) s. (S.KR 8000)

REE, Anita (1885-1933) German
£431 $733   (23-Oct-91 GD.B1241/R) Portrait of woman (43x30cm-17x12in) s. W/C
                        (S.FR 1100)
£756 $1384   (3-Jun-92 DO.H2867/R) Positano (63x49cm-25x19in) mono W/C over pencil
                        (DM 2200)

REED, Joseph (1822-1877) British
£920 $1766   (28-Jul-92 SWS249/R) The ferry (31x52cm-12x20in) s.d.73 W/C over pencil

REEDY, Leonard Howard (1899-1956) American
£395 $750   (28-Jun-92 LIT.L57) Indian raiders (20x30cm-8x12in) s. W/C

REEKERS, Hendrik (1815-1854) Dutch
£684 $1162   (24-Oct-91 D.V185/R) Still life of fruit (19x15cm-7x6in) s. panel
                        (A.S 14000)

REEKERS, Hendrik (attrib) (1815-1854) Dutch
£1774 $3157   (30-Oct-91 CH.AM95/R) Still life of flowers in vase and butterfly on
                        marble ledge (30x25cm-12x10in) s. panel (D.FL 5800)

REEKERS, Hendrik (style) (1815-1854) Dutch
£1087 $1870   (7-Mar-92 CH.AM246) Dead partridge and other fowl hanging, jug, grapes,
                        vegetables on plate on marble ledge (70x54cm-28x21in) with sig.
                        (D.FL 3500)

REES, Lloyd Frederick (1895-1988) Australian
£4255 $7532   (26-Apr-92 SY.ME334/R) Cathedral of France (54x41cm-21x16in) s.d.1969
                        canvas on board (A.D 10000)
£5507 $9912   (24-Nov-91 SY.S262/R) Geraniums, 1936 (28x33cm-11x13in) s. canvas on
                        board (A.D 12500)
£7660 $13557   (26-Apr-92 SY.ME245/R) Norhtern Hills, Bathurst (28x64cm-11x25in)
                        s.d.1968 (A.D 18000)
£8216 $13721   (19-Aug-91 SY.ME233/R) Dusk, Bathurst (30x61cm-12x24in) s.d. board
                        (A.D 17500)
£23474 $39202   (19-Aug-91 SY.ME242/R) Evening star, summertime, Bathurst
                        (88x121cm-35x48in) s.d.1979 i.verso (A.D 50000)
£34043 $60255   (26-Apr-92 SY.ME295/R) Anchorage (84x114cm-33x45in) s.d.78 (A.D 80000)
£1255 $2272   (19-May-92 JRL.S233) San Gimignano (20x27cm-8x11in) s.d.1966 W/C
                        (A.D 3000)
£1322 $2379   (24-Nov-91 SY.S369/R) Balls Head, Sydney Harbour (12x22cm-5x9in) s.d.1931
                        pencil (A.D 3000)
£1705 $3257   (21-Jul-92 JRL.S94) Oorie Beach (33x43cm-13x17in) s.d.77 ballpoint wash
                        (A.D 4400)
£1762 $3172   (24-Nov-91 SY.S515/R) From Omega near Gerringong (24x31cm-9x12in)
                        s.d.1950 pencil ink wash (A.D 4000)
£2481 $4738   (21-Jul-92 JRL.S85/R) Mosman Bay, Sydney Harbour (20x22cm-8x9in) s.d.1926
                        pen wash (A.D 6400)
£2810 $5367   (21-Jul-92 JRL.S245) Site of the ruined Abbey, Vezelay (30x36cm-12x14in)
                        s.d.1973 pen wash (A.D 7250)
£3198 $6108   (21-Jul-92 JRL.S151/R) House and garden, Cremorne (28x22cm-11x9in)
                        s.d.1926 pen wash (A.D 8250)
£3295 $6293   (21-Jul-92 JRL.S147/R) Caversham, Cremorne (24x23cm-9x9in) s.d.1926 pen
                        wash (A.D 8500)
£3304 $5947   (24-Nov-91 SY.S267/R) River II, Paris (23x31cm-9x12in) s.d.59 W/C pencil
                        (A.D 7500)
£10329 $17249   (19-Aug-91 SY.ME240/R) Werri Creek (55x74cm-22x29in) s.d.1980 crayon W/C
                        chl (A.D 22000)

REES, Otto van (1884-1957) Dutch
£576 $1042   (19-May-92 CH.AM22) Still life with fruit in a basket and a pipe
                        (24x30cm-9x12in) board (D.FL 1900)
£1389 $2528   (12-Dec-91 SY.AM117/R) Still life (80x60cm-31x24in) s.d.43 (D.FL 4500)
£1667 $3017   (21-May-92 SY.AM71/R) Landscape (4x27cm-2x11in) mono paper (D.FL 5500)
£1970 $3565   (19-May-92 CH.AM68) View of Bergen (54x63cm-21x25in) s. (D.FL 6500)

REESERT, J (19th C) ?
£687 $1271   (13-Jun-92 WK.M354/R) Still life of bowl with fruit and flowers
                        (42x33cm-17x13in) indis.s.d.1849 panel (DM 2000)

REEVES, Richard Stone (20th C) American
£1776 $3250   (5-Jun-92 SY.NY302/R) Barrera (81x96cm-32x38in) s.i.d.78
£2732 $5000   (5-Jun-92 SY.NY299/R) Katonka (66x81cm-26x32in) s.i.d.1976
£2732 $5000   (5-Jun-92 SY.NY300/R) Prismatical (81x96cm-32x38in) s.i.d.1982
£3005 $5500   (5-Jun-92 SY.NY269/R) Spectacular Bid with Shoemaker up (35x43cm-14x17in)
                        s.d.79 panel
£4098 $7500   (5-Jun-92 SY.NY270/R) Early Work at Saratoga (55x92cm-22x36in) s.i.
£4372 $8000   (5-Jun-92 SY.NY301/R) It's In The Air defeating Davona Dale
                        (40x71cm-16x28in) s.i.d.1979

REEVES, W (20th C) British
£550 $1001   (12-Dec-91 CSK133/R) The grub parade (46x61cm-18x24in) s. i.verso

REEVES, Walter (fl.1882-1900) British
£629 $1100   (23-Sep-91 S.SL244) View from the Bread-Walk looking towards Mill Street,
                        Weir, Ludlow (41x61cm-16x24in) s.i.d.1883 verso

REGAGNON, Albert (20th C) French
£1744 $3000   (12-Oct-91 SY.NY13/R) Barn (46x33cm-18x13in) s. panel

REGEMORTER, Petrus Johannes van (1755-1830) Flemish
£2300 $4209   (12-May-92 SWS812/R) Moonlit river landscape with fishermen bringing in
                     nets, figures by fire (26x37cm-10x15in) s.d.1790 panel

REGGIANI, Mauro (1897-1980) Italian
£7830 $14250   (9-Dec-91 CH.R145/R) Composizione n.39 (81x100cm-32x39in) s.i.d.1965
                     (I.L 17000000)
£8818 $16577   (19-Dec-91 F.M178/R) Paese della collina modenese (58x90cm-23x35in) s.
                     (I.L 19000000)
£12512 $22271   (26-Nov-91 SY.MI197/R) Composizione (89x115cm-35x45in) s. (I.L 27000000)
£14527 $25859   (29-Apr-92 F.F280/R) Composizione (101x73cm-40x29in) s. (I.L 32000000)

REGGIANINI, Vittorio (1858-?) Italian
£16000 $27360   (19-Mar-92 B103/R) Flirtation (76x58cm-30x23in) s.

REGILD, Carsten (1941-1992) Swedish
£1151 $2096   (25-May-92 RAS.K133/R) The opening of the coconuts (205x309cm-81x122in)
                     s.d.83 (D.KR 13000)

REGNARD, Jean (20th C) French
£678 $1200   (6-Nov-91 D.NY91/R) L'apres-midi sur le Seine (53x71cm-21x28in) s.

REGNAULT, Baron Jean Baptiste (1754-1829) French
£916 $1696   (12-Jun-92 ARC.P175 a) Mercure enlevant une fille de roi. Un sacrifice au
                     dieu Jupiter (24x19cm-9x7in) pen indian ink two (F.FR 9000)
£7716 $13966   (5-Dec-91 SY.MO66/R) Cupidon et psyche (30x225cm-12x89in) s. pen wash
                     htd.white gouache (F.FR 75000)
£8230 $14897   (5-Dec-91 SY.MO73/R) Pygmalion priant Venus d'animer sa statue. Dibutade
                     tracant le portraitde son berger (17x21cm-7x8in) both s. pen wash on
                     blk.chk. pair (F.FR 80000)

REGNAULT, Henri (1843-1871) French
£3371 $5899   (23-Feb-92 I.N94/R) Judith et Holopherne (72x100cm-28x39in) s.
                     (F.FR 33000)

REGNIER, Nicolas (1590-1667) Flemish
£12000 $23040   (8-Jul-92 S38/R) Young man playing the guitar (99x74cm-39x29in)
£93923 $170000   (21-May-92 CH.NY93/R) David with head of Goliath (136x106cm-54x42in)
                     bears i.

REGNIER, Nicolas (attrib) (1590-1667) Flemish
£17490 $31656   (5-Dec-91 SY.MO144/R) Saint Jean Baptiste (118x92cm-46x36in)
                     (F.FR 170000)

REGNIER, Nicolas (circle) (1590-1667) Flemish
£1100 $2002   (10-Dec-91 PH121/R) Penitent Magdalene (102x87cm-40x34in)

REGOS, Istvan (1954-) Hungarian
£827 $1423   (14-Oct-91 AT.P95) Poisson vivant (80x100cm-31x39in) s.d.1988 acrylic
                     (F.FR 8200)

REGTEREN ALTENA, Marie E van (1868-1958) Dutch
£917 $1633   (30-Oct-91 CH.AM141) Still life with porcelain bowl and fan on draped
                     table (50x60cm-20x24in) init. (D.FL 3000)

REGTERS, Tibout (1710-1768) Dutch
£2128 $3894   (12-May-92 SY.AM146/R) Fishwife (19x16cm-7x6in) panel (D.FL 7000)

REHDER, Julius Christian (1861-?) German
£745 $1326   (28-Nov-91 D.V86/R) Girl sewing (81x60cm-32x24in) s. (A.S 15000)
£1144 $1923   (27-Aug-91 RAS.K473) Doing homework (48x55cm-19x22in) s. panel
                     (D.KR 13000)

REHFISCH, Alison (1900-1975) Australian
£573 $1031   (24-Nov-91 SY.S5) Still life in glass vase (24x21cm-9x8in) s. canvasboard
                     (A.D 1300)
£705 $1269   (24-Nov-91 SY.S203/R) Still life - flowerpiece (29x23cm-11x9in) s. board
                     (A.D 1600)
£809 $1431   (26-Apr-92 SY.ME4/R) Bottlebrush still life (36x49cm-14x19in) s.i.d.1940
                     verso (A.D 1900)
£851 $1506   (26-Apr-92 SY.ME124/R) North coast landscape (36x53cm-14x21in) s. board
                     (A.D 2000)
£1047 $1999   (21-Jul-92 JRL.S47) Breton boats (59x49cm-23x19in) s. (A.D 2700)
£2092 $3787   (19-May-92 JRL.S93/R) Still life (60x50cm-24x20in) s. board (A.D 5000)
£3744 $6740   (24-Nov-91 SY.S276/R) Corner of studio, 1932 (30x35cm-12x14in) s. canvas
                     on board (A.D 8500)

REHN, Frank Knox Morton (1848-1914) American
£816 $1550   (28-Jun-92 LIT.L145) Sunset in harbour (41x71cm-16x28in) s. panel
£1167 $2100   (22-Nov-91 S.BM63/R) Long Beach, N.Y (41x71cm-16x28in) s.i. i.verso
£1638 $2900   (9-Nov-91 W.W175/R) Sunrise over Venice (76x127cm-30x50in) s.

REHN, Frank Knox Morton (1848-1914) American-cont.
£1724 $3000   (13-Sep-91 S.W2862/R) Coastal view - sunset on North shore
     (56x91cm-22x36in) s.d.79
£1730 $3200   (10-Jun-92 CE.NY185/R) Ships by foggy coast (57x91cm-22x36in) s.d.1881
£862 $1500   (15-Apr-92 SY.NY44/R) Crescent beach, Magnolia, Mass. Off coast Magnolia
     (41x71cm-16x28in) s. W/C paper on board pair

REICH, Adolf (1887-1963) Austrian
£1730 $3028   (19-Feb-92 D.V154/R) Musicians in interior (38x47cm-15x19in) s. panel
     (A.S 35000)

REICHEL, Hans (1892-1958) German
£6993 $12448   (30-Nov-91 VG.B220/R) Vertraumtes Haus (29x19cm-11x7in) mono.d.1928 W/C
     gouache pen (DM 20000)

REICHERT, C (19/20th C) Austrian?
£769 $1315   (19-Mar-92 N.M2817) White poodle (21x26cm-8x10in) s.d.14 panel (DM 2200)

REICHERT, Carl (1836-1918) Austrian
£488 $849   (19-Sep-91 D.V204/R) Portrait of dog (48x37cm-19x15in) (A.S 10000)
£1443 $2511   (21-Sep-91 SA.A1932/R) Hunting dog Hamlet (23cm-9ins circular) mono.
     i.verso board (DM 4200)
£1472 $2797   (25-Jun-92 D.V416/R) St Bernhard dogs. Bulldogs (13x34cm-5x13in) s. panel
     pair (A.S 30000)
£1709 $2905   (24-Oct-91 D.V102/R) Palazzo Venezia, Rome (45x56cm-18x22in) (A.S 35000)
£1709 $2905   (24-Oct-91 D.V104/R) Palazzo Venezia, Rome (45x56cm-18x22in) (A.S 35000)
£3418 $5811   (24-Oct-91 D.V48/R) Cats in artist's studio (28x33cm-11x13in) s.d.1892
     panel (A.S 70000)
£2687 $4621   (10-Oct-91 D.V318/R) Portraits of dogs (18x12cm-7x5in) mono.s. W/C six in
     one frame (A.S 55000)

REICHERT, Hermann (20th C) German
£1134 $1973   (21-Sep-91 SA.A547/R) Orchard in flowering field (58x78cm-23x31in)
     s.d.1915 (DM 3300)

REICHLE, Paul (1900-1981) German
£859 $1572   (2-Jun-92 FN.S2393/R) Composition landscape with white shape
     (36x52cm-14x20in) s.d.1966 i.d.verso board (DM 2500)

REICHLEN, Jean (1846-1913) Swiss
£1460 $2613   (6-May-92 GD.B1042/R) Sacra conversatione (40x27cm-16x11in) s.
     (S.FR 4000)

REID, Flora MacDonald (fl.1880-1938) British
£650 $1092   (26-Aug-91 S1124/R) Belgian mother (99x63cm-39x25in) s.d.1905

REID, George Agnew (1860-1947) Canadian
£800 $1432   (5-May-92 SWS225/R) A fresh breeze (48x28cm-19x11in) s.d.1903 pastel

REID, George Ogilvy (1851-1928) British
£700 $1267   (4-Dec-91 S155) Good likeness (30x41cm-12x16in) s.d.1877

REID, John Robertson (1851-1926) British
£650 $1190   (15-May-92 TE380/R) Sailing boats in estuary with children playing in
     foreground (30x61cm-12x24in) s.
£1200 $2172   (4-Dec-91 S256/R) Gleaners (35x53cm-14x21in) s.d.98 s.i.verso
£1800 $3330   (11-Jun-92 CSK225/R) The itinerant travellers (45x61cm-18x24in) s.d.98
£2500 $4450   (28-Apr-92 S212/R) Goose girl (58x44cm-23x17in) s.d.78

REID, Nano (1905-1981) Finnish
£1455 $2516   (2-Oct-91 A.D9/R) Turf cutters donkey (30x41cm-12x16in) s. canvasboard
     (E.P 1600)

REID, Robert (1862-1929) American
£1685 $3000   (29-Nov-91 MFA.C94/R) Portrait of lady in white (91x61cm-36x24in) s.
£1713 $3100   (24-May-92 JRB.C31/R) Portrait of a young girl (91x61cm-36x24in) s.
£1730 $3200   (10-Jun-92 CE.NY267/R) Portrait of lady (91x61cm-36x24in) s.
£2265 $4100   (24-May-92 JRB.C32/R) Portrait of a woman (91x61cm-36x24in)

REID, Robert Payton (1859-1945) British
£7000 $11760   (26-Aug-91 S1007/R) Roses (127x76cm-50x30in) s.
£9890 $18000   (27-May-92 CH.NY265/R) Summer's day in the flower garden
     (76x51cm-30x20in) s.

REID, Samuel (1854-1911) British
£2500 $4525   (4-Dec-91 S186/R) Boating on Kelsey Manor Lake (45x61cm-18x24in) s.

REID, Sir George (1841-1913) British
£1800 $3204   (28-Apr-92 S253/R) Attentive hearer of the Word (49x40cm-19x16in)
     mono.d.1865-6-7 W/C gouache

REID, Stephen (1873-1948) British
£5000 $8850   (6-Nov-91 S140/R) Ophelia (125x177cm-49x70in) s.d.1914 s.i.stretcher

REID-HENRY, David M (1919-1977) British
£420	$739	(6-Apr-92 WW108/R) Sparrows and other birds (28x37cm-11x15in) s. gouache W/C
£600	$1050	(25-Feb-92 C77/R) Mallards alighting (22x28cm-9x11in) s.d.1939 pencil W/C htd white
£650	$1138	(25-Feb-92 C30/R) Red-checked Bulbul (29x21cm-11x8in) s. i.verso pencil W/C bodycol
£700	$1225	(25-Feb-92 C24/R) Indian ring-necked parakeet (26x19cm-10x7in) s. pencil W/C bodycol
£750	$1313	(25-Feb-92 C149) Pheasants in snow (20x26cm-8x10in) s.d.39 W/C bodycol
£900	$1575	(25-Feb-92 C28/R) Mr. Hartlaub's Touraco (28x22cm-11x9in) s. pencil W/C bodycol
£1000	$1750	(25-Feb-92 C31/R) Scarlet Tanagers (39x27cm-15x11in) s. pencil W/C bodycol
£1000	$1750	(25-Feb-92 C26/R) Blue and gold macaw (25x20cm-10x8in) s. pencil W/C bodycol
£1600	$2800	(25-Feb-92 C25/R) African Pitta (28x19cm-11x7in) s. W/C bodycol
£1600	$2800	(25-Feb-92 C27/R) Hawk-headed parrot (37x27cm-15x11in) s. pencil W/C bodycol
£2100	$3675	(25-Feb-92 C22/R) Bearded tits (29x23cm-11x9in) s. i.verso pencil W/C bodycol

REIFFEL, Charles (1862-1942) American
£847	$1500	(12-Feb-92 B.SF510/R) Fall landscape (34x34cm-13x13in) s. pastel

REIGON, Francisco (fl.1840-1871) Spanish
£818	$1481	(20-May-92 ANS.M68/R) El bano de Diana (19x13cm-7x5in) s.d.1882 panel (S.P 150000)

REIKHET, Viktor (1922-) Russian
£665	$1184	(25-Nov-91 ARC.P38/R) La jeune femme en rouge (60x73cm-24x29in) s. (F.FR 6500)
£665	$1184	(25-Nov-91 ARC.P41) Nu assis (78x69cm-31x27in) s. (F.FR 6500)
£1597	$2842	(25-Nov-91 ARC.P37/R) La lecture (65x81cm-26x32in) s. (F.FR 15600)

REILLE, Comtesse Anna (19th C) French
£917	$1706	(18-Jun-92 SY.MO414/R) Gitane et son tambourin (105x85cm-41x33in) s. (F.FR 9000)

REILLE, Karl (1886-1975) French
£1114	$2017	(18-May-92 AT.P147) Jockey se rendant au depart (27x35cm-11x14in) s.d.1930 panel (F.FR 11000)
£1013	$1834	(18-May-92 AT.P29) Bat-l'eau (29x45cm-11x18in) mono.d.09 W/C (F.FR 10000)
£2837	$5135	(18-May-92 AT.P28/R) Cerf hallali (33x27cm-13x11in) s. gouache (F.FR 28000)

REIMANN, Walter (20th C) German
£632	$1137	(22-Nov-91 SA.A1758/R) Wannsee landscape (75x101cm-30x40in) s.d.1922 (DM 1800)

REIMER, F (fl.1830-1835) Italian
£885	$1700	(30-Jul-92 E.EDM329/R) Havana Packet, Havana, New York (56x74cm-22x29in) s. W/C

REIMPRE, Thibault de (1949-) French
£915	$1591	(16-Apr-92 FB.P270/R) Sans titre (60x60cm-24x24in) s.d.89 acrylic (F.FR 9000)

REIN, Johan Eimerich (1827-1900) Norwegian
£985	$1881	(21-Jul-92 UL.T203) Coastal landscape near Hellesund (34x61cm-13x24in) (N.KR 11000)

REINA, Antonio (?) ?
£1937	$3312	(17-Mar-92 FER.M117/R) Arrabal de Venecia con una gondola (20x15cm-8x6in) s. canvas laid down on panel (S.P 350000)

REINAGLE, George Philip (1802-1835) British
£6000	$10080	(15-Aug-91 B392/R) Dutch pinks and merchantmen off fortified jetty (49x75cm-19x30in) init.indist.d. panel

REINAGLE, P A (attrib) (fl.1804-1811) British
£652	$1225	(5-Jan-92 LIT.L355) Kill (51x61cm-20x24in)

REINAGLE, Philip (1749-1833) British
£11500	$20240	(10-Apr-92 C71/R) Landscapes with greyhounds and dead hare. Setters pointing (51x77cm-20x30in) one s.d.1799 pair
£26000	$46540	(13-Nov-91 S114/R) Pug dog with puppy by gate with lady and child beyond (37x49cm-15x19in)
£30000	$53700	(13-Nov-91 S109/R) Stag hound of the royal pack under tree at Windsor (37x49cm-15x19in)
£30000	$53700	(13-Nov-91 S106/R) Foxhounds in pursuit (37x49cm-15x19in)
£30000	$53700	(13-Nov-91 S104/R) Water dog carrying stick, rowing boat on river beyond (37x49cm-15x19in)
£700	$1232	(7-Apr-92 C136/R) Couple reading poetry beneath tree (36x52cm-14x20in) pencil W/C

REINAGLE, Philip (after) (1749-1833) British
£900 $1548 (8-Oct-91 PH50/R) Breaking cover, Colonel Thornton with his hounds
(71x91cm-28x36in)

REINAGLE, Philip (attrib) (1749-1833) British
£843 $1500 (30-Oct-91 D.NY58) The kill (51x61cm-20x24in)
£1000 $1710 (12-Mar-92 CSK176/R) Angler beside mill bothy (97x70cm-38x28in)

REINAGLE, Philip (circle) (1749-1833) British
£2600 $4628 (1-Nov-91 S420/R) Pair barn owls in landscape (60x75cm-24x30in)

REINAGLE, Ramsay Richard (1775-1862) British
£500 $930 (16-Jun-92 SWS212) Carnouise Glen (44x34cm-17x13in) s.d.1842
indis.s.i.stretcher
£1000 $1710 (16-Mar-92 LW1801/R) Portraits of Rev. Charles C. Beaty Powell, vicar of
Milton and wife, Catherine (38x30cm-15x12in) s.d.1848 i.verso pair
£3000 $5370 (13-Nov-91 S160/R) Family group in river landscape (86x68cm-34x27in)
£3200 $5728 (13-Nov-91 CG568/R) Figures by a bridge in an italianate landscape
(57x71cm-22x28in) s.d.1802

REINAGLE, Ramsay Richard (style) (1775-1862) British
£1200 $2052 (12-Mar-92 CSK122) Portrait of lady standing playing harp with dog at her
side in interior (56x36cm-22x14in)

REINBOTHE, Finn (20th C) Danish?
£722 $1235 (10-Mar-92 RAS.K14) Landscape (185x122cm-73x48in) s.d.1986verso oil
acrylic collage masonite (D.KR 8000)

REINDEL, Edna (1900-) American
£1892 $3500 (10-Jun-92 CE.NY451/R) Still life with tomato, eggplant and pommegranite
on table (66x56cm-26x22in) s.

REINHARD, Holga (1853-1902) Danish
£812 $1462 (19-Nov-91 RAS.K291/R) Interior with young couple (55x47cm-22x19in)
mono.d.1893 (D.KR 9000)
£1585 $2741 (2-Sep-91 BU.K23/R) Cottage interior with small girl reading
(70x90cm-28x35in) mono.d.1902 (D.KR 18000)

REINHARD, Josef (1749-1824) Swiss
£2196 $3931 (15-Nov-91 GK.Z5343/R) Vintner couple (62x47cm-24x19in) i.d.1798verso
canvas on pavatex (S.FR 5600)

REINHARDT, Ad (1913-1967) American
£21229 $38000 (12-Nov-91 CH.NY4/R) Blue composition (25x20cm-10x8in)
s.i.d.1959-60stretcher
£100559 $180000 (12-Nov-91 CH.NY6 a/R) Abstract painting (102x81cm-40x32in) s.d.41
£251397 $450000 (12-Nov-91 CH.NY30/R) Abstract painting (152x152cm-60x60in) s.i.d.1960
£251397 $450000 (6-May-92 SY.NY12/R) Abstract painting (203x102cm-80x40in)
s.i.d.1955verso

REINHARDT, Carl August (1818-1877) German
£559 $996 (26-Nov-91 KF.M244) Winter landscape with skaters (16x12cm-6x5in)
s.d.1850 gouache pencil (DM 1600)

REINHARDT, Georg Friedrich Theodor (?) ?
£2300 $4117 (5-May-92 SWS386) Still life of mixed roses in basket (47x38cm-19x15in)
s.

REINHARDT, J (?) ?
£1000 $1790 (15-Jan-92 BT168 b) Still life of flowers in a vase (58x48cm-23x19in) s.
board

REINHARDT, Louis (?-1870) German
£1745 $3123 (16-Jan-92 D.V57/R) Cattle watering in lake landscape (59x89cm-23x35in)
s. canvas on board (A.S 35000)

REINHARDT, Wilhelm (1815-1881) German
£519 $986 (24-Jun-92 KM.K1227) Farmhouse with view of Felbertal and Felbertauern
(80x100cm-31x39in) s. (DM 1500)

REINHART, Lea (1877-1970) Austrian
£550 $995 (21-May-92 CSK159) Still life of clock, roses in vase and other vases on
draped table (20x25cm-8x10in) s. panel

REINHERZ, Conrad (1835-1892) German
£1229 $2224 (22-May-92 GB.B6016) Horses watering (35x25cm-14x10in) s. panel (DM 3600)

REINHOLD, Franz (1816-1893) Austrian
£1097 $1963 (16-Jan-92 D.V109/R) Passeiertor near Meran (15x19cm-6x7in) s. paper
(A.S 22000)
£1199 $2062 (8-Oct-91 ZEL.L1678) Lake landscape with Austrian village
(57x102cm-22x40in) s. (DM 3500)
£1199 $2062 (8-Oct-91 ZEL.L1679/R) View of glacier (73x100cm-29x39in) s. (DM 3500)
£3100 $5363 (4-Oct-91 C79/R) Sportsmen conversing on the banks of lake
(26x44cm-10x17in) s. paper on canvas

REINHOLD, Franz (1816-1893) Austrian-cont.
£3497 $6294   (21-Nov-91 D.V74/R) Landscape (23x42cm-9x17in) i.verso (A.S 70000)
£4181 $7610   (11-Dec-91 N.M566/R) Wooded landscape with woodcutters (79x104cm-31x41in)
                  s. (DM 12000)
£2091   *$3805*   *(11-Dec-91 N.M264 a/R) Peasant woman and child on path in wooded*
                  landscape with village, Austria (38x55cm-15x22in) mono. W/C (DM 6000)

REINHOLD, Friedrich (younger) (1814-1881) Austrian
£1745 $3123   (16-Jan-92 D.V104/R) Horses watering (50x64cm-20x25in) s.d.1850
                  (A.S 35000)

REINHOLD, Thomas (1953-) Austrian
£769 $1369   (25-Nov-91 WK.M2054/R) Schwebende Knaben uber singende Madchen
                  (210x230cm-83x91in) s.d.1983 s.i.d.verso (DM 2200)
£978 $1740   (31-Oct-91 D.V186/R) Two figures (210x230cm-83x91in) s.d.83 (A.S 20000)
£1154 $2054   (25-Nov-91 WK.M2055/R) Singende Madchen unter schwebenden Knaben
                  (210x230cm-83x91in) s. s.i.d.1983verso (DM 3300)

REINICKE, Rene (1860-1926) German
£767 $1395   (12-Dec-91 L.K663) Still life of fruit, glass, bowl and stone ware
                  (51x57cm-20x22in) s.d.1910 (DM 2200)

REINIGER, Ernst (1841-1873) German
£2203 $3899   (23-Apr-92 RAS.V883/R) Mountain landscape with deer by lake
                  (88x160cm-35x63in) s.i. (D.KR 25000)

REINIGER, Otto (1863-1909) German
£3158 $5400   (13-Mar-92 FN.S2921/R) Schonbuch landscape (58x77cm-23x30in) s. (DM 9000)
£3436 $5979   (17-Sep-91 FN.S2507/R) Wooded landscape (67x39cm-26x15in) s.d.1889
                  (DM 10000)

REINIGER, Otto (attrib) (1863-1909) German
£775 $1402   (3-Dec-91 FN.S2400/R) Wooded river landscape with farmhouse and anglers
                  (31x51cm-12x20in) (DM 2200)

REINOLDS, C T (19th C) British
£500 $915   (12-May-92 H360) Reading the will s.d.1887

REINWALD, A (20th C) Belgian
£772 $1389   (22-Nov-91 SA.A388/R) Sunday tourists on Ostende beach (41x55cm-16x22in)
                  s.d.1913 (DM 2200)

REIPOLSKY, Anatoli (1945-) Russian
£504 $882   (24-Sep-91 ARC.P192/R) A la barre (60x80cm-24x31in) s. (F.FR 5000)

REISER, Carl (1877-?) German
£1568   *$2854*   *(11-Dec-91 WE.MU288) Pilgrimage church in mountain landscape*
                  (49x74cm-19x29in) s.d.1900 W/C (DM 4500)

REISMAN, Ori (1924-1991) Israeli
£1330 $2500   (5-Jan-92 GG.TA361/R) Portrait (54x46cm-21x18in) s.
£2444 $4400   (6-Jan-92 GG.TA438/R) Landscape (65x78cm-26x31in) s.
£4468 $8400   (5-Jan-92 GG.TA360/R) Landscape (55x73cm-22x29in) s.

REISMANN, Philip (1904-) American
£1149 $2000   (15-Apr-92 SY.NY186/R) Singing trip (54x36cm-21x14in) init.d.40 masonite
£1436 $2700   (18-Dec-91 SY.NY315/R) Ship skeleton (45x61cm-18x24in) s.d.1947 masonite
£851   *$1600*   *(18-Dec-91 SY.NY270/R) The shoe pedlar (45x35cm-18x14in) s.d.38 gouache*
                  masonite

REISS, Fritz (1857-1916) German
£1890 $3289   (17-Sep-91 FN.S2508/R) Two Black Forest girls whispering in landscape
                  (67x45cm-26x18in) s.i.verso (DM 5500)

REISS, Wallace (20th C) German?
£687 $1196   (17-Sep-91 FN.S2065) Return of the prophet (40x20cm-16x8in) s.d.1951
                  (DM 2000)

REISTRUP, K Hansen see HANSEN-REISTRUP, K

REITER, Johann Baptist (1813-1890) Austrian
£1854 $3225   (19-Sep-91 D.V23/R) Portrait of girl (32x37cm-13x15in) (A.S 38000)

REITER, Johann Baptist (circle) (1813-1890) Austrian
£3906 $6914   (5-Nov-91 GF.L2099/R) Mother and Child (69x59cm-27x23in) (S.FR 10000)

REMBRANDT (1606-1669) Dutch
£3800000 $7296000 (8-Jul-92 S86/R) Portrait of Johannes Uyittenbogaert (132x102cm-52x40in)
                  bears sig.i.d.1633

REMBRANDT (after) (1606-1669) Dutch
£780 $1420   (11-Dec-91 ZZ.B189) Self portrait (68x56cm-27x22in)
£800 $1440   (22-Nov-91 SWS166/R) The descent from the cross (56x46cm-22x18in) panel
£800 $1488   (16-Jun-92 SWS211) Study of heads of two men (38x56cm-15x22in)
£850 $1530   (21-Nov-91 CSK170) Girl at window (81x65cm-32x26in)

REMBRANDT (after) (1606-1669) Dutch-cont.
£1100	$1980	(30-Jan-92 TL23/R) Self portrait of the artist (73x61cm-29x24in)
£1101	$1894	(7-Oct-91 CH.E219/R) Judas casting down thirty pieces of silver (79x102cm-31x40in) (E.P 1200)
£1500	$2880	(8-Jul-92 S166/R) Portrait of Johannes Uyttenbogaert (34x25cm-13x10in)
£1900	$3629	(14-Jul-92 DR413) Self-portrait (66x53cm-26x21in)
£5136	$9193	(7-May-92 CH.AM108/R) Portrait of Nicolaes van Bambeeck, aged 44, standing at window (106x84cm-42x33in) with sig. (D.FL 17000)

REMBRANDT (circle) (1606-1669) Dutch
£2584	$4600	(22-Jan-92 D.NY55/R) Portrait of old man (61x46cm-24x18in) panel
£23743	$42500	(17-Jan-92 SY.NY179/R) Portrait of an oriental, possibly King Uzziah (102x80cm-40x31in)
£5028	$9000	(15-Jan-92 CH.NY141/R) Youth (12x5cm-5x2in) num.3 verso pen wash white

REMBRANDT (school) (1606-1669) Dutch
| £1235 | $2198 | (28-Apr-92 RAS.K477) The return of the Prodigal Son (34x60cm-13x24in) panel (D.KR 14000) |
| £2950 | $5252 | (25-Nov-91 CH.AM70/R) Christ at the column (29x18cm-11x7in) brush ink wash htd.white (D.FL 9500) |

REMBRANDT (studio) (1606-1669) Dutch
| £802 | $1436 | (12-Nov-91 SY.AM298/R) Death of St John the Baptist (17x19cm-7x7in) pen wash over chk (D.FL 2600) |

REMBRANDT (style) (1606-1669) Dutch
£750	$1373	(12-May-92 SWS622/R) Portrait of old man (93x77cm-37x30in)
£950	$1663	(27-Feb-92 CSK167) Portrait of man holding flute (47x37cm-19x15in)
£3200	$5600	(2-Apr-92 CSK127/R) Portrait of bearded man, in turban (60x48cm-24x19in)

REMDE, Friedrich (1801-1878) German
| £750 | $1298 | (3-Oct-91 CSK239) Portrait of Grand Duke Karl Frederick of Saxe Weimar Eisenbach (104x84cm-41x33in) |
| £1200 | $2076 | (3-Oct-91 CSK238/R) Portrait of Miss Remde, the younger daughter of the artist (130x97cm-51x38in) s.d.1854 |

REMFREY, David (20th C) British?
| £441 | $750 | (23-Oct-91 B.SF3730/R) Reclining girl (51x71cm-20x28in) s.d.1979 pencil chl |

REMINGTON, Frederic (1861-1909) American
£13187	$24000	(28-May-92 CH.NY112/R) Artillery Officer in fulldress (35x20cm-14x8in) s.
£703	$1300	(14-Jun-92 S.BM33/R) Fire-bag - illustration for Henry Wadsworth Longfellow's Song Hiawatha (28x23cm-11x9in) s.i. i.verso ink
£1395	$2400	(14-Oct-91 H.C131/R) Woman's shirt (28x20cm-11x8in) s.i. ink dr over pencil
£1453	$2500	(14-Oct-91 H.C133/R) Shirt-Blackfoot (25x20cm-10x8in) s.i. ink dr over pencil
£1512	$2600	(14-Oct-91 H.C132/R) Shield-Sioux (25x23cm-10x9in) s.i. ink dr over pencil
£2442	$4200	(14-Oct-91 H.C130/R) The wolf (25x20cm-10x8in) s.i. ink dr over pencil
£2527	$4750	(18-Dec-91 SY.NY377/R) Knife sheath, illustration from Song of Hiawatha (31x17cm-12x7in) i. pen board
£3052	$5250	(20-Oct-91 HG.C39) Bust of trooper (13x10cm-5x4in) s. W/C

REMISOFF, Nicolay (20th C) Russian
£1447	$2750	(24-Jun-92 B.SF6459/R) Summer on Lake Arrowhead (112x71cm-44x28in) s.
£449	$800	(2-Nov-91 IH.NY37/R) Theatre scene with man, stage and Punch (30x23cm-12x9in) s. gouache
£847	$1500	(7-Nov-91 SY.NY50/R) Soiree de Boston - design for the decor (30x45cm-12x18in) s.d.1920 gouache paper laid down on board

REMOND, Jean Charles Joseph (1795-1875) French
| £3289 | $6282 | (1-Jul-92 FB.P44/R) Esquisse pour l'enlevement de Proserpine (24x33cm-9x13in) (F.FR 32000) |
| £6116 | $11376 | (18-Jun-92 SY.MO86/R) Vue de la Baie de Naples (26x55cm-10x22in) s. i.verso paper laid down on canvas (F.FR 60000) |

REN YI (1840-1895) Chinese
£7396	$12944	(30-Mar-92 CH.HK159/R) White Phoenix perched on red rock beneath Wutong tree (135x59cm-53x23in) s.i.d.1886 ink W/C hanging scroll (HK.D 100000)
£8876	$15533	(30-Mar-92 CH.HK216/R) Cock and hens (138x66cm-54x26in) s.d.1874 ink W/C hanging scroll (HK.D 120000)
£51775	$90607	(30-Mar-92 CH.HK160/R) Figures, flowers and landscape (169x48cm-67x19in) s.i.d.1912 ink W/C four hanging scrolls (HK.D 700000)

RENARD, Pierre (19/20th C) French
| £670 | $1200 | (13-Nov-91 B.SF2340/R) L'Arc de Triomphe (30x41cm-12x16in) s. W/C paper laid down on board |

RENARD, Stephen J (1947-) British
£500	$840	(15-Aug-91 B274) Off Whitby (50x76cm-20x30in) s.d.89
£1000	$1800	(9-Jan-92 B273/R) New York Yacht Club Cruise 1937 (61x91cm-24x36in) s.d.89
£1300	$2184	(15-Aug-91 B406/R) Leander leading Cariad, 1902 (61x91cm-24x36in) s.d.90

RENARD, Stephen J (1947-) British-cont.
£2800	$5348	(17-Jul-92 C146/R) A winning tack (49x74cm-19x29in) s.d.89 pair
£5000	$9550	(17-Jul-92 C148) Jockeying for position (91x122cm-36x48in) s.d.92
£5500	$9240	(15-Aug-91 B423/R) Schooner Adela showing paces in good breeze overhauling Germania (76x102cm-30x40in) s.d.91

RENAUDIN, Alfred (1866-1944) French
£1067	$1857	(13-Apr-92 BG.P124) Maison abondonnee (50x73cm-20x29in) s.d.1917 (F.FR 10500)
£1575	$2741	(13-Apr-92 BG.P126/R) La butte Montmartre (50x73cm-20x29in) s.d.1916 (F.FR 15500)
£2138	$3956	(10-Jun-92 ZZ.F36/R) Les lavandieres a Traveton (50x73cm-20x29in) s.d.1919 (F.FR 21000)
£2240	$4145	(10-Jun-92 ZZ.F37) Vue d'Allarmont (110x170cm-43x67in) s.d.1926 (F.FR 22000)
£2747	$5000	(28-May-92 SY.NY149/R) Le moulin a eau (53x72cm-21x28in) s.i.
£4286	$7500	(20-Feb-92 SY.NY145/R) Vue de Fenetrange (50x73cm-20x29in) s.i.

RENAULT, Gaston (1855-?) French
£900	$1539	(17-Mar-92 PH140) Washing day (97x116cm-38x46in) s.d.1884

RENAULT, L (19th C) ?
£700	$1267	(3-Dec-91 HS67) Two masted sailing ship Agnes Cairns of New Quay in the Bay of Naples (36x48cm-14x19in) W/C
£2300	$4163	(3-Dec-91 HS66) Brigantine Pitho of Swansea under full sail at Leghorn (46x66cm-18x26in) s.d.1870 W/C

RENAULT, Luigi P (19th C) French
£1600	$2896	(20-May-92 S86/R) Schooner Lizzie and barque E.Plurilus Unnum. Schooner Lizzie (42x59cm-17x23in) i. one s.d.1863 pair

RENESSE, Constantin van (1626-1680) Dutch
£21118	$37590	(25-Nov-91 CH.AM73/R) Naaman before Elisha (27x29cm-11x11in) i. chk pen wash htd.white (D.FL 68000)

RENESSE, Constantin van (attrib) (1626-1680) Dutch
£800	$1456	(11-Dec-91 PH251/R) Job lying on the dunghill being mocked by friends (17x26cm-7x10in) pen wash

RENESSE, Constantin van (style) (1626-1680) Dutch
£2128	$3894	(12-May-92 SY.AM19/R) Committee of regents (120x165cm-47x65in) panel (D.FL 7000)

RENI (after) (1575-1642) Italian
£850	$1488	(27-Feb-92 B49) The Penitent Magdalen (76x63cm-30x25in)
£950	$1663	(27-Feb-92 B30) St. John preaching (65x49cm-26x19in)

RENI, Guido (1575-1642) Italian
£18000	$34560	(10-Jul-92 C61/R) Portrait of artist, in wide-brimmed hat (11x9cm-4x4in) with i.verso copper oval
£26000	$49920	(7-Jul-92 C170/R) Head of woman looking up (39x27cm-15x11in) i.d.1609 i.verso chk

RENI, Guido (after) (1575-1642) Italian
£750	$1335	(31-Oct-91 B70) St. John preaching (65x49cm-26x19in)
£773	$1400	(22-May-92 S.BM6/R) Massacre of the innocents (89x56cm-35x22in)
£800	$1536	(9-Jul-92 CSK333) The Chariot of Aurora (26x63cm-10x25in) panel
£800	$1536	(9-Jul-92 CSK341) The Chariot of Aurora (91x198cm-36x78in)
£850	$1488	(27-Feb-92 CSK83/R) The Immaculate Conception (100x74cm-39x29in) feigned oval
£850	$1530	(21-Nov-91 CSK112) The triumph of Apollo (60x122cm-24x48in)
£900	$1638	(12-Dec-91 B30/R) Aurora (34x75cm-13x30in)
£900	$1728	(10-Jul-92 C236/R) Vision of Saint Philip Neri (22x17cm-9x7in) copper
£900	$1575	(27-Feb-92 CSK43) Michael vanquishing the Devil (63x43cm-25x17in)
£1090	$1875	(7-Oct-91 ANS.M144/R) Susana y los Ancianos (116x151cm-46x59in) (S.P 200000)
£1098	$1900	(24-Mar-92 GRO.B6/R) Annunciation (165x94cm-65x37in)
£1200	$2100	(2-Apr-92 CSK12) Chariot of Aurora (76x156cm-30x61in)
£1200	$2160	(21-Nov-91 CSK78/R) Susannah and the Elders (30x39cm-12x15in)
£1279	$2200	(16-Oct-91 D.NY82) Apollo and Aurora (51x109cm-20x43in)
£1292	$2300	(22-Jan-92 SY.NY66/R) Mary Magdalene (95x79cm-37x31in)
£1300	$2275	(27-Feb-92 CSK112) Portrait of Beatrice Cenci (63x51cm-25x20in)
£1426	$2595	(11-Dec-91 LD.P31) Salome (65x59cm-26x23in) (F.FR 14000)
£1536	$2779	(3-Dec-91 AB.S4748/R) Sibylla (74x62cm-29x24in) (S.KR 16000)
£1600	$2880	(21-Nov-91 C71) Aurora (86x156cm-34x61in)
£2000	$3600	(22-Nov-91 SWS29/R) St Joseph with the Christ Child (47x40cm-19x16in) arched top
£2200	$3850	(27-Feb-92 CSK76/R) The Triumph of Aurora (86x167cm-34x66in)
£2321	$4177	(19-Nov-91 F.R128) La Fortuna (177x142cm-70x56in) (I.L 5000000)
£2400	$4272	(31-Oct-91 B26/R) Susanna and Elders (93x142cm-37x56in) after Guido Reni
£2487	$4750	(16-Jul-92 SY.NY194/R) Aurora (74x151cm-29x59in)
£3409	$6000	(9-Apr-92 FA.PH615 a) St Cecilia (71x56cm-28x22in)
£4800	$8544	(1-Nov-91 C47/R) Judith and Holofernes (225x149cm-89x59in)
£6500	$11375	(1-Apr-92 S171/R) Toilet of Venus (283x206cm-111x81in) indist.mono. i.d.1763

RENI, Guido (attrib) (1575-1642) Italian

£508	$900	(13-Feb-92 S.W1871) Presentation in the temple (18x13cm-7x5in) ink sepia washes

RENI, Guido (circle) (1575-1642) Italian

£900	$1575	(25-Feb-92 PH75/R) Madonna adoring the sleeping Christ Child (63x84cm-25x33in)
£1100	$1925	(25-Feb-92 PH80) The Agony in the Garden (57x43cm-22x17in)
£1884	$3240	(8-Oct-91 ZEL.L1681/R) Portrait of Madonna (48x38cm-19x15in) (DM 5500)
£2039	$3792	(18-Jun-92 SY.MO103) Vierge a l'Enfant (26x20cm-10x8in) copper (F.FR 20000)
£5525	$10000	(21-May-92 CH.NY173/R) Saint Joseph and infant Christ in landscape (117x84cm-46x33in)
£13953	$24000	(9-Oct-91 CH.NY10/R) Four Seasons (170x227cm-67x89in)

RENI, Guido (school) (1575-1642) Italian

£5233	$9000	(9-Oct-91 CH.NY56/R) Portia (89x76cm-35x30in)
£11317	$20484	(7-Dec-91 CH.MO2/R) David tenant la Tete de Goliath (222x151cm-87x59in) (F.FR 110000)

RENI, Guido (studio) (1575-1642) Italian

£4000	$7680	(7-Jul-92 PH215/R) Flight into Egypt (161x130cm-63x51in)
£4800	$9216	(7-Jul-92 PH143/R) Penitent Magdalen (161x128cm-63x50in)
£100000	$192000	(7-Jul-92 PH39/R) Lucretia (101x82cm-40x32in)

RENI, Guido (style) (1575-1642) Italian

£681	$1300	(16-Jul-92 SY.NY189/R) Mary with Jesus and John the Baptist (34x25cm-13x10in) panel
£750	$1440	(9-Jul-92 CSK67/R) The Mater Dolorosa (56x48cm-22x19in)
£800	$1400	(27-Feb-92 CSK14/R) The Madonna Annunciate (74x61cm-29x24in)
£1000	$1820	(26-May-92 PH130/R) Ecce Homo (66x51cm-26x20in)
£1067	$1900	(22-Jan-92 D.NY68) Penitent Magdalene (76x56cm-30x22in)
£1077	$2057	(15-Jul-92 CH.S774) Madonna and child (54x44cm-21x17in) (A.D 2800)
£1100	$2002	(12-Dec-91 B10 t) The incredulity of St.Thomas (152x132cm-60x52in)
£1172	$2074	(5-Nov-91 GF.L2335/R) St Peter (72x54cm-28x21in) (S.FR 3000)
£1300	$2340	(21-Nov-91 CSK94/R) Putti sharpening cupid's arrow (51x63cm-20x25in)
£1500	$2880	(8-Jul-92 S250) Ecce Homo (57x46cm-22x18in)
£1500	$2700	(21-Nov-91 CSK4) The Penitant Magdalen with putti (169x106cm-67x42in)
£1571	$3000	(16-Jul-92 SY.NY108/R) Head of an apostle (57x40cm-22x16in)
£1600	$2912	(13-Dec-91 C229/R) Portrait of Camillo Borghese as a Cardinal (65x49cm-26x19in)
£1600	$3072	(9-Jul-92 CSK70/R) Madonna Annunciate (67x49cm-26x19in)
£1963	$3729	(23-Jun-92 D.V172/R) The penitent Magdalen (116x91cm-46x36in) (A.S 40000)
£2000	$3500	(3-Apr-92 C90/R) Saint Dorothea (69x56cm-27x22in)
£2090	$3637	(13-Sep-91 C115/R) Angels making music (82x54cm-32x21in)
£2203	$3899	(7-Nov-91 D.V243/R) St Peter (128x93cm-50x37in) (A.S 45000)
£2235	$3823	(18-Mar-92 D.V199/R) Polyphem and Galathea (64x80cm-25x31in) (A.S 45000)
£2400	$4320	(21-Nov-91 C53) Saint Sebastian (129x99cm-51x39in)
£2600	$4680	(22-Nov-91 SWS28/R) The Holy Family (101x82cm-40x32in)
£2600	$4550	(28-Feb-92 C136/R) The Madonna and child (105x81cm-41x32in)
£4401	$7394	(27-Aug-91 RAS.K235/R) Cupid (82x110cm-32x43in) init. (D.KR 50000)
£7000	$12740	(11-Dec-91 S138/R) Penitent Magdalen (236x157cm-93x62in)
£7500	$13125	(2-Apr-92 CSK8/R) Saint John the Baptist (117x91cm-46x36in)

RENKER, G (?) German?

£683	$1242	(27-May-92 PH.DU172) Lake in wooded summer landscape (66x45cm-26x18in) s. board (DM 2000)

RENNAT, I B (attrib) (18th C) ?

£1509	$2672	(10-Nov-91 BU.M267) Cathedral interior (90x140cm-35x55in) s.d.1760verso (S.KR 16000)

RENNIE, George Melvin (20th C) British

£700	$1330	(24-Jun-92 LJ31) View of River Dee (44x60cm-17x24in) s.
£750	$1260	(26-Aug-91 S1003/R) Loch Benavian, Affric (51x76cm-20x30in) s.
£800	$1448	(4-Dec-91 S225/R) Dinnet Moor (41x61cm-16x24in) s. s.i.stretcher
£850	$1428	(26-Aug-91 S1002/R) Sound of Mull from Mull looking to mainland and Ben Cruichan (61x91cm-24x36in) s. i.stretcher
£1300	$2184	(26-Aug-91 S1001/R) Valley in the Highlands (40x61cm-16x24in) s.d.1925

RENOIR, Pierre Auguste (1841-1919) French

£14737	$26526	(21-Nov-91 L.K420/R) Trois roses (17x8cm-7x3in) mono. (DM 42000)
£16949	$30000	(6-Nov-91 CH.NY265/R) Composition mythologique (16x35cm-6x14in) st.sig. canvas on panel
£17143	$30000	(25-Feb-92 CH.NY11/R) Projet de decoration d'assiette (23cm-9ins circular) st.sig.
£19878	$36972	(21-Jun-92 LT.P71/R) Fruits sur la nappe blanche (17x24cm-7x9in) mono. (F.FR 195000)
£24000	$41280	(16-Oct-91 S10/R) Sucrier et citron (16x32cm-6x13in) s.
£25424	$45000	(6-Nov-91 CH.NY261/R) Tete de femme (14x11cm-6x4in) bears init. canvas on panel
£25714	$45000	(25-Feb-92 CH.NY10/R) Portrait de Pierre Renoir (15x15cm-6x6in) st.sig. oil pencil
£30000	$51900	(25-Mar-92 S11/R) Nature morte au citron et a la tasse du the (19x28cm-7x11in) s.

RENOIR, Pierre Auguste (1841-1919) French-cont.

£30395	$55015	(22-May-92 BL.P89/R) Femme vue de dos (20x11cm-8x4in) init. (F.FR 300000)
£37075	$69701	(16-Dec-91 AGS.P25/R) Jeune femme nue, en buste, vue de profil, le visage appuye sur les mains (18x19cm-7x7in) s. (F.FR 360000)
£40000	$69200	(25-Mar-92 S13/R) Paysage (22x33cm-9x13in) s.
£45198	$80000	(6-Nov-91 CH.NY263/R) Maisons dans les arbres (20x25cm-8x10in) s.
£45593	$82523	(24-May-92 GL.P57/R) Paysage de Cagnes (26x36cm-10x14in) s. (F.FR 450000)
£60109	$110000	(13-May-92 SY.NY50/R) L'arrosoir (23x29cm-9x11in) s.
£62842	$115000	(14-May-92 SY.NY241/R) Glaieuls (37x25cm-15x10in) s.
£64972	$115000	(6-Nov-91 CH.NY259/R) Nature morte aux peches et raisins (16x42cm-6x17in) s.
£73000	$139430	(1-Jul-92 S120/R) Paysage (29x38cm-11x15in) st.sig.
£86614	$148976	(16-Oct-91 G.Z14/R) Paysage au pont (22x32cm-9x13in) s.d.1901 (S.FR 220000)
£91185	$165046	(24-May-92 GL.P55/R) Clytemnestre (46x36cm-18x14in) studio st. (F.FR 900000)
£98361	$180000	(12-May-92 CH.NY109/R) Fille avec des bas rouges (31x23cm-12x9in) s.
£102145	$178754	(24-Feb-92 ARC.P23/R) Cagnes sur mer (18x32cm-7x13in) s. (F.FR 1000000)
£106557	$195000	(13-May-92 CH.NY207/R) Tama (37x31cm-15x12in) s.
£114754	$210000	(13-May-92 SY.NY47/R) Portrait de jeune fille en rose (28x26cm-11x10in) s.
£150000	$271500	(3-Dec-91 S23/R) Les baigneuses (34x46cm-13x18in) s.
£163934	$300000	(14-May-92 SY.NY242/R) Portrait de femme (34x28cm-13x11in) s.
£191257	$350000	(13-May-92 SY.NY45/R) Femme accoudee, Gabrielle (28x26cm-11x10in) s.
£256831	$470000	(13-May-92 SY.NY69/R) Paysage aux mimosas, Parc des Collettes (31x40cm-12x16in) s.
£295316	$546334	(12-Jun-92 AT.P20/R) Buste de femme au corsage rouge (41x37cm-16x15in) s. (F.FR 2900000)
£310734	$550000	(6-Nov-91 SY.NY36/R) Portrait de Madamoiselle Christine Lerolle (42x34cm-17x13in) s.
£320000	$579200	(2-Dec-91 C8/R) Alice Gamby au jardin, jeune femme assise dans l'herbe (73x85cm-29x33in)
£437158	$800000	(12-May-92 CH.NY102/R) La maison de Collette a Cagnes (47x55cm-19x22in) s.
£573771	$1050000	(13-May-92 SY.NY44/R) Paysage a La Roche-Guyon (46x56cm-18x22in) st.sig.
£1092896	$2000000	(12-May-92 CH.NY105/R) Yvonne et Jean (54x65cm-21x26in) s.
£1147541	$2100000	(13-May-92 SY.NY70/R) Portrait de Jean Renoir (41x32cm-16x13in) s.
£1242938	$2200000	(5-Nov-91 CH.NY27/R) L'alphabet, Jean et Gabrielle (56x46cm-22x18in) s.
£5561	$9989	(29-Nov-91 F.F94/R) Studio per decorazione di porta (32x41cm-13x16in) pencil (I.L 12000000)
£8239	$14089	(17-Mar-92 FB.P25/R) Nus (65x50cm-26x20in) s. red white chk. (F.FR 80000)
£15607	$27000	(2-Oct-91 SY.NY1/R) Etudes des nus (24x31cm-9x12in) init. wash chl
£21469	$38000	(7-Nov-91 SY.NY102 a/R) Enfant a la Charlotte (35x29cm-14x11in) s. conte crayon
£25000	$47750	(1-Jul-92 S110/R) Feuille d'etudes - tetes de jeune fille, fille assise et tete d'homme (52x32cm-20x13in) init. pen brush Indian ink htd chl
£70000	$126700	(3-Dec-91 S28/R) Baigneuses dans la foret (63x97cm-25x38in) s. pencil
£142077	$260000	(14-May-92 SY.NY107/R) Portrait de Mademoiselle Amelie Dieterle au chapeau (49x40cm-19x16in) init. chl
£409836	$750000	(12-May-92 CH.NY116/R) Portrait de fillette (38x29cm-15x11in) init. pastel paper on board
£508475	$900000	(5-Nov-91 CH.NY24/R) La loge (56x43cm-22x17in) s. pastel paper on board

RENOIR, Pierre Auguste (circle) (1841-1919) French

| £1380 | $2470 | (14-Nov-91 CH.R2) Casolare nel paesaggio (19x26cm-7x10in) s. canvas on board (I.L 3000000) |

RENOUARD, George (19/20th C) American?

| £506 | $910 | (23-Nov-91 YFA.M236/R) Porcelain vessels (46x56cm-18x22in) s. |

RENOUF, Edda (20th C) ?

| £515 | $892 | (23-Mar-92 CC.P118) One two (33x33cm-13x13in) s.i.d.1974 (F.FR 5000) |

RENOUX, Andre (?) French?

| £1279 | $2200 | (12-Oct-91 SY.NY97/R) Beaute divine (27x35cm-11x14in) s. s.i.verso |
| £1453 | $2500 | (12-Oct-91 SY.NY96/R) Librairie (28x46cm-11x18in) s. s.i.verso |

RENOUX, Charles (1795-1846) French

| £1839 | $3218 | (19-Feb-92 D.P10/R) Scene animee de personnages dans un cloitre (35x27cm-14x11in) s.d.1829 (F.FR 18000) |

RENOUX, Jules Ernest (1863-1932) French

£650	$1131	(19-Sep-91 CSK93) L'Arc du Carousel (33x40cm-13x16in) s.
£750	$1358	(2-Dec-91 CSK25/R) Notre Dame au choucher du soleil (27x35cm-11x14in) s. st.studio verso
£1000	$1810	(2-Dec-91 CSK23/R) Le Havre, Quai de Southampton (33x41cm-13x16in) s.i.st.studio verso
£1613	$3000	(16-Jun-92 RO.BA133) Rue de Paris (33x46cm-13x18in)
£1774	$3300	(16-Jun-92 RO.BA135) Le Pont des Arts (27x42cm-11x17in) panel

RENQVIST, Torsten (1924-) Swedish

| £720 | $1303 | (3-Dec-91 AB.S5143/R) Old woman (39x34cm-15x13in) s.d.52-56 (S.KR 7500) |

RENSHAW, A (?) ?

| £580 | $1061 | (5-Feb-92 CSK194) Young beauty (36x30cm-14x12in) s. painted oval |

RENSHAW, Ian (1967-) British
£500 $915   (3-Feb-92 B141/R) October (95x113cm-37x44in) init.d.90

RENTEL, Max (1850-?) German
£629 $1089   (25-Mar-92 KM.K1382) Sailor seated before cottage (41x31cm-16x12in)
                          s.d.87 panel (DM 1800)

RENTOIL, Henri Molte de (19/20th C) French
£2456 $4421   (22-Nov-91 SA.A1791/R) Water nymphs (121x104cm-48x41in) s. (DM 7000)

RENTZELL, August von and TRIEBEL, Carl (19th C) German
£2062 $3588   (17-Sep-91 FN.S2587/R) Animals and figures resting in mountain landscape,
                          thunderstorm rising (70x96cm-28x38in) s. (DM 6000)
£2168 $3750   (6-Sep-91 S.BM131/R) Genre scene with young shepherd and shepherdess
                          (69x97cm-27x38in) s.
£4530 $8244   (11-Dec-91 WE.MU144/R) Cattle and children in high mountain landscape
                          (69x97cm-27x38in) s. (DM 13000)

RENZ, Alfred (1877-1930) German
£1333 $2280   (13-Mar-92 FN.S2923/R) Hamburg Harbour (80x100cm-31x39in) s. (DM 3800)

REPETTO, Armando E (1893-1968) Argentinian
£559 $1000   (6-May-92 V.BA88) Barrio porteno (22x32cm-9x13in)
£698 $1200   (9-Oct-91 RO.BA593) Atardecer en Huacalera, Quebrada de Humahuaca, Jujuy
                          (14x20cm-6x8in) s. s.i.verso
£806 $1500   (16-Jun-92 RO.BA85) Homenaje (14x20cm-6x8in)
£814 $1400   (9-Oct-91 RO.BA405) Barcas en reparacion (40x50cm-16x20in) s.d.39
£1075 $2000   (16-Jun-92 RO.BA102) Desnudo (38x49cm-15x19in)
£1117 $2000   (6-May-92 V.BA90) En el puerto (40x50cm-16x20in)
£1163 $2000   (9-Oct-91 RO.BA591) De regreso (30x39cm-12x15in) s.d.51 panel
£2558 $4400   (9-Oct-91 RO.BA762) Dia de Lluvia (30x40cm-12x16in) s.d.51 panel
£2688 $5000   (16-Jun-92 RO.BA66) Paisaje (115x150cm-45x59in)

REPIN, Ilia (1844-1930) Russian
£2277 $4167   (14-May-92 BU.S194/R) Portrait of a man (42x32cm-17x13in) s.d.1881
                          (S.KR 24000)
£3036 $5556   (14-May-92 BU.S195/R) Barge pullers (22x28cm-9x11in) s. (S.KR 32000)
£4054 $6932   (12-Mar-92 GK.Z58) Self portrait (57x46cm-22x18in) indis.s. oval
                          (S.FR 10500)
£5090 $9263   (15-Dec-91 REM.W35) Study for The Zaporoze Cossacks (41x38cm-16x15in)
                          (P.Z 100000000)
£6319 $11500   (13-Dec-91 S.W2625/R) Portrait of Princess Paul Troubetosky
                          (53x43cm-21x17in) s.
£11000 $19580   (28-Nov-91 S407/R) Preparatory study for portrait of Sir George Buchanan,
                          Ambassador (21x12cm-8x5in) s.i.d.1917 panel
£950 $1644   (3-Oct-91 CSK2) Study for - They did not expect him (15x15cm-6x6in) s.
                          pencil
£2600 $4628   (28-Nov-91 S508/R) Study for portrait of Vera Repina - resting
                          (28x21cm-11x8in) s. graphite htd conte crayon white
£3000 $5580   (16-Jun-92 S12/R) General Otton Borisovich Richter (24x15cm-9x6in)
                          s.i.d.1886 chl oil cardboard
£4200 $7476   (28-Nov-91 S509/R) Study of seated lady with muff (41x31cm-16x12in)
                          s.i.d.1915 gouache over pencil

REPIN, Ilia (attrib) (1844-1930) Russian
£7042 $11831   (27-Aug-91 RAS.K154/R) Portrait of young man wearing fur hat
                          (68x48cm-27x19in) s. (D.KR 80000)

REPTON, John Adey (1775-1860) British
£4000 $7160   (14-Nov-91 S51/R) East Barsham Manor, Norfolk from the High Road. From
                          the Abbey Barn (26x43cm-10x17in) wash over pencil pair

RESCHI, Pandolfo (1643-1699) Polish
£6800 $11900   (31-Mar-92 PH80/R) Travellers being ambushed before natural arch spanning
                          country path (74x95cm-29x37in)
£11139 $20051   (19-Nov-91 F.R137/R) Battaglia (78x114cm-31x45in) (I.L 24000000)
£14403 $26070   (5-Dec-91 SY.MO228/R) Choc de cavalerie (89x115cm-35x45in) (F.FR 140000)
£22099 $40000   (22-May-92 SY.NY58/R) Landscape with herdsmen (119x171cm-47x67in)
£22099 $40000   (22-May-92 SY.NY58 a/R) Landscape with huntsmen (120x170cm-47x67in)

RESCHI, Pandolfo (circle) (1643-1699) Polish
£1840 $3165   (15-Oct-91 CH.R37/R) Viaggiatori a cavallo presso una siepe
                          (33x24cm-13x9in) (I.L 4000000)
£3937 $6810   (25-Mar-92 CH.R61/R) Mischia tra cavalieri (55x68cm-22x27in)
                          (I.L 8500000)

RESCHI, Pandolfo (style) (1643-1699) Polish
£838 $1600   (16-Jul-92 SY.NY172/R) Washerwomen in landscape (61x45cm-24x18in)

RESCHREITER, Rudolf (1868-?) German
£592 $1078   (13-Dec-91 BM.B789/R) View of St Moritz, winter (34x49cm-13x19in) s.
                          gouache (DM 1700)

RESEIGNO, V (19th C) Italian
£619 $1076   (21-Sep-91 SA.A1731/R) Diana and attendants in South Italian landscape
       s.d.1902 canvas on panel (DM 1800)

RESIO, Piro (19th C) Italian
£1465 $2490   (24-Oct-91 D.V130/R) Italian couple (46x26cm-18x10in) s. (A.S 30000)

RESNICK, Milton (1917-) American
£4624 $8000   (3-Oct-91 SY.NY15/R) Untitled (89x59cm-35x23in) s.d.59 linen laid down on
       board

RESNIKOFF, I (20th C) ?
£3243 $6000   (12-Jun-92 SY.NY50/R) Abstract cubist composition (61x51cm-24x20in) s.

RESTOUT, Jean (elder) (1663-1702) French
£3000 $5460   (10-Dec-91 PH176/R) Christ and woman from Samaria (87x57cm-34x22in)

RESTOUT, Jean (style) (17/18th C) French
£800 $1464   (12-May-92 SWS693/R) Virgin and child enthroned with saints
       (55x32cm-22x13in) painted arched top

RESTOUT, Jean (younger) (1692-1768) French
£5301 $9859   (20-Jun-92 CH.MO264/R) Saint Pelerin prechant aux habitants d'Auxerre
       (38x26cm-15x10in) black white chk (F.FR 52000)

RESTOUT, Jean (younger-attrib) (1692-1768) French
£2200 $4224   (8-Jul-92 PH199/R) Figures grouped around well together with livestock
       (23x32cm-9x13in) black chk htd white
£2854 $5309   (20-Jun-92 CH.MO265/R) Une academie d'homme allonge (24x40cm-9x16in) red
       white chk (F.FR 28000)

RETH, Alfred (1884-1966) French
£967 $1761   (11-Dec-91 ZZ.F73/R) Composition aux toits (46x38cm-18x15in) s. oil sable
       board (F.FR 9500)
£2033 $3537   (16-Apr-92 FB.P149/R) Composition (63x51cm-25x20in) s.d.58 oil sable
       panel (F.FR 20000)
£2618 $4451   (27-Oct-91 P.V13/R) Composition (48x41cm-19x16in) s.d.1947 oil sable
       gravel panel (F.FR 26000)
£3021 $5378   (28-Oct-91 GL.P198/R) Composition abstraite (46x55cm-18x22in) s.d.1959
       oil sable panel (F.FR 30000)
£3584 $6522   (30-May-92 VG.B353/R) Abstract composition (58x43cm-23x17in) s. oil sand
       gravel board (DM 10500)
£435 $774   (29-Nov-91 GAB.G2842) Baigneuses (22x27cm-9x11in) s.d.1908 W/C Indian ink
       (S.FR 1100)
£515 $881   (22-Mar-92 I.N25/R) Composition (61x46cm-24x18in) s.d.1951 lead pencil
       (F.FR 5000)
£864 $1503   (13-Apr-92 GL.P19) Composition (30x19cm-12x7in) s.d.1942 lead pencil
       stumping gouache (F.FR 8500)
£1118 $1945   (14-Apr-92 ZZ.F54/R) Harmonie de matiere (29x41cm-11x16in) s.d.51 mixed
       media sable plaster board (F.FR 11000)
£1442 $2465   (19-Mar-92 CSC.P14) Composition (55x45cm-22x18in) st.sig. oil collage
       canvas laid down on board (F.FR 14000)
£1829 $3183   (14-Apr-92 ZZ.F53/R) Compositon aux trois personnages (51x33cm-20x13in)
       s.d.59 mixed media plaster sable board (F.FR 18000)
£1829 $3183   (14-Apr-92 CSC.P39 b) Composition (62x47cm-24x19in) st.sig. oil collage
       (F.FR 18000)
£3893 $7008   (2-Feb-92 CSC.P86/R) Femme au chapeau de paille (63x49cm-25x19in) s.d.61
       oil collage panel (F.FR 38000)
£5664 $9686   (18-Mar-92 LT.P79/R) Paysage (68x102cm-27x40in) s.d.64 oil mixed media
       collage (F.FR 55000)
£8239 $14089   (19-Mar-92 CSC.P13/R) Composition (72x106cm-28x42in) s.d.64 oil mixed
       media collage panel (F.FR 80000)

RETHEL, Alfred (1816-1859) German
£1164 $2003   (11-Oct-91 AW.H1254) Allegory of death. Athlete (30x38cm-12x15in)
       i.d.1848 pencil double-sided (DM 3400)

RETHEL, Otto (1822-1892) German
£704 $1275   (3-Dec-91 FN.S2403/R) Boas finding Ruth gleaning (94x97cm-37x38in) s.
       (DM 2000)

RETHER, Alfred (?) ?
£573 $1031   (19-Nov-91 JRL.S145/R) German landscape (21x39cm-8x15in) init. board
       (A.D 1300)

RETS, Jean (1910-) Belgian
£4177 $7101   (22-Oct-91 C.A276/R) Koska (80x100cm-31x39in) s.verso (B.FR 250000)

RETTEGI, S W (20th C) ?
£2402 $4300   (16-Nov-91 WOL.C265/R) Still life of urn of flowers (122x66cm-48x26in)
       s.d.1928 board pair

RETTIG, John (1860-1932) American
£556 $1000   (24-Nov-91 JRB.C58/R) Provincetown pier (36x51cm-14x20in) s. gouache

RETZLAFF, E C W (1898-1976) German
£549 $933   (23-Oct-91 GD.B1244/R) Farmhouses in high mountains (60x80cm-24x31in) s.
(S.FR 1400)

REUMERT, Niels (1949-) ?
£1157 $2012   (18-Sep-91 KH.K165) Danish artists being used as bulldozers during
demonstration, Greenland (170x200cm-67x79in) s.d.1976verso (D.KR 13000)

REUSCH, Helga Ring (1865-1944) Norwegian
£930 $1693   (14-Dec-91 BU.O55/R) Landscape (37x50cm-15x20in) s.d.1911 (N.KR 10500)
£5348 $9251   (23-Mar-92 B.O103/R) Evening (95x185cm-37x73in) s.d.1897 (N.KR 60000)

REUSSWIG, William (1902-) American
£730 $1300   (2-May-92 IH.NY195/R) Three adults look on as boy greets puppy
(71x107cm-28x42in) s.
£955 $1700   (2-May-92 IH.NY1/R) Couple sitting on footbridge over stream
(89x89cm-35x35in) s.

REUTER, Fritz (1895-?) German
£2483 $4419   (28-Nov-91 D.V196/R) Rhododendron (50x40cm-20x16in) s.d.1933 board
(A.S 50000)

REUTERDAHL, Henry (1871-1925) American
*£787 $1400   (2-May-92 IH.NY22/R) Men stoking furnace, plant in distance
(41x38cm-16x15in) s.d.1911 W/C tempera*
*£899 $1600   (2-May-92 IH.NY163/R) Naval battle at close quarters. British ship in
battle s.d.1899 gouache grisaille*

REUTERSWARD, Carl Fredrik (1934-) Swedish
£1708 $3125   (12-May-92 GO.G144) Splendid isolation (116x89cm-46x35in) s. (S.KR 18000)
£1919 $3474   (3-Dec-91 AB.S5149/R) Horizontal game on orange waves (40x127cm-16x50in)
s. d.1986verso varnish tempera (S.KR 20000)
£1992 $3646   (12-May-92 GO.G145/R) Point de vue (89x116cm-35x46in) s. (S.KR 21000)
£2207 $3995   (3-Dec-91 AB.S5148/R) Game (38x61cm-15x24in) s. d.1961verso varnish
tempera (S.KR 23000)
£2372 $4341   (13-May-92 BU.S163/R) Dr Pratt Constructions (87x62cm-34x24in) s.
cardboard on canvas (S.KR 25000)
£3321 $6077   (13-May-92 BU.S162/R) From the Peking Opera, parade on red-brown
background (100x100cm-39x39in) s. (S.KR 35000)
*£776 $1404   (19-May-92 AB.S5308/R) The Pratt-Muller Empire, Beijing (96x65cm-38x26in)
s. varnish cardboard on canvas (S.KR 8200)*
*£1328 $2431   (13-May-92 BU.S164/R) Mrs Fortuna (59x88cm-23x35in) s.d.1962 varnish
tempera paper on cardboard (S.KR 14000)*
*£1613 $2952   (13-May-92 BU.S165/R) The Big Balance (28x103cm-11x41in) s. varnish
canvas (S.KR 17000)*

REUTERSWARD, Oscar (1915-) Swedish
£643 $1164   (3-Dec-91 AB.S5145/R) Devil's fork (170x38cm-67x15in) s. (S.KR 6700)
£787 $1424   (3-Dec-91 AB.S5144/R) Patriarch cross (160x115cm-63x45in) s. (S.KR 8200)

REUTLINGER, Jakob Heinrich (1802-1868) Swiss
£510 $913   (15-Nov-91 ZOF.Z1848) Brisenstock from Maiensass with goats and shepherd
returning home (36x50cm-14x20in) s.d.1832 i.verso board (S.FR 1300)

REVELLO DE TORO, Felix (20th C) Spanish
£2156 $4054   (16-Dec-91 ANS.M128/R) Saliendo del bano (65x50cm-26x20in) s.d.1966
(S.P 390000)

REVERON, Armando (1889-1954) Venezuelan
£19337 $35000   (19-May-92 SY.NY16/R) Paisaje con arbol (31x42cm-12x17in) s.
£45833 $82500   (18-Nov-91 SY.NY22/R) Cocoteros en la playa (47x60cm-19x24in) s.d.1926

REVILLA, Carlos (1940-) Peruvian
£1699 $2906   (21-Mar-92 KV.L438/R) Hommage a la Premiere femme volante
(114x147cm-45x58in) s.d.73 verso (B.FR 100000)

REVILLA, Justo (?) ?
£985 $1793   (11-Dec-91 FER.M107/R) Anciano sentado (100x82cm-39x32in) s. (S.P 180000)

REVOIL, Pierre (1776-1842) French
*£815 $1517   (18-Jun-92 SY.MO452/R) Jeune femme au clavecin (33x24cm-13x9in) mono. ink
wash (F.FR 8000)*
*£1529 $2844   (20-Jun-92 CH.MO247/R) Francois Ier, Henri II et la Reine Marguerite
assis dans un parc (21x27cm-8x11in) init.d.1816 pencil (F.FR 15000)*

REVOLD, Axel (1887-1962) Norwegian
£482 $897   (15-Jun-92 B.O128) Labourers (50x61cm-20x24in) mono. (N.KR 5500)
£834 $1435   (10-Oct-91 BU.O119/R) Sketch for embellishment on the vessel 'Oslofjord'
(81x101cm-32x40in) s. panel (N.KR 9500)
£922 $1586   (10-Oct-91 BU.O83/R) Landscape with houses (50x61cm-20x24in) s.d.48 panel
(N.KR 10500)
£922 $1586   (10-Oct-91 BU.O120) Coastal landscape with boat (51x60cm-20x24in) s.
(N.KR 10500)
£966 $1661   (7-Oct-91 B.O112/R) Landscape from North of Norway (50x60cm-20x24in) s.
panel (N.KR 11000)

REVOLD, Axel (1887-1962) Norwegian-cont.
£1667 $3100   (18-Jun-92 GWP.O78/R) Harbour scene (65x81cm-26x32in) s.d.47 (N.KR 19000)
£3161 $5436   (10-Oct-91 BU.O35/R) From Oslo harbour (76x80cm-30x31in) s. i.verso
            (N.KR 36000)

REY DE SARLAT, Charles (1819-?) French
£605 $1071   (8-Nov-91 CN.P31/R) Moulin a Montmartre (25x34cm-10x13in) s.d.1857
            (F.FR 6000)

REYCEND, Enrico (1855-1928) Italian
£12896 $23470   (12-Dec-91 F.M48/R) Nel frutteto (39x28cm-15x11in) s. board
            (I.L 28000000)

REYES, Andres Luis (?) Spanish
£498 $936   (16-Dec-91 ANS.M163/R) Soller, Mallorca (60x81cm-24x32in) s. s.i.verso
            (S.P 90000)

REYHER, Max (1862-1945) American
£1695 $3000   (9-Nov-91 W.W272/R) Flowers revenge (38x48cm-15x19in) s.d.1938 panel

REYL-HANISCH, Herbert von (1898-1937) Austrian
£2211 $3957   (5-May-92 ZEL.L1506/R) Mountain landscape (60x69cm-24x27in) s.d.1922
            board (DM 6500)
£3724 $6629   (28-Nov-91 D.V81/R) Self portrait (54x42cm-21x17in) mono.d.MCMXX panel
            (A.S 75000)

REYLANDER-BOHME, Ottilie (1882-1965) German
£756 $1406   (20-Jun-92 BM.B772/R) My sister Tene (58x47cm-23x19in) mono i.verso board
            (DM 2200)

REYMERSWAELE, Marinus van (studio) (1493-1567) Dutch
£7202 $13683   (26-Jun-92 AT.P5/R) Saint Jerome dans son cabinet de travail
            (99x50cm-39x20in) panel (F.FR 70000)

REYMOND, Casimir (1893-1969) Swiss
£474 $849   (6-May-92 GD.B1045/R) Le berceau (55x64cm-22x25in) s. (S.FR 1300)

REYNA MANESCAU, Antonio Maria de (1859-1937) Spanish
£3800 $6726   (14-Feb-92 C76/R) Monument to Bartolomeo Colleoni in Campo SS.Giovanni e
            Paolo (15x20cm-6x8in) s.i. board
£6500 $11830   (29-May-92 C365 a/R) Bacino de San Marco, Venice (34x75cm-13x30in) s.
£9000 $16380   (29-May-92 C365 b/R) Da d'Oro (34x75cm-13x30in) s.
£9000 $16380   (29-May-92 C400/R) Santa Maria del Giglio, Venice (33x72cm-13x28in) s.
            board
£11000 $19030   (4-Oct-91 C126/R) Piazetta from the Lagoon, Venice (35x75cm-14x30in) s.i.

REYNA, Antonio (20th C) Spanish
£1648 $3000   (26-May-92 CE.NY290/R) The fruit seller (38x22cm-15x9in) s.i. panel
£2217 $3924   (12-Feb-92 ANS.M128/R) Santa Maria della Salute, Venecia (18x13cm-7x5in)
            s. board (S.P 400000)
£2286 $4000   (18-Feb-92 CE.NY288/R) Fishing boats docked (25x39cm-10x15in) s.i.
£9302 $16000   (14-Oct-91 H.C47/R) View of the Doge's Palace, Venice (33x74cm-13x29in)
            s.i.
£10169 $18000   (6-Nov-91 D.NY40/R) Piazetta San Marco (35x76cm-14x30in) s.
£10857 $19000   (19-Feb-92 CH.NY114/R) Venetian canal scene (35x75cm-14x30in) s.i.
£10932 $18584   (22-Oct-91 DUR.M50/R) Veleros en un canal veneciano (34x74cm-13x29in) s.
            (S.P 2000000)
£12041 $20831   (24-Mar-92 CH.R85/R) Venezia, Palazzo Ducale (35x75cm-14x30in) s.
            (I.L 26000000)

REYNAUD, Francois (1825-1909) French
£592 $1078   (12-Dec-91 L.K664) Village street, Brittany (34x24cm-13x9in) s. board
            (DM 1700)

REYNIER, Gustave (1885-?) French
£572 $1002   (5-Apr-92 CSC.P100) Le pont Alexandre III (46x65cm-18x26in) s.
            (F.FR 5500)

REYNOLDS (after) (?) British
£750 $1335   (31-Oct-91 B160) Portrait of girl holding spaniel (77x61cm-30x24in)

REYNOLDS (studio) (?) ?
£1815 $3212   (6-Nov-91 LT.P28/R) Fillette en buste vu dans un medaillon ovale
            (54x43cm-21x17in) (F.FR 18000)

REYNOLDS, Alan (1926-) British
£1800 $3438   (16-Jul-92 B133/R) The village (81x112cm-32x44in) board
£920 $1628   (5-Nov-91 PH166/R) Sunrise. Study of dandelions (23x12cm-9x5in) first
            s.i.d.57 W/C htd.white second s.d.54 ink
£1000 $1770   (8-Nov-91 C205/R) Towards Adder Hill (26x28cm-10x11in) s.d. W/C wash
£2500 $4300   (6-Mar-92 C108/R) Legend in early autumn (33x42cm-13x17in) s.i.d.
            i.d.55verso W/C bodycol

REYNOLDS, Charles H (19/20th C) American?
£838 $1500   (13-Nov-91 B.SF2825/R) Aspen (61x76cm-24x30in) s.

REYNOLDS, Charles H (19/20th C) American?-cont.
£950 $1700 (13-Nov-91 B.SF2809/R) Navajo moving day (40x50cm-16x20in) s. board
£782 $1400 (13-Nov-91 B.SF2808/R) Old Sharp's Studio, Taos (39x49cm-15x19in) s.
gouache

REYNOLDS, Frederick George (1828-1921) British
£1709 $3043 (27-Apr-92 J.M1063) Grazing cattle (112x111cm-44x44in) s.d.1921
(A.D 4000)
£560 $1002 (14-Nov-91 S145) Woodland glade (13x29cm-5x11in) W/C over pencil
htd.white

REYNOLDS, Sir Joshua (1723-1792) British
£1047 $1800 (10-Oct-91 SY.NY151/R) Portrait of an artist (77x62cm-30x24in)
£4500 $8595 (15-Jul-92 S31/R) Portrait of a gentleman in red coat with fur collar
(46x37cm-18x15in)
£5500 $9680 (8-Apr-92 S48/R) Portrait of Sir Charles Pratt, 1st Earl Camden, wearing
judicial robes (72x60cm-28x24in)
£8000 $14320 (15-Nov-91 C22/R) Portrait of Richard Hopkins, in velvet jacket and white
stock (76x63cm-30x25in)
£22000 $42020 (15-Jul-92 S24/R) Portrait of Charlotte Walsingham (92x71cm-36x28in) i.
£38000 $66880 (8-Apr-92 S39/R) Portrait of Richard Boyle, 2nd Earl of Shannon
(118x98cm-46x39in)

REYNOLDS, Sir Joshua (after) (1723-1792) British
£750 $1373 (5-Feb-92 CSK231) Laughing girl (91x71cm-36x28in)
£850 $1479 (12-Sep-91 CSK105/R) Garrick between Comedy and Tragedy (76x94cm-30x37in)
£872 $1500 (10-Oct-91 SY.NY50/R) Portrait of Albany Wallis (77x64cm-30x25in)
£950 $1691 (30-Apr-92 CSK99) The Infant St John the Baptist (166x110cm-65x43in)
£1550 $2961 (15-Jul-92 S147/R) Portrait of Sir Richard Worsley (49x36cm-19x14in)

REYNOLDS, Sir Joshua (attrib) (1723-1792) British
£690 $1200 (16-Sep-91 B.SF2013/R) Sketch for portrait of Marchioness of Tavistock
(67x56cm-26x22in)
£1571 $3000 (16-Jul-92 SY.NY310/R) The bird (76x63cm-30x25in)

REYNOLDS, Sir Joshua (school) (1723-1792) British
£1657 $3000 (21-May-92 CH.NY127/R) Portrait of lady, said to be Miss Catherine Leigh,
Mrs C. Arcedeckne (126x100cm-50x39in)

REYNOLDS, Sir Joshua (studio) (1723-1792) British
£1600 $2816 (10-Apr-92 C103/R) Portrait of the Duke of Cumberland in uniform
(62x51cm-24x20in)

REYNOLDS, Sir Joshua (style) (1723-1792) British
£850 $1462 (8-Oct-91 PH32/R) Portrait of a lady, possibly Kitty Fisher
(75x62cm-30x24in)

REYNOLDS, W S (19/20th C) American
£2193 $3750 (12-Mar-92 MFA.C144) Lit pipe (25x41cm-10x16in) s.

REYNTJENS, Henrich Engelbert (1817-1900) Dutch
£867 $1500 (24-Mar-92 GRO.B53/R) Law suit (41x33cm-16x13in) s. panel
£980 $1755 (15-Nov-91 GK.Z5090) Couple in interior (16x22cm-6x9in) s. panel
(S.FR 2500)
£1364 $2414 (22-Apr-92 CH.AM94/R) An artist showing his work to a family of
connoisseurs (28x39cm-11x15in) s. panel (D.FL 4500)

REYSSCHOOT, Peter Jan van (attrib) (1702-1772) Flemish
£1900 $3401 (13-Nov-91 S141/R) Portrait of Sir Armine Wodehouse standing
(77x61cm-30x24in) i.

REZIA, Felice A (fl.1866-1902) British
£741 $1341 (19-May-92 GF.L2530/R) Busy village street, Northern Italy
(36x29cm-14x11in) s. panel (S.FR 2000)

REZNICEK, Ferdinand von (1868-1909) German
£388 $691 (28-Apr-92 D.V39/R) Room 2 (49x17cm-19x7in) s. grisaille mixed media
paper on board (A.S 8000)
£490 $871 (25-Nov-91 WK.M847/R) Street scene (35x26cm-14x10in) W/C indian ink over
pencil board (DM 1400)
£707 $1237 (3-Apr-92 BM.B695/R) Figures conversing (42x29cm-17x11in) s. W/C
htd.white (DM 2000)

REZVANI, Serge (1928-) French
£418 $778 (19-Jun-92 G.Z578) Abstract composition (41x27cm-16x11in) s.d.1960
i.stretcher mixed media canvas (S.FR 1100)

RHEAD, Louis John (1857-1926) British/American
£1500 $2550 (25-Oct-91 S211/R) Flamingo frieze (51x94cm-20x37in) s. gouache

RHEAM, Henry Meynell (1859-1920) British
£800 $1424 (28-Nov-91 L199/R) Fishing boats in Newlyn Harbour (25x36cm-10x14in) s.
W/C
£900 $1548 (10-Oct-91 L76/R) Fishermen in rowing boat in the Fal estuary
(20x41cm-8x16in) s.d.1919 W/C

RHEE, Seund Ja (1918-) Korean
£922 $1660   (27-Jan-92 GL.P138/R) Sans titre (81x65cm-32x26in) s.d.1963 (F.FR 9000)

RHEINER, Louis (1863-1924) Swiss
£784 $1333   (23-Oct-91 GD.B602/R) Arched bridge across river valley (27x35cm-11x14in) s. (S.FR 2000)
£1020 $1733   (23-Oct-91 GD.B603/R) Chateau Chillon (45x32cm-18x13in) s. s.d.1877verso (S.FR 2600)
£1704 $3084   (19-May-92 GF.L2618/R) Self portrait (16x14cm-6x6in) s. i.d.1882verso board (S.FR 4600)
£1953 $3457   (5-Nov-91 GF.L2279/R) Waiting near village (54x46cm-21x18in) indis.s.i. (S.FR 5000)
£1992   *$3606*   *(5-Dec-91 SY.Z65/R) Couchant vers le Brienzersee - Oberland Bernois (33x41cm-13x16in) s. s.i.verso pastel (S.FR 5000)*

RHEINERT, Adolf (1880-1958) German
£524 $907   (25-Mar-92 KM.K1383) Fisherfolk on beach waiting for boats (60x80cm-24x31in) s. board (DM 1500)

RHODES, Joseph (1782-1854) British
£860 $1531   (29-Oct-91 SWS129) Village wedding (28x37cm-11x15in) mono. panel

RHOMBERG, Hanno (1820-1869) German
£3429 $6000   (20-Feb-92 SY.NY205/R) Portrait of lady (86x68cm-34x27in) s.d.1845
£5233 $9000   (17-Oct-91 SY.NY256/R) First smoke (66x56cm-26x22in) s.d.1858 board

RHONSTAD, Eric (1909-) Swedish
£537 $955   (28-Oct-91 AB.S203) Frozen tarn, winter landscape from Varmland (44x53cm-17x21in) s. (S.KR 5700)

RIAN, Johannes (1891-1981) Norwegian
£571 $982   (7-Oct-91 B.O117/R) Landscape (51x65cm-20x26in) s. (N.KR 6500)
£614 $1142   (18-Jun-92 GWP.O223) Peasant woman (30x22cm-12x9in) s. paper (N.KR 7000)
£806 $1539   (21-Jul-92 UL.T205/R) Figures (80x85cm-31x33in) (N.KR 9000)
£1054 $1812   (7-Oct-91 B.O115/R) Half nude (66x37cm-26x15in) s.d.35 (N.KR 12000)
£1107 $2015   (9-Dec-91 B.O99/R) Street scene, Paris (55x45cm-22x18in) s.i.d.31 panel (N.KR 12500)
£1140 $2121   (18-Jun-92 GWP.O80/R) Composition (41x33cm-16x13in) s.d.76 panel (N.KR 13000)
£1229 $2114   (7-Oct-91 B.O118/R) Woman at piano (100x81cm-39x32in) s.d.33 (N.KR 14000)
£1949 $3547   (14-Dec-91 BU.O37/R) The farmer and the poet (66x135cm-26x53in) s. panel (N.KR 22000)
£2193 $4079   (18-Jun-92 GWP.O79/R) The window towards Mediterranean, Cagnes (38x46cm-15x18in) s.d.50 s.i.d.1949verso panel (N.KR 25000)
£2496 $4317   (23-Mar-92 B.O107/R) Semi-nude (55x45cm-22x18in) s. panel (N.KR 28000)
£3565 $6168   (23-Mar-92 B.O106/R) Yellow composition (100x85cm-39x33in) (N.KR 40000)
£7665 $13260   (23-Mar-92 B.O105/R) Red composition (100x81cm-39x32in) s.d.78 (N.KR 86000)
£8253 $14195   (10-Oct-91 BU.O55/R) Woman and man with concertina (48x58cm-19x23in) s. (N.KR 94000)
£9649 $17947   (15-Jun-92 B.O129/R) Yellow composition (90x80cm-35x31in) s.d.1960 (N.KR 110000)
£438   *$762*   *(14-Sep-91 BU.O311) Woman with cello (28x21cm-11x8in) s. W/C (N.KR 5000)*

RIBA ROVIRA, Francisco (1913-) Spanish?
£1368 $2490   (26-May-92 DUR.M76/R) Paisaje (46x55cm-18x22in) s. tablex (S.P 250000)

RIBAK, Zvi (20th C) Russian/Israeli
£8647 $15824   (17-May-92 GL.P196/R) Klezmerim (65x75cm-26x30in) s. (F.FR 85000)

RIBARZ, Rudolf (1848-1904) Austrian
£2997 $5395   (21-Nov-91 D.V129/R) Walking near the castle (59x45cm-23x18in) s. board (A.S 60000)
£9990 $17982   (21-Nov-91 D.V47/R) Sun flowers (135x43cm-53x17in) s. (A.S 200000)

RIBAS RIUS, Ramon (1903-1983) ?
£2800   *$4984*   *(28-Nov-91 CSK44/R) Ballet dancer at her toilette (89x71cm-35x28in) s. pastel*

RIBAS, Antonio (?) Spanish
£2529 $4451   (9-Apr-92 ANS.M153/R) El jardin (26x16cm-10x6in) s. board (S.P 460000)

RIBAS, Llobet (20th C) Spanish
£1053 $1895   (22-Nov-91 SA.A1770/R) Female nude (65x54cm-26x21in) i.verso (DM 3000)

RIBCOWSKY, Dey de (1880-?) Bulgarian/American
£514 $900   (3-Apr-92 S.W2452/R) California coast in moonlight (56x97cm-22x38in) s.

RIBEMONT-DESSAIGNES, Georges (1884-?) French
£2014 $3585   (31-Oct-91 LD.P212/R) Paysage aux pins maritimes (81x100cm-32x39in) (F.FR 20000)
£3659 $6366   (16-Apr-92 FB.P73/R) Femme allongee dans un paysage (65x78cm-26x31in) mono. board (F.FR 36000)

RIBERA, Jusepe de (1588-1656) Spanish
£30000	$57600	(8-Jul-92 S8/R) St Francis of Paula (73x52cm-29x20in) bears indis.sig
£200000	$364000	(29-May-92 C312/R) St Peter in Penitence (77x65cm-30x26in) indis.s.
£10000	*$18200*	*(10-Dec-91 C146/R) The head of a bearded man (22x17cm-9x7in) red chk.*
£22426	*$41713*	*(20-Jun-92 CH.MO212/R) Le Christ aux outrages (19x20cm-7x8in) i. chk ink*
		wash (F.FR 220000)
£50279	*$90000*	*(14-Jan-92 SY.NY58/R) St. Cecilia (26x21cm-10x8in) bears i. pen wash*

RIBERA, Jusepe de (attrib) (1588-1656) Spanish
£596	$1020	(13-May-92 FN.S2925) St Hieronymus holding scull and bible
		(85x74cm-33x29in) (DM 1700)
£3090	$5500	(28-Apr-92 PO.BA10) San Jeronimo (136x96cm-54x38in)
£9935	$16990	(18-Mar-92 D.V38/R) St Onofrio (87x92cm-34x36in) (A.S 200000)

RIBERA, Jusepe de (circle) (1588-1656) Spanish
£4200	$7476	(29-Oct-91 PH119/R) Jacob with the flock (170x226cm-67x89in)
£4651	$8000	(10-Oct-91 SY.NY177/R) Drunken Silenus (91x106cm-36x42in)
£9000	$16380	(29-May-92 C313/R) The Epistles of St Peter held by two hands
		(53x44cm-21x17in) i. fragment
£22099	$40000	(22-May-92 SY.NY101 a/R) Saint Andrew (74x59cm-29x23in)

RIBERA, Jusepe de (style) (1588-1656) Spanish
£2176	$3939	(19-May-92 AB.S4371/R) Saint Hieronymus (77x63cm-30x25in) . (S.KR 23000)
£3779	$6500	(10-Oct-91 SY.NY86/R) Saint Paul hermit (112x89cm-44x35in)
£6972	$12619	(3-Dec-91 SY.MI268) S.Pietro (97x49cm-38x19in) (I.L 15000000)
£11000	$20020	(13-Dec-91 C249/R) A Philosopher (116x91cm-46x36in)

RIBERA, Pedro see RIBERA, Pierre

RIBERA, Pierre (1867-1932) French
£683	$1182	(24-Mar-92 VN.R78/R) La senorita Espagnol (23x28cm-9x11in) s. panel
		(D.FL 2200)
£757	$1302	(20-Oct-91 I.N161) Le massif d'Hortensia (33x40cm-13x16in) s. panel
		(F.FR 7500)
£9000	$16020	(27-Nov-91 S381/R) Au jardin de Paris (33x41cm-13x16in) s.i. board
£10989	$20000	(28-May-92 SY.NY113/R) Sur le pont de bateau (64x76cm-25x30in) s.d.08
£467	*$841*	*(19-Nov-91 DUR.M42/R) Estudio de figuras (61x41cm-24x16in) s. dr*
		(S.P 85000)

RIBERA, Roman (1848-1935) Spanish
£7115	$12950	(26-May-92 DUR.M37/R) La leccion de musica (63x81cm-25x32in) s.
		(S.P 1300000)

RIBOT, Germain Theodore (1845-1893) French
£1099	$2000	(26-May-92 CE.NY89/R) The little chef (24x17cm-9x7in) s. board
£1714	$3033	(10-Nov-91 ZZ.F24/R) Le marmiton (34x27cm-13x11in) s. panel (F.FR 17000)
£1764	$3139	(28-Apr-92 RAS.K284) Young man reading (45x38cm-18x15in) s. (D.KR 20000)
£2007	$3593	(6-May-92 GD.B1051/R) Seamstresses (22x37cm-9x15in) s. (S.FR 5500)
£2393	$4188	(5-Apr-92 ZZ.F51/R) Vase de fleurs (73x60cm-29x24in) s. (F.FR 23000)
£3429	$6000	(20-Feb-92 SY.NY131/R) Nature morte aux fruits (34x41cm-13x16in) s. board

RIBOT, Theodule (1823-1891) French
£2198	$4000	(28-May-92 SY.NY136/R) Artist's mother (46x39cm-18x15in) s.
£5814	$10000	(16-Oct-91 CH.NY53/R) Old woman praying (56x46cm-22x18in) s.
£6593	$12000	(27-May-92 CH.NY188/R) A girl reading (46x38cm-18x15in) s.
£6977	$12000	(17-Oct-91 SY.NY160/R) L'incendie au village (91x53cm-36x21in) s.
£12000	$22320	(17-Jun-92 S468/R) La priere (92x125cm-36x49in) s.d.1862
£28571	$50000	(19-Feb-92 CH.NY11/R) Fete gallante (65x81cm-26x32in) s.

RIBOU (18th C) ?
£1600	*$2752*	*(4-Mar-92 C8/R) Gentleman, in blue coat and striped waistcoat and cravat*
		(6cm-2ins circular) min. s. set lid tortoiseshell box

RICARD-CORDINGLEY, Georges (1873-1939) French
£728	$1275	(5-Apr-92 ZZ.F90/R) Moutons dans les Alpilles (19x26cm-7x10in) s.
		(F.FR 7000)
£832	$1457	(5-Apr-92 ZZ.F87/R) Bateau dans l'estuaire (26x33cm-10x13in) s.
		(F.FR 8000)
£917	$1679	(1-Jun-92 W.T1423/R) Fisherfolk unloading (61x91cm-24x36in) s.d.92
		(C.D 2000)
£1093	$1912	(5-Apr-92 ZZ.F65/R) Vue de Boulogne (32x40cm-13x16in) s. (F.FR 10500)
£1301	$2276	(5-Apr-92 ZZ.F89/R) Tartane pres des cotes (61x46cm-24x18in) s.
		(F.FR 12500)

RICCARDI, Michele (1864-?) Italian
£697	$1262	(3-Dec-91 SY.MI8/R) Veduta di Piazza S. Marco (59x49cm-23x19in) s.
		(I.L 1500000)

RICCHI, Pietro (1605-1675) Italian
£6630	$12000	(21-May-92 CH.NY237/R) Judith with head of Holofernes, accompanied by
		maidservant (103x113cm-41x44in)

RICCHIARDI, Giovanni (?-1820) Italian
£2762	$5000	(22-May-92 SY.NY297/R) Portraits of Duke and Duchess of Aosta
		(87x69cm-34x27in) one s.i pair

RICCI, Arturo (1854-) Italian
£1685 $3000   (22-Jan-92 SY.NY534/R) Last drop (34x47cm-13x19in) s.i. i.verso board

RICCI, Dante (1879-1957) Italian
£2316 $4006   (24-Mar-92 CH.R103/R) Napoli, il Belvedere di Palazzo Reale (50x60cm-20x24in) s. mixed media (I.L 5000000)

RICCI, F (1608-1685) Spanish
£571 $1000   (18-Feb-92 CE.NY214) View of Rome (18x30cm-7x12in) i. panel

RICCI, Francisco (1608-1685) Spanish
£1300 $2366   (29-May-92 C346/R) Design for altarpiece of the crucifix with putti (54x36cm-21x14in) i. chk pen wash

RICCI, Giuseppe (19/20th C) Italian
£1220 $2209   (18-May-92 SY.MI55) Donne in chiesa (110x78cm-43x31in) s. (I.L 2700000)

RICCI, Guido (1836-1897) Italian
£1842 $3353   (10-Dec-91 F.R196/R) Ritorno dalla fienagione (22x32cm-9x13in) s. (I.L 4000000)

RICCI, Marco (1676-1729) Italian
£18000 $34560   (6-Jul-92 S99/R) Forest landscape with peasants fleeing from a bear (30x44cm-12x17in) tempera on kidskin
£18994 $34000   (14-Jan-92 SY.NY64/R) Extensive landscape with herdsmen and animals, buildings and river in distance (30x45cm-12x18in) tempera
£3500 $6370   (10-Dec-91 C161/R) A harbour (32x45cm-13x18in) bodycol. leather

RICCI, Marco (attrib) (1676-1729) Italian
£2400 $4176   (14-Apr-92 CSK100/R) Royal Yacht Fubbs in Italianate river landscape (63x107cm-25x42in)
£12000 $23040   (10-Jul-92 C279/R) Allegorical tomb of Sir Cloudsley Shovel (85x54cm-33x21in) en grisaille arched top
£13937 $25366   (12-Dec-91 L.K152/R) Winter landscape with figures and view of Verona (83x140cm-33x55in) (DM 40000)

RICCI, Marco (circle) (1676-1729) Italian
£1100 $2002   (12-Dec-91 B52/R) Wooded river landscape with figures fishing beside waterfall (69x53cm-27x21in) canvas laid down on panel
£1200 $2100   (31-Mar-92 PH49/R) Figures attending noble gentleman in palatial bedchamber (28x32cm-11x13in)
£1332 $2478   (16-Jun-92 SY.B231/R) Mountain landscape (48x52cm-19x20in) panel (B.FR 80000)
£3000 $5340   (29-Oct-91 PH15/R) Fishermen and other figures by a lake beneath ruins (37x62cm-15x24in)
£3200 $5824   (10-Dec-91 PH106/R) Rocky river landscape with mule train crossing wooden bridge (151x150cm-59x59in)
£9296 $16825   (4-Dec-91 CH.R107/R) Paesaggio con rovine antiche, approdo fluviale con armenti e pastori (107x82cm-42x32in) (I.L 20000000)

RICCI, Marco (style) (1676-1729) Italian
£780 $1357   (19-Sep-91 TL443) Venetian capriccio with figures being welcomed at landing stage (34x45cm-13x18in)
£800 $1400   (27-Feb-92 CSK126) Italianate landscape with soldier mounting his horse by ruin (33x25cm-13x10in) canvas laid down on panel
£1826 $3250   (22-Jan-92 SY.NY110/R) Rural landscape (31x40cm-12x16in) bears sig.
£2000 $3840   (9-Jul-92 CSK270/R) Italianate coastal landscape (58x81cm-23x32in)
£6484 $11217   (25-Mar-92 CH.R50/R) Porticciolo con rovine antiche. Marina con le rovine di tempio classico two (I.L 14000000)
£7000 $12250   (1-Apr-92 S165/R) Dismounted knight and other figures amid Roman ruins (91x119cm-36x47in)

RICCI, Pio (?-1919) Italian
£2057 $3600   (18-Feb-92 CE.NY160/R) Temptation (30x20cm-12x8in) s.d.1875
£2442 $4200   (14-Oct-91 H.C29/R) Lady embroidering - a labor of love (23x15cm-9x6in) s. panel
£3187 $5800   (26-May-92 CE.NY288/R) Musical trio (63x83cm-25x33in) s.
£3689 $6750   (17-May-92 DU.E1125/R) Courtship (76x84cm-30x33in) s. board
£5600 $9800   (27-Feb-92 GSP424) The rose (71x51cm-28x20in) s.

RICCI, Sebastiano (1659-1734) Italian
£11896 $21770   (16-May-92 F.L67/R) Giuseppe spiega i sogni al faraone (46x53cm-18x21in) (S.FR 32000)
£12000 $21480   (11-Nov-91 S482/R) Rocky estuary with boats in foreground (143x108cm-56x43in)
£75000 $144000   (10-Jul-92 C57/R) Alexander and Diogenes (104x137cm-41x54in)
£90000 $156600   (15-Apr-92 C52/R) Christ mourned by three angels at the foot of the cross (115x94cm-45x37in)
£1237 $2140   (27-Mar-92 CN.P4/R) Etudes de tetes rembranesques (22x19cm-9x7in) pen wash (F.FR 12000)

RICCI, Sebastiano (after) (1659-1734) Italian
£1987 $3398   (18-Mar-92 D.V207/R) Nessus raping Dejanira (62x78cm-24x31in) (A.S 40000)

RICCI, Sebastiano (attrib) (1659-1734) Italian

£3800	$6764	(30-Oct-91 S43/R) Two figures in landscape (25x34cm-10x13in)
£5000	$8950	(11-Nov-91 S477/R) Judgement of Paris (124x98cm-49x39in)
£13000	$23270	(11-Nov-91 S476/R) Venus and Adonis (124x100cm-49x39in)

RICCI, Sebastiano (circle) (1659-1734) Italian

£1800	$3456	(7-Jul-92 PH188/R) Offering of Abigail (91x110cm-36x43in)
£5200	$9100	(31-Mar-92 PH33/R) Resurrection (87x118cm-34x46in)
£11000	$19250	(1-Apr-92 S81/R) Temptation of Saint Anthony (88x75cm-35x30in)

RICCI, Sebastiano (studio) (1659-1734) Italian

£1987	$3398	(18-Mar-92 D.V14/R) Christ at the pond of Bethesda (60x97cm-24x38in) (A.S 40000)
£16000	$28000	(3-Apr-92 C120/R) Contest of Apollo and Marsyas (109x96cm⁻-43x38in)
£19000	$33250	(3-Apr-92 C119/R) Childhood of Castor and Pollux (109x96cm-43x38in)

RICCI, Sebastiano (style) (1659-1734) Italian

£1200	$2160	(21-Nov-91 CSK56/R) God the Father in Majesty with angels (24x76cm-9x30in)
£2200	$3850	(3-Apr-92 C126) Continence of Scipio (73x60cm-29x24in)
£2200	$3828	(13-Sep-91 C162/R) Belshazzar's feast (69x109cm-27x43in)
£2200	$3850	(3-Apr-92 C107/R) Personification of Africa (59x55cm-23x22in)
£2800	$5040	(21-Nov-91 C26/R) Elegant couple in clasical arcade and bath nearby (61x74cm-24x29in) i.verso
£3200	$5760	(21-Nov-91 CSK116) Shepherds resting by classical ruin. Family resting on track (91x71cm-36x28in) pair
£4800	$8400	(28-Feb-92 C107/R) Saint Martin dividing his cloak (78x54cm-31x21in)
£5000	$9100	(11-Dec-91 S104/R) Adoration of shepherds (92x73cm-36x29in)

RICCIARDELLI, Gabriele (fl.1745-1777) Italian

£30000	$52800	(10-Apr-92 C46/R) Prospect of Stillorgan Park and obelisk with Dublin and harbour beyond (36x82cm-14x32in)
£35000	$63700	(13-Dec-91 C99/R) View of Naples from the Vomero. View of the Gulf of Pozzuoli (50x128cm-20x50in) one i. pair
£50000	$96000	(10-Jul-92 C35/R) Naples from Santa Lucia. Posillipo from Chiaia (45x103cm-18x41in) canvas on board pair

RICCIARDELLI, Gabriele (circle) (fl.1745-1777) Italian

£30000	$54600	(13-Dec-91 C268/R) Capriccio view of London as a Mediterranean seaport (95x162cm-37x64in)

RICCIARDI, Oscar (1864-?) Italian

£604	$1094	(3-Dec-91 SY.MI11) Monumento al Colleoni (42x24cm-17x9in) s. (I.L 1300000)
£629	$1100	(18-Feb-92 CE.NY292) Return from market (14x27cm-6x11in) s. panel
£659	$1200	(26-May-92 CE.NY307/R) Bringing in the catch (20x30cm-8x12in) s. panel
£769	$1400	(26-May-92 CE.NY170) A fishing village (22x36cm-9x14in) s. panel
£927	$1668	(19-Nov-91 FP.M108) Rainy market scene (39x29cm-15x11in) s. board (C.D 1900)
£950	$1644	(3-Oct-91 CSK264/R) A Neapolitan Market (23x15cm-9x6in) s. panel
£996	$1844	(9-Jun-92 F.R72) Cortile rustico (30x20cm-12x8in) s. panel (I.L 2200000)
£1073	$1932	(19-Nov-91 FP.M206/R) Market square view (39x29cm-15x11in) s. board (C.D 2200)
£1111	$2000	(22-Nov-91 S.BM106/R) Cavaliers in grotto (15x23cm-6x9in) s.i. indist.i.verso canvasboard
£1175	$2127	(18-May-92 SY.MI18) Vicolo di Napoli (36x22cm-14x9in) s. panel (I.L 2600000)
£1204	$2083	(24-Mar-92 CH.R135) Mercatino presso il mare (19x28cm-7x11in) s. (I.L 2600000)
£1220	$2209	(18-May-92 SY.MI17/R) Veduta di Napoli (28x45cm-11x18in) s. (I.L 2700000)
£1300	$2314	(30-Oct-91 B51) On the Neapolitan Coast (41x31cm-16x12in) s. board pair
£1840	$3293	(14-Nov-91 CH.R97) Mercatino a Napoli (38x23cm-15x9in) s. (I.L 4000000)
£1900	$3363	(14-Feb-92 C125/R) Marina Grande, Capri (26x39cm-10x15in) s.
£2000	$3420	(17-Mar-92 PH209/R) Market scene (24x40cm-9x16in) s. panel
£2100	$3906	(16-Jun-92 PH82/R) Mediterranean coastal scene (46x36cm-18x14in) s.
£2200	$3894	(14-Feb-92 C129/R) Positano da Mare (40x24cm-16x9in) s.
£2200	$3806	(4-Oct-91 C188/R) Amalfi (40x30cm-16x12in) s.
£2299	$4116	(14-Nov-91 CH.R73) Mercatino a napoli (28x18cm-11x7in) s. canvas on board (I.L 5000000)
£2400	$4464	(16-Jun-92 PH87 a) Figures with mule and cart on coastal road (41x61cm-16x24in) s.i.
£2571	$4500	(18-Feb-92 CE.NY206/R) Bay of Naples with Vesuvius in distance (51x58cm-20x23in) s.
£2700	$4833	(15-Jan-92 BT146/R) View across the Bay of Naples. Neapolitan fishermen. Sunset over theDuomo,Venice (38x20cm-15x8in) s. pair
£3200	$5536	(4-Oct-91 C153/R) Costa Sorrentina (41x61cm-16x24in) s.i.
£3666	$6489	(7-Nov-91 F.M100/R) Veduta di Posillipo, Napoli (65x109cm-26x43in) s. i.verso (I.L 8000000)
£3685	$6706	(12-Dec-91 F.M95/R) Spiaggia meridonale con case e barche di pescatori (31x53cm-12x21in) s. (I.L 8000000)
£4800	$8496	(14-Feb-92 C128/R) Street scenes in Naples (20x10cm-8x4in) s.i. panel three
£1143	*$2000*	*(18-Feb-92 CE.NY272/R) Porta Capuana, Napoli (25x34cm-10x13in) s.i. W/C*

RICCIO, Domenico see BRUSASORCI, Domenico

RICE, Anne Estelle (1879-1959) American
£540 $967   (5-May-92 SWS490/R) La jeune fille (39x32cm-15x13in) studio st.verso board
£4200 $7056   (26-Aug-91 S1084/R) Ajaccio, Corse (53x63cm-21x25in) s.d.1913 stretcher
£5000 $8400   (26-Aug-91 S1083/R) Merry-go-round (71x91cm-28x36in) s. s.i.label frame

RICE-PEREIRA, Irene (1907-1971) American
£3000 $5250   (28-Feb-92 SY.NY262/R) Copper light. Untitled (46x61cm-18x24in) s.verso s.d.53 mixed media collage gouache pair

RICH, John Hubbard (1876-1954) American
£789 $1500   (24-Jun-92 B.SF6373/R) Floral still life (51x51cm-20x20in) s.
£3107 $5500   (12-Feb-92 B.SF576/R) Woman with flowers (69x58cm-27x23in) s.

RICH, William George (fl.1876-1884) British
£630 $1121   (29-Oct-91 SWS52) Evening (34x44cm-13x17in) s. s.i.d.1879 verso

RICHARD, Edna Vergon (1890-1985) American
£1073 $1900   (12-Feb-92 B.SF505/R) Doud's Hill, Big Sur (45x60cm-18x24in) s. canvasboard

RICHARD, Ernst (1819-1899) German
£859 $1495   (18-Sep-91 N.M666/R) Dog barking at angry bull and other domestic animals beyond (22x29cm-9x11in) s. (DM 2500)
£1049 $1794   (18-Mar-92 N.M623/R) Bull fight (22x29cm-9x11in) s. (DM 3000)

RICHARD, Fleury Francois (1777-1852) French
£1019 $1896   (18-Jun-92 SY.MO453/R) Renaud et Armide (18x14cm-7x6in) wash (F.FR 10000)

RICHARD, Hortense (1860-?) French
£464 $798   (16-Oct-91 FER.M272 a/R) Dama con toquilla (11x8cm-4x3in) min. s. silver frame (S.P 85000)

RICHARD, P (?) ?
£1339 $2517   (18-Dec-91 PR.P65) Fleurs et fruits (54x65cm-21x26in) s. (F.FR 13000)
£2571 $4500   (18-Feb-92 CE.NY306/R) Still life of roses by lake (81x116cm-32x46in) s.

RICHARD, Rene (1895-1982) Canadian
£750 $1328   (6-Nov-91 SY.T93) North shore, Quebec (29x39cm-11x15in) with sig. i.verso panel (C.D 1500)
£860 $1590   (9-Jun-92 FB.M142) Baie St. Paul (30x41cm-12x16in) s. board (C.D 1900)
£900 $1593   (6-Nov-91 SY.T201/R) Coastal seascape (45x61cm-18x24in) s. board (C.D 1800)
£1005 $1828   (26-May-92 JOY.T56/R) La vieille maison (50x60cm-20x24in) s. board (C.D 2200)
£1096 $1995   (26-May-92 JOY.T93/R) Baie St. Paul (45x60cm-18x24in) s. board (C.D 2400)
£1220 $2207   (2-Dec-91 R.T223/R) St Irenee (45x60cm-18x24in) s. masonite (C.D 2500)
£5936 $10804   (26-May-92 JOY.T234/R) Le campement (101x117cm-40x46in) s. board (C.D 13000)

RICHARDE, Ludvig (1862-1929) Swedish
£604 $1087   (19-Nov-91 GO.G152) Coastal landscape with sailingvessels (65x110cm-26x43in) s.d.95 (S.KR 6300)
£671 $1208   (19-Nov-91 GO.G151) Development in winter (40x58cm-16x23in) mono.d.87 (S.KR 7000)
£739 $1338   (3-Dec-91 AB.S4653/R) Seascape with breakers by rocky shore (70x162cm-28x64in) s. (S.KR 7700)
£787 $1424   (3-Dec-91 AB.S4654/R) Seascape with sailship in rough seas (112x85cm-44x33in) s. (S.KR 8200)
£1246 $2244   (19-Nov-91 GO.G153) Seascape with sailship in rough seas (108x70cm-43x28in) s.d.98 (S.KR 13000)

RICHARDS, Ceri (1903-1971) British
£1200 $2052   (11-Mar-92 S152/R) La Cathedrale Engloutie (30x19cm-12x7in) s.i.verso board
£452 $800   (9-Nov-91 W.W123/R) Mountainous landscape with bridge (28x38cm-11x15in) s.d.1946verso W/C
£550 $946   (5-Mar-92 CSK155/R) No. 20 - figure study - Rape of Sabines (28x20cm-11x8in) s.d.48 W/C pen
£600 $1032   (5-Mar-92 CSK139) Study for Relief Construction, 1936 (43x62cm-17x24in) init.d.36 pen brush
£750 $1373   (14-May-92 C129/R) Rape of sabines (27x19cm-11x7in) s.d.48 pen W/C
£1400 $2408   (6-Mar-92 C107/R) Costerwoman (38x27cm-15x11in) s.d.39 W/C pen ink
£1800 $3240   (20-Nov-91 S61/R) Design for dropcloth - homage to Dylan Thomas (49x74cm-19x29in) s.d.1953 pen brush chinese ink htd wht collage

RICHARDS, F (19/20th C) ?
£600 $1044   (12-Sep-91 CSK12/R) Young girl in straw hat seated by window (18x13cm-7x5in) s.d.90 pencil W/C

RICHARDS, F T (1864-1921) American
£1545 $2750   (2-Nov-91 IH.NY21/R) Seated nude woman (71x91cm-28x36in) s.

RICHARDS, Frank (fl.1892-1925) British
£7000 $13440   (30-Jul-92 BLH261) The Cornish orchard (48x38cm-19x15in)

1532

RICHARDS, John Inigo (?-1810) British
£6000 $10740   (15-Nov-91 C59/R) River landscape, possibly view from West End of Rochester Bridge, with boating party (41x51cm-16x20in)

RICHARDS, Richard Peter (1840-1877) British
£550 $979   (29-Oct-91 C56/R) Mother with her children on grassy bank (13x22cm-5x9in) s. pencil W/C htd white

RICHARDS, Thomas Addison (1820-1900) American
£904 $1600   (9-Nov-91 W.W129/R) Juliet (74x91cm-29x36in) s.d.June 1842verso

RICHARDS, William Trost (1833-1905) American
£528 $956   (3-Dec-91 FN.S2406) Mountain lake near Pulney with cattle watering and farmhouse with trees (31x50cm-12x20in) s. (DM 1500)
£925 $1600   (8-Sep-91 LIT.L104) Seascape (30x38cm-12x15in) s.
£957 $1800   (18-Dec-91 SY.NY78/R) Rocky coast (22x40cm-9x16in) s. board
£1147 $2065   (23-Nov-91 YFA.M238/R) Rocky shore (23x41cm-9x16in) s. board
£1854 $3300   (26-Jan-92 LIT.L161) A quiet cove, Rhode Island (23x41cm-9x16in) s. board
£2011 $3500   (15-Apr-92 SY.NY20/R) Seascape (53x38cm-21x15in) s.d.87 board
£3315 $6000   (5-Dec-91 SY.NY9/R) The pond at Oldmixon (14x23cm-6x9in) s. i.verso panel
£5848 $10000   (12-Mar-92 CH.NY67/R) The cliffs of Cornwall (71x112cm-28x44in) s.d.90 canvas on panel
£7735 $14000   (5-Dec-91 SY.NY10/R) Three coastal sketches one s. panel three
£7910 $14000   (14-Feb-92 DM.D2010) Along the coast (71x112cm-28x44in) s.d.1883
£8721 $15000   (18-Oct-91 DM.D2008/R) Along coast (71x112cm-28x44in) s.d.1883
£13260 $24000   (6-Dec-91 CH.NY88/R) Distant sails at dusk (56x91cm-22x36in) s.d.90
£15385 $28000   (28-May-92 CH.NY37/R) Along the shore (36x67cm-14x26in) s.d.1870
£18000 $32400   (19-Nov-91 PH34/R) Americas Coast, luminist coastal landscape (46x84cm-18x33in) indis.s. bears sig.d.1875 i.stretcher
£41436 $75000   (6-Dec-91 CH.NY72/R) Gathering leaves (61x51cm-24x20in) s.d.1876
£46703 $85000   (27-May-92 SY.NY4/R) Forest interior in autumn (76x63cm-30x25in) i.verso
£638 $1200   (18-Dec-91 SY.NY32/R) Breaking waves (40x64cm-16x25in) s.d.97 W/C board
£1453 $2600   (14-Nov-91 CE.NY155) Sea and cliffs (21x35cm-8x14in) W/C htd white gouache
£2339 $4000   (12-Mar-92 CH.NY34/R) Craggy rocks along the sea (19x34cm-7x13in) W/C pencil
£2684 $4750   (22-Apr-92 D.NY80) Coastal view with lighthouse in distance (18x33cm-7x13in) s.d.1871 W/C
£2762 $5000   (5-Dec-91 SY.NY12/R) Kynance Cove, Cornwall (23x36cm-9x14in) W/C
£3216 $5500   (12-Mar-92 CH.NY65/R) New Jersey shore (28x47cm-11x19in) s.d.1887 i.verso W/C

RICHARDSON, Charles (fl.1880-1901) British
£460 $773   (13-Aug-91 AG138/R) Cattle by upland burn (37x55cm-15x22in) s.d.1874 W/C

RICHARDSON, Charles Douglas (1853-1932) British
£936 $1657   (26-Apr-92 SY.ME38) Fishing (23x34cm-9x13in) s. (A.D 2200)

RICHARDSON, Frederick Stuart (1855-1934) British
£500 $885   (7-Nov-91 PHC643) First snow of winter (34x50cm-13x20in) s. i.verso W/C

RICHARDSON, Henry Burdon (c.1811-1874) British
£400 $692   (1-Oct-91 SWS1876) Children outside row of cottages (22x34cm-9x13in) s.d.1848 W/C bodycol over pencil
£820 $1394   (22-Oct-91 SWS136/R) Fresh breeze (23x35cm-9x14in) init.d.1849 i.verso W/C

RICHARDSON, Jonathan (17/18th C) British
£1200 $2112   (8-Apr-92 S164/R) Portrait of Charles Hawtrey (73x61cm-29x24in) oval
£3500 $6160   (10-Apr-92 C96/R) Portrait of lady seated with basket of flowers and landscape beyond (124x99cm-49x39in)

RICHARDSON, Jonathan (circle) (17/18th C) British
£1800 $3222   (15-Nov-91 C160/R) Portrait of gentleman, in cloak and stock (74x61cm-29x24in) oval

RICHARDSON, Jonathan (snr) (1665-1745) British
£1788 $3200   (15-Jan-92 CH.NY176/R) Portrait of Jonathan Richardson Jnr., as boy (13x10cm-5x4in) s.i.verso black lead vellum

RICHARDSON, Louis H (1853-1923) American
£774 $1300   (28-Aug-91 MFA.C75 a) Marsh scene (102x127cm-40x50in) s. canvas on board

RICHARDSON, Thomas Miles (19th C) British
£3500 $6685   (21-Jul-92 PH263/R) View of Edinburgh Castle from Port Hopetoun (78x108cm-31x43in) init.d.1828
£800 $1432   (15-Jan-92 BT92/R) At Taormina, Sicily (20x51cm-8x20in) s.d.1861 W/C
£1050 $1880   (15-Jan-92 BT91/R) A view in the Italian lakes (20x56cm-8x22in) s.d.1874 W/C

RICHARDSON, Thomas Miles (circle) (19th C) British
£800 $1456   (10-Dec-91 AG295/R) Port on south coast (40x62cm-16x24in)
£900 $1530   (22-Oct-91 S269) View of Whitby with beached fishing boats and fisherfolk in foreground (44x59cm-17x23in)

RICHARDSON, Thomas Miles (circle) (19th C) British-cont.
| £800 | $1456 | (10-Dec-91 AG179) Italian lake scene (23x43cm-9x17in) with init.d.1852 W/C |

RICHARDSON, Thomas Miles (jnr) (1813-1890) British
£900	$1674	(18-Jun-92 B81/R) Returning from labour (31x44cm-12x17in) s.i.verso panel
£450	$765	(22-Oct-91 SWS158) Figures in Scottish glen (23x34cm-9x13in) W/C gum arabic
£700	$1204	(3-Mar-92 AG194) Bamburgh Castle, Northumberland (19x45cm-7x18in) init.i.d.1849 W/C
£700	$1246	(29-Oct-91 C97/R) Glen Falloch (53x36cm-21x14in) i.d.58 pencil W/C htd white
£720	$1310	(10-Dec-91 SWS370) Bamborough Castle (18x45cm-7x18in) init.i.d.1849 W/C pencil
£740	$1258	(22-Oct-91 SWS140/R) Coastal scene with fisherfolk and beached boats (26x37cm-10x15in) init. W/C over pencil
£748	$1429	(16-Jul-92 S120) Village on the shores of lake (15x24cm-6x9in) s.d.1877 W/C over pencil bodycol
£950	$1596	(13-Aug-91 AG183/R) On the Blackmount, Argyleshire (31x85cm-12x33in) s.i.d.1856 W/C
£990	$1891	(16-Jul-92 S119) Fisherfolk on the shore, castle beyond (15x24cm-6x9in) s.d.1877 W/C over pencil bodycol
£1000	$1790	(11-Nov-91 PH145/R) Port and Castle d'Ostranter, Adriatic (14x23cm-6x9in) init. i.verso W/C over pencil
£1150	$1978	(3-Mar-92 AG195/R) Near Positano (19x46cm-7x18in) s.d.1866 W/C
£2000	$3580	(14-Nov-91 S118/R) Highland landscape (22x33cm-9x13in) W/C
£2700	$4536	(26-Aug-91 S780/R) Returning from the moors, Glen Kinglas, Argylshire (49x71cm-19x28in) s.d.1849 W/C
£3080	$5883	(16-Jul-92 S174/R) On the shores of the Bay of Naples (34x99cm-13x39in) s.d.1855 W/C over pencil htd bodycol
£4000	$7160	(14-Nov-91 S156/R) Goatfell, Glen Rossie, Isle of Arran (71x100cm-28x39in) s.d.1847 i.d.verso W/C over pencil htd.white
£7500	$13425	(14-Nov-91 S169/R) Sunset on Derwentwater from above Lodore (64x100cm-25x39in) s.d.1845 W/C over pencil htd.bodycol
£14000	$25060	(14-Nov-91 S171/R) The city of Durham (76x130cm-30x51in) s.d.1860 W/C over pencil htd.bodycol

RICHARDSON, Thomas Miles (snr) (1784-1848) British
| £726 | $1300 | (13-Nov-91 B.SF2187/R) Fishing boats, Tynemouth (30x51cm-12x20in) mono. board |
| £2000 | $3660 | (3-Jun-92 S8/R) Pulling in nets (41x61cm-16x24in) s. |

RICHARDSON, Thomas Miles (snr-attrib) (1784-1848) British
| £840 | $1529 | (10-Dec-91 AG342/R) Richmond Castle (28x42cm-11x17in) panel |
| £1512 | $2600 | (14-Oct-91 H.C53/R) River scene with fishing boats (41x61cm-16x24in) s. |

RICHARDSON, Thomas Miles (studio) (19th C) British
| £640 | $1165 | (10-Dec-91 AG175/R) Dover harbour and castle (20x32cm-8x13in) s.d.1835 W/C |

RICHARDSON, W (19th C) British
| £650 | $1144 | (8-Apr-92 CSK180) St. Clement Dane, Strand (41x30cm-16x12in) s.d.1874 s.i.d.1874 verso |

RICHARDT (19th C) ?
| £1099 | $2000 | (26-May-92 CE.NY291/R) A festive donkey (61x37cm-24x15in) s. |

RICHARDT, Ferdinand (1819-1895) Danish
£1408	$2366	(27-Aug-91 RAS.K458/R) Refreshment on table (41x46cm-16x18in) s.d.1867 (D.KR 16000)
£7735	$14000	(6-Dec-91 CH.NY28/R) Niagara Falls (32x92cm-13x36in) indis.s.
£13714	$24000	(20-Feb-92 SY.NY243/R) Visit of Edward, Prince of Wales and Princess Alexandra to Bernstorff Castle, Denmark (58x85cm-23x33in) s.d.1868

RICHE, I S J le (attrib) (18th C) French
| £899 | $1600 | (30-Oct-91 D.NY42) Vase de fleurs (58x46cm-23x18in) |

RICHEBE, Horace (1871-?) French
| £748 | $1339 | (5-May-92 ZEL.L1507/R) Seascape with sailing boats (48x87cm-19x34in) s.i.d.1934 (DM 2200) |

RICHENBERG, Robert (1917-) American
| £1397 | $2500 | (12-Nov-91 CE.NY25/R) The city (114x82cm-45x32in) s.d.60 s.d.verso acrylic |

RICHET, Leon (1847-1907) French
£2593	$4693	(19-May-92 GF.L2185/R) Farmhouse in moor landscape (27x41cm-11x16in) s. (S.FR 7000)
£2691	$4763	(5-Nov-91 SY.AM270/R) Wooded landscape with woman on path (49x64cm-19x25in) s. (D.FL 8800)
£2733	$4700	(15-Oct-91 CE.NY267/R) A thatched cottage in a meadow (38x55cm-15x22in) s.
£3200	$5952	(17-Jun-92 S465/R) Lady in boat in river landscape (46x61cm-18x24in) s.
£3364	$5988	(30-Oct-91 CH.AM246/R) Wooded landscape with peasant woman by pond (47x66cm-19x26in) s. (D.FL 11000)

RICHET, Leon (1847-1907) French-cont.

£3488	$6000	(16-Oct-91 CH.NY68/R) River landscape (41x62cm-16x24in) s.
£4857	$8500	(20-Feb-92 SY.NY143/R) Sunlit woodland clearing (55x65cm-22x26in) s.
£4942	$8500	(16-Oct-91 CH.NY69/R) A thatched cottage and a lone figure by a quiet pool (41x61cm-16x24in) s.d.1881
£5233	$9000	(16-Oct-91 CH.NY67/R) Fishermen in a wooded river landscape (45x65cm-18x26in) s.
£5814	$10000	(17-Oct-91 SY.NY163/R) Les fagotieres (93x74cm-37x29in) s.d.1882
£5926	$10726	(22-May-92 EA.Z148) Landscape with peasant cottages (80x106cm-31x42in) s.d.1872 panel (S.FR 16000)

RICHI (?) ?

| £500 | $930 | (17-Jun-92 B98) Bust portrait of pretty young girl (69x55cm-27x22in) s. |

RICHI, A (?) ?

| £1550 | $2945 | (22-Jun-92 HS176/R) Portrait of dark haired girl wearing green jacket with white and scarlet (65x52cm-26x20in) oval |

RICHIR, Herman (1866-1942) Belgian

| £8791 | $16000 | (28-May-92 SY.NY69/R) La femme au voile (157x109cm-62x43in) s. |

RICHLY, Rudolf (1886-1975) Austrian

| £1066 | $1941 | (26-May-92 D.V167/R) Still life with guitar (56x67cm-22x26in) s. (A.S 22000) |

RICHMOND, Agnes M (1870-1964) American

| £1520 | $2600 | (12-Mar-92 CH.NY183/R) Woman seated along the shore, Gloucester (96x81cm-38x32in) s.d.1920 |
| £1600 | $2800 | (26-Sep-91 CH.NY114/R) Olden times (55x39cm-22x15in) s. |

RICHMOND, Dorothy Kate (1861-1935) New Zealander

| *£586* | *$1061* | *(4-Dec-91 DS.W184) Twilight reflection (17x12cm-7x5in) s. W/C (NZ.D 1900)* |

RICHMOND, George (1809-1896) British

£420	*$769*	*(2-Jun-92 S706) Young man wearing olive green coat (8x?cm-3x?in) min.oval gilt metal mount framed*
£450	*$770*	*(12-Mar-92 CSK3) Portrait study of one girl seated and the other standing holding doll (51x41cm-20x16in) pencil W/C vignette*
£650	*$1177*	*(19-May-92 PH79/R) Portrait of Caroline Gibbs (57x43cm-22x17in) s.d.1846 W/C htd.white*
£800	*$1464*	*(2-Jun-92 S707) Young gentleman wearing black coat and landscape beyond (9x?cm-4x?in) min.mono.d.1830 framed*
£1600	*$3056*	*(14-Jul-92 DR371/R) Portrait of General George Powell Higginson in military uniform (46x29cm-18x11in) s.d.1837 W/C*

RICHMOND, Leonard (?-1965) British

| £750 | $1298 | (4-Sep-91 BT328/R) Zennor Village, Cornwall (48x61cm-19x24in) s. i.verso |
| £800 | $1400 | (27-Feb-92 L435/R) Figures on the beach and boats before Smeaton's Pier (48x58cm-19x23in) s. canvasboard |

RICHMOND, Sir William Blake (1842-1921) British

£4000	$7160	(11-Nov-91 S601/R) Portrait study of Rosalind, Countess of Carlisle (91x70cm-36x28in)
£4800	$8592	(11-Nov-91 S602/R) Vale of Sparta (89x150cm-35x59in)
£750	*$1328*	*(6-Nov-91 S331) Study for the figure of Sleep from Sarpedon (33x23cm-13x9in) chk*
£850	$1479	(10-Sep-91 RG2132/R) Study of male nude, studies of hands and forearms. Studies of female nude (30x36cm-12x14in) pencil htd white double-sided

RICHMOND, Sir William Blake (attrib) (1842-1921) British

| *£400* | *$716* | *(11-Nov-91 S619) Wooded landscape (26x35cm-10x14in) W/C htd white* |

RICHMOND, Thomas (1771-1837) British

| £1900 | $3401 | (13-Nov-91 S170/R) Whitenose, dark bay hunter, property of Mr H.J.Firth (59x74cm-23x29in) mono.d.1827 s.i.d.verso |
| £550 | $963 | (25-Feb-92 CSK12) Captain J L Fuller in blue cavalry uniform (7x?cm-3x?in) min.s.d.1816verso oval |

RICHMOND, Thomas (jnr) (1802-1874) British

| £3005 | $5500 | (5-Jun-92 SY.NY190/R) White Nose, dark bay hunter, property of H J Firth Esq. (61x76cm-24x30in) s.d.1827 |

RICHTER, Adrian Ludwig (1803-1884) German

| *£449* | *$800* | *(2-May-92 W.W10/R) Anficht des Amseltalles (15x10cm-6x4in) s. pen W/C paper on board* |

RICHTER, Aurel (1870-?) Hungarian

£409	*$748*	*(8-Feb-92 CSC.P71) Composition a la guitare (44x33cm-17x13in) mixed media (F.FR 4000)*
£491	*$898*	*(8-Feb-92 CSC.P90) L'accordeoniste (20x17cm-8x7in) mixed media (F.FR 4800)*
£545	*$987*	*(19-May-92 CH.AM85) Woman at a telephone (43x33cm-17x13in) s. gouache (D.FL 1800)*
£593	*$1085*	*(8-Feb-92 CSC.P79) Olga (43x41cm-17x16in) mixed media (F.FR 5800)*
£613	*$1123*	*(8-Feb-92 CSC.P73) Violoniste (32x25cm-13x10in) mixed media (F.FR 6000)*

RICHTER, Aurel (1870-?) Hungarian-cont.

£613	$1123	(8-Feb-92 CSC.P84) Les pecheurs (28x42cm-11x17in) mixed media (F.FR 6000)
£613	$1123	(8-Feb-92 CSC.P74/R) Nature morte au violon et raisins (30x40cm-12x16in) mixed media (F.FR 6000)
£613	$1123	(8-Feb-92 CSC.P75) Jeune fille au perroquet (28x33cm-11x13in) mixed media (F.FR 6000)
£665	$1216	(8-Feb-92 CSC.P72) Joueur de cartes (38x55cm-15x22in) mixed media (F.FR 6500)
£716	$1310	(8-Feb-92 CSC.P76) Couple (39x51cm-15x20in) mixed media (F.FR 7000)
£716	$1310	(8-Feb-92 CSC.P78/R) Cavaliers (31x34cm-12x13in) mixed media (F.FR 7000)
£864	$1573	(11-Dec-91 CH.AM53) Composition with houses and trees (55x45cm-22x18in) s. gouache (D.FL 2800)
£941	$1721	(8-Feb-92 CSC.P89) Course de voitures (25x31cm-10x12in) mixed media (F.FR 9200)
£971	$1778	(8-Feb-92 CSC.P86) Les avions (46x33cm-18x13in) mixed media (F.FR 9500)
£971	$1778	(8-Feb-92 CSC.P80/R) Au banjo (41x31cm-16x12in) mixed media (F.FR 9500)
£2658	$4865	(8-Feb-92 CSC.P91) Nature morte cubiste (50x75cm-20x30in) mixed media (F.FR 26000)

RICHTER, Carl August (1770-1818) German

£1127	$2039	(6-Dec-91 GB.B5975) Residenzschloss Werneck an der Werren (44x37cm-17x15in) W/C (DM 3200)

RICHTER, Christian II (1678-1732) Swedish

£650	$1144	(9-Apr-92 S126/R) Portrait of lady, with right hand raised to cheek (?x6cm-?x2in) min. vellum gilt frame oval
£700	$1232	(9-Apr-92 S127/R) Portrait of lady, hair over shoulder, wearing grey gown and blue drape (8x?cm-3x?in) min. vellum on card gilt frame ribbon tie oval

RICHTER, David (younger-attrib) (1664-1741) German

£474	$868	(14-May-92 BU.S100/R) Portrait of Ulrika Eleonora with her four dead babies on clouds (20x17cm-8x7in) indist.s.d.1723verso gouache (S.KR 5000)

RICHTER, Edouard Frederic Wilhelm (1844-1913) French

£12000	$21000	(19-Feb-92 CH.NY48/R) Teatime in garden (74x93cm-29x37in) s.

RICHTER, Emil Theodor (1801-1878) German

£1045	$1902	(13-Dec-91 BM.B708/R) Alpine river landscape (83x121cm-33x48in) s.d.1856 (DM 3000)
£2098	$3587	(18-Mar-92 N.M624/R) Castle Tyrol in the Etsch valley with Engelhorner (49x60cm-19x24in) s.d.1853 (DM 6000)

RICHTER, G (19/20th C) German

£784	$1333	(23-Oct-91 GD.B1247) Summer landscape. Winter landscape (25x39cm-10x15in) s. pair (S.FR 2000)

RICHTER, Gerhard (1932-) German

£1119	$1992	(25-Nov-91 WK.M849) Graublaue Kurven (40x45cm-16x18in) s.d.1971 acrylic paper (DM 3200)
£1800	$3096	(17-Oct-91 C116/R) Untitled (15x10cm-6x4in) s.d.31.1.89 oil on photograph
£2062	$3814	(11-Jun-92 HN.H389/R) Vermalung grau (40x40cm-16x16in) s.d.1971verso paper (DM 6000)
£2800	$4816	(17-Oct-91 C115/R) Untitled (10x15cm-4x6in) s.d.29.3.89 oil on photograph
£3500	$6020	(17-Oct-91 C113/R) Kerze (60x62cm-24x24in) s.d.1989 s.num.19/30 verso oil on photograph
£5307	$9500	(6-May-92 CH.NY239/R) Fingermalereien (40x40cm-16x16in) s.d.8.9.71 num.47/150 verso paper
£6936	$12000	(3-Oct-91 SY.NY128/R) Untitled no.48 (26x53cm-10x21in)
£7368	$13263	(19-Nov-91 L.K1028) Untitled (21x18cm-8x7in) s.i.d.1966verso (DM 21000)
£12849	$23000	(13-Nov-91 CH.NY255/R) Skizzen Zu Parkstuck (62x87cm-24x34in) s.d.1972 board mounted on linen
£19553	$35000	(6-May-92 CH.NY214/R) Untitled (42x60cm-17x24in) s.d.1984 num.561/4 verso
£21000	$36330	(26-Mar-92 C115/R) Mohn 618-2 (82x67cm-32x26in) s.i.d.1986verso
£28000	$48160	(17-Oct-91 C130/R) Stadtbild - M8 (85x90cm-33x35in) s.i.d.num.170/8 68 verso
£29000	$52490	(5-Dec-91 C40/R) Kleine Tur (50x50cm-20x20in) s.d.68verso
£47486	$85000	(13-Nov-91 CH.NY287/R) Abstraktes bild (105x100cm-41x39in) s.d.1984verso
£49123	$88421	(19-Nov-91 L.K1030/R) Parachute (60x45cm-24x18in) s.i.d.1977 (DM 140000)
£50279	$90000	(14-Nov-91 SY.NY193/R) Untitled (92x126cm-36x50in) s.d.1988 num.678-3 verso
£55866	$100000	(5-May-92 CH.NY47/R) Stadtbild SL3 (124x124cm-49x49in) s.i.d.69verso
£57143	$100000	(27-Feb-92 CH.NY49/R) Untitled (100x140cm-39x55in) s.d.1986verso
£70000	$133700	(2-Jul-92 C61/R) Abstract painting (200x200cm-79x79in) s.i.d.1977 426 verso
£75000	$143250	(2-Jul-92 C59/R) Korsika - sonne (85x90cm-33x35in) s.d.68 verso
£78212	$140000	(12-Nov-91 CH.NY64/R) Abstraktes Bild (125x150cm-49x59in) s.d.81verso
£95000	$181450	(2-Jul-92 C70/R) Untitled - 621 (300x300cm-118x118in) s.d.1987 verso
£111732	$200000	(5-May-92 CH.NY3/R) Untitled (70x55cm-28x22in) s.s.i.d.1982verso
£120000	$229200	(2-Jul-92 S42/R) Vesuv (70x100cm-28x39in) s.d.1976 panel
£122905	$220000	(5-May-92 CH.NY23/R) Untitled (260x201cm-102x79in) s.i.d.1986verso
£155000	$268150	(26-Mar-92 S50/R) Mondstein (101x151cm-40x59in) s.d.1981 verso
£195531	$350000	(12-Nov-91 CH.NY50/R) Gebirge (199x159cm-78x63in) s.i.d.68verso
£220000	$398200	(5-Dec-91 S35/R) Hirsch II (120x150cm-47x59in) s.d.1966 verso

RICHTER, Gerhard (1932-) German-cont.
£234637 $420000   (13-Nov-91 SY.NY1/R) Mustang Staffel (88x150cm-35x59in) s.i.verso
£240223 $430000   (13-Nov-91 SY.NY6/R) Zwei spanische Akte, Osterakte (140x148cm-55x58in)
  s.i.d.67verso
£2168 $3750   (3-Oct-91 SY.NY172/R) Untitled (29x21cm-11x8in) s.d.9.6.85 graphite
£2890 $5000   (3-Oct-91 SY.NY173/R) Untitled - candle (89x89cm-35x35in) s.d.89 oil on
colour photo mounted plexiglass

RICHTER, H Davis (1874-1955) British
£650 $1164   (13-Nov-91 ZZ.B130/R) Still life of red and yellow flowers
  (61x51cm-24x20in)
£900 $1611   (5-May-92 SWS489/R) Polyanthea in Chinese bowl (39x50cm-15x20in)
  s.i.verso
£1100 $1870   (22-Oct-91 SWS362/R) Gay harmony (49x60cm-19x24in) s.
£2200 $3696   (26-Aug-91 S1147/R) African marigolds (41x61cm-16x24in) s. i.overlap
£400 $724   (4-Dec-91 GA83) View of Continental town, with boats on river to fore
(64x51cm-25x20in) s. chl wash
£550 $1001   (12-Dec-91 CSK80) Polyanthus (38x35cm-15x14in) s. W/C pencil
£570 $980   (11-Oct-91 K340/R) Still life study of chrysanthemums in vase and
Japanese figure on table (53x43cm-21x17in) s. W/C

RICHTER, Hans (1888-) German
£2759 $4939   (14-Nov-91 F.M134/R) Composizione (44x60cm-17x24in) mono.d.1973
  (I.L 6000000)
£3685 $6706   (9-Dec-91 CH.R70/R) Moto-Ritmo 6 (135x35cm-53x14in) s.d.1959
  (I.L 8000000)

RICHTER, Hans Theo (1902-1969) German
£528 $956   (6-Dec-91 GB.B7024) Studies of heads (30x26cm-12x10in) s.d.1963 indian
  ink brush chk double-sided (DM 1500)
£751 $1359   (23-May-92 GB.B7152) Mother with child (47x31cm-19x12in) s.d.1948 chl
  (DM 2200)
£1024 $1853   (23-May-92 GB.B7151) Three figures on beach (27x39cm-11x15in) s.d.1951
  W/C over pen (DM 3000)
£1092 $1977   (23-May-92 GB.B7149/R) Woman with shoulder wrap. Female nude
  (48x32cm-19x13in) s.d.1944 bister double-sided (DM 3200)
£1126 $2039   (23-May-92 GB.B7150/R) Bathers on beach (27x38cm-11x15in) s.d.1951 W/C
  over pen (DM 3300)
£1585 $2868   (6-Dec-91 GB.B7023/R) Sisters, one seated the other standing
  (54x38cm-21x15in) s.d.1937 chk (DM 4500)

RICHTER, Henry James (style) (1772-1857) German
£1200 $2148   (14-Jan-92 SWS122/R) Family meal (51x41cm-20x16in) bears sig.

RICHTER, Henry Leopold (1870-1960) American
£971 $1700   (31-Mar-92 MOR.P31 a) California coastline (51x91cm-20x36in) s.

RICHTER, J (?) ?
£588 $1000   (23-Oct-91 GD.B1248) Wooded lake landscape with mountain range beyond
  (15x31cm-6x12in) s. (S.FR 1500)

RICHTER, Johan Anton (attrib) (1665-1745) Swedish
£66000 $126720   (7-Jul-92 PH56/R) Venice-view of Bacino di S. Marco. Venice-Molo looking
  towards Piazzetta (55x80cm-22x31in) pair

RICHTER, Johan Anton (style) (1665-1745) Swedish
£2000 $3640   (26-May-92 PH150/R) View of Grand Canal, Venice (62x102cm-24x40in)
£4400 $7656   (13-Sep-91 C94/R) Capriccio of San Giorgio Maggiore, Venice
  (53x109cm-21x43in) canvas on board

RICHTER, Ludwig (1803-1884) German
£478 $865   (22-May-92 GB.B6025/R) Pilgrim praying before wayside memorial
(12x9cm-5x4in) pencil wash (DM 1400)
£528 $956   (6-Dec-91 GB.B5979) Medieval scene with beggar woman approaching rich
man. Study of figure (12x10cm-5x4in) pen pencil double-sided sold with
another dr. (DM 1500)
£704 $1275   (6-Dec-91 GB.B5980/R) Children playing in graveyard (13x9cm-5x4in)
mono.indis.d.186. pen (DM 2000)
£775 $1402   (6-Dec-91 GB.B5976/R) Group of young trees (21x13cm-8x5in) s. pen wash
(DM 2200)
£853 $1544   (22-May-92 GB.B6021/R) Courting couple in landscape (24x17cm-9x7in)
i.d.185 pen (DM 2500)
£1126 $2039   (21-May-92 L.K324/R) Wie des Forsters Eltern Brautleute wurden
(9x8cm-4x3in) mono pencil W/C (DM 3300)
£8014 $14585   (12-Dec-91 L.K459/R) Peasant with ox-drawn cart and other figures in
landscape (16x23cm-6x9in) s.d.1836 W/C (DM 23000)

RICHTER, Robert Ludwig (19/20th C) Austrian
£3413 $6212   (30-May-92 VG.B155/R) Man standing with arm raised (45x19cm-18x7in)
s.d.1926 W/C over pencil (DM 10000)

RICHTER, Wilhelm (1824-1892) Austrian
£698 $1249   (16-Jan-92 D.V88/R) Portrait of lady holding fan (24x17cm-9x7in) s.d.1857
  board oval (A.S 14000)

RICHTER-REICH, F M (1896-) German
£1700 $2941   (3-Oct-91 CSK140) A flower market, Amsterdam (61x119cm-24x47in) s.

RICKLUND, Folke (1900-1986) Swedish
£665 $1157   (13-Apr-92 AB.S224) Early spring river landscape (31x40cm-12x16in) s.d.29 panel (S.KR 7000)
£815 $1467   (19-Nov-91 GO.G148) Rhythmical - spring landscape from Grovelsjon (50x62cm-20x24in) s.d.63 (S.KR 8500)
£895 $1592   (28-Oct-91 AB.S204) Reindeer in the mountains (32x40cm-13x16in) s. (S.KR 9500)
£1274 $2254   (25-Apr-92 SO.S581/R) Wilderness, mountain swamp (72x90cm-28x35in) s. (S.KR 13500)

RICKMAN, Philip (1891-1982) British
£400 $708   (13-Feb-92 B173/R) Pintail ducks startled by a moorhen (37x52cm-15x20in) gouache
£590 $1050   (26-Jan-92 LIT.L41) English snipe resting in dunes (36x51cm-14x20in) s.i. W/C
£650 $1138   (25-Feb-92 C81/R) Shelduck in estuary at low tide (25x34cm-10x13in) init.d.1930 pencil W/C
£700 $1225   (25-Feb-92 C143/R) Blackcock in flight (18x27cm-7x11in) s.d.1932 pencil W/C bodycol
£700 $1225   (25-Feb-92 C144/R) Woodcock and pheasant at edge of wood in winter (27x38cm-11x15in) s.d.1958 pencil W/C bodycol
£800 $1528   (21-Jul-92 LW1849/R) Lake scene with mallards (36x56cm-14x22in) s. W/C
£820 $1435   (25-Feb-92 C57) Kingfisher (35x71cm-14x28in) s.d.1968 pencil W/C bodycol
£850 $1488   (25-Feb-92 C84/R) Studies of lesser white-fronted and Canada geese (23x36cm-9x14in) s.i. pencil W/C htd white
£1000 $1750   (25-Feb-92 C87/R) Mallard (20x31cm-8x12in) s. pencil W/C bodycol
£1053 $1800   (13-Mar-92 S.BM258 a) Woodcock. Melting into the bracker (25x38cm-10x15in) s.i.verso W/C gouache ink paperboard pair
£1400 $2450   (25-Feb-92 C122/R) Peregrine falcon (55x37cm-22x15in) with sig.i. pencil W/C bodycol
£2100 $3675   (25-Feb-92 C72/R) Green-winged teal (81x46cm-32x18in) s.d.1970 pencil W/C bodycol
£3200 $5600   (25-Feb-92 C70/R) Carolina duck (78x56cm-31x22in) s.d.1970 W/C bodycol
£4000 $7000   (25-Feb-92 C69/R) Eider ducks at sea (57x82cm-22x32in) s.d.1966 W/C bodycol

RICKMAN, Thomas (1776-1841) British
£524 $1000   (16-Jul-92 SY.NY498/R) St Pancras New Church (64x48cm-25x19in) i. W/C India ink
£524 $1000   (16-Jul-92 SY.NY496/R) Design for St Pancras church (47x64cm-19x25in) s.i.d.1818 W/C India ink

RICO Y CEJUDO, Jose (1864-?) Spanish
£2046 $3846   (16-Dec-91 ANS.M108/R) Escena galante (45x30cm-18x12in) s. (S.P 370000)

RICO Y ORTEGA, Martin (1833-1908) Spanish
£3429 $6000   (18-Feb-92 CE.NY291/R) Venetian canal (36x25cm-14x10in) s.
£4571 $8000   (19-Feb-92 CH.NY113/R) Venetian view (46x73cm-18x29in) bears sig.
£7682 $13750   (14-Nov-91 GRO.B73/R) Camp by shore (18x36cm-7x14in) s. panel
£8140 $14000   (17-Oct-91 SY.NY364/R) Venetian cafe by lagoon (29x16cm-11x6in) s. paper on panel
£8721 $15000   (16-Oct-91 CH.NY158/R) A Venetian Canal scene (35x21cm-14x8in) s. panel
£8758 $15939   (26-May-92 DUR.M18/R) Rincon de Venecia (30x18cm-12x7in) panel (S.P 1600000)
£22857 $40000   (19-Feb-92 CH.NY110/R) Venetian canal scene (81x39cm-32x15in) s.
£25714 $45000   (19-Feb-92 CH.NY109/R) Grand Canal, Venice (47x73cm-19x29in) s.
£815 $1508   (9-Jun-92 F.R69) Il Canal Grande a Venezia (28x29cm-11x11in) s. W/C (I.L 1800000)
£874 $1600   (16-May-92 HG.C118) Canal scene (36x48cm-14x19in) s. W/C gouache
£2542 $4500   (6-Nov-91 D.NY35/R) Venetian fisherman preparing nets (47x30cm-19x12in) s. W/C
£10932 $18584   (22-Oct-91 DUR.M14/R) Venecia (35x53cm-14x21in) s. W/C (S.P 2000000)

RICO Y ORTEGA, Martin (attrib) (1833-1908) Spanish
£5495 $10000   (27-May-92 CH.NY229/R) Spring day in Venice (46x34cm-18x13in) s.

RICQUIER, L (1792-1884) Belgian
£680 $1278   (3-Jan-92 BW361) Young lady holding a child (38x33cm-15x13in) s. board

RICQUIER, Louis (1792-1884) Belgian
£6250 $11250   (2-Feb-92 ZZ.F67/R) Famille de pecheur sur un rivage Napolitain (44x68cm-17x27in) s.d.1845 panel (F.FR 61000)

RIDDEL, James (1858-1928) British
£750 $1335   (1-May-92 PHE1/R) Gravel bed on the Lossie (51x76cm-20x30in) s.
£850 $1632   (28-Jul-92 SWS437/R) A summer lane (44x59cm-17x23in) s.
£1750 $3133   (14-Jan-92 SWS252/R) The mill stream (39x50cm-15x20in) s.d.08 indis.i.verso
£3000 $5100   (24-Oct-91 CSK153/R) Children playing in a woodland clearing (91x107cm-36x42in) s.d.99

RIDELL, Annette Irwin (fl.1920-1930) American
£3421 $6500   (24-Jun-92 B.SF6351/R) Back Bay (69x79cm-27x31in) s.

RIDER, Arthur G (1886-1975) American
£4215 $7250   (12-Oct-91 DU.E86/R) Shoreline (30x36cm-12x14in) s. board
£537   *$950*   *(12-Feb-92 B.SF549/R) King's Canyon (36x46cm-14x18in) s. W/C*

RIDINGER, Johann Elias (1698-1767) German
£438 $784   *(6-May-92 GD.B1493) Eagle attacking chamois (30x23cm-12x9in) s.d.1741*
     pencil (S.FR 1200)
£850   *$1632*   (7-Jul-92 C108/R) Piebald horse (34x24cm-13x9in) i. chk
£1199   *$2062*   (11-Oct-91 AW.H1007/R) Dogs chasing hare in rocky landscape with bird of
     prey (30x24cm-12x9in) chk (DM 3500)
£1706 $3106   (26-May-92 KF.M210/R) Sacrifice scene before battle (49x51cm-19x20in)
     s.d.1723 sepia pen brush (DM 5000)
£1761 $3187   (6-Dec-91 GB.B5588/R) The wolf trap (34x23cm-13x9in) s.i.d.1708 pen wash
     (DM 5000)
£2448 $4357   (26-Nov-91 KF.M156/R) Stags caught in net in landscape (28x39cm-11x15in)
     sepia brush graphite (DM 7000)

RIDINGER, Johann Elias (attrib) (1698-1767) German
£1937 $3505   (3-Dec-91 FN.S2407/R) Stag with herd by the edge of the wood, evening
     (80x100cm-31x39in) (DM 5500)

RIDOLFI, Claudio (circle) (1570-1644) Italian
£3800 $6764   (1-Nov-91 C49/R) Martyrdom of Saint Sebastian (57x39cm-22x15in) panel

RIEBE, Carl (19th C) Swedish?
£660   *$1169*   *(10-Nov-91 BU.M9) Portrait of Esaias Tegner (20x15cm-8x6in) s. sold with*
     book (S.KR 7000)

RIECE, M (19th C) Scandinavian
£3200 $5536   (4-Oct-91 C115/R) Teatime (38x46cm-15x18in) s.

RIECKE, George (1848-1924) ?
£1291 $2310   (14-Nov-91 GRO.B77/R) Sheep in landscape (25x36cm-10x14in) s. pair

RIEDEL, Arthur (1888-1953) German
£989 $1839   (19-Jun-92 ZOF.Z2052/R) Winter in Basler Neubad (50x65cm-20x26in)
     s.i.d.33-34 panel (S.FR 2600)

RIEDEL, August (1799-1883) German
£20555 $39260   (1-Jul-92 FB.P79/R) Femmes et enfants (104x84cm-41x33in) s.d.1840
     (F.FR 200000)

RIEDEL, H (17th C) German
£597 $1050   (9-Apr-92 FA.PH652 c) The pleasure of smoke and drink (46x28cm-18x11in)
     s. panel

RIEDER, Marcel (1852-?) French
£1180 $2100   (22-Jan-92 SY.NY357/R) Reflections on wintry night (36x27cm-14x11in) s.
£1980 $3603   (27-May-92 PH.DU135/R) The Reading (57x71cm-22x28in) s.d.1901 (DM 5800)
£2616 $4500   (15-Oct-91 CE.NY213/R) Teatime on a winter afternoon (60x74cm-24x29in) s.
£3429 $6000   (20-Feb-92 SY.NY159/R) Seamstress by lamplight (60x73cm-24x29in) s.

RIEDMULLER, F X (1829-1901) German
£627 $1141   (12-Dec-91 N.M2828/R) River landscape with boats and figures
     (44x39cm-17x15in) s.d.72 (DM 1800)

RIEGEN, Nicolaas (1827-1889) Dutch
£729 $1269   (17-Sep-91 CH.AM418/R) The rescue (30x46cm-12x18in) s. (D.FL 2400)
£741 $1296   (18-Feb-92 CH.AM309/R) A stiff breeze (35x43cm-14x17in) s. panel
     (D.FL 2400)
£1061 $1877   (22-Apr-92 CH.AM125) Sailors in a rowingboat approaching a two-master at
     anchor (25x32cm-10x13in) s.d.57 panel (D.FL 3500)
£1484 $2597   (3-Apr-92 BM.B696/R) Lake landscape with fishermen (28x19cm-11x7in)
     s.indis.i.d.1858 (DM 4200)
£1500 $2670   (26-Nov-91 PH87) Shipping in calm at sunset (31x48cm-12x19in) s.
£2599 $4627   (30-Oct-91 CH.AM198/R) Sailors in fishing smack approaching Dutch
     two-master in choppy sea (65x99cm-26x39in) s.d.1871 (D.FL 8500)
£2752 $4899   (30-Oct-91 CH.AM181 a) Sailors in rowing boat approaching tow-master and
     scow nearby (66x92cm-26x36in) s. (D.FL 9000)
£2778 $5028   (19-May-92 GF.L2548/R) Sailing boats on calm sea (27x37cm-11x15in) s.
     panel (S.FR 7500)
£3058 $5443   (30-Oct-91 CH.AM14/R) Scow at full sail on choppy seas (44x67cm-17x26in)
     s. (D.FL 10000)
£5769 $10500   (28-May-92 SY.NY224/R) Hauling in catch (65x98cm-26x39in) s.d.1871
£455   *$786*   *(27-Mar-92 GRA.B2358/R) Sailing ships in stormy sea (15x22cm-6x9in) s.*
     W/C (DM 1300)

RIEGER, Albert (1834-1905) Austrian
£981 $1865   (25-Jun-92 D.V431/R) Village in mountain landscape (63x97cm-25x38in)
     s.d.1868 (A.S 20000)
£1214 $2160   (29-Apr-92 D.V861/R) Pond landscape (35x57cm-14x22in) indis.s.d.
     (A.S 25000)

RIEGER, Albert (1834-1905) Austrian-cont.
£1232 $2231   (3-Dec-91 FN.S2409) Moonlit Alpine lake landscape with riders on arched
                        stone bridge (104x162cm-41x64in) s. (DM 3500)
£1249 $2323   (16-Jun-92 RAS.V857 a/R) Mountain landscape with waterfall
                        (75x100cm-30x39in) s. (D.KR 14000)
£1707 $2971   (19-Sep-91 D.V131/R) Alpine landscape with stream, evening
                        (74x100cm-29x39in) s. (A.S 35000)
£1930 $3300   (13-Mar-92 FN.S2927/R) Alpine river landscape in thunderstorm
                        (79x115cm-31x45in) i.verso (DM 5500)
£1967 $3600   (5-Feb-92 D.NY79) Rushing mountain stream (74x104cm-29x41in) s.i.verso
£2062 $3588   (18-Sep-91 N.M667/R) Swedish coastal landscape with pilot station
                        (69x106cm-27x42in) s. i.stretcher (DM 6000)
£2913 $5184   (29-Apr-92 D.V745/R) River landscape (73x100cm-29x39in) s. (A.S 60000)
£8591 $14605   (25-Oct-91 BM.B814/R) Austrian warship before Triest (63x110cm-25x43in)
                        s.d.1859 (DM 25000)

RIEGER, Johann (attrib) (1655-1730) German
£651 $1119   *(11-Oct-91 AW.H1013/R) The vision of St Hyazinth, design for church*
                       (22x36cm-9x14in) pen wash htd.white squared (DM 1900)

RIEMERSCHMID, Richard (1868-1957) German
£674 $1200   (22-Jan-92 SY.NY272/R) Nude wading in forest stream (50x44cm-20x17in) s.
                       panel

RIEPER, August (1865-?) German
£1223 $2177   (30-Oct-91 CH.AM162) Elegant lady playing lute in bourgeois interior
                       (91x65cm-36x26in) s. (D.FL 4000)

RIERA Y ARAGO (1954-) Spanish
£987 $1756   *(26-Nov-91 BRO.B404) Untitled (58x40cm-23x16in) s.d.1991 mixed media*
                       (S.P 180000)
£1041 $1854   *(26-Nov-91 BRO.B341) Untitled (50x64cm-20x25in) s.d.1991 mixed media*
                       (S.P 190000)
£1094 $1948   *(29-Oct-91 BRO.B352) Untitled (50x64cm-20x25in) s.d.1991 mixed media*
                       collage (S.P 200000)
£1423 $2532   *(29-Oct-91 BRO.B310/R) Untitled (48x75cm-19x30in) s. mixed media collage*
                       panel (S.P 260000)
£1438 $2703   *(17-Dec-91 BRO.B415) Untitled (55x90cm-22x35in) s.d.1991 mixed media*
                       (S.P 260000)
£4700 $8836   *(17-Dec-91 BRO.B369/R) Untitled (118x224cm-46x88in) s.d.1988 mixed media*
                       canvas (S.P 850000)

RIESENER, Henri Francois (attrib) (1767-1828) French
£1744 $3000   (15-Oct-91 CE.NY1/R) An elegant lady in an interior (49x41cm-19x16in)

RIET, Willy van (?) Belgian
£531 $971   (12-May-92 C.A354/R) Ballerina (46x33cm-18x13in) s.d.1927 panel
                     (B.FR 32000)
£829 $1517   (12-May-92 C.A355) Still life with flowers (75x100cm-30x39in) s.d.1926
                     (B.FR 50000)

RIETER, H (?) ?
£950 $1644   *(3-Oct-91 CSK10 a) L'Arco Felice, Ischia (18x25cm-7x10in) s.i. bodycol.*

RIETSCHOOF, Jan Claes (attrib) (1652-1719) Dutch
£2210 $4000   (21-May-92 CH.NY229/R) Shipping in choppy sea (59x88cm-23x35in)
£2762 $5000   (22-May-92 SY.NY143/R) Dutch shipping in calm sea (48x59cm-19x23in)

RIETSCHOOF, Jan Claes (circle) (1652-1719) Dutch
£6647 $11897   (7-May-92 CH.AM148/R) Wijdschip going about as approaches Dutch
                       three-master, other shipping (75x103cm-30x41in) with mono. (D.FL 22000)

RIETTI, Arturo (1863-1942) Austrian
£695 $1202   (24-Mar-92 CH.R86) Busto di ragazza (55x45cm-22x18in) s.d.1933
                     (I.L 1500000)
£825 $1469   *(28-Apr-92 D.V175/R) Head (58x47cm-23x19in) s.d.04 mixed media paper on*
                     board (A.S 17000)

RIGAUD, Hyacinthe (1659-1743) French
£275229 $511927   (20-Jun-92 CH.MO91/R) Portrait de Pierre Vincent Bertin
                         (140x120cm-55x47in) (F.FR 2700000)

RIGAUD, Hyacinthe (after) (1659-1743) French
£3331 $6195   (16-Jun-92 SY.B241) Portrait of King Louis XIV (69x55cm-27x22in)
                     (B.FR 200000)
£7128 $13187   (10-Jun-92 ZZ.F64/R) Portrait de femme en buste (83x65cm-33x26in)
                     (F.FR 70000)

RIGAUD, Hyacinthe (attrib) (1659-1743) French
£7064 $12149   (16-Oct-91 AT.P102/R) Portrait d'un jeune home en buste (82x65cm-32x26in)
                     painted oval (F.FR 70000)
£7813 $13828   (5-Nov-91 GF.L2082/R) Portrait of nobleman (60x49cm-24x19in) (S.FR 20000)

RIGAUD, Hyacinthe (circle) (1659-1743) French
£2523 $4339   (16-Oct-91 AT.P112/R) Portrait presume de Francoiis Mansart
                  (46x37cm-18x15in) i.verso oval (F.FR 25000)
£6893 $13097   (26-Jun-92 AT.P110/R) Portrait d'homme en cuirasse (76x59cm-30x23in)
                  (F.FR 67000)

RIGAUD, Hyacinthe (studio) (1659-1743) French
£4115 $7819   (22-Jun-92 PIC.P10/R) Portrait du Regent en Marechal de France
                  (132x87cm-52x34in) (F.FR 40000)
£12257 $21450   (19-Feb-92 D.P9/R) Portrait de Maximilien Titon (104x106cm-41x42in)
                  (F.FR 120000)

RIGAUD, Hyacinthe (style) (1659-1743) French
£1571 $3000   (16-Jul-92 SY.NY259/R) Portrait of nobleman wearing Order of golden
                  Fleece (82x65cm-32x26in)
£3315 $6000   (22-May-92 SY.NY147/R) Portrait of Duc d'Orleans (136x103cm-54x41in)

RIGAUD, Jacques (attrib) (1681-1754) French
*£420 $764   (11-Dec-91 PH178/R) Mounted officers leading a parade (10x16cm-4x6in) pen
                  wash*

RIGAUD, Jean (1912-) French
£619 $1070   (27-Mar-92 PPB.P65/R) Gordes (59x92cm-23x36in) s.d.63 (F.FR 6000)
£759 $1351   (29-Apr-92 D.P163/R) Camaret (50x73cm-20x29in) s. d.67verso (F.FR 7500)

RIGAUD, Jean Baptiste (1700-1754) French
*£24000 $41760   (14-Apr-92 C156/R) View of the cascade at Chantilly (21x45cm-8x18in) i.
                  chk pen wash*
*£25000 $43500   (14-Apr-92 C157/R) Entrance to the Grand Trianon, Versailles
                  (23x47cm-9x19in) i. chk ink wash*

RIGBY, John Thomas (1922-) Australian
£427 $774   (2-Dec-91 AAA.S151) Seated nude (84x51cm-33x20in) s. (A.D 1000)
£806 $1500   (21-Jun-92 SY.ME69/R) Portrait of Judy (109x121cm-43x48in) s.d.1978
                  (A.D 2000)

RIGBY, Sarah (1962-) British
£750 $1373   (3-Feb-92 B128/R) Autumn (93x132cm-37x52in) s.

RIGG, Ernest H (20th C) British
£780 $1412   (20-May-92 BT234/R) Still life of flowers in Chinese vase
                  (33x28cm-13x11in) s. board

RIGHETTI, Luigi (19th C) British?
£420 $731   (14-Apr-92 C36/R) Design for fireplace (26x37cm-10x15in) i. chk pen W/C

RIGHETTI, Luigi (attrib) (19th C) British?
*£678 $1200   (13-Feb-92 S.W1856/R) Shepherd with flock in Arcadian landscape
                  (33x43cm-13x17in) s.d.1835 sepia ink washes*

RIGHINI, Sigismund (1870-1937) German
£478 $865   (4-Dec-91 G.Z1065) Mountain landscape (22x16cm-9x6in) board (S.FR 1200)
£876 $1586   (5-Dec-91 SY.Z63/R) Village street in Estavayer (22x29cm-9x11in)
                  mono.i.d.1911 board pencil study verso (S.FR 2200)
£2622 $4667   (29-Apr-92 G.Z190/R) Still life of fruit (28x38cm-11x15in) mono board
                  (S.FR 7000)
£3187 $5769   (4-Dec-91 G.Z1064) Yellow narcissi (48x35cm-19x14in) mono.d.1916 board
                  (S.FR 8000)
£4781 $8653   (5-Dec-91 SY.Z78/R) Still life of roses (53x39cm-21x15in) mono.d.1908
                  board (S.FR 12000)
£4781 $8653   (5-Dec-91 SY.Z85/R) Loewenzahn (46x53cm-18x21in) mono.d.06 (S.FR 12000)
£5976 $10817   (5-Dec-91 SY.Z77/R) Still life with cherries (36x48cm-14x19in)
                  mono.d.1912 (S.FR 15000)
£6767 $12383   (4-Jun-92 SY.Z386/R) Geraniums (41x55cm-16x22in) mono i.d.1916 board
                  (S.FR 18000)

RIGNANO, Domenico (attrib) (16th C) Italian
£650 $1131   (14-Apr-92 C94/R) Design for wall tomb (43x30cm-17x12in) i. chk pen wash

RIGOLOT, Albert (1862-1932) French
£625 $1106   (5-Nov-91 GF.L2746) Autumnal pond landscape (65x92cm-26x36in) s.
                  (S.FR 1600)
£926 $1759   (26-Jun-92 CSC.P110) Paysage (26x41cm-10x16in) s. panel (F.FR 9000)
£1986 $3574   (19-Nov-91 RAS.K115/R) Street in Laghouat (31x38cm-12x15in) s. panel
                  (D.KR 22000)
£2648 $4898   (10-Jun-92 ZZ.F39/R) Bord de la Loue (71x49cm-28x19in) (F.FR 26000)
£10440 $19000   (27-May-92 CH.NY197/R) Fishing on a summer day (60x81cm-24x32in) s.

RIGOLOT, Jean Gabriel (?) ?
£2235 $4000   (11-Nov-91 GC.M22/R) Paisaje Otonal (50x74cm-20x29in) s.

RIIS, Bendik (1911-) Norwegian
£1415 $2476   (25-Feb-92 UL.T228/R) 'Neptun' (57x135cm-22x53in) panel (N.KR 16000)

RIJ-ROUSSEAU, Jeanne (1870-1956) French
£10500 $18060   (16-Oct-91 S47/R) Le lecteur (72x53cm-28x21in) s.i.

RIJKELIJKHUYSEN, Hermanus Jan Hendrik (1813-1883) Dutch
£517 $899   (17-Sep-91 CH.AM578) A wooded landscape with a huntsman and a traveller conversing by a pond (37x63cm-15x25in) s. panel (D.FL 1700)

RIJKEVORSEL, G (?) ?
£1313 $2324   (26-Apr-92 FE.P95) Nature morte aux fruits (66x48cm-26x19in) s. (F.FR 13000)

RIJN, Harmensz van see REMBRANDT

RIKET, Leon (1876-1938) Belgian
£1233 $2121   (11-Oct-91 AW.H2890/R) Wooded river landscape with cows grazing (85x126cm-33x50in) s. (DM 3600)
£1362 $2451   (19-Nov-91 GM.B549/R) Maison au bord de l'eau (88x62cm-35x24in) s. wood (B.FR 80000)
£1658 $3035   (12-May-92 C.A275/R) Sunny spring day (51x73cm-20x29in) s. (B.FR 100000)

RILEY, Bridget (1931-) British
£5500 $10175   (11-Jun-92 C39/R) Kiss 1961 (122x122cm-48x48in) s.d.61 i.d.verso acrylic canvas
£14286 $25000   (25-Feb-92 SY.NY198/R) Tinct (145x141cm-57x56in) s.i.d.1972verso s.i.d.stretcher
£30000 $55500   (11-Jun-92 C38/R) Sheng-tung (96x228cm-38x90in) s.i.d.1974 verso acrylic canvas
£1543 $2700   (28-Feb-92 SY.NY306/R) Red enclosed by blue and green in different sequence (128x18cm-50x7in) s.d.73 gouache
£2100 $3717   (8-Nov-91 C259/R) Series 41 (98x63cm-39x25in) s.i.d.79 W/C bodycol.
£20000 $36200   (5-Dec-91 S28/R) Arrest III (192x175cm-76x69in) s.d.1965 verso emulsion linen

RILEY, John (1646-1691) British
£1800 $3168   (10-Apr-92 C94/R) Portrait of gentleman in coat with slashed sleeves (76x62cm-30x24in) painted oval cartouche
£2247 $4000   (22-Jan-92 D.NY21/R) Portrait of gentleman, said to be Reverend Henry Lucas (124x102cm-49x40in)
£2600 $4654   (13-Nov-91 S124/R) Portrait of gentleman (74x62cm-29x24in) painted oval

RILEY, John (circle) (1646-1691) British
£850 $1496   (8-Nov-91 S147/R) Portrait of lady, standing holding pearls (120x89cm-47x35in)
£2800 $4760   (22-Oct-91 S253/R) Portrait of gentleman, standing, wearing robes over armour (119x95cm-47x37in)

RILEY, John (style) (1646-1691) British
£1400 $2506   (14-Nov-91 CSK254/R) Portrait of boy seated with dove and spaniel at his feet (124x102cm-49x40in)

RILEY, Nicholas (1900-1944) American
£393 $700   (2-Nov-91 IH.NY71/R) Elderly woman outside, man crouched behind (43x48cm-17x19in) s. W/C

RILLAERT, Jan van (elder) (?-1568) Flemish
£3500 $6720   (7-Jul-92 C80/R) The Prophet Isaiah preaching to a crowd (67x54cm-26x21in) i. brush ink htd white olive prepared linen

RIMINGTON, Alexander Wallace (c.1854-1918) British
£1400 $2394   (13-Mar-92 C115/R) Taking the Sacrament to a sick person, Trau, Dalmatia (135x185cm-53x73in) init.

RINALDI, Angelo (1942-) Italian
£545 $970   (29-Apr-92 F.F70) Senza titolo (39x49cm-15x19in) s.d.1991 mixed media cardboard (I.L 1200000)

RINDISBACHER, Peter (1806-1834) Swiss
£24725 $45000   (28-May-92 CH.NY1/R) Buffalo hunt (21x41cm-8x16in) pen W/C board
£31429 $55000   (26-Sep-91 CH.NY10/R) Chase (20x30cm-8x12in) W/C

RING, L A (1854-1933) Danish
£794 $1413   (28-Apr-92 RAS.K604) Winter day near Auderod, thatched houses (20x16cm-8x6in) s.d.1901 (D.KR 9000)
£1083 $1949   (19-Nov-91 RAS.K289/R) Young girl with basket (34x25cm-13x10in) s.d.87 (D.KR 12000)
£1354 $2437   (19-Nov-91 RAS.K138/R) Interior with man by window (42x31cm-17x12in) s.d.81 (D.KR 15000)
£2256 $4061   (19-Nov-91 RAS.K112/R) Poplars near the church yard at Naestved, September evening (91x52cm-36x20in) s.d.1895 panel (D.KR 25000)
£2469 $4395   (28-Apr-92 RAS.K129/R) At the breakfast table (30x40cm-12x16in) s.d.1905 (D.KR 28000)
£3527 $6279   (28-Apr-92 RAS.K373/R) Gaabense ferry inn (33x54cm-13x21in) s. (D.KR 40000)
£4061 $7310   (19-Nov-91 RAS.K75/R) Peasant couple in Ring, man making bags, woman knitting (27x34cm-11x13in) s.d.87 (D.KR 45000)

RING, L A (1854-1933) Danish-cont.

£4513	$8123	(19-Nov-91 RAS.K76/R) Labourers at Sonderso water mains (155x185cm-61x73in) s.d.91 (D.KR 50000)
£7055	$12557	(28-Apr-92 RAS.K36/R) Young girl wearing strawhat looking out to sea (64x38cm-25x15in) s.d.97 sketch (D.KR 80000)
£8123	$14621	(19-Nov-91 RAS.K93/R) Early spring, Melby village (96x148cm-38x58in) s.d.1901 (D.KR 90000)
£2465	*$4141*	*(27-Aug-91 RAS.K85/R) Collecting corn - women and children in field landscape (33x48cm-13x19in) s.d.87 pastel (D.KR 28000)*

RING, Ludger Tom (younger-style) (1522-1584) German

£4800	$8400	(3-Apr-92 C77/R) Portrait of bearded gentleman, in black costume (25x18cm-10x7in) panel

RING, Ole (1902-1972) Danish

£713	$1226	(15-Oct-91 RAS.K222) From a boatyard (25x31cm-10x12in) s. (D.KR 8000)
£722	$1300	(19-Nov-91 RAS.K269) Old shed by the beach (22x33cm-9x13in) s. (D.KR 8000)
£812	$1462	(19-Nov-91 RAS.K516/R) Road through village (32x42cm-13x17in) s.d.1929 (D.KR 9000)
£881	$1498	(8-Aug-91 RAS.V979/R) Church and thatched house by village pond (36x46cm-14x18in) s. (D.KR 10000)
£882	$1570	(28-Apr-92 RAS.K544) Landscape, Vester Broby (25x33cm-10x13in) s. (D.KR 10000)
£1083	$1949	(19-Nov-91 RAS.K92/R) Autumn landscape (58x85cm-23x33in) s. (D.KR 12000)
£1230	$2202	(6-May-92 KH.K174/R) Summer day by the village pond (45x67cm-18x26in) s. (D.KR 14000)
£1354	$2437	(19-Nov-91 RAS.K206/R) Winter landscape at thaw (75x100cm-30x39in) s. (D.KR 15000)
£1496	$2514	(27-Aug-91 RAS.K488/R) From Hestehave near Praesto (18x30cm-7x12in) s.d.1942 (D.KR 17000)
£1585	$2662	(27-Aug-91 RAS.K133/R) Road through the village in spring (28x40cm-11x16in) s. (D.KR 18000)
£1715	$3087	(19-Nov-91 RAS.K94/R) Road through the village (52x70cm-20x28in) s. (D.KR 19000)
£1901	$3403	(16-Nov-91 FAL.M304/R) Store Tarnby near Koge (36x46cm-14x18in) s. (S.KR 20000)
£2115	$3595	(8-Aug-91 RAS.V983/R) Fishing boats and steamer on canal, Copenhagen (41x62cm-16x24in) s.d.1952 (D.KR 24000)
£3081	$5176	(27-Aug-91 RAS.K110/R) View of Wilders Plads (87x106cm-34x42in) s. (D.KR 35000)
£5722	$9613	(27-Aug-91 RAS.K131/R) View from Gammel Strand towards Hojbro Plads (82x106cm-32x42in) s. (D.KR 65000)

RING, Pieter de (style) (1615-1660) Dutch

£3665	$7000	(16-Jul-92 SY.NY274/R) Still life with cherries, grapes and gooseberries (51x63cm-20x25in)
£7509	$13590	(21-May-92 L.K124 a/R) Still life of fruit with lobster (83x109cm-33x43in) (DM 22000)

RINGEL, Franz (1940-) Austrian

£698	*$1249*	*(15-Jan-92 D.V283/R) Girl in profile (48x34cm-19x13in) s.i.d.1980 mixed media (A.S 14000)*
£733	*$1305*	*(31-Oct-91 D.V146/R) Langsee Fischer-Hutte, Prof.-Herbert-Bockl-Denkmal (40x30cm-16x12in) s.i.d.1980 col.pencil (A.S 15000)*
£1711	*$3045*	*(31-Oct-91 D.V101/R) Gansehaut III - Wo hort der Spass auf (61x57cm-24x22in) s.i.d.71 mixed media (A.S 35000)*
£2181	*$3970*	*(26-May-92 D.V283/R) Alles von Dolli und Franz (62x67cm-24x26in) s.i.d.1978 mixed media (A.S 45000)*
£2424	*$4411*	*(26-May-92 D.V282/R) Big and small twin (67x61cm-26x24in) s.d.71 mixed media (A.S 50000)*
£2688	*$4785*	*(31-Oct-91 D.V99/R) We misunderstand each other (74x61cm-29x24in) s.i.d.69 mixed media paper on paper (A.S 55000)*
£3177	*$5655*	*(31-Oct-91 D.V102/R) Renate (105x75cm-41x30in) s.d.75 s.d.verso mixed media oil board (A.S 65000)*

RINGELING, Hendrik (1812-1874) Dutch

£926	$1620	(18-Feb-92 CH.AM316/R) Peasant family in interior (66x53cm-26x21in) s. (D.FL 3000)

RINGQVIST, Bernt (1917-1966) Swedish

£569	$1042	(13-May-92 BU.S169/R) The picador (34x43cm-13x17in) s. panel (S.KR 6000)
£1186	$2170	(13-May-92 BU.S168/R) Birgit Cullberg (56x40cm-22x16in) s. panel (S.KR 12500)

RIO, Agusti (1923-) Spanish

£548	$976	(26-Nov-91 BRO.B317) Ensenada en una villa del Cantabrico (60x73cm-24x29in) s. (S.P 100000)

RIOPELLE, Jean-Paul (1923-) Canadian

£5143	$9000	(27-Feb-92 CH.NY2/R) Les ficelles (46x86cm-18x34in) s. acrylic paper on canvas
£6704	$12000	(13-Nov-91 CH.NY143/R) Opera des Pics (24x33cm-9x13in) s.
£6800	$11696	(17-Oct-91 S11/R) Abrupt (23x33cm-9x13in) s.
£7143	$12500	(27-Feb-92 CH.NY9/R) Des le matin (33x22cm-13x9in) s. s.i.d.67stretcher

RIOPELLE, Jean-Paul (1923-) Canadian-cont.

£7500	$12900	(17-Oct-91 S9/R) Argileux (24x33cm-9x13in) s. s.d.1957 stretcher
£8380	$15000	(6-May-92 CH.NY380/R) Serie Ste. Marguerite (111x71cm-44x28in) s. acrylic board
£9000	$15570	(26-Mar-92 C57/R) Iceberge no.19 (65x81cm-26x32in) s.i.stretcher
£14766	$27021	(3-Jun-92 PIC.P90/R) Les oies (73x92cm-29x36in) s. (F.FR 145000)
£19215	$33050	(8-Oct-91 CC.P34/R) Hublot (65x81cm-26x32in) s.d.1960 oval (F.FR 191000)
£21605	$39321	(12-Dec-91 SY.AM248/R) Tempete (54x66cm-21x26in) s.d.59 (D.FL 70000)
£23185	$40111	(4-Oct-91 CSC.P79/R) Au large (50x65cm-20x26in) s.d.57 (F.FR 230000)
£25140	$45000	(12-Nov-91 NY1/R) Printemps (35x24cm-14x9in) s.d.52
£33838	$59217	(25-Sep-91 EA.M502) Nadaka (76x91cm-30x36in) s.d.1947 verso (C.D 67000)
£36313	$65000	(13-Nov-91 CH.NY108/R) Untitled (55x34cm-22x13in) s.d.51verso
£39000	$70590	(5-Dec-91 C2/R) Arles (73x99cm-29x39in) s.
£50917	$94196	(12-Jun-92 AT.P48/R) Mouches a feu (73x92cm-29x36in) s.d.1958 (F.FR 500000)
£65856	$119200	(24-May-92 GL.P32/R) Point du jour (115x88cm-45x35in) s. (F.FR 650000)
£909	$1609	(24-Apr-92 CN.P207/R) Sans titre (49x65cm-19x26in) felt pen (F.FR 9000)
£5000	$8600	(17-Oct-91 C34/R) Untitled (17x28cm-7x11in) s.d.55 W/C ink
£5587	$10000	(13-Nov-91 CH.NY123/R) Untitled (45x50cm-18x20in) s.d.65 W/C gouache
£6286	$11000	(27-Feb-92 CH.NY10/R) Untitled (80x60cm-31x24in) s. col.chk
£10615	$19000	(13-Nov-91 CH.NY135/R) Untitled (108x75cm-43x30in) s.d.57 gouache

RIOS, Luigi da (1844-1892) Italian

£1500	$2595	(3-Oct-91 CSK244/R) A Venetian beauty (51x33cm-20x13in) s.d.1890
£6286	$11000	(20-Feb-92 SY.NY320/R) Venetian side canal (47x88cm-19x35in) s.d.1881 W/C bodycol

RIOULT, Louis Edouard (1790-1855) French

£10112	$18000	(22-Jan-92 SY.NY345/R) Une jeune baigneuse jette de l'eau au visage de sa compagne (140x173cm-55x68in) s.d.1831

RIP, Willem C (1856-1922) Dutch

£932	$1658	(26-Nov-91 VN.R95) Man on path in hilly landscape (42x52cm-17x20in) s.i. (D.FL 3000)
£1277	$2221	(17-Sep-91 CH.AM670) Summer, a polder landscape with a mill beyond (27x36cm-11x14in) indist.sig. panel (D.FL 4200)
£1835	$3266	(30-Oct-91 CH.AM210 a/R) Binnenhaven in 't Dorp de Heem (73x46cm-29x18in) s. s.i.verso (D.FL 6000)
£2094	$4000	(17-Jul-92 DM.D2181) Dutch landscape scene with boats (41x74cm-16x29in) s.
£734	$1306	(30-Oct-91 CH.AM355/R) River landscape with windmills (52x76cm-20x30in) s. W/C htd.white (D.FL 2400)
£846	$1505	(25-Nov-91 W.T1837/R) Windmills and rural figures (23x33cm-9x13in) s. W/C (C.D 1700)

RIPAMONTE, Carlos Pablo (1874-1968) Argentinian

£1099	$2000	(11-Dec-91 RO.BA239) Dos figuras de paisano (57x40cm-22x16in)
£1222	$2200	(20-Nov-91 V.BA85) Emponchado (46x30cm-18x12in) d.1944
£1285	$2300	(6-May-92 V.BA91) Gaucho a caballo (29x38cm-11x15in)
£1484	$2700	(11-Dec-91 RO.BA237) De un mismo pelo (63x51cm-25x20in) s.
£1868	$3400	(11-Dec-91 RO.BA49) Soldado trompeta (32x40cm-13x16in) s.d.933
£2688	$5000	(16-Jun-92 RO.BA72) El emponchao (37x30cm-15x12in)
£6183	$11500	(16-Jun-92 RO.BA49) Un alto en el camino (48x67cm-19x26in)
£24194	$45000	(16-Jun-92 RO.BA35) La Doma (106x142cm-42x56in)

RIPARI, Virgilio (1843-1902) Italian

£604	$1094	(3-Dec-91 SY.MI111) Bambina con cappuccio rosso (50x30cm-20x12in) s. (I.L 1300000)

RIPLEY, Aiden Lassell (1896-1969) American

£2632	$4500	(13-Mar-92 S.BM259/R) Moose hunting (43x66cm-17x26in) s.d.1941 i.verso W/C graphite
£3801	$6500	(13-Mar-92 S.BM257/R) Fishing, early spring (38x53cm-15x21in) s. i.verso W/C

RIPOLLES, Juan (?) Spanish?

£709	$1220	(16-Oct-91 FER.M166/R) Paisaje (72x91cm-28x36in) s.d.68 mixed media board (S.P 130000)

RIPPINGILLE, Edward Villiers (1798-1859) British

£1400	$2674	(15-Jul-92 S161/R) Settling the account (38x30cm-15x12in) s.panel

RIPPL-RONAI, Jozsef (1861-1930) Hungarian

£9500	$18145	(29-Jun-92 CSK68/R) Femme a la robe de chambre (47x42cm-19x17in) s.d.1905 board
£1013	$1834	(18-May-92 AT.P30) Femme au chapeau de paille (44x36cm-17x14in) s. pastel (F.FR 10000)

RIPPLINGER, Henry (1939-) Canadian

£385	$673	(17-Feb-92 HO.ED105) Chalk City (52x72cm-20x28in) s. W/C board (C.D 800)

RIQUER E INGLADA, Alejandro de (1856-1920) Spanish

£1935	$3638	(17-Dec-91 BRO.B406) Paisaje. Luz crepuscular (50x70cm-20x28in) s. (S.P 350000)

RIS, Cyriacus (18th C) German
£1220 $2220   (11-Dec-91 N.M349) Portrait of gentleman (52x39cm-20x15in) i.d.1770
               (DM 3500)

RISE, Bjarne (1904-1984) Norwegian
£709 $1290   (9-Dec-91 B.O102/R) View of Taormina (85x109cm-33x43in) s. (N.KR 8000)

RISEBOROUGH (20th C) American?
£936 $1600   (9-Mar-92 B.LA662/R) Trapeze artist (171x79cm-67x31in) s.d.52

RISS, Francois (1804-?) Russian
£3400 $6052   (28-Nov-91 CSK208) Portrait of lady wearing hat with ostrich feather
               (123x100cm-48x39in) s.d.1835

RISS, Thomas (1871-1959) Austrian
£687 $1196   (17-Sep-91 FN.S2066) Waiting for the prince - female nude
               (70x35cm-28x14in) s. board (DM 2000)
£3398 $6049   (28-Apr-92 D.V132/R) Grandmother telling tales (64x56cm-25x22in) s.panel
               (A.S 70000)

RISSALA, Kaapo (1900-1971) Finnish
£549 $961   (25-Sep-91 HOR.H81) Making coffee (65x54cm-26x21in) s.d.1932 (F.M 3900)

RISSET, E (20th C) Swiss
£863 $1467   (23-Oct-91 GD.B609/R) Genfersee landscape with vineyards
               (50x70cm-20x28in) s. i.d.1967 (S.FR 2200)

RISSOUKHINE, Iouri (1947-) Russian
£512 $911   (25-Nov-91 ZZ.F179/R) Autoportrait au maque (30x20cm-12x8in) s.verso
               panel (F.FR 5000)
£819 $1458   (25-Nov-91 ZZ.F181/R) Les trois graces Russes (120x135cm-47x53in) s.
               panel (F.FR 8000)
£1024 $1822   (25-Nov-91 ZZ.F182/R) Les tournesols enSeptembre (118x163cm-46x64in) s.
               panel (F.FR 10000)
£1024 $1822   (25-Nov-91 ZZ.F180/R) Carnaval a Orenbourg (118x163cm-46x64in) s. panel
               (F.FR 10000)
£2081 $3642   (30-Mar-92 ZZ.F77/R) Le marche aux oiseaux en Decembre
               (118x163cm-46x64in) s.d.1988 panel (F.FR 20000)
£3122 $5463   (30-Mar-92 ZZ.F81/R) Mars dans l'oural (118x163cm-46x64in) s. panel
               (F.FR 30000)

RISUENO, Jose (1665-1732) Spanish
£5000 $9100   (29-May-92 C335/R) The Trinity (110x83cm-43x33in)

RITCHIE, John (19th C) British
£1061 $1900   (13-Nov-91 B.SF2209/R) Life in the backwoods, a letter from home
               (46x61cm-18x24in) s.
£1400 $2506   (14-Jan-92 SWS124/R) Hide and seek (51x51cm-20x20in)
£1500 $2670   (1-May-92 PHE73/R) Skirmish with the enemy (51x41cm-20x16in) mono.

RITMAN, Louis (1889-1963) Russian/American
£944 $1700   (24-Nov-91 JRB.C141/R) Study for enchantment (36x43cm-14x17in) s.
£1437 $2500   (15-Apr-92 SY.NY144/R) Still life with basket of fruit and sugar bowl
               (39x62cm-15x24in) s. estate st.verso
£1445 $2500   (6-Sep-91 S.BM272/R) The pink collar (46x38cm-18x15in) s.
£2128 $4000   (18-Dec-91 SY.NY301/R) Village church (50x101cm-20x40in) s.
£3022 $5500   (28-May-92 BG.M552/R) Spring in Giverny (61x74cm-24x29in) s.
£3039 $5500   (7-Dec-91 LAE.L72/R) Verdun, France (51x64cm-20x25in) studio st.
£3714 $6500   (25-Sep-91 SY.NY76/R) Red-checked tablecloth (81x53cm-32x21in) s. bears
               estate st.verso
£3714 $6500   (25-Sep-91 SY.NY75/R) Under trees (53x81cm-21x32in) s. bears estate
               st.verso
£4000 $7000   (26-Sep-91 CH.NY90/R) On riverbank (54x65cm-21x26in) s. bears estate
               st.verso
£5747 $10000   (14-Sep-91 LAE.L302/R) Red head in white (66x81cm-26x32in) s.
£10497 $19000   (7-Dec-91 LAE.L71/R) Nina in the garden (102x74cm-40x29in) studio st.
£426   *$800*   *(18-Dec-91 SY.NY369/R) Galdioli garden (45x61cm-18x24in) s. W/C India ink*

RITSCHEL, William (1864-1949) American
£549 $950   (6-Sep-91 S.BM223/R) At the pier (25x20cm-10x8in) s. panel
£1011 $1850   (6-Jun-92 LAE.L98/R) Waves breaking in Pacific (51x30cm-20x12in) s.
£1412 $2500   (12-Feb-92 B.SF468/R) Seascape (32x58cm-13x23in) s. board
£1545 $2750   (26-Nov-91 MOR.P44) Sailboats and figures - evening tides
               (30x41cm-12x16in) s.d.1904 board
£1685 $3000   (26-Nov-91 MOR.P33 a) River barges (25x20cm-10x8in) s. panel
£1695 $3000   (12-Feb-92 B.SF577/R) Javanese girl (23x18cm-9x7in) s. board
£3689 $6750   (17-May-92 DU.E1102/R) Under sail near the California coast
               (53x43cm-21x17in) s.
£6077 $11000   (5-Dec-91 SY.NY104/R) Rockbound coast (77x102cm-30x40in) s.
£16949 $30000   (12-Feb-92 B.SF455/R) Outward bound (91x122cm-36x48in) s.
£960   *$1700*   *(12-Feb-92 B.SF469/R) Tahitian seascape (25x43cm-10x17in) s. W/C*

RITSCHL, Otto (20th C) German
£4561 $8211   (19-Nov-91 L.K1045/R) Composition (80x100cm-31x39in) s.d.1960 s.i.d.verso
               (DM 13000)

RITSCHL, Otto (20th C) German-cont.
£8532 $15529   (30-May-92 VG.B368/R) Composition (130x97cm-51x38in) s.d.1965 i.verso (DM 25000)
£825 $1509   (3-Jun-92 L.K400/R) Mother and child (45x29cm-18x11in) s.i.d.1927 W/C indian ink (DM 2400)
£825 $1509   (3-Jun-92 L.K401/R) Abstract composition (53x37cm-21x15in) s.d.1952 W/C (DM 2400)

RITSEMA, Coba (1876-1961) Dutch
£3517 $6225   (5-Nov-91 SY.AM242/R) Still life with pink flowers (100x66cm-39x26in) s. (D.FL 11500)
£9697 $17164   (22-Apr-92 CH.AM5/R) Lassitude (59x77cm-23x30in) i.stretcher (D.FL 32000)

RITTENBERG, Henry R (1879-1969) American
£860 $1540   (14-Nov-91 GRO.B106/R) Still life of fruit, brass bowl and samovar (89x114cm-35x45in) s. s.i.verso

RITTER, Caspar (1861-1923) German
£926 $1676   (19-May-92 GF.L2458/R) Cavalier smoking pipe in interior (52x81cm-20x32in) s.d.1882 (S.FR 2500)

RITTER, Eduard (1820-1892) German
£4847 $8822   (27-May-92 D.V523/R) The last penny (17x14cm-7x6in) s.d.1846 panel (A.S 100000)

RITTER, Henry (attrib) (1816-1853) Canadian
£3436 $5842   (25-Oct-91 BM.B817/R) Studio interior with artist and other figures (26x32cm-10x13in) mono.d.1845 (DM 10000)

RITTER, Lorenz (1832-1921) German
£893 $1555   (18-Sep-91 N.M268/R) Courtyard of Gothic monastery in Bavaria with churchtower (39x26cm-15x10in) s.d.1880 W/C (DM 2600)

RITTER, Paul (19/20th C) German
£820 $1500   (3-Jun-92 D.NY81) Artist in autumn landscape (51x91cm-20x36in) s.

RITTER, Wilhelm Georg (1850-1926) German
£2734 $4840   (5-Nov-91 GF.L2232/R) Rhine landscape (51x68cm-20x27in) s. (S.FR 7000)

RITTUN, Thorstein (1929-) Norwegian
£570 $1061   (18-Jun-92 GWP.O82/R) Woman and man (45x60cm-18x24in) s.d.54 (N.KR 6500)
£841 $1531   (14-Dec-91 BU.O86/R) Winter wood (54x65cm-21x26in) s.d.62 (N.KR 9500)
£1159 $2004   (23-Mar-92 B.O109/R) The family (81x100cm-32x39in) s.d. (N.KR 13000)
£1668 $2869   (7-Oct-91 B.O119/R) Women and seagulls (80x120cm-31x47in) s.d.1971 (N.KR 19000)

RITZ, Raphael (1829-1894) Swiss
£3386 $6129   (5-Dec-91 SY.Z38/R) Interior, Schloss Valere (46x56cm-18x22in) s. (S.FR 8500)
£6250 $11063   (5-Nov-91 GF.L2265/R) Girls wearing Kleinbremer costume winding flowers wreaths (35x51cm-14x20in) s. i.d.1909verso (S.FR 16000)

RITZBERGER, Albert (1853-1915) German
£878 $1528   (19-Sep-91 D.V242/R) Portrait of young girl (49x65cm-19x26in) board (A.S 18000)
£1748 $3111   (28-Apr-92 D.V116/R) Female nude (87x108cm-34x43in) s. (A.S 36000)
£3767 $6479   (8-Oct-91 ZEL.L1687/R) Salome dancing before Herodes (112x180cm-44x71in) s. (DM 11000)

RIVA (19/20th C) ?
£400 $708   (13-Feb-92 CSK73) Women of the Hareem (30x24cm-12x9in) s. indist.i. W/C

RIVAL, Denis (20th C) ?
£1310 $2320   (10-Nov-91 ZZ.F261/R) Le concert (80x80cm-31x31in) s.d.1990 (F.FR 13000)

RIVALZ, Antoine (1667-1735) French
£2039 $3792   (20-Jun-92 CH.MO225/R) La mort de Germanicus. Etude pour les deux soldats et un plan d'eglise (28x39cm-11x15in) s. chk wash ink double-sided (F.FR 20000)

RIVALZ, Antoine (circle) (1667-1735) French
£900 $1638   (10-Dec-91 PH147/R) Penitent Magdalen (99x81cm-39x32in)

RIVAS Y OLIVER, Antonio (19th C) Spanish
£2054 $3923   (2-Jul-92 ANS.M64/R) Vista urbana (27x17cm-11x7in) s. panel (S.P 375000)

RIVAS, Antonio (19th C) Italian
£659 $1200   (28-May-92 BG.M477/R) Choir boys singing in sanctuary (20x13cm-8x5in) s. panel
£2700 $4617   (17-Mar-92 PH203/R) In the harem (34x57cm-13x22in) s. panel
£2857 $5000   (18-Feb-92 CE.NY303/R) Fortune tellers (65x110cm-26x43in) s.d.85

RIVAS, Lucio (20th C) ?
£1247 $2182   (19-Feb-92 DUR.M1160/R) Interior de fabrica (85x100cm-33x39in) s. (S.P 225000)

RIVERA, Diego (1886-1957) Mexican

£20994	$38000	(18-May-92 CH.NY61/R) Calle de Vizcaya (27x18cm-11x7in) s. panel
£81384	$145677	(17-Nov-91 GL.P49/R) Village pres du champ (65x85cm-26x33in) s.d.11 (F.FR 800000)
£93923	$170000	(18-May-92 CH.NY60/R) Naturaleza muerta (27x38cm-11x15in) init.
£154696	$280000	(19-May-92 SY.NY19/R) Cazahuatl (116x95cm-46x37in) s.d.1937 s.i.d.verso
£155556	$280000	(19-Nov-91 CH.NY38/R) Retrato de Juanita (80x60cm-31x24in) s.d.1935 tempera linen on board
£160221	$290000	(19-May-92 SY.NY43/R) El nino en la fiesta (119x82cm-47x32in) s.d.1955 canvas laid down on masonite
£211111	$380000	(19-Nov-91 CH.NY46/R) Nino Chamula (76x60cm-30x24in) s.d.1950
£220994	$400000	(18-May-92 CH.NY10/R) Dos Tehuanas (80x60cm-31x24in) s.d.1934 tempera gessoed linen
£232044	$420000	(18-May-92 CH.NY35/R) Naturaleza muerta con tulipanes (68x54cm-27x21in) init. s.d.1916 verso
£344444	$620000	(18-Nov-91 SY.NY11/R) Paysage d'Arcueil (81x65cm-32x26in) s.d.18 s.i.d.verso
£607735	$1100000	(18-May-92 CH.NY19/R) Paisaje de Toledo (51x61cm-20x24in) s.d.1913
£1408840	$2550000	(19-May-92 SY.NY37/R) Mujer con Alcatraces (121x121cm-48x48in) s.d.1945
£1500000	$2700000	(19-Nov-91 CH.NY15/R) Venededora de flores (122x122cm-48x48in) s.d.1942 masonite
£2096	$3500	(20-Aug-91 RB.HY150/R) Man with mule (28x38cm-11x15in) s. pencil W/C parchment
£2486	$4500	(19-May-92 SY.NY117/R) Paisaje (32x23cm-13x9in) s. ink graphite
£2500	$4500	(19-Nov-91 CH.NY117/R) Michael Goodman trabajando con una regla de calculo (63x48cm-25x19in) s.d.31 pencil
£2778	$5000	(18-Nov-91 SY.NY107/R) Campesina (39x28cm-15x11in) s.d.36 chl rice paper
£3056	$5500	(18-Nov-91 SY.NY97/R) Vendedores de Canastas (28x38cm-11x15in) s.d.36 brush ink rice paper
£3222	$5800	(19-Nov-91 CH.NY123/R) La reconstruccion (29x21cm-11x8in) s.indis.d. pencil
£3333	$6000	(19-Nov-91 CH.NY120/R) Bocetos de chozas (17x23cm-7x9in) s.d.1947 chl set of three
£3889	$7000	(18-Nov-91 SY.NY95/R) El arresto (32x26cm-13x10in) s.i.d.1930 brush ink
£4444	$8000	(19-Nov-91 CH.NY119/R) Danzantes y Voladores de Paplanta (21x16cm-8x6in) s.d.55 pencil set of seven
£5525	$10000	(19-May-92 SY.NY116/R) Paisaje con cactus (17x32cm-7x13in) s.d.27 W/C col.pencil
£5556	$10000	(18-Nov-91 SY.NY12/R) Mademoiselle Vera (35x24cm-14x9in) s.d.1921 sanguine
£6111	$11000	(19-Nov-91 CH.NY116/R) Bocetos de cosechadores de arroz (9x15cm-4x6in) s.d.56 pencil set of fourteen
£7222	$13000	(18-Nov-91 SY.NY136/R) Boceto para la tierra fecunda o la tierra liberada (31x48cm-12x19in) s.d.25 chl
£7735	$14000	(19-May-92 SY.NY118/R) Mercado de flores (47x62cm-19x24in) s.d.27 chl
£8889	$16000	(19-Nov-91 CH.NY121/R) Mujeres en el Velorio (15x21cm-6x8in) s.d.1951 W/C
£10497	$19000	(18-May-92 CH.NY83/R) Vendedores callejeros (46x62cm-18x24in) s. wash rice paper
£11050	$20000	(19-May-92 SY.NY11/R) Boceto para germinacion (63x47cm-25x19in) s.d.27 chl
£11050	$20000	(19-May-92 SY.NY39/R) Nino (39x28cm-15x11in) s. chl sanguine rice paper
£11111	$20000	(18-Nov-91 SY.NY145/R) Campesinos (27x18cm-11x7in) s. W/C rice paper
£11602	$21000	(19-May-92 SY.NY109/R) Yucatan (32x43cm-13x17in) s. W/C chl rice paper
£11602	$21000	(19-May-92 SY.NY119/R) Zapatista (63x48cm-25x19in) s.d.27 chl
£12155	$22000	(18-May-92 CH.NY82/R) Vendedor de Ollas (47x61cm-19x24in) s.d.1940 W/C ink paper on board
£13812	$25000	(19-May-92 SY.NY30/R) Mercado (27x39cm-11x15in) s.d.1941 W/C rice paper
£13889	$25000	(18-Nov-91 SY.NY28/R) Hombre con pico (39x28cm-15x11in) s. W/C rice paper
£14365	$26000	(18-May-92 CH.NY153/R) Nina indigena (30x22cm-12x9in) s.d.1935 chl sanguine
£14365	$26000	(18-May-92 CH.NY157/R) Albanil (39x28cm-15x11in) s. W/C rice paper
£15000	$27000	(18-Nov-91 SY.NY137/R) Cantinflas (65x50cm-26x20in) s.d.53 graphite
£15470	$28000	(19-May-92 SY.NY168/R) Nino con perro (39x28cm-15x11in) s. W/C rice paper
£16575	$30000	(19-May-92 SY.NY134/R) Campesinos (40x32cm-16x13in) s.d.28 W/C rice paper
£16575	$30000	(18-May-92 CH.NY2/R) Vendedora de Cocos (28x38cm-11x15in) s. W/C rice paper
£17956	$32500	(19-May-92 SY.NY38/R) Autorretrato (31x24cm-12x9in) s.d.27 col.pencil
£22099	$40000	(19-May-92 SY.NY12/R) Acueducto (38x53cm-15x21in) s.d.V-18 graphite W/C
£22099	$40000	(18-May-92 CH.NY154/R) Cabeza de Nino (39x27cm-15x11in) s. chl W/C sanguine rice paper
£23611	$42500	(18-Nov-91 SY.NY135/R) Nina (39x28cm-15x11in) s.d.43 chl sanguine
£26389	$47500	(18-Nov-91 SY.NY32 a/R) Cargador (38x27cm-15x11in) s.d.1937 W/C rice paper
£31944	$57500	(18-Nov-91 SY.NY29/R) Cargadores (38x28cm-15x11in) s.d.37 W/C rice paper
£52486	$95000	(19-May-92 SY.NY31/R) Cargador de flores (38x28cm-15x11in) s.d.1954 W/C rice paper
£58333	$105000	(18-Nov-91 SY.NY13/R) Mujer sentada (30x39cm-12x15in) s.i.d.1914 W/C graphite

RIVERA, Manuel (20th C) Latin American?

£2075	$3549	(17-Mar-92 FER.M175/R) Casas (97x68cm-38x27in) s. tablex (S.P 375000)
£27488	$48378	(9-Apr-92 ANS.M119/R) Espejo en delirio (89x130cm-35x51in) s. polychrome metallic canvas (S.P 5000000)

RIVERO, L (?) ?
£710 $1292   (25-May-92 AT.P141/R) Nu sur fond de plumes (53x40cm-21x16in) s.d.30 crayon dr sanguine (F.FR 7000)

RIVERS, Elizabeth (1903-) British
£481 $843   (17-Feb-92 AD.D10) Lemons and oranges in wooden dish (51x30cm-20x12in) s. (E.P 520)
£537 $940   (17-Feb-92 AD.D12) Abstract - waves (46x58cm-18x23in) s. (E.P 580)

RIVERS, Larry (1923-) American
£9143 $16000   (25-Feb-92 SY.NY172/R) Silvia sunbathing (91x91cm-36x36in) s.d.80
£14525 $26000   (14-Nov-91 SY.NY341/R) Figures at table (39x40cm-15x16in) s.d.58 canvasboard
£41899 $75000   (12-Nov-91 CH.NY18/R) Last Civil War Veteran (76x58cm-30x23in) s.d.62 i.verso board
£69832 $125000   (14-Nov-91 SY.NY352/R) French money I (89x149cm-35x59in) s.d.62 verso
£1117 $2000   (12-Nov-91 CE.NY43/R) Untitled (20x19cm-8x7in) s.i. col.pencil graphite col.crayons
£1395 $2400   (12-Oct-91 SY.NY229/R) Untitled - nude studies (23x15cm-9x6in) one s. graphite pair
£2378 $4400   (12-Jun-92 SY.NY305/R) Portrait of Robert Fraser (34x42cm-13x17in) s.i.d.66 oil ink pencil collage airbrush
£2601 $4500   (3-Oct-91 SY.NY87/R) The Big D (45x60cm-18x24in) s.d.1975-76 pencil col.pencil
£3143 $5500   (27-Feb-92 CE.NY220/R) Carly Simon and Chinese information (77x111cm-30x44in) s. col.chk graphite masking tape paper collage
£3352 $6000   (6-May-92 CH.NY307/R) Untitled - Dreyfus Fund (49x35cm-19x14in) s.i.d.64 graphite col.crayons cellophane tape
£3429 $6000   (25-Feb-92 SY.NY167/R) Stencil camel (56x75cm-22x30in) s. spray paint pastel frisket on paper
£3631 $6500   (13-Nov-91 CH.NY179/R) Carly Simon and The Mongolian (71x104cm-28x41in) s.d.81 i.verso graphite col.crayons masking tape
£5780 $10000   (3-Oct-91 SY.NY84/R) In the artist's studio (62x71cm-24x28in) s. pencil prismacolour paper mounted foamboard
£15642 $28000   (13-Nov-91 CH.NY131/R) Untitled (36x42cm-14x17in) s.i.d.63 gouache graphite chl.tape collage

RIVERS, Leopold (1852-1905) British
£600 $1026   (12-Mar-92 CSK191) River landscape with angler in punt (61x107cm-24x42in) s.
£450 $860   (16-Jul-92 CSK52) Rustic idyll (37x53cm-15x21in) s. pencil W/C
£480 $821   (12-Mar-92 CSK77) Rustic idyll (36x53cm-14x21in) s. pencil W/C
£500 $850   (24-Oct-91 CSK67) A Hampshire Cottage (25x36cm-10x14in) s. W/C htd.white
£550 $946   (11-Oct-91 K426) Figures in trap about to ford stream and cottages beyond (48x74cm-19x29in) s. W/C
£980 $1754   (5-May-92 SWS196/R) Driving sheep near barn (51x78cm-20x31in) s. W/C

RIVERS, Leopold (circle) (1852-1902) British
£750 $1313   (23-Sep-91 PHB43) A view of Sunbury Weir (46x71cm-18x28in) s. i. verso

RIVERS, Montague (?) British
£1200 $2076   (25-Mar-92 AH186) Berkshire cottage (38x28cm-15x11in) W/C

RIVIERE, Adriaan de la (1857-1941) Dutch
£864 $1512   (25-Feb-92 VN.R284/R) The picnic (52x40cm-20x16in) s. (D.FL 2800)
£1056 $1880   (26-Nov-91 VN.R96/R) Figures outside an inn (81x111cm-32x44in) s.d.97 board (D.FL 3400)

RIVIERE, Briton (1840-1920) British
£7200 $13320   (12-Jun-92 C213/R) On the Road to Gloucester Fair (58x213cm-23x84in) s.i.d.1859 verso
£1200 $2052   (1-Aug-91 RBB546/R) Collies (43x58cm-17x23in) mono. W/C htd bodycol.

RIVIERE, Briton (attrib) (1840-1920) British
£830 $1452   (30-Mar-92 AAA.S144 d) Possession nine points of law (22x30cm-9x12in) panel (A.D 1900)

RIVIERE, Daniel Valentine (attrib) (1780-1854) British
£2000 $3400   (23-Oct-91 S190/R) Greek ladies of Pera, Constantinople (38x49cm-15x19in) W/C htd.bodycol gum arabic

RIVIERE, Henri (1864-1951) French
£509 $942   (12-Jun-92 ARC.P176) Paysage a Morgat en Bretagne (26x41cm-10x16in) i.d.1905 W/C black chk (F.FR 5000)
£1117 $2000   (9-May-92 CE.NY2/R) Pointe du Rez (41x26cm-16x10in) st.mono.i.d.1907 W/C pencil

RIVIERE, Henry Parsons (1811-1888) British
£480 $816   (22-Oct-91 SWS157/R) View of St. Peter's and Castell Saint Angelo (45x71cm-18x28in) s. W/C

RIVIERE, Hugh Goldwin (1869-1956) British
£750 $1305   (19-Sep-91 CSK79/R) Portrait of young man (32x26cm-13x10in) board

RIVOIRE, Francois (1842-1919) French
£611 $1130   (10-Jun-92 ZZ.F40) Bouquet de roses (27x39cm-11x15in) W/C (F.FR 6000)
£1461 $2600   (22-Jan-92 SY.NY352/R) Still life with roses (58x48cm-23x19in) s. W/C
£2571 $4500   (19-Feb-92 CH.NY55/R) Still life with roses (59x69cm-23x27in) s. W/C over
*   pencil*

RIXENS, Jean Andre (1846-1924) French
£38000 $70680   (16-Jun-92 PH138/R) Dejeuner du salon au Cafe la Cascade
                     (72x102cm-28x40in) s.d.1889

RIZI, Antonio (1560-1632) Italian
£9331 $16422   (11-Apr-92 AT.P1/R) Le Couronnement de la Vierge (130x92cm-51x36in)
                     i.verso panel (F.FR 92000)

RIZZI, Antonio (19th C) Italian
£1044 $1880   (20-Nov-91 DUR.M542/R) Salvando la muneca (65x46cm-26x18in) s. s.i.verso
                     (S.P 190000)
£1099 $1979   (20-Nov-91 DUR.M540/R) Venecia (38x55cm-15x22in) s. (S.P 200000)

RIZZI, Marco Antonio (attrib) (1648-1723) Italian
£3591 $6500   (21-May-92 CH.NY104/R) Mixed fruit in landscape (58x90cm-23x35in)

RIZZO, Arthur (1929-) Maltese
£520 $952   (3-Jun-92 ZZ.B177) Ballerina (109x50cm-43x20in) s. s.i.verso board

ROBBE, Louis (1806-1887) Belgian
£1000 $1790   (14-Jan-92 SWS205/R) Donkey and two chickens in barn (39x59cm-15x23in) s.
£1395 $2400   (14-Oct-91 H.C49/R) Paysage en Flanders (56x74cm-22x29in) s. canvas laid
                     down on board
£1764 $3122   (10-Nov-91 ZZ.F5/R) Moutons dans les alpages (23x31cm-9x12in) s.
                     (F.FR 17500)
£1966 $3500   (1-Nov-91 PO.BA25) Ovejas (50x71cm-20x28in) s.
£2747 $5000   (28-May-92 SY.NY230/R) Moutons dans un paysage (50x71cm-20x28in) s.
£4636 $8391   (23-May-92 KV.L464/R) Woman with cows in landscape (85x124cm-33x49in)
                     s.d.1868 (B.FR 280000)

ROBBINS, Horace Wolcott (1842-1904) American
£2210 $4000   (6-Dec-91 CH.NY34/R) Boating in autumn (27x46cm-11x18in) s.d.1870

ROBBINS, Lucy Lee (1865-?) American
£2446 $4257   (14-Apr-92 SY.AM95/R) Portrait of American lady in black hat
*   (52x37cm-20x15in) s. pastel (D.FL 8000)*

ROBELLAZ, Emile (1844-1882) Swiss
£3068 $5278   (7-Oct-91 CSC.P139/R) La lecture (49x39cm-19x15in) s. panel (F.FR 30500)

ROBERT, Henry (1881-1961) French
£1314 $2352   (6-May-92 GD.B1058/R) Matin a Gruyeres (55x73cm-22x29in) s. (S.FR 3600)
£745 $1267   (23-Oct-91 GD.B610/R) Lac de Chavannes (33x25cm-13x10in) s.i.d.1918
*   gouache (S.FR 1900)*

ROBERT, Hubert (1733-1808) French
£5071 $8925   (11-Apr-92 AT.P106/R) Le feu de camp (72x88cm-28x35in) s.d.178.
                     (F.FR 50000)
£10802 $19552   (5-Dec-91 SY.MO184/R) Personnages pres d'une colonne (36x27cm-14x11in)
                     (F.FR 105000)
£20950 $37500   (17-Jan-92 SY.NY60/R) A fantasy view of a gallery at the Coliseum, Rome
                     (85x95cm-33x37in)
£23464 $42000   (16-Jan-92 CH.NY65/R) Capriccio of Roman ruins with washerwomen
                     approaching archway and figures by column (77x87cm-30x34in) s.d.1796
£27933 $50000   (16-Jan-92 CH.NY78/R) Capriccio of Roman ruins including Pyramid Caius
                     Cestius, with figures by stream (119x82cm-47x32in) i.
£35678 $66361   (20-Jun-92 CH.MO68/R) Soldats parmi des ruines romaines
                     (99x135cm-39x53in) (F.FR 350000)
£35912 $65000   (21-May-92 CH.NY41/R) Capriccio with temple of Concordia, Arch of Titus
                     and Pyramid of Caius Cestius with figures (100x76cm-39x30in)
£37709 $67500   (16-Jan-92 CH.NY84/R) Mother and child drawing wine from barrel in ruined
                     wine cellar, dog to fore (72x59cm-28x23in) oval
£41899 $75000   (16-Jan-92 CH.NY70/R) Ruins of Roman bath, with figures promenading and
                     resting under arch (77x87cm-30x34in) s.d.1796
£111732 $200000   (16-Jan-92 CH.NY76/R) Antiquities of Provence, including Arena at Arles,
                     Maison Carree and Tour Magna at Nimes (56x79cm-22x31in)
£201117 $360000   (17-Jan-92 SY.NY63/R) Italian peasants resting among Roman ruins
                     (99x147cm-39x58in)
£1000 $1820   (11-Dec-91 PH68/R) Seated girl playing with dog (19x26cm-7x10in) chk
£1500 $2880   (7-Jul-92 C232) Washerwomen by fountain in park and stairway beyond
*   (37x48cm-15x19in) chk joined sheets made up*
£1800 $3132   (14-Apr-92 C163/R) Family watering horse by well with statue of Venus
*   (37x29cm-15x11in) chk*
£3073 $5500   (15-Jan-92 CH.NY95/R) Figures outside cottage by outcrop
*   (36x29cm-14x11in) s. red chk counterproof three*
£5144 $9311   (5-Dec-91 SY.MO35/R) Personnages dans des ruines devant une sculpture
*   (53x72cm-21x28in) s.i.d.1779 pen wash htd.W/C blk.chk. (F.FR 50000)*
£5500 $9570   (14-Apr-92 C162/R) Washerwomen in Egyptian temple (56x34cm-22x13in) chk
*   pen wash*

ROBERT, Hubert (1733-1808) French-cont.

£6000	$10920	(10-Dec-91 C210/R) A monumental bridge with figures beside a river (28x35cm-11x14in) red chk.
£7200	$13824	(8-Jul-92 PH188/R) Figures walking amongst classical ruins, before pyramidal tomb (36x29cm-14x11in) s. red chk over pen wash htd white
£7500	$13650	(10-Dec-91 C211/R) Design for a frontispiece (18x16cm-7x6in) i. ink wash
£7732	$13376	(26-Mar-92 PIC.P1/R) Les Ecuries du Pape Jules II (68x47cm-27x19in) s. pen Indian ink wash (F.FR 75000)
£13966	$25000	(14-Jan-92 SY.NY118 a) Washerwoman at stream. Entrance to chateau (36x29cm-14x11in) red chk pair
£15088	$26405	(3-Apr-92 AGS.P199/R) Le tombeau antique (42x33cm-17x13in) s.i.d.1760 sanguine (F.FR 145000)
£16277	$29786	(15-May-92 AT.P71/R) Terrasse d'une ville italienne (37x55cm-15x22in) sanguine (F.FR 160000)
£17329	$32232	(20-Jun-92 CH.MO274/R) Un gentilhomme portant un tricorne regardant une urne antique (51x39cm-20x15in) s.i. red chk (F.FR 170000)
£26749	$48416	(5-Dec-91 SY.MO13/R) Couple a dos d'ane dans les ruines d'un palais (55x66cm-22x26in) s.i.d.1760 pen wash W/C blk.chk. (F.FR 260000)

ROBERT, Hubert (after) (1733-1808) French

£800	$1376	(15-Oct-91 CSK632) The replantation of trees at Versailles (15x23cm-6x9in) bodycol.

ROBERT, Hubert (attrib) (1733-1808) French

£2514	$4500	(17-Jan-92 SY.NY163/R) Footbridge over river with figures along banks (40x62cm-16x24in)
£6116	$11376	(18-Jun-92 SY.MO256/R) Scenes campagnardes (11x15cm-4x6in) panel pair (F.FR 60000)
£15291	$28440	(18-Jun-92 SY.MO218/R) Lavandiere au bord d'un ruisseau. Lavandiere et petite fille (46x35cm-18x14in) panel pair (F.FR 150000)
£22099	$40000	(22-May-92 SY.NY77/R) Landscape with waterfall at Tivoli (113x65cm-44x26in)
£845	$1530	(3-Dec-91 FN.S1619) Classical landscape with ruins (32x26cm-13x10in) indis.s.d. W/C indian ink brush (DM 2400)
£1977	$3460	(3-Apr-92 AGS.P200/R) Vue de Grand Escalier de Versailles (39cm-15ins circular) pen W/C (F.FR 19000)

ROBERT, Hubert (circle) (1733-1808) French

£2523	$4339	(16-Oct-91 AT.P142/R) Bergers dans un paysage rocheux (44x36cm-17x14in) (F.FR 25000)
£950	$1700	(13-Jan-92 CE.NY180) A waterfall, Tivoli (37x27cm-15x11in) i.verso red chk.
£977	$1681	(10-Oct-91 D.V30/R) Landscape with ruins (36x51cm-14x20in) ochre (A.S 20000)

ROBERT, Hubert (school) (1733-1808) French

£782	$1400	(13-Jan-92 CE.NY177) Coastal landscape with a carriage. Reclining woman before a ruined house i. red chk. two

ROBERT, Hubert (style) (1733-1808) French

£1000	$1800	(22-Nov-91 SWS7) Landscape with figures by a bridge (60x52cm-24x20in)
£4000	$7000	(1-Apr-92 S167/R) Children playing among Roman ruins (39x52cm-15x20in)
£4094	$7288	(25-Nov-91 GL.P7/R) Vue d'un port (216x297cm-85x117in) (F.FR 40000)
£4119	$7745	(18-Dec-91 AT.P216/R) Scenes buccoliques (170x72cm-67x28in) four (F.FR 40000)

ROBERT, Leopold-Louis (1794-1835) French

£751	$1337	(29-Nov-91 GAB.G2167 b) Jeune femme romaine au crepuscule (111x83cm-44x33in) (S.FR 1900)

ROBERT, Leopold-Louis (attrib) (1794-1835) French

£2527	$4549	(19-Nov-91 RAS.K154/R) Young Greek sharpening his knife (52x43cm-20x17in) (D.KR 28000)
£6769	$12184	(19-Nov-91 RAS.K409/R) Italian harvesters having lunchbreak (85x116cm-33x46in) s. (D.KR 75000)

ROBERT, Marius Hubert (19/20th C) French

£520	$911	(5-Apr-92 ZZ.F94/R) Chateauneuf de Grasse a travers les oliviers (46x55cm-18x22in) s. (F.FR 5000)
£611	$1118	(2-Jun-92 AT.P205) La grande caravane (38x55cm-15x22in) s. board (F.FR 6000)

ROBERT, Maurice (1909-) Swiss

£706	$1200	(23-Oct-91 GD.B613/R) Autumn landscape near Neuveville (76x60cm-30x24in) s.d.1938 (S.FR 1800)

ROBERT, Nicolas (1614-1685) French

£12000	$23040	(7-Jul-92 C50/R) Barn owl (40x30cm-16x12in) chk bodycol vellum

ROBERT, Paul Andre Felix (1901-1977) Swiss

£1333	$2387	(15-Nov-91 ZOF.Z1853/R) Autumnal avenue (37x30cm-15x12in) s. pastel (S.FR 3400)

ROBERT, Philippe (1881-1930) Swiss
£608 $1088   (15-Nov-91 ZOF.Z1854/R) Bielersee landscape with view of Petersinsel and Jolimont (40x65cm-16x26in) s.d.1922 i.verso board (S.FR 1550)
£608 $1088   (15-Nov-91 ZOF.Z1855/R) Un tournant de la Thiele (40x65cm-16x26in) s.d.1922 i.verso board one of pair (S.FR 1550)

ROBERT, Theophile (1879-1954) Swiss
£1195 $2163   (5-Dec-91 SY.Z113/R) Bouquet de fleurs (73x61cm-29x24in) mono. paper on board (S.FR 3000)
£2451 $4362   (29-Nov-91 GAB.G2848/R) Nu au bouquet (61x46cm-24x18in) s.d.45 (S.FR 6200)
£3704 $6704   (19-May-92 GF.L2325/R) Mother and child (90x80cm-35x31in) s. (S.FR 10000)

ROBERT-FLEURY, Tony (1837-1912) French
£890 $1700   (16-Jul-92 SY.NY360/R) The prisoner (69x45cm-27x18in) s.

ROBERTI, R M (19th C) Italian
£584   *$1016*   *(18-Sep-91 N.M269) Pifferaro playing song for female leaning against chest (23x18cm-9x7in) s. W/C (DM 1700)*

ROBERTO, L (19th C) Italian
£400 $672   *(15-Aug-91 B271) Vito of Liverpool entering Bay of Naples (43x61cm-17x24in) s.i.d.1883 gouache*
£900 $1620   *(27-Jan-92 PH94) Yacht Isa off Napoli (41x63cm-16x25in) s.i. W/C pencil gouache*

ROBERTON, Alfred J (19th C) ?
£612 $1096   (5-May-92 ZEL.L1511/R) Still life of bowl of fruit, glass vase and roemer and drape (50x61cm-20x24in) s. (DM 1800)

ROBERTS, Alice T (20th C) American
£682 $1200   (9-Apr-92 FA.PH696) The model (69x89cm-27x35in) s.

ROBERTS, David (1796-1864) British
£2265 $4122   (11-Dec-91 WE.MU120/R) Street scene, Verona (29x38cm-11x15in) s. panel (DM 6500)
£5200 $9152   (6-Apr-92 WW23/R) Ruins of St. Andrews Cathedral and Church of St. Regulus, Fife, Scotland (46x35cm-18x14in) s.d.1830 panel
£8500 $14960   (8-Apr-92 S102/R) St. Stephen's, Vienna (23x34cm-9x13in) i. s.i.verso panel
£380000 $646000   (25-Oct-91 C1/R) Jerusalem (122x183cm-48x72in) s.d.1860
£382 $657   *(16-Oct-91 FER.M40/R) La llegada de los barcos al atardecer (17x24cm-7x9in) s. pencil dr W/C (S.P 70000)*
£600 $1020   *(22-Oct-91 SWS83) Lady Chapel, Chruch of St. Jacques, Dieppe, France (38x25cm-15x10in) i. wash over pencil*
£700 $1253   *(5-May-92 SWS20/R) Inside St.Mark's Basilica, Venice (17x12cm-7x5in) i. pencil wash*
£1320 $2521   *(16-Jul-92 S171/R) The Temple of Poseidon at Paestum, Italy (24x34cm-9x13in) i.d.1854 pencil wash htd white*
£3000 $5280   *(7-Apr-92 C158/R) Dieppe (23x31cm-9x12in) i.d.1828 pencil pen W/C htd white*
£3400 $6494   *(14-Jul-92 C150/R) Entrance to Court of Orange Trees, Seville (28x20cm-11x8in) pencil W/C htd white*
£3876 $7403   *(21-Jul-92 JRL.S175/R) Italian city square (35x55cm-14x22in) s.d.1847 W/C (A.D 10000)*
£5200 $9152   *(6-Apr-92 WW201/R) Street of San Bernardo and Church of Novitiate of Jesuits, Madrid (29x37cm-11x15in) s.d.1836 W/C htd white*
£7000 $12320   *(9-Apr-92 S85/R) Gauscin looking towards Gibraltar and coast of Barbary (23x33cm-9x13in) s.d.1834 W/C over pencil*
£11000 $21010   *(14-Jul-92 C153/R) Letter writer, Cairo (33x24cm-13x9in) s.i.d.22 pencil W/C htd white*

ROBERTS, David (circle) (1796-1864) British
£1100   *$1958*   *(1-Nov-91 S448) Ruins of Temple of Castor and Pollux, Forum, Rome (68x48cm-27x19in) W/C over pencil htd bodycol*

ROBERTS, David (style) (1796-1864) British
£1000 $1780   (30-Apr-92 CG868 a) Merchants on canal, Venice (92x72cm-36x28in) bears sig.d.1834

ROBERTS, Edwin (1840-1917) British
£1500 $2715   (20-May-92 BT182) Spanish fruit seller (89x69cm-35x27in) i.stretcher
£2200 $3740   (22-Oct-91 SWS288/R) Pet bird (76x67cm-30x26in) mono.d.1875
£2300 $4416   (28-Jul-92 SWS350/R) Proud little mother (33x25cm-13x10in) s.i.
£2586 $4500   (20-Sep-91 DM.D2030/R) Sweethearts love at first sight (46x36cm-18x14in) s. s.i.verso
£3161 $5500   (20-Sep-91 DM.D2029/R) Sweethears requited affection (46x36cm-18x14in) s. s.i.verso
£6000 $10320   (11-Oct-91 C83/R) Tea for two (63x51cm-25x20in) s. s.i.verso
£7500 $12900   (11-Oct-91 C82/R) Her only pair (61x45cm-24x18in) s. s.i.verso
£8000 $14000   (18-Feb-92 CE.NY104/R) Ladies first (71x91cm-28x36in) s. s.i.verso

ROBERTS, J (19th C) British
£615 $1100   (15-Nov-91 DM.D2137/R) Landscape with cottage by stream (53x97cm-21x38in) s.

ROBERTS, Paul (20th C) ?
£750 $1328   (13-Feb-92 CSK133 a) Figures on riverbank by boat (42x68cm-17x27in) s.

ROBERTS, R (19th C) British
£680 $1190   (26-Feb-92 MMB284) Dismasted schooner with salvage tug and life boat
      (61x107cm-24x42in) indis.s.

ROBERTS, T S (1760-1826) British
£3636 $6291   (2-Oct-91 A.D118/R) Pastoral river landscape with man watering horse
      (41x61cm-16x24in) panel (E.P 4000)

ROBERTS, Thomas E (1820-1901) British
£2800 $5180   (12-Jun-92 C245/R) The bashful suitor (61x50cm-24x20in) s.

ROBERTS, Thomas William (1856-1931) Australian
£1397 $2500   (13-Nov-91 B.SF2348/R) The letter (68x50cm-27x20in) s.d.1896 canvas laid
      down on masonite
£2564 $4564   (27-Apr-92 J.M311) Portrait of Ian MacAllister Moffat Pendor
      (99x89cm-39x35in) s.d.20 (A.D 6000)
£6388 $11498   (24-Nov-91 SY.S352) Hidden river (13x29cm-5x11in) s.d.1927 canvas on
      board (A.D 14500)
£7265 $12932   (28-Apr-92 CH.ME159/R) Autumn, England (43x34cm-17x13in) s. board
      (A.D 17000)
£7692 $13692   (28-Apr-92 CH.ME237/R) Edward Trenchard (107x76cm-42x30in) (A.D 18000)
£8295 $14433   (16-Sep-91 CH.ME79/R) Mt Warning and Macpherson Ranges, N.S.W. 1920
      (13x22cm-5x9in) s. board (A.D 18000)
£9390 $15681   (19-Aug-91 SY.ME198/R) Circular quay, Sydney (7x19cm-3x7in) s. panel
      (A.D 20000)
£11674 $21013   (24-Nov-91 SY.S466/R) Repatriated (22x13cm-9x5in) s.d.20 board
      (A.D 26500)
£12207   *$20385*   *(19-Aug-91 SY.ME351/R) Portrait of Lady Hopetoun (69x52cm-27x20in) pastel*
      (A.D 26000)

ROBERTS, William (1895-1980) British
£19000 $34770   (13-May-92 S73/R) The shoe-shop (91x61cm-36x24in) s.
£38000 $65360   (6-Mar-92 C98/R) The sunflowers (183x122cm-72x48in) s.
      s.indis.i.stretcher
£3200 $5664   (7-Nov-91 C22/R) Pollarding (55x36cm-22x14in) s. pencil blk.crayon W/C
£3800 $6498   (11-Mar-92 S110/R) Moonsnatchers (19x11cm-7x4in) s.i. pencil W/C
£6000 $10260   (11-Mar-92 S103/R) Springboard (50x35cm-20x14in) s.i. pencil W/C
£7000 $13370   (16-Jul-92 B54/R) The crabs (50x33cm-20x13in) s. W/C pencil
£9000 $16470   (5-Jun-92 C54/R) The gutter (21x39cm-8x15in) s. pencil W/C bodycol.

ROBERTS, William Goodridge (1904-1974) Canadian
£1194 $2125   (26-Nov-91 JOY.T96/R) Landscape in autumn (30x40cm-12x16in) s. board
      (C.D 2400)
£1484 $2716   (14-May-92 SY.T213/R) Laurentian hillside in winter (37x44cm-15x17in) s.
      board (C.D 3250)
£1500 $2655   (6-Nov-91 SY.T37) Summer landscape (37x44cm-15x17in) s. board (C.D 3000)
£1712 $3134   (14-May-92 SY.T217/R) Still life with green jug (30x41cm-12x16in) s.
      board (C.D 3750)
£3653 $6685   (14-May-92 SY.T208/R) Summer landscape (50x60cm-20x24in) s. board
      (C.D 8000)
£7073 $12732   (19-Nov-91 FP.M189/R) Nature morte (63x81cm-25x32in) s. board (C.D 14500)
£8219 $14959   (26-May-92 JOY.T76/R) Georgian Bay landscape (72x90cm-28x35in) s. board
      (C.D 18000)
£9132 $16621   (26-May-92 JOY.T39/R) Still life (50x60cm-20x24in) s. canvasboard
      (C.D 20000)
£12000 $21240   (6-Nov-91 SY.T46/R) Still life with pink roses and apples
      (76x51cm-30x20in) s. panel (C.D 24000)
£12626 $22096   (25-Sep-91 EA.M510 a) Still life with two bouquets and fruit s. masonite
      (C.D 25000)
£13242 $24100   (26-May-92 JOY.T25/R) Red cloth and yellow flowers (118x118cm-46x46in) s.
      board (C.D 29000)
£547   *$974*   *(26-Nov-91 JOY.T5/R) Summer landscape (34x44cm-13x17in) s. W/C (C.D 1100)*
£846   *$1505*   *(26-Nov-91 JOY.T186/R) Autumn landscape (22x28cm-9x11in) s. W/C*
      (C.D 1700)

ROBERTSON, Andrew (1777-1845) British
£1500 $2640   (9-Apr-92 S194/R) Portrait of lady, said to be Mary Brightwell, nee
      Wilkin (8x?cm-3x?in) min. gilt-metal frame rec.
£2100 $3612   (4-Mar-92 C74/R) Joseph Gwilt, holding plans of church (15x?cm-6x?in)
      min.mono.d.1810 gilt mount wood gesso frame rec

ROBERTSON, Charles (19th C) British
£620 $1085   (18-Feb-92 ACA837) Summer showers, Lyme Regis (30x46cm-12x18in) s.d.1888
      W/C
£750 $1335   (27-Nov-91 C241) Portrait of gentleman in coat, waistcoat and cravat
      (7x?cm-3x?in) min. gold frame oval hair verso
£1800 $3222   (11-Nov-91 PH165/R) Alleyway in Cairo (35x25cm-14x10in) s. W/C

ROBERTSON, Christina (19th C) British
£900   *$1647*   *(2-Jun-92 S709) Mother and child seated (13x?cm-5x?in) min.init.d.1836*
      arched ormolu frame

ROBERTSON, David T (1880-?) British
£600 $1008   (13-Aug-91 AG150) Sheep grazing by moorland stream (37x45cm-15x18in) s. W/C
£760 $1383   (10-Dec-91 AG157/R) Ploughman and team (33x52cm-13x20in) s. W/C
£950 $1729   (10-Dec-91 AG162) Sheep sheltering in byre during snow storm (20x74cm-8x29in) s. W/C

ROBERTSON, Henry (?) ?
£520 $993   (1-Jul-92 B98) Sheep by a tree (17x22cm-7x9in) mono. W/C

ROBERTSON, James D (?) British
£800 $1456   (29-May-92 PHG113) Landscape, evening (79x94cm-31x37in) s.

ROBERTSON, Percy (1868-?) British
£1676 $3000   (13-Nov-91 B.SF2346/R) High Holbord, London (18x30cm-7x12in) s.d.1903 W/ gouache

ROBERTSON, Suze (1856-1922) Dutch
£765 $1361   (30-Oct-91 CH.AM120) Farms and trees (23x37cm-9x15in) s. panel (D.FL 2500)
£1064 $1851   (17-Sep-91 CH.AM286/R) Binnenplaats (35x44cm-14x17in) s. panel (D.FL 3500)
£1080 $1890   (18-Feb-92 CH.AM112 e) Hanna (71x64cm-28x25in) s. (D.FL 3500)
£1284 $2273   (5-Nov-91 SY.AM185/R) Milk for cat (25x20cm-10x8in) s. panel (D.FL 4200)

ROBERTSON, Tom (1850-1947) British
£750 $1335   (28-Apr-92 S215/R) The City of Dreams (91x152cm-36x60in) s. s.i.stretcher

ROBERTSON, Walford Graham (1867-1948) British
£1200 $2088   (19-Sep-91 B45/R) Young woman seated at table (81x99cm-32x39in) s.d.1912

ROBERTY, G (19/20th C) ?
£1775 $3230   (25-May-92 ARC.P56 b) Jeune femme au bord d'une riviere (81x59cm-32x23in) s.d.1886 (F.FR 17500)

ROBIE, Jean Baptiste (1821-1910) Belgian
£17442 $30000   (16-Oct-91 CH.NY211/R) Still life with roses on a mossy bank (70x51cm-28x20in) s. panel
£28249 $50000   (6-Nov-91 D.NY19/R) Floral still life with apple blossoms, roses and viburnum in glen (100x76cm-39x30in) s.d.1867

ROBINET, Gustave Paul (younger) (1877-?) French
£1566 $2771   (22-Apr-92 ZZ.F138) Effets de Printemps, pres de Bonevoit (43x60cm-17x24in) s. (F.FR 15500)

ROBINS, Thomas Sewell (1814-1880) British
£440 $840   (16-Jul-92 S118) Shipping choppy seas (16x24cm-6x9in) W/C over pencil htd W/C
£500 $895   (11-Nov-91 PH144/R) Off the Dutch coast (17x35cm-7x14in) init.d.70 W/C
£520 $874   (15-Aug-91 B244) Sailing vessels in stormy seas (32x55cm-13x22in) s. W/C
£600 $1032   (4-Mar-92 DR79) Continental river landscape with sailing barges and church (26x36cm-10x14in) init.d.56 W/C
£800 $1368   (12-Mar-92 CSK53/R) On the Rhine, Cologne (36x53cm-14x21in) init.i.indis.d.1860 W/C htd.white
£1150 $2013   (17-Feb-92 HS191/R) Fishing boats outside harbour, with town in distance (35x50cm-14x20in) s.d.1851
£2310 $4412   (16-Jul-92 S121/R) On the Medway near Chatham Dockyard, Kent (18x25cm-7x10in) W/C over pencil htd bodycol
£2600 $4654   (14-Nov-91 S149/R) Fishing boats off the Needles (37x53cm-15x21in) s.d.1856 W/C over pencil htd.bodycol

ROBINS, Thomas Sewell (circle) (1814-1880) British
£1050 $1943   (11-Jun-92 CSK66) Fishing lugger approching Dutch port (38x53cm-15x21in) pencil W/C htd white

ROBINSON, Albert Henry (1881-1956) Canadian
£2500 $4425   (6-Nov-91 SY.T17/R) Cacouna (22x27cm-9x11in) s. panel (C.D 5000)
£2968 $5402   (26-May-92 JOY.T155/R) Noontime, Cacouna (21x26cm-8x10in) s.d.1921 panel (C.D 6500)
£3196 $5849   (14-May-92 SY.T67/R) Moonlight in basin, Louise Basin, Quebec City (33x40cm-13x16in) s. (C.D 7000)
£4566 $8311   (26-May-92 JOY.T235/R) Quebec harbour (28x32cm-11x13in) s.d.24 panel (C.D 10000)
£25571 $46539   (26-May-92 JOY.T100 h) Snow storm, Westmount (69x83cm-27x33in) s.d.1923 (C.D 56000)
£35000 $61950   (6-Nov-91 SY.T185/R) Murray River Valley (67x83cm-26x33in) s.d.1927 i.verso (C.D 70000)

ROBINSON, Annie Louisa see SWYNNERTON, Annie

ROBINSON, Chas Dorman (1847-1933) American
£474 $900   (24-Jun-92 B.SF6259/R) Cabin amongst Redwoods (61x46cm-24x18in) s.
£4474 $8500   (24-Jun-92 B.SF6288/R) Ships off Alcatraz (41x56cm-16x22in) s.
£4737 $9000   (24-Jun-92 B.SF6255/R) Yosemite (56x71cm-22x28in) s.d.1909

ROBINSON, Frederick Cayley (1862-1927) British
£850 $1547   (12-Dec-91 CSK43/R) Barbara reclining (32x66cm-13x26in) pastel chl.

ROBINSON, Hal (20th C) American
£506 $900   (26-Jan-92 LIT.L81) Wooded landscape with melting snow (46x30cm-18x12in) s.
£1064 $2000   (18-Dec-91 SY.NY224/R) Moonlit winter landscape (63x76cm-25x30in) s.

ROBINSON, P (?) British
£964 $1638   (23-Oct-91 EA.M483) Standing maiden in Egyptian dress (91x61cm-36x24in) s. (C.D 1850)

ROBINSON, Theodore (1852-1896) American
£2500 $4500   (24-Nov-91 JRB.C52/R) The bridge (13x20cm-5x8in) s. panel
£2869 $5250   (16-May-92 HG.C151/R) Brittany farm (23x33cm-9x13in) s.
£3801 $6500   (11-Mar-92 SY.NY50/R) Young man with scythe (26x16cm-10x6in) s.d.77 W/C panel
£3801 $6500   (11-Mar-92 SY.NY49/R) Nantucket windmill (18x25cm-7x10in) s.i. W/C

ROBINSON, Thomas (?-1810) British
£585 $1100   (18-Dec-91 SY.NY13/R) Landscape with cows by the shore (41x64cm-16x25in)

ROBINSON, William Heath (1872-1944) British
£440 $757   (10-Oct-91 L138) Motley's the only wear (20x15cm-8x6in) s.d.1916 ink wash
£600 $1092   (11-Dec-91 CSK41) The Little Old Cupid (25x18cm-10x7in) init. pen
£700 $1337   (1-Jul-92 B163/R) The seperation of England from France in prehistoric times (37x26cm-15x10in) s.i. pen monochrome
£720 $1246   (25-Mar-92 PHI506/R) The autograph album (40x29cm-16x11in) s.i. pen W/C
£1100 $2101   (1-Jul-92 B149/R) How to black-out (41x33cm-16x13in) s.i. pen monochrome
£1200 $2304   (10-Jul-92 CSK58/R) Curdling milk of human kindness on Christmas Eve (43x33cm-17x13in) s.i. pen col.pencil
£1500 $2880   (10-Jul-92 CSK60/R) Stand by everbody, for Big Ben and Weather report (41x30cm-16x12in) s.i. i.num.1672 verso pen wash
£2000 $3640   (11-Dec-91 CSK109/R) Interesting sidelights on the Wig Industry (41x30cm-16x12in) s.i. pencil ink wash

ROBINSON, William S (1861-?) American
£778 $1400   (22-Nov-91 S.BM187/R) Boats at pier, Gloucester (30x41cm-12x16in) s. i.verso board

ROBINSON, William T (1852-?) American
£893 $1500   (14-Aug-91 B.P159/R) Barnyard scene (18x25cm-7x10in) s.

ROBJENT, Richard (1937-) British?
£1000 $1750   (25-Feb-92 C117/R) Golden Eagles in Highlands (56x76cm-22x30in) s.d.1981 pencil W/C htd white
£2200 $3850   (25-Feb-92 C145/R) Blackgame at Lek (30x41cm-12x16in) s. W/C bodycol

ROBSON, Forster (19/20th C) British
£480 $869   (19-May-92 SWS426) April day, Shere Heath, Surrey (33x51cm-13x20in) s. W/C pencil

ROBSON, George Fennel (1788-1833) British
£450 $801   (27-Apr-92 PHB242) Ben Venu and Loch Ackray (29x43cm-11x17in) i.d.1811 verso pencil W/C
£620 $1184   (1-Jul-92 B3/R) Cattle by lake with mountains beyond (22x38cm-9x15in) W/C

ROBUSTI see TINTORETTO

ROCA SANS (20th C) Spanish?
£498 $862   (26-Mar-92 DUR.M956/R) Quinta Avenida, Nueva York (80x100cm-31x39in) s. (S.P 90000)

ROCA, Josep (1928-) Spanish
£663 $1246   (3-Jan-92 DUR.M48/R) Composicion (40x55cm-16x22in) s.d.58 mixed media canvas (S.P 120000)

ROCCA, G della (1788-1858) Italian
£3685 $6706   (12-Dec-91 F.M92/R) Giochi innocenti (37x67cm-15x26in) s. (I.L 8000000)

ROCCA, Michele (1670-1751) Italian
£12170 $21420   (10-Apr-92 AT.P6/R) Le Bapteme du Christ (47x73cm-19x29in) (F.FR 120000)

ROCCA, Michele (circle) (1670-1751) Italian
£757 $1302   (16-Oct-91 AT.P17) La Charite (41x33cm-16x13in) (F.FR 7500)

ROCCA, Michele (style) (1670-1751) Italian
£3511 $6250   (22-Jan-92 SY.NY142/R) Diana. Venus (48x43cm-19x17in) panel pair

ROCCHI, Fortunato (1822-1909) Italian
£453 $838   (9-Jun-92 F.R48) Gregge nella campagna romana (40x80cm-16x31in) s. (I.L 1000000)

ROCCHI, Francesco de (1902-) Italian
£5561 $9898   (26-Nov-91 SY.MI150/R) Interno nel mio studio (90x70cm-35x28in) s.d.63
                           (I.L 12000000)

ROCHARD, Francois Theodore (1798-1858) French
£580 $1032   (29-Nov-91 T200/R) Portrait of Barry Maxwell Close, aged 10 years
                           (30x23cm-12x9in) s.d.1839
£680 $1190   (25-Feb-92 CSK48) Charles, 4th Duke of Richmond and Lennox K G
                           (7x?cm-3x?in) min. gilt frame with scrolling foliate oval
£1400 $2492   (29-Nov-91 T202/R) Portraits of Vere Henry Close, aged 9 and Sophia
                           Caroline, aged 5 (43x30cm-17x12in) s.d.1839 W/C
£1500 $2670   (29-Nov-91 T201/R) Mrs Robert Close and her youngest child Emily Louisa
                           (43x30cm-17x12in) s.d.1839 W/C

ROCHAT, Alexandre (1895-) Swiss
£730 $1307   (6-May-92 GD.B1066/R) Still life with fruit and china (64x48cm-25x19in)
                           s. W/C (S.FR 2000)
£784 $1333   (23-Oct-91 GD.B615) Still life of flowers with book and fruit
                           (70x50cm-28x20in) mono. W/C (S.FR 2000)

ROCHAT, Willy (1920-) Swiss
£720 $1303   (6-Dec-91 GL.P219/R) La Place du Tertre et le Sacre-Coeur
                           (73x92cm-29x36in) s. i.verso (F.FR 7000)
£2000 $3460   (24-Mar-92 C114/R) Montmartre, le Moulin de la Galette (55x38cm-22x15in)
                           s.
£2500 $4325   (24-Mar-92 C117/R) Place de Foire aux arbres bleus (53x81cm-21x32in) s.
£628 $1136   (6-Dec-91 GL.P2227) Paris, Rue de la Mairie (27x35cm-11x14in) s. i.verso
                           pastel (F.FR 6100)
£844 $1545   (17-May-92 T.B234) La fenetre ouverte (40x32cm-16x13in) s. pastel
                           (F.FR 8300)
£1029 $1862   (6-Dec-91 GL.P217) Fleurs du jardin (40x32cm-16x13in) s. i.verso pastel
                           (F.FR 10000)
£1961 $3510   (15-Nov-91 GK.Z5226 c/R) Cat by window with view of bridge across the
                           Seine (55x38cm-22x15in) s. pastel board (S.FR 5000)
£3137 $5616   (15-Nov-91 GK.Z5226 a/R) Pont de la Concorde (60x79cm-24x31in) s. pastel
                           (S.FR 8000)

ROCHE, Alexander (1863-1921) British
£780 $1388   (1-May-92 PHE11/R) Sunlit avenue (37x44cm-15x17in) s.

ROCHE, Camille (20th C) French
£937 $1639   (30-Mar-92 ZZ.F162) Le singe roux. Le singe assis (32x26cm-13x10in)
                           st.sig. crayon chk.chl. pair (F.FR 9000)

ROCHE, Graeme (?) ?
£1277 $2260   (26-Apr-92 SY.ME86/R) Study for Listener (49x135cm-19x53in) s. (A.D 3000)
£1447 $2561   (26-Apr-92 SY.ME143/R) Study for Masseur (59x109cm-23x43in) s. (A.D 3400)
£2254 $3763   (19-Aug-91 SY.ME143/R) White dove and deckchairs (101x136cm-40x54in) s.
                           (A.D 4800)

ROCHE, Maria la (1870-1952) Swiss
£588 $1053   (15-Nov-91 ZOF.Z1780/R) Baselbieter Juralandschaft (50x38cm-20x15in) s.
                           paper on canvas (S.FR 1500)

ROCHE, Sampson Towgood (1759-1847) Irish
£400 $700   (24-Feb-92 SY.J765/R) Portrait of gentleman, wearing blue coat, grey
                           waistcoat and white jabot (7x?cm-3x?in) min. s.d.1789 gilt frame glazed
                           verso hair init (SA.R 2000)
£500 $955   (30-Jun-92 CSK520/R) Lady seated on sofa in decollete dress with lace
                           collar (10x?cm-4x?in) min.s. oval
£1009 $1736   (7-Oct-91 CH.E403/R) Lady Gwendoline Spencer, lace neckline adorned with
                           pearls, hair upswept (7x?cm-3x?in) min. s.d.1780 i.verso gilt frame
                           oval (E.P 1100)

ROCHEGROSSE, Georges (1859-1938) French
£1120 $2072   (10-Jun-92 ZZ.F41) Les horreurs de la guerre (34x55cm-13x22in) s.d.1915
                           (F.FR 11000)

ROCHER, M (19/20th C) French
£1099 $2100   (16-Jul-92 SY.NY409/R) La Conciergerie (35x45cm-14x18in) indis.s.

ROCHER, Maurice (1918-) French
£1222 $2261   (13-Jun-92 AT.P47/R) Personnage (65x50cm-26x20in) s. s.d.1988verso
                           (F.FR 12000)
£1524 $2652   (15-Apr-92 PLF.P102) Femme rose (61x50cm-24x20in) s.d.1982verso
                           (F.FR 15000)

ROCHFORT, I D (19th C) British?
£550 $995   (18-May-92 HS385/R) Three hunters in stable - Jack Shepherd, Black Prince
                           and Sancho (57x83cm-22x33in) s.d.1887 i.verso

ROCHUSSEN, Charles (1814-1894) Dutch
£765 $1353   (5-Nov-91 SY.AM385) Jeanne of Arc with army, burning city beyond
                           (75x126cm-30x50in) init.d.78 (D.FL 2500)

ROCHUSSEN, Charles (1814-1894) Dutch-cont.
£979 $1732   (5-Nov-91 SY.AM370/R) Battle between Dutch line of battleship Mars and three English men-o-war (42x57cm-17x22in) mono.d.1861 (D.FL 3200)
£1529 $2722   (30-Oct-91 CH.AM50/R) Sportsmen resting in landscape (23x35cm-9x14in) s.d.40 (D.FL 5000)
£612 $1083   (5-Nov-91 SY.AM431) Winter landscape with soldiers near mill (25x20cm-10x8in) init.d.90 W/C (D.FL 2000)

ROCHUSSEN, Charles and LEICKERT, Charles (19th C) Dutch/Belgian
£9174 $16239   (5-Nov-91 SY.AM77/R) Winter landscape with skaters and horse-drawn sledge on frozen river (44x73cm-17x29in) s. panel (D.FL 30000)

ROCK, Geoffrey (1923-) Canadian
£1000 $1770   (6-Nov-91 SY.T204/R) Shell, Ardmore, B.C (49x74cm-19x29in) s. s.d.1989 verso board (C.D 2000)
£1000 $1770   (6-Nov-91 SY.T255) Girl on beach (49x75cm-19x30in) s. s.d.1982 verso board (C.D 2000)

ROCKBURNE, Dorothea (20th C) Canadian
£1086 $1900   (28-Feb-92 SY.NY345/R) Paper folded upon itself (76x102cm-30x40in) s.d.72 graphite folded paper

ROCKENSCHAUB, Gerwald (1952-) Austrian
£894 $1600   (9-May-92 CE.NY197/R) Untitled (45x45cm-18x18in) init.d.86verso acrylic
£1564 $2784   (31-Oct-91 D.V231/R) Untitled (35x35cm-14x14in) mono.d.84verso acrylic (A.S 32000)

ROCKLINE, Vera (1896-1934) American
£16566 $31144   (21-Dec-91 PSA.W18) Man with pipe (92x65cm-36x26in) s. (P.Z 320000000)

ROCKSTUHL, Alois Gustav (1798-1877) Russian
£400 $680   (22-Oct-91 CSK6/R) Young boy, in profile to right, wearing low-cut gown (6x?cm-2x?in) min. s.gilt-metal mount carved wood case oval
£1185 $2145   (21-May-92 SY.G41/R) Portrait of Maria Feodorovna consort of Emperor Alexander II (11x?cm-4x?in) min.s.d.1864 gilt metal frame after Winterhalter (S.FR 3200)

ROCKWELL, Norman (1894-1978) American
£1170 $2200   (18-Dec-91 SY.NY203/R) Young Thai girl (45x38cm-18x15in) init. board
£5212 $9539   (3-Jun-92 R.T96/R) On top of world, also known as Boy on Weathervane (26x20cm-10x8in) i. oil pencil canvasboard (C.D 11363)
£5495 $10000   (28-May-92 CH.NY268/R) The long trek home (45x71cm-18x28in) s.d.1915 oil en grisaille
£6593 $12000   (27-May-92 SY.NY124/R) Mighty proud (24x20cm-9x8in) init. paper
£7602 $13000   (12-Mar-92 CH.NY144/R) Midnight encounter (60x46cm-24x18in) s.d.1916 en grisaille
£13812 $25000   (5-Dec-91 SY.NY116/R) Budwine boy (70x63cm-28x25in) s.
£20468 $35000   (11-Mar-92 SY.NY113/R) Steamship comfort (76x66cm-30x26in) s.
£38462 $70000   (27-May-92 SY.NY122/R) Is he coming (79x69cm-31x27in) s.
£52486 $95000   (5-Dec-91 SY.NY117/R) The magician (74x51cm-29x20in) s.i.
£55249 $100000   (6-Dec-91 CH.NY249/R) Merry Christmas - Concert Trio (102x76cm-40x30in) s.
£61404 $105000   (11-Mar-92 SY.NY112/R) Meeting clown (69x61cm-27x24in) s.
£1596 $3000   (18-Dec-91 SY.NY204/R) Study of an Arab (45x38cm-18x15in) init. oil chl. board
£3022 $5500   (13-Dec-91 DM.D2010/R) Image of boy and his future image as man punting football (43x36cm-17x14in) s. pencil

RODA, Leonardo (1868-1933) Italian
£908 $1688   (16-Jun-92 F.M47) Il Cervino (47x32cm-19x13in) s.d.1921 board (I.L 2000000)

RODAKOWSKI, Henryk (1823-1894) Polish
£1197 $2058   (20-Oct-91 UNI.W7) Releasing prisoners taken by the Tatars near Halicz (24x35cm-9x14in) W/C (P.Z 23000000)

RODCHENKO, Alexander (1891-1956) Russian
£40000 $69200   (25-Mar-92 S46/R) Composition (58x25cm-23x10in) s. panel

RODDE, Karl Gustav (1830-1906) German
£2456 $4421   (22-Nov-91 SA.A1618/R) River landscape near Hohen-Siegburg, Westfalen (51x71cm-20x28in) s. (DM 7000)

RODDE, Karl Gustav (attrib) (1830-1906) German
£1890 $3289   (18-Sep-91 N.M668/R) Italian coastal landscape with peasant girl on hilly path (70x100cm-28x39in) i. (DM 5500)

RODDE, Michel (1913-) French
£873 $1571   (19-Nov-91 FB.P90/R) Composition au pichet noir (50x73cm-20x29in) s. (F.FR 8500)

RODE, Christian Bernhard (1727-1797) German
£447 $786   (11-Apr-92 AW.H386/R) Reading donkey with scholars and allegory of happiness (30x22cm-12x9in) ochre (DM 1300)

RODECK, Karl (1841-1909) Dutch
£1095 $1917   (3-Apr-92 BM.B698/R) Wooded landscape, evening (38x55cm-15x22in) s.
i.verso (DM 3100)

RODER, Elselina (1820-1900) Dutch
£1500 $2595   (4-Oct-91 C75/R) Irises on marble slab (26x34cm-10x13in) s. panel

RODHE, Lennart (1916-) Swedish
£11353 $20549   (19-May-92 AB.S5310/R) The garden (57x117cm-22x46in) s. d.1958-59verso
tempera panel (S.KR 120000)
£617   *$1129*   *(13-May-92 BU.S171/R) Block drawing (17x19cm-7x7in) mono.d.54 Indian ink
(S.KR 6500)*

RODIN, Auguste (1840-1917) French
£383 $700   (6-Jun-92 LAE.L41/R) Dancing woman (46x30cm-18x12in) s. pencil wash
£546 $1000   (6-Jun-92 LAE.L40/R) Dancing figure with arm raised (48x33cm-19x13in) s.
pencil wash
£578 $1000   (29-Mar-92 MY.F71/R) The ballet (28x18cm-11x7in) s. pencil W/C board
£628 $1150   (6-Jun-92 LAE.L42/R) Cambodian dancer (46x30cm-18x12in) s. pencil wash
£809 $1400   (29-Mar-92 MY.F67/R) Lady in blue (33x23cm-13x9in) s. pencil W/C board
£809 $1400   (29-Mar-92 MY.F68/R) Nude (33x25cm-13x10in) s. pencil W/C board
£962 $1827   (25-Jun-92 GK.B640/R) Female nude kneeling (31x46cm-12x18in) i. brush over
pencil (S.FR 2500)
£1300 $2353   (2-Dec-91 CSK10/R) Etudes de tete (31x20cm-12x8in) s. pencil double-sided
£4096 $7454   (30-May-92 VG.B107/R) La vague (20x31cm-8x12in) s.i. pencil wash paper on
board (DM 12000)
£4887 $8845   (4-Dec-91 KH.K144/R) Seated nude woman (32x25cm-13x10in) s. W/C
(D.KR 54000)
£5000 $9500   (25-Jun-92 GK.B637/R) Two female nudes kneeling (44x32cm-17x13in) brush
over pencil (S.FR 13000)
£5119 $9266   (22-May-92 GB.B6033/R) Bathers (38x26cm-15x10in) s. W/C over pencil
(DM 15000)
£9040   *$16000*   (7-Nov-91 SY.NY107/R) Tete Casquee de profil - buste de Bellone
(12x10cm-5x4in) pen wash gouache over pencil paper on board
£14124   *$25000*   (7-Nov-91 SY.NY105/R) Three male figures (19x11cm-7x4in) i. pen sepia ink
wash pencil paper on board
£15254   *$27000*   (7-Nov-91 SY.NY106/R) Tete d'expression (15x10cm-6x4in) wash gouache over
pencil paper on board
£19209   *$34000*   (7-Nov-91 SY.NY104/R) Jeune femme et enfant (15x10cm-6x4in) pen wash
gouache over pencil chl paper on board
£51913   *$95000*   (13-May-92 SY.NY204/R) Le cercle des amours (19x14cm-7x6in) gouache
pencil pen

RODIN, Auguste (attrib) (1840-1917) French
£980 $1667   (23-Oct-91 GD.B1470) Seated female nude (19x24cm-7x9in) i. pencil W/C
(S.FR 2500)

RODO-BOULANGER, Graciela (20th C) Bolivian
£2471 $4250   (12-Oct-91 SY.NY207/R) El paso volante (61x46cm-24x18in) s.d.1967
£3779 $6500   (12-Oct-91 SY.NY206/R) Le vol (74x60cm-29x24in) s. i.verso

RODRIGO DE OSONA (elder-circle) (fl.1476-1484) Spanish
£4500 $8190   (29-May-92 C302/R) Coronation of the Virgin (52x74cm-20x29in) fragment
panel

RODRIGUEZ DE LOSADA, J M (c.1825-?) Spanish
£500 $875   (27-Feb-92 B42) The Penitent Magdalen (80x53cm-31x21in) s.d.1891 board

RODRIGUEZ LOSADA, Jose Maria (1826-1896) Spanish
£984 $1673   (23-Oct-91 DUR.M507/R) Guitarrista (83x61cm-33x24in) s. (S.P 180000)
£984 $1673   (23-Oct-91 DUR.M506/R) Joven (83x62cm-33x24in) s. (S.P 180000)

RODRIGUEZ SAN CLEMENT, Francisco (1861-1956) Spanish
£800 $1432   (5-May-92 SWS448/R) A Spanish dancer (64x79cm-25x31in) s.
£967 $1721   (21-Jan-92 DUR.M797/R) Bailarina de blanco (55x46cm-22x18in) s.
(S.P 175000)
£1150 $2001   (15-Apr-92 PHL159/R) Spanish dancer (72x60cm-28x24in) s.
£1207 $2076   (7-Oct-91 CSC.P143) Flamenco (61x50cm-24x20in) s. (F.FR 12000)
£1230 $2091   (22-Oct-91 DUR.M44/R) Bailarina (56x46cm-22x18in) s. (S.P 225000)
£1509 $2596   (7-Oct-91 CSC.P142/R) Espagnole (73x60cm-29x24in) s. (F.FR 15000)
£1779 $3238   (26-May-92 DUR.M141/R) Banistas (64x80cm-25x31in) s. (S.P 325000)
£1924 $3386   (9-Apr-92 ANS.M110/R) Dama con mantilla, en los toros (73x60cm-29x24in)
s. (S.P 350000)
£2189 $3984   (11-Dec-91 FER.M147/R) Tocando los palillos (81x65cm-32x26in) s. i.verso
(S.P 400000)
£2323 $3949   (22-Oct-91 DUR.M45/R) Belleza dormida (60x72cm-24x28in) s. (S.P 425000)

RODRIGUEZ, C N (19th C) ?
£1105 $2000   (19-May-92 SY.NY125/R) La batalla (36x47cm-14x19in) s.d.1850 panel

RODRIGUEZ, Dionisio (20th C) Spanish
£821 $1494   (27-May-92 DUR.M328/R) El perro blanco (116x89cm-46x35in) s. (S.P 150000)

RODRIGUEZ, Guillermo (20th C) Uruguayan?
£2312 $4000   (30-Sep-91 GC.M24) Ombu (75x75cm-30x30in) s.

RODRIGUEZ, Mariano (1912-1990) Cuban
£2210 $4000   *(19-May-92 SY.NY165/R) Hombre con sombrero (70x55cm-28x22in) s.d.48 W/C*
£7735 $14000   *(19-May-92 SY.NY164/R) Mujer con peces (90x72cm-35x28in) s.d.49 gouache*

RODVOGIN, Harris (20th C) American
£576 $1100   (3-Jul-92 S.W3813) Marilyn Monroe (76x102cm-30x40in) s.verso canvas on
                    panel

ROE, Clarence (?-1909) British
£459 $839   (1-Jun-92 W.T1342/R) Highland landscape at dusk (61x76cm-24x30in) s.
                    (C.D 1000)

ROE, Colin Graeme see   GRAEME, Colin

ROE, Robert Ernest (19th C) British
£750 $1328   (7-Nov-91 PHC745) Pool of London (61x107cm-24x42in) s.

ROE, Walter Herbert (fl.1882-1893) British
£1762 $3137   (26-Nov-91 J.M239) Vegetable pickers (91x121cm-36x48in) s.d.1889 verso
                    (A.D 4000)
£2400 $4104   (12-Mar-92 CSK270/R) The trysting place (127x71cm-50x28in) s.d.1901

ROED, Jorgen (1808-1888) Danish
£528 $887   (27-Aug-91 RAS.K371/R) Portrait of young girl (74x61cm-29x24in)
                    (D.KR 6000)
£3175 $5651   (28-Apr-92 RAS.K76/R) Achilleus visting Lycomedes' daughters
                    (73x60cm-29x24in) (D.KR 36000)
£3607 $6420   (25-Nov-91 BU.K10/R) A fisherman's family (63x79cm-25x31in) s.d.1857
                    (D.KR 40000)

ROED, Jorgen (attrib) (1808-1888) Danish
£2527 $4549   (19-Nov-91 RAS.K20/R) Bouquet of peonies, tulips and other flowers in
                    vase (35x29cm-14x11in) (D.KR 28000)

ROEDE, Jan (20th C) ?
£988 $1798   (11-Dec-91 CH.AM127) Composition with figures (114x146cm-45x57in) s.
                    (D.FL 3200)
£1061 $1920   (21-May-92 SY.AM324/R) Untitled (45x60cm-18x24in) s. (D.FL 3500)
£1758 $3181   (21-May-92 SY.AM186/R) Untitled (45x60cm-18x24in) s. (D.FL 5800)

ROEDERSTEIN, Ottilie Wilhelmine (1859-1937) Swiss
£588 $1053   (15-Nov-91 GK.Z5346) The model, portrait of woman with red hair
                    (67x47cm-26x19in) d.81 s.verso board (S.FR 1500)
£1065 $1980   (19-Jun-92 ZOF.Z2055/R) The first spring flowers (47x36cm-19x14in) d.1927
                    (S.FR 2800)

ROEDIG, Johann Christian (1751-1802) Dutch
£14365 $26000   (21-May-92 CH.NY43/R) Mixed flowers in glass vase on stone ledge
                    (91x75cm-36x30in) after Rachel Ruysch

ROEGGE, Wilhelm (snr) (1829-1908) German
£1742 $3171   (11-Dec-91 N.M570/R) Two girls in costume drinking beer (29x23cm-11x9in)
                    mono. i.stretcher (DM 5000)

ROEKENS, Paulette van (19/20th C) ?
£1023 $1750   (12-Mar-92 MFA.C198) Newport street scene (38x51cm-15x20in) s.

ROELOFS, Albert (1877-1920) Dutch
£2273 $4023   (22-Apr-92 CH.AM10) Guitaarspeelster (19x14cm-7x6in) s.d.1914 indist.i.
                    panel (D.FL 7500)
£2749 $5031   (2-Jun-92 FN.S2726/R) Young girl in dressing room with mirror
                    (37x27cm-15x11in) s. canvas on panel (DM 8000)

ROELOFS, Willem (1822-1897) Dutch
£745 $1289   (24-Mar-92 VN.R79/R) Drover with wading cattle (30x47cm-12x19in) s. board
                    (D.FL 2400)
£795 $1407   (5-Nov-91 SY.AM415) Wooded landscape with cattle grazing (18x25cm-7x10in)
                    s.i. panel (D.FL 2600)
£1170 $1988   (22-Oct-91 C.A907) Farm in Carlshaven (26x36cm-10x14in) s. panel
                    (B.FR 70000)
£1212 $2145   (22-Apr-92 CH.AM66) Cows in a meadow along a river (12x27cm-5x11in) s.i.
                    canvas laid down on panel (D.FL 4000)
£2630 $4655   (5-Nov-91 SY.AM141/R) View of river (30x44cm-12x17in) s. (D.FL 8600)
£2752 $4899   (30-Oct-91 CH.AM277/R) Polder landscape with farms (30x45cm-12x18in) s.
                    canvas on panel (D.FL 9000)
£3670 $6532   (30-Oct-91 CH.AM207/R) La mare aux vaches (44x70cm-17x28in) s.
                    (D.FL 12000)
£4893 $8709   (30-Oct-91 CH.AM275) Cows in meadow near trees (20x31cm-8x12in) s. panel
                    (D.FL 16000)
£11621 $20220   (14-Apr-92 SY.AM117/R) Grazing cattle by creek (45x70cm-18x28in) s.
                    (D.FL 38000)
£1223 $2128   (14-Apr-92 SY.AM321/R) The drawbridge (37x26cm-15x10in) s. W/C
                    (D.FL 4000)

ROEPEL, Coenraet (1678-1748) Dutch
£2500 $4800   (8-Jul-92 S159/R) Still life of fruit and flowers upon ornate fountain
     (151x123cm-59x48in) s.
£20112 $36000   (16-Jan-92 CH.NY74/R) Mixed flowers in glass vase on stone ledge
     (40x33cm-16x13in) bears sig.

ROERICH, Nikolai Konstantinovitch (1874-1947) American/Russian
£2200 $3916   (28-Nov-91 S436/R) Gifts (34x46cm-13x18in) init.i. tempera htd white
     paper on cardboard
£1309   *$2330*   *(31-Oct-91 LD.P146/R) Vue d'un village en Asie Centrale (31x45cm-12x18in)*
     mono. pastel htd.gouache (F.FR 13000)
£1400 $2604   (16-Jun-92 S88/R) The path, Putivl (17x21cm-7x8in) init. gouache over
     pencil

ROESCH, Kurt (1905-) American
£1040 $1800   (6-Sep-91 S.BM316/R) The star gazer (119x84cm-47x33in) s.

ROESEN, Severin (fl.1848-1871) German/American
£7143 $12500   (25-Sep-91 SY.NY6/R) Still life with strawberries (41x51cm-16x20in) s.
£10734 $19000   (13-Feb-92 S.W2820/R) Still life with mixed fruits, pilsner, and bird's
     nest (66x102cm-26x40in)
£18713 $32000   (12-Mar-92 CH.NY12/R) Still life with fruit and glass of wine
     (76x63cm-30x25in) bears sig. oval
£30387 $55000   (5-Dec-91 SY.NY1/R) Vase of flowers with bird's nest (76x63cm-30x25in) s.

ROESEN, Severin (attrib) (fl.1848-1871) German/American
£1864 $3300   (13-Feb-92 S.W2819/R) Still life of fruit with champagne flute
     (74x99cm-29x39in)

ROESLER, Ettore Franz see FRANZ, Ettore Roesler

ROESSINGH, Louis Albert (1873-1951) Dutch/Belgian
£751 $1321   (7-Apr-92 C.A204) Shepherd with his flock (29x46cm-11x18in) s.
     (B.FR 45000)
£1084 $1908   (7-Apr-92 C.A202/R) Storm over a cornfield (78x107cm-31x42in) s.d.1907
     (B.FR 65000)
£1711 $3097   (3-Dec-91 C.A267/R) Drenthe landscape (70x97cm-28x38in) s. (B.FR 100000)
£1882 $3406   (3-Dec-91 C.A266/R) Children playing on a heath (80x95cm-31x37in)
     s.d.1900 (B.FR 110000)
£2335 $4110   (7-Apr-92 C.A203) Shepherd with his flock (80x90cm-31x35in) s.
     (B.FR 140000)
£3336 $5872   (7-Apr-92 C.A201/R) Man with goats (97x130cm-38x51in) s. panel
     (B.FR 200000)

ROESSLER, Georg (1861-1925) German
£720 $1318   (5-Feb-92 KH.K109) Young woman (75x50cm-30x20in) s. (D.KR 8000)

ROESSLER, W (20th C) German
£748 $1338   (16-Jan-92 D.V55/R) Portrait of peasant with pipe (18x14cm-7x6in) s.i.
     panel (A.S 15000)

ROESTRATEN, Pieter Gerritsz van (1630-1700) Dutch
£5200 $9256   (1-Nov-91 C144/R) Ornate silver ewer with silver-gilt beaker, grapes and
     parakeet on marble ledge (76x62cm-30x24in) s.
£8980 $15894   (10-Feb-92 GL.P24/R) Nature morte au service a the (28x39cm-11x15in)
     (F.FR 88000)

ROESTRATEN, Pieter Gerritsz van (style) (1630-1700) Dutch
£1000 $1750   (27-Feb-92 CSK170/R) A vanitas still life with a skull, quill, and other
     objects on a table (49x80cm-19x31in) panel
£1800 $3456   (9-Jul-92 CSK285) Gilded nautilus cup by quiver, book, coins and other
     objects (36x48cm-14x19in) bears sig. panel
£3400 $6528   (9-Jul-92 B200/R) Still life of Chinese bowl, orange in roemer, spoon,
     strawberries on stone ledge (30x35cm-12x14in) init.
£5200 $9100   (1-Apr-92 S63/R) Still life of teapot, cups and saucers, vase, playing
     cards, on stone ledge (76x62cm-30x24in) bears init.
£6000 $10920   (11-Dec-91 S201/R) Still life of objects and books on table draped with
     carpet (84x104cm-33x41in)

ROETTIERS, Francois (18th C) French
£458   *$838*   *(15-May-92 AT.P205) Bacchanale (18x16cm-7x6in) s. pen (F.FR 4500)*

ROFFE, William John (fl.1845-1889) British
£683 $1229   (19-Nov-91 FP.M215/R) Coastal village view at low tide (51x76cm-20x30in)
     s. (C.D 1400)

ROFFIAEN, Jean Francois (1820-1898) Belgian
£2400 $4464   (17-Jun-92 S280/R) Shepherd and cattle by lake in mountainous landscape
     (50x70cm-20x28in) s.d.1851 panel
£3311 $5993   (23-May-92 KV.L281/R) Lac de Gozau et le Glacier du Dachstein
     (48x80cm-19x31in) s.d.1876 (B.FR 200000)
£9000 $16740   (19-Jun-92 C42/R) Le Lac Wallenstadt (72x121cm-28x48in) s.d.1865

ROFFO, Sergio (20th C) American
£497   *$850*   *(18-Mar-92 GRO.B12/R) Beacon Hill (71x97cm-28x38in) s.d.1987 W/C*

ROGER, Emili Bosch (1894-1980) Spanish?
£7661 $13636   (29-Oct-91 BRO.B342/R) Vista de Paris, con el Sena y Notre Dame (81x100cm-32x39in) s.d.1953 (S.P 1400000)
£821 $1461   *(29-Oct-91 BRO.B280) Puerto de Barcelona (34x46cm-13x18in) s.d.1926 W/C (S.P 150000)*

ROGER, Suzanne (1898-1986) French
£515 $881   (18-Mar-92 LT.P67) La procession (33x46cm-13x18in) s. (F.FR 5000)
£3021 $5378   (28-Oct-91 GL.P205/R) La maison de banlieue (73x60cm-29x24in) s. (F.FR 30000)
£4290 $7508   (21-Feb-92 LC.P50) Nuages blancs (72x60cm-28x24in) s. (F.FR 42000)

ROGERS, Claude (1907-) British
£5000 $8650   (2-Oct-91 S191/R) Negress (61x45cm-24x18in) s.d.38

ROGERS, D (19th C) ?
£480 $850   (24-Apr-92 DOU.M3) American sailing ship Julia (41x36cm-16x14in)

ROGERS, Philip Hutchins (1794-1853) British
£1939 $3529   (27-May-92 D.V640/R) Cattle in wooded landscape (66x82cm-26x32in) s.d.1825 (A.S 40000)

ROGERS, William P (fl.1842-1872) British
£3200 $6112   (17-Jul-92 C177/R) Fair wind off Dover. Haybarge and other vessels in a breeze (49x75cm-19x30in) s. pair

ROGGE, Emy (1866-?) German
£653 $1214   (20-Jun-92 BM.B773/R) Farmhouse (63x74cm-25x29in) s. canvas on board (DM 1900)

ROGGEMAN, Fons (1939-) Belgian
£400 $688   *(12-Oct-91 KV.L251) Self-portrait (47x37cm-19x15in) s. chk (B.FR 24000)*

ROGHMAN, Roeland (1597-1686) Dutch
£1533 $2790   *(12-Dec-91 L.K461/R) Wooded landscape with figures (13x18cm-5x7in) s. pen wash (DM 4400)*

ROGIER, Camille (19th C) French
£2077 $3759   (22-May-92 BL.P55) Scene orientale (36x23cm-14x9in) s. (F.FR 20500)

ROGNONI, Franco (1913-) Italian
£1006 $1911   *(23-Jun-92 F.M1) Citta antica (68x48cm-27x19in) s. mixed media (I.L 2200000)*

ROHDE, Fredrik (1816-1886) Danish
£527 $944   (6-May-92 KH.K176) Cliff landscape (22x34cm-9x13in) (D.KR 6000)
£1610 $2930   (12-Dec-91 RAS.V769/R) View of Lykkeaaborg in Blekinge (45x60cm-18x24in) s.d.1859 (D.KR 18000)
£1762 $2996   (8-Aug-91 RAS.V984/R) Milkmaid and boy on path near mill and Joenstrup college, summer (53x59cm-21x23in) mono.d.1850 (D.KR 20000)

ROHDE, Lennart see RODHE, Lennart

ROHDEN, A de (19th C) ?
£1600 $2848   (27-Nov-91 S89/R) Madonna and Child (57x37cm-22x15in) s.d.1878 panel

ROHDEN, Franz von (1817-1903) Italian
£3200 $5696   (27-Nov-91 S88/R) Nativity (265x189cm-104x74in) s.d.1853

ROHL, Karl Peter (1890-1975) German
£922 $1677   *(30-May-92 VG.B913/R) Composition black-red-brown (63x47cm-25x19in) s.d.1919 indian ink brush (DM 2700)*
£956 $1739   *(30-May-92 VG.B914/R) Eruption (72x45cm-28x18in) s.d.1919 indian ink brush (DM 2800)*

ROHLFS, Adolf (19th C) German
£1271 $2162   (25-Oct-91 BM.B818/R) Otter with fish (26x37cm-10x15in) s. (DM 3700)

ROHLFS, Christian (1849-1938) German
£8070 $14526   (21-Nov-91 L.K425/R) Corn fields (37x55cm-15x22in) s. canvas on panel (DM 23000)
£8874 $16150   (30-May-92 VG.B217/R) Blue mountains (30x46cm-12x18in) mono tempera (DM 26000)
£12281 $22105   (22-Nov-91 SA.A393/R) Beach woods near Weimar in autumn (69x53cm-27x21in) s.i.d.1890 (DM 35000)
£12632 $22737   (21-Nov-91 L.K428/R) Lago Maggiore (24x33cm-9x13in) mono.d.32 W/C over chk (DM 36000)
£14035 $25263   (21-Nov-91 L.K427/R) The white bridge (39x57cm-15x22in) mono.d.1931 i.verso water tempera (DM 40000)
£17143 $30000   (25-Feb-92 CH.NY33/R) Kohlkopfe (50x100cm-20x39in) init.d.10
£18771 $34164   (30-May-92 VG.B271/R) Echeverie (70x51cm-28x20in) mono.d.1929 tempera (DM 55000)
£22184 $40375   (30-May-92 VG.B215/R) Nude boy reclining on blue cloth (32x42cm-13x17in) mono tempera board (DM 65000)
£28249 $50000   (7-Nov-91 SY.NY155/R) Weiblicher akt (70x45cm-28x18in) init.d.16

ROHLFS, Christian (1849-1938) German-cont.
£30928	$57216	(12-Jun-92 HN.H743/R) Red blossoms (76x54cm-30x21in) mono.d.1930 tempera (DM 90000)
£420	$726	(27-Mar-92 GRA.B2846/R) Elegisches Mannchen (13x4cm-5x2in) mono. bodycol linen (DM 1200)
£756	$1406	(20-Jun-92 BM.B1072/R) Reclining female nude (49x62cm-19x24in) bears mono chl pencil (DM 2200)
£877	$1579	(23-Nov-91 N.M68/R) Hansel and Gretel (26x21cm-10x8in) mono.d.1919 W/C pen (DM 2500)
£1031	$1907	(12-Jun-92 HN.H745/R) Expulsion from Paradise (13x32cm-5x13in) s. tempera indian ink over woodcut (DM 3000)
£1638	$2982	(30-May-92 VG.B919/R) Fir trees in the mountains (56x41cm-22x16in) mono.d.1921 W/C chk paper on board (DM 4800)
£2113	$3824	(3-Dec-91 FN.S1877/R) Wooded lake landscape (49x34cm-19x13in) s.d.1900 col.chk (DM 6000)
£3484	$6341	(13-Dec-91 BM.B852/R) Meetings (22x27cm-9x11in) mono.d.1919 pen W/C (DM 10000)
£4098	$7500	(14-May-92 SY.NY122/R) Pauliturm in Soest (30x21cm-12x8in) gouache
£5802	$10560	(26-May-92 KF.M1213/R) Passion flower (26x38cm-10x15in) mono.d.1935 col.chk (DM 17000)
£6701	$11660	(21-Sep-91 SA.A602/R) Passion flower (16x24cm-6x9in) mono.d.33 col.chk (DM 19500)
£9605	$17000	(6-Nov-91 CH.NY136/R) Blumenstrauss (64x51cm-25x20in) init.d.22 gouache W/C
£14334	$26089	(30-May-92 VG.B216/R) Ticino houses (54x75cm-21x30in) i.verso W/C gouache (DM 42000)
£14754	$27000	(14-May-92 SY.NY124/R) Kniender Akt (49x40cm-19x16in) init. W/C gouache
£18557	$34330	(12-Jun-92 HN.H742/R) View of Ascona and Lago Maggiore, evening (33x50cm-13x20in) mono.d.1927 tempera bodycol (DM 54000)
£20619	$35876	(21-Sep-91 SA.A600/R) Busy street in Hagen (66x50cm-26x20in) i.d.20 water-tempera chk (DM 60000)
£51195	$93174	(29-May-92 VG.B31/R) Red tulips in glass (70x50cm-28x20in) mono.d.1926 tempera indian ink brush (DM 150000)

ROHLING, Carl (1849-1922) German
£1025	$1793	(3-Apr-92 BM.B699) Friedrich der Grosse playing the flute (38x30cm-15x12in) s. i.verso (DM 2900)

ROHNER, Georges (1913-) French
£904	$1600	(5-Nov-91 CE.NY54/R) Chemins sous les arbres (65x100cm-26x39in) s.d.49
£1644	$2828	(4-Mar-92 AT.P197/R) Les livres (54x65cm-21x26in) s.d.52 (F.FR 16000)
£1696	$2917	(4-Mar-92 AT.P198) Barques en bord de mer (19x33cm-7x13in) s. (F.FR 16500)
£1850	$3182	(4-Mar-92 AT.P196) Port breton - maree basse (27x46cm-11x18in) s. (F.FR 18000)
£4620	$8316	(19-Nov-91 FB.P78/R) Nature morte a l'etoffe rouge, livre et verre (81x116cm-32x46in) s. (F.FR 45000)
£740	$1273	(4-Mar-92 AT.P86) Barques au port (37x54cm-15x21in) s. W/C (F.FR 7200)

ROHRHIRSCH, K (1875-1954) German
£753	$1296	(11-Oct-91 AW.H2904/R) Bavarian mail coach before farmhouse (8x10cm-3x4in) s.i. panel (DM 2200)

ROIG Y SOLER, Juan (19/20th C) Spanish
£876	$1558	(29-Oct-91 BRO.B321) Torres de defensa (26x17cm-10x7in) s. canvas on panel (S.P 160000)
£9953	$18712	(17-Dec-91 BRO.B434/R) Barcas en una playa (39x53cm-15x21in) s. (S.P 1800000)
£10229	$19231	(17-Dec-91 BRO.B368/R) Port de la la Selva (39x53cm-15x21in) s. (S.P 1850000)

ROJAS, Francisco (20th C) Spanish?
£495	$890	(20-Nov-91 DUR.M1090/R) Espantapajaros (73x54cm-29x21in) s.d.72 (S.P 90000)

ROJAY, G (?) ?
£1530	$2800	(3-Jun-92 D.NY83) Lady's lesson (51x38cm-20x15in) s.i.d.83 panel

ROJKA, Fritz (1878-1939) Austrian
£1220	$2122	(19-Sep-91 D.V74/R) The pearl necklace (70x57cm-28x22in) s. (A.S 25000)

ROLAND DE LA PORTE, Henri Horace (1724-1793) French
£38470	$70016	(28-May-92 F.M96/R) Natura morta con strumenti musicali e partitura (85x110cm-33x43in) (I.L 85000000)
£117318	$210000	(17-Jan-92 SY.NY90/R) Still lifes of peaches and bread; cherries and wine; jug, wine and fruit; pears, grapes and glass (36x44cm-14x17in) four

ROLAND DE LA PORTE, Henri Horace (attrib) (1724-1793) French
£2500	$4800	(7-Jul-92 PH172/R) Still life of dead chicken on stone ledge with pair songbirds on nail (43x38cm-17x15in)
£3200	$5696	(1-Nov-91 C66/R) Peaches in basket and slice of melon on marble ledge (30x40cm-12x16in)

ROLAND DE LA PORTE, Henri Horace (circle) (1724-1793) French
£2000 $3500   (25-Feb-92 PH106/R) Still life of endives and sausages on table with cauldron (32x37cm-13x15in) bears sig.d.1650 canvas on board

ROLAND DE LA PORTE, Henri Horace (style) (1724-1793) French
£3500 $6230   (1-Nov-91 C67/R) Peaches and grapes in basket with redcurrants and gooseberries (30x35cm-12x14in)

ROLANDO, Charles (1842-?) Australian
£3917 $6816   (16-Sep-91 CH.ME177/R) Merri Creek at flood (60x103cm-24x41in) s. s.i.d.1885 verso (A.D 8500)
£5128 $9128   (28-Apr-92 CH.ME264/R) Cattle in river landscape (80x142cm-31x56in) s.d.1888 (A.D 12000)
£10213 $18077   (26-Apr-92 SY.ME494/R) Fossicking for gold (90x70cm-35x28in) (A.D 24000)

ROLDAN, E (19th C) Spanish
£511 $915   (6-May-92 GD.B1072/R) Still life with roses, narcissi and field flowers (46x61cm-18x24in) s. panel (S.FR 1400)
£511 $915   (6-May-92 GD.B1073/R) Still life of tulips, roses, carnations and lilac (51x41cm-20x16in) s. panel (S.FR 1400)

ROLDAN, Enrique (19th C) Spanish?
£1108 $1940   (18-Feb-92 DUR.M15/R) Plaza sevillana y la Giralda al fondo (31x23cm-12x9in) s.d.87 panel (S.P 200000)
£3879 $6789   (18-Feb-92 DUR.M16/R) Patio de la Alhambra (55x42cm-22x17in) s.d.90 (S.P 700000)

ROLFE, Henry Leonidas (19th C) British
£1278 $2300   (19-Nov-91 JRL.S93/R) Trout (44x75cm-17x30in) s.d.1866 (A.D 2900)
£2800 $4984   (28-Apr-92 S237/R) Brown trout and salmon (45x76cm-18x30in) s.d.1866

ROLFE, Henry Leonidas (attrib) (19th C) British
£872 $1500   (14-Oct-91 H.C43/R) Pike and perch (41x61cm-16x24in)
£2200 $3740   (22-Oct-91 S256/R) Coarse fish on river bank (59x72cm-23x28in)

ROLFSEN, Alf (1895-1979) Norwegian
£921 $1713   (15-Jun-92 B.O130/R) Sketch for wall decoration at Ulleval Hospital (37x75cm-15x30in) s. (N.KR 10500)

ROLING, Gerard Victor Alphons (1904-) Dutch
£4242 $7679   (19-May-92 CH.AM63/R) Still life of flowers and fruit (50x60cm-20x24in) init.d.40 (D.FL 14000)

ROLL, Alfred Philippe (1846-1919) French
£3613 $6900   (30-Jun-92 PO.BA5) Cheval au repos (65x80cm-26x31in) s.

ROLLAN, Jordi (1940-) Spanish
£713 $1268   (26-Nov-91 BRO.B390) Figura femenina sentada (100x81cm-39x32in) s.d.86 (S.P 130000)
£719 $1351   (17-Dec-91 BRO.B423) Figura echada, en escorzo (73x92cm-29x36in) s. (S.P 130000)

ROLLAND, Antoni Vidal (1889-1970) ?
£987 $1756   (26-Nov-91 BRO.B367) Placida lectura (65x81cm-26x32in) s. (S.P 180000)

ROLLET, Louis (?) French
£630 $1096   (13-Apr-92 BG.P90) Paysage du Japon (61x50cm-24x20in) s. panel (F.FR 6200)
£597   *$1123*   *(16-Dec-91 BG.P86) Scene de procession (52x36cm-20x14in) s. W/C (F.FR 5800)*

ROLLIN, J (19th C) French
£902 $1633   (5-Dec-91 D.V107) Fjord landscape (82x130cm-32x51in) s. (A.S 18000)

ROLLINS, Tim (1955-) American
£719   *$1200*   *(25-Aug-91 JRB.C42) Study for America, 1988 (18x13cm-7x5in) mixed media*
£3911   *$7000*   *(6-May-92 CH.NY192/R) Red badge of Courage XIII (61x91cm-24x36in) s.d.86-87 oil acrylic col.chk collage bookpages*

ROLLINS, Warren E (1861-1962) American
£737 $1400   (28-Jun-92 LIT.L53) Adobe in mountain landscape (30x41cm-12x16in) s. board
£1053 $2000   (24-Jun-92 B.SF6399/R) Evening seascape (36x56cm-14x22in) s.
£1257 $2250   (13-Nov-91 B.SF2818/R) Screen door (71x44cm-28x17in) s.

ROLSHOVEN, Julius (1858-1930) American
£1330 $2500   (18-Dec-91 SY.NY132/R) Tunisian dancer (184x101cm-72x40in) s.i.

ROLT, David (?) British
£860 $1643   (20-Jul-92 WW1) Elms at Fresden, October 4th (69x46cm-27x18in) mono.d.71

ROM, Henrik (1887-1919) Norwegian
£657 $1143   (14-Sep-91 BU.O312) Landscape with trees, spring thaw (57x65cm-22x26in) s. (N.KR 7500)

ROM, Henrik (1887-1919) Norwegian-cont.
£886 $1612   (14-Dec-91 BU.O20/R) Boats by jetty (70x85cm-28x33in) s.d.1915
                     (N.KR 10000)

ROMAGNONI, Bepi (1930-1964) Italian
*£6898 $12348   (14-Nov-91 F.M98/R) Racconto (100x100cm-39x39in) s.d.63 s.i.d.verso
                     collage mixed media (I.L 15000000)*

ROMAKO, Anton (1832-1889) Austrian
£1988 $3538   (30-Oct-91 CH.AM177/R) Portrait of girl in red (40x32cm-16x13in) s.
                     (D.FL 6500)
£11047 $19000   (17-Oct-91 SY.NY265/R) Reaper (135x100cm-53x39in) s.i.

ROMAN SCHOOL (?) Italian
£2324 $4206   (3-Dec-91 SY.MI246/R) Testa della Vergine (53x37cm-21x15in) c.1600 oval
                     (I.L 5000000)
£2523 $4339   (16-Oct-91 AT.P23/R) Bergers coversant le long d'un chemin
                     (54x67cm-21x26in) c.1700 (F.FR 25000)
£2938 $5318   (18-May-92 SY.MI275/R) La Maddalena in un paesaggio visitata dagli angeli
                     (28x40cm-11x16in) c.1700 (I.L 6500000)
£6054 $10414   (16-Oct-91 AT.P25/R) Scene de port mediterraneen (31x50cm-12x20in)
                     (F.FR 60000)
£10142 $17850   (11-Apr-92 AT.P16/R) Paysages de riviere avec ruines (73x59cm-29x23in)
                     pair (F.FR 100000)
£22634 $40967   (5-Dec-91 SY.MO164/R) Vase de fleurs dans un paysage (91x65cm-36x26in)
                     c.1700 (F.FR 220000)
£32441 $55474   (20-Mar-92 ZZ.F21/R) Paire de bouquets de fleurs dans des vases en bronze
                     avec un decor du putti (128x97cm-50x38in) c.1700 pair (F.FR 315000)

ROMAN SCHOOL, 16th C Italian
£37293 $67500   (22-May-92 SY.NY9/R) Portraits of Empresses Agrippina and Poppaea Sabina
                     (131x103cm-52x41in) i. pair
£2000 $3840   (7-Jul-92 C11) Two putti (13x8cm-5x3in) chk after Michelangelo
*£2300 $4416   (6-Jul-92 S106/R) Studies after the Antique. Studies of frames and a
                     capital (24x38cm-9x15in) bears.i. pen over chk. double-sided*
*£4000 $7320   (15-May-92 TE286) Beheading of Saint John the Baptist (15x18cm-6x7in) pen
                     wash*

ROMAN SCHOOL, 17th C Italian
£1859 $3365   (4-Dec-91 CH.R17) Paesaggio con figure e animali presso una torre
                     (33x33cm-13x13in) copper (I.L 4000000)
£2000 $3560   (30-Oct-91 S124/R) St Gregory (66x51cm-26x20in)
£2405 $4186   (18-Sep-91 N.M444/R) Madonna with Child, nuns and putti
                     (168x125cm-66x49in) (DM 7000)
£2724 $4848   (28-Apr-92 F.R21/R) Giovane donna con cesto di fiori (77x62cm-30x24in)
                     (I.L 6000000)
£2760 $4748   (15-Oct-91 CH.R52/R) Natura morta con uva, mele ed un'anguria
                     (50x62cm-20x24in) (I.L 6000000)
£3058 $5688   (18-Jun-92 SY.MO298/R) Angelots et composition aux fleurs
                     (99x74cm-39x29in) (F.FR 30000)
£3200 $5600   (1-Apr-92 S148/R) Landscape with shepherd and shepherdess resting near
                     ruins (50x67cm-20x26in)
£4183 $7571   (5-Dec-91 F.M86) Paesaggio con barche e figure. Paesaggio con figure e
                     specchio d'acqua (50x68cm-20x27in) pair (I.L 9000000)
£4641 $8355   (19-Nov-91 F.R66/R) Paesaggio con ninfa e satiro (73x106cm-29x42in)
                     (I.L 10000000)
£8840 $16000   (22-May-92 SY.NY224/R) Alexander visiting philosopher Diogenes
                     (117x166cm-46x65in)
£9774 $18570   (26-Jun-92 AT.P63/R) Bouquet de fleurs, artichauts et corbeille de fruits
                     devant un paysage (69x86cm-27x34in) (F.FR 95000)
£10690 $19349   (5-Dec-91 F.M95/R) Natura morta con vaso metallico e fiori
                     (51x64cm-20x25in) (I.L 23000000)
£12532 $22557   (19-Nov-91 F.R68/R) Vaso di garofani. Vaso di fiori (55x46cm-22x18in)
                     pair (I.L 27000000)
£12899 $23476   (28-May-92 F.M23/R) La bottega del maniscalco (215x180cm-85x71in)
                     (I.L 28500000)
£19321 $33233   (15-Oct-91 CH.R32/R) Veduta della Piazza e del Palazzo del Quirinale
                     (94x132cm-37x52in) i. (I.L 42000000)
£25000 $48000   (8-Jul-92 S91/R) Still life of melons, plums, figs and apples
                     (53x93cm-21x37in)
£32000 $58240   (11-Dec-91 S47/R) Coronation of Virgin with Saint John Baptist, Saint
                     Benedict, Saint Romuald and Saint Andrew (257x178cm-101x70in)
£37709 $67500   (17-Jan-92 SY.NY183/R) Still lifes of fruits, exotic birds and other
                     ojbects in landscapes (198x96cm-78x38in) pair
£43000 $78260   (11-Dec-91 S221/R) Still life of quinces, pomegranates and grapes hanging
                     from stone ledge (100x75cm-39x30in)
*£2500 $4350   (13-Apr-92 S166) Portrait said to be Gianlorenzo Bernini (19x15cm-7x6in)
                     black red chk htd white*

ROMAN SCHOOL, 18th C Italian
£1816 $3232   (28-Apr-92 F.R18) Immacolata Concezione (40x30cm-16x12in) (I.L 4000000)
£2035 $3500   (10-Oct-91 SY.NY98/R) Landscape with the baptism of Christ, God the
                     father and Holy Ghost (46x62cm-18x24in)
£2238 $4006   (13-Nov-91 PIC.P121/R) Nature morte a la barate, chaudron garni de fruits
                     et d'ecrevisses (12x29cm-5x11in) (F.FR 22000)

ROMAN SCHOOL, 18th C Italian-cont.

£2778	$4972	(12-Nov-91 SY.AM114/R) Holy Family (62x49cm-24x19in) (D.FL 9000)
£2779	$4807	(25-Mar-92 CH.R2/R) Veduta del Colosseo (63x49cm-25x19in) (I.L 6000000)
£3040	$5562	(12-May-92 SY.AM80/R) Pyramus and Thisbe (77x63cm-30x25in) (D.FL 10000)
£3122	$5463	(30-Mar-92 ZZ.F50/R) Le Bapteme du Christ (38x27cm-15x11in) shaped panel (F.FR 30000)
£3177	$5750	(20-May-92 D.NY92) The Holy Family with St Ann and St John the Baptist (97x127cm-38x50in)
£3495	$6397	(12-May-92 SY.AM143/R) Cleopatra (161x113cm-63x44in) (D.FL 11500)
£4000	$7120	(1-Nov-91 S422/R) Portraits of young girls (55x45cm-22x18in) painted oval pair
£4180	$7273	(13-Sep-91 C40/R) Leda and swan (76x66cm-30x26in)
£6021	$10416	(25-Mar-92 CH.R13/R) Veduta del Campidoglio (137x86cm-54x34in) (I.L 13000000)
£6186	$10763	(18-Sep-91 N.M445/R) Servus Servorum (136x94cm-54x37in) (DM 18000)
£6320	$11565	(16-May-92 F.L77/R) Paesaggi con figure (65x85cm-26x33in) oval pair (S.FR 17000)
£6500	$11830	(11-Dec-91 S118/R) Portrait of gentleman, seated, wearing badge of French military Order (81x65cm-32x26in)
£6500	$11570	(30-Oct-91 S178/R) The Liberation of St Peter (97x136cm-38x54in)
£6507	$11778	(3-Dec-91 SY.MI224/R) Paesaggi con figure (72x99cm-28x39in) pair (I.L 14000000)
£6552	$11598	(6-Nov-91 LT.P37/R) Vue d'architecture en perspective avec promeneurs (88x126cm-35x50in) (F.FR 65000)
£7000	$13440	(8-Jul-92 S259/R) Landscape with Diana and Callisto (60x89cm-24x35in)
£7241	$13179	(28-May-92 F.M108/R) Veduta ideale della campagna romana con figure (230x140cm-91x55in) (I.L 16000000)
£7437	$13460	(5-Dec-91 F.M89/R) Capriccio architettonico con rovine e figure (124x93cm-49x37in) (I.L 16000000)
£8000	$14000	(1-Apr-92 S100/R) Landscape with figures on road near waterfall (90x116cm-35x46in)
£34916	$62500	(17-Jan-92 SY.NY83/R) Still life of peaches in a glass bowl and flowers and fruit (128x93cm-50x37in)
£6116	*$11376*	*(18-Jun-92 SY.MO238/R) Vues de Rome (35x48cm-14x19in) bears sig. gouache pair (F.FR 60000)*

ROMAN SCHOOL, 19th C Italian

£24022	$43000	(17-Jan-92 SY.NY68/R) View of St Peter's Cathedral, Rome (52x84cm-20x33in)

ROMANACH, Leopoldo (1862-1951) Peruvian

£4167	$7500	(18-Nov-91 SY.NY150/R) El Borracho (67x86cm-26x34in) s.
£8840	$16000	(19-May-92 SY.NY85/R) Cruzando el rio (34x68cm-13x27in) s.

ROMANELLI, Giovanni Francesco (1610-1662) Italian

£1067	$1900	(30-Oct-91 D.NY82) Sibyl (107x79cm-42x31in)
£22346	$40000	(16-Jan-92 CH.NY21/R) Angelica and Medoro (68cm-27ins circular)

ROMANELLI, Giovanni Francesco (style) (1610-1662) Italian

£742	$1314	(5-Nov-91 GF.L2415) Lot and his daughters (35x47cm-14x19in) (S.FR 1900)

ROMANI, Juana (1869-1924) Italian

£13000	$24180	(17-Jun-92 S576/R) Self-portrait (128x95cm-50x37in) s. panel

ROMANI, Romolo (1884-1916) Italian

£927	*$1650*	*(27-Nov-91 F.M245/R) Il mistero (62x47cm-24x19in) s.i. graphite (I.L 2000000)*

ROMANINO, Girolamo (1484-1562) Italian

£7437	$13460	(3-Dec-91 SY.MI265/R) Tre teste (50x39cm-20x15in) tempera on linen (I.L 16000000)

ROMANITCHEV, Alexandre (1919-1989) Russian

£542	$966	(25-Nov-91 ARC.P188/R) Femme en blanc (60x48cm-24x19in) s. (F.FR 5300)
£624	$1093	(5-Apr-92 ARC.P80/R) Portrait d'un cosaque (56x37cm-22x15in) s.verso (F.FR 6000)
£1760	$3134	(25-Nov-91 ARC.P192/R) Le ponton (37x44cm-15x17in) s. board (F.FR 17200)

ROMANO, Antoniazzo (15th C) Italian

£123170	$222937	(5-Dec-91 F.M149/R) Madonna col Bambino e San Giovannino (70x50cm-28x20in) panel (I.L 265000000)

ROMANO, Daniela (20th C) ?

£1023	$1851	(3-Dec-91 F.R144) La bottega dell'antiquario (40x50cm-16x20in) s.verso acrylic (I.L 2200000)

ROMANO, Giulio (after) (1499-1546) Italian

£2498	$4646	(16-Jun-92 SY.B199/R) The Emperor Constantinus defeating Maxentius at Milvius Bridge near Rome (78x132cm-31x52in) (B.FR 150000)

ROMANO, Giulio (circle) (1499-1546) Italian

£1700	*$3264*	*(7-Jul-92 C9/R) Apollo on his chariot (27x34cm-11x13in) chk pen*

ROMANO, Umberto (1905-) American
£833 $1500 (24-Nov-91 JRB.C144/R) Portrait of the artist's wife (109x137cm-43x54in)
s.
£4598 $8000 (15-Sep-91 JRB.C95/R) Hunter (183x102cm-72x40in) s.d.1928

ROMANOV, Nikolai (1957-) Russian
£635 $1130 (25-Nov-91 ARC.P133) Gourzouff (84x90cm-33x35in) s. (F.FR 6200)
£709 $1284 (20-May-92 ARC.P52/R) Sous l'ombrelle (80x60cm-31x24in) s. (F.FR 7000)
£737 $1312 (25-Nov-91 ARC.P132/R) Ville du Sud (88x99cm-35x39in) s. (F.FR 7200)

ROMANOV, Viatcheslav (1952-) Russian
£564 $1014 (27-Jan-92 ARC.P14/R) Arbre d'automne (62x81cm-24x32in) s.verso
(F.FR 5500)
£619 $1058 (13-Mar-92 ARC.P37/R) Le fond du jardin (80x60cm-31x24in) s.verso
(F.FR 6000)
£663 $1232 (17-Jun-92 ARC.P140/R) Le chemin en automne (47x42cm-19x17in) s.
(F.FR 6500)
£666 $1199 (27-Jan-92 ARC.P13/R) Le ajrdin Anglais (51x60cm-20x24in) s.verso
(F.FR 6500)
£670 $1146 (13-Mar-92 ARC.P39) Ete dans le village (47x66cm-19x26in) s. (F.FR 6500)
£768 $1383 (27-Jan-92 ARC.P16/R) La Palais Chinois, St Petersbourg (15x27cm-6x11in)
s.verso board (F.FR 7500)
£927 $1623 (24-Sep-91 ARC.P198/R) L'eglis pres de la riviere (41x59cm-16x23in) s.
(F.FR 9200)
£1340 $2292 (13-Mar-92 ARC.P38/R) Reflets en sous bois (62x81cm-24x32in) s.verso
(F.FR 13000)
£1547 $2785 (27-Jan-92 ARC.P12/R) La pointe de l'ile de la Cite (44x54cm-17x21in)
s.verso (F.FR 15100)
£2062 $3526 (13-Mar-92 ARC.P40/R) Le palais chinois a St Petersbourg
(60x100cm-24x39in) s. (F.FR 20000)
£2664 $4795 (27-Jan-92 ARC.P15/R) Paturage au printemps (90x120cm-35x47in) s.verso
(F.FR 26000)

ROMANOVSKY, Dimitri (20th C) American
£534 $950 (29-Nov-91 MFA.C142) Stroll in the garden (25x18cm-10x7in) s.d.1909 board

ROMANTIC SCHOOL, 19th C Dutch
£3666 $6709 (5-Jun-92 D.P3/R) Portrait de jeune femme au turban pres d'un piano-forte
(81x64cm-32x25in) rem.sig.d.1818 (F.FR 36000)

ROMBERG DE VAUCORBEIL, Maurice (1862-1943) French
*£474 $900 (26-Jun-92 WOL.C467) Figures in marketplace outside Gate of Jerusalem
(36x53cm-14x21in) s. W/C*

ROMBOUTS, Gillis (attrib) (1630-1678) Dutch
£1107 $1970 (29-Nov-91 GAB.G3097/R) Paysage de riviere (31x39cm-12x15in) s. panel
(S.FR 2800)

ROMBOUTS, Salomon (attrib) (17th C) Dutch
£1569 $2808 (15-Nov-91 GK.Z5091/R) Figures resting on woodland clearing
(68x54cm-27x21in) panel (S.FR 4000)

ROMBOUTS, Theodor (1597-1637) Flemish
£3616 $6545 (18-May-92 SY.MI242/R) Un cantante (64x48cm-25x19in) s. (I.L 8000000)

ROMBOUTS, Theodor (circle) (1597-1637) Flemish
£2901 $5250 (22-May-92 SY.NY252/R) Bravo drinking (79x63cm-31x25in) mono.

ROMBOUTS, Theodor (style) (1597-1637) Flemish
£3800 $6840 (21-Nov-91 C82/R) Soldiers quarrelling over cards (90x132cm-35x52in)
£8000 $14000 (3-Apr-92 C20/R) Five senses - elegant company on wooded landscape
(57x77cm-22x30in)

ROMERO DE TORRES, Julio (1879-1930) Spanish
£9116 $16500 (4-Dec-91 NA.BA62) Pastora imperio (121x90cm-48x35in) s. oil tempera
£75000 $136500 (29-May-92 C407/R) Primavera (300x246cm-118x97in) s.i.verso

ROMERO OROZCO, Honorio (1867-c.1920) Spanish
£6635 $12474 (17-Dec-91 DUR.M14/R) Interior de un taller de costura
(200x140cm-79x55in) s.d.1897 (S.P 1200000)

ROMERO RESSENDI, Baldomero (1922-1977) Spanish
£1778 $3237 (11-Dec-91 FER.M168/R) Natividad (46x38cm-18x15in) s. panel (S.P 325000)

ROMERO Y LOPEZ, Jose Maria (c.1815-1880) Spanish
£1374 $2419 (9-Apr-92 ANS.M109/R) Retrato de dama sevillana (138x103cm-54x41in) s.
(S.P 250000)
£4424 $8316 (16-Dec-91 ANS.M95/R) Adoracion Eucaristica (104x84cm-41x33in) s.d.1846
(S.P 800000)

ROMERO, Carlos Orozco (20th C) Italian
£9945 $18000 (18-May-92 CH.NY85 a/R) Mujer en blanco (68x56cm-27x22in) s.d.1939
£10000 $18000 (18-Nov-91 SY.NY134/R) Paisaje montanoso (51x75cm-20x30in) s.d.1966

ROMERO, Juan (?) Spanish
£1501 $2581   (16-Oct-91 FER.M261/R) Saint Paul y su casa azul (100x81cm-39x32in)
s.d.1971 s.i.d.verso acrylic (S.P 275000)

ROMEYN, Willem (1624-1694) Dutch
£5594 $9678   (28-Mar-92 BOD.P1015) Herd of domestic animals with shepehrds near ruin
in southern landscape (36x41cm-14x16in) s. (DM 16000)

ROMEYN, Willem (circle) (1624-1694) Dutch
£842 $1516   (22-Nov-91 SA.A1513/R) South Italian mountain landscape with cattle
resting (34x40cm-13x16in) (DM 2400)

ROMIJN, Gust (1922-) Dutch
£515 $932   (21-May-92 SY.AM311) Untitled (47x65cm-19x26in) s.d.54 cardboard on panel
(D.FL 1700)

ROMITI, Gino (1881-1967) Italian
£507 $922   (12-Dec-91 F.M84) Livorno di notte (13x18cm-5x7in) s.d.57 masonite
(I.L 1100000)
£930 $1683   (3-Dec-91 SY.MI143) Scogli (30x40cm-12x16in) s. panel (I.L 2000000)
£1162 $1987   (19-Mar-92 F.M73) Paesaggio lacustre (10x15cm-4x6in) s. panel
(I.L 2500000)
£1627 $2945   (18-May-92 SY.MI22/R) Paesaggi (19x14cm-7x6in) s.d.52 cardboard set of
three (I.L 3600000)
£4982 $9218   (8-Jun-92 CH.R547/R) Ritorno dalla campagna (102x140cm-40x55in) s.d.1938
(I.L 11000000)

ROMITI, Sergio (1928-) Italian
£6208 $11113   (14-Nov-91 F.M99/R) Composizione (55x75cm-22x30in) s.d.1969
(I.L 13500000)
£6852 $11922   (14-Apr-92 F.M244/R) Composizione (50x80cm-20x31in) s.d.1969verso
(I.L 15000000)
£9282 $17450   (19-Dec-91 F.M220/R) Composizione (63x58cm-25x23in) s. (I.L 20000000)
£10674 $20067   (19-Dec-91 F.M203/R) Composizione (70x80cm-28x31in) s.d.1967
(I.L 23000000)

ROMNEY, George (1734-1802) British
£3600 $6336   (10-Apr-92 C110/R) Portrait of Master Thomas Wallace. Miss Elizabeth
Wallace (30x26cm-12x10in) pair
£11000 $19690   (15-Nov-91 C30/R) Portrait of Captain Henderson, in uniform
(75x62cm-30x24in) i.verso
£18000 $34380   (15-Jul-92 S37/R) Portrait of Elizabeth, Lady Forbes (75x62cm-30x24in)
£520 $993   (30-Jun-92 SWS1790) Study of Lady Hamilton (15x10cm-6x4in) pencil
£780 $1373   (9-Apr-92 S30) Study of standing figure with children (14x12cm-6x5in)
wash
£1500 $2685   (14-Nov-91 S73/R) Study of seated lady beneath tree (24x20cm-9x8in) pen
wash over pencil
£2500 $4775   (14-Jul-92 C39/R) Study of seated figures beneath tree (32x37cm-13x15in)
pen wash
£3090 $5500   (30-Oct-91 D.NY6) Woman kneeling beside pedestal. Standing woman
(25x43cm-10x17in) wash over pencil double-sided
£3500 $6720   (7-Jul-92 C110/R) The Fall of the Rebel Angels (31x26cm-12x10in) pencil
pen wash

ROMNEY, George (after) (1734-1802) British
£2400 $4296   (15-Nov-91 C175/R) Spinstress - portrait of Lady Hamilton, seated at
spinning, in doorway (219x152cm-86x60in)

ROMNEY, George (attrib) (1734-1802) British
£876 $1568   (6-May-92 GD.B1076/R) Portrait of young woman in lace dress
(78x63cm-31x25in) (S.FR 2400)
£2874 $5000   (16-Sep-91 B.SF2011/R) Portrait of Master Clitherow (76x62cm-30x24in)

ROMNEY, George (circle) (1734-1802) British
£800 $1424   (21-Jan-92 PH44) Portrait of lady, seated, with landscape beyond
(79x63cm-31x25in)
£1050 $1901   (6-Dec-91 TE529/R) Portrait of gentleman with his son (124x89cm-49x35in)
£1250 $2388   (21-Jul-92 PH238/R) Portrait of gentleman, wearing red coat and waistcoat
(76x63cm-30x25in)
£1490 $2548   (18-Mar-92 D.V255/R) Portrait of lady (76x63cm-30x25in) (A.S 30000)

ROMNEY, George (studio) (1734-1802) British
£1316 $2500   (25-Jun-92 BG.M503/R) Mrs Harriet Greer nee D'Oyly seated wearing plumed
hat (124x99cm-49x39in)
£1657 $3000   (22-May-92 SY.NY293/R) Portrait of John Flaxman sculpting bust of William
Hayley (72x58cm-28x23in)

ROMNEY, George (style) (1734-1802) British
£900 $1539   (18-Mar-92 CSK204) Portrait of young lady thought to be Miss Linnel
holding spaniel (193x160cm-76x63in)
£1500 $2565   (12-Mar-92 CSK120) Portrait of gentleman in waistcoat and jacket with
lingerie shirt (74x61cm-29x24in)
£1600 $2736   (12-Mar-92 CSK118) Portrait of gentleman in jacket with white cravat
(74x61cm-29x24in)

RONALD, William S (1926-) Canadian
£796 $1417   (26-Nov-91 JOY.T261/R) Abstract composition (56x76cm-22x30in) s.d.87 acrylic paper (C.D 1600)
£2125 $3761   (6-Nov-91 SY.T219/R) Maya (122x91cm-48x36in) s.d.57 acrylic canvas (C.D 4250)

RONAY, J L (19th C) ?
£1207 $2100   (13-Sep-91 S.W2350/R) Gypsy beauty (79x64cm-31x25in) s.
£1494 $2600   (13-Sep-91 S.W2351/R) Gypsy fiddler (79x64cm-31x25in) s.

RONCALLI, Cristoforo (attrib) (1552-1626) Italian
£2000   *$3480*   *(13-Apr-92 S41/R) Putto holding small palm tree (23x9cm-9x4in) black chk htd white squared*

RONCHELLI, Giovanni Battista (attrib) (1716-?) Italian
£2700 $5184   (7-Jul-92 PH184/R) Allegory of four virtues (52x52cm-20x20in) bozzeto

RONDEL, Frederick (1826-1892) American
£833 $1500   (22-Nov-91 S.BM85/R) Huntsman's companion (36x36cm-14x14in) s.
£1676 $3000   (14-Nov-91 CE.NY76) Swans wading (18x31cm-7x12in) s.
£2095 $3750   (6-May-92 D.NY2/R) Salvaging the wreck (76x127cm-30x50in) s.
£3457 $6500   (18-Dec-91 SY.NY34/R) Breaking surf with ship in distress (83x132cm-33x52in) s.
£5249 $9500   (6-Dec-91 CH.NY27/R) Pine Island, New York (20x26cm-8x10in) s. board
£447   *$800*   *(14-Nov-91 CE.NY83) Quaker Meeting House Bridge, Pomfret, CT (55x42cm-22x17in) s. W/C*

RONDEL, Henri (1857-1919) French
£1453 $2500   (15-Oct-91 CE.NY162/R) An elegant beauty (58x48cm-23x19in) s.
£1977 $3400   (15-Oct-91 CE.NY180/R) A young red haired beauty (71x61cm-28x24in) s. canvas laid down on board
£2791 $4800   (15-Oct-91 CE.NY100/R) An elegant lady, bust length (46x38cm-18x15in) s.

RONDI, P (?) Italian
£1815 $3376   (16-Jun-92 F.M49) Le tre fasi della vita (140x210cm-55x83in) s.d.1934 (I.L 4000000)

RONDONI, Ferdinando (?-1879) Italian
£500 $960   (9-Jul-92 B132) Penitent Magdalen (73x58cm-29x23in) s.i.d.1839 verso after Carlo Dolci

RONMY, Guillaume Frederic (1786-1854) French
£17329 $32232   (18-Jun-92 SY.MO74/R) Louis-Philippe d'Orleans et sa famille en 1822 au chateau de Neuilly (62x78cm-24x31in) s.d.1822 (F.FR 170000)

RONNE, Paul (?) Danish
£479 $863   (19-Nov-91 GO.G243) Interior (36x48cm-14x19in) s. (S.KR 5000)

RONNER, Henriette (1821-1909) Dutch
£550 $980   (30-Oct-91 CH.AM190) Rooster and two hens (8x8cm-3x3in) mono. panel (D.FL 1800)
£767 $1395   (11-Dec-91 WE.MU160/R) Hounds tracking down pheasant (18x22cm-7x9in) s. canvas on panel (DM 2200)
£870 $1504   (24-Mar-92 VN.R80/R) Sketch of kittens (27x37cm-11x15in) s. panel (D.FL 2800)
£917 $1596   (14-Apr-92 SY.AM214/R) High tea (30x23cm-12x9in) s. paper (D.FL 3000)
£994 $1709   (7-Mar-92 CH.AM247) Dog in kennel (16x11cm-6x4in) s.verso panel (D.FL 3200)
£1000 $1750   (27-Feb-92 HUN173/R) Study of three puppies (25x38cm-10x15in) s. board
£1107 $1970   (29-Nov-91 GAB.G2170) Les deux amis (27x35cm-11x14in) mono. panel (S.FR 2800)
£1483 $2595   (20-Feb-92 D.V451/R) Uninvited guests (19x16cm-7x6in) mono. panel (A.S 30000)
£1774 $3157   (30-Oct-91 CH.AM189/R) Expecting appraisal (18x15cm-7x6in) s. panel (D.FL 5800)
£1835 $3248   (5-Nov-91 SY.AM244/R) Cat with playful kittens (27x37cm-11x15in) s. paper on panel (D.FL 6000)
£2141 $3725   (14-Apr-92 SY.AM181/R) Portrait of boy with dog, landscape in distance (47x36cm-19x14in) s.d.1851 panel (D.FL 7000)
£2141 $3810   (30-Oct-91 CH.AM186) Kittens playing near basket (24x33cm-9x13in) s. paper on panel (D.FL 7000)
£2424 $4291   (22-Apr-92 CH.AM73/R) Cat, a dog and a parrot in an interior (41x30cm-16x12in) s. panel (D.FL 8000)
£2446 $4330   (5-Nov-91 SY.AM75/R) Sleeping with enemy (23x18cm-9x7in) s. panel (D.FL 8000)
£2879 $5095   (22-Apr-92 CH.AM71/R) Playful kittens (26x36cm-10x14in) s. paper laid down on panel (D.FL 9500)
£3058 $5321   (14-Apr-92 SY.AM130/R) Just good friends (25x20cm-10x8in) s. panel (D.FL 10000)
£5199 $9202   (5-Nov-91 SY.AM225/R) Musing kitten (21x16cm-8x6in) s. panel (D.FL 17000)
£7798 $14271   (3-Jun-92 R.T106/R) Kittens (46x36cm-18x14in) with sig. panel (C.D 17000)
£9786 $17321   (5-Nov-91 SY.AM67/R) Maternal love (24x32cm-9x13in) s.d.1906 panel (D.FL 32000)
£9786 $17028   (14-Apr-92 SY.AM298/R) Tea-time (23x32cm-9x13in) s.d.1905 panel (D.FL 32000)

RONNER, Henriette (1821-1909) Dutch-cont.

£11315 $19688   (14-Apr-92 SY.AM121/R) Two kittens with basket (23x31cm-9x12in) s. panel (D.FL 37000)

£12844 $22734   (5-Nov-91 SY.AM298/R) Dangerous game (34x45cm-13x18in) s. panel (D.FL 42000)

£13267 $24279   (12-May-92 C.A282/R) Family of cats (32x45cm-13x18in) s. panel (B.FR 800000)

£18349 $31927   (14-Apr-92 SY.AM236/R) Time flies (70x55cm-28x22in) s. (D.FL 60000)

£30581 $54434   (30-Oct-91 CH.AM213 b/R) Caged kittens (81x65cm-32x26in) s. (D.FL 100000)

£1376 $2394   (14-Apr-92 SY.AM157/R) Various studies of kittens (44x58cm-17x23in) s.d.96 W/C (D.FL 4500)

RONNER-KNIP, Henriette see RONNER, Henriette

RONNQUIST, Lotten (1864-1912) Swedish

£713 $1276   (16-Nov-91 FAL.M318/R) Children in town after snowfall, winter (72x60cm-28x24in) s.d.93 (S.KR 7500)

RONTINI, Alessandro (1854-?) Italian

£12000 $20520   (18-Mar-92 S179/R) Playing with the balloon (88x60cm-35x24in) s.i.

RONTINI, Ferruccio (20th C) Italian

£1899 $3436   (18-May-92 SY.MI91) Paesaggi (42x24cm-17x9in) s.d.42 cardboard set of four (I.L 4200000)

ROOFTHOOFT, Frans (1888-1957) Belgian

£993 $1798   (23-May-92 KV.L282) Still life of flowers (70x70cm-28x28in) s. (B.FR 60000)

ROOKER, Michael Angelo (1743-1801) British

£620 $1104   (30-Apr-92 T284) Ancient gateway at Dandelion, near Margate (15x23cm-6x9in) i. W/C

ROON, H (?) ?

£1000 $1700   (22-Oct-91 SWS337/R) Young model (22x11cm-9x4in) s. panel

ROONEY, Mick (20th C) ?

£1250 $2213   (8-Nov-91 C303/R) Two women meeting (42x33cm-17x13in) s.d.88 pastel gouache

ROOS, Cornelis Francois (1802-1874) Dutch

£673 $1191   (5-Nov-91 SY.AM7) River landscape with figures on sunny day (28x36cm-11x14in) s.d.1848 panel (D.FL 2200)

£917 $1624   (5-Nov-91 SY.AM430/R) Extensive summer landscape with figures by cottage (39x52cm-15x20in) s. panel (D.FL 3000)

ROOS, Jacob (1682-) Italian

£1524 $2652   (13-Apr-92 AT.P5) Berger et son troupeau (47x62cm-19x24in) (F.FR 15000)

ROOS, Jan (17/18th C) Dutch

£16293 $29654   (28-May-92 F.M104/R) La famiglia di Noe (106x137cm-42x54in) (I.L 36000000)

ROOS, Johann Heinrich (1631-1685) German

£2469 $4420   (14-Nov-91 CH.AM135/R) Horses watering at well on mountain pass (45x40cm-18x16in) (D.FL 8000)

£3000 $5760   (7-Jul-92 C268/R) Drover with family and cattle beside classical ruins (21x31cm-8x12in) s.d.1666 chk pen wash

ROOS, Johann Heinrich (circle) (1631-1685) German

£1379 $2372   (16-Oct-91 KM.K999/R) Shepherds with sheep, cattle and donkey in mountain landscape (57x72cm-22x28in) (DM 4000)

ROOS, Johann Melchior (1659-1731) German

£3632 $6465   (28-Apr-92 F.R59) Paesaggio con pastori e animali (22x32cm-9x13in) pair (I.L 8000000)

£4082 $7306   (5-May-92 ZEL.L1515/R) Pigs by pond in landscape, evening (62x51cm-24x20in) s.d.1715 (DM 12000)

£7426 $13367   (19-Nov-91 F.R170/R) Paesaggio con armenti (99x136cm-39x54in) (I.L 16000000)

ROOS, Philipp Peter (1657-1706) German

£1423 $2476   (13-Apr-92 AT.P47) Vision de Saint Jean l'Evangeliste dans l'ile de Patmos (54x43cm-21x17in) (F.FR 14000)

£2500 $4800   (7-Jul-92 PH214/R) Cavalry officer marshalling troops before battle (48x64cm-19x25in)

£2931 $5041   (16-Oct-91 KM.K998/R) Southern landscape with shepherds and animals near town with bridge (71x94cm-28x37in) (DM 8500)

£2990 $5143   (15-Oct-91 CH.R38) Paesaggio con armenti (48x73cm-19x29in) (I.L 6500000)

£3000 $5760   (8-Jul-92 S146/R) Dogs attacking bull (97x132cm-38x52in)

£3625 $6489   (7-May-92 CH.AM100/R) Sheep and goats resting in landscape (95x134cm-37x53in) (D.FL 12000)

£3729 $6750   (22-May-92 SY.NY173/R) Extensive landscape with sleeping herdsman and flock (96x133cm-38x52in)

1568

ROOS, Philipp Peter (1657-1706) German-cont.

£4420	$8000	(21-May-92 CH.NY205/R) Shepherd with horse attending sheep and goats by river, town beyond (94x147cm-37x58in)
£4938	$8938	(5-Dec-91 SY.MO233/R) Chien sur un coussin. Chien au noeud rouge (29x46cm-11x18in) pair (F.FR 48000)
£5500	$9570	(15-Apr-92 C176/R) Goat and two sheep in landscape, mounted herdsman with dog beyond (73x94cm-29x37in)
£5500	$10010	(12-Dec-91 B6) Shepherd boy seated in Italianate landscape with goats, sheep and sheepdog (67x65cm-26x26in)
£6077	$11000	(22-May-92 SY.NY174/R) Extensive landscape with herdsman and flock, ruins beyond (96x133cm-38x52in)
£6110	$11120	(28-May-92 F.M5) Paesaggio con pastori e armenti (75x102cm-30x40in) pair (I.L 13500000)
£6500	$11375	(1-Apr-92 S203/R) Goatherd with flock (63x92cm-25x36in)
£7452	$12742	(18-Mar-92 D.V212/R) Sheep and goats in southern landscape (112x171cm-44x67in) (A.S 150000)
£10334	$18705	(22-May-92 BL.P52/R) Cheval, moutons et berger. Berger, chien et son troupeau (105x146cm-41x57in) pair (F.FR 102000)
£21000	$38220	(13-Dec-91 C260/R) Elderly herdsman with bullock, bull, cow, horse, sheep, goats and dog (310x452cm-122x178in)
£514	*$884*	*(11-Oct-91 AW.H860/R) Sheep and horse with country folk (27x21cm-11x8in) pen wash (DM 1500)*

ROOS, Philipp Peter (attrib) (1657-1706) German

£2033	$3537	(13-Apr-92 AT.P11/R) Bergers gardant son troupeau (73x137cm-29x54in) (F.FR 20000)
£2981	$5097	(18-Mar-92 D.V217/R) Shepherd scene in the Roman campagna (63x99cm-25x39in) canvas on panel (A.S 60000)
£5060	$8500	(12-Aug-91 SG.M582) Pastoral landscape with village and mountains in background (61x48cm-24x19in) i.verso
£8989	$16000	(27-Apr-92 S.SL316/R) Shepherd wearing blue shirt and animal skin seated on rocky ledge, with horse, sheep and dogs (173x254cm-68x100in)

ROOS, Philipp Peter (circle) (1657-1706) German

| £1500 | $2880 | (9-Jul-92 CSK252/R) Saint John the Evangelist on Patmos writing, with drover and animals in foreground (51x43cm-20x17in) |
| £4000 | $7200 | (21-Nov-91 CSK130/R) Shepherd with horse, goats and cattle by bridge in Italianate landscape (71x96cm-28x38in) |

ROOS, Philipp Peter (studio) (1657-1706) German

| £1391 | $2379 | (18-Mar-92 D.V210/R) Domestic animals in Roman campagna (39x51cm-15x20in) (A.S 28000) |

ROOS, Philipp Peter (style) (1657-1706) German

£900	$1575	(2-Apr-92 CSK80/R) Horse, cow, donkey, sheep and goat in rocky landscape (37x47cm-15x19in)
£1000	$1750	(27-Feb-92 CSK123) A drover in a rocky landscape with sheep watering at a trough (25x35cm-10x14in) canvas laid down on panel
£1000	$1750	(28-Feb-92 C133) An Italianate river landscape with peasants, goats and cattle (63x76cm-25x30in)
£1571	$3000	(16-Jul-92 SY.NY63/R) Herder tending his flock (47x66cm-19x26in)
£1600	$2880	(22-Nov-91 SWS116/R) Landscape with a shepherd resting by his flock (68x89cm-27x35in)
£1826	$3250	(22-Jan-92 SY.NY186/R) Goatherd with goats and dog in landscape (96x73cm-38x29in)
£2500	$4375	(28-Feb-92 C109/R) Peasants watering cattle and sheep at rocky pools (34x29cm-13x11in) pair
£3280	$5575	(22-Oct-91 DUR.M2/R) Pastor con su rebano (127x180cm-50x71in) (S.P 600000)
£3600	$6300	(27-Feb-92 CSK250/R) The Boar hunt (94x148cm-37x58in)
£3700	$6660	(22-Nov-91 SWS115/R) Sheep and goats (74x93cm-29x37in) pair
£4400	$7920	(21-Nov-91 CSK133/R) Peasant girl carding wool and animals in Italianate landscape (96x137cm-38x54in)

ROOS, William (19th C) British

| £1147 | $2099 | (1-Nov-91 W.T1343/R) Gentleman with hunter and two dogs in stable yard (57x66cm-22x26in) s.d.1856 (C.D 2500) |

ROOSENBOOM, Albert (1845-1875) Belgian

£672	$1209	(19-Nov-91 GS.B3647) Young woman with mule on sandy beach (34x25cm-13x10in) s. panel (S.FR 1700)
£730	$1300	(22-Jan-92 SY.NY453/R) Still life with flowers in urn (24x23cm-9x9in) s. panel
£1009	$1796	(30-Oct-91 CH.AM72) Dog cart loaded with milkjugs (19x24cm-7x9in) s. (D.FL 3300)
£1829	$3200	(18-Feb-92 CE.NY100/R) Before party (24x20cm-9x8in) s.

ROOSENBOOM, Margaretha (1843-1896) Dutch

| £3509 | $6000 | (21-Mar-92 W.W41/R) Tabletop still-life with flowers in jug, wine glass, lemon, vegetables (23x18cm-9x7in) s. panel |
| £12121 | $21455 | (22-Apr-92 CH.AM79/R) A swag of pink roses (69x48cm-27x19in) s.d.90 (D.FL 40000) |

ROOSENBOOM, Nicolaas Johannes (1805-1880) Dutch

£523	$951	(11-Dec-91 WE.MU314) Skaters on canal (100x104cm-39x41in) mono.indis.d. (DM 1500)
£710	$1250	(12-Apr-92 LIT.L126) Ice skating scene with windmills in background (18x41cm-7x16in) s. copper
£1186	$2170	(12-May-92 GO.G232) Dutch winter landscape with skaters (20x28cm-8x11in) indist.s. panel oval (S.KR 12500)
£1326	$2400	(21-May-92 S.W2974/R) Sledging and skating on frozen river (11x14cm-4x6in) s. indis.i.verso panel
£1529	$2706	(5-Nov-91 SY.AM251/R) Winter landscape with figures on frozen river (45x57cm-18x22in) panel (D.FL 5000)
£1590	$2767	(14-Apr-92 SY.AM150/R) Figures on frozen river (14x20cm-6x8in) s. panel (D.FL 5200)
£2446	$4257	(14-Apr-92 SY.AM332/R) Winter landscape with figures on frozen river (25x38cm-10x15in) s.d.1870 panel (D.FL 8000)
£2500	$4450	(27-Nov-91 S34/R) Figures in winter landscape (20x30cm-8x12in) init. panel
£2932	$5131	(18-Feb-92 CH.AM336/R) Winter landscape with skaters and peasants conversing by farmhouse (26x35cm-10x14in) s. panel (D.FL 9500)
£3148	$5698	(20-May-92 GK.Z5074/R) Dutch winter landscape with skaters (27x35cm-11x14in) s. (S.FR 8500)
£3364	$5988	(30-Oct-91 CH.AM146/R) Winter landscape with windmill and skaters pushing sledge on frozen river (30x42cm-12x17in) s. panel (D.FL 11000)
£9174	$15963	(14-Apr-92 SY.AM263/R) Winter landscape with figures and horses on frozen river (55x66cm-22x26in) s. panel (D.FL 30000)

ROOSENBOOM, Nicolaas Johannes (circle) (1805-1880) Dutch

£1080	$1890	(18-Feb-92 CH.AM334) Winter skaters on frozen waterway by fortified mansion (18x23cm-7x9in) init. panel (D.FL 3500)

ROOSKENS, Anton (1906-1976) Dutch

£1173	$2135	(11-Dec-91 CH.AM355 a) Swarte Tijden (12x15cm-5x6in) init.d.58 s.d.verso paper on panel (D.FL 3800)
£1212	$2194	(21-May-92 SY.AM221/R) Untitled (32x39cm-13x15in) s.d.69 gouache wax crayon (D.FL 4000)
£3030	$5485	(21-May-92 SY.AM279/R) Composition no 511 (46x38cm-18x15in) init.d.73 i.verso (D.FL 10000)
£3348	$6060	(20-May-92 KH.K142/R) Composition (50x65cm-20x26in) s.d.75 acrylic paper on canvas (D.KR 38000)
£3636	$6582	(19-May-92 CH.AM283/R) Birds on the beach (51x40cm-20x16in) s.d.72 (D.FL 12000)
£4093	$7121	(17-Sep-91 RAS.K12/R) Man and birds (61x50cm-24x20in) s.d.74 i.verso (D.KR 46000)
£4321	$7864	(11-Dec-91 CH.AM369 a) Vogels ende Rode Zon (51x41cm-20x16in) s.d.58 (D.FL 14000)
£4448	$7740	(17-Sep-91 RAS.K92/R) The green planet (60x50cm-24x20in) s.d.67 (D.KR 50000)
£6228	$10836	(18-Sep-91 KH.K20/R) Figure composition (60x50cm-24x20in) s.d.66 panel (D.KR 70000)
£8000	$13760	(12-Oct-91 KV.L428/R) Beach scene (81x65cm-32x26in) s.d.70 (B.FR 480000)
£9091	$16455	(21-May-92 SY.AM266/R) Birds, composition no 556 (100x80cm-39x31in) s.d.73 i.d.73verso (D.FL 30000)
£9697	$17552	(19-May-92 CH.AM282/R) Woman with birds (80x100cm-31x39in) s.d.73 (D.FL 32000)
£11733	$20063	(12-Mar-92 RAS.K648/R) Composition with fantasy animal (73x92cm-29x36in) s. (D.KR 130000)
£12121	$21939	(19-May-92 CH.AM280/R) Girl with birds (97x130cm-38x51in) s.d.73 (D.FL 40000)
£12346	$22469	(11-Dec-91 CH.AM369/R) Symbolen in zwarte Vorm (100x120cm-39x47in) s.d.65 s.i.verso (D.FL 40000)
£23148	$42130	(12-Dec-91 SY.AM222/R) Compositie (139x200cm-55x79in) s.d.60 d.1960 stretcher (D.FL 75000)
£1667	$3017	(19-May-92 CH.AM290/R) Untitled (23x17cm-9x7in) s.d.49 gouache chk. (D.FL 5500)
£1818	$3291	(19-May-92 CH.AM339/R) Composition (33x11cm-13x4in) s.d.50 pencil gouache (D.FL 6000)
£2006	$3651	(11-Dec-91 CH.AM313) Composition with figures (59x48cm-23x19in) s.d.71 gouache (D.FL 6500)
£2273	$4114	(19-May-92 CH.AM288/R) Composition with birds (42x30cm-17x12in) s.d.52 gouache (D.FL 7500)
£2932	$5336	(11-Dec-91 CH.AM386/R) Composition (49x64cm-19x25in) s. gouache (D.FL 9500)
£3648	$6347	(18-Sep-91 KH.K60/R) Figure (48x65cm-19x26in) s.d.1973 gouache (D.KR 41000)

ROOTIUS, Jakobus (1644-1681) Dutch

£9063	$16224	(7-May-92 CH.AM132/R) Mixed flowers, plums in glass vase, with peaches and butterflies on stone ledge (65x50cm-26x20in) with indist.sig. (D.FL 30000)

ROOTIUS, Jan Albertsz (attrib) (1615-1674) Dutch

£2128	$3894	(12-May-92 SY.AM65/R) Still life of roemer, knife and fruit on pewter plate, on draped ledge (45x39cm-18x15in) indist.mono. (D.FL 7000)
£3779	$6500	(9-Oct-91 CH.NY154/R) Portrait of lady, standing wearing costume with bows, holding fan (123x98cm-48x39in)

ROOTIUS, Jan Albertsz (style) (1615-1674) Dutch
£4000 $7000   (2-Apr-92 CSK132/R) Fruit in basket on table by glass, pewter plate and gold vessel (28x39cm-11x15in)

ROOVER, Albert de (1892-1978) Belgian
£597 $1093   (12-May-92 C.A80) Reclining nude (23x34cm-9x13in) s.d.1948 panel (B.FR 36000)

ROPE, George Thomas (1846-1929) British
£680 $1204   (6-Nov-91 CB105/R) Study of fowl, two chicken and cockerel in farmyard (36x46cm-14x18in) s.d.1895
£900 $1647   (7-Feb-92 K296) River scene with distant view of figure and horse crossing wooden bridge (38x53cm-15x21in) s.
£925 $1693   (7-Feb-92 K300) Study of horses in meadow with cottage nearby (46x71cm-18x28in) s.

ROPELE, Walter (1934-) Swiss
£889 $1609   (19-May-92 GF.L2616/R) In the flower garden (60x73cm-24x29in) s.d.1991 (S.FR 2400)
£926 $1676   (19-May-92 GF.L2615/R) Breakfast (86x95cm-34x37in) s.d.1988 (S.FR 2500)

ROPS, Felicien (1833-1898) Belgian
£411   *$743*   *(7-Dec-91 KV.L270) Le faune (25x16cm-10x6in) s. pen (B.FR 24000)*
£1325   *$2397*   *(23-May-92 KV.L283) Le Rosaire de la Rosiere (21x10cm-8x4in) mono. pen (B.FR 80000)*

ROQUEPLAN (attrib) (19th C) French
£462   *$883*   *(1-Jul-92 CD.P52) Jules de Puysegur min. wood/ebony frame oval (F.FR 4500)*

ROQUEPLAN, Camille (1803-1855) French
£2976 $5000   (1-Sep-91 PO.BA1) Venus jugando con el Amor (45x55cm-18x22in) s. panel

RORBYE, Martinus (1803-1848) Norwegian
£1585 $2662   (28-Aug-91 KH.K173/R) Path through mountain cliffs (49x33cm-19x13in) init.i.d.1835 (D.KR 18000)
£44014 $73944   (27-Aug-91 RAS.K87/R) Hunter showing his wife the outcome of his first snipe shoot (39x50cm-15x20in) s.d.1839 (D.KR 500000)
£794   *$1413*   *(28-Apr-92 RAS.K704) View from Kolding (14x24cm-6x9in) i.d.1848 W/C (D.KR 9000)*

ROSA DA TIVOLI see ROOS, Philipp Peter

ROSA, Francesco de see ROSA, Pacecco di

ROSA, Herve di (1959-) French
£1426 $2609   (3-Jun-92 CSC.P223/R) Roc et Roll, etude no.4 (76x57cm-30x22in) s.d.89 acrylic paper (F.FR 14000)
£1564 $2800   (9-May-92 CE.NY303/R) Untitled (186x138cm-73x54in) s.d.83 acrylic
£1629 $2982   (3-Jun-92 CSC.P210) Roc et Roll - etude no.6 (76x57cm-30x22in) s.d.89 acrylic paper (F.FR 16000)
£1959 $3389   (23-Mar-92 CC.P142) L'asile de fous (155x105cm-61x41in) s.d.1990 acrylic paper laid down on canvas (F.FR 19000)
£2051 $3672   (19-Jan-92 CC.P60/R) L'arbre de vie (130x98cm-51x39in) s.i.d.1990 acrylic (F.FR 20000)
£3557 $6153   (29-Mar-92 P.V125/R) Le Scaphandrier (100x100cm-39x39in) s.d.1989 s.i.d.verso oil acrylic (F.FR 34500)
£8454 $14625   (23-Mar-92 CC.P65/R) La fin d'un monde (209x243cm-82x96in) s.i.d.84 acrylic (F.FR 82000)
£617   *$1123*   *(11-Dec-91 CH.AM459/R) Madonna with the big boobies (48x49cm-19x19in) pencil pen collage (D.FL 2000)*
£988   *$1798*   *(11-Dec-91 CH.AM457) Comic (48x49cm-19x19in) s. acrylic collage (D.FL 3200)*

ROSA, Pacecco di (1600-1654) Italian
£895 $1700   (26-Jun-92 WOL.C404/R) Madonna and Child (89x66cm-35x26in)
£7241 $13179   (28-May-92 F.M88/R) Santo Stefano (78x65cm-31x26in) (I.L 16000000)
£7694 $14003   (28-May-92 F.M89/R) San Lorenzo (78x65cm-31x26in) (I.L 17000000)

ROSA, Salvator (1615-1673) Italian
£3806 $7232   (24-Jun-92 KM.K954/R) Rocky wooded landscape with figures (64x76cm-25x30in) mono (DM 11000)
£45000 $81900   (13-Dec-91 C89/R) Saint John the Baptist preaching to the multitude (111x160cm-44x63in) s.
£400000 $696000   (15-Apr-92 C45/R) Portrait of artist wearing doublet, cap, torn glove and sword (115x94cm-45x37in)
£437   *$765*   *(3-Apr-92 AGS.P197) Etude de dragon (8x7cm-3x3in) pen (F.FR 4200)*
£1500   *$2730*   *(10-Dec-91 C145) Studies of heads and figures (7x11cm-3x4in) ink*
£2200   *$4224*   *(7-Jul-92 C30/R) Tree (78x54cm-31x21in) chk pen wash*
£2200   *$4224*   *(6-Jul-92 S7/R) Two figures, possibly study for Prodigal Son (8x10cm-3x4in) pen wash*
£2200   *$4224*   *(7-Jul-92 C31/R) Study of soldier holding pike on shoulder. Satyrs carrying off nymph (14x9cm-6x4in) chk pen wash double-sided*
£5019   *$8583*   *(12-Mar-92 GK.Z3/R) Mountain landscape with fir tree and two figures (62x41cm-24x16in) s. ink wash htd.white panel (S.FR 13000)*

ROSA, Salvator (1615-1673) Italian-cont.
£10615 $19000   *(14-Jan-92 SY.NY6/R) Woman sitting beneath tree in landscape (15x9cm-6x4in) pen wash*
£10615 $19000   *(14-Jan-92 SY.NY8/R) Two men seated on ground and two standing, fifth figure cut off on left (12x11cm-5x4in) pen wash over red chk*

ROSA, Salvator (after) (1615-1673) Italian
£1292 $2300   *(22-Jan-92 SY.NY111/R) La foret des philosophes (58x74cm-23x29in) i.verso*

ROSA, Salvator (attrib) (1615-1673) Italian
£4420 $8000   *(22-May-92 SY.NY161/R) Praying knight and attendant in grove (55x80cm-22x31in)*
£1237 $2289   *(13-Jun-92 HN.H123/R) Hiob and his friends (15x22cm-6x9in) pen wash (DM 3600)*

ROSA, Salvator (circle) (1615-1673) Italian
£3477 $5946   *(18-Mar-92 D.V26/R) The Temptation of St Anthony (50x69cm-20x27in) (A.S 70000)*

ROSA, Salvator (school) (1615-1673) Italian
£3925 $7458   *(23-Jun-92 D.V17/R) Erminia and the river god in wooded landscape, evening (150x138cm-59x54in) (A.S 80000)*

ROSA, Salvator (style) (1615-1673) Italian
£546 $1000   *(16-May-92 HG.C163) Battle scene (74x81cm-29x32in)*
£800 $1536   *(10-Jul-92 C289) Banditti conversing on rocky shore (33x36cm-13x14in)*
£880 $1531   *(13-Sep-91 C106/R) Hercules and Nemean lion (45x63cm-18x25in)*
£1000 $1920   *(9-Jul-92 CSK254/R) Wooded landscape with rocky pool (53x63cm-21x25in)*
£1067 $1900   *(22-Jan-92 SY.NY223/R) Ships in stormy sea (71x94cm-28x37in)*
£1100 $1925   *(27-Feb-92 B35) Bandits resting in a rocky wooded landscape, a bay beyond (46x38cm-18x15in)*
£1300 $2275   *(27-Feb-92 CSK133/R) Italianate lake landscape with shepherd and dog (38x56cm-15x22in)*
£1600 $3072   *(9-Jul-92 CSK261/R) Italianate landscape with castle ruins by river (57x81cm-22x32in)*
£1718 $3144   *(2-Jun-92 FN.S2728) Landscape with spring and shepherds (48x37cm-19x15in) (DM 5000)*
£1900 $3648   *(7-Jul-92 PH111/R) Brazen serpent (130x148cm-51x58in)*
£2247 $4000   *(22-Jan-92 SY.NY216/R) Fishermen in cove (56x119cm-22x47in)*
£2347 $4224   *(19-Nov-91 RAS.K433/R) Religious scene (102x76cm-40x30in) (D.KR 26000)*
£2700 $4860   *(22-Nov-91 SWS76/R) Hilly landscape with figures beside trees (63x47cm-25x19in)*
£3100 $5580   *(22-Nov-91 SWS174/R) A coastal landscape with galleys moored beneath a fort (98x126cm-39x50in)*
£3779 $6500   *(10-Oct-91 SY.NY85/R) Landscape with figures by a seaside grotto (95x131cm-37x52in)*
£4000 $7680   *(9-Jul-92 CSK249) Wooded Italianate landscape with hermits by grotto (127x101cm-50x40in)*
£4168 $7211   *(25-Mar-92 CH.R56/R) Paesaggio agreste (74x137cm-29x54in) (I.L 9000000)*
£10000 $19200   *(8-Jul-92 S110/R) Italianate landscape with soldiers and other figures by river (63x91cm-25x36in)*
£12500 $21875   *(3-Apr-92 C156) Rocky coastal landscape with banditti on shore (71x92cm-28x36in)*
£13000 $23660   *(13-Dec-91 C264/R) Italianate rocky landscape with banditti gambling by seashore (68x98cm-27x39in)*

ROSAI, Ottone (1895-1957) Italian
£2353 $4283   *(26-May-92 SY.MI65/R) Autoritratto (10x8cm-4x3in) s. board (I.L 5200000)*
£7193 $13524   *(19-Dec-91 F.M177/R) Due carabinieri (39x29cm-15x11in) s. panel (I.L 15500000)*
£7414 $13197   *(26-Nov-91 SY.MI139/R) Paesaggio (30x40cm-12x16in) s. panel (I.L 16000000)*
£8172 $14545   *(29-Apr-92 F.F181/R) Figure sedute intorno ad un tavolo (30x40cm-12x16in) s. (I.L 18000000)*
£10132 $18441   *(9-Dec-91 CH.R167/R) Omini al tavolo (30x40cm-12x16in) s. faesite (I.L 22000000)*
£11497 $20579   *(14-Nov-91 F.M95/R) Paesaggio con le case (50x70cm-20x28in) s. (I.L 25000000)*
£13356 $24309   *(9-Dec-91 CH.R182/R) La curva (50x40cm-20x16in) s. i.d.1955verso faesite (I.L 29000000)*
£13578 $24711   *(26-May-92 SY.MI191/R) Cinque a tavola (45x55cm-18x22in) s.d.44 (I.L 30000000)*
£13703 $23844   *(14-Apr-92 F.M169/R) Paesaggio (70x50cm-28x20in) s. board (I.L 30000000)*
£27239 $48485   *(29-Apr-92 F.F294/R) Crocifissione (100x70cm-39x28in) (I.L 60000000)*
£545 $970   *(29-Apr-92 F.F37/R) Ritratto (15x13cm-6x5in) s. ink paper on canvas (I.L 1200000)*
£973 $1732   *(29-Nov-91 F.F31) Ritratto (28x20cm-11x8in) s. chl paper on cardboard (I.L 2100000)*
£1297 $2310   *(29-Nov-91 F.F92/R) Natura morta (44x33cm-17x13in) s. chl (I.L 2800000)*
£3402 $6226   *(12-May-92 F.R100/R) Paesaggio con muro e case (40x51cm-16x20in) s. W/C (I.L 7500000)*

ROSALES, Eduardo (1836-1873) Spanish
£465 $847   *(11-Dec-91 FER.M6/R) Maternidad (45x23cm-18x9in) s. pencil htd white (S.P 85000)*

ROSAM, Walter Alfred (1883-1916) German
£2825 $5000   (6-Nov-91 D.NY54/R) Aeneas and Dido (199x149cm-78x59in) s.

ROSASPINA, Antonio (1830-1871) Italian
£1934 $3500   (21-May-92 S.W2907/R) Boy with violin (48x38cm-19x15in) s.d.1867

ROSATI, Albert (19th C) ?
£2000 $3460   *(4-Oct-91 C131/R) Arabs in street (53x36cm-21x14in) s. W/C htd.white*

ROSATI, Giulio (1858-1917) Italian
£4000 $7240   (22-May-92 C219 a/R) Carpet sellers (37x53cm-15x21in) s. pencil W/C htd
                   white
£10935 $20011   (13-May-92 FER.M109/R) En el estudio del pintor (40x65cm-16x26in)
                   s.d.1883 (S.P 2000000)
£3600 $6120   *(23-Oct-91 S252/R) Arab horseman and carpet seller (34x24cm-13x9in) s.*
                   W/C
£6000 $10860   *(22-May-92 C213/R) Mending carpet (52x37cm-20x15in) s. pencil W/C*
£6500 $11765   *(22-May-92 C212/R) Carpet seller (52x35cm-20x14in) s. pencil W/C htd*
                   white

ROSCH, Carl (1884-?) German
£2353 $4000   (23-Oct-91 GD.B617/R) Still life of candle, book and coffee pot on chair
                   (92x65cm-36x26in) mono.d.48 tempera (S.FR 6000)

ROSCH, Ludwig (1865-1936) Austrian
£777 $1383   *(28-Apr-92 D.V7) Danube landscape (46x62cm-18x24in) s. chl chk htd.white*
                   canvas on board (A.S 16000)
£971 $1728   *(28-Apr-92 D.V6) Stephanskirche (68x46cm-27x18in) s. chl chk (A.S 20000)*
£1456 $2592   *(29-Apr-92 D.V672/R) View of Vienna with Stefanskirche beyond*
                   (36x28cm-14x11in) s. mixed media oval (A.S 30000)

ROSE, Guy (1867-1925) American
£42582 $77500   (27-May-92 SY.NY67/R) Off Mission Point (62x74cm-24x29in) s.

ROSE, Herbert (1882-1955) British
£684 $1217   (27-Apr-92 J.M410) Street cafe (39x44cm-15x17in) s. (A.D 1600)

ROSE, Iver (?) ?
£988 $1700   (7-Mar-92 LAE.L145/R) Vegetable sellers (51x76cm-20x30in) s.d.42 masonite

ROSE, J (19th C) ?
£867 $1500   (24-Mar-92 GRO.B32/R) Ships in harbour (38x58cm-15x23in) s.d.1875 canvas
                   on panel

ROSE, Julius (1828-1911) German
£704 $1176   (19-Aug-91 SY.ME181) Figures by German lake (59x116cm-23x46in) s.d.1882
                   (A.D 1500)
£785 $1500   (16-Jul-92 SY.NY417/R) Fisherboats near Elagusa Dalmatia
                   (31x39cm-12x15in) s.
£1461 $2600   (22-Jan-92 SY.NY248/R) Greek harbour on blustery day (37x58cm-15x23in) s.
£1512 $2812   (20-Jun-92 BM.B883/R) Young woman and peasant boy standing on woodland
                   path (30x40cm-12x16in) s. (DM 4400)
£1600 $2896   (22-May-92 C161/R) Kings Lacke near Berchtesgaden, Bavaria
                   (61x119cm-24x47in) s.i.d.1882 with i.verso

ROSE, Knut (1936-) Norwegian
£1228 $2284   (15-Jun-92 B.O131/R) Composition (46x38cm-18x15in) s.d.1970verso
                   (N.KR 14000)
£2105 $3916   (18-Jun-92 GWP.O83/R) Composition (55x61cm-22x24in) s. s.i.d.1969verso
                   (N.KR 24000)

ROSE, Manuel (20th C) South American
£1156 $2000   (30-Sep-91 GC.M36/R) Bailarina en el Tocador (51x40cm-20x16in) board
£3933 $7000   (28-Oct-91 GC.M40/R) Rina en el cafetin (87x106cm-34x42in) s.
£3978 $7200   (2-Dec-91 GC.M51/R) Rosedal en la quinta del artista (100x100cm-39x39in)
                   s.
£6906 $12500   (2-Dec-91 GC.M52/R) Sendero en las piedras (81x116cm-32x46in) s.d.1917
£1078 $1800   *(19-Aug-91 GC.M13/R) Dama sentada en taburete (63x42cm-25x17in) s.d.1929*
                   pastel

ROSE, Samuel (1941-) American?
£889 $1600   (24-Nov-91 JRB.C160/R) R.H. Ives Gammell Studio interior at Williamstown
                   (61x36cm-24x14in) s.

ROSE, William (1930-) Australian
£968 $1800   (21-Jun-92 SY.ME45/R) Untitled s.d.1982 plywood (A.D 2400)

ROSE-INNES, Alexander (1915-) South African
£565 $999   (4-Nov-91 SY.J133) Woman seated on couch (44x59cm-17x23in) s. (SA.R 2800)

ROSELAND, Harry (1868-1950) American
£1149 $2000   (15-Aug-92 SY.NY68/R) maternal kiss (36x51cm-14x20in) s.i.verso
£1519 $2750   (22-May-92 S.BM77/R) Her favourite flfowers (20x28cm-8x11in) s. board
£1657 $3000   (7-Dec-91 LAE.L117/R) The coloured palmist (25x36cm-10x14in) s. s.i.verso

ROSELAND, Harry (1868-1950) American-cont.
£2088 $3800   (15-Dec-91 LIT.L340) Fortune teller with two young girls (41x61cm-16x24in) s.d.30
£2632 $4500   (12-Mar-92 CH.NY75/R) A watched pot never boils (30x23cm-12x9in) s. canvasboard
£2807 $4800   (12-Mar-92 CH.NY73/R) Purl one, drop two (30x23cm-12x9in) s. canvasboard
£3243 $6000   (10-Jun-92 CE.NY260/R) Reading tea leaves (49x77cm-19x30in) s.d.32
£9669 $17500   (2-Dec-91 S.SL302/R) Look out to sea (122x76cm-48x30in) s.d.08

ROSELL, Alexander (19/20th C) British
£600 $1044   (12-Sep-91 CSK254) Out of the wreck. Crib (36x46cm-14x18in) s. pair
£700 $1246   (21-Jan-92 PH143) Wedding present (25x33cm-10x13in) s.
£950 $1634   (11-Oct-91 K518/R) Granny's advice (51x71cm-20x28in) s.
£3779 $6500   (17-Oct-91 SY.NY304/R) Allied forces (76x63cm-30x25in) s.d.1900

ROSEN, Charles (1878-1950) American
£15385 $28000   (28-May-92 CH.NY187/R) Morning along the canal (102x81cm-40x32in) s.

ROSEN, Ernest (1877-1926) American
£1494 $2600   (15-Apr-92 SY.NY72/R) Woman holding cigarette (99x69cm-39x27in) s.

ROSEN, Georg von (1843-1923) Scandinavian
£474 $868   (17-May-92 BU.M262/R) Spring - Romantic landscape with funeral procession of monks (122x92cm-48x36in) s.d.1907-1917 (S.KR 5000)

ROSEN, Jan (1854-?) Polish
£1392 $2519   (3-Dec-91 AB.S4749/R) Portraits of horse and rider (17x24cm-7x9in) s.d.1888 panel pair (S.KR 14500)

ROSENBERG, Edward (1858-1934) Swedish
£2207 $3995   (3-Dec-91 AB.S4655/R) Late winter landscape with house and trees by water, evening (60x94cm-24x37in) s. (S.KR 23000)
£3053 $5435   (28-Nov-91 BU.S31/R) River landscape, Kolmarden (164x258cm-65x102in) s.d.1883 (S.KR 32000)

ROSENBERG, W C (?) ?
£550 $1056   (29-Jul-92 CSK281) A penny for the song (50x40cm-20x16in) s.

ROSENFELD, Eugen (1870-1953) German
£488 $844   (3-Oct-91 D.V137/R) Portrait of girl (50x36cm-20x14in) board (A.S 10000)

ROSENGREN, Jean (1894-1965) Swedish
£551 $987   (16-Nov-91 FAL.M309/R) Farm in Skane with geese by river (49x69cm-19x27in) s. (S.KR 5800)
£570 $1021   (16-Nov-91 FAL.M306/R) Monday's breakfast (59x78cm-23x31in) s.d.1932 (S.KR 6000)

ROSENQUIST, James (1933-) American
£22346 $40000   (6-May-92 CH.NY305/R) Exit (76x84cm-30x33in) s.d.1961 verso
£81006 $145000   (6-May-92 SY.NY54/R) The bird of paradise approaches the hot water plant (244x213cm-96x84in) oil acrylic
£811 $1500   (12-Jun-92 SY.NY312/R) Drawing No.19 for time colours time (50x71cm-20x28in) s.i.d.1980 dry pigment
£1081 $2000   (12-Jun-92 SY.NY315/R) Drawing No.18 for time colours time (50x71cm-20x28in) s.i.d.1980 dry pigment
£5491 $9500   (3-Oct-91 SY.NY71/R) Giselle star pale (107x79cm-42x31in) s.i.d.1974 ink acrylic paper collage two sheets
£11732 $21000   (14-Nov-91 SY.NY372/R) Drawing for star sack (131x209cm-52x82in) s.d.1974 acrylic paper cloth collage

ROSENSOHN, Lennart (1918-) Swedish
£1622 $2887   (27-Nov-91 BU.S30/R) The story-teller (80x95cm-31x37in) s.d.1985 (S.KR 17000)
£1622 $2887   (27-Nov-91 BU.S32/R) Man with birds (96x84cm-38x33in) s.d.1990 (S.KR 17000)
£1987 $3596   (19-May-92 AB.S5311/R) Women on Bali (130x100cm-51x39in) s.d.83 (S.KR 21000)
£391 $688   (11-Apr-92 FAL.M355/R) Man with fish (42x32cm-17x13in) s.d.1989 W/C (S.KR 4100)
£615 $1113   (19-May-92 AB.S5312/R) Composition (54x74cm-21x29in) s.d.1985 mixed media (S.KR 6500)

ROSENSTAND, Vilhelm (1838-1915) Danish
£2285 $4090   (6-May-92 KH.K11/R) Young Italian woman with water jug (71x49cm-28x19in) s.i.d.1875 (D.KR 26000)

ROSENTHAL, Albert (1863-?) American
£506 $910   (23-Nov-91 YFA.M256/R) Village in snow (66x79cm-26x31in) s.

ROSENTHALIS, Moshe (20th C) ?
£585 $1100   (5-Jan-92 GG.TA356/R) Still life (54x46cm-21x18in) s.

ROSENTHALS, Jan (1866-1916) Latvian
£712 $1302   (14-May-92 BU.S101/R) Spring offerings (32x48cm-13x19in) mono. mixed media (S.KR 7500)

ROSHARDT, Walter (1897-1966) Swiss
£588 $1053   (15-Nov-91 ZOF.Z1856/R) Half nude girl (29x21cm-11x8in) mono.i. pencil
                        (S.FR 1500)

ROSI, Alessandro (attrib) (1627-1707) Italian
£850 $1479   (13-Apr-92 S159/R) Study of standing figure, wearing cloak and hat
                        (41x26cm-16x10in) bears i. black red chk

ROSIER, A (18/19th C) ?
£2026 $3668   (23-May-92 G.SB486) Deux-mats dans la rade a Constantinople
                        (41x27cm-16x11in) s. panel (F.FR 20000)

ROSIER, Amedee (1831-) French
£3119 $5364   (7-Oct-91 CSC.P137/R) Vue de Venise (54x73cm-21x29in) s. (F.FR 31000)
£8800 $15224   (4-Oct-91 C45/R) Boats on the lagoon, Venice (61x82cm-24x32in) s.

ROSIER, Jean Guillaume (1858-1931) Belgian
£498 $910   (12-May-92 C.A285) In the studio (60x40cm-24x16in) s. (B.FR 30000)
£829 $1517   (12-May-92 C.A284) Design for the church in Mechelen (107x66cm-42x26in)
                        mono. panel triptich (B.FR 50000)
£2239 $4097   (12-May-92 C.A283) Time for tea (65x62cm-26x24in) s.d.10 (B.FR 135000)

ROSIERSE, Johannes (1818-1901) Dutch
£2000 $3720   (18-Jun-92 B146/R) Family in candlelit interior (66x54cm-26x21in)
                        s.d.1852 panel
£6116 $10642   (14-Apr-92 SY.AM123/R) Family gathering (64x80cm-25x31in) s. panel
                        (D.FL 20000)
£7000 $12460   (27-Nov-91 S47/R) Bird's nest (49x63cm-19x25in) s. panel

ROSINI, Umberto (20th C) Italian
£1754 $3158   (22-Nov-91 SA.A1569/R) Neapolitan coastal landscape with houses and
                        palaces (110x164cm-43x65in) s.i. (DM 5000)

ROSLIN, Alexander (1718-1793) Swedish
£9461 $17124   (19-May-92 AB.S4269/R) Portrait of the French Crown Princess Marie
                        Josephe (73x59cm-29x23in) s.d.1776 (S.KR 100000)
£70547 $125573   (28-Apr-92 RAS.K22/R) Portrait of young lady with flowers in her hair
                        (80x63cm-31x25in) s.d.1781 oval (D.KR 800000)
£144014 $263546   (5-Feb-92 KH.K114/R) Portrait of Christian VII wearing Coronation robes
                        (115x87cm-45x34in) i. (D.KR 1600000)

ROSLIN, Alexander (circle) (1718-1793) Swedish
£963 $1743   (19-May-92 GF.L2434/R) Portrait of nobleman (60x50cm-24x20in) (S.FR 2600)
£7500 $13650   (10-Dec-91 PH156/R) Portrait of Tsar Paul I. Portrait of Empress Maria
                        Feodorowna (82x62cm-32x24in) pair

ROSLIN, Alexander (studio) (1718-1793) Swedish
£3200 $5696   (30-Apr-92 CG875/R) Young woman decorating statue of Cupid with garland
                        of flowers (146x107cm-57x42in)

ROSNER, Charles (20th C) German/American
£726 $1300   (15-Nov-91 RB.HY193/R) Packet ship Washington Irving, under full sail
                        against sunset sky (25x38cm-10x15in) s.d.35 W/C

ROSS, Alvin (20th C) American?
£638 $1200   (18-Dec-91 SY.NY419/R) Kitchen sink (52x40cm-20x16in) s.i.d.1960 verso

ROSS, James (18/19th C) British
£398 $700   (9-Apr-92 FA.PH725) Silent earth (33x51cm-13x20in) s. W/C
£414 $750   (5-Dec-91 FA.PH545) Country near Flemington New Jersey (53x74cm-21x29in)
                        s. W/C
£426 $750   (9-Apr-92 FA.PH726) Time for soup and mittens (53x76cm-21x30in) s. W/C
£426 $750   (9-Apr-92 FA.PH727) Eastern point light (51x71cm-20x28in) s. W/C
£525 $950   (5-Dec-91 FA.PH531/R) Art Museum and Waterworks (33x48cm-13x19in) s. W/C

ROSS, Sir William Charles (1794-1860) British
£400 $700   (24-Sep-91 CSK12) Gentleman in black coat and blue waistcoat
                        (9x?cm-4x?in) min.s.i.d.1846 verso rec.leather case
£600 $1056   (9-Apr-92 S200) Portrait of gentleman, wearing brown topcoat
                        (11x?cm-4x?in) min. gilt-metal mount wood frame oval

ROSS, Stuart (20th C) American
£526 $900   (18-Mar-92 GRO.B20) Evening light (66x102cm-26x40in) s.d.1987 acrylic
                        canvas

ROSSANDER, Armand (1914-1976) Swedish
£568 $1027   (19-May-92 AB.S5313/R) View of the lock, Stockholm (49x70cm-19x28in)
                        s.d.60 (S.KR 6000)
£1390 $2502   (23-Nov-91 SO.S588/R) Composition (66x114cm-26x45in) s. (S.KR 14500)

ROSSANO, Federico (1835-1912) Italian
£5500 $9515   (4-Oct-91 C174/R) The young harvesters (19x32cm-7x13in) s. panel
£14000 $24780   (13-Feb-92 CSK226/R) Country farmstead (60x50cm-24x20in) s.

ROSSEELS, Jacques (1828-1912) Flemish
£919 $1562   (22-Oct-91 C.A910) Landscape (62x33cm-24x13in) s. (B.FR 55000)

ROSSELLI, Bernardo (fl.1532-1569) Italian
£30726 $55000   (17-Jan-92 SY.NY36/R) The Virgin with the infant Saint John the Baptist
         adoring Christ (80x44cm-31x17in) tempera panel arched top
£240223 $430000   (17-Jan-92 SY.NY6/R) Scenes from the life of King David, with the battle
         of David and Goliath (40x141cm-16x56in) tempera panel gilt detail

ROSSELLI, Bernardo di Stefano (1450-1526) Italian?
£22346 $40000   (16-Jan-92 CH.NY48/R) Madonna of Girdle, with Saint Thomas and donor at
         prayer (131x72cm-52x28in) panel arched top

ROSSELLI, Bernardo di Stefano (circle) (1450-1526) Italian?
£6000 $10920   (10-Dec-91 PH112/R) Annunciation - Virgin and Angel of Annunciation
         (27x20cm-11x8in) panel pair

ROSSELLI, Matteo (1578-1650) Italian
£550 $957   (13-Apr-92 S222) Standing apostle (40x26cm-16x10in) black chk
£1800 $3456   (7-Jul-92 C177/R) Prone man and study of the same. Four studies of men
         (20x37cm-8x15in) chk

ROSSETTI, Cesare (17th C) Italian
£400 $728   (11-Dec-91 PH179/R) A naval battle (16x18cm-6x7in) pen wash chk.htd.white
         shaped

ROSSETTI, Dante Gabriel (1828-1882) British
£8000 $14240   (29-Oct-91 C14/R) Portrait of Fanny Cornforth (32x24cm-13x9in) pencil
£8200 $15170   (12-Jun-92 C78/R) Elizabeth Siddal reclining on a bank holding a parasol
         (10x9cm-4x4in) pen wash
£30000 $53400   (27-Nov-91 S171/R) Christmas carol (45x37cm-18x15in) mono.d.1867 red
         white chk
£80000 $136800   (13-Mar-92 C81/R) Calliope Coronio (72x49cm-28x19in) mono.i.d.1869
         col.chk two joined sheets
£80000 $148000   (12-Jun-92 C93/R) Portrait of Mrs William Stillman nee Marie Spartali
         (62x47cm-24x19in) mono.d.1869 col.chk.

ROSSI (?) ?
£1300 $2379   (15-May-92 CBS226) Boy shepherd playing pipe (48x41cm-19x16in) s.

ROSSI, A M (19th C) British
£903 $1543   (12-Mar-92 RAS.V971) Italian scene with figures and poultry
         (45x61cm-18x24in) s. (D.KR 10000)

ROSSI, Alberto (1858-1936) Italian
£3901 $7023   (18-Nov-91 AT.P371/R) Fellahal chez l'ecrivain public (34x46cm-13x18in)
         s. panel (F.FR 38000)

ROSSI, Alberto Maria (1879-1965) Argentinian
£729 $1400   (4-Aug-92 V.BA91/R) El baile (42x34cm-17x13in)
£955 $1700   (1-Nov-91 PO.BA34) Personajes del circo (54x44cm-21x17in) s. panel
£2135 $3800   (28-Apr-92 PO.BA29) Personajes del circo (62x80cm-24x31in) s.
£3763 $7000   (16-Jun-92 RO.BA70) Venecia (105x110cm-41x43in)

ROSSI, Alexander M (fl.1870-1905) British
£1300 $2236   (4-Mar-92 S143/R) On jetty (25x35cm-10x14in) indist.s. paper on canvas
£1600 $2768   (24-Mar-92 PHC443/R) Girls in meadow (13x21cm-5x8in) i.verso board
£1700 $2924   (11-Oct-91 C109/R) Day dreaming (36x25cm-14x10in) s.
£2400 $4128   (11-Oct-91 C6/R) On the riverbank (52x33cm-20x13in) s. card laid down on
         canvas
£3200 $5440   (22-Oct-91 SWS315/R) Marguerite (150x105cm-59x41in) s. with large
         decorated frame
£8721 $15000   (16-Oct-91 CH.NY259/R) The card game (71x91cm-28x36in)
£980 $1676   (12-Mar-92 CSK74/R) Spring idyll (51x69cm-20x27in) s.d.1898 W/C bodycol
£2000 $3560   (30-Apr-92 CG835/R) The little Neapolitan (55x43cm-22x17in) s. W/C htd
         bodycol. paper laid down on canvas

ROSSI, C (19th C) ?
£2195 $3820   (19-Sep-91 D.V95/R) Grape harvest (100x140cm-39x55in) s.d.890 (A.S 45000)

ROSSI, Francesco del see SALVIATI, Francesco

ROSSI, Giambattista (style) (1494-1541) Italian
£1400 $2450   (27-Feb-92 B57) The Madonna and Child with St. Anne, St. John and two
         angels (27x16cm-11x6in) panel

ROSSI, Gino (1884-1947) Italian
£25950 $46191   (29-Nov-91 F.F161 b) Paesaggio asolano (28x37cm-11x15in) i.verso
         cardboard (I.L 56000000)

ROSSI, Joseph (19/20th C) French
£1046 $1799   (13-Oct-91 REM.W23) Street scene (45x38cm-18x15in) s. board
         (P.Z 20000000)

ROSSI, L (?) ?
£540 $978   (4-Dec-91 DS.W79) Reclining nude (50x70cm-20x28in) s. (NZ.D 1750)

ROSSI, Lucius (1846-1913) French
£576 $1100   (19-Jul-92 LIT.L1) Portrait of semi-nude young woman (53x46cm-21x18in) s.
£2615 $4498   (13-Oct-91 REM.W24) Garden scene (35x28cm-14x11in) s. (P.Z 50000000)

ROSSI, Luigi (1853-1923) Swiss
£8850 $16460   (16-Jun-92 F.M273/R) Primi approcci (48x78cm-19x31in) s.d.1884
                            (I.L 19500000)
£697 $1262   (3-Dec-91 SY.MI113) Ritratto di vecchio (56x39cm-22x15in) s. pastel
*   cardboard (I.L 1500000)*

ROSSI, Mariano (1731-1807) Italian
£3400 $5950   (3-Apr-92 C14/R) Cephalus and Procris (23x29cm-9x11in)
£4074 $7374   (19-May-92 GF.L2097/R) Bozzetto for ceiling fresco with apotheosis of a
                            pope (70x99cm-28x39in) (S.FR 11000)

ROSSI, Roberto (1896-1957) Argentinian
£838 $1500   (6-May-92 V.BA96) Composicion (63x48cm-25x19in)
£1006 $1750   (19-Sep-91 V.BA89) Naturaleza muerta con jarra (47x65cm-19x26in)
£1022 $1900   (16-Jun-92 RO.BA84) La Blusa Blanca (73x55cm-29x22in)

ROSSIGNOL, Lily (19/20th C) French
£4942 $8500   (16-Oct-91 CH.NY26/R) Castel San Angelo, Rome (90x135cm-35x53in) s.d.91

ROSSLE, Herta (1906-) German
£528 $956   (3-Dec-91 FN.S1875/R) Three men standing before multistoried houses
                            (79x70cm-31x28in) s.d.1926 panel (DM 1500)

ROSSLER, Adalbert von (1853-1922) German
£4035 $7263   (22-Nov-91 SA.A1772/R) Palace scene with harem ladies (130x74cm-51x29in)
                            s. (DM 11500)

ROSSLER, Rudolf (1864-?) Austrian
£680 $1210   (29-Apr-92 D.V849) Little girl with her dog (32x24cm-13x9in) s.
                            (A.S 14000)
£1453 $2500   (15-Oct-91 CE.NY33/R) Children singing (53x122cm-21x48in) s.

ROSSMANN, Augusta Charlotte Cornelie (1863-1945) Belgian
£602 $1101   (4-Jun-92 SY.Z590/R) Little girl seated (46x55cm-18x22in) (S.FR 1600)
£827 $1514   (4-Jun-92 SY.Z560/R) Study of vegetables and fruit (35x57cm-14x22in)
                            (S.FR 2200)
£2444 $4472   (4-Jun-92 SY.Z589/R) Interior with lobster (67x100cm-26x39in) s.
                            mono.verso (S.FR 6500)

ROSSO (?) Italian
£820 $1500   (3-Jun-92 D.NY85) Lesson (43x33cm-17x13in) masonite

ROSSO, Jose D (1898-1958) Argentinian
£677   . $1300   (4-Aug-92 V.BA93) Velero (38x48cm-15x19in) tempera
£729 $1400   (4-Aug-92 V.BA94/R) Naturaleza muerta (44x46cm-17x18in) tempera

ROSSUM DU CHATTEL, Fredericus Jacobus van (1856-1917) Dutch
£2484 $4422   (26-Nov-91 VN.R25) Figure in rowingboat in river landscape
                            (26x35cm-10x14in) s. (D.FL 8000)
£3976 $7037   (5-Nov-91 SY.AM74/R) Boat on canal by estate (32x40cm-13x16in) s. panel
                            (D.FL 13000)

ROSSUM DU CHATTEL, Jan Hendrik van (1820-1878) Dutch
£2062 $3588   (17-Sep-91 FN.S2223/R) Dutch river landscape with fishing boats, ferry
                            and windmills beyond (39x65cm-15x26in) s. (DM 6000)

ROSSUM, Jan van (17th C) Dutch
£8333 $14917   (14-Nov-91 CH.AM128/R) Godard Philip van Lynden d'Aspremont and sister
                            Jacoba in landscape (134x134cm-53x53in) s.i.d.1667 i.coat of arms
                            (D.FL 27000)

ROSTOCK, F (19/20th C) French
£1875 $3319   (5-Nov-91 GF.L2554/R) Harbour view, winter (59x77cm-23x30in) s.d.1897
                            (S.FR 4800)

ROSTRUP-BOYESEN, P (1882-1952) Danish
£535 $920   (16-Oct-91 KH.K230) Summer's day, Dragor (57x70cm-22x28in) mono.
                            (D.KR 6000)

ROTARI, Pietro (1707-1762) Italian
£5385 $10285   (15-Jul-92 CH.S767/R) Czarevich Paul of Russia (54x45cm-21x18in)
                            (A.D 14000)
£6704 $12000   (17-Jan-92 SY.NY54/R) Portrait of a girl in red wearing a white cap
                            (43x34cm-17x13in)
£23743 $42500   (17-Jan-92 SY.NY53/R) Portrait of a girl in a blue dress and cap
                            (43x33cm-17x13in)

ROTARI, Pietro (attrib) (1707-1762) Italian
£14525 $26000   (16-Jan-92 CH.NY86/R) Young woman asleep. Young woman gesturing. Young woman looking over shoulder. Young woman to right (49x40cm-19x16in) four

ROTARI, Pietro (style) (1707-1762) Italian
£3927 $7030   (7-May-92 CH.AM25/R) Portrait of young woman, wearing fur-trimmed blue coat and red bonnet (45x35cm-18x14in) canvas on board (D.FL 13000)
£6363 $11263   (7-Nov-91 D.V1/R) Portrait of girl wearing blue ribbon around neck (45x35cm-18x14in) one of pair (A.S 130000)
£6363 $11263   (7-Nov-91 D.V2/R) Portrait of young lady wearing black dress (45x35cm-18x14in) one of pair (A.S 130000)

ROTELLA, Mimmo (1918-) Italian
£795 $1438   (23-May-92 KV.L285) Composition (34x23cm-13x9in) s. collage (B.FR 48000)
£2085 $3712   (26-Nov-91 SY.MI104/R) Le olive (116x118cm-46x46in) s. photograph on paper on panel (I.L 4500000)
£2741 $4769   (14-Apr-92 F.M79/R) Il ferito (33x55cm-13x22in) s. s.i.d.verso collage canvas (I.L 6000000)
£2781 $4755   (18-Mar-92 LT.P139) Abraction (25x52cm-10x20in) s.d.1958 torn posters laid down on canvas (F.FR 27000)
£3178 $5657   (29-Apr-92 F.F209/R) Sempre buona (140x98cm-55x39in) s.d.1971 artypo plexiglass (I.L 7000000)
£3178 $5657   (29-Apr-92 F.F208/R) Manus (19x29cm-7x11in) s. s.i.d.1962 decollage canvas (I.L 7000000)
£10000 $17200   (17-Oct-91 S41/R) Untitled (85x148cm-33x58in) s. poster decollage canvas

ROTH, Dieter (1930-) German
£512 $932   (25-May-92 WK.M1072/R) 5 x 3 unstabile (23x24cm-9x9in) s.i.d.1975 col.felt tip pen pencil collage board (DM 1500)
£512 $932   (25-May-92 WK.M1073/R) Bottom (23x33cm-9x13in) s.i.d.1975 pencil felt tip pen board (DM 1500)
£624 $1129   (3-Dec-91 AB.S5151/R) '5x3 Unstabile' (24x34cm-9x13in) s.d.75 mixed media (S.KR 6500)
£672 $1216   (3-Dec-91 AB.S5150/R) 'Hintern' (24x33cm-9x13in) s.d.75 pencil Indian ink (S.KR 7000)
£1181 $2031   (16-Oct-91 G.Z151/R) Conversation (21x29cm-8x11in) s.i.d.1975 pencil (S.FR 3000)

ROTH, Dieter and RAINER, Arnulf (20th C) German/Austrian
£6119 $10892   (26-Nov-91 KF.M975/R) Untitled (44x62cm-17x24in) s.i.d.1976 mixed media board (DM 17500)

ROTH, George Andries (1809-1887) Dutch
£1884 $3240   (8-Oct-91 ZEL.L1690/R) Wooded landscape with figures on path (24x30cm-9x12in) s.d.1874 panel (DM 5500)

ROTH, L M (1858-?) German
£1490 $2667   (15-Nov-91 ZOF.Z1427/R) The joy of motherhood (107x63cm-42x25in) s.i. (S.FR 3800)

ROTH, Leo (1910-) ?
£691 $1300   (5-Jan-92 GG.TA357/R) Still life and figure (81x60cm-32x24in) s.d.1968

ROTH, Philipp (1841-1921) German
£515 $897   (18-Sep-91 N.M670) Gravel pit (18x26cm-7x10in) s. board (DM 1500)
£697 $1268   (11-Dec-91 WE.MU72/R) Autumnal lake landscape (23x33cm-9x13in) s.d.1861 board on panel (DM 2000)
£756 $1315   (18-Sep-91 N.M669/R) River landscape (29x33cm-11x13in) s. board (DM 2200)
£1742 $3171   (12-Dec-91 L.K671) View of Dutch town and windmills (21x23cm-8x9in) s. board (DM 5000)
£1742 $3171   (12-Dec-91 L.K670) Landscape with telegraph poles near Munich (20x27cm-8x11in) s. i.verso board (DM 5000)
£2113 $3824   (3-Dec-91 FN.S2415 a/R) River landscape with reed and waterlilies (29x31cm-11x12in) s.i. canvas on board (DM 6000)
£3521 $6373   (3-Dec-91 FN.S2415/R) Cattle on path returning from pastures in wooded landscape (45x63cm-18x25in) s. (DM 10000)
£5842 $10691   (2-Jun-92 FN.S2727/R) Cattle watering in Amper landscape and thunderstorm rising (46x85cm-18x33in) s.i.d.1889 (DM 17000)
£993 $1708   (11-Oct-91 AW.H1266/R) Farmhouse in Dachauer Moos (30x38cm-12x15in) s. chk htd.white (DM 2900)
£2963 $5363   (19-May-92 GF.L2158/R) Farmhouses near Gern (24x39cm-9x15in) s. W/C (S.FR 8000)

ROTH, Willi (1908-1952) Swiss
£471 $800   (23-Oct-91 GD.B625/R) Landscape near Munchenstein (45x54cm-18x21in) s.d.32 panel (S.FR 1200)
£510 $913   (15-Nov-91 ZOF.Z1858/R) Rhine landscape with view of Basle at night (25x20cm-10x8in) s.d.36 pencil (S.FR 1300)

ROTHAUG, Alexander (1870-1946) Austrian
£1582 $2768   (19-Feb-92 D.V18/R) The first ray of sunshine (61x31cm-24x12in) s. (A.S 32000)
£583 $1037   (28-Apr-92 D.V239/R) By the fountain (46x38cm-18x15in) s. mixed media board (A.S 12000)

ROTHAUG, Alexander (1870-1946) Austrian-cont.
£736 $1398   (25-Jun-92 D.V711/R) Einzug mit Amor (9x20cm-4x8in) s. pen brush indian
                 ink (A.S 15000)

ROTHE, G H (20th C) American?
£698 $1200   (12-Oct-91 SY.NY372/R) Untitled (183x89cm-72x35in) gold leaf oil panel on
                 linen-covered panel
£698 $1200   (12-Oct-91 SY.NY371/R) Untitled (188x90cm-74x35in) s.d.1987 verso gold
                 leaf oil panel

ROTHENBERG, Susan (1945-) American
£3352 $6000   (5-May-92 CH.NY158/R) Untitled (66x59cm-26x23in) s.d.85verso paper
£22857 $40000   (25-Feb-92 SY.NY157/R) Somebody else's hand (55x91cm-22x36in)
                    s.i.d.1979verso acrylic flashe
£62857 $110000   (27-Feb-92 CH.NY106/R) Greenfield (198x282cm-78x111in) s.d.1980verso
£64246 $115000   (13-Nov-91 SY.NY75/R) Untitled - head (170x198cm-67x78in) s.d.1978 verso
                    acrylic canvas
£89385 $160000   (13-Nov-91 SY.NY50/R) Patches (221x297cm-87x117in)
£122905 $220000   (5-May-92 CH.NY11/R) Grandmother (226x286cm-89x113in) s.i.d.1983-84verso
£1286 $2250   (28-Feb-92 SY.NY343/R) Untitled (44x36cm-17x14in) graphite
£6286 $11000   (27-Feb-92 CH.NY103/R) Untitled (56x79cm-22x31in) s.d.1985verso chl
                    graphite
£8380 $15000   (5-May-92 CH.NY138/R) Head and spine (76x111cm-30x44in) s.d.1983verso oil
                    chl
£15363 $27500   (14-Nov-91 SY.NY230/R) Untitled (68x100cm-27x39in) chl

ROTHENSTEIN, Sir William (1872-1945) British
£500 $900   (20-Nov-91 B63) Artist's house, Iles Farm, Far Oakridge, Gloucestershire
                  (56x91cm-22x36in)
£1800 $3132   (19-Sep-91 B69/R) Portrait of girl in pink (53x43cm-21x17in)
£8000 $14400   (20-Nov-91 S96/R) Portrait of Robbie (34x24cm-13x9in) s.i.d.1898 col.chk

ROTHKO, Mark (1903-1970) American
£55714 $97500   (25-Feb-92 SY.NY123/R) Untitled (61x44cm-24x17in) s.verso paper on canvas
£134078 $240000   (5-May-92 CH.NY33/R) Untitled (122x103cm-48x41in) acrylic paper on board
£217877 $390000   (6-May-92 SY.NY8 a/R) Untitled (84x76cm-33x30in)

ROTHLISBERGER, William (1862-1943) Swiss
£553 $996   (19-Nov-91 GS.B3235) Le Vully (55x89cm-22x35in) s.d.1933 s.i.d.verso
                board (S.FR 1400)

ROTHLISBERGER, Willy (1914-) Swiss?
£1020 $1733   (23-Oct-91 GD.B620) Self portrait with daughter (90x70cm-35x28in) mono.
                 pavatex (S.FR 2600)
£1176 $2000   (23-Oct-91 GD.B619/R) Silsersee landscape (74x94cm-29x37in) mono. i.verso
                 (S.FR 3000)

ROTHSTEN, Carl Abraham (1826-1877) Swedish
£527 $949   (23-Nov-91 SO.S590/R) Summer landscape with hunters and fox
                 (58x73cm-23x29in) mono.d.1851 (S.KR 5500)
£1296 $2345   (3-Dec-91 AB.S4657/R) Summer landscape with Skokloster Palace
                 (52x74cm-20x29in) s.d.1868 (S.KR 13500)
£1698 $3006   (5-Nov-91 BA.S157/R) View of Lovstadt Palace (40x55cm-16x22in)
                 init.d.1854 (S.KR 18000)
£2657 $4861   (14-May-92 BU.S58/R) Sailingboats near Gripsholm's Castle
                 (53x65cm-21x26in) mono.d.1857 (S.KR 28000)

ROTHWELL, Richard (attrib) (1800-1868) British
£4500 $8055   (15-Nov-91 C189/R) Group portrait of mother and two daughters, one seated
                 reading book (91x100cm-36x39in)

ROTHWELL, Selim (1815-1881) British
£520 $941   (19-May-92 PH42) Arch of Titus at Rome (45x73cm-18x29in) s.d.1878 W/C
£750 $1328   (13-Feb-92 B162) Figures outside a Milanese Palace (55x77cm-22x30in) s.i.
                 W/C htd.white

ROTIER, Peter (1887-1963) American
£575 $1000   (15-Sep-91 H.C777) Buffalo hunting (61x76cm-24x30in) s. board

ROTIG, Georges Frederic (1873-1961) French
£1376 $2450   (30-Oct-91 CH.AM239/R) Boars in snowy forest along brook
                 (33x41cm-13x16in) s.d.47 (D.FL 4500)
£2081 $3642   (30-Mar-92 ZZ.F123/R) Cerf et biches a l'automne (146x60cm-57x24in)
                 s.d.1920 (F.FR 20000)
£4069 $7284   (17-Nov-91 LL.LH102/R) La horde de sangliers (46x61cm-18x24in) s.d.1903
                 (F.FR 40000)
£864 $1511   (30-Mar-92 ZZ.F118/R) Sangliers dans la neige (10x12cm-4x5in) s.d.1911
                 crayon ink (F.FR 8300)
£884 $1548   (30-Mar-92 ZZ.F117/R) Sangliers au bord du lac (11x9cm-4x4in) s.i. crayon
                 ink (F.FR 8500)
£1041 $1821   (30-Mar-92 ZZ.F115/R) Les Cockers et Setter Gordon et Laverach
                 (23x33cm-9x13in) s. crayon (F.FR 10000)
£1353 $2367   (30-Mar-92 ZZ.F116/R) Les Rapaces (24x32cm-9x13in) s.d.1922 gouache
                 (F.FR 13000)

ROTTA, Antonio (1828-1903) Italian
£34000 $58140   (20-Mar-92 C60/R) Nuovi amichetti (42x52cm-17x20in) s.d.1879 panel

ROTTA, Antonio (attrib) (1828-1903) Italian
£8929 $15000   (12-Aug-91 SG.M580) Young girl holding her cat up to birdcage
        (43x33cm-17x13in) s.d.1890 panel

ROTTENHAMMER, Hans (16/17th C) German
£8500 $16320   (7-Jul-92 PH22/R) Holy Family accompanied by two angels (38x28cm-15x11in)
        copper
£11583 $19807   (12-Mar-92 GK.Z6/R) Reclining Venus and two putti (33x44cm-13x17in)
        s.indis.d.1601 copper (S.FR 30000)
£26132 $47561   (11-Dec-91 N.M352/R) The Judgement of Paris (32x43cm-13x17in) copper
        (DM 75000)

ROTTENHAMMER, Hans (attrib) (16/17th C) German
£7000 $12250   (1-Apr-92 S170/R) Adoration of Magi (49x40cm-19x16in) copper
£584 $1069   (3-Jun-92 DO.H2392/R) Jesus and the Woman of Samaria (20x16cm-8x6in) i.
        indian ink pen wash (DM 1700)

ROTTENHAMMER, Hans (circle) (16/17th C) German
£2500 $4575   (12-May-92 SWS805/R) Judgement of Paris (50x68cm-20x27in) copper
£4530 $8244   (12-Dec-91 L.K153/R) Bacchanale (34x43cm-13x17in) copper (DM 13000)

ROTTENHAMMER, Hans (school) (16/17th C) German
£1646 $3128   (24-Jun-92 CSC.P39) Leda (22x30cm-9x12in) copper (F.FR 16000)

ROTTENHAMMER, Hans (style) (16/17th C) German
£1358 $2431   (12-Nov-91 SY.AM87) Diana and Actaeon (38x56cm-15x22in) panel (D.FL 4400)
£1490 $2548   (18-Mar-92 D.V394/R) Scene from the life of St Catherin of Alexandria
        (42x31cm-17x12in) copper one of pair (A.S 30000)
£1490 $2548   (18-Mar-92 D.V392/R) Scene from the life of St Catherin of Alexandria
        (42x31cm-17x12in) copper one of pair (A.S 30000)

ROTTENHAMMER, Johann (1564-1625) German
£750 $1365   (11-Dec-91 PH316/R) The Nativity (30x20cm-12x8in) pen htd.white

ROTTENHAMMER, Johann (attrib) (1564-1625) German
£12000 $23040   (8-Jul-92 S77/R) Ecce Homo and Christ carrying the Cross (22x28cm-9x11in)
        copper

ROTTENHAMMER, Johann (circle) (1564-1625) German
£1900 $3325   (31-Mar-92 PH50/R) Holy Family with Saint Elizabeth (30x24cm-12x9in)
        copper

ROTTENHAMMER, Johann (studio) (1564-1625) German
£4000 $7280   (10-Dec-91 PH136/R) Adoration of shepherds (20x25cm-8x10in) bears sig.
        copper

ROTTMANN, Carl (1798-1850) German
£13380 $24218   (4-Dec-91 DO.H2901/R) Pronoia (25x30cm-10x12in) i.verso (DM 38000)

ROTTMANN, Mozart (1874-?) Hungarian
£856 $1473   (8-Oct-91 ZEL.L1691/R) The paternity suit (61x81cm-24x32in) s. (DM 2500)
£1706 $3089   (21-May-92 L.K477) The beautiful slave (89x114cm-35x45in) s.d.11
        (DM 5000)

ROTTMAYR, Johann Michael (1654-1730) Austrian
£10453 $19024   (11-Dec-91 N.M354/R) Homage of Godess (90x58cm-35x23in) (DM 30000)
£16575 $30000   (21-May-92 CH.NY79/R) Good Samaritan (148x197cm-58x78in)

ROUAN, Francois (1943-) French
£2138 $3956   (13-Jun-92 AT.P64/R) La lampe a petrole (65x50cm-26x20in) s. (F.FR 21000)
£29050 $52000   (12-Nov-91 CE.NY87/R) Porta Ardeatina (201x171cm-79x67in)
        s.i.d.1972-1974stretcher woven canvas strips

ROUARGUE, S (19th C) French
£471 $900   (16-Jul-92 SY.NY334/R) Artist in her garden (74x52cm-29x20in) s.d.1828
        pastel

ROUAULT, Georges (1871-1958) French
£13834 $24625   (29-Nov-91 GAB.G2868/R) Paysage au Cypres (14x10cm-6x4in) bears studio
        st.verso panel (S.FR 35000)
£27597 $50502   (3-Jun-92 PIC.P60/R) Tristes Os - clown (32x20cm-13x8in) s.i. tracing
        paper (F.FR 271000)
£30000 $57300   (1-Jul-92 S147/R) Paysage biblique (16x24cm-6x9in) studio st. paper laid
        down on canvas
£45000 $85950   (30-Jun-92 C181/R) La sainte face (63x49cm-25x19in)
£50000 $90500   (3-Dec-91 C279/R) La passion (11x25cm-4x10in) s. i.stretcher
£65574 $120000   (14-May-92 SY.NY275/R) Christ, Passion (44x33cm-17x13in) s. paper on
        canvas
£218579 $400000   (13-May-92 SY.NY93/R) Clown a la grosse caisse (68x49cm-27x19in) s. paper
        on canvas
£280000 $506800   (2-Dec-91 C32/R) Femme a la rose (71x61cm-28x24in) s.

ROUAULT, Georges (1871-1958) French-cont.

£4578	$8194	(13-Nov-91 CD.P13/R) Premier projet pour Passion (31x20cm-12x8in) Indian ink wash gouache (F.FR 45000)
£7000	$13370	(1-Jul-92 S160/R) Petit breton (30x18cm-12x7in) gouache chl
£7650	$14000	(13-May-92 CH.NY233/R) Bon electeur (31x20cm-12x8in) s.indist.d.1918 i.verso gouache
£8197	$15000	(13-May-92 CH.NY228/R) Mademoiselle Irma (33x20cm-13x8in) s.d.1918 gouache brush ink col.wax crayon
£10383	$19000	(13-May-92 CH.NY229/R) Fleau colon (38x25cm-15x10in) s.d.1918 i.verso gouache
£10929	$20000	(13-May-92 CH.NY230/R) Cristal de Roche (31x20cm-12x8in) s.d.1918 gouache brush wash
£12022	$22000	(13-May-92 CH.NY227/R) L'administrateur colonial (38x25cm-15x10in) s.d.1918 i.verso gouache col. wax crayons
£13000	$23530	(3-Dec-91 C111/R) Nu de dos (39x26cm-15x10in) init.d.1915 gouache paper laid down on card
£15301	$28000	(13-May-92 CH.NY231/R) Le politicard (38x25cm-15x10in) s.d.1918 i.verso gouache
£16393	$30000	(13-May-92 CH.NY232/R) Paysage tropical (36x22cm-14x9in) s.d.1918 i.verso gouache
£17486	$32000	(13-May-92 CH.NY226/R) Sainte-Nitouche (29x19cm-11x7in) s.d.1918 i.verso gouache col.wax crayon
£22599	$40000	(6-Nov-91 CH.NY156/R) Etoile du soir, clos ma paupiere ... (20x31cm-8x12in) s.d.1932 gouache brush india ink
£191257	$350000	(12-May-92 CH.NY128/R) Acrobat XIII (104x73cm-41x29in) s.d.1913 gouache paper on canvas

ROUBAL, Franz (1884-1967) Austrian

£602	$1089	(5-Dec-91 D.V239) Cows grazing (60x80cm-24x31in) s.d.1933 (A.S 12000)

ROUBAUD, Franz (1856-1928) Russian

£1203	$2093	(18-Sep-91 N.M671/R) Caucasian rider in prairie (22x30cm-9x12in) s.d.1890 panel (DM 3500)
£3136	$5707	(11-Dec-91 WE.MU315) Cossacks racing in mountain landscape (62x46cm-24x18in) s. (DM 9000)
£4577	$8285	(3-Dec-91 FN.S2420/R) Riders and horse-drawn carts crossing ford in mountain landscape (60x84cm-24x33in) s. (DM 13000)

ROUBAUD, Franz (attrib) (1856-1928) Russian

£1134	$1973	(18-Sep-91 N.M672) Arabian riders before town (11x25cm-4x10in) i. panel (DM 3300)

ROUBINE, Yefime (1912-) Russian

£720	$1303	(6-Dec-91 ARC.P24) La moisson (74x101cm-29x40in) s. (F.FR 7000)

ROUBINSKI, Igor (1919-) Russian

£963	$1754	(27-May-92 GL.P67/R) Enfants devant la datcha (80x121cm-31x48in) s. (F.FR 9500)

ROUEN SCHOOL, 17th C French

£2900	$5568	(7-Jul-92 PH202/R) Madonna and child attended by angels (76x61cm-30x24in)

ROUETTE, Gabriel (attrib) (18th C) French

£3242	$5868	(20-May-92 CSC.P19/R) Deux chiens se disputant un jeu de cartes (67x105cm-26x41in) (F.FR 32000)

ROUGEMONT, Philippe de (1891-1965) Swedish

£475	$851	(16-Nov-91 FAL.M312/R) Nude model (73x60cm-29x24in) s. (S.KR 5000)
£617	$1074	(13-Apr-92 AB.S230) Nude woman reclining of sofa (56x91cm-22x36in) s. (S.KR 6500)
£659	$1173	(28-Oct-91 AB.S207/R) Nude model seated by mirror (76x73cm-30x29in) s.d.43 (S.KR 7000)
£679	$1202	(25-Apr-92 SO.S582/R) Ballet dancers (60x46cm-24x18in) s. (S.KR 7200)

ROUGERON, Jules James (1841-1880) French

£1400	$2534	(22-May-92 C152/R) Park bench (33x24cm-13x9in) s.
£2875	$5175	(20-Nov-91 CN.P218/R) La lettre (45x61cm-18x24in) s.d.77 board laid down on canvas (F.FR 28000)

ROULAND, Orlando (1871-?) American

£1111	$2000	(22-Nov-91 S.BM114/R) Plaza reflections Central Park, New York (53x74cm-21x29in) with i.verso

ROULET, Henry (1915-) Swiss

£1711	$3183	(19-Jun-92 ZOF.Z2062/R) Intimite (50x61cm-20x24in) s.i.d.1971 (S.FR 4500)

ROULLET, Gaston (1847-1925) French

£610	$1061	(13-Apr-92 BG.P87) Le Hvre de Thuyen (27x18cm-11x7in) s.d.1886 wood (F.FR 6000)
£900	$1629	(19-May-92 SWS288) Le vieux Chateau de Fougeres Bretagne (89x68cm-35x27in) s.i.

ROUMIANTSEVA, Galina (1927-) Russian

£1486	$2674	(27-Jan-92 ARC.P77/R) Le soir de Noel (70x90cm-28x35in) s. (F.FR 14500)
£1537	$2766	(27-Jan-92 ARC.P80/R) La table fleurie (80x120cm-31x47in) s. (F.FR 15000)

ROUMIANTSEVA, Kapitolina (1925-) Russian
£504	$882	(24-Sep-91 ARC.P96/R) Dans le jardin (50x75cm-20x30in) s. board (F.FR 5000)
£514	$900	(24-Sep-91 ARC.P100/R) Fleurs dans champs (81x62cm-32x24in) s. (F.FR 5100)
£605	$1058	(24-Sep-91 ARC.P94/R) La premiere peche (61x81cm-24x32in) s. board (F.FR 6000)
£789	$1420	(27-Jan-92 ARC.P165/R) Le banc du jardin (72x100cm-28x39in) s. (F.FR 7700)
£1025	$1844	(27-Jan-92 ARC.P164/R) Pres de la maison (99x100cm-39x39in) s. (F.FR 10000)
£1076	$1936	(27-Jan-92 ARC.P166/R) Bouquet des champs (119x79cm-47x31in) s. (F.FR 10500)

ROUNTREE, Harry (1878-1950) British
£900	$1728	(10-Jul-92 CSK43/R) We must burn the house down (30x20cm-12x8in) s. pencil W/C htd white

ROUPE, Lennart (1918-) Swedish
£541	$942	(13-Apr-92 AB.S231/R) Vessels at anchor, Stockholm (88x91cm-35x36in) s.d.86 (S.KR 5700)

ROURE, Auguste Louis (1878-?) French
£815	$1483	(13-Dec-91 ZZ.F34) Garrigue (36x59cm-14x23in) s. (F.FR 8000)

ROUSSE, Frank (fl.1897-1915) British
£520	$884	(24-Oct-91 RS59) Unloading the catch (25x43cm-10x17in) s. W/C

ROUSSEAU (?) ?
£370	$670	(21-May-92 GK.Z1707 b) Portrait of young gentleman wearing patterned silk gilet (7x5cm-3x2in) min.s.d.1830 (S.FR 1000)

ROUSSEAU, Emmanuel (19th C) French
£803	$1437	(6-May-92 GD.B1087/R) Still life of onions, garlic, laurel, parsley and pot on wall (39x23cm-15x9in) s.i. board (S.FR 2200)

ROUSSEAU, Helen (1898-) American
£632	$1200	(24-Jun-92 B.SF6465/R) Barnyard - November Haze (61x76cm-24x30in) s. board
£2825	$5000	(12-Feb-92 B.SF546/R) Sailing lesson (81x91cm-32x36in) s. board

ROUSSEAU, Henri (style) (1844-1910) French
£1000	$1730	(3-Oct-91 CSK48) A faggot gatherer on a woodland track (64x76cm-25x30in) with sig.

ROUSSEAU, Henri Emilien (1875-1933) French
£1728	$3006	(13-Apr-92 AT.P208) Le lancement du faucon (20x16cm-8x6in) s. board (F.FR 17000)
£2182	$3993	(14-May-92 BU.S174/R) Still life of flowers (61x51cm-24x20in) s. (S.KR 23000)
£11294	$20329	(18-Nov-91 AT.P376/R) Les cavaliers (55x74cm-22x29in) s.d.1929 (F.FR 110000)
£681	$1300	(16-Jul-92 SY.NY403/R) Course en Camargue (48x63cm-19x25in) s.d.29 W/C gouache chl.
£4268	$7427	(13-Apr-92 AT.P163/R) Caid fauconnier a cheval (61x47cm-24x19in) s. W/C over chl dr (F.FR 42000)

ROUSSEAU, Jacques de (1600-1638) Dutch
£48000	$92160	(10-Jul-92 C13/R) Lute player accompanying old man holding musical score (122x101cm-48x40in) mono.d.1631

ROUSSEAU, Jacques de (attrib) (1600-1638) Dutch
£1685	$3000	(22-Jan-92 D.NY42) Mother and daughter (66x99cm-26x39in)

ROUSSEAU, Jules Antoine (1710-1782) French
£10288	$18621	(7-Dec-91 CH.MO63/R) Un paneau de porte pour un cabinet turc (93x70cm-37x28in) painted with J.H. and J.S.Rousseau panel (F.FR 100000)

ROUSSEAU, Margarite (1888-1948) Belgian
£632	$1100	(11-Sep-91 D.NY71) Cabanas along shore (38x56cm-15x22in) s.d.19 board
£925	$1600	(2-Oct-91 D.NY86) The boating party (38x53cm-15x21in) s. board
£1500	$2580	(12-Oct-91 KV.L256) Sunday afternoon (38x55cm-15x22in) s.d.15 canvas on panel (B.FR 90000)
£1667	$2867	(12-Oct-91 KV.L255/R) The coaches (46x55cm-18x22in) s.d.17 (B.FR 100000)
£1714	$3000	(28-Feb-92 SY.NY165/R) Afternoon at beach (38x55cm-15x22in) s.
£18286	$32000	(19-Feb-92 CH.NY145/R) Regatta (54x72cm-21x28in) s.d.13 canvas on board

ROUSSEAU, Maurice (19th C) French
£916	$1750	(16-Jul-92 SY.NY524/R) Shepherdess and her flock (50x65cm-20x26in) s.

ROUSSEAU, Philippe (1816-1887) French
£728	$1275	(5-Apr-92 ZZ.F72/R) Nature morte aux poissons (46x61cm-18x24in) init. (F.FR 7000)

ROUSSEAU, Philippe (1816-1887) French-cont.

£15429 $27000   (20-Feb-92 SY.NY3/R) La chaise de poste, paysage (102x119cm-40x47in) s.d.1841

ROUSSEAU, Theodore (1812-1867) French

£2372	$4246	(6-May-92 GD.B1088/R) Woodlands with pond and figures, autumn (31x50cm-12x20in) mono paper on canvas (S.FR 6500)
£2624	$4750	(21-May-92 S.W2897/R) Forest interior (23x38cm-9x15in) s. panel
£3670	$6826	(18-Jun-92 SY.MO359/R) Un peintre parmi les rochers (30x25cm-12x10in) paper laid down on canvas (F.FR 36000)
£5106	$9241	(7-Dec-91 WK.M478/R) Landscape near Barbizon (49x60cm-19x24in) s. (DM 14500)
£6620	$12049	(12-Dec-91 L.K672/R) Hilly landscape near Barbizon at dusk (65x71cm-26x28in) s. panel (DM 19000)
£8140	$14000	(16-Oct-91 CH.NY77 a/R) Le petit pecheur (15x21cm-6x8in) bears init. panel
£11628	$20000	(16-Oct-91 CH.NY77/R) L'Etude des Marais de Tiffauge en Vendee (22x33cm-9x13in) s. panel
£13937	$25366	(14-Dec-91 BOD.P744) Cows watering in pond in forest of Fontainebleau (29x46cm-11x18in) mono (DM 40000)
£15385	$28000	(27-May-92 CH.NY171/R) L'Etang (35x53cm-14x21in) s. panel
£21978	$40000	(27-May-92 CH.NY170/R) Soleil couchant (26x50cm-10x20in) s.
£52326	$90000	(13-Oct-91 H.C44/R) Plains of Meudon (36x48cm-14x19in) init.d.1844 panel
£407	$754	(12-Jun-92 ARC.P179) Chemin a la lisiere d'un bois (19x28cm-7x11in) studio st. black crayon (F.FR 4000)
£470	$861	(3-Feb-92 SD.P195) Paysage (7x12cm-3x5in) bears st.mono. lead pencil stumping (F.FR 4600)
£601	$1112	(12-Jun-92 ARC.P180) Paysage avec personnage (11x18cm-4x7in) studio st. black crayon (F.FR 5900)
£772	$1321	(18-Mar-92 PIC.P95/R) Pres de Viroflay (18x25cm-7x10in) init.d.1958 crayon dr htd pastel (F.FR 7500)
£1512	$2600	(13-Oct-91 H.C43/R) Landscape with building among trees (13x23cm-5x9in) bears atelier st. pen pencil
£1977	$3400	(13-Oct-91 H.C41/R) Pont de pierre dans la campagne (15x23cm-6x9in) bears atelier st. pencil
£4000	$7120	(27-Nov-91 S230/R) Bergere gardant ses troupeaux (37x51cm-15x20in) st. black chk
£5601	$10362	(12-Jun-92 ARC.P178/R) Vue d'une mare pres d'une chaumiere (12x18cm-5x7in) studio st. pen wash htd W/C (F.FR 55000)

ROUSSEAU, Theodore (attrib) (1812-1867) French

£878 $1589   (3-Dec-91 R.T203/R) Setting sun, Barbizon Forest (77x98cm-30x39in) bears sig (C.D 1800)

ROUSSEL, Charles-Emanuel-Joseph (1861-1936) French

£922	$1660	(2-Feb-92 ZZ.F73/R) Le pecheur a la barbe blanche (55x46cm-22x18in) s. (F.FR 9000)
£2601	$4553	(5-Apr-92 ZZ.F5/R) Le retour des pecheurs (33x46cm-13x18in) s. (F.FR 25000)
£3538	$6191	(5-Apr-92 ZZ.F2/R) La preparation des filets (33x46cm-13x18in) s. (F.FR 34000)

ROUSSEL, Ker Xavier (1867-1944) French

£4096	$7250	(6-Nov-91 D.NY46/R) Dance pour la nymphe (28x37cm-11x15in) s. cardboard
£4802	$8500	(5-Nov-91 CE.NY1/R) Le faune et les deux nymphes (27x37cm-11x15in) s. board
£565	$1016	(19-Nov-91 FB.P13/R) Personnage dans un jardin (23x36cm-9x14in) s. pastel paper laid down on board (F.FR 5500)
£769	$1462	(25-Jun-92 GK.B644) Le dejeuner sur l'herbe (19x29cm-7x11in) s. W/C bodycol over chk (S.FR 2000)
£875	$1497	(22-Mar-92 LT.P38) Paysage (30x49cm-12x19in) s. pastel (F.FR 8500)
£1459	$2510	(4-Mar-92 AT.P87/R) Triomphe de Bacchus (24x34cm-9x13in) s. pastel (F.FR 14200)
£2837	$5135	(19-May-92 FB.P53) Femme nue dans un paysage (29x45cm-11x18in) s. pastel (F.FR 28000)
£5295	$9690	(3-Jun-92 PIC.P32/R) Baigneuse au bord de l'eau (21x34cm-8x13in) s. pastel (F.FR 52000)

ROUSSEL, Pierre (20th C) French

£900	$1629	(2-Dec-91 CSK63/R) Panorama de la vallee du Loire (61x82cm-24x32in) s. board
£1387	$2400	(25-Mar-92 D.NY63/R) Paysage (64x66cm-25x26in) s.
£750	$1358	(2-Dec-91 CSK61/R) La lampe Japonaise (61x67cm-24x26in) s. pastel

ROUSSEL, Theodore (1847-1926) British

£800 $1392   (19-Sep-91 B34/R) Portrait of Hettie Pettigrew (61x46cm-24x18in)

ROUSSEL-MASURE (1863-1919) French

£1025 $1844   (2-Feb-92 ZZ.F93/R) Riviere pres d'un village de Bourgogne (60x73cm-24x29in) s. (F.FR 10000)

ROUVIERE (20th C) French

£867 $1500   (2-Oct-91 D.NY83) Cosmos blancs (71x56cm-28x22in) s. s.i.verso

ROUX, Antoine (elder) see ROUX, Joseph Ange Antoine

ROUX, Eugene le (?) ?
£16097 $27686   (7-Oct-91 CSC.P138/R) La carte a payer (57x46cm-22x18in) s.d.73
       (F.FR 160000)

ROUX, Francois Geoffroy (1811-1882) French
£1408 $2549   (4-Dec-91 DO.H2540/R) English frigate leaving Marseille Harbour
       (42x54cm-17x21in) s.i.d.1846 W/C indian ink pen over pencil (DM 4000)
£8147 $15071   (10-Jun-92 ZZ.F69/R) Le brick de transport no.31 'L'Alcyon' partant de
       Toulon 1828 (44x57cm-17x22in) s.d.1830 W/C wash htd gouache
       (F.FR 80000)

ROUX, Francois Geoffroy (attrib) (1811-1882) French
£750 $1358   (20-May-92 S94/R) American frigate (37x53cm-15x21in) W/C pen over pencil

ROUX, Frederic (1805-1874) French
£420 $748   (28-Nov-91 CSK63) Fortifications at the entrance to harbour, Valletta
       (15x20cm-6x8in) pencil W/C
£900 $1629   (20-May-92 S109/R) Theoxena, J G Borland Capt (40x56cm-16x22in)
       s.i.d.1851 s.i.d.verso W/C

ROUX, Gaston Louis (1904-) French
£650 $1242   (29-Jun-92 CSK119/R) Homme (72x54cm-28x21in) s.d.28 oil mixed media
       canvas

ROUX, J (19th C) French
£7202 $13035   (5-Dec-91 SY.MO269/R) Paysage de bord de mer (51x66cm-20x26in) s.d.1773
       (F.FR 70000)

ROUX, Joseph Ange Antoine (1765-1835) French
£2800 $5040   (22-Nov-91 C8/R) The brig Le Duc d'Angouleme off Marseilles
       (43x58cm-17x23in) s.i.d.1818 pencil W/C htd.white
£6925 $12811   (10-Jun-92 ZZ.F70/R) Le brick francais 'La Precieuse' (41x60cm-16x24in)
       s.d.1803 pen W/C (F.FR 68000)
£7637 $14129   (10-Jun-92 ZZ.F71/R) Le Lougre, gree en goelette - l'Aigle se preparant a
       rentrer a Marseille s.d.1803 pen W/C (F.FR 75000)

ROUX, Louis (1817-1903) French
£1139 $2040   (5-May-92 ZEL.L1519/R) Moonlit river landscape with windmill
       (27x38cm-11x15in) s.i. panel (DM 3350)

ROUX, Mathieu Antoine (19th C) ?
£550 $995   (20-May-92 S79) The brig Soleil in storm (32x43cm-13x17in) s.i. W/C pen
£800 $1448   (20-May-92 S74) Brig in heavy seas (21x36cm-8x14in) s.d.1817 W/C pen
£850 $1539   (20-May-92 S71/R) Saint Esprit buffeted by wind (32x43cm-13x17in)
       s.i.d.1817 W/C pen

ROUX, Oswald (1880-1960) Austrian
£736 $1398   (25-Jun-92 D.V641/R) Sunday (35x53cm-14x21in) s. board (A.S 15000)

ROUX, Paul (?-1918) French
£2528 $4500   (22-Jan-92 SY.NY310/R) Landscape near Eole with figure by stream
       (89x147cm-35x58in) s.i.

ROUX-CHAMPION, Joseph Victor (1871-1953) French
£400 $696   (19-Sep-91 CSK101) Villas amidst trees (32x47cm-13x19in) s. W/C pencil

ROUZEE, M (19th C) French
£575 $1000   (11-Sep-91 D.NY69) Children on quai (51x41cm-20x16in) s. masonite

ROVELLO, A (?) ?
£3600 $6408   (28-Nov-91 CSK199 a/R) Still life of fruit by salver, book and vase of
       flowers on table (73x100cm-29x39in) s.

ROW, D E (20th C) ?
£650 $1164   (11-Nov-91 S689) Propelled airship (34x49cm-13x19in) s.d.1916 W/C

ROWAN, Marian Ellis (1858-1922) Australian
£489 $836   (16-Mar-92 MGS.S153) Native roses (41x21cm-16x8in) s. W/C (A.D 1100)
£741 $1274   (14-Oct-91 MGS.S349) Wattle (37x26cm-15x10in) s. W/C (A.D 1600)
£793 $1427   (19-Nov-91 JRL.S23) Wattle (18x26cm-7x10in) s. W/C (A.D 1800)
£846 $1616   (15-Jul-92 CH.S798/R) Lesser bird of Paradise (23cm-9ins circular) s.
       gouache (A.D 2200)
£900 $1638   (28-May-92 C80/R) Laburnum (76x57cm-30x22in) s.i. gouache
£900 $1638   (28-May-92 C79/R) Pyracantha (51cm-20ins circular) s. gouache
£1957 $3465   (26-Apr-92 SY.ME368/R) Orchids (53x36cm-21x14in) s. W/C (A.D 4600)

ROWBOTHAM, Charles (fl.1877-1914) British
£440 $840   (1-Jul-92 B53) Continental river landscape with figures by stone bridge
       (25x43cm-10x17in) W/C
£450 $765   (22-Oct-91 SWS164/R) Meta near Sorrento, Bay of Naples (17x30cm-7x12in)
       W/C htd gouache
£480 $917   (1-Jul-92 B89) Children fishing by Rydal Water (13x22cm-5x9in) s. W/C
       bodycol.
£500 $840   (13-Aug-91 AG167/R) Bay of Naples (12x19cm-5x7in) s. W/C
£500 $880   (6-Apr-92 PH99) The coast, Genoa (15x27cm-6x11in) s.d.1907 W/C bodycol.

1584

ROWBOTHAM, Charles (fl.1877-1914) British-cont.

£520	$993	(1-Jul-92 B58/R) Lake St Moritz, Switzerland (19x28cm-7x11in) s. W/C bodycol.
£580	$1021	(6-Apr-92 PH107/R) Alpine scene (20x29cm-8x11in) s. W/C bodycol.
£600	$1068	(29-Oct-91 C133) Figures on quayside by estuary (32x45cm-13x18in) studio st.verso pencil W/C scratching out
£600	$1146	(16-Jul-92 CSK53) Peasants gossiping on coastal path above Bay of Naples (29x39cm-11x15in) s.d.1919 W/C bodycol
£660	$1135	(3-Mar-92 AG167 a/R) Near Mennagio on Lake Como (20x42cm-8x17in) s.d.1901 i.verso W/C
£680	$1163	(12-Mar-92 CSK58/R) Beilstein on the Moselle (13x18cm-5x7in) s.i.d.1899 pencil W/C htd.white
£680	$1170	(3-Mar-92 AG167) Gerano, Gulf of Spezzia (20x42cm-8x17in) s.d.1901 i.verso W/C
£700	$1337	(13-Jul-92 PH99) Church and town of Loretto (22x50cm-9x20in) s. W/C bodycol
£720	$1210	(13-Aug-91 AG168/R) Near Taormina Sicily (27x43cm-11x17in) s. W/C
£750	$1433	(16-Jul-92 CSK125/R) Peasants and goats by ruins on Italian coast (20x25cm-8x10in) s.d.1906 i.verso pen W/C htd white
£780	$1396	(14-Jan-92 SWS24/R) Esa near Nice (20x48cm-8x19in) s.d.1890 i.verso W/C bodycol
£800	$1368	(17-Mar-92 SWS1467) Vesuvius across the Bay of Naples (20x40cm-8x16in) s. W/C htd.bodycol.over traces pencil
£820	$1435	(1-Apr-92 B108) Castle on the Rhine (20x38cm-8x15in) s. W/C
£860	$1462	(22-Oct-91 SWS159/R) Pazzuoli, Bay of Naples (18x34cm-7x13in) s.i.d.1902 W/C htd gouache
£950	$1615	(24-Oct-91 CSK22) Gossip at the fountain, Scilla, Calabria (20x15cm-8x6in) s.d.1903 i. verso pencil W/C htd.white
£950	$1615	(24-Oct-91 CSK23) A goatherder gossiping with peasant women on a coastal path at Calabria (15x23cm-6x9in) i. verso pencil W/C htd.white
£1200	$2292	(13-Jul-92 PH114/R) View from terrace overlooking the Italian coast (30x61cm-12x24in) s.d.1887 W/C bodycol
£1650	$3152	(13-Jul-92 PH113) Beside an Italian lake (30x60cm-12x24in) s.d.1887 W/C bodycol
£3200	$5504	(4-Mar-92 S209/R) Bay of Sorrento. Pozzuoli Bay of Naples (14x25cm-6x10in) s.d.1892 W/C

ROWBOTHAM, Claude (fl.1892-1913) British

£400	$696	(9-Sep-91 PH223) Streatley on Thames (35x52cm-14x20in) s.d.1892 W/C htd.white
£440	$757	(4-Mar-92 DR101) Streatley (20x48cm-8x19in) s.i.d.1892 W/C htd white
£500	$890	(30-Apr-92 T300/R) Figures on river bank - houses beyond (20x46cm-8x18in) s. W/C

ROWBOTHAM, Thomas Charles Leeson (1823-1875) British

£400	$712	(29-Oct-91 SWS420) Figures on lakeside path in Italy (24x56cm-9x22in) W/C over pencil htd white
£400	$728	(10-Dec-91 AG177) Fishing boat drawn up on beach for repair (14x37cm-6x15in) s.i.d.1860 W/C
£420	$739	(9-Apr-92 B41/R) Lago Maggiore from Baveno (13x20cm-5x8in) s.i.d.1843 W/C htd.white
£650	$1242	(21-Jul-92 PH270) Ben Ruaidh - Argyllshire (22x30cm-9x12in) s.d.1856 W/C htd white
£700	$1253	(15-Jan-92 BT104/R) French coasters in a swell (25x28cm-10x11in) init.d.1846 W/C
£700	$1204	(4-Mar-92 DR43/R) Mediterranean scene with fishermen and fort (20x46cm-8x18in) s.d.1874 W/C bodycol gum arabic
£800	$1376	(4-Mar-92 S203/R) Off Whitby (21x32cm-8x13in) s.d.1858 W/C
£988	$1700	(15-Oct-91 CE.NY148/R) Monastary on a cliff with the sea beyond (25x54cm-10x21in) s.i.d.1867 W/C gouache board
£2200	$3784	(4-Mar-92 S204/R) Fishing boats by sea (26x53cm-10x21in) s.d.1861 W/C htd white

ROWBOTHAM, Thomas Leeson (1783-1853) British

£900	$1611	(14-Nov-91 S135) Fisherfolk by Carnarvon Castle, Wales (29x23cm-11x9in) bears sig.indis.d.18.. W/C over pencil

ROWDEN, Thomas (1842-1926) British

£398	$708	(25-Nov-91 W.T1809) Belstone Tor, Dartmoor (19x40cm-7x16in) s. W/C (C.D 800)
£498	$886	(25-Nov-91 W.T1810/R) Shepherd and sheep (52x34cm-20x13in) s. W/C (C.D 1000)
£620	$1147	(11-Jun-92 T320/R) Sheep, pony and rider on Dartmoor (25x38cm-10x15in) s.d.98 W/C
£700	$1246	(28-Nov-91 PHX356) Dartmoor with ponies watering (36x64cm-14x25in) s.i.d.1903 W/C

ROWE, Algernon (?) British?

£1350	$2417	(14-Jan-92 SWS271/R) Studio still life (76x62cm-30x24in) sold with another picture
£2000	$3700	(12-Jun-92 C129/R) The rehearsal (127x76cm-50x30in) s.

ROWE, E Arthur (?-1922) British

£650	$1203	(11-Jun-92 CSK16/R) Villa Aldobrandim (25x36cm-10x14in) s.i.verso pencil W/C

ROWE, E Arthur (?-1922) British-cont.

£950	$1815	(13-Jul-92 PH130) Ravello (16x23cm-6x9in) s.i. W/C
£1100	$1881	(12-Mar-92 CSK37/R) The west border, Hatfield (18x23cm-7x9in) s. W/C
£1200	$2160	(27-Jan-92 PH130/R) Entrance to Hotel Times, Taormina, Sicily (34x24cm-13x9in) s. i.verso W/C
£1500	$2820	(19-Dec-91 C17/R) Under the terrace, Penshurst (28x38cm-11x15in) s. s.i.verso W/C

ROWE, William B (1854-1933) British

£625	$1106	(5-Nov-91 GF.L2618/R) Landscape with haystack (20x34cm-8x13in) board (S.FR 1600)

ROWLAND, C J (19th C) ?

£700	$1239	(12-Feb-92 B48/R) Portrait of officer of Madras Infantry (42x28cm-17x11in) s.d.1840 verso

ROWLANDSON, George Derville (1861-?) British

£3142	$5750	(5-Jun-92 SY.NY100/R) Picking up the scent (50x76cm-20x30in) s.
£4000	$6880	(11-Oct-91 C58/R) Over the ditch. The kill (61x91cm-24x36in) s. pair
£5500	$9735	(6-Nov-91 S102/R) New friends (40x61cm-16x24in) s.

ROWLANDSON, Thomas (1756-1827) British

£468	$867	(12-Jun-92 ARC.P182) Le service de la soupe (30x23cm-12x9in) s.d.1800 pen W/C (F.FR 4600)
£480	$830	(25-Mar-92 PHI474) Quizzing a country girl (11x14cm-4x6in) pen W/C over pencil
£480	$816	(22-Oct-91 SWS56/R) Huntsman dragged (10x18cm-4x7in) pen W/C
£520	$905	(12-Sep-91 CSK5) Homeward bound (10x13cm-4x5in) s. pencil ink W/C
£608	$1100	(21-May-92 GRO.B12/R) The cat club (10x18cm-4x7in) s.i. W/C
£750	$1433	(13-Jul-92 PH5/R) Travelling actors (26x19cm-10x7in) indis.i. W/C ink
£780	$1334	(12-Mar-92 CSK1) Nasty tumble (10x18cm-4x7in) bears sig. pen ink W/C
£791	$1400	(9-Nov-91 W.W87/R) Old Bartholomews and Hamlin's Inn (18x25cm-7x10in) i. pen W/C paper mounted on board
£820	$1394	(22-Oct-91 SWS58/R) Musical entertainers (12x16cm-5x6in) bears sig. pen W/C
£829	$1500	(20-May-92 D.NY2) The doctor's visit (15x23cm-6x9in) s. pen ink wash
£840	$1428	(22-Oct-91 SWS55/R) Bathers by lake (13x21cm-5x8in) bears sig. pen ink W/C
£850	$1496	(7-Apr-92 C122/R) Illustration to Sterne's 'Sentimental Journey' (12x18cm-5x7in) pencil ink W/C
£858	$1639	(16-Jul-92 S91) Margate, Kent (12x21cm-5x8in) i. pen W/C
£860	$1462	(22-Oct-91 SWS57/R) Rape of Europa (15x20cm-6x8in) bears sig. pen col.wash
£880	$1540	(1-Apr-92 B24) Figures and sailing vessels in coastal landscape (13x21cm-5x8in) pen ink W/C
£900	$1719	(13-Jul-92 PH10/R) Mars and Venus with putti (19x15cm-7x6in) s.i. W/C ink
£900	$1611	(12-Nov-91 C63 a) Woman and a goose (10x13cm-4x5in) pencil pen W/C
£940	$1598	(22-Oct-91 SWS54/R) Loading carrier's cart (10x16cm-4x6in) bears sig.d.1800 W/C pen col.ink
£950	$1615	(23-Oct-91 MMB217/R) Military toast (10x18cm-4x7in) pen sepia ink wash
£1000	$1720	(4-Mar-92 DR14/R) Three old salts (19x15cm-7x6in) bears sig. pen W/C
£1000	$1760	(6-Apr-92 PH26/R) The unsuccessful suitor (27x22cm-11x9in) bears sig.d.1799 W/C ink
£1008	$1784	(8-Nov-91 CN.P18) La promenade (16x14cm-6x6in) pen crayon W/C (F.FR 10000)
£1017	$1800	(9-Nov-91 W.W88/R) The connoisseur and hired boy (20x15cm-8x6in) s.i. pen W/C
£1060	$1844	(17-Sep-91 JRL.S358 a/R) Vicar and curate (26x19cm-10x7in) s.d.1787 W/C (A.D 2300)
£1100	$1969	(14-Nov-91 S95) Church wardens and overseers settling the poor rate (15x25cm-6x10in) s.i.d.1807 W/C pen
£1178	$2250	(3-Jul-92 S.W3846/R) Dr. Sangado and patient (25x23cm-10x9in) i. W/C
£1200	$2076	(4-Sep-91 BT39/R) The elopement (13x23cm-5x9in) W/C
£1500	$2640	(7-Apr-92 C121/R) Hussars with horses in stables (21x26cm-8x10in) pencil ink W/C
£1600	$2816	(9-Apr-92 S39/R) Glutton (29x23cm-11x9in) pen W/C over pencil
£1700	$2992	(9-Apr-92 S36/R) Vicar of Stuffwell (27x16cm-11x6in) pen W/C over pencil
£1800	$3222	(14-Nov-91 S75) Near Truro, Cornwall (16x23cm-6x9in) s.i. W/C pen ink over pencil
£1900	$3344	(9-Apr-92 S109/R) Mouth of river (31x47cm-12x19in) W/C over pencil
£1900	$3401	(12-Nov-91 C65/R) The Breedwell family (10x18cm-4x7in) pen W/C over pencil
£2000	$3580	(14-Nov-91 S71/R) Cats' chorus (13x21cm-5x8in) pen W/C over pencil
£2100	$3612	(4-Mar-92 DR13/R) Off to war, soldier, drummer and dog leaving lady with two babies (27x21cm-11x8in) pen W/C
£2100	$3696	(9-Apr-92 S43/R) Childsren outside cottage in woods (20x27cm-8x11in) i. pen W/C over pencil
£2100	$3759	(14-Nov-91 S74/R) Sunday morning (16x23cm-6x9in) W/C pen
£2200	$4202	(16-Jul-92 S78/R) Field preaching (30x21cm-12x8in) pen W/C over pencil
£2200	$3872	(7-Apr-92 C120/R) English hussar and French cuirassier (21x27cm-8x11in) pencil ink W/C
£2200	$3938	(12-Nov-91 C73/R) Trinity Library, Cambridge (21x29cm-8x11in) i.verso pencil ink W/C
£2400	$4224	(7-Apr-92 C119/R) English hussar and French cuirassier (21x27cm-8x11in) pencil ink W/C

ROWLANDSON, Thomas (1756-1827) British-cont.

£2600	$4654	(12-Nov-91 C63/R) Changing horses at the Swan Inn, Brixton (14x23cm-6x9in) pen W/C
£2640	$5042	(16-Jul-92 S77/R) At the butcher's shop (28x23cm-11x9in) pen W/C
£3000	$5280	(9-Apr-92 S40/R) Chamber of Genius (21x28cm-8x11in) s.d.1805 pen W/C over pencil
£3300	$6303	(16-Jul-92 S84/R) Gentlemen on horseback watching race (14x21cm-6x8in) pen W/C
£3500	$6265	(12-Nov-91 C66/R) The library of the Royal Instution, Albermarle Street (20x28cm-8x11in) pencil pen W/C
£4400	$8404	(16-Jul-92 S75/R) French diligence (33x53cm-13x21in) i. pen W/C over pencil
£4500	$8595	(14-Jul-92 C5/R) Ugly Club (23x37cm-9x15in) s.i.d.1807 pencil pen W/C
£4500	$8595	(14-Jul-92 C9/R) Writing will. Reading will (24x32cm-9x13in) s.d.1786 pen W/C pair
£4600	$8786	(14-Jul-92 C8/R) Gaming table (27x37cm-11x15in) pencil pen W/C
£5000	$8950	(14-Nov-91 S16/R) Bonaparte's carriage taken at Waterloo (15x24cm-6x9in) indis.i. pen W/C
£5060	$9665	(16-Jul-92 S83/R) Near the finishing post (14x21cm-6x8in) pen W/C
£11000	$19690	(12-Nov-91 C68/R) Sale of English beauties in the East Indies (24x34cm-9x13in) i. pencil pen W/C

ROWNTREE, Kenneth (1915-) British

£520	$920	(6-Nov-91 CB134/R) Chatsworth from the park (33x43cm-13x17in) s.

ROWORTH, Edward (1880-1964) British

£544	$964	(4-Nov-91 SY.J107/R) The old bridge, Somerset west (34x47cm-13x19in) s. board (SA.R 2700)
£700	$1190	(22-Oct-91 C61/R) House in Cape (71x91cm-28x36in) s.
£835	$1453	(13-Apr-92 SY.J341/R) Eikenhof (76x100cm-30x39in) s. (SA.R 4200)

ROXBURGH, Rachel (1915-) Australian

£881	$1586	(24-Nov-91 SY.S314/R) Near Oxford (42x52cm-17x20in) board (A.D 2000)

ROY, A (?) ?

£650	$1112	(19-Mar-92 B65) Under the trees (61x66cm-24x26in) s.

ROY, Jean Baptiste de (1759-1839) Belgian

£1112	$2013	(3-Dec-91 C.A78) Still life of flowers (52x48cm-20x19in) s. oval (B.FR 65000)
£1748	$3024	(25-Mar-92 KM.K990) Cattle in river landscape with village (33x54cm-13x21in) s. one of pair (DM 5000)
£1923	$3327	(25-Mar-92 KM.K991/R) Cattle grazing in river landscape with houses and figures (32x53cm-13x21in) s. one of pair (DM 5500)
£7251	$12979	(7-May-92 CH.AM144/R) Bull and cows on river bank with peasant family, castle of Laeken beyond (81x116cm-32x46in) s.d.1794 panel (D.FL 24000)

ROY, Pierre (1880-1950) Italian

£28000	$53480	(1-Jul-92 S193/R) Composition aux poids et mesures (92x60cm-36x24in) s.
£2264	$3893	(12-Oct-91 SY.MO197/R) Maquette pour le decor - Le Jeu de Cartes (32x25cm-13x10in) init. pencil gouache (F.FR 22500)

ROYBET, Ferdinand (1840-1920) French

£1160	$2100	(22-May-92 S.BM95/R) Young shepherds, twilight (41x25cm-16x10in) s. panel
£1400	$2394	(17-Mar-92 PH166/R) Portrait of gentleman wearing green cloak (81x64cm-32x25in) s. panel
£1475	$2700	(17-May-92 DU.E1103/R) Cavalier (64x51cm-25x20in) s. panel
£1493	$2657	(25-Nov-91 W.T1993/R) Le cavalier (61x45cm-24x18in) s. panel (C.D 3000)
£1702	$3250	(16-Jul-92 SY.NY400/R) The cavalier (66x55cm-26x22in) s. panel
£2035	$3500	(18-Oct-91 DM.D2005/R) Young Prince (53x46cm-21x18in) s. cradled panel
£2592	$4458	(16-Oct-91 FER.M216/R) El trovador (53x37cm-21x15in) s. panel (S.P 475000)
£3211	$5587	(14-Apr-92 SY.AM233/R) Portrait of an officer (79x62cm-31x24in) s. panel (D.FL 10500)

ROYE, Joseph van de (1861-1941) Belgian

£2500	$4475	(15-Jan-92 BT150/R) Still life of fruit and a melon on a table (64x99cm-25x39in) s.i.d.1928
£3080	$5574	(3-Dec-91 C.A321/R) Still life of flowers (46x36cm-18x14in) s. panel (B.FR 180000)

ROYEN, Peter (20th C) Swiss?

£486	$870	(15-Nov-91 KM.K614) Signals (80x60cm-31x24in) s.d.52 i.verso (DM 1400)

ROYER, Henri (1869-1938) French

£3024	$5353	(5-Nov-91 ZZ.F120/R) Jeune femme au vase (46x33cm-18x13in) s.d.97 (F.FR 30000)

ROYER, Pierre (attrib) (fl.1769-1779) French

£2854	$5309	(19-Jun-92 CN.P60/R) Paysage neo-classique (73x62cm-29x24in) (F.FR 28000)

ROYLE, Herbert (1870-1958) British

£1000	$1720	(16-Oct-91 PHL310) Bolton Abbey on Wharfe (60x50cm-24x20in) s.
£1000	$1820	(10-Dec-91 HAR755) Winter feeding, Wharfedale (38x48cm-15x19in) s. board
£1100	$2101	(16-Jul-92 CSK161) Dee estuary from Caldy Hill (86x108cm-34x43in) s.

ROYLE, Herbert (1870-1958) British-cont.
£1150 $2093 (10-Dec-91 HAR777) Bolton Bridge, Wharfedale (18x23cm-7x9in) s. board
£1450 $2422 (21-Aug-91 HAR391/R) Yorkshire moorland (41x53cm-16x21in) s.i.verso
£1450 $2494 (16-Oct-91 PHL336) Figures picking bluebells before ruined abbey
     (60x50cm-24x20in) s.
£1550 $2821 (10-Dec-91 HAR780) Bolton Abbey (23x18cm-9x7in) s. board
£2300 $3841 (21-Aug-91 HAR389/R) Landscape with hay makers (79x43cm-31x17in) s.
£2600 $4472 (16-Oct-91 PHL311/R) Haymaking (40x60cm-16x24in) s.
£2800 $4900 (27-Sep-91 C118/R) Richmond Castle (76x102cm-30x40in) s.
£3000 $5160 (16-Oct-91 PHL343/R) Cattle in river landscape (76x127cm-30x50in) s.
£3200 $5664 (6-Nov-91 CB136/R) The homeward rest with plough horses watering in
     stream and figures (76x61cm-30x24in) s.
£3600 $6552 (11-Dec-91 PHL129) Bolton Abbey on the Wharfe (100x136cm-39x54in) s.
£440 $757 (16-Oct-91 PHL53/R) Castleberg Hill (35x45cm-14x18in) s.d.1925 col.wash

ROYLE, Stanley (1888-1961) British
£1150 $2047 (1-May-92 PHE39) Snow covered river landscape. Village church
     (29x39cm-11x15in) one s.d.1929 board pair
£2100 $3570 (22-Oct-91 SWS369/R) Fulwood Valley (70x90cm-28x35in) s.d.1922
£2740 $4712 (8-Oct-91 ZEL.L1693/R) River landscape with arched stone bridge and ruin
     beyond, autumn (122x153cm-48x60in) s. (DM 8000)

ROYO, Jose (19/20th C) Spanish
£1232 $2241 (27-May-92 DUR.M420/R) Nina con frutas (73x60cm-29x24in) (S.P 225000)
£2175 $3872 (28-Apr-92 DUR.M583) Descanso en el jardin (82x100cm-32x39in) s.
     (S.P 400000)

ROZEN, George (20th C) American
£1826 $3250 (2-May-92 IH.NY171/R) Man on horseback being lassoed (51x38cm-20x15in) s.

ROZEN, Jerome (20th C) American
£730 $1300 (2-May-92 IH.NY204/R) Glowering man with whip confronts woman, baby and
     dog (69x51cm-27x20in) s.
£1180 $2100 (2-Nov-91 IH.NY191/R) Cowboy on white horse (71x51cm-28x20in) s.

ROZIER, Dominique Hubert (1840-1901) French
£977 $1729 (5-Nov-91 GF.L2519/R) Dead rabbit (65x54cm-26x21in) s. (S.FR 2500)

ROZIER, Jules (1821-1882) French
£694 $1200 (6-Sep-91 S.BM151/R) The Garden Wall (36x28cm-14x11in) s.
£1100 $1913 (18-Sep-91 N.M673/R) Washer woman in river landscape (23x40cm-9x16in) s.
     panel (DM 3200)
£1200 $2052 (17-Mar-92 PH132/R) Washing at river bank (25x41cm-10x16in) s. panel

RUBBIANI, Felice (1677-1752) Italian
£8000 $14240 (1-Nov-91 C13/R) Peaches on stone ledge (22x47cm-9x19in)

RUBBIANI, Felice and VELLANI, Francesco (18th C) Italian
£18785 $34000 (22-May-92 SY.NY35/R) Still life of flowers in vase, fruit and grapes and
     antique frieze (83x143cm-33x56in) s.d.34

RUBBO, Anthony Dattilo (1870-1955) Australian
£1145 $2062 (24-Nov-91 SY.S11/R) Moi-Meme (55x45cm-22x18in) s. s.i.verso (A.D 2600)

RUBCZAK, Jan (1884-1949) Polish
£1781 $3242 (15-Dec-91 REM.W36) Brittany landscape (51x75cm-20x30in) s. board
     (P.Z 35000000)

RUBELLI, Egidio de (19th C) Italian
£1173 $2052 (18-Feb-92 CH.AM264) A couple in a gondola in the lagoon near Venice
     (66x105cm-26x41in) s. (D.FL 3800)
£1463 $2722 (16-Jun-92 VN.R268/R) Elegant figures in a gondola on the Grand Canal,
     Venice (63x92cm-25x36in) s. (D.FL 4800)

RUBELLI, Giuseppe de (1844-1916) Italian
£1394 $2384 (19-Mar-92 F.M28/R) Effetto lunare (53x71cm-21x28in) s. (I.L 3000000)

RUBEN, Franz Leo (1842-1920) Austrian
£893 $1555 (18-Sep-91 N.M675) Sphinx in park landscape (50x70cm-20x28in) s.
     (DM 2600)

RUBEN, Franz Leo (attrib) (1842-1920) Austrian
£1103 $1996 (5-Dec-91 D.V108) Small town in the mountains (26x34cm-10x13in) i. board
     (A.S 22000)

RUBENS (after) (1577-1640) Flemish
£750 $1350 (21-Nov-91 CSK77) The Descent from the Cross (114x84cm-45x33in)
£800 $1400 (25-Feb-92 PH61/R) The Assumption of the Virgin (36x44cm-14x17in)
£800 $1464 (12-May-92 SWS628/R) Portrait of artist (87x64cm-34x25in)
£850 $1547 (10-Dec-91 PH180/R) Lot and daughters leaving Sodom (63x76cm-25x30in)
£850 $1488 (2-Apr-92 CSK120) Portrait of Albert and Nicolas Rubens (94x58cm-37x23in)
£851 $1557 (12-May-92 SY.AM77) Presentation of Christ to assorted saints
     (101x88cm-40x35in) (D.FL 2800)
£900 $1620 (22-Nov-91 SWS154) The meeting of Abraham and Melchizedek
     (107x144cm-42x57in)

RUBENS (after) (1577-1640) Flemish-cont.

£926	$1657	(14-Nov-91 CH.AM99) The Conversion of St Paul (81x110cm-32x43in) panel (D.FL 3000)
£994	$1800	(20-May-92 D.NY30) Nocturnal flight into Egypt (46x51cm-18x20in) panel
£1000	$1920	(9-Jul-92 CSK335) Putti in landscape (115x190cm-45x75in)
£1200	$2100	(3-Apr-92 C21) Wooded river landscape at sunset with resting shepherd on path (30x46cm-12x18in)
£1235	$2210	(14-Nov-91 CH.AM101) Madonna and Child at stone niche decorated with flowers (83x67cm-33x26in) (D.FL 4000)
£1264	$2250	(22-Jan-92 SY.NY197/R) Chateau de Steen (30x46cm-12x18in)
£1413	$2430	(16-Oct-91 AT.P81) La Crucifixion (42x35cm-17x14in) panel (F.FR 14000)
£1605	$2873	(14-Nov-91 CH.AM65) Cows being milked in meadow with sportsmen nearby and wood beyond (26x35cm-10x14in) copper (D.FL 5200)
£1764	$3139	(28-Apr-92 RAS.K385/R) Woman and satyr holding basket of flowers (105x76cm-41x30in) (D.KR 20000)
£1964	$3515	(7-May-92 CH.AM67) Couple embracing (85x72cm-33x28in) (D.FL 6500)
£2300	$4140	(22-Nov-91 SWS230/R) The lion hunt (113x142cm-44x56in)
£2315	$4144	(12-Nov-91 SY.AM175) The birth of Louis XIII (113x86cm-44x34in) (D.FL 7500)
£2326	$4000	(9-Oct-91 CH.NY61/R) Death of Adonis (34x52cm-13x20in) panel
£2500	$4800	(9-Jul-92 CSK338) Hercules and the Nemean Lion (166x152cm-65x60in)
£2778	$4972	(14-Nov-91 CH.AM66/R) The tribute money (113x179cm-44x70in) (D.FL 9000)
£2932	$5248	(12-Nov-91 SY.AM174/R) Diana and Callisto (84x99cm-33x39in) (D.FL 9500)
£3000	$5370	(11-Nov-91 S490/R) Meeting of Abraham and Melchizedek (156x166cm-61x65in)
£3395	$6077	(12-Nov-91 SY.AM94) Herod's feast (156x234cm-61x92in) (D.FL 11000)
£3484	$6341	(12-Dec-91 N.M2701/R) Cimon and Iphigenie (170x240cm-67x94in) c.1617 (DM 10000)
£3521	$5915	(27-Aug-91 RAS.K230/R) Horror of war (105x185cm-41x73in) (D.KR 40000)
£3800	$7258	(14-Jul-92 DR409/R) Farmers in landscape (104x147cm-41x58in)
£4073	$7250	(22-Jan-92 SY.NY51/R) Three Graces (116x98cm-46x39in)
£4144	$7500	(21-May-92 CH.NY241/R) Holy Family with Saint Anne and infant Saint John the Baptist (122x91cm-48x36in)
£4500	$8640	(10-Jul-92 C155/R) Lot and family fleeing from Solomon (181x226cm-71x89in)
£4990	$9033	(3-Dec-91 AB.S4750/R) Adoration of the Kings (53x41cm-21x16in) copper (S.KR 52000)

RUBENS (attrib) (1577-1640) Flemish

£1242	*$2211*	*(25-Nov-91 CH.AM51/R) Head of satyr (26x21cm-10x8in) chk wash cut corners (D.FL 4000)*

RUBENS (circle) (1577-1640) Flemish

£942	$1800	(16-Jul-92 SY.NY257/R) Portrait of man (40x30cm-16x12in) canvas on panel
£950	$1824	(10-Jul-92 PH79/R) Raising of Lazarus (60x51cm-24x20in) panel
£1800	$3150	(25-Feb-92 PH31/R) Marriage of the Virgin (145x115cm-57x45in)
£2062	$3567	(27-Mar-92 CD.P5/R) Bacchus (61x51cm-24x20in) (F.FR 20000)
£2300	$4094	(1-Nov-91 C101/R) Victory of Eucharistic truth over Heresy (67x94cm-26x37in) panel
£3086	$5586	(5-Dec-91 SY.MO207/R) Saint Georges (124x102cm-49x40in) (F.FR 30000)
£3488	$6000	(9-Oct-91 CH.NY60/R) Gideon overcoming Midianites (62x77cm-24x30in) panel
£3779	$6500	(10-Oct-91 SY.NY83/R) Mary Magdalene (35x25cm-14x10in) panel
£1050	*$1827*	*(13-Apr-92 S302/R) Standing draped figure and separate sketches of head, lion's head, foot (20x15cm-8x6in) red chk pen*
£8500	*$14790*	*(13-Apr-92 S72/R) Figure studies, including Apollo and Daphne (24x33cm-9x13in) bears i. black red chk pen double-sided*

RUBENS (school) (1577-1640) Flemish

£1587	$2825	(28-Apr-92 RAS.K49/R) Animals near watering place (65x82cm-26x32in) (D.KR 18000)
£2203	$3899	(7-Nov-91 D.V273/R) Portrait of bishop (60x47cm-24x19in) (A.S 45000)
£2768	$5260	(24-Jun-92 KM.K955/R) Meleager presenting the head of the Calydonian boar to Atalante (124x101cm-49x40in) (DM 8000)
£2901	$5250	(20-May-92 D.NY29) St Jerome (89x64cm-35x25in) panel
£3039	$5500	(21-May-92 CH.NY198/R) Judgement of Paris (58x86cm-23x34in)
£3651	$6426	(11-Apr-92 AT.P43/R) Le denier de Cesar (72x106cm-28x42in) panel (F.FR 36000)
£1725	*$3089*	*(15-Nov-91 GK.Z6187) Battle composition (25x41cm-10x16in) sepia bister wash W/C ochre (S.FR 4400)*

RUBENS (studio) (1577-1640) Flemish

£2700	$4806	(29-Oct-91 PH56/R) The reconcilliation of Jacob and Esau (46x41cm-18x16in) panel
£4500	$7875	(28-Feb-92 C40/R) The Holy Family in landscape with angel bearing fruit (114x147cm-45x58in)
£40055	$72500	(22-May-92 SY.NY17/R) Portrait of Anne of Austria (150x119cm-59x47in)

RUBENS (style) (1577-1640) Flemish

£880	$1584	(22-Nov-91 SWS209) The holy family with Saint Anne and the infant Saint John the Baptist (53x46cm-21x18in)
£900	$1647	(12-May-92 H363) The garden of love (104x135cm-41x53in)
£994	$1699	(18-Mar-92 D.V294/R) Crucifixion (102x78cm-40x31in) (A.S 20000)
£1000	$1820	(12-Dec-91 B75) Cephalus and Procris (39x49cm-15x19in)
£1166	$2168	(16-Jun-92 SY.B203) Latona with her children imploring the help of the gods (120x102cm-47x40in) (B.FR 70000)
£1180	$2100	(22-Jan-92 D.NY89) Holy Family (122x84cm-48x33in)

RUBENS (style) (1577-1640) Flemish-cont.

£1600	$2800	(27-Feb-92 B28/R) St.Christopher (126x88cm-50x35in) panel
£1600	$2912	(10-Dec-91 PH191/R) Study of putti from Rubens sketch Apotheosis of James and other studies (51x70cm-20x28in) canvas on board
£1626	$2829	(13-Apr-92 AT.P57) Salome et la tete de Saint Jean Baptiste (85x115cm-33x45in) (F.FR 16000)
£1665	$3097	(16-Jun-92 SY.B249/R) David and Abigail (206x189cm-81x74in) (B.FR 100000)
£1700	$3060	(21-Nov-91 CSK1/R) The pieta (104x103cm-41x41in)
£1702	$3250	(17-Jul-92 DM.D2177) Holy Family with St. John the Baptist (64x91cm-25x36in)
£1900	$3477	(12-May-92 SWS802/R) Three crosses (95x62cm-37x24in) panel
£2220	$3818	(16-Oct-91 AT.P63/R) Suzanne et les vieillards (38x29cm-15x11in) copper (F.FR 22000)
£2245	$3973	(10-Feb-92 GL.P4/R) Le Martyre de Saint Barthelemy (73x60cm-29x24in) i.verso (F.FR 22000)
£2265	$4190	(8-Jun-92 CH.R757/R) Sant'Anna e San Gioacchino conducono la Vergine al matrimonio (75x119cm-30x47in) (I.L 5000000)
£2400	$4392	(12-May-92 SWS742) Moses and brazen serpent (53x74cm-21x29in) panel
£2500	$4800	(8-Jul-92 S123/R) St Jerome in Penitence (60x47cm-24x19in) panel
£2600	$4628	(31-Oct-91 B87/R) Triumph of Christianity over Paganism (68x87cm-27x34in) metal
£2800	$4984	(31-Oct-91 B35/R) Salome presented with head of St. John the Baptist (104x180cm-41x71in)
£3100	$5673	(12-May-92 SWS682/R) Infant Christ and Saint John with cherubs (47x64cm-19x25in) panel
£3714	$6500	(21-Feb-92 BG.M271/R) Battle of the Lapiths and the Centaurs (30x43cm-12x17in) copper panel
£6079	$11125	(12-May-92 SY.AM139/R) Portrait of gentleman (112x82cm-44x32in) sig. (D.FL 20000)
£6458	$11043	(18-Mar-92 D.V371/R) Returning from the work in the fields at the end of the day (112x197cm-44x78in) (A.S 130000)
£9302	$16000	(10-Oct-91 SY.NY174/R) Huntsmen and dogs bringing down a wild boar (81x101cm-32x40in) copper laid down on panel
£546	$939	(16-Oct-91 FER.M43/R) Caballero (20x14cm-8x6in) pencil sanguine dr (S.P 100000)

RUBENS, Sir Peter Paul (1577-1640) Flemish

£850	$1479	(14-Apr-92 C65) Diana and nymphs hunting (30x43cm-12x17in) chk
£6800	$13056	(6-Jul-92 S91/R) Soldiers demolishing a bridge (39x28cm-15x11in) chk.pen wash oil

RUBIN, Reuven (1893-1974) Israeli

£3514	$6500	(12-Jun-92 SY.NY208/R) The fisherman (33x24cm-13x9in) s.
£4237	$7500	(5-Nov-91 CE.NY66/R) Still life with fruit (23x44cm-9x17in) s.
£7429	$13000	(26-Sep-91 SY.I13/R) Vase of anemones (31x26cm-12x10in) s.
£8286	$14500	(26-Sep-91 SY.I12/R) Red poppies in vase (41x29cm-16x11in) s.
£8571	$15000	(26-Sep-91 SY.I10/R) Vase with mimosas (33x25cm-13x10in) s.
£9143	$16000	(26-Sep-91 SY.I11/R) Poppies and cyclamens in vase (34x29cm-13x11in) s.
£10571	$18500	(26-Sep-91 SY.I63/R) Pomegranates (33x41cm-13x16in) s.
£11732	$21000	(13-Nov-91 B.SF2380/R) Still life with white flowers (92x74cm-36x29in) s.
£16393	$30000	(13-May-92 CH.NY303/R) Yellow daffodils (72x54cm-28x21in) s.
£17486	$32000	(13-May-92 CH.NY278/R) Landscape with olive tree (81x65cm-32x26in) s.
£22340	$42000	(5-Jan-92 GG.TA352/R) Ancient olive trees in Galilee (65x81cm-26x32in) s.
£22857	$40000	(26-Sep-91 SY.I23/R) Mimosas in vase (80x64cm-31x25in) s.d.1949
£22857	$40000	(26-Sep-91 SY.I14/R) Spring bouquet (74x60cm-29x24in) s.
£22951	$42000	(13-May-92 CH.NY298/R) Road to Galilee - springtime in Galilee (66x81cm-26x32in) s. s.i.stretcher
£23121	$40000	(2-Oct-91 SY.NY88/R) harvest time in Nazareth (87x114cm-34x45in) s.
£24000	$42000	(26-Sep-91 SY.I18/R) Jerusalem landscape (61x50cm-24x20in) s.
£28571	$50000	(26-Sep-91 SY.I9/R) Californian villa (66x87cm-26x34in) s.
£40000	$70000	(26-Sep-91 SY.I22/R) Seder outside the walls of Jerusalem (113x161cm-44x63in) s.d.1949
£44571	$78000	(26-Sep-91 SY.I19/R) Maternity (64x74cm-25x29in) s.
£46857	$82000	(25-Feb-92 CH.NY34/R) Self-portrait (91x63cm-36x25in) s. canvas on masonite
£865	$1600	(8-Jun-92 GG.TA252/R) Man at prayer (54x36cm-21x14in) s. gouache pastel
£1875	$3319	(10-Nov-91 ZZ.F230/R) Vase de fleurs (24x20cm-9x8in) s.d.1942 W/C (F.FR 18600)
£2235	$4000	(9-May-92 CE.NY88/R) Mother and Child (62x46cm-24x18in) s. pen brush wash col.chk
£2857	$5000	(26-Sep-91 SY.I108/R) Galilean fisherman (65x49cm-26x19in) s. indian ink W/C
£3459	$6400	(8-Jun-92 GG.TA250/R) Shepherd, herds of camels and sheep (78x52cm-31x20in) s. W/C ink
£3714	$6500	(26-Sep-91 SY.I61/R) Two reclining donkeys (34x44cm-13x17in) s. W/C pencil
£6216	$11500	(9-Jun-92 GG.TA441/R) Safed jew (34x28cm-13x11in) s.i.d.1923 W/C
£6383	$12000	(5-Jan-92 GG.TA350/R) View from the window to the Old City (40x32cm-16x13in) s. W/C

RUBINSHTEIN, David (1902-) Russian

£665	$1184	(25-Nov-91 ARC.P141 a) Orchestre (41x56cm-16x22in) s. (F.FR 6500)
£409	$729	(25-Nov-91 ARC.P140/R) Au concert philharmonique (26x39cm-10x15in) s. W/C (F.FR 4000)

RUBINSHTEIN, David (1902-) Russian-cont.

£819	$1458	(25-Nov-91 ARC.P139/R) Concerto pour violonn et orchestre (30x41cm-12x16in) s. W/C (F.FR 8000)
£819	$1458	(25-Nov-91 ARC.P139 b) Le chef d'orchestre (50x70cm-20x28in) s. W/C (F.FR 8000)
£963	$1742	(20-May-92 ARC.P225/R) La femme en rouge (52x41cm-20x16in) s. pastel (F.FR 9500)

RUBIO, Louis (?-1882) Italian

£6911	$12024	(13-Apr-92 AT.P205/R) Portrait du Sultan Abdul-Medjid Khan, peint d'apres nature a Constantinople (65x54cm-26x21in) s.d.1847 (F.FR 68000)

RUDAUX, Henri Edmond (?-1927) French

£1214	$2160	(29-Apr-92 D.V764/R) Still life of geraniums (39x71cm-15x28in) s.d.1901 (A.S 25000)

RUDBERG, Gustav (1915-) Swedish

£518	$922	(28-Oct-91 AB.S209) Field of snow, Hven (30x74cm-12x29in) s.d.44 (S.KR 5500)
£753	$1341	(28-Oct-91 AB.S208) 'Juryman's house' - view from Hven (47x59cm-19x23in) s. (S.KR 8000)
£918	$1661	(19-May-92 AB.S5316/R) Farm at Hven (58x94cm-23x37in) s. (S.KR 9700)
£1041	$1884	(19-May-92 AB.S5314/R) Ocean and shore (52x85cm-20x33in) s. (S.KR 11000)
£1708	$3125	(13-May-92 BU.S176/R) From Kyrkeviken, Hven (58x72cm-23x28in) s. (S.KR 18000)
£1898	$3472	(13-May-92 BU.S172/R) Hills at Hven (49x64cm-19x25in) s. (S.KR 20000)
£1898	$3472	(13-May-92 BU.S173/R) Backafall, Hven (55x68cm-22x27in) s. (S.KR 20000)
£2372	$4341	(11-May-92 NOR.S96/R) Land and sea, Hven (35x97cm-14x38in) s. (S.KR 25000)
£2941	$5382	(13-May-92 BU.S175/R) Seascape with boat off Hven (59x57cm-23x22in) s. (S.KR 31000)
£3036	$5556	(11-May-92 NOR.S97/R) Beach, Hven (78x83cm-31x33in) s. (S.KR 32000)
£5821	$10361	(28-Nov-91 BU.S106/R) Boat at anchor by Hven (77x87cm-30x34in) s. (S.KR 61000)

RUDE, Olaf (1886-1957) Danish

£632	$1080	(12-Mar-92 RAS.K712) Seated man and woman (110x117cm-43x46in) s.d.37 (D.KR 7000)
£817	$1431	(1-Apr-92 KH.K282/R) Still life (65x46cm-26x18in) (D.KR 9000)
£891	$1533	(16-Oct-91 KH.K220/R) Landscape with houses, Bornholm (65x92cm-26x36in) s.d.30 (D.KR 10000)
£891	$1533	(16-Oct-91 KH.K286/R) Summer landscape with houses among rocks (60x81cm-24x32in) s. (D.KR 10000)
£894	$1628	(10-Dec-91 RAS.K156) Coastal landscape, Bornholm (56x66cm-22x26in) s. (D.KR 10000)
£925	$1637	(23-Apr-92 RAS.V1011/R) Coastal landscape, Bornholm (56x66cm-22x26in) s. (D.KR 10500)
£1181	$2066	(1-Apr-92 KH.K109/R) Poultry yard (60x73cm-24x29in) s.d.28 (D.KR 13000)
£1426	$2453	(16-Oct-91 KH.K236/R) From the balcony, grey day (73x100cm-29x39in) s.d.1930 (D.KR 16000)
£1629	$2948	(4-Dec-91 KH.K14/R) View from the studio (50x65cm-20x26in) s. (D.KR 18000)
£1693	$2913	(16-Oct-91 KH.K116/R) View over the sea, Bornholm summer 1932 (50x65cm-20x26in) s.d.32 (D.KR 19000)
£1726	$3020	(1-Apr-92 KH.K128/R) Raod through landscape, Bornholm (58x69cm-23x27in) s.d.25 (D.KR 19000)
£1805	$3087	(12-Mar-92 RAS.K711/R) View across roof tops (50x70cm-20x28in) s.d.40 (D.KR 20000)
£2089	$3656	(1-Apr-92 KH.K30/R) Pine forest (133x150cm-52x59in) s.d.35 (D.KR 23000)
£2089	$3656	(1-Apr-92 KH.K148/R) Ballet dancer (49x39cm-19x15in) s. (D.KR 23000)
£2139	$3679	(16-Oct-91 KH.K154/R) Autumn day by the sea, Bornholm (97x130cm-38x51in) s.d.30 (D.KR 24000)
£2228	$3832	(16-Oct-91 KH.K80/R) Early spring in Italian wineyard (54x65cm-21x26in) s.d.25 (D.KR 25000)
£2361	$4133	(1-Apr-92 KH.K221/R) Landscape (97x130cm-38x51in) s. (D.KR 26000)
£2674	$4599	(16-Oct-91 KH.K109/R) Autumn landscape, Gronnedal, Bronholm (73x91cm-29x36in) s. (D.KR 30000)
£4977	$9009	(4-Dec-91 KH.K26/R) Still life (73x92cm-29x36in) s. (D.KR 55000)
£5348	$9198	(16-Oct-91 KH.K47/R) Nature morte (70x80cm-28x31in) s.d.23 (D.KR 60000)
£5450	$9537	(1-Apr-92 KH.K88/R) Storm approaching (100x126cm-39x50in) s.d.28 (D.KR 60000)
£9774	$17690	(4-Dec-91 KH.K20/R) Still life (80x100cm-31x39in) s.d.45 (D.KR 108000)
£22624	$40950	(4-Dec-91 KH.K1/R) Cubist composition (125x97cm-49x38in) s.d.17 (D.KR 250000)

RUDELL, Carl (1852-1920) German

£769	$1331	(25-Mar-92 KM.K1756) Spectators watching horse dressage in circus (17x25cm-7x10in) s. W/C (DM 2200)

RUDGE, Bradford (19th C) British

£400	$764	(30-Jun-92 SWS1728) Near Glendwr Mill, Barmouth, North Wales (49x38cm-19x15in) i. W/C over pencil htd bodycol gum arabic

RUDISUHLI, Eduard (attrib) (1875-1938) Swiss
£756 $1315   (18-Sep-91 N.M676) Silver birch trees in autumn landscape
                    (51x78cm-20x31in) i. board (DM 2200)

RUDISUHLI, Hermann (1864-1945) Swiss
£732 $1245   (24-Oct-91 D.V78/R) Trees in landscape (32x48cm-13x19in) (A.S 15000)

RUDISUHLI, Jakob Lorenz (1835-1918) Swiss
£4815 $8715   (19-May-92 GF.L2249/R) Seaside castle in storm, autumn (78x119cm-31x47in)
                    s. (S.FR 13000)
£7059 $12000   (23-Oct-91 GD.B627/R) Vierwaldstattersee at sunset (80x120cm-31x47in)
                    s.i.d.1873 (S.FR 18000)

RUDNICKI, Marek (1927-?) Polish
£1230 $2128   (6-Oct-91 E.LA133/R) Femme et arlequin (55x46cm-22x18in) s.d.89
                    (F.FR 12200)
*£605 $1046   (6-Oct-91 E.LA134) Femme au chapeau bleu (46x38cm-18x15in) s. mixed media
                    laid down (F.FR 6000)*

RUDOLPH, Wilhelm (1889-) German
£1042 $1865   (15-Nov-91 KM.K619) Still life with watering can and bucket
                    (37x46cm-15x18in) s. tempera board (DM 3000)
£387 $701   (6-Dec-91 GB.B7057) Peasant feeding geese (33x36cm-13x14in) s.d.1925 W/C
                    (DM 1100)

RUE, Louis-Felix de la (attrib) (1731-1765) French
£509 $910   (17-Nov-91 LT.P3/R) Bacchanales (24x18cm-9x7in) pen wash (F.FR 5000)

RUEDA, Gerardo (1926-) Spanish
£2629 $4495   (17-Mar-92 FER.M176/R) Barcas de vela (55x78cm-22x31in) s.d.1953 mixed
                    media (S.P 475000)

RUEFF, A (19th C) Austrian
£584 $1045   (6-May-92 GD.B1092) Two elegant gentlemen looking at drawings
                    (32x22cm-13x9in) s.d.1889 panel (S.FR 1600)

RUEGG, Albert (1902-1986) Swiss
£547 $980   (6-May-92 GD.B1094/R) Passenger on board of ship looking out on choppy
                    seas (60x80cm-24x31in) s.d.1963 i.d.verso (S.FR 1500)
£657 $1176   (6-May-92 GD.B1093/R) Bunch of spring flowers in vase (81x60cm-32x24in)
                    s.d.1962 i.d.verso (S.FR 1800)

RUEGG, Eduard (?-1903) Swiss
£1141 $2122   (19-Jun-92 ZOF.Z2065/R) Thunersee near Interlaken (52x75cm-20x30in)
                    s.i.d.1882 (S.FR 3000)

RUELLAN, Andree (?) ?
£546 $1000   (17-May-92 DU.E1244) Two clowns (76x61cm-30x24in) s.

RUETER, Georg (1875-1966) Dutch
£578 $1005   (17-Sep-91 CH.AM430) A still life with roses in a vase (40x37cm-16x15in)
                    s. (D.FL 1900)
£617 $1080   (18-Feb-92 CH.AM32/R) Still life with roses in a glass (30x26cm-12x10in)
                    s.d.48 panel (D.FL 2000)
£973 $1692   (17-Sep-91 CH.AM429) A still life with carnations in a vase
                    (43x45cm-17x18in) s.d.50 (D.FL 3200)

RUFALO, Carlos R (?) Uruguayan
£562 $1000   (25-Nov-91 GC.M73/R) Vista desde el Cerro (45x51cm-18x20in) s. board
£782 $1400   (6-May-92 CAS.M32) En la playa (32x24cm-13x9in) panel
£983 $1700   (30-Sep-91 GC.M17) Personajes en la playa (19x29cm-7x11in) s. panel
£1564 $2800   (6-May-92 CAS.M31) Playa Pocitos (21x18cm-8x7in) panel

RUFFI, Gianni (1938-) Italian
£2497 $4444   (29-Apr-92 F.F204/R) Dinamite (80x90cm-31x35in) s.verso tempera rope
                    panel (I.L 5500000)

RUGENDAS, Christian Johann (attrib) (1708-1781) German
£3600 $6408   (30-Oct-91 S181/R) Battle scenes between Turkish and christian soldiers
                    (39x53cm-15x21in) pair

RUGENDAS, Georg Philipp (17/18th C) German
*£2235 $3823   (18-Mar-92 D.V412/R) Siege (15x22cm-6x9in) pen (A.S 45000)
£2484 $4247   (18-Mar-92 D.V411/R) Surrender and defeat of Schloss Mayland
                    (23x26cm-9x10in) s.i.d.1707 pen (A.S 50000)*

RUGENDAS, Georg Philipp (circle) (17/18th C) German
*£994 $1699   (18-Mar-92 D.V318/R) Encampment (16x20cm-6x8in) gouache one of pair
                    (A.S 20000)
£994 $1699   (18-Mar-92 D.V317/R) Soldiers marching in river landscape (16x19cm-6x7in)
                    gouache one of pair (A.S 20000)*

RUGENDAS, Georg Philipp (style) (17/18th C) German
£1000 $1780   (30-Oct-91 S180) Battle scene (40x51cm-16x20in)

RUGENDAS, Georg Philipp I (1666-1742) German
£11747 $20793   (7-Nov-91 D.V91/R) After the battle (72x137cm-28x54in) one of pair
                                 (A.S 240000)
£13705 $24258   (7-Nov-91 D.V90/R) Skirmish (72x137cm-28x54in) one of pair (A.S 280000)

RUGENDAS, Georg Philipp I (attrib) (1666-1742) German
£1768 $3200   (19-May-92 CE.NY299) Cavalry skirmish (30x38cm-12x15in)
£3436 $5979   (18-Sep-91 N.M446/R) Skirmish (40x54cm-16x21in) (DM 10000)

RUGENDAS, Georg Philipp II (1701-1774) German
£3426 $6065   (7-Nov-91 D.V330/R) Skirmish between Royals and Turks (43x63cm-17x25in)
                                 (A.S 70000)

RUGENDAS, Johann Moritz (1802-1858) German
£29006 $52500   (19-May-92 SY.NY5/R) Saliendo de la iglesia (49x39cm-19x15in)

RUGGERI, Piero (1930-) Italian
£914 $1590   (14-Apr-92 F.M121/R) Composizione (50x40cm-20x16in) s. tempera paper on
                               canvas (I.L 2000000)
£920 $1646   (14-Nov-91 F.M2) Composizione (80x60cm-31x24in) s.d.1972verso
                               (I.L 2000000)
£8222 $14306   (14-Apr-92 F.M140/R) Studio da Rembrandt (143x126cm-56x50in) s.d.1957
                               (I.L 18000000)

RUGGIERO, Pasquale (1851-1916) Italian
£3403 $6500   (16-Jul-92 SY.NY585/R) The letter (47x35cm-19x14in) s.d.79

RUGGIERO, Pasquale (attrib) (1851-1916) Italian
£851 $1481   (17-Sep-91 CH.AM391) A woman in a courtyard, Naples (46x32cm-18x13in)
                               s.i. (D.FL 2800)

RUHLE, Clara (1885-1947) German
£653 $1195   (2-Jun-92 FN.S2401/R) Seated female nude with bowl of fruit
                               (23x20cm-9x8in) canvas on board (DM 1900)

RUIN, Ingrid (1881-1956) Finnish
£1833 $3226   (12-Apr-92 HOR.H191) Young lady (80x65cm-31x26in) s.d.1923 (F.M 14500)

RUINART DE BRINANT, Jules (1838-1898) French
£2222 $4022   (19-May-92 GF.L2727) Neapolitan Harbour scene with figures
                               (24x34cm-9x13in) s. panel (S.FR 6000)
£2400 $4152   (4-Oct-91 C117/R) The concert (38x26cm-15x10in) s.i.d.89 panel
£7143 $13000   (28-May-92 SY.NY186/R) Still life (51x81cm-20x32in) s.d.76

RUITH, Horace van (19/20th C) British
£12000 $20400   (23-Oct-91 S327/R) Procession, Mysore (94x74cm-37x29in) s.

RUIZ DE CACERES (19th C) Spanish
£2690 $4600   (13-Mar-92 WOL.C439/R) Afternoon rest in the garden (33x23cm-13x9in)
                               s.i.d.1875 panel

RUIZ DE LA CASA, Angel (?) Spanish?
£470 $836   (21-Jan-92 DUR.M38/R) Canal de Brujas (81x65cm-32x26in) s. (S.P 85000)
£497 $885   (21-Jan-92 DUR.M77/R) Regreso de las barcas (54x65cm-21x26in) s.
                               s.i.d.91verso (S.P 90000)
£552 $1038   (3-Jan-92 DUR.M71/R) Sol de tarde (81x65cm-32x26in) s. s.i.d.1991
                               (S.P 100000)

RUIZ SANCHEZ MORALES, Manuel (1853-1922) Spanish
£415 $748   (29-Jan-92 FER.M232) Vista de la Alhambra (19x30cm-7x12in) s. W/C
                               (S.P 75000)
£415 $748   (29-Jan-92 FER.M233/R) Patio de los leones de la Alhambra
                               (19x30cm-7x12in) s. W/C (S.P 75000)
£1230 $2251   (13-May-92 FER.M77/R) La casa del pueblo con la mula a la puerta
                               (56x34cm-22x13in) s. W/C (S.P 225000)
£1650 $2954   (5-May-92 SWS140/R) Market stalls in Spanish backstreet (53x36cm-21x14in)
                               s. W/C

RUIZ, Antonio (1897-1964) Mexican
£4444 $8000   (18-Nov-91 SY.NY91/R) Escena de Cristo (25x34cm-10x13in) s.d.20 graphite

RUIZ, B Yamero (fl.1890-1910) American
£1000 $1900   (24-Jun-92 B.SF6274/R) Woman sitting by river bank (33x53cm-13x21in) s.

RUIZ, Joseph (?) Spanish?
£7500 $13125   (1-Apr-92 S190/R) Mediterranean harbour scene (42x84cm-17x33in)

RUIZ, Juan (circle) (18th C) Spanish
£54845 $99270   (4-Dec-91 CH.R134/R) Veduta di Napoli dalla spiaggia di Mergellina con il
                               Vesuvio (50x131cm-20x52in) (I.L 118000000)

RUIZ, Tomasso (18th C) Spanish
£17442 $30000   (9-Oct-91 CH.NY136/R) View of Bay of Naples, Vesuvius beyond
                               (26x59cm-10x23in) s.d.1741

RUIZ, Tomasso (18th C) Spanish-cont.
£30479 $53339   (20-Feb-92 SY.EP.M16/R) Dos vistas de Napoles (42x102cm-17x40in) one s. pair
    (S.P 5500000)
£44000 $77000   (31-Mar-92 PH104/R) View of Naples from Castel dell Ovo
    (47x130cm-19x51in) s.

RUIZ, Tomasso (attrib) (18th C) Spanish
£4115 $7819   (26-Jun-92 AT.P61/R) Vue d'un port au soleil levant avec Civitta Vecchia
    (74x104cm-29x41in) (F.FR 40000)

RUIZ-PIPO, Manolo (1929-) Spanish
£751 $1427   *(26-Jun-92 AGS.P20/R) Couple de paysans (49x31cm-19x12in) s.d.1959 W/C*
    gouache (F.FR 7300)
£2081 $3642   *(5-Apr-92 ZZ.F205/R) Les Arlequins (56x38cm-22x15in) s. gouache*
    (F.FR 20000)

RUL, Henri (1862-?) Belgian
£1040 $1809   (14-Apr-92 SY.AM395) Wooded landscape (101x65cm-40x26in) s. (D.FL 3400)
£1223 $2128   (14-Apr-92 SY.AM364/R) Dune landscape near Heyst (80x100cm-31x39in) s.
    (D.FL 4000)
£1400 $2506   (14-Jan-92 SWS223/R) Pluie d'automne (79x99cm-31x39in) s. s.i.verso

RUMMELSPACHER, Joseph (1852-1921) German
£741 $1298   (19-Feb-92 D.V45/R) Alpine summer farm cottage, Tyrol (66x95cm-26x37in)
    s. i.verso (A.S 15000)

RUMOHR, Knut (1916-) Norwegian
£482 $897   (18-Jun-92 GWP.O85/R) Mountainside (68x86cm-27x34in) s.d.70 (N.KR 5500)
£713 $1234   (23-Mar-92 B.O111/R) Composition with red (80x100cm-31x39in) s.d.1967
    (N.KR 8000)
£713 $1234   (23-Mar-92 B.O110/R) Mountains (79x98cm-31x39in) s.d.78 (N.KR 8000)
£1053 $1958   (18-Jun-92 GWP.O84/R) Small opening (85x120cm-33x47in) s.d.1970
    (N.KR 12000)

RUMP, Godfred (1816-1880) Danish
£628 $1112   (11-Feb-92 RAS.K150) Winter landscape with sunshine (45x57cm-18x22in)
    init. (D.KR 7000)
£762 $1372   (30-Jan-92 RAS.V674) Ladies walking in park, summer (56x68cm-22x27in)
    s.d.1874 (D.KR 8500)

RUMPF, Emil (1860-?) German
£2226 $3829   (11-Oct-91 AW.H2911/R) Mail coach in snow storm outside hotel waiting for
    travellers (51x80cm-20x31in) s. (DM 6500)

RUMPLER, Franz (1848-1922) Austrian
£1994 $3569   (16-Jan-92 D.V121/R) Loretto Kapelle in Haida (16x23cm-6x9in) panel
    (A.S 40000)

RUNDT, Hans Hinrich (1660-c.1750) German
£4070 $7000   (10-Oct-91 SY.NY94/R) Christ in the garden of Gethsemane
    (108x136cm-43x54in) s.d.1729

RUNGE, Philipp Otto (1777-1810) German
£7560 $13986   *(13-Jun-92 HN.H233/R) Studies of head and hands (21x39cm-8x15in) chk*
    htd.white (DM 22000)

RUNGIUS, Carl (1869-1959) American/German
£1073 $1900   (9-Nov-91 W.W261/R) Wyoming landscape (23x28cm-9x11in) s.
£1073 $1900   (9-Nov-91 W.W267/R) Yukon territory (23x28cm-9x11in) s.
£1073 $1900   (9-Nov-91 W.W251/R) Rocky mountain landscape (23x28cm-9x11in) s.
£1638 $2900   *(9-Nov-91 W.W248/R) Siesta - a preparatory drawing and etching*
    (20x28cm-8x11in) pencil crayon two

RUNGUN, D K (20th C) Balinese
£1147 $2099   *(1-Jun-92 W.T1234) Flora and fauna composition (67x43cm-26x17in) s.i. W/C*
    fabric laid down (C.D 2500)

RUOKOKOSKI, Jalmari (1886-1936) Finnish
£1527 $2718   (28-Nov-91 BU.S32/R) Still life of flowers (50x56cm-20x22in) s.d.1918
    (S.KR 16000)
£1552 $2763   (1-Dec-91 HOR.H193) Flowers (36x40cm-14x16in) s.d.1935 (F.M 12000)
£1643 $2893   (12-Apr-92 HOR.H193) The harbour (46x57cm-18x22in) s.d.1926 (F.M 13000)
£1682 $2994   (1-Dec-91 HOR.H192) Road to town (38x46cm-15x18in) s.d.1924 (F.M 13000)
£2070 $3684   (1-Dec-91 HOR.H191) The blue river (41x41cm-16x16in) s. (F.M 16000)
£2402 $4228   (12-Apr-92 HOR.H194) Still life of flowers (45x53cm-18x21in) s.d.1920
    (F.M 19000)
£3752 $6678   (1-Dec-91 HOR.H189/R) View of Borga in winter (46x55cm-18x22in) s.d.1929
    (F.M 29000)

RUOPPOLO, Gian Battista (1620-1685) Italian
£5525 $10000   (20-May-92 D.NY60) Still life of grapes, peaches, pears, cherries and
    figs on stone step (64x94cm-25x37in) i.verso
£38000 $72960   (8-Jul-92 S81/R) Still life of pomegranates and other fruit and flowers
    on stone ledge (111x86cm-44x34in)

RUOPPOLO, Gian Battista (attrib) (1620-1685) Italian
£13966 $25000   (17-Jan-92 SY.NY177/R) Still life with fruit (72x96cm-28x38in)

RUOPPOLO, Giuseppe (attrib) (1639-1710) Italian
£28219 $50229   (28-Apr-92 RAS.K70/R) Still life of fruit, flowers and two rabbits
         (95x145cm-37x57in) (D.KR 320000)

RUOPPOLO, Giuseppe (circle) (1639-1710) Italian
£18000 $32760   (10-Dec-91 PH218/R) Still lives of fruit scattered by ledges and in
         landscapes (73x97cm-29x38in) pair

RUPERTI, Madya (1903-1981) Swiss
£457 $800   *(28-Feb-92 SY.NY280/R) Plymouth (119x81cm-47x32in) s.d.63 collage wash*
         masonite

RUSCHA, Edward (1937-) American
£36313 $65000   (14-Nov-91 SY.NY181/R) Do az I do (140x188cm-55x74in) s.d.1988 verso
         acrylic canvas
£39106 $70000   (5-May-92 CH.NY62/R) Days of the week (56x203cm-22x80in)
         s.i.d.1979stretcher
£67039 $120000   (12-Nov-91 CH.NY67/R) Nota bad world, is it (252x202cm-99x80in)
         s.d.1983verso
£4749 $8500   (13-Nov-91 CH.NY165/R) The briefcase (37x58cm-15x23in) s.d.1973 gun
         powder
£8380 $15000   (7-May-92 SY.NY326/R) More poison (56x76cm-22x30in) s.d.1984 dry pigment
£8939 $16000   (7-May-92 SY.NY322/R) Rain (58x74cm-23x29in) s.d.1970 s.num.840 verso gun
         powder pastel
£9497 $17000   (14-Nov-91 SY.NY343 a/R) Various cruelties (91x102cm-36x40in) blueberry
         extract on rayon-crepe

RUSCHE, Moritz Albert (1888-1969) German
£853 $1553   (27-May-92 PH.DU174) North German flatlands (75x100cm-30x39in) mono.
         (DM 2500)

RUSHBURY, Sir Henry (1889-1968) British
£600 $1044   (15-Apr-92 PHL89/R) Campo S. Magherita, Venice (26x32cm-10x13in)
         s.i.d.1957 pencil col.wash
£650 $1190   (4-Jun-92 CSK115) Piccadilly Circus (33x41cm-13x16in) s.d.1921 pencil W/C

RUSINOL, Santiago (1861-1931) Spanish
£7188 $13514   (17-Dec-91 BRO.B380/R) Arboles en las margenes de un rio (23x32cm-9x13in)
         s. panel (S.P 1300000)
£13372 $23000   (16-Oct-91 CH.NY156/R) The garden wall (52x32cm-20x13in) s.
£60824 $114349   (17-Dec-91 BRO.B433) Llac casa Bades, Arbucies (112x144cm-44x57in) s.
         (S.P 11000000)

RUSKIEWICZ, F (1819-1883) Polish
£509 $926   (15-Dec-91 REM.W38) Figures in landscape (42x55cm-17x22in) s.
         (P.Z 10000000)

RUSKIN, John (1819-1900) British
£7200 $12672   (9-Apr-92 S82/R) Val Anzasca, Italy (16x22cm-6x9in) i. pen W/C over
         pencil htd bodycol
£10000 $17900   (12-Nov-91 C145/R) The Bridge of Rheinfelden (37x55cm-15x22in) pencil ink
         W/C htd.white

RUSS, C B (19th C) ?
£621 $1100   (25-Apr-92 YFA.M259/R) View from Trempeauleau Cliff, Upper Mississippi
         River (30x51cm-12x20in) s.d.1887

RUSS, Franz (19th C) Austrian
£3000 $5340   (26-Nov-91 PH122/R) Portrait of lady seated wearing feathered hat
         (79x63cm-31x25in) s.d.1897

RUSS, Franz (younger) (1844-1906) Austrian
£1400 $2492   (28-Nov-91 CSK158) Idyll (69x53cm-27x21in) init.

RUSS, Karl (1779-1843) Austrian
£971 $1728   (29-Apr-92 D.V840/R) The founding of Maria Hietzing (48x54cm-19x21in)
         s.d.1822 panel (A.S 20000)

RUSS, Robert (1847-1922) Austrian
£1845 $3283   (29-Apr-92 D.V870/R) Street scene in southern town (28x17cm-11x7in) s.
         panel (A.S 38000)
£2670 $4752   (29-Apr-92 D.V631/R) Wooden benches in woodland clearing (23x34cm-9x13in)
         s. mixed media board (A.S 55000)

RUSSELL, Charles M (1865-1926) American
£17582 $32000   (28-May-92 CH.NY115/R) Deer in a snowy forest (19x28cm-7x11in) init.
         d.1906 gouache pencil board
£27624 $50000   (5-Dec-91 SY.NY46/R) Misplaced confidence (32x44cm-13x17in) s. W/C
         gouache paperboard en grisaille
£37363 $68000   (27-May-92 SY.NY47/R) Trappers crossing the Prairie (29x53cm-11x21in)
         s.d.1901 W/C paperboard

RUSSELL, Charles M (1865-1926) American-cont.
£71429 $130000   (28-May-92 CH.NY109/R) A campsite by the lake (35x56cm-14x22in) s.i.d.1908 W/C gouache pencil board

RUSSELL, Charles M (attrib) (1865-1926) American
£3571 $6000   (12-Aug-91 SG.M593) The Ambush (61x91cm-24x36in) s.

RUSSELL, George (1867-?) British
£780 $1450   (17-Jun-92 A.D67) Summer evening, Hill of Howth (33x38cm-13x15in) mono. (E.P 850)
£872 $1621   (17-Jun-92 A.D153) Figures on seashore at twilight (41x51cm-16x20in) mono. (E.P 950)
£1028 $1779   (25-Mar-92 A.D157) Mother and child in moonlight landscape (41x53cm-16x21in) mono. (E.P 1100)
£1147 $2133   (17-Jun-92 A.D9/R) Mountainous landscape at dusk with sheep (38x51cm-15x20in) mono. (E.P 1250)
£1169 $2070   (4-Nov-91 SY.J236/R) Mother and daughter in landscape (40x52cm-16x20in) mono. (SA.R 5800)
£1193 $2218   (17-Jun-92 A.D52) Children in sand dunes (38x51cm-15x20in) init. (E.P 1300)

RUSSELL, George Horne (1861-1933) Canadian
£505 $923   (2-Jun-92 R.T510/R) Marine coast of Nova Scotia (56x79cm-22x31in) s. (C.D 1100)
£548 $1003   (14-May-92 SY.T3) Scottish landscape (45x60cm-18x24in) s. (C.D 1200)
£995 $1771   (26-Nov-91 JOY.T43/R) Sailing vessels on river s. (C.D 2000)
£1000 $1770   (6-Nov-91 SY.T172/R) Lunenburg, Nova Scotia (30x50cm-12x20in) s. (C.D 2000)
£1650 $2921   (6-Nov-91 SY.T203/R) Harbour scene at dusk (58x105cm-23x41in) s. (C.D 3300)
£1951 $3532   (2-Dec-91 R.T230/R) Woman clam digging, Bay of Fundy, New Brunswick (76x102cm-30x40in) s. s.verso (C.D 4000)

RUSSELL, Gyrth (1892-1970) Canadian
£600 $1044   (19-Sep-91 B27/R) Harbour at Mevagissey (53x38cm-21x15in) s.
£720 $1289   (5-May-92 SWS480/R) Harbour entrance, Polperro (52x75cm-20x30in) s. i.verso
£720 $1289   (14-Jan-92 PH42/R) Fishing boats in harbour (38x53cm-15x21in) s.
£1000 $1850   (12-Jun-92 TE626) St Ives, Cornwall (56x76cm-22x30in) s.
£3000 $5160   (10-Oct-91 L401/R) Fishing boats returning to Newlyn Harbour and moored before lighthouse (53x76cm-21x30in) s.

RUSSELL, J B (19/20th C) British
£600 $1110   (11-Jun-92 CSK185/R) Inquisitive kittens (66x50cm-26x20in) s.

RUSSELL, John (1745-1806) British
£1923 $3673   (15-Jul-92 CH.S758/R) Portrait of gentleman, in blue coat (61x50cm-24x20in) s.d.1788 (A.D 5000)
£4144 $7500   (21-May-92 CH.NY149/R) Portrait of nobleman, said to be robert Grosvenor, Viscount Belgrave (30x25cm-12x10in) s.d.1788
£580 $1038   (5-May-92 SWS83/R) Portrait of John Webbe Weston (60x45cm-24x18in) s. pastel

RUSSELL, John (after) (1745-1806) British
£880 $1681   (14-Jul-92 DR321) Portrait of Martha Higginson and son, Powell (91x71cm-36x28in) pastel

RUSSELL, John (attrib) (1745-1806) British
£1600 $2848   (21-Jan-92 PH59/R) Portrait of young boy as Cupid (91x71cm-36x28in)
£4500 $8595   (15-Jul-92 S45/R) Portrait of Mary and William Warren (81x71cm-32x28in)
£1200 $2148   (14-Nov-91 S52/R) View of Guildford High Street, Surrey (29x41cm-11x16in) i.d.1765 W/C over pen

RUSSELL, John (circle) (1745-1806) British
£1400 $2506   (11-Nov-91 S529/R) Two children playing cards (39x29cm-15x11in) pastel

RUSSELL, John (19th C) British
£850 $1471   (24-Mar-92 CG834) Salmon and trout on a rocky bank (45x91cm-18x36in) s.
£1100 $1958   (28-Apr-92 S219/R) Grouse (46x69cm-18x27in) s. s.i.verso
£1200 $2016   (26-Aug-91 S878/R) Trout (26x46cm-10x18in) s. panel
£1400 $2492   (28-Apr-92 S239/R) Trout and salmon (45x91cm-18x36in) s.
£2100 $3738   (28-Apr-92 S238/R) Salmon (45x90cm-18x35in) s.
£2600 $4706   (4-Dec-91 S165/R) Two salmon (37x75cm-15x30in) s.
£5738 $10500   (5-Jun-92 SY.NY104/R) The day's catch (80x120cm-31x47in) s.d.1871

RUSSELL, John Peter (1859-1931) Australian
£11538 $20538   (28-Apr-92 CH.ME155/R) Young man, head and shoulders in profile (33x41cm-13x16in) s.d.1912 (A.D 27000)
£96916 $172511   (26-Nov-91 J.M14/R) Belle Ile (53x64cm-21x25in) s.i.d.1900 (A.D 220000)
£158120 $281453   (28-Apr-92 CH.ME186/R) Cruach en Mahr, Martin, Belle Ile en Mer (60x73cm-24x29in) s. s.i.stretcher (A.D 370000)
£1709 $3043   (27-Apr-92 J.M132/R) Solitude (26x38cm-10x15in) s.i.d.20 W/C (A.D 4000)
£2137 $3803   (27-Apr-92 J.M612) By the lake (32x49cm-13x19in) s.i. W/C (A.D 5000)
£2863 $5154   (24-Nov-91 SY.S472/R) Cagnes (25x36cm-10x14in) s.i.d.20 W/C (A.D 6500)

RUSSELL, John Peter (1859-1931) Australian-cont.
£3000 $5340   (28-Nov-91 C38/R) Foggy evening at Belle-Ile (25x35cm-10x14in) s.i.d.10 W/C

RUSSELL, John Wentworth (1879-1959) Canadian
£900 $1593   (6-Nov-91 SY.T29) Figure seated by garden (27x34cm-11x13in) s.d.11 board (C.D 1800)
£1393 $2480   (25-Nov-91 W.T1562) Still life with figurines and flowers (116x89cm-46x35in) s. (C.D 2800)

RUSSELL, Morgan (1886-1953) American
£552 $1000   (4-Dec-91 D.NY76/R) Quarry (64x81cm-25x32in) s.

RUSSELL, Robert (1808-1900) Australian
£553 $979   (26-Apr-92 SY.ME173) Lady with riding crop (16x11cm-6x4in) s.d.1878 W/C ivory (A.D 1300)

RUSSIAN SCHOOL (?) Russian
£2437 $4386   (19-Nov-91 RAS.K276/R) Road through wood (118x79cm-46x31in) s. (D.KR 27000)
£3704 $6704   (19-May-92 GF.L2280/R) Sleigh ride (61x50cm-24x20in) c.1900 indis.s. (S.FR 10000)

RUSSIAN SCHOOL, 17th C
£3254 $5889   (3-Dec-91 SY.MI212/R) Abramo e i tre angeli (61x47cm-24x19in) tempera on panel gold ground (I.L 7000000)

RUSSIAN SCHOOL, 18th C
£2091 $3805   (12-Dec-91 L.K155 a/R) Portrait of Tsar Peter III of Russia (85x72cm-33x28in) i.verso (DM 6000)

RUSSIAN SCHOOL, 19th C
£2767 $4980   (19-Nov-91 GS.B3649) Troika in winter landscape (50x90cm-20x35in) indis.s.d.1882 (S.FR 7000)
£5524 $10053   (14-Dec-91 BA.S108/R) Small girl with hat (120x80cm-47x31in) (S.KR 58000)

RUSSIAN SCHOOL, 20th C
£594 $1058   (26-Nov-91 KF.M1003) Woman with bucket (20x18cm-8x7in) gouache board (DM 1700)

RUSSO, Mario (1925-) Italian
£557 $1047   (19-Dec-91 F.M82) Il carro sulla neve (62x100cm-24x39in) s.d.1956 s.i.d.verso (I.L 1200000)

RUSSO, Nicola Maria (attrib) (1647-1702) Italian
£7202 $13035   (5-Dec-91 SY.MO266/R) Allegorie de la chasse (87x85cm-34x33in) oval (F.FR 70000)

RUSSO, Raul (1912-1984) Argentinian
£948 $1650   (19-Sep-91 V.BA91) Delta (30x35cm-12x14in) tempera
£1613 $3000   (16-Jun-92 RO.BA83) Naturaleza muerta (26x33cm-10x13in)
£1744 $3000   (9-Oct-91 RO.BA214) La Grua (59x89cm-23x35in) s.
£2083 $4000   (4-Aug-92 V.BA96) Paisaje (60x49cm-24x19in)
£2611 $4700   (20-Nov-91 V.BA89/R) Paisaje en azul (40x50cm-16x20in)
£3226 $6000   (16-Jun-92 RO.BA82) Suburbio (81x100cm-32x39in)
£6180 $11000   (1-Nov-91 PO.BA71) Barcas (62x72cm-24x28in)

RUSSOLO, Luigi (1885-1947) Italian
£2514 $4777   (23-Jun-92 F.M224/R) Il pioppo sotto la luna (40x28cm-16x11in) s.d.1946 s.i.verso panel (I.L 5500000)

RUST, Graham (?) British
£1900 $3458   (12-Dec-91 CSK188/R) A view of Sandwich Park, Wiltshire in Exotic parkland (101x137cm-40x54in) s.d.74 board

RUST, Johan Adolph (1828-1915) Dutch
£1143 $2000   (18-Feb-92 CE.NY118/R) Fishing village (28x36cm-11x14in) s.

RUSTIN, Jean (1928-) French
£2959 $5238   (12-Feb-92 GL.P97) Nu (41x33cm-16x13in) s.d.1971 (F.FR 29000)
£4167 $7250   (13-Apr-92 GL.P190/R) Tete d'homme (40x40cm-16x16in) s.d.1985 i.verso (F.FR 41000)
£4303 $7746   (27-Jan-92 GL.P154) Nu couche (38x46cm-15x18in) s.d.1971 (F.FR 42000)

RUSZCZYC, Ferdynand (1870-1936) Polish
£1425 $2594   (15-Dec-91 REM.W37) Forest (24x34cm-9x13in) s. (P.Z 28000000)
£2529 $4527   (17-Nov-91 REM.W24) At sea (27x36cm-11x14in) s. (P.Z 49000000)
£4710 $8149   (8-Sep-91 REM.W29) Landscape with trees and river (31x46cm-12x18in) s. (P.Z 90000000)
£569 $1071   (21-Dec-91 HO.P4) Cranes (29x24cm-11x9in) s. W/C (P.Z 11000000)

RUSZKOWSKI, Zdzislaw (1907-1990) Polish
£500 $915   (14-May-92 C100) Nude against light (99x79cm-39x31in) s. mono.verso
£700 $1281   (14-May-92 C97/R) Pansies (35x43cm-14x17in) s.
£850 $1556   (14-May-92 C95/R) Beside loch (66x96cm-26x38in) s.

RUSZKOWSKI, Zdzislaw (1907-1990) Polish-cont.
£1050 $1922   (14-May-92 C99/R) Cyprus window (98x68cm-39x27in) s.
£1800 $3294   (14-May-92 C98/R) View from boatyard (106x75cm-42x30in) s.

RUTHART, Karl Andreas (1630-1703) German
£44053 $77974   (7-Nov-91 D.V99/R) Lions and tiger fighting and other animals in cave
                  with sarcophagus (97x114cm-38x45in) s. (A.S 900000)

RUTHART, Karl Andreas (attrib) (1630-1703) German
£6969 $12683   (11-Dec-91 N.M355/R) Dogs attacking two bears in mountainous landscape
                  (70x87cm-28x34in) (DM 20000)
£8123 $14621   (19-Nov-91 RAS.K23/R) Eagle attacking swans and ducks (160x230cm-63x91in)
                  (D.KR 90000)

RUTHENBECK, Reiner (1937-) German
£632 $1137   (19-Nov-91 L.K1060) Glass balloon in box (21x30cm-8x12in) s.i.d.1970
                  pencil felt tip pen (DM 1800)
£632 $1137   (19-Nov-91 L.K1059) Untitled (21x30cm-8x12in) s.i.d.c.1970 pencil
                  col.pencil (DM 1800)
£702 $1263   (19-Nov-91 L.K1058) Untitled (21x29cm-8x11in) s.d.c.1968 pencil (DM 2000)

RUTHS, Valentin (1825-1905) German
£616 $1035   (27-Aug-91 RAS.K475) Wooded landscape (53x75cm-21x30in) s. panel
                  (D.KR 7000)
£1587 $2825   (28-Apr-92 RAS.K465/R) Schwerer sturm (85x140cm-33x55in) s.d.1899
                  (D.KR 18000)
£1761 $3187   (4-Dec-91 DO.H2904/R) View of Fritzlar, winter evening (50x72cm-20x28in)
                  s.i.indis.d.1872 (DM 5000)

RUTTIMANN, Hans (1940-) Swiss
£401 $719   (6-May-92 GD.B1097/R) Siesta (31x41cm-12x16in) s.d.92 indian ink pen
                  (S.FR 1100)

RUXLEBEN, Bruno von (19th C) ?
£2744 $5076   (13-Jun-92 CH.AM187/R) Rabbits with vegetables in landscape. Ducks and
                  ducklings on riverbank (67x83cm-26x33in) init.d.1839 pair (D.FL 9000)
£2896 $5358   (13-Jun-92 CH.AM186/R) Greyhound watching dead hare. Fox watching
                  pheasant in landscape (67x83cm-26x33in) s.init.d.1838 pair (D.FL 9500)

RUYSCH, Rachel (1664-1750) Dutch
£46296 $82870   (14-Nov-91 CH.AM122/R) Forest floor still life of flowers, fungi, insects
                  and butterflies (64x52cm-25x20in) s.d.1683 (D.FL 150000)

RUYSCH, Rachel (after) (1664-1750) Dutch
£1224 $2166   (7-Nov-91 D.V314/R) Bunch of flowers in glass vase (46x34cm-18x13in)
                  panel (A.S 25000)

RUYSCH, Rachel (attrib) (1664-1750) Dutch
£80000 $139200 (15-Apr-92 C2/R) Roses and other flowers with butterflies in glass vase
                  in casement (76x63cm-30x25in)

RUYSCH, Rachel (circle) (1664-1750) Dutch
£2718 $5028   (8-Jun-92 CH.R764) Piccolo festone di fiori (31x36cm-12x14in)
                  (I.L 6000000)
£24912 $46088   (8-Jun-92 CH.R755/R) Vaso con fiori poggiato su un piano di pietra
                  (78x63cm-31x25in) (I.L 55000000)
£30000 $53400   (30-Oct-91 S145/R) Still life of flowers in glass vase on marble ledge
                  draped with cloth (92x71cm-36x28in)

RUYSCH, Rachel (style) (1664-1750) Dutch
£3436 $5979   (18-Sep-91 N.M447/R) Still life of tulips and other flowers in glass vase
                  on table with snail (68x54cm-27x21in) (DM 10000)
£4180 $7273   (13-Sep-91 C125/R) Mixed flowers in vase with butterflies, frog and other
                  insects (111x77cm-44x30in)

RUYSDAEL, Jacob Salomonsz van (1630-1681) Dutch
£7500 $13050   (15-Apr-92 C118/R) Wooded landscape with drover on track by pond
                  (82x112cm-32x44in)
£8000 $14000   (1-Apr-92 S42/R) Bosky landscape with cattle and sleeping herder
                  (56x84cm-22x33in) indist.s.d. panel

RUYSDAEL, Jacob van (1628-1682) Dutch
£6186 $10763   (17-Sep-91 FN.S2510/R) Dutch wooded landscape with farmhouses and
                  shepherd with flock (50x68cm-20x27in) panel (DM 18000)
£19000 $34580   (13-Dec-91 C205/R) Wooded dune landscape with peasants on track
                  (48x64cm-19x25in) s. panel
£40000 $76800   (8-Jul-92 S53/R) Wooden landscape with figures near stream
                  (64x81cm-25x32in) bears sig
£180000 $313200 (15-Apr-92 C24/R) Wooded landscape with shepherd and shepherdess
                  conversing by river (51x61cm-20x24in) s.

RUYSDAEL, Jacob van (after) (1628-1682) Dutch
£4115 $7449   (5-Dec-91 SY.MO294/R) Paysage avec promeneurs (108x160cm-43x63in)
                  (F.FR 40000)

RUYSDAEL, Jacob van (style) (1628-1682) Dutch
£2344 $4148   (5-Nov-91 GF.L2349/R) River landscape (40x55cm-16x22in) bears sig. panel
          (S.FR 6000)
£4800 $8400   (28-Feb-92 C78/R) Wooded river landscape with a woman washing outside a
          cottage (74x63cm-29x25in)

RUYSDAEL, Salomon van (1600-1670) Dutch
£16838 $29299   (18-Sep-91 N.M448/R) Tower standing in landscape with rider and coach
          beyond (110x83cm-43x33in) s.d.1641 (DM 49000)
£24839 $42474   (18-Mar-92 D.V133/R) Wooded landscape with huntsmen (56x72cm-22x28in)
          mono (A.S 500000)
£58000 $105560   (11-Dec-91 S37/R) View along river Rhine looking upstream towards
          Arnheim, with cattle and boats (62x94cm-24x37in) s.d.1652 panel

RUYSDAEL, Salomon van (attrib) (1600-1670) Dutch
£1754 $3000   (13-Mar-92 FN.S2936/R) Dutch canal landscape with shipping
          (30x40cm-12x16in) panel (DM 5000)

RUYTEN, Jan Michael (1813-1881) Belgian
£10365 $18968   (12-May-92 C.A287/R) Dutch harbour scene (41x29cm-16x11in) s. panel
          (B.FR 625000)

RUYTINX, Alfred (1871-?) Belgian
£916 $1704   (16-Jun-92 SY.B317) Kitchen still life (99x138cm-39x54in) s. (B.FR 55000)

RUZICKA, Othmar (1877-?) Austrian
£629 $1089   (25-Mar-92 KM.K1392) Bohemian peasant girls wearing Sunday costume on
          path (60x80cm-24x31in) s. (DM 1800)

RUZICKA-LAUTENSCHLAGER, Hans (20th C) Austrian
£993 $1768   (28-Nov-91 D.V115/R) Kurkonzert (64x79cm-25x31in) s. (A.S 20000)

RYAN, Adrian (1920-) British
£500 $915   (6-Feb-92 DLY530/R) Motor racing (38x48cm-15x19in) s.

RYAN, Thomas (1929-) Irish
£463 $843   (11-Dec-91 A.D180) St.Peter's, Drogheda, 1980 (23x18cm-9x7in) s. board
          (E.P 500)
£833 $1517   (11-Dec-91 A.D136) Line of trees at home (51x41cm-20x16in) s. board
          (E.P 900)
£833 $1517   (11-Dec-91 A.D31/R) 'The Orchestral Pit', self-portrait (18x28cm-7x11in)
          s. s.i.verso board (E.P 900)

RYBACK, Issachar (1897-1935) Russian
£2778 $5056   (11-Dec-91 CH.AM310/R) Girl harvesting (100x81cm-39x32in) s.
          s.i.d.1920verso (D.FL 9000)
£4286 $7500   (26-Sep-91 SY.I82/R) Market scene (65x50cm-26x20in) s. s.i.indis.d.verso
£6857 $12000   (26-Sep-91 SY.I33/R) Portrait of Raya Garbusoya (100x80cm-39x31in) s.
£638 $1200   (5-Jan-92 GG.TA358/R) Yeshiva student (62x46cm-24x18in) s. pastel
£1453 $2600   (9-May-92 CE.NY54/R) Yeshiva boy (32x25cm-13x10in) s. W/C

RYBKOWSKI, Tadeusz (1848-1926) Polish
£509 $926   (15-Dec-91 REM.W39) Easter market in Lwow (21x36cm-8x14in) s. W/C
          (P.Z 10000000)
£781 $1367   (29-Sep-91 AG.W14) Easter Market in Lwow (21x36cm-8x14in) s. W/C
          (P.Z 15000000)

RYCK, Pieter Cornelisz van (style) (1568-c.1628) Dutch
£850 $1522   (5-May-92 ZEL.L1552/R) Still life of dead game, swan and lobster
          (54x88cm-21x35in) (DM 2500)

RYCKAERT, David III (1612-1661) Flemish
£3591 $6500   (22-May-92 SY.NY166/R) Card players in interior (60x80cm-24x31in) s.
          panel

RYCKAERT, Marten (1587-1631) Flemish
£30000 $54600   (11-Dec-91 S52/R) Figures on banks of river (27x34cm-11x13in) panel

RYCKAERT, Marten (attrib) (1587-1631) Flemish
£1804 $3229   (15-Nov-91 GK.Z5094/R) Italian lake landscape with hunting party before
          ruin (30cm-12ins circular) panel (S.FR 4600)
£2778 $5028   (19-May-92 GF.L2038/R) Hilly wooded landscape with two shepherds
          (20x36cm-8x14in) indis.i.verso panel (S.FR 7500)

RYCKERE, Bernard de (circle) (1535-1590) Flemish
£5961 $10194   (18-Mar-92 D.V50/R) Diana with nymphs and Acteon (38x33cm-15x13in) copper
          (A.S 120000)

RYCKHALS, Frans (circle) (1600-1647) Dutch
£1100 $1958   (29-Oct-91 PH77/R) An interior with a woman preparing vegetables in an
          upturned barrel (41x36cm-16x14in) panel

RYD, Carl (1883-1958) Swedish
£659 $1173   (28-Oct-91 AB.S211) After the thunderstorm, harvesting landscape
          (37x45cm-15x18in) s.d.48 (S.KR 7000)

RYD, Carl (1883-1958) Swedish-cont.
£665 $1157   (13-Apr-92 AB.S233) Winter landscape with snow covered pine
(54x45cm-21x18in) s.d.25 (S.KR 7000)

RYDBERG, Gustaf (1835-1933) Swedish
£1226 $2171   (5-Nov-91 BA.S159/R) Fishermen in punt (21x32cm-8x13in) init. panel
(S.KR 13000)
£2081 $3767   (19-May-92 AB.S4272/R) Winter landscape with woman and sledge
(36x45cm-14x18in) s.d.88 panel (S.KR 22000)
£2281 $4084   (16-Nov-91 FAL.M314/R) From Bordighera, Italy (38x60cm-15x24in) s.d.1902
(S.KR 24000)

RYDER, Chauncey F (1868-1949) American
£556 $950   (13-Mar-92 S.BM241/R) Stream at the foot of the hill. Autumnal study
(15x20cm-6x8in) s. s.verso board double-sided
£894 $1600   (14-Nov-91 CE.NY178/R) Cape Porpoise, Maine (16x21cm-6x8in) s. i.verso
panel
£929 $1700   (9-Feb-92 LIT.L281) Through arch (30x41cm-12x16in) s. board
£944 $1700   (22-Nov-91 S.BM135/R) Stream at foot of hill. Autumnal sketch
(15x20cm-6x8in) s. board double-sided
£1040 $1800   (6-Sep-91 S.BM218/R) Up hill on Essex Road (41x51cm-16x20in) s. i. verso
£1117 $2100   (18-Dec-91 SY.NY98/R) The lane to the pasture (30x40cm-12x16in) s.
£2155 $3750   (15-Apr-92 SY.NY101/R) Approaching storm (30x41cm-12x16in) s.
£3509 $6000   (12-Mar-92 CH.NY170/R) Autumn hills (54x76cm-21x30in) s. canvas on
masonite on panel
£4396 $8000   (28-May-92 CH.NY135/R) The old road (63x76cm-25x30in) s. canvas on
masonite
£5143 $9000   (26-Sep-91 CH.NY92/R) Deep hollow (63x76cm-25x30in) s. canvas on panel

RYLAARSDAM, Jan (1911-) Dutch
£492 $900   (17-May-92 DU.E1056/R) Market park (46x64cm-18x25in) indis.s. i.verso

RYLAND, Henry (1856-1924) British
£900 $1539   (19-Mar-92 B77) A classical beauty (74x25cm-29x10in) s. board
£400 $720   (30-Jan-92 TL135) Portrait study of Simonetta (28x22cm-11x9in) init.
pencil drawing
£1200 $2136   (29-Oct-91 C59/R) Surprised (37x53cm-15x21in) s. i.verso pencil W/C
£1710 $2941   (10-Oct-91 D.V308/R) Portrait of young girl before peonies
(50x33cm-20x13in) s. chk W/C (A.S 35000)
£2125 $3845   (18-May-92 SY.MI4/R) Le quattro stagioni (33x50cm-13x20in) s. W/C htd
white set of four (I.L 4700000)
£4000 $7320   (3-Jun-92 S287/R) Greeting (37x53cm-15x21in) s. W/C
£4900 $8673   (6-Nov-91 S277/R) La Primavera (63x44cm-25x17in) s. s.i.stretcher W/C
over pencil htd.white
£8033 $13736   (18-Mar-92 ARC.P11 c) Jeune femme au chapelet (71x37cm-28x15in) s.d.1897
W/C pastel (F.FR 78000)

RYLAND, Robert K (1873-1951) American
£1170 $2000   (12-Mar-92 CH.NY220/R) No rooms in Manhattan (41x33cm-16x13in) board
£1796 $3250   (21-May-92 GRO.B220/R) Seated woman with pears (91x69cm-36x27in) s.d.1916

RYLANDER, Hans Chr (20th C) Swedish?
£581 $1058   (10-Dec-91 RAS.K105) 'Harehop og sakrale tilfojelser' (103x67cm-41x26in)
init. s.d.1980-81verso (D.KR 6500)
£934 $1625   (17-Sep-91 RAS.K117) Perished body placed to rest (111x121cm-44x48in)
s.d.67verso (D.KR 10500)

RYLOV, Arkadij (1870-1939) Russian
£949 $1736   (14-May-92 BU.S196/R) Beet-pickers (49x60cm-19x24in) s. (S.KR 10000)

RYMAN, Herbert D (20th C) American
£368 $700   (24-Jun-92 B.SF6514/R) Circus canvas mender's wagon (51x74cm-20x29in)
s.d.1949 s.verso W/C

RYMAN, Robert (1930-) American
£17143 $30000   (25-Feb-92 SY.NY206/R) Untitled (46x46cm-18x18in) s.d.69 mylar
£46243 $80000   (3-Oct-91 SY.NY96/R) Untitled (33x33cm-13x13in) s. i.d.1961 linen
£167598 $300000   (13-Nov-91 SY.NY62/R) Director (238x213cm-94x84in) s.d.83 verso oil
fibreglass aluminium
£9714 $17000   (27-Feb-92 CH.NY53/R) Bent line drawing (50x50cm-20x20in) s.i.d.70verso
blue felt-tip pen fabric on board
£30000 $54300   (5-Dec-91 S60/R) Courier (87x82cm-34x32in) s.d.82 verso oil enamelac
fibreglass aluminium

RYN, Jan van de (1610-1678) Flemish
£748 $1339   (5-May-92 ZEL.L1509/R) Portrait of young man decorated with laurels
(19x18cm-7x7in) (DM 2200)

RYSBRACK, Pieter (circle) (1655-1729) Flemish
£1300 $2496   (10-Jul-92 PH81/R) Still life of dead water- and song-birds upon bank
(77x64cm-30x25in)
£1800 $3276   (10-Dec-91 PH207/R) Landscape with dead game, beneath tree
(89x75cm-35x30in)

RYSBRACK, Pieter Andreas (1690-1748) Flemish
£12601 $22303   (6-Nov-91 LT.P49/R) La lecon de dessin. Scene de marche (70x88cm-28x35in) pair (F.FR 125000)

RYSER, Fritz (1910-) Swiss
£784 $1333   (23-Oct-91 GD.B631) Hay stack in field (38x55cm-15x22in) s.d.64 (S.FR 2000)

RYSSELBERGHE, Theo van (1862-1926) Belgian
£2616	$4500	(12-Oct-91 SY.NY19/R) Portrait of Jacques Copeau (91x72cm-36x28in) mono.
£6200	$11842	(1-Jul-92 S105/R) Femme a la robe verte (35x18cm-14x7in) s. panel
£12000	$20640	(16-Oct-91 S30/R) Portrait de femme (44x34cm-17x13in) mono.d.1918 canvas on board
£17000	$30770	(3-Dec-91 C214/R) Paysage du midi (19x24cm-7x9in) panel
£23000	$39330	(12-Mar-92 B31/R) Landscape in yellow and purple (46x56cm-18x22in) mono.
£24000	$43440	(3-Dec-91 C227/R) Vue de Veere, Brume matinale (59x72cm-23x28in) mono.d.VR06
£494	$938	(22-Jun-92 AT.P85) Portrait d'Emile Verhaeren (23x19cm-9x7in) mono. studio st. pencil (F.FR 4800)
£962	$1780	(12-Jun-92 HN.H751/R) Female nude resting (36x47cm-14x19in) mono brush (DM 2800)
£1387	$2400	(25-Mar-92 D.NY64) Panoramic view of a village (15x23cm-6x9in) mono.d.03 W/C
£2483	$4495	(23-May-92 KV.L409/R) Elisabeth endormie a l'age de 4 ans (37x31cm-15x12in) mono. pastel board (B.FR 150000)
£15000	$28650	(1-Jul-92 S144/R) Femme nu devant le miroir (58x71cm-23x28in) mono.d.05 pastel paper laid down on canvas

RYSWYCK, Jan van (?) ?
£756 $1315   (17-Sep-91 FN.S2071) White hydrangea on tiled ground (105x92cm-41x36in) s.d.1923 (DM 2200)

RZEPINSKI, Czeslav (1905-) Polish
£785 $1358   (8-Sep-91 REM.W30) Forest landscape (54x80cm-21x31in) s. (P.Z 15000000)

S F (?) ?
£750 $1275   (23-Oct-91 S146/R) The road to Athens (28x41cm-11x16in) s.i.d.1852 W/C over pencil

S O (?) ?
£529 $942   (28-Apr-92 RAS.K588) Wild flowers (22x16cm-9x6in) init.d.79 (D.KR 6000)

SAABYE, Carl Anton (1807-1878) Danish
£2256 $4061   (19-Nov-91 RAS.K27/R) Norwegian fjord landscape (120x158cm-47x62in) s.d.1849 (D.KR 25000)

SAALBORN, Louis (1890-1957) Dutch
£545	$987	(21-May-92 SY.AM35) Landhuis te Bloemendaal (50x60cm-20x24in) s. s.i.verso cardboard (D.FL 1800)
£617	$1123	(11-Dec-91 CH.AM64) View on farm yard, Heerden (60x80cm-24x31in) s. s.i.d.49verso board (D.FL 2000)
£617	$1123	(12-Dec-91 SY.AM154/R) Stilleven met flessen (50x60cm-20x24in) s.d.1915 canvas on board (D.FL 2000)
£758	$1371	(19-May-92 CH.AM45) Shells on a beach, Bergen aan Zee (64x75cm-25x30in) s.indis.d. board (D.FL 2500)
£1080	$1966	(11-Dec-91 CH.AM56) View on farmyard (64x76cm-25x30in) s.d.49 (D.FL 3500)
£1152	$2084	(21-May-92 SY.AM168) View of the church at Bergen aan Zee (73x92cm-29x36in) s.d.50 s.d.verso (D.FL 3800)

SAAR, Karl von (1797-1853) Austrian
£437	$778	(29-Apr-92 D.V727/R) Portrait of young bearded gentleman (14x11cm-6x4in) s. W/C (A.S 9000)
£440	$788	(11-Nov-91 PH27) Portrait of Frank Boghurst wearing uniform and holding hat in hand (22x?cm-9x?in) min.s. wood frame
£1942	$3456	(29-Apr-92 D.V726/R) Portrait of young woman with curly hairstyle (11x9cm-4x4in) min.s.d.836 W/C (A.S 40000)

SAARINEN, Yrjo (1899-1958) Finnish
| £8538 | $15198 | (1-Dec-91 HOR.H195/R) Junipers (100x81cm-39x32in) s.d.1947 (F.M 66000) |
| £451 | $798 | (6-Nov-91 HOR.H113) From the beach (33x41cm-13x16in) s.d.1946 W/C (F.M 3200) |

SAAVEDRA, M (?) ?
£526 $947   (29-Jan-92 FER.M198) Jovenes campesinos con cesto de frutos y hortalizas (84x78cm-33x31in) s. (S.P 95000)

SABATELLI, Giuseppe (1813-1843) Italian
£750 $1365   (10-Dec-91 C188) A nude rending a garment. A coastal scene at sunrise (22x22cm-9x9in) s.i. blk.lead ink double-sided

SABATELLI, Giuseppe (after) (1813-1843) Italian
£1815 $3376   (16-Jun-92 F.M11) Farinata degli Uberti tenta di salvare Cece de
     Buondelmonti (62x77cm-24x30in) (I.L 4000000)

SABATELLI, Luigi (1772-1850) Italian
£1400   *$2548*   *(10-Dec-91 C187/R) Indolence (37x45cm-15x18in) s.i. ink*

SABATER, Daniel (1888-1951) Spanish
£771 $1326   (4-Mar-92 AT.P199) Mon Dieu, quelle chaleur (65x81cm-26x32in) s.i.
     (F.FR 7500)
£1041 $1987   (2-Jul-92 ANS.M132/R) Es posible... (37x46cm-15x18in) s. board
     (S.P 190000)
£1505 $2739   (26-May-92 DUR.M117/R) Monja (96x76cm-38x30in) s. (S.P 275000)

SABBAGH, Georges (1887-1951) French
£511 $915   (6-May-92 GD.B1098) Riverside houses (59x73cm-23x29in) s. board
     (S.FR 1400)
£1628 $2979   (17-May-92 T.B206/R) Ferme du Tregor (33x61cm-13x24in) s.d.24
     (F.FR 16000)
£511   *$936*   *(3-Feb-92 SD.P198) Le Repos du modele (46x61cm-18x24in) s.d.23 pastel*
     (F.FR 5000)
£1353   *$2367*   *(5-Apr-92 ZZ.F189/R) Nu allonge (46x61cm-18x24in) s.d.1923 pastel*
     (F.FR 13000)

SABBATINI, Lorenzo (c.1530-1577) Italian
£8721 $15000   (10-Oct-91 SY.NY143 a/R) The Annunciation (105x84cm-41x33in)

SABBATINI, Lorenzo (circle) (c.1530-1577) Italian
£6200 $10850   (31-Mar-92 PH113/R) Madonna and child with St. Elizabeth and infant St.
     John the Baptist (61x79cm-24x31in) panel

SABIRZYANOV, Farkhat (1933-) Russian
£532 $947   (25-Nov-91 ZZ.F175/R) La Datcha (82x60cm-32x24in) s. (F.FR 5200)
£560 $1019   (11-Dec-91 ZZ.F37/R) Le couple (75x95cm-30x37in) s.verso (F.FR 5500)
£1426 $2595   (11-Dec-91 ZZ.F38/R) Lenine au Kremlin (90x83cm-35x33in) s.verso
     (F.FR 14000)
£815   *$1483*   *(11-Dec-91 ZZ.F32/R) Lenine et le Comte Central (36x44cm-14x17in) s.verso*
     gouache (F.FR 8000)

SABLET, Francois Jean (1745-1819) French
£3037 $5497   (19-May-92 GF.L2451/R) Portrait of gentleman. Portrait of lady
     (23x20cm-9x8in) pair (S.FR 8200)

SABLET, Jacques Henri (attrib) (1749-1803) Swiss
£3018 $5191   (11-Oct-91 HC.P5/R) Paysage fluvial au clair de lune (45x61cm-18x24in)
     attrib to Jacques Francois (F.FR 30000)

SABOURAUD, Emile (1900-) French
£497 $900   (19-May-92 CE.NY277) Rue de village (53x74cm-21x29in) s.
£608 $1100   (20-May-92 FB.P232) Enfants de Neuville (61x81cm-24x32in) s. (F.FR 6000)
£678 $1200   (9-Nov-91 W.W73/R) Les bords de Lardques a Dieppe (38x81cm-15x32in) s.
     i.stretcher
£724 $1246   (11-Oct-91 HC.P34) Femme endormie (61x74cm-24x29in) s. (F.FR 7200)
£1143 $2000   (19-Feb-92 D.NY76) Bouquet de roses sur fond jaune (64x46cm-25x18in)
     s.d.1949 i.verso
£1440 $2607   (6-Dec-91 GL.P197 b) Le bateau-phare a Dunkerque (60x92cm-24x36in) s.
     (F.FR 14000)

SABY, Bernard (20th C) French?
£1509 $2596   (8-Oct-91 CC.P22/R) Sans titre (73x60cm-29x24in) s.d.9.VI.55 (F.FR 15000)
£2515 $4326   (8-Oct-91 CC.P17/R) Sans titre (73x100cm-29x39in) s.d.1956-1957
     (F.FR 25000)

SABY-VIRICES, Philippe see ARTIAS, Philippe

SACCAGGI, Cesare (1868-?) Italian
£1721 $3184   (9-Jun-92 F.R108) Cascata in Val di Susa (27x40cm-11x16in) s. panel
     (I.L 3800000)
£817   *$1519*   *(16-Jun-92 F.M66) Ritratto di giovinetto (49x36cm-19x14in) s.d.1927 W/C*
     (I.L 1800000)

SACCARO, John (1913-1981) American
£690 $1200   (14-Sep-91 LAE.L304/R) Blue Lovers (74x53cm-29x21in) s. s.i.verso
£2684 $4750   (12-Feb-92 B.SF639/R) Composition no.21 (117x147cm-46x58in) s.
£6471 $11000   (23-Oct-91 B.SF3708/R) Untitled (137x137cm-54x54in) s.

SACCHI, Andrea (1599-1661) Italian
£3600   *$6912*   *(6-Jul-92 S123/R) The Madonna and Child with St Jerome (14x16cm-6x6in)*
     chk.

SACCHI, Andrea (attrib) (1599-1661) Italian
£2000   *$3480*   *(14-Apr-92 C114/R) Hercules seated in wooded landscape (29x41cm-11x16in)*
     chk

SACCHI, Andrea (circle) (1599-1661) Italian
£1134 $2075   (2-Jun-92 FN.S2735/R) Portrait of cardinal Bernadinos Spada
                  (62x47cm-24x19in) (DM 3300)
£4420 $8000   (21-May-92 CH.NY174/R) Saint Gregory, seated at desk, with Holy Spirit
                  descending (112x146cm-44x57in)

SACHAROFF, Olga (1889-) Russian
£4101 $7504   (13-May-92 FER.M167/R) El jardin de mi casa (60x73cm-24x29in) s.
                  (S.P 750000)

SACHERI, Giuseppe (1863-1950) Italian
£1237 $2190   (7-Nov-91 F.M64) Marina presso Nervi (23x33cm-9x13in) s.d.930verso panel
                  (I.L 2700000)
£2299 $4116   (14-Nov-91 CH.R190) Mareggiata (39x44cm-15x17in) s. board (I.L 5000000)

SACKENHEIM, Rolf (1921-) German
£526 $947   *(19-Nov-91 L.K1066) Untitled (25x37cm-10x15in) s.d.1984 indian ink*
                  (DM 1500)
£561 $1011   *(19-Nov-91 L.K1062) Untitled (32x24cm-13x9in) s.d.78 pen indian ink*
                  (DM 1600)
£561 $1011   *(19-Nov-91 L.K1067) Untitled (25x29cm-10x11in) s.d.1987 indian ink brush*
                  (DM 1600)

SACKS, Joseph (1887-1974) American
£1163 $2000   (10-Oct-91 FA.PH906/R) Portrait of Mrs. Victor C. Mathers, seated with
                  riding crop (91x76cm-36x30in)

SACO (19th C) Italian
£1660 $2839   (17-Mar-92 FER.M198/R) Virgen orando (11x9cm-4x4in) min. s.d.1835 carved
                  wood frame (S.P 300000)

SACRE, Emile (1844-1882) Belgian
£1284 $2235   (14-Apr-92 SY.AM22/R) Lady with fan (55x37cm-22x15in) s. panel
                  (D.FL 4200)

SADABA (?) Spanish
£712   *$1295   (26-May-92 DUR.M102/R) Rincon granadino (69x42cm-27x17in) s. W/C*
                  (S.P 130000)

SADELER, Egidius II (c.1570-c.1629) Flemish
£702 $1263   (22-Nov-91 SA.A1521/R) Sokrates taking the cup (45x55cm-18x22in)
                  indis.mono.d.1600 panel (DM 2000)

SADLER, Kate (fl.1880-94) British
£1400   *$2408   (4-Mar-92 S299/R) White anemones (44x25cm-17x10in) s.d.82 W/C bodycol htd*
                  gum arabic

SADLER, Walter Dendy (1854-1923) British
£3106 $5839   (22-Dec-91 AG.W8) After the battle (74x54cm-29x21in) s. (P.Z 60000000)
£4286 $7500   (20-Feb-92 SY.NY261/R) It's always largest fish that's lost
                  (71x112cm-28x44in) s.d.81

SADLER, William (18/19th C) British
£600 $1068   (21-Jan-92 SWS907) Departure of Princess Caroline for England
                  (22x36cm-9x14in) panel
£688 $1280   (17-Jun-92 A.D171) Fishing boats in choppy seas (23x33cm-9x13in) panel
                  (E.P 750)
£880 $1601   (11-Dec-91 A.D37) Dublin coastal scene with figures (20x30cm-8x12in)
                  board (E.P 950)
£1560 $2901   (17-Jun-92 A.D103) Extensive wooded landscape with houses and figures
                  (20x33cm-8x13in) panel (E.P 1700)
£2600 $4524   (18-Sep-91 CG103) Fishermen by stream near Chapelizod with Dublin in
                  distance. Horsemen and cart on road (23x33cm-9x13in) panel pair

SADLER, William (attrib) (18/19th C) British
£1850 $3219   (15-Apr-92 PHL209/R) Anglers by river in wooded, rocky gorge
                  (23x34cm-9x13in) panel

SADLER, William (jnr) (1782-1839) British
£1435 $2512   (17-Feb-92 AD.D42) View of Heuston Bridge and Dublin Quays from Phoenix
                  Park (20x30cm-8x12in) panel (E.P 1550)
£2400 $4224   (8-Apr-92 S192/R) Duke of Wellington at La Haye Sainte, Battle of
                  Waterloo (33x57cm-13x22in) panel

SADLER, William (snr-attrib) (?-1788) British
£880 $1584   (22-Nov-91 SWS284) Fishermen on the banks of a river (42x56cm-17x22in)

SADUN, Piero (20th C) ?
£2177 $3985   (12-May-92 F.R112) Spazio plastico (117x101cm-46x40in) d.1959 s.verso
                  (I.L 4800000)
£4648 $8413   (3-Dec-91 F.R186/R) Senza titolo (120x110cm-47x43in) s. s.d.1972verso
                  (I.L 10000000)

SAEDELEER, Elisabeth de (20th C) Belgian
£1325 $2397   (23-May-92 KV.L106) Farm in landscape (40x50cm-16x20in) s. (B.FR 80000)

SAEDELEER, Valerius de (1867-1941) Belgian
£110092 $193761   (7-Apr-92 C.A107/R) Trees in winter landscape (147x157cm-58x62in) s.
              (B.FR 6600000)

SAEGHER, Romain de (1907-1986) Belgian
£430 $779   (23-May-92 KV.L109) The road to Emmaus (26x35cm-10x14in) s.d.1981 gouache
              (B.FR 26000)
£476 $814   (21-Mar-92 KV.L101) The entry of Christ (26x35cm-10x14in) s.d.77 gouache
              (B.FR 28000)
£546 $989   (23-May-92 KV.L107) Bridge over a river (49x51cm-19x20in) s.d.76 W/C
              (B.FR 33000)
£565 $1022   (7-Dec-91 KV.L112) The Last Supper (35x27cm-14x11in) s. gouache
              (B.FR 33000)

SAETTI, Bruno (1902-1984) Italian
£3244 $5774   (29-Nov-91 F.F160/R) Natura morta (26x26cm-10x10in) s. s.verso
              (I.L 7000000)
£5059 $9055   (14-Nov-91 F.M62/R) Maschere (44x64cm-17x25in) s.d.1934 s.verso panel
              (I.L 11000000)
£5792 $10310   (29-Nov-91 F.F161/R) Ragazzo (44x26cm-17x10in) s. s.d.1944verso canvas on
              panel (I.L 12500000)
£1485 $2792   (19-Dec-91 F.M7/R) Musico (63x62cm-25x24in) s.d.43 sanguine cardboard
              (I.L 3200000)
£2320 $4362   (19-Dec-91 F.M154/R) Sole (24x31cm-9x12in) s. fresco (I.L 5000000)

SAEYS, Jakob Ferdinand (attrib) (1658-1725) Flemish
£2600 $4758   (12-May-92 SWS713/R) Architectural capriccio with return of prodigal son
              (67x84cm-26x33in)
£11500 $19550   (23-Oct-91 S30/R) Architectural capriccio with Turkish figures
              (152x167cm-60x66in)

SAEYS, Jakob Ferdinand (circle) (1658-1725) Flemish
£2600 $4680   (21-Nov-91 CSK128) Hawking party before palace (69x87cm-27x34in)

SAEYS, Jakob Ferdinand (style) (1658-1725) Flemish
£2200 $4224   (10-Jul-92 C165/R) Facade of palace with gentlefolk in oriental costume
              (33x40cm-13x16in)

SAEZ, Carlos F (?) South American
£843 $1500   (28-Oct-91 GC.M10/R) Mujer (17x16cm-7x6in) ink

SAEZ, Martin (1923-) Spanish
£872 $1500   (7-Oct-91 ANS.M181/R) Bodegon de caza (55x39cm-22x15in) s. (S.P 160000)
£1108 $1962   (12-Feb-92 ANS.M76/R) Concierto de arlequines (80x100cm-31x39in) s.
              (S.P 200000)
£1908 $3282   (7-Oct-91 ANS.M151/R) Velada musical (80x100cm-31x39in) s. (S.P 350000)

SAFFER, Hans Konrad (1860-1940) German
£977 $1660   (24-Oct-91 D.V42/R) The village politician (37x49cm-15x19in) s.
              (A.S 20000)

SAFLUND, Martin (1894-1976) Swedish
£550 $946   (19-Oct-91 UA.U400/R) Uppsala Seminarium in evening light
              (90x100cm-35x39in) s. (S.KR 5800)

SAFONOF, Serguei (1914-) Russian
£520 $911   (5-Apr-92 ARC.P106/R) Les glaeuls (99x69cm-39x27in) s. (F.FR 5000)

SAFTLEVEN, Cornelis (1607-1681) Dutch
£1573 $2691   (18-Mar-92 N.M451/R) Cows and goats (44x54cm-17x21in) (DM 4500)
£2800 $5096   (10-Dec-91 PH200/R) Domestic fowl beside pond (47x64cm-19x25in) panel
£4863 $8900   (12-May-92 SY.AM79/R) Shepherd and shepherdesses with cattle outside barn
              (74x103cm-29x41in) s. panel (D.FL 16000)
£2640 $4699   (25-Nov-91 CH.AM124/R) The ruins of the Huis te Spangen at Overschie near
              Rotterdam (20x31cm-8x12in) s.i.d.1649 chk wash (D.FL 8500)

SAFTLEVEN, Cornelis (attrib) (1607-1681) Dutch
£850 $1488   (3-Apr-92 C59/R) Witches driving away demons (55x82cm-22x32in)

SAFTLEVEN, Cornelis (style) (1607-1681) Dutch
£850 $1530   (21-Nov-91 CSK190/R) Woman preparing vegetables in kitchen
              (49x43cm-19x17in)

SAFTLEVEN, Herman (1609-1685) Dutch
£2930 $5186   (5-Nov-91 GF.L2041/R) River landscape with two boats (10x14cm-4x6in)
              mono. panel (S.FR 7500)
£12346 $22099   (12-Nov-91 SY.AM97/R) Peasants journeying along path in Italianate
              landscape (42x67cm-17x26in) mono.d.1649 panel (D.FL 40000)
£12650 $22011   (13-Sep-91 C33/R) Shepherd on bluff beneath cottage, peasants on track
              below (22x26cm-9x10in) mono.d.1671 panel
£14000 $24500   (1-Apr-92 S2/R) Rhenish river landscape with boats moored beneath houses
              (15x36cm-6x14in) mono.d.1664 panel
£20062 $35910   (14-Nov-91 CH.AM126/R) Rhenish river landscape with shipping and village
              beyond (18x23cm-7x9in) s.d.1655 panel (D.FL 65000)

SAFTLEVEN, Herman (1609-1685) Dutch-cont.

£20370	$36870	(19-May-92 GF.L2040/R) Rhine landscape (25x33cm-10x13in) panel (S.FR 55000)
£621	$1106	(25-Nov-91 CH.AM126/R) Rocky river landscape with traveller on path (20x31cm-8x12in) mono. chk wash (D.FL 2000)
£926	$1657	(12-Nov-91 SY.AM360/R) View of Petronella Chapel in village of de Bilt near Utrecht (10x15cm-4x6in) chk brush wash (D.FL 3000)
£1180	$2101	(25-Nov-91 CH.AM125/R) View inside the Ramparts of Utrecht with the Mariakerk beyond (15x19cm-6x7in) mono. i.verso chk wash (D.FL 3800)
£2174	$3870	(25-Nov-91 CH.AM135/R) Boat under sail with church beyond (9x6cm-4x2in) chk wash (D.FL 7000)
£2174	$3870	(25-Nov-91 CH.AM136/R) Boat moored by timberyard (8x6cm-3x2in) chk wash (D.FL 7000)
£2174	$3870	(25-Nov-91 CH.AM127/R) Three boats moored by cottage (10x8cm-4x3in) mono chk wash (D.FL 7000)
£2484	$4422	(25-Nov-91 CH.AM128/R) Barge at quay with man broaching barrels (10x9cm-4x4in) mono. chk wash (D.FL 8000)
£2484	$4422	(25-Nov-91 CH.AM133/R) Vessels moored by tower (10x9cm-4x4in) chk wash (D.FL 8000)
£2484	$4422	(25-Nov-91 CH.AM129/R) Two barges moored by angle turret of city wall (10x9cm-4x4in) mono. chk wash (D.FL 8000)
£3416	$6081	(25-Nov-91 CH.AM130/R) Sailing boat moored near inn (10x9cm-4x4in) mono. chk wash (D.FL 11000)
£3571	$6357	(25-Nov-91 CH.AM134/R) Boats oored by river bank with family on the shore (10x9cm-4x4in) mono. chk wash (D.FL 11500)
£3571	$6357	(25-Nov-91 CH.AM132/R) Men with wheelbarrows loading small sailing vessels in canal (10x9cm-4x4in) mono. chk wash (D.FL 11500)
£4037	$7186	(25-Nov-91 CH.AM85/R) Study of huntsman seen from behind (30x19cm-12x7in) mono. chk wash upper corners trimmed (D.FL 13000)
£4500	$8640	(6-Jul-92 S31/R) Rhine landscape with moored boat, figures in foreground (16x25cm-6x10in) chk.wash
£5307	$9500	(15-Jan-92 CH.NY144/R) Man carrying sack, walking to right (30x18cm-12x7in) mono. black red chk wash

SAFTLEVEN, Herman (attrib) (1609-1685) Dutch

£4070	$7000	(9-Oct-91 CH.NY51/R) Mountainous landscape with peasants fording river (36x60cm-14x24in) panel
£6379	$11545	(5-Dec-91 SY.MO325/R) Paysage Rhenan (25x33cm-10x13in) bears d.AO/1657 (F.FR 62000)
£1160	$2100	(22-May-92 GB.B5393) River landscape with boat (10x8cm-4x3in) chk wash (DM 3400)
£1570	$2842	(22-May-92 GB.B5392) River landscape with tower and angler (11x15cm-4x6in) mono chk wash (DM 4600)

SAGRESTANI, Giovanni Camillo (1660-1731) Italian

£6395	$11000	(9-Oct-91 CH.NY183/R) Triumph of Galatea (116x88cm-46x35in)

SAGRESTANI, Giovanni Camillo (circle) (1660-1731) Italian

£1100	$2112	(7-Jul-92 PH120/R) Penitent Magdalen (81x107cm-32x42in)

SAIKINA, Alexandra (1925-) Russian

£608	$1100	(20-May-92 ARC.P29/R) Andrioucha (75x84cm-30x33in) s. (F.FR 6000)
£1013	$1834	(20-May-92 ARC.P28/R) Les phlox (88x74cm-35x29in) s. (F.FR 10000)

SAILMAKER, Isaac (attrib) (1633-1721) British

£2000	$3600	(22-Nov-91 C135/R) Two three-deckers and other shipping off Portsmouth (28x39cm-11x15in) panel

SAILMAKER, Isaac (style) (1633-1721) British

£3500	$6720	(10-Jul-92 C105/R) Galley, Dutch frigate lowering sail and other shipping beyond (117x98cm-46x39in)

SAIN, Edouard Alexandre (1830-1910) French

£619	$1076	(17-Sep-91 FN.S2516) Girls collecting berries in landscape (20x31cm-8x12in) s. i.verso (DM 1800)
£2260	$4000	(13-Feb-92 S.W2680/R) Kiarella (86x66cm-34x26in) s.d.1865 i.verso
£5233	$9000	(17-Oct-91 SY.NY187/R) Rosina (105x63cm-41x25in) s.i.

SAIN, Paul Jean Marie (1853-1908) French

£700	$1329	(26-Jun-92 CSC.P115) La lavandiere (27x41cm-11x16in) s. (F.FR 6800)
£766	$1341	(19-Feb-92 D.P32) Une Vespree d'Avignon (40x56cm-16x22in) s.i.d.1896 (F.FR 7500)
£813	$1544	(26-Jun-92 CSC.P114/R) Jeune femme au bord de la riviere (46x60cm-18x24in) s. (F.FR 7900)
£912	$1633	(6-May-92 GD.B1099/R) Provence landscape in spring (38x55cm-15x22in) s. (S.FR 2500)

ST BRICE, Robert (20th C) Haitian

£4696	$8500	(19-May-92 SY.NY189/R) Twin Loas (173x89cm-68x35in) s.d.55

ST JOHN, E (19th C) British?

£1000	$1900	(24-Jun-92 DR61/R) Genoa (68x122cm-27x48in) s. W/C

T JOHN, Edwin (?) British
£400 $744   (18-Jun-92 CSK68) Fishing vessels on continental lake (38x61cm-15x24in)
     s. pencil W/C htd.gum arabic
£520 $894   (4-Mar-92 DR42/R) Near Cohsem, on Rhine (41x61cm-16x24in) s. W/C bodycol

T JOHN, S H (19th C) American
£930 $1600   (16-Oct-91 D.NY58) Faithful hunting hounds (135x102cm-53x40in) s.d.1879

T JOHN-JONES, Herbert (fl.1905-1923) British
£700 $1225   (27-Feb-92 GSP450) Horse portrait of Shirley Fly in a walled garden
     (41x51cm-16x20in) s.d.1910 i.verso
£750 $1313   (27-Feb-92 GSP451) Horse portrait of Glenavon Fireworks in a walled
     garden (41x51cm-16x20in) s.d.1910 i.verso

AINT, Daniel (school) (1778-1847) French
£2469 $4691   (26-Jun-92 AGS.P64/R) Portrait du Prince Alexandre M. Golitzine
     (10x8cm-4x3in) min. gilded bronze frame oval (F.FR 24000)

AINT-AUBIN, Augustin de (1736-1807) French
£366 $700   (3-Jul-92 S.W3700/R) 18th century peasant man (13x8cm-5x3in) sepia chk
£366 $700   (3-Jul-92 S.W3699/R) 18th Century peasant woman (13x8cm-5x3in) sepia chk
£700 $1274   (10-Dec-91 C223/R) Portrait de Sophie le Couteulx du Moley
     (17x13cm-7x5in) pencil touches red chk.
£2200 $4224   (6-Jul-92 S126/R) Portrait of man in profile (12cm-5ins circular) chk.
£2793 $5000   (15-Jan-92 CH.NY88/R) Presumed portrait of artist's wife, Louise-Nicole
     Godeau. Self-portrait (8x6cm-3x2in) d.1767 black lead htd white pair

AINT-AUBIN, Gabriel de (1724-1780) French
£22634 $40967   (5-Dec-91 SY.MO99/R) Catalogue des tableaux... catalogue (F.FR 220000)
£23464 $42000   (14-Jan-92 SY.NY61/R) Apollo and Mars playing chess, with Jupiter, Juno
     and other gods (12x17cm-5x7in) s.d.1775 pen wash htd white over black
     chk
£52469 $94969   (5-Dec-91 SY.MO100/R) Catalogue des tableaux... catalogue (F.FR 510000)

AINT-DELIS, Henri de (1878-1949) French
£3557 $6189   (19-Apr-92 ZZ.F71/R) Honfleur, bateaux a quais (26x33cm-10x13in) s.
     hardboard (F.FR 35000)
£2747 $5026   (17-May-92 T.B65/R) Procession de la Fete Dieu a Honfleur - Place Ste
     Catherine (48x62cm-19x24in) s. W/C (F.FR 27000)

AINT-GERMIER, Joseph (1860-1925) French
£718 $1285   (19-Jan-92 CSC.P122) Femmes dans un interieur mauresque (35x27cm-14x11in)
     s. panel (F.FR 7000)

AINT-IGNY, Jean de (c.1600-c.1649) French
£5144 $9311   (5-Dec-91 SY.MO14/R) Etudes de tetes de personnages (23x17cm-9x7in)
     sanguine pair (F.FR 50000)

AINT-JEAN, Simon (1808-1860) French
£2559 $4555   (29-Nov-91 ARC.P99/R) Nature morte (44x53cm-17x21in) s. (F.FR 25000)
£7545 $12978   (7-Oct-91 CSC.P146) Nature morte (19x30cm-7x12in) s.d.57 board
     (F.FR 75000)
£9684 $18012   (18-Jun-92 SY.MO84/R) Compagnie de perdrix (73x95cm-29x37in) s.d.1839
     (F.FR 95000)
£11047 $19000   (17-Oct-91 SY.NY76/R) Still life of roses, carnations, grapes and peaches
     on forest floor (46x61cm-18x24in) s.d.1853

AINT-JOHN, J Allen (1872-?) American
£1186 $2100   (9-Nov-91 W.W222/R) After the storm (51x76cm-20x30in) s.

AINT-OURS, Jean-Pierre (1752-1809) Swiss
£579 $990   (12-Mar-92 GK.Z86) Head of winged angel (26x32cm-10x13in) s.d.1808verso
     oval panel (S.FR 1500)

AINT-QUENTIN, Jacques Philippe Jos de (1783-?) French
£2216 $3766   (25-Oct-91 AT.P133/R) Lavandiere avec un jeune enfant (36x26cm-14x10in)
     s.d.1765 pierre noire wash htd.white (F.FR 22000)

AINTHILL, Loudon (1918-1969) Australian
£751 $1254   (19-Aug-91 SY.ME21) Sisters (61x49cm-24x19in) s.i.d.1949 pencil
     (A.D 1600)
£940 $1674   (27-Apr-92 J.M114/R) Tree creature (58x40cm-23x16in) s.i. gouache ink
     (A.D 2200)
£1800 $3204   (28-Nov-91 C4/R) Figure with guitar (76x56cm-30x22in) s.i.d.50 pen W/C
     black chk gouache

AINTIN, Henri (1846-1899) French
£618 $1100   (22-Jan-92 SY.NY305/R) Drawing water along river (65x100cm-26x39in) s.
£632 $1080   (13-Mar-92 FN.S2937) Coastal landscape, evening (38x60cm-15x24in) s.
     (DM 1800)
£902 $1633   (5-Dec-91 D.V119) Duck hunt (23x39cm-9x15in) s.d.92 panel (A.S 18000)
£999 $1858   (16-Jun-92 SY.B284) Winter (39x26cm-15x10in) s.d.1884 panel (B.FR 60000)
£1800 $3114   (4-Oct-91 C50/R) At the watermill, spring (181x132cm-71x52in) s.d.1888

SAKAI, Kazuya (c.1927-) Argentinian
£2762 $5000   (18-May-92 CH.NY211/R) De la serie blanco y negro (110x100cm-43x39in)
        s.d.58 verso s.i.verso

SALA Y FRANCES, Emilio (1850-1910) Spanish
£1424 $2720   (2-Jul-92 ANS.M84/R) Desnudo femenino (62x37cm-24x15in) board
        (S.P 260000)
£1786 $3000   (1-Sep-91 PO.BA15) Escena galante (23x31cm-9x12in) panel
£1915 $3486   (11-Dec-91 FER.M149/R) Mirando por la ventana (101x80cm-40x31in) s.
        (S.P 350000)
£2078 $3678   (12-Feb-92 ANS.M129/R) Jardin (33x35cm-13x14in) (S.P 375000)
£3602 $6304   (18-Feb-92 DUR.M20/R) Muneca abandonada (33x19cm-13x7in) s. panel
        (S.P 650000)
£769   *$1400*   *(11-Dec-91 RO.BA69) Escena de teatro (29x41cm-11x16in) s. grisaille*

SALA, Jean (1895-) Spanish
£2424 $4291   (26-Apr-92 FE.P62) Ville de Grenade (92x65cm-36x26in) s. (F.FR 24000)
£1368   *$2476*   *(22-May-92 LD.P5) Elegante au chapeau bleu (130x88cm-51x35in) s. pastel*
        oval (F.FR 13500)

SALA, Juan (1867-1918) Spanish
£5714 $10000   (19-Feb-92 CH.NY124/R) Teatime by river (50x62cm-20x24in) s.

SALA, Paolo (1859-1929) Italian
£1000 $1790   (5-May-92 SWS442/R) Fishing boats at dusk, Lago Maggiore (33x24cm-13x9in)
        s. panel
£1000 $1900   (24-Jun-92 LJ244) Equestrian figures in mountainous landscape
        (22x38cm-9x15in) s. board
£1852 $3205   (24-Mar-92 CH.R73) Figure presso un ruscello (13x24cm-5x9in) s.i.d.1888
        panel (I.L 4000000)
£1859 $3365   (3-Dec-91 SY.MI79/R) Engadina (20x30cm-8x12in) s.d.1906 panel
        (I.L 4000000)
£2600 $4654   (5-May-92 SWS434/R) At the water's edge (19x28cm-7x11in) s. panel
£4648 $7948   (19-Mar-92 F.M80/R) Mattinata veneziana (25x40cm-10x16in) s.i.
        (I.L 10000000)
£5270 $9328   (7-Nov-91 F.M11/R) Isola dei Pescatori sul Lago Maggiore
        (34x50cm-13x20in) s. i.verso panel (I.L 11500000)
£8500 $15130   (29-Nov-91 C61/R) On the Embankment with Cleopatra's Needle, Waterloo
        Bridge beyond, London (19x30cm-7x12in) s. panel
£12831 $22711   (7-Nov-91 F.M46/R) Paesaggio lacustre (98x148cm-39x58in) s.
        (I.L 28000000)
£515   *$897*   *(18-Sep-91 N.M271) Mountain lake landscape with peasant woman on path*
        (24x40cm-9x16in) s. W/C over pencil (DM 1500)
£1040   *$1882*   *(18-May-92 SY.MI28) Villa sul lago (22x48cm-9x19in) s.d.1979 W/C*
        (I.L 2300000)
£1047   *$1800*   *(15-Oct-91 CE.NY299/R) St. Paul's Cathedral, London (23x33cm-9x13in) s.i.*
        W/C paperboard
£1725   *$2933*   *(23-Oct-91 GD.B1261) Canale Grande, Venice (29x45cm-11x18in) s.i. W/C*
        (S.FR 4400)
£2400   *$4200*   *(18-Feb-92 CE.NY224/R) Panorama di Venezia (35x52cm-14x20in) s.i. W/C*
£2747   *$5000*   *(27-May-92 CH.NY209/R) Dance of Spring (97x67cm-38x26in) s. W/C paper on*
        board
£3800   *$7068*   *(17-Jun-92 S564/R) View of Parliament Square, London (35x51cm-14x20in)*
        s.i. W/C

SALABET, Jean (20th C) French
£519 $950   (4-Jun-92 GOM.M19/R) Avenue de l'Opera (28x35cm-11x14in) s.d.1954

SALADO, Diego Santiago (1965-) Spanish
£818 $1406   (7-Oct-91 ANS.M180/R) Farol y granadas (73x60cm-29x24in) s.d.91
        s.i.d.verso (S.P 150000)
£1366 $2323   (24-Oct-91 DUR.M1028/R) Bodegon de cristales (73x91cm-29x36in) s.d.91
        (S.P 250000)

SALANSON, Eugenie Marie (19th C) French
£4717 $8349   (5-Nov-91 BA.S164/R) Fishergirl (136x87cm-54x34in) s.d.1884 (S.KR 50000)
£5769 $10500   (28-May-92 SY.NY143/R) Lobster catch (135x86cm-53x34in) s.d.1884

SALANTINE (19th C) German
£1832 $3500   (16-Jul-92 SY.NY420/R) The schoolmaster's discovery (57x49cm-22x19in)
        s.d.1852

SALCES Y GUTIERREZ, Manuel (1861-1932) Spanish
£551 $986   (14-Nov-91 ANS.M130/R) Plato con el Nacimiento (37x27cm-15x11in) s.d.96
        (S.P 100000)
£691 $1299   (16-Dec-91 ANS.M145/R) Paisaje con rocas (13x15cm-5x6in) s. (S.P 125000)
£940 $1767   (16-Dec-91 ANS.M150/R) Paisaje con casa (14x18cm-6x7in) s. (S.P 170000)

SALCI, Gabriele (18th C) Italian
£10871 $20111   (8-Jun-92 CH.R684/R) Natura morta con due cavoli, verdure ed un cesto di
        frutta ed uccellagione (96x132cm-38x52in) (I.L 24000000)

SALEC, de (?) ?
£2690 $4600   (13-Mar-92 WOL.C112/R) The baptism. Audience with the Cardinal
        (46x61cm-18x24in) s. pair

SALEH, Radeaa (1814-1880) Javanese
£10398 $18508   (30-Oct-91 CH.AM200/R) Three-master in distress (78x122cm-31x48in) s.d.1869 (D.FL 34000)

SALEMME, Attilio (1911-1955) American
£6286 $11000   (28-Feb-92 SY.NY263/R) Vintage of uncertainties (41x107cm-16x42in) s.d.49
£8649 $16000   (12-Jun-92 SY.NY239/R) The assignation (119x149cm-47x59in) s.d.52

SALENTIN, Hubert (1822-1910) German
£4409 $7848   (28-Apr-92 RAS.K119/R) Wooded landscape with young girl gathering twigs (127x95cm-50x37in) s.i.d.1885 (D.KR 50000)

SALES, Francisco (1905-) Spanish
£1232 $2241   (26-May-92 DUR.M63/R) Jarra y limon (46x33cm-18x13in) s.d.75 (S.P 225000)

SALICATH, Ornulf (1888-1962) Norwegian
£490 $848   (23-Mar-92 B.O112/R) Mountain landscape with lake (61x75cm-24x30in) s. panel (N.KR 5500)

SALIERES, Paul (19th C) French
£11628 $20000   (17-Oct-91 SY.NY175/R) Twin boys (161x112cm-63x44in) s.

SALIETTI, Alberto (1892-) Italian
£5337 $10034   (19-Dec-91 F.M110/R) Fiori di primavera (90x70cm-35x28in) s. panel (I.L 11500000)
£5714 $10856   (23-Jun-92 F.M135/R) Paesaggio di Andora (120x80cm-47x31in) s. (I.L 12500000)
£7771 $14764   (23-Jun-92 F.M205/R) Carnevale a Venezia (132x127cm-52x50in) s. masonite (I.L 17000000)

SALIGER, Ivo (1894-1975) Austrian
£589 $1119   (25-Jun-92 D.V627/R) By the fountain (78x69cm-31x27in) s. board (A.S 12000)
£971 $1728   (28-Apr-92 D.V232/R) Card game (70x80cm-28x31in) s. panel (A.S 20000)
£2196 $3799   (3-Oct-91 D.V218/R) Bathing women (160x110cm-63x43in) s. (A.S 45000)
£874 $1555   *(28-Apr-92 D.V244/R) Justice (67x49cm-26x19in) mixed media board (A.S 18000)*

SALIMBENI, Ventura (attrib) (1567-1613) Italian
£976   *$1865*   *(3-Jul-92 SD.P74) Tete de femme (21x16cm-8x6in) black chk sanguine (F.FR 9500)*

SALINAS Y TERUEL, Augustin (1862-1915) Spanish
£1585 $2933   (9-Jun-92 F.R89) Marina di Anzio (25x50cm-10x20in) s.d.1913 (I.L 3500000)
£1760 $3045   (24-Mar-92 CH.R54) Ritratto di giovane donna con cappellino (100x60cm-39x24in) s.d.85 (I.L 3800000)
£2624 $4932   (3-Jan-92 DUR.M11/R) Pueblo italiano (26x34cm-10x13in) s.d.1919 (S.P 475000)
£6076 $11422   (3-Jan-92 DUR.M4/R) Junto a la fuente (14x23cm-6x9in) s. panel (S.P 1100000)
£6602 $11092   (27-Aug-91 RAS.K157/R) Italians returning home after day's work in wineyard (23x40cm-9x16in) s.i (D.KR 75000)

SALINAS Y TERUEL, Augustin (attrib) (1862-1915) Spanish
£920 $1646   (14-Nov-91 CH.R12) Ragazza in costume spagnolo (31x19cm-12x7in) panel (I.L 2000000)

SALINAS, Pablo (1871-1946) Spanish
£2265 $4190   (9-Jun-92 F.R140/R) Gitani (40x66cm-16x26in) s. (I.L 5000000)
£5193 $8828   (22-Oct-91 DUR.M60/R) Picador (13x21cm-5x8in) s. panel (S.P 950000)
£8848 $16811   (22-Jun-92 AT.P90/R) Chez le cardinal (29x46cm-11x18in) s. (F.FR 86000)
£12000 $21840   (29-May-92 C360/R) The letter (24x22cm-9x9in) s.
£14277 $25985   (12-Dec-91 F.M12/R) Partita a carte (23x38cm-9x15in) s. panel (I.L 31000000)
£17000 $30940   (29-May-92 C359/R) Word of advice (14x24cm-6x9in) s.i. panel
£19131 $32523   (22-Oct-91 DUR.M61/R) Concierto (23x40cm-9x16in) s. panel (S.P 3500000)
£62857 $110000   (20-Feb-92 SY.NY77/R) Wedding party (39x67cm-15x26in) s.i.

SALINAS, Porfirio (1910-1972) American
£710 $1300   (6-Jun-92 LAE.L85/R) Texas hill country in autumn (23x30cm-9x12in) s. canvasboard

SALINI, Tommaso (1575-1625) Italian
£6000 $10920   (10-Dec-91 PH68/R) Still life of mixed vegetables in basket, with flowers, meat on ledge (49x71cm-19x28in)
£29070 $50000   (10-Oct-91 SY.NY146/R) The education of Jupiter (161x112cm-63x44in)
£36327 $62482   (15-Oct-91 PPB.P20/R) Jeune femme attachant un bouc (165x115cm-65x45in) (F.FR 360000)

SALISBURY, Frank O (1874-1962) British
£510 $913   (5-May-92 ZEL.L1523/R) Wisteria in Lord Inverforth's garden (91x71cm-36x28in) s.d.1944 i.verso (DM 1500)
£540 $977   (20-May-92 BT229/R) Lilium Delphinium and Boccania (89x69cm-35x27in) s. i.verso

SALISBURY, Frank O (1874-1962) British-cont.
£650 $1131   (19-Sep-91 CSK203/R) Edward the Confessor's Chapel, Westminster Abbey
                 (76x63cm-30x25in) s.
£1800 $3150   (26-Feb-92 MMB252) The musicians (76x102cm-30x40in) s.

SALLE, David (1952-) American
£19553 $35000 (5-May-92 CH.NY122 a/R) B.A.I.A. (110x160cm-43x63in) acrylic
£19553 $35000 (5-May-92 CH.NY113/R) Untitled (147x215cm-58x85in) oil acrylic two panels
£27933 $50000 (13-Nov-91 CH.NY294/R) Swimmer (167x234cm-66x92in) oil acrylic diptych
£30726 $55000 (7-May-92 SY.NY142/R) He aspires to condition of the...
                 (122x178cm-48x70in) s.verso acrylic canvas
£72626 $130000 (5-May-92 CH.NY56/R) Skintight world (224x288cm-88x113in) oil acrylic
£2857 $5000 (25-Feb-92 SY.NY239/R) Untitled (46x61cm-18x24in) s.d.84 W/C
£3352 $6000 (6-May-92 CH.NY203/R) Untitled (57x76cm-22x30in) brush ink
£3911 $7000 (13-Nov-91 CH.NY314/R) Untitled (51x70cm-20x28in) s.d.1986 W/C graphite
£5714 $10000 (27-Feb-92 CH.NY124/R) Untitled (36x51cm-14x20in) s.d.1985 W/C graphite
£8939 $16000 (5-May-92 CH.NY163/R) Untitled (46x61cm-18x24in) s.i.d.1982-1986 W/C
                 graphite
£10056 $18000 (13-Nov-91 CH.NY301/R) Untitled (46x60cm-18x24in) s.d.84 W/C graphite
£14857 $26000 (27-Feb-92 CH.NY109/R) Engagement rings (153x107cm-60x42in) oil acrylic
                 fabric collage on canvas
£72626 $130000 (7-May-92 SY.NY138/R) Collapsing sheet (214x255cm-84x100in) oil acrylic
                 fabric canvas wood object

SALLINEN, T (1879-1955) Finnish
£23388 $41163 (12-Apr-92 HOR.H197/R) In the sauna II (120x110cm-47x43in) s.d.1922
                 (F.M 185000)
£493 $863 (25-Sep-91 HOR.H85) Beach hut (29x42cm-11x17in) s.d.1945 W/C (F.M 3500)

SALLINEN, Tyko (1879-1955) Scandinavian
£2587 $4605 (1-Dec-91 HOR.H197/R) Summer's day (46x54cm-18x21in) s.d.1925 (F.M 20000)

SALMI, Max (1931-) Finnish
£712 $1266 (1-Dec-91 HOR.H200) Spring (34x50cm-13x20in) s.d.1967 (F.M 5500)
£759 $1335 (12-Apr-92 HOR.H198) Composition (41x40cm-16x16in) s.d.1972 (F.M 6000)
£759 $1389 (13-May-92 BU.S177/R) The painter's jacket (98x68cm-39x27in) s.d.65
                 (S.KR 8000)

SALMON, John Cuthbert (1844-1917) British
£800 $1424 (28-Nov-91 PHX415/R) Fishermen and distressed vessel in stormy seas.
                 Retrieving the wreckage (23x53cm-9x21in) s.d.1867 W/C htd.white pair

SALMON, John Francis (c1814-c1875) British
£1100 $1980 (27-Jan-92 PH69/R) Return of fishing fleet (35x66cm-14x26in) s.d.1861 W/C
                 htd white

SALMON, Robert (1775-1844) American
£4532 $7750 (13-Mar-92 S.BM171/R) Fishing scene (25x36cm-10x14in) d.1840 i.verso
                 panel
£6593 $12000 (27-May-92 SY.NY7/R) Cunard lighthouse (24x30cm-9x12in) s.i.d.1828 board
£6818 $12000 (9-Apr-92 FA.PH814/R) Ships off the Scottish coast (25x30cm-10x12in)
                 panel
£15205 $26000 (12-Mar-92 CH.NY4/R) Shipping off Greenock (51x76cm-20x30in) s.d.1826
                 i.verso panel
£25000 $47750 (17-Jul-92 C153/R) An armed brig shown in two positions off little
                 Cumbrae on the Clyde (52x78cm-20x31in) init.d.1814
£89820 $150000 (20-Aug-91 RB.HY200/R) No.723 Revenue Schooner, Boston Harbor
                 (41x61cm-16x24in) s.d.1831 panel

SALMSON, Hugo (1844-1894) Swedish
£1755 $3212 (12-May-92 GO.G149) Peasantwoman (62x46cm-24x18in) s.i.d.1879
                 (S.KR 18500)
£1900 $3287 (4-Oct-91 C114/R) The road home (67x94cm-26x37in) s. panel
£4528 $8106 (7-May-92 RAS.S13/R) Family returning from the field (125x175cm-49x69in)
                 s. (S.KR 48000)
£9434 $16887 (7-May-92 RAS.S14/R) Returning from church (66x81cm-26x32in) s.d.1868
                 (S.KR 100000)

SALOKIVI, Santeri (1886-1940) Finnish
£845 $1479 (25-Sep-91 HOR.H87) Man with beard (49x39cm-19x15in) s. (F.M 6000)
£1686 $2917 (28-Mar-92 UA.U469/R) Sunny farm scene (28x35cm-11x14in) s. i.verso
                 (S.KR 17500)
£5692 $10132 (1-Dec-91 HOR.H201) Cleaning fish at Vano (32x46cm-13x18in) s.
                 (F.M 44000)

SALOME (20th C) ?
£3593 $6468 (19-Nov-91 FB.P249/R) Scene romantique (183x276cm-72x109in) s.i.d.83
                 acrylic (F.FR 35000)

SALOMON LE TROPEZIEN (19/20th C) French
£706 $1215 (20-Oct-91 I.N21) Tartane a Saint-Tropez (54x65cm-21x26in) s. (F.FR 7000)

SALONEN, Ivan (?) Scandinavian
£515 $937 (11-Dec-91 HOR.H104) February (60x90cm-24x35in) s. (F.M 4000)

SALT, J (19th C) British
£900 $1557   (4-Oct-91 BW412) Ancient Italy (76x127cm-30x50in) s. after J M W Turner

SALT, James (19th C) British
£3000 $5130   (12-Mar-92 CSK304/R) Venetian capriccio (76x127cm-30x50in) s.
£3500 $6650   (23-Jun-92 PH194/R) Venetian waterways (90x124cm-35x49in) s.

SALT, John (20th C) British
£5587 $10000   (6-May-92 CH.NY311/R) Arrested vehicle - fat seats (132x194cm-52x76in)
£10405 $18000   (3-Oct-91 SY.NY58/R) Catskill pastoral (116x147cm-46x58in)

SALTER, John William (19th C) British
£400 $692   (4-Sep-91 BT126/R) View of Babbacombe (18x25cm-7x10in) s.d.1890 W/C

SALTER, William (1804-1875) British
£750 $1335   (29-Oct-91 PH128) Madonna della scala (123x17cm-48x7in) after Antonio
                 Allegri
£1892 $3425   (19-May-92 AB.S4372/R) The day - Madonna and Child with saints
                 (195x145cm-77x57in) i.verso after Corregio (S.KR 20000)

SALTIEL-MARSHALL, Alice (?) American
£366 $659   (18-Nov-91 HO.ED38/R) Untitled - mountain landscape (31x41cm-12x16in) s.
                 W/C (C.D 750)

SALTO, Axel (1889-?) Danish
£1713 $3050   (25-Nov-91 BU.K49/R) Stags in battle (131x171cm-52x67in) (D.KR 19000)

SALTOFT, Edvard Anders (1883-1939) Danish
£802 $1380   (15-Oct-91 RAS.K233) Liva Weel entertaining (105x80cm-41x31in) s.i.
                 gouache (D.KR 9000)

SALVI, Giovanni Battista see SASSOFERRATO

SALUCCI, Alessandro (17th C) Italian
£18159 $32323   (28-Apr-92 F.R98/R) Capriccio architettonico con interno di palazzo e
                 gallerie (74x100cm-29x39in) (I.L 40000000)

SALVANA, John (1873-1956) Australian
£513 $913   (27-Apr-92 J.M1149) Mawor River, NSW 1920 (40x61cm-16x24in) s. (A.D 1200)
£548 $959   (23-Sep-91 AAA.S108) New South Wales landscape (30x45cm-12x18in) s. board
                 (A.D 1200)
£2137 $3803   (27-Apr-92 J.M325) Meadow bank (94x145cm-37x57in) s.d.1913 canvas on
                 board (A.D 5000)
£407 $777   (21-Jul-92 JRL.S240) Burragorang Valley (32x53cm-13x21in) s.d.1927 W/C
                 (A.D 1050)

SALVATORE, Anna (1923-1978) Italian
£4641 $8725   (19-Dec-91 F.M142/R) Ragazzi in campagna (156x260cm-61x102in)
                 (I.L 10000000)

SALVIATI, Francesco (1510-1563) Italian
£19000 $33060   (14-Apr-92 C87/R) Bearded man seated on trunk of tree (33x22cm-13x9in) i.
                 chk wash htd.white

SALVIATI, Francesco (attrib) (1510-1563) Italian
£22222 $40222   (19-May-92 GF.L2014/R) Portrait of Cosimo I de Medici with view of
                 Florence beyond (127x86cm-50x34in) (S.FR 60000)
£6704 $12000   (15-Jan-92 CH.NY5/R) Soldier shielding eyes (35x26cm-14x10in) black chk

SALVIATI, Francesco (circle) (1510-1563) Italian
£4469 $8000   (17-Jan-92 SY.NY192/R) The Adoration of the Shepherds (84x107cm-33x42in)

SALVIATI, Francesco (style) (1510-1563) Italian
£1389 $2486   (14-Nov-91 CH.AM94) Road to Calvary. Christ among the Doctors.
                 Crucifixion shaped copper plates triptych (D.FL 4500)
£13000 $24960   (9-Jul-92 CSK53 a/R) Christ washing the disciples' feet. The Last Supper
                 (25x46cm-10x18in) panel pair

SALVIATI, Giovanni (1881-?) Italian
£921 $1676   (12-Dec-91 F.M46) Marina con pescatori (30x36cm-12x14in) s. panel
                 (I.L 2000000)

SALVO (1947-) Italian
£914 $1737   (23-Jun-92 F.M74/R) Il naviglio (34x48cm-13x19in) s.i.d.1981 tempera
                 cardboard (I.L 2000000)
£1131 $2059   (26-May-92 SY.MI46/R) Composizione (16x29cm-6x11in) s.id.1981verso
                 (I.L 2500000)
£1280 $2432   (23-Jun-92 F.M81) Senza titolo (29x34cm-11x13in) paper (I.L 2800000)
£1370 $2384   (14-Apr-92 F.M95/R) Camion (38x26cm-15x10in) paper (I.L 3000000)
£1472 $2634   (14-Nov-91 F.M119/R) Paesaggio (24x18cm-9x7in) s.d.1985 board oval
                 (I.L 3200000)
£1934 $3521   (9-Dec-91 CH.R84/R) Senza titolo (51x36cm-20x14in) s.d.1990 board
                 (I.L 4200000)
£2270 $4040   (29-Apr-92 F.F171/R) Senza titolo (35x50cm-14x20in) (I.L 5000000)
£2317 $4124   (29-Nov-91 F.F115) Senza titolo (35x50cm-14x20in) paper (I.L 5000000)

SALVO (1947-) Italian-cont.
£2497	$4444	(29-Apr-92 F.F172/R) Isola Tiburtina (48x40cm-19x16in) cardboard on canvas (I.L 5500000)
£3200	$6079	(23-Jun-92 F.M120/R) Citta (100x80cm-39x31in) s.verso (I.L 7000000)
£6395	$11127	(14-Apr-92 F.M242/R) Ottomania (100x80cm-39x31in) s.d.1985 (I.L 14000000)
£6395	$11127	(14-Apr-92 F.M171/R) Paesaggio (80x100cm-31x39in) s.d.1991verso (I.L 14000000)

SALZMANN, Gottfried (1943-) Austrian
| £399 | $714 | *(15-Jan-92 D.V242) Landscape (22x18cm-9x7in) W/C (A.S 8000)* |
| £1246 | $2231 | *(15-Jan-92 D.V241/R) Untitled (46x48cm-18x19in) s.d. W/C (A.S 25000)* |

SALZMANN, Louis Henri (1887-1955) Swiss
| £620 | $1111 | (6-May-92 GD.B1102/R) Idyllic village scene (50x65cm-20x26in) s.d.44 (S.FR 1700) |

SAMACCHINI, Orazio (1532-1577) Italian
| £9269 | $17425 | (18-Dec-91 AT.P1/R) La Vierge et l'Enfant couronnant Sainte Cecile entre Saint Jerome et Saint Francois (144x116cm-57x46in) (F.FR 90000) |

SAMACCHINI, Orazio (attrib) (1532-1577) Italian
| £18592 | $33651 | (4-Dec-91 CH.R47/R) Cristo Pantocratore (117x90cm-46x35in) (I.L 40000000) |
| £25484 | $47401 | (18-Jun-92 SY.MO14/R) Sainte Famille (66x55cm-26x22in) panel (F.FR 250000) |

SAMACCHINI, Orazio (circle) (1532-1577) Italian
| £8000 | $14240 | (1-Nov-91 C22/R) Holy Family with infant Saint John the Baptist (15x11cm-6x4in) panel |

SAMARAS, Lucas (1936-) American
£523	$900	*(12-Oct-91 SY.NY255/R) Untitled (28x22cm-11x9in) init.d.63 Indian ink W/C*
£811	$1500	*(12-Jun-92 SY.NY248/R) Untitled (32x24cm-13x9in) pastel*
£811	$1500	*(12-Jun-92 SY.NY247) Untitled (30x22cm-12x9in) init.i.d.62 verso pastel*
£1216	$2250	*(12-Jun-92 SY.NY246/R) Embracing (22x30cm-9x12in) init.d.62 verso pastel*
£1221	$2100	*(12-Oct-91 SY.NY249/R) Untitled (28x21cm-11x8in) init.d.62 verso Indian ink W/C*
£2000	$3500	*(28-Feb-92 SY.NY312/R) Nude by red table (30x23cm-12x9in) init.d.62 verso pastel*
£2035	$3500	*(12-Oct-91 SY.NY373/R) Reconstruction No.104 (137x134cm-54x53in) sewn fabric collage*
£15029	$26000	*(3-Oct-91 SY.NY143/R) Head group no.2 (246x338cm-97x133in) ink wash on 22 pieces paper mounted ragboard*

SAMBA, Cheri (1956-) Zairean
£1546	$2675	(23-Mar-92 CC.P136/R) Amoureux chatie (90x90cm-35x35in) s.d.1981 (F.FR 15000)
£1649	$2854	(23-Mar-92 CC.P128) Immortalisons l'amitie (92x84cm-36x33in) s.d.1980 (F.FR 16000)
£1649	$2854	(23-Mar-92 CC.P126/R) Armour transfere (94x88cm-37x35in) s.d.1981 (F.FR 16000)
£1701	$2943	(23-Mar-92 CC.P131/R) Deux ans.. Conge ya bolingo (94x76cm-37x30in) s.d.1980 (F.FR 16500)

SAMBERGER, Leo (1861-1940) German
| £859 | $1495 | *(18-Sep-91 N.M272/R) Self portrait with hat (59x44cm-23x17in) mono.d.1903 s.d.verso grisaille chk chl oval (DM 2500)* |

SAMMICHELI, Michele (circle) (1484-1559) Italian
| £4800 | $8352 | *(14-Apr-92 C97/R) Design for palace (28x42cm-11x17in) chk pen wash sold with two other drawings* |

SAMMONS, Carl (1888-1968) American
£674	$1200	(26-Nov-91 MOR.P21) Carmel coast (30x41cm-12x16in) s. canvasboard
£686	$1200	(31-Mar-92 MOR.P71) Monterey coastal (46x61cm-18x24in) s. canvas on board
£843	$1500	(26-Nov-91 MOR.P14) California coastal scene (30x41cm-12x16in) s. canvasboard
£1073	$1900	(12-Feb-92 B.SF569/R) Smoke trees, Palm Springs (30x39cm-12x15in) s. canvas on board

SAMOKHVALOV, Alexandre (1894-1971) Russian
£594	$1057	(25-Nov-91 ARC.P120/R) Jeune fille au bouquet (38x30cm-15x12in) s. (F.FR 5800)
£614	$1093	(25-Nov-91 ARC.P121/R) En attendant (69x49cm-27x19in) s. (F.FR 6000)
£1013	$1834	(20-May-92 ARC.P59/R) Modele (139x59cm-55x23in) s. (F.FR 10000)
£1024	$1822	(25-Nov-91 ARC.P118/R) Nu allonge (35x52cm-14x20in) s. (F.FR 10000)
£2866	$5101	(25-Nov-91 ARC.P122/R) La Parisienne (147x88cm-58x35in) s. (F.FR 28000)
£3480	$6194	(25-Nov-91 ARC.P119/R) La fille au chapeau (136x113cm-54x44in) s. (F.FR 34000)

SAMOKICH, Nicolai (1860-1944) Russian
| £1000 | $1780 | (28-Nov-91 S401/R) Dawn raid (50x39cm-20x15in) s. panel |
| £524 | $1000 | *(16-Jul-92 SY.NY449/R) Village market with carriage (28x22cm-11x9in) s. W/C pen* |

SAMPLE, Paul (1896-1974) American
£1596 $3000 (18-Dec-91 SY.NY314/R) Haying (40x50cm-16x20in) s.
£2811 $5200 (10-Jun-92 CE.NY385/R) Fox by winter stream (51x67cm-20x26in) s.
£395 $750 (24-Jun-92 B.SF6510/R) Back Alley (25x32cm-10x13in) s. W/C
£410 $750 (16-May-92 HG.C69 b) Boxer (30x46cm-12x18in) s. gouache
£429 $750 (22-Feb-92 YFA.M168) Winter landscape (38x56cm-15x22in) s. W/C
£514 $900 (31-Mar-92 MOR.P87 a) Salinas Valley (15x33cm-6x13in) s.i.d.29 W/C

SAMSONOV, Marat (1925-) Russian
£815 $1517 (17-Jun-92 ARC.P117/R) Jeunes paysannes vietnamiennes (58x71cm-23x28in) s. panel (F.FR 8000)

SAN JOSE GONZALEZ, Francisco (1919-1981) Spanish
£798 $1429 (14-Nov-91 ANS.M111/R) Altar mayor de Arenas de San Pedro (65x46cm-26x18in) s. ink dr (S.P 145000)

SAN JOSE, Francisco (20th C) Spanish
£1093 $2001 (13-May-92 FER.M150/R) La silla del Avila, Caracas (50x61cm-20x24in) s.d.1976 (S.P 200000)
£2075 $3549 (17-Mar-92 FER.M168/R) Iglesia de Vallecas (55x46cm-22x18in) s.d.1974 (S.P 375000)
£525 $988 (17-Dec-91 DUR.M109/R) Casa (21x27cm-8x11in) s. W/C (S.P 95000)

SANAHUJA, Manuel Fernandez (19th C) Spanish?
£930 $1693 (11-Dec-91 FER.M61/R) Puerto de Vigo (42x28cm-17x11in) s.d.1879 W/C (S.P 170000)

SANBORN, Percy A (1849-1929) American
£3059 $5750 (18-Dec-91 SY.NY31/R) Glory of the Seas (55x86cm-22x34in) s.i.

SANCHEZ (?) Spanish
£1000 $1810 (21-May-92 CSK310) Spanish villa (71x91cm-28x36in) s.

SANCHEZ BARBUDO, Salvador see BARBUDO, Salvador Sanchez

SANCHEZ COELLO, Alonso (c.1531-c.1588) Spanish
£240000 $436800 (29-May-92 C311/R) Portrait of Hernan Cortes wearing hat with badge by table with clock (123x104cm-48x41in) i.

SANCHEZ COELLO, Alonso (after) (c.1531-1588) Spanish
£5000 $9550 (15-Jul-92 S12/R) Portrait of King Philip of Spain (45x34cm-18x13in) panel

SANCHEZ COELLO, Alonso (studio) (c.1531-c.1588) Spanish
£2851 $5275 (12-Jun-92 ARC.P57/R) Portrait d'une dame de qualite (64x55cm-25x22in) (F.FR 28000)

SANCHEZ SOLA, E (19th C) Spanish
£2797 $4839 (25-Mar-92 KM.K1394/R) Altar servants preparing for mass in church interior (88x130cm-35x51in) s. (DM 8000)

SANCHEZ SOLA, Emilio (c.1874-c.1925) Spanish
£1800 $3348 (16-Jun-92 SWS241/R) Woman arranging vase of roses (88x128cm-35x50in) s.
£3139 $5336 (6-Aug-91 UL.T230/R) Woman with flowers (90x130cm-35x51in) (N.KR 36000)

SANCHEZ, Edgar (1940-) Venezuelan
£4696 $8500 (18-Nov-91 CH.NY188/R) Rostro y Piel 202 (150x150cm-59x59in) s.i.verso acrylic canvas
£5000 $9000 (19-Nov-91 CH.NY178/R) Imagen, vision B2000 (140x170cm-55x67in) acrylic

SANCHEZ, Emilio (1921-) Cuban
£2210 $4000 (18-May-92 CH.NY217/R) Untitled (122x122cm-48x48in) init.
£3333 $6000 (19-Nov-91 CH.NY203/R) Una casita verde (137x96cm-54x38in) init. i.stretcher

SANCHEZ, Pedro (16th C) Spanish
£32535 $58889 (5-Dec-91 F.M20/R) Crocefissione (209x117cm-82x46in) panel (I.L 70000000)

SANCHEZ, Tomas (1948-) Central American
£16667 $30000 (19-Nov-91 CH.NY191 a/R) La nube y su sombra (109x150cm-43x59in) s.d.88 s.i.d.verso
£33149 $60000 (18-May-92 CH.NY106/R) Meditacion (108x149cm-43x59in) s.d.87 s.i.d.verso acrylic canvas

SANCHEZ-PERRIER, Emilio (1855-1907) Spanish
£6742 $12000 (22-Jan-92 SY.NY546/R) Boating on river (18x30cm-7x12in) s.i. panel
£7000 $12740 (29-May-92 C380/R) Figures in wooded river landscape (37x24cm-15x9in) s.i. i.verso panel
£7429 $13000 (20-Feb-92 SY.NY92/R) Fishing along river (27x35cm-11x14in) s. panel
£8721 $15000 (17-Oct-91 SY.NY106/R) Rowing on lake (33x41cm-13x16in) s.i. panel
£9143 $16000 (20-Feb-92 SY.NY90/R) Rower on quiet river (21x27cm-8x11in) s.i. panel
£9302 $16000 (17-Oct-91 SY.NY380 a/R) On river's edge at dusk (52x92cm-20x36in) s. cradled panel
£9302 $16000 (17-Oct-91 SY.NY380/R) Sevilla (26x35cm-10x14in) s. panel

SANCHEZ-PERRIER, Emilio (1855-1907) Spanish-cont.
£13143 $23000   (20-Feb-92 SY.NY91/R) On river de Huelva, near Seville (22x41cm-9x16in)
                s.i. panel
£15698 $27000   (17-Oct-91 SY.NY107/R) El Rialaje - Alcala (36x55cm-14x22in) s.i. panel

SANCHO, Jose (20th C) Spanish
£3597 $6151   (17-Mar-92 FER.M156/R) Planchadora leyendo una carta (73x54cm-29x21in) s.
                (S.P 650000)

SANCHO, Manuel (20th C) Spanish?
£664 $1136   (17-Mar-92 FER.M75/R) Terminando la faena (60x81cm-24x32in) s.
                (S.P 120000)

SAND, Lennart (1946-) Scandinavian?
£1423 $2448   (19-Oct-91 UA.U347/R) Brown bear (73x93cm-29x37in) s.d.1988 (S.KR 15000)
£3962 $7013   (5-Nov-91 BA.S162/R) White-tailed eagles attacking goosander
                (135x195cm-53x77in) s. (S.KR 42000)

SANDBERG, Einar (1876-1947) Norwegian
£797 $1451   (10-Dec-91 UL.T215) From Malumsaetre (50x60cm-20x24in) panel (N.KR 9000)

SANDBERG, Johan Gustaf (1782-1854) Swedish
£4771 $8492   (28-Nov-91 BU.S33/R) Valkyrior riding to battle (140x201cm-55x79in)
                (S.KR 50000)

SANDBERG, Ragnar (1902-1972) Swedish
£1727 $3127   (3-Dec-91 AB.S5152/R) The bath (28x39cm-11x15in) s. panel (S.KR 18000)
£1898 $3472   (13-May-92 BU.S181/R) Self portrait with pipe (40x30cm-16x12in) init.
                (S.KR 20000)
£2087 $3820   (13-May-92 BU.S180/R) French sailors (24x33cm-9x13in) init.d.1937
                cardboard (S.KR 22000)
£4364 $7987   (13-May-92 BU.S179/R) It's windy on the jetty (30x54cm-12x21in) init.
                (S.KR 46000)
£4744 $8681   (13-May-92 BU.S178/R) Man and birds (44x53cm-17x21in) init. (S.KR 50000)
£20873 $38197   (11-May-92 NOR.S81/R) Man with doves (63x69cm-25x27in) init.
                (S.KR 220000)

SANDBY, Paul (1725-1809) British
£1210 $2311   (16-Jul-92 S86/R) Church by lake in wooded landscape (22x26cm-9x10in) pen
                W/C
£1600 $2864   (14-Nov-91 S79/R) Figure with horse, donkey and dog in landscape with
                country house beyond (39x54cm-15x21in) init.d.1796 W/C over pencil
£1870 $3572   (16-Jul-92 S85/R) Traveller passing castle in landscape (24x30cm-9x12in)
                pen W/C
£1900 $3401   (14-Nov-91 S9/R) Cart horses pulling timber waggon (8x22cm-3x9in) W/C
                over pencil sold with two other pictures
£2000 $3520   (9-Apr-92 S50/R) Horse and cart on country road. Horseman in thunderstorm
                (7x9cm-3x4in) gouache pair
£2600 $4966   (14-Jul-92 C6/R) Lake landscape with drover and cattle in foreground
                (31x46cm-12x18in) bodycol
£3000 $5280   (9-Apr-92 S19/R) Conway Castle, Wales. Llyn Peris with Dolbadarn Castle,
                Wales (18x33cm-7x13in) indist.i.verso gouache pair
£3800 $6802   (14-Nov-91 S56/R) The bagpiper with his dancing dog (20x15cm-8x6in) pen
                ink W/C over pencil
£3800 $6802   (14-Nov-91 S64/R) Bridge over river, Wales (40x50cm-16x20in) gouache
£4800 $8448   (7-Apr-92 C101/R) Figures on lane before Rochester Castle
                (49x63cm-19x25in) pen W/C
£5000 $8950   (14-Nov-91 S63/R) Llanthony Abbey, Monmouthshire (20x29cm-8x11in) i. W/C
                over pencil
£6200 $10974   (4-Nov-91 WW214) Shrewsbury Bridge (71x99cm-28x39in) gouache paper on
                canvas
£7500 $13425   (12-Nov-91 C75/R) Caernarvon Castle, with a harper in the foreground
                (49x70cm-19x28in) bodycol.
£9500 $17005   (14-Nov-91 S59/R) The church at Hampton on the Thames (26x36cm-10x14in)
                gouache pencil
£19000 $34010   (14-Nov-91 S57/R) Haymakers at work near the Medway, Kent
                (29x43cm-11x17in) s.d.1802 gouache pencil
£19000 $33440   (7-Apr-92 C100/R) St. George's Gate, Canterbury (32x51cm-13x20in)
                num.2556 verso pencil pen W/C

SANDBY, Paul (attrib) (1725-1809) British
£2550 $4412   (4-Sep-91 BT108/R) Figure in wooded garden (46x61cm-18x24in) gouache

SANDBY, Paul (circle) (1725-1809) British
£950 $1701   (11-Nov-91 S538) Matlock High Tor from river (33x44cm-13x17in) i.verso
                W/C over pen pair

SANDBY, Paul (style) (1725-1809) British
£800 $1376   (8-Oct-91 PH8) Figures on a cart before a cottage with cattle, landscape
                beyond (67x107cm-26x42in)

SANDBY, Thomas (1721-1798) British
£620 $1073   (4-Sep-91 BT41/R) Elegant figures walking in park (15x20cm-6x8in) s. W/C
                over pencil

SANDELS, Gosta (1877-1919) Swedish
£480 $869   (3-Dec-91 AB.S5153/R) View (34x21cm-13x8in) s.d.1916 Indian ink wash
        (S.KR 5000)
£815 $1467   (19-Nov-91 GO.G287) Wooded glade, Sandhamn (38x54cm-15x21in) s.d.06 chl
        chk (S.KR 8500)

SANDER, Ludwig (1906-) American
£1163 $2000   (12-Oct-91 SY.NY277/R) Pensacola IV (61x51cm-24x20in) s.d.1960 verso

SANDERS, Christopher (1905-1991) British
£540 $983   (28-May-92 B290) Lescoril (60x70cm-24x28in) s.
£850 $1556   (14-May-92 C152/R) Buckingham Palace from Mall (37x44cm-15x17in) s.
£1200 $2196   (14-May-92 C153/R) Le Grau du Roi, South of France (50x60cm-20x24in) s.
        s.i.stretcher

SANDERS, Julius (20th C) ?
£456 $831   (25-May-92 AT.P135/R) Portrait au bonnet rose (30x23cm-12x9in) s. gouache
        (F.FR 4500)

SANDERS, Walter G (fl.1882-1892) British
£1800 $3168   (8-Apr-92 CSK200/R) Roses in bowl on marble ledge (30x44cm-12x17in)
        s.d.1895

SANDERSON, Robert (fl.1858-1908) British
£750 $1335   (1-May-92 PHE8) Homeward bouand on snow covered country road
        (50x75cm-20x30in) s.d.1891
£1300 $2184   (26-Aug-91 S847/R) The race (30x21cm-12x8in) s.d.1894 panel
£2100 $4011   (16-Jul-92 PHX383/R) Pets (33x25cm-13x10in) mono.d.1878 panel

SANDERSON, William (20th C) British
£550 $995   (6-Dec-91 TE513/R) The washing day (71x51cm-28x20in) s.d.1924 W/C
        bodycol.

SANDERSON-WELLS (1872-1955) British
£600 $1098   (12-May-92 H361) Two horses taking fence through open country with hound
        chasing (91x71cm-36x28in)

SANDERSON-WELLS, John (1872-1955) British
£550 $1007   (14-May-92 CSK266/R) The musician (18x30cm-7x12in) s. panel
£900 $1665   (11-Jun-92 CSK218/R) Returning home (20x28cm-8x11in) s. panel
£950 $1653   (19-Sep-91 TL499) The end of the day (27x37cm-11x15in) s.
£1900 $3268   (4-Mar-92 S85/R) Fine hunting morn (51x40cm-20x16in) s.
£2881 $5100   (14-Feb-92 DM.D2019/R) English Horse racing scene (41x61cm-16x24in) s.
£3300 $5610   (6-Aug-91 H370/R) The Gleaners (61x51cm-24x20in) s.
£800 $1464   (4-Jun-92 CSK49/R) Devon and Somerset stag hounds (26x35cm-10x14in) s.
        W/C bodycol
£900 $1665   (11-Jun-92 CSK31/R) A fair critic (43x36cm-17x14in) s. pencil W/C

SANDIG, Armin (1929-) German
£619 $1144   (11-Jun-92 HN.H414/R) Reise ins Blaue (49x65cm-19x26in) s.i.d.1972 W/C
        over pencil (DM 1800)

SANDIG, Emerich (1903-1973) Austrian
£596 $1061   (28-Nov-91 D.V98/R) Napoleon on journey to St Helena (110x160cm-43x63in)
        s.d.1931 (A.S 12000)

SANDORFI, Istvan (1948-) French
£3150 $5482   (16-Apr-92 FB.P242/R) Nu s'etant foule la cheville dans l'escalier suite
        a Marcel Duchamp (193x97cm-76x38in) s.d.Septembre 1984 i.verso
        (F.FR 31000)

SANDOZ, Claude (1946-) Swiss
£524 $934   (25-Nov-91 WK.M2057) Kleiner Mann ganz gross (194x154cm-76x61in)
        s.i.d.1982verso acrylic (DM 1500)
£874 $1556   (25-Nov-91 WK.M2056/R) Herzwesen im Lande der Schwarzhute
        (228x370cm-90x146in) s.i.d.1981verso acrylic (DM 2500)
£1049 $1867   (25-Nov-91 WK.M2059) Redblue flower (101x140cm-40x55in) s.i.d.1982
        acrylic (DM 3000)

SANDREUTER, Hans (1850-1901) Swiss
£451 $826   (4-Jun-92 SY.Z563/R) BLago Maggiore with barges (17x26cm-7x10in) mono W/C
        pencil (S.FR 1200)

SANDROCK, Leonhard (1867-?) German
£699 $1210   (25-Mar-92 KM.K1395) River landscape with steamer, possibly Lower Elbe
        s. canvas on board (DM 2000)
£825 $1509   (2-Jun-92 FN.S2403/R) Harbour worker in boat (46x57cm-18x22in) s. board
        (DM 2400)
£1433 $2595   (23-May-92 GB.B785) Railway bridge with workmen at night (32x24cm-13x9in)
        s. board (DM 4200)

SANDS, H H (fl.1886-1906) British
£583 $1049   (30-Jan-92 RAS.V675/R) Woodsman returning home with horses
        (85x121cm-33x48in) s.d.1899 (D.KR 6500)

SANDYS, Emma (1834-1877) British
£2000 $3440 (4-Mar-92 S53 a/R) Medieval beauty (30x25cm-12x10in) mono.d.1866 panel

SANDYS, Emma (attrib) (1834-1877) British
£550 $995 (5-Dec-91 CSK240) The hand of cards (36x25cm-14x10in) board

SANDYS, Frederick (1832-1904) British
£27000 $48600 (19-Nov-91 PH61/R) Portrait of Lady Grace Rose (56x45cm-22x18in) i.d.1866
panel
£500 *$860* *(4-Mar-92 S320/R) Portrait of young girl (58x42cm-23x17in) col.chk*
£3200 *$5504* *(4-Mar-92 S321/R) Gypsy girl (37x31cm-15x12in) col.chk*

SANDYS-LUMSDAINE, Leesa (1936-) British
£1200 $2304 (28-Jul-92 SWS166/R) Top sprinters So Blssed and Be Friendly
(89x120cm-35x47in) s.d.69

SANEJOUAND, Jean Michel (1934-) French
£963 *$1742* *(20-May-92 FB.P233/R) Untitled (110x110cm-43x43in) oil gouache*
(F.FR 9500)

SANESI, Nicola (1818-1889) Italian
£2475 $4380 (7-Nov-91 F.M31/R) La lettura della mano (54x43cm-21x17in) s.d.1861
(I.L 5400000)
£4561 $7800 (13-Mar-92 FN.S2938/R) Carneval in Venice (98x72cm-39x28in) s.d.1862
(DM 13000)

SANETY, Gide (20th C) ?
£683 $1250 (17-May-92 DU.E1158) Portrait of brunette (56x46cm-22x18in) indis.s.

SANGER, Grace H C (1881-?) American
£562 $1000 (29-Nov-91 MFA.C102/R) Seated woman under umbrella (41x30cm-16x12in)
s.verso board

SANGIOVANNI, A (18th C) Italian
£8140 $14000 (10-Oct-91 SY.NY77/R) Still life of flowers in urns with fruit and a
bird, all in a landscape (49x62cm-19x24in) indist.s.

SANI, Alessandro (19/20th C) Italian
£2383 $4218 (5-Nov-91 GF.L2167/R) The courted woman (66x51cm-26x20in) s. (S.FR 6100)
£3048 $5334 (18-Feb-92 DUR.M46/R) El galante vencedor (51x64cm-20x25in) s.
(S.P 550000)
£3279 $6000 (16-May-92 HG.C196/R) Pleasant serenade (64x51cm-25x20in) s.
£4857 $8500 (18-Feb-92 CE.NY99/R) Serving meal (49x65cm-19x26in) s.

SANI, David (19/20th C) Italian
£3022 $5500 (26-May-92 CE.NY161/R) Blowing bubbles for baby (55x77cm-22x30in)
s.i.d.89
£4074 $7374 (19-May-92 GF.L2205/R) Mother and Child in kitchen interior
(63x50cm-25x20in) s. (S.FR 11000)

SANLOT-BAGNINAULT, Rene (19th C) French
£553 $996 (19-Nov-91 GS.B3651) Portrait of Alice de Mugent (24x19cm-9x7in)
mono.d.1852 (S.FR 1400)

SANNUY, J (19/20th C) Uruguayan?
£449 *$800* *(28-Oct-91 GC.M1/R) Soldado y Escopeta (29x12cm-11x5in) s.d.1897 W/C*
£545 *$970* *(25-Nov-91 GC.M85) Infante Trompeta (10x6cm-4x2in) s.d.1893 W/C*
£867 *$1500* *(30-Sep-91 GC.M20/R) Infante Tambor (50x35cm-20x14in) s.d.1893 W/C*

SANO di PIETRO (1406-1481) Italian
£25000 $48000 (10-Jul-92 C223/R) Madonna and child with saints John the Baptist and
Leonard, two angels (47x38cm-19x15in) tempera gold ground panel

SANO di PIETRO (style) (1406-1481) Italian
£3867 $7000 (21-May-92 CH.NY133/R) Madonna and Child with adoring angels
(46x32cm-18x13in) panel

SANSOM, Gareth Laurence (1939-) Australian
£2621 $4875 (21-Jun-92 SY.ME140/R) Untitled (197x213cm-78x84in) s.d.74 acrylic
(A.D 6500)

SANT, J (1820-1916) British
£1350 $2417 (5-May-92 SWS304/R) Crossing the brook (44x54cm-17x21in) s.d.1835 after
George Vincent

SANT, James (1820-1916) British
£1350 $2336 (25-Mar-92 PHI559/R) Mother and child, the reading lesson
(25x20cm-10x8in) mono oval
£1800 $3150 (23-Sep-91 PHB52/R) Portrait of an Italian boy (76x63cm-30x25in) mono.
oval
£3297 $6000 (28-May-92 SY.NY300/R) Day dreaming (56x46cm-22x18in) mono.
£4200 $7182 (12-Mar-92 CSK269/R) The sound of the lark (76x63cm-30x25in) mono. oval

SANT, James (circle) (1820-1916) British
£4000 $7080   (6-Nov-91 S173/R) Miss Edith Denny and her sister on her marriage to Edmund Power (142x112cm-56x44in)

SANTA MARIA, Marceliano (19/20th C) Spanish
£8260 $14785   (14-Nov-91 ANS.M80/R) La ermita, la fuente y el rio (44x51cm-17x20in) s. i.verso (S.P 1500000)
£9400 $17672   (16-Dec-91 ANS.M99/R) Riberas del Jarama (40x50cm-16x20in) s. i.verso (S.P 1700000)

SANTACROCE, Girolamo I (attrib) (?-1556) Italian
£6704 $12000   (13-Nov-91 B.SF2101/R) Sacra conversazione (46x141cm-18x56in)

SANTAFEDE, Fabrizio (1559-) Italian
£8000 $13920   (15-Apr-92 C160/R) Christ mourned by two angels (132x107cm-52x42in)

SANTAOLARIA, Vicente (1886-?) Spanish
£2058 $3909   (26-Jun-92 CSC.P109/R) Danseuses espagnoles (100x80cm-39x31in) s. (F.FR 20000)

SANTASUSAGNA, Ernest (1900-1964) ?
£713 $1268   (26-Nov-91 BRO.B319) Figura femenina (91x72cm-36x28in) s. (S.P 130000)
£1699 $3024   (26-Nov-91 BRO.B384) Figura femenina sobre fondo urbano (100x81cm-39x32in) s.d.39 (S.P 310000)

SANTERRE, Jean Baptiste (1651-1717) French
£1337 $2421   (5-Dec-91 SY.MO369/R) Femme et enfant dans un interieur (71x56cm-28x22in) (F.FR 13000)

SANTERRE, Jean Baptiste (after) (1651-1717) French
£3000 $5760   (10-Jul-92 C192 a/R) Kitchen maid preparing cabbage at table (92x74cm-36x29in)

SANTERRE, Jean Baptiste (attrib) (1651-1717) French
£2575 $4840   (18-Dec-91 AT.P179/R) Portrait d'un gentilhomme en manteau bleu (82x65cm-32x26in) oval (F.FR 25000)

SANTERRE, Jean Baptiste (circle) (1651-1717) French
£2732 $4672   (18-Mar-92 D.V257/R) Portrait of young lady (70x86cm-28x34in) (A.S 55000)

SANTIAGO, Carlos de (?) ?
£1421 $2600   (4-Jun-92 GOM.M51) Campina de Villa Rica, Chile (60x75cm-24x30in) s. s.i.verso fibre
£2570 $4600   (6-May-92 CAS.M28/R) Quinta (100x90cm-39x35in)

SANTOMASO, Giuseppe (1907-1990) Italian
£4526 $8237   (26-May-92 SY.MI44/R) Natura morta (39x62cm-15x24in) s. (I.L 10000000)
£8172 $14545   (29-Apr-92 F.F276/R) Spazio grigio (45x33cm-18x13in) s.d.1968 oil sand (I.L 18000000)
£14000 $24080   (17-Oct-91 C42/R) Spazio Aperto (73x55cm-29x22in) s.d.61
£19914 $36243   (26-May-92 SY.MI230/R) Gialli e neri a leme (162x96cm-64x38in) s.d.58 (I.L 44000000)
£38588 $68687   (29-Apr-92 F.F278/R) Il battipalo (110x70cm-43x28in) s.d.1953 (I.L 85000000)
£1564 $2800   *(12-Nov-91 CE.NY141/R) Untitled (46x36cm-18x14in) s.d.83 col.chk crayons chl ink paper collage*
£4869 $8667   *(29-Apr-92 G.Z52/R) Composition in brown (51x36cm-20x14in) s.d.1977 mixed media (S.FR 13000)*
£5906 $10157   *(16-Oct-91 G.Z48/R) Astrazione (61x45cm-24x18in) s.d.1986 mixed media collage paper on panel (S.FR 15000)*
£11975 $21794   *(9-Dec-91 CH.R144/R) Notturno (100x81cm-39x32in) s.i.d.1982 oil collage (I.L 26000000)*
£13165 $23434   *(29-Apr-92 F.F277) Composizione (47x57cm-19x22in) s. oil mixed media canvas (I.L 29000000)*
£18536 $32994   *(29-Nov-91 F.F137/R) Doppio segno (92x72cm-36x28in) s.d.1973 oil collage canvas (I.L 40000000)*

SANTORO, Francesco Raffaello (1844-?) Italian
£1966 $3500   (22-Jan-92 SY.NY539/R) Flirtation (63x96cm-25x38in) s.i.

SANTORO, Rubens (1859-1942) Italian
£5714 $10000   (19-Feb-92 CH.NY94/R) Portrait of North African man (24x18cm-9x7in) s. panel
£7558 $13000   (17-Oct-91 SY.NY363/R) Venetian sunset (20x28cm-8x11in) s. canvasboard
£10225 $18508   (3-Dec-91 SY.MI147/R) Marina di Sapri (26x39cm-10x15in) s. (I.L 22000000)
£19000 $35340   (17-Jun-92 S550/R) Salviati Palace, Venice (32x23cm-13x9in) s. panel
£19061 $35453   (16-Jun-92 F.M218/R) Scena veneziana (33x23cm-13x9in) s. panel (I.L 42000000)
£22000 $37620   (20-Mar-92 C58/R) Gondolas on the Grand Canal with S.Maria della Salute, Venice (26x45cm-10x18in) s.
£23256 $40000   (16-Oct-91 CH.NY184/R) A Venetian Canal Scene (33x24cm-13x9in) s. panel
£25000 $42750   (18-Mar-92 S180/R) Neapolitan women in a sunny street (63x36cm-25x14in) s.d.90
£34884 $60000   (16-Oct-91 CH.NY185/R) The wine harvest (51x39cm-20x15in) s.d.1883 panel

SANTRY, Terence John (1910-1990) Australian
£595	$1070	(24-Nov-91 SY.S112) Street scene (29x39cm-11x15in) s. canvasboard (A.D 1350)
£1322	$2352	(26-Nov-91 J.M204/R) Viaduct, Roselle (48x60cm-19x24in) s. canvas on board (A.D 3000)
£1542	$2775	(24-Nov-91 SY.S133/R) Industrial landscape. Sydney Street scene (49x57cm-19x22in) s. canvas on board double-sided (A.D 3500)
£2423	$4313	(26-Nov-91 J.M136/R) Young boy, Paddington (74x83cm-29x33in) s. canvas on board (A.D 5500)
£783	*$1363*	*(16-Sep-91 CH.ME8) Ship at Wharf, Pyrmont (54x75cm-21x30in) s. ink W/C htd white (A.D 1700)*

SANTVOORT, Dirck van (1610-1680) Dutch
£12916	$22086	(18-Mar-92 D.V94/R) Portrait of nobleman wearing white lace collar (89x57cm-35x22in) panel (A.S 260000)

SANTVOORT, Dirck van (circle) (1610-1680) Dutch
£21802	$37500	(10-Oct-91 SY.NY90/R) Portrait of a young couple standing in an interior (64x56cm-25x22in) panel

SANTVOORT, Pieter Dircksz van (1604-1635) Dutch
£3416	*$6081*	*(25-Nov-91 CH.AM121/R) Mountainous wooded river landscape with village. Wooded landscape (18x28cm-7x11in) d.1623 chk pen wash double-sided (D.FL 11000)*

SANUCCA, Jean (18/19th C) ?
£1800	*$3060*	*(23-Oct-91 S46/R) Building of the bridge of Canaro, Alexandria (56x91cm-22x36in) i.d.1804 pen W/C over pencil*
£3000	*$5100*	*(23-Oct-91 S59/R) Night view of the building of the bridge at Canaro, Alexandria (59x92cm-23x36in) s.i.d.1804 pen W/C over pencil bodycol*

SANVITELLI (19th C) Italian
£2234	$3887	(17-Sep-91 FN.S2518/R) View of Naples with Vesuvio beyond and fisherfolk dancing on terrace (55x81cm-22x32in) s. (DM 6500)

SANZ, Bernard Lukas (1650-c.1710) Italian
£3315	$6000	(22-May-92 SY.NY289/R) Extensive mountainous river landscape with travellers on path (67x91cm-26x36in) s.

SAPP, Allen (1929-) Canadian
£550	$974	(6-Nov-91 SY.T196) That's all for the day (29x39cm-11x15in) s. acrylic canvas (C.D 1100)
£596	$1091	(1-Jun-92 W.T1118 a) Father thinking about something (46x61cm-18x24in) s.i.d.1975verso acrylic (C.D 1300)
£1000	$1770	(6-Nov-91 SY.T154/R) Visiting (61x91cm-24x36in) s. acrylic canvas (C.D 2000)
£1261	$2308	(1-Jun-92 W.T1108) Days end (76x122cm-30x48in) s. (C.D 2750)
£1279	$2327	(26-May-92 JOY.T49/R) Charlie Frank and friend (60x90cm-24x35in) s. acrylic canvas (C.D 2800)

SARACENI, Carlo (style) (1585-1620) Italian
£1268	$2346	(8-Jun-92 CH.R687) Scena di banchetto (57x43cm-22x17in) panel (I.L 2800000)

SARBURGH, Bartholomeus (attrib) (1590-?) Italian
£11328	$20051	(5-Nov-91 GF.L2026/R) Portrait of Abel Socin. His wife Catharina Verzasgha (93x70cm-37x28in) i.coat of arms d.1618 pair (S.FR 29000)

SARDI, Jean (1947-) French
£613	$1073	(23-Feb-92 LT.P72/R) Animation dans une vieille rue (46x56cm-18x22in) s. (F.FR 6000)
£686	$1180	(20-Oct-91 LT.P41) Rencontre (60x73cm-24x29in) s. (F.FR 6800)
£692	$1267	(7-Jun-92 LT.P127) Neige a Revest (60x73cm-24x29in) s. (F.FR 6800)
£746	$1320	(10-Nov-91 LT.P3/R) Port Anime (65x81cm-26x32in) s. (F.FR 7400)

SARDINIAN SCHOOL, 15th C Italian
£13000	$23660	(13-Dec-91 C235/R) Madonna and Child enthroned, Crucifixion above. Saints Jerome and Benedict (42x42cm-17x17in) gold ground panel triptych

SARET, Alan (1944-) American
£838	*$1500*	*(9-May-92 CE.NY258/R) Suprise at the entrance of Varla (77x89cm-30x35in) s.i.d.1988verso col.pencil*

SARGENT, John Singer (1856-1925) American/British
£14917	$27000	(6-Dec-91 CH.NY140/R) A mosque, Cairo 1891 (35x47cm-14x19in)
£32967	$60000	(27-May-92 SY.NY97/R) Male model resting (56x71cm-22x28in)
£52632	$90000	(11-Mar-92 SY.NY46/R) Olive trees in Corfu (52x62cm-20x24in)
£209945	$380000	(5-Dec-91 SY.NY77/R) 'Expectancy' - portrait of Frances Winifred Hill (102x86cm-40x34in) s.
£435	*$774*	*(29-Nov-91 GAB.G2171 a) Portrait du banquier s.i. crayon (S.FR 1100)*
£1100	*$1881*	*(19-Mar-92 T90) Figures on balcony (23x18cm-9x7in) s.d.23 W/C*
£1200	*$2088*	*(10-Sep-91 HS61) Landscape with figures (13x18cm-5x7in) s. pencil dr htd white*
£8187	*$14000*	*(11-Mar-92 SY.NY54/R) Portrait of Princess Henrietta Maria Stuart - copy after Bartholomeus Van der Helst (54x37cm-21x15in) W/C paperboard*

ARGENT, John Singer (1856-1925) American/British-cont.
£8772 $15000   (11-Mar-92 SY.NY52/R) Becalmed (21x28cm-8x11in) i. pencil
£10500 $18060   (6-Mar-92 C26/R) At Siena, cow and calf in stall (25x36cm-10x14in) s.
                              pencil W/C gum arabic
£13000 $22360   (6-Mar-92 C25/R) Palace and gardens, Spain (45x30cm-18x12in) pencil W/C
£13736 $25000   (27-May-92 SY.NY63/R) Berles-au-Bois, France (39x53cm-15x21in) s.i.d.1919
                              W/C
£23352 $42500   (27-May-92 SY.NY62/R) Venetian canal (25x36cm-10x14in) s.i. W/C
£29000 $49880   (6-Mar-92 C27/R) Reflections, rocks and water (25x30cm-10x12in) W/C
                              bodycol
£260000 $475800   (5-Jun-92 C18/R) The green parasol (47x35cm-19x14in) pencil W/C bodycol

ARGENT, John Singer (after) (1856-1925) American/British
£809 $1400   (29-Mar-92 MY.F146/R) Carlotta (41x38cm-16x15in) s.

ARGENT, Paul Turner (1880-?) American
£552 $950   (12-Oct-91 DU.E115) Spring landscape (51x61cm-20x24in) s.d.27stretcher

ARGENT, Richard (1911-1978) American
£1826 $3250   (2-Nov-91 IH.NY118/R) Man struggling with coat hangers in closet
                              (69x53cm-27x21in) s. board

ARKISIAN, Sarkis (1909-) American
£655 $1100   (16-Aug-91 DM.D2004/R) Rasputin (58x43cm-23x17in) s. mixed media
£714 $1200   (16-Aug-91 DM.D2003/R) Sunflowers in shaped vase (56x36cm-22x14in) s.
                              mixed media board

ARLUIS, Leonard (1874-1949) French
£515 $881   (18-Mar-92 ARC.P11 b) Adoration des rois mages (100x72cm-39x28in) s.
                              (F.FR 5000)

ARNARI, Franco (1933-) Italian
£2284 $3974   (14-Apr-92 F.M30/R) Omaggio a Ingres (94x95cm-37x37in) s.verso
                            (I.L 5000000)

ARONI, Sergio (1935-) Italian
£5253 $9140   (14-Apr-92 F.M133/R) Figura ferita (150x120cm-59x47in) s.
                            s.i.d.1960/61verso (I.L 11500000)

ARTAIN, William (1843-1924) American
£1462 $2500   (13-Mar-92 S.BM180/R) Drink by the shade trade (33x46cm-13x18in) s.

ARTELLE, Herbert (1885-1955) American
£737 $1400   (24-Jun-92 B.SF6342/R) Spring valley (71x91cm-28x36in) s.

ARTO, Andrea del (1487-1530) Italian
£1606 $2938   (3-Jun-92 R.T188/R) Holy Family with John the Baptist (60x46cm-24x18in)
                            i.num.15 verso panel (C.D 3500)

ARTO, Andrea del (after) (1487-1530) Italian
£909 $1573   (25-Mar-92 KM.K992) The Risen Christ (61x44cm-24x17in) (DM 2600)
£2744 $5076   (13-Jun-92 CH.AM188) The Madonna and Child (111x77cm-44x30in) i.verso
                            (D.FL 9000)
£4070 $7000   (10-Oct-91 SY.NY2/R) The Pieta, with SS. John, Mary Magdalene, Catherine,
                            Peter and Paul (73x60cm-29x24in) panel
£10497 $19000   (22-May-92 SY.NY128/R) Virgin and Child with Infant Saint John the
                            Baptist (117x90cm-46x35in)

ARTO, Andrea del (circle) (1487-1530) Italian
£4115 $7449   (5-Dec-91 SY.MO205/R) Vierge a l'enfant et Saint Jean-Baptiste
                            (105x80cm-41x31in) panel (F.FR 40000)

ARTO, Andrea del (style) (1487-1530) Italian
£950 $1663   (2-Apr-92 CSK20/R) Holy Family (14x9cm-6x4in) panel
£1300 $2275   (2-Apr-92 CSK31) Madonna and Child with two angels (42x21cm-17x8in) gold
                            ground panel shaped triptych
£2800 $4984   (1-Nov-91 C155/R) Madonna and Child with infant Saint John the Baptist
                            (111x83cm-44x33in) panel
£3000 $5250   (2-Apr-92 CSK15) Betrothal of Virgin. Virgin and Saint Elizabeth
                            (24x32cm-9x13in) panel pair
£4180 $7273   (13-Sep-91 C58/R) Scholar holding open book (67x54cm-26x21in) panel
£9669 $17500   (21-May-92 CH.NY100/R) Madonna and child with infant Saint John the
                            Baptist (104x77cm-41x30in) panel

ARTO, J H (19/20th C) Italian
£600 $1026   (19-Mar-92 B51) The Serenade (70x50cm-28x20in) s.

ARTO, Pietro (1930-) Italian
£863 $1467   (23-Oct-91 GD.B634/R) Seated nude (36x43cm-14x17in) s. pastel (S.FR 2200)

ARTORE, Hugo (1935-) Uruguayan
£618 $1100   (28-Oct-91 GC.M23) Gente en el Bar (52x54cm-20x21in) s.
£1236 $2200   (28-Oct-91 GC.M22/R) En el Bar (89x110cm-35x43in) s.d.1965 fibre

SARTORI, Benedetto (18th C) Italian
£5245 $8969   (18-Mar-92 N.M452/R) Trompe l'oeil still lifes (92x69cm-36x27in) pair
                         (DM 15000)

SARTORI, Giulio (1840-1907) Italian
£900 $1557   (3-Oct-91 CSK241/R) Portrait of a lady in a dark lace trimmed dress
                         (86x64cm-34x25in) s.

SARTORIO, G A (1861-1932) Italian
£705   *$1255*   *(26-Nov-91 J.M572) Laneway (57x62cm-22x24in) s.d.1901 mixed media*
                         (A.D 1600)

SARTORIO, Giulio Aristide (1861-1932) Italian
£4070 $7000   (17-Oct-91 SY.NY381/R) Allegoria (50x62cm-20x24in) s.d.1892
£7410 $12819   (24-Mar-92 CH.R12/R) Il piccolo leopardo (38x68cm-15x27in) s.i.
                         (I.L 16000000)
£575   *$1000*   *(15-Sep-91 JRB.C109/R) Country road (15x56cm-6x22in) s.d.1892 pastel*
£906   *$1676*   *(9-Jun-92 F.R94) Autunno (44x25cm-17x10in) s. pastel (I.L 2000000)*
£2072   *$3750*   *(21-May-92 GRO.B11/R) The island of penguins (25x53cm-10x21in)*
                         s.i.d.MCMXXIV pastel

SARTORIUS, Francis (elder) (1734-1804) British
£1700 $2992   (8-Apr-92 S205/R) Dark bay racehorse with jockey up (22x28cm-9x11in) s.
£9500 $16720   (10-Apr-92 C74/R) Crop, iron grey racehorse beating Faith, bay racehorse
                         at Newmarket (65x92cm-26x36in)
£10000 $17600   (10-Apr-92 C73/R) Goldfinder, bay racehorse with jockey up, other horses
                         and riders beyond (63x76cm-25x30in)
£15847 $29000   (5-Jun-92 SY.NY8/R) The Duke of Kingston's Christophus by Snap
                         (63x76cm-25x30in) s.indis.d.
£17000 $29920   (8-Apr-92 S120/R) Setting out (73x159cm-29x63in)

SARTORIUS, Francis (elder-circle) (1734-1804) British
£2000 $3480   (12-Sep-91 CSK200/R) Fox in lair with dead cockerel, a hunt in full cry
                         beyond (74cm-29ins circular)
£3000 $5730   (15-Jul-92 S178/R) Gentleman out shooting with his dog (51x60cm-20x24in)

SARTORIUS, John Nott (1759-1828) British
£1500 $2640   (8-Apr-92 S204/R) Gentlemen out coursing (36x52cm-14x20in) s.
£1700 $2907   (12-Mar-92 CSK133/R) Bay hunter in landscape (33x42cm-13x17in) s.d.1818
£2200 $4070   (11-Jun-92 CSK167/R) Hunstman and hound. The kill (35x44cm-14x17in)
                         s.d.1794 pair
£2400 $4584   (21-Jul-92 PH245/R) Still life of fruit (18x23cm-7x9in) s. pair
£17500 $30800   (8-Apr-92 S123/R) Three hunters in wooded landscape with huntsman and
                         groom (90x116cm-35x46in) s.
£19126 $35000   (5-Jun-92 SY.NY28/R) The check. Full cry (62x74cm-24x29in) s.d.1810 pair

SARTORIUS, John Nott (attrib) (1759-1828) British
£1490 $2533   (23-Oct-91 GD.B1266/R) Horse standing (70x87cm-28x34in) (S.FR 3800)
£2158 $4100   (26-Jun-92 WOL.C441/R) Horse and jockey in landscape (48x69cm-19x27in)
£5721 $10184   (25-Nov-91 W.T1936/R) Mounted huntsmen and hounds in landscape
                         (82x112cm-32x44in) (C.D 11500)

SARTORIUS, William (18th C) British
£1900 $3401   (13-Nov-91 S215/R) Still life of fruit, ewer and basket on ledge
                         (47x57cm-19x22in)
£6200 $10912   (8-Apr-92 S110/R) Still life of fruit, birds and insects in grotto
                         (59x66cm-23x26in)

SARTORIUS, William (circle) (18th C) British
£1650 $2822   (16-Mar-92 LW1858) Still life with dead wild fowl and basket of fruit in
                         landscape with cat (64x76cm-25x30in)
£1900 $3439   (5-Dec-91 CG310/R) Still life with bullfinch feeding from melon and fruit
                         by grapevine (48x38cm-19x15in)

SARYAN, Martiros (20th C) Russian
£5000   *$9300*   *(16-Jun-92 S77/R) Still life with fruit (48x59cm-19x23in) s.d.1913*
                         gouache

SARZANA see FIASELLA, Domenico

SASSENBERG, I I D (19th C) Swiss
£772   *$1320*   *(13-Mar-92 FN.S2939/R) Rhine landscape with monastery and village*
                         (56x73cm-22x29in) s.d.1824 gouache (DM 2200)

SASSENBROUCK, Achille van (1886-1979) Belgian
£497 $899   (23-May-92 KV.L369) Ternat landscape (38x45cm-15x18in) s. panel
                         (B.FR 30000)
£596 $1079   (23-May-92 KV.L370) Ternat landscape (38x45cm-15x18in) s. panel
                         (B.FR 36000)
£829 $1517   (12-May-92 C.A429) Old corner of Mechelen (86x75cm-34x30in) s.
                         (B.FR 50000)
£1454 $2632   (7-Dec-91 KV.L338) Still life with fish (100x110cm-39x43in) s.d.1928
                         (B.FR 85000)

ASSI, Pietro (1834-1905) Italian
2681 $1266   (16-Jun-92 F.M54) Guardiana di tacchini (30x46cm-12x18in) s. paper
        (I.L 1500000)
2874 $1564   (14-Nov-91 CH.R154) Paesaggio con gregge (11x18cm-4x7in) s. panel
        (I.L 1900000)

ASSOFERRATO (1609-1685) Italian
2850 $1556   (12-May-92 SWS651) Virgin at prayer (46x38cm-18x15in)
1900 $3325   (3-Apr-92 C152/R) Madonna and Child (69x61cm-27x24in) with studio
2572 $4655   (5-Dec-91 SY.MO202/R) Vierge (42x35cm-17x14in) (F.FR 25000)
3500 $6230   (1-Nov-91 C26/R) Madonna (50x37cm-20x15in)
3591 $6500   (21-May-92 CH.NY223/R) Madonna and Child surrounded by cherubs
        (75x100cm-30x39in)
8500 $15470   (13-Dec-91 C244/R) The Madonna at prayer (49x37cm-19x15in)
8853 $15758   (28-Apr-92 F.R88/R) Madonna (49x38cm-19x15in) (I.L 19500000)
16327 $28898   (10-Feb-92 GL.P23/R) Vierge a l'Enfant (64x48cm-25x19in) (F.FR 160000)
41752 $75988   (11-Dec-91 LD.P56/R) La Vierge aux mains jointes, dite aussi la Vierge en
        oraison (74x59cm-29x23in) (F.FR 410000)

ASSOFERRATO (attrib) (1609-1685) Italian
2060 $3872   (18-Dec-91 AT.P136/R) L'Enfant Jesus endormi (63x120cm-25x47in)
        (F.FR 20000)
3466 $6446   (18-Jun-92 SY.MO276/R) Vierge (49x39cm-19x15in) (F.FR 34000)

ASSOFERRATO (circle) (1609-1685) Italian
2962 $5184   (24-Feb-92 ARC.P4/R) Sainte Famille (27x27cm-11x11in) copper octagonal
        (F.FR 29000)

ASSOFERRATO (school) (1609-1685) Italian
1707 $3090   (3-Dec-91 R.T15/R) Madonna praying (50x38cm-20x15in) (C.D 3500)
2320 $4200   (19-May-92 CE.NY342) madonna in prayer (51x38cm-20x15in)

ASSOFERRATO (studio) (1609-1685) Italian
3800 $6916   (13-Dec-91 C246) The Madonna and Child (73x58cm-29x23in)

ASSOFERRATO (style) (1609-1685) Italian
800    $1400   (2-Apr-92 CSK28/R) Immaculate Conception (73x47cm-29x19in)
890    $1700   (16-Jul-92 SY.NY183/R) Madonna and Christ (68x55cm-27x22in)
903    $1625   (19-Nov-91 RAS.K368) Madonna praying (47x37cm-19x15in) (D.KR 10000)
1200 $2196   (12-May-92 SWS692) Madonna and Child (71x59cm-28x23in)
1210 $2105   (13-Sep-91 C55/R) Madonna at prayer (70x57cm-28x22in)

ASSOON, Theresa Georgina see THORNYCROFT, Theresa G

ASSU, Aligi (1912-) Italian
13578 $24711   (26-May-92 SY.MI180/R) Nudo su una poltrona verde (97x64cm-38x25in)
        (I.L 30000000)
15779 $29665   (19-Dec-91 F.M180/R) Wanda (45x35cm-18x14in) s. s.i.d.1952verso
        (I.L 34000000)
22706 $40417   (29-Nov-91 F.F180/R) Divina Provvidenza s.d.1961 (I.L 49000000)
26493 $46098   (14-Apr-92 F.M188/R) Cavalli spaventati dalla tempesta (60x95cm-24x37in)
        s. s.d.1946verso (I.L 58000000)
1266 $2291   *(21-May-92 F.M257) Cavallo (20x14cm-8x6in) s. pastel (I.L 2800000)*
1356 $2455   *(21-May-92 F.M199) Cavallo balzano. Piccolo caffe (6x16cm-2x6in) s.i.*
        s.d.1981verso W/C pair (I.L 3000000)
1356 $2455   *(21-May-92 F.M281) I cavalli del pastore. Cavalli sulla spiaggia*
        (6x17cm-2x7in) s.i. s.d.1981verso W/C cardboard pair (I.L 3000000)
1492 $2700   *(21-May-92 F.M221/R) Cavaliere (39x30cm-15x12in) s. W/C (I.L 3300000)*
1492 $2700   *(21-May-92 F.M325) Cavallo. Cavaliere nel paesaggio s. one pastel one*
        W/C two (I.L 3300000)
1808 $3273   *(21-May-92 F.M51) Due cavalli (29x41cm-11x16in) s. ink acrylic*
        (I.L 4000000)
1946 $3464   *(29-Nov-91 F.F121/R) Colomba (33x32cm-13x13in) s. ink acrylic cardboard*
        (I.L 4200000)
3347 $6057   *(3-Dec-91 F.R102/R) La famiglia (43x65cm-17x26in) s. s.verso gouache*
        paper on canvas (I.L 7200000)
3847 $7002   *(26-May-92 SY.MI26/R) Toeletta (45x64cm-18x25in) s.i.verso gouache paper*
        on canvas (I.L 8500000)

ATO, Key (1906-1978) Japanese
3143 $5500   (28-Feb-92 SY.NY271/R) Son de l'eau (91x73cm-36x29in) s.d.63
927    $1585   *(21-Mar-92 AT.P79) Sans titre (19x32cm-7x13in) s. mixed media crumpled*
        paper (F.FR 9000)
1236 $2113   *(21-Mar-92 AT.P77/R) Sans titre (25x31cm-10x12in) s.d.73 mixed media*
        crumpled paper (F.FR 12000)

ATO, Tadashi (1923-) American
702    $1200   (12-Mar-92 CH.NY245/R) Abstraction in blue and grey (46x58cm-18x23in)
        s.i.d.1948stretcher

ATORY, Joseph August (19th C) Austrian
2622 $4484   (18-Mar-92 N.M628/R) Still life of flowers and fruit on window ledge
        before curtain (33x48cm-13x19in) s.d.1836 (DM 7500)

SATTLER, Hubert (1817-1904) Austrian
£976	$1698	(19-Sep-91 D.V154/R) View of Lake Constance and Bregenz (15x19cm-6x7in) i.verso board (A.S 20000)
£981	$1865	(25-Jun-92 D.V432/R) Wartburg in Thuringia (13x19cm-5x7in) mono panel (A.S 20000)
£989	$1730	(20-Feb-92 D.V327/R) View of Thun, Lake Thun (13x19cm-5x7in) s. i.verso board (A.S 20000)
£989	$1730	(20-Feb-92 D.V442/R) View of Lucerne (11x16cm-4x6in) mono L B board (A.S 20000)
£989	$1730	(20-Feb-92 D.V441/R) View of Montreux (13x18cm-5x7in) s.R.Ritschard panel (A.S 20000)
£1220	$2122	(19-Sep-91 D.V161/R) Castle Neuschwanstein (14x19cm-6x7in) indis.mono. panel (A.S 25000)
£1236	$2163	(20-Feb-92 D.V467/R) View of Vevey, Lake Geneva (11x16cm-4x6in) s.G.Stahly-Richen panel (A.S 25000)
£1865	$3543	(25-Jun-92 D.V496/R) Festung Hohensalzburg (10x14cm-4x6in) mono metal (A.S 38000)
£1865	$3543	(25-Jun-92 D.V413/R) View of Luzern (13x19cm-5x7in) board (A.S 38000)
£2224	$3893	(20-Feb-92 D.V319/R) Berchtesgaden (14x19cm-6x7in) mono. panel (A.S 45000)
£2498	$4496	(21-Nov-91 D.V158/R) View of Schloss Anif near Salzburg (13x17cm-5x7in) mono. board (A.S 50000)
£30581	$56881	(18-Jun-92 SY.MO85/R) Vue du vieux port a Genes (72x99cm-28x39in) inits. (F.FR 300000)

SATZBERGER, I C (16th C) German
£3916	$6931	(7-Nov-91 D.V80/R) The Mourning of Christ (26x17cm-10x7in) s. panel (A.S 80000)

SAUBER, Robert (1868-1936) British
£5500	$9790	(28-Apr-92 PH51/R) Portrait of Marie Sauber, artist's wife (243x130cm-96x51in) s.

SAUBES, Leon Daniel (1855-1922) French
£528	$887	(27-Aug-91 RAS.K333) Small child giving bread to a beggar (91x78cm-36x31in) s. (D.KR 6000)

SAUBIDET, Tito (1891-1953) Argentinian
£955	$1700	(1-Nov-91 PO.BA8) Pareja bajo el ombu (59x59cm-23x23in) s. panel
£500	*$900*	*(20-Nov-91 V.BA90) Caballo (26x36cm-10x14in) W/C*

SAUBIER-HEULER (19/20th C) French
£572	*$1002*	*(5-Apr-92 ZZ.F59/R) Nature morte aux pommes et aux raisins (52x63cm-20x25in) s. W/C (F.FR 5500)*

SAUER, Walter (1889-1972) Belgian
£633	*$1089*	*(12-Oct-91 KV.L261) Religieuse (50x29cm-20x11in) mono.d.1918 chk (B.FR 38000)*
£1614	*$2760*	*(21-Mar-92 KV.L254) Woman (42x33cm-17x13in) mono.d.1918 chk pastel (B.FR 95000)*

SAUERWEID, Nicolas Alexandrovitch (1836-1866) Russian
£6500	$11635	(15-Nov-91 C149/R) Battle of Waterloo, with Wellington on Copenhagen (206x340cm-81x134in)

SAUNDERS, Charles L (19th C) British
£872	$1500	(15-Oct-91 CE.NY398/R) Twilight on a Canal, Devonshire (61x96cm-24x38in) init.

SAUNDERS, Norman (1906-1988) American
£730	$1300	(2-Nov-91 IH.NY194/R) Roping a bull (76x94cm-30x37in) s.
£478	*$850*	*(2-May-92 IH.NY121/R) Batman confronts villain (8x13cm-3x5in) gouache*

SAURA, Antonio (1930-) Spanish
£1667	$3017	(19-May-92 CH.AM315) A face (26x20cm-10x8in) s.d.1977 verso acrylic (D.FL 5500)
£23000	$41860	(29-May-92 C452/R) Retrato (60x73cm-24x29in) s.indis.i.d.61
£26612	$47369	(30-Nov-91 FB.P17/R) Autoportrait (65x81cm-26x32in) s.d.56 (F.FR 260000)
£36000	$65520	(29-May-92 C463/R) Noa (129x97cm-51x38in) s.d.59 s.i.d.verso
£40223	$72000	(13-Nov-91 CH.NY101/R) Untitled (160x129cm-63x51in)
£55000	$100100	(29-May-92 C453/R) Mademoiselle Tamara (161x129cm-63x51in) s.d.67
£831	*$1437*	*(26-Mar-92 DUR.M981/R) Cabezas (25x36cm-10x14in) s.d.1968verso ink dr (S.P 150000)*
£884	*$1574*	*(21-Jan-92 DUR.M44/R) Rostro sobre manuscrito (59x34cm-23x13in) s. ink (S.P 160000)*
£2313	*$4025*	*(18-Sep-91 KH.K41/R) Composition (30x27cm-12x11in) s.d.1879verso mixed media acrylic double-sided (D.KR 26000)*
£6857	*$12000*	*(25-Feb-92 SY.NY138/R) Composition (76x102cm-30x40in) s.d.66 gouache ink*
£8199	*$13938*	*(22-Oct-91 DUR.M99/R) Auto de fe (30x46cm-12x18in) s.d.89 s.i.d.verso mixed media (S.P 1500000)*
£8571	*$15000*	*(25-Feb-92 SY.NY130/R) Untitled (76x102cm-30x40in) s.d.66 gouache ink*
£8755	*$15584*	*(29-Oct-91 BRO.B334/R) Cuatro temas one s.d.59 three s.d.60 mixed media four joined (S.P 1600000)*
£22118	*$41581*	*(17-Dec-91 BRO.B393/R) Cocktail party (62x90cm-24x35in) s.d.62 mixed media (S.P 4000000)*

AURFELT, Leonard (19th C) French
£750 $1365   (10-Dec-91 SWS126) Le Theatre Tabarin (61x31cm-24x12in) s. panel

AUTER, Georg (19/20th C) German
£2500 $4325   (4-Oct-91 C100/R) Resurrection or Der Ruf zum Licht und Leben
       (163x136cm-64x54in) s.d.08 s.i.stretcher

AUTIN, Rene (1881-1968) French
£1387 $2386   (4-Mar-92 AT.P201) Neige sur la Risle a Pont-Audemer (65x92cm-26x36in)
       s.d.1930 i.verso (F.FR 13500)
£2294 $4266   (21-Jun-92 LT.P72 b/R) Vapeur sur la Seine (46x55cm-18x22in) s.
       (F.FR 22500)

AUTS, D (17th C) Dutch
£6098 $10610   (15-Apr-92 CB.P5/R) Nature morte aux fruits sur un entablement
       (41x35cm-16x14in) (F.FR 60000)

AUTS, Dirck (17th C) ?
£5000 $8750   (31-Mar-92 PH66/R) Still life with bird on plate with oysters and crab,
       grapes and wine, on draped stone ledge (42x38cm-17x15in) panel

AUVAGE, Arsene (19th C) French
£862 $1500   (11-Sep-91 D.NY72) Young child with hoop on country lane
       (74x53cm-29x21in) init.

AUVAGE, P (18/19th C) French/Flemish
£1800 $3096   (15-Oct-91 CSK616/R) A girl feeding birds in a kitchen (33x24cm-13x9in)
       s.

AUVAGE, Pieter Joseph (school) (1744-1818) Flemish
£3229 $5554   (16-Oct-91 AT.P133/R) Motifs d'amours entourant des cassolettes de
       guirlandes de fleurs (65x120cm-26x47in) four semi-circle (F.FR 32000)

AUVAGEOT, Charles Theodore (1826-1883) French
£510 $948   (17-Jun-92 I.N107) Bord de riviere (22x27cm-9x11in) s. panel (F.FR 5000)

AUZAY, Adrien Jacques (1841-1928) French
£1844 $3300   (14-Nov-91 GRO.B60/R) Houseboat (33x51cm-13x20in) s. panel

AVAGE, Anne (1896-1971) Canadian
£814 $1507   (9-Jun-92 FB.M39/R) At Lake Wonish, Quebec (30x41cm-12x16in) board
       double-sided (C.D 1800)
£1393 $2480   (26-Nov-91 JOY.T95/R) Little apple tree, pasture, Lake Wonish
       (30x35cm-12x14in) s. panel (C.D 2800)
£1553 $2826   (26-May-92 JOY.T137/R) Metis along lower St. Lawrence (30x35cm-12x14in)
       s. panel (C.D 3400)
£1791 $3188   (26-Nov-91 JOY.T191/R) House at Cape a L'Aigle (30x35cm-12x14in) s. panel
       (C.D 3600)
£1826 $3324   (26-May-92 JOY.T35/R) House in Laurentians, winter, Sixteen Island Lake
       (40x45cm-16x18in) s. panel double-sided (C.D 4000)
£2189 $3897   (25-Nov-91 W.T1572/R) Evening (66x79cm-26x31in) s. i.verso (C.D 4400)

AVAGE, Cedric (1901-1969) New Zealander
£525 $950   (4-Dec-91 DS.W48) Boats on the wind (49x59cm-19x23in) s. (NZ.D 1700)
£537 $962   (6-May-92 DS.W51) Boats under trees (49x59cm-19x23in) s. (NZ.D 1800)
£597 $1069   (6-May-92 DS.W92) Afternoon shadows (43x58cm-17x23in) s. i.verso
       (NZ.D 2000)
£716 $1282   (6-May-92 DS.W91) Cafe, Sitges, Spain (39x48cm-15x19in) s. i.verso
       (NZ.D 2400)
£1235 $2235   (4-Dec-91 DS.W65) Landscape with stream (44x54cm-17x21in) s. (NZ.D 4000)
£617   *$1117*   *(4-Dec-91 DS.W49) The beach market (51x63cm-20x25in) s. W/C (NZ.D 2000)*
£1065   *$1779*   *(21-Aug-91 DS.W16) Castle of Rhodes (45x61cm-18x24in) s. W/C (NZ.D 3100)*

AVAGE, Eugene (1883-1978) American
£939 $1700   (24-May-92 LIT.L277) Beach scene (74x74cm-29x29in) s.d.45

AVARY, Robert (1920-) French
£1027 $1848   (22-Nov-91 ZZ.F82) Notre Dame de Paris (73x60cm-29x24in) s. (F.FR 10000)

AVELIEVA, Valentina (1938-) Russian
£655 $1147   (24-Sep-91 ARC.P202/R) Les dernieres nouvelles (122x73cm-48x29in) s.
       (F.FR 6500)

AVERY, Hans (attrib) (1597-1654) Dutch
£1481 $2652   (12-Nov-91 SY.AM121/R) Horses and bull in wood (34x43cm-13x17in) panel
       (D.FL 4800)
£1571 $3000   (16-Jul-92 SY.NY120/R) Dutch shipping in rough water off a coast
       (35x50cm-14x20in) panel

AVERY, Roeland (1576-1639) Dutch
£6000 $10680   (1-Nov-91 C137/R) Cow, deer, goats, macaws, herons and sheep by
       waterfall, castle beyond (32x43cm-13x17in) with sig.d.1623 panel
£34000 $60520   (1-Nov-91 C134/R) Rocky coastline with fishermen unloading catch on
       beach, rainclouds in sky, sun breaking through (49cm-19ins circular)
       panel

SAVERY, Roeland (attrib) (1576-1639) Dutch
£5000 $9600   (10-Jul-92 C117/R) Extensive mountainous landscape with hunting party on forest path (32x42cm-13x17in) with sig.d.1613 copper

SAVERYS, Albert (1886-1964) Belgian
£4010 $6817   (22-Oct-91 C.A280/R) Winter on the Leie (50x60cm-20x24in) s. panel (B.FR 240000)
£8278 $14983   (23-May-92 KV.L488/R) Orchard in winter (80x100cm-31x39in) s.d.62 (B.FR 500000)
£8278 $14983   (23-May-92 KV.L485/R) Winter on the Leie (60x87cm-24x34in) s.d.59 (B.FR 500000)
£11000 $18920   (12-Oct-91 KV.L462/R) Leie landscape (67x73cm-26x29in) s. (B.FR 660000)
£13594 $23246   (21-Mar-92 KV.L460/R) Still life of fish on a table (126x136cm-50x54in) s. (B.FR 800000)
£13687 $24773   (7-Dec-91 KV.L399/R) Beside the Leie (45x55cm-18x22in) s. (B.FR 800000)
£17515 $30826   (7-Apr-92 C.A205/R) Still life of fish (130x160cm-51x63in) s. (B.FR 1050000)
£2500 $4300   (12-Oct-91 KV.L263) Zuiders beach scene (48x68cm-19x27in) s. W/C (B.FR 150000)

SAVIGNAC, R (?) French
£3081 $5176   (27-Aug-91 RAS.K174/R) Gladiolus and flox in vase (92x72cm-36x28in) s. (D.KR 35000)

SAVIN, Maurice (1894-1973) French
£520 $998   (7-Jul-92 ARC.P96) Bouquet de fleurs (92x73cm-36x29in) s. (F.FR 5000)
£2062 $3567   (23-Mar-92 CC.P13) Femme a la robe rouge (55x46cm-22x18in) s. (F.FR 20000)
£8745 $15828   (6-Dec-91 GL.P198/R) Les habitues du bar (92x65cm-36x26in) s. (F.FR 85000)

SAVINI, Alfonso (1836-1908) Italian
£2000 $3620   (21-May-92 CSK279/R) New baby (29x42cm-11x17in) s. panel
£3058 $5443   (30-Oct-91 CH.AM83/R) Steeling a kiss (33x43cm-13x17in) s. panel (D.FL 10000)

SAVINIO, Alberto (1891-1952) Italian
£29509 $52525   (29-Apr-92 F.F293/R) Composizione (24x31cm-9x12in) s. tempera cardboard (I.L 65000000)
£136612 $250000   (12-May-92 CH.NY133/R) Les collegians (65x54cm-26x21in) s.d.1929
£2531 $4582   (21-May-92 F.M252/R) Il longevo (25x17cm-10x7in) s.i.d.1948 pencil (I.L 5600000)

SAVINIO, Ruggero (1934-) Italian
£998 $1826   (12-May-92 F.R149) Distanza dal paesaggio n.15 (49x40cm-19x16in) d.1972/73 panel (I.L 2200000)
£1179 $2158   (12-May-92 F.R111) Distanza dal paesaggio (50x40cm-20x16in) d.1973 panel (I.L 2600000)

SAVINOV, Gleb (1915-) Russian
£507 $917   (20-May-92 ARC.P66) Les jasmins (63x56cm-25x22in) s. (F.FR 5000)
£510 $948   (17-Jun-92 ARC.P119/R) Dans le jardin (81x60cm-32x24in) s. (F.FR 5000)
£709 $1284   (20-May-92 ARC.P64/R) Au bord de la mer (32x49cm-13x19in) s. (F.FR 7000)
£795 $1479   (17-Jun-92 ARC.P120/R) La datcha (46x67cm-18x26in) s. (F.FR 7800)
£819 $1458   (25-Nov-91 ARC.P112/R) Le lac (128x96cm-50x38in) s. (F.FR 8000)
£870 $1549   (25-Nov-91 ARC.P108/R) La fille au piano (84x65cm-33x26in) s. (F.FR 8500)
£1146 $2041   (25-Nov-91 ARC.P109/R) Le jardin fleuri (79x61cm-31x24in) s. (F.FR 11200)
£1165 $2109   (20-May-92 ARC.P65/R) La place de Vatslav, Prague (69x85cm-27x33in) s. (F.FR 11500)

SAVIO, John (1902-1938) Scandinavian
£701 $1219   (14-Sep-91 BU.O316) Wooded landscape with tarn (35x49cm-14x19in) s. W/C (N.KR 8000)

SAVONANZI, Emilio (1580-1660) Italian
£70994 $129209   (26-May-92 FB.P8/R) Le Sacrifice d'Isaac (153x118cm-60x46in) (F.FR 700000)

SAVOSTIANOV, Fiodor (1924-) Russian
£756 $1323   (24-Sep-91 ARC.P105/R) Dans les haltes herbes (69x84cm-27x33in) s. (F.FR 7500)
£773 $1322   (13-Mar-92 ARC.P23/R) L'ete a la campagne (69x89cm-27x35in) s. (F.FR 7500)
£866 $1612   (17-Jun-92 ARC.P102/R) Le bois pour la cheminee (60x80cm-24x31in) s. (F.FR 8500)
£1937 $3602   (17-Jun-92 ARC.P104/R) Vacances d'ete (109x84cm-43x33in) s. (F.FR 19000)
£2067 $3616   (24-Sep-91 ARC.P104/R) Rivalite (109x101cm-43x40in) s. (F.FR 20500)

SAVRASOV, Aleksei Kondratievitch (1830-1897) Russian
£1579 $2843   (19-Nov-91 RAS.K369) Russian village (49x74cm-19x29in) s.d.1884 (D.KR 17500)

SAVTCHENKOVA, Maria (1917-) Russian
£563 $1002   (25-Nov-91 ARC.P69) Fillette a la table (33x50cm-13x20in) s. board (F.FR 5500)

SAVTCHENKOVA, Maria (1917-) Russian-cont.

£594	$1057	(25-Nov-91 ARC.P70) Au travail (48x35cm-19x14in) s. board (F.FR 5800)
£768	$1366	(25-Nov-91 ARC.P67/R) Jeune fille au soleil (33x24cm-13x9in) s. (F.FR 7500)
£809	$1439	(25-Nov-91 ARC.P66/R) Au jardin (100x70cm-39x28in) s. (F.FR 7900)

SAWREY, Hugh (1923-) Australian

£502	$879	(23-Sep-91 AAA.S160) Farriers cottage (20x31cm-8x12in) s. board (A.D 1100)
£812	$1470	(2-Dec-91 AAA.S81) The horse catcher (19x19cm-7x7in) s. board (A.D 1900)
£913	$1598	(23-Sep-91 AAA.S155) White cocky (30x40cm-12x16in) s. (A.D 2000)
£1156	$1976	(16-Mar-92 MGS.S89) Stingey Jones (29x34cm-11x13in) s. (A.D 2600)
£1172	$2238	(29-Jun-92 AAA.S81) Charlie Peacock and his pack horse (30x35cm-12x14in) s. board (A.D 3000)
£1200	$2052	(17-Mar-92 JRL.S54) Mooraberrie Pack-horses (25x30cm-10x12in) s. (A.D 2700)
£1674	$3013	(24-Nov-91 SY.S482) Sting Jones' woolies (49x59cm-19x23in) s. i.verso (A.D 3800)
£1709	$3043	(27-Apr-92 J.M79) Aces coming up (50x60cm-20x24in) s. (A.D 4000)
£1747	$3057	(30-Mar-92 AAA.S86) Travelling mob (51x61cm-20x24in) s. (A.D 4000)
£1762	$3137	(26-Nov-91 J.M261) Artist's camp (48x58cm-19x23in) s. board (A.D 4000)
£1875	$3581	(29-Jun-92 AAA.S152) The mud crabbers (50x61cm-20x24in) s. board (A.D 4800)
£1923	$3423	(27-Apr-92 J.M116/R) The stockman (120x135cm-47x53in) s. board (A.D 4500)
£1953	$3730	(29-Jun-92 AAA.S73) The Boulia Picnic Races (51x61cm-20x24in) s. board (A.D 5000)
£2030	$3674	(2-Dec-91 AAA.S140/R) Smithy's Wheat Farm (50x60cm-20x24in) s. board (A.D 4750)
£2511	$4395	(23-Sep-91 AAA.S163) Blackjack (51x61cm-20x24in) s. (A.D 5500)
£2643	$4705	(26-Nov-91 J.M192/R) Getting sheep for missus (74x99cm-29x39in) s. board (A.D 6000)
£2968	$5194	(23-Sep-91 AAA.S138) Packing nags (51x61cm-20x24in) s. (A.D 6500)
£3819	$6569	(14-Oct-91 MGS.S201) The rogue packhorse, Monkira Station (60x75cm-24x30in) s. (A.D 8250)
£3930	$6878	(30-Mar-92 AAA.S133) Cattlemen by Heifer Creek (76x102cm-30x40in) s. (A.D 9000)
£4487	$8122	(2-Dec-91 AAA.S129) The holdup (76x101cm-30x40in) s. (A.D 10500)
£6008	$11475	(21-Jul-92 JRL.S159/R) Smith's sawmill (148x198cm-58x78in) s. (A.D 15500)
£7752	$14806	(21-Jul-92 JRL.S161/R) Binde Banjo (148x198cm-58x78in) s. sold with print (A.D 20000)

SAWYER, Amy (19th C) British

| £1600 | $2864 | (14-Jan-92 SWS245/R) Down in the valley where the daisies grow (19x25cm-7x10in) s. panel |

SAWYER, Clifton Howard (1896-1966) American

| £737 | $1400 | (24-Jun-92 B.SF6341/R) Verbena (46x56cm-18x22in) s.d.63 |

SAWYER, Helen (1900-) American

| £1844 | $3300 | (14-Nov-91 GRO.B177/R) In studio - self-portrait (81x71cm-32x28in) s. |

SAWYER, Wells M (1863-1961) American

| £575 | $1000 | (15-Sep-91 JRB.C114/R) Over New York roofs (41x51cm-16x20in) s. masonite |

SAY, Frederick Richard (attrib) (c.1827-1860) British

| £1685 | $3000 | (30-Oct-91 D.NY56) Portrait of two brothers with dog (53x43cm-21x17in) |

SAY, Frederick Richard (circle) (c.1827-1860) British

| £2600 | $4992 | (9-Jul-92 B90) Portrait of lady, seated with daughter beside her holding shoe (77x63cm-30x25in) |

SAYERS, Reuben (1815-1888) British

| £720 | $1238 | (3-Mar-92 SWS1634/R) Maternal Love (29x39cm-11x15in) s.i.d.1849verso |

SAYMOUR, Sam (19/20th C) ?

| £928 | $1614 | (17-Sep-91 FN.S2521) Still life of flowers in vase on table with bird's nest (55x45cm-22x18in) s. panel (DM 2700) |

SAYRE, F Grayson (1879-1938) American

| £562 | $1000 | (26-Nov-91 MOR.P110 a) Eucalyptus landscape (25x36cm-10x14in) s. gouache |

SCACCIATI, Andrea (1642-1704) Italian

| £9784 | $18393 | (18-Dec-91 AT.P141/R) Corbeille de fleurs et noisettes. Corbeille de fleurs et caroubes (43cm-17ins circular) wood pair (F.FR 95000) |
| £16227 | $28560 | (10-Apr-92 AT.P32/R) Nature morte aux perroquets et vase de Chine (85x115cm-33x45in) (F.FR 160000) |

SCACCIATI, Andrea (attrib) (1642-1704) Italian

| £11481 | $20781 | (19-May-92 GF.L2096/R) Still lifes of flowers (65x50cm-26x20in) pair (S.FR 31000) |
| £28000 | $48720 | (15-Apr-92 C46/R) Lilies, roses and other flowers in sculpted urn on stone ledge (100x80cm-39x31in) |

SCACCIATI, Pietro Neri (style) (?) Italian
£5000 $9600   (8-Jul-92 S272/R) Two turkeys, chicks in basket and fruit
                      (66x78cm-26x31in)

SCAFFAI, Luigi (1837-?) Italian
£1724 $3000   (13-Sep-91 S.W2857) Figures in interior (23x18cm-9x7in) s. panel
£2053 $3900   (26-Jun-92 WOL.C438/R) The bashful maid (43x30cm-17x12in) s. panel
£9000 $15930   (14-Feb-92 C99/R) The doctor's visit (65x85cm-26x33in) s.

SCALBERT, Jules (1851-?) French
£995 $1842   (9-Jun-92 FB.M188) Les baigneuses (27x21cm-11x8in) s. board (C.D 2200)
£3911 $7000   (16-Nov-91 WOL.C279/R) Satyr and nymphs (81x66cm-32x26in) s.
£8242 $15000   (28-May-92 SY.NY96/R) Les baigneuses (72x100cm-28x39in) s.
£10465 $18000   (17-Oct-91 SY.NY110/R) Hommage a Louis Pasteur (128x166cm-50x65in) s.

SCALI, Vincent (1956-) French
£1644 $3141   (30-Jun-92 ZZ.F38/R) Composition (192x171cm-76x67in) s.d.1991verso paper
                      laid down on canvas (F.FR 16000)

SCANAVINO, Emilio (1922-1986) Italian
£623 $1084   (17-Sep-91 RAS.K166/R) Pro Memoria I (60x50cm-24x20in) s. d.1962-63verso
                      cardboard on canvas (D.KR 7000)
£1668 $2969   (29-Nov-91 F.F45/R) Composizione (44x46cm-17x18in) s. acrylic cardboard
                      on panel (I.L 3600000)
£1766 $3197   (3-Dec-91 F.R167) Senza titolo (50x60cm-20x24in) s. board on canvas
                      (I.L 3800000)
£1903 $3577   (19-Dec-91 F.M103/R) Composizione (52x50cm-20x20in) s. (I.L 4100000)
£2989 $5351   (14-Nov-91 F.M33/R) Composizione (68x92cm-27x36in) s. acrylic panel
                      (I.L 6500000)
£3178 $5657   (29-Apr-92 F.F214) Il nodo (60x60cm-24x24in) s. s.i.verso (I.L 7000000)
£3945 $7416   (19-Dec-91 F.M125/R) Costruzione (65x44cm-26x17in) s. s.i.verso
                      (I.L 8500000)
£4339 $7551   (14-Apr-92 F.M139/R) Vitalita (40x50cm-16x20in) s. s.i.d.1958verso
                      (I.L 9500000)
£4880 $8833   (3-Dec-91 F.R241/R) Tramatura (60x60cm-24x24in) s. s.i.d.1975verso
                      (I.L 10500000)
£5253 $9140   (14-Apr-92 F.M258/R) Composizione (50x70cm-20x28in) s.d.1957
                      (I.L 11500000)
£1188   *$2258*   *(23-Jun-92 F.M13/R) Situazione 2 (45x55cm-18x22in) s. mixed media*
                      cardboard (I.L 2600000)

SCANLAN, Robert Richard (?-1876) British
£5429 $9500   (20-Feb-92 SY.NY264/R) Donneybrooke fair (103x142cm-41x56in)
£398   *$697*   *(17-Feb-92 AD.D18) Young man hunting (23x33cm-9x13in) s.d.1861 W/C*
                      (E.P 430)

SCANNEL, Edith M S (fl.1880-1921) British
£520 $894   (3-Mar-92 AG267) Young girl holding yellow bird (43cm-17ins circular)
                      s.i.verso

SCARBOROUGH, Frank William (fl.1896-1939) British
£460 $791   (3-Mar-92 AG188) Fishing boats at harbour mouth (49x33cm-19x13in) s. W/C
£460 $851   (11-Jun-92 CSK61/R) Sunset, Pool of London (23x18cm-9x7in) s.i. pencil
                      W/C
£460 $851   (11-Jun-92 CSK60) Off Wapping, London (23x18cm-9x7in) s.i. pencil W/C
£1450 $2596   (5-May-92 SWS201/R) Sunrise, Lowestoft. Sunset, Pittenweem
                      (23x34cm-9x13in) s. W/C bodycol. pair
£1450 $2465   (22-Oct-91 SWS147/R) Tower Bridge, London (28x59cm-11x23in) s.i. W/C
                      gouache over pencil
£1500 $2550   (22-Oct-91 SWS146/R) Tower Bridge, London. Greenwich Reach, London
                      (34x24cm-13x9in) s.i. W/C over pencil htd bodycol pair
£3000 $5400   (9-Jan-92 B259/R) The Pool of London, shipping before Tower Bridge.
                      Sunset, Port of London (17x51cm-7x20in) s. W/C pair

SCARBOROUGH, Frederick W (fl.1896-1939) British
£480   *$835*   *(9-Sep-91 PH139) Robin Hood's Bay (18x52cm-7x20in) s. W/C over pencil*
£732   *$1324*   *(3-Dec-91 R.T181/R) London Bridge (25x35cm-10x14in) s.i. W/C bodycol*
                      (C.D 1500)
£1700   *$2975*   *(23-Sep-91 PHB14/R) Unloading off Wapping, Port of London. Fishing boats*
                      off a jetty (49x33cm-19x13in) s.i. W/C pair

SCARCELLINO, Ippolito (1551-1620) Italian
£10000 $19200   (8-Jul-92 S315/R) Mars and Venus (49x40cm-19x16in)

SCARCELLINO, Ippolito (circle) (1551-1620) Italian
£1800 $3204   (29-Oct-91 PH71/R) The Holy Family with St Clare (73x63cm-29x25in)
£1800 $3276   (10-Dec-91 PH236/R) Holy Family with St. Dominic (29x21cm-11x8in)

SCARCELLINO, Ippolito (style) (1551-1620) Italian
£1105 $2000   (20-May-92 D.NY79) Jesus riding into Jerusalem (25x53cm-10x21in)
£1200 $2160   (21-Nov-91 C37) Three scenes from the life of St Anthony of Padua
                      (42x32cm-17x13in) panel
£2100 $3843   (12-May-92 SWS699/R) Adoration of Magi (41x32cm-16x13in) panel

SCARFE, Gerald (1936-) British
£2500 $4275   *(11-Mar-92 S171/R) Turning point (84x59cm-33x23in) s.i. pen*
£3000 $5130   *(11-Mar-92 S173/R) New slim-line Luciano (84x59cm-33x23in) s.i. pen*
£3200 $5472   *(11-Mar-92 S172/R) Pig in middle (84x59cm-33x23in) s.i. pen wash*

SCARLETT, Rolph (1884-1984) American
£1622 $3000   *(10-Jun-92 CE.NY608/R) Divided (92x122cm-36x48in) s. i.stretcher*
£2632 $4500   *(12-Mar-92 CH.NY253/R) Geometric abstraction (102x121cm-40x48in) s.*
£1064 $2000   *(18-Dec-91 SY.NY437/R) Abstract composition (40x48cm-16x19in) s. gouache*
                ink graphite
£1170 $2200   *(18-Dec-91 SY.NY436/R) Abstract composition (45x45cm-18x18in) s. gouache*
                ink graphitew

SCARLETTI, E G (19/20th C) ?
£750 $1343   *(14-Nov-91 CSK349) Roman beauty (51x76cm-20x30in) s.d.1900*

SCARPA, Gino (1924-) Italian
£829 $1500   *(19-May-92 CE.NY280) Chi deve venire (53x64cm-21x25in) s.d.1956 panel*

SCARPITTA, Salvatore (1919-) American
£3486 $6310   *(3-Dec-91 F.R111/R) Composizione (104x71cm-41x28in) s.d.1956 tempera*
                paper on canvas (I.L 7500000)

SCARVELLI (?) Italian
£725 $1341   *(8-Jun-92 CH.R628) Vicolo orientale (35x24cm-14x9in) s. W/C (I.L 1600000)*
£2500 $4450   *(27-Nov-91 B36/R) The citadel Corfu. Pontikonissi, Corfu (18x29cm-7x11in)*
                s. W/C pair

SCARVELLI, S (19/20th C) Greek
£500 $890   *(26-Nov-91 PH180) Feluccas and steamboats on the Nile (26x43cm-10x17in)*
                s. W/C over pencil
£1500 $2790   *(18-Jun-92 B11/R) The Citadel, Corfu. Pontikonissi, Corfu*
                (17x29cm-7x11in) s. W/C pair
£2400 $4080   *(23-Oct-91 S166/R) Fisherman of the Citadel, Corfu (26x43cm-10x17in) s.*
                W/C over pencil
£3000 $5100   *(23-Oct-91 S167/R) Corfu (26x44cm-10x17in) s. W/C over pencil*
£6500 $11050   *(23-Oct-91 S254/R) Gateway of mosque. Near Eastern street*
                (38x21cm-15x8in) s. W/C over pencil pair sold with Nile view

SCATIZZI, Sergio (1918-) Italian
£880 $1567   *(29-Nov-91 F.F99) Natura morta con uva e frutti (50x72cm-20x28in) s.*
                s.i.d.1982 board (I.L 1900000)
£1142 $1987   *(14-Apr-92 F.M164/R) Paesaggio (71x55cm-28x22in) s. cardboard*
                (I.L 2500000)
£1362 $2424   *(29-Apr-92 F.F100) Natura morta (36x51cm-14x20in) s. s.i.d.1967 board*
                (I.L 3000000)
£1622 $2887   *(29-Nov-91 F.F104/R) Paesaggio a Valdinievole (60x80cm-24x31in) s.*
                s.i.d.1946/47verso (I.L 3500000)
£1634 $2909   *(29-Apr-92 F.F90) Laguna (47x63cm-19x25in) s. s.i.d.1950verso board*
                (I.L 3600000)
£1634 $2909   *(29-Apr-92 F.F94/R) Fiori (50x60cm-20x24in) s. (I.L 3600000)*
£772 $1374   *(29-Apr-92 F.F22/R) Nudino. Natura morta (29x29cm-11x11in) s.d.1955*
                s.verso mixed media cardboard pair (I.L 1700000)

SCAUFLAIRE, Edgar (1893-1960) Belgian
£2039 $3487   *(21-Mar-92 KV.L259/R) Les Forains (47x63cm-19x25in) s.d.1928 pastel*
                (B.FR 120000)

SCHAAP, Hendrik (1878-1955) Dutch
£520 $925   *(29-Oct-91 VN.R263/R) View of Rotterdam harbour (39x59cm-15x23in) s.*
                (D.FL 1700)

SCHAAR, Sipke van der (1879-1961) Dutch
£917 $1624   *(5-Nov-91 SY.AM145/R) Figures in oasis (94x140cm-37x55in) s. (D.FL 3000)*

SCHABRATZKY, Josef (fl.1880-1919) Austrian
£488 $830   *(24-Oct-91 D.V227/R) View of Maria Zell (20x15cm-8x6in) s.i.d.1911 W/C*
                (A.S 10000)

SCHACHNER, Therese (1890-C.1930) Austrian
£702 $1270   *(5-Dec-91 D.V123) Rising thunderstorm (29x50cm-11x20in) s. (A.S 14000)*

SCHACK, Sophus (1811-1864) Danish
£3081 $5176   *(27-Aug-91 RAS.K165/R) The artist and his girlfriend (100x75cm-39x30in)*
                s.d.1853 (D.KR 35000)

SCHAD, Christian (1894-1982) German
£8000 $15280   *(30-Jun-92 C159/R) Halbakt (30x22cm-12x9in) s.d.30 pencil col.crayons*

SCHADE, Karl Martin (1862-1954) Austrian
£781 $1351   *(3-Oct-91 D.V40) Flowering heath (80x110cm-31x43in) s. i.verso*
                (A.S 16000)

SCHADOW, Gottfried (1764-1850) German
£845 $1530   *(6-Dec-91 GB.B6000/R) The three graces (18x13cm-7x5in) pen (DM 2400)*

SCHADOW, Wilhelm von (1788-1862) German
£853 $1544   (22-May-92 GB.B6048) Shepherd finding sheep. Christ with penitent sinner and angels (23x22cm-9x9in) pencil wash htd white gold paper on board pair (DM 2500)
£2676 $4844   (6-Dec-91 GB.B6004/R) Study of male nude (28x20cm-11x8in) i. pencil (DM 7600)

SCHAEFELS, Hendrik Frans (1827-1904) Belgian
£1100 $2046   (16-Jun-92 PH41/R) Buying fabric (38x31cm-15x12in) s.d.1880
£2934 $4900   (25-Aug-91 LIT.L196) Interior scene of man playing lute (64x48cm-25x19in) s.d.1869 panel

SCHAEFELS, Lucas (1824-1885) Belgian
£2035 $3500   (15-Oct-91 CE.NY125/R) Still life with fruit and dead hare (124x85cm-49x33in) s.d.1871
£8989 $16000   (22-Jan-92 SY.NY452/R) Still life with Chinese vase. Still life with goldfish bowl (86x69cm-34x27in) one s. s.d.1883 verso one s.d.1883 verso pair

SCHAEFER, Carl Fellman (1903-) Canadian
£1000 $1770   (6-Nov-91 SY.T178/R) Lemon and gourds (29x39cm-11x15in) s.d.51 board (C.D 2000)
£597 $1063   (25-Nov-91 W.T1594) Wheatfield from the pinnacle (28x38cm-11x15in) s.i.d.56verso W/C (C.D 1200)
£642 $1175   (1-Jun-92 W.T1085) On the Huron Road near Waterloo County (30x41cm-12x16in) s.d.72 i.verso W/C (C.D 1400)
£642 $1175   (1-Jun-92 W.T1126) On the Kennisis River, Haliburton (28x38cm-11x15in) s.i.d.69verso (C.D 1400)
£780 $1427   (1-Jun-92 W.T1115) Spring, Raven Lake, Haliburton (28x37cm-11x15in) s.d.72 i.verso W/C (C.D 1700)

SCHAEFFER, August (1833-1916) Austrian
£732 $1245   (24-Oct-91 D.V209/R) Spring landscape (34x47cm-13x19in) panel (A.S 15000)

SCHAEFFER, Henri (1900-1975) French
£509 $931   (17-May-92 T.B207) Entree de Port en Bretagne (46x61cm-18x24in) s. (F.FR 5000)
£550 $957   (19-Sep-91 B180) Parisian market (40x51cm-16x20in) s.

SCHAEFFER, Mead (1898-1980) American
£7303 $13000   (2-Nov-91 IH.NY93/R) People skiing through heavy snow (89x69cm-35x27in) s.

SCHAEP, Henri Adolphe (1826-1870) Dutch
£959 $1649   (8-Oct-91 ZEL.L1707/R) River landscape with figures in boat and town, evening (26x34cm-10x13in) s.d.1845 (DM 2800)

SCHAERER, Hans (1927-) Swiss
£9195 $15908   (23-Mar-92 AB.L94/R) Madonna framboise (113x89cm-44x35in) s.d.1972 oil objects pavatex (S.FR 24000)

SCHAFER, Frederick (1839-1927) American
£842 $1600   (24-Jun-92 B.SF6256/R) John Muir's Valley (76x131cm-30x52in) s.
£1184 $2250   (24-Jun-92 B.SF6254/R) Morning on Merced River, California (76x127cm-30x50in) s.
£1579 $3000   (24-Jun-92 B.SF6253/R) On Slate Creek, California (76x127cm-30x50in) s.

SCHAFER, Henry (19th C) British/French
£500 $955   (30-Jun-92 SWS1514) Rue de la Pucelle, Rouen, Normandy (39x29cm-15x11in) s.d.1890 s.i.verso
£700 $1246   (28-Nov-91 B78) Antwerp, Belgium (25x20cm-10x8in) s.i.verso
£700 $1253   (5-May-92 SWS400/R) Old Gateway, Huy, Belgium (39x30cm-15x12in) s.i.verso
£700 $1211   (24-Mar-92 PHC386/R) Market Square, Fecamp, Normandy (45x35cm-18x14in) s.i.
£700 $1204   (8-Oct-91 PH94) Nuremberg, Germany (41x30cm-16x12in) s.d.1890 i.verso
£800 $1488   (18-Jun-92 B60/R) Metz, Lorraine (38x28cm-15x11in) mono.d.1884
£850 $1479   (11-Sep-91 MMB316/R) Am Markt, Frankfort Am Main (41x30cm-16x12in) s.i.verso
£900 $1557   (24-Mar-92 PHC414) Figures in continental town scene (39x29cm-15x11in) mono.d.1885
£1300 $2327   (5-May-92 SWS389/R) Frankfort am Main, Germany. Honfleur, France (19x14cm-7x6in) s. s.i.verso pair
£2000 $3600   (19-Nov-91 PH90/R) St Maclou, Rouen, Normandy (61x51cm-24x20in) s. s.i.verso
£3300 $5610   (22-Oct-91 SWS264/R) Fecamp, Normandy. St. Pierre, Caen, Normandy (29x22cm-11x9in) s.d.80 s.i.verso pair
£420 $718   (18-Mar-92 CSK133) Fishermen by the Rock of Gibraltar (28x41cm-11x16in) s. pencil pen ink W/C htd.white
£520 $926   (28-Nov-91 CSK10) St Stephen's Cathedral, Vienna (61x46cm-24x18in) s.i. pencil W/C htd.white
£540 $961   (29-Oct-91 SWS465) Burgos Cathedral, Spain (62x44cm-24x17in) s.i. W/C over pencil htd white
£550 $946   (3-Mar-92 AG202) Berne, Switzerland (44x74cm-17x29in) mono.i. W/C

SCHAFER, Henry (19th C) British/French-cont.
£930 $1600   (15-Oct-91 CE.NY93/R) Louviers, Normandy (63x46cm-25x18in) s.i. W/C paperboard
£1400 $2408   (4-Mar-92 S212/R) Chapel of high altar, cathedral of Toledo, Spain. San Miguel, Xeres (61x44cm-24x17in) s.i. W/C pair

SCHAFER, Henry (attrib) (19th C) British/French
£600 $1050   (23-Sep-91 HS336) Abbeville - figures in market place with buildings and cathedral beyond (40x30cm-16x12in) s.d.1857 i.verso

SCHAFER, Henry (circle) (19th C) British/French
£2200 $4092   (17-Jun-92 B131/R) Continental street scene, with market sellers in foreground (85x66cm-33x26in) indist.s. pair

SCHAFER, Henry Thomas (19/20th C) British
£3371 $6000   (22-Jan-92 SY.NY461/R) Daisy chain. Ivy blossoms (58x29cm-23x11in) s.d.1886 pair
£395 $700   (9-Nov-91 W.W99/R) Street scene, Normandy (46x36cm-18x14in) s.i. W/C

SCHAFER, Herman (19th C) German
£2584 $4497   (13-Apr-92 SY.J252/R) Freiburg, Baden. Morlaix, Brittany (21x9cm-8x4in) mono.d.1883 board pair (SA.R 13000)

SCHAFFNER, Marcel (1931-) Swiss
£575 $994   (23-Mar-92 AB.L184/R) Untitled (60x42cm-24x17in) s.d.1987 gouache (S.FR 1500)
£996 $1723   (23-Mar-92 AB.L185/R) Untitled (62x86cm-24x34in) s.d.1985 gouache (S.FR 2600)
£1533 $2651   (23-Mar-92 AB.L188/R) Untitled (70x100cm-28x39in) d.1984/85 gouache grease chk (S.FR 4000)

SCHAGEN, Gerbrand Frederik van (1880-1968) Dutch
£795 $1415   (30-Oct-91 CH.AM27) Moored boats in canal, winter (24x31cm-9x12in) s. canvas on panel (D.FL 2600)
£917 $1633   (30-Oct-91 CH.AM28/R) River landscape with draw bridge (50x70cm-20x28in) s. (D.FL 3000)

SCHAIK, Hugo van (1872-1946) Dutch
£559 $968   (25-Mar-92 KM.K1397) Peasant woman and young boy on path in heath landscape (26x38cm-10x15in) s. (DM 1600)

SCHALCKE, Cornelis Simonsz van der (attrib) (1611-1671) Dutch
£1041 $1884   (19-May-92 AB.S4374/R) River Vecht breaking through dam, 1st October 16.. (25x34cm-10x13in) panel (S.KR 11000)

SCHALCKEN, Godfried (1643-1706) Dutch
£4115 $7819   (26-Jun-92 AT.P95/R) Portrait allegorique (18x15cm-7x6in) copper oval (F.FR 40000)
£10500 $20160   (7-Jul-92 PH85/R) Young girl teaching tricks to pet spaniel (21x16cm-8x6in) panel shaped top
£12000 $23040   (10-Jul-92 C136/R) Narcissus (42x34cm-17x13in) s.

SCHALCKEN, Godfried (circle) (1643-1706) Dutch
£1700 $3264   (10-Jul-92 C139/R) Portrait of lady, in blue dress (25x8cm-10x3in) copper inset panel with swags flowers

SCHALCKEN, Godfried (style) (1643-1706) Dutch
£925 $1767   (1-Jul-92 CD.P14) Portrait d'un geographe (27x20cm-11x8in) panel (F.FR 9000)
£990 $1723   (13-Sep-91 C108/R) Hermit writing by candlelight (38x30cm-15x12in) panel
£1685 $3000   (22-Jan-92 SY.NY146/R) Reading of lady's palm (84x69cm-33x27in)
£2400 $4200   (27-Feb-92 CSK191/R) Elderly man courting serving wench in cellar (48x37cm-19x15in) panel
£3000 $5460   (13-Dec-91 C160/R) Boy at table holding up candle to light pipe (24x18cm-9x7in) panel

SCHALL, Jean Frederic (1752-1825) French
£2947 $5600   (26-Jun-92 WOL.C414/R) The courtship (43x38cm-17x15in)
£7202 $13035   (5-Dec-91 SY.MO270/R) Scene galante dans un parc (37x30cm-15x12in) (F.FR 70000)
£18349 $34128   (18-Jun-92 SY.MO71/R) Le reveil de Psyche (77x123cm-30x48in) (F.FR 180000)
£26243 $47500   (22-May-92 SY.NY74/R) Lover listened to L'Amant Ecoute (25x22cm-10x9in) copper

SCHALL, Jean Frederic (attrib) (1752-1825) French
£1530 $2769   (20-May-92 CSC.P9) La jeune jardiniere (16x23cm-6x9in) (F.FR 15100)
£30896 $52832   (20-Mar-92 ZZ.F25/R) Les incroyables (120x52cm-47x20in) screen four parts (F.FR 300000)

SCHALL, Jean Frederic (circle) (1752-1825) French
£8939 $16000   (17-Jan-92 SY.NY147/R) A girl watering roses in a garden setting (39x30cm-15x12in)

SCHALL, Jean Frederic (studio) (1752-1825) French
£2539 $4494   (5-Nov-91 GF.L2078/R) The broken fan (30x25cm-12x10in) panel (S.FR 6500)

SCHALL, Lothar (20th C) ?
£2632 $4500   (13-Mar-92 FN.S2589/R) Untitled (172x200cm-68x79in) s. (DM 7500)

SCHAMBERG, Morton Livingston (1881-1918) American
£7143   *$13000*   *(28-May-92 CH.NY252/R) Composition (22x16cm-9x6in) pastel pencil*

SCHANTZ, Philip von (1928-) Swedish
£662 $1199   (19-May-92 AB.S5320/R) Still life with jug and knife (50x28cm-20x11in) s.d.52 (S.KR 7000)
£901 $1649   (13-May-92 BU.S185/R) Still life of jug (24x46cm-9x18in) s. (S.KR 9500)
£1920 $3437   *(16-Nov-91 FAL.M323/R) Vegetable (39x49cm-15x19in) s.d.1978 W/C (S.KR 20200)*

SCHANZ, Heinz (1927-) German
£2730 $4969   (25-May-92 WK.M1095/R) Head (75x60cm-30x24in) s.d.1958 s.d.verso egg tempera (DM 8000)
£3780 $6918   (2-Jun-92 L.K923/R) Head (64x50cm-25x20in) s.d.1961 egg tempera paper (DM 11000)
£7167 $13044   (25-May-92 WK.M1099/R) Head (90x89cm-35x35in) s.d.1960 egg tempera hessian (DM 21000)
£7167 $13044   (25-May-92 WK.M1097/R) Blue head figure (99x71cm-39x28in) s.d.1959verso egg oil tempera (DM 21000)
£7167 $13044   (25-May-92 WK.M1096/R) Female figure (98x85cm-39x33in) s.d.1959 s.d.verso egg tempera hessian (DM 21000)
£7509 $13666   (25-May-92 WK.M1098/R) Red head (93x76cm-37x30in) s.d.60 s.d.59/60verso egg tempera (DM 22000)
£8247 $15093   (2-Jun-92 L.K922/R) Untitled (136x112cm-54x44in) s.d.1959verso egg tempera hessian (DM 24000)
£683   *$1242*   *(25-May-92 WK.M1104) Composition (38x26cm-15x10in) s. col.wax crayon double-sided (DM 2000)*
£683   *$1242*   *(25-May-92 WK.M1105/R) Untitled (47x29cm-19x11in) s. indian ink brush (DM 2000)*
£853   *$1553*   *(25-May-92 WK.M1101/R) Composition (28x37cm-11x15in) s.d.1958 col.chk (DM 2500)*
£853   *$1553*   *(25-May-92 WK.M1102) Composition with figures (26x13cm-10x5in) s.d.1958 crayon board (DM 2500)*
£2218   *$4038*   *(25-May-92 WK.M1103) Composition (59x42cm-23x17in) s.d.1962 gouache paper on board (DM 6500)*

SCHARF, Kenny (1958-) American
£4190 $7500   (9-May-92 CE.NY222/R) Greenorite over blupoint (81x60cm-32x24in) s.i.d.84verso
£5028 $9000   (9-May-92 CE.NY225/R) The hero to the rescue (59x59cm-23x23in) s.i.d.84verso acrylic spray enamel panel
£5143 $9000   (27-Feb-92 CH.NY138/R) Gleem (94x119cm-37x47in) s.i.d.88verso acrylic oil plastic canvas
£18286 $32000   (27-Feb-92 CH.NY133/R) Elroy and Leroy (152x244cm-60x96in) s.i.d.82verso acrylic
£1220   *$2122*   *(14-Apr-92 CSC.P90) Je ne sais pas (46x61cm-18x24in) s.d.84 ink (F.FR 12000)*
£5143 $9000   (25-Feb-92 SY.NY252/R) Solsu n luis violetch (65x91cm-26x36in) s.i.d.84verso acrylic spray enamel canvas
£5714 $10000   (25-Feb-92 SY.NY254/R) Starring the star (122cm-48ins circular) s.i.d.85verso acrylic spray enamel canvas
£11173 $20000   (7-May-92 SY.NY224/R) In ecstasy (227x273cm-89x107in) s.d.82 stretcher acrylic spray paint canvas
£12849 $23000   (5-May-92 CH.NY181/R) Tune in, tune on, flip out (183x122cm-72x48in) s.d.83verso oil spray enamel canvas
£15896 $27500   (3-Oct-91 SY.NY179 a/R) Pikki Taki Chop (222x183cm-87x72in) s.i.d.84-85verso acrylic enamel spray paint oil
£16760 $30000   (5-May-92 CH.NY185/R) Major blast (244x244cm-96x96in) s.i.d.84verso oil spray enamel canvas

SCHARFF, Erwin (1887-1955) German
£772   *$1389*   *(21-Nov-91 L.K433/R) Man with horses (36x51cm-14x20in) mono.d.1945 W/C (DM 2200)*

SCHARFF, William (1866-1959) Danish
£1112 $1935   (17-Sep-91 RAS.K675/R) Pine forest (62x107cm-24x42in) s. (D.KR 12500)
£3156 $5618   (25-Nov-91 BU.K48/R) Pine forest, autumn (160x225cm-63x89in) s.d.1939 (D.KR 35000)
£2725 $4768   (1-Apr-92 KH.K205/R) Sketch for exhibition poster (65x50cm-26x20in) s. W/C gouache (D.KR 30000)

SCHARL, Josef (1896-1954) German
£2105 $3789   (23-Nov-91 N.M276/R) Cow with calf (53x72cm-21x28in) s.d.1923 (DM 6000)
£683   *$1242*   *(30-May-92 VG.B945/R) Rows of trees and clouded sky (33x50cm-13x20in) s.d.1936 gouache (DM 2000)*
£699   *$1245*   *(26-Nov-91 KF.M1012) Male portrait (51x35cm-20x14in) s.d.1948 brush wash (DM 2000)*
£956   *$1739*   *(30-May-92 VG.B946/R) Portrait of melancholic male (51x30cm-20x12in) s.d.1949 gouache (DM 2800)*

SCHARL, Josef (1896-1954) German-cont.
£1024 $1863   (26-May-92 KF.M1231/R) Landscape (38x49cm-15x19in) s.d.1936 gouache (DM 3000)
£1053 $1895   (23-Nov-91 N.M278/R) Jungle people (37x50cm-15x20in) s.i.d.1936 gouache (DM 3000)
£1053 $1895   (23-Nov-91 N.M279/R) Portrait of gentleman (42x33cm-17x13in) s.d.1936 gouache (DM 3000)

SCHARP, Henri (19th C) ?
£1856 $3100   (20-Aug-91 RB.HY231/R) The refuge (61x81cm-24x32in) s.d.18 indist.

SCHARY, Saul (1904-1978) American
£9890 $18000   (28-May-92 CH.NY231/R) Pierrot (146x114cm-57x45in) s.d.29

SCHATZ, Manfred (20th C) German
£550 $1023   (20-Jun-92 BM.B960) Peasant with oxen (40x50cm-16x20in) s.d.55 i.verso panel (DM 1600)
£1394 $2537   (13-Dec-91 BM.B796) Flooded landscape with ducks, winter (60x80cm-24x31in) s. (DM 4000)
£1916 $3488   (13-Dec-91 BM.B794/R) Wooded moor landscape with pheasants (61x81cm-24x32in) s. (DM 5500)
£2439 $4439   (13-Dec-91 BM.B795/R) Hunted boars in snow covered wooded landscape (60x90cm-24x35in) s. (DM 7000)

SCHATZ, Otto Rudolf (1901-1961) Austrian
£1236 $2163   (19-Feb-92 D.V192/R) Reconstruction of Vienna (32x37cm-13x15in) mono. panel (A.S 25000)
£1367 $2364   (3-Oct-91 D.V232/R) Erzberg landscape (28x41cm-11x16in) mono. oil tempera board (A.S 28000)
£583 $1037   (28-Apr-92 D.V278/R) New York (44x59cm-17x23in) s. W/C (A.S 12000)
£631 $1123   (28-Apr-92 D.V277/R) St Stephan (28x36cm-11x14in) mono mixed media (A.S 13000)
£643 $1125   (19-Feb-92 D.V216/R) Geisselung (18x24cm-7x9in) mono. W/C (A.S 13000)
£728 $1296   (28-Apr-92 D.V280/R) Nude girl wearing hat (42x29cm-17x11in) mono mixed media (A.S 15000)
£777 $1383   (28-Apr-92 D.V279/R) New York (44x58cm-17x23in) s. W/C (A.S 16000)

SCHAUB, J Friedrich Wilhelm (fl.1776-1788) German
£563 $1020   (6-Dec-91 GB.B5600) Capriccio of ruins with figures and cattle s.i.d.1782 pen wash htd.white over chl (DM 1600)

SCHAUENBERG, Walter (1884-1943) Swiss
£494 $919   (19-Jun-92 ZOF.Z2071/R) Farmhouse in summer landscape (28x40cm-11x16in) s. board (S.FR 1300)
£494 $919   (19-Jun-92 ZOF.Z2072) Heiternplatz (40x60cm-16x24in) s.d. board (S.FR 1300)
£570 $1061   (19-Jun-92 ZOF.Z2073) Farmhouse in spring (20x28cm-8x11in) s. board (S.FR 1500)
£684 $1273   (19-Jun-92 ZOF.Z2074) Farmhouse in autumn landscape (28x40cm-11x16in) s. board (S.FR 1800)
£684 $1273   (19-Jun-92 ZOF.Z2070/R) Farmhouse in winter landscape (28x40cm-11x16in) s. board (S.FR 1800)

SCHAUENSTEIN-INDRA, Hedwig (1896-1988) Austrian
£491 $932   (25-Jun-92 D.V636/R) Das wilde Gamseck (46x52cm-18x20in) s.d.1928 i.verso (A.S 10000)

SCHAUFFELEIN, Hans Leonard (1480-1540) German
£15464 $26907   (18-Sep-91 N.M450/R) Resurection (74x82cm-29x32in) altar panel (DM 45000)

SCHAUFFELEIN, Hans Leonard (circle) (1480-1540) German
£2315 $4144   (14-Nov-91 CH.AM203/R) The Beheading of St Paul (134x60cm-53x24in) panel (D.FL 7500)

SCHAUMAN, Sigrid (1877-1979) Finnish
£1770 $3115   (12-Apr-92 HOR.H201) In the garden (31x23cm-12x9in) s. (F.M 14000)
£1811 $3224   (1-Dec-91 HOR.H203) Tolo sugar refinery (18x25cm-7x10in) s. (F.M 14000)
£2458 $4375   (1-Dec-91 HOR.H202) Soderlangvik farm (27x35cm-11x14in) s.d.1961 (F.M 19000)

SCHAUSS, Ferdinand (1832-1916) German
£2234 $3797   (25-Oct-91 BM.B820/R) Nude girl seated by stream holding bunch of field flowers (138x108cm-54x43in) s. (DM 6500)
£10989 $20000   (28-May-92 SY.NY61/R) Young Saint John the Baptist (157x126cm-62x50in) s.

SCHAWINSKY, Xanti (1904-1979) Italian
£1371 $2605   (23-Jun-92 F.M22/R) Composizione (70x60cm-28x24in) s.d.1974verso (I.L 3000000)
£2529 $4375   (23-Mar-92 AB.L170/R) Composition (30x30cm-12x12in) s.d.1961 (S.FR 6600)
£3158 $5684   (21-Nov-91 L.K434/R) Abstract composition (23x30cm-9x12in) s.d.1951 (DM 9000)
£4651 $8000   (12-Oct-91 SY.NY236/R) Double profile (61x46cm-24x18in) s. acrylic burlap
£4743 $8538   (22-Nov-91 EA.Z98) Hochhauser (48x48cm-19x19in) s.d.1961 acrylic pavatex (S.FR 12000)

SCHAWINSKY, Xanti (1904-1979) Italian-cont.
£3780 $6653   (10-Apr-92 KM.K532/R) Composition Sp 527 (57x50cm-22x20in)
  s.i.d.1977verso col.spray technique gauze panel (DM 11000)

SCHEBEK, Ferdinand (1875-1949) Austrian
£1565 $2801   (5-May-92 ZEL.L1524/R) Berlin lake with ducks in spring
  (79x119cm-31x47in) s.i.d.1942 (DM 4600)

SCHEDRIN, Sylvester Feodosievich (1791-1830) Russian
£22000 $39160   (28-Nov-91 S421/R) Bay of Naples (50x61cm-20x24in)

SCHEELE, Kurt (1905-) German
£1024 $1853   (23-May-92 GB.B7191) Dancing figure, Pulcinella by Stravinski
  (27x21cm-11x8in) s.i.d.36 W/C pen (DM 3000)

SCHEERES, Hendricus Johannes (1829-1864) Dutch
£1135 $2055   (19-May-92 AB.S4375/R) Interior with man resting (21x17cm-8x7in) s.d.1855
  panel (S.KR 12000)
£1333 $2413   (19-May-92 GF.L2200/R) Lady buying jewellery (21x17cm-8x7in) s. panel
  (S.FR 3600)

SCHEFFEL, Johan Hendrik (1690-1781) Swedish
£1325 $2397   (19-May-92 AB.S4273/R) Portrait of Margareta Katarina Ugla as a child
  (50x40cm-20x16in) (S.KR 14000)

SCHEFFER, Arnold (1839-1873) French
£9000 $16020   (28-Nov-91 B188 d) Portrait of soldier, probably Lieutenant of French
  Horse Artillery (122x96cm-48x38in) s.d.1860

SCHEFFER, Ary (1795-1858) French
£3909 $7428   (26-Jun-92 AT.P121/R) Marguerite au rouet (121x90cm-48x35in) (F.FR 38000)
£449 $787   (21-Feb-92 LC.P13) Saint Jean-Baptiste prechant dans le desert
  (27x24cm-11x9in) s. pierre noire (F.FR 4400)
£17500 $29750   (23-Oct-91 S55/R) Study for La Defense de Missolonghi (26x19cm-10x7in)
  W/C htd.bodycol gum arabic

SCHEFFER, Robert (1859-?) Austrian
£874 $1555   (29-Apr-92 D.V911/R) Oblarn station, Steiermark (22x32cm-9x13in) s.
  i.d.1911verso board (A.S 18000)
£977 $1660   (24-Oct-91 D.V154/R) Farmstead in mountain landscape (26x37cm-10x15in)
  s.d.97 board (A.S 20000)
£1074 $1826   (24-Oct-91 D.V153/R) Mondsee landscape (24x29cm-9x11in) s. i.d.1907verso
  board (A.S 22000)
£1236 $2163   (19-Feb-92 D.V39/R) View of Purgg, Steiermark (25x30cm-10x12in) s.d.1935
  canvas on board (A.S 25000)
£1483 $2595   (20-Feb-92 D.V478/R) The arts enthusiast (46x35cm-18x14in) s.i.d.1922
  board (A.S 30000)
£1570 $2983   (25-Jun-92 D.V472/R) View of Purgg, Steiermark s.i.d.1925verso board
  (A.S 32000)
£1939 $3529   (27-May-92 D.V549/R) Interior (82x64cm-32x25in) s.d.1928 i.verso
  (A.S 40000)
£3600 $6228   (3-Oct-91 CSK218/R) The artist's studio (81x64cm-32x25in) s.
£1214 $2160   (29-Apr-92 D.V654/R) The return (42x53cm-17x21in) s.i.verso W/C
  (A.S 25000)

SCHEFFLER, Rudolf (1884-?) American
£2948 $5100   (8-Sep-91 LIT.L66) Pumpkin flowers and sunflowers (71x102cm-28x40in)
  s.estate st.verso

SCHEGGI, Paolo (1940-1971) Italian
£632 $1100   (15-Sep-91 JRB.C243/R) Shaped canvas, 1964 (51x71cm-20x28in) s.verso
  tempera
£1463 $2779   (23-Jun-92 F.M16/R) Senza titolo (100x100cm-39x39in) s.d.1964verso three
  canvases overlapping (I.L 3200000)
£2989 $5351   (14-Nov-91 F.M1) Zone riflesse (60x60cm-24x24in) s.i.d.1963verso
  overlapping canvas (I.L 6500000)

SCHEGGIA, Giovanni di Ser Giovanni (1407-1486) Italian
£35912 $65000   (22-May-92 SY.NY3/R) Madonna and child with two angels (86x49cm-34x19in)
  tempera panel arched top

SCHEGGIA, Giovanni di Ser Giovanni (attrib) (1407-1486) Italian
£8721 $15000   (10-Oct-91 SY.NY68/R) The Madonna and Child (51x34cm-20x13in) tempera
  panel

SCHEIBER, Hugo (1873-1950) Hungarian
£528 $956   (6-Dec-91 GB.B7074) View over rooftops (38x48cm-15x19in) board (DM 1500)
£565 $1016   (20-Nov-91 CN.P62) L'homme au drapeau (57x47cm-22x19in) s. gouache
  (F.FR 5500)
£585 $1100   (5-Jan-92 GG.TA394/R) Nude amongst trees (41x28cm-16x11in) s. oil gouache
£649 $1200   (8-Jun-92 GG.TA265/R) Seated man (60x43cm-24x17in) s. gouache
£674 $1200   (29-Apr-92 G.Z1/R) Portrait of man (63x48cm-25x19in) s. gouache board
  (S.FR 1800)
£700 $1274   (12-Dec-91 CSK108) Girls with fruit bowl (54x40cm-21x16in) s. gouache
£733 $1261   (12-Oct-91 KV.L267) Four figures (21x33cm-8x13in) s. gouache (B.FR 44000)

SCHEIBER, Hugo (1873-1950) Hungarian-cont.

£745	$1326	(28-Nov-91 D.V219/R) Deep in thoughts (50x41cm-20x16in) s. mixed media paper on board (A.S 15000)
£894	$1600	(9-May-92 CE.NY135/R) Village path (57x42cm-22x17in) s. col.chk over pencil paper on paper
£1049	$1867	(30-Nov-91 VG.B968/R) Busy street at night with policeman (70x51cm-28x20in) s. gouache pastel (DM 3000)
£1073	$1900	(5-Nov-91 CE.NY93/R) Seated man (70x50cm-28x20in) s. gouache pastel
£1356	$2400	(5-Nov-91 CE.NY91/R) Man leaning against tree (59x47cm-23x19in) s. gouache W/C
£1424	$2606	(17-May-92 GL.P144/R) La route (68x47cm-27x19in) s. gouache pastel (F.FR 14000)
£1540	$2772	(20-Nov-91 CN.P61/R) Les deux maisons (67x46cm-26x18in) s. gouache (F.FR 15000)
£1667	$2867	(12-Oct-91 KV.L457/R) Two figures (46x38cm-18x15in) s. gouache (B.FR 100000)
£1667	$3033	(12-Dec-91 SY.AM78/R) Village (44x36cm-17x14in) s. gouache (D.FL 5400)
£1673	$3112	(19-Jun-92 G.Z25/R) The artist and his model (31x21cm-12x8in) s. gouache (S.FR 4400)
£1833	$3153	(12-Oct-91 KV.L458/R) The black coach (48x31cm-19x12in) s. gouache (B.FR 110000)
£2763	$5029	(9-Dec-91 CH.R98/R) Donna (50x45cm-20x18in) s. mixed media (I.L 6000000)
£3232	$6011	(19-Jun-92 G.Z51/R) Deux filles assises (69x49cm-27x19in) s. mixed media (S.FR 8500)
£4297	$7605	(5-Nov-91 GF.L2207/R) Acrobatics (65x48cm-26x19in) s. mixed media (S.FR 11000)

SCHEIBL, Hubert (1951-) Austrian

| £997 | $1785 | (15-Jan-92 D.V277/R) Untitled (78x57cm-31x22in) s.d.89 mixed media (A.S 20000) |

SCHEID, Lore (1889-1946) German

| £752 | $1361 | (5-Dec-91 D.V241) Salzkammergut landscape (52x65cm-20x26in) s.d.1932 (A.S 15000) |

SCHEINS, Karl Ludwig (1808-1879) German

| £1031 | $1753 | (25-Oct-91 BM.B821/R) Moonlit lake landscape with hunters around campfire (80x68cm-31x27in) s. (DM 3000) |
| £1254 | $2283 | (12-Dec-91 L.K684) Mountainous landscape with traveller by water and hilltop monastery (34x48cm-13x19in) mono.d.1842 (DM 3600) |

SCHEIRMAN, A (?) ?

| £1300 | $2496 | (9-Jul-92 CSK271/R) Dutch wooded river landscape with barge, figures walking on track (28x36cm-11x14in) s. panel |

SCHELCK, Maurice (1906-1978) Belgian

£1325	$2397	(23-May-92 KV.L290) Flower vase (80x60cm-31x24in) s. canvas on panel (B.FR 80000)
£1417	$2437	(12-Oct-91 KV.L272) Cornfield (50x60cm-20x24in) s. canvas on panel (B.FR 85000)
£1490	$2697	(23-May-92 KV.L291/R) Ardeur de la Tenacite (150x81cm-59x32in) s. (B.FR 90000)
£1501	$2642	(7-Apr-92 C.A211) Sunny landscape in Lathem (50x60cm-20x24in) s.d.1963 panel (B.FR 90000)
£2005	$3409	(22-Oct-91 C.A283/R) Still life (100x80cm-39x31in) s. (B.FR 120000)
£3342	$5681	(22-Oct-91 C.A284/R) Bouquet of flowers (76x56cm-30x22in) s.d.1947 panel (B.FR 200000)
£4078	$6974	(21-Mar-92 KV.L471/R) Winter landscape at sunset (80x100cm-31x39in) s. s.d.71 verso canvas on panel (B.FR 240000)
£5338	$9394	(7-Apr-92 C.A210/R) Landscape in Flanders (120x100cm-47x39in) s. panel (B.FR 320000)

SCHELFHOUT, Andreas (1787-1870) Dutch

£10286	$18000	(19-Feb-92 CH.NY129/R) Skaters in frozen winter landscape (36x58cm-14x23in) s.
£18960	$33749	(30-Oct-91 CH.AM137/R) Peasants conversing by boat on frozen river (30x44cm-12x17in) s. panel (D.FL 62000)
£21407	$38104	(30-Oct-91 CH.AM184 a/R) Figures and horse-drawn sledge on frozen waterway by fortified mansion (26x31cm-10x12in) s.d.49 panel (D.FL 70000)
£55046	$97982	(30-Oct-91 CH.AM285/R) Winter landscape with figures on frozen waterway and Dordrecht beyond (48x66cm-19x26in) s.d.1846 panel (D.FL 180000)
£113636	$201136	(22-Apr-92 CH.AM223/R) Peasants by a booth and skaters on a frozen waterway, windmill beyond (58x78cm-23x31in) s.d.57 panel (D.FL 375000)
£428	$745	(14-Apr-92 SY.AM349) Coastal landscape (22x28cm-9x11in) s.verso pen brush (D.FL 1400)
£1818	$3218	(22-Apr-92 CH.AM300/R) Extensive winterlandscape with numerous skaters (26x35cm-10x14in) s.d.51 pastel (D.FL 6000)

SCHELFHOUT, Andreas (attrib) (1787-1870) Dutch

| £3364 | $5853 | (14-Apr-92 SY.AM222) Figures in winter landscape (53x71cm-21x28in) s. panel (D.FL 11000) |

SCHELFHOUT, Andreas (circle) (1787-1870) Dutch
£1543 $2701   (18-Feb-92 CH.AM338/R) Winter view of the IJ, Amsterdam, with moored three masters and figures (25x33cm-10x13in) s. panel (D.FL 5000)

SCHELFHOUT, Andreas (style) (1787-1870) Dutch
£900 $1602   (26-Nov-91 PH84) Skaters in winter landscape (35x43cm-14x17in) bears sig

SCHELFHOUT, Andreas and VERBOECKHOVEN, Eugene (19th C) Dutch/Belgian
£19697 $34864   (22-Apr-92 CH.AM223/R) Winterscene with peasant on a snowy path, a skater and other figures (53x70cm-21x28in) s.both artists panel (D.FL 65000)

SCHELLENBERG, Carolus (1849-1923) Dutch
£683 $1182   (24-Mar-92 VN.R82) Figures resting by the water in polder landscape (26x43cm-10x17in) s. (D.FL 2200)

SCHELLER, H D (18th C) German
£806 $1427   (10-Nov-91 ZZ.F53/R) Etudes de feuilles de murier avec insectes (30x21cm-12x8in) s. one d.1796 pen W/C htd.gouache pair (F.FR 8000)

SCHELLINKS, Willem (attrib) (1627-1678) Dutch
£3600 $6912   (8-Jul-92 S201/R) Southern landscape with figures and animals on path beside stream (80x114cm-31x45in)

SCHELOUMOFF, A (1912-1976) Russian
£592 $1078   (11-Dec-91 WE.MU145/R) Wolves attacking troika (30x40cm-12x16in) s. (DM 1700)
£592 $1078   (11-Dec-91 WE.MU146/R) Escaping the wolves (30x40cm-12x16in) s. (DM 1700)

SCHELTEMA, Jan Hendrik (1861-1938) Dutch
£661 $1176   (26-Nov-91 J.M163) Drinking pool (37x28cm-15x11in) s. canvas on board (A.D 1500)
£699 $1223   (30-Mar-92 AAA.S106) Post and rail fence (29x35cm-11x14in) s. board (A.D 1600)
£1502 $2509   (19-Aug-91 SY.ME73) Breakers on rocky shore (29x38cm-11x15in) s. canvas on board (A.D 3200)
£1795 $3195   (28-Apr-92 CH.ME108/R) Morning on the Buffalo River (29x21cm-11x8in) s. canvas on board (A.D 4200)
£2137 $3803   (27-Apr-92 J.M102/R) Cattle drinking (49x75cm-19x30in) s. (A.D 5000)
£2203 $3921   (26-Nov-91 J.M52/R) Droving sheep (60x103cm-24x41in) s. (A.D 5000)
£2350 $4184   (27-Apr-92 J.M304) Cattle on the road (29x44cm-11x17in) s. canvas on board (A.D 5500)
£3084 $5489   (26-Nov-91 J.M187 a) Milking time (28x42cm-11x17in) s. canvas on board (A.D 7000)
£3500 $5950   (22-Oct-91 C111/R) Cows at pool (65x46cm-26x18in) s.
£3500 $5950   (22-Oct-91 C110/R) Horses grazing (46x56cm-18x22in) s.
£4060 $7226   (27-Apr-92 J.M78) Sheep grazing (40x60cm-16x24in) s. (A.D 9500)
£4681 $8285   (26-Apr-92 SY.ME353/R) Droving, early morning (59x103cm-23x41in) s. canvas on board (A.D 11000)
£5286 $9410   (26-Nov-91 J.M295/R) Misty morning in Mallee (66x100cm-26x39in) s. (A.D 12000)
£17521 $31188   (28-Apr-92 CH.ME168/R) Going to market, Western District (59x130cm-23x51in) s. i.stretcher (A.D 41000)
£19824 $35286   (26-Nov-91 J.M13/R) The round-up (80x125cm-31x49in) s. (A.D 45000)

SCHELVER, August Franz (1805-1844) German
£2091 $3805   (12-Dec-91 L.K686/R) Shepherd and shepherd boy on horse in heath landscape (42x32cm-17x13in) s.d.1840 panel (DM 6000)

SCHENAU, Johann Eleazar (1737-1806) German
£3315 $6000   (22-May-92 S.BM32/R) Charmed - a genre scene (33x23cm-13x9in) s.

SCHENCK, August Friedrich Albrecht (1828-1901) Danish
£890 $1700   (16-Jul-92 SY.NY466/R) Driving sheep home in a snowstorm (46x61cm-18x24in) s.
£1041 $1821   (30-Mar-92 ZZ.F134) Le troupeau de moutons dans la neige (35x50cm-14x20in) s. (F.FR 10000)
£1440 $2750   (16-Jul-92 SY.NY465/R) In the snow storm (87x121cm-34x48in) s.
£1913 $3500   (17-May-92 DU.E1063/R) Leading the flock home (61x48cm-24x19in) s.

SCHENDEL, Petrus van (1806-1870) Belgian
£820 $1500   (16-May-92 HG.C117/R) Letter by candlelight (23x18cm-9x7in) s.d.1853 panel
£900 $1557   (3-Oct-91 CSK236) A girl, head and shoulders by candlelight (43x36cm-17x14in) s.
£1277 $2221   (17-Sep-91 CH.AM362/R) Rotterdam on fire (69x82cm-27x32in) s. (D.FL 4200)
£2446 $4355   (30-Oct-91 CH.AM221/R) Lady carrying basket (17x20cm-7x8in) s. panel (D.FL 8000)
£2688 $4784   (29-Nov-91 GAB.G3100/R) Marche a la volaille (49x38cm-19x15in) s. (S.FR 6800)
£3137 $5616   (15-Nov-91 ZOF.Z1428/R) School lessons at night (49x40cm-19x16in) s.s. panel (S.FR 8000)
£5495 $10000   (27-May-92 CH.NY239/R) Scullery maid and young mistress of the house in kitchen interior (76x63cm-30x25in) s.d.1835
£7068 $13500   (16-Jul-92 SY.NY444/R) The candlelit market (57x42cm-22x17in) s.d.1856 panel

SCHENDEL, Petrus van (1806-1870) Belgian-cont.
£7600 $13224   (18-Sep-91 PHS584) Poultry seller at candlelit stall (36x30cm-14x12in)
  s.i.d.1847 panel
£31000 $57660   (17-Jun-92 S290/R) Poultry stall in Antwerp at night (77x60cm-30x24in)
  s.i. panel
£32000 $54720   (19-Mar-92 B102/R) A vegetable stall at night (65x51cm-26x20in) s. panel
£34000 $63240   (17-Jun-92 S294/R) Groenmarkt at night, Hague (89x72cm-35x28in) s.d.1868

SCHENDEL, Petrus van (attrib) (1806-1870) Belgian
£5924 $10368   (24-Feb-92 ARC.P14/R) Les bulles de savon (51x64cm-20x25in) panel
  (F.FR 58000)

SCHENK, Karl (1780-1827) German
£1204 $2156   (6-May-92 GD.B1118/R) Old man lighting fire and young woman with child
  leaning against tree (60x45cm-24x18in) s. pavatex (S.FR 3300)
£1569 $2667   (23-Oct-91 GD.B639/R) Bear (18x34cm-7x13in) s. pavatex (S.FR 4000)
£2737 $4900   (6-May-92 GD.B1116/R) The first bunch of flowers (60x48cm-24x19in) s.
  panel (S.FR 7500)
£2920 $5226   (6-May-92 GD.B1119/R) Don Quichote and Sancho Pansa (243x120cm-96x47in)
  s. panel (S.FR 8000)
£3529 $6000   (23-Oct-91 GD.B638/R) Small girl picking flowers in field
  (53x42cm-21x17in) s. panel (S.FR 9000)

SCHENKEL, Jan Jacob (1829-1900) Dutch
£1988 $3538   (30-Oct-91 CH.AM224/R) Interior of Oude Kerk with tomb of William the
  Silent of Orange, Delft (68x50cm-27x20in) s.d.1858 panel (D.FL 6500)

SCHENLOOP, C P (20th C) ?
£2105 $3600   (13-Mar-92 FN.S2591/R) Composition with circles and diagonals
  (80x60cm-31x24in) mono. i.d.1928verso (DM 6000)

SCHENONE PUIG, Dolcey (?) Uruguayan?
£636 $1100   (30-Sep-91 GC.M25) Casona del Prado (71x56cm-28x22in) s.
£1202 $2200   (4-Jun-92 GOM.M60/R) Fuente (61x75cm-24x30in) s.

SCHENZER, Ph (19th C) ?
£2266 $4260   (18-Dec-91 FB.P161) Bouquet de fleurs dans un vase (28x22cm-11x9in)
  s.d.1846 pair (F.FR 22000)

SCHERBRING, Carl (1859-1899) German
£546 $988   (22-May-92 GB.B6050) Field with group of trees (44x52cm-17x20in)
  (DM 1600)

SCHERER, Hermann (1893-1927) Swiss
£815 $1475   (19-May-92 GF.L2840) Davos landscape (42x56cm-17x22in) oil chk
  (S.FR 2200)

SCHERFIG, Hans (20th C) Danish
£1073 $1953   (10-Dec-91 RAS.K260/R) Tapir and young in the jungle (30x35cm-12x14in)
  s.d.1954 masonite (D.KR 12000)
£1444 $2469   (12-Mar-92 RAS.K737/R) Tapirs in the jungle (38x46cm-15x18in) s.d.45
  masonite (D.KR 16000)
£1538 $2785   (4-Dec-91 KH.K139/R) Elephant in jungle (67x76cm-26x30in) s. tempera
  (D.KR 17000)
£1957 $3406   (17-Sep-91 RAS.K677/R) Pink flamingoes in jungle landscape
  (30x42cm-12x17in) s.d.1950 masonite (D.KR 22000)

SCHERMER, Cornelis (1824-1915) Dutch
£2584 $4495   (17-Sep-91 CH.AM365/R) The horse fair (62x97cm-24x38in) s. (D.FL 8500)

SCHERRER, Jean Jacques (19th C) French
£5557 $9614   (24-Mar-92 CH.R4/R) La predizione (176x132cm-69x52in) s.d.1883
  (I.L 12000000)

SCHERREWITZ, Johan (1868-1951) Dutch
£621 $1068   (16-Oct-91 KM.K1351) Beach scene with horse-drawn cart and fishermem
  (25x42cm-10x17in) s. panel (DM 1800)
£1100 $1958   (28-Nov-91 B11/R) Milking time (46x31cm-18x12in) s. bears sig.i.verso
£1155 $2010   (17-Sep-91 CH.AM550/R) A peasant-woman gathering wood on the edge of a
  forest (40x55cm-16x22in) s. (D.FL 3800)
£1481 $2593   (18-Feb-92 CH.AM49/R) Wooded dunelandscape with peasant on horse-drawn
  cart (45x55cm-18x22in) s. (D.FL 4800)
£1667 $2950   (22-Apr-92 CH.AM32) Peasant and cows on a farmyard, Heeze
  (32x52cm-13x20in) s. (D.FL 5500)
£2300 $4117   (5-May-92 SWS409/R) Shell fishers (26x49cm-10x19in) s. panel
£3143 $5500   (18-Feb-92 CE.NY190/R) Seaweed gatherer returning home (35x51cm-14x20in)
  s.
£3211 $5716   (30-Oct-91 CH.AM287/R) The return to the barn (70x101cm-28x40in) s.
  (D.FL 10500)
£3266 $5814   (29-Oct-91 PH.T11/R) Beaching fishing boat (88x118cm-35x46in) s.
  (C.D 6500)
£3976 $7076   (30-Oct-91 CH.AM129/R) Peasant loading horse-drawn cart (51x91cm-20x36in)
  s. (D.FL 13000)

SCHETKY, John Christian (style) (1778-1874) British
£1000 $1740   (14-Apr-92 CSK101) Merchantman wrecked on rocky coastline (57x71cm-22x28in) mono.

SCHEUBEL, Johann Joseph III (attrib) (1733-1801) German
£2439 $4439   (11-Dec-91 N.M357/R) Little girl picking flower from rosebush in park landscape (71x57cm-28x22in) oval (DM 7000)

SCHEUERER, Julius (1859-1913) German
£619 $1132   (2-Jun-92 FN.S2740) Poultry by banks of stream (12x16cm-5x6in) s. board (DM 1800)
£1150 $2093   (11-Dec-91 N.M574) Ducks and geese at water by fence (16x40cm-6x16in) (DM 3300)
£1498 $2727   (11-Dec-91 N.M573/R) Pheasants, swan and ducks at the water (13x10cm-5x4in) s. panel (DM 4300)
£1713 $2964   (25-Mar-92 KM.K1400) Poultry by the edge of the wood (32x52cm-13x20in) s. (DM 4900)
£1951 $3395   (19-Sep-91 D.V26/R) Poultry in pond landscape (35x70cm-14x28in) s.i. (A.S 40000)
£2313 $4140   (5-May-92 ZEL.L1525/R) Poultry before stable (28x18cm-11x7in) s.i. panel (DM 6800)

SCHEUERER, Otto (1862-1934) German
£512 $927   (22-May-92 GB.B6051) Capercaillies performing courtship dance (30x40cm-12x16in) s. board (DM 1500)
£619 $1076   (18-Sep-91 N.M682/R) Ducks and chicks at pond beneath tree near farmhouse (16x21cm-6x8in) s.i. panel (DM 1800)
£756 $1315   (18-Sep-91 N.M683) Turkey, cockerel, chicken and chicks feeding before barn (24x34cm-9x13in) s.i. (DM 2200)
£893 $1555   (18-Sep-91 N.M681/R) Turkey, cockerel and chicken feeding before barn (26x37cm-10x15in) s.i. board (DM 2600)

SCHEUERMANN, Hedwig (19/20th C) Swiss
£646 $1202   (19-Jun-92 ZOF.Z2077/R) Stetten, Aargau (59x80cm-23x31in) s.d.1910 i.verso board (S.FR 1700)

SCHEUREN, Caspar Johann Nepomuk (1810-1887) German
£1056 $1911   (3-Dec-91 AB.S4753/R) Summer landscape with buildings and figures by lake (30x42cm-12x17in) s.d.1850 (S.KR 11000)
£2448 $4234   (25-Mar-92 KM.K1399/R) Thunderstorm rising in river landscape (30x42cm-12x17in) s.d.1880 (DM 7000)
£563   *$1020*   *(4-Dec-91 DO.H2912/R) Fishing hut on Dutch coast (26x37cm-10x15in) s. W/C over indian ink pen (DM 1600)*
£1185   *$2156*   *(12-Dec-91 L.K472/R) Easter Sunday of artist, illustrations for poem by Catharina Diez (29x24cm-11x9in) s.d.1846 pen W/C board set of six (DM 3400)*

SCHEUREN, Caspar Johann Nepomuk (attrib) (1810-1887) German
£1276 $2194   (16-Oct-91 KM.K1352/R) Woodland landscape with cottage by stream and thunderstorm rising (57x51cm-22x20in) i. (DM 3700)

SCHEX, Joseph (1819-1894) German
£1276 $2194   (16-Oct-91 KM.K1354/R) Portrait of gentleman standing with arms folded s.d.1849 oval one of pair (DM 3700)
£1379 $2372   (16-Oct-91 KM.K1353/R) Portrait of lady seated on terrace s.d.1849 oval one of pair (DM 4000)

SCHIANCHI, Federico (?) Italian
£1382 $2515   (10-Dec-91 F.R202/R) Il Tevere a Castel Sant'Angelo (18x25cm-7x10in) s. panel (I.L 3000000)
£9211 $16765   (10-Dec-91 F.R206/R) Veduta del Foro Romano e di Via della Consolazione (74x98cm-29x39in) s. (I.L 20000000)

SCHIAVO, Paolo (1397-1478) Italian
£38674 $70000   (21-May-92 CH.NY24/R) Venus reclining on pillows holding garland of flowers with putto, in landscape (51x170cm-20x67in) tempera panel inside of cassone lid

SCHIAVONE, Andrea (1522-1563) Italian
£16500 $28875   (1-Apr-92 S16/R) Madonna and child with infant Saint John and Saint Anne (97x111cm-38x44in)

SCHIAVONE, Andrea (attrib) (1522-1563) Italian
£1236 $2323   (16-Dec-91 AGS.P37/R) La derniere Cene (51x43cm-20x17in) panel (F.FR 12000)

SCHIAVONI, Natale (1777-1858) Italian
£1684 $3032   (22-Nov-91 SA.A1556/R) Portrait of Venetian lady with fur (66x52cm-26x20in) (DM 4800)

SCHICK, R (?) German
£1379 $2400   (11-Sep-91 D.NY73) Allegory of friendship (30cm-12ins circular) s.i.

CHICKHARDT, Karl (1866-1933) German
£982 $1680   (13-Mar-92 FN.S2942) Enz landscape with farmhouse amongst trees (40x50cm-16x20in) s. board (DM 2800)

CHIDER, Fritz (1846-1907) Austrian
£6274 $11669   (19-Jun-92 ZOF.Z2078/R) Lady with kitten in interior (88x69cm-35x27in) s. (S.FR 16500)
£451 $826   (4-Jun-92 SY.Z562/R) Peaches (20x28cm-8x11in) W/C (S.FR 1200)
£1316 $2408   (4-Jun-92 SY.Z564/R) Still life with fan of ostrich feathers (46x62cm-18x24in) mono W/C (S.FR 3500)

CHIDONE, Bartolomeo (attrib) (1578-1615) Italian
£4000 $7280   (11-Dec-91 S194/R) Charity (56x44cm-22x17in)

CHIDONE, Bartolomeo (style) (1578-1615) Italian
£950 $1710   (21-Nov-91 CSK34) Madonna and Child (61x49cm-24x19in)
£1500 $2745   (12-May-92 SWS614/R) Madonna and child (53x41cm-21x16in)

CHIEDGES, Peter Paulus (1812-1876) Dutch
£525 $918   (18-Feb-92 CH.AM305) Shepherdess and flock (47x66cm-19x26in) s. (D.FL 1700)
£612 $1064   (14-Apr-92 SY.AM56) Vessels in calm sea (9x16cm-4x6in) s. panel (D.FL 2000)
£950 $1710   (22-Nov-91 C129/R) Beached fishing boats (21x28cm-8x11in) s.indis.d.1869 panel
£1284 $2286   (30-Oct-91 CH.AM195) Sailors in rowing boat approaching two-master and steamer beyond (24x34cm-9x13in) s.d.61 panel (D.FL 4200)
£4587 $7982   (14-Apr-92 SY.AM141/R) Sailors in rowing-boat hooking a 'Tjalk' (34x50cm-13x20in) s.d.56 panel (D.FL 15000)

CHIEFER, Johannes (20th C) ?
£809 $1400   (25-Mar-92 D.NY66) Rue des Bois (66x76cm-26x30in) s.d.1936verso

CHIELE, Egon (1890-1918) Austrian
£2456 $4421   (23-Nov-91 N.M281/R) Study of head (48x32cm-19x13in) mono.d.1907 chk htd.white (DM 7000)
£20341 $36818   (21-May-92 F.M226/R) Nudo femminile (29x46cm-11x18in) s.d.1917 crayon (I.L 45000000)
£23000 $43930   (1-Jul-92 S152/R) Bildnis Hofrat V (45x29cm-18x11in) s.i.d.1918 chl
£44687 $79543   (28-Nov-91 D.V39/R) Girl reclining (48x32cm-19x13in) s.d.1911 pencil (A.S 900000)
£50000 $95500   (1-Jul-92 S153/R) Frau mit kopftuch (46x29cm-18x11in) s.d.1916 pencil
£50000 $95500   (30-Jun-92 C160/R) Weiblicher akt, kniend, nach links vornubergebeugt (31x50cm-12x20in) s.d.1918 W/C black crayon
£55000 $105050   (30-Jun-92 S29/R) Stehender knabe. Stehendes madchen - Gertrude Schiele (44x32cm-17x13in) init.d.10 gouache W/C pencil double-sided
£85000 $153850   (3-Dec-91 S34/R) Nacktes paar (37x52cm-15x20in) init.d.1911 st.verso gouache W/C pencil
£87432 $160000   (13-May-92 CH.NY223/R) Portrait eines knaben (45x31cm-18x12in) init.d.10 gouache over pencil
£92308 $175385   (26-Jun-92 GK.B135/R) Torso of kneeling young girl (48x32cm-19x13in) s.i.d.1913 W/C over pencil (S.FR 240000)
£100000 $191000   (30-Jun-92 S28/R) Zwei proletarierkinder (44x30cm-17x12in) s.d.10 black chk gouache
£120219 $220000   (12-May-92 CH.NY150/R) Stehender mann - selstbildnis (44x31cm-17x12in) s.d.1911 st.verso W/C gouache over pencil
£123077 $233846   (26-Jun-92 GK.B134/R) Half nude girl supporting head (45x32cm-18x13in) mono.d.1911 bodycol W/C htd white over pencil (S.FR 320000)
£135593 $240000   (6-Nov-91 SY.NY49/R) Sitzender akt. Bildnis (30x47cm-12x19in) s.d.1913 W/C blk.crayon pencil double-sided
£140000 $253400   (3-Dec-91 S33/R) Zwei gassenbuben (39x32cm-15x13in) init.d.10 gouache W/C over pencil
£230000 $439300   (30-Jun-92 S26/R) Stehendes madchen im blauen kleid und grunen strumpfen, ruckenansicht (48x31cm-19x12in) s.d.1913 pencil gouache
£520000 $993200   (30-Jun-92 S25/R) Bildnis der Edith Schiele, sitzend (51x40cm-20x16in) s.d.1915 pencil gouache

CHIELE, H (?) ?
£2289 $3845   (27-Aug-91 RAS.K611/R) Still life of roses, pansies and irises on table (86x100cm-34x39in) s. oval (D.KR 26000)

CHIER, Franz (1852-1922) German
£2035 $3500   (15-Oct-91 CE.NY90/R) The romantic suitor (12x95cm-5x37in) s.

CHIERTZ, August Ferdinand (1804-1878) German
£1571 $3000   (16-Jul-92 SY.NY439/R) Sentries halting travellers on rural path (34x47cm-13x19in) s.d.1839 panel

CHIERTZ, Franz Wilhelm (1813-1887) German
£1407 $2547   (19-May-92 GF.L2480/R) Midnight sun and polar bears playing, Bergen, Norway (36x54cm-14x21in) s.d.1881 i.verso (S.FR 3800)

CHIESS, Ernst Traugott (1872-1919) Swiss
£941 $1685   (15-Nov-91 ZOF.Z1868) Shepherd and goats II (30x45cm-12x18in) i.verso board (S.FR 2400)

SCHIESS, Ernst Traugott (1872-1919) Swiss-cont.
£1418 $2452   (23-Mar-92 AB.L32/R) Three beduin women (42x52cm-17x20in) board
                        (S.FR 3700)

SCHIESS, Hans Rudolf (1904-1978) Swiss
£1176 $2000   (23-Oct-91 GD.B640/R) Composition (80x50cm-31x20in) s.d.65 (S.FR 3000)
£1303 $2254   (23-Mar-92 AB.L171/R) The eye (30x25cm-12x10in) s. s.i.verso pavatex
                        (S.FR 3400)

SCHIESS, Tobias (1925-) Swiss
*£575 $994   (23-Mar-92 AB.L5/R) Double self portrait (47x65cm-19x26in) s.d.48
                       s.i.d.verso W/C tempera over indian ink (S.FR 1500)*

SCHIESS, Traugott (1834-1869) Swiss
£1481 $2681   (19-May-92 GF.L2251/R) Shepherd boy with flock by stream
                       (67x54cm-26x21in) s.i.d.1863 (S.FR 4000)

SCHIESTL-ARDING, Albert (20th C) ?
£1394 $2537   (13-Dec-91 BM.B541/R) Still life with fruit and dahlias (71x65cm-28x26in)
                       mono. i.verso (DM 4000)

SCHIFANO, Mario (1934-) Italian
£463 $825   (26-Nov-91 SY.MI64) Paesaggio (40x50cm-16x20in) s.verso acrylic
                       (I.L 1000000)
£463 $825   (29-Nov-91 F.F52) Senza titolo (30x40cm-12x16in) s. s.verso cardboard on
                       canvas (I.L 1000000)
£630 $1083   (16-Oct-91 G.Z42/R) Paesaggio (45x45cm-18x18in) s.i.verso (S.FR 1600)
£640 $1216   (23-Jun-92 F.M102) Paesaggio (75x98cm-30x39in) s. (I.L 1400000)
£699 $1196   (21-Mar-92 WK.M561/R) Cornfield (62x92cm-24x36in) s.verso acrylic
                       (DM 2000)
£817 $1494   (12-May-92 F.R157) Paesaggio anemico (60x80cm-24x31in) s. acrylic
                       (I.L 1800000)
£920 $1646   (14-Nov-91 F.M39) Composizione (87x135cm-34x53in) s. acrylic
                       (I.L 2000000)
£1023 $1851   (3-Dec-91 F.R159) Paesaggio anemico (100x100cm-39x39in) s. acrylic paper
                       on canvas (I.L 2200000)
£1049 $1794   (21-Mar-92 WK.M563/R) Tomatoes (91x91cm-36x36in) s.verso (DM 3000)
£1096 $1908   (14-Apr-92 F.M10/R) Colle (70x100cm-28x39in) s.i.d.1987verso
                       (I.L 2400000)
£1096 $1908   (14-Apr-92 F.M47) Paesaggio (100x70cm-39x28in) s.verso (I.L 2400000)
£1205 $2145   (29-Nov-91 F.F47) Albero (73x95cm-29x37in) s. (I.L 2600000)
£1208 $2187   (3-Dec-91 F.R182) Televisore (74x104cm-29x41in) s.verso acrylic
                       emulsioned canvas (I.L 2600000)
£1329 $2272   (21-Mar-92 WK.M560/R) Palm tree (91x62cm-36x24in) s.verso acrylic
                       (DM 3800)
£1392 $2617   (19-Dec-91 F.M106) Vortice (90x90cm-35x35in) s.verso (I.L 3000000)
£1622 $2887   (26-Nov-91 SY.MI21/R) Albero (60x80cm-24x31in) s. acrylic (I.L 3500000)
£1656 $2963   (14-Nov-91 F.M120/R) Acerbi (115x164cm-45x65in) s.verso oval
                       (I.L 3600000)
£1829 $3183   (16-Apr-92 FB.P255/R) Sans titre (210x110cm-83x43in) s. acrylic
                       (F.FR 18000)
£1854 $3299   (26-Nov-91 SY.MI99/R) Coca Cola (70x100cm-28x39in) s. acrylic
                       (I.L 4000000)
£1946 $3464   (26-Nov-91 SY.MI91/R) Tutte stelle (100x70cm-39x28in) s.verso acrylic
                       (I.L 4200000)
£2270 $4040   (29-Apr-92 F.F223/R) Senza titolo (79x100cm-31x39in) s. (I.L 5000000)
£2448 $4185   (21-Mar-92 WK.M562/R) Esso (100x100cm-39x39in) s.verso acrylic sold with
                       s.photograph (DM 7000)
£4526 $8237   (26-May-92 SY.MI115/R) Paesaggio (160x190cm-63x75in) s.verso acrylic
                       paper on canvas (I.L 10000000)
£7437 $13460   (3-Dec-91 F.R249/R) Venerde di Milo 4 (90x74cm-35x29in) s.verso acrylic
                       panel (I.L 16000000)
*£417 $742   (27-Nov-91 F.M179) Senza titolo (100x70cm-39x28in) s. collage ink acrylic
                       collage col.plexiglass (I.L 900000)*
*£440 $784   (27-Nov-91 F.M297) Senza titolo (100x70cm-39x28in) s. collage ink acrylic
                       (I.L 950000)*
*£640 $1216   (23-Jun-92 F.M18) Erotico (43x53cm-17x21in) s.verso emulsioned canvas
                       (I.L 1400000)*
*£741 $1320   (26-Nov-91 SY.MI126) Composizione (100x70cm-39x28in) s. gouache collage
                       (I.L 1600000)*
*£817 $1494   (12-May-92 F.R163/R) Casa sulla sabbia (50x60cm-20x24in) s.verso enamel
                       canvas (I.L 1800000)*
*£908 $1616   (29-Apr-92 F.F68) Senza titolo (100x70cm-39x28in) s. collage
                       (I.L 2000000)*
*£914 $1737   (23-Jun-92 F.M97) Composizione (70x100cm-28x39in) s.verso enamel
                       (I.L 2000000)*
*£1021 $1919   (19-Dec-91 F.M127/R) Carra nel 1914 (75x50cm-30x20in) s.verso emulsion
                       enamel canvas (I.L 2200000)*
*£1096 $1908   (14-Apr-92 F.M9/R) Televisore (40x50cm-16x20in) s.verso emulsioned canvas
                       (I.L 2400000)*
*£1114 $2094   (19-Dec-91 F.M114/R) Picasso (70x50cm-28x20in) s.i.verso emulsion enamel
                       canvas (I.L 2400000)*
*£1380 $2470   (14-Nov-91 F.M34) Gigli d'acqua (81x111cm-32x44in) s.verso oil enamel
                       canvas (I.L 3000000)*

SCHIFANO, Mario (1934-) Italian-cont.

£1380	$2470	*(14-Nov-91 F.M61/R) Coca cola (70x100cm-28x39in) s.verso enamel paper on canvas (I.L 3000000)*
£1498	$2667	*(29-Apr-92 F.F222/R) Coca Cola (80x60cm-31x24in) s.verso mixed media paper on canvas (I.L 3300000)*
£1622	$2887	*(26-Nov-91 SY.MI122/R) Coca Cola (100x70cm-39x28in) s. acrylic pencil paper on canvas (I.L 3500000)*
£1720	$3130	*(25-May-92 CH.R70/R) Reticolo (102x140cm-40x55in) s. enamel canvas (I.L 3800000)*
£1810	$3295	*(25-May-92 CH.R67/R) Futurismo rivisitato a colori (70x100cm-28x39in) s. enamel canvas (I.L 4000000)*
£1946	$3464	*(26-Nov-91 SY.MI43/R) Particolare di esterno (70x100cm-28x39in) s.init.d.62 enamel pencil (I.L 4200000)*
£2037	$3707	*(25-May-92 CH.R65/R) Coca Cola (70x100cm-28x39in) s.verso enamel paper on canvas (I.L 4500000)*
£2377	$4516	*(23-Jun-92 F.M77/R) Particolare di paesaggio (151x99cm-59x39in) s.i.d.1969 enamel collage (I.L 5200000)*
£3244	$5774	*(29-Nov-91 F.F53) Senza titolo (100x80cm-39x31in) s. mixed media paper on canvas (I.L 7000000)*
£3621	$6590	*(26-May-92 SY.MI127/R) Veramente (70x105cm-28x41in) oil pastel pencil collage paper on canvas (I.L 8000000)*
£3654	$6358	*(14-Apr-92 F.M150/R) Romazzano, la casa di Alighiero (260x200cm-102x79in) s.i. s.d.1988verso enamel acrylic canvas (I.L 8000000)*
£4375	$7963	*(9-Dec-91 CH.R129/R) Propaganda (130x100cm-51x39in) s.i.d.1962 enamel paper on canvas (I.L 9500000)*
£4990	$9131	*(12-May-92 F.R226/R) Figura in movimento (160x130cm-63x51in) s.i.d.1965verso enamel paper on canvas (I.L 11000000)*
£6789	$12356	*(26-May-92 SY.MI225/R) Senza titolo (110x110cm-43x43in) s.d.61verso enamel paper on canvas (I.L 15000000)*
£6810	$12121	*(29-Apr-92 F.F224/R) Senza propaganda (148x100cm-58x39in) mixed media paper on canvas (I.L 15000000)*

SCHIFFER, Anton (1811-1876) Austrian

£3333	$6033	*(19-May-92 GF.L2135/R) View of Malnitzer Tauern with crossing to Gastein (49x38cm-19x15in) s.d.1873 i.verso board (S.FR 9000)*
£515	$897	*(18-Sep-91 N.M274/R) View of Tivoli (24x32cm-9x13in) s.d.1828 chl chk pencil (DM 1500)*

SCHILDER, Andrei Nikolaevich (1861-1919) Russian

£3605	$6598	*(14-May-92 BU.S199/R) Snowy park landscape (69x115cm-27x45in) s. (S.KR 38000)*

SCHILDT, N M (?) Dutch?

£497	$860	*(24-Mar-92 VN.R83) Peasant woman with milk cans (105x72cm-41x28in) s. (D.FL 1600)*

SCHILL, A (?) ?

£550	$952	*(1-Oct-91 SWS1629) Curate's letter (11x18cm-4x7in) s. panel*

SCHILL, Emil (1870-1958) Swiss

£627	$1167	*(19-Jun-92 ZOF.Z2080/R) Winter landscape, Innerschweiz s. i.verso panel (S.FR 1650)*

SCHILLE, Alice (?-1955) American

£3448	$6000	*(15-Apr-92 SY.NY211/R) Figures walking in wooded landscape (51x43cm-20x17in) s. W/C*

SCHILTER, Hans (1918-) Swiss?

£1250	$2213	*(5-Nov-91 GF.L2659) The forest, Hunenberg near Cham (42x59cm-17x23in) s.i.d.1962 s.i.d.verso tempera paper (S.FR 3200)*
£1250	$2213	*(5-Nov-91 GF.L2656) Autumn landscape (40x58cm-16x23in) s.i.d.1955 tempera paper (S.FR 3200)*
£1484	$2627	*(5-Nov-91 GF.L658) Two men seated beneath tree at the end of the day (35x28cm-14x11in) mono.d.1953 tempera oil indian ink panel (S.FR 3800)*
£1719	$3042	*(5-Nov-91 GF.L2660) Railway embankment Rothenthurm (54x113cm-21x44in) mono.d.1959 s.i.d.verso (S.FR 4400)*

SCHINAGEL, Emil (1899-1943) Polish

£2615	$4498	*(13-Oct-91 REM.W29) Forest Madonna (99x68cm-39x27in) (P.Z 50000000)*

SCHINDLER, Carl (1821-1842) Austrian

£684	$1176	*(10-Oct-91 D.V116/R) Portrait of old woman wearing lace cap (17x14cm-7x6in) i.d.1838 pencil study verso (A.S 14000)*

SCHINDLER, Emil Jakob (1842-1892) Austrian

£8991	$16184	*(21-Nov-91 D.V152/R) Woodland path (63x47cm-25x19in) s. (A.S 180000)*
£59940	$107892	*(21-Nov-91 D.V49/R) Ragusa street scene (39x24cm-15x9in) s.d.883 panel (A.S 1200000)*

SCHINKEL, Karl Friedrich (circle) (1781-1841) German

£2289	$4143	*(6-Dec-91 GB.B6010/R) Schloss Predjama with figures (52x63cm-20x25in) (DM 6500)*

SCHINNAGL, Maximilian Joseph (1697-1762) German
£1987 $3398   (18-Mar-92 D.V175/R) Wooded landscape with figures (19x27cm-7x11in) panel
                  (A.S 40000)

SCHINNERER, Adolf (1876-1949) German
£2982 $5368   (23-Nov-91 N.M282/R) Winter landscape with dogs fighting
                  (75x98cm-30x39in) s. (DM 8500)

SCHIOLER, Inge (1908-1971) Swedish
£949 $1736   (12-May-92 GO.G153) Tarn, Partille (32x38cm-13x15in) s. (S.KR 10000)
£2372 $4341   (12-May-92 GO.G154) Mountain-ash (18x24cm-7x9in) s.d.1958 (S.KR 25000)
£3036 $5556   (13-May-92 BU.S189/R) Winter wood (50x55cm-20x22in) s.d.1969 (S.KR 32000)
£3241 $5704   (11-Apr-92 FAL.M371/R) View from Inges mountain, Koster (34x42cm-13x17in)
                  s.d.1960 (S.KR 34000)
£3595 $6507   (19-May-92 AB.S5322/R) Landscape with trees and blue sky
                  (65x54cm-26x21in) s.d.56 panel (S.KR 38000)
£3795 $6945   (13-May-92 BU.S187/R) Breakers (55x50cm-22x20in) s. (S.KR 40000)
£4163 $7535   (19-May-92 AB.S5321/R) Sea and cliffs, Koster (43x42cm-17x17in) s.d.1960
                  (S.KR 44000)
£4364 $7987   (13-May-92 BU.S188/R) Meadow near sea (50x54cm-20x21in) s.d.1969
                  (S.KR 46000)
£5849 $10527   (19-Nov-91 GO.G161/R) Glistening sun (39x42cm-15x17in) s.d.1960
                  (S.KR 61000)
£6736 $12327   (12-May-92 GO.G156/R) Coastal landscape with beach hut (50x56cm-20x22in)
                  s.d.1969 (S.KR 71000)
£8588 $15286   (28-Nov-91 BU.S107/R) Landscape with houses near Koster fjor
                  (50x57cm-20x22in) s. (S.KR 90000)
£10355 $18639   (19-Nov-91 GO.G162/R) Mild summer day, Koster (50x55cm-20x22in) s.d.1962
                  (S.KR 108000)
£13283 $24307   (13-May-92 BU.S186/R) View of Nord and South Koster (61x72cm-24x28in)
                  s.d.1958 (S.KR 140000)
£15180 $27780   (11-May-92 NOR.S78/R) Koster in full bloom (64x74cm-25x29in) s.d.1959
                  (S.KR 160000)
£1088   *$1969*   *(19-May-92 AB.S5324/R) Hazel bush (40x53cm-16x21in) s.d.1959 pastel*
                  (S.KR 11500)
£1152   *$2084*   *(3-Dec-91 AB.S5154/R) Boy of coastal cliff (41x32cm-16x13in) s.d.56*
                  pastel chk (S.KR 12000)
£1328   *$2431*   *(12-May-92 GO.G280) Grapes and apples (38x45cm-15x18in) s. gouache*
                  (S.KR 14000)
£1419   *$2569*   *(19-May-92 AB.S5323/R) The mountain, landscape with trees*
                  (38x46cm-15x18in) s. pastel (S.KR 15000)
£1423   *$2604*   *(13-May-92 BU.S190/R) Park interior (36x44cm-14x17in) s. pastel chk*
                  (S.KR 15000)
£1518   *$2778*   *(12-May-92 GO.G282) The pear tree (47x38cm-19x15in) s. pastel*
                  (S.KR 16000)

SCHIOTT, August (1823-1895) Danish
£661 $1170   (23-Apr-92 RAS.V886/R) Two children paddling (45x33cm-18x13in) s.
                  (D.KR 7500)
£747 $1337   (6-May-92 KH.K12/R) Small girl frightened by turkey (53x43cm-21x17in)
                  s.d.1868 (D.KR 8500)
£400   *$712*   *(26-Nov-91 PH154) Cairo street scene (30x22cm-12x9in) s.i. W/C*

SCHIOTTZ-JENSEN, N F (1855-1941) Danish
£539 $953   (11-Feb-92 RAS.K151) Landscape from Ulvig in Hardanger (43x62cm-17x24in)
                  s.i. (D.KR 6000)
£560 $957   (12-Mar-92 RAS.V976 a) West coast landscape with fisherman and beached
                  boats (33x48cm-13x19in) s.d.1906 (D.KR 6200)
£651 $1119   (15-Oct-91 RAS.K238/R) Italian woman on mountain road (50x70cm-20x28in)
                  s. (D.KR 7300)
£835 $1494   (6-May-92 KH.K183) Italian woman by town gate (50x65cm-20x26in)
                  s.i.d.1925 (D.KR 9500)
£923 $1652   (6-May-92 KH.K184) Italian with ox and cart (50x80cm-20x31in) s.i.d.1914
                  (D.KR 10500)

SCHIOTTZ-JENSEN, Niels F (1855-1941) Danish
£1055 $1889   (16-Nov-91 FAL.M324/R) Hunter with dog in wood (48x72cm-19x28in) s.d.1893
                  (S.KR 11100)

SCHIOTTZ-JENSEN, Niels F (attrib) (1855-1941) Danish
£906 $1594   (11-Apr-92 FAL.M372/R) Woman on beach (69x51cm-27x20in) bears sig.
                  (S.KR 9500)

SCHIPPERS, Joseph (1868-1950) Belgian
£900 $1602   (28-Nov-91 B135/R) The miser (25x33cm-10x13in) s.d.1915 s.i.d.verso panel

SCHIPPERUS, Pieter Adrianus (1840-1929) Dutch
£420   *$718*   *(19-Mar-92 B6/R) Woman with barrow on heath (44x70cm-17x28in) s. gouache*
£745   *$1289*   *(24-Mar-92 VN.R84/R) Farm in the forest (57x39cm-22x15in) s. W/C*
                  (D.FL 2400)

SCHIRMER, Johann Wilhelm (1807-1863) German
£1585 $2868   (4-Dec-91 DO.H2914/R) Wooded landscape with footbridge (87x110cm-34x43in)
                  (DM 4500)

SCHIRMER, Johann Wilhelm (1807-1863) German-cont.

£2817	$5099	(4-Dec-91 DO.H2915/R) Bay of Naples with Vesuvio, evening (27x33cm-11x13in) paper on board (DM 8000)
£6485	$11802	(27-May-92 PH.DU39/R) Wooded landscape (56x74cm-22x29in) mono.d.1842 (DM 19000)
£10563	$19120	(4-Dec-91 DO.H2916/R) Landscape near Tivoli (28x44cm-11x17in) mono. paper on board (DM 30000)
£378	$692	(3-Jun-92 DO.H2415/R) The Rhine near Koblenz (47x71cm-19x28in) i. W/C pencil (DM 1100)
£423	$765	(4-Dec-91 DO.H2922/R) Eifel landscape (45x66cm-18x26in) W/C (DM 1200)
£447	$786	(11-Apr-92 AW.H689/R) Landscape near Civitella (33x56cm-13x22in) i.d.1839 pencil col.chk (DM 1300)
£584	$1069	(3-Jun-92 DO.H2414/R) Near Wolfsanger (55x68cm-22x27in) i. W/C pencil (DM 1700)
£584	$1069	(3-Jun-92 DO.H2409/R) Moon rising in evening landscape (37x55cm-15x22in) chl htd.white (DM 1700)
£584	$1069	(3-Jun-92 DO.H2408/R) Sunday morning landscape with shepherds and flock (60x87cm-24x34in) chl htd.white (DM 1700)
£810	$1466	(4-Dec-91 DO.H2921/R) Siebengebirge near Bonn (42x69cm-17x27in) i.verso W/C over pencil (DM 2300)
£825	$1509	(3-Jun-92 DO.H2412/R) Path leading through Eifel landscape (38x52cm-15x20in) W/C (DM 2400)
£825	$1509	(3-Jun-92 DO.H2405/R) Mountainous landscape with shepherd (25x32cm-10x13in) mono indian ink pen wash (DM 2400)
£825	$1509	(3-Jun-92 DO.H2416/R) Aar landscape with fishermen (37x41cm-15x16in) mono. W/C over pencil (DM 2400)
£893	$1635	(3-Jun-92 DO.H2417/R) Rocky wooded landscapes (58x72cm-23x28in) W/C indian ink pen two (DM 2600)
£962	$1761	(3-Jun-92 DO.H2410/R) Landscape with church, moonlit evening (36x52cm-14x20in) W/C (DM 2800)
£986	$1785	(4-Dec-91 DO.H2919/R) Clemens-Kapelle (24x31cm-9x12in) i. W/C bodycol (DM 2800)
£986	$1785	(4-Dec-91 DO.H2917/R) Alpine lake landscape with travellers resting by campfire (39x52cm-15x20in) indis.i.verso W/C (DM 2800)
£1065	$1949	(3-Jun-92 DO.H2411/R) Night sky (51x70cm-20x28in) W/C (DM 3100)
£1134	$2075	(3-Jun-92 DO.H2413/R) Hilly Eifel landscape with road (35x72cm-14x28in) W/C (DM 3300)
£1203	$2201	(3-Jun-92 DO.H2419/R) Stream in Black Forest landscape (48x71cm-19x28in) W/C indian ink pen htd.white (DM 3500)
£1268	$2294	(4-Dec-91 DO.H2932/R) Flight to Egypt in landscape (56x74cm-22x29in) s. chl (DM 3600)
£1408	$2549	(4-Dec-91 DO.H2927/R) Campagna landscape (46x62cm-18x24in) W/C over pencil (DM 4000)
£1479	$2677	(4-Dec-91 DO.H2920/R) Kloster Laach near Koblenz (43x68cm-17x27in) W/C htd.white (DM 4200)
£1546	$2830	(3-Jun-92 DO.H2406/R) Campagna landscape (10x14cm-4x6in) i.verso W/C board (DM 4500)
£1549	$2804	(4-Dec-91 DO.H2918/R) Wetterhorn (49x41cm-19x16in) W/C indian ink pen (DM 4400)
£1585	$2868	(4-Dec-91 DO.H2930/R) Wooded landscape with shepherd and cattle (36x52cm-14x20in) W/C (DM 4500)
£1718	$3144	(3-Jun-92 DO.H2421/R) Studies of plants and stones W/C over indian ink pen (DM 5000)
£1890	$3459	(3-Jun-92 DO.H2404/R) Farewell scene before monastery in wooded landscape (23x30cm-9x12in) indian ink pen W/C (DM 5500)
£1937	$3505	(4-Dec-91 DO.H2931) Forest scenes s. one st.sig. two (DM 5500)
£1937	$3505	(4-Dec-91 DO.H2933/R) The Samaritan (40x52cm-16x20in) s. indian ink brush pen (DM 5500)
£1993	$3508	(11-Apr-92 AW.H687/R) Wetterhorn landscape with torrent (50x41cm-20x16in) W/C over indian ink pen (DM 5800)
£2405	$4402	(3-Jun-92 DO.H2423/R) Landscape views, South of France one d.1836 three W/C pen pencil set of 6 (DM 7000)
£2993	$5417	(4-Dec-91 DO.H2926/R) Italian landscape with buildings (40x39cm-16x15in) W/C (DM 8500)
£2993	$5417	(4-Dec-91 DO.H2924/R) Italian composition with bathers (35x56cm-14x22in) W/C over pencil (DM 8500)
£3345	$6055	(4-Dec-91 DO.H2923/R) Rocky landscape (72x104cm-28x41in) W/C over pencil (DM 9500)
£3436	$6289	(3-Jun-92 DO.H2407/R) Studies of Italian costumes (27x37cm-11x15in) i.d.1839/40 indian ink pen W/C two (DM 10000)
£3521	$6373	(4-Dec-91 DO.H2925/R) Italian landscape with shepherds (37x53cm-15x21in) W/C pen (DM 10000)

SCHIRMER, Johann Wilhelm (attrib) (1807-1863) German

| £1433 | $2595 | (21-May-92 L.K485) Moonlit lake landscape (52x66cm-20x26in) mono.d.1849 (DM 4200) |

SCHIRREN, Ferdinand (1872-1944) Belgian

£434	$739	(22-Oct-91 C.A288) Seated woman (63x48cm-25x19in) s.d.1912 wash (B.FR 26000)
£799	$1487	(16-Jun-92 SY.B357/R) Madonna (51x39cm-20x15in) s. W/C (B.FR 48000)
£1667	$2867	(12-Oct-91 KV.L273) Still life (33x27cm-13x11in) s. W/C (B.FR 100000)
£2165	$4027	(16-Jun-92 SY.B364/R) Path in wooded landscape (54x45cm-21x18in) s. W/C (B.FR 130000)
£2673	$4545	(22-Oct-91 C.A286/R) Still life (62x51cm-24x20in) s. W/C (B.FR 160000)

SCHIVERT, Victor (1863-?) Rumanian
£549 $1000   (11-Dec-91 RO.BA467) Jeune femme reposant (93x77cm-37x30in) s.
£828 $1423   (16-Oct-91 KM.K1359) Female nude on rocky outcrop with view of lake
           (93x78cm-37x31in) s. (DM 2400)

SCHJELDERUP, Leif (19/20th C) Norwegian
£2096 $3500   (23-Aug-91 DOU.M8) Luminous landscape (99x74cm-39x29in)
£7429 $13000   (19-Feb-92 CH.NY81/R) See-saw by sea (116x157cm-46x62in) s.

SCHJERFBECK, H (1862-1946) Finnish
£1136 $2000   (12-Apr-92 LIT.L231) Fruit and ivy (18x25cm-7x10in) init.d.1880 W/C

SCHJERFBECK, Helene (1862-1946) Finnish
£31132 $55726   (7-May-92 RAS.S38/R) Blue madonna (48x45cm-19x18in) init.i. (S.KR 330000)
£5310 $9345   (12-Apr-92 HOR.H202) Confirmation candidate (51x33cm-20x13in) s. col chk
           (F.M 42000)
£11860 $21703   (14-May-92 BU.S102/R) Egyptian girl (33x30cm-13x12in) init. sketch chl
           (S.KR 125000)
£47438 $86812   (11-May-92 NOR.S41/R) Girl by the fence (45x35cm-18x14in) init. W/C
           (S.KR 500000)

SCHLAGETER, Karl (1894-) Swiss
£591 $1016   (16-Oct-91 G.Z150/R) Composition (77x65cm-30x26in) s. (S.FR 1500)

SCHLATTER, Ernst Emil (1883-1954) Swiss
£760 $1414   (19-Jun-92 ZOF.Z2082/R) Schloss Tarasp (24x32cm-9x13in) s. i.verso board
           (S.FR 2000)

SCHLEGEL, Friedrich (?) ?
£4000 $7240   (21-May-92 CSK190/R) Harem beauties (90x124cm-35x49in) s.

SCHLEGEL, Julius (1830-?) German
£1115 $2074   (16-Jun-92 RAS.V863/R) Castle von Ischia (62x89cm-24x35in) s.d.1861
           (D.KR 12500)

SCHLEGEL, Julius (attrib) (1830-?) German
£1526 $2900   (22-Jun-92 SG.M659) Mountain landscape (71x94cm-28x37in) s.

SCHLEICH, Eduard (elder) (1812-1874) German
£7843 $14039   (15-Nov-91 GK.Z5098/R) Moor landscape with farmstead, evening
           (37x58cm-15x23in) s. panel (S.FR 20000)
£7904 $13753   (18-Sep-91 N.M684/R) Rising thunderstorm in lake Starnberg landscape with
           view of Seeshaupt (38x63cm-15x25in) s. canvas on panel (DM 23000)

SCHLEICH, Eduard (elder-attrib) (1812-1874) German
£1573 $2691   (18-Mar-92 N.M630/R) Moonlit Dutch river landscape with shipping and
           windmills (45x80cm-18x31in) (DM 4500)

SCHLEICH, Eduard (younger) (1853-1893) German
£815 $1475   (19-May-92 GF.L2474/R) Wooded pond landscape (34x46cm-13x18in) i.verso
           (S.FR 2200)
£1742 $3171   (11-Dec-91 N.M576/R) Woodcutters working on woodland clearing
           (39x58cm-15x23in) s.i. (DM 5000)

SCHLEICH, Hans (1834-1912) German
£1338 $2489   (16-Jun-92 RAS.V864/R) Fishermen on beach at Arkona, Rugen
           (68x108cm-27x43in) s.d.80 (D.KR 15000)

SCHLEICH, Robert (1845-1934) German
£1706 $3089   (22-May-92 GB.B6055) Lake landscape, evening (16x30cm-6x12in) s. panel
           (DM 5000)
£4437 $8075   (27-May-92 PH.DU138/R) Figures and cows in landscape (53x88cm-21x35in)
           s.d.1879 (DM 13000)
£10989 $20000   (28-May-92 SY.NY30/R) Haystacks (23x39cm-9x15in) s.

SCHLEICHER, Carl (19th C) Austrian
£900 $1539   (19-Mar-92 B72/R) Again empty (19x15cm-7x6in) s.i.verso panel

SCHLEIDEN, Eduard (1809-C1883) French
£1340 $2493   (20-Jun-92 BM.B886/R) Traveller resting with view of valley
           (34x39cm-13x15in) s.indis.d.1850 (DM 3900)

SCHLEISNER, C (19th C) ?
£615 $1101   (6-May-92 KH.K186/R) Young girl with cup (21x17cm-8x7in) init.d.1861
           panel (D.KR 7000)
£791 $1416   (6-May-92 KH.K13/R) Grandmother reading with children (40x30cm-16x12in)
           s.d.1872 (D.KR 9000)
£1246 $2231   (16-Jan-92 D.V12/R) Portrait of hunter, probably Rosenblattl
           (34x28cm-13x11in) s.indis.i.d.1842 (A.S 25000)
£1354 $2437   (19-Nov-91 RAS.K252/R) Midday nap (45x57cm-18x22in) s. (D.KR 15000)

SCHLEISNER, C A (1810-1882) Danish
£1496 $2514   (27-Aug-91 RAS.K151/R) Birdcatcher showing his captures to small children
           (40x31cm-16x12in) s. (D.KR 17000)

SCHLEISNER, Christian Andreas (1810-1882) Danish
£852 $1534   (30-Jan-92 RAS.V676/R) Boy and girl by beached boat (45x53cm-18x21in) s.d.1859 (D.KR 9500)
£2632 $4737   (22-Nov-91 SA.A1694/R) The sought after song bird (41x31cm-16x12in) s. (DM 7500)

SCHLEMMER, Oskar (1888-1943) German
£1100 $2034   (12-Jun-92 HN.H753/R) Flowers (22x15cm-9x6in) glass (DM 3200)
£9790 $17427   (28-Nov-91 SY.BE10/R) View over roofs and chimneys (28x41cm-11x16in) s. (DM 28000)
£8392 $14937   (28-Nov-91 SY.BE58/R) Seated and standing figures in room perspective (9x22cm-4x9in) pencil W/C paper laid down (DM 24000)
£130000 $235300   (3-Dec-91 C159/R) HK 1926 (55x40cm-22x16in) W/C pencil

SCHLESINGER, C (19/20th C) ?
£872 $1500   (20-Oct-91 HG.C58) Portrait of young lady holding mask (43x36cm-17x14in) s. tin

SCHLESINGER, Felix (1833-1910) German
£651 $1119   (8-Oct-91 ZEL.L1710/R) Portrait of old man wearing hat (28x23cm-11x9in) s. (DM 1900)
£2273 $3886   (18-Mar-92 N.M631/R) The sausage thief (29x37cm-11x15in) s.i.d.1854 (DM 6500)
£4945 $9000   (27-May-92 CH.NY80/R) A visit from grandfather (40x48cm-16x19in) s,
£11047 $19000   (17-Oct-91 SY.NY250/R) Young girl with rabbits (30x22cm-12x9in) s.
£20000 $35600   (29-Nov-91 C38/R) The departure for America (82x110cm-32x43in) s.d.1859

SCHLESINGER, Henri-Guillaume (1814-1893) French
£1600 $2864   (13-Nov-91 WI1194/R) Reveries, study of lady in 18th century dress (45x30cm-18x12in) s.d.1870
£1608 $2911   (19-May-92 AB.S4376/R) Girl wearing national costume feeding goat (91x71cm-36x28in) indist.sig.d.1856 (S.KR 17000)
£17000 $31620   (17-Jun-92 S489/R) Ce n'est pas moi (81x100cm-32x39in)

SCHLESINGER, Henri-Guillaume (attrib) (1814-1893) French
£1200 $2136   (28-Nov-91 B188 a) Pretty Spanish girl playing guitar (90x67cm-35x26in)

SCHLESINGER, Karl (1825-1893) Swiss
£1143 $2000   (18-Feb-92 CE.NY229/R) Before masked ball (43x36cm-17x14in) s. metal

SCHLICHTER, Rudolf (1890-1955) German
£683 $1242   (26-May-92 KF.M1235/R) Old farmstead in the Jura (50x65cm-20x26in) s.i.d.1934 indian ink board (DM 2000)
£1890 $3250   (16-Oct-91 G.Z100/R) Das Stehaufmannchen (65x47cm-26x19in) s.i.d.1927 pencil (S.FR 4800)

SCHLICHTKRULL, J C (1866-1945) Danish
£553 $1029   (16-Jun-92 RAS.V865) Old woman knitting by seaside (67x49cm-26x19in) s.d.91 (D.KR 6200)

SCHLICHTKRULL, Johan Christopher (1866-1945) Danish
£490 $843   (15-Oct-91 RAS.K241/R) Doing homework (105x90cm-41x35in) s.d.1926 (D.KR 5500)

SCHLIER, Michael (1744-1807) German
£2000 $3840   (8-Jul-92 S306/R) Church interior (25x29cm-10x11in) s.d.1789 panel

SCHLIMARSKI, Heinrich Hans (1859-?) Austrian
£750 $1334   (28-Apr-92 RAS.K402/R) Salomes' dance (80x120cm-31x47in) s. (D.KR 8500)
£1472 $2797   (25-Jun-92 D.V455) Still life of flowers and fruit (131x111cm-52x44in) s. (A.S 30000)
£1300 $2314   (27-Nov-91 S131/R) Portrait of lady (63x48cm-25x19in) s. pastel cardboard

SCHLISSER, E (19th C) ?
£5500 $9350   (22-Oct-91 C86/R) Colonial house in Singapore (48x60cm-19x24in) s.i.d.1857 indist.i.verso

SCHLITT, Heinrich (1849-?) German
£1162 $2103   (7-Dec-91 WK.M486/R) Bremer Stadtmusikanten (49x60cm-19x24in) s. mixed media board (DM 3300)

SCHLOBACH, Willy (1865-1951) Belgian
£4500 $7965   (14-Feb-92 C50/R) Les elements en mouvement (142x185cm-56x73in) mono.d.1900

SCHLOEMANN, Eduard (1888-1940) German
£1202 $2176   (7-Dec-91 AL.W7) Sea and rocks (63x85cm-25x33in) s. (P.Z 24000000)

SCHLOSSER, Bernhard (1802-1859) German
£3000 $5580   (17-Jun-92 S369/R) Praying for sick child (52x48cm-20x19in) s.d.1839

SCHLOSSER, Gerard (1931-) French
£1031 $1784   (23-Mar-92 CC.P61/R) Sans titre (80x100cm-31x39in) s. acrylic (F.FR 10000)

SCHLOSSER, Gerard (1931-) French-cont.
£2577	$4459	(29-Mar-92 P.V82/R) Peut-etre avant (162x130cm-64x51in) s.d.1986verso acrylic sand (F.FR 25000)
£5092	$9267	(15-Dec-91 P.V57/R) OUF II (130x162cm-51x64in) s.i.d.1966verso acrylic (F.FR 50000)

SCHLOTTHAUER (19th C) German
£1134	$1973	(18-Sep-91 N.M686/R) Portrait of Friederike Neidhardt (63x51cm-25x20in) i.stretcher painted oval (DM 3300)

SCHLUNKE, David (1942-) Australian
£685	$1275	(21-Jun-92 SY.ME44/R) Acacia portrait (121x183cm-48x72in) s.d.1979 (A.D 1700)

SCHLUTER (20th C) German
£767	$1395	(11-Dec-91 N.M578/R) Southern coastal landscape with sailing boats, possibly Cap d'Antibes (59x106cm-23x42in) s.i. (DM 2200)

SCHLUTER, August (1858-1928) German
£488	$844	(3-Oct-91 D.V172/R) Spring in Garmisch-Partenkirchen (41x53cm-16x21in) s. (A.S 10000)

SCHMALIX, Hubert (1952-) Austrian
£2218	$4038	(25-May-92 WK.M1113/R) Yellow head (140x140cm-55x55in) d.1980 (DM 6500)
£2730	$4969	(25-May-92 WK.M1114/R) Female rice picker (138x170cm-54x67in) (DM 8000)
£3147	$5601	(25-Nov-91 WK.M2061/R) Melancholy (140x150cm-55x59in) d.1984 (DM 9000)
£3393	$6175	(26-May-92 D.V325/R) Untitled (141x140cm-56x55in) s.d.1982verso acrylic (A.S 70000)
£3393	$6175	(26-May-92 D.V324/R) Untitled (140x140cm-55x55in) s.d.82 dispersion acrylic (A.S 70000)
£3910	$6960	(31-Oct-91 D.V229/R) The bay (138x120cm-54x47in) s.d.1986 (A.S 80000)
£4399	$7830	(31-Oct-91 D.V139/R) Untitled (130x150cm-51x59in) acrylic canvas (A.S 90000)
£4545	$8091	(25-Nov-91 WK.M2060/R) Hector Berlioz (200x200cm-79x79in) d.1981 (DM 13000)
£6786	$12351	(26-May-92 D.V323/R) Man with boat (200x200cm-79x79in) acrylic (A.S 140000)
£586	*$1020*	*(12-Sep-91 D.V210) Untitled (60x45cm-24x18in) s.d.83 W/C gouache (A.S 12000)*
£897	*$1606*	*(15-Jan-92 D.V275/R) Untitled (31x23cm-12x9in) s.d.83 mixed media (A.S 18000)*
£897	*$1606*	*(15-Jan-92 D.V247/R) Untitled (50x64cm-20x25in) s.d.82 pen indian ink W/C (A.S 18000)*
£969	*$1764*	*(26-May-92 D.V318/R) Untitled (62x44cm-24x17in) s.d.82 acrylic dispersion (A.S 20000)*
£1097	*$1963*	*(15-Jan-92 D.V249/R) Profile 3 (50x38cm-20x15in) s.i.d.1980verso gouache (A.S 22000)*
£1212	*$2206*	*(26-May-92 D.V312/R) Untitled (38x50cm-15x20in) s.d.82 gouache (A.S 25000)*
£1369	*$2436*	*(31-Oct-91 D.V141/R) Heads I (50x38cm-20x15in) s.i.d.1981verso gouache (A.S 28000)*
£1857	*$3306*	*(31-Oct-91 D.V140/R) Head (50x38cm-20x15in) d.1980 s.verso gouache (A.S 38000)*

SCHMALZ, Herbert Gustave (1857-1935) British
£1600	$2752	(11-Oct-91 C8/R) Iphigenia (35x23cm-14x9in) s.i.verso panel

SCHMALZIGAUG, Jules (1882-1917) Belgian
£600	*$1032*	*(12-Oct-91 KV.L274) Portrait of Isidoor Verheyden (34x25cm-13x10in) st.sig.verso chk (B.FR 36000)*

SCHMID, Mathias (1835-1923) Austrian
£767	$1380	(29-Jan-92 N.M822/R) Young woman (22x10cm-9x4in) s. panel (DM 2200)
£3906	$6641	(24-Oct-91 D.V207/R) At the spinning wheel (42x34cm-17x13in) s.d.99 (A.S 80000)
£13986	$23916	(18-Mar-92 N.M633/R) The little vet (93x76cm-37x30in) s. (DM 40000)

SCHMID, Richard (20th C) American
£4651	$8000	(12-Oct-91 DU.E89/R) Reclining nude

SCHMID, Wilhelm (1892-1971) Swiss
£940	$1720	(4-Jun-92 SY.Z379/R) Still life (53x42cm-21x17in) s. s.i.verso (S.FR 2500)
£2835	$4905	(23-Mar-92 AB.L36/R) Le duel (33x41cm-13x16in) s.i. (S.FR 7400)

SCHMIDT (?) ?
£4808	$8750	(28-May-92 SY.NY147/R) Harvesters (88x114cm-35x45in) s.
£3711	*$6346*	*(15-Mar-92 DA.R7/R) Scene de la vie quotidienne des femmes de marins pecheurs (71x100cm-28x39in) s.d.1904 pastel canvas pair (F.FR 36000)*

SCHMIDT, Albert (1883-1970) Swiss
£706	$1200	(23-Oct-91 GD.B645/R) Figures walking in fields (45x38cm-18x15in) s.d.1923 board (S.FR 1800)
£1098	$1867	(23-Oct-91 GD.B644/R) The oath (59x41cm-23x16in) s.d.68 st.studio verso (S.FR 2800)

SCHMIDT, Albert (1883-1970) Swiss-cont.
£1116 $2019   (5-Dec-91 SY.Z122/R) Printemps, Lac Leman (25x34cm-10x13in) mono.i.d.1905 board (S.FR 2800)
£1204 $2156   (6-May-92 GD.B1129/R) Fields (38x46cm-15x18in) s.d.1921 (S.FR 3300)
£1412 $2400   (23-Oct-91 GD.B646/R) Tree in flowering garden with houses beyond (71x47cm-28x19in) s. st.studio verso (S.FR 3600)
£2628 $4704   (6-May-92 GD.B1130/R) Tree on rocks (38x46cm-15x18in) s.d.1907 (S.FR 7200)

SCHMIDT, Carl (19/20th C) German
£789 $1500   (24-Jun-92 B.SF6421/R) Mountain snow (41x51cm-16x20in) s. canvasboard

SCHMIDT, Eduard (19/20th C) German
£6007 $10512   (3-Apr-92 BM.B702/R) View of Cape Town (45x68cm-18x27in) s. (DM 17000)

SCHMIDT, Eduard Allan (19th C) German
£1049 $1815   (25-Mar-92 KM.K1406) Gentlemen in interior decorated with hunting regalia (67x88cm-26x35in) s.d.1886 (DM 3000)
£1271 $2250   (13-Feb-92 S.W2691/R) The blacksmith's shop (13x10cm-5x4in) init. panel

SCHMIDT, H (?) ?
£1375 $2392   (18-Sep-91 N.M687/R) Village before hill with fortified castle (19x24cm-7x9in) s.d.1867 (DM 4000)

SCHMIDT, Hans (1877-?) German
£1394 $2537   (11-Dec-91 N.M579/R) Mules by sunlit wall near market (71x102cm-28x40in) s. (DM 4000)

SCHMIDT, Hans W (1859-1950) German
£1690 $3059   (3-Dec-91 FN.S2433/R) Portrait of Kaiser Friedrich I wearing uniform with orders (90x72cm-35x28in) s.i.d.1914 (DM 4800)

SCHMIDT, Harold von (20th C) German?
£4121 $7500   (27-May-92 SY.NY45/R) Ghost column (76x76cm-30x30in) s.d.1932
£8287 $15000   (5-Dec-91 SY.NY50/R) The searchers (76x114cm-30x45in) s.d.1950
£9392 $17000   (5-Dec-91 SY.NY49/R) Bunch quitters (61x127cm-24x50in) s.d.1931 s.i.d.1931-32verso panel

SCHMIDT, Johann Martin (1718-1801) German
£1031 $1887   (2-Jun-92 FN.S2744 a) Sts Jacob and Sebastian kneeling on clouds (24x16cm-9x6in) metal oval top (DM 3000)
£2944 $5594   (23-Jun-92 D.V119/R) Mater Dolorosa (49x37cm-19x15in) (A.S 60000)
£1570 $2857   (26-May-92 KF.M220/R) Angel with eucharist floating on clouds (29x19cm-11x7in) pen over chk htd white (DM 4600)

SCHMIDT, Leonhard (1892-?) German
£5263 $9000   (13-Mar-92 FN.S2947) Stuttgart street scene with figures (66x67cm-26x26in) s.d.1931 (DM 15000)

SCHMIDT, Reinhold (1861-?) German
£859 $1495   (18-Sep-91 N.M688/R) Horse Cuisine and foal grazing (35x46cm-14x18in) s. (DM 2500)

SCHMIDT, Robert G (1923-) French
£1431 $2620   (5-Feb-92 FB.P225 a) Le quai des pecheurs (63x92cm-25x36in) s. i.verso (F.FR 14000)

SCHMIDT, Rudolf (19/20th C) Austrian
£700 $1246   (26-Nov-91 PH119/R) Flower market in square (13x15cm-5x6in) s. W/C
£977 $1681   (10-Oct-91 D.V261/R) Blumenmark am Hof (13x16cm-5x6in) s.d.1923 W/C (A.S 20000)
£1212 $2206   (27-May-92 D.V662/R) Blumenmarkt am Hof (9x11cm-4x4in) s. W/C (A.S 25000)

SCHMIDT, Werner (1888-1964) German
£1573 $2801   (25-Nov-91 WK.M896/R) Open air cafe (76x57cm-30x22in) mono. panel (DM 4500)
£583 $1037   (29-Apr-92 D.V650/R) Monte Cimon della Paza, Rolle-Pass (38x25cm-15x10in) mono.i. gouache (A.S 12000)

SCHMIDT, Willem Hendrik (1809-1849) Dutch
£765 $1353   (5-Nov-91 SY.AM315/R) Invitation (37x34cm-15x13in) s.d.40 panel (D.FL 2500)

SCHMIDT-ROTTLUFF (1884-?) German
£94406 $168042   (29-Nov-91 VG.B32/R) Still life in landscape (76x90cm-30x35in) s.i.stretcher (DM 270000)

SCHMIDT-ROTTLUFF, Karl (1884-) German
£29371 $52280   (30-Nov-91 VG.B176/R) Still life with jug and vases (73x65cm-29x26in) s. (DM 84000)
£31579 $56842   (21-Nov-91 L.K443/R) Pot plant (74x66cm-29x26in) s. s.i.verso panel (DM 90000)
£99656 $184364   (12-Jun-92 HN.H754/R) Lake landscape (99x125cm-39x49in) s. s.i.d.1935stretcher (DM 290000)

SCHMIDT-ROTTLUFF, Karl (1884-) German-cont.

£120000	$217200	(2-Dec-91 C19/R) Stilleben mit apfeln und flasche (51x71cm-20x28in) s. board
£4211	$7579	(21-Nov-91 L.K444/R) Still life (70x75cm-28x30in) s. W/C board (DM 12000)
£5119	$9317	(30-May-92 VG.B228/R) Rooftops and woods (40x54cm-16x21in) s. indian ink brush col.chk (DM 15000)
£5245	$9336	(26-Nov-91 KF.M1017/R) Pensive woman (9x14cm-4x6in) s. pencil chk postcard (DM 15000)
£5802	$10560	(30-May-92 VG.B180/R) Woman standing (14x9cm-6x4in) mono.i.verso indian ink pen col.chk postcard (DM 17000)
£6873	$12577	(3-Jun-92 L.K418/R) Coral - blue snail (50x69cm-20x27in) s. i.verso W/C indian ink brush (DM 20000)
£7037	$12737	(20-May-92 GK.Z5001) Landscape with cornfield (27x35cm-11x14in) s. ink grease chk (S.FR 19000)
£7560	$13835	(3-Jun-92 L.K417/R) Flowering tree (50x65cm-20x26in) s.i.d.1956 W/C indian ink brush (DM 22000)
£8532	$15529	(25-May-92 WK.M1117/R) Still life with flower pot and masks (52x40cm-20x16in) s. col.chk W/C (DM 22000)
£9556	$17392	(30-May-92 VG.B181/R) Female nude reclining on green drape (14x9cm-6x4in) s.i.verso indian ink pen col.pencil postcard (DM 28000)
£9556	$17392	(30-May-92 VG.B179/R) Dangaster landscape (14x9cm-6x4in) d.1910 i.verso col.chk postcard (DM 28000)
£13652	$24846	(30-May-92 VG.B182/R) Poppies in field (9x14cm-4x6in) s.i.verso col.pencil indian ink postcard (DM 40000)
£13993	$25468	(30-May-92 VG.B229/R) Garden gate (69x53cm-27x21in) s.i. i.verso W/C indian ink brush over pencil (DM 41000)
£17133	$30497	(30-Nov-91 VG.B175/R) Still life with apples and oranges (50x74cm-20x29in) s. i.d.1928verso W/C (DM 49000)
£18881	$33608	(29-Nov-91 VG.B21/R) Landscape with level crossing, Holstein (50x69cm-20x27in) s. W/C indian ink brush (DM 54000)
£19931	$36873	(12-Jun-92 HN.H758/R) Vase by window (69x50cm-27x20in) s.i. W/C indian ink pen board (DM 58000)
£22727	$40455	(29-Nov-91 VG.B22/R) Bridge across the Elbe near Dessau (50x70cm-20x28in) s. W/C (DM 65000)
£22727	$40455	(30-Nov-91 VG.B180/R) Goats (49x63cm-19x25in) s. i.verso W/C (DM 65000)
£23077	$41077	(29-Nov-91 VG.B29/R) Torre di Nerone at night (66x49cm-26x19in) W/C over indian ink brush (DM 66000)
£24573	$44724	(30-May-92 VG.B221/R) Bauernhof in Rumbke am Lebasee (50x70cm-20x28in) s. W/C indian ink brush (DM 72000)
£34364	$63574	(12-Jun-92 HN.H756/R) Portrait of girl (37x31cm-15x12in) s.d.1913 W/C over pencil (DM 100000)
£58419	$108076	(12-Jun-92 HN.H755/R) Still life with vase and jug (56x42cm-22x17in) s.d.1909 W/C (DM 170000)
£59727	$108703	(29-May-92 VG.B32/R) Girl wearing yellow blouse (70x50cm-28x20in) s. W/C brush over chk (DM 175000)
£64846	$118020	(29-May-92 VG.B21/R) Landscape (32x44cm-13x17in) s.d.1911 W/C over pencil (DM 190000)

SCHMIS, Richard (?) ?

£1711	$3250	(24-Jun-92 D.NY72) Figures in courtyard (61x91cm-24x36in) s.

SCHMITT (?) ?

£1411	$2498	(10-Nov-91 ZZ.F22/R) Cheval et jeune poulain (50x61cm-20x24in) s. (F.FR 14000)

SCHMITT, Nathanael (1847-1918) German

£4124	$7546	(2-Jun-92 FN.S2745/R) Ludwigskirche in Saarbrucken with artist's wife Cornelie von Ammon (82x64cm-32x25in) s.i.d.1883 (DM 12000)

SCHMITT, Victor (?) German?

£524	$907	(25-Mar-92 KM.K1407) Kitchen interior with elderly man seated in armchair doing experiment (18x24cm-7x9in) s. (DM 1500)

SCHMITZ, Ernst (1859-1917) German

£9714	$17000	(20-Feb-92 SY.NY31/R) In der werkstatte (69x95cm-27x37in) s.i.

SCHMITZ, L (19th C) ?

£547	$968	(5-Nov-91 GF.L2489/R) Rhine landscape near Oberwesel (47x66cm-19x26in) s. (S.FR 1400)

SCHMITZ, Philipp (1824-1887) German

£2091	$3805	(12-Dec-91 L.K692) Portrait of Solingen Kaufmann Friedrich Eduard Stricker. His wife (66x55cm-26x22in) s.i.d.49 pair (DM 6000)

SCHMOGNER, Walter (?) ?

£391	$696	(31-Oct-91 D.V110/R) Weckerl mit laufendem Kummel (41x59cm-16x23in) s.i.d.78 pencil col.pencil (A.S 8000)
£437	$778	(28-Apr-92 D.V373) Wunderbare Verganglichkeit (31x42cm-12x17in) s.i.d.75 pencil col.pencil W/C (A.S 9000)
£440	$783	(31-Oct-91 D.V109/R) Insect island (41x59cm-16x23in) s.i.d.78 pencil col.pencil (A.S 9000)

SCHMUD, M (18th C) Continental

£1047	$2000	(16-Jul-92 SY.NY149/R) Family portrait in classical setting (66x81cm-26x32in) s.

SCHMURR, Wilhelm (1878-?) German
£7560 $13835 (3-Jun-92 L.K423 a/R) Women conversing (51x41cm-20x16in) s. i.d.1945verso panel (DM 22000)

SCHMUTZER, Jakob Matthias (attrib) (1733-1811) Austrian
£1300 $2496 (6-Jul-92 S51/R) Head of young man (58x42cm-23x17in) chk.htd.

SCHMUTZLER, Leopold (1864-1941) German
£1375 $2515 (2-Jun-92 FN.S2746) Portrait of young woman (57x43cm-22x17in) s.i. (DM 4000)
£1399 $2490 (25-Nov-91 WK.M902/R) Young woman with lyra (100x75cm-39x30in) s. i.stretcher (DM 4000)
£2439 $4439 (11-Dec-91 WE.MU182/R) Muse (102x76cm-40x30in) s. board (DM 7000)
£3429 $6000 (19-Feb-92 CH.NY73/R) Water carrier (95x69cm-37x27in) s.
£14286 $25000 (20-Feb-92 SY.NY85/R) Domestic bliss (77x94cm-30x37in) s.

SCHNABEL, Julian (1951-) American
£7514 $13000 (3-Oct-91 SY.NY187/R) Journey of the lost tooth (128x76cm-50x30in) s.d.82 tempera paper map
£65714 $115000 (25-Feb-92 SY.NY234/R) Sad vase (274x213cm-108x84in) s.i.d.1983stretcher velvet
£72626 $130000 (14-Nov-91 SY.NY204/R) Against moderism - what to do with corner in Madrid (244x234cm-96x92in) s.d.2/27/79 verso oil wax canvas
£162011 $290000 (6-May-92 SY.NY47/R) Maria Callas no 4 (274x310cm-108x122in) velvet
£2826 $5398 (30-Jun-92 ZZ.F89/R) Portrait de Jean Cocteau (32x24cm-13x9in) s.d.1989 ink double-sided (F.FR 27500)
£33520 $60000 (13-Nov-91 CH.NY315/R) Forms of Insanity (253x203cm-100x80in) s.d.89 oil fabric paper collage paper on canvas
£44693 $80000 (14-Nov-91 SY.NY232/R) Memory or stimulus for memory - marriage of Mary Boone and Michael Werner (290x400cm-114x157in) oil fibreglass tarpaulin

SCHNACKENBERG, Walter (1880-1961) German
£455 $809 (26-Nov-91 KF.M1020) Girl with cactus (48x36cm-19x14in) pen W/C i.verso board (DM 1300)

SCHNAKENBERG, Henry (1892-1970) American
£629 $1100 (26-Sep-91 CH.NY255/R) Central Park (43x56cm-17x22in) s.d. i.verso W/C board

SCHNARRENBERGER, Wilhelm (1892-?) German
£2560 $4659 (30-May-92 VG.B254/R) Still life with sculpture (37x48cm-15x19in) mono.d.1948 (DM 7500)
£4778 $8696 (30-May-92 VG.B253/R) Two wine glasses on round table (47x37cm-19x15in) mono.d.1943 (DM 14000)
£478 $870 (30-May-92 VG.B954/R) By the water (21x30cm-8x12in) mono.d.1948 W/C (DM 1400)
£683 $1242 (30-May-92 VG.B953/R) Summer night (42x36cm-17x14in) mono.d.1937 W/C board (DM 2000)

SCHNARS-ALQUIST, Hugo (1855-1939) German
£4545 $7864 (25-Mar-92 KM.K1409/R) Seascape with shipping (60x90cm-24x35in) s.d.1905 (DM 13000)

SCHNEIDAU, Christian von (1893-1976) American
£537 $950 (12-Feb-92 B.SF562/R) Winter fairyland (76x91cm-30x36in) s.
£678 $1200 (12-Feb-92 B.SF553/R) Waves among rocks (91x112cm-36x44in) s.
£737 $1400 (24-Jun-92 B.SF6501/R) Signe - artist's wife (122x102cm-48x40in) s.
£1086 $1900 (31-Mar-92 MOR.P118) Sunday on Provincetown Wharf (46x58cm-18x23in) s. board

SCHNEIDER, B (19th C) German
£662 $1192 (29-Jan-92 N.M830) Fun on the ice by the town canal (56x71cm-22x28in) s.d.1863 (DM 1900)

SCHNEIDER, Gerard (1896-1986) Swiss
£2062 $3567 (23-Mar-92 CC.P34) Composition (49x64cm-19x25in) s. acrylic paper (F.FR 20000)
£2079 $3992 (7-Jul-92 ARC.P97/R) Composition sur fond vert (38x55cm-15x22in) s.d.74 peinture a l'essence paper (F.FR 20000)
£2243 $4171 (15-Jun-92 GL.P95/R) Untitled (54x74cm-21x29in) s.d.1975 acrylic paper laid down on canvas (F.FR 22000)
£3141 $5685 (21-May-92 CC.P30/R) Untitled (74x108cm-29x43in) s.d.1975 acrylic paper laid down on canvas (F.FR 31000)
£3692 $6609 (19-Jan-92 CC.P76/R) Composition (38x46cm-15x18in) s.d.1976 acrylic (F.FR 36000)
£3802 $7072 (19-Jun-92 G.Z92/R) Composition (74x106cm-29x42in) s.d.1974 acrylic paper (S.FR 10000)
£3971 $7228 (15-Dec-91 P.V35/R) Composition (75x108cm-30x43in) s.d.1975 acrylic paper (F.FR 39000)
£4024 $6922 (8-Oct-91 CC.P70/R) Composition (74x106cm-29x42in) s.d.1975 acrylic paper (F.FR 40000)
£4632 $7875 (27-Oct-91 P.V20/R) 61 L (81x100cm-32x39in) s.d.1975 i.verso acrylic (F.FR 46000)
£5097 $9480 (15-Jun-92 GL.P39/R) 49 L (50x61cm-20x24in) s.d.1976 i.verso acrylic (F.FR 50000)

SCHNEIDER, Gerard (1896-1986) Swiss-cont.

£7202	$13035	(6-Dec-91 GL.P300/R) Sans titre (104x147cm-41x58in) s.d.1984 acrylic paper laid down on canvas (F.FR 70000)
£7724	$13208	(17-Mar-92 FB.P50/R) Composition (147x147cm-58x58in) s.d.83 acrylic paper laid down on canvas (F.FR 75000)
£9054	$15573	(7-Oct-91 RY.P105/R) Sans titre (96x150cm-38x59in) acrylic paper (F.FR 90000)
£9278	$16052	(29-Mar-92 P.V29/R) Composition (60x73cm-24x29in) s.d.1963 (F.FR 90000)
£12794	$22774	(30-Nov-91 FB.P10/R) Composition (40x61cm-16x24in) s.d.10.52 (F.FR 125000)
£14330	$25507	(1-Dec-91 I.N40/R) Composition (150x147cm-59x58in) s.d.1983 acrylic paper (F.FR 140000)
£14403	$26070	(6-Dec-91 GL.P299/R) Opus 52 K (97x130cm-38x51in) s.d.1974 acrylic (F.FR 140000)
£30000	$54300	(5-Dec-91 S41/R) Opus 75 F (100x81cm-39x32in) s.d.6-63
£1030	$1761	(22-Mar-92 I.N6) Composition (21x17cm-8x7in) s.d.1947 Indian ink (F.FR 10000)
£1236	$2113	(22-Mar-92 I.N19) Composition (37x47cm-15x19in) s.d.1979 gouache (F.FR 12000)
£1324	$2409	(11-Dec-91 ZZ.F143/R) Composition (48x63cm-19x25in) s.d.48 col.chks. (F.FR 13000)
£1612	$2934	(9-Dec-91 CH.R68/R) Composition (23x30cm-9x12in) s. mixed media paper on canvas (I.L 3500000)
£2060	$3522	(22-Mar-92 I.N38/R) Composition (21x30cm-8x12in) s.d.1980 gouache W/C pastel ink paper on canvas (F.FR 20000)
£2881	$5473	(26-Jun-92 FB.P38/R) Composition (52x74cm-20x29in) s.d.1968 gouache (F.FR 28000)
£5664	$9686	(17-Mar-92 FB.P55/R) Composition (50x59cm-20x23in) s. gouache paper laid down on canvas (F.FR 55000)

SCHNEIDER, Herbert (1924-1984) German

| £417 | $746 | (15-Nov-91 KM.K639) Siegeltanz (28x40cm-11x16in) s.d.80 s.i.verso collage (DM 1200) |

SCHNEIDER, Jean Claude (?) ?

| £562 | $983 | (23-Feb-92 FE.P137) Nu (33x41cm-13x16in) s. (F.FR 5500) |

SCHNEIDER, Otto Ludwig (1858-?) German

| £1031 | $1887 | (2-Jun-92 FN.S2747/R) View of Berchtesgaden with Watzmann beyond (80x121cm-31x48in) s. (DM 3000) |

SCHNEIDER, Wilhelm (1821-1900) German

| £1724 | $2966 | (16-Oct-91 KM.K1360) Snowy landscape with frozen stream and farmhouse beyond (43x64cm-17x25in) (DM 5000) |

SCHNEIDER-SEENUSS, Leo (1868-?) German

| £698 | $1249 | (15-Jan-92 D.V57/R) Sackwiesensee landscape, Steiermark (50x64cm-20x25in) s. i.verso (A.S 14000) |

SCHNEIDT, Max (1858-1937) German

| £1045 | $1902 | (11-Dec-91 N.M580/R) Young peasant couple in kitchen interior (19x13cm-7x5in) s.d.1896 panel (DM 3000) |

SCHNITZLER, Michael (1782-1861) German

| £1718 | $2990 | (18-Sep-91 N.M689/R) Fox grabbing chicken in yard (34x42cm-13x17in) s. copper (DM 5000) |
| £1742 | $3171 | (11-Dec-91 N.M358/R) Three dead birds hanging from strings (25x21cm-10x8in) s. i.verso panel (DM 5000) |

SCHNORR VON CAROLSFELD, Julius (1794-1872) German

| £3873 | $7011 | (4-Dec-91 DO.H2937/R) Portrait of Ferdinand von Olivier (16x13cm-6x5in) pencil (DM 11000) |

SCHNORR VON CAROLSFELD, Julius (attrib) (1794-1872) German

| £1045 | $1902 | (12-Dec-91 L.K693/R) Ruth and Esther in wooded landscape (48x57cm-19x22in) (DM 3000) |

SCHNYDER, Albert (1898-1989) German

£3102	$5553	(6-May-92 GD.B1134/R) Boy drawing at table (69x84cm-27x33in) s.i.d.1934verso (S.FR 8500)
£3922	$6667	(23-Oct-91 GD.B651/R) La baignade (73x60cm-29x24in) s.i.d.1957verso (S.FR 10000)
£4887	$8944	(4-Jun-92 SY.Z442/R) Maison dans les gorges (73x91cm-29x36in) s.i.d.1961 (S.FR 13000)
£7510	$13518	(19-Nov-91 GS.B3246) En attendant le bateau (81x61cm-32x24in) s.i.d.1973verso (S.FR 19000)
£14444	$26144	(20-May-92 GK.Z5164/R) La rout et la ferme (50x73cm-20x29in) d.1965 bears sig.i.stretcher (S.FR 39000)
£784	$1333	(23-Oct-91 GD.B2275/R) Horses before farmhouse (45x60cm-18x24in) s.i.d.1945verso pencil (S.FR 2000)
£863	$1467	(23-Oct-91 GD.B2276) Rider with two horses returning to farmhouse (19x24cm-7x9in) pencil (S.FR 2200)

SCHOBINGER, Karl Friedrich (1879-1951) Swiss

| £586 | $1037 | (5-Nov-91 GF.L602) Autumnal fruit trees (57x78cm-22x31in) s. (S.FR 1500) |

SCHOBINGER, Karl Friedrich (1879-1951) Swiss-cont.
£2344 $4148   (5-Nov-91 GF.L2601/R) *Study of stream near Wurzenbach* (78x57cm-31x22in)
     s.d.1906 mono.verso (S.FR 6000)
£2539 $4494   (5-Nov-91 GF.L2603/R) *Die Schwarze Lutschine* (95x71cm-37x28in) s.
     (S.FR 6500)
£431 $772   (12-Nov-91 GF.L5361) *Soldier wearing helmet and sword* (45x32cm-18x13in)
     W/C over pencil (S.FR 1100)

SCHODL, Max (1834-1921) Austrian
£1977 $3460   (20-Feb-92 D.V418/R) *Still life of antiques* (23x17cm-9x7in) s.d.1897
     panel (A.S 40000)
£2119 $3856   (10-Dec-91 F.R197) *Natura morta con tappeto ed elmo* (48x31cm-19x12in)
     s.d.1880 panel (I.L 4600000)

SCHODLBERGER, Johann Nepomuk (1779-1853) Austrian
£684 $1176   (10-Oct-91 D.V187/R) *Wooded landscape with well near Frascati*
     (40x33cm-16x13in) s. W/C (A.S 14000)

SCHOELFFT, August Theodor (1809-1888) Hungarian
£527 $954   (22-May-92 BL.P56) *Dame de qualite au chale indien* (110x92cm-43x36in)
     s.d.1837 (F.FR 5200)

SCHOELLER, Johann Christian (1782-1851) Austrian
£444 $804   (21-May-92 SY.G45) *Portrait of gentleman wearing coat, waistcoat and*
     pleated jabot (9x?cm-4x?in) min.oval gilt metal mount lacquer frame
     (S.FR 1200)

SCHOENFELD, Eduard (1839-1885) German
£906 $1631   (29-Jan-92 N.M832/R) *Grape harvest at the Mosel* (31x42cm-12x17in) s.
     panel (DM 2600)

SCHOENMANN, Joseph (1799-1879) Austrian
£5437 $9516   (20-Feb-92 D.V336/R) *Mythological scene* (134x170cm-53x67in) (A.S 110000)

SCHOEVAERDTS, Mathys (1665-1694) Flemish
£5800 $10324   (1-Nov-91 C127/R) *Travellers and pilgrims resting and watering horses at*
     fountain by ruins (29x41cm-11x16in) s. panel

SCHOEVAERDTS, Mathys (attrib) (1665-1694) Flemish
£2400 $4200   (28-Feb-92 C132) *Peasants on track by stream, hillside town beyond*
     (24x333cm-9x131in) canvas laid down on panel
£3500 $6370   (11-Dec-91 S95) *Coastal landscape with figures in Oriental costume by*
     town (44x61cm-17x24in)

SCHOEVAERDTS, Mathys (circle) (1665-1694) Flemish
£2400 $4200   (28-Feb-92 C57/R) *Wooded landscape with washerwomen by fountain and*
     drover on track (20x24cm-8x9in) panel

SCHOEVAERDTS, Mathys (style) (1665-1694) Flemish
£979 $1733   (7-Nov-91 D.V289/R) *Wooded landscape with travellers* (20x26cm-8x10in)
     panel on panel (A.S 20000)
£1235 $2210   (14-Nov-91 CH.AM46) *Village by river with peasants* (38x49cm-15x19in)
     (D.FL 4000)
£1800 $3150   (27-Feb-92 CSK131/R) *A religious procession* (28x36cm-11x14in) panel
£4532 $8112   (7-May-92 CH.AM14/R) *Peasants and travellers merry-making by village*
     inns, in wooded landscapes (47x63cm-19x25in) pair (D.FL 15000)
£4950 $8613   (13-Sep-91 C124/R) *Peasants at harbour inlet* (49x68cm-19x27in)

SCHOFER (19th C) ?
£1000 $1770   (13-Feb-92 CSK114/R) *Tree lined avenue* (69x104cm-27x41in) s.d.1876

SCHOFIELD, Kershaw (fl.1900-1938) British
£500 $860   (16-Oct-91 PHL309) *Study of drying lines* (24x33cm-9x13in) s. board
£600 $1032   (16-Oct-91 PHL308) *Flowers in bowl and Oriental statuette on ledge*
     (32x42cm-13x17in) s. board
£880 $1531   (15-Apr-92 PHL167) *Summer landscape* (50x70cm-20x28in) s. board

SCHOFIELD, Walter E (1867-1944) American
£1599 $2750   (20-Oct-91 HG.C7) *Coastal cliffs* (76x91cm-30x36in) s.
£2339 $4000   (11-Mar-92 SY.NY68/R) *Rocky coastline* (51x61cm-20x24in) s.
£3158 $6000   (24-Jun-92 B.SF6401/R) *Laguna beach* (63x76cm-25x30in) s.
£4121 $7500   (27-May-92 SY.NY66/R) *Cliffs* (76x91cm-30x36in) s.

SCHOLDER, Fritz (1937-) American
£1744 $3000   (12-Oct-91 SY.NY356/R) *Possession with lion* (76x56cm-30x22in) s. d.1989
     verso acrylic paper
£5523 $9500   (12-Oct-91 SY.NY360/R) *Indian at bar* (76x76cm-30x30in) s.d.1969
     overlap acrylic canvas

SCHOLL, H J (?) ?
£851 $1557   (12-May-92 SY.AM135/R) *View of Schloss Ampsen at Lochem* (18x48cm-7x19in)
     s. pencil W/C (D.FL 2800)

SCHOLLHORN, Hans (1892-1981) Swiss
£667 $1201   (19-Nov-91 FB.P37/R) Coin de Rue a Geneve (55x46cm-22x18in) s.
       i.d.1930verso (F.FR 6500)
£1481 $2681   (20-May-92 GK.Z5159) Mulatto woman seated (65x54cm-26x21in) s.
       (S.FR 4000)

SCHOLTE, Rob (1958-) ?
£2160 $3932   (11-Dec-91 CH.AM462/R) Vallende Poolster (120x150cm-47x59in)
       s.i.d.1984/87verso acrylic (D.FL 7000)

SCHOLTEN, Hendrik Jacobus (1824-1907) Dutch
£2080 $3618   (14-Apr-92 SY.AM127/R) A happy mother (38x51cm-15x20in) s.d.1895 panel
       (D.FL 6800)

SCHOLTZ, Heinz (1925-) ?
£1103 $1953   (6-Nov-91 N.M1136) Viktualienmarkt, Munich (30x23cm-12x9in) s. copper
       (DM 3200)
£1103 $1953   (6-Nov-91 N.M1135) View of Marienplatz, Munich (24x39cm-9x15in) s. copper
       (DM 3200)

SCHOLTZ, Robert (1877-?) German
£550 $1023   (18-Jun-92 CSK160) Mallards (91x147cm-36x58in) s. board

SCHOLZ, Werner (1898-1982) German
£2901 $5280   (30-May-92 VG.B282/R) Hillside house (49x44cm-19x17in) mono.d.1977
       i.d.verso panel (DM 8500)
£550 $1017   (12-Jun-92 HN.H764/R) Girl (48x29cm-19x11in) mono pastel (DM 1600)

SCHONBERG, Torsten (1882-?) Scandinavian
£472 $835   (5-Nov-91 BA.S163/R) Portrait of the artist Anders Trulson
       (40x31cm-16x12in) s.d.1909 panel (S.KR 5000)

SCHONBERGER, Armand (1885-) Hungarian
£1014 $1805   (25-Nov-91 WK.M905/R) Suburbian street (43x40cm-17x16in) s.d.1922 board
       on board (DM 2900)
*£631 $1123   (28-Apr-92 D.V179/R) In the cafe (31x39cm-12x15in) s.d.1921 W/C pencil
       (A.S 13000)*

SCHONBRUNNER, Ignaz (1835-1921) Austrian
£962 $1674   (19-Sep-91 N.M2810/R) Still life with cyclamen, sugar bowl and coffee
       service (70x101cm-28x40in) s. (DM 2800)

SCHONBURG-GAUERNITZ, Prinz Ernst (?) German
£523 $951   (13-Dec-91 BM.B800/R) Portrait of ruler in 18th century costume
       (107x80cm-42x31in) mono.d.1912 (DM 1500)

SCHONFELD, Johann Heinrich (attrib) (1609-1682) German
£9500 $18240   (10-Jul-92 C293/R) Crucifixion (136x89cm-54x35in)

SCHONIAN, Alfred (1856-1936) German
£890 $1557   (20-Feb-92 D.V368) Chickens and turkeys (15x25cm-6x10in) s. (A.S 18000)
£1034 $1779   (16-Oct-91 KM.K1361/R) Cockerel and two chicken before bush
       (12x16cm-5x6in) s. paper (DM 3000)
£1100 $1958   (30-Apr-92 CSK7) Poultry and ducks by pond (24x48cm-9x19in) s. panel
£1384 $2422   (20-Feb-92 D.V367) Chicken and ducks (15x25cm-6x10in) s. (A.S 28000)
£1573 $2691   (18-Mar-92 N.M635/R) Schneckenpost. Wetterfrosche (16x24cm-6x9in) s.i.
       panel pair (DM 4500)

SCHONLEBER, Gustav (1851-1917) German
£1203 $2093   (17-Sep-91 FN.S2538/R) View of Dinkelsbuhl (19x27cm-7x11in) s. board
       (DM 3500)
£1544 $2640   (13-Mar-92 FN.S2952) View of Frisian farmhouse (27x34cm-11x13in) s.d.1877
       canvas on board (DM 4400)
£2113 $3824   (3-Dec-91 FN.S2436/R) Fishing boat on beach at dusk (53x73cm-21x29in)
       s.d.1902 i.verso (DM 6000)
£2131 $3622   (26-Oct-91 WK.M638/R) Cobra an der Alten Liebe, Cuxhven (41x55cm-16x22in)
       s. i.verso canvas on board (DM 6200)
£2622 $4537   (28-Mar-92 BOD.P1022) Coastal landscape with windmill and sailing boats
       (22x42cm-9x17in) s. board (DM 7500)
£3484 $6341   (12-Dec-91 L.K694/R) View of houses and walls of medieval town by river
       (42x54cm-17x21in) s.d.1897 panel (DM 10000)
£4561 $7800   (13-Mar-92 FN.S2950/R) Der Thurm von Overschie (51x23cm-20x9in)
       s.i.d.1885 i.verso board (DM 13000)
£5155 $8969   (17-Sep-91 FN.S2537/R) The Waal near Nymwegen with shipping
       (37x47cm-15x19in) s.d.1879 canvas on board (DM 15000)

SCHONN, Alois (1826-1897) Austrian
£46715 $84086   (18-Nov-91 AT.P375) Le repos sous les ombrages (107x163cm-42x64in)
       s.d.1871 (F.FR 455000)

SCHONPFLUG, Fritz (1873-1951) Austrian
*£388 $691   (28-Apr-92 D.V23/R) Confirmation in the Prater (23x35cm-9x14in)
       s.i.d.1910 W/C htd.white (A.S 8000)*
*£445 $779   (19-Feb-92 D.V31/R) Officers around 1910 (22x33cm-9x13in) s.d.1942
       i.verso W/C pen indian ink htd.white (A.S 9000)*

SCHONPFLUG, Fritz (1873-1951) Austrian-cont.
£643 $1125   (19-Feb-92 D.V32/R) Mein liebes Kind, lass es dich nicht verdriessen (39x47cm-15x19in) s.i.d.1945 W/C pen indian ink htd.white (A.S 13000)

SCHOONHOVEN VAN BEURDEN, Alexander Franciscus van (1883-1963) Dutch
£848 $1536   (21-May-92 SY.AM111/R) Voorjaar te Laren (46x72cm-18x28in) s. s.l.stretcher (D.FL 2800)

SCHOONHOVEN, Jan J (1914-) Dutch
£424 $768   (21-May-92 SY.AM192) T 80-65 (39x26cm-15x10in) s.d.1980 s.i.d.190verso ink (D.FL 1400)
£463 $843   (11-Dec-91 CH.AM145) T79-19 (49x32cm-19x13in) s.i.d.1979 pen (D.FL 1500)
£556 $1011   (12-Dec-91 SY.AM212) Untitled (20x20cm-8x8in) s.d.66 ink (D.FL 1800)
£556 $1011   (11-Dec-91 CH.AM414) T75-96 (50x32cm-20x13in) s.i.d.1975 pen (D.FL 1800)
£679 $1236   (11-Dec-91 CH.AM422) T62-46 (45x28cm-18x11in) s.i.verso pen (D.FL 2200)
£741 $1348   (11-Dec-91 CH.AM183) T76-52 (49x32cm-19x13in) s.i.d.1976 pencil brush ink (D.FL 2400)
£1030 $1865   (21-May-92 SY.AM211/R) Untitled (38x28cm-15x11in) init.d.51 W/C ink (D.FL 2400)
£4630 $8426   (12-Dec-91 SY.AM210/R) R 70-80 (33x33cm-13x13in) s.d.1970 verso white paint papier mache (D.FL 15000)
£6061 $10970   (21-May-92 SY.AM224/R) R72-15 (43x35cm-17x14in) s.i.d.1972verso white paint paper mache (D.FL 20000)

SCHOONOVER, Frank E (1877-1972) American
£6180 $11000   (2-May-92 IH.NY157/R) Man and dog in deep snow (71x97cm-28x38in) s.d.
£8427 $15000   (2-Nov-91 IH.NY114/R) Ahuitzotl and the ocelot (91x69cm-36x27in)
£447 $800   (16-Nov-91 WOL.C643/R) Western shootout (46x76cm-18x30in) s. gouache

SCHOOR, Abraham van der (17th C) Dutch
£700 $1246   (29-Oct-91 PH60/R) Portrait of man, wearing a black jacket (61x48cm-24x19in) s.d.1651
£19757 $36155   (12-May-92 SY.AM157/R) Esther and Mordecai (141x172cm-56x68in) s.d.1643 (D.FL 65000)

SCHOOTEN, Floris van (fl.1605-1655) Dutch
£3000 $5340   (1-Nov-91 C149/R) Fruit stall in Dutch street (58x63cm-23x25in) init. panel
£21000 $40320   (10-Jul-92 C177/R) Engraved silver beaker and spoon, with bread roll, mixed fruit on draped table (40x55cm-16x22in) s. panel

SCHOPIN, Frederic Henri (1804-1880) French
£9174 $17064   (19-Jun-92 ARC.P107/R) Meleagre reprenant les armes a la sollicitation de son epouse (112x145cm-44x57in) (F.FR 90000)

SCHOTANUS, Petrus (17th C) Dutch
£14334 $25945   (21-May-92 L.K140/R) Vanitas still life with globe, candle, dead birds and nuts (83x59cm-33x23in) s. panel (DM 42000)

SCHOTEL, Anthonie Pieter (1890-1958) Dutch
£1111 $1944   (25-Feb-92 VN.R327) View on an inland harbour (54x65cm-21x26in) s. (D.FL 3600)

SCHOTEL, Jan Christianus (1787-1838) Dutch
£2128 $3702   (17-Sep-91 CH.AM427) A platbodem approaching a two-mater on a choppy sea off a jetty (46x61cm-18x24in) s. (D.FL 7000)
£9174 $16330   (30-Oct-91 CH.AM201/R) Dutch tjalk Johanna sailing off jetty and other shipping in choppy sea (85x126cm-33x50in) s. (D.FL 30000)
£1835 $3193   (14-Apr-92 SY.AM327/R) Estuary scene with shipping in rough seas (63x98cm-25x39in) s.d.1826 W/C (D.FL 6000)

SCHOTEL, Petrus Jan (1808-1865) Dutch
£2141 $3725   (14-Apr-92 SY.AM90/R) Sailings vessels on the Zuiderzee (26x36cm-10x14in) s. panel (D.FL 7000)
£788 $1395   (22-Apr-92 CH.AM257/R) The famous return of Admiral de Ruyter (23x37cm-9x15in) s. col.ink wash (D.FL 2600)
£788 $1395   (22-Apr-92 CH.AM259) The seabattle of Scheveningen, 10 August 1653 (26x36cm-10x14in) s. col.ink wash (D.FL 2600)

SCHOTH (?) ?
£1000 $1780   (28-Nov-91 CSK123/R) Pilgrims gathered by shrine outside Jerusalem (67x108cm-26x43in) s.

SCHOTH, A (1859-1906) German
£520 $910   (25-Sep-91 HUN3) Estuary scene (28x58cm-11x23in)
£520 $967   (18-Jun-92 CSK229) Boulogne (58x117cm-23x46in) s. panel

SCHOTT, Max (19th C) ?
£1067 $1900   (22-Jan-92 SY.NY281/R) Portrait of lady (65x55cm-26x22in) s.d.1904

SCHOUBROECK, Peter (1570-1607) Flemish
£15000 $27300   (10-Dec-91 PH82/R) Conversion of St. Paul (28x39cm-11x15in) copper

SCHOUK, Cornelis (style) (17th C) Dutch
£1642 $2940   (6-May-92 GD.B1136/R) Seascape with two master anchoring
                             (40x50cm-16x20in) i. panel (S.FR 4500)

SCHOUMAN, Aert (1710-1792) Dutch
£1553 $2764   *(25-Nov-91 CH.AM175/R) Gooseberry bush in mountainous landscape*
                             (36x25cm-14x10in) s. W/C (D.FL 5000)

SCHOUMAN, Aert (circle) (1710-1792) Dutch
£1543 $2762   *(12-Nov-91 SY.AM244/R) Peacock and other exotic birds by urn in park*
                             (47x31cm-19x12in) W/C gouache (D.FL 5000)
£2006 $3591   *(12-Nov-91 SY.AM243/R) Hoopoe, lapwing and wren in wooded landscape*
                             (47x32cm-19x13in) W/C gouache (D.FL 6500)

SCHOUMAN, Izaak (1801-1878) Dutch
£912 $1587   (17-Sep-91 CH.AM334) Portrait of a lady, standing three quarter length
                             wearing a blue dress (106x84cm-42x33in) s.d.1852 canvas laid down on
                             board (D.FL 3000)

SCHOUMAN, Martinus (1770-1840) Dutch
£7722 $13205   (12-Mar-92 GK.Z107/R) Seascape with sailing ships (79x96cm-31x38in)
                             s.d.1817 i.verso panel (S.FR 20000)

SCHOUTEN (?) ?
£1080 $1900   (8-Apr-92 D.NY62) Floral still life (102x76cm-40x30in) s.
£1136 $2000   (8-Apr-92 D.NY63) Floral still life (102x76cm-40x30in) s.

SCHOUTEN, Henri (1864-1927) Belgian
£617 $1080   (18-Feb-92 CH.AM186/R) Sheep and lambs in landscape (63x48cm-25x19in) s.
                             (D.FL 2000)
£673 $1171   (14-Apr-92 SY.AM300) Draught-horses (58x88cm-23x35in) s. (D.FL 2200)
£833 $1458   (24-Sep-91 GM.B266/R) La Moisson (80x100cm-31x39in) s. (B.FR 50000)
£862 $1483   (16-Oct-91 KM.K1362) Beach scene with three donkeys (100x80cm-39x31in) s.
                             (DM 2500)
£917 $1624   (5-Nov-91 SY.AM456/R) Ploughman (58x88cm-23x35in) s. (D.FL 3000)
£979 $1732   (5-Nov-91 SY.AM156) Cows watering (78x57cm-31x22in) s. (D.FL 3200)
£1040 $1840   (5-Nov-91 SY.AM284/R) Shepherd resting with flock (63x98cm-25x39in) s.
                             (D.FL 3400)
£1101 $1949   (5-Nov-91 SY.AM226/R) Shepherdess with goats by gate (63x48cm-25x19in) s.
                             (D.FL 3600)
£1162 $2057   (5-Nov-91 SY.AM112/R) Shepherd resting with dogs (78x58cm-31x23in) s.
                             (D.FL 3800)
£1223 $2165   (5-Nov-91 SY.AM463/R) Farmer ploughing (58x88cm-23x35in) s. (D.FL 4000)
£1590 $2815   (5-Nov-91 SY.AM113/R) Hunter (80x60cm-31x24in) s. (D.FL 5200)
£1714 $3000   (23-Sep-91 S.SL250) Poultry in a landscape (69x91cm-27x36in) s.
£2727 $4827   (22-Apr-92 CH.AM149/R) Souvenir d'Ecosse (101x151cm-40x59in)
                             s.indist.d.1892 i.verso (D.FL 9000)

SCHOUTEN, Henry (1791-1835) Dutch
£667 $1167   (24-Sep-91 GM.B587) Fermier et deux chevaux (60x80cm-24x31in) s.
                             (B.FR 40000)
£700 $1225   (24-Sep-91 GM.B373) Bergere et son troupeau (40x50cm-16x20in) s. wood
                             (B.FR 42000)
£880 $1593   (3-Dec-91 FN.S2439/R) Three hunting dogs by fence in field
                             (80x60cm-31x24in) s. (DM 2500)
£916 $1704   (16-Jun-92 SY.B294) Shepherdess with her flock (69x99cm-27x39in) s.d.1920
                             verso (B.FR 55000)
£1947 $3504   (2-Feb-92 ZZ.F36/R) Depart pour la chasse (43x34cm-17x13in) s. panel
                             (F.FR 19000)
£1998 $3596   (2-Feb-92 ZZ.F49/R) Le retour de chasse (43x34cm-17x13in) s. panel
                             (F.FR 19500)
£2664 $4795   (2-Feb-92 ZZ.F17/R) Bredouille, il faut acheter du gibier
                             (43x53cm-17x21in) s. i.verso panel (F.FR 26000)

SCHOVELIN, Axel Thorsen (1827-1893) Danish
£535 $920   (15-Oct-91 RAS.K246) Landscape with view towards Fredensborg Palace
                             (43x64cm-17x25in) init. (D.KR 6000)
£798 $1429   (16-Nov-91 FAL.M326/R) Wooded glade with house, pond and cattle
                             (69x94cm-27x37in) s. (S.KR 8400)
£880 $1523   (2-Sep-91 BU.K58/R) Storks by thatched farm (62x46cm-24x18in) s. metal on
                             gilded wood - firescreen (D.KR 10000)
£1408 $2366   (27-Aug-91 RAS.K578/R) Lake landscape from outskirts of wood
                             (68x95cm-27x37in) s. (D.KR 16000)
£1463 $2546   (19-Sep-91 D.V121/R) Lake landscape with boat by shore (60x94cm-24x37in)
                             s. (A.S 30000)
£1761 $2958   (27-Aug-91 RAS.K482/R) View of Heidelberg with ruins of Jettenbuhl Palace
                             (88x125cm-35x49in) s. (D.KR 20000)

SCHOVILL, L (18th C) ?
£1536 $2779   (3-Dec-91 AB.S4755/R) Belsassar's feast (57x73cm-22x29in) indist.sig.
                             (S.KR 16000)

SCHOYEN, E (?) Scandinavian
£585 $1036   *(15-Feb-92 BU.O116) Winter landscape with house (37x52cm-15x20in) s.*
                             pastel (N.KR 6600)

CHOYERER, Josef (1844-1923) German
£934 $1775   (27-Jun-92 FN.L1162) Bodensee landscape (13x16cm-5x6in) s. board
                               (DM 2700)
£1049 $1867   (26-Nov-91 KF.M249/R) Landscape near Hofgastein (30x43cm-12x17in) s.i.
                               s.i.d.1911verso panel (DM 3000)
£1119 $1992   (26-Nov-91 KF.M252/R) River landscape with farmstead beyond
                               (46x68cm-18x27in) canvas on board (DM 3200)
£1375 $2337   (25-Oct-91 BM.B825/R) Vierwaldstatter See landscape with figures
                               (81x147cm-32x58in) s. i.verso (DM 4000)
£1538 $2738   (26-Nov-91 KF.M250/R) Wooded lake landscape with view of village
                               (36x48cm-14x19in) canvas on board (DM 4400)
£1546 $2830   (2-Jun-92 FN.S2751/R) View of Schloss Neuschwanstein with cattle grazing
                               (24x36cm-9x14in) s. (DM 4500)
£1958 $3485   (26-Nov-91 KF.M248/R) Glonntal landscape near Grafing (49x72cm-19x28in)
                               s. s.i.indis.d.1894verso (DM 5600)
£2120 $3710   (3-Apr-92 BM.B705/R) Mountain landscape with figures, late summer
                               (44x54cm-17x21in) s. (DM 6000)

CHOYERER, Josef (attrib) (1844-1923) German
£906 $1649   (11-Dec-91 N.M582/R) Mountainous river landscape with figures
                               (45x63cm-18x25in) i. (DM 2600)

CHRADER, Julius Friedrich Anton (1815-1900) German
£5814 $10000   (17-Oct-91 SY.NY253/R) Cupid caught napping (122x171cm-48x67in) s.d.1867

CHRADER, Rudolf (attrib) (1853-?) German
£592 $1066   (29-Jan-92 N.M833/R) Rape field (36x46cm-14x18in) d.21 i.verso board
                               (DM 1700)

CHRADER-VELGEN, Carl Hans (1876-?) German
£4211 $7579   (23-Nov-91 N.M287/R) Burggarten, wooded landscape (80x65cm-31x26in) s.
                               (DM 12000)
£6316 $11368   (23-Nov-91 N.M286/R) Flowers in Delft vase (67x59cm-26x23in) s.
                               (DM 18000)

CHRAM, Alois Hans (1864-1919) Austrian
£8889 $15200   (17-Mar-92 JRL.S139/R) Allegoric nude by lake (113x148cm-44x58in)
                               s.d.1909 (A.D 20000)
*£440 $756   (10-Oct-91 D.V309/R) Portrait of young lady wearing gold embroidered
                               dress (48x38cm-19x15in) s.d.1915 pastel (A.S 9000)*

CHRAMM, V (?) ?
£513 $913   (27-Apr-92 J.M458) In the drawing room (46x37cm-18x15in) s. board
                               (A.D 1200)

CHRAMM, Viktor (1865-1929) Rumanian
£1775 $3230   (27-May-92 PH.DU36/R) Portrait of a woman (64x58cm-25x23in) s. panel
                               (DM 5200)

CHRAMM-ZITTAU, Rudolf (1874-1929) German
£488 $844   (3-Oct-91 D.V129/R) Ducks (14x24cm-6x9in) s.d.1943verso board (A.S 10000)
£586 $1013   (3-Oct-91 D.V124/R) Sea gulls (35x60cm-14x24in) s. (A.S 12000)
£699 $1196   (18-Mar-92 N.M637/R) Mountain landscape (60x79cm-24x31in) s. (DM 2000)
£748 $1339   (5-May-92 ZEL.L1529/R) St Francis talking to the birds in the forest,
                               spring (40x55cm-16x22in) (DM 2200)
£976 $1689   (3-Oct-91 D.V123/R) Chickens (35x60cm-14x24in) (A.S 20000)
£997 $1785   (15-Jan-92 D.V148) Dachauer Moor (60x79cm-24x31in) s. (A.S 20000)
£1220 $2111   (3-Oct-91 D.V126/R) Alpine landscape (50x70cm-20x28in) s. (A.S 25000)
£1678 $2870   (18-Mar-92 N.M636/R) Alpine summer farm on the mountains with peasant
                               woman and son (50x70cm-20x28in) s. (DM 4800)
£1952 $3377   (3-Oct-91 D.V125/R) Turkeys in pheasant garden (29x49cm-11x19in) s. panel
                               (A.S 40000)

CHRANZ, Anton (1769-1839) Austrian
£850 $1445   (23-Oct-91 S47/R) The Temple of Seti I at Gourna, Thebes
                               (45x60cm-18x24in) s.d.1843stretcher paper on canvas
£8000 $14320   (13-Nov-91 S12/R) Grand Harbour, Valetta, Malta, with HMS Britannia
                               (29x45cm-11x18in)
£26000 $45760   (8-Apr-92 S2/R) Entry of Dowager Queen Adelaide on board H.M.S. Hastings,
                               Valetta, 1838 (58x64cm-23x25in)

CHRANZ, Giovanni (circle) (?) Italian
*£1450 $2581   (27-Nov-91 B24/R) Grand Harbour, Valetta, with fisherfolk
                               (17x27cm-7x11in) bears sig.d.1801 pencil W/C*

CHRANZ, John (1794-1882) Austrian
*£1300 $2249   (4-Oct-91 C136/R) Looking North across Garitsa bay towards the Palaion
                               Frourion, Corfu (13x20cm-5x8in) pencil W/C*

CHRANZ, John (attrib) (1794-1882) Austrian
£850 $1445   (23-Oct-91 S164) The Bay of Navarino (26x36cm-10x14in) wash over pencil

CHRANZ, John (style) (1794-1882) Austrian
*£22000 $39160   (29-Nov-91 C90/R) Extensive view of Lisbon on River Tejo with Praca do
                               Terreiro do Paco (91x152cm-36x60in) bears i.*

SCHRANZ, Joseph (1803-?) German
£18000 $32400   (22-Nov-91 C29/R) British men-o-war and paddle steamer in squall off
                        Valetta, Malta (44x71cm-17x28in) s.d.1866
£1176   *$2000*   *(23-Oct-91 GD.B1272/R) Harbour view. View of Mon Repos with town beyond,*
                        Korfu (?x45cm-?x18in) s. W/C two (S.FR 3000)

SCHRANZ, Joseph (attrib) (1803-?) German
£1700 $3060   (22-Nov-91 C116/R) HMS Rodney struck by lightning Dec 1838 off Malta and
                        other shipping (30x44cm-12x17in) paper on canvas

SCHRAUDOLPH, Johann (attrib) (1808-1879) German
£1568 $2854   (12-Dec-91 L.K695/R) The mystic marriage of St Catherine
                        (42x30cm-17x12in) panel (DM 4500)

SCHRAUDOLPH, Robert (1887-?) German
£1049 $1794   (19-Mar-92 N.M2834/R) Oberstdorf houses (60x74cm-24x29in) s. (DM 3000)

SCHREIBER, Charles Baptiste (?-1903) French
£1600 $2768   (3-Oct-91 CSK168/R) A musical interlude (53x51cm-21x20in) s.

SCHREIBER, Conrad Peter (1816-1894) German
£3500 $6510   (19-Jun-92 C32/R) Lake Averno, with Vesuvius (41x52cm-16x20in) s.d.1856
                        canvas laid down on board

SCHREIBER, Georges (1904-1977) American
£957 $1800   (18-Dec-91 SY.NY309/R) Village landscape (65x78cm-26x31in) s.d.28

SCHREIBER, Georges (1866-1943) French
£748 $1339   (5-May-92 ZEL.L1532/R) Sunlit spring landscape, Provence
                        (32x45cm-13x18in) s. (DM 2200)

SCHREINER, Friedrich Wilhelm (1836-?) German
£1189 $2033   (18-Mar-92 N.M638) Fisherboys by beached boat on southern coast
                        (128x105cm-50x41in) s. (DM 3400)

SCHREITTER von SCHWARZENFELD, Adolf (1854-?) Austrian
£728 $1296   (29-Apr-92 D.V837) Girl with fruit (38x47cm-15x19in) s.d.1905 (A.S 15000)

SCHRETER, Zygmunt (c.1896-?) French
£509 $931   (17-May-92 GL.P83) Paysage (50x65cm-20x26in) s. st.verso (F.FR 5000)

SCHREUER, Wilhelm (1866-1933) German
£1062 $1826   (8-Oct-91 ZEL.L1714/R) Village street with peasants conversing
                        (38x43cm-15x17in) mono. board (DM 3100)
£761   *$1446*   *(24-Jun-92 KM.K1251) Artillery withdrawing (57x69cm-22x27in) mono mixed*
                        media (DM 2200)
£874   *$1512*   *(25-Mar-92 KM.K1418) Three Dutch fisher women seated at table in interior*
                        (69x55cm-27x22in) mono mixed media (DM 2500)
£909   *$1573*   *(25-Mar-92 KM.K1414/R) Cellar tavern with figures seated at table playing*
                        cards (70x56cm-28x22in) mono. mixed media paper on panel (DM 2600)
£979   *$1694*   *(25-Mar-92 KM.K1416/R) Ferry crossing (60x75cm-24x30in) mono mixed media*
                        (DM 2800)
£1049   *$1815*   *(25-Mar-92 KM.K1417/R) Figures in gothic interior before council meeting*
                        (60x80cm-24x31in) mono mixed media paper on canvas (DM 3000)
£1195   *$2174*   *(27-May-92 PH.DU139) Rider and hounds by a river (39x54cm-15x21in) mono.*
                        mixed media paper on canvas (DM 3500)
£1706   *$3089*   *(21-May-92 L.K486/R) Street scene with horse-drawn cart and figures*
                        conversing (50x60cm-20x24in) mono mixed media board (DM 5000)
£2439   *$4439*   *(12-Dec-91 L.K696/R) Die frohliche Runde (60x80cm-24x31in) mono. mixed*
                        media paper on canvas (DM 7000)
£4437   *$8031*   *(21-May-92 L.K488/R) Elegant party in ball room interior*
                        (65x80cm-26x31in) mono mixed media board (DM 13000)

SCHREYER, Adolf (1828-1899) German
£702 $1200   (13-Mar-92 FN.S2954) Beduins on horseback in desert (36x51cm-14x20in) s.
                        (DM 2000)
£1134 $1973   (18-Sep-91 N.M693/R) Rider in autumnal woods (11x17cm-4x7in) s. panel
                        (DM 3300)
£1826 $3250   (29-Nov-91 MFA.C239/R) Wallachian horsemen (18x46cm-7x18in) panel
£3846 $7000   (26-May-92 CE.NY45/R) A haywagon (33x50cm-13x20in) s. panel
£5757 $9960   (8-Sep-91 REM.W31) Arab on horseback (23x33cm-9x13in) s. (P.Z 110000000)
£25581 $44000   (16-Oct-91 CH.NY98/R) Halt of the Arab Chiefs (59x96cm-23x38in) s.
£62857 $110000   (19-Feb-92 CH.NY72/R) Arab horseman at pool (87x119cm-34x47in) s.

SCHREYER, Adolf (attrib) (1828-1899) German
£629 $1120   (29-Nov-91 ZEL.L1102/R) Arab seated on white horse, evening
                        (48x36cm-19x14in) canvas on panel (DM 1800)

SCHREYER, Adolf (style) (1828-1899) German
£1150 $2059   (6-May-92 ZZ.B197) Arab warriors on horseback (45x75cm-18x30in) bears sig

SCHREYER, Franz (1858-?) German
£1463 $2663   (13-Dec-91 BM.B713/R) Posilippo near Naples (31x51cm-12x20in) s.d.01
                        i.verso (DM 4200)

CHREYER, Greta (1917-) Austrian
£1396 $2499   (15-Jan-92 D.V235) Walk into Mystery from Secret Places
(76x101cm-30x40in) s. (A.S 28000)

CHREYER, Lothar (1886-1966) German
£756 $1399   (12-Jun-92 HN.H766/R) Composition (12x12cm-5x5in) s.d.1925 gouache
(DM 2200)
£764 $1413   (10-Jun-92 CSC.P184) Untitled (27x19cm-11x7in) mono.d.1917 gouache
(F.FR 7500)

CHRIECK, Otto Marseus van (style) (1619-1678) Dutch
£926 $1657   (12-Nov-91 SY.AM135/R) Wildfowl, flowers and insects at foot of tree
(45x30cm-18x12in) copper (D.FL 3000)
£960 $1700   (23-Apr-92 S.BM710/R) Still life with snails, butterfly, grasshopper and
snake (36x28cm-14x11in) panel

CHRIMPF, Georg (1898-1938) German
£54196 $96469   (26-Nov-91 KF.M1023) Portrait of Oskar Maria Graf (65x47cm-26x19in)
s.d.1918 (DM 155000)

CHRODER, Albert (?) ?
£1375 $2392   (17-Sep-91 FN.S2531) 17th century Dutch interior with cavaliers seated at
table (62x76cm-24x30in) s.i. (DM 4000)

CHRODER, Albert Friedrich (1854-1939) German
£1029 $1800   (3-Apr-92 S.W2445/R) Gentleman with long stem pipe at table
(23x33cm-9x13in) s. panel

CHRODER, Carl Julius Hermann (1802-1867) German
£1031 $1794   (17-Sep-91 FN.S2532/R) Sunday afternoon scene in the English Garden,
Munich (35x42cm-14x17in) s. oval (DM 3000)

CHRODER, Max (19th C) German
£1134 $1973   (18-Sep-91 N.M694/R) North African river landscape with figures before
Roman ruins at dusk (66x89cm-26x35in) s. board (DM 3300)
£1399 $2392   (18-Mar-92 N.M640/R) Seascape with surf and rocky coast
(87x141cm-34x56in) s.d.1871 (DM 4000)

CHRODER, Poul (1894-1957) Danish
£1056 $1827   (2-Sep-91 BU.K78/R) Still life of flowers in glass vase (96x67cm-38x26in)
init. (D.KR 12000)
£1090 $1907   (1-Apr-92 KH.K212) Still life of flowers (95x66cm-37x26in) s.
(D.KR 12000)
£1381 $2376   (16-Oct-91 KH.K247) Interior (90x118cm-35x46in) s. (D.KR 15500)
£1900 $3440   (4-Dec-91 KH.K5/R) Still life of books on table (89x116cm-35x46in) s.
(D.KR 21000)

CHRODER, Sierk (?) ?
£1368 $2380   (17-Sep-91 CH.AM122) A girl reading (50x45cm-20x18in) s.d.77 W/C
(D.FL 4500)

CHRODER, Theodor (19th C) ?
£1271 $2365   (20-Jun-92 BM.B962/R) Bunch of summer flowers in basket (70x82cm-28x32in)
s.verso (DM 3700)

CHRODER-GREIFSWALD, Max (1858-?) German
£2921 $5082   (21-Sep-91 SA.A1887/R) Prinz Heinrich mit Panzerkorvette Prinz Adalbert
beim Landgang (34x48cm-13x19in) s.i.d.87 i.verso (DM 8500)

CHRODER-SONNENSTERN, Friedrich (1892-1982) German
£853 $1544   (23-May-92 GB.B7220) Der Zauberfrosch (73x51cm-29x20in) mono.d.1960
col.pencil board (DM 2500)
£956 $1739   (26-May-92 KF.M1247/R) Die 3 Weisen aus dem Abendland (20x28cm-8x11in) i.
col.pencil pencil (DM 2800)
£990 $1791   (23-May-92 GB.B7221) Die komisch moralische Eifersucht
(73x51cm-29x20in) s.i.d.1962 col.pencil board (DM 2900)
£1053 $1895   (23-Nov-91 N.M290/R) Die Kunstler Knochen-Ehrung (50x35cm-20x14in)
s.i.d.1959 s.mono.d.verso col.pencil board (DM 3000)
£1160 $2100   (23-May-92 GB.B7222) Des Teufels Himmelfahrt (72x51cm-28x20in)
mono.d.1964 s.i.d.verso col.pencil board (DM 3400)
£1423 $2604   (13-May-92 BU.S191/R) The mermaidswan and the flying snake
(68x98cm-27x39in) s.d.1956 crayon (S.KR 15000)
£1546 $2830   (2-Jun-92 L.K932/R) Damon der Leerlaufredner oder die sogennante
Viermachtkonferenz Berlin (47x69cm-19x27in) s.i.d.1963 col.pencil
(DM 4500)
£2028 $3610   (25-Nov-91 WK.M911/R) Das Schicksalsduplikat oder der Lebensdauerlaufer
(47x69cm-19x27in) s.i.d.1956 s.d.verso pencil.chk board (DM 5800)
£2797 $4979   (30-Nov-91 VG.B316/R) Die mondmoralische Kurfurstendammsau
(49x70cm-19x28in) s.i.d.1959 s.d.verso col.pencil board (DM 8000)
£2797 $4979   (30-Nov-91 VG.B317/R) Wettlauf zwischen Beine und Kopf oder der
Lebensnarrenlaufer (47x69cm-19x27in) s.i.d.1957 i.verso col.pencil
board (DM 8000)
£3043 $5417   (29-Nov-91 GAB.G2528/R) Das Moralische drei Dimensionale
Monobrautwerbung's Derdy (51x70cm-20x28in) s. col.crayons (S.FR 7700)

SCHRODL, Anton (1823-1906) Austrian
£643 $1125   (20-Feb-92 D.V340/R) View of yard, Weissenkirchen at the Danube
                          (31x38cm-12x15in) board (A.S 13000)
£1697 $3088   (27-May-92 D.V569/R) Rocky coastal landscape (74x102cm-29x40in) s.
                          (A.S 35000)
£1754 $3175   (5-Dec-91 D.V128) To the stable (44x65cm-17x26in) s. board (A.S 35000)
£3878 $7058   (27-May-92 D.V552/R) Arriving on the high mountains summer pastures
                          (89x133cm-35x52in) s. (A.S 80000)

SCHRODTER, Adolf (1805-1875) German
£1463 $2546   (19-Sep-91 D.V202/R) Falstaff with cork screw (70x61cm-28x24in)
                          mono.d.1841 board (A.S 30000)

SCHROEDER, Georg Engelhardt (1684-1750) Swedish
£1139 $2083   (14-May-92 BU.S61/R) Portrait of Ulrika Juliana Brahe (80x66cm-31x26in)
                          s.verso (S.KR 12000)
£1750 $3168   (19-May-92 AB.S4274/R) Portrait of Cardinal de Fleury (158x128cm-62x50in)
                          i.d.1738verso after Hyacinthe Rigaud (S.KR 18500)
£2846 $5209   (14-May-92 BU.S60/R) Appelles and Kampasbe (61x93cm-24x37in) s.verso
                          (S.KR 30000)

SCHROTTER, Alfred von (1856-1935) Austrian
£1854 $3300   (22-Jan-92 SY.NY391/R) Conscription officer (16x11cm-6x4in) s.d.1888
                          panel
£4360 $7500   (17-Oct-91 SY.NY269 b/R) Sportsman (38x30cm-15x12in) s.d.1889 panel

SCHROTZBERG, Franz (1811-1889) Austrian
£1939 $3529   (27-May-92 D.V529/R) Portrait of lady (126x95cm-50x37in) rem.sig
                          (A.S 40000)

SCHRYVER, Louis Marie de (1862-1942) French
£52198 $95000   (28-May-92 SY.NY88/R) Marchande de fleurs, Avenue de L'Opera
                          (69x98cm-27x39in) s.d.1891 s.d.1891 verso
£60465 $104000   (16-Oct-91 CH.NY7 a/R) Le Marche de Fleurs de la Madeleine
                          (55x65cm-22x26in) s.d.1891
£82418 $150000   (27-May-92 CH.NY61/R) Summer flowers (102x157cm-40x62in) s.d.1888

SCHUBACK, Emil Gottlieb (1820-1902) German
£4828 $8303   (16-Oct-91 KM.K1368/R) Interior with boy and girl lighting grandfather's
                          pipe (54x48cm-21x19in) s. (DM 14000)

SCHUBERT, Heinrich Carl (1827-1897) Austrian
£3061 $5480   (5-May-92 ZEL.L1533/R) Danube landscape near Bratislava with view of
                          Thebener Kogel and ruin (56x79cm-22x31in) s.d.1850 (DM 9000)
*£1221 $2101   (10-Oct-91 D.V218/R) Sunset in Wienerwald landscape (29x38cm-11x15in)
                          s.d.1866 W/C (A.S 25000)*

SCHUBERT, Hugo (1874-1913) Austrian
£902 $1633   (5-Dec-91 D.V243) View of Neustift, Cobenzl and Kahlenberg
                          (50x68cm-20x27in) s.d.1906 (A.S 18000)

SCHUBERT, Otto (1892-?) German
£1706 $3106   (27-May-92 PH.DU177) Autumn landscape near Graupa (76x100cm-30x39in) s.
                          (DM 5000)

SCHUBERT, W (?) ?
£1074 $1857   (3-Oct-91 D.V76/R) View of Frauenkirche, Munich (27x20cm-11x8in) i. board
                          on panel (A.S 22000)

SCHUCH, Carl (attrib) (1846-1903) Austrian
£619 $1132   (2-Jun-92 FN.S2752) Alpine lake landscape with figures and thunderstorm
                          rising (18x32cm-7x13in) rem.mono canvas on board (DM 1800)

SCHUCH, N W (?) ?
£769 $1315   (19-Mar-92 N.M2835) Friedrich II on horseback with entourage
                          (89x68cm-35x27in) (DM 2200)

SCHUCH, Werner Wilhelm Gustav (1843-1918) German
£2921 $5082   (21-Sep-91 SA.A1881/R) Soldiers fleeing through woodlands
                          (101x160cm-40x63in) s.d.1879 (DM 8500)
£4211 $7579   (22-Nov-91 SA.A1711/R) General Seydlitz near Rossbach (76x51cm-30x20in)
                          s. (DM 12000)
£4211 $7579   (22-Nov-91 SA.A1712/R) General Zieten near Katholisch-Hennersdorf
                          (77x51cm-30x20in) s. (DM 12000)

SCHUCHARDT, B (19th C) ?
£3746 $6743   (21-Nov-91 D.V51/R) Still life with roses (49x39cm-19x15in) s.d.1863
                          (A.S 75000)

SCHUESSLER, C (19th C) ?
£930 $1600   (14-Oct-91 H.C33/R) Guinevere and Lancelot (160x122cm-63x48in) s.d.1859

SCHUFFENECKER, Claude Emile (1851-1934) French
£6500 $12415   (29-Jun-92 CSK73/R) Portrait of Count Antonie de la Rochefoucauld
                          (70x56cm-28x22in)

SCHUFFENECKER, Claude Emile (1851-1934) French-cont.
£570 $1043   *(17-May-92 T.B91) Paysage a l'arbre bleu (19x13cm-7x5in) studio st. pastel (F.FR 5600)*

SCHUFRIED, Dominik (1810-?) Austrian
£981 $1865   (25-Jun-92 D.V433/R) Alpine landscape with cattle (44x60cm-17x24in) mono (A.S 20000)
£1454 $2647   (27-May-92 D.V510/R) Deer by road in wooded landscape (60x84cm-24x33in) mono (A.S 30000)
£2200 $3740   (22-Oct-91 SWS325/R) Country homestead. Quiet mooring (33x41cm-13x16in) s.d.1867 pair
£2908 $5293   (27-May-92 D.V520/R) Riverside hut in mountain landscape (69x84cm-27x33in) s. (A.S 60000)

SCHUHKNECHT, Adolf (1889-?) German
£979 $1694   (25-Mar-92 KM.K1420) Rhine landscape near Bacharach, autumn (80x112cm-31x44in) s. (DM 2800)

SCHUHMACHER, Wim (1894-1988) Dutch
£3030 $5485   (21-May-92 SY.AM49/R) Self portrait (38x28cm-15x11in) s.d.1914 canvas on panel (D.FL 10000)
£6061 $10970   (19-May-92 CH.AM31/R) Still life with gladioli (73x91cm-29x36in) s. (D.FL 20000)
£6790 $12358   (11-Dec-91 CH.AM216/R) Winter landscape (47x94cm-19x37in) s.d.1915 (D.FL 22000)
£15152 $27424   (21-May-92 SY.AM61/R) Flowering trees (108x95cm-43x37in) s. (D.FL 50000)
£1970 $3565   *(19-May-92 CH.AM77/R) Seated male nude (115x63cm-45x25in) s.d.1926 ink (D.FL 6500)*

SCHUKIN (after) (19th C) Russian
£900 $1674   (16-Jun-92 S14/R) Emperor Pavel Petrovich (73x57cm-29x22in)

SCHULDT, Fritiof (1891-1978) Swedish
£1140 $1983   (13-Apr-92 AB.S238) Young Norwegian girl in interior (79x64cm-31x25in) s. (S.KR 12000)

SCHULMAN, David (1881-1966) Dutch
£612 $1064   (14-Apr-92 SY.AM377) View in Edam (29x39cm-11x15in) s. (D.FL 2000)
£932 $1612   (24-Mar-92 VN.R87/R) Village in winter (39x58cm-15x23in) s. (D.FL 3000)
£1376 $2436   (5-Nov-91 SY.AM149/R) Woodcutters (76x90cm-30x35in) s. (D.FL 4500)
£1455 $2575   (22-Apr-92 CH.AM30) View of the harbour of Spakenburg, with a moored fishingfleet (41x60cm-16x24in) s. (D.FL 4800)
£1590 $2815   (5-Nov-91 SY.AM465/R) Blaricum in snow (35x64cm-14x25in) s. (D.FL 5200)
£1896 $3299   (14-Apr-92 SY.AM137) View of Laren, in winter (65x116cm-26x46in) s. (D.FL 6200)
£3704 $6481   (18-Feb-92 CH.AM1/R) A view of Amsterdam with the Central Station and the St. Nicolaas church beyond (50x70cm-20x28in) s. (D.FL 12000)

SCHULMAN, Lion (1851-1942) Dutch
£848 $1502   (22-Apr-92 CH.AM111) Elegant ladies and gentlemen conversing and strolling in a forest (27x22cm-11x9in) s. panel (D.FL 2800)
£864 $1512   (18-Feb-92 CH.AM331 a/R) Wooded landscape with stream and peasants on track near Osterbeek (39x52cm-15x20in) s.d.1886 (D.FL 2800)

SCHULMAN, Lion (attrib) (1851-1942) Dutch
£673 $1171   (14-Apr-92 SY.AM289) Figures in wooded landscape, village beyond (25x36cm-10x14in) panel (D.FL 2200)
£775 $1402   (3-Dec-91 FN.S2447/R) Peasant transporting wood with horse-drawn cart on snow-covered path (30x47cm-12x19in) s. (DM 2200)

SCHULTEN, Curtius (1893-?) ?
£759 $1305   (16-Oct-91 KM.K1370) Flowering Eifel landscape (54x66cm-21x26in) s. paper (DM 2200)

SCHULTZ, A (?) ?
£580 $1050   (5-Dec-91 FA.PH483 a) River landscape (66x99cm-26x39in) s.d.1891
£619 $1083   (25-Feb-92 UL.T231 b/R) Landscape (46x54cm-18x21in) (N.KR 7000)

SCHULTZ, Alexander (1901-1981) Norwegian
£966 $1661   (7-Oct-91 B.O120/R) Winter landscape (50x61cm-20x24in) s. (N.KR 11000)
£980 $1696   (23-Mar-92 B.O116/R) Landscape with houses (50x61cm-20x24in) s. panel (N.KR 11000)
£1070 $1850   (23-Mar-92 B.O115/R) Summer (50x62cm-20x24in) s.d.65 (N.KR 12000)
£1097 $1888   (7-Oct-91 B.O121/R) Landscape (55x46cm-22x18in) s. panel (N.KR 12500)
£1240 $2257   (10-Dec-91 UL.T217) Landscape (N.KR 14000)
£1240 $2257   (10-Dec-91 UL.T216) Landscape with trees (50x61cm-20x24in) (N.KR 14000)
£2193 $4079   (15-Jun-92 B.O135/R) The fisherman and the dreamer (81x100cm-32x39in) s.d.76 (N.KR 25000)
£400 $732   *(6-Feb-92 B.O214 a) Landscape with house (36x63cm-14x25in) s.d.81 W/C (N.KR 4500)*
£616 $1084   *(8-Apr-92 GWP.O64/R) House in landscape (35x54cm-14x21in) s.d.1978 W/C (N.KR 7000)*

SCHULTZ, George F (1869-?) American
£765 $1400   (17-May-92 DU.E1205) Quiet fishing village (51x76cm-20x30in) s.
          i.stretcher

SCHULTZ, Julius (19th C) Danish
£619 $1052   (25-Oct-91 BM.B827/R) Winter landscape with hunter transporting dead stag
          on horse-drawn sleigh (90x72cm-35x28in) s. (DM 1800)

SCHULTZBERG, Anshelm (1862-1945) Swedish
£1709 $2974   (13-Apr-92 AB.S236) Mountainous landscape, Gavinana, North Italy
          (86x100cm-34x39in) s.d.1911238 (S.KR 18000)
£1727 $3127   (3-Dec-91 AB.S4661/R) Seascape with boats and breakers (48x98cm-19x39in)
          s.i.d.1891 (S.KR 18000)
£2863 $5095   (28-Nov-91 BU.S34/R) Winter landscape at dusk (75x100cm-30x39in) s.
          (S.KR 30000)
£2925 $5235   (7-May-92 RAS.S69/R) April evening near Skarklitt's chalets, Alfdalen,
          Dalarne 1909 (70x110cm-28x43in) s. (S.KR 31000)
£3510 $6424   (12-May-92 GO.G158/R) Winter landscape from Bjorkbodarne, Dalarne
          (50x75cm-20x30in) s.d.1941 (S.KR 37000)
£3774 $6679   (5-Nov-91 BA.S166/R) The farm, Vesay, Alvdalen, Dalarna (60x80cm-24x31in)
          s.d.1943 (S.KR 40000)
£3795 $6945   (14-May-92 BU.S63/R) Winter landscape, Bergslagen (68x105cm-27x41in) s.
          (S.KR 40000)
£3890 $7119   (12-May-92 GO.G159/R) Country road to the sea (81x116cm-32x46in)
          s.i.d.1918 (S.KR 41000)
£4123 $7421   (19-Nov-91 GO.G164) Wooded landscape (160x200cm-63x79in) s.d.1913
          (S.KR 43000)
£4389 $7813   (28-Nov-91 BU.S35/R) Winter landscape with chalets, evening sun
          (80x100cm-31x39in) s.d.1910 (S.KR 46000)
£4432 $7667   (28-Mar-92 UA.U435/R) Winter landscape with morning sunshine
          (87x111cm-34x44in) s. (S.KR 46000)
£4607 $8338   (3-Dec-91 AB.S4660/R) Wooded landscape with tarn, sunny winter's day
          (80x113cm-31x44in) s. (S.KR 48000)
£5000 $9000   (22-Nov-91 S.BM140/R) Winter woodland (71x91cm-28x36in) s.d.1922
£5464 $10000   (3-Feb-92 S.SL361/R) Landscape with flowering lilac bower
          (102x109cm-40x43in) s. canvas on board
£5693 $10417   (14-May-92 BU.S62/R) Winter landscape, Alvdals, Dalarna
          (90x127cm-35x50in) s. (S.KR 60000)

SCHULTZE-BLUHM, Ursula see URSULA

SCHULTZE, Bernard (1915-) German
£5703 $10608   (19-Jun-92 G.Z42/R) The flying Dutchman (120x80cm-47x31in) s.d.1986
          (S.FR 15000)
£12238 $21783   (29-Nov-91 VG.B64/R) Aus Gestrupp (57x71cm-22x28in) s.i.d.1955 board
          (DM 35000)
£14035 $25263   (19-Nov-91 L.K1079/R) Lichtung (95x140cm-37x55in) s.d.1977 s.i.d.verso
          (DM 40000)
£561 $1011   (19-Nov-91 L.K1087) Abstract s.i. pencil (DM 1600)
£561 $1011   (23-Nov-91 N.M291) Composition (10x15cm-4x6in) s. col.pencil (DM 1600)
£825 $1526   (11-Jun-92 HN.H423/R) Composition (27x21cm-11x8in) s.i.d.1957 col. chk
          bodycol over indian ink pen (DM 2400)
£1100 $2034   (11-Jun-92 HN.H422/R) Composition (27x61cm-11x24in) mono. s.i.d.1952verso
          (DM 3200)
£1474 $2653   (19-Nov-91 L.K1082/R) Composition (49x74cm-19x29in) mono. chl col.chk
          board (DM 4200)
£1970 $3565   (21-May-92 SY.AM205/R) Untitled (49x62cm-19x24in) s.d.57 W/C col.crayon
          (D.FL 6500)
£2448 $4357   (30-Nov-91 VG.B365/R) Landscape on two feet (73x102cm-29x40in) s.i.d.1976
          indian ink pen board (DM 7000)
£2749 $5031   (2-Jun-92 L.K937/R) 6/11/57-59 (61x43cm-24x17in) s.i. i.verso mixed media
          (DM 8000)
£2901 $5280   (30-May-92 VG.B372/R) Composition 34 (61x45cm-24x18in) s.d.1958 gouache
          frottage (DM 8500)
£4196 $7469   (28-Nov-91 SY.BE79/R) Countries and customs (51x73cm-20x29in) s.i.d.66
          indian ink pen collage W/C chk gouache (DM 12000)
£5118 $8803   (16-Oct-91 G.Z65/R) Hommage a Stifter (73x102cm-29x40in) s.i.d.1980 W/C
          board (S.FR 13000)
£5263 $9474   (19-Nov-91 L.K1080/R) Abstract composition (68x98cm-27x39in) s.d.1961 W/C
          pen (DM 15000)

SCHULTZE, Carl (1856-?) German
£523 $951   (11-Dec-91 N.M586/R) Sunlit fjord landscape (60x80cm-24x31in) s.i.
          (DM 1500)
£3739 $6692   (16-Jan-92 D.V3/R) Engstersee landscape (84x110cm-33x43in) s.i.
          (A.S 75000)

SCHULTZE, Max (1845-1926) German
£1718 $2990   (18-Sep-91 N.M695/R) South Italian coastal landscape with buildings on
          hillside and figures (24x36cm-9x14in) s. (DM 5000)

SCHULTZE, Robert (1828-) German
£4296 $7474   (21-Sep-91 SA.A1791/R) Near Murren, Berner Oberland (101x151cm-40x59in)
          s. i.verso (DM 12500)

SCHULTZENHEIM, Ida von (1859-1940) Swedish
£2800 $5208   (17-Jun-92 S344/R) Boy with two greyhounds (129x189cm-51x74in) s.d.90

SCHULZ, Carl (19th C) German
£1146 $2041   (28-Apr-92 RAS.K197/R) Watermill by river (31x38cm-12x15in) s.d.1835 (D.KR 13000)

SCHULZ, Charles M (1922-) American
£843 $1500   (2-May-92 IH.NY140/R) Lucy flies tiny kite (38x56cm-15x22in) s. pen ink
£2247 $4000   (2-May-92 IH.NY141/R) Lucy and Snoopy dancing. Snoopy relaxes with head in water dish (13x69cm-5x27in) s. pen ink two

SCHULZ-RUMPOLD, Volkmar (1956-) German
£1181 $2031   (16-Oct-91 G.Z142/R) Das verwirrte Gesicht (55x37cm-22x15in) s.i.d.1986verso canvas on board (S.FR 3000)
£4811 $8804   (2-Jun-92 L.K947/R) Neuerdings gibt's Leute (118x82cm-46x32in) mixed media hessian (DM 14000)

SCHULZ-STRADTMANN, Otto (1892-1960) German
£557 $1015   (11-Dec-91 WE.MU105/R) Stream in wooded landscape, spring (60x80cm-24x31in) s. (DM 1600)
£1031 $1907   (13-Jun-92 WK.M358/R) Schloss Nymphenburg (70x100cm-28x39in) s. (DM 3000)
£1394 $2537   (11-Dec-91 N.M587/R) Viktualienmarkt, Munich (60x80cm-24x31in) s.i.d.1925 (DM 4000)

SCHULZE, Andreas (1955-) German
£2857 $5000   (27-Feb-92 CE.NY290/R) Untitled (209x359cm-82x141in) acrylic diptych
£3073 $5500   (6-May-92 CH.NY260/R) Untitled (200x400cm-79x157in) s.d.82 verso acrylic canvas diptych
£3911 $7000   (14-Nov-91 SY.NY224/R) Untitled (201x401cm-79x158in) s.d.1984 verso acrylic cotton two parts

SCHUMACHER, C J (19/20th C) ?
£1271 $2300   (24-May-92 LIT.L66) German landscape (53x102cm-21x40in) s.d.1874

SCHUMACHER, Emil (1912-) German
£12238 $21783   (26-Nov-91 KF.M1029/R) Composition (62x49cm-24x19in) s.d.1960 board (DM 35000)
£21053 $37895   (19-Nov-91 L.K1089/R) Untitled (70x50cm-28x20in) s.d.1960 (DM 60000)
£34130 $62116   (29-May-92 VG.B84/R) Liba (80x60cm-31x24in) s.d.1959 (DM 100000)
£82000 $141860   (26-Mar-92 S55/R) Tecins (77x181cm-30x71in) s.d.62 board
£3158 $5684   (19-Nov-91 L.K1092/R) Djerba (28x38cm-11x15in) s.i.d.1975 indian ink (DM 9000)
£5634 $10197   (6-Dec-91 GB.B7106/R) Mythical creatures (37x46cm-15x18in) s.d.1956 mixed media W/C (DM 16000)
£7018 $12632   (19-Nov-91 L.K1091/R) Rome (33x25cm-13x10in) s.i.d.1963 indian ink gouache (DM 20000)
£10239 $18635   (30-May-92 VG.B371/R) G-67 (49x66cm-19x26in) s.d.84 mixed media board (DM 30000)
£17065 $31058   (30-May-92 VG.B370/R) Composition (35x54cm-14x21in) s.d.1962 mixed media board on board (DM 50000)
£83916 $149371   (29-Nov-91 VG.B77/R) Boras (125x170cm-49x67in) s.d.1984 mixed media oil sand board (DM 240000)

SCHUMANN (?) ?
£787 $1400   (22-Jan-92 SY.NY263/R) Two peasant women in field (41x42cm-16x17in) s.
£1100 $1947   (13-Feb-92 CSK32/R) Still life of carnations, peonies and other mixed flowers in vase (63x47cm-25x19in) s.d.1894 pencil W/C bodycol.

SCHUPPEN, Jacob van (1670-1751) Dutch
£5500 $10560   (10-Jul-92 C211/R) Portrait of Victor Graf Philippi, General Commander of Bareuter Dragoons (145x123cm-57x48in) with sig.i.d.1723

SCHURCH, Johann Robert (1895-1941) Swiss
£1116 $2019   (5-Dec-91 SY.Z92/R) Saleve au matin (38x51cm-15x20in) s. s.i.verso board (S.FR 2800)
£1673 $3112   (19-Jun-92 ZOF.Z2085/R) Still life with vegetables (46x55cm-18x22in) s.i.indis.d.verso (S.FR 4400)
£2390 $4327   (4-Dec-91 G.Z1128/R) Christ (61x37cm-24x15in) (S.FR 6000)
£2789 $5048   (4-Dec-91 G.Z1127/R) Portrait of woman (46x55cm-18x22in) s. (S.FR 7000)
£2988 $5408   (4-Dec-91 G.Z1126/R) St Sebastian (55x46cm-22x18in) s. (S.FR 7500)
£398 $721   (4-Dec-91 G.Z1138) Pensive thoughts, possibly selfportrait. Figure study (34x25cm-13x10in) s.d.1916 pencil double-sided (S.FR 1000)
£444 $804   (20-May-92 GK.Z5139) Still life with pot plant and bowl (51x40cm-20x16in) s.d.1917 grease chk (S.FR 1200)
£558 $1010   (4-Dec-91 G.Z1141) Descent from the Cross (29x45cm-11x18in) s.d.1919 pencil (S.FR 1400)
£558 $1010   (4-Dec-91 G.Z1137) Two women (51x39cm-20x15in) s. pencil (S.FR 1400)
£613 $1061   (23-Mar-92 AB.L44/R) Reclining female nude (25x33cm-10x13in) pencil (S.FR 1600)
£637 $1154   (4-Dec-91 G.Z1133) La fuite en Egypte (51x39cm-20x15in) pencil (S.FR 1600)
£797 $1442   (4-Dec-91 G.Z1136) The hurdy gurdy player. Figure studies (44x31cm-17x12in) s.d.1916 double-sided (S.FR 2000)

1658

SCHURCH, Johann Robert (1895-1941) Swiss-cont.
£876	$1586	(4-Dec-91 G.Z1129/R) The Samaritan (45x30cm-18x12in) s.d.1919 pencil (S.FR 2200)
£977	$1789	(4-Jun-92 SY.Z389/R) Vom Zirkus (27x21cm-11x8in) s.i.d.27 indian ink pen (S.FR 2600)
£1073	$1856	(23-Mar-92 AB.L45/R) Two female nudes (26x21cm-10x8in) s.i. W/C indian ink (S.FR 2800)
£1573	$2800	(29-Apr-92 G.Z14/R) Three women (21x27cm-8x11in) indian ink pen wash (S.FR 4200)
£2191	$3966	(5-Dec-91 SY.Z89/R) Vor dem Wirtshaus (33x24cm-13x9in) s.d.24 chl pastel (S.FR 5500)

SCHURCH, Paul (1886-1939) Swiss
| £494 | $919 | (19-Jun-92 ZOF.Z2086/R) San Bernardino (59x74cm-23x29in) s.i.d.1933 (S.FR 1300) |

SCHURCHARDT, F (?) ?
| £920 | $1600 | (11-Sep-91 D.NY75) Day's end (86x112cm-34x44in) s.d.84 |

SCHURIG, Otto (19th C) German
| £825 | $1435 | (19-Sep-91 N.M2812) Danae (85x120cm-33x47in) s.d.1898 after van Dyck (DM 2400) |

SCHURJIN, Raul (1907-1983) Argentinian
£604	$1100	(11-Dec-91 RO.BA249) Costeras (52x38cm-20x15in) s.i.
£1292	$2300	(28-Apr-92 PO.BA40) Senoritas en la playa (44x90cm-17x35in) s.d.59 hardboard
£1404	$2500	(28-Apr-92 PO.BA41) Coqueluche (70x30cm-28x12in) s. hardboard

SCHURR, Claude (1920-) French
| £1230 | $2213 | (2-Feb-92 ZZ.F213/R) Le bateau vert (46x55cm-18x22in) s. (F.FR 12000) |
| £2330 | $4218 | (20-May-92 I.N179/R) Prelassement (130x97cm-51x38in) s. (F.FR 23000) |

SCHUSTER, Donna (1883-1953) American
£1130	$2000	(12-Feb-92 B.SF586/R) Tulips (76x63cm-30x25in) s.
£1447	$2750	(23-Jun-92 MOR.P92) California landscape (38x38cm-15x15in) s. board
£1714	$3000	(31-Mar-92 MOR.P96) Hollywood hills (46x61cm-18x24in) st.studio board
£2286	$4000	(31-Mar-92 MOR.P33) Boats in harbour (41x30cm-16x12in) s. board
£2401	$4250	(12-Feb-92 B.SF587/R) Apples and daisies (71x56cm-28x22in) s.
£3143	$5500	(31-Mar-92 MOR.P94) Self portrait (61x56cm-24x22in) s.
£3933	$7000	(26-Nov-91 MOR.P74) Kitchen still life (64x76cm-25x30in) s.
£674	$1200	(26-Nov-91 MOR.P74 a) Fishing boats at rest (36x46cm-14x18in) s. W/C

SCHUSTER, Franz (1870-1903) Austrian
| £1659 | $3119 | (17-Dec-91 DUR.M33/R) El despertar de la Primavera (77x120cm-30x47in) s. (S.P 300000) |

SCHUSTER, Josef (1812-1890) Austrian
| £1697 | $3088 | (27-May-92 D.V606/R) Flowers surrounded by cartouche (106x84cm-42x33in) s. (A.S 35000) |
| £2908 | $5293 | (27-May-92 D.V576/R) View of Venice (105x78cm-41x31in) s.d.1833 (A.S 60000) |

SCHUSTER, Joseph (1873-1945) Austrian
| £1027 | $1767 | (8-Oct-91 ZEL.L1716/R) Still life of fruit on plate and silver tea jug (40x49cm-16x19in) s.d.1926 panel (DM 3000) |

SCHUSTER, Karl Maria (1871-1953) Austrian
£488	$844	(3-Oct-91 D.V81/R) Rectory, Krumbach, Lower Austria (64x50cm-25x20in) s.d.1948 (A.S 10000)
£1300	$2496	(28-Jul-92 SWS412/R) Quiet moments (49x38cm-19x15in) s.
£1384	$2422	(19-Feb-92 D.V4/R) Girl reading in interior (81x72cm-32x28in) s.d.1918 (A.S 28000)
£1444	$2599	(19-Nov-91 RAS.K139/R) Interior with girl reading book (107x76cm-42x30in) s.indist.d.19.3 (D.KR 16000)

SCHUSTER, Rudolf (1848-1902) German
| £859 | $1495 | (17-Sep-91 FN.S2535/R) Village street of Waldenbuch with figures (28x37cm-11x15in) mono.i.d.1879 pencil (DM 2500) |

SCHUSTER-WOLDAN, Raffael (1870-1951) German
| £1557 | $2958 | (24-Jun-92 KM.K1256/R) Portrait of young woman (66x58cm-26x23in) s.d.1928 (DM 4500) |
| £1923 | $3327 | (25-Mar-92 KM.K1423/R) Female nude reclining (62x77cm-24x30in) s. (DM 5500) |

SCHUTT, Gustav (1890-1968) Austrian
| £878 | $1520 | (3-Oct-91 D.V235/R) Landscape (31x39cm-12x15in) board (A.S 18000) |
| £1092 | $1944 | (28-Nov-91 D.V181/R) Birds' house (55x68cm-22x27in) s. (A.S 22000) |

SCHUTZ, Christian Georg (18/19th C) German
| £6993 | $12098 | (25-Mar-92 KM.K993/R) Romantic Rhine landscape with shipping and figures (24x33cm-9x13in) s. panel (DM 20000) |
| £7215 | $12555 | (15-Apr-92 CB.P6) Paysage d'hiver (71x115cm-28x45in) (F.FR 71000) |

SCHUTZ, Christian Georg (18/19th C) German-cont.
£7813 $13828   (5-Nov-91 GF.L2077/R) River landscape with fortified castle
     (23x35cm-9x14in) (S.FR 20000)
£9259 $17593   (24-Jun-92 CSC.P50/R) Vue de la vallee du Rhin (38x57cm-15x22in)
     (F.FR 90000)
£10465 $18000   (10-Oct-91 SY.NY106/R) Extensive mountainous river landscape with a
     castle, village beyond (29x39cm-11x15in) s.

SCHUTZ, Christian Georg (attrib) (18/19th C) German
£2486 $4500   (22-May-92 SY.NY165/R) Extensive river landscape with figures and town on
     bank (41x57cm-16x22in)

SCHUTZ, Christian Georg I (1718-1791) German
£3575 $6256   (24-Feb-92 CSC.P23/R) Paysage fluvial anime de promeneurs
     (24x31cm-9x12in) (F.FR 35000)
£5670 $9866   (18-Sep-91 N.M451/R) Hilly river landscape with buildings and figures
     (29x40cm-11x16in) s. panel (DM 16500)
£6485 $11737   (21-May-92 L.K141/R) Rhine landscape with town and hillside church ruin
     (28x36cm-11x14in) s. copper (DM 19000)
£9500 $17290   (10-Dec-91 PH3/R) River landscape with vessels moored before castle
     (39x54cm-15x21in)
£14684 $25991   (7-Nov-91 D.V89/R) Wooded landscape with shepherds resting by stream and
     town beyond (39x32cm-15x13in) s. panel one of pair (A.S 300000)
£14684 $25991   (7-Nov-91 D.V88/R) Wooded landscape with shepherdesses by waterfall,
     evening (39x32cm-15x13in) s. panel one of pair (A.S 300000)
£17000 $32640   (8-Jul-92 S325/R) Rhenish landscapes (20x29cm-8x11in) s. panel pair

SCHUTZ, Christian Georg I (attrib) (1718-1791) German
£4623 $7952   (8-Oct-91 ZEL.L1715/R) Figures resting in grotto (22x29cm-9x11in)
     (DM 13500)

SCHUTZ, Christian Georg I (circle) (1718-1791) German
£7500 $13500   (21-Nov-91 CSK120/R) Rhenish landscapes with drovers and cattle
     (28x40cm-11x16in) panel pair

SCHUTZ, Christian Georg I (style) (1718-1791) German
£3800 $6764   (30-Oct-91 S149/R) Rhenish landscape with figures crossing bridge
     (30x51cm-12x20in) panel

SCHUTZ, Christian Georg II (1758-1823) German
£4938 $8840   (12-Nov-91 SY.AM96/R) Rhineland landscape (50x63cm-20x25in) (D.FL 16000)

SCHUTZ, Christian Georg II (attrib) (1758-1823) German
£1272 $2226   (3-Apr-92 BM.B597/R) Landscape with watermill (23x30cm-9x12in) panel
     (DM 3600)
£2412 $4367   (19-May-92 AB.S4377/R) Landscape with windmill and figures
     (25x34cm-10x13in) panel (S.KR 25500)
£3873 $7011   (4-Dec-91 DO.H2942/R) River landscape (22x30cm-9x12in) panel (DM 11000)

SCHUTZ, Franz (1751-1781) German
£7948 $13592   (18-Mar-92 D.V177/R) Rhine landscape (25x32cm-10x13in) s. panel
     (A.S 160000)

SCHUTZ, Heinrich (1875-?) German
£549 $1000   (26-May-92 CE.NY70/R) Load of firewood (55x73cm-22x29in) s.d.16 board
£619 $1052   (25-Oct-91 BM.B949/R) Peasant with horse-drawn plough (51x71cm-20x28in)
     s. (DM 1800)

SCHUTZ, Jan Frederik (1817-1888) Dutch
£795 $1415   (30-Oct-91 CH.AM261) Sailors by rowing boat on beach (15x24cm-6x9in)
     s.d.61 panel (D.FL 2600)
£1150 $2082   (19-May-92 SWS173) Barge and other shipping in calm waters
     (32x50cm-13x20in) s.d.79 card
£2752 $5037   (1-Jun-92 W.T1377/R) Dutch wydschip and brigantine in heavy seas
     (44x80cm-17x31in) s. (C.D 6000)

SCHUTZ, Johann Georg (1755-1813) German
£1835 $3413   (18-Jun-92 SY.MO258/R) Paysage fluvial avec chateau (23x30cm-9x12in)
     (F.FR 18000)
£2572 $4655   (5-Dec-91 SY.MO324/R) Paysage Rhenan (21x29cm-8x11in) (F.FR 25000)
£3870 $7043   (11-Dec-91 LD.P49/R) Bord du Rhin (38x47cm-15x19in) sig. (F.FR 38000)

SCHUTZ, Johann Georg (attrib) (1755-1813) German
£3024 $5292   (25-Sep-91 CSC.P12/R) Paysage rocheux au moulin (112x81cm-44x32in)
     (F.FR 30000)

SCHUTZ, Johannes (20th C) Swiss
£843 $1500   (28-Apr-92 PO.BA9) Vista de St.Moritz (62x82cm-24x32in) s.d.1931
£1333 $2413   (19-May-92 GF.L2581/R) View of St Moritz lake and Piz Languard
     (60x80cm-24x31in) s.d.1937 (S.FR 3600)
£2205 $4102   (19-Jun-92 ZOF.Z1620/R) View of Piz della Margina (62x82cm-24x32in)
     d.1936 s.i.verso (S.FR 5800)

SCHUTZ, Willem Joannes (1854-1933) Dutch
£825 $1435   (17-Sep-91 FN.S2539/R) Fishing boats on Scheweningen beach at low tide (27x36cm-11x14in) s. (DM 2400)

SCHUTZE, Wilhelm (1840-1898) German
£530 $928   (3-Apr-92 BM.B796) Still life of lobster (63x94cm-25x37in) s. (DM 1500)
£13000 $23140   (27-Nov-91 S136/R) Adorable kittens (74x60cm-29x24in) s.i.

SCHUYFF, Peter (1958-) Dutch
£1341 $2400   (12-Nov-91 CE.NY143/R) Mr America no 1 (84x61cm-33x24in) s.d.84verso acrylic
£1714 $3000   (25-Feb-92 SY.NY222/R) Untitled (107x91cm-42x36in) s.d.85verso acrylic linen
£2286 $4000   (25-Feb-92 SY.NY219/R) Untitled blue (190x191cm-75x75in) acrylic
£2312 $4000   (3-Oct-91 SY.NY180 a/R) The weld (305x305cm-120x120in) acrylic linen
£3911 $7000   (12-Nov-91 CE.NY145/R) Untitled (190x190cm-75x75in) s.d.87verso acrylic linen
£3911 $7000   (13-Nov-91 CH.NY322/R) Master tone (305x305cm-120x120in) acrylic
£4624 $8000   (3-Oct-91 SY.NY181/R) Untitled (305x305cm-120x120in) acrylic linen

SCHWAB, Vladimir (20th C) ?
£1232 $2218   (19-Nov-91 FB.P149/R) Composition (83x62cm-33x24in) (F.FR 12000)

SCHWABE, Carlos (1866-1926) Swiss
£4348 $7739   (29-Nov-91 GAB.G2872/R) Implorantes (17x11cm-7x4in) s. (S.FR 11000)
£7312 $13016   (29-Nov-91 GAB.G2871/R) La mort intimidee (17x11cm-7x4in) s. (S.FR 18500)
£438   *$797*   *(11-Dec-91 ZZ.F39) La virginite (14x10cm-6x4in) s.d.1909 gouache W/C (F.FR 4300)*

SCHWABE, Randolphe (1885-?) British
£1800 $3078   (11-Mar-92 S6/R) Braunton, Devon (75x61cm-30x24in) s. s.i.verso board

SCHWALBACH, Carl (1885-1983) German
£629   *$1120*   *(25-Nov-91 WK.M926/R) Age, summer evening (73x120cm-29x47in) s.i.d.1940/41 oil chk canvas (DM 1800)*

SCHWALBE, Ole (1929-) Danish
£578 $1006   (18-Sep-91 KH.K174) Composition (55x46cm-22x18in) s.d.56verso masonite (D.KR 6500)
£617 $1116   (20-May-92 KH.K170) Composition (105x121cm-41x48in) (D.KR 7000)

SCHWANFELDER, Charles Henry (1774-1837) British
£2186 $4000   (5-Jun-92 SY.NY6/R) A bay hunter (58x76cm-23x30in) s.d.1826
£3200 $5728   (15-Nov-91 C103/R) Isaac, saddled grey racehorse held by owner Sam Darling, on gallops (63x76cm-25x30in) s.d.1837
£7000 $11760   (26-Aug-91 S858/R) Rough shooting (84x111cm-33x44in)

SCHWARTZ, Andrew T (1867-1942) American
£703 $1300   (10-Jun-92 CE.NY435/R) Purple mountains (66x76cm-26x30in) s.
£5263 $9000   (12-Mar-92 CH.NY175/R) Annisquam River (82x92cm-32x36in) s.d.1911

SCHWARTZ, C A (19th C) ?
£414   *$750*   *(20-May-92 D.NY11) Card game in tavern (15x10cm-6x4in) s.i. gouache*

SCHWARTZ, Daniel and FISHBURNE, St Julian (20th C) American
£1371   *$2400*   *(26-Sep-91 CH.NY277/R) New Paltz, New York. Head of young girl. Weehawken at sunrise (46x77cm-18x30in) two s.d. one s.i.d. pastel one oil three*

SCHWARTZ, Frans (1850-1917) Danish
£528 $887   (27-Aug-91 RAS.K498) Young nude girl seen from behind (26x25cm-10x10in) sketch (D.KR 6000)
£1408 $2366   (27-Aug-91 RAS.K497) Apollo passing Poseidon and his daughters (63x64cm-25x25in) (D.KR 16000)
£2646 $4709   (28-Apr-92 RAS.K135/R) Young girl with oak wreath (65x49cm-26x19in) mono.d.1889 (D.KR 30000)

SCHWARTZ, Mommie (20th C) Dutch?
£3939 $7130   (21-May-92 SY.AM41/R) Still life (45x55cm-18x22in) s. (D.FL 13000)

SCHWARTZ, William S (1896-) American
£3837 $6600   (20-Oct-91 HG.C41) Russian village (76x66cm-30x26in) s.
£7018 $12000   (12-Mar-92 CH.NY200/R) The hurdy-gurdy man (92x102cm-36x40in) s.d.1929 i.verso
£640   *$1100*   *(20-Oct-91 HG.C42) Farm landscape (56x76cm-22x30in) s. gouache board*

SCHWARTZE, Theresa (1851-1918) Dutch
£795   *$1383*   *(14-Apr-92 SY.AM418) Portrait of girl in hat (37x27cm-15x11in) s. black chk htd white (D.FL 2600)*

SCHWARZ, Christoph (circle) (1545-1592) German
£5385 $10285   (15-Jul-92 CH.S766/R) Saint Cecilia (35x30cm-14x12in) panel (A.D 14000)

SCHWARZ, Feri (1869-1923) Russian
£471   *$842*   *(12-Nov-91 GF.L5365/R) View of Stephansplatz with figures and cathedral, Vienna (20x15cm-8x6in) s. W/C (S.FR 1200)*

SCHWARZ, Wenzel (1842-1919) German
£902 $1633   (5-Dec-91 D.V173) Wien I, Schonlaterngasse (14x10cm-6x4in) s.i. W/C
                 (A.S 18000)

SCHWARZENBACH, Armin (1914-) Swiss
£627 $1067   (23-Oct-91 GD.B657/R) Rocks with Alpine flowers (47x37cm-19x15in) s.
                 board (S.FR 1600)

SCHWARZENBACH, Hans (1911-1983) Swiss
£791 $1423   (19-Nov-91 GS.B3249) Still life of silver thistles (30x45cm-12x18in)
                 s.d.44 pavatex (S.FR 2000)
£1314 $2352   (6-May-92 GD.B1143/R) Still life with silver thistles and blue jug
                 (29x43cm-11x17in) s.d.42 board (S.FR 3600)

SCHWARZENFELD, Adolf von see SCHREITTER von SCHWARZENFELD, Adolf

SCHWARZER, Bernd (1954-) German
£1873 $3333   (29-Apr-92 G.Z88/R) Hanging ox (30x18cm-12x7in) acrylic pavatex
                 (S.FR 5000)
£5243 $9333   (29-Apr-92 G.Z86/R) Head with leaves - German head with leaves
                 (72x53cm-28x21in) s.i.d.1954 acrylic board (S.FR 14000)

SCHWARZER, Ludwig (1912-) Austrian
£2234 $3977   (28-Nov-91 D.V249/R) O3Y (42x58cm-17x23in) s.d.67 panel (A.S 45000)

SCHWARZLER, K (20th C) ?
£989 $1730   (19-Feb-92 D.V79) Woodland path (47x38cm-19x15in) s. board (A.S 20000)

SCHWEGE, E von (19th C) Polish?
£3716 $6429   (8-Sep-91 REM.W32) Forest skirmish (120x105cm-47x41in) s. (P.Z 71000000)

SCHWEICKHARDT, Hendrik Willem (1746-1797) German
£900 $1575   (27-Feb-92 CSK160/R) Sheep grazing on a hill (14x18cm-6x7in) s. panel
£1158 $1980   (13-Mar-92 FN.S2957/R) Dutch 17th century interior with figures playing
                 tric trac (32x25cm-13x10in) panel (DM 3300)
£2700 $5184   (9-Jul-92 B156/R) Sailing boats and rowing boats on river, windmills and
                 villages beyond (32x44cm-13x17in) panel

SCHWEICKHARDT, Hendrik Willem (attrib) (1746-1797) German
£3874 $7205   (20-Jun-92 CH.MO38 a/R) Scene de patinage (27x40cm-11x16in) panel
                 (F.FR 38000)

SCHWEICKHARDT, Hendrik Willem (circle) (1746-1797) German
£2800 $5348   (21-Jul-92 PH242/R) Figures skating on frozen river before cow shed
                 (22x32cm-9x13in) panel

SCHWEICKHARDT, Hendrik Willem (style) (1746-1797) German
£2500 $4250   (23-Oct-91 S79/R) Arcadian landscape (112x143cm-44x56in)

SCHWEINFURTH, Ernst (1818-1877) German
£8500 $14450   (23-Oct-91 S64/R) In the Roman campagna (81x119cm-32x47in) s.d.1857

SCHWEIZER, Albert (1886-1948) Swiss
£608 $1132   (19-Jun-92 ZOF.Z2087) Baselbieter Jura landscape (43x65cm-17x26in) s.
                 (S.FR 1600)

SCHWEMMINGER, Josef (1804-1895) Austrian
£699 $1210   (25-Mar-92 KM.K1424) View of castle and figures, possibly Burg Werfen,
                 Salzburger Land (116x164cm-46x65in) (DM 2000)
£1951 $3551   (11-Dec-91 WE.MU319) Figures in cornfield (9cm-4ins circular) s. i.verso
                 paper (DM 5600)
£3093 $5381   (18-Sep-91 N.M696/R) Burg Golling near Salzburg (42x34cm-17x13in) s.
                 i.stretcher (DM 9000)
£976 $1698   (19-Sep-91 D.V247/R) Sunset near farmhouse. Mountainous lake landscape
                 (15x19cm-6x7in) s. W/C pair (A.S 20000)

SCHWENINGER, Carl (19th C) Austrian
£890 $1557   (20-Feb-92 D.V385/R) Fortified castle in mountainous landscape
                 (50x40cm-20x16in) mono.d.1876 (A.S 18000)
£11000 $19580   (29-Nov-91 C43/R) Ein Plauderstundchen (68x95cm-27x37in) s.i.
£12000 $22320   (19-Jun-92 C77/R) Sylvia (48x60cm-19x24in) s.

SCHWENINGER, Carl (attrib) (19th C) Austrian
£748 $1338   (16-Jan-92 D.V119) Traunsee landscape with boats (63x84cm-25x33in)
                 (A.S 15000)

SCHWENINGER, Carl (elder) (1818-1887) Austrian
£2439 $4244   (19-Sep-91 D.V15/R) Achensee landscape with coach arriving, Tyrol
                 (48x63cm-19x25in) mono. indis.i.verso (A.S 50000)

SCHWENINGER, Carl (younger) (1854-1903) Austrian
£752 $1361   (5-Dec-91 D.V132) Deep in thoughts (47x38cm-19x15in) (A.S 15000)

SCHWICHTENBERG, Martel (1896-1945) German
£1329 $2365   (26-Nov-91 KF.M1038/R) Still life with Japanese doll (76x60cm-30x24in) s.
                     (DM 3800)

SCHWINGE, Friedrich Wilhelm (1852-1913) German
£893 $1662   (20-Jun-92 BM.B888/R) Wooded heath landscape (217x122cm-85x48in) s.
                     (DM 2600)
£1031 $1753   (25-Oct-91 BM.B828/R) Children walking on path in heath landscape with
                     thunderstorm rising (55x75cm-22x30in) s.d.1885 board (DM 3000)
£1329 $2272   (19-Mar-92 N.M2837/R) Pond with waterlilies in park landscape
                     (103x151cm-41x59in) s.d.1913 (DM 3800)

SCHWITTERS, Kurt (1887-1948) German
£950 $1700   (9-May-92 CE.NY4/R) Cabin near Hotel Djupvasshytta (23x17cm-9x7in)
                     init.d.38 s.d.verso panel
£4811 $8419   (27-Sep-91 GRA.B2832/R) S Style (8x7cm-3x3in) d.1946 collage board
                     (DM 14000)
£8000 $13840   (25-Mar-92 S55/R) Collage (6x5cm-2x2in) init.d.47 collage
£9000 $16290   (4-Dec-91 S135/R) Das herz geht zur muhle (26x29cm-10x11in) init.d.1919
                     W/C red crayon
£14000 $24220   (25-Mar-92 S56/R) Collage (26x22cm-10x9in) s.d.47 collage
£24742 $45773   (12-Jun-92 HN.H769/R) Red coffee mill (18x16cm-7x6in) s. stamp drawing
                     (DM 72000)
£26230 $48000   (13-May-92 CH.NY266/R) Untitled (28x22cm-11x9in) s.d.1930 init.d.1930
                     verso collage
£28249 $50000   (5-Nov-91 CH.NY6/R) Merzbild (18x14cm-7x6in) collage
£35000 $63350   (4-Dec-91 S150/R) M.Z.30,3 (32x22cm-13x9in) s.d.1930 collage
£37801 $69175   (3-Jun-92 L.K428/R) Merzzeichnung (10x7cm-4x3in) s.i.d.1920 mixed media
                     collage (DM 110000)
£48023 $85000   (5-Nov-91 CH.NY3/R) Merzbild (17x14cm-7x6in) init.d.22 collage paper
£68259 $124232   (29-May-92 VG.B47/R) Merzzeichnung 54, fallende Werte (15x12cm-6x5in)
                     s.i.d.1920 collage paper fabric painted (DM 200000)
£124294 $220000   (6-Nov-91 SY.NY32/R) Merzbild 9A (16x19cm-6x7in) s.i.d.verso assemblage
                     collage oil cardboard

SCHYL, Jules (1893-1977) Swedish
£496 $872   (11-Apr-92 FAL.M374/R) Landscape with horse grazing (27x35cm-11x14in)
                     s.d.46 panel (S.KR 5200)
£665 $1191   (16-Nov-91 FAL.M327/R) Still life of flowers (35x27cm-14x11in) s.d.1966
                     panel (S.KR 7000)
£757 $1370   (19-May-92 AB.S5325/R) Still life of cut flowers (75x61cm-30x24in) s.
                     (S.KR 8000)
£906 $1594   (11-Apr-92 FAL.M377/R) Composition with woman (51x42cm-20x17in) s.
                     (S.KR 9500)
£913 $1633   (16-Nov-91 FAL.M328/R) Avignon, Ville-Neuf, 1924 (56x47cm-22x19in) s.
                     (S.KR 9600)
£1141 $2042   (16-Nov-91 FAL.M330/R) Reclining model (48x56cm-19x22in) s.d.1928
                     (S.KR 12000)
£2186 $3913   (16-Nov-91 FAL.M332/R) Spanish lady (79x63cm-31x25in) s.d.XXII
                     (S.KR 23000)

SCIALOJA, Toti (1914-) Italian
£2041 $3736   (12-May-92 F.R144) Senza titolo (68x95cm-27x37in) s.d.1973 faesite
                     (I.L 4500000)
£2556 $4627   (3-Dec-91 F.R161) Senza titolo (100x70cm-39x28in) s.d.1988 paper
                     (I.L 5500000)
£2763 $5029   (9-Dec-91 CH.R86/R) Parigi (65x54cm-26x21in) s.i.d.1950verso
                     (I.L 6000000)
£2942 $5354   (25-May-92 CH.R52/R) Natura morta (60x81cm-24x32in) s.d.54 s.d.verso
                     (I.L 6500000)
£3685 $6706   (9-Dec-91 CH.R119/R) Natura morta (100x65cm-39x26in) s.d.1954
                     (I.L 8000000)
£5097 $9073   (29-Nov-91 F.F135/R) Viola (126x173cm-50x68in) s.i.d.1978 tempera
                     canvasboard (I.L 11000000)
£3200 $6079   (23-Jun-92 F.M203/R) Intermittenze piccole (64x136cm-25x54in)
                     s.i.d.1966verso mixed media canvas (I.L 7000000)

SCIFONI, Anatolio (1841-1884) Italian
£4372 $8000   (16-May-92 HG.C57/R) Offering (66x53cm-26x21in) s. panel

SCILLA, Agostino (1629-1700) Italian
£4800 $8544   (1-Nov-91 C17/R) Dead hare, pair Lapwing, Red Mullet, oysters and lemons
                     on rock (69x96cm-27x38in)

SCILTIAN, Gregorio (1900-1985) Russian
£7890 $14832   (19-Dec-91 F.M230/R) Ritratto di donna (54x45cm-21x18in) s. panel
                     (I.L 17000000)
£8147 $14827   (26-May-92 SY.MI162/R) Natura morta con libri (41x52cm-16x20in)
                     s.d.XXXVII (I.L 18000000)
£1297 $2310   (29-Nov-91 F.F84) Nudo (45x35cm-18x14in) s. mixed media cardboard
                     (I.L 2800000)

SCIUTI, Giuseppi (1835-1911) Italian
£16096 $28811   (14-Nov-91 CH.R102/R) Il Tempio di Venere (54x74cm-21x29in) s.
                     (I.L 35000000)

CKELL, Ludwig (1833-1912) German
£1229 $2224   (21-May-92 L.K480) View of Altausser lake, Salzkammergut (16x25cm-6x10in)
            s. panel (DM 3600)
£1407 $2505   (29-Oct-91 PH.T30/R) Wooded landscape with figure on path
            (46x61cm-18x24in) s.d.1869 (C.D 2800)
£1916 $3488   (11-Dec-91 N.M592/R) View of village with Eiger, Monch and Jungfrau,
            Berner Oberland (40x52cm-16x20in) mono.d.1856 (DM 5500)
£3985 $7292   (14-May-92 BU.S175/R) Mill house in Tyrol (52x40cm-20x16in) s. panel
            (S.KR 42000)
£4530 $8244   (11-Dec-91 WE.MU290) Landscape with figures (46x61cm-18x24in) s.d.1869
            (DM 13000)
£6993 $11958   (18-Mar-92 N.M641/R) View of Partenkirchen (64x85cm-25x33in) s.
            i.stretcher (DM 20000)

COGNAMIGLIO, E (19th C) Italian
£686 $1200   (18-Feb-92 CE.NY223/R) Gypsy woman (30x19cm-12x7in) s. panel
£1571 $3000   (16-Jul-92 SY.NY584/R) Gypsy musicians in an interior (74x48cm-29x19in)
            s.

COPPA, Giuseppe (19th C) Italian
£3351 $5965   (28-Apr-92 RAS.K287/R) Prospect view of Napoli (43x66cm-17x26in) i.verso
            gouache (D.KR 38000)

COPPETTA, Pietro (1863-1920) Italian
£2326 $4000   (17-Oct-91 SY.NY362 a/R) Dans le parc (11x18cm-4x7in) s.
£5233 $9000   (17-Oct-91 SY.NY373/R) L'Arc du Carrousel et Les Tuileries
            (11x17cm-4x7in) s. board
£7267 $12500   (17-Oct-91 SY.NY374/R) L'Arc du Carrousel au Louvre (14x20cm-6x8in) s.
            board
£11497 $20579   (14-Nov-91 CH.R57/R) Vedute di Parigi (13x20cm-5x8in) s. set of four
            (I.L 25000000)
£552 $988   (14-Nov-91 CH.R33) Donna seduta (39x28cm-15x11in) s.verso pencil
            (I.L 1200000)

COREL, Jan van (style) (1495-1562) Dutch
£4405 $7797   (7-Nov-91 D.V124/R) St Sebastian in mountainous river landscape with
            stone bridge (104x74cm-41x29in) (A.S 90000)

CORIEL, J B (1883-?) Belgian
£600 $1044   (14-Apr-92 GM.B500/R) Fond St Jean a Montigny (80x110cm-31x43in) s.
            (B.FR 36000)

CORIEL, Jean Baptiste (1883-?) Belgian
£2483 $4495   (23-May-92 KV.L294/R) Orchard in the spring (50x80cm-20x31in) s.
            (B.FR 150000)

CORZELLI, Eugenio (1890-1958) Italian
£779 $1379   (7-Nov-91 F.M27) Villa a Resina, Napoli (50x40cm-20x16in) s.
            (I.L 1700000)
£916 $1622   (7-Nov-91 F.M29) Gregge nel villaggio di Fittleworth (50x40cm-20x16in) s.
            (I.L 2000000)
£2088 $3883   (16-Jun-92 F.M312/R) Spiaggia al tramonto con figure (50x81cm-20x32in) s.
            (I.L 4600000)
£3857 $7175   (16-Jun-92 F.M314/R) Piazza Saint Denis, Parigi (44x61cm-17x24in) s.
            (I.L 8500000)
£4631 $8012   (24-Mar-92 CH.R118) Parigi, Sulla senna (20x30cm-8x12in) s. canvas on
            board pair (I.L 10000000)
£5650 $10227   (18-May-92 SY.MI63/R) Passeggiata a Parigi (49x82cm-19x32in) s.
            (I.L 12500000)

COTT, Adam Sherriff (1887-1980) Canadian
£1194 $2125   (26-Nov-91 JOY.T254/R) Plains Indian Chieftain portrait (75x60cm-30x24in)
            s. (C.D 2400)

COTT, Clyde Eugene (1884-1959) American
£1271 $2250   (12-Feb-92 B.SF552/R) Shimmering sands, Laguna beach (76x102cm-30x40in)
            s.

COTT, David (1806-1849) British
£632 $1200   (24-Jun-92 D.NY73) View across the lake (61x91cm-24x36in) s.
£750 $1283   (11-Mar-92 S140) Lagoon (76x61cm-30x24in) init.d.76 verso
£2400 $4152   (2-Oct-91 S159/R) Noonday beach (152x122cm-60x48in) init.d.78verso

COTT, Frank Edwin (1862-1929) American
£1461 $2600   (3-May-92 LIT.L126) St Germain des Pres, Paris (84x91cm-33x36in) s.

COTT, Howard (1902-1983) American
£449 $800   (2-May-92 IH.NY97/R) Three men's heads, holding beer glasses
            (38x91cm-15x36in) s. gouache

COTT, J W A (1815-1907) British
£667 $1200   (22-Nov-91 E.EDM994/R) The Bullard Mansion, Cambridge, Massachusetts
            (30x51cm-12x20in) s.d.1866 board

SCOTT, James (?) British
£1300 $2262   (12-Sep-91 CSK114) Portrait of lady in black and white dress in interior (163x96cm-64x38in)

SCOTT, John (19th C) British
£662 $1199   (19-May-92 AB.S5326/R) Untitled (52x49cm-20x19in) s.d.87verso metal (S.KR 7000)
£3100 $5642   (10-Dec-91 AG350/R) Snow-rigged brig Welcome off Tynemouth (52x75cm-20x30in) s.

SCOTT, John W A (1815-1907) British
£505 $950   (18-Dec-91 SY.NY2/R) Still life of fruit on tabletop (35x50cm-14x20in) s.

SCOTT, Julian (1846-1901) American
£1130 $2000   (9-Nov-91 W.W193/R) Union soldier (30x18cm-12x7in) s.d.1894 board
£1250 $2200   (12-Apr-92 LIT.L244) Spinning (74x58cm-29x23in) s.d.1884

SCOTT, Robert (20th C) British
£1000 $1720   (10-Oct-91 CSK33/R) Astra, Candida, Velsheda and Britannia racing off Needles, Isle of Wight (76x102cm-30x40in) s.d.91 s.i.verso

SCOTT, Samuel (1703-1772) British
£9500 $17005   (13-Nov-91 S1/R) The morning gun (27x35cm-11x14in) s.

SCOTT, Samuel (circle) (1703-1772) British
£1309 $2500   (16-Jul-92 SY.NY230/R) View of London (21x32cm-8x13in) panel
£17000 $30430   (15-Nov-91 C51/R) View of quadrangle of Christ's Hospital, with members of school to fore (74x117cm-29x46in)

SCOTT, Septimus Edwin (1879-?) British
£5500 $9460   (6-Mar-92 C120/R) Lords, Eton and Harrow (23x39cm-9x15in) s. W/C bodycol
£5500 $9460   (6-Mar-92 C119/R) Henley Regatta (38x30cm-15x12in) s. W/C bodycol

SCOTT, Sir Peter (1909-1989) British
£620 $1110   (5-May-92 SWS499/R) The evening clearance - mallards (24x34cm-9x13in) s.d.1981
£900 $1611   (14-Jan-92 SWS273/R) Pinkfeet on Arnafellsalda, Central Iceland (61x51cm-24x20in) s.d.1952
£1150 $2001   (17-Sep-91 PH40/R) Eight penguins (38x45cm-15x18in) s.d.1975
£1300 $2275   (25-Feb-92 C60/R) Early morning pintails (49x75cm-19x30in) s.d.1934 i.verso
£2459 $4500   (5-Jun-92 SY.NY284/R) A pearly dawn (38x45cm-15x18in) s.d.1939
£2800 $4900   (25-Feb-92 C51/R) Widgeon displaying (37x45cm-15x18in) s.d.1932
£3000 $5040   (26-Aug-91 S941/R) Lone long-tailed drake (50x76cm-20x30in) s.d.1959 i.overlap
£3500 $6125   (25-Feb-92 C54/R) Pink-footed geese over marshes (36x44cm-14x17in) s.d.1936 with i.verso
£3500 $6125   (25-Feb-92 C52/R) Looking west towards lighthouse (37x44cm-15x17in) s.d.1935 with i.
£3800 $6878   (4-Dec-91 S235/R) Mallards jumping (63x91cm-25x36in) s.d.1952 i.stretcher
£4200 $7350   (25-Feb-92 C56/R) Migration - red-breasted geese (70x90cm-28x35in) s.d.1974
£4500 $8055   (13-Nov-91 CG555/R) On the top of the tide at moonrise, the edge of the Salting si alive with Wigeon (51x76cm-20x30in) s.d.1935 i.verso
£5200 $8736   (26-Aug-91 S942/R) Slimbridge (63x76cm-25x30in) s.d.1947

SCOTT, Tom (1859-1927) British
£800 $1480   (9-Jun-92 AG160/R) St. Mary's Church, Wareham, Dorset (25x36cm-10x14in) s.i.d.1911 verso W/C
£1000 $1780   (1-May-92 PHE28/R) Warrior's rest, Yarrow (67x100cm-26x39in) s.d.1911 W/C
£3100 $5518   (1-May-92 PHE26/R) Mosstrooper scout (91x75cm-36x30in) s.d.96 W/C

SCOTT, William (1913-1989) British
£7800 $13806   (8-Nov-91 C251/R) Poem for a jug, blue on white (51x51cm-20x20in) s.verso
£11000 $19800   (20-Nov-91 S194/R) Orchard of pears (61x61cm-24x24in) s.d.83verso
£21000 $36540   (19-Sep-91 B79/R) Still life with flowers on table (51x61cm-20x24in)
£800 $1480   (9-Jun-92 RG2342) Girl at table (36x43cm-14x17in) s. pencil W/C
£1600 $2832   (8-Nov-91 C248/R) Related form (40x58cm-16x23in) s.d.74 pencil
£5000 $8850   (8-Nov-91 C202/R) Lovers beside a wood (27x38cm-11x15in) s.d.45 W/C bodycol.pen brush

SCOTT, William Bell (1811-1890) British
£1500 $2580   (3-Mar-92 AG269/R) John Bunyan's dream (41cm-16ins circular) s.i.d.1853stretcher
£440 $840   (13-Jul-92 PH59) Enchanted corner (19x26cm-7x10in) s.i.verso WC bodycol

SCOTT-RUUD, Gunnar (1897-1953) Norwegian
£1317 $2344   (29-Oct-91 UL.T213 a/R) Interior with still life and guitar (60x90cm-24x35in) s.d.1923 (N.KR 15000)

SCOTTISH SCHOOL, 18th C
£2900 $5104   (6-Apr-92 WW39) Inver ferry on Tay near Dunkeld (71x91cm-28x36in)

SCOTTISH SCHOOL, 20th C
£12022 $22000   (3-Jun-92 D.NY87) Roses in glass beside bowl of peaches (38x28cm-15x11in)
     bears indist.sig. board

SCOUEZEC, Maurice le (1881-1940) French
£3052 $5585   (17-May-92 T.B179/R) Paysage - vue sur la Baie de Douarnenez
     (45x63cm-18x25in) studio st. panel (F.FR 30000)
£5697 $10425   (17-May-92 T.B336/R) Femme au chapeau cloche (60x45cm-24x18in) s.d. paper
     laid down on panel (F.FR 56000)
£7630 $13962   (17-May-92 T.B178/R) Nu au fond bleu (75x51cm-30x20in) studio st. paper
     laid down on panel (F.FR 75000)

SCOUGALL, John (1645-1730) British
£1300 $2288   (10-Apr-92 C9/R) Portrait of John, 8th Earl of Rothes, in armour with
     white cravat (30x25cm-12x10in) i. canvas on panel oval
£2800 $4928   (10-Apr-92 C10/R) Portraits of Lady Christina Leslie. Lady Ann Lindsay
     before curtain (?x29cm-?x11in) i. painted oval pair
£3500 $6160   (10-Apr-92 C8/R) Portraits of Lady Susanna Hamilton. Margaret, Countess
     of Rothes (?x29cm-?x11in) i. painted oval pair

SCOULER, James (1740-1812) British
£1600 $2752   (4-Mar-92 C88/R) Lady, in white dress with double frilled collar, surcoat
     pearl clasp (7x?cm-3x?in) min.s.d.1790 gold frame plaited hair verso
     oval

SCOVOLO, Mario di (1840-1884) italian
£1600 $2848   (28-Nov-91 CSK72) Cavalry of General Villary (38x89cm-15x35in) s.i.d.1866

SCROTS, William (16th C) Dutch
£1185 $2145   (19-May-92 GF.L2342/R) Portrait of young prince (34x26cm-13x10in) panel
     oval (S.FR 3200)

SCROTS, William (circle) (16th C) Dutch
£2762 $5000   (21-May-92 CH.NY161/R) Portrait of bearded gentleman, wearing costume and
     cap with medallion (31x24cm-12x9in) panel

SCROTS, William (studio) (16th C) Dutch
£48000 $91680   (15-Jul-92 S7/R) Portrait of Edward VI (35x30cm-14x12in) panel

SCUBERTH, C George (1860-1929) ?
£491 $868   (25-Apr-92 SO.S589/R) Portrait of woman (58x44cm-23x17in) s. panel
     (S.KR 5200)

SCULLY, Sean (1946-) American
£3352 $6000   (6-May-92 CH.NY360/R) Change no.1 (25x52cm-10x20in) s.d.1975 oil masking
     tape
£3429 $6000   (28-Feb-92 SY.NY340 a/R) P7 (59x49cm-23x19in) s.d.1980 acrylic paper
£4000 $6920   (26-Mar-92 C92/R) Change 30 (59x79cm-23x31in) s.i.d.1975 paper collage
£21965 $38000   (3-Oct-91 SY.NY116/R) Zembra (76x76cm-30x30in) s.i.d.1985verso
£47486 $85000   (7-May-92 SY.NY147/R) For Charles Choset (190x230cm-75x91in)
£89385 $160000   (12-Nov-91 CH.NY63/R) Manus II (152x131cm-60x52in) s.i.d.1.83verso
£89385 $160000   (13-Nov-91 SY.NY77/R) Darkness here (254x335cm-100x132in) s.d.12.89 verso
£1000 $1730   (26-Mar-92 C94/R) Untitled (48x65cm-19x26in) s.d.71 gouache
£1427 $2654   (15-Jun-92 GL.P26/R) Untitled (44x62cm-17x24in) s.d.1971 gouache
     (F.FR 14000)
£1500 $2595   (26-Mar-92 C93/R) Untitled (61x61cm-24x24in) s.d.77 gouache
£1543 $2700   (28-Feb-92 SY.NY341 a/R) No.8 (77x59cm-30x23in) s.d.1981 chl
£1800 $3114   (26-Mar-92 C90 a/R) Drawing No 11 (70x102cm-28x40in) s.i.d.74 W/C tape
£3500 $6020   (17-Oct-91 C121 a/R) Untitled (77x71cm-30x28in) s.d.78 oil on paper
     collage
£8380 $15000   (7-May-92 SY.NY192/R) Untitled (77x96cm-30x38in) s.d.5.13.89 pastel

SCURR, M (19/20th C) ?
£1500 $2715   (20-May-92 S108/R) Ship entering harbour (71x114cm-28x45in) s.d.1860

SEABROOKE, Elliott (1886-?) British
£400 $752   (18-Dec-91 C29) Boats on river (30x48cm-12x19in) s. pencil W/C
£400 $752   (18-Dec-91 C28/R) French coastal scene (30x48cm-12x19in) s. pencil W/C

SEABY, Allen William (1867-1953) British
£460 $823   (15-Jan-92 BT115/R) Redshanks at the water's edge (30x41cm-12x16in) s.
     gouache linen

SEAFORTH, Charles Henry (1801-?) British
£3200 $5760   (22-Nov-91 C74/R) Merchantmen off the Indian Coast at dusk
     (50x75cm-20x30in) s.d.1867
£8500 $14960   (8-Apr-92 S8/R) Admiral's barge returning to shore (75x105cm-30x41in) s.

SEAFORTH, Charles Henry (attrib) (1801-?) British
£2200 $3828   (14-Apr-92 CSK154/R) English brig being attacked by Corsairs in Straits
     of Gibraltar (43x71cm-17x28in) indist.i.verso panel

SEAGO, Edward (1910-1974) British
£2200 $4026   (5-Jun-92 C78/R) Protector and Wave Chief in rough seas from Britannia
     (28x41cm-11x16in) s. board

SEAGO, Edward (1910-1974) British-cont.

£2419	$4282	(4-Nov-91 SY.J224) Seascape (24x39cm-9x15in) s. board (SA.R 12000)
£2667	$4560	(17-Mar-92 JRL.S116/R) October afternoon, Gorleston (26x40cm-10x16in) s. canvasboard (A.D 6000)
£3000	$5460	(12-Dec-91 CSK102) The coast near Estroil, Portugal (31x40cm-12x16in) s. board
£3200	$5856	(5-Jun-92 C76/R) Britannia and escorting warship (30x41cm-12x16in) s. board
£3500	$6020	(6-Mar-92 C96/R) Red dogwood, winter (39x59cm-15x23in) s. board
£3800	$6954	(5-Jun-92 C90/R) Snow and mist, Norfolk (39x60cm-15x24in) s. board
£4878	$8829	(3-Dec-91 R.T140/R) Quai de Montebello, Paris (66x91cm-26x36in) s. i.verso (C.D 10000)
£5000	$8750	(27-Sep-91 C20/R) Castle on the Seine, Chateau Gaillard (34x49cm-13x19in) s. board
£5025	$8945	(29-Oct-91 PH.T131/R) Street in Navplion, Greece (51x65cm-20x26in) s. masonite (C.D 10000)
£5500	$9460	(6-Mar-92 C92/R) Flowers in glass vase (59x44cm-23x17in) s. board
£6000	$10980	(13-May-92 S4/R) Tall ships in harbour (30x40cm-12x16in) s. board
£6000	$10740	(14-Jan-92 PH69/R) Marsh track, winter, Norfolk (51x76cm-20x30in) s. board
£6600	$11418	(2-Oct-91 S69/R) Suffolk landscape, summer (30x51cm-12x20in) s. i.verso board
£6977	$12000	(17-Oct-91 SY.NY324/R) Barnyard in Norfolk (51x76cm-20x30in) s. board
£7200	$12528	(17-Sep-91 SWS211/R) 'Trimdon', dark bay racehorse in yard (57x75cm-22x30in) s.d.34
£7500	$13275	(5-Nov-91 PH39/R) The still pool, winter (65x91cm-26x36in) s. board
£8000	$14160	(7-Nov-91 C61/R) Summer flowers in a stoneware jar (59x49cm-23x19in) s.
£8000	$13920	(19-Sep-91 B37/R) Upton Dyke, Norfolk (36x51cm-14x20in) s. board
£8197	$15000	(17-May-92 DU.E1118/R) Thames barges off Harwich (51x76cm-20x30in) s. i.verso masonite
£8500	$14790	(17-Sep-91 SWS212/R) 'Trilogy', a bay mare and foal in paddock (70x90cm-28x35in) s.d.34
£8543	$15206	(29-Oct-91 PH.T124/R) Norfolk hedgerow (48x74cm-19x29in) s. masonite (C.D 17000)
£9000	$15570	(2-Oct-91 S122/R) The village pasture (63x76cm-25x30in) s.
£9000	$16470	(13-May-92 S18/R) Shacks in the dunes (35x51cm-14x20in) s. i.verso board
£10000	$17700	(7-Nov-91 C62/R) Norfolk landscape (34x50cm-13x20in) s. board
£11000	$20130	(13-May-92 S8/R) Cattle by a stream (51x76cm-20x30in) s.
£12000	$21600	(20-Nov-91 S86/R) Ludlow (80x117cm-31x46in) s.
£12000	$20640	(6-Mar-92 C94/R) The wide field, Ludham, Norfolk (49x75cm-19x30in) s. board
£13000	$23790	(13-May-92 S9/R) Thames barges at half tide (41x61cm-16x24in) s. i.verso board
£20000	$34400	(6-Mar-92 C93/R) Chestnut trees, Champs Elysees, Paris (66x91cm-26x36in) s.
£21000	$37800	(20-Nov-91 S90/R) The marshman's cottage, river Thurne, Norfolk (64x90cm-25x35in) s. board
£420	*$802*	*(16-Jul-92 B25/R) Yacht in full sail in an estuary (17x26cm-7x10in) s. W/C*
£940	*$1683*	*(14-Jan-92 SWS95/R) Side street in Bruges (18x27cm-7x11in) s. bears i.verso W/C over pencil*
£1600	*$3008*	*(18-Dec-91 C18/R) Drumlanrig, Scotland (28x38cm-11x15in) s. pen ink W/C*
£1600	*$2848*	*(28-Apr-92 RG2560) On the Seine near Amfreville (25x36cm-10x14in) s. W/C*
£1600	*$2768*	*(2-Oct-91 S113/R) Two views of Ormesby Broad, Norfolk in winter (18x24cm-7x9in) s. W/C two*
£1700	*$2941*	*(2-Oct-91 S115/R) Norfolk cottages (27x37cm-11x15in) s. W/C*
£2300	*$4117*	*(14-Jan-92 PH74/R) Rue Galande, paris (27x38cm-11x15in) s. W/C over pencil*
£3000	*$5550*	*(12-Jun-92 K487/R) The Quadriga Hyde Park Corner with sculpture of Peace above (25x36cm-10x14in) s.d.1953 W/C*
£3800	*$6650*	*(27-Sep-91 C22/R) The Hayfield, Norfolk (32x47cm-13x19in) s. pencil W/C*
£4900	*$8575*	*(27-Sep-91 C23/R) The waterfront, Aberdeen, - Hong Kong (33x51cm-13x20in) s. pencil W/C*
£5000	*$8650*	*(2-Oct-91 S114/R) Norfolk evenings init. s.i.verso board pair*
£5000	*$8650*	*(2-Oct-91 S131/R) The flooded marsh (37x53cm-15x21in) s. W/C*

SEAGO, Edward (attrib) (1910-1974) British

£1000	$1910	(2-Jul-92 D168/R) Windmill in landscape with cat (15x23cm-6x9in) bears sig. board

SEALY, Allen Culpeper (19th C) British

£900	$1647	(5-Feb-92 CSK236/R) Chestnut racehorse with jockey up, racecourse beyond (53x65cm-21x26in) s.d.1905
£8197	$15000	(5-Jun-92 SY.NY171/R) The meet (52x67cm-20x26in) s.d.1892

SEALY, Douglas (1937-) Australian

£1542	$2744	(26-Nov-91 J.M44/R) Rock fisherman (75x101cm-30x40in) s. canvas on board (A.D 3500)

SEARLE, Ronald (1920-) British

£820	*$1574*	*(10-Jul-92 CSK54/R) Sweeping up Inebriates (51x36cm-20x14in) s.i.d.1964 pencil pen wash*
£900	*$1728*	*(10-Jul-92 CSK53/R) Hamburg Haven (48x38cm-19x15in) s.i.d.1964 s.i.verso pen wash collage*

SEARS, Benjamin Willard (1846-1905) American
£904 $1600   (12-Feb-92 B.SF426/R) Sentinel Rock, Yosemite (66x46cm-26x18in) s. init.d.1903 verso

SEARS, Olga (?) American
£497 $950   (19-Jul-92 JRB.C141/R) Teddy and friend (36x46cm-14x18in) s. canvasboard

SEATH, Ethel (?) Canadian
£2488 $4428   (26-Nov-91 JOY.T131) St. Sulpice Garden (40x30cm-16x12in) s. panel (C.D 5000)

SEBASTIAN CHICHARRO, Bernardino (20th C) Spanish?
£998 $1746   (18-Feb-92 DUR.M44/R) Uvas y paquete (38x46cm-15x18in) s. (S.P 180000)
£1243 $2336   (3-Jan-92 DUR.M14/R) Paquetes (38x46cm-15x18in) s. tablex (S.P 225000)
£1381 $2596   (3-Jan-92 DUR.M15/R) Nueces (55x46cm-22x18in) s. (S.P 250000)

SEBEN, Henri van (1825-1913) Belgian
£650 $1177   (21-May-92 CSK241/R) Picking wild flowers (25x18cm-10x7in) init.
£1396 $2499   (16-Jan-92 D.V97/R) Children (21x16cm-8x6in) s. panel (A.S 28000)
£1538 $2800   (26-May-92 CE.NY163/R) Playing with hoops (72x62cm-28x24in) s.d.58

SEBEN, Henri van (attrib) (1825-1913) Belgian
£3125 $5250   (12-Aug-91 SG.M598) The snowball fight (81x66cm-32x26in) s.

SEBIRE, Gaston (20th C) French
£546 $1000   (17-May-92 DU.E1106) Village le soir (23x64cm-9x25in) s. board
£656 $1200   (17-May-92 DU.E1038/R) Les roses du jardin (38x30cm-15x12in) s.
£751 $1300   (25-Mar-92 D.NY69/R) Roses et Boutons (41x33cm-16x13in) s.
£820 $1500   (5-Feb-92 D.NY81) Le bouquet rouge (53x38cm-21x15in) s. s.i.stretcher
£950 $1700   (6-May-92 D.NY118/R) Fleurs de Jocelyne (40x33cm-16x13in) s. i.verso
£1093 $2000   (17-May-92 DU.E1105/R) La Marine aux Remorqueurs, Havre (61x81cm-24x32in) s.
£1184 $2250   (22-Jun-92 SG.M548) Dans le jardin au Havre (81x102cm-32x40in) s.i.
£1229 $2200   (9-May-92 CE.NY24/R) Campagne Normande (74x100cm-29x39in) s. s.verso
£1486 $2600   (27-Feb-92 CE.NY144/R) Vase de fleurs (55x38cm-22x15in) s.
£1536 $2750   (13-Nov-91 B.SF2378/R) Bleuets et roses (52x44cm-20x17in) s.
£1899 $3400   (6-May-92 D.NY81/R) Matinee a la plage (49x74cm-19x29in) s. init.i.stretcher

SEBREGTS, Lode (20th C) Belgian
£568 $966   (22-Oct-91 C.A919) Pan (70x60cm-28x24in) s. tempera (B.FR 34000)

SEBRON, Hippolyte Victor Valentin (1801-1879) French
£3000 $5580   (16-Jun-92 PH143/R) View of harbour town by moonlight (70x106cm-28x42in) s.d.1844
£2134 $3713   (13-Apr-92 AT.P157/R) La fontaine de Selim III a Constantinople (32x48cm-13x19in) s.d.1864 W/C (F.FR 21000)

SECQUEVILLE, Maxime (20th C) French
£515 $885   (20-Oct-91 LT.P110) Les hauts de Rouen (46x61cm-18x24in) s. (F.FR 5100)
£626 $1076   (20-Oct-91 LT.P30/R) La berge fleurie a Nogent (50x65cm-20x26in) s. (F.FR 6200)
£664 $1162   (23-Feb-92 LT.P81/R) Bord de Marne en Automne (54x65cm-21x26in) s. (F.FR 6500)
£706 $1215   (20-Oct-91 LT.P40/R) Paysage a Saint Mammes (60x73cm-24x29in) s. (F.FR 7000)

SEDANER, L (?) ?
£1040 $1893   (27-May-92 DUR.M345/R) Atardecer (61x90cm-24x35in) s. (S.P 190000)

SEDLACEK, Stephan (19/20th C) Austrian
£570 $1021   (16-Nov-91 FAL.M333/R) Rococo interior with figures merrymaking (65x92cm-26x36in) s. (S.KR 6000)
£697 $1268   (13-Dec-91 BM.B717/R) Gentlemen gathered round table and women by fountain in courtyard (71x102cm-28x40in) s. (DM 2000)
£1609 $2783   (28-Mar-92 UA.U397) Rococo interior with figures (70x140cm-28x55in) s. (S.KR 16700)
£2500 $4650   (17-Jun-92 S357/R) Game of billiards (72x114cm-28x45in) s.

SEDLACEK, Stephan (style) (19/20th C) Austrian
£2600 $4628   (28-Nov-91 CSK127/R) The slave trader (57x79cm-22x31in) bears sig.

SEEGER, Hermann (1857-?) German
£3400 $6018   (14-Feb-92 C60/R) On the beach (90x72cm-35x28in) s.
£17000 $31620   (19-Jun-92 C58/R) Summer's Delight (90x70cm-35x28in) s.d.1899

SEEHAUS, Paul Adolf (1891-1919) German
£697 $1268   (14-Dec-91 BOD.P748/R) Window with flowers (67x74cm-26x29in) s.d.1904 (DM 2000)

SEEKATZ, Johann Conrad (1719-1768) German
£3800 $7296   (10-Jul-92 C212/R) Christ and woman of Samaria at well (22x29cm-9x11in) panel
£8500 $16320   (8-Jul-92 S104/R) Landscapes with shepherds and flock. Peasant girls washing clothes (30x23cm-12x9in) mono pair

SEEKATZ, Johann Conrad (1719-1768) German-cont.

£13500	$23625	(1-Apr-92 S11/R) Peasant boy with dog and firebrand. Peasant boy with hurdy-gurdy, smoking pipe (50x38cm-20x15in) pair
£38462	$65769	(18-Mar-92 N.M453/R) Peasant children feeding goats before farmhouse in hilly landscape (55x41cm-22x16in) s.d.1762 (DM 110000)
£375	*$680*	*(22-May-92 GB.B5691) Portrait of boy with hat (37x27cm-15x11in) brush (DM 1100)*

SEEKATZ, Johann Conrad (style) (1719-1768) German

£1300	$2340	(21-Nov-91 CSK101) Hercules in the Garden of the Hesperides (36x41cm-14x16in)
£3000	$5760	(8-Jul-92 S149/R) Soldiers and women in encampment at night (31x40cm-12x16in)

SEELOS, Gottfried (1829-1900) Austrian

£3155	$5617	(29-Apr-92 D.V796/R) Southern coastal landscape (90x73cm-35x29in) s.d.877 (A.S 65000)

SEELOS, Gustav (1831-1911) Austrian

£1951	$3395	(19-Sep-91 D.V224/R) Near Villafranca (16x32cm-6x13in) s.d.872 i.verso panel (A.S 40000)
£4496	$8092	(21-Nov-91 D.V57/R) South Tyrolean landscape (36x55cm-14x22in) s. (A.S 90000)

SEELOS, Ignaz (1827-1902) Austrian

£756	*$1315*	*(18-Sep-91 N.M277) Bunch of spring flowers (48x27cm-19x11in) s. W/C bodycol (DM 2200)*

SEEMAN, E (17/18th C) German/Polish

£2100	$3570	(21-Oct-91 H260) Portrait of young girl, holding vine leaf and grapes, seated in landscape (86x71cm-34x28in)

SEEMAN, Enoch (17/18th C) German/Polish

£1700	$2992	(8-Apr-92 S162/R) Portrait of gentleman, wearing coat and silver embroidered waistcoat (75x61cm-30x24in) painted oval
£5500	$9845	(13-Nov-91 S33/R) Portrait of lady, probably Mary Fermor, seated holding hat (124x99cm-49x39in) bears i.d.1685
£5500	$9845	(15-Nov-91 C12/R) Portrait of Mary Rand, seated, holding pearl necklace, by draped curtain (127x102cm-50x40in) i.

SEEMAN, Enoch (studio) (17/18th C) German/Polish

£2400	$4320	(22-Nov-91 SWS262/R) Portrait of George Blackall. Portrait of John Blackall (74x61cm-29x24in) painted ovals pair

SEERY, John (1941-) American

£503	$900	(12-Nov-91 CE.NY52/R) Soft entry (139x109cm-55x43in) s.i.d.70verso acrylic
£571	$1000	(27-Feb-92 CE.NY208/R) Cliffs (102x198cm-40x78in) s.d.1980 s.stretcher acrylic canvas
£1117	$2000	(12-Nov-91 CE.NY54/R) Yankee clipper (76x74cm-30x29in) s.d.1976verso acrylic
£1856	$3100	(25-Aug-91 JRB.C67) Wet wind (145x152cm-57x60in) s.d.87

SEEVAGEN, Lucien (1887-1959) French?

£651	$1191	(17-May-92 T.B208/R) Balise de chenal en Bretagne Nord (45x54cm-18x21in) s. canvas laid down on board (F.FR 6400)
£1064	$1926	(23-May-92 G.SB490) Chaumieres sur la cote a Brehat (73x117cm-29x46in) s. (F.FR 10500)

SEEWALD, Richard Josef (1889-1976) German

£5119	$9317	(25-May-92 WK.M1147/R) Palm tree, Elba (75x58cm-30x23in) s.d.1921 s.i.d.verso (DM 15000)
£515	*$876*	*(26-Oct-91 WK.M669/R) Robinson (36x33cm-14x13in) s.d.1923 W/C over pencil (DM 1500)*
£1024	*$1863*	*(30-May-92 VG.B927/R) Self portrait with pipe. Portrait study (63x46cm-25x18in) s.d.1930 pencil double-sided (DM 3000)*

SEGAAR, Bram (1888-1962) Dutch

£517	$899	(17-Sep-91 CH.AM219) A polder landscape in summer (35x50cm-14x20in) s. canvas laid down on panel (D.FL 1700)

SEGAL, Arthur (1875-1944) Rumanian

£2857	$5000	(26-Sep-91 SY.I97/R) Vase of thistles (73x57cm-29x22in) s. panel
£6007	$10512	(3-Apr-92 BM.B941/R) Azaleas (63x41cm-25x16in) s.d.1910 board (DM 17000)
£6360	$11131	(3-Apr-92 BM.B940/R) Geraniums (70x59cm-28x23in) s.d.1910 board (DM 18000)
£6514	$11790	(6-Dec-91 GB.B7116/R) Wooded landscape with farmhouse (62x43cm-24x17in) s.d.1909 canvas on board (DM 18500)
£17000	$30770	(3-Dec-91 C238/R) Segelboot im Hafen (62x82cm-24x32in) s.d.1912
£17065	$31058	(30-May-92 VG.B235/R) View of street and church tower (105x70cm-41x28in) s.indis.d.1924 board on panel (DM 50000)
£32000	$57920	(4-Dec-91 S134/R) Schlafende frau (79x98cm-31x39in) s.d.1925 board
£1910	*$3418*	*(15-Nov-91 KM.K652/R) Geometric composition (36x39cm-14x15in) s.d.1922 gouache (DM 5500)*
£1944	*$3500*	*(6-Jan-92 GG.TA429 a/R) In the circus (30x22cm-12x9in) s.d.1908-12 W/C*

SEGAL, Arthur (1875-1944) Rumanian-cont.
£2000 $3500   (26-Sep-91 SY.I40/R) Composition (35x32cm-14x13in) gouache
£2571 $4500   (26-Sep-91 SY.I41/R) Face of woman (37x35cm-15x14in) gouache

SEGAL, George (1924-) American
£1029 $1800   (28-Feb-92 SY.NY311/R) Seated nude (46x30cm-18x12in) s.d.61 pastel
£3146 $5694   (23-May-92 KV.L451/R) Composition with shoe (62x47cm-24x19in) s.d.75
     pastel (B.FR 190000)

SEGANTINI, Giovanni (1858-1899) Italian
£13746 $23918   (17-Sep-91 FN.S1828) Peasants harvesting, evening (20x28cm-8x11in) s.
     pencil (DM 40000)

SEGANTINI, Gottardo (1882-1974) Italian
£2549 $4333   (23-Oct-91 GD.B693/R) Gioconda (42x39cm-17x15in) s.d.1949 pavatex
     (S.FR 6500)
£3187 $5769   (5-Dec-91 SY.Z173/R) Val Bondasca in winter (60x40cm-24x16in) s.d.1963
     pavatex (S.FR 8000)
£4815 $8715   (20-May-92 GK.Z5125 a) Engadin (52x62cm-20x24in) s.d.1947 pavatex
     (S.FR 13000)
£7171 $12980   (5-Dec-91 SY.Z172/R) Summer landscape in Engadin (60x50cm-24x20in)
     s.d.1954 pavatex (S.FR 18000)
£9960 $18028   (5-Dec-91 SY.Z154/R) Snowcovered mountain landscape with ski track
     (70x60cm-28x24in) s.d.1926 s.i.d.verso canvas on panel (S.FR 25000)

SEGAR, William (circle) (16/17th C) British
£1800 $3222   (13-Nov-91 S116/R) Portrait of Lord Burroughs, Deputy of Ireland,
     standing (123x98cm-48x39in) i.d.1588
£9000 $16110   (15-Nov-91 C2/R) Portrait of man, with hand offering horoscope
     (39x32cm-15x13in) i. panel oval

SEGE, Alexandre (1818-1885) French
£1296 $2346   (19-May-92 GF.L2512/R) Coastal landscape, Normandy (31x45cm-12x18in) s.
     (S.FR 3500)

SEGELCKE, Severin (1867-?) Norwegian
£482 $897   (15-Jun-92 B.O136/R) Three brothers and sister (75x91cm-30x36in) s.d.1908
     (N.KR 5500)

SEGELITZ, Carl (20th C) German
£526 $947   (22-Nov-91 SA.A1713/R) Friedrich der Grosse in the battle near Zorndorf
     in 1758 (90x120cm-35x47in) i. i.verso (DM 1500)

SEGERS, A (1876-1950) Belgian
£683 $1216   (26-Nov-91 VN.R110/R) Shipping in an inland harbour in winter
     (91x111cm-36x44in) s. (D.FL 2200)

SEGERSTRAHLE, Lennart (1892-1975) Finnish
£1264 $2225   (12-Apr-92 HOR.H206) Falling mask (64x49cm-25x19in) s.d.1966 (F.M 10000)
£4804 $8455   (12-Apr-92 HOR.H204/R) Eagles (76x115cm-30x45in) s.d.1924 (F.M 38000)
£517 $921   (1-Dec-91 HOR.H204) Field near coast (47x58cm-19x23in) s. W/C (F.M 4000)

SEGHERS, Daniel (1590-1661) Flemish
£9877 $17679   (12-Nov-91 SY.AM218/R) Allegory of the Passage of Youth
     (124x97cm-49x38in) (D.FL 32000)
£138889 $263889   (26-Jun-92 AGS.P53/R) Roses, tulipes et fleurs d'oranger dans un vase de
     cristal (26x18cm-10x7in) mono. copper (F.FR 1350000)

SEGHERS, Daniel (attrib) (1590-1661) Flemish
£2985 $5313   (29-Oct-91 UL.T175 c/R) The Holy Family surrounded by garland of flowers
     (54x66cm-21x26in) (N.KR 34000)

SEGHERS, Daniel (school) (1590-1661) Flemish
£2800 $4844   (23-Mar-92 HS219/R) Still life of garlands of spring and summer flowers
     (49x100cm-19x39in)

SEGHERS, Daniel (style) (1590-1661) Flemish
£1895 $3241   (10-Mar-92 RAS.K29/R) Madonna and Child on niche with garland of flowers
     (71x71cm-28x28in) (D.KR 21000)
£5800 $11136   (9-Jul-92 CSK121/R) Portrait of nobleman, decorated with swags of mixed
     flowers (91x71cm-36x28in) i.stretcher verso
£6800 $13056   (9-Jul-92 CSK110/R) Madonna and Child surrounded by garland of flowers
     and fruit (102x72cm-40x28in) bears sig.d.1638 panel

SEGHERS, Gerard (studio) (1591-1651) Flemish
£3377 $5977   (6-Nov-91 LT.P75) L'Extase de Sainte Therese (22x17cm-9x7in) copper
     (F.FR 33500)

SEGHERS, Hercules (after) (1590-1638) Dutch
£850 $1522   (11-Nov-91 S481) Denial of St. Peter (40x47cm-16x19in)

SEGHERS, Hercules (style) (1590-1638) Dutch
£1000 $1830   (12-May-92 SWS794/R) Mountainous landscape with travellers
     (53x97cm-21x38in)

SEGIETH, Paul (1884-?) German
£512 $932   (26-May-92 KF.M1256) Riding school (49x47cm-19x19in) s.d.1913 gouache
                    board on board (DM 1500)

SEGNA, Niccolo di (style) (14th C) Italian
£9000 $16020   (29-Oct-91 PH95/R) The Madonna and child (36x26cm-14x10in) tempera panel

SEGNER, E B (20th C) American
£730 $1300   (2-May-92 IH.NY213/R) Newlyweds leaving registrar's office
                    (102x76cm-40x30in) s.

SEGOND, Philippe (1961-) French
£1030 $1761   (21-Mar-92 AT.P34/R) Paysage aux arbres (130x162cm-51x64in) s.d.mai
                    91verso mixed media canvas (F.FR 10000)

SEGONZAC, Andre Dunoyer de see DUNOYER DE SEGONZAC, Andre

SEGOVIA, Andres (c.1929-) Spanish
£571 $1000   (29-Sep-91 LIT.L469) Nature morte (71x91cm-28x36in) s.

SEGRELLES, Eustaquio (19/20th C) Spanish
£962 $1693   (9-Apr-92 ANS.M151/R) El Roncal (80x50cm-31x20in) s. (S.P 175000)
£1364 $2347   (16-Oct-91 FER.M232/R) Pescadoras en la Albufera de Valencia
                    (38x55cm-15x22in) s. s.i.verso (S.P 250000)
£1504 $2752   (13-May-92 FER.M135/R) Barcos en el puerto de Valencia (44x58cm-17x23in)
                    s. (S.P 275000)
£1769 $3327   (16-Dec-91 ANS.M133/R) Playa de Levante (38x55cm-15x22in) s.d.1990
                    s.i.d.verso (S.P 320000)
£2460 $4502   (13-May-92 FER.M133/R) Playa de Valencia (50x65cm-20x26in) s.d.91
                    (S.P 450000)
£2719 $4840   (28-Apr-92 DUR.M551/R) Sol y sombra (54x73cm-21x29in) s. s.i.verso
                    (S.P 500000)
£3007 $5503   (13-May-92 FER.M134/R) Sacando la barca, playa de Levante
                    (54x65cm-21x26in) s. (S.P 550000)
£3420 $6224   (11-Dec-91 FER.M158/R) Arrastrando la barca con los bueyes en una playa
                    valenciana (60x100cm-24x39in) s.d.90 (S.P 625000)
£3560 $6799   (2-Jul-92 ANS.M123/R) Pescadores del Palmar, Valencia (73x101cm-29x40in)
                    s.d.86 (S.P 650000)
£3834 $7322   (2-Jul-92 ANS.M122/R) El Caballo, El Palmar, Valencia (73x100cm-29x39in)
                    s.d.86 (S.P 700000)

SEGRELLES, Jose (1885-?) Spanish
£547 $1001   (13-May-92 FER.M80/R) El hijo del contrabandista (32x22cm-13x9in) s. W/C
                    (S.P 100000)

SEGUI, Antonio (1934-) Argentinian
£802 $1460   (12-Dec-91 SY.AM280) Personnage con flores (31x24cm-12x9in) s.d.62 panel
                    (D.FL 2600)
£988 $1798   (12-Dec-91 SY.AM231) Figura contra biomb (31x24cm-12x9in) s.d.1961 panel
                    (D.FL 3200)
£1049 $1910   (12-Dec-91 SY.AM306/R) Escapulario (31x24cm-12x9in) s.d.1961 panel
                    (D.FL 3400)
£3315 $6000   (18-May-92 CH.NY203/R) Untitled (61x90cm-24x35in) s.d.50
£4024 $6922   (8-Oct-91 CC.P62/R) Sans titre (81x100cm-32x39in) s.d.1985 (F.FR 40000)
£4047 $7285   (2-Feb-92 CSC.P85/R) Abstraction (50x40cm-20x16in) s.d.60 (F.FR 39500)
£4637 $8208   (10-Nov-91 ZZ.F253/R) Amore (100x81cm-39x32in) s. (F.FR 46000)
£5233 $9000   (12-Oct-91 SY.NY215/R) Boss (178x178cm-70x70in)
£7222 $13000   (19-Nov-91 CH.NY154/R) Ciegos en el jardin (65x92cm-26x36in) s.d.80
                    st.studio s.i.d.80verso
£7735 $14000   (19-May-92 SY.NY199/R) El que piensa mucho (72x91cm-28x36in)
                    s.i.d.14-5.83
£12155 $22000   (18-May-92 CH.NY202/R) Untitled (180x129cm-71x51in) s.d.81
£12155 $22000   (18-May-92 CH.NY99/R) Malos Pensamientos (129x161cm-51x63in) s.d.84
£2464 $4435   (19-Nov-91 FB.P199/R) Personnage au chien (79x58cm-31x23in) s. oil pastel
                    (F.FR 24000)
£3090 $5283   (17-Mar-92 FB.P96/R) Personnage (53x66cm-21x26in) s.d.87 mixed media
                    paper (F.FR 30000)
£4420 $8000   (18-May-92 CH.NY180/R) Hombre en un interior (78x57cm-31x22in) s.d.1972
                    mixed media
£6501 $11767   (7-Dec-91 KV.L497/R) Paris 1913 (194x194cm-76x76in) s.d.73 pastel canvas
                    (B.FR 380000)
£9724 $17308   (1-Dec-91 I.N77/R) Sans titre (114x145cm-45x57in) s. mixed media canvas
                    (F.FR 95000)

SEGUIN-BERTAULT, Paul (1869-1964) French
£914 $1600   (27-Feb-92 CE.NY14/R) Jardin du Luxembourg (61x81cm-24x32in) s.

SEGURA, Agustin (19/20th C) Spanish
£1659 $3119   (17-Dec-91 DUR.M100/R) Viejo (85x85cm-33x33in) s. (S.P 300000)

SEIDEL, August (1820-1904) German
£699 $1196   (18-Mar-92 N.M643) Rocky mountain valley with stream and shepherd with
                    animals (37x50cm-15x20in) (DM 2000)
£1333 $2280   (13-Mar-92 FN.S2959) Lake Starnberg landscape with peasant girls in field
                    (15x27cm-6x11in) mono. board (DM 3800)

SEIDEL, August (1820-1904) German-cont.
£1399 $2392   (18-Mar-92 N.M642/R) Summer landscape with farmhouse (19x33cm-7x13in) mono. canvas on board (DM 4000)
£1603 $2917   (12-Dec-91 L.K674) Forest workmen by mountain stream (60x50cm-24x20in) s. (DM 4600)

SEIDEN, Regina (1897-?) Canadian
£800 $1416   (6-Nov-91 SY.T143) Nuns with children (53x73cm-21x29in) s. (C.D 1600)

SEIDL-SEITZ, Josef (1908-) German
£772 $1389   (23-Nov-91 N.M294/R) View of Florence (85x110cm-33x43in) s.d.1957 s.i.verso (DM 2200)

SEIFERT (?) ?
£1203 $2093   (18-Sep-91 N.M698/R) Turkeys, ducks and geese by water (41x36cm-16x14in) s.i.d.1899 (DM 3500)

SEIFERT, Alfred (1850-1901) Czechoslovakian
£874 $1495   (18-Mar-92 N.M644/R) Blonde girl with rose on dress (27x20cm-11x8in) s. panel (DM 2500)
£1047 $1800   (15-Oct-91 CE.NY179/R) A young beauty (13x10cm-5x4in) s. panel
£4587 $8165   (30-Oct-91 CH.AM166/R) Shady thoughts, boy day-dreaming (116x101cm-46x40in) s. (D.FL 15000)

SEIFFERT, Carl Friedrich (1809-1891) German
£1031 $1794   (18-Sep-91 N.M700/R) Tegernsee landscape (43x57cm-17x22in) s.d.1878 (DM 3000)
£423 $765   (6-Dec-91 GB.B6019) Country estate in the Roman campagna (26x36cm-10x14in) s. W/C (DM 1200)

SEIGNAC, Guillaume (1870-1924) French
£2326 $4000   (15-Oct-91 CE.NY84/R) A basket of cherries (55x46cm-22x18in) s.
£6000 $11160   (17-Jun-92 S504/R) Wave (50x65cm-20x26in) s.
£54945 $100000   (28-May-92 SY.NY66/R) Psyche (176x96cm-69x38in) s.

SEIGNAC, Paul (1826-1904) French
£2100 $3570   (8-Aug-91 GSP425) First lessons (30x23cm-12x9in) s. panel
£4397 $7827   (29-Oct-91 PH.T139/R) Feeding little brother (31x23cm-12x9in) s. panel (C.D 8750)
£6800 $12172   (13-Nov-91 CG520/R) Dolly's toilet (36x28cm-14x11in) s. panel

SEILER, Carl Wilhelm Anton (1846-1921) German
£789 $1350   (22-Mar-92 LIT.L137) Genre scene with church official (38x30cm-15x12in) s.i.d.1890
£1200 $2136   (26-Nov-91 PH116) The apothecary (20x15cm-8x6in) s.d.1884 panel
£1400 $2506   (14-Jan-92 SWS220/R) The flautist (22x15cm-9x6in) s.d.1914 panel
£1400 $2422   (4-Oct-91 C99/R) The dandy (23x15cm-9x6in) s.d.1884 panel
£1684 $3032   (22-Nov-91 SA.A1703/R) Party merrymaking (55x69cm-22x27in) s. (DM 4800)
£1742 $3171   (11-Dec-91 WE.MU234/R) Gentleman before city gate (22x15cm-9x6in) s.d.1884 panel (DM 5000)
£6849 $11781   (8-Oct-91 ZEL.L1718/R) Two gentlemen seated at draped table in interior (27x33cm-11x13in) s.d.1878 panel (DM 20000)

SEILER, Joseph Albert (19th C) Austrian
£5233 $9000   (15-Oct-91 CE.NY108/R) Christmas morning service in St Nepomuk (84x65cm-33x26in) s.

SEITZ, Anton (1829-1900) German
£2921 $4966   (25-Oct-91 BM.B830/R) Young woman seated at table reading love letter and female spinning (12x9cm-5x4in) s. panel (DM 8500)

SEITZ, Georg (1810-1870) German
£1220 $2220   (11-Dec-91 N.M593/R) Still life of flowers in vase and fruit on table (68x57cm-27x22in) oval (DM 3500)
£1394 $2537   (11-Dec-91 N.M594/R) Still life of flowers and fruit (55x68cm-22x27in) (DM 4000)
£2424 $4411   (27-May-92 D.V575/R) Still life of fruit and roses (68x55cm-27x22in) s. (A.S 50000)
£3322 $5747   (25-Mar-92 KM.K1428/R) Still life of fruit and vine branch with bird on marble table (55x68cm-22x27in) s. (DM 9500)
£9000 $16740   (17-Jun-92 S378/R) Still life of flowers and bird's nest on marble ledge (77x62cm-30x24in) s.

SEITZ, Gustav (1906-1969) German
£412 $763   (12-Jun-92 HN.H774) Female half nude (18x15cm-7x6in) s. indian ink brush (DM 1200)
£447 $826   (12-Jun-92 HN.H775/R) Marina (28x35cm-11x14in) pencil (DM 1300)
£550 $1017   (12-Jun-92 HN.H778/R) Portrait of Bert Brecht (24x23cm-9x9in) chk (DM 1600)
£893 $1635   (3-Jun-92 L.K430/R) Couple (31x23cm-12x9in) s. blue pencil (DM 2600)
£1031 $1907   (12-Jun-92 HN.H776/R) Portrait study of Bert Brecht (39x24cm-15x9in) s. indian ink pen (DM 3000)

SEITZ, Maximilian (1811-1869) German
£1531 $2740   (5-May-92 ZEL.L1535/R) Christ in glory surrounded by angels (153x117cm-60x46in) s.i.d.1869 (DM 4500)

SEITZ, Otto (1846-1912) German
£557 $1015   (12-Dec-91 L.K675) The tobacco sniffer (12x8cm-5x3in) s. panel (DM 1600)

SEIWERT, Franz Wilhelm (1894-1933) German
£13333 $24000   (21-Nov-91 L.K463) Still life (60x50cm-24x20in) mono.d.1925 (DM 38000)

SEKOTO, Gerard (1913-) South African
£968 $1713   (4-Nov-91 SY.J327/R) Girl in checked dress (18x14cm-7x6in) s. board (SA.R 4800)
£994 $1730   (13-Apr-92 SY.J365/R) Township scene (45x60cm-18x24in) s.d.74 board (SA.R 5000)
£1010 $1727   (12-Mar-92 SY.J436/R) Group of women (32x45cm-13x18in) s.d.60 board (SA.R 5000)
£1889 $3286   (13-Apr-92 SY.J367/R) Amused (30x40cm-12x16in) s. canvasboard (SA.R 9500)
£2621 $4639   (4-Nov-91 SY.J326/R) Figures in shebeen (25x33cm-10x13in) s. canvasboard (SA.R 13000)
£2783 $4843   (13-Apr-92 SY.J366/R) Women in conversation (24x29cm-9x11in) s. canvasboard (SA.R 14000)
£4435 $7851   (4-Nov-91 SY.J328/R) The Zulu war dancers (33x41cm-13x16in) s. paper on board (SA.R 22000)
£8871 $15702   (4-Nov-91 SY.J33/R) Children at prayer (48x60cm-19x24in) s. panel (SA.R 44000)
£517 $899   (13-Apr-92 SY.J222) African head (57x27cm-22x11in) s.d.80 W/C (SA.R 2600)
£1815 $3212   (4-Nov-91 SY.J325/R) Three men at railway station (24x35cm-9x14in) s. W/C (SA.R 9000)

SEKULA, Sonja (1918-1963) Swiss/American
£449 $800   (29-Apr-92 G.Z175) I try (23x21cm-9x8in) s.i.d.1955 collage (S.FR 1200)
£562 $1000   (29-Apr-92 G.Z174) Soi (51x35cm-20x14in) s.i.d.1958 gouache (S.FR 1500)
£1514 $2740   (4-Dec-91 G.Z39/R) Le printemps, composition III (48x34cm-19x13in) s.d.1961 collage (S.FR 3800)

SELIGMANN (19/20th C) ?
£1660 $2955   (29-Nov-91 GAB.G2687/R) Effet de lumiere sur la Seine (39x50cm-15x20in) s.d.1912 (S.FR 4200)

SELIGMANN, Kurt (1900-1961) Swiss
£1992 $3606   (4-Dec-91 G.Z195/R) Three men at table (58x50cm-23x20in) board (S.FR 5000)
£3343 $5750   (12-Oct-91 SY.NY49/R) Surrealist figure (60x47cm-24x19in) pen indian ink

SELL, Christian (1831-1883) German
£784 $1404   (15-Nov-91 ZOF.Z1430/R) Patrol (2x26cm-1x10in) s. (S.FR 2000)
£859 $1495   (18-Sep-91 N.M701/R) Soldiers on guard duty during Thirty Year War (27x31cm-11x12in) s.d.1860 (DM 2500)
£883 $1546   (3-Apr-92 BM.B709/R) Soldiers attacking at dawn (9x12cm-4x5in) s. panel (DM 2500)
£1923 $3500   (26-May-92 CE.NY44/R) The out-post (52x74cm-20x29in) s.d.1860
£2800 $4984   (27-Nov-91 S97/R) En route to battle (29x40cm-11x16in) s.

SELLAER, Vincent (16th C) Flemish
£16201 $29000   (17-Jan-92 SY.NY109/R) Madonna and Child with Saint Elizabeth and other members of the Holy Family (95x109cm-37x43in) panel

SELLAER, Vincent (style) (16th C) Flemish
£1300 $2275   (27-Feb-92 CSK4) The Madonna and child (72x51cm-28x20in) panel

SELLAIO, Jacopo del (1441-1493) Italian
£41436 $75000   (21-May-92 CH.NY48/R) Holy Family with infant Saint John the Baptist in landscape (68cm-27ins circular) panel

SELLENY, Josef (1824-1875) Austrian
£1717 $3263   (25-Jun-92 D.V482/R) Shipwreck in coastal landscape (62x88cm-24x35in) s.d.859 (A.S 35000)

SELLMAYR, Ludwig (1834-1901) German
£550 $1023   (16-Jun-92 PH9) Hunters with horse and kill on rocky mountain pass (27x21cm-11x8in) s. panel

SELMYHR, Conrad (1877-1944) Norwegian
£650 $1157   (26-Nov-91 PH172) Fjord scene with steam ship and other vessels (60x100cm-24x39in) s.

SELTZER, Olaf C (1877-1957) American
£7429 $13000   (25-Sep-91 SY.NY43/R) King's mirror (91x122cm-36x48in) s.d.1904
£4787 $9000   (18-Dec-91 SY.NY379/R) Indians on the plains (33x45cm-13x18in) s. W/C gouache pencil board

SELVA, E (?) Italian
£920 $1646   (14-Nov-91 CH.R205) Scorcio di Venezia (27x47cm-11x19in) s. panel (I.L 2000000)

SELWYN, John (?) British
£600 $1092   (28-May-92 B28) The Front, Southsea (50x64cm-20x25in) init.

SEMEGHINI, Pio (1878-1964) Italian
£454 $808   (29-Apr-92 F.F44/R) Due volti (14x21cm-6x8in) panel (I.L 1000000)
£4139 $7409   (14-Nov-91 F.M116/R) I tetti rossi (28x36cm-11x14in) masonite (I.L 9000000)
£4409 $8289   (19-Dec-91 F.M132/R) Fanciulla con mela (37x28cm-15x11in) s.d.1941 s.i.verso panel (I.L 9500000)
£8573 $15260   (29-Nov-91 F.F179/R) Bambina con golfino a righe (44x33cm-17x13in) s. panel (I.L 18500000)
£772 $1374   (29-Apr-92 F.F27/R) Intero con sculture (45x31cm-18x12in) s. sanguine cut corners (I.L 1700000)

SEMENOWSKY, Eisman (19th C) French
£765 $1353   (5-Nov-91 SY.AM109) Girl in Oriental costume (27x21cm-11x8in) s.d.1890 panel (D.FL 2500)
£1648 $3000   (28-May-92 SY.NY180/R) Skater (70x44cm-28x17in) s.d.1889 s.verso panel

SEMIAN, Jean (1910-) Spanish
£812 $1389   (12-Mar-92 RAS.K642/R) Le brasero bleu (92x65cm-36x26in) s.d.1950 (D.KR 9000)

SEMINO, Andrea (16th C) Italian
£1461 $2600   (22-Jan-92 D.NY63) Venus with cupids (102x84cm-40x33in) canvas en rosaille

SEMINO, Francesco (1832-1883) Italian
£2303 $4191   (12-Dec-91 F.M45/R) Allegoria dell'Italia (57x51cm-22x20in) (I.L 5000000)

SEMITECOLO, Nicoletto (14th C) Italian
£86957 $154783   (29-Nov-91 GAB.G3088/R) Christ au tombeau entre la Vierge et Saint Jean l'evangeliste (60x78cm-24x31in) tempera panel (S.FR 220000)

SEMPERE, Eusebio (1924-) Spanish
£3560 $6799   (2-Jul-92 ANS.M108/R) Composicion (60x45cm-24x18in) s. gouache (S.P 650000)
£7748 $13248   (17-Mar-92 FER.M184/R) Abstracto con blancas, negras y corcheas (49x64cm-19x25in) s. mixed media (S.P 1400000)
£10332 $18390   (28-Apr-92 EP.M15/R) Del cuadrado al circulo No.3 (49x32cm-19x13in) s.d.68 s.i.d.1968verso pencil gouache panel (S.P 1900000)

SEMPLE, J (19th C) British?
£1955 $3500   (15-Nov-91 DM.D1013/R) Ship Countess of Dublin (20x33cm-8x13in) s.d.1869 board

SENAPE, Antonio (?) Italian
£515 $907   (11-Apr-92 AW.H710/R) Veduta di Catania et Etna (17x25cm-7x10in) i. indian ink pen sepia (DM 1500)
£800 $1448   (21-May-92 CSK4) Marina di Palermo e Monte Pellegrino. Porto di Messina (20x30cm-8x12in) i. pen pair

SENAT, Prosper L (1852-1925) American
£585 $1000   (12-Mar-92 MFA.C103) Capri (69x48cm-27x19in) s. board

SENAVE, Jacques Albert (1758-1829) Belgian
£550 $963   (28-Feb-92 C112/R) Peasant family in barn (16x21cm-6x8in) indist.s.

SENBERGS, Jan (1939-) Australian
£1855 $3450   (21-Jun-92 SY.ME125/R) Collapsed object no 2 (168x183cm-66x72in) d.1969 s.i.verso (A.D 4600)
£1855 $3450   (21-Jun-92 SY.ME75/R) The main body (183x137cm-72x54in) s. s.i.d.1965verso enamel board (A.D 4600)

SENEQUE, Clement (1896-1930) South African
£605 $1071   (4-Nov-91 SY.J283/R) Landscape with trees, Durban (31x39cm-12x15in) s.d.25 board (SA.R 3000)
£994 $1730   (13-Apr-92 SY.J358) Bay from Albert Park, Durban (23x32cm-9x13in) s.d.25 board (SA.R 5000)
£1008 $1784   (4-Nov-91 SY.J284/R) Landscape sunset (55x68cm-22x27in) s.d.21 (SA.R 5000)

SENET, R (1856-1926) Spanish
£521 $885   (23-Oct-91 MA.V182) Venetian Canal scene (38x18cm-15x7in) s. W/C (C.D 1000)

SENET, Rafael (1856-1926) Spanish
£1000 $1780   (26-Nov-91 PH245 a) Venetian canal (9x14cm-4x6in) s. panel
£5466 $9292   (22-Oct-91 DUR.M35/R) Pescadoras (34x60cm-13x24in) s. (S.P 1000000)
£6400 $11648   (11-Dec-91 PHL93/R) View of the Grand Canal towards Santa Maria della Salute (49x60cm-19x24in) s.
£6897 $12000   (13-Sep-91 S.W2786/R) Entrance to Grand Canal (30x51cm-12x20in) s.
£10169 $18000   (6-Nov-91 D.NY38/R) View of the Grand Canal (53x98cm-21x39in) s.
£1776 $3020   (22-Oct-91 DUR.M36/R) El Gran Canal (30x47cm-12x19in) s. W/C (S.P 325000)

SENGL, Peter (1945-) ?
£342 $609   *(31-Oct-91 D.V111/R) Cat walking on stilts (64x49cm-25x19in) s.d.1975*
           pencil chl col.pencil (A.S 7000)
£391 $696   *(31-Oct-91 D.V112/R) Teufelsgefahrt mit lachender und*
           Nachrechts-blickender (50x62cm-20x24in) s.i.d.74 mixed media (A.S 8000)
£489 $870   *(31-Oct-91 D.V113/R) Lowen-Tiger-Brause fur Kleinkletterfiguren*
           (48x63cm-19x25in) s.i.d.1975 mixed media (A.S 10000)

SENIOR, Mark (1864-1927) British
£520 $894   (16-Oct-91 PHL330) Rough sea (22x27cm-9x11in) s. s.i.d.1924 verso board
£7000 $12180   (15-Apr-92 PHL199/R) June (60x49cm-24x19in) s. s.i.verso

SENKEVITCH, Serafina (1941-) Russian
£1527 $2795   (3-Jun-92 ARC.P154/R) Fleurs et fruits (130x161cm-51x63in) s.
           (F.FR 15000)

SENTERIKA, V (19th C) Russian
£1915 $3390   (10-Nov-91 ZZ.F131/R) Scene familiale dans la vieille Russie
           (42x49cm-17x19in) s. (F.FR 19000)

SEOANE, Luis (1910-1979) Argentinian
£3044 $5205   (17-Mar-92 FER.M172/R) Mujer en azul (101x81cm-40x32in) s. (S.P 550000)
£1640 $2788   *(23-Oct-91 DUR.M529/R) Paisaje con mar al fondo (50x64cm-20x25in) s.d.79*
           pastel gouache (S.P 300000)
£1776 $3020   *(23-Oct-91 DUR.M528/R) El vikingo que vino a casa (64x50cm-25x20in)*
           s.d.79 pastel gouache (S.P 325000)

SEPESHY, Zoltan L (1898-?) American
£1667 $3000   (10-Jan-92 DM.D2005/R) City scene (91x86cm-36x34in) s.

SEPHTON, George Harcourt (19th C) British
£500 $895   (14-Nov-91 CSK168) Still life of bowl of poppies (97x104cm-38x41in)
           s.d.1897
£1025 $1844   (2-Feb-92 ZZ.F22/R) Jeune femme et petits moutons dans le sous-bois
           (63x76cm-25x30in) s. (F.FR 10000)
£2000 $3580   (11-Nov-91 S664/R) Portrait of Charles, Lord Howard of Effingham, Earl of
           Nottingham (49x39cm-19x15in)
£600 $1068   *(1-May-92 PHE34/R) The letter (34x26cm-13x10in) s.d.1903 W/C*

SEQUEIRA, Domingos Antonio de (1768-1837) Portuguese
£634 $1147   (6-Dec-91 GB.B5605/R) Teaching Christianity (28x40cm-11x16in) s.d.1805 indian ink pen wash (DM 1800)

SERANGELI, Giacchino Giuseppe (1768-1852) French
£24474 $43319   (7-Nov-91 D.V6/R) The Three Graces crowning Venus (100x75cm-39x30in) (A.S 500000)

SERAPHINE DE SENLIS (1864-1942) French
£1850 $3533   (3-Jul-92 GL.P158/R) Cerises (36x49cm-14x19in) s. (F.FR 18000)
£3800 $6536   (16-Oct-91 S114/R) Fleurs sur fond bleu (21x26cm-8x10in) s. panel

SEREBRIAKOFF, Alexandre (20th C) Russian
£654 $1125   (12-Oct-91 SY.MO189) Maquette pour le decor - La Sylphide, Act I (31x37cm-12x15in) pen indian ink W/C htd gouache (F.FR 6500)
£654 $1125   (12-Oct-91 SY.MO190) Maquette pour le decor - La Sylphide, Act II (24x34cm-9x13in) pen indian ink W/C (F.FR 6500)
£1107 $1903   (12-Oct-91 SY.MO188/R) Maquette pour le decor - La Sylphide, Act I (33x42cm-13x17in) pen indian ink W/C htd gouache (F.FR 11000)
£1509 $2596   (12-Oct-91 SY.MO187/R) La Sylphide (43x62cm-17x24in) s.d.1947 W/C pen indian ink (F.FR 15000)
£3018 $5191   (12-Oct-91 SY.MO222/R) Interieur - Welcome (23x28cm-9x11in) pen indian ink W/C htd gouache gold paint (F.FR 30000)
£3421 $5883   (12-Oct-91 SY.MO223/R) Les toits - vue de Rue Casimir-Delavigne (47x35cm-19x14in) s.d.47 pen indian ink W/C htd gouache pencil (F.FR 34000)
£5030 $8652   (12-Oct-91 SY.MO225/R) Interieur - le vestibule - Rue Casimir-Delavigne (33x45cm-13x18in) s.d.1947 pen indian ink W/C htd gouache pencil (F.FR 50000)
£6539 $11247   (12-Oct-91 SY.MO228/R) Interieur - la chambre de Boris Kochno (39x41cm-15x16in) s.d.1947 pen indian ink W/C htd gouache pencil (F.FR 65000)
£6640 $11421   (12-Oct-91 SY.MO224/R) Trompe l'oeil - Rue Casimir-Delavigne (26x39cm-10x15in) s.i.d.1948 W/C pen indian ink (F.FR 66000)
£12072 $20765   (12-Oct-91 SY.MO229/R) Interieur - la chambre de Christian Berard (34x49cm-13x19in) s.d.1947 pen indian ink W/C htd gouache pencil (F.FR 120000)
£31187 $53642   (12-Oct-91 SY.MO226/R) Atelier de M. Christian Berard - Rue Casimir-Delavigne a Paris (39x57cm-15x22in) s.d.1948 pen indian ink W/C htd gouache pencil (F.FR 310000)
£32193 $55372   (12-Oct-91 SY.MO227/R) Interieur - l'atelier de Boris Kochno et de Christian Berard (42x59cm-17x23in) s.d.1946 pen indian ink W/C htd gouache (F.FR 320000)

SEREBRIAKOVA, Zinaida (1884-1967) Russian
£11000 $19580   (28-Nov-91 S427/R) Self-portrait - portrait of artist in studio (47x37cm-19x15in) s. pastel

SERGEL, Johan Tobias (1740-1814) Swedish
£665 $1157   (13-Apr-92 AB.S412) Sketch after satyric atland in Palazzo Fernese (54x40cm-21x16in) red chk (S.KR 7000)

SERGENT, Rene (20th C) Belgian
£750 $1275   (23-Oct-91 S96) The ampitheatre, Nimes (31x64cm-12x25in) s.d.1885 W/C over pencil

SERISAWA, Sueo (1910-) Japanese
£1412 $2500   (12-Feb-92 B.SF589/R) Red canna (76x66cm-30x26in) s.d.38

SERNA, Ismael de la (1897-1968) Spanish
£1287 $2420   (18-Dec-91 PR.P96/R) Bouquet de fleurs a la fenetre (19x25cm-7x10in) s.i.verso board (F.FR 12500)
£1643 $3138   (2-Jul-92 ANS.M78/R) Pleine lune (72x100cm-28x39in) s. panel (S.P 300000)
£1829 $3237   (12-Feb-92 ANS.M106/R) Composicion (50x45cm-20x18in) tempera tablex (S.P 330000)
£2203 $3943   (14-Nov-91 ANS.M61/R) Composicion (50x45cm-20x18in) tempera tablex (S.P 400000)
£2369 $4050   (18-Mar-92 PIC.P54/R) Nature morte et verre (31x68cm-12x27in) inlaid stucco (F.FR 23000)
£4105 $7471   (26-May-92 DUR.M51/R) Bodegon del libro abierto (55x36cm-22x14in) s. board (S.P 750000)
£4153 $7475   (28-Jan-92 EP.M71/R) Carguero negro (95x82cm-37x32in) s. board (S.P 750000)
£4707 $8472   (28-Jan-92 EP.M53/R) Velero (105x80cm-41x31in) s. board (S.P 850000)
£5179 $8907   (7-Oct-91 ANS.M114/R) Frutero (34x26cm-13x10in) s. board (S.P 950000)
£6912 $12994   (16-Dec-91 ANS.M111/R) Velador con bodegon (46x35cm-18x14in) s. tablex (S.P 1250000)
£10756 $18500   (12-Oct-91 SY.NY124/R) Still life (81x65cm-32x26in) s.d.50 s.verso masonite
£11000 $19030   (25-Mar-92 S51/R) Nature morte aux citrons (73x91cm-29x36in) s.d.28
£22118 $41581   (16-Dec-91 ANS.M76/R) El arbol (106x75cm-42x30in) s. (S.P 4000000)
£1988 $3697   (17-Jun-92 I.N141/R) La mappemonde (51x36cm-20x14in) s. gouache (F.FR 19500)
£2627 $4675   (29-Oct-91 BRO.B301) La ciudad (45x80cm-18x31in) s. i.verso oil collage board (S.P 480000)

SERNE, Adrianus (1773-1853) Dutch
£1706 $3106   (27-May-92 PH.DU143) Wanderer and woman in conversation in wooded river
                  landscape (39x51cm-15x20in) mono. (DM 5000)

SERNE, Adrianus (attrib) (1773-1853) Dutch
£556 $972   (18-Feb-92 CH.AM322) A shaded landscape with travellers and a horse on a
                track near a cottage (51x45cm-20x18in) canvas laid down on board
                (D.FL 1800)

SERNEELS, Clement (20th C) Belgian
£1168 $2055   (7-Apr-92 C.A585/R) The model (90x70cm-35x28in) s. panel (B.FR 70000)
£1392 $2421   (13-Apr-92 SY.J343) Proteas (90x70cm-35x28in) s.d.68 (SA.R 7000)

SERNER, Otto (1854-?) Swiss
£733 $1260   *(10-Oct-91 D.V274/R) Bay of Naples with Vesuvio (29x47cm-11x19in) s.d.97
                mixed media board (A.S 15000)*

SERPAN, Jaroslav (1922-1976) Czechoslovakian
£1524 $2652   (16-Apr-92 FB.P143/R) Feuns (92x60cm-36x24in) s.d.54 i.verso (F.FR 15000)
£1955 $3500   *(13-Nov-91 CH.NY102/R) Dgrugi (135x129cm-53x51in) s.i.d.19.6.1958verso
                oil string paper collage*

SERPIONI, Alberro (?) ?
£503 $900   *(16-Nov-91 WOL.C136/R) The cavalier (53x36cm-21x14in) s.i. W/C*

SERRA Y AUQUE, Enrico (1859-1918) Spanish
£934 $1682   (19-Nov-91 DUR.M53/R) La garza (51x76cm-20x30in) s.d.93 (S.P 170000)
£1129 $2033   (20-Nov-91 CN.P214/R) Femme en priere (81x57cm-32x22in) s.d.1894
                (F.FR 11000)
£1359 $2473   (13-Dec-91 BM.B719/R) Romantic landscape with pond, autumn
                (114x86cm-45x34in) s.i.d.1905 (DM 3900)
£1363 $2535   (16-Jun-92 EP.M19/R) Paisaje (39x26cm-15x10in) s. panel (S.P 250000)
£1505 $2739   (26-May-92 DUR.M80/R) Lagunas pontinas (26x42cm-10x17in) s.d.1887
                (S.P 275000)
£2057 $3600   (18-Feb-92 CE.NY256/R) Shrine in marsh (58x94cm-23x37in) s.d.1901
£2200 $3916   (27-Nov-91 S375/R) Woodland lake at Malmaison (92x67cm-36x26in) s.i.
£3200 $5472   (17-Mar-92 PH214/R) Floral tribute by wonded river (97x112cm-38x44in)
                s.i.d.1905
£4000 $7120   (27-Nov-91 S374/R) Ruins by lake at sunset (72x114cm-28x45in) s.i.

SERRA Y FARNES, Pedro (1890-1974) Spanish
£1528 $2765   (20-May-92 ANS.M140/R) Paisaje (51x60cm-20x24in) s. (S.P 280000)

SERRA Y PORSON, Jose (1824-1910) Spanish
£2771 $4849   (18-Feb-92 DUR.M1/R) Pintor en su estudio (31x23cm-12x9in) s.d.96 panel
                (S.P 500000)

SERRA, F (?) ?
£714 $1286   (20-Nov-91 DUR.M1094/R) Ninas en la playa (65x81cm-26x32in) s. panel
                (S.P 130000)

SERRA, Luigi (1846-1888) Italian
£815 $1475   (20-May-92 GK.Z5073) Nun kissing picture of Christ in candle lit interior
                (26x17cm-10x7in) s.i.d.1874 panel (S.FR 2200)

SERRA, P (?) ?
£879 $1583   (19-Nov-91 DUR.M50/R) Maja con mantilla y abanico (105x68cm-41x27in) s.
                (S.P 160000)

SERRA, Richard (1939-) American
£22346 $40000   (13-Nov-91 CH.NY220/R) Untitled (115x205cm-45x81in) black oilstick
£10405 $18000   *(3-Oct-91 SY.NY113/R) Untitled (113x288cm-44x113in) s.d.74 paintstick*
£25140 $45000   *(14-Nov-91 SY.NY163/R) Judgments on sheet (152x360cm-60x142in) paintstick
                paper*

SERRAS, Giovanni Tomasso (19th C) ?
£602 $1096   (27-May-92 DUR.M351/R) Puerto de Mahon (34x42cm-13x17in) s.d.1810 panel
                (S.P 110000)

SERRASANTA (1916-) Argentinian
£1991 $3742   (17-Dec-91 BRO.B420) Gitanos (50x61cm-20x24in) s. (S.P 360000)

SERRES, Dominic (1722-1793) British
£2400 $4584   (21-Jul-92 PH256/R) Man-o'-War and other shipping off continental town
                (46x68cm-18x27in)
£9800 $17542   (13-Nov-91 S7/R) The attack on Moro Castle, July 1st, 1762
                (49x75cm-19x30in) s.d.1767
£38000 $66880   (8-Apr-92 S61/R) Intendant's Palace, Quebec. Bishops house with ruined
                town of Quebec (34x52cm-13x20in) s.d.1760 pair
£650 $1170   *(9-Jan-92 B240) At Charlton, sailing vessels off a coastline
                (18x32cm-7x13in) init.i.d.7th-9th-1780 pen wash*
£900 $1611   *(12-Nov-91 C79) Three-decker vice-admiral of the red, two-decker beyond.
                A merchantman passing Calshot Castle (23x29cm-9x11in) both init.d.1788
                pencil W/C two*

SERRES, Dominic (1722-1793) British-cont.
£1400 $2380   (22-Oct-91 SWS59/R) British man-o'-war off over (21x32cm-8x13in) s.d.1790
     W/C pen

SERRES, Dominic (circle) (1722-1793) British
£1100 $2112   (9-Jul-92 B62/R) British Man-o'-War, flying red ensign and common pendant
     (70x75cm-28x30in)
£1500 $2715   (20-May-92 S4/R) Rounding a lighthouse (20x25cm-8x10in)

SERRES, John Thomas (1759-1825) British
£4400 $8404   (21-Jul-92 PH259/R) Coastal vessels and hay barges in Waterford Harbour,
     Ireland (36x46cm-14x18in) s.d.1788 i.d.1788 verso
£5738 $10500   (5-Jun-92 SY.NY240/R) Leith Harbour (50x96cm-20x38in) s.d.1825
£8500 $15300   (19-Nov-91 PH25/R) View of lighthouse at Genoa harbour with shipping
     (111x129cm-44x51in) s.d.1795
£16000 $28800   (19-Nov-91 PH24/R) View of Florence from Arno with figures and fishing
     boats (50x65cm-20x26in) s.d.1799
£726 $1300   (15-Jan-92 CH.NY185/R) Fishermen with cart by shore (20x28cm-8x11in)
     s.d.1808 black white chk

SERRES, John Thomas (style) (1759-1825) British
£800 $1384   (4-Sep-91 BT304/R) British squadron engaging shore batteries
     (71x119cm-28x47in)

SERRITELLI (?) Italian
£5500 $9790   (27-Nov-91 S317/R) Figures on beach near Naples (37x65cm-15x26in) s.
£7037 $12737   (19-May-92 GF.L2210/R) View of Naples and Vesuvius (55x81cm-22x32in) s.
     (S.FR 19000)

SERRITELLI, Giovanni (?) Italian?
£1186 $2100   (13-Feb-92 S.W1606) Figures and cattle in Arcadian landscape
     (48x84cm-19x33in) s.

SERT Y BADIA, Jose Maria (1876-1945) Spanish
£2510 $4542   (20-May-92 ANS.M111/R) Maqueta para un mural (39x176cm-15x69in) paper on
     panel (S.P 460000)

SERT, Henri (1938-) French
£479 $863   (19-Nov-91 GO.G156) Fantasy animal (87x111cm-34x44in) s.d.1959
     (S.KR 5000)
£493 $849   (15-Oct-91 GO.G1142/R) Composition with two figures (82x122cm-32x48in) s.
     (S.KR 5200)
£417 $718   (15-Oct-91 GO.G1143) Female figure (105x75cm-41x30in) s.d.1959 panel
     (S.KR 4400)

SERUSIER, Paul (1863-1927) French
£12729 $23167   (15-Dec-91 T.B229/R) Paysge aux arbres jaunes (71x50cm-28x20in) s.d.17
     (F.FR 125000)
£16277 $29135   (17-Nov-91 GL.P23/R) Nature morte a la plante verte et aux trois pommes
     (60x73cm-24x29in) s.d.1903 (F.FR 160000)
£1611 $2868   (28-Oct-91 GL.P114/R) Etude de bretonnes, scene bretonne (18x16cm-7x6in)
     gouache (F.FR 16000)
£2385 $4531   (25-Jun-92 GK.B652/R) Paysage de Bretagne (24x36cm-9x14in) col.chk
     (S.FR 6200)
£3323 $5915   (28-Oct-91 GL.P122/R) La foret (30x23cm-12x9in) st.init. lead pencil
     pastel (F.FR 33000)

SERVAES, Albert (1883-1966) Belgian
£2673 $4545   (22-Oct-91 C.A290) Swiss landscape (46x61cm-18x24in) s.d.1948
     (B.FR 160000)
£4078 $6974   (21-Mar-92 KV.L461/R) Haystack in evening landscape (60x65cm-24x26in)
     s.d.1929 (B.FR 240000)
£993 $1798   (23-May-92 KV.L298) Reconciliation (48x36cm-19x14in) s.d.1951 chl.
     (B.FR 60000)

SERVANDONI, Jean Nicolas (1695-1766) French
£8454 $14625   (27-Mar-92 CN.P51/R) Tempete pres des cotes. Bateaux pres d'une cote avec
     monuments (47x132cm-19x52in) (F.FR 82000)

SERVANDONI, Jean Nicolas (attrib) (1695-1766) French
£5801 $10500   (21-May-92 CH.NY222/R) Figures before ruined portico in landscape, ruined
     archway beyond (89x127cm-35x50in)

SERVEAU, Clement (1886-1972) French
£1093 $2000   (17-May-92 DU.E1089) Floral still life with bell jar (64x48cm-25x19in)
     s.d.1945
£1304 $2322   (29-Nov-91 GAB.G2635) Nature morte, fruits et bouteilles
     (79x65cm-31x26in) s. board (S.FR 3300)
£2058 $3724   (6-Dec-91 GL.P238) La chaise (65x50cm-26x20in) s. (F.FR 20000)
£2305 $4150   (2-Feb-92 CSC.P45/R) Nature morte aux fruits (22x27cm-9x11in) s.d.1950
     (F.FR 22500)
£2372 $4221   (29-Nov-91 GAB.G2636) Bouquet de fleurs (52x65cm-20x26in) s. board
     (S.FR 6000)
£3000 $5580   (17-Jun-92 S523/R) Still life of flowers and fruit (91x71cm-36x28in)
     s.d.1926

SERVEAU, Clement (1886-1972) French-cont.
£432 $821   (24-Jun-92 GL.P170 b) Nature morte (32x24cm-13x9in) s.d.1953 gouache
           (F.FR 4200)
£463 $880   (24-Jun-92 GL.P171) Composition aux fruits (32x24cm-13x9in) s.d.1953
           gouache (F.FR 4500)
£6865 $12357   (2-Feb-92 CSC.P55/R) Composition dubiste au violon (43x36cm-17x14in)
           s.d.22 pastel crayon (F.FR 67000)

SERVRANCKX, Victor (1897-) Belgian
£375 $683   (30-May-92 VG.B931/R) Composition (29x39cm-11x15in) s.d.1923 gouache over
           indian ink brush (DM 1100)

SESSIONS, James (1882-1962) American
£710 $1300   (17-May-92 DU.E1039/R) Near Aquilla, Mexico, Southeast of El Paso
           (18x23cm-7x9in) s.verso graphite W/C
£957 $1800   (18-Dec-91 SY.NY384/R) End of the trail - The old trading post
           (50x64cm-20x25in) s. gouache board

SESTO, Cesare da (after) (1477-1523) Italian
£3500 $6720   (10-Jul-92 PH63/R) Salome (132x87cm-52x34in)

SESTO, Cesare da (attrib) (1477-1523) Italian
£3529 $6318   (15-Nov-91 GK.Z5096/R) Mary Magdalen holding pot of ointment
           (76x61cm-30x24in) panel (S.FR 9000)

SETHER, Gulbrand (fl.1890-1910) Norwegian
£628 $1200   (16-Jul-92 SY.NY469/R) Fisherman's port in Norway (68x99cm-27x39in) s.

SETKOWICZ, Adam (1875-1945) Polish
£523 $905   (8-Sep-91 REM.W33) Rest in the field (41x64cm-16x25in) s. board
           (P.Z 10000000)

SETOS, de los (?) Spanish
£719 $1351   (16-Dec-91 ANS.M143/R) Feria campesina (46x61cm-18x24in) s. (S.P 130000)

SETTANNI, Luigi (1909-1984) American
£1047 $1800   (10-Oct-91 FA.PH908/R) Seated nude (41x28cm-16x11in) s.

SETTERBERG, Carl (1897-?) American
£447 $800   (13-Nov-91 B.SF2806/R) Pueblo church (37x53cm-15x21in) s. W/C

SETTLE, William F (1821-1897) British
£3500 $6300   (22-Nov-91 C124/R) British frigate and cutter (18x26cm-7x10in)
           mono.d.1880 panel
£800 $1440   (9-Jan-92 B245/R) H M S Eurydice (22x33cm-9x13in) init.d.76 i.verso W/C

SEUPEL, Johann Friedrich (18th C) German
£21000 $40320   (10-Jul-92 C183/R) Ocelot watching over dead parrot (103x126cm-41x50in)
           s.d.1791

SEURAT, Georges (1859-1891) French
£1643 $2957   (20-Nov-91 CN.P63/R) Trois hommes et deux femmes (14x23cm-6x9in) lead
           pencil (F.FR 16000)
£7000 $12670   (4-Dec-91 S104/R) Jeune guerrier casque (15x20cm-6x8in) st. pencil
£13559 $24000   (6-Nov-91 CH.NY107/R) Guerrier Casque, de profil (64x49cm-25x19in) conte
           crayon
£452696 $810326   (17-Nov-91 GL.P28/R) Le moissonneur (30x23cm-12x9in) d.1881 Conte crayon
           (F.FR 4450000)

SEVEHON, Francky Boy (1954-) French?
£661 $1149   (16-Apr-92 FB.P238/R) Adieu valerie (123x157cm-48x62in) s.i.d.87 acrylic
           (F.FR 6500)

SEVERA, Carlo (20th C) Italian
£772 $1374   (29-Apr-92 F.F83) Ricerca di luce (44x100cm-17x39in) d.1983 mixed media
           panel (I.L 1700000)

SEVERDONCK, Franz van (1809-1889) Belgian
£879 $1600   (26-May-92 CE.NY92/R) Poultry feeding (19x25cm-7x10in) s.d.1885 panel
£887 $1543   (14-Apr-92 SY.AM159) Two roosters (18x24cm-7x9in) s.d.1864 panel
           (D.FL 2900)
£917 $1624   (5-Nov-91 SY.AM271) Sheep and hens in meadow (17x24cm-7x9in) s.d.1864
           panel (D.FL 3000)
£925 $1600   (6-Sep-91 S.BM119/R) Belle-cour avec pigeons (15x23cm-6x9in) s.d.1861 i.
           verso panel
£955 $1700   (22-Jan-92 SY.NY440/R) Fowl in landscape (18x24cm-7x9in) s.d.1863 panel
£979 $1703   (14-Apr-92 SY.AM125) Poultry in meadow (17x24cm-7x9in) s.d.1864 panel
           (D.FL 3200)
£1000 $1750   (21-Feb-92 BG.M270/R) Interior of barn with roosters and chickens
           (18x25cm-7x10in) s.d.1874
£1019 $1854   (14-Dec-91 BU.O44/R) Sheep and ducks in landscape (18x26cm-7x10in)
           s.d.1844 sig.i.verso panel (N.KR 11500)
£1149 $2000   (13-Sep-91 S.W2852/R) Gamecocks fighting (18x25cm-7x10in) s.d.1889 panel
£1168 $2090   (14-Nov-91 GRO.B20/R) Farmyard (18x25cm-7x10in) s.d.1878 panel

SEVERDONCK, Franz van (1809-1889) Belgian-cont.

£1223	$2165	(5-Nov-91 SY.AM239/R) Bull and goat in meadow (20x26cm-8x10in) s.d.1864 panel (D.FL 4000)
£1223	$2165	(5-Nov-91 SY.AM157) Cattle in meadow (20x26cm-8x10in) s.d.1864 panel (D.FL 4000)
£1394	$2537	(12-Dec-91 L.K676) Sheep, ducks and cows in landscape (22x32cm-9x13in) s.d.1856 panel (DM 4000)
£1678	$2987	(30-Nov-91 VG.B100/R) Hunter and peasant woman conversing in landscape (54x81cm-21x32in) s. (DM 4800)
£1800	$3204	(28-Nov-91 B154/R) Cockerls, pigeons and ducks in landscape (18x26cm-7x10in) s. s.i.verso panel pair
£1832	$3500	(16-Jul-92 SY.NY482/R) Sheep and ducks in landscape (17x26cm-7x10in) s.d.1889 panel
£1900	$3287	(23-Mar-92 HS196/R) Sheep and lambs in moorland landscape. Two sheep and two lambs upon hill (17x25cm-7x10in) s.d.1878 board
£2405	$4402	(2-Jun-92 FN.S2759/R) Sheep with lambs in hilly landscape and thunderstorm rising (48x68cm-19x27in) s.d.1888 (DM 7000)
£3488	$6000	(15-Oct-91 CE.NY116/R) Sheep and poultry grazing in a landscape (18x26cm-7x10in) s.d.1833 i. verso

SEVERDONCK, Franz van and MOREL, Jan Evert (19th C) Belgian

£1728	$3300	(16-Jul-92 SY.NY485/R) Shepherd tending his flock (33x29cm-13x11in) s.d.187- panel

SEVEREN, Dan van (20th C) Belgian?

£917	$1615	(7-Apr-92 C.A266) Composition (42x35cm-17x14in) s.d.1971 dr. (B.FR 55000)
£1001	$1761	(7-Apr-92 C.A265/R) Composition (57x37cm-22x15in) s.d.1971 dr. (B.FR 60000)
£1170	$1988	(22-Oct-91 C.A320) Composition (43x28cm-17x11in) s.d.1965 coloured dr. (B.FR 70000)
£1337	$2272	(22-Oct-91 C.A319) Composition (50x42cm-20x17in) s.d.1970 dr. (B.FR 80000)
£2002	$3523	(7-Apr-92 C.A264/R) Composition (120x94cm-47x37in) s.d.1975 dr. (B.FR 120000)

SEVERINI, Gino (1883-1966) Italian

£1267	$2306	(25-May-92 CH.R13/R) Studio per gioielli (12x18cm-5x7in) s. tempera (I.L 2800000)
£1267	$2306	(25-May-92 CH.R14/R) Disegno per spilla (13x18cm-5x7in) s. tempera paper (I.L 2800000)
£2881	$5473	(24-Jun-92 GL.P178/R) Beaute de la courbe (102x72cm-40x28in) s. tempera board (F.FR 28000)
£5424	$9818	(21-May-92 F.M260/R) Poesie algebrique (64x50cm-25x20in) s. tempera (I.L 12000000)
£12435	$22632	(9-Dec-91 CH.R162/R) Tracteurs acricoles (23x22cm-9x9in) s. tempera paper on canvas (I.L 27000000)
£19067	$33939	(29-Apr-92 F.F291/R) Composizione (25x60cm-10x24in) tempera cardboard (I.L 42000000)
£22107	$40235	(9-Dec-91 CH.R113/R) Natura morta con strumento musicale, frutta e vasi (51x36cm-20x14in) s. tempera paper (I.L 48000000)
£33930	$61413	(3-Dec-91 F.R245/R) Natura morta con bottiglie e fruttiera (24x28cm-9x11in) s. panel (I.L 73000000)
£35271	$66309	(19-Dec-91 F.M162/R) Natura morta (45x34cm-18x13in) s. i.d.verso panel (I.L 76000000)
£39548	$70000	(6-Nov-91 CH.NY308/R) Les choses deviennent Peinture (65x46cm-26x18in) s.d.1964 s.i.d.verso
£64706	$111294	(12-Oct-91 F.L223/R) Natura morta con bottiglia, frutta e dolce (53x73cm-21x29in) s. (S.FR 165000)
£76575	$143961	(19-Dec-91 F.M226/R) Lumiere et mouvement, ballet a l'opera (116x80cm-46x31in) s. s.i.d.1953verso (I.L 165000000)
£1564	$2800	(9-May-92 CE.NY130/R) Natura morta (18x27cm-7x11in) s.indis.i.d.55 pen indian ink
£1673	$3029	(3-Dec-91 F.R125/R) Natura morta scomposta (26x19cm-10x7in) s. ink (I.L 3600000)
£1955	$3500	(9-May-92 CE.NY132/R) Natura morta (20x28cm-8x11in) s. pen indian ink
£2170	$3927	(21-May-92 F.M108/R) La foi (27x20cm-11x8in) mono.d. ink (I.L 4800000)
£4571	$8000	(25-Feb-92 CH.NY61/R) Pulcinella e Arlecchino (29x23cm-11x9in) s. pen indian ink
£6124	$11207	(12-May-92 F.R199/R) Ritmo di oggetti (25x33cm-10x13in) s.d.1948/50 mixed media (I.L 13500000)

SEVERINUS, A de (19th C) Italian

£690	$1200	(11-Sep-91 D.NY78) Cavalier comes to call (81x61cm-32x24in) bears sig.

SEVERN, Joseph Arthur Palliser (1842-1931) British

£750	$1335	(28-Nov-91 CSK65/R) Sunset, Notre Dame and Ile de la Cite (58x86cm-23x34in) pencil W/C htd.white
£780	$1427	(14-May-92 CSK113) Sunset, Notre Dame and Ile de la Cite from the left bank (58x86cm-23x34in) pencil W/C htd.white

SEVILLE SCHOOL, 17th C Spanish

£2753	$4928	(14-Nov-91 ANS.M86/R) La conversion de San Pablo (115x168cm-45x66in) i. (S.P 500000)
£2765	$5198	(17-Dec-91 BRO.B371) Entierro de Santa Catalina (195x137cm-77x54in) studio of Zurbaran (S.P 500000)

SEVILLE SCHOOL, 17th C Spanish-cont.
£8177 $14064   (7-Oct-91 ANS.M95/R) Sacrificio de Isaac (175x116cm-69x46in)
(S.P 1500000)

SEVILLE SCHOOL, 18th C Spanish
£2319 $3989   (16-Oct-91 FER.M89/R) El regreso del hijo prodigo (30x30cm-12x12in)
(S.P 425000)

SEVILLE SCHOOL, 19th C Spanish
£5537 $9967   (28-Jan-92 EP.M22/R) Escena campestre (81x139cm-32x55in) indist.mono.
(S.P 1000000)

SEVIN, Pierre Paul (attrib) (1650-1710) French
*£800 $1424   (27-Nov-91 C204/R) Lady in decollete dress with pearl necklace
(3x?cm-1x?in) mins.s. gilt metal frame enamel border oval*

SEXTON, Frederick Lester (1889-?) American
£683 $1250   (9-Feb-92 LIT.L301) House in winter (51x71cm-20x28in) s.
£893 $1500   (28-Aug-91 MFA.C166/R) Autumn landscape (36x36cm-14x14in) board

SEYBEL (20th C) ?
£815 $1491   (3-Jun-92 CSC.P27) La plage Trouville-Roches noires (23x46cm-9x18in) s.
(F.FR 8000)

SEYBEL, Lyne (20th C) ?
£811 $1477   (25-May-92 D.P211) Paris - Ile de la Cite (33x41cm-13x16in) s.
(F.FR 8000)

SEYDEL, Eduard (1822-1881) Luxembourger
£1300 $2314   (28-Nov-91 B63/R) Figures before woodland cottage (25x33cm-10x13in)
s.d.1861
£2610 $4750   (28-May-92 SY.NY250/R) Coffee time (36x42cm-14x17in) s.d.1859

SEYLER, J (1873-1958) German
£488 $878   (29-Jan-92 N.M834) Cattle by stream (27x49cm-11x19in) s. (DM 1400)
*£483 $854   (6-Nov-91 N.M1145) Rider in savannah (20x27cm-8x11in) s. mixed media
(DM 1400)*

SEYLER, Julius (1873-1958) German
£515 $897   (17-Sep-91 FN.S2541) Courting couple beneath trees (21x14cm-8x6in) s.
board (DM 1500)
£699 $1196   (19-Mar-92 N.M2839/R) Shrimp fishermen (40x66cm-16x26in) s. board
(DM 2000)
£753 $1296   (11-Oct-91 AW.H3037/R) Courting couple in landscape (33x43cm-13x17in)
board (DM 2200)
£859 $1495   (18-Sep-91 N.M705) Shrimpfisher on beach (70x90cm-28x35in) s. panel
(DM 2500)
£877 $1579   (23-Nov-91 N.M295) Peasant ploughing with oxen (71x99cm-28x39in) s. board
(DM 2500)
£962 $1674   (17-Sep-91 FN.S541 a/R) Shrimp fishermen with horses on beach at low tide
(68x98cm-27x39in) s. board (DM 2800)
£1020 $1825   (15-Nov-91 ZOF.Z1431/R) Peasant ploughing with oxen (23x34cm-9x13in) s.
board (S.FR 2600)
£1031 $1794   (18-Sep-91 N.M703/R) Shrimpfisher on beach (70x100cm-28x39in) s. board
(DM 3000)
£1049 $1815   (25-Mar-92 KM.K1435) Beach scene with fishermen and horse-drawn carts
(47x72cm-19x28in) s. (DM 3000)
£1237 $2153   (18-Sep-91 N.M704/R) Peasant ploughing with horses (50x69cm-20x27in) s.
board (DM 3600)
£1719 $3042   (5-Nov-91 GF.L2628) Team of oxen in avenue lined with birch tree
(50x70cm-20x28in) s. board (S.FR 4400)
£1852 $3352   (20-May-92 GK.Z5084/R) Shrimp fishing, Normandy (70x100cm-28x39in) s.
(S.FR 5000)
£2166 $3704   (12-Mar-92 RAS.V981/R) Figures and oxcart (66x100cm-26x39in) s.
(D.KR 24000)
£3136 $5707   (11-Dec-91 WE.MU252/R) Indian (100x70cm-39x28in) s. board (DM 9000)
*£683 $1242   (25-May-92 WK.M1156/R) Horses on beach (32x43cm-13x17in) s. oil gouache
(DM 2000)*
*£683 $1242   (25-May-92 WK.M1157/R) Two scouts (32x43cm-13x17in) s. oil gouache
(DM 2000)*

SEYMOUR, James (1702-1752) British
£10000 $17600   (8-Apr-92 S122/R) Bay racehorse with jockey up by gap at Newmarket
(23x29cm-9x11in) s.
£18033 $33000   (5-Jun-92 SY.NY2/R) Saddled grey with jockey up exercising on Newmarket
Heath (64x76cm-25x30in)
£20000 $35800   (13-Nov-91 S94/R) The Hon John Smith Barry out hunting with his hounds
(62x101cm-24x40in)

SEYMOUR, James (after) (1702-1752) British
£3400 $5916   (10-Sep-91 RG2297) Stable interiors with horses and grooms
(25x36cm-10x14in) pair

SEYMOUR, Samuel (1775-?) American
£6704 $12000   (14-Nov-91 CE.NY20/R) Two Indian braves and squaw (13x16cm-5x6in)
     init.i.d.1806 W/C pencil sepia ink

SEYSSAUD (1867-1952) French
£8454 $14456   (11-Mar-92 CJ.N272/R) Paysage rocheux (65x80cm-26x31in) (F.FR 82000)

SEYSSAUD, R (1867-1952) French
£1423 $2476   (13-Apr-92 BG.P132) La riviere au peuplier (55x46cm-22x18in) s.
     (F.FR 14000)

SEYSSAUD, Rene (1867-1952) French
£3086 $5617   (11-Dec-91 CH.AM244/R) Paysage aus cerisiers (46x55cm-18x22in) s.
     (D.FL 10000)
£5595 $10015   (13-Nov-91 PIC.P84) Paysage a l'arbre (55x46cm-22x18in) s. (F.FR 55000)
£7345 $13000   (5-Nov-91 CE.NY223/R) Moisson a Aurel (60x73cm-24x29in) s.

SHACKLETON, John (18th C) British
£900 $1584   (8-Apr-92 S171/R) Portrait of Jane Pescod, Mrs Carew Mildmay
     (239x147cm-94x58in)
£3500 $6405   (15-May-92 TE358/R) Portrait of Queen Anne, seated holding orb
     (236x137cm-93x54in)
£4500 $8235   (15-May-92 TE357/R) Portrait of Queen Mary, in diamond-studded dress,
     standing by table (236x137cm-93x54in)

SHADBOLT, Jack (1909-) Canadian
£2736 $4871   (26-Nov-91 JOY.T9/R) Organic forms - winter (50x65cm-20x26in) s.d.51
     s.d.52 acrylic ink (C.D 5500)
£4338 $7895   (26-May-92 JOY.T161/R) Heat devils (140x187cm-55x74in) s.d.85 acrylic
     canvas (C.D 9500)
£4390 $7946   (2-Dec-91 R.T211/R) Bottles (73x92cm-29x36in) s. i.d.1958 st.studio
     stretcher (C.D 9000)
£1005 $1828   (26-May-92 JOY.T168) Indoor sculpture (54x48cm-21x19in) s. mixed media
     (C.D 2200)
£1005 $1828   (26-May-92 JOY.T218) Trapped bird (46x36cm-18x14in) s.d.48 ink W/C
     (C.D 2200)
£1461 $2659   (26-May-92 JOY.T206) Studies of boats at dock (30x37cm-12x15in) s.d.63
     chl wash pair (C.D 3200)
£1625 $2876   (6-Nov-91 SY.T52/R) Dock view with boats (79x53cm-31x21in) s.d.62 W/C ink
     paper on board (C.D 3250)
£2511 $4571   (26-May-92 JOY.T189/R) Old west end store, Robson Street, Vancouver, B.C
     (67x46cm-26x19in) s.d.46 W/C (C.D 5500)
£3250 $5753   (6-Nov-91 SY.T129/R) Vancouver School of Art (77x56cm-30x22in) s.d.46 W/C
     pen (C.D 6500)

SHAHN, Ben (1898-1969) American
£690 $1200   (15-Apr-92 SY.NY249/R) Eyes and nose (10x14cm-4x6in) ink
£2128 $4000   (18-Dec-91 SY.NY340/R) Moon for the Misbegotten (43x35cm-17x14in) s.
     India ink

SHALDERS, George (1826-1873) British
£600 $1026   (18-Mar-92 CSK153) Returning home with flock (20x38cm-8x15in) init.d.1861
£1500 $2880   (28-Jul-92 SWS325/R) Views in Glengariff (25x36cm-10x14in) s.i.d.1861
     pair
£500 $885   (13-Feb-92 B195/R) Children by a fence watching a mother and calf
     (26x21cm-10x8in) s. W/C bodycol.
£650 $1105   (24-Oct-91 CSK50/R) Homeward bound (25x46cm-10x18in) s.d.65 pencil W/C
     bodycol.
£720 $1224   (22-Oct-91 SWS198) Cattle and sheep in landscape (29x50cm-11x20in)
     s.d.1872 W/C bodycol gum arabic
£2100 $3717   (6-Nov-91 S254/R) Taking the flock to new pastures (19x30cm-7x12in)
     s.d.65 W/C htd.bodycol
£8200 $14022   (12-Mar-92 CSK44/R) Wensleydale (46x79cm-18x31in) s.d.1866 i.verso pencil
     W/C bodycol

SHANKS, Nelson (20th C) American
£984 $1800   (7-Jun-92 LIT.L72) Black nude (41x41cm-16x16in) s.i.d.1973verso

SHANKS, William Somerville (1864-1951) British
£1400 $2492   (28-Apr-92 S264) Making butter (61x91cm-24x36in) s.
£3200 $5696   (30-Apr-92 CG936/R) Still life with lobster on plate and brown crock on
     marble ledge (51x61cm-20x24in) s.

SHANNON, Charles Haslewood (1865-1937) British
£1397 $2500   (13-Nov-91 B.SF2349/R) The wounded Amazon (102x83cm-40x33in) s.d.1922

SHANNON, David Michael (20th C) Australian
£1026 $1826   (28-Apr-92 CH.ME81) Gleesons farm (75x55cm-30x22in) s.d.86 (A.D 2400)
£1613 $2806   (16-Sep-91 CH.ME182/R) Marshalling Yards V (76x102cm-30x40in) s.d.71
     (A.D 3500)
£2304 $4009   (16-Sep-91 CH.ME102/R) Daisy with parasol (107x107cm-42x42in) s.d.69
     (A.D 5000)
£2308 $4408   (19-Jul-92 SY.ME22/R) Little Collins Street, Melbourne (121x75cm-48x30in)
     s. masonite (A.D 6000)

SHANNON, David Michael (20th C) Australian-cont.
£2350	$4184	(28-Apr-92 CH.ME279) Jugiong landscape no II (100x75cm-39x30in) s.d.87 (A.D 5500)
£3341	$5813	(16-Sep-91 CH.ME72/R) City skyline (120x150cm-47x59in) s. (A.D 7250)
£5991	$10424	(16-Sep-91 CH.ME91/R) Heathcote landscape (100x200cm-39x79in) s.d.85 (A.D 13000)

SHANNON, Sir James Jebusa (1862-1923) British
| £580 | $969 | (22-Aug-91 CSK187) Portrait of young boy (69x56cm-27x22in) s. |
| £17442 | $30000 | (17-Oct-91 SY.NY115/R) Portrait of Miss Annie Beebe (114x87cm-45x34in) s.d.1886 |

SHAO FEI (1954-) Chinese
| £6575 | $11243 | (22-Mar-92 SY.TA71/R) Dance (72x89cm-28x35in) s. (T.D 286000) |
| £2811 | $4919 | (30-Mar-92 CH.HK377/R) Golden autumn (91x117cm-36x46in) s.d.1986 ink W/ scroll (HK.D 38000) |

SHAPIRO, Joel (1941-) American
£2793	$5000	(9-May-92 CE.NY260/R) Untitled (40x51cm-16x20in) init.d.1985verso chl chk
£3911	$7000	(6-May-92 CH.NY348/R) Untitled (47x35cm-19x14in) s.d.1987 verso col.chk chl
£7821	$14000	(13-Nov-91 CH.NY272/R) Untitled (78x58cm-31x23in) s.d.87verso chl.col.chks.
£13295	$23000	(3-Oct-91 SY.NY158/R) Untitled (135x145cm-53x57in) chl.chk.
£21788	$39000	(6-May-92 CH.NY359/R) Untitled (153x102cm-60x40in) s.d.1988 verso chl col.chk

SHAPLEIGH, F H (1842-1906) American
| £500 | $950 | (28-Jun-92 LIT.L237) The old Spanish Fort at Maranzas (51x36cm-20x14in) s. i.verso |

SHAPLEIGH, Frank Henry (1842-1906) American
£642	$1150	(6-May-92 B.P51/R) Abandoned dory (18x30cm-7x12in) s.d.1873 panel
£958	$1600	(20-Aug-91 RB.HY115/R) Lake Lucerne, Switzerland (66x122cm-26x48in) s.d.1866
£1667	$2900	(13-Sep-91 S.W2863/R) Italian lake scene (66x122cm-26x48in) s.d.1868
£4571	$8000	(4-Apr-92 E.EDM385/R) Quebec from Point Levi (76x122cm-30x48in) s.d.1883

SHARP, Dorothea (1874-1955) British
£500	$850	(5-Aug-91 WW71) Still life of flowers (55x44cm-22x17in) s. board
£500	$890	(30-Apr-92 T100/R) Flowers in vase (28x23cm-11x9in)
£1300	$2249	(2-Oct-91 S44/R) Day at the beach (18x25cm-7x10in) canvas on board
£1400	$2506	(14-Jan-92 PH40) Feeding chickens (48x41cm-19x16in)
£1500	$2610	(14-Apr-92 ZZ.B17) Still life with vase of mixed garden flowers (44x36cm-17x14in) s. board sold with two col.prints
£1520	$2584	(22-Oct-91 SWS403/R) Summer's day on beach (26x34cm-10x13in) oil sketch panel
£1700	$2924	(6-Mar-92 C117/R) Summer flowers in blue vase (31x28cm-12x11in) board
£1800	$3132	(19-Sep-91 B41/R) Still life of flowers in vase (52x62cm-20x24in) s. board
£2200	$3806	(2-Oct-91 S125/R) Paddling (29x37cm-11x15in) board
£2200	$4026	(4-Jun-92 CSK100/R) Summer flowers in brown vase on table (46x36cm-18x14in) init.
£2400	$4392	(5-Jun-92 C33/R) Lilies and summer flowers in earthenware vase (43x36cm-17x14in) s. board
£2400	$4272	(1-May-92 PHE87/R) Shrimping (38x50cm-15x20in)
£2800	$4816	(6-Mar-92 C118/R) Children at the Peter Pan Monument, Kensington Gardens (36x25cm-14x10in) panel
£3000	$5310	(7-Nov-91 C72/R) Honeysuckle, daisies, hollyhocks and fuchsia on a window ledge (51x41cm-20x16in) board
£3200	$5664	(5-Nov-91 PH34/R) Two children on rocks (35x46cm-14x18in) s. panel
£3200	$5568	(17-Sep-91 PH13) Picking flowers on a cliff top (35x45cm-14x18in) s. panel
£3500	$6405	(14-May-92 C25/R) Summer flowers in earthenware vase (41x33cm-16x13in)
£3800	$6650	(27-Sep-91 C73/R) In the Luxembourg Gardens (37x44cm-15x17in) s. panel
£5000	$8750	(27-Sep-91 C72/R) Summer flowers (37x43cm-15x17in) s. board
£5200	$9256	(1-May-92 PHE60/R) Through the waves (34x44cm-13x17in) s.
£6000	$10260	(11-Mar-92 S134/R) Cornish holiday (51x61cm-20x24in) s.
£6000	$10980	(14-May-92 C186/R) Children paddling in shallows (56x56cm-22x22in) s.
£7500	$12975	(2-Oct-91 S100/R) The campfire (63x76cm-25x30in) s.
£8000	$13760	(6-Mar-92 C115/R) On the beach (40x48cm-16x19in) s.
£9000	$15930	(7-Nov-91 C74) Marcella Smith at the beach, the Languedoc, South of France (77x96cm-30x38in)
£9000	$15480	(6-Mar-92 C116/R) At the seaside (40x48cm-16x19in) s.
£29000	$53070	(5-Jun-92 C32/R) Crossing the Etang (91x107cm-36x42in) s.

SHARP, Joseph Henry (1859-1953) American
£838	$1500	(13-Nov-91 B.SF2731/R) Sunset on pond (15x22cm-6x9in) s. board
£1257	$2250	(13-Nov-91 B.SF2680/R) Roses and blue vase (61x91cm-24x36in) s.
£2095	$3750	(13-Nov-91 B.SF2824/R) Ranch at Lodge Grass (25x36cm-10x14in) s. board
£3073	$5500	(14-Nov-91 CE.NY315/R) Acoma, New Mexico (77x61cm-30x24in) s.
£3723	$7000	(18-Dec-91 SY.NY381/R) Western landscape (24x34cm-9x13in) s. i.verso board
£4795	$8200	(13-Mar-92 WOL.C456/R) Fort Washakie NY (23x33cm-9x13in) s. canvas on board

HARP, Joseph Henry (1859-1953) American-cont.
£4945 $9000   (28-May-92 CH.NY122/R) The artist's Pueblo studio (24x35cm-9x14in) s.
            canvasboard
£6044 $11000   (28-May-92 CH.NY121/R) Still life with snapdragons in blue bowl
            (51x61cm-20x24in) s.
£7459 $13500   (6-Dec-91 CH.NY122/R) Marigolds and asters in a china vase
            (56x69cm-22x27in) s.
£7821 $14000   (13-Nov-91 B.SF2721/R) Autumn in Taos Canyon (56x69cm-22x27in) s.
£8380 $15000   (13-Nov-91 B.SF2720/R) Aspens, Cottonwoods and Spruce, Taos Canyon
            (65x76cm-26x30in) s. s.d.1932 verso
£9392 $17000   (6-Dec-91 CH.NY163/R) The Flagships Connecticut and Kansas
            (50x76cm-20x30in) s.
£13187 $24000   (28-May-92 CH.NY118/R) Portrait of an Indian, Taos (46x28cm-18x11in) s.i.
            board
£23077 $42000   (28-May-92 CH.NY108/R) Evening on Crow Reservation, Montana
            (30x45cm-12x18in) s.
£391   *$700*   *(13-Nov-91 B.SF2817/R) Indian head (9x14cm-4x6in) s. ink*

HARP, Louis H (1875-1946) American
£789 $1500   (23-Jun-92 MOR.P113) South Point Lobos (64x76cm-25x30in) s.
£1124 $2000   (26-Nov-91 MOR.P62) Coastal Gibson Beach, South Point Lobos
            (64x76cm-25x30in) s.
£1397 $2500   (13-Nov-91 B.SF2796/R) Navajo spring (51x66cm-20x26in) s.d.1915 s.verso

HARPLES, James (1752-1811) American
£1000   *$1760*   *(7-Apr-92 C56/R) Portrait of gentleman seated in chair, in coat,*
            waistcoat and cravat (23x22cm-9x9in) pastel

HARPLES, Rolinda (1794-1838) British
£42000 $80220   (15-Jul-92 S85/R) Rownham Ferry with portraits (84x120cm-33x47in) s.

HATTUCK, Aaron Draper (1832-1928) American
£689 $1150   (25-Aug-91 LIT.L250) Across Lake George (13x23cm-5x9in) i. verso paper
£1033 $1860   (23-Nov-91 YFA.M265/R) Pre-Raphaelite landscape (41x30cm-16x12in) s.
£1124 $2000   (26-Jan-92 JRB.C44/R) Hudson Valley, Esopus Creek (25x43cm-10x17in)
            canvas on board

HAUL, Dedi Ben (1930-) ?
£904 $1700   (5-Jan-92 GG.TA182/R) Jerusalem (96x105cm-38x41in) s. board

HAW, C H (?) ?
£793 $1411   (26-Nov-91 J.M1044) Droving (59x90cm-23x35in) s. (A.D 1800)

HAW, Charles Green (1892-1974) American
£698 $1200   (12-Oct-91 SY.NY268/R) Duet (152x102cm-60x40in) s.
£3714 $6500   (26-Sep-91 CH.NY207/R) Revolt (127x102cm-50x40in) s.
£4310 $7500   (15-Apr-92 SY.NY253/R) Abstract composition (41x51cm-16x20in) s.d.1941
            verso canvasboard
£1514   *$2800*   *(10-Jun-92 CE.NY463) Now September (11x18cm-4x7in) s. W/C*

HAW, George (?) ?
£857 $1500   (19-Feb-92 D.NY79) Sunday sailors, Loire (51x41cm-20x16in) s. i.stretcher
£925 $1600   (25-Mar-92 D.NY70) The Meadow on the Oise (51x61cm-20x24in) s. i.verso

HAW, Harry Hutchinson (1897-?) American
£1111 $1900   (13-Mar-92 S.BM249/R) Southern Ohio Hills, Ridge (102x122cm-40x48in)
            s.d.1931

HAW, James (18th C) British
£4500   *$7650*   *(23-Oct-91 S302/R) View of Adelaide, South Australia (29x43cm-11x17in)*
            s.d.1851 oil W/C paper on board

HAW, John Byam (1872-1919) British
£520 $889   (12-Mar-92 CSK277/R) Be not righteous over much, neither make thyself
            over wise (38x27cm-15x11in) s.d.1901 panel
£1050 $1806   (4-Mar-92 ZZ.B227) Pegasus ploughing (36x62cm-14x24in) s. panel
£1650 $3152   (14-Jul-92 DR428/R) Road to Calvary (35x25cm-14x10in) s. panel
£2000 $3540   (6-Nov-91 S192/R) As it happeneth to the fool, so it happeneth even to me
            .... (40x30cm-16x12in) s.d.1901 i.verso panel
£720   *$1375*   *(13-Jul-92 PH104) The Kelpie and the Highlander (56x45cm-22x18in) s. W/C*
            bodycol

HAW, Joshua (1776-1861) British
£2011 $3500   (15-Apr-92 SY.NY7/R) Mount Katahdin (44x34cm-17x13in) s.d.1819
            i.stretcher

HAW, Joshua (attrib) (1776-1861) British
£791 $1400   (9-Nov-91 W.W133/R) Boys playing, a scene near a mill (61x81cm-24x32in)

HAW, Walter (1851-1933) British
£650 $1157   (28-Nov-91 PHX522) Ground swell, Padstow (51x102cm-20x40in) s.i.verso

HAWHAN, Ada Romer (1865-1947) American
£684 $1300   (24-Jun-92 B.SF6320/R) By window (30x36cm-12x14in) s.

SHAYER, Charles (attrib) (19th C) British
£2800 $4872   (11-Sep-91 PHG14) Gossips by an Inn (95x127cm-37x50in)

SHAYER, H and C (19th C) British
£2105 $4000   (26-Jun-92 WOL.C409/R) English countryside with figures (30x41cm-12x16in)
    s. pair

SHAYER, Henry and Charles (19th C) British
£3500 $6230   (28-Apr-92 PH119/R) Gypsy encampment (36x31cm-14x12in) pair

SHAYER, William (19th C) British
£1100 $1958   (21-Jan-92 PH14/R) Fisherfolk on coast, cottage beyond (23x30cm-9x12in)
    s. board
£1132 $2004   (5-Nov-91 BA.S165/R) Fisherfamily on beach (36x46cm-14x18in) s.d.1850
    (S.KR 12000)
£1412 $2500   (5-Nov-91 BG.M668/R) Cows, horse and rider in mountainous river landscape
    (43x36cm-17x14in) s.d.1850
£1500 $2580   (11-Oct-91 C114/R) Fishermen bringing in the catch (18x23cm-7x9in)
£1796 $3000   (20-Aug-91 RB.HY116/R) Fishmongers at the shore (46x61cm-18x24in) s.
£1800 $3384   (19-Dec-91 C161/R) Cattle in barn (46x56cm-18x22in)
£2000 $3700   (11-Jun-92 CSK98/R) Boy with dog, donkey and goats on track
    (53x43cm-21x17in) s.
£3600 $6480   (19-Nov-91 PH65/R) Fisherfolk on the sea shore (46x61cm-18x24in) s.
£3700 $7104   (28-Jul-92 SWS372/R) The ploughman's rest (69x90cm-27x35in)
£6200 $11160   (19-Nov-91 PH26/R) The plough team. Drover with charges (36x30cm-14x12in)
    s. panel pair
£6600 $11550   (27-Feb-92 L400/R) Cottage interior with family by hearthside
    (71x91cm-28x36in) s.
£8000 $14800   (11-Jun-92 CSK96/R) Bargaining for fish (71x91cm-28x36in) s.
£9302 $16000   (16-Oct-91 CH.NY239/R) The harvest (71x92cm-28x36in) s.
£10500 $18060   (11-Oct-91 C97/R) The cornfield (76x102cm-30x40in) s. s.i.stretcher
£11000 $20350   (12-Jun-92 C212/R) Fisherfolk on the beach (76x101cm-30x40in) s.
£12000 $20640   (11-Oct-91 C95/R) Encampment in New Forest (102x84cm-40x33in) s.

SHAYER, William (attrib) (19th C) British
£520 $931   (15-Jan-92 BT207) Figures on a beach (28x48cm-11x19in) bears sig.d.1844
£571 $1000   (18-Feb-92 CE.NY29) Haywagon (74x107cm-29x42in) canvas on masonite
£769 $1400   (26-May-92 CE.NY26) Harvesters in wooded landscape (89x89cm-35x35in)
    bears sig.
£838 $1500   (6-May-92 D.NY57/R) Southampton (48x79cm-19x31in) s.d.1841
£1500 $2550   (24-Oct-91 CSK139/R) Fisherfolk on a beach with a pony (71x91cm-28x36in)
£2200 $3762   (12-Mar-92 CSK216/R) Cattle watering at pool, drover beyond
    (76x102cm-30x40in) bears sig.d.1851

SHAYER, William (circle) (19th C) British
£1450 $2422   (21-Aug-91 HAR375/R) Coastal scene with fishing village in foreground
    (58x112cm-23x44in)

SHAYER, William (snr) (1787-1879) British
£1800 $3204   (21-Jan-92 PH115/R) Marekt man (35x30cm-14x12in) s. s.i.verso panel
£2023 $3500   (29-Mar-92 MY.F58/R) The traders (76x64cm-30x25in) s.
£2500 $4450   (21-Jan-92 PH114/R) Fisherman (35x30cm-14x12in) s.i.verso panel
£2800 $5124   (7-Feb-92 K394/R) Mid-day rest scene. Evening rustic scene
    (15x23cm-6x9in) one s. panel pair
£3200 $5728   (15-Nov-91 C72/R) Gypsy encampment in clearing in wooded landscape
    (76x63cm-30x25in) s.
£3500 $6685   (21-Jul-92 PH264/R) Fisherfolk and beached fishing vessels on foreshore
    (71x91cm-28x36in) s.d.1852
£4000 $7000   (20-Feb-92 SY.NY253/R) On south coast (67x81cm-26x32in) indist.s.
£4500 $8055   (15-Nov-91 C45/R) Itinerant trinket seller (76x63cm-30x25in)
£5714 $10000   (20-Feb-92 SY.NY252/R) Fishing boats at low tide (45x61cm-18x24in) s.
    panel
£7115 $12806   (19-Nov-91 GS.B3659/R) Figures with beached sailing boat near fisher huts
    (51x61cm-20x24in) s. (S.FR 18000)
£9143 $16000   (19-Feb-92 CH.NY164/R) Bringing in catch (77x103cm-30x41in) s.d.1837
£29070 $50000   (17-Oct-91 SY.NY295 a/R) Fruit sellers (72x91cm-28x36in) s.d.1833

SHAYER, William (snr) and WILLIAMS, Edward Charles (19th C) British
£9000 $15840   (8-Apr-92 S99/R) Landscape with cattle watering (70x90cm-28x35in) s.

SHAYER, William (style) (19th C) British
£747 $1300   (15-Sep-91 H.C816) Coastal scene with fisherman's family
    (69x91cm-27x36in) bears sig.
£800 $1456   (10-Dec-91 AG341/R) Water cart (33x44cm-13x17in)

SHAYER, William J (1811-1892) British
£750 $1425   (23-Jun-92 PH192/R) Cattle and boy in landscape (32x26cm-13x10in) d.1847
    board
£900 $1665   (11-Jun-92 CSK108/R) Figures before an abbey ruin (29x24cm-11x9in) s.
    board
£1150 $2059   (5-May-92 SWS345/R) A plough team (33x44cm-13x17in) s.i.d.1875
£1500 $2790   (18-Jan-92 B168) At the rabbit hole (45x61cm-18x24in) s.d.1861
£1800 $3294   (3-Jun-92 S51/R) Farmyard scene beside the sea (23x32cm-9x13in)
    bears.sig.
£1800 $3204   (28-Nov-91 B81/R) Setting off (15x23cm-6x9in) s.d.86 board pair

HAYER, William J (1811-1892) British-cont.
2600 $4758   (15-May-92 TE366/R) Plough team (51x69cm-20x27in) s.d.1861
3000 $5370   (15-Nov-91 C101/R) Colonel Pearson's Achievement, with J. Chalmer up, in
                  landscape (36x46cm-14x18in) s.d.1867
:3400 $5814   (12-Mar-92 CSK206) Wayside conversation (76x127cm-30x50in) s.d.1870

HAYER, William J (circle) (1811-1892) British
:820 $1410   (3-Mar-92 SWS1574) A farmyard scene (35x46cm-14x18in) bears sig.

HAYER, William and WILLIAMS, Edward Charles (19th C) British
:5400 $10368   (28-Jul-92 SWS373/R) A roadside Inn, Sussex (74x92cm-29x36in)
:13000 $23790   (3-Jun-92 S38/R) Near Wantage, Berkshire (77x128cm-30x50in) s.d.51

HEARER, Christopher H (1840-1926) American
1136 $2000   (9-Apr-92 FA.PH753) River landscape (51x76cm-20x30in) s.d.1885

HED, Charles D (1818-1893) American
:1053 $2000   (24-Jun-92 B.SF6287/R) Sailboats and steamship (46x81cm-18x32in) s.

HEDD, Marvin Kingsley (1906-1982) ?
:499 $892   (15-Jan-92 D.V175/R) New York (101x84cm-40x33in) s. (A.S 10000)

HEE, Sir Martin Archer (1769-1850) British
:1000 $1910   (17-Jul-92 C71/R) Portrait of a gentleman in black coat and white cravat
                  (76x63cm-30x25in)
:4200 $7518   (13-Nov-91 S157/R) Portrait of Sir Richard Hardinge seated at table
                  (125x100cm-49x39in)

HEE, Sir Martin Archer (attrib) (1769-1850) British
:8500 $15215   (13-Nov-91 S60/R) Portrait of gentleman, said to be Gawen William Rowan
                  Hamilton-Rowan (76x63cm-30x25in)
:10000 $17900   (13-Nov-91 S57/R) Portrait of boy seated on bank (126x100cm-50x39in)

HEERBOOM, Andrew (19th C) British
:750 $1298   (3-Oct-91 CSK179) The arrival (51x71cm-20x28in) s.d.1876 canvas laid down
                  on board

HEETS, Millard (1907-1989) American
:492 $900   (17-May-92 DU.E1232) Burma (30x23cm-12x9in) s.i. W/C
:500 $950   (26-Jun-92 WOL.C118) Burma (25x36cm-10x14in) s. W/C pencil
:1974 $3750   (24-Jun-92 B.SF6468/R) Two figures in landscape (56x76cm-22x30in)
                  s.d.1939 W/C
:1974 $3750   (24-Jun-92 B.SF6471/R) Beach near Kailua-Kona, Hawaii (57x75cm-22x30in)
                  s.d.1950 verso W/C
:2105 $4000   (24-Jun-92 B.SF6470/R) Ladies in morning, Hawaii, 1950 (57x75cm-22x30in)
                  W/C
:2368 $4500   (24-Jun-92 B.SF6472/R) Approaching storm (55x75cm-22x30in) s.d.verso W/C
:3684 $7000   (24-Jun-92 B.SF6469/R) Tower, Alamos, Mexico (56x76cm-22x30in) s.d.1963
                  W/C

HEFFIELD, George (1839-1892) British
:700 $1218   (12-Sep-91 CSK34) Cattle watering in parkland landscape
                  (107x165cm-42x65in) s.d.1884 pastel

HELDON, Charles Gates (1889-1961) American
:421 $750   (2-May-92 IH.NY43/R) Two women on Paris street (48x41cm-19x16in) s. pen
                  ink wash

HELLEY, Samuel (c.1750-1808) British
:600 $1050   (24-Sep-91 CSK38/R) The Rev. William Dodd in cleric's robes
                  (11x?cm-4x?in) min.s.d.1774 oval
:850 $1513   (27-Nov-91 C228/R) Portrait of gentleman in coat with shirt and cravat
                  (4x?cm-2x?in) min. gold bracelet clasp frame oval
:926 $1759   (26-Jun-92 AGS.P65) Portrait presume de Louis Philippe Joseph, duc
                  d'Orleans (7x6cm-3x2in) min. gilded metal border in gold frame oval
                  (F.FR 9000)

HEMI, Menachem (1896-1951) Israeli
:4362 $8200   (5-Jan-92 GG.TA397/R) Donkey train (40x26cm-16x10in) s.
:8511 $16000   (5-Jan-92 GG.TA396/R) Safed on the background of Mount Atsmon
                  (53x71cm-21x28in) s.
:8777 $16500   (5-Jan-92 GG.TA395/R) Self portrait (81x60cm-32x24in) s.twice
:22162 $41000   (9-Jun-92 GG.TA448/R) Pioneer. Effendis (68x58cm-27x23in) double-sided

HEN ZENGZHI and WU CHANGSHUO (19/20th C) Chinese
:1849 $3236   (30-Mar-92 CH.HK381/R) Plum blossoms and calligraphy (18x51cm-7x20in)
                  s.i.d.1920 ink W/C two fans hanging scroll (HK.D 25000)

HENTON, Annie F (fl.1900-1906) British
3000 $5370   (14-Jan-92 B211/R) An Irish Water Spaniel and a Yorkshire Terrier in a
                  landscape (81x71cm-32x28in) s.d.16/4/1900

HEPARD, Ernest Howard (1879-1976) British
:900 $1728   (10-Jul-92 CSK64) Winnie-the-Pooh and friends outside treehouse
                  (28x23cm-11x9in) s. s.i.verso pencil pen W/C bodycol htd white

SHEPARD, Ernest Howard (1879-1976) British-cont.

£1500	$2880	(10-Jul-92 CSK65) Had a pleasant evening (13x8cm-5x3in) init. s.verso pen
£1500	$2880	(10-Jul-92 CSK67) But I don't know 'Good King Wenceslas' said Peter 'And I can't sing' said Benjie (18x15cm-7x6in) init. s.verso pen htd white
£2000	$3840	(10-Jul-92 CSK66/R) Now we'll go right up to the house and sing our carols under windows (18x15cm-7x6in) pen htd white
£2200	$4224	(10-Jul-92 CSK68) Waiting at window (18x13cm-7x5in) s.i. s.i.d.1959 verso pencil pen
£2200	$4224	(10-Jul-92 CSK69/R) Politeness (18x10cm-7x4in) s.i.d.1959 pencil pen
£2400	$4368	(11-Dec-91 CSK66/R) The wrong house s. pen htd.white two in same mount
£3000	$5460	(11-Dec-91 CSK62/R) Expotitions (13x15cm-5x6in) i. s.verso pencil pen
£3000	$5460	(11-Dec-91 CSK67/R) Mole (18x15cm-7x6in) init. pencil ink htd.white
£4800	$9216	(10-Jul-92 CSK70/R) It had HUNNY written on it. And ot is honey, right way down (18x23cm-7x9in) pencil vignettes two one sheet
£6000	$11520	(10-Jul-92 CSK71/R) Pooh and Owl visiting in Owl's parlour (13x18cm-5x7in) pencil pen col.chk
£8000	$15360	(10-Jul-92 CSK73/R) So he started to climb out of hole (10x10cm-4x4in) init. pencil pen
£8200	$15744	(10-Jul-92 CSK72/R) So Pooh pushed and pushed and pushed way through hole (10x10cm-4x4in) pencil pen
£9000	$16380	(11-Dec-91 CSK74/R) What's inside it (23x18cm-9x7in) s. pencil ink W/C htd.white

SHEPHERD, David (1931-) British

£6000	$10260	(11-Mar-92 S88/R) Backs, Cambridge (51x76cm-20x30in) s. i.verso
£8500	$14535	(11-Mar-92 S133/R) Bull elephant (66x107cm-26x42in) s.d.72

SHEPHERD, George (19th C) British

£3600	$6336	(6-Apr-92 PH32/R) Exmouth from Powderham Park (58x83cm-23x33in) W/C htd white

SHEPHERD, George Sydney (?-1858) British

£700	$1337	(14-Jul-92 C44/R) Babbacombe Bay, Devonshire (23x39cm-9x15in) s.i.d.1850 pencil W/C htd white gum arabic
£3600	$6876	(14-Jul-92 C51/R) View West Stratton, Hants. Rye, Sussex. Houses, Luton. Woking, Surrey. Houghton Conquest House (16x24cm-6x9in) s.i.d.1822 pencil W/C five

SHEPPARD, Warren W (1859-1937) American

£778	$1300	(20-Aug-91 RB.HY233) Seascape (51x76cm-20x30in) s.
£914	$1600	(28-Sep-91 YFA.M216) Coastal sunrise (51x76cm-20x30in) s.
£1243	$2250	(21-May-92 GRO.B42/R) Sailboats in the lagoon, Venice (46x76cm-18x30in) s.
£1676	$3000	(14-Nov-91 CE.NY156/R) Sailboat in moonlight (53x41cm-21x16in) s.d.88
£1730	$3200	(10-Jun-92 CE.NY208/R) Venetian canal scene (61x41cm-24x16in) s.
£2299	$4000	(15-Apr-92 SY.NY27/R) Ships sailing by sunset (62x92cm-24x36in) s.d.1894 canvas on board
£5407	$9300	(10-Oct-91 FA.PH869/R) Schooner in choppy seas (56x91cm-22x36in) s.

SHERIDAN, Henrique (c.1835-1860) ?

£1800	$3276	(28-May-92 C11/R) Distant view of Montevideo (28x38cm-11x15in) s. board

SHERMAN, Albert (1882-1971) Australian

£638	$1130	(26-Apr-92 SY.ME127) River Vista (44x36cm-17x14in) s. canvasboard (A.D 1500)
£830	$1452	(30-Mar-92 AAA.S125) Still life (40x46cm-16x18in) s. board (A.D 1900)
£933	$1596	(17-Mar-92 JRL.S170/R) Still life with camelias (39x50cm-15x20in) s. (A.D 2100)
£983	$1719	(30-Mar-92 AAA.S80 f) Spring flowers (56x41cm-22x16in) s. (A.D 2250)
£1026	$1826	(28-Apr-92 CH.ME236/R) Still life of camellias in blue bowl (24x29cm-9x11in) s. board (A.D 2400)
£1250	$2150	(14-Oct-91 MGS.S130) Still life (28x42cm-11x17in) s. board (A.D 2700)
£1282	$2282	(27-Apr-92 J.M193) Melody - roses (30x25cm-12x10in) s. board (A.D 3000)
£1322	$2352	(26-Nov-91 J.M200/R) Still life with figure (34x52cm-13x20in) s. board (A.D 3000)
£2564	$4564	(28-Apr-92 CH.ME157/R) Still life, bowl of camellias (58x66cm-23x26in) s. (A.D 6000)
£3191	$5649	(26-Apr-92 SY.ME302/R) Spring flowers (53x43cm-21x17in) s. masonite (A.D 7500)

SHERRIN, D (19/20th C) British

£500	$865	(6-Sep-91 BW313) River landscape at sunset (51x76cm-20x30in) s.
£759	$1305	(16-Oct-91 KM.K1383) Harvest in hill landscape (60x101cm-24x40in) s. (DM 2200)

SHERRIN, Daniel (20th C) British

£498	$886	(25-Nov-91 W.T1903) Surrey common (24x32cm-9x13in) s. (C.D 1000)
£524	$1000	(16-Jul-92 SY.NY544/R) Cottage by the shore (61x107cm-24x42in) s.d.1902
£550	$990	(9-Jan-92 B317/R) An open seascape with a clipper on the Horizon (76x127cm-30x50in) s.
£550	$941	(12-Mar-92 CSK198 a/R) Sussex landscape (51x77cm-20x30in) s.
£680	$1265	(18-Jun-92 CSK272) Figures walking on country track (41x61cm-16x24in) s.
£720	$1231	(12-Mar-92 CSK198) Surrey common (46x76cm-18x30in) bears sig.
£880	$1478	(27-Aug-91 SWS1451) Harvest time (50x76cm-20x30in) s.
£920	$1647	(14-Jan-92 SWS151/R) Children in landscape (49x75cm-19x30in) s.

SHERRIN, Daniel (20th C) British-cont.
£1200 $2160   (22-Nov-91 C60/R) On the high seas (77x64cm-30x25in) one s. pair
£1400 $2408   (11-Oct-91 C19) The Valley of the Wye (51x76cm-20x30in) s.
£1600 $2976   (18-Jun-92 B96/R) The edge of the wood. Evening light (50x76cm-20x30in)
     s.i.verso pair
£1884 $3240   (8-Oct-91 ZEL.L1721/R) Surrey river landscape, evening (51x76cm-20x30in)
     s. (DM 5500)
£2400 $4560   (23-Jun-92 PH205/R) Children in landscape (76x127cm-30x50in) s.
£2800 $4704   (26-Aug-91 S814/R) Highland cattle by loch (60x92cm-24x36in) s.
£4570 $8500   (16-Jun-92 RO.BA139) Peaceful evening (76x127cm-30x50in)

SHERRIN, John (1819-1896) British
£460 $787   (1-Aug-91 RBB528/R) Group of sheep in meadow with old trees beyond
     (28x48cm-11x19in) s. W/C
£620 $1116   (27-Jan-92 PH29) Plums and gooseberries (21x32cm-8x13in) s.d.1869 W/C
     bodycol

SHERWIN, Frank (1896-?) British
£550 $968   (9-Apr-92 B62/R) The ferry, Concarneau (37x44cm-15x17in) s. W/C

SHERWOOD, Mary (20th C) American
£838 $1400   (25-Aug-91 JRB.C210) Brief history - Part I s.i.d.86

SHEVCHENKO, Alexander (1883-1943) Russian
£1916 $3314   (28-Mar-92 F.L55/R) Progetto per scenografia (26x41cm-10x16in) s.d.1910
     pastel (S.FR 5000)

SHI FU (1946-) Chinese
£5917 $10355   (30-Mar-92 CH.HK334/R) Nudes and Lotus (67x134cm-26x53in) s. ink W/C
     scroll (HK.D 80000)

SHI LU (1919-1982) Chinese
£847 $1500   (7-Nov-91 B.SF1227/R) Flower (33x33cm-13x13in) s. ink colour scroll
£904 $1600   (7-Nov-91 B.SF1228/R) Lotus (33x33cm-13x13in) s. ink colour scroll
£3698 $6472   (30-Mar-92 CH.HK263/R) Standard script calligraphy - kai shu
     (176x93cm-69x37in) s. ink hanging scroll (HK.D 50000)
£4438 $7766   (30-Mar-92 CH.HK248/R) Roses (136x65cm-54x26in) s.i.d.1971 ink W/C
     hanging scroll (HK.D 60000)
£5178 $9061   (30-Mar-92 CH.HK309/R) Bole examining horse (31x74cm-12x29in) i. ink W/C
     scroll (HK.D 70000)
£8876 $15533   (30-Mar-92 CH.HK250/R) Jujube tree (165x65cm-65x26in) s.i.d.1972 ink W/C
     scroll (HK.D 120000)
£51775 $90607   (30-Mar-92 CH.HK264/R) Landscape of Jialing River (182x97cm-72x38in) s.
     ink scroll (HK.D 700000)
£53254 $93195   (30-Mar-92 CH.HK195/R) Girl picking mulberry leaves (66x51cm-26x20in)
     s.i. ink W/C scroll (HK.D 720000)
£73964 $129438   (30-Mar-92 CH.HK251/R) Mount Hua (246x106cm-97x42in) s.i. ink W/C hanging
     scroll (HK.D 1000000)

SHIELS, William (1785-1857) British
£7000 $12530   (15-Nov-91 C113/R) Pony, with Landseer and Newfoundland dogs, sea loch
     with castle beyond (135x191cm-53x75in) s.

SHIKLER, Aaron (1922-) American
£843 $1500   (2-May-92 W.W99/R) Provincetown (51x76cm-20x30in) s.d.74
£1600 $2800   (26-Sep-91 CH.NY269/R) Jo in studio (26x36cm-10x14in) s.d.
£1714 $3000   (26-Sep-91 CH.NY275/R) Egg tomatoes (27x37cm-11x15in) s.d. panel

SHILLING, Arthur (1941-1986) Canadian
£573 $974   (23-Oct-91 MA.V91) Clothesline (46x61cm-18x24in) s.d.1976 acrylic aper
     (C.D 1100)
£780 $1413   (2-Dec-91 R.T203/R) Canadian fall (30x41cm-12x16in) s.i.verso canvasboard
     (C.D 1600)
£1659 $3002   (2-Dec-91 R.T202/R) Landscape with canoe, Green Island, Lake Couchiching
     (68x81cm-27x32in) s.d.76 i.d.verso masonite (C.D 3400)
£1735 $3158   (26-May-92 JOY.T48/R) Ojibway children lying in bed (60x90cm-24x35in)
     s.d.76 (C.D 3800)
£2000 $3540   (6-Nov-91 SY.T187/R) Portrait of young Indian boy (62x51cm-24x20in) s.
     board (C.D 4000)
£366 $659   (18-Nov-91 HO.ED25/R) Bewaben (20x25cm-8x10in) s.d.82 pencil (C.D 750)

SHILTSOV, Pavel Savvich (1820-1893) Russian
£3800 $6764   (28-Nov-91 S391/R) Portrait of Italian peasant girl (54x49cm-21x19in)
     oval

SHIMA, Matsu (20th C) ?
£2615 $4995   (15-Jul-92 CH.S809/R) Flowers in vase (52x44cm-20x17in) gouache
     (A.D 6800)

SHIMIDZU, H (20th C) Japanese
£782 $1400   (15-Nov-91 RB.HY147/R) Portrait of freighter Corona with Mt. Fuji in
     background (33x48cm-13x19in) s. mixed media silk

SHINN, Everett (1876-1953) American
£1389 $2500   (24-Nov-91 JRB.C204/R) The shop (61x51cm-24x20in) s.

SHINN, Everett (1876-1953) American-cont.

£2973	$5500	(10-Jun-92 CE.NY560/R) Reclining nude (24x33cm-9x13in) canvasboard
£7692	$14000	(28-May-92 CH.NY219/R) Clown antics (25x20cm-10x8in) s.d.1946 panel
£8242	$15000	(27-May-92 SY.NY107 a/R) After dinner turn (25x20cm-10x8in) board
£87912	$160000	(28-May-92 CH.NY218/R) The singer (67x44cm-26x17in) s.d.1902
£857	$1500	(26-Sep-91 CH.NY231/R) Study of nude model. Study for Belasco Theatre Proscenium (25x19cm-10x7in) one s.d. W/C pencil paper on board pair
£1229	$2200	(14-Nov-91 CE.NY121/R) Boston Tea Party (33x40cm-13x16in) s. W/C pencil gouache board
£1339	$2250	(14-Aug-91 B.P78/R) Nude, washing (18x28cm-7x11in) s. crayon chk.paperboard
£1404	$2500	(2-Nov-91 IH.NY78/R) Children playing in snow in front of building (28x38cm-11x15in) s.d.ink W/C
£1404	$2500	(2-Nov-91 IH.NY79/R) Barefoot man in cloak. My conscience is clear one s.d.1941 W/C pair
£4420	$8000	(6-Dec-91 CH.NY177/R) Girl in a chair (30x33cm-12x13in) s.d.1912 pastel chl
£4678	$8000	(13-Mar-92 S.BM308/R) The dressing room (46x30cm-18x12in) s.i.d.1934 pastel paperboard
£10440	$19000	(27-May-92 SY.NY90/R) Horsedrawn bus (55x75cm-22x30in) s.d.99 pastel
£19337	$35000	(6-Dec-91 CH.NY172/R) The Dewey Arch, Madison Square (34x44cm-13x17in) s. pastel
£44199	$80000	(6-Dec-91 CH.NY178/R) The tightrope walker (30x33cm-12x13in) s.d.1904 pastel

SHINZEL, W (?) ?

£549	$1000	(28-May-92 BG.M468/R) Four water fowl (61x51cm-24x20in) s.

SHIRLEY, Henry (19th C) British

£580	$1114	(28-Jul-92 SWS324/R) Evening landscape with party of young anglers (34x57cm-13x22in) s.
£900	$1548	(4-Mar-92 S41/R) Sorting fish (36x59cm-14x23in) s.

SHIRREFF, Charles (c.1750-?) British

£2200	$3872	(9-Apr-92 S179/R) Portrait of officer, wearing scarlet uniform (6x?cm-2x?in) min. gold frame glass verso with hair lock oval

SHISHKIN, Ivan Ivanovich (1832-1898) Russian

£500	$890	(28-Nov-91 S514) In forest (38x31cm-15x12in) init.d.1874
£524	$1000	(16-Jul-92 SY.NY454 a/R) In the pine forest (23x14cm-9x6in) init.
£1233	$2257	(14-May-92 BU.S197/R) Green tree by river (30x39cm-12x15in) init. (S.KR 13000)
£1803	$3299	(14-May-92 BU.S198/R) Field in flower (20x30cm-8x12in) s. (S.KR 19000)
£700	$1302	(16-Jun-92 S4/R) View over lake in the forest (24x33cm-9x13in) s.d.86 sepia W/C over pencil

SHLIE, Charles (19th C) ?

£1600	$2896	(20-May-92 S84/R) Pacific of Montrose at Riga in Latvia (48x63cm-19x25in) i.d.1829 W/C htd.white panel

SHOESMITH, Kenneth Denton (1890-1939) British

£700	$1267	(20-May-92 S243) Rio (23x35cm-9x14in) s. W/C htd.bodycol

SHOKLER, Harry (1896-?) American

£4121	$7500	(28-May-92 CH.NY223/R) Duryea's Dock, Montauk (66x81cm-26x32in) s.

SHOOSMITH, Thurston Laidlaw (1865-1933) British

£520	$926	(27-Nov-91 B122) Street scene with figures (38x27cm-15x11in) init.d.1904 pencil W/C

SHOR, Zvi (1898-1979) Israeli

£479	$900	(5-Jan-92 GG.TA382/R) Trees (38x46cm-15x18in) s.twice
£486	$900	(8-Jun-92 GG.TA260/R) Alley in Petach Tiqva (41x33cm-16x13in) s. s.d.1967 verso
£532	$1000	(5-Jan-92 GG.TA383/R) Wood (33x41cm-13x16in) s.twice
£532	$1000	(5-Jan-92 GG.TA381/R) Shenkin Garden in Tel Aviv (33x41cm-13x16in) s.
£541	$1000	(8-Jun-92 GG.TA259/R) Suburb in Petach Tiqva (33x49cm-13x19in) s. board
£703	$1300	(9-Jun-92 GG.TA442/R) Woman painter (34x26cm-13x10in) s.

SHORE (?) ?

£850	$1624	(23-Jul-92 CSK190) Summer still life (61x51cm-24x20in) s.d.52

SHORT, Obadiah (1803-1886) British

£500	$880	(10-Apr-92 K493) Figure in lane by Crome's Mill, Mousehold (20x23cm-8x9in)

SHORT, William (19/20th C) Australian

£3404	$6026	(26-Apr-92 SY.ME414/R) Botanical gardens, Melbourne (57x105cm-22x41in) s.d.1879 (A.D 8000)

SHREVE, Carl (20th C) American?

£674	$1200	(2-Nov-91 IH.NY57/R) People around open fireplace (81x74cm-32x29in) s.

SHRUBSOLE, W G (?-1889) British
£677 $1218   (19-Nov-91 RAS.K373) Mountainous landscape with waterfall
     (92x147cm-36x58in) s.d.1880 (D.KR 7500)
£1200 $2064   (4-Mar-92 ME1) Extensive scene of Port Penrhyn, Bangor (58x89cm-23x35in)
     s.

SHULZ, Adolph Robert (1869-1963) American
£1860 $3200   (14-Oct-91 H.C143) Autumn landscape (64x86cm-25x34in) s.

SHURTLEFF, R M (1838-1915) American
£795 $1400   (12-Apr-92 LIT.L197) Landscape (86x61cm-34x24in) s.

SHURTLEFF, Roswell Morse (1838-1915) American
£556 $950   (13-Mar-92 S.BM170) Autumn in Keene Valley, New York view
     (30x41cm-12x16in) s.i. i.verso
£663 $1200   (5-Dec-91 GRO.B477/R) Shadows of big rock - in Adirondacks
     (51x64cm-20x25in) s.

SIBERDT, Eugene (1851-1931) Belgian
£2322 $4249   (12-May-92 C.A296) Peasant woman with children (90x63cm-35x25in) s.
     (B.FR 140000)

SIBERECHTS, Jan (1627-1700) Flemish
£8500 $16320   (10-Jul-92 C112/R) Peasant woman on horseback in stream beside wood
     (64x56cm-25x22in)

SIBERECHTS, Jan (circle) (1627-1700) Flemish
£1600 $2912   (13-Dec-91 C130/R) Landscape with drovers fording stream
     (52x120cm-20x47in)

SICARDI, Louis Marie (1746-1825) French
£412 $782   (26-Jun-92 AGS.P61) Portrait d'homme en habit gris clair (4x3cm-2x1in)
     min. lock of hair verso oval (F.FR 4000)
£1800 $3096   (4-Mar-92 C39/R) Lady, in brown dress with lace collar, pearl set comb in
     hair (7x?cm-3x?in) min. s.d.1806 gilt mount scrolls panel oval

SICHULSKI, Kazimierz (1879-1942) Polish
£916 $1667   (15-Dec-91 REM.W40) Woman with lamb (76x68cm-30x27in) s. (P.Z 18000000)
£2071 $3893   (21-Dec-91 PSA.W19) Still life of flowers and blue vase
     (100x69cm-39x27in) s. board (P.Z 40000000)
£1047 $1811   (8-Sep-91 REM.W34) Hutsul woman (75x55cm-30x22in) s. pastel
     (P.Z 20000000)

SICILIA, Jose Maria (1954-) Spanish
£8380 $15000   (13-Nov-91 CH.NY244/R) Brown flower (92x92cm-36x36in) s.i.d.86verso
     acrylic four panels
£8939 $16000   (14-Nov-91 SY.NY236/R) Flower bunch 3 (162x81cm-64x32in) acrylic canvas
£12849 $23000   (7-May-92 SY.NY226/R) Frame flower I (276x132cm-109x52in) acrylic canvas
£16760 $30000   (13-Nov-91 CH.NY245/R) Flor 13 (302x204cm-119x80in) s.d.85verso acrylic
     four panels
£17143 $30000   (25-Feb-92 SY.NY247/R) Untitled (100x100cm-39x39in) s.d.85verso acrylic
£17401 $30973   (28-Apr-92 EP.M42/R) Flor Linea Negra (100x100cm-39x39in) s.i.d.87verso
     acrylic (S.P 3200000)
£27933 $50000   (5-May-92 CH.NY130/R) Tulip 6 (260x249cm-102x98in) s.i.d.85verso

SICIOLANTE DA SERMONETA, Girolamo (attrib) (1521-c.1580) Italian
£488 $894   (15-May-92 AT.P210) La mort des enfants de Niobe (23x28cm-9x11in) pen
     wash htd white (F.FR 4800)

SICKERT, Oswald (1828-1885) British
£2230 $4148   (16-Jun-92 RAS.V867/R) Figures by house, sea at background
     (51x61cm-20x24in) s.d.1846 panel (D.KR 25000)

SICKERT, Walter Richard (1860-1942) British
£5200 $9204   (7-Nov-91 C85/R) Rue Aguado, Dieppe (19x24cm-7x9in) s.d.August 1914 board
£6000 $10980   (13-May-92 S25/R) Le Port de Dieppe (38x46cm-15x18in) s.i.d.1900
£6000 $10380   (2-Oct-91 S38/R) The road to the Casino, Dieppe (20x25cm-8x10in) s. board
£7500 $13725   (13-May-92 S76/R) The Happy Valley, Envermeu (38x56cm-15x22in) s.
£8000 $14640   (5-Jun-92 C42/R) Statue of Duquesne, Dieppe (33x23cm-13x9in) s.
£10500 $18585   (7-Nov-91 C84/R) The Grand Canal, Venice (16x24cm-6x9in) s. i.verso panel
£17000 $30090   (7-Nov-91 C86/R) La Rue du Mortier d'Or, Dieppe (19x24cm-7x9in) s.d.1903
     panel
£17500 $30100   (6-Mar-92 C55/R) Portrait of lady (40x32cm-16x13in) s.
£38000 $68400   (20-Nov-91 S113/R) Nuit d'ete (51x41cm-20x16in)
£60000 $106200   (5-Nov-91 PH29/R) The Belgian soldier (91x71cm-36x28in) s.d.1914
£100000 $180000   (20-Nov-91 S112/R) Ennui (46x38cm-18x15in) s.i.d.1916
£520 $941   (19-May-92 SWS368) Figure study of lady in elegant dress and hat
     (24x24cm-9x9in) s.i. pen crayon htd.chk
£700 $1225   (27-Sep-91 C12/R) Ponte della Maravegie, San Trovaso, Venice
     (33x26cm-13x10in) s.i. pencil
£800 $1376   (5-Mar-92 CSK62/R) Study of female nude (33x24cm-13x9in) s. pencil
£1500 $2565   (11-Mar-92 S55/R) Mantelpiece mirror (38x20cm-15x8in) init. black chk htd
     white
£1800 $3078   (11-Mar-92 S56/R) Study of Roald Kristian for 'Little Tea Party'
     (31x20cm-12x8in) s.i. pencil

SICKERT, Walter Richard (1860-1942) British-cont.
£2900 $5307   *(14-May-92 C58/R) St. Jacques, Dieppe (23x18cm-9x7in) s.i. pen W/C pencil squared*

SICKLES, Noel (1910-1982) American
£787 $1400   *(2-May-92 IH.NY131/R) Men by campfire (13x61cm-5x24in) s. pen ink*

SIDANER, Henri le (1862-1939) French
£5544 $9814   (10-Nov-91 ZZ.F142/R) Dunes a Etaples (38x56cm-15x22in) s. (F.FR 55000)
£7209 $13553   (16-Dec-91 AGS.P18/R) La Maison de Gerbery (54x68cm-21x27in) s. (F.FR 70000)
£14754 $27000   (14-May-92 SY.NY258/R) Les roses sur la maison, Gerberoy (27x35cm-11x14in) s.
£20576 $39095   (24-Jun-92 GL.P156/R) Crepuscule a Quimperle (65x54cm-26x21in) s. (F.FR 200000)
£21516 $38730   (2-Feb-92 ZZ.F107/R) Maison de l'artiste a Gerberoy (54x68cm-21x27in) s. (F.FR 210000)
£24000 $41520   (24-Mar-92 C54/R) La jetee (32x41cm-13x16in) s. panel
£27976 $50076   (17-Nov-91 GL.P55/R) La maison du canal, Malines (73x60cm-29x24in) s. (F.FR 275000)
£38000 $65360   (16-Oct-91 S26/R) Le vieux pont sur l'Elle (66x81cm-26x32in) s.
£41850 $74493   (26-Nov-91 J.M6/R) Le Moulin Gris, Montreuil Bellay (64x80cm-25x31in) s. (A.D 95000)
£42000 $76020   (3-Dec-91 C228/R) Le jardin blanc, Gerberoy (38x58cm-15x23in) s. panel
£42000 $72660   (25-Mar-92 S29/R) Le vieux moulin (81x65cm-32x26in) s.
£45317 $77039   (21-Oct-91 ARC.P16/R) Pont en automne, Gisors (54x81cm-21x32in) s. (F.FR 450000)
£45778 $81943   (17-Nov-91 GL.P56/R) Le 14 juillet, Gerberoy (82x100cm-32x39in) s. (F.FR 450000)
£57143 $100000   (25-Feb-92 SY.NY13/R) Great Gate, Hampton Court (79x99cm-31x39in) s.
£531 $929   *(5-Apr-92 ZZ.F83/R) Maisons a Gerberoy (15x19cm-6x7in) s. ink wash col.crayon (F.FR 5100)*
£720 $1303   *(6-Dec-91 GL.P148) Maisons sur le canal (14x19cm-6x7in) crayon htd.col.crayons (F.FR 7000)*
£1029 $1862   *(6-Dec-91 GL.P147) La table et la maison, Gerberoy (25x15cm-10x6in) s. crayon htd.pen col.crayons (F.FR 10000)*
£1639 $2951   *(2-Feb-92 ZZ.F102/R) Maison sur le canal (14x19cm-6x7in) s. col.crayons (F.FR 16000)*
£7056 $12208   *(6-Oct-91 E.LA66/R) Vue de Bruges (27x35cm-11x14in) s. oil pastel laid down on panel (F.FR 70000)*
£18000 $34380   *(30-Jun-92 C201/R) Le Canal au Crepuscule, Nemours (56x80cm-22x31in) pastel canvas*

SIDDELL, Peter (1935-) New Zealander
£648 $1173   (4-Dec-91 DS.W176) Side street (21x16cm-8x6in) s.i.d.83verso (NZ.D 2100)
£1173 $2123   (4-Dec-91 DS.W175) Houses and pines (50x40cm-20x16in) s.d.1983 i.verso acrylic (NZ.D 3800)

SIDLEY, Samuel (1829-1896) British
£2000 $3440   (4-Mar-92 S159/R) Girl in wood (132x76cm-52x30in) s.d.1879

SIDNEY, Herbert (1858-1923) British
£820 $1460   (29-Apr-92 B118/R) Two doves (102x62cm-40x24in) s. s.i.d.1886verso

SIDOROV, Vitaly (1922-) Russian
£713 $1304   (3-Jun-92 ARC.P21/R) La plage (79x109cm-31x43in) s. (F.FR 7000)
£815 $1491   (3-Jun-92 ARC.P19/R) Les pivoines (66x61cm-26x24in) s. (F.FR 8000)

SIDOROVICZ, Sigmund (1846-1881) Austrian
£1300 $2314   (26-Nov-91 PH145/R) Figures with haycart in river landscape (42x34cm-17x13in) s.d.1879

SIEBENTHAL, Adolphe de (1895-1958) Swiss
£553 $985   (29-Nov-91 GAB.G2876) En Catalogne (50x61cm-20x24in) s. (S.FR 1400)

SIEFFERT, Paul (1874-?) French
£633 $1145   (18-May-92 SY.MI16) Nudo sdraiato (50x73cm-20x29in) s. (I.L 1400000)
£1660 $2988   *(19-Nov-91 GS.B3660) Female nude seen from behind reclining on sheepskin reading (53x80cm-21x31in) s. pastel (S.FR 4200)*

SIEGARD, Par (1877-1961) Swedish
£558 $960   (8-Mar-92 BU.M71) Madonna and Child (34x23cm-13x9in) s.d.1923 (S.KR 5800)
£759 $1389   (17-May-92 BU.M493) Midsummer night's dream (37x87cm-15x34in) s. (S.KR 8000)
£1236 $2212   (16-Nov-91 FAL.M334/R) Red flowers (43x30cm-17x12in) s. (S.KR 13000)
£2002 $3523   (11-Apr-92 FAL.M383/R) Still life of flowers (62x46cm-24x18in) s.d.35 panel (S.KR 21000)

SIEGEN, August (19th C) German
£820 $1460   (28-Nov-91 CSK89) Figures in town street (140x104cm-55x41in) s. panel
£900 $1602   (28-Nov-91 CSK186) Continental river town (50x82cm-20x32in) s.
£955 $1700   (28-Apr-92 PO.BA25) Vista de Montevideo (50x83cm-20x33in) s.
£1900 $3363   (13-Feb-92 CSK117/R) Sienna (52x41cm-20x16in) s. panel
£2098 $3587   (18-Mar-92 N.M648/R) View of Danzig harbour (97x143cm-38x56in) s. i.stretcher (DM 6000)

SIEGEN, August (19th C) German-cont.
£2400 $4152   (4-Oct-91 C130/R) Arab street scene (98x142cm-39x56in) s. canvas on board
£2448 $4185   (18-Mar-92 N.M647/R) View of Venice with market scene before Palazzo
                della Raggione (52x41cm-20x16in) s. i.verso panel (DM 7000)
£3525 $5992   (23-Oct-91 ZZ.F32/R) Rue au Caire (58x80cm-23x31in) s. (F.FR 35000)

SIEGER, Frederik (1902-) Dutch
£864 $1573   (12-Dec-91 SY.AM288/R) Composition (50x60cm-20x24in) s. d.1981 stretcher
                (D.FL 2800)

SIEGER, Viktor (1843-1905) Austrian
£2000 $3720   (18-Jun-92 B49/R) Country romance (64x83cm-25x33in) s.i.

SIEGERT, August Friedrich (1820-1883) German
£3670 $6495   (5-Nov-91 SY.AM56/R) Expectation (72x60cm-28x24in) s.d.1876 (D.FL 12000)

SIEGFRIED, Edwin C (1889-1955) American
£506 $900   (26-Nov-91 MOR.P58) Afterglow, sunset on marshes, San Francisco Bay near
                Alameda (66x81cm-26x32in) s. pastel
£737 $1400   (24-Jun-92 B.SF6314/R) Alameda Estuary (57x84cm-22x33in) s. pastel

SIEGRIEST, Louis Bassi (1899-1989) American
£4520 $8000   (12-Feb-92 B.SF594/R) House among trees (43x48cm-17x19in) s.

SIEGRIEST, Lundy (1925-) American
£1471 $2500   (23-Oct-91 B.SF3799/R) Steer and trees (41x51cm-16x20in) s. s.i.d.verso

SIEGUMFELDT, Hermann Carl (1833-1912) Danish
£3086 $5494   (28-Apr-92 RAS.K100/R) Two tired small orange sellers (72x53cm-28x21in)
                s.d.1865 (D.KR 35000)

SIEHL-FREYSTETT, Georg (1868-1919) German
£1134 $2109   (20-Jun-92 BM.B774/R) Path lined with birch trees in evening sunlight
                (76x92cm-30x36in) s. i.verso (DM 3300)

SIEMERING, Fritz (?-1883) German
£777 $1360   (3-Apr-92 BM.B712/R) Studio interior with old peasant woman looking at
                picture (53x41cm-21x16in) s.d.1875 (DM 2200)

SIEMIRADZKI, Hendrik (1843-1902) Polish
£1018 $1853   (15-Dec-91 REM.W41) Portrait of a woman (17x22cm-7x9in) s. panel
                (P.Z 20000000)
£3097 $5543   (17-Nov-91 REM.W25) Scene from antiquity (20x35cm-8x14in) s. panel
                (P.Z 60000000)
£3676 $6910   (21-Dec-91 PSA.W20) Portrait of an Italian woman (46x31cm-18x12in) s.
                (P.Z 71000000)

SIENESE SCHOOL, 14th C Italian
£3367 $5960   (10-Feb-92 GL.P16) La vierge (36x21cm-14x8in) panel (F.FR 33000)
£26000 $47320   (11-Dec-91 S23/R) Coronation of Virgin with infant Christ, Saint
                Catherine and other saint (22x38cm-9x15in) i.verso oil tempera panel
                gold ground arched

SIENESE SCHOOL, 16th C Italian
£2209 $3800   (9-Oct-91 CH.NY13/R) Saints Paul and Clare, Holy Ghost above
                (79x58cm-31x23in) panel
£7435 $13606   (16-May-92 F.L12/R) Madonna col bambino (46x34cm-18x13in) panel
                (S.FR 20000)
£23704 $42905   (5-Dec-91 F.M94/R) Diana ed Atteone (59cm-23ins circular) panel
                (I.L 51000000)

SIERHUIS, Jan (1928-) Dutch
£679 $1236   (11-Dec-91 CH.AM119) Aan het strand (50x64cm-20x25in) s.d.65 s.i.verso
                acrylic paper (D.FL 2200)
£848 $1536   (19-May-92 CH.AM351) Alicante (68x48cm-27x19in) s.d.64 (D.FL 2800)
£1364 $2468   (19-May-92 CH.AM234) Two figures (60x23cm-24x9in) s.i.d.1964 verso
                dyptich in one frame (D.FL 4500)
£1852 $3370   (12-Dec-91 SY.AM221/R) Zomerse liefde (80x85cm-31x33in) s.d.60
                (D.FL 6000)
£667 $1207   (19-May-92 CH.AM365) Faces (65x51cm-26x20in) s.d.65 gouache (D.FL 2200)
£926 $1685   (11-Dec-91 CH.AM146) Two figures (72x94cm-28x37in) s. gouache (D.FL 3000)
£1061 $1920   (19-May-92 CH.AM254/R) De bespieder (100x64cm-39x25in) s.i.d.1965 verso
                gouache (D.FL 3500)

SIERICH, Ludwig Casimir (1834-1919) Dutch
£970 $1716   (22-Apr-92 CH.AM103) Winterlandscape with skaters on a frozen river by a
                castle (19x26cm-7x10in) s. panel (D.FL 3200)
£1162 $2103   (3-Dec-91 FN.S2459/R) Moor landscape with peasant family
                (26x37cm-10x15in) s. (DM 3300)

SIERIG, Ferdinand Carl (1839-1905) Dutch
£459 $817   (29-Oct-91 VN.R274) Winters bosgezicht (58x76cm-23x30in) s. (D.FL 1500)

SIEVERT, H (19th C) German
£515 $897   (21-Sep-91 SA.A1721/R) Portrait of young lady on terrace with view of
       lake beyond (38x31cm-15x12in) s.d.1849 pastel (DM 1500)

SIGALON, Xavier (1787-1837) French
£1987 $3398   (18-Mar-92 D.V197/R) Portrait of young lady wearing beret
       (87x69cm-34x27in) s. (A.S 40000)

SIGG, Hermann-Alfred (1924-) Swiss
£1373 $2333   (23-Oct-91 GD.B700/R) Late autumn II (80x50cm-31x20in) s.d.61 i.verso
       (S.FR 3500)

SIGMUND, Benjamin D (fl.1880-1904) British
£400 $668   (22-Aug-91 CSK20) Feeding the chickens (25x36cm-10x14in) s. pencil W/C
       htd bodycol. white
£640 $1222   (23-Jul-92 T270/R) Woman by thatched cottage - sea beyond
       (25x36cm-10x14in) s. W/C
£650 $1242   (13-Jul-92 PH90/R) Girl and ducks by stream (26x35cm-10x14in) s. W/C htd
       white
£681 $1300   (16-Jul-92 SY.NY488/R) Summer landscape with grazing sheep
       (36x53cm-14x21in) s. W/C board
£720 $1296   (29-Jan-92 RBB882/R) The Thames near Cleveden, river scene with cattle
       (20x36cm-8x14in) s. W/C
£850 $1513   (29-Oct-91 C116/R) Spring - sheep in orchard (27x18cm-11x7in) s.i. pencil
       W/C bodycol.
£900 $1602   (29-Oct-91 C111/R) Burnham Beeches (18x27cm-7x11in) s. s.i.verso pencil
       W/C bodycol.
£950 $1710   (27-Jan-92 PH31/R) In cottage garden (26x37cm-10x15in) s. W/C bodycol

SIGMUND, Benjamin D (attrib) (fl.1880-1904) British
£520 $967   (16-Jun-92 SWS355) Under the orchard trees (30x23cm-12x9in) i.verso W/C
       gouache

SIGNAC, Paul (1863-1935) French
£16000 $27680   (24-Mar-92 C13/R) L'echafaudage du Sacre Coeur, Montmartre
       (51x33cm-20x13in) s.i.d.82 panel
£141243 $250000   (6-Nov-91 SY.NY38/R) Le Chenal de la Rochelle (46x55cm-18x22in) s.d.1927
£160000 $289600   (2-Dec-91 C14/R) Le port de Constantinople (41x33cm-16x13in) s.i.
£327869 $600000   (12-May-92 CH.NY122/R) Antibes, le nuage rose (73x92cm-29x36in) s.d.1916
£1423 $2533   (29-Nov-91 GAB.G2877/R) Le port de Concarneau (32x24cm-13x9in) s.i. wash
       crayon (S.FR 3600)
£1581 $2814   (29-Nov-91 GAB.G2878/R) Le Pont sur la riviere (21x28cm-8x11in) s. lead
       pencil (S.FR 4000)
£1749 $3323   (24-Jun-92 GL.P119) Voiliers dans le port du Pouliguen (9x13cm-4x5in)
       s.d.1928 W/C (F.FR 17000)
£1809 $3400   (5-Jan-92 GG.TA299/R) Seascape (10x14cm-4x6in) W/C
£2675 $4842   (6-Dec-91 GL.P158/R) Venise (16x21cm-6x8in) s.d.1908 W/C (F.FR 26000)
£2820 $5019   (28-Oct-91 GL.P115/R) Bourg Saint-Andre (18x24cm-7x9in) s. W/C lead
       pencil (F.FR 28000)
£3488 $6000   (12-Oct-91 SY.NY33/R) Bateau de pecheur en port (11x17cm-4x7in) s. W/C
       chl graph paper
£4500 $7740   (16-Oct-91 S2/R) Montelimar, la petite place (12x20cm-5x8in) s.i. W/C
       pencil
£4571 $8000   (25-Feb-92 SY.NY3/R) Honfleur (11x15cm-4x6in) s.i. W/C pencil paper on
       board
£4857 $8500   (25-Feb-92 SY.NY4/R) Samois (11x16cm-4x6in) s.i.d.00 W/C over pencil
       paper on board
£5144 $9311   (6-Dec-91 GL.P157/R) Les gondoles (19x25cm-7x10in) s.d.1908 W/C
       (F.FR 50000)
£5200 $8996   (25-Mar-92 S1/R) Venise, La croix de Saint-Marc (13x25cm-5x10in)
       s.indist.i. W/C pencil paper laid down on card
£6173 $11173   (6-Dec-91 GL.P156/R) Camaret (28x44cm-11x17in) st.sig.d.27b juin 1927
       (F.FR 60000)
£7500 $14325   (1-Jul-92 S128/R) Vue de la Seine (25x37cm-10x15in) s. W/C
£7500 $14325   (30-Jun-92 C121/R) Le port Paimpol (29x44cm-11x17in) s.d.25 W/C pencil
       paper on card
£7514 $13000   (2-Oct-91 SY.NY8/R) Penmarche (26x35cm-10x14in) s.d.22 W/C chl paper on
       board
£7599 $13754   (24-May-92 GL.P3/R) Douarnenez (21x27cm-8x11in) s.d.1927 W/C (F.FR 75000)
£7634 $13588   (28-Nov-91 BU.S57/R) The harbour in La Rochelle (21x27cm-8x11in) s.i. W/C
       chl (S.KR 80000)
£8000 $14480   (3-Dec-91 C119/R) Les Ables d'Olone (26x41cm-10x16in) s.i.d.Sept. 30
       pencil W/C
£8500 $15385   (3-Dec-91 C161/R) St.Tropez (28x44cm-11x17in) st.sig.i.d.12 Avril 30 W/C
       pencil
£9290 $17000   (13-May-92 CH.NY252/R) Audierne (28x23cm-11x9in) s.d.27 W/C over black
       chk paper on board
£12000 $22920   (30-Jun-92 C122/R) Les maisons du port, St Tropez (32x40cm-13x16in)
       s.i.d.1914 W/C pencil paper on card
£13559 $24000   (6-Nov-91 CH.NY159/R) Le lac d'Annecy (28x40cm-11x16in) s.i. W/C chk
£13849 $25344   (3-Jun-92 PIC.P66/R) La Rochelle (24x39cm-9x15in) s. W/C (F.FR 136000)
£15819 $28000   (6-Nov-91 CH.NY146/R) Landerneau (28x39cm-11x15in) st.sig.d.24 gouache
       W/C chk paper on board
£20101 $33769   (16-Aug-91 ZZ.F37/R) Le port de la Rochelle (28x43cm-11x17in) s. W/C
       (F.FR 200000)

SIGNAC, Paul (1863-1935) French-cont.

| £21000 | $36330 | (24-Mar-92 C8/R) Marche a Antibes (29x42cm-11x17in) s.i.d.1919 W/C pencil paper on card |
| £22000 | $39820 | (3-Dec-91 C117/R) Vue d'un Port, Paimpol (30x77cm-12x30in) init. W/C soft pencil two sheets joined paper |

SIGNAC, Paul (attrib) (1863-1935) French

| £3114 | $5948 | (4-Jul-92 BOD.P645) Portrait of young man in wooded park landscape (46x41cm-18x16in) s. (DM 9000) |

SIGNORE, Littorio del (1938-) ?

| £647 | $1151 | (26-Nov-91 JOY.T266/R) Une rue de Montreal (60x75cm-24x30in) s. (C.D 1300) |
| £758 | $1326 | (25-Sep-91 EA.M530 a) Rue St. Paul, Montreal (61x91cm-24x36in) s. d.1989 verso (C.D 1500) |

SIGNORET, Charles Louis (1867-1932) French

| £6742 | $12000 | (27-Apr-92 S.SL531/R) Enfants cueillant des fruits dans le midi (79x109cm-31x43in) s. |

SIGNORET, Charles Louis (attrib) (1867-1932) French

| £522 | $898 | (19-Oct-91 UA.U352/R) Mountain landscape with travellers (50x80cm-20x31in) (S.KR 5500) |

SIGNORINI, Giovanni (1808-1864) Italian

| £7500 | $12825 | (18-Mar-92 S144/R) Marina del Porto (82x133cm-32x52in) s. |

SIGNORINI, Giovanni (attrib) (1808-1864) Italian

| £6859 | $11729 | (12-Mar-92 RAS.V982/R) Southern landscape with figures resting by waterhole (102x154cm-40x61in) s. (D.KR 76000) |

SIGNORINI, Giovanni Battista (?) Italian

| £4930 | $8923 | (7-Dec-91 WK.M492/R) Flight into Egypt (100x152cm-39x60in) s. (DM 14000) |

SIGNORINI, Giuseppe (1857-1932) Italian

£562	$1000	(29-Nov-91 MFA.C204/R) Cavalier (33x25cm-13x10in) s. W/C
£629	$1100	(19-Feb-92 CH.NY98/R) Mandolin player (37x28cm-15x11in) s.i. W/C over pencil board
£1836	$3250	(6-Nov-91 D.NY33/R) Moor standing on prayer rug (54x37cm-21x15in) s.d.78 s.verso W/C
£2743	$4800	(19-Feb-92 CH.NY97/R) Painter's studio (45x30cm-18x12in) s.i. W/C gouache pencil gum arabic board
£2907	$5000	(16-Oct-91 CH.NY203/R) The tea party (38x48cm-15x19in) s.i. W/C htd.white over traces pencil board
£4200	$7266	(4-Oct-91 C176/R) The proposal (45x60cm-18x24in) s.i. W/C bodycol card
£4268	$7427	(13-Apr-92 AT.P154/R) La priere (55x38cm-22x15in) s.d.79 W/C (F.FR 42000)
£8242	$15000	(28-May-92 SY.NY302/R) Discussion (69x93cm-27x37in) s.i. W/C gouache board
£11628	$20000	(17-Oct-91 SY.NY36/R) Harem (88x62cm-35x24in) s.i. W/C

SIGNORINI, Telemaco (1835-1901) Italian

| £38422 | $69545 | (18-May-92 SY.MI128/R) Careggi dopo la pioggia (31x41cm-12x16in) s. (I.L 85000000) |
| £54459 | $101293 | (16-Jun-92 F.M281/R) Croce di via a Settignano (28x19cm-11x7in) mono panel (I.L 120000000) |

SIGNOVERT, Jean (1919-1981) French

£491	$875	(1-Dec-91 I.N14) Les pelerins d'Emmaus (36x46cm-14x18in) s.i.d.1946 col.crayon (F.FR 4800)
£619	$1126	(25-May-92 D.P212) Composition abstraite (33x23cm-13x9in) s.d.59 mixed media (F.FR 6100)
£665	$1184	(1-Dec-91 I.N1) Composition (47x29cm-19x11in) s. gouache (F.FR 6500)

SIGRIST, Franz I (attrib) (1727-1803) Austrian

| £1200 | $2304 | (7-Jul-92 PH203/R) Martyrdom of St. Lucy (42x31cm-17x12in) shaped top |

SIGRISTE, Guido (1864-1915) Swiss

| £1011 | $1800 | (22-Jan-92 SY.NY387/R) Arrest of Carmen (33x41cm-13x16in) s. panel |
| £2593 | $4693 | (19-May-92 GF.L2636/R) Napoleon and officers riding over battle field (10x15cm-4x6in) s. panel (S.FR 7000) |

SIJTHOFF, Gisbertus Jan (1867-1949) Dutch

| £673 | $1191 | (5-Nov-91 SY.AM409) View of Bruges (48x59cm-19x23in) s. (D.FL 2200) |

SILAS, L (?) ?

| £3000 | $5580 | (17-Jun-92 S501/R) Still life of mixed flowers (105x150cm-41x59in) s. |

SILAS, Louis (?) ?

| £660 | $1195 | (20-May-92 B119/R) Venetian still life (69x89cm-27x35in) s. panel |
| £3900 | $6708 | (4-Mar-92 CBB13/R) Still life of a vase of flowers with insects (152x99cm-60x39in) s. |

SILBERT, Marie Jose Jean Raymond (1862-1939) French

| £13347 | $24025 | (18-Nov-91 AT.P377/R) Le marche a Kairouan (110x167cm-43x66in) s. (F.FR 130000) |

SILBERT, Max (1871-?) French
£1676 $3000   (6-May-92 D.NY65/R) Lacemakers (55x46cm-22x18in) s.

SILLEM, Charles (19th C) British?
£2000 $3360   (26-Aug-91 S851/R) In a crofter's cottage (91x63cm-36x25in) s.d.1893

SILLEN, Herman (1857-1908) Swedish
£4269 $7813   (14-May-92 BU.S64/R) Seascape with sailingboats (57x97cm-22x38in)
                  s.d.1895 (S.KR 45000)
£2657   *$4861*   *(11-May-92 NOR.S64/R) Stockholm (20x42cm-8x17in) s.d.1900 W/C*
                  (S.KR 28000)

SILO, Adam (1674-1772) Dutch
£24474 $43319   (7-Nov-91 D.V168/R) Frigate and other shipping in choppy sea
                  (43x62cm-17x24in) s. (Ä.S 500000)

SILO, Adam (style) (1674-1772) Dutch
£3000 $5490   (12-May-92 SWS752/R) Shipping in choppy waters, town beyond
                  (51x61cm-20x24in)

SILVA, Benjamin (1927-) Brazilian
£3315 $6000   (18-May-92 CH.NY215/R) Painter's studio (100x100cm-39x39in) s. i.d.1973
                  num.8 stretcher

SILVA, Francis Augustus (1835-1886) American
£6433 $11000   (12-Mar-92 CH.NY17/R) Hudson River at Kingston Point (36x61cm-14x24in)
                  indis.s.
£9659 $17000   (9-Apr-92 FA.PH822/R) Passing showers (51x91cm-20x36in) s.
£13500 $25110   (16-Jun-92 PH60/R) Sunset (61x51cm-24x20in) s.d.79 i.verso
£18286 $32000   (26-Sep-91 CH.NY12/R) Moonrise (35x61cm-14x24in) s.d.72

SILVA, J de (19th C) ?
£600 $1062   (7-Nov-91 PHC735) Steamship Hyana at sea (51x79cm-20x31in) s.d.1872

SILVA, Ramon (1890-1919) Argentinian
£8377 $16000   (30-Jun-92 PO.BA21) Vista de Palermo (33x42cm-13x17in) s.d.1912 board
£14607 $26000   (1-Nov-91 PO.BA44) Jardin botanico (42x55cm-17x22in) s. board
£2473   *$4500*   *(11-Dec-91 RO.BA39) Paisaje (48x61cm-19x24in) s.d.1913 W/C*

SILVA, William P (1859-1948) American
£506 $910   (23-Nov-91 YFA.M269/R) Fishing boats at dock (30x38cm-12x15in) s. board
£1447 $2750   (24-Jun-92 B.SF6333/R) Windblown cypress, Monterey (51x61cm-20x24in) s.

SILVAIN, Christian (1950-) Belgian
£513   *$929*   *(7-Dec-91 KV.L289) Oiseau-cage (93x69cm-37x27in) s.d.89 acrylic collage*
                  (B.FR 30000)
£650   *$1177*   *(7-Dec-91 KV.L287 a) Les messagers (100x49cm-39x19in) s.d.88 mixed media*
                  (B.FR 38000)

SILVESTRE, Israel (attrib) (16/17th C) French
£850   *$1632*   *(7-Jul-92 C51) Le marche d'esclaves or la petite vue de Paris*
                  (15x21cm-6x8in) i. chk pen

SILVESTRE, Louis (studio) (17/18th C) French
£4137 $7116   (16-Apr-91 AT.P111/R) Portrait en buste de l'electeur de Saxe Frederic
                  Auguste 1st (81x64cm-32x25in) (F.FR 41000)

SILVESTRE, Louis (style) (17/18th C) French
£800 $1400   (1-Apr-92 S115) Portrait of nobleman, wearing insignia of Russian Order
                  of White Eagle (82x66cm-32x26in)

SILVESTRE, Louis (younger) (1675-1760) French
£23464 $42000   (16-Jan-92 CH.NY107/R) Portrait of Maria Josepha, Queen of Poland,
                  standing by parrot eating grapes on ledge (146x112cm-57x44in)
£6320   *$11755*   *(20-Jun-92 CH.MO223/R) Saint Paul guerissant le paralytique*
                  (35x27cm-14x11in) i. black white chk (F.FR 62000)

SILVESTRE, Nicolas Charles de (1699-1767) French
£520   *$905*   *(13-Apr-92 S287) Landscape with church and bridge (10x19cm-4x7in) bears*
                  i. red chk

SILVEYRA, C (1890-?) Argentinian
£1488 $2500   (1-Sep-91 PO.BA28) Combate de la escuadra (17x48cm-7x19in) s. panel

SIMBARI, Nicola (1927-) Italian
£1130 $2000   (5-Nov-91 CE.NY117/R) At sea (79x58cm-31x23in) s.d.57
£1216 $2250   (12-Jun-92 SY.NY225/R) Boats along the Adriatic (59x80cm-23x31in) s.
£1469 $2600   (5-Nov-91 CE.NY147/R) Standing woman (80x100cm-31x39in) s.
£2035 $3500   (12-Oct-91 DU.E171) Girl and flowers (58x71cm-23x28in)
£2326 $4000   (12-Oct-91 SY.NY185/R) Red and gold flowers (90x100cm-35x39in) s.d.63
£2326 $4000   (12-Oct-91 SY.NY186/R) Figure sulla spiaggia (57x57cm-22x22in)
                  s.indist.d.
£2733 $4700   (12-Oct-91 SY.NY183/R) Round table (61x81cm-24x32in) s.d.68
£2737 $5200   (26-Jun-92 WOL.C525/R) Beachscape with figures (48x69cm-19x27in) s.d.67
£2793 $5000   (9-May-92 CE.NY95/R) Nostalgia del mare (80x100cm-31x39in) s.d.62

SIMBARI, Nicola (1927-) Italian-cont.
£2838	$5250	(12-Jun-92 SY.NY223/R) Beach at Ostia (69x88cm-27x35in) s.
£3023	$5200	(12-Oct-91 SY.NY184/R) Girl on bicycle (60x80cm-24x31in) s.
£3390	$6000	(5-Nov-91 CE.NY242/R) Elfrida a tavola (101x110cm-40x43in) s.d.67
£4000	$7000	(28-Feb-92 SY.NY167/R) Capri (81x99cm-32x39in) s.d.66
£811	$1500	(12-Jun-92 SY.NY224/R) Paris at 6 pm (69x100cm-27x39in) s. gouache paper on canvas

SIMBERG, Hugo (1873-1917) Finnish
| £40455 | $71201 | (12-Apr-92 HOR.H207/R) Winter's day in Antrea (57x90cm-22x35in) s.d.1900 (F.M 320000) |
| £2587 | $4605 | (1-Dec-91 HOR.H206/R) Vessels in harbour (25x32cm-10x13in) s.i.d.1901 gouache (F.M 20000) |

SIMBOLI, Raymond (1894-1964) American
| £2924 | $5000 | (12-Mar-92 CH.NY212/R) Factories, Pittsburgh (76x91cm-30x36in) s. |

SIMCOCK, Jack (1929-) British
| £420 | $764 | (11-Dec-91 ZZ.B296) Building and wall (38x61cm-15x24in) s.d.60 W/C board |

SIME, Sidney Herbert (1867-1941) British
| £1023 | $1800 | (6-Apr-92 B.LA2362/R) The diver (34x24cm-13x9in) s.i.verso W/C gouache over pencil board |

SIMENSEN, Sigvald (?-1920) Norwegian
£490	$843	(15-Oct-91 RAS.K249) Fjord landscape (105x148cm-41x58in) s. (D.KR 5500)
£615	$1094	(29-Oct-91 UL.T216) Fjord landscape, Vestland (100x150cm-39x59in) (N.KR 7000)
£665	$1177	(15-Feb-92 BU.O119) From a fishing village in Lofoten (100x150cm-39x59in) s. (N.KR 7500)
£701	$1219	(14-Sep-91 BU.O322) Landscape (95x73cm-37x29in) s. (N.KR 8000)
£790	$1406	(29-Oct-91 UL.T215) Fjord landscape (103x160cm-41x63in) (N.KR 9000)

SIMI, Filadelfo (1849-1923) Italian
| £1348 | $2305 | (19-Mar-92 F.M51) Il Vince (41x47cm-16x19in) i.verso W/C (I.L 2900000) |

SIMIONOV, Alexandre (1890-1970) Russian
| £1080 | $1955 | (6-Dec-91 ARC.P223/R) L'entree en cage (58x59cm-23x23in) s. (F.FR 10500) |
| £2572 | $4655 | (6-Dec-91 ARC.P225/R) Les trapezistes (57x79cm-22x31in) s. (F.FR 25000) |

SIMKHOVITCH, Simka (1893-?) Russian
| £15385 | $28000 | (28-May-92 CH.NY233/R) The picnic (111x126cm-44x50in) s.d.1934-35 |

SIMKIN, Richard (1840-1926) British
| £580 | $1038 | (15-Jan-92 BT68/R) Troopers of the 21st Lancers (25x20cm-10x8in) s.i. W/C |

SIMMERS, Melvin (1907-1991) British
| £576 | $979 | (21-Oct-91 SY.J425/R) Flower sellers (50x60cm-20x24in) s. board (SA.R 2800) |

SIMMLER, Friedrich Karl Joseph (1801-1872) German
| £986 | $1785 | (4-Dec-91 DO.H2949/R) Sheep on hillside (19x28cm-7x11in) s. panel (DM 2800) |

SIMMONS, Edward Emerson (1852-1932) American
| £1784 | $3318 | (19-Jun-92 CN.P64) L'enlevement d'Europe (32x41cm-13x16in) (F.FR 17500) |
| £1215 | $2150 | (10-Nov-91 LIT.L149) Cattle in landscape (30x46cm-12x18in) s. W/C |

SIMMONS, Eyres (fl.1902-1914) British
| £410 | $750 | (6-Feb-92 DLY52) Yacht aground, Penzance harbour (33x25cm-13x10in) s. W/C |

SIMMONS, Freeman Willis (?-1926) American
| £820 | $1500 | (5-Feb-92 D.NY83) Communicant (79x58cm-31x23in) s. |

SIMON, A (?) ?
| £1163 | $2000 | (12-Oct-91 SY.NY110/R) Market place (60x71cm-24x28in) s. |

SIMON, Auguste (?) French
| £611 | $1130 | (10-Jun-92 LD.P130) L'attente du modele (32x40cm-13x16in) s. panel (F.FR 6000) |

SIMON, E (?) ?
| £653 | $1136 | (19-Sep-91 N.M2818/R) Village fair before church in Brittany (37x46cm-15x18in) s. panel (DM 1900) |

SIMON, Lucien (1861-1945) French
£2337	$4067	(16-Apr-92 FB.P139/R) Place animee (108x150cm-43x59in) s. (F.FR 23000)
£2472	$4325	(19-Feb-92 D.V125/R) At the end of the day (70x51cm-28x20in) s.indis.d. (A.S 50000)
£3665	$7000	(16-Jul-92 SY.NY352/R) Dans l'atelier (54x65cm-21x26in) s.
£4595	$7720	(1-Sep-91 PO.BA4) Interior con modelo (55x64cm-22x25in) s.
£1459	$2640	(4-Dec-91 NA.BA66) Femme et petit enfant derriere un table (70x47cm-28x19in) s. W/C
£2000	$3820	(29-Jun-92 CSK20/R) Les Communiants (60x93cm-24x37in) s. gouache W/C

SIMON, T F (1877-1942) Czechoslovakian
£1083 $1949   (19-Nov-91 RAS.K227/R) Model resting (66x53cm-26x21in) s. (D.KR 12000)

SIMON, Tavik Frantisek (1877-1942) Czechoslovakian
£706 $1264   (15-Nov-91 GK.Z5257/R) Wooded landscape with figures (100x80cm-39x31in)
        s.d.1905 (S.FR 1800)
£5000 $8650   (4-Oct-91 C90/R) Onival beach (46x55cm-18x22in) s.d.1904

SIMON, Yohanan (1905-1976) Israeli
£1596 $3000   (5-Jan-92 GG.TA297/R) Imaginary landscape (40x52cm-16x20in) s.d.1961twice
        board on canvas
£2595 $4800   (9-Jun-92 GG.TA405/R) In Kibbutz Gan Schmuel (23x29cm-9x11in) s.d.42
        s.verso
£4571 $8000   (26-Sep-91 SY.I109/R) Kibbutzniks (53x79cm-21x31in)
£5319 $10000   (5-Jan-92 GG.TA295/R) Figures in landscape (60x73cm-24x29in) s.d.1960
£865   *$1600*   *(8-Jun-92 GG.TA211/R) Douceur nocturne (16x22cm-6x9in) s.d.68 oil mixed*
        media canvas on board

SIMONE, A de (19th C?) Italian?
£2600 $4524   (14-Apr-92 CSK169/R) British iron-clad lying at anchor and drying sails
        in Bay of Naples (53x71cm-21x28in) s.d.1866
£440   *$796*   *(19-May-92 SWS348) The steam yacht Norseman off Naples (44x63cm-17x25in)*
        s.i. gouache
£550   *$990*   *(22-Nov-91 C7) The screw schooner Gelert (37x57cm-15x22in) s.i. pencil*
        bodycol
£750   *$1290*   *(10-Oct-91 CSK41) RYS Calista, in swell (43x65cm-17x26in) s.d.1902*
        bodycol
£800   *$1392*   *(14-Apr-92 CSK71/R) S.S. Ocean Prince in Bay of Naples (40x62cm-16x24in)*
        s.d.86 bodycol
£950   *$1653*   *(14-Apr-92 CSK78/R) S.Y. Ulva in Bay of Naples (40x65cm-16x26in) s.i.d.95*
        pencil bodycol
£1100   *$1980*   *(22-Nov-91 C4/R) R.V.Y.C. Chevy Chase in the Bay of Naples*
        (46x61cm-18x24in) s.i.d.90 gouache
£1100   *$1980*   *(22-Nov-91 C6) The steam yacht Varuna with Naples beyond*
        (42x62cm-17x24in) s.d.1906 W/C bodycol
£1100   *$1980*   *(22-Nov-91 C5/R) S.Y. Shellah in the Bay of Naples (38x63cm-15x25in)*
        s.i.d.91 W/C bodycol

SIMONE, A de (attrib) (19th C?) Italian
£850   *$1479*   *(14-Apr-92 CSK75/R) S.S. India in Bay of Naples (42x65cm-17x26in) i.*
        bodycol
£850   *$1479*   *(14-Apr-92 CSK72) Schooner-rigged steam yacht (46x68cm-18x27in) bodycol*

SIMONE, Alfredo de (?) ?
£1138 $1900   (19-Aug-91 GC.M12/R) Lavanderas (18x23cm-7x9in) s. board
£2370 $4100   (30-Sep-91 GC.M46/R) Calle del Barrio Sur (26x35cm-10x14in) s. board
£2601 $4500   (30-Sep-91 GC.M45/R) Calle del Barrio Sur (26x34cm-10x13in) board
£2732 $5000   (4-Jun-92 GOM.M41/R) Calle del Barrio Sur (75x55cm-30x22in) s.
£4309 $7800   (2-Dec-91 GC.M57/R) Barrio Sur (63x45cm-25x18in) s. arpillera
£6180 $11000   (28-Oct-91 GC.M41/R) 'Calle' o 'Mi Barrio' (80x85cm-31x33in) s.

SIMONE, G de (20th C) ?
£520   *$905*   *(14-Apr-92 CSK74) Sloop under sail (38x49cm-15x19in) s. bodycol oval*

SIMONE, Michele de (19/20th C) Italian
£736 $1317   (14-Nov-91 CH.R87) Passeggiata sul lungomare (13x19cm-5x7in) s. panel
        (I.L 1600000)

SIMONE, Nicolo de (circle) (17th C) Italian
£7247 $13407   (8-Jun-92 CH.R698) Baccanale (140x180cm-55x71in) (I.L 16000000)

SIMONE, Tommaso de (19th C) Italian
£450   *$770*   *(19-Mar-92 B27) An Ironclad in the Bay of Naples (30x46cm-12x18in)*
        s.d.1991 gouache
£820   *$1476*   *(9-Jan-92 B166 d) The Schooner, Sierra Sadena, at sea (30x46cm-12x18in)*
        s. gouache
£862   *$1500*   *(13-Sep-91 S.W2769/R) Yacht Varuna with Vesuvius erupting in distance*
        (43x64cm-17x25in) s.d.1906 W/C
£900   *$1512*   *(15-Aug-91 B221) S.S. Isobel of Whitby in Bay of Naples. In Bay of Biscay*
        (43x66cm-17x26in) i. gouache pair
£1050   *$1890*   *(9-Jan-92 B237) The S Y Monsoon in the Bay of Naples (35x64cm-14x25in)*
        s.i. gouache
£1750   *$2940*   *(15-Aug-91 B191) Steam and sail yacht, Mera in Bay of Naples. S.Y.Mera in*
        squall (44x63cm-17x25in) one s.i.d.1905 one s.i.d.1907 gouache pair
£1800   *$3240*   *(9-Jan-92 B243/R) The steam yacht, Giralda, in the Bay of Naples,*
        Vesuvius beyond (44x60cm-17x24in) s.i.d.90 gouache
£1900   *$3420*   *(9-Jan-92 B262) R M Y C - Vol-au-Vent, in the bay of Naples, Vesuvius*
        erupting beyond (39x57cm-15x22in) s.i.d.99 gouache

SIMONE, de (?) Italian
£440   *$792*   *(27-Jan-92 PH92) Steam yacht in choppy sea (35x55cm-14x22in) s. gouache*
£650   *$1177*   *(20-May-92 S159/R) Schooner off the Bay of Naples (30x43cm-12x17in) s.*
        W/C

SIMONETTI, A (19/20th C) Italian
£600 $1116   (16-Jun-92 PH73/R) Figure on lane in landscape (38x70cm-15x28in) s.

SIMONETTI, Amedeo (1874-1922) Italian
£852 $1500   (10-Apr-92 DM.D2015/R) Drawing room scene, depicting male string duet
                    entertaining two women (79x64cm-31x25in) s.
£500 $895   (16-Jan-92 B150/R) Lady and gallante in elegant interior
                    (36x54cm-14x21in) s.i. W/C
£1279 $2200   (14-Oct-91 H.C48/R) Flower seller (51x38cm-20x15in) s.i. W/C

SIMONETTI, Attilio (1843-1925) Italian
£1197 $2179   (10-Dec-91 F.R150/R) Ragazza in costume (52x41cm-20x16in) s.d.1869
                    (I.L 2600000)

SIMONETTI, Ettore (19th C) Italian
£2094 $4000   (16-Jul-92 SY.NY602/R) The presentation (76x55cm-30x22in) s.d.1885 W/C
                    pencil board
£9890 $18000   (28-May-92 SY.NY50/R) Trying on shoes (76x55cm-30x22in) s.i. W/C
£11628 $20000   (17-Oct-91 SY.NY35/R) Shoe shop (78x56cm-31x22in) s.i. W/C

SIMONI, Cesare (19th C) Italian
£2528 $4500   (22-Jan-92 SY.NY526/R) Port scene lit by moonlight (69x92cm-27x36in)
                    indist.s.

SIMONI, Gustavo (1846-?) Italian
£920 $1646   (14-Nov-91 CH.R153) Odalisca (52x34cm-20x13in) s.i.d.1902 W/C
                    (I.L 2000000)

SIMONI, Scipione (19/20th C) Italian
£2235 $4000   (13-Nov-91 B.SF2247/R) The entertaining jester (16x23cm-6x9in) s.d.1880
                    panel
£2247 $4000   (22-Jan-92 SY.NY513/R) Women conversing on steps in village
                    (85x53cm-33x21in) s. W/C paper on board
£4631 $8012   (24-Mar-92 CH.R26/R) Ceccano (100x65cm-39x26in) s.d.1893 W/C
                    (I.L 10000000)

SIMONI, Stefan (1860-1950) Austrian
£1221 $2075   (24-Oct-91 D.V40/R) Park landscape (40x50cm-16x20in) s. board (A.S 25000)
£2600 $4602   (14-Feb-92 C57/R) The Zoo, Schonbrunn (39x49cm-15x19in) s.

SIMONIDY, Michel (1870-1933) Rumanian
£4722 $8500   (8-Jan-92 D.NY80) Winter perfume (81x74cm-32x29in) s.d.1902

SIMONIN, Francine (1942-) Canadian
£466 $844   (24-May-92 AT.P115/R) Les chaises IV (56x76cm-22x30in) s. oil chl pastel
                    (F.FR 4600)

SIMONIN, Victor (1877-1946) Belgian
£632 $1080   (13-Mar-92 FN.S2960) Red roses in blue vase on white table cloth
                    (32x50cm-13x20in) s. canvas on panel (DM 1800)

SIMONINI, Francesco (1686-1753) Italian
£3058 $5688   (18-Jun-92 SY.MO197) Cavalier jouant de la trompette (41x32cm-16x13in)
                    (F.FR 30000)
£9497 $17000   (16-Jan-92 CH.NY117/R) Battle scene (74x99cm-29x39in)
£9500 $16625   (1-Apr-92 S119/R) Studies of footsoldiers and cavalrymen
                    (58x47cm-23x19in) pair
£15317 $27570   (19-Nov-91 F.R144/R) Cavalieri in marcia (51x72cm-20x28in) (I.L 33000000)
£2389 $4324   (22-May-92 GB.B5695/R) Skirmish with fortified castle and outlines of
                    town beyond (40x59cm-16x23in) chk wash (DM 7000)

SIMONINI, Francesco (attrib) (1686-1753) Italian
£1118 $1945   (13-Apr-92 AT.P10) Engagement de cavaliers (22x30cm-9x12in) (F.FR 11000)
£7558 $13000   (10-Oct-91 SY.NY153/R) Battle scene (71x97cm-28x38in)

SIMONINI, Francesco (circle) (1686-1753) Italian
£942 $1800   (16-Jul-92 SY.NY125/R) Battle scene (22x29cm-9x11in) canvas on panel
£1832 $3500   (16-Jul-92 SY.NY122/R) Battle scene (35x47cm-14x19in)
£4405 $7797   (7-Nov-91 D.V47/R) Figures and riders before tent (56x117cm-22x46in)
                    (A.S 90000)

SIMONINI, Francesco (style) (1686-1753) Italian
£1500 $2880   (9-Jul-92 CSK208/R) Cavalrymen engaging Turks (44x71cm-17x28in)
£1700 $3264   (9-Jul-92 CSK204/R) Cavalry engagement (25x34cm-10x13in)
£1702 $3250   (16-Jul-92 SY.NY123/R) Battle scene (36x47cm-14x19in)
£2800 $5040   (22-Nov-91 SWS124/R) A Cavalry battle (33x42cm-13x17in)

SIMONNET, Lucien (1849-1926) French
£674 $1200   (1-Dec-91 DU.E1137/R) Pastoral scene with sheep (38x56cm-15x22in) s.

SIMONSEN, Johanne (19th C) Scandinavian
£3200 $5952   (17-Jun-92 S298/R) Still life of summer flowers in basket
                    (42x56cm-17x22in) init.

SIMONSEN, Niels (1807-1885) Danish

£792	$1331	(27-Aug-91 RAS.K499) Young girl in National costume (47x30cm-19x12in) s.d.1857 (D.KR 9000)
£990	$1812	(5-Feb-92 KH.K117/R) From the beach near Lokken (33x50cm-13x20in) s.d.1856 (D.KR 11000)
£1173	$2112	(19-Nov-91 RAS.K113/R) Three Arabian girls and a Bedouin by a well (54x80cm-21x31in) s. (D.KR 13000)
£4332	$7798	(19-Nov-91 RAS.K33/R) Being attacked by pilots (71x95cm-28x37in) s.d.1882 (D.KR 48000)
£16000	$27360	(18-Mar-92 S39/R) The last stand (78x109cm-31x43in) s.d.1867

SIMONSEN, Simon (1841-1928) Danish

£496	$883	(25-Nov-91 BU.K25/R) Landscape with gundog (30x42cm-12x17in) s.d.1885 panel (D.KR 5500)
£511	$858	(28-Aug-91 KH.K178) A Saint Bernhard (29x33cm-11x13in) s.d.1899 (D.KR 5800)
£669	$1244	(16-Jun-92 RAS.V869/R) Dachshund puppy by tree (25x33cm-10x13in) s.d.1916 (D.KR 7500)
£674	$1200	(29-Nov-91 MFA.C56/R) Spaniel (20x25cm-8x10in) s.d.1897 board
£847	$1576	(16-Jun-92 RAS.V868/R) Puppies in basket (26x35cm-10x14in) s.d.1891 (D.KR 9500)
£1337	$2299	(15-Oct-91 RAS.K251/R) The pointers resting (20x29cm-8x11in) s.d.1892 (D.KR 15000)
£1937	$3254	(27-Aug-91 RAS.K163/R) In the dog kennel (20x34cm-8x13in) s.d.1903 (D.KR 22000)
£2113	$3549	(27-Aug-91 RAS.K127/R) The four deer reared at Hjortekaershuset, summer 1892 (108x140cm-43x55in) s.d.1892 (D.KR 24000)
£2293	$4081	(28-Apr-92 RAS.K60/R) From the Roman Campagna with horse and waggon (29x41cm-11x16in) s.d.1877 (D.KR 26000)
£2641	$4437	(27-Aug-91 RAS.K128/R) Horses in Vallo Dyrehave (80x115cm-31x45in) s.d.1902 (D.KR 30000)
£2852	$5105	(16-Nov-91 FAL.M338/R) Unsafe in a strange place, two puppies in poultry yard (31x43cm-12x17in) s.d.18 (S.KR 30000)
£4296	$7474	(21-Sep-91 SA.A1829/R) Farmyard with chickens, ducks and dog (37x57cm-15x22in) s.d.1893 (DM 12500)
£5415	$9260	(12-Mar-92 RAS.V983/R) Dachshund with puppies seated in farmyard (70x85cm-28x33in) s.d.1885 (D.KR 60000)
£12556	$22601	(30-Jan-92 RAS.V679/R) Pointer with six puppies (82x103cm-32x41in) s.d.1891 (D.KR 140000)

SIMONSON, David (attrib) (1831-1896) German

| £698 | $1200 | (16-Oct-91 D.NY89) Mother and child playing in a garden (48x53cm-19x21in) bears sig. |

SIMONSON-CASTELLI, Ernst Oskar (1864-1919) German

| £524 | $1000 | (16-Jul-92 SY.NY421/R) Young girl with flowers (80x62cm-31x24in) s. |

SIMONSSON, Birger (1883-1938) Swedish

£572	$1007	(11-Apr-92 FAL.M384/R) Southern landscape with house (40x33cm-16x13in) s. panel (S.KR 6000)
£959	$1726	(19-Nov-91 GO.G166/R) Still life of flowers and figurine (54x45cm-21x18in) init. (S.KR 10000)
£1198	$2157	(19-Nov-91 GO.G165/R) Green interior (70x62cm-28x24in) (S.KR 12500)

SIMONSSON, Konrad (1843-1916) Swedish

£652	$1174	(19-Nov-91 GO.G168) Girl on path (35x29cm-14x11in) s. panel (S.KR 6800)
£700	$1260	(19-Nov-91 GO.G169) Path by clump of trees in garden (35x29cm-14x11in) s. panel (S.KR 7300)
£874	$1520	(13-Apr-92 AB.S239/R) Lake landscape with trees (28x45cm-11x18in) s. panel (S.KR 9200)

SIMPKINS, Henry J (1906-) Canadian

| £450 | $797 | (6-Nov-91 SY.T285) Steaming up at Sugar Camp - St. Janvier, Quebec (47x62cm-19x24in) s. W/C (C.D 900) |

SIMPSON, Charles (?) ?

£2000	$3500	(27-Sep-91 C114/R) Becher's Brook, The Grand National (71x102cm-28x40in) s.
£1100	$1991	(21-May-92 B173/R) The morning ride (37x52cm-15x20in) s. gouache
£1500	$2670	(29-Oct-91 HB550/R) Left behind (51x74cm-20x29in) gouache

SIMPSON, Charles Walter (1885-1971) British

| £502 | $914 | (26-May-92 JOY.T208) Le retour de la messe de minuit (22x34cm-9x13in) s. ink wash (C.D 1100) |

SIMPSON, Ethel H (fl.1890) British

| £620 | $1128 | (10-Dec-91 SWS247) English village, summertime (59x87cm-23x34in) init.d.1866 s.i.stretcher |

SIMPSON, John (18/19th C) British

| £1600 | $2816 | (9-Apr-92 S191/R) Portrait of Admiral Sir Charles Napier (8x?cm-3x?in) min. gilt mount frame oval |

SIMPSON, Tom (20th C) British

| £400 | $696 | (19-Sep-91 B6) Barrage balloon (21x27cm-8x11in) s.i.d.1918 W/C chl |

SIMPSON, William (1823-1899) British
£420 $752   (16-Jan-92 B173/R) Brindjarries - Indian Salt - merchants (25x35cm-10x14in) s.i.d.1863 pencil W/C htd white
£2800 $4928   (7-Apr-92 C184/R) Temple of Martund, Kashmir (35x50cm-14x20in) s.i.d.1862 pencil W/C htd white
£2800 $4928   (7-Apr-92 C185/R) Vale of Kashmir (35x50cm-14x20in) s.i.d.1863 pencil W/C bodycol

SIMS, Charles (1873-1926) British
£900 $1611   (5-May-92 SWS477/R) Legend (98x129cm-39x51in)
£900 $1719   (16-Jul-92 B40/R) Mother and child (37x52cm-15x20in) s. paper
£1176 $2106   (15-Nov-91 ZOF.Z1434/R) Ianthe (43x40cm-17x16in) s. panel (S.FR 3000)

SIMSCH, Walter (20th C) German?
£580 $1056   (30-May-92 VG.B932/R) Still life with jug (62x48cm-24x19in) s.d.1932 W/C over pencil (DM 1700)

SIMSON, William (1800-1847) British
£13000 $23400   (19-Nov-91 PH27/R) The shooting party (65x95cm-26x37in) s.d.1829 panel

SINCLAIR, Frances (20th C) British
£500 $870   (18-Sep-91 CG151) Sheep grazing, near Baily, Howth (43x53cm-17x21in) s.d.10 s.i.verso canvas on board

SINCLAIR, G (19th C) British
£1900 $3344   (10-Apr-92 C189/R) Twin Beast, shorthorn Devon cross bull in meadow and village beyond (46x62cm-18x24in) i.d.1867

SINCLAIR, H W (19/20th C) British
£500 $895   (11-Nov-91 PH142 a) Sailing off Cowes (28x45cm-11x18in) init.d.1907 W/C

SINCLAIR, Max (19th C) British
£1000 $1680   (15-Aug-91 B283) Steamship and yacht on open seas (30x51cm-12x20in) s. mono.i.verso pair
£1000 $1720   (17-Oct-91 GSP430/R) At timber wharf - harbour scene with steam tug Chum, pulling ship (41x61cm-16x24in) s.verso

SINDING, Otto Ludvig (1842-1909) Norwegian
£746 $1387   (15-Jun-92 B.O138/R) Mountain pass (49x36cm-19x14in) s. (N.KR 8500)
£1070 $1850   (23-Mar-92 B.O118/R) Plants and wood (37x29cm-15x11in) s.d.1879 (N.KR 12000)
£1203 $2093   (18-Sep-91 N.M706/R) Lambs in field, spring (38x50cm-15x20in) s. (DM 3500)
£2289 $4143   (3-Dec-91 FN.S2458) Peasant proposing to girl in mountain landscape with cattle grazing (54x51cm-21x20in) s. (DM 6500)

SINDING, Sigmund (1875-1936) Norwegian
£526 $979   (18-Jun-92 GWP.O90/R) Coastal landscape, winter (71x92cm-28x36in) s. (N.KR 6000)
£1374 $2432   (15-Feb-92 BU.O120) Street scene, Oslo (61x49cm-24x19in) s. panel (N.KR 15500)
£7617 $13864   (14-Dec-91 BU.O10/R) Figures at Stortorvet (117x99cm-46x39in) s. (N.KR 86000)

SINDING-LARSEN, Kristoffer (1873-1948) Scandinavian
£579 $1002   (23-Mar-92 B.O119/R) Summer night in Nevlunghavn (68x80cm-27x31in) s. (N.KR 6500)

SINEMUS, Wim (20th C) Dutch
£1049 $1910   (12-Dec-91 SY.AM177/R) Untitled (64x49cm-25x19in) s.d.63 gouache pastel (D.FL 3400)

SINET, Andre (1867-?) French
£7429 $13000   (19-Feb-92 CH.NY64/R) At opera (40x27cm-16x11in) s.d. pastel canvas

SINGDAHLSEN, Andreas (1855-?) Norwegian
£613 $1067   (14-Sep-91 BU.O326) Winter landscape (33x48cm-13x19in) s. (N.KR 7000)
£613 $1067   (14-Sep-91 BU.O325) Hay-stacks (33x48cm-13x19in) s. (N.KR 7000)
£657 $1143   (14-Sep-91 BU.O327) Chickens in yard (33x48cm-13x19in) s. (N.KR 7500)
£697 $1186   (6-Aug-91 UL.T80) Autumn landscape (80x64cm-31x25in) (N.KR 8000)
£966 $1661   (7-Oct-91 B.O123/R) River landscape, winter (46x73cm-18x29in) s. (N.KR 11000)
£1771 $3224   (14-Dec-91 BU.O56/R) Winter landscape with horse and sleigh, Skaugumsasen (42x58cm-17x23in) s. (N.KR 20000)
£576 $1048   (9-Dec-91 B.O104/R) Winter landscape, Asker (30x48cm-12x19in) s. W/C (N.KR 6500)

SINGER, Clyde (1908-) American
£791 $1400   (22-Apr-92 D.NY84) Rendezvous at 84th Street (46x71cm-18x28in) s. s.i.d.1970 verso masonite
£851 $1600   (18-Dec-91 SY.NY278/R) 44st Night (55x70cm-22x28in) s. board
£4889 $8800   (22-Nov-91 E.EDM598/R) Tug boat with buildings in background (81x102cm-32x40in) s.d.38

SINGER, William Henry (jnr) (1868-1943) American
£511 $894   (19-Feb-92 D.P34) Paysage de neige (54x45cm-21x18in) s.d.1930 pastel
                               (F.FR 5000)

SINGIER, Gustave (1909-1985) French
£16185 $28000   (2-Oct-91 SY.NY77/R) Provence-La Vielle Ville I (81x100cm-32x39in) s.d.59
£514 $915   (29-Nov-91 GAB.G2879 a) Variation humaine (56x44cm-22x17in) s.d.61 W/C
                               Indian ink (S.FR 1300)
£624 $1093   (5-Apr-92 R.P189/R) Sans titre (31x22cm-12x9in) s. W/C (F.FR 6000)
£771 $1472   (3-Jul-92 GL.P161) Untitled (44x55cm-17x22in) s. W/C (F.FR 7500)
£1078 $1940   (19-Nov-91 FB.P138/R) Composition (65x45cm-26x18in) s.d.1973 W/C
                               (F.FR 10500)
£1129 $2033   (19-Nov-91 FB.P120/R) Composition (55x43cm-22x17in) s.d.76 W/C
                               (F.FR 11000)
£1232 $2218   (19-Nov-91 FB.P179/R) Composition (54x37cm-21x15in) s.d.79 W/C
                               (F.FR 12000)
£1232 $2218   (19-Nov-91 FB.P175/R) Composition (35x60cm-14x24in) s.d.67 W/C
                               (F.FR 12000)
£1600 $2768   (26-Mar-92 C14) Theocrite et la flute de pan (32x25cm-13x10in) s.d.48
                               pastel W/C paper mounted on board
£1611 $2739   (24-Oct-91 CSC.P68/R) Rythmes (54x42cm-21x17in) s.d.73 W/C (F.FR 16000)
£1700 $2941   (26-Mar-92 S2/R) Peniches a Clichy (24x31cm-9x12in) s.d.50 W/C paper on
                               card

SINGLETON, Henry (1766-1839) British
£1143 $2000   (18-Feb-92 CE.NY105/R) Sewing lesson (63x76cm-25x30in) s.
£1200 $2160   (21-Nov-91 WA145) Heath 'Old' Hall, with Wakefield Bridge beyond
                               (91x119cm-36x47in)

SINGLETON, Henry (attrib) (1766-1839) British
£700 $1246   (21-Jan-92 PH61) Classical figure on rock, dog at feet (91x77cm-36x30in)
£800 $1440   (22-Nov-91 SWS295) The new pet (75x62cm-30x24in)

SINGLETON, Henry (circle) (1766-1839) British
£750 $1373   (12-May-92 SWS748/R) Ruth and Boaz (124x89cm-49x35in)
£950 $1615   (24-Oct-91 CSK158/R) A milkmaid holding an open letter in a wooded
                               landscape (30x25cm-12x10in)

SINIBALDI, Jean Paul (1857-1909) French
£3143 $5500   (20-Feb-92 SY.NY279/R) Christening (46x61cm-18x24in) s.

SINIBALDO, T (?) Italian
£988 $1700   (9-Oct-91 RO.BA196) La visita del Cardenal (55x46cm-22x18in) s.

SINTENIS, Renee (1888-1965) German
£6873 $12715   (12-Jun-92 HN.H789/R) Futuristic composition (23x29cm-9x11in) s.indis.i.
                               indian ink brush pencil col.chk (DM 20000)

SIPKES, Joseph and KAMPHUYSEN, Jan (19th C) Dutch
£2019 $3472   (7-Mar-92 CH.AM228/R) Launching of ship with various onlookers
                               (62x79cm-24x31in) s.d.1826 (D.FL 6500)

SIQUEIROS, David (1896-1974) Mexican
£16575 $30000   (18-May-92 CH.NY8/R) Mujer con Rebozo (76x52cm-30x20in) s. masonite
£22099 $40000   (18-May-92 CH.NY73/R) Figura (79x59cm-31x23in) s.d.5-22-69 s.i.d.verso
                               composite board
£44199 $80000   (18-May-92 CH.NY16/R) Retrato de Blanca Luz (92x69cm-36x27in) s.d.1931
                               gessoed burlap
£518 $892   (16-Oct-91 FER.M35/R) Retrato de Picasso (21x15cm-8x6in) s.i. chl dr
                               (S.P 95000)
£2095 $3750   (13-Nov-91 B.SF2760/R) Mother and child (27x36cm-11x14in) s. gouache
£2353 $4000   (23-Oct-91 B.SF3790/R) Figure study (42x32cm-17x13in) s.d.4-64 gouache
£12155 $22000   (18-May-92 CH.NY72/R) Mujer en un Mundo de Hambre y Terror
                               (56x38cm-22x15in) s.d.64 politec paper on masonite
£22099 $40000   (19-May-92 SY.NY40/R) Paisaje (61x76cm-24x30in) s.d.54 pyroxylin masonite
£41436 $75000   (19-May-92 SY.NY13/R) Picadores de piedra (100x75cm-39x30in) s.d.26 oil
                               pyroxylin masonite
£44444 $80000   (19-Nov-91 CH.NY36/R) Dos cabezas (89x59cm-35x23in) s.d.57 piroxyline
                               masonite
£47222 $85000   (18-Nov-91 SY.NY20/R) Retrato de Ione Robinson (86x58cm-34x23in) s.d.31
                               oil pyroxylin burlap
£52486 $95000   (19-May-92 SY.NY20/R) Esclavo, simbolo del Luchador Sacrificado
                               (101x65cm-40x26in) s.d.1948 duco canvas on masonite

SIRANI, Elisabetta (1638-1665) Italian
£3916 $6931   (7-Nov-91 D.V33/R) Salome with the head of John (137x99cm-54x39in) after
                               Guido Reni (A.S 80000)

SIRANI, Elisabetta (attrib) (1638-1665) Italian
£1650 $2871   (11-Sep-91 MMB345/R) Madonna and child (74x61cm-29x24in)
£5200 $9100   (31-Mar-92 PH24/R) Magdalen (74x61cm-29x24in)
£6000 $11520   (7-Jul-92 PH12/R) Sibyl (88x68cm-35x27in)

SIRANI, Giovanni Andrea (1610-1670) Italian
£600 $1092   (11-Dec-91 PH286/R) The return of the Prodigal Son (16x22cm-6x9in) pen wash over chk.

SIRONI, Mario (1885-1961) Italian
£1390 $2475   (27-Nov-91 F.M172/R) Paesaggio (11x13cm-4x5in) s. tempera paper (I.L 3000000)
£1622 $2887   (27-Nov-91 F.M234/R) Figura orante (36x25cm-14x10in) s. tempera paper on board (I.L 3500000)
£5714 $10000   (25-Feb-92 SY.NY40/R) Colloquio (22x28cm-9x11in) s.
£8626 $15354   (29-Apr-92 F.F292/R) Paesaggio (23x34cm-9x13in) s.d.1949 tempera board (I.L 19000000)
£8804 $15672   (26-Nov-91 SY.MI158/R) Figure (27x28cm-11x11in) board (I.L 19000000)
£11121 $19796   (26-Nov-91 SY.MI140/R) Composizione in rosso (44x55cm-17x22in) s. (I.L 24000000)
£13902 $24745   (26-Nov-91 SY.MI128/R) Composizione (32x40cm-13x16in) s. (I.L 30000000)
£18286 $32000   (25-Feb-92 CH.NY92/R) Paesaggio (46x39cm-18x15in) board on canvas
£22276 $41880   (19-Dec-91 F.M181/R) Composizione (60x50cm-24x20in) s. (I.L 48000000)
£25331 $46102   (9-Dec-91 CH.R186/R) Casolari in alta montagna (37x50cm-15x20in) s. d.1948verso (I.L 55000000)
£58011 $109061   (19-Dec-91 F.M153/R) Composizione (110x140cm-43x55in) s. (I.L 125000000)
£74255 $139599   (19-Dec-91 F.M212/R) Composizione (90x97cm-35x38in) s. (I.L 160000000)
£82778 $148172   (14-Nov-91 F.M82/R) I bevitori (80x70cm-31x28in) (I.L 180000000)
£94275 $168751   (14-Nov-91 F.M113/R) Composizione (53x68cm-21x27in) s. (I.L 205000000)
£678 $1227   (21-May-92 F.M278) Figure (18x11cm-7x4in) s. ink W/C (I.L 1500000)
£695 $1237   (27-Nov-91 F.M186) Paesaggio (10x12cm-4x5in) mono. pencil (I.L 1500000)
£1090 $1939   (29-Apr-92 F.F24/R) Figure (26x18cm-10x7in) s. pencil gouache paper on cardboard (I.L 2400000)
£1176 $2024   (12-Oct-91 F.L202/R) Nudo femminile (12x8cm-5x3in) s. pencil (S.FR 3000)
£1412 $2428   (12-Oct-91 F.L215/R) Nudo femminile (10x11cm-4x4in) s. Indian ink (S.FR 3600)
£1451 $2496   (12-Oct-91 F.L203/R) Nudo femminile (11x8cm-4x3in) s. ink (S.FR 3700)
£1487 $2692   (3-Dec-91 F.R115/R) Studio per paesaggio con figure (22x15cm-9x6in) s. pencil (I.L 3200000)
£1569 $2698   (12-Oct-91 F.L210/R) Untitled (16x15cm-6x6in) s. pencil (S.FR 4000)
£1808 $3273   (21-May-92 F.M99/R) Testa d'uomo (37x29cm-15x11in) s. gouache (I.L 4000000)
£2285 $4342   (23-Jun-92 F.M67/R) Bozzetto per la Giustizia (20x31cm-8x12in) i. chl (I.L 5000000)
£2359 $4317   (12-May-92 F.R79/R) Parete (30x22cm-12x9in) s. mixed media (I.L 5200000)
£3244 $5774   (26-Nov-91 SY.MI29/R) Figure. Figura (21x32cm-8x13in) mixed media.pencil W/C double-sided (I.L 7000000)
£3621 $6590   (26-May-92 SY.MI118/R) Composizione con uomo e bottiglia (50x32cm-20x13in) mixed media paper on canvas (I.L 8000000)
£3714 $6500   (25-Feb-92 SY.NY41/R) L'uomo seduto (25x16cm-10x6in) s. gouache paper on canvas
£3847 $7002   (25-May-92 CH.R42/R) Figure (50x40cm-20x16in) s. s.d.1961verso mixed media paper on canvas (I.L 8500000)
£6563 $11944   (25-May-92 CH.R20/R) Senza titolo (25x22cm-10x9in) s. pencil ink tempera paper on canvas (I.L 14500000)
£9143 $16000   (25-Feb-92 CH.NY75/R) Cavallo e cavaliere (45x56cm-18x22in) s. gouache pencil paper on canvas
£9827 $17000   (2-Oct-91 SY.NY58/R) I Filosofi (42x43cm-17x17in) s.gouache brush ink
£10117 $18110   (14-Nov-91 F.M94/R) Colloquio (70x53cm-28x21in) mixed media (I.L 22000000)
£10506 $18280   (14-Apr-92 F.M241/R) Composizione (34x53cm-13x21in) s. mixed media cardboard (I.L 23000000)
£11121 $19796   (26-Nov-91 SY.MI178/R) Il bevitore (84x74cm-33x29in) s. mixed media paper on canvas (I.L 24000000)
£11514 $20956   (9-Dec-91 CH.R99/R) Studio per parete (28x50cm-11x20in) d.1944 mixed media (I.L 25000000)
£11765 $20235   (12-Oct-91 F.L212/R) Donna (27x21cm-11x8in) d.1915 ink board (S.FR 30000)

SISKOV, Ludmil (1936-) Czechoslovakian
£864 $1469   (21-Oct-91 SY.J330/R) Lemon party (124x159cm-49x63in) mono. acrylic canvas (SA.R 4200)

SISLEY, Alfred (1839-1899) French
£259563 $475000   (13-May-92 SY.NY49/R) Chantier a Saint Mammes (50x65cm-20x26in) s.d.80
£282486 $500000   (5-Nov-91 CH.NY20/R) Rue a Veneux (55x74cm-22x29in) s.
£292044 $496475   (21-Oct-91 ARC.P31/R) Les falaises au Pays de Galles (60x92cm-24x36in) s.d.97 (F.FR 2900000)
£327869 $600000   (13-May-92 SY.NY46/R) Rue de village, temps gris (38x56cm-15x22in) s.d.74
£409605 $725000   (6-Nov-91 SY.NY4/R) Printemps a Veneux (73x91cm-29x36in) s.

SISSON, Laurence P (1928-) American
£663 $1200   (22-Nov-91 S.BM227/R) Tidal pool, autumn (117x76cm-46x30in) masonite

SITJE, Joronn (1897-1982) Norwegian
£527 $906   (10-Oct-91 BU.O100/R) Woman (48x38cm-19x15in) s.d.45 panel (N.KR 6000)
£702 $1305   (18-Jun-92 GWP.O92/R) Woman and boy (61x50cm-24x20in) s. panel (N.KR 8000)
£877 $1632   (15-Jun-92 B.O139/R) Tunes (100x81cm-39x32in) s.d.56 (N.KR 10000)

SITTER, Inger (1929-) Norwegian
£614 $1142   (15-Jun-92 B.O140/R) Self portrait (54x46cm-21x18in) s. panel (N.KR 7000)

SITTOW, Michiel (after) (1469-1525) Dutch
£2100 $3654   (10-Sep-91 H203) Portrait of Henry VIII holding red rose of Lancaster
                            (33x23cm-13x9in) panel

SIVERS, Clara von (1854-?) German
£15984 $28771   (21-Nov-91 D.V132/R) Lilac in vase (111x88cm-44x35in) s. (A.S 320000)

SIVORI, Edouardo (1847-1918) Argentinian
£1124 $2000   (28-Apr-92 PO.BA26) Desnudo femenino de espaldas (86x34cm-34x13in) canvas
                            laid down on board
£1333 $2400   (20-Nov-91 V.BA92) Autorretrato (22x17cm-9x7in)
£2022 $3600   (28-Apr-92 PO.BA27) Desnudo femenino (90x37cm-35x15in)
£2111 $3800   (20-Nov-91 V.BA93) Paisaje (23x34cm-9x13in) d.1895
£6492 $12400   (30-Jun-92 PO.BA16) Atardecer en la pampa (25x40cm-10x16in) s.
£23077 $42000   (11-Dec-91 RO.BA8/R) Ninos en el parque Lezama (150x100cm-59x39in) s.
£391 $750   (4-Aug-92 V.BA99/R) Paisaje (19x14cm-7x6in) W/C

SJAMAAR, Pieter Geerard (1819-1876) Dutch
£1835 $3193   (14-Apr-92 SY.AM128/R) Man in window eating fish (34x27cm-13x11in)
                            s.d.1860 panel (D.FL 6000)

SJOBERG, Axel (1866-1950) Swedish
£949 $1736   (12-May-92 GO.G164) Coastal landscape with boats (68x100cm-27x39in)
                            s.d.41 (S.KR 10000)
£2216 $3833   (28-Mar-92 UA.U398/R) Female nude (92x74cm-36x29in) s.d.89 (S.KR 23000)
£2217 $3924   (5-Nov-91 BA.S171/R) Gulls on rock (70x90cm-28x35in) s.d.1907
                            (S.KR 23500)
£4744 $8681   (11-May-92 NOR.S59/R) Dusk by Landsorts lighthouse (94x130cm-37x51in) s.
                            (S.KR 50000)
*£395 $704   (28-Oct-91 AB.S403) Sailing vessels at Kanholmsfjarden, Sandhamn
                            (37x55cm-15x22in) s.d.1913 W/C (S.KR 4200)*

SJOFTVANO (19th C) ?
£845 $1530   (3-Dec-91 FN.S2462) The Judgement of Salomon (126x156cm-50x61in) s.
                            (DM 2400)

SJOHOLM, Charles (1933-) Swedish
£659 $1173   (28-Oct-91 AB.S216/R) Street scene with buss number 59, Stockholm
                            (54x46cm-21x18in) s. (S.KR 7000)
*£408 $711   (13-Apr-92 AB.S244) Boats at quay, Nybrohamn, Stockholm (37x44cm-15x17in)
                            s. mixed media (S.KR 4300)*

SJOLANDER, Waldemar (1906-1988) Swedish
£949 $1736   (12-May-92 GO.G166) Flowers in blue vase (53x38cm-21x15in) s.
                            double-sided (S.KR 10000)
£1151 $2071   (19-Nov-91 GO.G172) Harbour view with figures on jetty (49x53cm-19x21in)
                            s. (S.KR 12000)
*£422 $759   (19-Nov-91 GO.G292) Mexican landscape with women (50x65cm-20x26in)
                            s.d.1953 gouache (S.KR 4400)*
*£455 $833   (12-May-92 GO.G284) Mexican lady (64x50cm-25x20in) s.i. gouache
                            (S.KR 4800)*
£479 $863   (19-Nov-91 GO.G291) Procession (50x65cm-20x26in) s.i. gouache (S.KR 5000)

SJOSTEDT, Yvonne (20th C) ?
£610 $1061   (16-Apr-92 FB.P69/R) Portrait de jeune fille (100x81cm-39x32in) s.
                            (F.FR 6000)

SJOSTROM, Ina (?) Finnish
£507 $887   (25-Sep-91 HOR.H90) Autumn colours (32x48cm-13x19in) s. (F.M 3600)

SJOSTROM, L P (1820-1896) Swedish
*£624 $1073   (15-Oct-91 RAS.K394) Ships portrait 'Magneten from Landskrona'
                            (41x56cm-16x22in) s.d.1875 W/C gouache (D.KR 7000)*

SJOSTROM, Vilho (1873-1944) Finnish
£1264 $2225   (12-Apr-92 HOR.H211) The farewell (62x50cm-24x20in) s.d.1920 (F.M 10000)
£3234 $5757   (1-Dec-91 HOR.H207) Red dress (99x51cm-39x20in) s.d.1911 (F.M 25000)
£3364 $5987   (1-Dec-91 HOR.H209) Reflections in coastal water (73x60cm-29x24in)
                            s.d.1941 (F.M 26000)
£3881 $6908   (1-Dec-91 HOR.H208/R) Landscape with rowingboat near logfloating
                            (60x74cm-24x29in) s.d.1942 (F.M 30000)

SKAGERFORS, Olle (1920-) Swedish
£815 $1467   (19-Nov-91 GO.G173) Still life (37x59cm-15x23in) init. (S.KR 8500)
£854 $1563   (12-May-92 GO.G167) Landscape with cottage (48x57cm-19x22in) init.d.47
                            (S.KR 9000)
£1423 $2604   (12-May-92 GO.G168/R) Still life of jug and cup (46x60cm-18x24in) init.
                            (S.KR 15000)

SKARBINA, Franz (1849-1910) German
£2218 $4038   (30-May-92 VG.B129/R) Village church, Tyrol (35x34cm-14x13in) s.d.1896
                            canvas on board (DM 6500)

SKARBINA, Franz (1849-1910) German-cont.

£2752	$4872	(5-Nov-91 SY.AM195/R) Figures on beach of Duinkerken (34x49cm-13x19in) s. (D.FL 9000)
£6873	$12784	(20-Jun-92 BM.B1077/R) Berlin street scene (56x40cm-22x16in) s. (DM 20000)
£7018	$12632	(22-Nov-91 SA.A1754/R) Horse-drawn coach before palace (31x39cm-12x15in) s. (DM 20000)
£8247	$14351	(21-Sep-91 SA.A1920/R) Interior of Catharinenkirche in Hamburg with figures (111x67cm-44x26in) s.i.d.1892 (DM 24000)
£10465	$18000	(16-Oct-91 CH.NY92/R) Leipzigerstrasse, Berlin (37x29cm-15x11in) s.d.15 Dec 1904 i. verso canvas laid on board
£909	$1573	(25-Mar-92 KM.K1436) Alpine landscape with village (48x63cm-19x25in) s. pastel (DM 2600)

SKARI, Edvard (1839-1903) Norwegian

£531	$928	(25-Feb-92 UL.T233) Fjord landscape with boats (30x46cm-12x18in) (N.KR 6000)
£587	$1056	(19-Nov-91 RAS.K376/R) Waves hitting breakwater (34x52cm-13x20in) s.i. (D.KR 6500)
£740	$1332	(19-Nov-91 RAS.K377) Cliffs near Lofoten (39x79cm-15x31in) s.i. (D.KR 8200)
£797	$1451	(9-Dec-91 B.O105/R) Seascape (64x95cm-25x37in) s.indist.d.1879 (N.KR 9000)
£2107	$3624	(7-Oct-91 B.O125/R) Vessels off Kronborg Palace (106x168cm-42x66in) s.d.1897 (N.KR 24000)
£2326	$4233	(12-Dec-91 RAS.V782/R) Norwegian seascape with several line-of-battle ships (79x126cm-31x50in) s. (D.KR 26000)
£2719	$5058	(15-Jun-92 B.O141/R) Landscape (106x145cm-42x57in) s.i.d.1866 (N.KR 31000)

SKEAPING, John (1901-1980) British

£546	$1000	(5-Jun-92 SY.NY297/R) Around the track (33x45cm-13x18in) s.d.63
£824	$1500	(26-May-92 CE.NY39/R) Bay stallion Kenneth Rowntree at the races (50x76cm-20x30in) s.i. panel
£1200	$2100	(27-Sep-91 C55/R) On the gallops (52x75cm-20x30in) s.d.69
£2500	$4475	(15-Jan-92 BT149/R) Coming through the crowd (109x94cm-43x37in) s.d.62
£700	$1281	(14-May-92 C113/R) Reed buck (23x35cm-9x14in) s.d.29 pen col.crayon bodycol
£700	$1253	(14-Jan-92 PH81/R) Three gazelles (29x37cm-11x15in) s.d.30 pencil
£700	$1274	(12-Dec-91 CSK213) Tiger sketch (20x33cm-8x13in) chl.brn.chk.
£1000	$1730	(2-Oct-91 S167/R) Grazing deer (28x35cm-11x14in) s. pencil
£1200	$2064	(4-Mar-92 DR86) Racehorse going away (42x52cm-17x20in) s.d.62 W/C bodycol
£1350	$2322	(4-Mar-92 DR87) Galloping racehorse (51x73cm-20x29in) s.d.70 W/C

SKELL, Ludwig (1843-1905) German

£3158	$5400	(13-Mar-92 FN.S2962/R) Lake Starnberg landscape with farmhouse and figures (53x64cm-21x25in) s.d.1874 (DM 9000)

SKELTON, Joseph Ratcliffe (fl.1888-1927) British

£480	$859	(14-Nov-91 B178/R) Fortune in the fire (51x36cm-20x14in) s. W/C bodycol

SKENE OF RUBISLAW, James (1775-1864) British

£1200	$2040	(23-Oct-91 S186/R) Castel a mare, Gulf of Smyrna (23x48cm-9x19in) s.d.1838 W/C over pencil

SKILLING, William (20th C) British/American

£929	$1700	(3-Jun-92 D.NY89) White show horse (152x122cm-60x48in) s.
£1093	$1903	(13-Apr-92 SY.J27) Maharajah's elephant (120x151cm-47x59in) s. (SA.R 5500)
£1530	$2800	(3-Jun-92 D.NY88/R) Greyhound with whelp in landscape (152x122cm-60x48in) s.

SKIPWORTH, Frank Markham (1854-1929) British

£500	$925	(9-Jun-92 RG2352) Portrait, believed to be Ellen Terry (53x38cm-21x15in) mono.d.91
£900	$1674	(18-Jun-92 B105/R) A young beauty (66x53cm-26x21in) init.
£9143	$16000	(19-Feb-92 CH.NY171/R) Lesson (65x87cm-26x34in) s.

SKLAR, Dorothy (20th C) American

£743	$1300	(31-Mar-92 MOR.P82) L.A. street scene (33x51cm-13x20in) s.d.45 W/C

SKOCZYLAS, Wladyslaw (1883-1934) Polish

£417	$729	(29-Sep-91 AG.W15) Garden scene (34x34cm-13x13in) s. W/C (P.Z 8000000)

SKOLD, Otte (1894-1958) Swedish

£518	$922	(28-Oct-91 AB.S218/R) Still life of carnations in vase (72x39cm-28x15in) s. glass (S.KR 5500)
£384	$695	(3-Dec-91 AB.S5156/R) Harbour scene, Tangier (24x36cm-9x14in) s. W/C (S.KR 4000)

SKOPTSOV, Semyon Sergeevich (1917-) Russian

£500	$905	(4-Dec-91 S382/R) Lake, cloudy day (50x72cm-20x28in) s. d.1954 verso card

SKOTNES, C (?) ?
£500 $910   (28-May-92 B271) Primeval Man (122x119cm-48x47in) s. mixed media on carved panel

SKOU, Sigurd (attrib) (1878-1929) American
£552 $1000   (24-May-92 JRB.C142/R) Fisherman, Brittany (53x46cm-21x18in) canvas on panel
£1447 $2750   (22-Jun-92 SG.M585) Ladies of Brittany (66x81cm-26x32in) s.d.1926

SKOUINE, Elena (1908-1986) Russian
£912 $1650   (20-May-92 ARC.P137/R) Au piano, portrait de Piotr Tchaikovsky (80x106cm-31x42in) s. (F.FR 9000)

SKOVGAARD, P C (1817-1875) Danish
£484 $813   (28-Aug-91 KH.K179) Italian landscape (19x26cm-7x10in) (D.KR 5500)
£617 $1048   (8-Aug-91 RAS.V991/R) Wooded river landscape (48x38cm-19x15in) i.verso (D.KR 7000)
£903 $1625   (19-Nov-91 RAS.K127/R) Path along water (36x58cm-14x23in) i.verso (D.KR 10000)
£990 $1812   (5-Feb-92 KH.K120/R) Early evening near Knabstrup (23x38cm-9x15in) i.d.1874 (D.KR 11000)
£1323 $2354   (28-Apr-92 RAS.K61/R) Landscape, warm summer's day (30x46cm-12x18in) d.1860 (D.KR 15000)
£1427 $2655   (16-Jun-92 RAS.K264/R) River running through wood (48x38cm-19x15in) i.verso (D.KR 16000)
£2636 $4719   (6-May-92 KH.K191/R) Landscape, Bondedammen near Hellebaek (58x78cm-23x31in) mono.d.1852 (D.KR 30000)

SKRAMSTAD, Ludwig (1855-1912) Norwegian
£570 $1061   (15-Jun-92 B.O143/R) Green landscape with two boys (45x75cm-18x30in) s. (N.KR 6500)
£663 $1160   (25-Feb-92 UL.T234/R) Morning landscape (33x43cm-13x17in) (N.KR 7500)
£754 $1334   (15-Feb-92 BU.O123) Winter landscape (39x63cm-15x25in) s.i.verso panel (N.KR 8500)
£877 $1632   (15-Jun-92 B.O142/R) Winter landscape (53x97cm-21x38in) s. (N.KR 10000)
£877 $1632   (15-Jun-92 B.O144/R) Autumn landscape with man (34x27cm-13x11in) s.d.1879 panel (N.KR 10000)
£1054 $1875   (2-Nov-91 BU.O58) Norwegian fjord landscape (75x125cm-30x49in) s. (N.KR 12000)
£1149 $2011   (25-Feb-92 UL.T236/R) View from Hardangerfjord (40x58cm-16x23in) (N.KR 13000)
£1923 $3288   (18-Mar-92 N.M649/R) Woodland pond in early autumn (82x136cm-32x54in) s. (DM 5500)
£3012 $5481   (9-Dec-91 B.O106/R) View of a valley (72x122cm-28x48in) s.d.84 (N.KR 34000)
£6234 $10722   (10-Oct-91 BU.O17/R) Lake landscape (120x170cm-47x67in) s. (N.KR 71000)

SKREDSVIG, Christian (1854-1924) Scandinavian
£1019 $1854   (10-Dec-91 UL.T220) Evening mood (23x16cm-9x6in) (N.KR 11500)
£7000 $13020   (17-Jun-92 S324/R) La vie moderne (18x30cm-7x12in) s.
£7558 $13000   (16-Oct-91 CH.NY127/R) Cows watering at quiet pool (62x100cm-24x39in) s.d.1881
£9211 $17132   (15-Jun-92 B.O146/R) Lake landscape, Djuptjern (46x70cm-18x28in) s. (N.KR 105000)
£13421 $24963   (15-Jun-92 B.O145/R) Evening landscape, Eggedal (109x201cm-43x79in) s.d.1918 (N.KR 153000)
£22282 $38547   (23-Mar-92 B.O121/R) The flower seller, Paris (100x160cm-39x63in) s.i.d.1885 (N.KR 250000)
£1228 $2284   (15-Jun-92 B.O147/R) Man and dog hunting (12x15cm-5x6in) s.d.90 gouache (N.KR 14000)

SKRETA, Karl (attrib) (1610-1674) Austrian
£2442 $4200   (9-Oct-91 CH.NY44/R) Saint Luke painting Virgin (71x73cm-28x29in)

SKULASON, Thorvaldur (1906-1984) Icelandic
£447 $814   (10-Dec-91 RAS.K158) Composition with fruit (30x28cm-12x11in) s. W/C (D.KR 5000)

SKUM, Nils Nilsson (1872-1951) Swedish
£570 $991   (13-Apr-92 AB.S415) Landscape with reindeer, Lappland (26x35cm-10x14in) s.d.1942 Indian ink chk (S.KR 6000)
£678 $1207   (28-Jan-92 AB.S405) Reindeer in the mountains (25x32cm-10x13in) s. pencil chk (S.KR 7200)
£712 $1239   (13-Apr-92 AB.S414) Reindeer in the mountains (25x34cm-10x13in) s.d.1944 i.verso chk (S.KR 7500)

SLABBINCK, Rik (1914-1991) Belgian
£1337 $2272   (22-Oct-91 C.A291 b) Still life (73x61cm-29x24in) s. (B.FR 80000)
£1671 $2840   (22-Oct-91 C.A292) Still life (73x61cm-29x24in) s. (B.FR 100000)
£1711 $3097   (3-Dec-91 C.A523/R) The red house (60x75cm-24x30in) s. (B.FR 100000)
£5004 $8807   (7-Apr-92 C.A217/R) The pink tablecloth (95x129cm-37x51in) s. (B.FR 300000)

SLADE, Cora (?-1937) American
£526 $900   (12-Mar-92 MFA.C161) Orange and grapes (13x23cm-5x9in) s.

SLADE, Cora (?-1937) American-cont.
£556 $950   (12-Mar-92 MFA.C160) Cherries (15x23cm-6x9in) s.
£585 $1000   (12-Mar-92 MFA.C162) Plums (10x23cm-4x9in) s.
£877 $1500   (12-Mar-92 MFA.C163) Oranges (18x25cm-7x10in) s.

SLAGER, Jeanette (1881-1945) Dutch
£547 $952   (17-Sep-91 CH.AM318) Red poppies in a copper pan (71x102cm-28x40in) s.
             (D.FL 1800)

SLAGER, Piet (elder) (1841-1912) Dutch
£1040 $1840   (5-Nov-91 SY.AM269/R) Two young girls by fire (23x17cm-9x7in) s. panel
             (D.FL 3400)

SLAMA, Viktor Theodor (1890-1973) Austrian
£586 $1013   (3-Oct-91 D.V189/R) Maiandacht (110x87cm-43x34in) s.i.verso (A.S 12000)

SLATER, John Falconar (1857-1937) British
£520 $874   (13-Aug-91 AG232) Mist descending on upland river valley
             (125x99cm-49x39in) s.
£540 $907   (13-Aug-91 AG219) River rushing down mountain valley (91x120cm-36x47in)
             s.d.1919 board
£700 $1274   (10-Dec-91 AG275) Quiet river bend (24x34cm-9x13in) s. with i.verso
£820 $1378   (13-Aug-91 AG220/R) Walled garden in summer (55x78cm-22x31in) s. board
£1210 $2141   (4-Nov-91 SY.J212/R) Coastal landscape (80x152cm-31x60in) s. board
             (SA.R 6000)
£1500 $2580   (3-Mar-92 SWS1580) The riverside path (50x90cm-20x35in) s. pair
£2450 $4214   (11-Oct-91 K522/R) Wooded river landscape at sunset with cottage
             (66x102cm-26x40in) s.
£2700 $4590   (22-Oct-91 SWS402/R) Cottage and garden (59x95cm-23x37in) s. panel
£1000   *$1820*   *(10-Dec-91 AG200/R) Horseman approaching farm in snow (44x59cm-17x23in)*
             s. gouache

SLAUGHTER, Stephen (?-1765) British
£5000 $9550   (17-Jul-92 C5/R) Portrait of Lord Bowes of Clonlyon (127x101cm-50x40in)
£9000 $16110 (13-Nov-91 S44/R) Portrait of Captain John Long Bateman standing in
             uniform holding sword (124x99cm-49x39in) s.i.d.1744

SLAUGHTER, Stephen (attrib) (?-1765) British
£1826 $3250   (22-Jan-92 D.NY18/R) Portrait of young girl holding rose
             (127x102cm-50x40in)

SLEATOR, James Sinton (?-1950) British
£6422 $11945 (17-Jun-92 A.D93/R) Corner of studio (61x51cm-24x20in) (E.P 7000)

SLENDZINSKI, Ludomir (1899-1980) Polish
£2615 $4498   (13-Oct-91 REM.W30) Helios (100x100cm-39x39in) s. panel (P.Z 50000000)

SLEVOGT, Max (1868-1932) German
£2098 $3734   (28-Nov-91 SY.BE3/R) Portrait of Otto Blumenfeld (43x35cm-17x14in) s.d.15
             panel (DM 6000)
£4082 $7306   (5-May-92 ZEL.L1538/R) Portrait of Dr Manasse (81x66cm-32x26in) s.d.1895
             (DM 12000)
£5498 $10062 (2-Jun-92 FN.S2761/R) Tintoretto self portrait (34x38cm-13x15in) mono.
             i.verso after Tintoretto (DM 16000)
£13287 $23650 (28-Nov-91 SY.BE4/R) The defeat of the Mamelukes (55x67cm-22x26in)
             s.d.1917 (DM 38000)
£13986 $24895 (28-Nov-91 SY.BE2/R) Cafe waiter (38x31cm-15x12in) s.d.07 (DM 40000)
£14676 $26710 (30-May-92 VG.B138/R) Still life of prawns (49x61cm-19x24in) s.d.1913
             panel (DM 43000)
£8392   *$14937* *(28-Nov-91 SY.BE42/R) Palm trees and village. The blue sea*
             (14x22cm-6x9in) s.d.1914 i.d.verso W/C over pencil htd.white two
             (DM 24000)

SLINGELANDT, Pieter van (1640-1691) Dutch
£28000 $53760 (8-Jul-92 S84/R) Lady with child standing in courtyard of country house
             (31x24cm-12x9in) s.d.1681 panel
£760   *$1375*   *(22-May-92 LD.P53/R) Portrait de femme en buste (16x13cm-6x5in) ink wash*
             vellum (F.FR 7500)
£2623   *$4696*   *(12-Nov-91 SY.AM293) Portrait of young man in landscape (21x17cm-8x7in)*
             s.d.1673 col.chk vellum (D.FL 8500)
£3200   *$5824*   *(11-Dec-91 PH169/R) Portrait of young girl holding a puppy*
             (17x13cm-7x5in) mono. chk.htd.bodycol chk

SLINGELANDT, Pieter van (attrib) (1640-1691) Dutch
£13000 $24960 (10-Jul-92 C146/R) Portrait of girl, aged nine, wearing grey dress with
             lace collar (18x14cm-7x6in) i. copper
£554   *$942*   *(25-Oct-91 AT.P135) Portrait de femme lisant (21x16cm-8x6in) i. pen wash*
             (F.FR 5500)

SLINGELANDT, Pieter van (circle) (1640-1691) Dutch
£1400 $2688   (9-Jul-92 B146/R) lacemaker (20x14cm-8x6in) panel

SLIPPER, Gary P (1934-) Canadian
£548 $997   (26-May-92 JOY.T238/R) Forest (20x25cm-8x10in) s.d.67 board (C.D 1200)

SLOAN, John (1871-1951) American
£12281 $21000   (11-Mar-92 SY.NY101/R) Portrait of Stuart Davis (81x66cm-32x26in) s.
£23464 $42000   (6-May-92 D.NY55/R) Wind on the bay (64x76cm-25x30in) s.
£30387 $55000   (6-Dec-91 CH.NY174/R) Nude glancing back (81x66cm-32x26in) s.
£649 $1200   (10-Jun-92 CE.NY572/R) Here it is Sir, hope you'll like it (30x27cm-12x11in) s.i.d.1926 pencil paperboard

SLOAN, Marianna (1875-1954) American
£540 $950   (9-Apr-92 FA.PH789) Afternoon, Chelsea England (25x33cm-10x13in) pastel

SLOANE, Eric (1910-) American
£1214 $2100   (6-Sep-91 S.BM249/R) The huntsman (41x51cm-16x20in) s. masonite
£1326 $2400   (4-Dec-91 D.NY39/R) Canvasbacks flying over marsh (86x117cm-34x46in) masonite
£1436 $2600   (4-Dec-91 D.NY2/R) Sea fox (61x74cm-24x29in) s.i. board
£1528 $2750   (10-Jan-92 DM.D2018/R) New snow (43x61cm-17x24in) s.i. board
£1923 $3500   (13-Dec-91 DM.D2043/R) Ready for blow (74x99cm-29x39in) s.
£1965 $3400   (8-Sep-91 LIT.L42) Bridge (53x69cm-21x27in) s. masonite
£2000 $3500   (26-Sep-91 CH.NY149/R) Slope (51x61cm-20x24in) s.i. canvasboard
£2765 $4950   (14-Nov-91 GRO.B166 a/R) Autumn hay (46x91cm-18x36in) s. masonite
£4084 $7800   (19-Jul-92 LIT.L118) Covered bridge with childrens and dog, West Arlington, Vermont (61x76cm-24x30in) s. masonite
£4945 $9050   (9-Feb-92 LIT.L157) Vermont, October (61x91cm-24x36in) s.
£9945 $18000   (6-Dec-91 CH.NY246/R) Berkshire Barn (61x101cm-24x40in) s.i. masonite

SLOANE, George (19/20th C) British
£791 $1400   (6-Nov-91 D.NY32/R) Noble pursuit (30x41cm-12x16in) s.d.1909 board
£1751 $3100   (13-Feb-92 S.W2837/R) The charmer s.i.d.1902 panel

SLOBODKINA, Esphyr (1914-) American
£4094 $7000   (12-Mar-92 CH.NY246/R) Abstract forms in space (34x21cm-13x8in) s.verso oil pencil masonite

SLOCOMBE, Frederick (1847-?) British
£1707 $3072   (23-Nov-91 SO.S605/R) Woman and cat (51x33cm-20x13in) s. W/C (S.KR 17800)

SLOCOMBE, Shirley Charles (19th C) British
£3000 $5280   (8-Apr-92 B124/R) Portrait of Mr G H Garnett-Orme Esq (236x145cm-93x57in) s.d.1908 i.verso
£3100 $5456   (8-Apr-92 B125/R) Portrait of Mrs G H Garnett-Orme Esq (236x145cm-93x57in) s.d.1908-9 i.verso
£500 $900   (27-Jan-92 PH108) Lacquer cabinet (37x26cm-15x10in) s.d.1905 W/C bodycol

SLOMAN, Joseph (1883-?) American
£511 $900   (9-Apr-92 FA.PH691) Veranda on Rittenhouse (51x66cm-20x26in) s. i.verso

SLOTT-MOLLER, Agnes (1862-1937) Danish
£946 $1712   (19-May-92 AB.S4379/R) Danish lake landscape with punt, summer (52x102cm-20x40in) s. (S.KR 10000)

SLOTT-MOLLER, Harald (1864-1937) Danish
£1146 $2041   (28-Apr-92 RAS.K513/R) Young girl in rowing boat at sunset (48x68cm-19x27in) s. (D.KR 13000)
£1471 $2529   (15-Oct-91 RAS.K257/R) Migratory birds - illustration for a poem (140x168cm-55x66in) s.d.MCMIX (D.KR 16500)
£5714 $10000   (20-Feb-92 SY.NY244/R) Poet, Holger Drachman, surrounded by muses (119x201cm-47x79in) s.d.1911-1912
£13500 $24030   (27-Nov-91 S72/R) Morgenkaffen (83x67cm-33x26in) s.

SLOW, John (19th C) British?
£2000 $3460   (24-Mar-92 CG811/R) H.M.S. Amphion leaving Malta (32x42cm-13x17in) s.i.d.1837verso board

SLUITER, Willy (1873-1949) Dutch
£796 $1417   (25-Nov-91 W.T1959/R) Preparing for a crop (61x86cm-24x34in) s. board (C.D 1600)
£979 $1732   (5-Nov-91 SY.AM266/R) Girl in Volendam costume (43x33cm-17x13in) s.d.1911 panel (D.FL 3200)
£1529 $2661   (14-Apr-92 SY.AM331/R) Playing time (23x25cm-9x10in) s.d.1903 panel (D.FL 5000)
£2752 $4789   (14-Apr-92 SY.AM113/R) Figures on terrace in Scheveningen (47x64cm-19x25in) s.d.39 W/C (D.FL 9000)

SLUSSER, Jean Paul (1886-?) American
£539 $975   (7-Dec-91 LAE.L28/R) Village scene (64x84cm-25x33in) s.verso

SLUYS, Theo van (19th C) Belgian
£1257 $2250   (13-Nov-91 B.SF2233/R) Sheep with lambs and chickens in manger (56x48cm-22x19in) s. i.verso

SLUYTERS, Jan (1881-1957) Dutch
£1173 $2052   (18-Feb-92 CH.AM135/R) Portrait of a black gentleman (60x50cm-24x20in) s. (D.FL 3800)
£1543 $2809   (11-Dec-91 CH.AM217) Toledo (31x24cm-12x9in) s.i.d.1910 board (D.FL 5000)

SLUYTERS, Jan (1881-1957) Dutch-cont.

£1852	$3241	(18-Feb-92 CH.AM159/R) Still life with white tulips in vase (53x48cm-21x19in) s. (D.FL 6000)
£2128	$3702	(17-Sep-91 CH.AM28/R) A portrait of Ysbrand Hiddes Galema (100x85cm-39x33in) s. (D.FL 7000)
£2576	$4662	(21-May-92 SY.AM26/R) De voyeur (45x47cm-18x19in) s.d.1902 (D.FL 8500)
£5455	$9873	(19-May-92 CH.AM154/R) Portrait of two children (150x115cm-59x45in) s. (D.FL 18000)
£5758	$10421	(19-May-92 CH.AM166/R) Portrait of lady in fur coat (88x79cm-35x31in) s. (D.FL 19000)
£6790	$12358	(11-Dec-91 CH.AM238/R) Orchids in glass vase (65x54cm-26x21in) s. (D.FL 22000)
£9091	$16455	(19-May-92 CH.AM195/R) View of Schinkelkade near the Overtoon, Amsterdam (58x71cm-23x28in) s. (D.FL 30000)
£11515	$20842	(19-May-92 CH.AM194/R) Still life of pansies and forget-me-nots in vase (52x49cm-20x19in) s. (D.FL 38000)
£13889	$25278	(11-Dec-91 CH.AM242/R) Outskirts of Amsterdam (42x33cm-17x13in) mono.d.07 (D.FL 45000)
£15152	$27424	(19-May-92 CH.AM153/R) Standing nude seen from the back (73x55cm-29x22in) (D.FL 50000)
£18519	$33704	(11-Dec-91 CH.AM243/R) Moonnight (41x33cm-16x13in) mono.d.10 (D.FL 60000)
£34848	$63076	(19-May-92 CH.AM176/R) Wooded lane (34x51cm-13x20in) s.d.10 (D.FL 115000)
£45455	$82273	(19-May-92 CH.AM178/R) Cubist portrait of a lady (107x95cm-42x37in) s. (D.FL 150000)
£455	$823	(21-May-92 SY.AM5) Nurse collecting for the Red Cross (23x23cm-9x9in) s. W/C ink chk (D.FL 1500)
£463	$843	(12-Dec-91 SY.AM126/R) Reclining nude (20x27cm-8x11in) init. ink gouache (D.FL 1500)
£545	$987	(21-May-92 SY.AM169) Portrait (26x17cm-10x7in) mono.s.d.1908 W/C (D.FL 1800)
£669	$1164	(17-Sep-91 CH.AM38) A standing nude (33x18cm-13x7in) s. pencil W/C (D.FL 2200)
£790	$1375	(17-Sep-91 CH.AM41) Two female bathers (17x24cm-7x9in) init. pencil W/C (D.FL 2600)
£909	$1645	(19-May-92 CH.AM33) Portrait of a baby (44x37cm-17x15in) s. Chl.W/C (D.FL 3000)
£912	$1587	(17-Sep-91 CH.AM36) A portrait of a baby (23x41cm-9x16in) s. pencil W/C (D.FL 3000)
£926	$1685	(11-Dec-91 CH.AM211) Female nude standing (46x23cm-18x9in) s. pencil chk W/C (D.FL 3000)
£1064	$1851	(17-Sep-91 CH.AM55/R) Nocturne (47x63cm-19x25in) s.d.nov.1905 pencil chk. (D.FL 3500)
£1235	$2247	(11-Dec-91 CH.AM256) Nude smoking (34x21cm-13x8in) init. pencil W/C pen (D.FL 4000)
£1235	$2247	(11-Dec-91 CH.AM234) Spanish dancer (26x20cm-10x8in) s.i.d.06 pencil cryaon brush ink (D.FL 4000)
£1520	$2644	(17-Sep-91 CH.AM24/R) A nude seated on a draped chair (30x14cm-12x6in) s. pencil W/C (D.FL 5000)
£1818	$3291	(19-May-92 CH.AM164/R) Spanish lady (31x23cm-12x9in) pencil chk crayon W/C (D.FL 6000)
£1852	$3370	(11-Dec-91 CH.AM236/R) Apachedans (26x20cm-10x8in) pencil crayon W/C (D.FL 6000)
£2469	$4494	(11-Dec-91 CH.AM222/R) Salome (26x40cm-10x16in) s.d.18 chk W/C cardboard (D.FL 8000)
£2879	$5211	(19-May-92 CH.AM95/R) Reclining nude (21x43cm-8x17in) s. pencil W/C (D.FL 9500)
£3395	$6179	(11-Dec-91 CH.AM235/R) Two dancing women (26x20cm-10x8in) pencil pen brush (D.FL 11000)
£4012	$7302	(11-Dec-91 CH.AM237) Quadrille au Tabarin (25x20cm-10x8in) d.06 pencil col.crayons (D.FL 13000)
£4545	$8227	(19-May-92 CH.AM156/R) The loge (26x20cm-10x8in) s.d.07 pencil crayon W/C (D.FL 15000)
£5247	$9549	(11-Dec-91 CH.AM264/R) Boslandschap met badende vrouwen (53x73cm-21x29in) s. pencil pastel W/C (D.FL 17000)
£5556	$10111	(11-Dec-91 CH.AM224/R) Nude seated on bench (34x32cm-13x13in) pencil W/C htd.white (D.FL 18000)
£6061	$10970	(19-May-92 CH.AM151/R) Two women seen from the back (26x20cm-10x8in) pencil W/C (D.FL 20000)
£6173	$11235	(11-Dec-91 CH.AM231/R) Still life with flowers in vase with Portugese landscape beyond (82x63cm-32x25in) s.i. pastel htd.white (D.FL 20000)

SLUYTERS, Jan (jnr) (1914-) Dutch

£760	$1322	(17-Sep-91 CH.AM69) A landscape in spring near Geleen, Limberg (64x80cm-25x31in) s. (D.FL 2500)

SMADJA, Alex (20th C) ?

£1220	$2122	(16-Apr-92 FB.P147/R) Composition (116x81cm-46x32in) s. (F.FR 12000)
£1527	$2780	(11-Dec-91 ZZ.F138/R) Composition (41x31cm-16x12in) s. chl.oil paper laid down on board (F.FR 15000)

SMALL, Florence (c.1860-1933) British

£1300	$2470	(23-Jun-92 PH118/R) Girl in chair (56x46cm-22x18in) s.

SMALL, Frank O (1860-?) American

£1734	$3000	(6-Sep-91 S.BM190/R) The welcoming smile (56x41cm-22x16in) s.

SMALL, William (1843-1929) British
£1600 $3056   *(1-Jul-92 B66/R) The kitchen garden (27x40cm-11x16in) init.d.1871 W/C bodycol*

SMALLFIELD, Frederick (1829-1915) British
£400 $768   *(29-Jul-92 CSK12) The accordion player (33x22cm-13x9in) s.d.1858 W/C*
£700 $1197   *(13-Mar-92 C1/R) The ghost story (9x12cm-4x5in) init.i. W/C*

SMALT, Abraham Samuel (1852-1930) Dutch
£926 $1685   *(11-Dec-91 CH.AM97) View of village, Dordrecht (48x68cm-19x27in) s. (D.FL 3000)*

SMART (18/19th C) British
£800 $1432   *(13-Nov-91 WI1092/R) Portrait of boy in midshipman's uniform min.*

SMART, Jeffrey (1921-) Australian
£1255 $2272   *(19-May-92 JRL.S234) Head of boy (47x36cm-19x14in) s.d.43 board (A.D 3000)*
£3205 $5705   *(27-Apr-92 J.M94 a) Study for the Ball Game, Athens (36x35cm-14x14in) s. board (A.D 7500)*
£5500 $9735   *(10-Feb-92 B27/R) Satellite dish (99x119cm-39x47in) s.*
£6167 $11101   *(24-Nov-91 SY.S335/R) Piraeus II (49x60cm-19x24in) s.d.1964 (A.D 14000)*
£6809 $12051   *(26-Apr-92 SY.ME474 a/R) Study for Morning, Yarragon Siding, 1982/84 (36x57cm-14x22in) (A.D 16000)*
£7048 $12687   *(24-Nov-91 SY.S376) Study for Placard and Underpass, 1986 (38x47cm-15x19in) s. board (A.D 16000)*
£7660 $13557   *(26-Apr-92 SY.ME474 i/R) Study for Five Factories, 1988 (29x51cm-11x20in) (A.D 18000)*
£11894 $21410   *(24-Nov-91 SY.S266/R) Variation on theme by Ian Bent, 1968/69 (59x68cm-23x27in) i.verso (A.D 27000)*
£16170 $28621   *(26-Apr-92 SY.ME321/R) Self portrait (64x80cm-25x31in) s.d.64 hardboard (A.D 38000)*
£18298 $32387   *(26-Apr-92 SY.ME385/R) Breakwater, Fiumicino (66x130cm-26x51in) s. (A.D 43000)*

SMART, John (snr) (1742-1811) British
£950 $1767   *(17-Jun-92 PHS434/R) Portrait of Thomas Lewin min.W/C i. plaited hair verso*
£2600 $4576   *(9-Apr-92 S158/R) Portrait of gentleman, with powdered hair, wearing scarlet coat (3x?cm-1x?in) min. s.d.1778 gilt bezel lacquer frame oval*
£3242 $5869   *(22-May-92 L.K1110/R) Portrait of lady wearing low cut dress with blue ribbon on neckline (7x5cm-3x2in) min.mono oval (DM 9500)*
£4600 $7958   *(25-Mar-92 PHS507/R) Portrait of Mary Lewin (5x?cm-2x?in) min.mono.i.verso oval gold frame*
£5800 $10208   *(9-Apr-92 S183/R) Portrait of Richard, 7th Earl of Cavan (5x?cm-2x?in) min. init.d.1783 ormolu frame oval*
£6500 $11440   *(9-Apr-92 S165/R) Portrait of William Domville (8x?cm-3x?in) min. init.d.1807 i.verso gold frame oval*

SMART, John (snr-circle) (1742-1811) British
£2048 $3706   *(22-May-92 L.K1111/R) Portrait of Elizabeth Voisy (5x4cm-2x2in) min. (DM 6000)*

SMART, John IV (1838-1899) British
£700 $1330   *(23-Jun-92 CG668/R) Moonrise on Wye, Below Monmouth (28x41cm-11x16in) s.i.verso*
£1100 $1969   *(13-Nov-91 CG642) Loch Coruisk, Isle of Sky (75x124cm-30x49in) s.d.1881 W/C htd.scratching out*

SMELLIE, John (?-1925) British
£750 $1358   *(4-Dec-91 S302/R) Stone gathering on coast near Porthlethen (31x51cm-12x20in) s. s.i.verso*

SMET, Gustave de (1877-1943) Belgian
£6173 $11235   *(12-Dec-91 SY.AM44/R) Marin (39x31cm-15x12in) s.d.15-5-1923 paper (D.FL 20000)*
£8200 $14186   *(24-Mar-92 C49/R) Verger au soleil couchant (40x52cm-16x20in) s. panel*
£8292 $15174   *(12-May-92 C.A81/R) Chickens by a farm (46x59cm-18x23in) s. (B.FR 500000)*
£8354 $14202   *(22-Oct-91 C.A159/R) Head of a fisherman (38x30cm-15x12in) s. board (B.FR 500000)*
£11728 $21346   *(11-Dec-91 CH.AM282/R) Riverlandscape with goat (49x68cm-19x27in) s. (D.FL 38000)*
£14545 $26327   *(19-May-92 CH.AM186/R) Fishing boats returning from sea (70x79cm-28x31in) s. (D.FL 48000)*
£18820 $34063   *(7-Dec-91 KV.L401/R) Working in the fields (42x52cm-17x20in) s. (B.FR 1100000)*
£21721 $36926   *(22-Oct-91 C.A158/R) Still life with bowl of fruit s. (B.FR 1300000)*
£1479 $2677   *(4-Dec-91 DO.H3403/R) Artist and wife (25x19cm-10x7in) mono. indian ink pen htd.white (DM 4200)*

SMET, Henri de (1865-1940) Belgian
£917 $1596   *(14-Apr-92 SY.AM53/R) The visit (48x37cm-19x15in) s.d.1901 (D.FL 3000)*

SMET, Leon de (1881-1966) Belgian
£2167 $3770   (14-Apr-92 GM.B498/R) Coucher de soleil (75x110cm-30x43in) s.
                  (B.FR 130000)
£8500 $14705   (24-Mar-92 C50/R) Buste de femme, une rose a la main (69x56cm-27x22in)
                  s.d.1925

SMET, de (19/20th C) Belgian
£2667 $4587   (12-Oct-91 KV.L85/R) Fun on the ice (52x63cm-20x25in) s.d.1871
                  (B.FR 160000)
£7000 $13020   (19-Jun-92 C5/R) Tales of the hunt (70x89cm-28x35in)

SMETANA, Jan (1918-) Czechoslovakian
£1241 $2210   (29-Nov-91 D.V154/R) Landscape upside down (100x73cm-39x29in) s.d.
                  (A.S 25000)

SMETHAM, James (1821-1889) British
£1050 $1911   (12-Dec-91 GSP532) Milkmaid in byre, surrounded by animals, swain looking
                  in (74x61cm-29x24in)

SMIDTH, Hans (1839-1917) Danish
£529 $942   (27-Apr-92 BU.K11/R) Heath landscape (37x56cm-15x22in) s. (D.KR 6000)
£722 $1300   (19-Nov-91 RAS.K253/R) Heath landscape (36x60cm-14x24in) s. (D.KR 8000)
£838 $1491   (27-Apr-92 BU.K2/R) Boys by jetty (25x38cm-10x15in) s. (D.KR 9500)
£882 $1570   (28-Apr-92 RAS.K199/R) Kriegbaum's farm in Resen-Faelde, Alheden
                  (43x74cm-17x29in) s.d.1913 (D.KR 10000)
£993 $1787   (19-Nov-91 RAS.K136/R) Intkerior of old house in country
                  (39x58cm-15x23in) s. (D.KR 11000)
£993 $1787   (19-Nov-91 RAS.K270/R) Avenue of large trees (49x41cm-19x16in) s.
                  (D.KR 11000)
£1159 $1993   (15-Oct-91 RAS.K259/R) Landscape with houses (36x53cm-14x21in) s.
                  (D.KR 13000)
£1235 $2198   (28-Apr-92 RAS.K127/R) Peasants in a railway compartment
                  (67x95cm-26x37in) s.d.1888 (D.KR 14000)
£1367 $2433   (28-Apr-92 RAS.K262/R) Farmer returning home to farm (44x62cm-17x24in) s.
                  (D.KR 15500)
£1764 $3139   (28-Apr-92 RAS.K639/R) Landscape with thatched houses (36x63cm-14x25in)
                  s. (D.KR 20000)

SMILLIE, George H (1840-1921) American
£526 $900   (13-Mar-92 S.BM176/R) The fields across the stream, spring landscape
                  (30x36cm-12x14in) s.d.1914
£797 $1450   (15-Dec-91 LIT.L424) The Cobblestone Lane (76x51cm-30x20in) s.
£896 $1550   (29-Mar-92 MY.F99/R) Morning walk (51x76cm-20x30in) s.
£1064 $2000   (18-Dec-91 SY.NY90/R) Landscape at sunset (40x61cm-16x24in) s.
£2926 $5500   (18-Dec-91 SY.NY67/R) Springtime (50x76cm-20x30in) s.

SMILLIE, James (1807-1885) American
£4327 $7400   (12-Mar-92 MFA.C217 a) Western horseman (30x38cm-12x15in) s. board

SMIRKE, Robert (1752-1845) British
£2000 $3580   (15-Nov-91 C193/R) Portrait of Sir Thomas Horsley Curties, Senior Exon of
                  Yeoman of Guard (112x86cm-44x34in) i.verso
£1800   *$3060*   *(23-Oct-91 S1/R) West end of the Parthenon (29x43cm-11x17in) pen W/C over*
                  pencil
£2400   *$4080*   *(23-Oct-91 S2/R) West end of the Parthenon. Entrance to the Acropolis*
                  one i. W/C over pencil two

SMIRKE, Robert (attrib) (1752-1845) British
£628 $1200   (16-Jul-92 SY.NY244/R) Two men of letters (46x56cm-18x22in)
£900 $1584   (8-Apr-92 S168/R) Portrait of Lady Mary Isabella, Duchess of Rutland,
                  standing in grounds of Haddon Hall (69x58cm-27x23in) after Sir Joshua
                  Reynolds

SMIRNOV, Youri (1925-) Russian
£515 $881   (13-Mar-92 ARC.P219/R) Le bouquet de flox (118x66cm-46x26in) s.
                  (F.FR 5000)
£536 $917   (13-Mar-92 ARC.P218/R) Les fleurs (68x116cm-27x46in) s. (F.FR 5200)

SMISSEN, Dominicus van der (1704-1760) German
£6873 $12715   (13-Jun-92 HN.H181/R) Self portrait. Artist's wife (53x47cm-21x19in)
                  s.i.indis.d.1759 pair (DM 20000)

SMIT, Philippe (1887-1948) Dutch
£703 $1224   (14-Apr-92 SY.AM342/R) Place de la Concorde in Paris (48x70cm-19x28in) s.
                  board (D.FL 2300)

SMITH OF CHICHESTER, George (1714-1776) British
£4000 $7040   (8-Apr-92 S108/R) Still life of bread and cheese and decanter of wine
                  (62x74cm-24x29in)
£5525 $10000   (22-May-92 SY.NY227/R) Extensive landscape, said to be view of Chichester
                  with Isle of Wight in distance (65x107cm-26x42in) s.d.1750
£9500 $17005   (13-Nov-91 S63/R) Landscape with artist seated sketching
                  (75x100cm-30x39in)
£9500 $17005   (13-Nov-91 S64/R) Landscape with figures by fallen tree and distant lake
                  (75x100cm-30x39in)

SMITH OF CHICHESTER, William (1707-1764) British
£3477 $5946   (18-Mar-92 D.V70/R) River landscape with shepherd and flock, evening (33x48cm-13x19in) one of pair (A.S 70000)
£3477 $5946   (18-Mar-92 D.V69/R) River landscape with wooden bridge, evening (33x48cm-13x19in) s.d.1757 one of pair (A.S 70000)

SMITH OF DERBY, Thomas (?-1767) British
£9000 $15840   (10-Apr-92 C60/R) River landscapes with countryfolk (46x102cm-18x40in) pair

SMITH, Albert (1896-1940) American
£665 $1184   (27-Nov-91 LD.P215/R) Cabaret (65x51cm-26x20in) s.d.1932 (F.FR 6500)

SMITH, Albert F (1862-1940) American?
£506 $900   (29-Nov-91 MFA.C220/R) Cos Cob landscape s. board

SMITH, Alexis (20th C) American
£3911 $7000   (9-May-92 CE.NY221/R) How ya gonna keep 'em down on the farm (40x176cm-16x69in) cardboard photos plastic animal collage board

SMITH, Alice Ravenel Huger (1876-?) American
£492 $900   (15-May-92 DM.D2052) Black woman subject (25x18cm-10x7in) init. W/C
£492 $900   (15-May-92 DM.D2037) Black woman subject (25x18cm-10x7in) init. W/C

SMITH, Archibald Cary (1837-1911) American
£3324 $5750   (29-Mar-92 MY.F138/R) Bay sunrise (28x53cm-11x21in) s.

SMITH, Archibald Cary (attrib) (1837-1911) American
£811 $1500   (10-Jun-92 CE.NY145/R) Ships on high seas (41x66cm-16x26in) s.

SMITH, Arthur Reginald (1871-1934) British
£1150 $1978   (16-Oct-91 PHL34/R) Ghaishills, Grassington (36x53cm-14x21in) s. i.verso col.wash

SMITH, C A (1853-1946) British
£1197 $2130   (27-Apr-92 J.M508) White bonnett (38x27cm-15x11in) init.d.1886 canvas on board (A.D 2800)

SMITH, Carlton A (1853-1946) British
£1950 $3413   (26-Feb-92 MMB229/R) Woman reading by fireside s.
£2700 $4887   (20-May-92 BT189/R) Feeding jackdaw (33x20cm-13x8in) s.d.1905 board
£2924 $5000   (13-Mar-92 WOL.C417/R) Lazy moments (30x18cm-12x7in) board
£3000 $5340   (28-Apr-92 PH145/R) Gypsy girl (52x35cm-20x14in) s.d.1907
£3000 $5490   (3-Jun-92 S131/R) Sunday morning (91x71cm-36x28in) s.d.1887
£4340 $7681   (25-Apr-92 SO.S595/R) Interior with women feeding birds (75x48cm-30x19in) s.d.1892 (S.KR 46000)
£1700 $2958   (18-Sep-91 WI1105/R) Leisure moments (36x25cm-14x10in) s. W/C
£3000 $5340   (29-Oct-91 C51/R) Girl seated in interior (39x27cm-15x11in) s. pencil W/C
£3200 $5504   (4-Mar-92 S296/R) Leisure moments (36x26cm-14x10in) s. W/C
£3500 $6125   (23-Sep-91 PHB9/R) Sisters (29x19cm-11x7in) s.d.1908 W/C
£4000 $7120   (29-Oct-91 C52/R) The spoilt child (39x28cm-15x11in) s.d.99 i.verso pencil W/C htd white
£4000 $6880   (4-Mar-92 S295/R) Sisters (29x19cm-11x7in) s.d.1908 W/C
£4506 $8111   (19-Nov-91 GO.G293) Interior with mother and daughter (47x70cm-19x28in) s.d.1906 W/C (S.KR 47000)
£5000 $9150   (3-Jun-92 S262/R) The fairy tale (39x56cm-15x22in) s.d.96 W/C
£5000 $8900   (29-Oct-91 C50/R) The jewel box (49x35cm-19x14in) s.d.97 pencil W/C
£5500 $9460   (4-Mar-92 S294/R) Birthday book (55x36cm-22x14in) s. W/C
£6500 $11505   (6-Nov-91 S303/R) A stitch in time (48x70cm-19x28in) s.d.1905 i.verso W/C
£9000 $16470   (3-Jun-92 S284/R) Christmas Eve (75x123cm-30x48in) s.d.1901 W/C htd.
£9200 $16100   (1-Apr-92 B125/R) New friends (48x69cm-19x27in) s.d.1906 W/C

SMITH, Charles (19th C) British
£659 $1200   (26-May-92 CE.NY263/R) Peasant woman by a brook (48x61cm-19x24in) s. canvas on board

SMITH, Charles L A (1871-1937) American
£734 $1300   (12-Feb-92 B.SF492/R) Autumn trees (56x69cm-22x27in) s.
£1966 $3500   (26-Nov-91 MOR.P57) Landscape - in Santa Maria Valley, California (48x58cm-19x23in) s.d.1920 W/C

SMITH, Colvin (1795-1875) British
£1200 $2088   (12-Sep-91 CSK104) Portrait of Archibald Campbell of Blythswood (264x148cm-104x58in)
£1500 $2685   (13-Nov-91 S155/R) Portrait of Francis, Lord Jeffrey standing (91x71cm-36x28in)

SMITH, Dan (?) ?
£730 $1300   (2-May-92 IH.NY101/R) Uniformed man on horseback (43x36cm-17x14in) s. pen ink

SMITH, David (1906-1965) American
£1279 $2200   (20-Oct-91 HG.C83) Untitled composition (43x64cm-17x25in) s.d.2-13-59 W/C brush

SMITH, David (1906-1965) American-cont.
£8380 $15000   *(13-Nov-91 CH.NY228/R) Untitled (50x66cm-20x26in) st.verso enamel spray paint*

SMITH, Edward (?) British
£3200 $5440   *(22-Oct-91 S264/R) Coastal scene at Llanstephan, Carmarthenshire (61x84cm-24x33in) s.*

SMITH, Edwin D (1800-?) British
£420 $722   *(16-Oct-91 CSK33) Three boys with violin and cello (38x32cm-15x13in) s.d.1841 W/C htd white*

SMITH, Edwin J (20th C) British
£550 $979   *(1-Nov-91 PHE35) Children playing in rock pools (58x63cm-23x25in) s.d.1916 panel*

SMITH, Ernest Browning (1866-1951) American
£632 $1200   *(24-Jun-92 B.SF6409/R) California cove (51x42cm-20x17in) s.*
£686 $1200   *(31-Mar-92 MOR.P40 a) Landscape (41x51cm-16x20in) st.studio*

SMITH, Ernst (20th C) Swedish
£959 $1726   *(23-Nov-91 SO.S606/R) Sailingboat at sea (41x58cm-16x23in) s. panel (S.KR 10000)*

SMITH, Francis (20th C) ?
£2128 $3851   *(18-May-92 AT.P151) Le parterre (35x27cm-14x11in) s.d. panel (F.FR 21000)*
£2634 $4768   *(18-May-92 AT.P150) Rue au Portugal (41x33cm-16x13in) s. panel (F.FR 26000)*
£1317 $2384   *(18-May-92 AT.P35) Jardin au Portugal (23x31cm-9x12in) s. gouache (F.FR 13000)*
£1378 $2494   *(18-May-92 AT.P36/R) Une journee a la campagne (37x45cm-15x18in) s. gouache (F.FR 13600)*
£2163 $3698   *(22-Mar-92 LT.P96) La nativite (55x46cm-22x18in) s. gouache (F.FR 21000)*
£2357 $4242   *(2-Feb-92 ZZ.F162/R) Aux Deux Magots (34x26cm-13x10in) s. gouache (F.FR 23000)*

SMITH, Francis Hopkinson (1838-1915) American
£1064 $2000   *(18-Dec-91 SY.NY11/R) Picnic by a stream (64x46cm-25x18in) s.d.75 W/C gouache*
£1676 $3000   *(14-Nov-91 CE.NY221/R) Battery Park, New York City (34x62cm-13x24in) W/C chl gouache*
£2162 $4000   *(10-Jun-92 CE.NY181/R) Gleaners (33x59cm-13x23in) s. W/C gouache*
£2749 $4700   *(11-Mar-92 SY.NY53/R) Inn of William the Conqueror (37x65cm-15x26in) s. W/C gouache*
£3315 $6000   *(22-May-92 S.BM81/R) Blossoms by the wishing well (43x64cm-17x25in) s. W/C gouache chl graphite paperboard*
£3429 $6000   *(26-Sep-91 CH.NY48/R) Italian courtyard (37x63cm-15x25in) s.d. W/C gouache pencil paper on board*
£8772 $15000   *(12-Mar-92 CH.NY101/R) Summer morning, inn of William the Conqueror (59x91cm-23x36in) s. gouache chl paper on board*

SMITH, Frank Vining (1879-1967) American
£1215 $2200   *(22-May-92 S.BM133/R) South shore road, Cohasset view 1918 (61x71cm-24x28in) s.*
£1833 $3300   *(22-Nov-91 E.EDM660/R) Storming along (71x91cm-28x36in) s. masonite*
£1989 $3600   *(5-Dec-91 GRO.B520/R) Full sail (102x86cm-40x34in) s.*

SMITH, Frederick Carl (1868-1955) American
£632 $1200   *(24-Jun-92 B.SF6340/R) Field of Hollyhocks (46x61cm-18x24in) s.*

SMITH, George (1829-1901) British
£1300 $2184   *(26-Aug-91 S950/R) Feeding time (30x40cm-12x16in) s. canvas board*
£1600 $2688   *(26-Aug-91 S959/R) Loading a cart (30x40cm-12x16in) s. canvas board*
£3000 $5310   *(6-Nov-91 S128/R) The last scene in the gambler's house (51x76cm-20x30in) s.d.1871*
£3500 $5880   *(26-Aug-91 S946/R) Cattle at trough (69x92cm-27x36in) s.*
£3500 $6475   *(12-Jun-92 C249/R) A sketch for 'The Raffle' (22x35cm-9x14in) s.d.1868*
£3800 $6384   *(26-Aug-91 S945/R) Feeding the calves (76x96cm-30x38in) s.*
£4000 $6720   *(26-Aug-91 S944/R) Bringing in the calves (63x76cm-25x30in) s. board*
£8146 $14500   *(30-Oct-91 D.NY53/R) The old stone bridge (81x99cm-32x39in) s.d.1769*

SMITH, Gordon Appelby (1919-) Canadian
£1750 $3098   *(6-Nov-91 SY.T218) July sea (132x152cm-52x60in) s.d.1973 verso acrylic canvas (C.D 3500)*
£2439 $4415   *(2-Dec-91 R.T217/R) Nocturne (86x122cm-34x48in) s. (C.D 5000)*

SMITH, Grace Cossington (1892-1984) Australian
£1809 $3201   *(26-Apr-92 SY.ME443/R) After bush fire (24x33cm-9x13in) s.d.1953 board (A.D 4250)*
£2128 $3766   *(26-Apr-92 SY.ME309/R) Bay view pier (49x41cm-19x16in) s.d.1943 s.i.verso board (A.D 5000)*
£2128 $3766   *(26-Apr-92 SY.ME318) Ku-Ring-Gai Avenue, Turramurra (32x28cm-13x11in) s. board (A.D 5000)*
£3524 $6344   *(24-Nov-91 SY.S435/R) Wamberal Lake No. 1, 1927-28 (26x21cm-10x8in) s. board (A.D 8000)*

SMITH, Grace Cossington (1892-1984) Australian-cont.

£5111	$8740	(17-Mar-92 JRL.S192) Still life with tankard (30x23cm-12x9in) s.d.53 canvasboard (A.D 11500)
£7265	$12932	(27-Apr-92 J.M10/R) Artist's bedroom window (54x42cm-21x17in) s.d.46 board (A.D 17000)
£7981	$13329	(19-Aug-91 SY.ME199/R) Gum blossom (30x24cm-12x9in) s.d.1944 board (A.D 17000)
£8547	$15214	(28-Apr-92 CH.ME180/R) Nasturtiums (49x36cm-19x14in) s.d.44 s.i.verso board (A.D 20000)
£9000	$16020	(28-Nov-91 C49/R) Still life with leaves (53x43cm-21x17in) s.d.53 canvas on board
£14097	$25374	(24-Nov-91 SY.S342/R) Calf in landscape (37x48cm-15x19in) s. board (A.D 32000)
£641	$1141	(27-Apr-92 J.M591) Chestnut tree, Sussex 1949 (22x29cm-9x11in) s.i. crayon (A.D 1500)

SMITH, Graham (20th C) British

| £400 | $768 | (9-Jul-92 B152/R) Valentine's Brook, Grand National (37x55cm-15x22in) s.d.1949 W/C bodycol |

SMITH, Hassel (1915-) American

| £585 | $1000 | (9-Mar-92 B.LA799/R) Mouse Hole, Cornwall (91x87cm-36x34in) |

SMITH, Hely Augustus Morton (1862-1941) British

| £500 | $895 | (5-May-92 SWS491/R) Clipper at sea (74x100cm-29x39in) s. |

SMITH, Henry Pember (1854-1907) American

£1064	$2000	(18-Dec-91 SY.NY111/R) The time of sunset - River Zan (30x40cm-12x16in) s.
£1168	$2090	(14-Nov-91 GRO.B95/R) Landscape with lake and house (30x41cm-12x16in) s.
£1322	$2300	(15-Apr-92 SY.NY81/R) Guidecca canal (36x51cm-14x20in) s.
£2514	$4500	(14-Nov-91 CE.NY87/R) Cottage by forest clearing (48x74cm-19x29in) s.d.
£489	$850	(15-Apr-92 B.SF3348/R) Venetian canal scene (43x58cm-17x23in) s. W/C
£690	$1200	(15-Apr-92 SY.NY83/R) Venetian view (59x98cm-23x39in) s. W/C gouache board
£894	$1600	(14-Nov-91 CE.NY312) Back canal of Venice (25x35cm-10x14in) s. W/C paperboard

SMITH, J (?) ?

| £1477 | $2600 | (8-Apr-92 D.NY64) Figures along inland waterway (79x119cm-31x47in) |

SMITH, Jack Carrington (1908-) Australian

| £969 | $1744 | (24-Nov-91 SY.S228) Derwent from studio (39x54cm-15x21in) s.d.71 i.verso (A.D 2200) |

SMITH, Jack W (1874-1949) American

£1974	$3750	(23-Jun-92 MOR.P124) Lakes in San Gabriel Canyon (30x41cm-12x16in) s.
£3933	$7000	(26-Nov-91 MOR.P32) Seascape (61x71cm-24x28in) s.
£7865	$14000	(26-Nov-91 MOR.P82) Tide pools (51x61cm-20x24in) s.
£10169	$18000	(12-Feb-92 B.SF466/R) Rocks and surf (58x79cm-23x31in) s.

SMITH, James Burrell (?-1897) British

| £580 | $1056 | (10-Dec-91 AG212) Highlanders resting on path overlooking Argyllshire loch (54x111cm-21x44in) s.d.1861 indist.i.verso W/C |
| £1300 | $2184 | (26-Aug-91 S774/R) Sitting by a loch. Walking by a loch (23x54cm-9x21in) s.d.1861 W/C pair |

SMITH, Jeremy (1946-) Canadian

| £5936 | $10863 | (14-May-92 SY.T124/R) Young woman in doorway (173x79cm-68x31in) s. d.1982 verso egg tempera panel (C.D 13000) |

SMITH, Jesse Willcox (1863-1935) American

| £8146 | $14500 | (2-May-92 IH.NY91/R) Two young girls looking at their reflections (53x36cm-21x14in) s. chl W/C |

SMITH, John Brandon (19th C) British

£1400	$2492	(28-Apr-92 PH108) Old bridge on Dulas, South Wales (36x46cm-14x18in) s.d.1880
£1700	$2890	(22-Oct-91 SWS271/R) On Dulas, South Wales (36x49cm-14x19in) s.d.1893
£1850	$3312	(14-Jan-92 SWS135/R) Waterfall on the Dulas, South Wales (44x34cm-17x13in) s.

SMITH, John Guthrie Spence (1880-1951) British

| £1000 | $1680 | (26-Aug-91 S1006/R) Quayside - Etaples (51x60cm-20x24in) s. s.i.verso board |

SMITH, John Raphael (1752-1812) British

| £520 | $910 | (1-Apr-92 B39/R) Little girl holding orange (25x20cm-10x8in) pastel |

SMITH, John Thomas (attrib) (1766-1833) British

| £900 | $1719 | (13-Jul-92 PH46/R) High Ongar Church and parsonage (21x30cm-8x12in) i.verso W/C sold with another W/C |

SMITH, John Warwick (1749-1831) British

£660	$1122	(22-Oct-91 SWS45/R) Temple of Clitumnus (17x25cm-7x10in) s.verso W/C over pencil
£1000	$1790	(11-Nov-91 S541) Italian landscape with building by road (32x45cm-13x18in) s.verso W/C
£1150	$1990	(4-Sep-91 BT107/R) Manor house in extensive parkland (33x48cm-13x19in) s. W/C
£1320	$2521	(16-Jul-92 S103/R) Near Geneva on the banks of the Rhone (17x24cm-7x9in) s.d.1788 W/C over pencil
£1500	$2640	(7-Apr-92 C135/R) Rocky waterfall in Wales (31x44cm-12x17in) s.d.1785 pencil W/C
£2000	$3580	(14-Nov-91 S93/R) Pont Rhianellt near Llangollen (13x21cm-5x8in) i.verso W/C over pencil gum arabic
£2600	$4654	(14-Nov-91 S92/R) View of Holyhead, Anglesey (15x23cm-6x9in) W/C over pencil

SMITH, Joseph Lindon (1863-1950) American

£565	$1000	(25-Apr-92 YFA.M269/R) Flowers by pond (46x36cm-18x14in) s.
£1462	$2500	(13-Mar-92 S.BM211/R) Temple along the nile, view of Egyptian ruins (69x58cm-27x23in) s. canvasboard
£1580	$2750	(10-Sep-91 BG.M642/R) Trompe d'oeil of Egyptian relief (74x48cm-29x19in) s.

SMITH, Joshua (1905-) Australian

| £468 | $829 | (26-Apr-92 SY.ME46) Inlet and bridge (35x48cm-14x19in) s. board (A.D 1100) |

SMITH, Ken (?) ?

| £726 | $1293 | (27-Apr-92 J.M94) Haze (69x89cm-27x35in) s. board (A.D 1700) |

SMITH, Kiki (1954-) ?

| £1453 | $2600 | (9-May-92 CE.NY210/R) For Mr G (80x168cm-31x66in) ink silver paint dyed fabric |

SMITH, Kimber (1922-) American

| £787 | $1354 | (16-Oct-91 G.Z23/R) Composition (34x48cm-13x19in) mono. indian ink brush over oil chk (S.FR 2000) |

SMITH, Lance (1950-) British

| £550 | $974 | (23-Apr-92 B76) Catacomb (213x244cm-84x96in) s.i.d.1990verso |

SMITH, Leon Polk (1906-) American

£2571	$4500	(27-Feb-92 CE.NY151/R) Caddo (64x51cm-25x20in) s.d.1958 verso oil metallic paint
£4797	$8250	(12-Oct-91 SY.NY276/R) Constellation K (120x60cm-47x24in) s.d.1969 verso acrylic joined canvas
£9249	$16000	(3-Oct-91 SY.NY29/R) Correspondence (173x109cm-68x43in) s.i.d.1962verso
£669	$1150	(12-Oct-91 SY.NY244/R) Untitled (24x29cm-9x11in) s.d.45 W/C ink
£1117	$2000	(9-May-92 CE.NY362/R) Blue on black (65x49cm-26x19in) s.d.1960 paper collage

SMITH, Mathilde (1826-1882) Norwegian

| £2897 | $4983 | (7-Oct-91 B.O127/R) From Larvik (38x56cm-15x22in) s.d.1848 (N.KR 33000) |

SMITH, Miller (fl.1885-1920) British

| £800 | $1480 | (11-Jun-92 CSK46/R) At the kitchen door. An old cottage and garden (58x28cm-23x11in) s. pencil W/C htd.white pair |

SMITH, Pauline (1967-) British

| £550 | $1007 | (3-Feb-92 B5/R) Square blue sun (168x152cm-66x60in) |

SMITH, Reginald (19th C) British

| £630 | $1203 | (16-Jul-92 PHX369/R) Rocky coastal outcrop (102x76cm-40x30in) s. |

SMITH, Richard (1931-) British

£7000	$12040	(17-Oct-91 S70/R) Album (183x122cm-72x48in) s.d.62 verso
£650	$1131	(19-Sep-91 CSK257/R) Untitled (58x77cm-23x30in) s.d.72 paper collage
£1300	$2236	(17-Oct-91 S117/R) Blue drawing (89x151cm-35x59in) s.d.70 pastel collage
£1400	$2408	(17-Oct-91 S99/R) Mr 1970 (74x151cm-29x59in) s.d.70 pastel collage

SMITH, Robert (1792-1882) Irish

| £6500 | $11050 | (23-Oct-91 S332/R) The Qutb Mosque, Delhi, showing the screen and iron pillar (89x122cm-35x48in) |
| £11000 | $18700 | (23-Oct-91 S331/R) Qutb Mosque, Delhi, showing Qutb-Ub-Din screen and iron pillar (89x102cm-35x40in) s.d.1830 |

SMITH, Russell (1812-1896) American

£565	$1000	(9-Nov-91 W.W128/R) Two miles above Catawisa, Pennsylvania (18x28cm-7x11in) s.d.July 30th 1839 i.verso board
£669	$1150	(10-Oct-91 FA.PH825/R) Cabin on Wissahickin (30x46cm-12x18in) init. s.d.1838 verso
£3911	$7000	(14-Nov-91 CE.NY72/R) Lafayette College, Easton, Pennsylvania (46x69cm-18x27in)

SMITH, Sir Matthew (1879-1959) British
£3500	$6405	(5-Jun-92 C53/R) Coastal landscape (21x26cm-8x10in) s.d.1911 panel
£4000	$7640	(16-Jul-92 B106/R) Portrait of Meraud Guinness (29x25cm-11x10in)
£7500	$13500	(20-Nov-91 S2/R) St. Paul du Var (40x53cm-16x21in)
£12000	$21600	(20-Nov-91 S3/R) Draped nude (61x73cm-24x29in)
£20000	$36600	(13-May-92 S62/R) Tulips and daffodils (76x63cm-30x25in) init.
£22000	$40260	(13-May-92 S47/R) The Rowlandson jug (66x66cm-26x26in) init.
£32000	$57600	(20-Nov-91 S107/R) Tulips in bowl (55x65cm-22x26in)
£1200	*$2124*	*(5-Nov-91 PH153/R) Still life with fruit (49x37cm-19x15in) s. col.chks.*
£1550	*$2775*	*(14-Jan-92 PH97) Fruit in bowl (37x48cm-15x19in). W/C*
£2300	*$3933*	*(11-Mar-92 S65/R) Still life - fruit bowl and sculpted head (37x47cm-15x19in) s. col.chk*

SMITH, Stephen Catterson (attrib) (19/20th C) British
£1800	$3438	(15-Jul-92 S144/R) Portrait of a lady with flamingo (249x164cm-98x65in)

SMITH, Stephen Catterson (elder) (1806-1872) British
£1400	$2590	(12-Jun-92 TE612/R) Portrait of Mrs Penrose Fitzgerald (53x38cm-21x15in) s.d.1855 panel

SMITH, Sydney Ure (20th C) Australian
£430	*$821*	*(29-Jun-92 AAA.S198) Early vaucluse (24x34cm-9x13in) s. chl W/C (A.D 1100)*

SMITH, Thomas Noel see NOELSMITH, Thomas

SMITH, Treania (1901-1990) Australian
£562	$1011	(24-Nov-91 SY.S237/R) Mountain road (44x56cm-17x22in) s.d.1946 board (A.D 1275)
£573	$1031	(24-Nov-91 SY.S218/R) Kissing Point Road, Turramurra (21x28cm-8x11in) s. s.i.verso canvas on board (A.D 1300)
£881	$1586	(24-Nov-91 SY.S259/R) Richmond Bridge, Tasmania (23x28cm-9x11in) s.d.1938 canvasboard (A.D 2000)
£1498	$2696	(24-Nov-91 SY.S274/R) Church point (34x36cm-13x14in) s. canvas on board (A.D 3400)

SMITH, Victor see SPARRE, Victor

SMITH, Walter Granville (1870-1938) American
£1081	$2000	(10-Jun-92 CE.NY329) Fishing off coast (13x30cm-5x12in) s.
£2924	$5000	(12-Mar-92 CH.NY193/R) Skating by the mill (76x102cm-30x40in) s.d.1938
£3073	$5500	(6-May-92 B.P83/R) Taking walk - portrait of artist's wife (76x56cm-30x22in) s.

SMITH, Wilhelm (1867-1949) Swedish
£2500	$4425	(5-Nov-91 BA.S167/R) Ducks swimming in spring river landscape (65x50cm-26x20in) s. (S.KR 26500)

SMITH, William Collingwood (1815-1887) British
£1100	*$2035*	*(12-Jun-92 C2) Haddon Hall from the river (23x55cm-9x22in) s. pencil W/C*

SMITH, William H (fl.1863-1880) British
£552	$950	(20-Oct-91 HG.C48) Grape still life (36x30cm-14x12in) s.d.1878

SMITH, William Harding (1848-1922) British
£859	$1495	(21-Sep-91 SA.A1768/R) Still life of fruit (35x44cm-14x17in) s.indis.d.1870 board (DM 2500)
£420	*$701*	*(22-Aug-91 CSK66) A repast, Haddon Hall (43x61cm-17x24in) s. s.i.label backboard pencil W/C htd white*

SMITH, William St Thomas (1862-1926) Canadian
£365	*$665*	*(26-May-92 JOY.T228/R) Milking time at homestead (36x52cm-14x20in) s. W/C (C.D 800)*

SMITH, Xanthus (1838-1929) American
£537	$950	(10-Nov-91 LIT.L143) Study of fisherman (36x28cm-14x11in) mono.d.1916 s.i.d.verso
£857	$1500	(28-Sep-91 YFA.M221/R) Scene at Oban, coast of Scotland (41x56cm-16x22in) s.d.1919
£1197	$2250	(18-Dec-91 SY.NY20/R) The American Falls (20x30cm-8x12in) s.d.1879 canvas on masonite
£1429	$2500	(4-Apr-92 E.EDM339/R) Unknown American clipper ship (36x56cm-14x22in) s.
£3509	$6000	(12-Mar-92 CH.NY37/R) The Lizzie Driscoll at dock (39x59cm-15x23in) s.d.1878
£6077	$11000	(6-Dec-91 CH.NY40/R) Abandoned (51x77cm-20x30in) s.d.1880

SMITH-HALD, Bjorn (1883-?) Norwegian
£704	$1238	(8-Apr-92 GWP.O139) Moonlit landscape (45x64cm-18x25in) s. (N.KR 8000)
£833	$1550	(18-Jun-92 GWP.O94/R) Child asleep (70x60cm-28x24in) s. (N.KR 9500)
£8070	*$15011*	*(15-Jun-92 B.O147 a/R) Admiring look - flirt (72x60cm-28x24in) s. mixed media (N.KR 92000)*

SMITH-HALD, Frithjof (1846-1903) Norwegian
£674	$1159	(19-Oct-91 UA.U355) Breakers by the coast (26x35cm-10x14in) s. panel (S.KR 7100)

SMITH-HALD, Frithjof (1846-1903) Norwegian-cont.
£1620 $2819   (14-Sep-91 BU.O332) Landscape from Borrevannet (26x35cm-10x14in) s. panel
             (N.KR 18500)
£1860 $3385   (9-Dec-91 B.O107/R) Evening on the fjord (45x63cm-18x25in) s.
             (N.KR 21000)
£2000 $3620   (22-May-92 C45/R) Winter landscape with cottage (42x52cm-17x20in) s.
£3166 $5573   (7-Apr-92 UL.T231/R) Winter landscape (67x94cm-26x37in) (N.KR 36000)

SMITHER, Michael (1939-) New Zealander
£710 $1285   (4-Dec-91 DS.W52) Export butter (85x97cm-33x38in) init.d.77 (NZ.D 2300)
£2663 $4448   (21-Aug-91 DS.W101) Joseph - with four teeth (119x104cm-47x41in) s.
             (NZ.D 7750)
£2749 $4591   (21-Aug-91 DS.W77/R) War games (125x120cm-49x47in) init.d.78 (NZ.D 8000)

SMITHERS, Collier (fl.1892-1936) British
£500 $915   (6-Feb-92 PHF165) Portrait of young lady seated on grassy bank with
             Pekinese on lap (110x84cm-43x33in) s.
£9884 $17000   (17-Oct-91 SY.NY33/R) Angel of fortune (140x120cm-55x47in) s.d.1901

SMITHSON, Robert (1938-1973) American
£4469 $8000   *(14-Nov-91 SY.NY157/R) Asphalt spiral (31x38cm-12x15in) s.d.71 felt*
             marker pencil
£4469 $8000   *(14-Nov-91 SY.NY158/R) Granite crystal (48x61cm-19x24in) s.i.d.72 pencil*
£5500 $9515   *(26-Mar-92 S106/R) Madrone spiral (60x48cm-24x19in) s.d.1972 pencil*

SMITS, Jakob (1856-1928) Belgian
£2772 $4990   (20-Nov-91 CN.P216) L'enfant au beret (36x28cm-14x11in) init.
             (F.FR 27000)
£4975 $9104   (12-May-92 C.A299/R) The washerwoman (41x33cm-16x13in) panel
             (B.FR 300000)
£15013 $26422   (7-Apr-92 C.A219/R) The little knitter (40x30cm-16x12in) s. W/C
             (B.FR 900000)
£18079 $32000   (6-Nov-91 D.NY43/R) Peasant family in interior (65x71cm-26x28in) s.
£21240 $36321   (21-Mar-92 KV.L459/R) Woman sewing in an interior (69x84cm-27x33in) s.
             (B.FR 1250000)
£668 $1136   *(22-Oct-91 C.A295) Village scene (16x19cm-6x7in) s. dr. (B.FR 40000)*
£728 $1319   *(23-May-92 KV.L307) In the stall. The seamstress (19x24cm-7x9in) s. chk.*
             double-sided (B.FR 44000)

SMITS, Jan Gerard (1823-1910) Dutch
£772 $1350   (18-Feb-92 CH.AM15) View of the Groenburgwal, Amsterdam (55x85cm-22x33in)
             s. (D.FL 2500)
£1009 $1756   *(14-Apr-92 SY.AM229) In the Dunes of Scheveningen (26x44cm-10x17in)*
             s.d.1908 W/C (D.FL 3300)

SMOLDERS, Pol (20th C) Belgian
£1170 $1988   (22-Oct-91 C.A924/R) Girl with a doll (62x50cm-24x20in) s. (B.FR 70000)
£430 $779   *(23-May-92 KV.L310) Child in a coat (53x30cm-21x12in) s. W/C (B.FR 26000)*

SMOORENBERG, Dirk (1883-1960) Dutch
£606 $1097   (19-May-92 CH.AM15) Mountain landscape (18x27cm-7x11in) s.d.24 board
             (D.FL 2000)
£667 $1207   (21-May-92 SY.AM124) Landscape (36x43cm-14x17in) s. (D.FL 2200)
£741 $1348   (12-Dec-91 SY.AM23) Water lillies (53x41cm-21x16in) (D.FL 2400)
£802 $1460   (12-Dec-91 SY.AM88/R) Still life with anemones (58x71cm-23x28in) s.d.24
             (D.FL 2600)
£926 $1685   (12-Dec-91 SY.AM5/R) View of Loosdrechtse Plassen (43x65cm-17x26in) s.
             (D.FL 3000)
£1389 $2528   (12-Dec-91 SY.AM108/R) Water lillies (55x80cm-22x31in) s.d.23 (D.FL 4500)
£1667 $3017   (19-May-92 CH.AM101/R) Trees along a pond (46x73cm-18x29in) s.d.12
             (D.FL 5500)
£1852 $3241   (18-Feb-92 CH.AM95) Waterlillies (42x65cm-17x26in) s. (D.FL 6000)
£2273 $4114   (21-May-92 SY.AM20/R) Water lillies (54x73cm-21x29in) s. (D.FL 7500)
£4630 $8426   (12-Dec-91 SY.AM50/R) View of Lac Leman (65x90cm-26x35in) s.d.12
             (D.FL 15000)

SMOUKROVITCH, Piotr (1928-) Russian
£512 $922   (27-Jan-92 ARC.P176/R) Funerailles de Lenine (60x111cm-24x44in) s.verso
             (F.FR 5000)
£563 $1002   (25-Nov-91 ARC.P135) Travaux des champs (45x74cm-18x29in) s. (F.FR 5500)
£594 $1057   (25-Nov-91 ARC.P137/R) Veronika (38x59cm-15x23in) s. (F.FR 5800)
£676 $1202   (25-Nov-91 ARC.P136/R) Les nouveaux livres (35x55cm-14x22in) s.
             (F.FR 6600)
£1126 $2004   (25-Nov-91 ARC.P134/R) Les revisions (63x80cm-25x31in) s. (F.FR 11000)

SMOUKROVITCH, Vitold (1967-) Russian
£533 $959   (27-Jan-92 ARC.P170/R) Les trois barques (76x69cm-30x27in) s. (F.FR 5200)
£574 $1033   (27-Jan-92 ARC.P169/R) Sur le balcon (60x70cm-24x28in) s. (F.FR 5600)

SMOUT, Lucas (younger) (1671-1713) ?
£762 $1326   (13-Apr-92 AT.P70) Marche au poissons (39x51cm-15x20in) (F.FR 7500)

SMYTH, John Richard Coke (1808-1882) Canadian?
£400 $680   *(22-Oct-91 C36/R) Cape Diamond and Wolfe's Cove, Quebec (25x35cm-10x14in)*
             pencil W/C

SMYTH, William (1813-1878) Irish
£1900 $3230   *(23-Oct-91 S275/R) Illustrations to George Back's Narrative of Expedition of HMS Terror four s.i. two d. W/C over pencil 6 in 3 frames*

SMYTHE, Edward Robert (1810-1899) British
£546 $1000   (17-May-92 DU.E1054) Barn interior with ferrier at work (61x91cm-24x36in) s. board
£800 $1416   (6-Nov-91 CB126/R) Boy with dog and white pony resting on shoreline (33x51cm-13x20in)
£900 $1647   (3-Jun-92 S81/R) By the wicket gate (23x30cm-9x12in) init.
£950 $1739   (3-Jun-92 S75/R) A rustic family (30x26cm-12x10in) s.indis.d.
£1100 $2013   (3-Jun-92 S77/R) A gypsy camp (30x40cm-12x16in) s.indis.d.
£1300 $2405   (11-Jun-92 CSK102/R) Fisherfolk on the seashore with horses (50x76cm-20x30in) s.
£1400 $2562   (3-Jun-92 S76/R) The basket maker's camp (30x41cm-12x16in) s.
£2200 $3784   (4-Mar-92 S22/R) Cherry tree Woodbridge (30x41cm-12x16in) s.

SMYTHE, Emily R (fl.1850-1874) British
£597 $1063   (25-Nov-91 W.T1885) Good friends (30x46cm-12x18in) mono. (C.D 1200)

SMYTHE, H (19th C) ?
£4800 $8448   (8-Apr-92 S90/R) Landscape with Vale of Towy (70x90cm-28x35in)

SMYTHE, Lionel Percy (1839-1913) British
£2200 $3894   (6-Nov-91 S203/R) Weary (111x82cm-44x32in) s.d.1879 and 82 s.indis.i.stretcher
£524 $1000   *(16-Jul-92 SY.NY495/R) Buttercups and daisies (21x31cm-8x12in) s.d.1883 W/C gouache*
£600 $1026   *(13-Mar-92 C10) Farmyard at Chateau d'Honvault, Wimereux in the Pas de Calais (18x31cm-7x12in) s. i.verso pencil W/C*

SMYTHE, Thomas (1825-1906) British
£850 $1488   (25-Sep-91 CSK279) A Gypsy encampment (25x41cm-10x16in) s. canvas laid down on board
£2000 $3520   (10-Apr-92 K484/R) Resting companions (28x43cm-11x17in) s.
£2100 $3990   (24-Jun-92 PHI615/R) Couple in conversation at the garden gate (20x25cm-8x10in) s. sold with another painting pair
£2200 $3806   (24-Mar-92 PHC401) Two tethered donkeys (22x42cm-9x17in) s. pair
£2600 $4810   (12-Jun-92 C216/R) Outside the inn (24x38cm-9x15in) s. panel
£2800 $4816   (11-Oct-91 K514/R) Work horses by and in stable with domestic poultry, summer (28x43cm-11x17in) s.
£2800 $5320   (24-Jun-92 PHI612) Man with two horses pulling timber drug, believed to be near Ipswich (36x46cm-14x18in) s.
£3200 $6144   (28-Jul-92 SWS375/R) Gathering brushwood in the snow (35x62cm-14x24in) s. board
£3200 $5536   (25-Mar-92 PHI597/R) By Suffolk stream (29x39cm-11x15in) s.
£3800 $7220   (24-Jun-92 PHI619) Horsemen and other figures before inn in snow covered landscape (35x62cm-14x24in) s. board
£4000 $7080   (6-Nov-91 S13/R) Mending nets. Outside boat house (30x40cm-12x16in) s. pair
£4098 $7500   (5-Jun-92 SY.NY78/R) The midday rest (45x61cm-18x24in) s.
£4300 $7396   (11-Oct-91 K513/R) Horses being lead into stables after a days work, winter (28x43cm-11x17in) s.
£7000 $12810   (3-Jun-92 S78/R) At the cottage door (23x33cm-9x13in) s.
£7000 $13300   (24-Jun-92 PHI618/R) The Orwell from Woolverstone Park (51x75cm-20x30in) s.

SNAFFLES see PAYNE, Charles Johnson

SNAPE, Martin (fl.1874-1901) British
£520 $926   *(29-Nov-91 T196) Bridges over estuary with buildings, figures and swans (28x43cm-11x17in) s. W/C*
£530 $954   *(20-Nov-91 RB620) Entrance to Southampton Water from Hillhead (23x36cm-9x14in) s. W/C*

SNAPE, William H (fl.1885-1892) British
£880 $1690   (28-Jul-92 SWS335/R) Cottage interior (41x31cm-16x12in) s.d.1890 panel

SNAYERS, Peeter (1592-1666) Flemish
£5226 $9512   (12-Dec-91 L.K160/R) Battle szene with riders in mountainous landscape (99x134cm-39x53in) (DM 15000)

SNAYERS, Peeter (style) (1592-1666) Flemish
£850 $1479   (19-Sep-91 TL398) The skirmish (63x76cm-25x30in)
£2800 $5040   (21-Nov-91 CSK117/R) Cavalry skirmish (63x76cm-25x30in)
£4630 $8287   (14-Nov-91 CH.AM19/R) Cavalry skirmishes (45x81cm-18x32in) pair (D.FL 15000)

SNAYERS, Peeter and MOMPER, Joos de (17th C) Flemish
£5000 $8750   (3-Apr-92 C53/R) Ambush in gorge (55x85cm-22x33in) panel

SNELL, Henry Bayley (1858-1943) American
£20468 $35000   (12-Mar-92 CH.NY169/R) Low tide (86x112cm-34x44in) s.

SNELL, J H (1861-1935) British
£500 $940   (3-Jan-92 BW129) Drover with sheep (30x43cm-12x17in) s. WC

SNELL, James Herbert (1861-1935) British
£517 $921   (1-Dec-91 HOR.H18) Boat trip on the river (30x40cm-12x16in) s. (F.M 4000)
£1150 $2082   (19-May-92 SWS245/R) Carbis Bay (40x65cm-16x26in) s. s.i.verso

SNELLINCK, Cornelis (?-1669) Dutch
£5965 $10737   (22-Nov-91 SA.A1524/R) River landscape with figures (41x52cm-16x20in)
         panel (DM 17000)

SNELLING, Matthew (1621-1678) British
£3800 $6536   (4-Mar-92 C97/R) Gentleman, in black cloak and white shirt, long brown
         hair and moustache (5x?cm-2x?in) min. init.d.1651 verso card wood frame
         oval

SNELLMAN, Anita (1924-) Finnish
£1517 $2670   (12-Apr-92 HOR.H212) Apple blossom (99x50cm-39x20in) s.d.1950 (F.M 12000)

SNELLMAN, Eero (1890-1951) Finnish
£1011 $1780   (12-Apr-92 HOR.H213) From Paris (60x60cm-24x24in) s.d.1913 (F.M 8000)
£1294 $2303   (1-Dec-91 HOR.H213) Elk in winter landscape (60x76cm-24x30in) s.d.1944
         (F.M 10000)

SNOECK, Jacques (1881-1921) Dutch
£1463 $2663   (12-Dec-91 L.K678) Peasant woman with child in interior (48x42cm-19x17in)
         s. (DM 4200)

SNOEYERBOSCH, Cornelius Johannes (1891-1955) Dutch
£838 $1600   (3-Jul-92 S.W3079/R) Sunflowers (122x76cm-48x30in) s.
£838 $1600   (3-Jul-92 S.W3080) Irises (122x76cm-48x30in) s.

SNYDER, Peter Etril (20th C) Canadian
£439 $790   (18-Nov-91 HO.ED116/R) Sugar shanty buchart (46x61cm-18x24in) (C.D 900)

SNYDERS, Frans (1579-1657) Dutch
£55866 $100000   (16-Jan-92 CH.NY111/R) Table laden with game birds, glass vase flowers
         and basket fruit and two dogs (229x168cm-90x66in) s.i.
£5247 $9497   (5-Dec-91 SY.MO71/R) Nature morte (27x35cm-11x14in) pen brush wash
         (F.FR 51000)

SNYDERS, Frans (after) (1579-1657) Dutch
£800 $1424   (1-Nov-91 S382) Lion and mouse (47x68cm-19x27in)
£820 $1402   (16-Mar-92 LW1843/R) Figure, hound and cat around table of dead game and
         fruit (76x102cm-30x40in) s.i.
£1591 $2800   (8-Apr-92 D.NY66) Exotic birds in landscape (66x99cm-26x39in)

SNYDERS, Frans (attrib) (1579-1657) Dutch
£4800 $9216   (8-Jul-92 S152/R) Still life of game and songbirds (33x45cm-13x18in)
         panel
£50968 $94801   (20-Jun-92 CH.MO33/R) La chasse a l'ours (210x328cm-83x129in) painted
         with studio (F.FR 500000)

SNYDERS, Frans (circle) (1579-1657) Dutch
£11000 $21120   (10-Jul-92 C120/R) Boar hunt (203x348cm-80x137in)

SNYDERS, Frans (school) (1579-1657) Dutch
£5233 $9000   (9-Oct-91 CH.NY22/R) Turkey and cockerel fighting, with other fowl in
         landscape (148x199cm-58x78in)

SNYDERS, Frans (studio) (1579-1657) Dutch
£4564 $8032   (11-Apr-92 AT.P42/R) Nature morte de poissons (67x105cm-26x41in) panel
         (F.FR 45000)
£20992 $37366   (28-Nov-91 BU.S74/R) Fight between a lion and a wild boar
         (171x200cm-67x79in) (S.KR 220000)

SNYDERS, Frans (style) (1579-1657) Dutch
£1800 $3456   (10-Jul-92 C121/R) Boar hunt (114x136cm-45x54in) with indist.sig.
£8146 $14500   (22-Jan-92 SY.NY183/R) Still life with game, fowl, fruit and lobster
         (117x167cm-46x66in)
£8287 $15000   (22-May-92 SY.NY121/R) Dogs attacking bear (115x199cm-45x78in) bears
         sig.d.1610
£15000 $27300   (13-Dec-91 C185 a/R) Game stall with man holding boar's head
         (209x340cm-82x134in)
£55000 $100100   (13-Dec-91 C185/R) Fruit and vegetable stall with lady examining peach
         offered by old woman (212x330cm-83x130in)

SNYDERS, Frans and WILDENS, Jan (attrib) (17th C) Dutch/Flemish
£11500 $20125   (28-Feb-92 C155/R) Hounds attacking a wolf over a dead buck
         (171x25cm-67x10in)

SNYDERS, Frans and WILDENS, Jan (style) (17th C) Dutch/Flemish
£5500 $10560   (10-Jul-92 C119/R) Wolf and hounds fighting over dead buck
         (262x296cm-103x117in)

SNYERS, Pieter (1681-1752) Flemish
£4321	$7735	(12-Nov-91 SY.AM42/R) Elderly kitchen maid preparing vegetables and fruit by park fountain (87x61cm-34x24in) s. (D.FL 14000)
£8800	$16896	(8-Jul-92 S291/R) Still life of fruit and vegetables with rabbit in landscape (19x30cm-7x12in) copper
£13619	$24242	(28-Apr-92 F.R92/R) Sottobosco con fagiano (112x84cm-44x33in) s. cardboard (I.L 30000000)
£35000	$63700	(11-Dec-91 S35/R) Still life of flowers in glass vase, shells, bird of Paradise and snake in glass jar, on desk, with (33x40cm-13x16in) s. copper

SNYERS, Pieter (attrib) (1681-1752) Flemish
| £2208 | $4195 | (23-Jun-92 D.V111/R) Still life of fruit (45x57cm-18x22in) (A.S 45000) |

SNYERS, Pieter (circle) (1681-1752) Flemish
| £2778 | $4972 | (12-Nov-91 SY.AM40/R) Still life of herring and spring onions on draped ledge in landscape (56x76cm-22x30in) (D.FL 9000) |

SOBRADO, Pedro (?) Spanish
£829	$1559	(17-Dec-91 DUR.M111/R) Pareja de campesinos (65x54cm-26x21in) s. (S.P 150000)
£1013	$1843	(26-May-92 DUR.M74/R) De vuelta del trabajo (60x73cm-24x29in) s. (S.P 185000)
£1022	$1820	(21-Jan-92 DUR.M75/R) El anticuario (65x81cm-26x32in) s. (S.P 185000)
£1099	$1979	(19-Nov-91 DUR.M92/R) El Rastro (54x65cm-21x26in) s. (S.P 200000)
£1247	$2182	(18-Feb-92 DUR.M74/R) Contemplando las flores (54x65cm-21x26in) s. (S.P 225000)
£1662	$2875	(24-Mar-92 DUR.M491/R) El sillon rojo (65x81cm-26x32in) s. (S.P 300000)

SOBRINO (?) ?
| £752 | *$1278* | *(22-Oct-91 C.A925) Composition (100x64cm-39x25in) s.d.1969 mixed media (B.FR 45000)* |

SOCHTIG, Paul Werner (?) ?
| £853 | $1553 | (27-May-92 PH.DU179/R) Scene at the Ratinger Gate (49x68cm-19x27in) s. board (DM 2500) |

SOCKWELL, Cassael (20th C) ?
| £605 | $1071 | (7-Nov-91 AT.P67) Chevrons (89x93cm-35x37in) s.d.1968verso acrylic (F.FR 6000) |

SOCRATE, Carlo (1889-1967) Italian
| £4990 | $9131 | (12-May-92 F.R235/R) Dormiente (30x39cm-12x15in) s. (I.L 11000000) |

SOCRATE, Mario (20th C) Italian
| £1529 | $2722 | (29-Nov-91 F.F71/R) Ponte sul fiume (8x11cm-3x4in) s. panel (I.L 3300000) |

SODEN, John E (19th C) British
| £1200 | $2088 | (12-Sep-91 CSK203/R) The huntsman's story (30x41cm-12x16in) s. panel |

SODRING, Frederik (1809-1862) Danish
£632	$1137	(19-Nov-91 RAS.K301) Magefjeldet at Walderhaug (30x48cm-12x19in) s.i.d.1834 (D.KR 7000)
£2076	$3736	(19-Nov-91 RAS.K26 a/R) Shepherdess and sheep in rocky river landscape (55x80cm-22x31in) s.d.1831 (D.KR 23000)
£2439	$4439	(12-Dec-91 L.K680/R) Schloss Burresheim near Mayen (30x32cm-12x13in) s. (DM 7000)
£2439	$4439	(12-Dec-91 L.K679/R) View of monastery Maria Laach (28x37cm-11x15in) (DM 7000)

SOER, Chris (1882-1961) Dutch
| £586 | $1026 | (18-Feb-92 CH.AM64 a/R) River landscape with peasant in rowing boat moored along field (41x60cm-16x24in) s. (D.FL 1900) |
| £854 | $1588 | (16-Jun-92 VN.R284/R) Shipping by a tower (69x59cm-27x23in) s. (D.FL 2800) |

SOEST, Gerard van (attrib) (c.1637-1681) British
| £1279 | $2200 | (9-Oct-91 CH.NY99/R) Portrait of gentleman, wearing black costume with lace shirt (76x63cm-30x25in) |

SOEST, Louis W van (1867-1948) Dutch
| £486 | $846 | (17-Sep-91 CH.AM673) Winter landscape with peasant woman on stone bridge (16x20cm-6x8in) s. panel (D.FL 1600) |
| £729 | $1269 | (17-Sep-91 CH.AM407) A brook in a forest in winter (65x60cm-26x24in) s.indist.d.1910 (D.FL 2400) |

SOEST, Pierre Gerardus Cornelis van (1930-) Dutch
| £1394 | $2523 | (21-May-92 SY.AM306/R) Untitled (116x97cm-46x38in) s.d.64 acrylic (D.FL 4600) |

SOEST, Pieter Cornelisz van (attrib) (17th C) Dutch
| £3395 | $6077 | (12-Nov-91 SY.AM14/R) Naval battle (48x94cm-19x37in) panel (D.FL 11000) |

SOFFICI, Ardengo (1879-1964) Italian
£13713 $26054   (23-Jun-92 F.M173/R) Paesaggio di Poggio a Caiano (50x35cm-20x14in)
s.d.1947 s.i.verso paper on canvas (I.L 30000000)

SOGLOW, Otto (1900-1975) ?
£393 $700   (2-Nov-91 IH.NY143/R) Little King finds note in bottle, Louie wants to
paint mountains (69x51cm-27x20in) s.i. pen

SOHL, Will (1906-1969) German
£418 $761   (14-Dec-91 BOD.P754) Beach scene (44x64cm-17x25in) s.d.1958 indian ink
dr. (DM 1200)

SOHLBERG, Harald (1869-1935) Norwegian
£21071 $37507   (29-Oct-91 UL.T220/R) Coastal landscape, Naersnesbukta 1930
(40x60cm-16x24in) (N.KR 240000)
£1320 $2218   (27-Aug-91 RAS.K678) Jonasgaarden, Roros, Norway (25x31cm-10x12in)
init.i.d.29 pastel (D.KR 15000)

SOHN, Carl Ferdinand (1805-1867) German
£2439 $4439   (12-Dec-91 L.K681/R) The two Leonoras in Southern landscape, after
Goethe's Tasso (42x33cm-17x13in) (DM 7000)

SOHN, Hermann (1895-1971) German
£515 $897   (17-Sep-91 FN.S2081) Nude pair beneath trees on shore with outlines of
town beyond (66x85cm-26x33in) s.d.1922 (DM 1500)

SOIRON, Jean Francois (school) (1756-1813) French
£400 $680   (22-Oct-91 CSK7/R) Lady, to right, in low-cut dress with ribbon and
necklace (6cm-2ins circular) min. enamel fitted red leather case
circular

SOISALO, Juha (1941-) Finnish
£1423 $2533   (1-Dec-91 HOR.H214) In the bath (134x118cm-53x46in) s.d.1989 (F.M 11000)

SOKOLOFF, Ivan Ivanovitch (1823-1918) Russian
£471 $810   (13-Oct-91 REM.W25) Autumn (32x47cm-13x19in) s. tempera (P.Z 9000000)

SOKOLOV, Nikolai (1903-) Russian
£676 $1184   (30-Mar-92 ZZ.F77) Flamenco (110x80cm-43x31in) s. (F.FR 6500)
£691 $1202   (13-Apr-92 ARC.P168/R) A Paris (25x34cm-10x13in) s. (F.FR 6800)
£765 $1422   (17-Jun-92 ARC.P93/R) A Paris (18x28cm-7x11in) s. board (F.FR 7500)
£861 $1559   (20-May-92 ARC.P114/R) Vieille rue à Riga (43x31cm-17x12in) s. board
(F.FR 8500)
£861 $1559   (20-May-92 ARC.P117) Vieux quartier de Rome (35x25cm-14x10in) s. board
(F.FR 8500)
£1013 $1834   (20-May-92 ARC.P115/R) Vieille cour a Moscou (25x30cm-10x12in) s. isorel
(F.FR 10000)
£1169 $2034   (13-Apr-92 ARC.P167/R) A Prague (35x49cm-14x19in) s. (F.FR 11500)
£1677 $2918   (13-Apr-92 ARC.P166/R) A Venise (25x34cm-10x13in) s. board (F.FR 16500)
£1874 $3393   (20-May-92 ARC.P113/R) Petite rue en Italie (35x25cm-14x10in) s. board
(F.FR 18500)

SOKOLOV, Vassili (1915-) Russian
£504 $882   (24-Sep-91 ARC.P55/R) Plage en Crimee (98x78cm-39x31in) s.d.49
(F.FR 5000)
£520 $911   (5-Apr-92 ARC.P84/R) Bateau sur la greve (65x79cm-26x31in) s. (F.FR 5000)
£716 $1275   (25-Nov-91 ARC.P177) Un secret de fillettes (100x90cm-39x35in) s.
(F.FR 7000)
£720 $1303   (6-Dec-91 ARC.P95/R) La plage de Gourzouff (50x70cm-20x28in) s. board
(F.FR 7000)
£772 $1397   (6-Dec-91 ARC.P94/R) Jeune reveuse (48x33cm-19x13in) s. (F.FR 7500)
£798 $1421   (25-Nov-91 ARC.P174/R) La veranda (80x60cm-31x24in) s. (F.FR 7800)
£819 $1458   (25-Nov-91 ARC.P173/R) Le printemps (109x89cm-43x35in) s. (F.FR 8000)
£972 $1731   (25-Nov-91 ARC.P176/R) La lecture (48x33cm-19x13in) s. board (F.FR 9500)
£1029 $1862   (6-Dec-91 ARC.P98) Devant le magasin. Village de Crimee s. pair
(F.FR 10000)
£1873 $3278   (5-Apr-92 ARC.P83/R) Le parc de Pouchkine (136x90cm-54x35in) s.d.56
(F.FR 18000)

SOKOLOVA, Anastassia (1967-) Russian
£514 $931   (6-Dec-91 ARC.P179) Les vases de Chine (50x50cm-20x20in) s. (F.FR 5000)
£561 $1043   (17-Jun-92 ARC.P87/R) Au petit dejeuner (60x60cm-24x24in) s. (F.FR 5500)
£566 $1024   (6-Dec-91 ARC.P182/R) Bouquet d'automne (81x65cm-32x26in) s. (F.FR 5500)
£589 $1026   (13-Apr-92 ARC.P33/R) La Traviata (60x60cm-24x24in) s. (F.FR 5800)
£638 $1155   (6-Dec-91 ARC.P185) Bouquet dans un verre rose (73x60cm-29x24in) s.
(F.FR 6200)
£700 $1266   (6-Dec-91 ARC.P183 a/R) Un reve (54x63cm-21x25in) s. (F.FR 6800)
£716 $1275   (25-Nov-91 ARC.P41 b/R) Au salon (61x46cm-24x18in) s. (F.FR 7000)
£760 $1375   (20-May-92 ARC.P95/R) Jeune fille au salon (73x60cm-29x24in) s.
(F.FR 7500)
£813 $1415   (13-Apr-92 ARC.P28/R) Le jardin du Luxembourg (24x34cm-9x13in) s. board
(F.FR 8000)
£823 $1490   (6-Dec-91 ARC.P184/R) La toilette (61x50cm-24x20in) s. (F.FR 8000)
£864 $1503   (13-Apr-92 ARC.P29/R) Un coin du salon (65x50cm-26x20in) s. (F.FR 8500)
£915 $1591   (13-Apr-92 ARC.P31/R) Ma soeur Ania (55x38cm-22x15in) s. (F.FR 9000)

SOKOLOVA, Anastassia (1967-) Russian-cont.

£957	$1732	(6-Dec-91 ARC.P180/R) La salle a manger (74x54cm-29x21in) s. (F.FR 9300)
£968	$1801	(17-Jun-92 ARC.P89/R) Nu pres du paravent (81x65cm-32x26in) s. (F.FR 9500)
£1114	$2017	(20-May-92 ARC.P96/R) L'attente (65x54cm-26x21in) s. (F.FR 11000)
£1118	$1945	(13-Apr-92 ARC.P32/R) Nature morte pres du psyche (60x73cm-24x29in) s. (F.FR 11000)
£1376	$2560	(17-Jun-92 ARC.P86/R) Nu (54x64cm-21x25in) s. (F.FR 13500)
£1440	$2607	(6-Dec-91 ARC.P181/R) Les ballons (46x55cm-18x22in) s. (F.FR 14000)
£1529	$2844	(17-Jun-92 ARC.P85/R) La nappe a rayures (81x65cm-32x26in) s. (F.FR 15000)
£1543	$2793	(6-Dec-91 ARC.P176/R) La coquette (61x46cm-24x18in) s. (F.FR 15000)
£1595	$2886	(6-Dec-91 ARC.P177) Le petit dejeuner (55x46cm-22x18in) s. (F.FR 15500)
£1626	$2829	(13-Apr-92 ARC.P30/R) Pres de la cheminee (60x73cm-24x29in) s. (F.FR 16000)
£1626	$2829	(13-Apr-92 ARC.P27/R) Le cafe du soir (73x60cm-29x24in) s. (F.FR 16000)
£1631	$3034	(17-Jun-92 ARC.P84/R) Dans le boudoir (64x54cm-25x21in) s. (F.FR 16000)
£1842	$3279	(25-Nov-91 ARC.P41 a/R) Apres-midi d'ete (65x81cm-26x32in) s. (F.FR 18000)
£2077	$3759	(20-May-92 ARC.P98/R) Composition orange (81x42cm-32x17in) s. (F.FR 20500)
£2229	$4034	(20-May-92 ARC.P99/R) Primadonna (100x45cm-39x18in) s. (F.FR 22000)
£2330	$4218	(20-May-92 ARC.P97/R) La couture (61x46cm-24x18in) s. (F.FR 23000)
£2846	$4951	(13-Apr-92 ARC.P26/R) Nature morte au vase de Chine (92x65cm-36x26in) s. (F.FR 28000)
£3040	$5502	(20-May-92 ARC.P94/R) Les fleurs du jardin (91x56cm-36x22in) s. (F.FR 30000)

SOKOLOVA, Elena Ilinichna (1919-) Russian

| £659 | $1200 | (27-May-92 GL.P38/R) La tasse de the (69x70cm-27x28in) s. (F.FR 6500) |

SOLA, Ignacio (20th C) Argentinian

| £1124 | $2000 | (1-Nov-91 PO.BA73) Turf (55x70cm-22x28in) s.d.81 |

SOLANA, Jose Gutierrez (1885-1945) Spanish

£68157	$126772	(16-Jun-92 EP.M33/R) Un mascaron (68x53cm-27x21in) s. (S.P 12500000)
£69233	$119773	(24-Mar-92 EP.M16/R) Bodegon de la coliflor (63x73cm-25x29in) s. (S.P 12500000)
£5814	*$10465*	*(28-Jan-92 EP.M47/R) Mascara, Cocinera (45x28cm-18x11in) s. pencil (S.P 1050000)*

SOLAND, Gottlieb (1928-) ?

| £627 | $1123 | (15-Nov-91 GK.Z5768) Untitled (120x130cm-47x51in) s.d.1977verso (S.FR 1600) |

SOLARI, Achille (1835-?) Italian

| £2600 | $4602 | (14-Feb-92 C119/R) Capril from the Amalfitan Coast. Bay of Naples from Posillipo (26x40cm-10x16in) one s. pair |

SOLARI, Luis A (20th C) Uruguayan

£663	$1180	(30-Apr-92 GOM.M61) Descubrimiento de America (40x45cm-16x18in) s. oil acrylic board
£1180	$2100	(28-Oct-91 GC.M29) Hombre del Mono Rojo (67x55cm-26x22in) s.d.63 board
£2431	$4400	(2-Dec-91 GC.M69) Figuras animales (72x92cm-28x36in) s. fibre
£607	*$1080*	*(30-Apr-92 GOM.M60) Tres Mascarones (28x37cm-11x15in) s. mixed media*

SOLARIO, Andrea (circle) (1460-1522) Italian

| £5557 | $9614 | (25-Mar-92 CH.R66/R) La testa di San Giovanni Battista (38x48cm-15x19in) panel (I.L 12000000) |

SOLBRIG, H (19th C) Austrian

| £615 | $1100 | (16-Nov-91 WOL.C494) The last beams (30x46cm-12x18in) s. panel |

SOLDAN-BROFELDT, Venny (1863-1945) Finnish

| £885 | $1558 | (12-Apr-92 HOR.H215) View of the field (21x48cm-8x19in) s.d.1892 (F.M 7000) |
| £2717 | $4836 | (1-Dec-91 HOR.H215) On the sandy beach (37x46cm-15x18in) s.d.1929 (F.M 21000) |

SOLDATI, Atanasio (1896-1953) Italian

£2317	$4124	(27-Nov-91 F.M272/R) L'angelo azzurro (19x12cm-7x5in) s. tempera (I.L 5000000)
£8685	$16501	(23-Jun-92 F.M155/R) Composizione (32x23cm-13x9in) s.d.1934 tempera cardboard (I.L 19000000)
£35870	$64208	(14-Nov-91 F.M80/R) Composizione con pesce (54x73cm-21x29in) s. (I.L 78000000)
£2085	*$3712*	*(26-Nov-91 SY.MI55/R) Composizione (19x9cm-7x4in) mono. gouache paper on canvas (I.L 4500000)*

SOLDENHOFF, Alexander Leo (1882-1951) Swiss

£657	$1176	(6-May-92 GD.B1213/R) Wurmer Schnee im Linthal (70x60cm-28x24in) s. st.studio s.i.d.1919verso (S.FR 1800)
£926	$1676	(19-May-92 GF.L2608/R) Girl on the beach, evening (70x120cm-28x47in) s. s.i.d.1942verso (S.FR 2500)
£1481	$2681	(19-May-92 GF.L2607/R) Female half nude (80x66cm-31x26in) s. (S.FR 4000)

SOLDENHOFF, Alexander Leo (1882-1951) Swiss-cont.
£1667	$3017	(19-May-92 GF.L2609/R) The washerwomen (95x75cm-37x30in) s. s.i.d.1940verso (S.FR 4500)
£2980	$5067	(23-Oct-91 GD.B706/R) Girl sleeping (70x120cm-28x47in) s. i.d.1925verso (S.FR 7600)
£3711	$6568	(5-Nov-91 GF.L2440/R) Three bathing women (200x170cm-79x67in) s.d.1927 (S.FR 9500)

SOLDI, Andrea (1703-1771) Italian
| £6000 | $10800 | (19-Nov-91 PH23/R) Portrait of gentleman standing wearing gold embroidered waistcoat (127x103cm-50x41in) |

SOLDI, Andrea (circle) (1703-1771) Italian
| £7200 | $12888 | (15-Nov-91 C16/R) Portrait of Edmund Peers, in braided coat, resting hand on stone wall (127x103cm-50x41in) |
| £7500 | $13425 | (15-Nov-91 C17/R) Portrait of Newsham Peers, in uniform, battle beyond (127x103cm-50x41in) |

SOLDI, Raul (1905-) Argentinian
£879	$1600	(11-Dec-91 RO.BA440) Paisaje (17x23cm-7x9in) s.
£2688	$5000	(16-Jun-92 RO.BA6) Cabeza (30x24cm-12x9in)
£4213	$7500	(1-Nov-91 RO.BA64) Quinto junto al rio (46x56cm-18x22in) s.d.48
£4271	$8200	(4-Aug-92 V.BA103/R) La volanta (25x34cm-10x13in)
£6283	$12000	(30-Jun-92 PO.BA26) Figuras (51x69cm-20x27in) s. hardboard
£6742	$12000	(1-Nov-91 PO.BA63) Paisaje con coche (46x55cm-18x22in) s.d.57
£6977	$12000	(9-Oct-91 RO.BA28/R) El Nino de la Silla (65x55cm-26x22in) s.
£7865	$14000	(28-Apr-92 PO.BA39) Mujer peinandose (96x66cm-38x26in) s.
£8621	$15000	(19-Sep-91 V.BA97/R) Paisaje urbano (45x60cm-18x24in) d.1938
£10215	$19000	(16-Jun-92 RO.BA43) La pareja (46x30cm-18x12in)
£13372	$23000	(9-Oct-91 RO.BA29/R) Figura (87x60cm-34x24in) s.d.50
£20349	$35000	(9-Oct-91 RO.BA27/R) Labor cotidiana (80x60cm-31x24in) s.d.45 tempera
£25843	$46000	(1-Nov-91 PO.BA62) Planchadoras (93x76cm-37x30in) s.d.49-50
£10440	*$19000*	*(11-Dec-91 RO.BA25/R) Nina Miranda (156x108cm-61x43in) s. mixed media*

SOLE JORBA, Vicenc (1904-1949) Spanish
| £10506 | $19751 | (17-Dec-91 BRO.B387/R) Mercado de ganado (59x78cm-23x31in) s.d.33 (S.P 1900000) |

SOLE, Giovan Gioseffo dal (1654-1719) Italian
£2100	$3675	(31-Mar-92 PH47/R) St. Cecilia (26x22cm-10x9in) copper oval
£9000	$16020	(1-Nov-91 C27/R) Personification of visual arts appearing to Pope (25x35cm-10x14in) paper on canvas
£38000	$72960	(8-Jul-92 S10/R) Diana and Endymion (67x98cm-26x39in)

SOLE, Giovan Gioseffo dal (attrib) (1645-1719) Italian
| £1987 | $3398 | (18-Mar-92 D.V241/R) Madonna with Child sleeping (17cm-7ins circular) copper (A.S 40000) |

SOLE, Stelio (1932-) Canadian
| £2533 | $4585 | (24-May-92 AT.P36) Porta dorata confinestra No.2 (140x78cm-55x31in) s. oil pigments canvas 22 carat gold (F.FR 25000) |

SOLENGHI, Giuseppe (1879-1944) Italian
£1116	$2019	(3-Dec-91 SY.MI76) Milano sotto la neve (29x38cm-11x15in) s. panel (I.L 2400000)
£1162	$2103	(3-Dec-91 SY.MI75/R) Milano, veduta dell'Arco della Pace (48x37cm-19x15in) s. panel (I.L 2500000)
£1512	$2677	(7-Nov-91 F.M78) La messa di mezzanotte (30x50cm-12x20in) s. i.verso panel (I.L 3300000)

SOLER, Antonio (19th C) ?
| £3315 | $6000 | (19-May-92 SY.NY78/R) Portrait of Juan Jose Flores, First President of Ecuador (104x74cm-41x29in) s.i.d.1835 |

SOLER, Rigoberto (1896-1968) Spanish
| £2629 | $4495 | (17-Mar-92 FER.M140/R) Bodegon de peces y caracola (90x75cm-35x30in) s.d.1952 (S.P 475000) |

SOLIMENA (circle) (17/18th C) Italian
| £1546 | $2675 | (27-Mar-92 CD.P4/R) Marie Madeleine repentante (80x68cm-31x27in) (F.FR 15000) |

SOLIMENA, Francesco (1657-1747) Italian
£1543	$2793	(5-Dec-91 SY.MO197/R) Portrait d'homme (19x13cm-7x5in) (F.FR 15000)
£6000	$10920	(10-Dec-91 PH45/R) Saint Paul (61x47cm-24x19in)
£7500	$13650	(10-Dec-91 PH75/R) Saint John of Damascus (36x31cm-14x12in)
£8287	$15000	(22-May-92 SY.NY269/R) Vision of Saint Francis (97x98cm-38x39in) bears sig.
£37037	$67037	(5-Dec-91 SY.MO156/R) Le festin d'Herode (75x100cm-30x39in) panel (F.FR 360000)

SOLIMENA, Francesco (attrib) (1657-1747) Italian
| £1615 | $2777 | (16-Oct-91 AT.P36/R) Noli me tangere (70x52cm-28x20in) (F.FR 16000) |
| £7437 | $13460 | (4-Dec-91 CH.R58/R) Ritratto del cardinale Althann con beretta e con lettera nella mano (95x75cm-37x30in) i. (I.L 16000000) |

SOLIMENA, Francesco (attrib) (1657-1747) Italian-cont.
£1412 $2527   *(12-Nov-91 GF.L5140) Ceiling design with saints ochre two sold with another drawing (S.FR 3600)*

SOLIMENA, Francesco (circle) (1657-1747) Italian
£1094 $2002   (12-May-92 SY.AM119) Christ as man of sorrows (57x45cm-22x18in) canvas on board (D.FL 3600)
£2263 $4097   (5-Dec-91 SY.MO240/R) Allegorie de la force (50x62cm-20x24in) (F.FR 22000)
£3086 $5586   (5-Dec-91 SY.MO359/R) Scene de l'histoire ancienne (66x47cm-26x19in) (F.FR 30000)
£4200 $7476   (1-Nov-91 C35/R) Noli me Tangere (63x49cm-25x19in)
£1900 $3648   *(7-Jul-92 C36/R) Cardinal supervising the construction of facade (17x37cm-7x15in) chk pen wash two joined sheets*

SOLIMENA, Francesco (school) (1657-1747) Italian
£3405 $6061   (28-Apr-92 F.R24/R) Assunzione della Vergine (130x103cm-51x41in) (I.L 7500000)

SOLIMENA, Francesco (studio) (17/18th C) Italian
£2037 $3707   (11-Dec-91 LD.P39/R) Allegorie de l'Afrique (82x69cm-32x27in) arched (F.FR 20000)
£3631 $6500   (13-Nov-91 B.SF2097/R) Christ and the woman taken in adultery (103x155cm-41x61in)
£4800 $8400   (1-Apr-92 S213/R) Child presented to Madonna and Child, with male saint in attendance (82x68cm-32x27in)
£8000 $14000   (31-Mar-92 PH18/R) Maurus and Placidus received by St. Benedict (74x154cm-29x61in)

SOLIMENA, Francesco (style) (1657-1747) Italian
£1461 $2600   (22-Jan-92 SY.NY88/R) Madonna and Child (30x23cm-12x9in)

SOLIMENA, Francesco and BRUEGHEL, Abraham (17th C) Italian/Flemish
£40000 $72800   (11-Dec-91 S32/R) Girl picking grapes from trellis, still life flowers in urn and fruit, in landscape setting (76x101cm-30x40in)

SOLIS, Virgil (circle) (16th C) German
£893 $1573   *(11-Apr-92 AW.H303/R) Diana and attendants setting out for the hunt (20x21cm-8x8in) W/C pen (DM 2600)*

SOLLMANN, Paul (1886-) German
£408 $731   *(5-May-92 ZEL.L1166/R) View of Rothenburg ob der Tauber (53x66cm-21x26in) s.i. W/C (DM 1200)*

SOLOMON, Abraham (1824-1862) British
£2400 $4512   (19-Dec-91 C173/R) Frosty evening (20x15cm-8x6in) init. board

SOLOMON, Lance Vaiben (1913-1989) Australian
£504 $962   (21-Jul-92 JRL.S40) Fisherman Wallis Lake (24x28cm-9x11in) s. board (A.D 1300)
£598 $1065   (27-Apr-92 J.M777) Morning walk (32x36cm-13x14in) s.d.1938 canvas on board (A.D 1400)
£889 $1520   (17-Mar-92 JRL.S74) Rural scene (20x29cm-8x11in) s. board (A.D 2000)
£1111 $1978   (28-Apr-92 CH.ME162/R) Silver and grey (60x50cm-24x20in) s. i.verso board (A.D 2600)
£1135 $1987   (30-Mar-92 AAA.S99) Cattle grazing near Creek (46x40cm-18x16in) s. board (A.D 2600)
£1198 $2085   (16-Sep-91 CH.ME49) Landscape, 1962 (43x39cm-17x15in) s. board (A.D 2600)

SOLOMON, Simeon (1840-1905) British
£900 $1548   *(4-Mar-92 S322/R) Love and Hate (30x41cm-12x16in) red chk*
£1000 $1850   *(12-Jun-92 C81) Mystical head in profile (25x17cm-10x7in) indis.s.d.189-pencil W/C*
£2200 $4026   *(14-May-92 CSK60) Delphike (30x18cm-12x7in) init.i.d.1890 red chk*
£2800 $5180   *(12-Jun-92 C77/R) Quia Multum Amavit (35x40cm-14x16in) mono.d.1892 red chk.*

SOLTAU, Pauline (1833-1902) German
£4396 $8000   (28-May-92 SY.NY244/R) Mother's favourite (116x89cm-46x35in) s.i.

SOMAVILLA, Godofredo (attrib) (?) ?
£615 $1100   (11-Nov-91 GC.M48/R) Pintando a la modelo (66x37cm-26x15in) board

SOMER, Paul van (attrib) (16/17th C) Flemish/Dutch
£3800 $6688   (8-Apr-92 S11/R) Portrait of Sir Thomas Peyton (105x89cm-41x35in)

SOMER, Paul van (style) (16/17th C) Flemish/Dutch
£1200 $2052   (12-Mar-92 CSK91/R) Portrait of gentleman in white ruff and gold embroidered doublet (58x46cm-23x18in) panel

SOMERSCALES, Thomas (1842-1927) British
£5000 $9100   (28-May-92 C18/R) Lowering tender (46x61cm-18x24in)
£5500 $9350   (22-Oct-91 C4 a) Valle del Rio Renegado, Cerca de los Banos de Chillan (36x56cm-14x22in) s.d.92 i.verso

SOMERSCALES, Thomas (1842-1927) British-cont.
£17000 $28900   (22-Oct-91 C4/R) Ponte sobre el Rio Aconagua, Chile (46x65cm-18x26in)
                   s.d.1911
£22000 $37400   (22-Oct-91 C3/R) Rio Aconagua, Chile (58x91cm-23x36in) s.d.1911

SOMERVILLE, Edith Oenone (1858-1949) British
£650 $1118   (16-Oct-91 ZZ.B56) Ross Bay (22x28cm-9x11in) s. board
£650 $1131   (18-Sep-91 CG124/R) Gorse bushes by river (22x27cm-9x11in) s. panel

SOMM, Henry (1844-1907) French
£457 $796   (19-Apr-92 ZZ.F9/R) Jeune femme allongee (30x49cm-12x19in) s. W/C ink
                   wash (F.FR 4500)
£554 $986   (28-Oct-91 GL.P100) Elegante au bord de la riviere (23x15cm-9x6in) s. pen
                   W/C (F.FR 5500)
£828 $1466   (24-Apr-92 CN.P145) A l'atelier (20x27cm-8x11in) s. W/C (F.FR 8200)

SOMMAR, Hindric (after) (1702-1790) Swedish
£4415 $7990   (3-Dec-91 AB.S4663/R) Portrait of Lovisa Ulrika (80x65cm-31x26in) sold
                   with portrait of Adolf F by unknown artist (S.KR 46000)

SOMMAVILLA, E (19th C) Italian
£1115 $2029   (11-Dec-91 N.M595/R) Still life of flowers in vase, fruit in basket and
                   wine glass with bottle (60x100cm-24x39in) s. (DM 3200)

SOMME, Jacob (1862-1940) Norwegian
£570 $1061   (15-Jun-92 B.O158/R) View of Stavanger (26x34cm-10x13in) s. (N.KR 6500)
£1240 $2257   (9-Dec-91 B.O116/R) Winter in Old Stavanger (31x43cm-12x17in) s.d.1904
                   (N.KR 14000)

SOMMER, O (?) ?
£524 $897   (19-Mar-92 N.M2841/R) Female half nude by lake shore (84x50cm-33x20in) s.
                   (DM 1500)
£862 $1526   (6-Nov-91 N.M1148/R) Female nude by lake shore (84x50cm-33x20in) s.
                   (DM 2500)

SOMMER, William (19/20th C) American
£395 $750   (26-Jun-92 WOL.C112) Figural composition (25x33cm-10x13in) s. W/C ink

SOMMERS, Otto (19th C) American
£2234 $3887   (18-Sep-91 N.M708/R) Mountain valley with river and cows on wooden bridge
                   (73x102cm-29x40in) s.i.d.1874 (DM 6500)
£8791 $16000   (28-May-92 CH.NY22/R) View of Conway, New Hampshire (79x117cm-31x46in) s.

SOMOV, Konstantin (1869-1939) Russian
£800 $1424   (28-Nov-91 S475) Nude with roses (19x16cm-7x6in) s. pencil htd ink oval

SOMVILLE, Roger (1923-) Belgian
£4790 $8671   (7-Dec-91 KV.L441/R) Un peintre (162x130cm-64x51in) s.d.1974
                   (B.FR 280000)
£565 $1022   (7-Dec-91 KV.L295) Nude (27x25cm-11x10in) s.d.1980 pen wash (B.FR 33000)

SON, Joris van (1623-1667) Flemish
£20000 $36400   (11-Dec-91 S216/R) Still life of fruit hanging from nail in stone niche
                   (59x42cm-23x17in) s.
£35642 $65937   (12-Jun-92 ARC.P67/R) Nature morte au verre monte et fruits
                   (59x43cm-23x17in) s. panel (F.FR 350000)
£66000 $126720   (7-Jul-92 PH24/R) Breakfast still life with basket assorted fruit, pie,
                   shellfish, chalice and roemer on draped table (71x91cm-28x36in)
                   indist.s.

SON, Joris van (circle) (17th C) Flemish
£4471 $7645   (18-Mar-92 D.V355/R) Garland of fruit (34x42cm-13x17in) canvas on panel
                   (A.S 90000)
£6000 $10920   (10-Dec-91 PH195/R) Still life of mixed fruit (52x36cm-20x14in) pair

SON, Joris van (studio) (17th C) Flemish
£2823 $4996   (6-Nov-91 LT.P50/R) Guirlande de fruits (34x42cm-13x17in) canvas laid
                   down on panel (F.FR 28000)

SON, Joris van (style) (17th C) Flemish
£2400 $4608   (10-Jul-92 C176/R) Orange and grapes in porcelain bowl, with glass and
                   moth on stone ledge (41x33cm-16x13in) panel
£3704 $6630   (12-Nov-91 SY.AM127/R) Fruit and cob of corn in niche (56x44cm-22x17in)
                   canvas on board (D.FL 12000)
£5000 $8500   (22-Oct-91 S234/R) Still life of roemer, mixed fruit on stone ledge
                   (24x33cm-9x13in)
£5000 $8500   (22-Oct-91 S235/R) Still life of mixed fruit with song bird
                   (24x33cm-9x13in)
£11000 $20020   (11-Dec-91 S185/R) Still life of roemer, fruit in bowl, with seafish and
                   lemon on pewter dishes on table (39x57cm-15x22in)
£14000 $24500   (3-Apr-92 C32/R) Lobsters, oyster on pewter plate, grapes, glasses and
                   lemons on draped table (39x59cm-15x23in) panel

SONDERBORG, Kurt R H (1923-) Danish
£11945	$21741	(30-May-92 VG.B341/R) Composition (55x70cm-22x28in) s.d.1958 egg tempera board on canvas (DM 35000)
£22184	$40375	(29-May-92 VG.B83/R) Composition 3-IX-62 11.25-11.42 (109x70cm-43x28in) s.d.62 egg tempera photoboard on canvas (DM 65000)
£2560	*$4659*	*(30-May-92 VG.B343/R) Composition (30x41cm-12x16in) s.d.1953 indian ink brush pen (DM 7500)*
£3162	*$5786*	*(2-Jun-92 L.K954) Untitled (77x56cm-30x22in) s.i.d.1961 indian ink (DM 9200)*
£6143	*$11181*	*(30-May-92 VG.B342/R) Composition (52x67cm-20x26in) s.i.d.1955/56 s.i.d.1957verso board (DM 18000)*
£6485	*$11802*	*(30-May-92 VG.B340/R) Nasva (49x70cm-19x28in) s.i.d.1952 gouache indian ink pen brush board (DM 19000)*
£12969	*$23604*	*(29-May-92 VG.B82/R) Composition (65x45cm-26x18in) s.d.1961 mixed media photoboard on panel (DM 38000)*

SONDERGAARD, Jens (1895-1957) Danish
£560	$957	(12-Mar-92 RAS.V1109) Landscape with rocks by the sea (66x91cm-26x36in) (D.KR 6200)
£722	$1235	(10-Mar-92 RAS.K169/R) Reclining negro woman (90x115cm-35x45in) s.d.1954verso (D.KR 8000)
£801	$1393	(17-Sep-91 RAS.K696) Three figures watching oncoming storm over ocean (71x92cm-28x36in) s.d.32 (D.KR 9000)
£891	$1533	(16-Oct-91 KH.K67/R) Sea and cliffs on the West coast (84x100cm-33x39in) s.d.1931verso (D.KR 10000)
£891	$1533	(16-Oct-91 KH.K268) Hundested harbour (87x97cm-34x38in) s.d.55-56verso (D.KR 10000)
£1082	$1926	(25-Nov-91 BU.K54/R) Evening (120x105cm-47x41in) s.d.42 (D.KR 12000)
£1090	$1907	(1-Apr-92 KH.K252) Ferries in Hundested Harbour (90x100cm-35x39in) s.d.54verso (D.KR 12000)
£1151	$2096	(25-May-92 RAS.K165) Evening by the sea (65x79cm-26x31in) s. d.1942verso (D.KR 13000)
£1159	$1993	(16-Oct-91 KH.K200/R) Hilly landscape, Thy (62x75cm-24x30in) s. (D.KR 13000)
£1181	$2066	(1-Apr-92 KH.K253) Lynaes fjord (80x100cm-31x39in) s.d.56verso (D.KR 13000)
£1345	$2422	(30-Jan-92 RAS.V758) Sea and cliffs (85x100cm-33x39in) s.d.1931 (D.KR 15000)
£1426	$2453	(16-Oct-91 KH.K187/R) Figures by the sea (100x100cm-39x39in) s. (D.KR 16000)
£1426	$2453	(16-Oct-91 KH.K95/R) Figures by the sea (100x120cm-39x47in) s.d.55 (D.KR 16000)
£2147	$3907	(10-Dec-91 RAS.K172/R) Fishing boats going out to sea (79x121cm-31x48in) s. (D.KR 24000)

SONDERMANN, Hermann (1832-1901) German
| £2671 | $4595 | (11-Oct-91 AW.H1308/R) Pipe smoking peasant with daughter seated on lap (28x23cm-11x9in) s.i.d.1880 panel (DM 7800) |
| £9020 | $15333 | (23-Oct-91 GD.B1286/R) The marriage contract (92x120cm-36x47in) s. (S.FR 23000) |

SONG YUGUI (1940-) Chinese
| *£25148* | *$44009* | *(30-Mar-92 CH.HK341/R) Waterfall in autumn (133x82cm-52x32in) s.d.1991 ink W/C silk hanging scroll (HK.D 340000)* |

SONJE, Jan Gabrielsz (1625-1707) Dutch
| £2600 | $4628 | (30-Oct-91 S170/R) River landscape with figures near wood (76x62cm-30x24in) s. |
| £2657 | $4861 | (14-May-92 BU.S144/R) Landscape with figures (33x44cm-13x17in) s. panel (S.KR 28000) |

SONMANS, William (attrib) (?-1708) British
| £2000 | $3420 | (12-Mar-92 CSK103) Portrait of lady in dress with low cut trimmed bodice (76x63cm-30x25in) |

SONNE, Jorgen Valentin (1801-1890) Danish
£616	$1035	(27-Aug-91 RAS.K361/R) Scene from an Italian shepherd family - wolf in the flock of sheep (24x34cm-9x13in) init (D.KR 7000)
£720	$1318	(5-Feb-92 KH.K122) Moor landscape, summer evening (30x45cm-12x18in) init. (D.KR 8000)
£1408	$2366	(27-Aug-91 RAS.K114/R) Mrs Signe Puggaard walking in garden with her two daughters (76x69cm-30x27in) s.d.1883 (D.KR 8000)
£1498	$2651	(23-Apr-92 RAS.V896/R) Mrs Signe Puggaard walking in the garden with her two daughters (76x69cm-30x27in) s.d.1883 (D.KR 17000)
£9227	$16516	(6-May-92 RAS.K15/R) Wedding procession, soldier finding his fiance as someone else's bride (91x132cm-36x52in) s.d.1856 (D.KR 105000)

SONNIER, Keith (20th C) ?
| *£1006* | *$1730* | *(8-Oct-91 CC.P43/R) Sans titre (57x51cm-22x20in) mono.d.1970 col.crayons paint (F.FR 10000)* |

SONNLEITHNER, Rudolf (1883-1952) Austrian
| £599 | $1083 | (3-Dec-91 FN.S2464) Woodland lake with duck flying off, autumn (40x50cm-16x20in) s. (DM 1700) |

SONNTAG, William L (1822-1900) American
£1064 $2000   (18-Dec-91 SY.NY36/R) The old mill (25x30cm-10x12in) s.
£1081 $2000   (10-Jun-92 CE.NY155/R) Cabin hidden in woods (30x25cm-12x10in) s.i.
£1458 $2800   (31-Jul-92 E.EDM102/R) Forest glade (25x46cm-10x18in) s.
£2077 $3800   (7-Jun-92 LIT.L144) Fishermen at Mascot Lake, New Hampshire (30x51cm-12x20in) s.
£2128 $4000   (18-Dec-91 SY.NY21/R) Autumn landscape (22x30cm-9x12in) s.
£2456 $4200   (12-Mar-92 CH.NY30/R) On the Pontomac (50x76cm-20x30in) s.
£2842 $5400   (26-Jun-92 WOL.C416) Landscape (48x74cm-19x29in) s.
£3351 $6200   (10-Jun-92 CE.NY234/R) Mountains in twilight (76x27cm-30x11in) s.
£3509 $6000   (12-Mar-92 CH.NY31/R) On the Shenandoah (50x75cm-20x30in) s.
£14835 $27000   (28-May-92 CH.NY7/R) Duck hunters on the Ohio River (89x127cm-35x50in) s.d.1850
£15385 $28000   (28-May-92 CH.NY63/R) Mountain stream from the foot of Mt. Carter, New Hampshire (102x140cm-40x55in) s.i.
£16575 $30000   (6-Dec-91 CH.NY32/R) Afterglow, Massanutten Mountains (91x142cm-36x56in) s.d.1865
£726   *$1300*   *(13-Nov-91 B.SF2766/R) View across field (13x19cm-5x7in) s. W/C*

SONNTAG, William L (jnr) (1870-?) American
£2155 $3750   (20-Sep-91 DM.D2019/R) London and Northwestern railroad (43x130cm-17x51in)

SOOLMAKER, Jan Frans (1635-1685) Flemish
£3500 $6720   (9-Jul-92 CSK246/R) Wooded landscape at sunset with drover and cattle (73x65cm-29x26in) panel

SOONIUS, Louis (1883-1956) Dutch
£1162 $2069   (30-Oct-91 CH.AM48) Children playing in the dunes (30x41cm-12x16in) s. (D.FL 3800)

SOORD, Alfred Usher (1868-1915) British
£500   *$865*   *(1-Oct-91 SWS1863) Lady ironing in interior (44x37cm-17x15in) s.d.1903 W/C*

SOPER, Eileen A (1905-1990) British
£750   *$1283*   *(10-Mar-92 B155) Eva reading in a hammock (63x72cm-25x28in)*
£420   *$718*   *(10-Mar-92 B139) Red squirrels on a branch (39x28cm-15x11in) s. W/C*
£450   *$770*   *(10-Mar-92 B166/R) Pine Martens (38x54cm-15x21in) s. W/C*
£500   *$855*   *(10-Mar-92 B170/R) Red Squirrels (39x28cm-15x11in) s. W/C*
£650   *$1112*   *(10-Mar-92 B186/R) Badgers (40x58cm-16x23in) s. W/C*
£750   *$1283*   *(10-Mar-92 B161/R) Dormice (39x28cm-15x11in) s. W/C*
£850   *$1454*   *(10-Mar-92 B213) Watch for the vixen (29x39cm-11x15in) s. W/C pair*
£900   *$1539*   *(10-Mar-92 B214/R) Otter studies (44x35cm-17x14in) s. W/C htd.white*
£900   *$1539*   *(10-Mar-92 B219/R) Water-Voles feeding (27x38cm-11x15in) s. W/C*
£950   *$1625*   *(10-Mar-92 B201/R) Fox cubs sniffing the air (39x58cm-15x23in) W/C*
£950   *$1625*   *(10-Mar-92 B211) Red squirrel on a pine branch (59x39cm-23x15in) s. W/C*

SOPER, George (1870-1942) British
£650   *$1112*   *(10-Mar-92 B92/R) Horses pulling a hay cart (72x51cm-28x20in)*
£400   *$680*   *(24-Oct-91 CSK56) The fruit pickers (25x20cm-10x8in) s.d.20/89 pencil W/C*
£420   *$752*   *(14-Nov-91 B192) The haywain (25x38cm-10x15in) s.i. W/C htd.white*
£580   *$992*   *(10-Mar-92 B97/R) A man and dog in a horse-drawn cart (41x56cm-16x22in) W/C*
£720   *$1231*   *(10-Mar-92 B44/R) Polo players (40x58cm-16x23in) pencil W/C*
£1000   *$1710*   *(10-Mar-92 B85/R) The Circus (31x48cm-12x19in) pencil W/C*
£1400   *$2394*   *(10-Mar-92 B66/R) The Logging Team (39x57cm-15x22in) pencil W/C*

SOPER, J H (?) British
£700   *$1295*   *(11-Jun-92 CSK132) Shepherd with sheep on track near Haslemere (45x61cm-18x24in) s.*

SORBI, Giulio (1883-1975) Italian
£690   *$1235*   *(14-Nov-91 CH.R158) Carabiniere a cavallo (17x12cm-7x5in) s. panel (I.L 1500000)*

SORBI, Raffaello (1844-1931) Italian
£1162 $2103   (3-Dec-91 SY.MI53) Aia con tacchino e gallini (7x10cm-3x4in) s. panel (I.L 2500000)
£1487 $2692   (3-Dec-91 SY.MI49/R) Scena di storia Romana (10x21cm-4x8in) s.d.1866 panel (I.L 3200000)
£1859 $3365   (3-Dec-91 SY.MI34/R) Musicanti (10x5cm-4x2in) s. panel (I.L 4000000)
£2092 $3786   (3-Dec-91 SY.MI56/R) Giovinetta con Vestito Rosa (10x7cm-4x3in) s. panel (I.L 4500000)
£2556 $4627   (3-Dec-91 SY.MI51) Strada con cipressi (12x9cm-5x4in) s. panel (I.L 5500000)
£3254 $5889   (3-Dec-91 SY.MI57/R) Donna con bambino (10x7cm-4x3in) s. panel (I.L 7000000)
£12000 $21240   (14-Feb-92 C85/R) Feeding the doves. Preparing to bathe (58x45cm-23x18in) one s.d.1868 one i.verso pair
£30000 $52500   (20-Feb-92 SY.NY66/R) Girotondo (40x75cm-16x30in) s.d.1877
£395   *$715*   *(3-Dec-91 SY.MI30/R) Dante e Beatrice a S.Miniato (20x29cm-8x11in) s. chl (I.L 850000)*

SOREAU, Isaak (attrib) (1604-?) Dutch
£7167 $12973   (21-May-92 L.K133/R) Still life of strawberries in bowl and single
                           carnation (25x35cm-10x14in) (DM 21000)

SOREAU, Isaak (style) (1604-?) Dutch
£3700 $7104   (8-Jul-92 S233/R) Still life of flowers in basket with butterfly on stone
                           ledge (43x82cm-17x32in)

SORENSEN, C F (1818-1879) Danish
£502 $889   (23-Apr-92 RAS.V905) Seascape with sailship off the coast
                           (20x43cm-8x17in) s.d.1878 (D.KR 5700)
£538 $969   (30-Jan-92 RAS.V684) Coastal landscape with sailship (32x46cm-13x18in) s.
                           (D.KR 6000)
£539 $953   (11-Feb-92 RAS.K169) Seascape at sunset (20x28cm-8x11in) s.d.77
                           (D.KR 6000)
£573 $1020   (28-Apr-92 RAS.K530) Venetian canal scene (30x44cm-12x17in) i.d.1862
                           (D.KR 6500)
£624 $1161   (16-Jun-92 RAS.K255) Seascape with sailship, morning (31x46cm-12x18in)
                           init.d.1870 (D.KR 7000)
£718 $1271   (11-Feb-92 RAS.K168) Seascape with vessels off Mandal (29x46cm-11x18in)
                           init.i.d.1875 (D.KR 8000)
£748 $1257   (27-Aug-91 RAS.K520) Seascape with sailship (12x16cm-5x6in) init.d.1848
                           (D.KR 8500)
£750 $1334   (28-Apr-92 RAS.K307) Coastal landscape (24x37cm-9x15in) s. (D.KR 8500)
£948 $1706   (19-Nov-91 RAS.K246/R) Along Sjaelland's coast (40x59cm-16x23in) init.
                           (D.KR 10500)
£1762 $2996   (8-Aug-91 RAS.V995/R) Seascape with sailship off coastal cliffs
                           (35x53cm-14x21in) s.d.1876 (D.KR 20000)
£2201 $3697   (28-Aug-91 KH.K190/R) Swedish fishermen under Kullen, herring season
                           (45x57cm-18x22in) s.d.1871 (D.KR 25000)
£2205 $3924   (28-Apr-92 RAS.K657) Seascape near Capri (40x108cm-16x43in) s.d.1873
                           (D.KR 25000)
£2498 $4646   (16-Jun-92 RAS.V877/R) Seascape with sailingboats in a calm, sunset
                           (45x57cm-18x22in) s.d.1871 (D.KR 28000)
£2817 $4732   (27-Aug-91 RAS.K53/R) Swedish fishermen by Kullen in the herring season
                           (90x133cm-35x52in) s.d.1871 (D.KR 32000)
£3169 $5324   (27-Aug-91 RAS.K51/R) Seascape with fishingboat (83x118cm-33x46in)
                           s.d.1867 (D.KR 36000)
£3961 $6655   (27-Aug-91 RAS.K28/R) Seascape with approaching storm (61x87cm-24x34in)
                           s.d.1848 (D.KR 45000)

SORENSEN, Carl Frederick (1818-1879) Danish
£500 $860   (5-Mar-92 D82/R) Shipping in harbour at sunrise (36x48cm-14x19in) s.
£900 $1629   (20-May-92 S29/R) Man of war (30x26cm-12x10in) indis.s.i.
£1134 $1973   (21-Sep-91 SA.A1924/R) Portrait of young lady standing on terrace with
                           view of landscape (46x40cm-18x16in) s.d.1852 (DM 3300)
£8057 $15389   (21-Jul-92 UL.T215/R) Seascape (158x230cm-62x91in) (N.KR 90000)

SORENSEN, Eiler (1869-1953) Danish
£522 $935   (14-Nov-91 GRO.B164 a/R) Sunlit interior with flowers (28x20cm-11x8in) s.
                           canvas on board
£902 $1605   (25-Nov-91 BU.K24/R) Woman and gundog by garden fence (82x86cm-32x34in)
                           s.d.1905 (D.KR 10000)

SORENSEN, Henrik (1882-1962) Norwegian
£664 $1209   (14-Dec-91 BU.O174) Landscape with rowingboat (55x50cm-22x20in)
                           (N.KR 7500)
£1011 $1780   (7-Apr-92 UL.T233/R) From Telemark (54x49cm-21x19in) (N.KR 11500)
£1107 $2015   (14-Dec-91 BU.O175) Grey day over Digerronden (40x65cm-16x26in)
                           mono.d.1959 (N.KR 12500)
£1395 $2371   (6-Aug-91 UL.T232/R) Landscape 1960 (50x60cm-20x24in) (N.KR 16000)
£2139 $3701   (23-Mar-92 B.O126/R) The oak, Stoa (38x45cm-15x18in) mono.d.1945 panel
                           (N.KR 24000)
£2456 $4568   (15-Jun-92 B.O160/R) Marianne listening (55x46cm-22x18in) mono. panel
                           (N.KR 28000)
£7456 $13868   (15-Jun-92 B.O159/R) Marianne from Tyros (130x54cm-51x21in) mono.d.54
                           (N.KR 85000)

SORGH, H M (1611-1670) Dutch
£2111 $3610   (17-Mar-92 JRL.S141/R) Rotterdam fish seller (55x48cm-22x19in)
                           s.indist.d. (A.D 4750)

SORGH, Hendrik Martensz (1611-1670) Dutch
£4144 $7500   (22-May-92 SY.NY164/R) Kitchen interior with maid at work and two boys
                           playing in background (49x64cm-19x25in) s. panel
£4630 $8287   (14-Nov-91 CH.AM202 a/R) Peasant couple in barn with barrels and kitchen
                           ware nearby (45x57cm-18x22in) indis.s.d.16.. panel (D.FL 15000)
£20000 $35000   (1-Apr-92 S26/R) Shipping on Zuider Zee (72x107cm-28x42in) s. bears seal
                           verso

SORGH, Hendrik Martensz (circle) (1611-1670) Dutch
£2417 $4326   (7-May-92 CH.AM84/R) Maid standing by kitchen utensils near well in barn
                           (37x51cm-15x20in) with init.d. panel (D.FL 8000)

SORGH, Hendrik Martensz (style) (1611-1670) Dutch
£900 $1575   (27-Feb-92 B61) Peasants drinking and smoking at a table outside a country cottage (33x26cm-13x10in) panel

SORIA, Eduardo (19/20th C) Italian?
£821 $1494   (11-Dec-91 FER.M102/R) Indolencia (50x39cm-20x15in) s. (S.P 150000)
£1239 $2218   (14-Nov-91 ANS.M58/R) Mujer en rojo (46x38cm-18x15in) s. (S.P 225000)

SORIA, Florentino (?) ?
£982 $1689   (16-Oct-91 FER.M122) El rio Cares a su paso por Cabrales, Asturias (32x23cm-13x9in) s. panel (S.P 180000)

SORIA, Martin de (15th C) Italian
£14525 $26000   (17-Jan-92 SY.NY8/R) The adoration of the shepherds. The adoration of the Magi (147x71cm-58x28in) tempera panel pair

SORIANO, Juan (1920-) Mexican
£14365 $26000   (18-May-92 CH.NY194/R) La Hija de Rapaccini (65x155cm-26x61in) s.d.56
£23333 $42000   (19-Nov-91 CH.NY68/R) Paisaje lirico (105x80cm-41x31in) s.d.49-51
£1105 $1900   (12-Oct-91 SY.NY196/R) Man sitting on park bench (43x55cm-17x22in) s. chl indian ink W/C
£1667 $3000   (18-Nov-91 SY.NY109/R) La familia (65x50cm-26x20in) s.d.44 distemper

SORKAU, Albert (1874-?) French
£700 $1246   (28-Nov-91 B109/R) At the dressing table (55x46cm-22x18in) s.
£843 $1500   (1-Nov-91 PO.BA17) La Leccion (55x46cm-22x18in) s.

SORMANI, Gian Luciano (1867-?) Italian
£608 $1132   (19-Jun-92 G.2145/R) La Riva degli Schiavoni, Venice (43x29cm-17x11in) s. W/C (S.FR 1600)

SOROKINE, Ivan (1910-1986) Russian
£666 $1199   (27-Jan-92 ARC.P25/R) La ravaudage des filets (74x99cm-29x39in) s. (F.FR 6500)

SOROLLA Y BASTIDA, Joaquin (1863-1923) Spanish
£3318 $6237   (17-Dec-91 BRO.B426) Monte Igueldo. San Sebastian (14x19cm-6x7in) board (S.P 600000)
£3318 $6237   (17-Dec-91 BRO.B363/R) Mercado al aire libre en Castilla (8x14cm-3x6in) panel (S.P 600000)
£7631 $14346   (16-Dec-91 ANS.M84/R) Cielo y mar (9x17cm-4x7in) s. panel (S.P 1380000)
£13631 $25354   (16-Jun-92 EP.M24/R) En la barca (9x12cm-4x5in) s. panel (S.P 2500000)
£14377 $27028   (17-Dec-91 DUR.M26/R) El hombre del sombrero de paja (55x46cm-22x18in) (S.P 2600000)
£20459 $38463   (16-Dec-91 ANS.M82/R) Mar y veleros en el puerto (14x18cm-6x7in) s. board (S.P 3700000)
£21978 $40000   (28-May-92 SY.NY128/R) Fiesta Callejera (14x19cm-6x7in) s. panel
£26163 $45000   (17-Oct-91 SY.NY122/R) Barcos en la playa (14x25cm-6x10in) s.i. panel
£40000 $72800   (29-May-92 C372/R) Nino con fondo de vides (44x28cm-17x11in) s.
£47486 $85000   (11-Nov-91 GC.M67/R) Regreso de pescadores (20x40cm-8x16in) s.
£70493 $119839   (21-Oct-91 ARC.P29/R) Les barques (40x64cm-16x25in) s.d.1894 (F.FR 700000)
£90000 $163800   (29-May-92 C367/R) Sketch for Sad Inheritance, boceto para Triste Herencia (28x24cm-11x9in) s.i.d.1903 panel
£180000 $327600   (29-May-92 C373/R) Traineras, Zarauz, near San Sebastian (68x78cm-27x31in) s.d.1910
£285714 $500000   (20-Feb-92 SY.NY107/R) Barcas - Playa de Valencia (51x85cm-20x33in) s. num.327 verso
£1105 $1967   (21-Jan-92 DUR.M67/R) Apunte de bueyes (23x31cm-9x12in) pencil dr (S.P 200000)
£1777 $3252   (13-May-92 FER.M131/R) Campesino (18x11cm-7x4in) W/C htd gouache (S.P 325000)
£2601 $4969   (2-Jul-92 ANS.M76/R) Desnudo de mujer de espaldas (77x62cm-30x24in) chl pastel (S.P 475000)

SOTO (20th C) ?
£435 $774   (29-Nov-91 GAB.G2175/R) Parvis de la cathedrale St Marco (22x16cm-9x6in) i.verso panel (S.FR 1100)

SOTO, Jesus Raphael (1923-) Venezuelan
£17103 $29417   (12-Oct-91 GL.P36 b/R) Vibrations en gris (120x100cm-47x39in) s.d.1960 metal trellis gouache board hardboard (F.FR 170000)

SOTO, Rafael Fernandez de (1915-1984) Spanish
£521 $927   (26-Nov-91 BRO.B408) Olot (50x61cm-20x24in) s. i.d.1945verso (S.P 95000)

SOTTER, George William (1879-?) American
£2260 $4000   (9-Nov-91 W.W282/R) Sailing off the Jersey coast (58x66cm-23x26in) s.d.48 board

SOTTOCORNOLA, Giovanni (1855-1917) Italian
£10500 $18690   (27-Nov-91 S385/R) Still life of peaches on foliage (48x78cm-19x31in) s.d.1888

SOTTSASS, Ettore (20th C) ?
£3823 $6575   *(13-Oct-91 SY.MO8/R) Projet de meuble - Casablanca (30x23cm-12x9in) s.i.*
             col.crayon (F.FR 38000)

SOUBRE, Charles (1821-1895) Belgian
£2000 $3560   (27-Nov-91 S14/R) Violent attack (149x109cm-59x43in) s.d.1847

SOUCEK, Karel (1915-1982) Czechoslovakian
£501 $912   (10-Dec-91 RAS.K259) 'Der Morgen' (54x64cm-21x25in) s.d.68 (D.KR 5600)
£1241 $2210   (29-Nov-91 D.V91/R) Mothers (73x90cm-29x35in) (A.S 25000)

SOUDAN, Maurice (1878-1948) Belgian
£628 $1080   (13-Oct-91 REM.W26) Portrait of girl in white bow (44x69cm-17x27in) s.
             (P.Z 12000000)

SOUKHOROUKIKH, Anatoli (1935-) Russian
£512 $911   (25-Nov-91 ARC.P183/R) Dans l'atelier (99x75cm-39x30in) s. board
             (F.FR 5000)
£532 $947   (25-Nov-91 ARC.P185) Un marche dans le Sud (69x79cm-27x31in) s.
             (F.FR 5200)
£716 $1275   (25-Nov-91 ARC.P186/R) Un roman d'amour (90x100cm-35x39in) s. (F.FR 7000)

SOUKHOV, Alexandre (1921-) Russian
£559 $973   (13-Apr-92 ARC.P195) Soir d'hiver (49x69cm-19x27in) s. board (F.FR 5500)
£610 $1061   (13-Apr-92 ARC.P198) Au mois de mars (30x40cm-12x16in) s. board
             (F.FR 6000)
£762 $1326   (13-Apr-92 ARC.P193/R) Le livre d'images (35x50cm-14x20in) s. board
             (F.FR 7500)

SOULACROIX, Frederic (1825-1879) French
£5814 $10000   (16-Oct-91 CH.NY32/R) An elegant lady holding a pink bonnet
             (74x37cm-29x15in) s.
£8242 $15000   (27-May-92 CH.NY22/R) Elegant lady seated at a piono-forte
             (49x31cm-19x12in) s.
£11628 $20000   (17-Oct-91 SY.NY176/R) Basketful of carnations and daffodils
             (61x100cm-24x39in) s.
£15934 $29000   (28-May-92 SY.NY80/R) La demande en mariage (91x74cm-36x29in) s.i. canvas
             on masonite
£16201 $29000   (6-May-92 D.NY63/R) The love letter (77x47cm-30x19in) s.i.
£55233 $95000   (16-Oct-91 CH.NY28/R) Three beautiful connoisseurs (89x69cm-35x27in) s.i.

SOULAGES, Pierre (1919-) French
£15259 $27925   (14-May-92 BG.P43/R) Composition (64x50cm-25x20in) s. paper laid down on
             canvas (F.FR 150000)
£17329 $32232   (15-Jun-92 GL.P53/R) Peinture (80x60cm-31x24in) s. s.d.1969verso
             (F.FR 170000)
£25225 $43387   (4-Mar-92 KH.K192/R) Composition (81x100cm-32x39in) s. i.d.71
             (D.KR 280000)
£25706 $44471   (4-Oct-91 CSC.P84/R) Composition (33x46cm-13x18in) s. d.1952 verso
             (F.FR 255000)
£30395 $55015   (24-May-92 GL.P26/R) Composition (65x80cm-26x31in) s.d.50 (F.FR 300000)
£32000 $61120   (2-Jul-92 S47/R) Peinture, 12 Decembre 1965 (130x97cm-51x38in) s.
             s.d.12.12.65 i.verso
£45593 $82523   (24-May-92 GL.P28/R) Untitled (116x89cm-46x35in) s. (F.FR 450000)
£55000 $99550   (5-Dec-91 C4/R) 19 Mars 60 (130x130cm-51x51in) s. d.19 Mars 60verso
£171198 $291037   (27-Oct-91 P.V24/R) Composition (130x89cm-51x35in) s. d.21 Sept.1956verso
             (F.FR 1700000)
£13780 $23701   *(16-Oct-91 G.Z21/R) Abstraction (103x76cm-41x30in) d.1953/54 indian ink*
             (S.FR 35000)

SOULES, Eugene Edouard (1811-1876) French
£460   *$833*   *(19-May-92 PH99/R) Figures by ruined abbey (12x18cm-5x7in) s. W/C*

SOULIE, Tony (1955-) French
£611 $1118   (3-Jun-92 CSC.P127/R) Toros (68x97cm-27x38in) s.d.1991 acrylic varnish
             (F.FR 6000)

SOULIER, Eugene (?) ?
£2569   *$4419*   *(4-Mar-92 AT.P88) Paris, place de la Bourse (19x28cm-7x11in) s. W/C*
             (F.FR 25000)

SOUROVTCEV, Andrei (1931-) Russian
£614 $1093   (25-Nov-91 ARC.P24) Fillette en rouge (45x33cm-18x13in) s. board
             (F.FR 6000)
£716 $1275   (25-Nov-91 ARC.P21/R) La fete populaire (33x58cm-13x23in) s. board
             (F.FR 7000)
£798 $1421   (25-Nov-91 ARC.P23) Fete villageoise (32x49cm-13x19in) s. board
             (F.FR 7800)
£972 $1731   (25-Nov-91 ARC.P22/R) Courrier d'amour (44x30cm-17x12in) s. board
             (F.FR 9500)

SOUTER, Camille (1929-) British
£787   *$1432*   *(11-Dec-91 A.D93) Abstract landscape (56x74cm-22x29in) s.d.1984 mixed*
             media (E.P 850)

SOUTER, Camille (1929-) British-cont.
£1495	$2587	(25-Mar-92 A.D161) As if they could fly (36x38cm-14x15in) s. mixed media (E.P 1600)

SOUTER, John Bulloch (1890-1972) British
£500	$870	(19-Sep-91 CSK91) Red and white roses (41x30cm-16x12in) s. artist's board
£650	$1190	(14-May-92 C73/R) Three pink roses in jug (30x41cm-12x16in) s. board
£1200	$2136	(28-Apr-92 S287/R) Still life with pink rose and glass (30x40cm-12x16in) s. canvasboard
£3571	$6500	(28-May-92 SY.NY297/R) Diana (53x41cm-21x16in) s. board

SOUTH GERMAN SCHOOL, 15th C
£2000	$3500	(3-Apr-92 C155) Crucifixion (79x53cm-31x21in) panel
£10381	$19723	(24-Jun-92 KM.K959/R) St Catherine of Alexandria conversing with the philosophers (70x50cm-28x20in) panel (DM 30000)

SOUTH GERMAN SCHOOL, 16th C
£4800	$8736	(11-Dec-91 S178/R) Male saints (82x41cm-32x16in) panel pair
£5226	$9512	(12-Dec-91 C174/R) Portrait of young man holding book (44x35cm-17x14in) i.d.1528 vellum on panel (DM 15000)
£6977	$12000	(10-Oct-91 SY.NY134/R) The flight into Egypt (101x85cm-40x33in) gold ground panel
£7558	$13000	(10-Oct-91 SY.NY135/R) Christ among the doctors (107x86cm-42x34in) gold ground panel
£8380	$15000	(16-Jan-92 CH.NY101/R) Presentation of Virgin in Temple (78x57cm-31x22in) d.1537 panel

SOUTHALL, Joseph Edward (1861-1944) British
£3800	$6954	(5-Jun-92 C1/R) Pont Henri IV (23x21cm-9x8in) mono.d.1937 tempera
£2800	$4844	(2-Oct-91 S52/R) Banbury Market Place (33x45cm-13x18in) mono.d.1905-6 W/C
£3600	$6228	(4-Sep-91 BT36/R) The trippers (15x25cm-6x10in) mono.d.1933 i.backboard W/C

SOUTHERN, Clara (?) Australian?
£2137	$3803	(27-Apr-92 J.M318) The studio (24x35cm-9x14in) s. (A.D 5000)
£16740	$29797	(26-Nov-91 J.M19/R) The artist's orchard (44x80cm-17x31in) s. (A.D 38000)

SOUTHGATE, Frank (1872-1916) British
£1100	$1925	(25-Feb-92 C178/R) Sportsmen conversing by Wildfowler's punt (24x39cm-9x15in) s. grisaille
£1950	$3413	(25-Feb-92 C174/R) Duck-shooting over field of stubble (34x52cm-13x20in) s. i.verso canvas on card grisaille
£3200	$5600	(25-Feb-92 C183/R) Re-loading - snipe overhead (25x35cm-10x14in) s. grisaille
£3400	$5950	(25-Feb-92 C176/R) Shooting geese (40x60cm-16x24in) s. grisaille
£3800	$6650	(25-Feb-92 C177/R) Concealed fowler observing Brent Geese (40x60cm-16x24in) s. grisaille
£500	$865	(25-Mar-92 PHI489) Snipe in the reeds (52x31cm-20x12in) s.d.1902 W/C bodycol
£800	$1400	(25-Feb-92 C173/R) Pink-footed geese on shore (39x59cm-15x23in) s. W/C en grisaille
£900	$1575	(25-Feb-92 C179) Shooting (33x41cm-13x16in) s. i.verso W/C grisaille
£1250	$2188	(25-Feb-92 C175/R) Judy had two birds gathered in twinkling (34x46cm-13x18in) s. i.d. num.verso grisaille
£2200	$3850	(25-Feb-92 C180/R) Flighting. Scaup duck leading Black Duck on Wash (30x45cm-12x18in) s. i.d.num.verso black chk pair
£2400	$4200	(25-Feb-92 C181/R) Canada geese flighting over estuary (37x57cm-15x22in) s. W/C bodycol
£2400	$4200	(25-Feb-92 C182/R) Autumn arrivals, Golden Plover (39x60cm-15x24in) s. i.verso W/C bodycol
£2800	$4900	(25-Feb-92 C152/R) Cock pheasants under beech tree (39x57cm-15x22in) pencil W/C bodycol

SOUTINE, Chaim (1893-1943) Russian
£84746	$150000	(6-Nov-91 SY.NY39/R) Arbres a Ceret (54x73cm-21x29in)
£112994	$200000	(5-Nov-91 CH.NY41/R) Nature morte au faisan (90x58cm-35x23in)
£142857	$250000	(25-Feb-92 SY.NY38/R) Vue de Montmartre (66x81cm-26x32in) s.
£285132	$527495	(12-Jun-92 AT.P22/R) La femme au bain, torse (54x62cm-21x24in) s. (F.FR 2800000)
£327684	$580000	(5-Nov-91 CH.NY50/R) La petite fille en rose (73x54cm-29x21in)

SOUTO (19/20th C) Spanish
£1404	$2400	(12-Mar-92 MFA.C264) View of Toledo (43x58cm-17x23in) s. pastel

SOUTTER, Louis (1871-1942) Swiss
£1581	$2814	(29-Nov-91 GAB.G2530/R) Roses (31x23cm-12x9in) i. Indian ink (S.FR 4000)
£1912	$3461	(5-Dec-91 SY.Z121/R) Purite (22x17cm-9x7in) i. indian ink pen (S.FR 4800)
£2047	$3521	(16-Oct-91 G.Z25/R) Femmes devant des portailles (22x17cm-9x7in) pen (S.FR 5200)
£3299	$5905	(12-Nov-91 HW.H3209/R) Deux femmes devant un miroir (21x27cm-8x11in) indian ink pen (DM 9500)
£3360	$5980	(29-Nov-91 GAB.G2529/R) Ulysse et Penelope (35x26cm-14x10in) i. Indian ink (S.FR 8500)
£3472	$6215	(12-Nov-91 HW.H3208/R) Vieillesse (27x21cm-11x8in) i. indian ink pen (DM 10000)

SOUTTER, Louis (1871-1942) Swiss-cont.
£4811 $8804   *(2-Jun-92 L.K964/R) Le salut du cheminot (20x31cm-8x12in) i. indian ink pen (DM 14000)*
£4811 $8804   *(2-Jun-92 L.K965/R) L'Annonciation. La Mort (18x28cm-7x11in) i. indian ink pen two on one sheet (DM 14000)*
£26236 $48798   *(19-Jun-92 G.Z21/R) Quatre personnages (51x68cm-20x27in) d.1937/42 indian ink (S.FR 69000)*

SOUVERBIE, Jean (1891-1981) French
£3055 $5652   *(12-Jun-92 ARC.P16/R) Les Trois Graces (65x40cm-26x16in) s. (F.FR 30000)*
£3360 $5980   *(29-Nov-91 GAB.G2881) Les Baigneuses (57x39cm-22x15in) s. hardboard (S.FR 8500)*
£3429 $6000   *(27-Feb-92 CE.NY83/R) Aphrodite et Helios (46x55cm-18x22in) s.d.47 s.d.1947 verso board*
£4057 $7383   *(26-May-92 RY.P101/R) Femme au turban (92x73cm-36x29in) s. (F.FR 40000)*
£4559 $8207   *(2-Feb-92 CSC.P41/R) Les baigneuses (43x62cm-17x24in) s. hardboard (F.FR 44500)*
£4857 $8500   *(28-Feb-92 SY.NY63/R) Repose by sea (50x61cm-20x24in) s.*

SOUZA, Alberto Augusto de (1880-1962) Portuguese
£831 $1455   *(18-Feb-92 DUR.M67/R) Mercado en Vila Franca de Xira (34x28cm-13x11in) s. W/C (S.P 150000)*

SOWDEN, John (1838-1926) British
£500 $875   *(23-Sep-91 HS152) Fair Maids of February - study of snowdrops and other flowers (26x20cm-10x8in) s. W/C*
£1200 $2064   *(4-Mar-92 S301/R) Fair maids of February (25x20cm-10x8in) s. s.i.d.1867 verso W/C htd bodycol arched top*

SOWERBY, Millicent (fl.1900-1909) British
£650 $1242   *(1-Jul-92 B158/R) The Princess and the Frog (18x15cm-7x6in) s.d.08 pen W/C*

SOYA-JENSEN, C M (1860-1912) Danish
£540 $988   *(5-Feb-92 KH.K123) River landscape with houses, France (33x54cm-13x21in) s. (D.KR 6000)*

SOYER, Moses (1899-1974) American
£526 $1000   *(26-Jun-92 WOL.C113/R) Two seated dancers (48x28cm-19x11in)*
£726 $1300   *(14-Nov-91 CE.NY411) Dancer rsting (56x23cm-22x9in) s. canvasboard*
£811 $1500   *(10-Jun-92 CE.NY574/R) Portrait of composer virgil Thomson (76x63cm-30x25in) estate st.*
£1405 $2600   *(10-Jun-92 CE.NY549/R) Head of girl (35x25cm-14x10in) s.*
£1596 $3000   *(18-Dec-91 SY.NY241/R) Ballet class (40x50cm-16x20in) s.d.1938*
£1706 $2900   *(11-Aug-91 LIT.L124) Female nude (61x51cm-24x20in) s.*
£2586 $4500   *(15-Apr-92 SY.NY193/R) Dancer in red skirt (50x26cm-20x10in) s.d.52*
£3073 $5500   *(15-Nov-91 DM.D2000/R) The fitting (58x43cm-23x17in) s.*
£3457 $6500   *(18-Dec-91 SY.NY245/R) Fortune teller (58x52cm-23x20in) s.*
£733 $1400   *(3-Jul-92 S.W3862/R) Reclining nude (30x41cm-12x16in) s. sepia chk chl*

SOYER, Paul Constant (1823-1903) French
£733 $1276   *(14-Apr-92 GM.B651) Bouquet de pivoines (52x64cm-20x25in) s. (B.FR 44000)*

SOYER, Raphael (1899-1987) American
£973 $1800   *(10-Jun-92 CE.NY496) Portrait of woman with blue robe (45x46cm-18x18in) s. board*
£1148 $2100   *(7-Jun-92 LIT.L159) Portrait of seated woman (43x53cm-17x21in) s.*
£1351 $2500   *(10-Jun-92 CE.NY565) Kate (30x23cm-12x9in) s.*
£1871 $3200   *(12-Mar-92 CH.NY216/R) Blue cardigan (60x44cm-24x17in) s.*
£2924 $5000   *(12-Mar-92 CH.NY210/R) The conversation (82x56cm-32x22in) s.*
£402 $700   *(13-Sep-91 S.W2295) Reclining female nude (20x25cm-8x10in) s. ink wash*
£419 $700   *(25-Aug-91 LIT.L201) Two figures (18x23cm-7x9in) s. ink*
£419 $700   *(25-Aug-91 LIT.L199) Self Portrait (23x18cm-9x7in) s. pen*
£546 $950   *(15-Apr-92 SY.NY199/R) Women in my brother's house (48x36cm-19x14in) s.i. pencil*
£747 $1300   *(15-Apr-92 SY.NY195/R) Four views of standing female nude (37x42cm-15x17in) s. W/C pencil*

SPACIC, Jan (1892-?) Czechoslovakian
£1633 $2922   *(5-May-92 ZEL.L1540/R) View of Prague with Laurenzikirche (97x144cm-38x57in) s.d.1924 (DM 4800)*

SPADA, Valerio (17th C) Italian
£1200 $2304   *(7-Jul-92 C160/R) Buildings on river bank. Herdsman by gnarled trunk. Trees near farmstead i. chk pen three on one mount*

SPADARI, Gian Giacomo (1938-) Italian
£548 $954   *(14-Apr-92 F.M76) Per un personaggio (80x80cm-31x31in) s.i.d.1964/65verso (I.L 1200000)*
£834 $1485   *(29-Nov-91 F.F54) Ebollizione (90x80cm-35x31in) s.d.1969 mixed media (I.L 1800000)*

SPADARO, Micco see GARGIULIO, Domenico

SPADINI, Armando (1883-1925) Italian
£29892 $53507   (14-Nov-91 CH.R148/R) Amore materna, la moglie con la figlia Anna
                   (62x50cm-24x20in) s. (I.L 65000000)
£29937 $54485   (10-Dec-91 F.R217/R) Primavera nuvolosa (72x94cm-28x37in) s.
                   (I.L 65000000)

SPADINO, Giovanni Paolo (17th C) Italian
£12155 $22000   (21-May-92 CH.NY72/R) Mixed fruit on stone ledge (34x56cm-13x22in)

SPADINO, Giovanni Paolo (attrib) (17th C) Italian
£6000 $10920   (11-Dec-91 S132/R) Still life of mixed fruit (24x51cm-9x20in)

SPAENDONCK, Cornelis van (style) (1756-1840) French
£3488 $6000   (10-Oct-91 SY.NY55/R) Still life of flowers in a glass vase with
                   pomegranate and grapes on a ledge (64x54cm-25x21in)
£8000 $15360   (8-Jul-92 S155/R) Still life of flowers in gilt and porphyry urn
                   (119x97cm-47x38in)

SPAENDONCK, Gerard van (1746-1822) French
£2174 $3913   (21-Nov-91 SY.G15/R) Still life of roses and other flowers in vase with
                   bird's nest and basket (7cm-3ins circular) min.init. gilt metal mount
                   wood frame (S.FR 5500)
£8696 $15652   (21-Nov-91 SY.G16/R) Still life with roses and other flowers in basket
                   and bird's nest (6cm-2ins circular) min. gilt metal mount wood frame
                   (S.FR 22000)

SPAGNOLETTO, lo see RIBERA, Jusepe de

SPAHN, Victor (20th C) French
£1109 $1963   (10-Nov-91 ZZ.F267/R) Le golfeur (65x54cm-26x21in) s. (F.FR 11000)

SPALA, Vaclav (1885-1946) Czechoslovakian
£4561 $8211   (23-Nov-91 N.M380/R) River landscape, Hotel Praha (74x92cm-29x36in)
                   s.d.1935 (DM 13000)
£9123 $16421   (23-Nov-91 N.M379/R) Bunch of summer flowers before landscape
                   (91x61cm-36x24in) s.d.1936 (DM 26000)

SPALDING, C B (19th C) British
£5000 $8950   (13-Nov-91 S164/R) Haidee, chestnut racehorse in stable. Dark bay
                   racehorse in landscape (80x105cm-31x41in) s.d.1841 pair

SPAMPANI, Giovanni Battista (?-1745) Italian
£780 $1498   (8-Jul-92 PH21/R) Stage design of palatial stairway (38x46cm-15x18in)
                   i.graphite

SPANGENBERG, George (1907-1954) American
£789 $1500   (24-Jun-92 B.SF6410/R) Devil's Cauldron, Carmel, California
                   (34x46cm-13x18in) s. board

SPANISH SCHOOL (?) Spanish
£2123 $3800   (6-May-92 CAS.M48/R) Feria (48x38cm-19x15in)
£21605 $38673   (12-Nov-91 SY.AM51) The Nativity. The Baptism of Christ (66x57cm-26x22in)
                   panel pair (D.FL 70000)

SPANISH SCHOOL, 16th C
£2210 $4000   (21-May-92 CH.NY130/R) Saint Michael slaying Satan (48x44cm-19x17in) gold
                   ground panel part retable
£2730 $4942   (21-May-92 L.K134) Madonna and Child with Apostle (36x29cm-14x11in) gold
                   ground panel (DM 8000)
£2838 $5137   (19-May-92 AB.S4401/R) Jesus carrying the cross (102x53cm-40x21in) panel
                   (S.KR 30000)
£3315 $6000   (22-May-92 SY.NY307/R) Crowning of episcopal saint (92x85cm-36x33in)
                   tempera oil gilt panel
£4500 $7875   (3-Apr-92 C96/R) Saints Roch, Vincent Ferrer, Nicholas and Peter Martyr
                   (58x112cm-23x44in) panel two sections
£6800 $12104   (30-Oct-91 S37/R) The martyrdom of a saint (113x93cm-44x37in) panel
£8000 $14240   (30-Oct-91 S140/R) Bishop, queen and other figures at bedside of king
                   (148x100cm-58x39in) panel
£9000 $16020   (30-Oct-91 S137/R) Sacrifice near castle (146x78cm-57x31in) panel
£9000 $16020   (30-Oct-91 S138/R) King with courtiers celebrating birth of royal infant
                   (150x84cm-59x33in) panel
£9500 $16910   (30-Oct-91 S139/R) Three figures standing in interior (149x63cm-59x25in)
                   panel
£18000 $34560   (7-Jul-92 PH51/R) Lamentation, Crucifixion and entombment. Christ before
                   Pontius Pilate (112x169cm-44x67in) panel triptych double-sided
£18592 $33651   (5-Dec-91 F.M138/R) Deposizione (100x135cm-39x53in) c.1540 panel
                   (I.L 40000000)
£4037 $7307   (20-May-92 ANS.M52/R) Virgen con Nino (17x11cm-7x4in) ink dr (S.P 740000)

SPANISH SCHOOL, 17th C
£1976 $3518   (29-Nov-91 GAB.G2996) Le martyre de Sainte Catherine (32x26cm-13x10in)
                   panel (S.FR 5000)
£2000 $3560   (30-Oct-91 S123/R) The vision of St Anthony of Padua (142x110cm-56x43in)
                   indis.s.i.

SPANISH SCHOOL, 17th C-cont.

£2018	$3471	(16-Oct-91 AT.P4/R) La Vierge et l'Enfant apparaissant a un ange gardien (89x109cm-35x43in) (F.FR 20000)
£2180	$3750	(10-Oct-91 SY.NY36/R) Return from the flight into Egypt (67x56cm-26x22in)
£2183	$3754	(16-Oct-91 FER.M198/R) Imposicion del cingulo de castidad a Sto.Tomas (88x76cm-35x30in) (S.P 400000)
£2191	$4184	(2-Jul-92 ANS.M49/R) Piedad (106x79cm-42x31in) (S.P 400000)
£2447	$4332	(7-Nov-91 D.V49/R) Prophet (63x75cm-25x30in) (A.S 50000)
£3557	$6473	(11-Dec-91 FER.M125/R) El Bautismo de Cristo (35x29cm-14x11in) copper (S.P 650000)
£4942	$8500	(9-Oct-91 CH.NY135/R) Mixed flowers in sculpted urn with parrot on draped table (80x97cm-31x38in)
£4968	$8495	(18-Mar-92 D.V195/R) Portrait of gentleman wearing ruff (67x52cm-26x20in) (A.S 100000)
£6087	$10410	(17-Mar-92 FER.M103/R) Dama con perrito (130x88cm-51x35in) (S.P 1100000)
£35568	$63311	(29-Oct-91 EP.M9/R) Retrato de una nina (114x70cm-45x28in) (S.P 6500000)

SPANISH SCHOOL, 18th C

£2074	$3898	(17-Dec-91 DUR.M127/R) Jose con su rebano de ovejas (150x183cm-59x72in) (S.P 375000)
£2212	$4158	(17-Dec-91 DUR.M123/R) Susana y los viejos (213x150cm-84x59in) (S.P 400000)
£2215	$3987	(29-Jan-92 FER.M125/R) Jarron de flores (62x49cm-24x19in) (S.P 400000)
£2779	$4807	(25-Mar-92 CH.R26/R) Ritratto di dama con cagnolino (105x87cm-41x34in) (I.L 6000000)
£2946	$5332	(20-May-92 ANS.M156/R) Inmaculada Concepcion (98x48cm-39x19in) panel (S.P 540000)
£3010	$5718	(23-Jun-92 DUR.M122/R) La Virgen con el Nino rodeada de santos (63x49cm-25x19in) (S.P 550000)
£3041	$5717	(17-Dec-91 DUR.M136/R) San Joaquin, Santa Ana, La Virgen y San Jose (170x225cm-67x89in) (S.P 550000)
£3528	$6245	(6-Nov-91 LT.P13) Trois lapins (46x46cm-18x18in) (F.FR 35000)
£4354	$7750	(22-Jan-92 D.NY11) Portrait of young lady wearing embroidered dress in landscape (86x69cm-34x27in)
£4420	$8000	(22-May-92 SY.NY309/R) Supper at Emmaus (55x72cm-22x28in)

SPANISH SCHOOL, 18th/19th C

£2488	$4678	(18-Dec-91 DUR.M609/R) Bodegon con cesta de frutas y botella (40x54cm-16x21in) (S.P 450000)

SPANISH SCHOOL, 19th C

£2046	$3520	(16-Oct-91 FER.M103/R) Caballero con casaca (95x70cm-37x28in) (S.P 375000)
£2442	$4200	(9-Oct-91 CH.NY32) Portrait of child, standing holding tambourine (56x44cm-22x17in)
£2445	$4279	(30-Mar-92 ZZ.F101) Taureau et Toreador (43x56cm-17x22in) (F.FR 23500)
£2460	$4502	(13-May-92 FER.M55/R) Haciendo las labores al calor del hogar (62x84cm-24x33in) bears indist.sig. (S.P 450000)
£3010	$5718	(23-Jun-92 DUR.M488/R) Retrato de Fernando VII (137x104cm-54x41in) (S.P 550000)
£3200	$5792	(22-May-92 C267/R) At ball (19x30cm-7x12in) with sig. panel

SPANISH SCHOOL, 19th/20th C

£825	$1451	(9-Apr-92 ANS.M165/R) En la sacristia (67x49cm-26x19in) (S.P 150000)

SPANISH-FLEMISH SCHOOL

£3400	$6052	(30-Oct-91 S187/R) St John the Baptist preaching (46x59cm-18x23in) c.1600 copper
£4200	$7350	(1-Apr-92 S181/R) Christ carrying cross (103x93cm-41x37in) panel c.1600

SPANISH-FLEMISH SCHOOL, 16th C

£5461	$9884	(21-May-92 L.K135/R) The Lamentation of Christ with view of town beyond (62x46cm-24x18in) c.1500 panel (DM 16000)

SPANO, Maria (1843-?) Italian

£1204	$2083	(24-Mar-92 CH.R118 b) Marina con pescatore che rammenda le reti (13x22cm-5x9in) s.d.1889 panel (I.L 2600000)

SPANOGHE, Leon (1874-1955) Belgian?

£1711	$3097	(7-Dec-91 KV.L298) View of Dendermonde (50x71cm-20x28in) s. panel (B.FR 100000)

SPANYI, Bela von (1852-1914) Hungarian

£1079	$2051	(25-Jun-92 D.V468/R) Stork in birch wood (78x69cm-31x27in) s. (A.S 22000)

SPARE, Austin Osman (1888-1956) British

£400	$688	(4-Mar-92 ZZ.B252) Serpent temptation init.d.54 pastel over pencil panel
£400	$712	(21-Jan-92 SWS1265) Portrait study of man in cap, smoking cigarette (37x28cm-15x11in) init.d.37 col.pastel
£500	$890	(23-Jan-92 CSK146) Ghosts are sidereal (46x37cm-18x15in) init.d.55 s.i.d.verso pencil pastel
£780	$1349	(4-Sep-91 BT85/R) Wrestlers in landscape (38x28cm-15x11in) init. W/C
£850	$1471	(4-Sep-91 BT88/R) Self-portrait (38x28cm-15x11in) init. chl pastel
£1000	$1740	(19-Sep-91 TL481) Charmante (55x40cm-22x16in) i.verso mixed media panel

SPARE, Austin Osman (1888-1956) British-cont.
| £1100 | $1903 | (4-Sep-91 BT92/R) Realism - Psycho-realism - Psycho-revisionism (38x56cm-15x22in) init.i.d.37 pencil chl pastel |
| £1250 | $2163 | (4-Sep-91 BT89/R) Chaos (30x25cm-12x10in) mono.i.d.One 04 ink |

SPARKS, Herbert Blande (fl.1892-1893) British
| £603 | $1073 | (29-Oct-91 PH.T75/R) Young lady on lakeside terrace (44x29cm-17x11in) s. W/C over pencil (C.D 1200) |
| £700 | $1204 | (4-Mar-92 S266) Garden seat (46x30cm-18x12in) s. W/C |

SPARRE, Louis (1863-1964) Swedish/Finnish
£494	$859	(13-Apr-92 AB.S250) Trees by manor house (45x45cm-18x18in) s.d.19 (S.KR 5200)
£678	$1207	(28-Oct-91 AB.S220) Sunlit cliffs, Blahall, Gotland (36x53cm-14x21in) s. (S.KR 7200)
£3161	$5563	(12-Apr-92 HOR.H219/R) The fishing fleet in harbour (36x46cm-14x18in) s. (F.M 25000)
£4551	$8010	(12-Apr-92 HOR.H217) Atlantic breakers (59x80cm-23x31in) s.d.1941 (F.M 36000)
£5692	$10132	(1-Dec-91 HOR.H216/R) Chord in B minor (100x83cm-39x33in) s.d.1908 (F.M 44000)

SPARRE, Victor (1919-) Norwegian?
| £2456 | $4568 | (18-Jun-92 GWP.O95/R) Fugetives in exile (105x135cm-41x53in) s.d.78 s.i.verso (N.KR 28000) |

SPARRGREN, Lorentz Lars Svensson (1763-1828) Swedish
| £1235 | $2198 | (28-Apr-92 RAS.K41/R) Prince Eugen and Princess Augusta Amalia of Leuchtenberg (17x14cm-7x6in) init. pair (D.KR 14000) |

SPAT, Gabriel (?) ?
£586	$1013	(3-Oct-91 D.V154/R) Man and woman (18x12cm-7x5in) d.1910 canvas on board (A.S 12000)
£1714	$3000	(28-Sep-91 YFA.M222/R) Entr'acte (25x20cm-10x8in) s. board
£1757	$3250	(12-Jun-92 SY.NY118/R) Le Bois de Boulogne (38x50cm-15x20in) s.
£546	$1000	(5-Feb-92 D.NY85) La Conciergerie a Paris (28x36cm-11x14in) s.i. W/C

SPAZZAPAN, Luigi (1890-1958) Italian
£2270	$4040	(29-Apr-92 F.F110/R) Figura. Ritratto (48x36cm-19x14in) s. tempera chl double-sided (I.L 5000000)
£2549	$4537	(29-Nov-91 F.F97) Figura (48x36cm-19x14in) s. tempera cardboard (I.L 5500000)
£834	$1485	(27-Nov-91 F.M226/R) Nudo femminile (48x36cm-19x14in) s. gouache (I.L 1800000)

SPEAR, Ruskin (1911-1990) British
£1000	$1830	(14-May-92 C144/R) Financial Times, Geoffrey Howe (119x47cm-47x19in) s.i. board
£1000	$1740	(19-Sep-91 CSK254/R) Road to river (81x59cm-32x23in) s. board
£1100	$2013	(14-May-92 C159/R) Chimpanzee (40x40cm-16x16in) s. board
£1500	$2565	(11-Mar-92 S147/R) Bridge (34x40cm-13x16in) i.verso board
£1600	$3056	(16-Jul-92 B113/R) Boating on the river (75x61cm-30x24in) s.d.1956
£1800	$3132	(17-Sep-91 PH155) A view from the artist's studio (29x38cm-11x15in) s. board
£2000	$3480	(17-Sep-91 PH156/R) Farm buildings (39x50cm-15x20in) s. board
£2200	$3806	(2-Oct-91 S197/R) Frankly speaking (91x129cm-36x51in) s. board

SPECKAERT, Hans (?-c.1577) Flemish
| £39106 | $70000 | (16-Jan-92 CH.NY35/R) Death of Sisera (171x171cm-67x67in) |

SPEICHER, Eugene (1883-1962) American
£719	$1200	(25-Aug-91 LIT.L248) November Landscape (41x51cm-16x20in) s.
£872	$1500	(13-Oct-91 LIT.L111) Old brick house (41x51cm-16x20in) s.
£877	$1500	(12-Mar-92 MFA.C97) Kingston, N.Y. Factory Square (41x51cm-16x20in) s.
£930	$1600	(20-Oct-91 HG.C46) Hudson River scene (41x51cm-16x20in) s.

SPELMAN, John A (1880-1941) American
| £1027 | $1900 | (10-Jun-92 CE.NY437/R) Red barn amongst blue mountains (75x93cm-30x37in) s. |

SPENCE, Percy Frederick Seaton (1868-1933) Australian
| £661 | $1176 | (26-Nov-91 J.M690) Charge (47cm-19ins circular) s.d.1922 (A.D 1500) |

SPENCELAYH, Charles (1865-1958) British
£1400	$2492	(28-Apr-92 PH154/R) Portrait of girl (41x30cm-16x12in) s.d.1893
£1500	$2655	(6-Nov-91 S113/R) Flowers (24x31cm-9x12in) s.d.1948
£1800	$3078	(13-Dec-91 C170/R) 2nd June 1953 (76x56cm-30x22in) s.d.53
£2000	$3420	(13-Mar-92 C171/R) The broken chair (14x9cm-6x4in) s. panel
£2500	$4550	(10-Dec-91 AG352/R) Happy moments - portrait of artist's son Vernon (24x34cm-9x13in) s.d.1893
£3191	$5649	(26-Apr-92 SY.ME219/R) Writing letter (39x29cm-15x11in) s. (A.D 7500)
£3800	$7144	(19-Dec-91 C210/R) Sweet peas (38x30cm-15x12in) s. s.i.backing board
£4800	$8496	(6-Nov-91 S185/R) Once too often (23x17cm-9x7in) s. i.verso panel
£6000	$10320	(4-Mar-92 S176/R) Old tea caddy (26x21cm-10x8in) s. s.i.verso panel
£7400	$12728	(4-Mar-92 S174/R) New sovereign (31x25cm-12x10in) s. panel

SPENCELAYH, Charles (1865-1958) British-cont.

£12500	$23875	(2-Jul-92 D179/R) The philatelist (36x23cm-14x9in) s.
£13000	$23010	(6-Nov-91 S186/R) Part of my stock-in-trade (60x51cm-24x20in) s.d.1948
£16000	$28320	(6-Nov-91 S193/R) Grandfather's and grandmother's treasures (41x51cm-16x20in) s.d.1945
£18000	$31860	(6-Nov-91 S195/R) His old wedding hat (51x61cm-20x24in) s.d.1943 s.i.verso
£24000	$41280	(4-Mar-92 S173/R) Unexpected (51x38cm-20x15in) s. s.i.verso
£28000	$47880	(13-Mar-92 C172/R) She stoops to conquer (63x76cm-25x30in) s.
£9000	$15480	(4-Mar-92 S310/R) Much noise little music (26x37cm-10x15in) s. i.verso W/C

SPENCER, Fred (fl.1891-1924) British

£960	$1632	(22-Oct-91 SWS205/R) Corner of library (17x25cm-7x10in) s. W/C
£2400	$4128	(4-Mar-92 S293/R) Antiquarian books (17x26cm-7x10in) s. W/C

SPENCER, Gervase (?-1763) British

£650	$1190	(2-Jun-92 S680/R) Lady wearing ermine trimmed gown (4x?cm-2x?in) min.init.d.1757 oval gold frame

SPENCER, Gilbert (1892-1979) British

£513	$928	(2-Dec-91 AAA.S173) Sailing on Middle harbour (90x108cm-35x43in) s. board (A.D 1200)
£2400	$4176	(19-Sep-91 TL389/R) Goring Gap (53x77cm-21x30in) s.d.1959

SPENCER, John C (19/20th C) American

£508	$900	(9-Nov-91 W.W158/R) Game birds (51x36cm-20x14in) s.d.1884

SPENCER, R B (19th C) British

£4800	$8352	(14-Apr-92 CSK119/R) Wooden barque Glengairn under full sail off Dover (58x94cm-23x37in) s.

SPENCER, Robert (1879-1931) American

£6044	$11000	(28-May-92 CH.NY181/R) Note of the City, No.I (28x36cm-11x14in) s.

SPENCER, Sir Stanley (1891-1959) British

£13000	$23010	(7-Nov-91 C50/R) Fernlea, Cookham (25x35cm-10x14in) pencil oil paper laid over panel
£36000	$65880	(13-May-92 S75/R) Self-portrait (35x25cm-14x10in) s.d.57 s.i.verso panel
£220000	$402600	(13-May-92 S74/R) Seated nude (76x51cm-30x20in)
£350000	$640500	(13-May-92 S78/R) The Daughters of Jerusalem (54x115cm-21x45in)
£1000	$1730	(2-Oct-91 S140/R) Portrait of man (29x21cm-11x8in) s.d.1922 pencil
£1500	$2610	(19-Sep-91 B49/R) Head portrait of girl (30x26cm-12x10in) s. pencil
£1500	$2865	(16-Jul-92 B100 c) Out walking Hilda (39x24cm-15x9in) d. pencil
£2900	$5539	(16-Jul-92 B100 b) Sewing on a button (40x27cm-16x11in) pencil
£3200	$5856	(14-May-92 C55/R) Picking walnuts at Fernlea, Cookham (26x35cm-10x14in) pencil

SPENCER, Thomas (18th C) British

£4800	$9168	(15-Jul-92 S87/R) A grey racehorse, proabaly Jason, with jockey at racecourse (79x125cm-31x49in)

SPENCER, Vera (20th C) British

£1000	$1710	(11-Mar-92 S149/R) Leviathan (47x54cm-19x21in) s. board

SPENCER-BOWER, Olivia (1905-) New Zealander

£432	$782	(4-Dec-91 DS.W50) Portrait of woman arranging flowers (53x42cm-21x17in) s. W/C (NZ.D 1400)

SPENCER-BOWER, Rosa (19/20th C) New Zealander

£299	$534	(6-May-92 DS.W42) Otira Gorge (36x55cm-14x22in) s. W/C (NZ.D 1000)

SPENDER, Humphrey (1910-) British

£750	$1433	(16-Jul-92 B156/R) The sea (29x49cm-11x19in) init.d.1941 collage

SPENLOVE, Frank Spenlove (1868-1933) British

£440	$748	(8-Aug-91 B193) Her love had gone a sailing (28x43cm-11x17in) s. W/C htd.white

SPERL, Johann (1840-1914) German

£2120	$3710	(3-Apr-92 BM.B714/R) Farmhouse in the Bavarian Alps (45x71cm-18x28in) s. (DM 6000)

SPERLI, Johann Jakob (1770-1841) Swiss

£1128	$2064	(4-Jun-92 SY.Z333/R) Health resort in the Ostschweiz (39x51cm-15x20in) s.d.1823 pencil W/C (S.FR 3000)

SPERLICH, J (19th C) German

£2281	$4105	(22-Nov-91 SA.A1589/R) Who is first (16x32cm-6x13in) s.i. panel (DM 6500)

SPERLICH, Sophie (19th C) German

£517	$900	(15-Sep-91 JRB.C91/R) Portrait of two kittens (15x20cm-6x8in) s. panel

SPERLING, Heinrich (1844-1924) German
£2091 $3805   (11-Dec-91 N.M598/R) Hunting dogs standing in field (33x38cm-13x15in)
       s.d.1885 one canvas on panel pair (DM 6000)

SPERLING, J W (19th C) ?
£1800 $3060   (22-Oct-91 C60/R) Ramanankoraisina, Ranera, Raharolahy and Rasatranabo -
*   all Ambassadors (29x23cm-11x9in) i. col.chk ovals four*

SPERLING, Johann Christian (1690-1746) German
£15642 $28000   (16-Jan-92 CH.NY90/R) Danae (49x59cm-19x23in) s.i.d.1724 copper

SPEY, Martinus (1777-?) Flemish
£14525 $26000   (17-Jan-92 SY.NY87/R) Still life of grapes, peaches, flowers with
       butterflies and snails ona ledge (68x54cm-27x21in) s.

SPEYER, Christian (1855-1928) German
£4096 $7454   (27-May-92 PH.DU145) Horse-breaker on the shore (106x140cm-42x55in) s.
       (DM 12000)

SPICUZZA, Francesco J (1883-1962) American
£536 $970   (7-Dec-91 SG.M438) Stormy sea (61x74cm-24x29in) s. pastel

SPICUZZA, Francesco J (attrib) (1883-1962) American
£789 $1500   (22-Jun-92 SG.M640) Mother's portrait (74x58cm-29x23in) s. board
£658 $1250   (22-Jun-92 SG.M671) View of Lake Michigan (38x48cm-15x19in) s. pastel

SPIEGEL, Ferdinand (1879-) German
£909 $1555   (19-Mar-92 N.M2842/R) The Schlern, South Tyrol (79x100cm-31x39in) s.
       i.d.29verso (DM 2600)

SPIEGLER, Franz Josef (attrib) (1691-1757) German
£1020 $1827   (5-May-92 ZEL.L1541/R) Mary instructing Ann and putti above
       (82x58cm-32x23in) (DM 3000)
£2265 $4122   (11-Dec-91 N.M365/R) Skirmish in mountain landscape (51x43cm-20x17in)
       (DM 6500)
£2962 $5390   (11-Dec-91 N.M364/R) The Lamentation of Christ (44x55cm-17x22in)
       (DM 8500)

SPIERINCKS, Karel Philips (circle) (1608-1639) Flemish
£1800 $3204   (1-Nov-91 S374/R) Putti playing with bubbles (72x97cm-28x38in)

SPIERS, Harry (1869-?) American
£395 $700   (25-Apr-92 YFA.M273) Park Street church (51x41cm-20x16in) s. W/C

SPIGEL, Natan (1902-1942) Polish
£837 $1449   (8-Sep-91 REM.W35) In a back alley (60x44cm-24x17in) s. pastel
       (P.Z 16000000)

SPILHACZEK, Max (1876-?) Austrian
£537 $929   (3-Oct-91 D.V144/R) Tree lined path through landscape, late summer
       (47x63cm-19x25in) s. board on canvas (A.S 11000)
£878 $1520   (3-Oct-91 D.V143/R) Wienerwald landscape with house (47x62cm-19x24in) s.
       canvas on board (A.S 18000)

SPILHAUS, Nita (1878-1967) German
£605 $1071   (4-Nov-91 SY.J285/R) Farmhouse with aveue of trees (17x22cm-7x9in) init.
       board (SA.R 3000)
£1034 $1799   (13-Apr-92 SY.J346/R) Mamre (31x40cm-12x16in) init. board (SA.R 5200)
£1109 $1963   (4-Nov-91 SY.J286/R) Cape wooded landscape (31x40cm-12x16in) mono. board
       (SA.R 5500)

SPILIMBERGO, Adriano (1908-1975) Italian
£4139 $7409   (14-Nov-91 F.M100/R) Veduta di Lecco (60x80cm-24x31in) s. (I.L 9000000)
£4409 $8289   (19-Dec-91 F.M156/R) Isola di S.Giorgio (45x55cm-18x22in) s.
       (I.L 9500000)

SPILIMBERGO, Lino Eneas (1896-1964) Argentinian
£5220 $9500   (11-Dec-91 RO.BA28/R) Contemplacion (61x43cm-24x17in) s.
£7865 $14000   (1-Nov-91 PO.BA55) Paisaje de San Juan (43x57cm-17x22in) s.d.1930
£10753 $20000   (16-Jun-92 RO.BA20) Termas de Rio Hondo (40x60cm-16x24in)
£12209 $21000   (9-Oct-91 RO.BA26/R) Paisaje Norteno (61x47cm-24x19in) s.d.1941
£16129 $30000   (16-Jun-92 RO.BA41) Cabeza de nina (37x29cm-15x11in)
£25269 $47000   (16-Jun-92 RO.BA30) Paisaje (67x127cm-26x50in)
£26163 $45000   (9-Oct-91 RO.BA25/R) Familia Coya (188x106cm-74x42in) s.
£61798 $110000   (1-Nov-91 PO.BA54) Chico de pelo rojo (103x77cm-41x30in) s.
£124084 $237000   (30-Jun-92 PO.BA22) Meditando (193x143cm-76x56in) s.
£2688 $5000   (16-Jun-92 RO.BA19) Suburbio (35x47cm-14x19in) W/C
£2793 $5000   (6-May-92 V.BA102/R) Paisaje de Francia (32x42cm-13x17in) W/C
£3779 $6500   (9-Oct-91 RO.BA199/R) Figura (61x45cm-24x18in) s.d.59 pastel
£4121 $7500   (11-Dec-91 RO.BA29) Paisaje (49x34cm-19x13in) s.i. mixed media

SPILLIAERT, Leon (1881-1946) Belgian
£9167 $15767   (12-Oct-91 KV.L456/R) Karreveld-snowy landscape (60x47cm-24x19in)
       s.d.1920 panel (B.FR 550000)
£752 $1278   (22-Oct-91 C.A299) The cockfight (25x35cm-10x14in) s. W/C (B.FR 45000)

SPILLIAERT, Leon (1881-1946) Belgian-cont.

£1418	$2495	(7-Apr-92 C.A226/R) Houses with red rooftops (29x39cm-11x15in) s.d.1930 W/C (B.FR 85000)
£1501	$2642	(7-Apr-92 C.A227) The poachers (25x32cm-10x13in) s. colour dr. (B.FR 90000)
£3003	$5284	(7-Apr-92 C.A225/R) Park in Ostend (30x47cm-12x19in) s.d.1930 W/C (B.FR 180000)
£3636	$6582	(19-May-92 CH.AM172/R) Sunlovers on the beach Ostende (26x34cm-10x13in) s.d.1921 W/C pencil (D.FL 12000)
£5004	$8807	(7-Apr-92 C.A227 c/R) Still life (47x60cm-19x24in) s.d.1927 W/C (B.FR 300000)
£5004	$8807	(7-Apr-92 C.A223/R) Woman before a belfry (73x48cm-29x19in) s. pastel (B.FR 300000)
£6672	$11743	(7-Apr-92 C.A227 b/R) Portrait of Madeleine (63x48cm-25x19in) s.d.1922 gouache (B.FR 400000)
£9410	$17032	(7-Dec-91 KV.L397/R) Snowy landscape (55x38cm-22x15in) s.d.1920 gouache W/C (B.FR 550000)
£10833	$18633	(12-Oct-91 KV.L392/R) the card player (50x35cm-20x14in) s.d.1929 W/C (B.FR 650000)
£14542	$26322	(7-Dec-91 KV.L398/R) The dolls (49x62cm-19x24in) s.d.1931 W/C (B.FR 850000)
£16681	$29358	(7-Apr-92 C.A222/R) The Pulpit in Ostend (70x90cm-28x35in) s.d.1913 pastel (B.FR 1000000)
£19071	$34900	(12-May-92 C.A301/R) Woodland scene in winter (150x99cm-59x39in) s.d.1917 W/C (B.FR 1150000)
£20000	$34600	(24-Mar-92 C25/R) Plage (62x49cm-24x19in) s. pastel gouache chl card
£33417	$56809	(22-Oct-91 C.A298/R) Woman in a hat (31x40cm-12x16in) s.d.1909 W/C (B.FR 2000000)
£53068	$97114	(12-May-92 C.A300/R) Sunset over the sea in October (66x87cm-26x34in) s.d.1913 chk. (B.FR 3200000)
£66834	$113617	(22-Oct-91 C.A297/R) Mary Magdalen removes the crown of thorns (70x88cm-28x35in) s.d.1913 mixed media (B.FR 4000000)

SPIN, Jacob (1806-1885) Dutch

£1304	$2257	(24-Mar-92 VN.R89) Portrait of th ship 'Hillechiena van Delfziel' (47x63cm-19x25in) s.d.1848 W/C (D.FL 4200)
£1304	$2257	(24-Mar-92 VN.R90/R) Portrait of the barque 'President van Buren' (55x68cm-22x27in) s.d.1857 W/C (D.FL 4200)
£1515	$2682	(22-Apr-92 CH.AM264) The bark Johannes off the coast, Texel (47x63cm-19x25in) s.i.d.1870 ink W/C htd.white (D.FL 5000)

SPINDLER, Jake Ed (19th C) ?

| £765 | $1361 | (30-Oct-91 CH.AM100) Wooded river landscape with sheep (102x152cm-40x60in) s.d.1891 (D.FL 2500) |

SPINKS, Thomas (19th C) British

£720	$1289	(14-Jan-92 SWS143/R) Angler by river valley below ruined abbey (34x49cm-13x19in) s.
£1150	$1978	(8-Oct-91 PH101) Snowdon from Bryntuch, Capel Curig. Betws-y-Coed s.d.1890 i.stretcher s.d.1889 pair
£1200	$2016	(27-Aug-91 SWS1551/R) Herding cattle. River landscape (50x76cm-20x30in) s.d.1896 pair

SPINNY, Guillaume Jean Joseph de (1721-1785) Flemish

| £843 | $1500 | (22-Jan-92 SY.NY168/R) Portrait of lady holding gold cup (93x78cm-37x31in) s. painted oval |
| £893 | $1500 | (1-Sep-91 PO.BA11) Retrato de Mme.Elizabeth (73x57cm-29x22in) s.d.1761 |

SPIRIDON, Ignace (20th C) Italian

| £3500 | $6055 | (4-Oct-91 C43/R) Feeding time (76x100cm-30x39in) s.d.1869 |

SPIRO, Eugen (1874-1972) German

£771	$1472	(1-Jul-92 FB.P76) Le matador (56x35cm-22x14in) s. panel (F.FR 7500)
£4211	$7579	(21-Nov-91 L.K468/R) Woman in landscape (45x50cm-18x20in) s.d.1918 canvas on board (DM 12000)
£4561	$8211	(22-Nov-91 SA.A416/R) Summer flowers in green vase (75x65cm-30x26in) s.d.1934 (DM 13000)

SPIRO, Georges (1909-) French

£649	$1200	(12-Jun-92 SY.NY203/R) Sunset (50x61cm-20x24in) s.d.59
£1117	$2000	(13-Nov-91 B.SF2417/R) Paysage surrealiste (45x55cm-18x22in) s.
£1228	$2100	(21-Mar-92 W.W60/R) Le soleil et ses symboles (81x102cm-32x40in) s.d.1951 s.verso masonite

SPITZER, Walter (1927-) Polish

£1628	$2979	(17-May-92 GL.P262/R) Jerusalem d'or (46x60cm-18x24in) s. s.i.verso (F.FR 16000)
£1676	$3000	(13-Nov-91 B.SF2331) Portrait of seated woman in festive dress (55x47cm-22x19in) s.
£560	$1024	(17-May-92 GL.P22) Carnaval de Venise (32x39cm-13x15in) s. W/C gouache (F.FR 5500)
£1871	$3348	(10-May-92 LT.P69/R) Hommage a I.B.Singer (70x58cm-28x23in) s. gouache collage (F.FR 18500)
£2183	$4191	(6-Jul-92 HC.P59/R) Le Messager (64x47cm-25x19in) s. gouache htd (F.FR 21000)

SPITZWEG, Carl (1808-1885) German

£10811	$18486	(12-Mar-92 GK.Z92/R) Landscape with houses and church beyond (8x8cm-3x3in) i.verso panel (S.FR 28000)
£10997	$19134	(17-Sep-91 FN.S2549/R) King David seated with harp on terrace (34x8cm-13x3in) (DM 32000)
£62718	$114146	(13-Dec-91 BM.B723/R) The astrologer (29x18cm-11x7in) mono. panel (DM 180000)
£62718	$114146	(11-Dec-91 WE.MU77/R) Der Sonntagsjager (33x41cm-13x16in) panel (DM 180000)
£75601	$131546	(17-Sep-91 FN.S2546/R) Rocky landscape at night (31x53cm-12x21in) s.rhombus panel (DM 220000)
£206186	$358763	(17-Sep-91 FN.S2545/R) Die Nachhilfestunde - cleric kissing girl in landscape (23x29cm-9x11in) s.rhombus panel (DM 600000)
£515	$902	(27-Sep-91 GRA.B2482/R) Sketch of Oriental standing (16x13cm-6x5in) pencil (DM 1500)
£523	$951	(11-Dec-91 N.M269/R) Der schuchterne Freier (17x21cm-7x8in) pencil (DM 1500)
£619	$1076	(18-Sep-91 N.M278) Bushes by the edge of wood (10x21cm-4x8in) W/C (DM 1800)
£704	$1275	(3-Dec-91 FN.S2470) Wooded mountain landscape (31x20cm-12x8in) pencil (DM 2000)
£1068	$1901	(29-Apr-92 D.V561/R) Studies of mother holding child. Figures (27x20cm-11x8in) pencil double-sided (A.S 22000)
£2048	$3706	(21-May-92 L.K334/R) Figure with hunchback conversing with girl (21x15cm-8x6in) pencil (DM 6000)

SPLITGERBER, August (1844-1918) German

£524	$897	(18-Mar-92 N.M652) Shepherd with flock on woodland path (13x12cm-5x5in) s. panel (DM 1500)
£687	$1258	(2-Jun-92 FN.S2763) Village in hilly landscape with shepherd and sheep on path, evening (11x19cm-4x7in) s. panel (DM 2000)
£825	$1435	(18-Sep-91 N.M709) Landscape with traveller in fields (10x24cm-4x9in) s. panel (DM 2400)
£825	$1509	(2-Jun-92 FN.S2762) Wooded lake landscape and thunderstorm rising (11x19cm-4x7in) s. panel (DM 2400)
£836	$1522	(11-Dec-91 N.M600/R) Schloss Pottenstein, Franconia (23x15cm-9x6in) s.i. board (DM 2400)
£1045	$1882	(29-Jan-92 N.M835) Peasant woman with cows by stream in landscape (9x19cm-4x7in) s. panel (DM 3000)
£1045	$1902	(12-Dec-91 L.K683) Young girl with goat before tower in town wall (27x21cm-11x8in) (DM 3000)
£1220	$2220	(13-Dec-91 BM.B724/R) Shepherd and flock in autumnal wood (23x36cm-9x14in) s. (DM 3500)
£1812	$3298	(11-Dec-91 WE.MU114/R) The hermit (23x12cm-9x5in) s. panel (DM 5200)

SPODE, Samuel (19th C) British

£1000	$1740	(12-Sep-91 CSK205/R) 'Asteriod', chestnut racehorse in loose box (48x58cm-19x23in) i.
£1300	$2327	(13-Nov-91 S166/R) Dido and Fop, two favourite pointers (44x58cm-17x23in) i.
£1800	$3078	(12-Mar-92 CSK144/R) Sportsman mounted on chestnut hunter with two pointers in landscape (71x91cm-28x36in)
£4000	$7160	(14-Jan-92 SWS162/R) Voltigeur. The Flying Dutchman (45x60cm-18x24in) s.i. pair

SPODE, Samuel (style) (19th C) British

£2077	$3800	(5-Jun-92 SY.NY169/R) The start of the St Leger (46x83cm-18x33in) i.

SPOERRI, Daniel (20th C) ?

£800	$1464	(4-Jun-92 CSK204) Untitled (50x50cm-20x20in) s.d.77 verso collage
£993	$1698	(12-Mar-92 RAS.K541) Collage (50x50cm-20x20in) s.d.72verso (D.KR 11000)

SPOHLER (19th C) Dutch

£900	$1548	(10-Oct-91 L285/R) Farmstead by figure and skaters on lake with distant windmill (43x71cm-17x28in) panel

SPOHLER, Jan Jacob (1811-1866) Dutch

£1284	$2286	(29-Oct-91 VN.R286/R) Landscape with mill (27x38cm-11x15in) s. panel (D.FL 4200)
£2905	$5171	(30-Oct-91 CH.AM268) Wooded river landscape with shipping and figures near windmill (27x21cm-11x8in) s. panel (D.FL 9500)
£7200	$13392	(19-Jun-92 C3/R) River landscape with figures by windmill (56x71cm-22x28in) s. panel
£7509	$13590	(21-May-92 L.K483/R) Dutch street scene (53x44cm-21x17in) s. (DM 22000)
£8485	$15018	(22-Apr-92 CH.AM205/R) Shipping on river near a windmill, anglers in the foreground (57x74cm-22x29in) s. (D.FL 28000)
£9898	$17915	(21-May-92 L.K482/R) Fun on the ice on Dutch canal (43x63cm-17x25in) s. panel (DM 29000)

SPOHLER, Jan Jacob Coenraad (1837-1923) Dutch

£1000	$1860	(18-Jun-92 B56/R) Windmills by a river (18x15cm-7x6in) s. panel
£1789	$3221	(22-Nov-91 SA.A1669/R) Dutch harbour with windmills and figures (26x21cm-10x8in) s. panel (DM 5100)
£1831	$3314	(3-Dec-91 FN.S2471/R) Dutch river landscape with sailing boats and figures on path (47x66cm-19x26in) s. (DM 5200)

SPOHLER, Jan Jacob Coenraad (1837-1923) Dutch-cont.
£12000 $21360   (27-Nov-91 S24/R) Ferry (62x82cm-24x32in) s.

SPOHLER, Jan Jacob Coenraad (circle) (1837-1923) Dutch
£1800 $3078   (17-Mar-92 PH28/R) Figures on path beside canal (43x65cm-17x26in) bears
                sig.

SPOHLER, Johannes Franciscus (1853-1894) Dutch
£1034 $1779   (16-Oct-91 KM.K1391) View of Dutch town with figures (16x20cm-6x8in) s.
                panel (DM 3000)
£2202 $3897   (5-Nov-91 SY.AM296/R) Town scene (33x25cm-13x10in) s.d.1873 panel
                (D.FL 7200)
£3000 $5130   (17-Mar-92 PH1/R) Dutch street scene (45x36cm-18x14in) s.
£5500 $10230   (17-Jun-92 S267/R) Canal scene, Amsterdam (46x61cm-18x24in) s.
£6800 $12104   (27-Nov-91 S4/R) Dutch canal scene (44x35cm-17x14in) s.

SPOHLER, Johannes Franciscus (attrib) (1853-1894) Dutch
£550 $995   (21-May-92 CSK131) Figures in Dutch street (20x16cm-8x6in) with sig.
                panel

SPOLDI, Aldo (1950-) Italian
*£1180 $2101   (29-Apr-92 F.F72/R) Senza titolo (100x64cm-39x25in) s. mixed media
                cardboard (I.L 2600000)*

SPOON, Arij (1859-1945) Dutch
£466 $829   (26-Nov-91 VN.R117) View of Rotterdam (35x51cm-14x20in) s.d.1902
                (D.FL 1500)

SPOONER, Arthur (20th C) British
£7200 $12888   (14-Jan-92 PH106/R) Hauling up cobbles, Flamborough (122x191cm-48x75in)
                s. s.i.verso
£15000 $27900   (17-Jun-92 S418/R) Iris (152x61cm-60x24in) s.d.1905

SPOONER, Charles (fl.1885-1904) British
£700 $1211   (26-Mar-92 CSK67) Porchester castle (66x92cm-26x36in) s.d.1886

SPOONER-LILLINGSTON, G B Percy (fl.1871-1930) British
£520 $952   (4-Jun-92 DLY101) Fishing boats (91x61cm-36x24in) s.d.14
£3100 $5549   (14-Jan-92 PH43/R) Trawler's boat (76x138cm-30x54in) s.d.94 s.stretcher

SPORNBERG, J (18th C) ?
*£400 $712   (21-Jan-92 SWS1726/R) Portrait of gentleman, with receding grey hair, in
                brown jacket (7x?cm-3x?in) min. s.d.1795 turned giltwood frame*

SPOWERS, Ethel (1890-1947) Australian
£385 $685   (27-Apr-92 J.M987) Spring (23x33cm-9x13in) s.d.1946 W/C (A.D 900)

SPRANGER, Bartholomaeus (1546-1611) Flemish
£1575 $2710   (8-Oct-91 ZEL.L1727/R) Mythological allegory in rocky landscape with
                Caritas and truth (44x32cm-17x13in) panel (DM 4600)

SPRANGER, Bartholomaeus (circle) (1546-1611) Flemish
£6363 $11263   (7-Nov-91 D.V269/R) Crucifixion (104x83cm-41x33in) panel (A.S 130000)

SPRANGER, Bartholomaeus (style) (1546-1611) Flemish
£6800 $12444   (12-May-92 SWS764/R) Mercury and Venus (161x119cm-63x47in)
£8000 $14000   (25-Feb-92 PH35/R) The three fates (38cm-15ins circular) W/C bodycol
                vellum pair

SPREAFICO, Eugenio (1856-1919) Italian
£5113 $8743   (19-Mar-92 F.M62/R) Case a Magreglio (24x30cm-9x12in) s. panel
                (I.L 11000000)

SPRECKELS, R C (19th C) Dutch
£559 $950   (25-Oct-91 S.W2361/R) Cows and sheep - pastoral landscape
                (25x36cm-10x14in) s. panel

SPRICK, Johann (19th C) German
£999 $1858   (16-Jun-92 SY.B281/R) Young lady and her child seated on Gothic chair
                (116x94cm-46x37in) s. (B.FR 60000)

SPRINCHORN, Carl (1887-1971) American
£833 $1400   (14-Aug-91 B.P143/R) Bend in the river (41x51cm-16x20in) s. d.44 verso
                canvasboard
£4315 $7250   (14-Aug-91 B.P142/R) April showers (64x76cm-25x30in) s. i. verso
*£391 $700   (6-May-92 B.P121/R) Crystal Cage - Nat Henson's camp at East Branch
                Penobscot at Matagamon (30x46cm-12x18in) s. i.verso gouache*

SPRING, Alfons (1843-1908) German
£4500 $7965   (14-Feb-92 C54/R) At church (52x32cm-20x13in) s.i. panel

SPRINGER, Cornelis (1817-1891) Dutch
£23368 $39725   (25-Oct-91 BM.B833/R) View of Harlem with figures (30x41cm-12x16in) s.
                panel (DM 68000)

SPRINGER, Cornelis (1817-1891) Dutch-cont.

£32423	$59010	(27-May-92 PH.DU43/R) The Michaelis Gate of Xanten in romantic surroundings (44x54cm-17x21in) mono.d.1841 (DM 95000)
£42813	$76208	(30-Oct-91 CH.AM284/R) View of Vismarkt, Harderwyk, with villagers (31x41cm-12x16in) s.d.1864 s.i.d.verso panel (D.FL 140000)
£82857	$145000	(20-Feb-92 SY.NY6/R) De Wijdstraat te Oudewater bij Zomer (56x74cm-22x29in) s.d.78 s.i.verso panel
£88000	$150480	(20-Mar-92 C6/R) The house of Admiral Martin van Rossum in Zaltbommel (75x97cm-30x38in) s.d.1860
£150000	$267000	(29-Nov-91 C15/R) The Rokin, Amsterdam, towards Langebrugsteeg (60x77cm-24x30in) s. mono.i.d.1854verso panel
£520	$920	(5-Nov-91 SY.AM318) Wooded landscape with heron in creek (41x31cm-16x12in) init. black chk (D.FL 1700)
£909	$1609	(22-Apr-92 CH.AM301) Figures resting at the back of a church (15x12cm-6x5in) s.d.61 pencil pen W/C (D.FL 3000)
£1162	$2057	(5-Nov-91 SY.AM165) View of town in winter (40x34cm-16x13in) init.indist.d. brown chk (D.FL 3800)
£2446	$4330	(5-Nov-91 SY.AM3/R) Het melkpad, Hilversum (29x39cm-11x15in) s.i.d.90 black brown chk (D.FL 8000)
£2599	$4601	(5-Nov-91 SY.AM293/R) Street scene, Edam (60x45cm-24x18in) s.i.d.79 black chk (D.FL 8500)
£2691	$4763	(5-Nov-91 SY.AM143/R) Karnemelksgracht, Enkhuizen (29x40cm-11x16in) s.i.indist.d. black brown chk (D.FL 8800)
£4848	$8582	(22-Apr-92 CH.AM341/R) View of the Waag, Deventer, with several villagers on the Brink (75x100cm-30x39in) s.i.d.1868 blk.brown chks. (D.FL 16000)
£9786	$17419	(30-Oct-91 CH.AM372/R) View of Nieuwe Zijds Voorburgwal, Amsterdam with figures and boats (39x55cm-15x22in) s.d.1884 pencil pen W/C htd.white (D.FL 32000)

SPRINGER, Leendert (jnr) (1831-1894) Dutch

£459	$817	(29-Oct-91 VN.R287) Winter landscape with windmill (33x24cm-13x9in) s. (D.FL 1500)

SPRINGOLO, Nino (1886-?) Italian

£5105	$9597	(19-Dec-91 F.M108) Case d'autunno (67x82cm-26x32in) s. panel (I.L 11000000)

SPROTTE, Siegward (1913-) German

£1024	$1853	(23-May-92 GB.B7263) Dune landscape with blue sky (34x27cm-13x11in) s.d.1981 board (DM 3000)
£1993	$3687	(12-Jun-92 HN.H793/R) Landscape near Potsdam (22x27cm-9x11in) s.d.1937 tempera oil panel (DM 5800)
£1468	$2656	(23-May-92 GB.B7264) Still life with delphinum (65x47cm-26x19in) s. W/C (DM 4300)

SPURLING, Jack (1871-1933) British

£1702	$3013	(26-Apr-92 SY.ME193/R) Torrens (37x52cm-15x20in) s.d.1928 gouache W/C (A.D 4000)
£2000	$3620	(20-May-92 S237/R) The ship Samuel Plimsoll (43x66cm-17x26in) s.d.1926 W/C bodycol

SPURRIER, Steven (1878-?) British

£400	$680	(22-Oct-91 SWS424/R) At ball (17x28cm-7x11in) s.i.d.1934 pencil W/C htd bodycol

SQUIRE, Helen (fl.1889-1905) British

£650	$1235	(23-Jun-92 PH121/R) Girl reading by window (24x33cm-9x13in) s.d.95 indis.i.verso panel
£720	$1303	(19-May-92 PH87/R) A quiet read (29x45cm-11x18in) init. W/C htd.white

SQUIRRELL, Leonard (1893-1979) British

£460	$819	(21-Jan-92 SWS1330/R) Canterbury Cathedral (51x37cm-20x15in) s. s.i.mount W/C bodycol over pencil
£500	$895	(14-Jan-92 SWS99/R) Sunlit valley (30x21cm-12x8in) s.d.1932 W/C over pencil
£750	$1350	(28-Jan-92 RG2655) Coastal scene, September afternoon, Pakefield near Lowestoft (20x38cm-8x15in) s.d.1948 W/C

STAATEN, Louis van (19th C?) Dutch

£420	$819	(15-Jan-92 CSK109) Dutch barges moored in harbour by windmill (41x60cm-16x24in) s.pencil W/C htd white
£420	$781	(16-Jun-92 RB398) Dutch canal scene with windmill and barges (38x58cm-15x23in) s. W/C
£800	$1376	(11-Oct-91 K342/R) Govingheim. Douvecht (58x38cm-23x15in) s. W/C pair

STABLI, Adolf (attrib) (1842-1901) Swiss

£2910	$5180	(28-Apr-92 RAS.K482) River landscape (19x24cm-7x9in) s.d.1891 panel (D.KR 33000)

STACEY, Anna Lee (1871-1943) American

£2374	$4250	(13-Nov-91 B.SF2662/R) View of Gloucester Bay (61x91cm-24x36in) s.

STACEY, H E (19th C) British

£670	$1179	(8-Apr-92 CSK279) Encampment around ark of Covenant (173x234cm-68x92in) s.d.86

STACEY, John F (attrib) (1859-?) American
£684 $1300   (22-Jun-92 SG.M591) Through the nut trees to Rogers Lake (91x112cm-36x44in) s.

STACHE, Adolphe (1823-1862) Belgian
£2200 $3762   (17-Mar-92 SWS1287) A talkative friend (34x27cm-13x11in) s. panel

STACHE, Hermann (1867-?) German
£685 $1178   (11-Oct-91 AW.H3075/R) Black Forest house in landscape (32x43cm-13x17in) s.d.1905 i.verso board (DM 2000)

STACHOWSKI, Wladyslaw von (1852-1932) Polish
£952 $1705   (5-May-92 ZEL.L1543/R) Seascape with frigate and fishing boat (75x116cm-30x46in) s. (DM 2800)

STACK, Josef Magnus (1812-1868) Swedish
£2021 $3557   (11-Apr-92 FAL.M397/R) Ships at anchor in moonlight (67x82cm-26x32in) s.d.1857 (S.KR 21200)
£2863 $5095   (28-Nov-91 BU.S37/R) Winter scene with family fishing (59x86cm-23x34in) s.d.1854 (S.KR 30000)
£6000 $10680   (29-Nov-91 C97/R) Marina Grande, Capri (62x93cm-24x37in) s.d.1867

STACKHOUSE, Emily (1811-1870) British
£445 $779   (20-Feb-92 D.V533/R) Lily (41x30cm-16x12in) s.d.1864 W/C oval (A.S 9000)

STACQUET, Henri (1838-1907) Belgian
£500 $875   (24-Sep-91 GM.B749) Village sous la neige (B.FR 30000)

STADEMANN, Adolf (1824-1895) German
£699 $1196   (18-Mar-92 N.M655) Frozen lake landscape with skaters (17x26cm-7x10in) mono. board (DM 2000)
£1569 $2808   (15-Nov-91 GK.Z5101/R) Winter landscape with skaters (24x31cm-9x12in) (S.FR 4000)
£2216 $3900   (9-Apr-92 FA.PH651/R) Children playing in winter landscape (13x23cm-5x9in) s. panel
£3297 $6000   (27-May-92 CH.NY65/R) Faggot gatherers in winter landscape (30x46cm-12x18in) s. board
£3571 $6250   (20-Feb-92 SY.NY215/R) Winter landscape (22x32cm-9x13in) s. panel
£5245 $8969   (18-Mar-92 N.M653/R) Frozen river landscape with figures in evening sunshine (32x39cm-13x15in) s. (DM 15000)
£6873 $11959   (18-Sep-91 N.M710/R) Skaters in frozen river landscape with cottage (49x61cm-19x24in) s. (DM 20000)
£15331 $27902   (11-Dec-91 WE.MU82/R) Fun on the ice (61x101cm-24x40in) s. (DM 44000)

STADLER, P (19/20th C) Austrian
£514 $884   (8-Oct-91 ZEL.L2286/R) Portrait of girl wearing black jacket with lace and ermine (8x6cm-3x2in) min. (DM 1500)
£2200 $4026   (2-Jun-92 S716) Triumphal entry of Prince Charles into Antwerp with rejoicing crowds (24x?cm-9x?in) min.

STAEGER, Ferdinand (1880-1975) German
£500 $865   (3-Oct-91 CSK219) The old cow herd (71x86cm-28x34in) s.
£1031 $1814   (10-Apr-92 KM.K553/R) Prager Grabenbummel (54x114cm-21x45in) s.d.1900 (DM 3000)
£1375 $2419   (10-Apr-92 KM.K554/R) Aus Wirrnis entsprungen (102x163cm-40x64in) s.d.1924 i.verso (DM 4000)

STAEL, Nicolas de (1914-1955) French
£27000 $48870   (3-Dec-91 C280/R) Composition (38x46cm-15x18in) s.
£70000 $126700   (2-Dec-91 C47/R) Florence (14x22cm-6x9in) s.i.verso
£160000 $289600   (5-Dec-91 S13/R) Composition (61x50cm-24x20in) s.
£5500 $10505   (30-Jun-92 C202/R) Abstract composition (55x75cm-22x30in) s.d.51 ink paper on board
£9290 $17000   (11-May-92 CH.NY48/R) Le picador (29x22cm-11x9in) st.sig. collage
£21000 $36330   (26-Mar-92 S22/R) Composition, fond vert clair (32x22cm-13x9in) s. s.d.53 verso paper collage card

STAFL, Otakar (?) ?
£1468 $2554   (14-Apr-92 SY.AM202/R) The Wenceslaus Square in Prague (31x39cm-12x15in) s. panel (D.FL 4800)

STAGER, Balz (1861-1937) Swiss
£2431 $4352   (15-Nov-91 ZOF.Z1885/R) Evening near Niederurnen (46x38cm-18x15in) s.d.1898 i.verso (S.FR 6200)

STAGLIANO, Arturo (1870-1936) Italian
£1013 $1844   (12-Dec-91 F.M43) Figura femminile con fiori di pesco (59x41cm-23x16in) s. (I.L 2200000)
£3242 $5608   (24-Mar-92 CH.R110/R) Testa di ragazza (64x51cm-25x20in) s. panel (I.L 7000000)

STAGURA, Albert (1866-1947) German
£989 $1730   (19-Feb-92 D.V40/R) View of glacier (130x94cm-51x37in) s.i. (A.S 20000)
£1930 $3300   (13-Mar-92 FN.S2968/R) Alpine landscape with sheep and fog rising (122x101cm-48x40in) s.i.d.1925 panel (DM 5500)

STAGURA, Albert (1866-1947) German-cont.

£1056	$1912	(3-Dec-91 FN.S2473) Snow covered river landscape, evening (63x74cm-25x29in) s.i. pastel (DM 3000)
£1375	$2392	(21-Sep-91 SA.A1962/R) Autumnal landscape with mountain range beyond (80x72cm-31x28in) s.i.d.1922 pastel board (DM 4000)
£1394	$2537	(11-Dec-91 N.M270/R) River in moor landscape with snow covered mountains (73x82cm-29x32in) s.indis.d.1932 pastel (DM 4000)
£1408	$2549	(3-Dec-91 FN.S2472/R) View of village near pond in rising thunderstorm (74x69cm-29x27in) s.i. pastel (DM 4000)
£1748	$2990	(18-Mar-92 N.M305/R) Lake Chiemsee landscape with Fohn clouds (58x67cm-23x26in) indis.s.d.1926 pastel (DM 5000)
£1748	$2990	(18-Mar-92 N.M306) Moon rising in moor landscape (58x63cm-23x25in) s.i.d.1912 pastel (DM 5000)
£1986	$3535	(28-Nov-91 D.V132/R) Chiemsee landscape with fisherman (73x83cm-29x33in) s.d.1941 mixed media paper on board (A.S 40000)

STAHL, Benjamin Albert (1910-) American

£2388	$4250	(2-Nov-91 IH.NY69/R) Young woman in white blouse (46x61cm-18x24in) s.

STAHL, Friedrich (1863-1940) German

£1143	$2000	(28-Feb-92 SY.NY53/R) Portrait of Diana Silvarum (34x25cm-13x10in) s.i.d.1920 panel
£1672	$3044	(12-Dec-91 L.K701/R) St Eligius seated with couple standing beside him (45x44cm-18x17in) s.d.1922-23 panel (DM 4800)
£3500	$6335	(22-May-92 C175/R) Mixed flowers in vase with bowl of cherries on table (50x44cm-20x17in) s.d.1911 panel
£4587	$8165	(30-Oct-91 CH.AM161/R) Among the holyhocks (100x60cm-39x24in) s.d.1882 (D.FL 15000)

STAHLSCHMIDT, Max (1854-?) German

£1549	$2804	(3-Dec-91 FN.S2475/R) Peasants washing horses in stream and arched bridge in wooded landscape (72x106cm-28x42in) s. (DM 4400)

STAHR, Paul (1883-1953) American

£1966	$3500	(2-May-92 IH.NY202/R) Woman with torch, man with gun attacked by tiger (64x58cm-25x23in) s.

STAHRE, Hakan (1944-) Swedish

£706	$1257	(28-Oct-91 AB.S221) Picking potatoes in field (45x54cm-18x21in) s. (S.KR 7500)

STAINFORTH, Martin (20th C) Australian

£598	$1065	(28-Apr-92 CH.ME131) At the stables, Randwick N.S.W. (24x29cm-9x11in) s. (A.D 1400)
£989	$1800	(13-Dec-91 DM.D2003/R) English horse race (69x94cm-27x37in) board
£1700	$3094	(28-May-92 C76/R) Finishing post (60x98cm-24x39in) s. board
£5000	$8550	(17-Mar-92 JRL.S191/R) Passing winning post (62x101cm-24x40in) s. (A.D 11250)

STAINTON, George (19th C) British

£619	$1076	(18-Sep-91 N.M711/R) Fishing boat and flotsam on choppy seas offshore (40x61cm-16x24in) s. (DM 1800)
£880	$1681	(16-Jul-92 PHX368/R) On Thames (41x61cm-16x24in) s. i.verso
£900	$1566	(14-Apr-92 CSK149/R) Coastyal lugger in fair wind off-shore (40x61cm-16x24in) s.
£1100	$2112	(28-Jul-92 RJ136) Shipping in rough seas in the Channel (53x58cm-21x23in) s.
£2600	$4706	(20-May-92 S49/R) Penarth (51x76cm-20x30in) s. s.i.stretcher

STALBEMT, Adriaen van (1580-1662) Flemish

£6200	$11036	(30-Oct-91 S104/R) The Judgement of Verity (52x78cm-20x31in) panel

STALBEMT, Adriaen van (attrib) (1580-1660) Flemish

£10000	$19200	(10-Jul-92 C110/R) Winter landscape with skaters on frozen river by tower (9x10cm-4x4in) copper
£12963	$23204	(14-Nov-91 CH.AM200 a/R) Rest on the Flight into Egypt (26x19cm-10x7in) copper oval (D.FL 42000)

STALLER, Gerard Johan (1880-1956) Dutch

£581	$1028	(5-Nov-91 SY.AM426/R) Figure in Oriental landscape (107x162cm-42x64in) s.d.1930 (D.FL 1900)

STAMMBACH, Eugen (1876-1966) German

£515	$897	(17-Sep-91 FN.S2558) Fir trees (41x52cm-16x20in) s. (DM 1500)
£619	$1076	(17-Sep-91 FN.S2561/R) Black Forest peasant interior with cast iron stove (36x50cm-14x20in) s. board on panel (DM 1800)
£912	$1560	(13-Mar-92 FN.S2970/R) Still life of magnolias in vase (46x56cm-18x22in) s. (DM 2600)
£1404	$2400	(13-Mar-92 FN.S2969) Still life of flowers (36x23cm-14x9in) s. i.d.1963verso board (DM 4000)
£1512	$2631	(17-Sep-91 FN.S2555/R) Wildsee near Wildbad (75x110cm-30x43in) s. (DM 4400)
£1512	$2631	(17-Sep-91 FN.S2557/R) Still life of flowers (53x36cm-21x14in) s. canvas on board (DM 4400)

STAMMBACH, Eugen (1876-1966) German-cont.
£2234 $3887   (17-Sep-91 FN.S2556/R) View of Swabian farmhouse with fruit tree (87x52cm-34x20in) s.d.1929 (DM 6500)

STAMMEL, Eberhard (1833-1906) German
£917 $1633   (30-Oct-91 CH.AM169/R) Nobleman enjoying oysters (35x29cm-14x11in) s. (D.FL 3000)
£1404 $2500   (22-Jan-92 SY.NY275/R) Nosegay (42x34cm-17x13in) s.d.1863 canvas on masonite

STAMMHAMMER, Ferdinand (1901-1973) Austrian
£393 $746   (25-Jun-92 D.V593/R) Still life with king of hearts (33x47cm-13x19in) s. gouache (A.S 8000)

STAMOS, Theodoros (1922-) American
£857 $1500   (28-Feb-92 SY.NY272/R) Untitled (23x30cm-9x12in) s. s.d.1959 stretcher
£1143 $2000   (27-Feb-92 CE.NY199/R) Untitled (61x48cm-24x19in) s.d.74 acrylic paper
£1143 $2000   (27-Feb-92 CE.NY150/R) Wm. Blake-Sun box (41x173cm-16x68in) s.d.1959 overlap
£1676 $3000   (9-May-92 CE.NY371/R) Interference (61x48cm-24x19in) s. board
£2093 $3600   (12-Oct-91 SY.NY315/R) Infinity field lefkada series (77x56cm-30x22in) s.d.1975 acrylic paper
£2171 $3800   (27-Feb-92 CE.NY149/R) Star of midnight field (178x58cm-70x23in) s. d.1954 stretcher
£2235 $4000   (12-Nov-91 CE.NY142/R) Infinity field lefkada series for Caspar David Friedrich (56x77cm-22x30in) s.i.d.1981-2 acrylic
£2326 $4000   (12-Oct-91 SY.NY275/R) Infinity field (132x142cm-52x56in) s.d.1969-70 stretcher
£5378 $9250   (12-Oct-91 SY.NY242/R) Mistra (76x60cm-30x24in) s.d.49 masonite
£5714 $10000   (27-Feb-92 CH.NY6/R) Cleft (41x107cm-16x42in) s. s.i.d.1956verso
£17341 $30000   (3-Oct-91 SY.NY55/R) Infinity field lefkada series (244x193cm-96x76in) s.i.d.1980 acrylic
£2746   *$4750*   *(6-Sep-91 S.BM324/R) Untitled abstraction (43x58cm-17x23in) s.d.1950 gouache*

STAMPFLI, Peter (1937-) Swiss
£1423 $2476   (16-Apr-92 FB.P210/R) Albion (192x168cm-76x66in) s.i.d.84verso acrylic (F.FR 14000)
£1722 $3118   (20-May-92 FB.P23 a) Optimo (198x125cm-78x49in) s.d.86 verso acrylic canvas (F.FR 17000)
£2026 $3668   (20-May-92 FB.P21 a) Pioneer (203x212cm-80x83in) s.d.87 verso acrylic canvas (F.FR 20000)
£2533 $4585   (20-May-92 FB.P22 a/R) Coronado (200x154cm-79x61in) s.d.85-86 verso acrylic canvas (F.FR 25000)

STAN, Walter (1917-) American
£843 $1450   (10-Oct-91 FA.PH756) At piano (74x89cm-29x35in) s. double-sided

STANESBY, Alexander (19th C) British
£650 $1125   (1-Oct-91 SWS1705) Still life of fruits on draped table (30x38cm-12x15in) s.d.1874 board

STANFIELD, C (1793-1867) British
£2550 $4386   (4-Mar-92 RBB923/R) Rhenish landscapes with boats and figures on shore, buildings beyond (30x41cm-12x16in) s. pair

STANFIELD, Clarkson (1793-1867) British
£1100 $2012   (3-Jun-92 DO.H2430/R) Upper Italian lake landscape with boats (37x53cm-15x21in) s. board (DM 3200)
£1150 $2139   (16-Jun-92 ACA780) Street scene (46x38cm-18x15in) s.d.1848 panel
£2459 $4500   (5-Jun-92 SY.NY235/R) Harbour at dusk (97x128cm-38x50in) s.d.1842
£8000 $15280   (17-Jul-92 C182/R) On the South coast (77x117cm-30x46in) indis.s.d.18--
£400   *$720*   *(22-Nov-91 C2) Off Dover (13x20cm-5x8in) s. pencil W/C htd.white*
£580   *$1027*   *(11-Feb-92 PH132) Crossing bridge (22x32cm-9x13in) s.d.39 W/C*
£1500   *$2685*   *(12-Nov-91 C115/R) Ischia (20x30cm-8x12in) pencil W/C htd.bodycol.scratching out*
£1860   *$3200*   *(15-Oct-91 CE.NY391/R) A village square (25x34cm-10x13in) s. ink pencil W/C gouache*
£3600   *$6444*   *(12-Nov-91 C117/R) Pavia (24x36cm-9x14in) pencil W/C htd.white scratching out*
£4400   *$8404*   *(16-Jul-92 S117) Dover (16x25cm-6x10in) W/C over pencil htd bodycol*

STANFIELD, Clarkson (circle) (1793-1867) British
£900 $1512   (29-Aug-91 CG116) Smallships in rough seas off the Dutch coast (71x91cm-28x36in) s.
£900 $1512   (15-Aug-91 B309) Vessels in Dutch harbour (40x60cm-16x24in)
£650   *$1242*   *(1-Jul-92 B42) Figures and boats on Continental river (17x27cm-7x11in) W/C*

STANFIELD, Clarkson (style) (1793-1867) British
£2000 $3620   (20-May-92 S1/R) The Battle of Trafalgar, late in the day (76x153cm-30x60in)

STANFIELD, George Clarkson (1828-1878) British
£1580 $2750   (13-Sep-91 S.W2865/R) Coastal scene (69x102cm-27x40in) s.

STANFIELD, George Clarkson (1828-1878) British-cont.
£1600 $2768   (23-Mar-92 HS233/R) Extensive continental river scene with figures
                       crossing a bridge (49x74cm-19x29in) indist.s.d.1857
£1700 $3111   (3-Jun-92 S6/R) Angera on Lago Maggiore (38x58cm-15x23in) s.d.1862
£5000 $8550   (12-Mar-92 CSK294/R) Mosel landscape with fishing boats and castles
                       (35x53cm-14x21in) s.d.51 and 52 pair

STANFIELD, George Clarkson (style) (1828-1878) British
£1300 $2327   (14-Jan-92 SWS160/R) Peasants on shores of North Italian lake
                       (59x107cm-23x42in) indis.init.

STANFIELD, William Clarkson see STANFIELD, Clarkson

STANGE, Bernhard (1807-1880) German
£2055 $3534   (8-Oct-91 ZEL.L1729/R) View of cataracts in Formazzotal with figures on
                       arched stone bridge (138x102cm-54x40in) mono.d.1878 i.verso (DM 6000)

STANGL, Heinz (1942-) Austrian
£440 $783   (31-Oct-91 D.V81/R) Bathtime (34x25cm-13x10in) s.d.1974 pencil W/C
                       (A.S 9000)
£538 $957   (31-Oct-91 D.V80/R) Conversation (35x25cm-14x10in) s.d.1973 pencil W/C
                       (A.S 11000)

STANHOPE, John Roddam Spencer (1829-1908) British
£25000 $44500   (27-Nov-91 S172/R) Song of Solomon (107x260cm-42x102in) gouache triptych
                       eight compartments

STANIEK, A (19th C) German
£976 $1766   (3-Dec-91 R.T163/R) Serenading the friar (56x46cm-22x18in) s.i.d.1883
                       (C.D 2000)

STANIER, Henry (?-1892) British
£1100 $1903   (24-Mar-92 PHC385) Milton reciting prose to daughters (98x153cm-39x60in)
                       s.d.1861

STANISLAWSKI, Jan (1860-1907) Russian
£1445 $2587   (17-Nov-91 REM.W26) Corn stooks (18x24cm-7x9in) s. board (P.Z 28000000)
£2278 $4282   (21-Dec-91 PSA.W21) Podole landscape (15x23cm-6x9in) s. board
                       (P.Z 44000000)
£2917 $5104   (29-Sep-91 AG.W18) In the Ukraine (21x32cm-8x13in) s. (P.Z 56000000)
£3003 $5645   (22-Dec-91 AG.W9) Kiev, Padol Suburb (24x32cm-9x13in) s. cardboard
                       (P.Z 58000000)

STANKO, Michal (1901-1969) Polish
£1047 $1811   (8-Sep-91 REM.W36) Mountain pasture (71x50cm-28x20in) s. panel
                       (P.Z 20000000)

STANKOWSKI, Anton (1906-) ?
£2062 $3814   (11-Jun-92 HN.H441/R) Deception (50x50cm-20x20in) s.d.1979 (DM 6000)

STANLEY, Bob (1932-) American
£2098 $3629   (28-Mar-92 BOD.P1027) Beatles George and John (61x61cm-24x24in)
                       s.i.d.1965verso liquitex canvas (DM 6000)

STANLEY, Caleb Robert (1795-1868) British
£2200 $4136   (19-Dec-91 C141/R) Continental river landscape with church overlooking
                       gorge (76x112cm-30x44in) s.
£1200 $2148   (14-Nov-91 S151/R) On the Thames at Battersea (19x29cm-7x11in) s. W/C
                       over pencil

STANLEY, H (?) ?
£1000 $1720   (4-Mar-92 S216/R) St. George's Hall, Liverpool (49x75cm-19x30in) s.d.76
                       W/C over pencil

STANLEY, Harold John (1817-1867) British
£1100 $2046   (18-Jun-92 B69/R) Portrait of young lady holding a fan (52x43cm-20x17in)
                       s.

STANLEY, Lady Dorothy Tennant see TENNANT, Dorothy

STANLEY, Mrs (19th C) British
£850 $1624   (14-Jul-92 DR295/R) Panoramic view in County Down from Carlingford to
                       Benyon (22x127cm-9x50in) s.i.d.1813 pen monochrome wash

STANNARD, Alexander Molyneux (1878-1975) British
£440 $748   (22-Oct-91 SWS199) Leafy lane (24x35cm-9x14in) s. W/C
£480 $859   (6-May-92 MMB217) Country cottage with garden (18x23cm-7x9in) s.indis.d.
                       W/C htd.white
£750 $1305   (12-Sep-91 CSK54/R) Berkshire village (36x61cm-14x24in) s. pencil W/C

STANNARD, Alfred (1806-1889) British
£700 $1337   (21-Jul-92 PH262/R) Ferry (65x86cm-26x34in)

STANNARD, Eloise Harriet (c.1828-1915) British

£1150	$1978	(16-Oct-91 HAR445/R) Still life with fruit, red poppies and bullfinches (53x43cm-21x17in) s.d.1876
£1700	$2890	(22-Oct-91 SWS311/R) Still life of pears by basket (30x50cm-12x20in) s.d.1911
£2000	$3540	(6-Nov-91 S108/R) Still life of pears, grapes, basket and butterfly (25x35cm-10x14in) s.
£2200	$4070	(12-Jun-92 C188/R) Grapes on silver plate (22x30cm-9x12in) s.d.1893
£3200	$5440	(24-Oct-91 CSK162/R) Roses by a upturned basket on a ledge (28x33cm-11x13in) s.d.1881
£3200	$5920	(12-Jun-92 C187/R) Strawberries in wicker basket on ledge (21x30cm-8x12in) s.d.1895
£4500	$7965	(6-Nov-91 S104/R) Still life of grapes, peaches and raspberries on marble ledge (43x35cm-17x14in) s.d.1886
£6000	$10560	(10-Apr-92 K497/R) Study of strawberries on cabbage leaf in basket upon ledge (36x23cm-14x9in) s.d.1891
£6000	$10980	(3-Jun-92 S207/R) Yellow roses (33x41cm-13x16in) s.d.1892
£6200	$10912	(10-Apr-92 K498/R) Black grapes in cut glass bowl with mixed fruit on marble ledge (36x23cm-14x9in) s.d.1891

STANNARD, Eva (?) ?

| £534 | $950 | (26-Jan-92 JRB.C30) Still life with cherries (25x36cm-10x14in) s. canvas on board |

STANNARD, Henry (1844-1920) British

£710	$1349	(24-Jun-92 MMB298/R) Cart horses watering (23x33cm-9x13in) s.
£520	$931	(14-Jan-92 SWS42/R) Summer (35x54cm-14x21in) s.i.verso W/C htd bodycol
£550	$935	(8-Aug-91 B196) A good chance for a double (34x66cm-13x26in) s. W/C bodycol.
£620	$1122	(20-May-92 B131/R) Peacock walk (24x35cm-9x14in) s. W/C htd. bodycol.
£900	$1548	(15-Oct-91 CHAP285) Two to one on the second barrel - pheasant shoot (33x53cm-13x21in) s. W/C

STANNARD, Henry Sylvester (1870-1951) British

£740	$1339	(19-May-92 SWS381/R) Cottage garden path (34x24cm-13x9in) s. W/C
£400	$692	(4-Sep-91 BT114/R) Sheep on heath (13x20cm-5x8in) s. W/C
£420	$802	(16-Jul-92 CSK139) Flock of sheep by cottages on edge of heath (30x52cm-12x20in) pencil W/C htd white
£440	$752	(12-Mar-92 CSK73) Sunny lane, Cotswolds (28x38cm-11x15in) s. W/C htd.white
£460	$800	(16-Apr-92 PHX336/R) Selworthy - nr Exmoor (38x56cm-15x22in) s. W/C htd white
£500	$905	(6-Dec-91 K496) Heath pond at evening (25x33cm-10x13in) s. W/C
£550	$974	(13-Feb-92 B138/R) The windmill at High Salvington, Sussex (27x37cm-11x15in) s. W/C
£550	$974	(13-Feb-92 B190/R) Bisham Abbey, Buckinghamshire (38x54cm-15x21in) s.d.Nov.1941 W/C
£550	$985	(16-Jan-92 B211/R) Stream running through primrose filled wood (39x100cm-15x39in) s. W/C bodycol
£565	$1000	(13-Feb-92 S.W1341) Evening mist over Ellen's Isle (51x33cm-20x13in) s. W/C
£600	$1116	(18-Jun-92 CSK10) Children by dog cart at dusk (43x69cm-17x27in) s. W/C
£700	$1190	(22-Oct-91 LW2170/R) Wordsworths Cottage at Grasmere s.i.verso W/C
£740	$1413	(23-Jul-92 T264) Landscape with flock of sheep grazing (25x36cm-10x14in) s. W/C
£760	$1300	(19-Mar-92 T231) Sheep in country lane (18x25cm-7x10in) s. W/C
£780	$1404	(28-Jan-92 RG2739) View of country house garden (25x38cm-10x15in) s. W/C
£800	$1392	(11-Sep-91 MMB204) Daffodil time, the wilderness, Hampton Court (15x23cm-6x9in) s.i. verso
£820	$1566	(16-Jul-92 CSK138/R) Feeding chickens (30x52cm-12x20in) s. W/C
£880	$1566	(27-Nov-91 B193/R) Cottages in spring landscape (18x27cm-7x11in) s. W/C pair
£900	$1611	(5-May-92 SWS189/R) The chairmender (34x45cm-13x18in) s. i.verso W/C
£900	$1530	(22-Oct-91 LW2172) Children examining birds nest in landscape (36x25cm-14x10in) W/C
£950	$1720	(20-May-92 B155/R) June flowers, Bakewell, Derbyshire (36x49cm-14x19in) s. W/C
£1000	$1800	(27-Jan-92 PH79/R) Minding flock (33x60cm-13x24in) s. W/C
£1100	$2013	(14-May-92 CSK144) Shepherds gossiping at dusk by country tavern (33x61cm-13x24in) s. W/C
£1300	$2379	(3-Jun-92 S242/R) Way across the common, Beds (35x52cm-14x20in) s.d.1901 W/C
£1300	$2405	(12-Jun-92 C26/R) An old Bedfordshire cottage (26x36cm-10x14in) s.d.1884 pencil W/C
£1300	$2301	(6-Nov-91 S267/R) Sunny spot in Sussex (25x35cm-10x14in) s. W/C
£1500	$2820	(19-Dec-91 C27/R) Anne Hathaway's Cottage (24x34cm-9x13in) s. pencil W/C htd white
£1500	$2745	(3-Jun-92 S259/R) Heathland (33x50cm-13x20in) s. W/C
£1500	$2625	(23-Sep-91 PHB17/R) Feeding the kitten (34x24cm-13x9in) s. W/C
£1500	$2595	(24-Mar-92 PHC362/R) At Riseley, Bedfordshire (26x37cm-10x15in) s. W/C pair
£1500	$2865	(1-Jul-92 B115/R) Little fishers (50x35cm-20x14in) W/C
£1600	$2736	(13-Mar-92 C27/R) By the brook, Evenholt, Bedfordshire. Gathering acorns at Flitwick (36x25cm-14x10in) s. i.verso pencil W/C htd.white pair
£1800	$3438	(1-Jul-92 B111/R) Flower gatherers (52x35cm-20x14in) W/C

STANNARD, Henry Sylvester (1870-1951) British-cont.

£1900 $3420   (27-Jan-92 PH32) Feeding time, near Witley, Surrey (25x34cm-10x13in) s. W/C

£2000 $3540   (6-Nov-91 S270/R) By the hencoop, Worcestershire lane (25x35cm-10x14in) s. s.i.verso W/C htd.white

£2050 $3936   (28-Jul-92 RG2668) Haywains in landscapes (36x61cm-14x24in) s. W/C pair

£2100 $3948   (3-Jan-92 BW351/R) Rural landscape with sheep grazing in foreground. Village scene (25x36cm-10x14in) s. W/C pair

£2400 $4512   (19-Dec-91 C12/R) Young girl feeding chickens outside cottage (34x49cm-13x19in) rem.sig. pencil W/C htd white

£2600 $4550   (1-Apr-92 B86) Sheep in lane in summer landscape (34x53cm-13x21in) s. W/C

£2600 $4550   (1-Apr-92 B85/R) Young girl by cornstooks in field with farm cottages (33x51cm-13x20in) s. W/C

£2900 $5133   (6-Nov-91 S269/R) Outside a cottage (25x35cm-10x14in) s. W/C htd.white

£2900 $5191   (14-Jan-92 SWS62/R) Her pet kitten (25x34cm-10x13in) s. W/C

£3200 $5600   (20-Feb-92 LE259) Children playing by a brook (25x36cm-10x14in) W/C

£3200 $5760   (27-Jan-92 PH141/R) In sweet September (42x66cm-17x26in) s. W/C

£4000 $6800   (22-Oct-91 SWS206/R) Visit to Grandma. Her first bird's nest (36x25cm-14x10in) i.verso W/C over pencil pair

£4400 $7480   (22-Oct-91 SWS251/R) Bedfordshire cottage. Warwickshire cottage (25x36cm-10x14in) s. W/C pair

STANNARD, Joseph (1797-1830) British

£1500 $2865   (21-Jul-92 PH269/R) Man-o'-War and barges off jetty (53x76cm-21x30in)

STANNARD, Lilian (1877-1944) British

£1400 $2506   (14-Jan-92 SWS86/R) Glorious summer (24x34cm-9x13in) s. W/C bodycol

£1400 $2534   (20-May-92 B314/R) Through the garden (33x24cm-13x9in) s. W/C

£1900 $3439   (20-May-92 B318/R) The old garden gateway (34x24cm-13x9in) s. W/C

£1913 $3500   (17-May-92 DU.E1071) The old garden wall (25x33cm-10x13in) s. W/C

STANNARD, Theresa Sylvester (1898-1947) British

£1200 $2100   (1-Apr-92 B150/R) View from flower garden (24x34cm-9x13in) s.d.1926 W/C

£1300 $2301   (6-Nov-91 S271/R) Rustic cottage (35x25cm-14x10in) s. W/C

£1300 $2379   (6-Feb-92 DLY309/R) Thatched cottage in summertime (25x33cm-10x13in) s. W/C bodycol

£1300 $2483   (13-Jul-92 PH79/R) Poppies in cottage garden (35x25cm-14x10in) s. W/C

£1350 $2417   (14-Jan-92 SWS63/R) The cottage garden (17x25cm-7x10in) s. W/C pair

£1404 $2500   (22-Jan-92 SY.NY471/R) Perennial garden with sundial (36x25cm-14x10in) s.d.1926 W/C paper on board

£1500 $2670   (29-Oct-91 C82/R) The cottage garden (37x26cm-15x10in) s. pencil W/C htd white

£1521 $2646   (17-Sep-91 JRL.S358) Old garden, Bedfordshire (24x34cm-9x13in) s. W/C (A.D 3300)

STANOWSKY, Eugen (?) ?

£885 $1558   (12-Apr-92 HOR.H222) Coastal breakers (66x100cm-26x39in) s.d.1914 (F.M 7000)

STANTON, Ernest (?) British

£600 $1044   (19-Sep-91 TL352) Gathering flowers (29x38cm-11x15in)

STANZEL, Rudi (1958-) Austrian

£873 $1588   (26-May-92 D.V366/R) Untitled (129x129cm-51x51in) s.d.85verso acrylic canvas (A.S 18000)

STANZIONE, Massimo (1585-1656) Italian

£13966 $25000   (17-Jan-92 SY.NY167/R) Adoration of the Shepherds (116x154cm-46x61in) mono.

£110000 $200200   (13-Dec-91 C86/R) Madonna and Child (127x96cm-50x38in) mono.

STANZIONE, Massimo (style) (1585-1656) Italian

£1300 $2314   (29-Oct-91 PH151) The Madonna and child (126x103cm-50x41in)

£2800 $5376   (10-Jul-92 C255/R) Shepherd, head and shoulders (36x30cm-14x12in)

STAPHORST, Abraham (c.1638-1696) Dutch

£6200 $11842   (15-Jul-92 S9/R) Portrait of William Car of Ferniehurst and his wife (20x16cm-8x6in) one s. both i.panel pair

STAPLES, Owen (1866-1949) British

£885 $1505   (23-Oct-91 MA.V190) Young girl with sheep (79x53cm-31x21in) s.d.1891 (C.D 1700)

STAPLES, Sir Robert Ponsonby (1853-1943) British

£511 $858   (28-Aug-91 KH.K185) Portrait of woman wearing white dress (102x76cm-40x30in) s. (D.KR 5800)

£803 $1493   (16-Jun-92 RAS.V874/R) Portrait of woman wearing white dress (102x76cm-40x30in) s. (D.KR 9000)

£600 $1044   (16-Apr-92 PHX323) In Kensington Gardens (33x51cm-13x20in) s. i.verso W/C

£2300 $4117   (5-May-92 SWS275/R) The home farm field (53x69cm-21x27in) s. mono.i.verso pastel

STARK, James (1794-1859) British

£1900 $3401   (13-Nov-91 S194/R) Study of beech trees (38x45cm-15x18in) paper on board

STARK, James (1794-1859) British-cont.
£3800	$6764	(21-Jan-92 PH18/R) Drover with cattle in meadow, hilly landscape beyond (30x46cm-12x18in) board
£5200	$9932	(21-Jul-92 PH266/R) Edge of Norfolk Common (27x44cm-11x17in) panel
£6800	$12172	(13-Nov-91 S73/R) Hampstead Heath (44x60cm-17x24in)
£18000	$34380	(21-Jul-92 PH261/R) Figures, horse and horse drawn cart before cottage in wooded landscape (57x77cm-22x30in) panel

STARK, James (circle) (1794-1859) British
£718	$1300	(2-Dec-91 S.SL285/R) Shepherdess with cattle watering beside large tree with workers in field (91x71cm-36x28in)
£900	$1575	(23-Sep-91 PHB40/R) A rest by the wayside (35x46cm-14x18in) panel

STARK, Josef August (1782-1838) Austrian
£1987	$3398	(18-Mar-92 D.V311/R) Self portrait (71x58cm-28x23in) i.d.1812verso (A.S 40000)

STARK, Otto (1859-1926) American
£344	*$620*	*(23-Nov-91 YFA.M275/R) Sunset (33x48cm-13x19in) s.d.1909 pastel*

STARKER, Erwin (1872-1938) German
£526	$900	(13-Mar-92 FN.S2972) Schnee am Gahkopf mit Blick zum Burgholzhof (35x51cm-14x20in) s. i.d.1910verso board (DM 1500)
£702	$1200	(13-Mar-92 FN.S2978) Bathers in wooded river landscape (34x49cm-13x19in) s. canvas on board (DM 2000)
£982	$1680	(13-Mar-92 FN.S2975/R) Flowering fruit trees in landscape (30x40cm-12x16in) s. board (DM 2800)
£2456	$4200	(13-Mar-92 FN.S2979/R) View of Stuttgart from vineyard, winter (59x72cm-23x28in) s. board (DM 7000)
£3169	$5736	(3-Dec-91 FN.S2476) Sunset in Bopserwald near open air theatre (27x35cm-11x14in) s. (DM 9000)
£386	*$660*	*(13-Mar-92 FN.S2976) View towards Schwieberdingen and Ludwigsburg from water reservoir (37x50cm-15x20in) s. i.d.1934 pastel (DM 1100)*

STARKER, Erwin (attrib) (1872-1938) German
£702	$1200	(13-Mar-92 FN.S2980/R) Wooded landscape near Ditzingen with corn stooks (44x54cm-17x21in) s. (DM 2000)

STARN TWINS (1961-) American
£2793	*$5000*	*(5-May-92 CH.NY145/R) Between here and there (183x275cm-72x108in) s.i.d.85-88verso cellophane tape photo collage*
£4749	*$8500*	*(5-May-92 CH.NY123/R) Large blue Ian test strip with holes (292x182cm-115x72in) s.d.85-86verso photo collage cellophane tape*
£8000	*$14000*	*(27-Feb-92 CH.NY73/R) Blue and yellow Louvre floor (213x488cm-84x192in) s.d.85-88verso photocoll. 6 panels sheet metal*
£20950	*$37500*	*(14-Nov-91 SY.NY195/R) Ascension (229x610cm-90x240in) toned silverprint tape ortho film wood glass*

STARN, Doug and Mike see STARN TWINS

STARNINA, Gherardo (1354-1413) Italian
£20408	$36122	(10-Feb-92 GL.P19/R) Sainte Catherine d'Alexandrie et Saint Jean-Baptiste (26x30cm-10x12in) tempera gold sheet panel (F.FR 200000)

STAUDACHER, Hans (1923-) Swiss
£2048	$3727	(26-May-92 KF.M1279/R) Untitled (50x40cm-20x16in) s.i.d.1961verso (DM 6000)
£440	*$765*	*(12-Sep-91 D.V222) Spring ... (30x22cm-12x9in) s.i. mixed media (A.S 9000)*
£449	*$803*	*(15-Jan-92 D.V257/R) Untitled (25x35cm-10x14in) s.i.d.1972 pen brush indian ink W/C (A.S 9000)*
£489	*$850*	*(12-Sep-91 D.V220) African war dance (32x24cm-13x9in) s.i. pen brush indian ink W/C htd.white (A.S 10000)*
£499	*$892*	*(15-Jan-92 D.V255/R) Untitled (27x38cm-11x15in) s.d.1973 pen brush indian ink W/C (A.S 10000)*
£499	*$892*	*(15-Jan-92 D.V254/R) 2 dkg lustrosa, 5 dkg Wiesengrun und auf in die Natur (32x24cm-13x9in) s.i. pen brush indian ink W/C (A.S 10000)*
£586	*$1013*	*(3-Oct-91 D.V270/R) Female seated (35x25cm-14x10in) s.i.d.52 pen indian ink wash (A.S 12000)*
£587	*$1044*	*(31-Oct-91 D.V3/R) Untitled (35x58cm-14x23in) s.d.59 pen brush indian ink (A.S 12000)*
£593	*$1038*	*(19-Feb-92 D.V242/R) Untitled (24x32cm-9x13in) s.i.d.1985 mixed media (A.S 12000)*
£630	*$1147*	*(26-May-92 D.V293/R) My feelings in Paris (32x25cm-13x10in) s.i.d.1970 pen indian ink W/C dispersion (A.S 13000)*
£630	*$1147*	*(26-May-92 D.V207/R) Untitled (53x38cm-21x15in) mono pen indian ink htd white paper on board (A.S 13000)*
£728	*$1296*	*(28-Apr-92 D.V331/R) Sheep (33x48cm-13x19in) s.d.1951 pen brush indian ink wash (A.S 15000)*
£777	*$1383*	*(28-Apr-92 D.V332/R) Untitled (25x17cm-10x7in) s.d.71 mixed media (A.S 16000)*
£791	*$1384*	*(19-Feb-92 D.V240/R) Untitled (30x22cm-12x9in) s.d.1982 pen indian ink W/C (A.S 16000)*
£791	*$1384*	*(19-Feb-92 D.V241/R) Untitled (30x22cm-12x9in) s.d.1982 pen indian ink W/C gouache (A.S 16000)*

STAUDACHER, Hans (1923-) Swiss-cont.
£847	$1517	(15-Jan-92 D.V253/R) Untitled (24x32cm-9x13in) s. mixed media (A.S 17000)
£1365	$2485	(26-May-92 KF.M1280/R) Stations of the Cross (64x76cm-25x30in) s.i.d.1958
		mixed media (DM 4000)
£1466	$2610	(31-Oct-91 D.V40/R) Untitled (35x50cm-14x20in) s.i.d.62 pen brush indian
		ink W/C (A.S 30000)
£6800	$11696	(17-Oct-91 C47/R) Irrtum (90x130cm-35x51in) s.d.59 i.d.59 v. oil gouache
		ink crayon board

STAUFFER, Fred (1892-1980) Swiss
£630	$1140	(19-May-92 GF.L2905) Female head IV (68x454cm-27x179in) s.d.1957 i.verso
		panel (S.FR 1700)
£1504	$2752	(4-Jun-92 SY.Z414/R) Saw mill (55x100cm-22x39in) s.d.40 (S.FR 4000)
£2174	$3913	(19-Nov-91 GS.B3266) Emmental landscape, late autumn (80x106cm-31x42in)
		s.d.65 pavatex (S.FR 5500)
£2256	$4128	(4-Jun-92 SY.Z404/R) Landte im Regen (80x70cm-31x28in) s.d.39 s.i.verso
		(S.FR 6000)
£2738	$5092	(19-Jun-92 ZOF.Z2095/R) Meeting (50x41cm-20x16in) s.d.26 board
		(S.FR 7200)
£2920	$5226	(6-May-92 GD.B1226/R) Near Heimenschwand, evening (126x122cm-50x48in)
		s.d.74 panel (S.FR 8000)
£3137	$5333	(23-Oct-91 GD.B715/R) Moor landscape near Koniz (68x109cm-27x43in) s.d.63
		i.verso pavatex (S.FR 8000)
£3137	$5333	(23-Oct-91 GD.B716/R) Wooded landscape with view of town in November
		(85x90cm-33x35in) s. (S.FR 8000)
£5138	$9249	(19-Nov-91 GS.B3265) Winter landscape, Saanenland (80x65cm-31x26in)
		s.d.42 (S.FR 13000)
£471	$800	(23-Oct-91 GD.B719/R) Farmhouse in Emmental (35x42cm-14x17in) s. oil chk
		(S.FR 1200)
£474	$849	(6-May-92 GD.B1227/R) Railway line near Bern, Lorraine (33x45cm-13x18in)
		s. gouache (S.FR 1300)

STAUFFER-BERN, Karl (1857-1891) Swiss
| £3861 | $6602 | (12-Mar-92 GK.Z90 a) Sleeping girl seated in armchair (136x96cm-54x38in) |
| | | (S.FR 10000) |

STAUN, Jeppe Pedersen (1747-1826) Danish
| £705 | $1248 | (23-Apr-92 RAS.V898/R) Children in school's playground with teachers |
| | | (33x41cm-13x16in) s.d.1777verso (D.KR 8000) |

STAVERNUS, Petrus (1634-1654) Dutch
| £3137 | $5616 | (15-Nov-91 GK.Z5103 a) Laughing boy with fishes (73x60cm-29x24in) |
| | | (S.FR 8000) |

STAVRIANOS, Wendy (1941-) Australian
| £685 | $1275 | (21-Jun-92 SY.ME117) Parchment fragment,tribute to Mishima |
| | | (152x213cm-60x84in) s.d.1979 acrylic (A.D 1700) |

STAZEWSKI, Henryk (1894-?) Polish
£606	$1097	(19-May-92 CH.AM213/R) Composition (18x14cm-7x6in) s. gouache (D.FL 2000)
£611	$1112	(15-Dec-91 REM.W42) Abstract composition mixed media (P.Z 12000000)
£774	$1386	(17-Nov-91 REM.W27) Abstract composition (26x22cm-10x9in) s. gouache
		(P.Z 15000000)

STEA, Cesare (1893-?) American
| £686 | $1200 | (28-Feb-92 SY.NY57) Self-portrait (13x9cm-5x4in) s. gouache |

STEAD, Fred (1863-1940) British
| £560 | $997 | (21-Jan-92 SWS1023) Fauns in wooded landscape (49x164cm-19x65in) s. |
| £3143 | $5500 | (18-Feb-92 CE.NY106/R) Admiring jewels (164x45cm-65x18in) s. |

STEADMAN, Ralph Idris (?) ?
£500	$960	(10-Jul-92 CSK51/R) Whatever happened to sense of values
		(76x56cm-30x22in) s.i.d.1964 pencil pen htd white
£550	$1056	(10-Jul-92 CSK50/R) Welcome to London Hilton Sir. Take your money, Sir
		(48x69cm-19x27in) s.i. pencil col.chk W/C bodycol
£618	$1100	(2-May-92 IH.NY117/R) Nixon and Prime Minister Wilson shaking hands
		through charred body (48x69cm-19x27in) s. pen ink

STEEL, John Sydney (1863-?) British
| £580 | $1038 | (14-Jan-92 SWS248/R) Moorish girl (33x23cm-13x9in) s. panel |

STEELE, Christopher (1730-?) British
| £5800 | $11078 | (15-Jul-92 S17/R) Portrait of young boy with dog in landscape |
| | | (133x100cm-52x39in) |

STEELE, Daniel (19th C) American
| £526 | $1000 | (26-Jun-92 WOL.C427) Portrait of a gentleman (66x53cm-26x21in) |

STEELE, E (19th C) British
| £780 | $1396 | (15-Jan-92 BT127) Still life with flowers in a vase on a ledge |
| | | (89x69cm-35x27in) s.d.1910 |

STEELE, Edwin (19th C) British
£791 $1423   (19-Nov-91 GS.B3666) Still life of roses, carnations and other flowers in basket (46x61cm-18x24in) s. (S.FR 2000)
£1200 $2172   (20-May-92 B229/R) Roses in an urn on a table (86x63cm-34x25in) s.d.1849

STEELE, Juliette (1909-1980) American
£1554 $2750   (12-Feb-92 B.SF635/R) Powerline (51x61cm-20x24in) s.d.1952 tempera masonite
£1554 $2750   (12-Feb-92 B.SF636/R) Circus (51x61cm-20x24in) s.d.1952 tempera masonite

STEELE, Mary E (?) British
£750 $1358   (5-Dec-91 CSK246) Feeding the ducks (112x142cm-44x56in) s.

STEELE, Tim (20th C) American
£449   *$750*   *(25-Aug-91 JRB.C213) Construction II chl triptych*

STEELINK, Willem (1826-1913) Dutch
£917 $1624   (5-Nov-91 SY.AM104) Sheep on heath between Laren and Blaricum (51x66cm-20x26in) s. (D.FL 3000)
£1040 $1840   (5-Nov-91 SY.AM6/R) Shepherd with flock (49x67cm-19x26in) s. (D.FL 3400)

STEELL, David George (1856-1930) British
£720 $1289   (14-Jan-92 B143/R) A terrier with his ball (59x51cm-23x20in) s.d.1873
£2200 $3938   (14-Jan-92 B234/R) By the day's bag (56x72cm-22x28in) s.d.1878 board
£2200 $3696   (26-Aug-91 S875/R) An awkward charge (51x66cm-20x26in) s. i.overlap
£3005 $5500   (5-Jun-92 SY.NY157 a/R) The messenger (29x24cm-11x9in) s.i.d.95

STEEN, Germain van der (20th C) Belgian?
£1304   *$2322*   *(29-Nov-91 GAB.G2533/R) Le chat a barbe noire (65x50cm-26x20in) s. W/C col.crayons (S.FR 3300)*

STEEN, Jan (1623-1679) Dutch
£10142 $17850   (10-Apr-92 AT.P17/R) Le charlatan du village (35x24cm-14x9in) traces sig. panel (F.FR 100000)
£26000 $47320   (13-Dec-91 C30/R) Wood in dunes with peasant family resting in foreground (27x34cm-11x13in) s. panel

STEEN, Jan (attrib) (1623-1679) Dutch
£2067 $3782   (12-May-92 SY.AM70/R) Young man making obscene gesture (12x9cm-5x4in) panel oval (D.FL 6800)
£2979 $5451   (12-May-92 SY.AM9/R) Head of young boy (15x12cm-6x5in) bears mono. panel (D.FL 9800)

STEEN, Jan (style) (1623-1679) Dutch
£1976 $3616   (12-May-92 SY.AM58/R) Twelfth night (30x40cm-12x16in) bears sig. panel (D.FL 6500)
£2400 $4200   (3-Apr-92 C63/R) Family celebrating birth of twins (75x66cm-30x26in) with sig.
£4300 $7783   (20-May-92 BT186/R) Merry company (58x46cm-23x18in) bears sig. panel
£4630 $8287   (14-Nov-91 CH.AM162/R) The Feast of Epiphany (80x73cm-31x29in) indis.s. (D.FL 15000)

STEENWYCK, H van (17th C) Dutch
£3200 $5600   (27-Feb-92 GSP444) Perspective interior of a cathedral with figures at various persuits (61x84cm-24x33in)

STEENWYCK, Harmen van (1612-1656) Dutch
£14781 $27492   (18-Jun-92 SY.MO221/R) Nature morte aux oiseaux, canard, panier de fruits et chat (48x93cm-19x37in) panel (F.FR 145000)

STEENWYCK, Hendrik van (17th C) Dutch
£4800 $9216   (10-Jul-92 C166/R) Christ and Nicodemus (12x14cm-5x6in) init. copper

STEENWYCK, Hendrik van (younger) (1580-1649) Flemish
£1121 $2086   (19-Jun-92 ARC.P82/R) Interieur d'eglise avec deux personnages (13x8cm-5x3in) s.d.1626 copper (F.FR 11000)
£33520 $60000   (16-Jan-92 CH.NY10/R) Saint Jerome in Gothic church (20x28cm-8x11in) init.d.1625 copper

STEENWYCK, Hendrik van (younger) and BRUEGHEL, Jan (17th C) Flemish
£15000 $28800   (10-Jul-92 C4/R) Nave of Gothic church, with Mass being said (74x105cm-29x41in) with i. panel transferred canvas

STEENWYCK, Hendrik van (younger-style) (1580-1649) Flemish
£2800 $4984   (30-Oct-91 S52/R) Church interior (26x31cm-10x12in) panel

STEEPLE, John (?-1887) British
£480   *$869*   *(19-May-92 SWS301) Farmers' gossip (44cm-17ins circular) s.d.1855 W/C over pencil htd.white gum arabic*
£780   *$1357*   *(9-Sep-91 PH177/R) Cattle in a moorland (48x73cm-19x29in) s. W/C*

STEER, Henry Reynolds (1858-1928) British
£420   *$718*   *(12-Mar-92 CSK69/R) Homeless (43x66cm-17x26in) s. s.i.verso pencil W/C htd.bodycol*

TEER, Philip Wilson (1860-1942) British
£5000	$9150	(5-Jun-92 C19/R) Strand-on-the-Green (19x27cm-7x11in) st.init. panel
£6500	$11505	(7-Nov-91 C14/R) The rape of the Sabines (71x94cm-28x37in) s.
£640	$1114	(15-Apr-92 PHL43) White yacht (24x34cm-9x13in) s.d.1921 pencil wash
£660	$1148	(15-Apr-92 PHL42/R) Yachts on river inlet (23x33cm-9x13in) s.d.1920 pencil wash
£700	$1190	(22-Oct-91 SWS229/R) Framlingham Castle (22x33cm-9x13in) s. W/C
£900	$1602	(21-Jan-92 SWS1253) Beached boats. Street scene in Santiago (22x30cm-9x12in) one s.d.1934 one s.i. W/C pencil sepia ink pair

TEFANI, Vincenzo de (1859-?) Italian
| £6448 | $11735 | (12-Dec-91 F.M36/R) Ragazza in lettura (105x86cm-41x34in) s.d.1895 (I.L 14000000) |

TEFANO, Vincenzo de (1861-?) Italian
| £511 | $925 | (3-Dec-91 SY.MI91) Nudo con drappo bianco (61x37cm-24x15in) s.d.61 (I.L 1100000) |

TEFANONI, Tino (1937-) Italian
| £507 | $922 | (9-Dec-91 CH.R55/R) Le piramidi (96x81cm-38x32in) s.d.1975 (I.L 1100000) |
| £511 | $960 | (19-Dec-91 F.M12) I bicchieri grigi (80x95cm-31x37in) s. i.verso acrylic (I.L 1100000) |

TEFANSSEN, Jon (1881-1962) Icelandic
| £2543 | $4450 | (1-Apr-92 KH.K168/R) Wild flowers in jug (54x46cm-21x18in) s. (D.KR 28000) |

TEFFAN, Johann Gottfried (1815-1905) Swiss
£1111	$2011	(19-May-92 GF.L2638/R) Mountain stream on the Klaussenpass (20x26cm-8x10in) s.i.d.1899 (S.FR 3000)
£1742	$3171	(11-Dec-91 N.M603/R) Torrent in mountain landscape (85x117cm-33x46in) s. (DM 5000)
£1875	$3319	(5-Nov-91 GF.L2547/R) Boathouse by lake (19x26cm-7x10in) mono.d.1891 (S.FR 4800)
£9774	$17887	(4-Jun-92 SY.Z334/R) High Alpine mountains with cattle, Canton Glarus Switzerland (69x91cm-27x36in) s.i.d.1866 i.verso (S.FR 26000)
£10370	$18770	(19-May-92 GF.L2265/R) Murgsee landscape near the border of St Gallen and Glarus (93x126cm-37x50in) s.i.d.1873 i.verso (S.FR 28000)
£10588	$18953	(15-Nov-91 ZOF.Z1887/R) Lontsch, Glarn mountainlandscape with stream and cows grazing (110x85cm-43x33in) s.i.d.1882 (S.FR 27000)
£17928	$32450	(5-Dec-91 SY.Z25/R) Shepherd with cattle in Kloentalersee landscape (107x100cm-42x39in) s.i.d.1864 (S.FR 45000)

TEFFANI, Luigi (1827-1898) Italian
£6200	$11532	(17-Jun-92 S583/R) Ploughing field (68x108cm-27x43in) s.
£6275	$10730	(19-Mar-92 F.M1/R) Marina olandese con barche e pescatori (64x112cm-25x44in) s. (I.L 13500000)
£6908	$12573	(12-Dec-91 F.M1/R) Marina con pescatori (74x145cm-29x57in) s. (I.L 15000000)

TEFFEK, Carl (1818-1890) German
| £4124 | $7175 | (21-Sep-91 SA.A1777/R) Two Italian women (97x74cm-38x29in) (DM 12000) |

TEFFELAAR, Cornelis (1795-1861) Dutch
| £486 | $846 | (17-Sep-91 CH.AM607) A river landscape in summer with a sailing boat on the water, farm beyond (24x35cm-9x14in) s. panel (D.FL 1600) |

TEFFEN, Eduard (19th C) Austrian
| £2577 | $4485 | (18-Sep-91 N.M712/R) Village street with milk cart (36x44cm-14x17in) s.d.1886 (DM 7500) |

TEFFEN, Walter (1924-1982) Swiss
| £547 | $980 | (6-May-92 GD.B1232/R) Sunflowers (60x81cm-24x32in) s.d.73 (S.FR 1500) |

TEFFENS, Louise (1841-1865) Belgian
| £857 | $1543 | (19-Nov-91 RAS.K221/R) Novice mistress and her novices (64x100cm-25x39in) s.d.1863 (D.KR 9500) |

TEFFENSEN, Poul (1866-1923) Danish
£492	$895	(12-Dec-91 RAS.V787) Peasantboy with two cows (58x89cm-23x35in) s. (D.KR 5500)
£529	$936	(23-Apr-92 RAS.V899) Landscape with woman watering cows (51x75cm-20x30in) s.d.1918 (D.KR 6000)
£808	$1430	(11-Feb-92 RAS.K14 a) Field landscape with grazing cows (70x101cm-28x40in) s.d.1890 (D.KR 9000)
£924	$1553	(28-Aug-91 KH.K186) Cattle (57x88cm-22x35in) s.d.1917 (D.KR 10500)
£987	$1776	(30-Jan-92 RAS.V682/R) Driving the geese home (56x96cm-22x38in) (D.KR 11000)
£1218	$2193	(19-Nov-91 RAS.K264/R) Field landscape with cows (70x101cm-28x40in) s.d.1890 (D.KR 13500)
£1399	$2518	(19-Nov-91 RAS.K263/R) Cows and horses in farmyard (55x93cm-22x37in) s.d.1892 (D.KR 15500)
£2905	$5026	(2-Sep-91 BU.K18/R) Potatoe harvesting (98x130cm-39x51in) init.d.1905 (D.KR 33000)

STEFFENSON, G (?) ?
£800 $1392   (10-Sep-91 RG2283) River landscape with cattle watering and figures in foreground (43x89cm-17x35in) s.

STEGEMANN, Heinrich (1888-1945) German
£423 $765   (4-Dec-91 DO.H3407/R) S. Silvestre, Florence (35x47cm-14x19in) s.i. W/C over pencil (DM 1200)

STEIDL, Melchior (1660-1727) Austrian
£444 $803   (22-May-92 GB.B5408/R) Madonna and Child on clouds with St Dominic. Study of drape (28x20cm-11x8in) pen ochre double-sided (DM 1300)

STEIDLER, P (19th C) Austrian
£790 $1375   (21-Sep-91 SA.A1135/R) Portrait of young woman wearing dress with lace trim and gold necklace (6x5cm-2x2in) min.s. tempera oval emaille brass frame (DM 2300)

STEIN, Georges (20th C) French
£2791 $4800   (15-Oct-91 CE.NY423/R) Place de la Concorde (15x22cm-6x9in) s.i. panel
£3659 $6366   (19-Apr-92 ZZ.F147/R) Paris au crepuscule, les Halles et l'eglise Saint-Eustache s. panel (F.FR 36000)
£3779 $6500   (17-Oct-91 SY.NY210/R) Boulevard des Italiens (27x41cm-11x16in) s.i.
£3779 $6500   (15-Oct-91 CE.NY420/R) Place de l'OPera (15x22cm-6x9in) s.i. panel
£3862 $6720   (19-Apr-92 ZZ.F146/R) La parvis de Notre-Dame s. panel (F.FR 38000)
£4065 $7073   (19-Apr-92 ZZ.F145/R) Le pont des Saints Peres (22x16cm-9x6in) s. panel (F.FR 40000)
£4472 $7780   (19-Apr-92 ZZ.F144/R) L'avenue du bois de Boulogne (16x22cm-6x9in) s. panel (F.FR 44000)
£5500 $9735   (13-Feb-92 CSK121/R) A street, Bern (47x66cm-19x26in) s.i.
£9547 $17029   (28-Oct-91 GL.P223) Notre Dame (22x16cm-9x6in) s. panel (F.FR 95000)
£407 $707   (19-Apr-92 ZZ.F47) Trois elegantes (12x20cm-5x8in) st.sig. W/C (F.FR 4000)
£509 $910   (17-Nov-91 FB.P4) Pont d'Iena et Ancien Trocadero (15x31cm-6x12in) s. pastel W/C (F.FR 5000)
£610 $1061   (19-Apr-92 ZZ.F49) La place de la Concorde (12x20cm-5x8in) st.sig. W/C (F.FR 6000)
£1331 $2368   (27-Nov-91 AT.P60/R) Elegante au bal (27x19cm-11x7in) s. gouache (F.FR 13000)
£2400 $4248   (14-Feb-92 C1 a/R) Elegant figures before Arc de Triomphe, Paris (40x51cm-16x20in) s.i. W/C col.chks.bodycol.card

STEIN, Peter (1922-) Swiss
£547 $980   (6-May-92 GD.B1233/R) Composition (34x26cm-13x10in) s.d.61 gouache (S.FR 1500)

STEIN-WIESE, Ida (1910-1966) German
£559 $968   (25-Mar-92 KM.K1447) Geese in wooded landscape with farmhouses (55x77cm-22x30in) (DM 1600)
£909 $1573   (25-Mar-92 KM.K1452) Peasant servant seated (80x60cm-31x24in) (DM 2600)
£1399 $2420   (25-Mar-92 KM.K1442/R) Peasants seated in interior studying letter (136x110cm-54x43in) s.d.1947 (DM 4000)
£2098 $3629   (25-Mar-92 KM.K1443/R) Peasant women in interior getting ready for church (142x157cm-56x62in) s. (DM 6000)

STEINACKER, Alfred (1838-?) Austrian
£777 $1383   (29-Apr-92 D.V794/R) Called by horn (13x26cm-5x10in) s. panel (A.S 16000)
£777 $1383   (29-Apr-92 D.V793/R) Over the fence (13x26cm-5x10in) s. panel (A.S 16000)
£971 $1728   (29-Apr-92 D.V843/R) Woodland path (61x50cm-24x20in) bears sig.d.1897 (A.S 20000)
£989 $1730   (20-Feb-92 D.V375/R) Hunting scene (21x31cm-8x12in) s. panel (A.S 20000)

STEINBERG, Saul (1914-) American
£2743 $4800   (28-Feb-92 SY.NY317/R) Hohner music machine (48x32cm-19x13in) s.d.66 indian ink paper collage sheet music
£2884 $4931   (17-Mar-92 FB.P85/R) Trois cartes postales (36x28cm-14x11in) s.d.71 oil W/C ink (F.FR 28000)
£3911 $7000   (7-May-92 SY.NY296/R) 71st street treaty - document (76x102cm-30x40in) s.d.67 indian ink wash rubber stamps pencil
£4545 $8045   (24-Apr-92 CN.P215/R) Trois voyageurs (36x28cm-14x11in) W/C ink (F.FR 45000)
£6704 $12000   (6-May-92 CH.NY293/R) No.4 Railroad (58x37cm-23x15in) s.d.1958 pen col.crayons
£7263 $13000   (6-May-92 CH.NY318/R) Pyramid (51x76cm-20x30in) s.d.1972 W/C graphite in rubber stamp gold
£7263 $13000   (13-Nov-91 CH.NY176/R) Dropouts (58x74cm-23x29in) s.d.1978 i.verso col.pencils graphite

STEINER, Heinz (1905-) Austrian
£583 $1037   (28-Apr-92 D.V272) Near Hochrotherd, Wienerwald (74x100cm-29x39in) (A.S 12000)

STEINER, Johann Nepomuk (1725-1793) Czechoslovakian
£2326 $4000   (10-Oct-91 SY.NY152/R) Portrait of Johan Wenzina (46x37cm-18x15in) i. verso

STEINER, Josef (20th C) Austrian
£909 $1600   (12-Apr-92 LIT.L210) Still life of flowers (53x41cm-21x16in) s.
£1293 $2314   (5-May-92 ZEL.L1548/R) Bouquet of tulips, roses and other flowers on marble ledge (50x39cm-20x15in) s. panel (DM 3800)
£1460 $2613   (6-May-92 GD.B1237/R) Still life of flowers on stone ledge and view of landscape (63x76cm-25x30in) s. (S.FR 4000)
£1582 $2768   (20-Feb-92 D.V391/R) Still life of flowers (59x50cm-23x20in) s. panel (A.S 32000)

STEINFELD, Franz (1787-1868) Austrian
£2424 $4411   (27-May-92 D.V653/R) Forest interior with huntsman (35x27cm-14x11in) s. board on canvas (A.S 50000)
£3213 $5623   (20-Feb-92 D.V349/R) Mountain lake (44x31cm-17x12in) s. (A.S 65000)
£3878 $7058   (27-May-92 D.V630/R) The Hintere Langbathsee near Gmunden (27x35cm-11x14in) s.d.1863 paper on panel (A.S 80000)

STEINFELD, Wilhelm (1816-1854) Austrian
£1375 $2392   (18-Sep-91 N.M714/R) Watzmann near Salzburg with harvest scene (31x37cm-12x15in) s.d.1857 i.stretcher (DM 4000)

STEINHARDT, Friedrich (1844-?) German
£769 $1331   (25-Mar-92 KM.K1453/R) Annunciation to the Shepherds (80x54cm-31x21in) s.d.1892 one of pair (DM 2200)
£979 $1694   (25-Mar-92 KM.K1454/R) Adoration of the Magi (79x53cm-31x21in) one of pair (DM 2800)
£1717 $3263   (25-Jun-92 D.V404 r) Two ladies in Chinese salon (55x41cm-22x16in) s. (A.S 35000)

STEINHARDT, Jakob (1887-1968) Israeli
£691 $1300   (5-Jan-92 GG.TA385/R) Landscape (37x50cm-15x20in) s.d.1955 paper on board
£2556 $4600   (6-Jan-92 GG.TA440/R) Jerusalem, path in garden (60x60cm-24x24in) s.d.1939 s.d.verso
£3511 $6600   (5-Jan-92 GG.TA386/R) Funeral procession (82x100cm-32x39in) d.1922 s.verso
£16000 $28000   (26-Sep-91 SY.I42/R) Job amidst the mountains. Expressionist mountainscape (149x105cm-59x41in) s.d.1913 double-sided
£1027 $1900   (9-Jun-92 GG.TA294/R) Mount Moriah (46x60cm-18x24in) s. chl

STEINHAUSEN, Wilhelm (1846-1924) German
£2405 $4089   (25-Oct-91 BM.B838/R) Portrait of artist's child (43x37cm-17x15in) mono.d.88 board (DM 7000)

STEINHAUSEN, Wilhelm (attrib) (1846-1924) German
£969 $1841   (24-Jun-92 KM.K1270) Taunus landscape (19x29cm-7x11in) mono board (DM 2800)

STEINLE, Eduard Jacob von (1810-1886) Austrian/German
£887 $1606   (21-May-92 L.K339/R) St Cacilie with organ in landscape (52x21cm-20x8in) pencil wash htd.white (DM 2600)

STEINLEN, Theophile Alexandre (1859-1923) Swiss
£1304 $2322   (29-Nov-91 GAB.G2883/R) La perche gourmande (31x48cm-12x19in) s. panel (S.FR 3300)
£3378 $6250   (12-Jun-92 SY.NY30/R) Vase de fleurs et livres (63x44cm-25x17in) s.d.20verso
£10196 $17333   (23-Oct-91 GD.B725/R) Le chat gris (33x50cm-13x20in) s.d.1919 board (S.FR 26000)
£10980 $18667   (23-Oct-91 GD.B726/R) Deux chats (63x52cm-25x20in) s. monotype (S.FR 28000)
£392 $702   (15-Nov-91 GK.Z5611) Chez grand mere (34x26cm-13x10in) st.sig. chl (S.FR 1000)
£392 $702   (15-Nov-91 GK.Z5610) Les trois arbres (26x21cm-10x8in) s. indian ink (S.FR 1000)
£410 $741   (22-May-92 GB.B6066) Court scene with judges wearing robes (39x51cm-15x20in) W/C bodycol over pencil (DM 1200)
£435 $774   (29-Nov-91 GAB.G2885) L'allegorie (38x23cm-15x9in) bears studio st. chl. (S.FR 1100)
£447 $783   (3-Apr-92 AGS.P203) Pierrot et bergere (29x24cm-11x9in) s. pen blue crayon (F.FR 4300)
£462 $883   (3-Jul-92 GL.P165) Sevices graves (37x30cm-15x12in) s. col.crayon dr (F.FR 4500)
£510 $948   (21-Jun-92 LT.P9) Les porteuses d'eau (47x31cm-19x12in) s. chl (F.FR 5000)
£612 $1064   (14-Apr-92 SY.AM490/R) In the pub (39x29cm-15x11in) s. mixed media (D.FL 2000)
£616 $1060   (11-Oct-91 AW.H1316/R) Street musicians (32x21cm-13x8in) s. pen htd.chk board (DM 1800)
£627 $1123   (15-Nov-91 GK.Z5613) Les evacues de Verdun (24x32cm-9x13in) s. indian ink wash (F.FR 1800)
£692 $1315   (25-Jun-92 GK.B660) Nude young woman seated on bed (24x19cm-9x7in) s. chk paper on board (S.FR 1800)
£702 $1193   (22-Oct-91 C.A929) Seated nude (60x45cm-24x18in) s. dr. (B.FR 42000)
£800 $1376   (5-Mar-92 CSK145/R) Les chats (11x44cm-4x17in) s. W/C wash two one mount
£989 $1730   (3-Apr-92 AGS.P202) Les fiances de la Rue Lepic (15x27cm-6x11in) s.i.d.94 blue crayon (F.FR 9500)

STEINLEN, Theophile Alexandre (1859-1923) Swiss-cont.

£1167	$2100	(6-Jan-92 GG.TA428/R) Musicians and painter (26x19cm-10x7in) s. W/C pencil
£2352	$4304	(3-Feb-92 SD.P221/R) Blanchisseuses (48x36cm-19x14in) s. chl.stumping (F.FR 23000)
£2515	$4326	(7-Oct-91 CSC.P148) Nathalie Madore (49x30cm-19x12in) studio st.verso chl.chk. (F.FR 25000)
£3714	$6500	(20-Feb-92 SY.NY240/R) Le 18 Mars au Pere Lachaise (37x52cm-15x20in) s.i. black blue chk wash paper on card
£3823	$6575	(12-Oct-91 SY.MO1/R) La chaussee clignancourt. Il avait chien. Couple et gendarmes. Soulaud (32x28cm-13x11in) s.i. crayon pen collage four (F.FR 38000)
£4000	$7640	(30-Jun-92 C109/R) Les trottins (32x27cm-13x11in) s. col.crayons pencil
£6000	$11460	(30-Jun-92 C110/R) Les grands douleurs (47x35cm-19x14in) s. col.crayons pen pencil

STEINMETZ-NORIS, Fritz (1860-?) German

£2286	$4000	(3-Apr-92 S.W2447/R) Morning joy (69x46cm-27x18in) s.d.87

STEIR, Pat (20th C) ?

£10983	$19000	(3-Oct-91 SY.NY175/R) Samari tree (152x457cm-60x180in) s.d.83 in three panels

STELLA, Eduard (1884-1955) Austrian

£598	$1071	(15-Jan-92 D.V4/R) Vintner (181x81cm-71x32in) i.d.1914 (A.S 12000)
£1396	$2499	(15-Jan-92 D.V3/R) Female gardener (181x81cm-71x32in) i.d.1914verso (A.S 28000)

STELLA, Frank (1936-) American

£15607	$27000	(3-Oct-91 SY.NY102/R) Palmito ranch - small version, orange (30x30cm-12x12in)
£18000	$31140	(26-Mar-92 C72) Polar Co-ordinate (96x96cm-38x38in) s.i.d.CTPIII 80 acrylic screenprint oil
£21229	$38000	(12-Nov-91 CH.NY17/R) Greek key (30x30cm-12x12in) acrylic
£27933	$50000	(14-Nov-91 SY.NY140/R) Untitled (30x30cm-12x12in) s.d.1/10/61 verso
£33237	$57500	(3-Oct-91 SY.NY93/R) Island No.10 (30x30cm-12x12in)
£72626	$130000	(12-Nov-91 CH.NY10/R) Untitled (30x30cm-12x12in) masonite
£100559	$180000	(13-Nov-91 SY.NY57/R) Scramble - descending orange values - descending spectrum (175x175cm-69x69in) s.d.77 verso acrylic canvas
£108939	$195000	(7-May-92 SY.NY304/R) Double concentric squares (206x409cm-81x161in) acrylic canvas
£139665	$250000	(5-May-92 CH.NY45/R) Double scramble (172x350cm-68x138in) s.i.d.78stretcher acrylic
£3529	$6000	(23-Oct-91 B.SF3739/R) Untitled (43x56cm-17x22in) init. W/C col.pencil
£4749	$8500	(13-Nov-91 CH.NY227/R) Untitled (44x56cm-17x22in) s. col.pencils graphite graph paper
£6145	$11000	(14-Nov-91 SY.NY165/R) Untitled (17x17cm-7x7in) s.d.63 verso col.pencil
£8485	$15358	(21-May-92 SY.AM271/R) Study for grondo (80x76cm-31x30in) s.i.d.73 mixed media paper on board (D.FL 28000)
£9827	$17000	(3-Oct-91 SY.NY139/R) Polar coordinate (96x96cm-38x38in) s.d.1980 screenprint lithograph acrylic others
£13143	$23000	(25-Feb-92 SY.NY187/R) Untitled, polar co-ordinates IV (96x96cm-38x38in) s.d.80 gouache crayon over lithograph
£15607	$27000	(3-Oct-91 SY.NY107/R) Hagmatana (43x56cm-17x22in) init.d.66 col.felt marker pencil
£16760	$30000	(6-May-92 CH.NY386/R) Green solitaire (153x215cm-60x85in) s.d.81 silkscreen acrylic glitter paper canvas
£30726	$55000	(13-Nov-91 CH.NY192/R) Wake Island rail (153x214cm-60x84in) s.d.77 silkscreen acrylic collage glitter linen
£36313	$65000	(14-Nov-91 SY.NY373/R) Bermuda petrel (152x213cm-60x84in) s.d.81 screenprint mixed media Tycore panel
£111732	$200000	(13-Nov-91 SY.NY29/R) Joatinga I (244x335cm-96x132in) mixed media honey-combed aluminium
£184358	$330000	(6-May-92 SY.NY41/R) Steller's alabtross, 5X (305x419cm-120x165in) mixed media on aluminum

STELLA, Giacomo di Marco Antonio (attrib) (1555-1630) Italian

£3167	$5732	(3-Dec-91 AB.S4756/R) Landscape with putti by ruins (60x73cm-24x29in) (S.KR 33000)

STELLA, Jacques de (1596-1657) French

£10649	$18742	(10-Apr-92 AT.P24/R) Salomon recevant la reine de Saba (98x142cm-39x56in) (F.FR 105000)

STELLA, Jacques de (attrib) (1596-1657) French

£3000	$5760	(10-Jul-92 C203/R) Bacchanalian revel (105x81cm-41x32in)
£13953	$24000	(10-Oct-91 SY.NY164/R) Reclining Venus attended by Putti (12x21cm-5x8in) octagonal oil gilt slate

STELLA, Jacques de (circle) (1596-1657) French

£1966	$3500	(22-Jan-92 SY.NY127/R) St. Cecelia (36x30cm-14x12in) copper octagonal

STELLA, Joseph (1877-1946) American

£4972	$9000	(6-Dec-91 CH.NY220/R) Toys (51x40cm-20x16in) s.d.1943

STELLA, Joseph (1877-1946) American-cont.
£5848	$10000	(12-Mar-92 CH.NY234/R) Vesuvius (20x17cm-8x7in) s. canvas on canvas on aluminum
£6044	$11000	(28-May-92 CH.NY247/R) Dog on a balcony, Paris (53x45cm-21x18in) canvas on panel
£8857	$15145	(17-Mar-92 FB.P53/R) Village sur le lac (38x61cm-15x24in) s. (F.FR 86000)
£20468	$35000	(12-Mar-92 CH.NY244/R) Study for Battle of Light, Coney Island (24x29cm-9x11in) s.
£366	$700	(3-Jul-92 S.W2732) Elephant (25x20cm-10x8in) s. oil crayon
£747	$1300	(15-Apr-92 SY.NY205/R) Hibiscus blossom (28x22cm-11x9in) s. pencil col.pencil W/C
£757	$1400	(10-Jun-92 CE.NY561/R) Back of man (20x13cm-8x5in) s. pencil
£2857	$5000	(26-Sep-91 CH.NY213/R) Pink flower (56x38cm-22x15in) s. s.i.verso crayon silverpoint
£3509	$6000	(12-Mar-92 CH.NY227/R) Abstraction, dance (25x20cm-10x8in) W/C paper on paper
£4000	$7000	(26-Sep-91 CH.NY252/R) Head of old man. Sketch of man's head (29x23cm-11x9in) s.d. lithographic crayon double-sided
£6433	$11000	(12-Mar-92 CH.NY226/R) Flower bud (56x69cm-22x27in) s. conte crayon pencil
£6857	$12000	(26-Sep-91 CH.NY285/R) Telegraph poles (17x23cm-7x9in) s.d.1915 W/C

STELLA, Joseph and MYERS, Jerome (20th C) American
£3143	$5500	(26-Sep-91 CH.NY248/R) Self-portrait. Sketches of woman's head. Sketch of Parisian postman. Man (28x21cm-11x8in) one bears sig. chl pencil oil four

STELLETSKY, Dimitri (1875-1947) Russian
£1000	$1810	(22-May-92 C95/R) Falconer (65x54cm-26x21in) s.

STELLWAG, F (19th C) Dutch
£656	$1200	(3-Jun-92 D.NY91) Bear trainer (58x97cm-23x38in) s.

STELZNER, Heinrich (1833-1910) German
£773	$1400	(21-May-92 GRO.B47/R) The scholar (36x25cm-14x10in) s.i.d.1883 panel

STEMATSKY, Avigdor (1908-1989) Israeli
£4054	$7500	(8-Jun-92 GG.TA208/R) Untitled (91x65cm-36x26in) s.
£4286	$7500	(26-Sep-91 SY.I114/R) Composition (46x55cm-18x22in) s. s.i.verso
£4757	$8800	(9-Jun-92 GG.TA402/R) Landscape in Rishon Le'Zhion (35x40cm-14x16in) s. s.d.1934 verso
£8108	$15000	(8-Jun-92 GG.TA207/R) Figures in landscape (81x100cm-32x39in) s.d.56 s.verso
£798	$1500	(5-Jan-92 GG.TA291/R) Untitled (33x48cm-13x19in) s.d.1952 W/C
£944	$1700	(6-Jan-92 GG.TA429/R) Figures in landscape (48x68cm-19x27in) s. W/C
£2162	$4000	(9-Jun-92 GG.TA403/R) Landscapes (42x34cm-17x13in) s. W/C double-sided
£2811	$5200	(9-Jun-92 GG.TA404/R) Landscape in Rishon Le'Zhion (35x45cm-14x18in) s. W/C
£3243	$6000	(9-Jun-92 GG.TA401/R) Landscape. Intellectual (40x30cm-16x12in) s. W/C double-sided
£3351	$6200	(9-Jun-92 GG.TA400/R) Portrait of woman (49x40cm-19x16in) s.d.1930 W/C
£3404	$6400	(5-Jan-92 GG.TA290/R) Interior (40x33cm-16x13in) s.d.1940 W/C

STEN, John (1879-1922) Swedish
£949	$1736	(12-May-92 GO.G170/R) Cubistic nude (81x65cm-32x26in) s. (S.KR 10000)
£1248	$2258	(3-Dec-91 AB.S5157/R) Seated nude (56x46cm-22x18in) s. panel (S.KR 13000)
£1898	$3472	(12-May-92 GO.G169/R) L'Abondance (98x165cm-39x65in) s. sketch (S.KR 20000)
£569	$1042	(12-May-92 GO.G288) Palm trees, Bali (36x26cm-14x10in) gouache (S.KR 6000)
£806	$1476	(12-May-92 GO.G285/R) Flowers in vase (36x24cm-14x9in) s.d.1921 gouache (S.KR 8500)
£1139	$2083	(12-May-92 GO.G289) Nature morte (36x25cm-14x10in) s.i.d.1915 W/C (S.KR 12000)
£1248	$2258	(3-Dec-91 AB.S5158/R) Reclining female nude (53x64cm-21x25in) s. W/C (S.KR 13000)

STENBERG, Emerik (1873-1972) Swedish
£1836	$3268	(28-Oct-91 AB.S222) Interior with pastry-board (89x74cm-35x29in) s.d.1912 (S.KR 19500)

STENBERG, Georgiy (1900-1933) Russian
£1801	$3115	(28-Mar-92 F.L52/R) Due ballerini (29x35cm-11x14in) mono. pencil tempera (S.FR 4700)

STENERSEN, Gudmund (1863-1934) Norwegian
£790	$1359	(7-Oct-91 B.O128/R) Winter landscape with goats (66x97cm-26x38in) s. (N.KR 9000)

STENGELIN, Alphonse (1852-?) French
£1025	$1844	(2-Feb-92 ZZ.F77/R) Bateau pres du rivage (29x40cm-11x16in) s. (F.FR 10000)

STENIUS, Per (1922-) Finnish
£2199 $3915   (1-Dec-91 HOR.H218) Street scene in India (44x36cm-17x14in) s.
(F.M 17000)
£4678 $8233   (12-Apr-92 HOR.H224/R) Three beauties (59x83cm-23x33in) s.d.1984
(F.M 37000)

STENVINKEL, Jan (1933-1989) Swedish
£911 $1640   (19-Nov-91 GO.G174) Cumulus tempel (116x89cm-46x35in) s. (S.KR 9500)
£1007 $1812   (19-Nov-91 GO.G175) Cumulus tempel (130x97cm-51x38in) s. (S.KR 10500)
£1518 $2778   (13-May-92 BU.S194/R) The tree giving nourishment to birds
(117x89cm-46x35in) s.d.1975 (S.KR 16000)

STEPHAN, A (?) ?
£628 $1200   (17-Jul-92 DM.D2030/R) Parlour scene (84x135cm-33x53in) s.

STEPHAN, Gary (1942-) American
£2000 $3500   (27-Feb-92 CE.NY215/R) Binding knowledge (229x122cm-90x48in) s.d.1981
verso acrylic two panels
£2514 $4500   (9-May-92 CE.NY299/R) World (244x152cm-96x60in) s.i.d.1982verso canvas
linen three panels

STEPHAN, Joseph (1709-1786) German
£5800 $10150   (1-Apr-92 S174/R) Market by walls of town (38x50cm-15x20in) mono.

STEPHANOFF, James (1787-1874) British
*£7000 $12320   (7-Apr-92 C111/R) Fair, held on 1st August, in Hyde Park
(42x60cm-17x24in) s.d.1815 pencil W/C htd white*

STEPHENS, Alice Barber (1858-1932) American
£899 $1600   (2-Nov-91 IH.NY48/R) Woman on white horse reviewing troops
(61x43cm-24x17in) s. grisaille board

STEPHENS, Ethel Anna (?-1944) Australian
£1022 $1748   (17-Mar-92 JRL.S55/R) Still life (37x49cm-15x19in) s. board (A.D 2300)
£2423 $4361   (24-Nov-91 SY.S281/R) Quai Vert, Bruges (37x44cm-15x17in) s.d.1922
(A.D 5500)

STEPHENSON, Willie (fl.1893-1938) British
£400 $692   (1-Oct-91 SWS1828) Path to river (39x59cm-15x23in) s. W/C

STEPPE, Romain (1859-1927) Belgian
£513 $929   (3-Dec-91 C.A288) Windmill at evening (100x70cm-39x28in) s. (B.FR 30000)
£1493 $2731   (12-May-92 C.A302/R) Fishing boats on the North Sea (122x180cm-48x71in)
s. (B.FR 90000)
£2141 $3810   (30-Oct-91 CH.AM64/R) Orage, steamer at full sea (120x180cm-47x71in) s.
s.i.d.1908verso (D.FL 7000)

STEPPES, Edmund (1873-?) German
£1199 $2062   (8-Oct-91 ZEL.L1732/R) Moonlit wooded lake landscape with rocks
(100x85cm-39x33in) s.d.1904 (DM 3500)
*£524 $934   (25-Nov-91 WK.M953/R) Erlebnis (26x39cm-10x15in) s.d.1943 s.i.d.verso
gouache panel (DM 1500)*

STERKENBURG, Piet (20th C) Dutch
£701 $1297   (13-Jun-92 CH.AM192) Fishing fleet setting out on choppy sea and jetty
(80x110cm-31x43in) s.d.81 (D.FL 2300)

STERLING, Marc (1898-?) Russian
£973 $1800   (8-Jun-92 GG.TA209/R) Children in fancy dress (60x50cm-24x20in) s.
£1383 $2600   (5-Jan-92 GG.TA293/R) Vase with flowers and little doll (65x53cm-26x21in)
s.

STERN, Ignaz (1680-1748) German
£5664 $10649   (18-Dec-91 AT.P142/R) Vierge a l'Enfant dans une guirlande de fleurs
(45x36cm-18x14in) bears i. (F.FR 55000)
£6341 $11731   (8-Jun-92 CH.R722/R) L'angelo custode (43x31cm-17x12in) s.d.1725
(I.L 14000000)
£7500 $13125   (3-Apr-92 C9/R) Glaucus and Scylla (127x103cm-50x41in)

STERN, Ignaz (circle) (1680-1748) German
£1700 $3264   (9-Jul-92 CSK328/R) The toilet of Bathsheba (56x44cm-22x17in)

STERN, Ignaz and Ludovico (18th C) German/Italian
£4183 $7571   (5-Dec-91 F.M85) Composizione floreale con amorino (48x76cm-19x30in) pair
(I.L 9000000)

STERN, Irma (1894-1966) South African
£6500 $11050   (22-Oct-91 C64/R) Harvesting (69x61cm-27x24in) s.d.1955
£9073 $16058   (4-Nov-91 SY.J317/R) Three African women (58x58cm-23x23in) s.d.1941
(SA.R 45000)
£11928 $20755   (13-Apr-92 SY.J352/R) African masks and lilies in jug (60x60cm-24x24in)
s.d.1954 (SA.R 60000)
£12922 $22485   (13-Apr-92 SY.J356/R) Pensive Malay woman (55x50cm-22x20in) s.d.1954
(SA.R 65000)

STEPHAN WELZ & CO.

In Association With

SOTHEBY'S

FOUNDED 1744

Irma Stern (1894 – 1966)
MALAY GIRL WITH FLOWERS
signed and dated 1934, 75 by 65 cm
Sold on 4 November 1991 for SA Rand 154,000
A record auction price for the artist

JOHANNESBURG: 13 Biermann Avenue, Rosebank, Johannesburg
P O Box 52431, Saxonwold 2132, South Africa
Telephone: +27(11)880-3125/9. Fax: +27(11)880-2656.

CAPE TOWN: 86 Hout Street, Cape Town
P O Box 2374, Cape Town 8000, South Africa
Telephone: +27(21)23-4728. Fax: +27(21)248700

SOUTH AFRICA'S LARGEST FINE ART AUCTIONEERS

STERN, Irma (1894-1966) South African-cont.
£14911	$25944	(13-Apr-92 SY.J354/R) Amphora and Proteas (89x69cm-35x27in) s.d.1963 (SA.R 75000)
£23857	$41511	(13-Apr-92 SY.J355/R) Still life with tulips and fruit (85x68cm-33x27in) s.d.1959 (SA.R 120000)
£28226	$49960	(4-Nov-91 SY.J314/R) Malay girl with flowers (75x65cm-30x26in) s.d.1934 (SA.R 140000)
£444	$760	(12-Mar-92 SY.J413) Still life with clay pots (61x51cm-24x20in) s.d.1944 W/C (SA.R 2200)
£550	$1001	(28-May-92 C51) Native boy (70x54cm-28x21in) s.d.1941 red chk
£1193	$2029	(21-Oct-91 SY.J350) Two female figures (37x26cm-15x10in) indist.s.d. mixed media (SA.R 5800)
£1512	$2676	(4-Nov-91 SY.J316/R) Group of Africans (24x34cm-9x13in) s.d.1942 gouache (SA.R 7500)
£1749	$2973	(21-Oct-91 SY.J349/R) African woman with headscarf (62x47cm-24x19in) s.d.1938 chl (SA.R 8500)
£1811	$3078	(21-Oct-91 SY.J347/R) Congolese woman with clay pot (26x21cm-10x8in) s.d.1945 gouache pencil (SA.R 8800)
£2621	$4639	(4-Nov-91 SY.J313/R) Watussi, woman, East Africa (62x47cm-24x19in) s.d.1948 chl (SA.R 13000)
£3226	$5710	(4-Nov-91 SY.J315/R) Watussi woman (59x46cm-23x18in) s.d.1935 chl (SA.R 16000)
£5169	$8994	(13-Apr-92 SY.J357/R) In harem (30x24cm-12x9in) s.d.1945 gouache (SA.R 26000)

STERN, Kurt (20th C) ?
£572	$1098	(6-Jul-92 HC.P84/R) Composition LA (62x42cm-24x17in) s. panel (F.FR 5500)

STERN, Max (1872-) German
£2388	$4250	(22-Jan-92 SY.NY260/R) Peasants by church at night (60x75cm-24x30in) s.
£2448	$4357	(30-Nov-91 VG.B1009/R) Dutch fisherfolk on beach (59x50cm-23x20in) s. (DM 7000)

STERNE, Maurice (1878-1957) American
£2123	$3800	(14-Nov-91 CE.NY374/R) Marigolds in vase (74x60cm-29x24in) s.d.1928

STERRE DE JONG, Jacobus (1866-1920) Dutch
£663	$1200	(2-Dec-91 S.SL286/R) Interior with mother and child (48x38cm-19x15in) s.

STERRER (?) ?
£3122	$5463	(3-Apr-92 ZZ.F115) La lecture (116x89cm-46x35in) s. (F.FR 30000)

STERRER, Karl (1885-1960) Austrian
£1738	$3093	(28-Nov-91 D.V135/R) Hind (90x62cm-35x24in) s.d.1943 chl W/C gouache paper on board (A.S 35000)

STERRY, Carl (1861-?) German
£7671	$13809	(19-Nov-91 RAS.K65/R) Young Oriental woman seated with string instrument (174x96cm-69x38in) s.d.1888 (D.KR 85000)
£7800	$13806	(14-Feb-92 C89/R) An Odalisque (175x97cm-69x38in) s.d.1888

STETSON, Charles Walter (1858-1911) American
£952	$1600	(28-Aug-91 MFA.C271) Pepper trees, Pasadena (51x61cm-20x24in) s.d.1889

STETTLER, Marthe (1870-1945) Swiss
£3906	$6914	(5-Nov-91 GF.L2294/R) Mother with two children in park (81x100cm-32x39in) s. (S.FR 10000)

STEUDNER, Daniel (fl.1700-1740) German
£485	$864	(29-Apr-92 D.V707/R) Farmhouse interior with figures (12x15cm-5x6in) i.verso W/C vellum (A.S 10000)

STEVART, James Everett (19th C) ?
£1423	$2604	(14-May-92 BU.S176/R) Indian village by Columbia river (26x36cm-10x14in) s.d.1893 (S.KR 15000)

STEVENS, Agapit (19th C) Belgian
£3005	$5500	(17-May-92 DU.E1087/R) Woman with fan (84x46cm-33x18in) s.
£720	$1339	(17-Jun-92 S320/R) Girl with poppies in hair (52x43cm-20x17in) s. pastel

STEVENS, Aime (1879-?) Belgian
£2395	$4335	(7-Dec-91 KV.L304/R) Hiercheuse (100x120cm-39x47in) s. (B.FR 140000)

STEVENS, Alfred (1823-1906) Belgian
£734	$1277	(14-Apr-92 SY.AM278) View of Le Havre by moonlight (35x26cm-14x10in) s.d.82 panel (D.FL 2400)
£2058	$3909	(24-Jun-92 GL.P149/R) Marine (41x32cm-16x13in) s. panel (F.FR 20000)
£2117	$3747	(4-Nov-91 SY.J240/R) Beach scene (33x24cm-13x9in) s. panel (SA.R 10500)
£3080	$5544	(20-Nov-91 CN.P213/R) Femme a l'eventail (57x42cm-22x17in) init. (F.FR 30000)
£8721	$15000	(16-Oct-91 CH.NY212/R) Femme assise a l'eventail (21x16cm-8x6in) mono. panel
£9143	$16000	(19-Feb-92 CH.NY143/R) Lady in black (50x40cm-20x16in) s. panel
£27000	$48060	(27-Nov-91 S77/R) La douloureuse certitude (80x60cm-31x24in) s.

STEVENS, Alfred (style) (1823-1906) Belgian
£3500 $6055   (4-Oct-91 C76/R) Artist at work (82x60cm-32x24in) i.

STEVENS, Dorothy (1888-1966) Canadian
£731 $1337   (14-May-92 SY.T225/R) Nude bathers on rock by lake (32x39cm-13x15in) s. panel (C.D 1600)
£1000 $1770   (6-Nov-91 SY.T10/R) Woman and child (90x69cm-35x27in) s. (C.D 2000)

STEVENS, George (19th C) British
£1300 $2483   (17-Jul-92 C99/R) Larders with dead game (30x35cm-12x14in) s. pair

STEVENS, George (attrib) (19th C) British
£900 $1530   (24-Oct-91 CSK123) A greyound in an open landscape, Windsor Castle beyond (33x43cm-13x17in) indist.i.d.1830 panel

STEVENS, J D (19th C) British?
£1040 $1851   (29-Oct-91 VN.R289) Dienstbode bij boekenkast (50x70cm-20x28in) (D.FL 3400)
£2800 $4900   (17-Feb-92 HS343/R) Flemish interior with lady holding basket of fruit, dead game on table (60x46cm-24x18in) s. panel

STEVENS, Leopold (1866-1935) French
£655 $1126   (16-Oct-91 FER.M117/R) Pareja de enamorados (54x40cm-21x16in) s. (S.P 120000)

STEVENS, Pieter (1567-1624?) Flemish
£10802   *$19336*   *(12-Nov-91 SY.AM264/R) Landscape with castle (20x27cm-8x11in) pen W/C (D.FL 35000)*

STEVENS, William Dodge (1870-?) American
£2907 $5000   (12-Oct-91 DU.E93/R) The Kingdom round the corner (66x102cm-26x40in) s.

STEVENS, William Lester (1888-1969) American
£684 $1300   (28-Jun-92 LIT.L217) Fishing shack (61x76cm-24x30in) s.
£690 $1200   (15-Apr-92 SY.NY157/R) Winter landscape with stream (71x89cm-28x35in) s.
£691 $1250   (24-May-92 LIT.L216) Harbour at Port Clyde (58x74cm-23x29in) s. i.verso board
£983 $1760   (14-Nov-91 GRO.B139/R) Southwest Head, Grand Manan (81x91cm-32x36in) s. masonite
£1094 $2100   (31-Jul-92 E.EDM39/R) Coastal scene (64x76cm-25x30in) s.
£1600 $2800   (3-Apr-92 DOU.M1) The Merton Batcheldor Barn (107x89cm-42x35in)
£1045   *$1870*   *(14-Nov-91 GRO.B167/R) Waiting for breakfast (69x94cm-27x37in) s.i. W/C pencil*

STEVENSON, William Grant (1849-1919) British
£700 $1267   (4-Dec-91 S150/R) Feeding pet lamb (46x61cm-18x24in) s.

STEVENSON, William Leroy (1905-1966) Canadian
£1024 $1844   (18-Nov-91 HO.ED105/R) First autumn (61x76cm-24x30in) s. board (C.D 2100)

STEVER, Jorge (1940-) German
£537 $973   (3-Dec-91 AB.S5159/R) Grey composition (120x100cm-47x39in) (S.KR 5600)

STEVNS, Niels Larsen (1864-) Danish
£1090 $1907   (1-Apr-92 KH.K187/R) Road near Christiansdal 1919 (50x70cm-20x28in) (D.KR 12000)
£1604 $2759   (16-Oct-91 KH.K201/R) Grey day by the sea (46x61cm-18x24in) (D.KR 18000)

STEWART, Allan (1865-1951) British
£2600 $4472   (11-Oct-91 C152/R) William Penn receiving Charter of Pennsylvania from Charles II (122x183cm-48x72in) s.d.1913

STEWART, Frank Algernon (1877-1945) British
£480 $869   *(5-Dec-91 CG20/R) The Earl of Berkeley's hounds in Marlingwood (38x28cm-15x11in) s. W/C htd.bodycol*

STEWART, Helen Mary (20th C) New Zealander
£1718 $2869   (21-Aug-91 DS.W86/R) Abstract Blenheim landscape (59x74cm-23x29in) s. (NZ.D 5000)

STEWART, J (19th C) British
£1300 $2353   (20-May-92 S156/R) The steam ship Cumbrae (41x66cm-16x26in) s.d.1875

STEWART, J L (19/20th C) ?
£2800 $4816   (16-Oct-91 CSK269) Venetian backwater (65x47cm-26x19in) s.i.d.1909 with 3 pictures different artists

STEWART, J Oswald (fl.1880-1885) British
£720 $1253   (11-Sep-91 PHG33/R) Rob Roy in Glasgow jail (81x151cm-32x59in) s.d.1871

STEWART, James (1791-1863) British
£1100 $1958   (27-Apr-92 PHB268) Portrait group of five children (125x97cm-49x38in) s.i.verso

STEWART, James Lawson (fl.1883-1889) British
£450 $765   (24-Oct-91 CSK65) Chelcote Manor House (61x97cm-24x38in) s. pencil W/C htd.bodycol.

STEWART, John (20th C) British
£1300 $2340   (22-Nov-91 C130/R) The yacht Norma in the Clyde (46x61cm-18x24in) s.d.1886

STEWART, Julius L (1855-1919) American
£4400 $7832   (28-Nov-91 CSK152/R) Summer in the Alps (81x49cm-32x19in) init.i.
£4848 $8582   (24-Apr-92 CN.P191/R) Elegante au sofa (91x64cm-36x25in) s. (F.FR 48000)
£42857 $75000   (26-Sep-91 CH.NY55/R) Picnic under trees (54x100cm-21x39in) s.d.96

STEWART, Julius L (circle) (1855-1919) American
£47222 $85000   (8-Jan-92 D.NY81/R) Five O'Clock tea (147x211cm-58x83in) i.

STICKS, George Blackie (1843-1938) British
£590 $1015   (3-Mar-92 AG265) Morning, Coast of Marsden (45x38cm-18x15in) s.d.1885 i.verso
£1150 $2105   (5-Feb-92 CSK252/R) Dunstonburgh Castle, evening (77x102cm-30x40in) s.d.1882 s.i.d.82 verso

STICKS, Harry (?-1938) British
£500 $915   (5-Feb-92 ZZ.B115) In Weardale (30x46cm-12x18in) s. i.verso
£740 $1369   (9-Jun-92 AG308/R) In Weardale (29x44cm-11x17in) s.

STIEGEL, Eduard (1818-1879) German
£550 $1023   (20-Jun-92 BM.B894/R) Wooded Hessian landscape with architecture and figures (36x27cm-14x11in) s. W/C (DM 1600)

STIELER, Joseph Karl (1781-1858) German
£7000 $12460   (27-Nov-91 S99/R) Portrait of King Oskar of Sweden as Crown Prince (73x60cm-29x24in)

STIENON DU PRE, C (?) ?
£2217 $4167   (17-Dec-91 GM.B886/R) Marine (16x25cm-6x10in) s. (B.FR 130000)

STIEPEVICH, Vincent G (19th C) Russian
£1868 $3250   (13-Sep-91 S.W2859/R) Girl spinning thread (76x51cm-30x20in) s. s.i.stretcher
£3198 $5500   (15-Oct-91 CE.NY287/R) In the Harem (46x61cm-18x24in) s.

STIERHOF, Ernst (1918-) German
£2234 $3887   (17-Sep-91 FN.S2569/R) Young girl seated with rabbit by stable entrance (40x30cm-16x12in) s.i. (DM 6500)

STIFTER, Moritz (1857-1905) Austrian
£5437 $9516   (20-Feb-92 D.V317/R) Oriental bazaar (39x29cm-15x11in) s.d.1890 panel (A.S 110000)
£5523 $9500   (17-Oct-91 SY.NY265/R) Looking glass (39x32cm-15x13in) s.d.1890 panel

STIGLMAYER (19th C) German
£1394 $2537   (12-Dec-91 N.M2839) Konigssee with view of St Bartholoma (14x24cm-6x9in) s.d.1886 panel (DM 4000)

STIGLMAYER, Johann (19th C) German
£894 $1600   (13-Nov-91 B.SF2318/R) Cabin in clearing (57x96cm-22x38in) s.d.1842

STILLMAN, Marie Spartali (1844-1927) British
£1056 $1900   (22-Nov-91 S.BM148/R) Certain ladies...gathering themselves unto Beatrice - illus.from Dante (79x61cm-31x24in) mono.d.80 W/C gouache graphite
£3800 $6954   (14-May-92 TL214/R) Kelmscott Manor from front garden (28x51cm-11x20in) W/C
£8000 $14800   (12-Jun-92 C96/R) Portrait of Effie holding a lily and posy of roses (47x36cm-19x14in) mono.d.76 pencil W/C bodycol.htd.gum arabic
£11500 $21275   (12-Jun-92 C94/R) First meeting of Petrarch and Laura in Church of Santa Chiara at Avignon (57x50cm-22x20in) mono.d.1889 pencil W/C bodycol.htd.gum arabic
£15000 $25500   (25-Oct-91 C20/R) Pharmakeutria - brewing the love philtre (52x47cm-20x19in) mono. W/C gum arabic bodycol paper on panel
£16000 $29600   (12-Jun-92 C95/R) La Pensierosa (54x47cm-21x19in) mono.d.79 pencil W/C bodycol.htd.gum arabic

STIMMER, Tobias (1539-1584) Swiss
£17000 $32640   (7-Jul-92 C96/R) Portrait of bearded man seated at table (29x21cm-11x8in) mono.i.d.1576 pen

STIMMER, Tobias (circle) (1539-1584) Swiss
£1004 $1717   (12-Mar-92 GK.Z11) Flagellation of Christ (57x44cm-22x17in) (S.FR 2600)

STINTON, James (1870-1961) British
£540 $972   (29-Jan-92 RBB903) Pair of pheasants in woodland clearing (18x13cm-7x5in) s. W/C

STIRLING-BROWN, A E D G (19/20th C) British?
£920 $1601   (18-Sep-91 PHS565/R) Portrait of racehorse Cicero in stable
(69x89cm-27x35in) s.i.d.1909

STIRNER, Karl (1882-1943) German
£471   *$842*   *(12-Nov-91 GF.L5371) Wooded lake landscape with figure, early spring*
(21x18cm-8x7in) mono. gouache (S.FR 1200)

STITT, Hobart D (1880-?) American
£1105 $2000   (24-May-92 JRB.C25/R) Springtime (76x91cm-30x36in) s.

STIXRUD, Christoffer (1900-1968) Norwegian
£702 $1305   (18-Jun-92 GWP.O97/R) Street scene, Abelhaugen (56x67cm-22x26in) s.
i.verso (N.KR 8000)
£704 $1238   (8-Apr-92 GWP.O71/R) From the garden (59x66cm-23x26in) s. (N.KR 8000)
£967 $1703   (8-Apr-92 GWP.O70/R) Girl with flowers (66x59cm-26x23in) s. (N.KR 11000)
£1019 $1854   (14-Dec-91 BU.O69/R) Girl with flowers (100x82cm-39x32in) s. i.verso
(N.KR 11500)

STOBBAERTS, Jan (1838-1914) Belgian
£791 $1407   (29-Nov-91 GAB.G2177 a) La reception mondaine (35x55cm-14x22in) panel
(S.FR 2000)
£1170 $1988   (22-Oct-91 GM.B331/R) Chien attele (35x48cm-14x19in) s. wood (B.FR 70000)
£6005 $10569   (7-Apr-92 C.A229/R) The cow herder (100x125cm-39x49in) s. (B.FR 360000)

STOBBAERTS, Marcel (1899-) Belgian
£795 $1438   (23-May-92 KV.L317) La famille-Chez Jacques Maes (60x80cm-24x31in) s.
(B.FR 48000)

STOCK, Henry John (circle) (1853-1931) British
£3000   *$5340*   *(29-Oct-91 C25/R) Maidens at woodland spring (76x51cm-30x20in) i. pencil*
W/C bodycol.paper laid down on linen

STOCK, Ignatius van der (17th C) Dutch
£3927 $7030   (7-May-92 CH.AM89/R) Italianate wooded landscape with muleteer and
peasant woman on track (57x84cm-22x33in) (D.FL 13000)
£9000 $17280   (7-Jul-92 PH4/R) Extensive wooded landscape with figure on horse beside
pool (137x178cm-54x70in) s.

STOCK, Joseph Whiting (1815-1855) American
£824 $1500   (30-May-92 S.BM107/R) Portrait of bearded gentleman, possibly of New
Bedford (76x64cm-30x25in)

STOCKLEIN, Christian (1741-1795) Swiss
£33149 $60000   (21-May-92 CH.NY81/R) Imaginary church interior with figures
(66x78cm-26x31in) s.i. bears sig. panel

STOCKLER, Emanuel (1819-1893) German
£5500   *$10230*   *(17-Jun-92 S366/R) Grand Gallery in Louvre (40x57cm-16x22in) s.d.1870 W/C*

STOCKMAN, Billy (20th C) Australian
£507 $882   (16-Sep-91 CH.ME153/R) Wild potato dreaming (91x61cm-36x24in) board
(A.D 1100)

STOCKMAN, Jan Gerritsz (?-1670) Dutch
£4641 $8355   (19-Nov-91 F.R145/R) Paesaggio con frammenti classici e figure
(147x132cm-58x52in) (I.L 10000000)

STOCKUM, Hilda van (1908-) Dutch
£2545 $4404   (2-Oct-91 A.D32) Still life with chinese plate, jug and bread
(38x46cm-15x18in) init. (E.P 2800)

STOCKWELL, John B (20th C) American
£497 $850   (18-Mar-92 GRO.B59) Rolling fields (51x71cm-20x28in) s.d.89 pastel
£526 $900   (18-Mar-92 GRO.B29) Cypress tree (51x71cm-20x28in) s.d.89 pastel

STODDART, Margaret Olrog (1865-1934) New Zealander
£684   *$1238*   *(2-Dec-91 AAA.S111) Spring in the orchard (26x28cm-10x11in) s. W/C*
(A.D 1600)
£896 $1603   (6-May-92 DS.W20) Wooded river (35x24cm-14x9in) s. W/C (NZ.D 3000)
£1389 $2514   (4-Dec-91 DS.W183) Approaching the village (25x35cm-10x14in) s.d.1901 W/C
(NZ.D 4500)
£5864 $10614   (4-Dec-91 DS.W18/R) Still life of chrysanthemums (67x49cm-26x19in)
s.d.1895 W/C (NZ.D 19000)

STOECKL, Rupert (1923-) German
£769 $1369   (25-Nov-91 WK.M955/R) Lustige Schritte (48x30cm-19x12in) s.d.1954
i.d.verso gouache board (DM 2200)
£1294 $2303   (26-Nov-91 KF.M1066/R) Composition before blue (57x81cm-22x32in) s.d.1956
d.verso gouache board (DM 3700)

STOECKLI, Paul (1906-1992) Swiss
£588 $1000   (23-Oct-91 GD.B729/R) Half portrait (37x28cm-15x11in) s.indis.d. tempera
pavatex (S.FR 1500)

STOECKLI, Paul (1906-1992) Swiss-cont.

£460	$795	(23-Mar-92 AB.L56) Untitled (35x34cm-14x13in) s.d.1983 collage gouache board (S.FR 1200)
£460	$795	(23-Mar-92 AB.L58) Untitled (19x22cm-7x9in) mono.d.1979 gouache (S.FR 1200)
£460	$795	(23-Mar-92 AB.L59) Untitled (22x22cm-9x9in) mono.d.1979 collage board (S.FR 1200)
£460	$795	(23-Mar-92 AB.L55) Schnittzeichnung (22x27cm-9x11in) mono.d.1986 gouache board (S.FR 1200)
£498	$862	(23-Mar-92 AB.L57) Untitled (24x36cm-9x14in) s.d.1986 collage gouache (S.FR 1300)
£575	$994	(23-Mar-92 AB.L68) Composition with circle (29x29cm-11x11in) s. gouache collage (S.FR 1500)
£627	$1123	(15-Nov-91 ZOF.Z1893) Untitled (34x35cm-13x14in) s. indian ink pen board (S.FR 1600)
£728	$1259	(23-Mar-92 AB.L54/R) Schnittzeichnung (22x22cm-9x9in) mono gouache board (S.FR 1900)
£1149	$1989	(23-Mar-92 AB.L67/R) Untitled (35x33cm-14x13in) s. gouache paper on board (S.FR 3000)
£1303	$2254	(23-Mar-92 AB.L60/R) Page of diary (100x70cm-39x28in) s.d.1985 indian ink pen newspaper collage board (S.FR 3400)
£1762	$3049	(23-Mar-92 AB.L65/R) Diary page (100x70cm-39x28in) s. indian ink pen gouache newspaper collage (S.FR 4600)

STOECKLIN, Niklaus (1896-1982) Swiss

£2256	$4128	(4-Jun-92 SY.Z392/R) Oase Oued von Gabes (37x46cm-15x18in) s.d.26 board (S.FR 6000)
£2353	$4212	(15-Nov-91 GK.Z5354/R) Basket with pears (23x28cm-9x11in) s. pavatex (S.FR 6000)
£3922	$7020	(15-Nov-91 ZOF.Z1896/R) Orange branch (33x24cm-13x9in) s.d.54 panel (S.FR 10000)
£6538	$12423	(25-Jun-92 GK.B664/R) Pumpkin with butterfly (28x36cm-11x14in) s.d.1948 pavatex (S.FR 17000)
£7115	$13519	(25-Jun-92 GK.B662/R) San Gimignano (44x50cm-17x20in) s.d.1920 (S.FR 18500)
£13944	$25239	(5-Dec-91 SY.Z139/R) Forest interior (81x65cm-32x26in) s.d.26 panel (S.FR 35000)
£456	$849	(19-Jun-92 ZOF.Z2102/R) Village view with view of towers of San Gimignano (21x16cm-8x6in) mono.i. W/C indian ink pen (S.FR 1200)
£1000	$1900	(25-Jun-92 GK.B663) Wild strawberries with fruit and flowers in vase (21x14cm-8x6in) s.d.1934 W/C over pencil (S.FR 2600)
£1049	$1867	(29-Apr-92 G.Z12) Rotes Ordensband (22x16cm-9x6in) s.i.d.1945 W/C indian ink over pencil (S.FR 2800)
£1504	$2752	(4-Jun-92 SY.Z394/R) Bundesfeuer I (14x10cm-6x4in) gouache (S.FR 4000)
£1729	$3165	(4-Jun-92 SY.Z393/R) Bundesfeuer II (10x14cm-4x6in) gouache (S.FR 4600)

STOFF, Alois (1846-?) Austrian

£1977	$3460	(20-Feb-92 D.V482/R) Girl seated in landscape (31x22cm-12x9in) s.d.1880 panel (A.S 40000)

STOFFE, Jan van der (1611-1682) Dutch

£1800	$3456	(10-Jul-92 C131/R) Cavalry skirmish (40x51cm-16x20in) s. panel
£3800	$7296	(8-Jul-92 S319/R) Skirmish between cavalry and pikemen (35x46cm-14x18in) s. panel
£10465	$18000	(10-Oct-91 SY.NY39/R) A cavalry skirmish (34x56cm-13x22in) s. panel

STOFFE, Jan van der (attrib) (1611-1682) Dutch

£1320	$2297	(13-Sep-91 C30/R) Cavalry skirmish between Turks and Crusaders (36x49cm-14x19in) indist.s. oval
£1742	$3100	(22-Jan-92 SY.NY209/R) Cavalry skirmish (30x39cm-12x15in) panel
£2558	$4808	(18-Dec-91 GM.B4128) Scene de cavalerie (50x67cm-20x26in) (B.FR 150000)

STOFFE, Jan van der (style) (1611-1682) Dutch

£2863	$5095	(28-Nov-91 BU.S75/R) Battle scene (50x95cm-20x37in) panel (S.KR 30000)

STOHNER, Karl (1894-?) German

£700	$1211	(3-Oct-91 CSK221) The ballerinas (41x56cm-16x22in) st.sig.
£1100	$1947	(13-Feb-92 CSK162) Arranging the lillies (91x69cm-36x27in) st.sig.

STOHRER, Walter (1937-) German

£1224	$2117	(28-Mar-92 BOD.P1029) Heads (49x69cm-19x27in) s.d.1972 gouache (DM 3500)
£1404	$2526	(19-Nov-91 L.K1116/R) Nichts als Ketschup and Windhunde (73x53cm-29x21in) s.d.1978 i.verso mixed media over etching (DM 4000)
£3413	$6212	(30-May-92 VG.B402/R) Sand ... plastic landscape (63x49cm-25x19in) s.i.d.1965 mixed media (DM 10000)
£3754	$6833	(30-May-92 VG.B400/R) Untitled (90x62cm-35x24in) s.d.1969 mixed media board (DM 11000)
£4778	$8696	(30-May-92 VG.B401/R) Untitled (87x62cm-34x24in) s.d.1974 mixed media board (DM 14000)
£8392	$14937	(25-Nov-91 WK.M957/R) Doris II (100x60cm-39x24in) s.i.d.1975verso oil collage canvas (DM 24000)
£20478	$37270	(29-May-92 VG.B89/R) Paranoischer Kopf (199x174cm-78x69in) s.d.1975 i.d.verso mixed media canvas (DM 60000)
£27273	$48545	(29-Nov-91 VG.B83/R) Untitled (197x300cm-78x118in) mixed media paper collage canvas (DM 78000)

STOILOFF, Constantin (1850-1924) Russian
£600 $1146   (21-Jul-92 ZZ.B1) Russian snow scene (28x43cm-11x17in) s.
£865 $1644   (24-Jun-92 KM.K1272) Cossacks riding in winter landscape
                            (48x63cm-19x25in) s. (DM 2500)
£1264 $2274   (19-Nov-91 RAS.K382) Sleigh pursued by wolves (71x106cm-28x42in) s.
                            (D.KR 14000)
£1508 $2700   (16-Nov-91 WOL.C672/R) Cossacks in pursuit (66x53cm-26x21in) s.
£1786 $3250   (28-May-92 SY.NY261 a/R) Cossack's charges (69x56cm-27x22in) s.
£506 $850   (28-Aug-91 MFA.C208/R) Winter sleigh ride (23x33cm-9x13in) s. W/C

STOITZNER, Constantin (1863-1934) Austrian
£850 $1522   (5-May-92 ZEL.L1553/R) Still life of fruit, jug and wine glass on draped
                            table (61x92cm-24x36in) mono (DM 2500)
£872 $1500   (15-Oct-91 CE.NY57/R) Elderly man and a child by a harbour
                            (81x54cm-32x21in) s.
£1384 $2422   (20-Feb-92 D.V500) World news (51x41cm-20x16in) s. (A.S 28000)

STOITZNER, Constantin (attrib) (1863-1934) Austrian
£490 $847   (25-Mar-92 KM.K1460) Figures seated at table before window in tavern
                            (57x36cm-22x14in) s. (DM 1400)

STOITZNER, Josef (1884-1951) Austrian
£1761 $3187   (3-Dec-91 FN.S2484/R) Still life with dead game, basket with vegetables
                            and bowl with fruit (74x101cm-29x40in) s. (DM 5000)
£3800 $6878   (2-Dec-91 CSK24/R) Kahlenbergerdorf (69x55cm-27x22in) s.
£7756 $14115   (26-May-92 D.V85/R) Farmhouse garden (68x55cm-27x22in) s. (A.S 160000)
£485 $864   (28-Apr-92 D.V91/R) Flowering field (29x43cm-11x17in) s.d.1913 pencil
                            htd.white (A.S 10000)
£777 $1383   (29-Apr-92 D.V629/R) Farmhouse with flowering lilac (36x25cm-14x10in)
                            s.d.1908 W/C (A.S 16000)

STOITZNER, Siegfried (20th C) Austrian
£1483 $2595   (19-Feb-92 D.V259) View of Durnstein (48x78cm-19x31in) s.d.1935 panel
                            (A.S 30000)

STOITZNER, Walter (1890-1921) Austrian
£566 $967   (12-Mar-92 SY.J351/R) View of farmhouse in mountains (57x49cm-22x19in) s.
                            board (SA.R 2800)

STOJANOW, Pjotr (19th C) Russian
£825 $1435   (18-Sep-91 N.M715/R) Wolves attacking troika (32x53cm-13x21in) s.
                            (DM 2400)
£1236 $2200   (22-Jan-92 SY.NY438/R) Napoleon riding in troika at front of troops
                            (30x53cm-12x21in) s.

STOK, Jacobus van der (1795-1864) Dutch
£1600 $3072   (28-Jul-92 SWS380/R) The travellers' rest (29x38cm-11x15in) s. panel
£1667 $2950   (22-Apr-92 CH.AM102/R) Wooded riverlandscape with shepherds and flock on
                            wooden bridge (37x45cm-15x18in) s.d.1827 panel (D.FL 5500)

STOKES, Adrian (1854-1935) British
£700 $1225   (27-Sep-91 C100/R) Ascona landscape (59x73cm-23x29in) init.d.48 stretcher
£2116 $3767   (28-Apr-92 RAS.K88/R) Helga Ancher, born 1883, seated in the grass
                            (26x20cm-10x8in) init.i. (D.KR 24000)
£800 $1392   (19-Sep-91 CSK188) Portrait of two children with rose (57x47cm-22x19in)
                            s.d.1886 pencil W/C paper on canvas

STOKES, George Vernon (1873-1954) British
£920 $1647   (14-Jan-92 B238/R) A Sheepdog in a sunlit landscape (38x48cm-15x19in) s.
                            board

STOKES, Margaret (1916-) British?
£1111 $2022   (11-Dec-91 A.D18) A little red and black coming through (43x53cm-17x21in)
                            inits. (E.P 1200)

STOKES, Marianne (1855-1927) British
£500 $910   (12-Dec-91 CSK100/R) A little Slovak (25x20cm-10x8in) init. panel
£514 $884   (8-Oct-91 ZEL.L1734/R) White lilies (60x30cm-24x12in) mono. board
                            (DM 1500)
£900 $1530   (22-Oct-91 SWS363/R) Roses (30x18cm-12x7in) bears i.verso panel

STOKES, Wendy (?) ?
£513 $913   (27-Apr-92 J.M668) Tide (100x130cm-39x51in) s.i. paper (A.D 1200)

STOLERENKO, Piotr (1925-) Russian
£659 $1192   (20-May-92 ARC.P11/R) La jetee (50x71cm-20x28in) s. board (F.FR 6500)
£711 $1238   (13-Apr-92 ARC.P148/R) Sur le balcon (67x50cm-26x20in) s. board (F.FR 7000)
£772 $1397   (6-Dec-91 ARC.P19) Le matin (80x53cm-31x21in) s. (F.FR 7500)
£813 $1415   (13-Apr-92 ARC.P145/R) Les chaises longues (50x80cm-20x31in) s. board
                            (F.FR 8000)
£866 $1612   (17-Jun-92 ARC.P159/R) Au mois de septembre (50x59cm-20x23in) s.
                            (F.FR 8500)
£1216 $2201   (20-May-92 ARC.P8/R) Au bord de la mer (49x69cm-19x27in) s. board
                            (F.FR 12000)

STOLERENKO, Piotr (1925-) Russian-cont.

£1317	$2384	(20-May-92 ARC.P10/R) La maison au bord de la mer (25x34cm-10x13in) s. board (F.FR 13000)
£1321	$2299	(13-Apr-92 ARC.P146/R) La maison du pecheur (25x35cm-10x14in) s. board (F.FR 13000)
£1376	$2560	(17-Jun-92 ARC.P158/R) Sous la tonnelle (80x80cm-31x31in) s. (F.FR 13500)
£1520	$2751	(20-May-92 ARC.P9/R) La cour ensoleillee (50x40cm-20x16in) s. board (F.FR 15000)
£1535	$2733	(25-Nov-91 ARC.P101/R) Petite cour en Crimee (40x50cm-16x20in) s. board (F.FR 15000)
£1931	$3360	(13-Apr-92 ARC.P147/R) La terrase rose (64x70cm-25x28in) s. (F.FR 19000)
£2033	$3537	(13-Apr-92 ARC.P143/R) Le printemps (75x85cm-30x33in) s. (F.FR 20000)
£2033	$3537	(13-Apr-92 ARC.P144/R) La petite cour au bord de la mer (70x90cm-28x35in) s. (F.FR 20000)
£2881	$5214	(6-Dec-91 ARC.P18/R) Au jardin (86x104cm-34x41in) s. board (F.FR 28000)
£2938	$5318	(20-May-92 ARC.P7/R) Le passage vers la plage (70x50cm-28x20in) s. board (F.FR 29000)
£4401	$7834	(25-Nov-91 ARC.P100/R) Le jardin fleuri (91x99cm-36x39in) s. (F.FR 43000)
£5732	$10203	(25-Nov-91 ARC.P99/R) L'Heure du the (91x100cm-36x39in) s. (F.FR 56000)

STOLITSA, Evgeni Ivanovich (1870-1929) Russian

£485	$864	(29-Apr-92 D.V878/R) Wooded landscape (27x34cm-11x13in) indis.s. board (A.S 10000)

STOLK, Alida Elisabeth van (attrib) (1830-c.1884) Dutch

£1515	$2682	(22-Apr-92 CH.AM77) Still life with fruit in a basket and dead game on a stone ledge (69x57cm-27x22in) s.d.52 canvas laid down on panel (D.FL 5000)

STOLKER, Jan (1724-1785) Dutch

£1000	$1820	(10-Dec-91 PH198/R) Two angels in clouds (73x100cm-29x39in) s.d.1759
£2652	$4800	(21-May-92 CH.NY116/R) Portraits of Sir Anthony van Dyck. Hans Holbein younger. Frans Hals. Albrecht Durer and Rembrandt (10x8cm-4x3in) s.i.copper five

STOLTENBERG, Hans John (1879-?) German

£1287	$2200	(13-Mar-92 WOL.C429) Landscape with stormy sky (20x28cm-8x11in) s. board

STOLTENBERG, Mattias (1799-1871) Norwegian

£7024	$12502	(29-Oct-91 UL.T221/R) Interior with Engel Stoltenberg (25x22cm-10x9in) (N.KR 80000)
£9658	$17191	(29-Oct-91 UL.T222/R) Rainbow, with Vang church, Hedmarken in background (28x36cm-11x14in) (N.KR 110000)

STOLTENBERG-LERCHE, Vincent (1837-1892) Norwegian

£2480	$4514	(10-Dec-91 UL.T223/R) Evening meal at the monastery (35x28cm-14x11in) s.d.1887 (N.KR 28000)

STOLZ SEGUI, Ramon (1872-1924) Spanish

£968	$1656	(17-Mar-92 FER.M66/R) Bodegon de claveles (41x33cm-16x13in) s. (S.P 175000)

STOLZ, Erwin (1896-1987) Austrian

£544	$974	(5-May-92 ZEL.L1170/R) Unicorn before oak tree (38x28cm-15x11in) mono tempera (DM 1600)
£612	$1096	(5-May-92 ZEL.L1555/R) The Garden of Eden (37x54cm-15x21in) board triptych (DM 1800)
£884	$1583	(5-May-92 ZEL.L1556/R) Flamenco dancer (40x42cm-16x17in) (DM 2600)
£884	$1583	(5-May-92 ZEL.L1554/R) Th stolen bride (50x40cm-20x16in) s. canvas on board (DM 2600)
£596	*$1061*	*(28-Nov-91 D.V59/R) Silent Night, Holy Night (81x49cm-32x19in) gouache paper molino (A.S 12000)*
£645	*$1149*	*(28-Nov-91 D.V58/R) Clown and Kasperl (44x41cm-17x16in) mixed media (A.S 13000)*

STOMER, Mathaus I (c.1600-c.1650) Flemish

£85885	$155453	(18-May-92 SY.MI272/R) Adorazione dei re Magi (127x177cm-50x70in) (I.L 190000000)

STOMER, Matthias (style) (17th C) Flemish

£4420	$8000	(22-May-92 SY.NY262/R) Mocking of Christ (126x164cm-50x65in)

STONE (?) ?

£1550	$2713	(2-Apr-92 HB624) Hunt in full cry. Crossing ditch (41x69cm-16x27in) s. pair

STONE, A (?) ?

£1220	$2098	(16-Oct-91 PHL325/R) At full cry (15x30cm-6x12in) s. panel pair

STONE, Marcus (1840-1921) British

£1200	$2256	(19-Dec-91 C166/R) Sketch for 'Bad news' (34x22cm-13x9in)
£3800	$7144	(19-Dec-91 C193/R) Olivia (21x15cm-8x6in) s.d.1880 s.i.d.verso panel
£10000	$18500	(12-Jun-92 C250/R) Henry VIII and Anne Boleyn observed by Queen Katharine (122x183cm-48x72in) s.d.70

STONE, Marcus (1840-1921) British-cont.
£14000 $24080   (4-Mar-92 S132/R) Henry VIII and Anne Boleyn observed by Queen Katharine (122x183cm-48x72in) s.d.70

STONE, Margaret (20th C) ?
£556 $989   (27-Apr-92 J.M1029) Luculea grandiflora (32x29cm-13x11in) s.i.d.1975 W/C (A.D 1300)

STONE, Marland (20th C) American
£899 $1600   (2-May-92 IH.NY81/R) Man tying woman's bowtie (64x51cm-25x20in) s. pastel

STONE, R (20th C) Australian
£2400 $4272   (21-Jan-92 PH117/R) In paddock. At start. Neck and neck. Final stretch (15x31cm-6x12in) s. panel four

STONE, Reynolds (1909-) British
£1988 $3538   (26-Nov-91 VN.R118/R) Two hunting scene (15x30cm-6x12in) s. panel pair (D.FL 6400)

STONE, Richard (20th C) British
£618 $1100   (2-Nov-91 IH.NY120/R) Woman in yellow dress with red umbrella (56x46cm-22x18in) s. gouache

STONE, Robert (20th C) Australian
£1913 $3500   (5-Jun-92 SY.NY199/R) On the scent. The kill (15x31cm-6x12in) s. panel pair
£3005 $5500   (5-Jun-92 SY.NY193/R) The meet. Passing a stagecoach. Over a ditch. Full cry (15x30cm-6x12in) 2 s. set of four
£3552 $6500   (5-Jun-92 SY.NY172/R) View halloo. Full cry. Over the fence. The kill (15x30cm-6x12in) 2 s. set of four

STONE, Rudolf (19th C) ?
£3100 $5673   (4-Jun-92 DLY157/R) Huntings scenes (15x30cm-6x12in) s. set of four
£3400 $6086   (5-May-92 SWS307/R) The meet. The start. Full cry. The finish (15x31cm-6x12in) s. panel set of four

STONE, Sarah (18th C) ?
£689 $1240   (23-Nov-91 YFA.M279/R) Variety Lark. Blue Grossbeak (36x25cm-14x10in) one s. one d.1795 W/C pair
£1100 $1969   (12-Nov-91 C47/R) A pink flamingo (36x25cm-14x10in) i.mount pencil W/C
£1100 $1969   (12-Nov-91 C50/R) A crowned crane (38x27cm-15x11in) s.d.1783 i.mount pencil W/C htd.white
£1100 $1969   (12-Nov-91 C48/R) Night Heron (38x28cm-15x11in) s.d.1782 i.mount pencil W/C gum arabic
£1200 $2148   (12-Nov-91 C49/R) Little blue heron (40x29cm-16x11in) s.d.1782 i.mount pencil W/C bodycol.

STONE, W (19/20th C) British
£800 $1376   (8-Oct-91 PH102) Dartmouth, Devon (46x82cm-18x32in) s.

STOOP, Dirk (1618-1681) Dutch
£3072 $5560   (21-May-92 L.K144/R) Hunting scene with figures and dogs (63x51cm-25x20in) panel (DM 9000)
£4749 $8500   (11-Nov-91 GC.M57/R) L'Aubrevoir (22x29cm-9x11in) panel

STOOP, Dirk (attrib) (1618-1681) Dutch
£1600 $2928   (12-May-92 SWS605/R) Man leading grey horse outside inn (30x24cm-12x9in) panel

STOOP, Dirk (circle) (1618-1681) Dutch
£5123 $9221   (27-Jan-92 CSC.P45/R) Choc de cavalerie (59x84cm-23x33in) panel (F.FR 50000)

STOOPENDAAL, Georg (1866-1953) Swedish
£522 $955   (12-May-92 GO.G172) Waggon load of timber (50x76cm-20x30in) s. (S.KR 5500)

STOOPENDAAL, Mosse (1901-1948) Swedish
£616 $1059   (8-Mar-92 BU.M350) Tree-pipit (21x26cm-8x10in) s. panel (S.KR 6400)
£1342 $2416   (23-Nov-91 SO.S613/R) Crows (22x29cm-9x11in) s. panel (S.KR 14000)
£1376 $2518   (12-May-92 GO.G180) Winter landscape with crows in flight (34x54cm-13x21in) s. (S.KR 14500)
£1412 $2514   (28-Oct-91 AB.S223) Autumn landscape with woodcock at dusk (54x67cm-21x26in) s.d.23 (S.KR 15000)
£1415 $2505   (25-Apr-92 SO.S600/R) Bird in bushes (40x36cm-16x14in) s. (S.KR 15000)
£1540 $2649   (8-Mar-92 BU.M42) Crows (25x50cm-10x20in) s.d.1938 panel (S.KR 16000)
£1630 $2934   (23-Nov-91 SO.S611/R) Seagulls on rocks (38x58cm-15x23in) s. (S.KR 17000)
£1992 $3646   (12-May-92 GO.G175) Ducks in flight by tarn (45x60cm-18x24in) s. (S.KR 21000)
£2176 $3939   (19-May-92 AB.S4278/R) Winter landscape with running hare (50x70cm-20x28in) s.d.1940 (S.KR 23000)
£2182 $3993   (14-May-92 BU.S67/R) Great tits among autumn leaves (45x60cm-18x24in) s.d.1944 (S.KR 23000)
£2453 $4342   (25-Apr-92 SO.S599/R) Bird by tree (31x43cm-12x17in) s.d.38 (S.KR 26000)

STOOPENDAAL, Mosse (1901-1948) Swedish-cont.

£2495	$4516	(3-Dec-91 AB.S4667/R) Coastal landscape with ducks in flight, winter (41x53cm-16x21in) s. (S.KR 26000)
£2589	$4660	(23-Nov-91 SO.S612/R) Great tits on branch (48x59cm-19x23in) s.d.1946 (S.KR 27000)
£2649	$4795	(19-May-92 AB.S4277/R) Blackbirds in winter tree (33x45cm-13x18in) s.d.38 (S.KR 28000)
£3071	$5559	(3-Dec-91 AB.S4668/R) Fox and mallards (46x55cm-18x22in) s. d.1942verso (S.KR 32000)
£3260	$5868	(19-Nov-91 GO.G177/R) Woodcock (46x55cm-18x22in) s.d.1938 (S.KR 34000)
£3272	$5628	(8-Mar-92 BU.M469) Gulls on a skerry (55x86cm-22x34in) s.d.1943 (S.KR 34000)
£3359	$6080	(3-Dec-91 AB.S4666/R) Bullfinches in winter (38x46cm-15x18in) s.d.1939 (S.KR 35000)
£3416	$6250	(12-May-92 GO.G177/R) Flowering marshes with geese (60x90cm-24x35in) s.d.1937 (S.KR 36000)
£3453	$6250	(19-May-92 AB.S4279/R) Mallard and ducklings swimming among reeds (35x49cm-14x19in) s. (S.KR 36500)
£3605	$6598	(11-May-92 NOR.S15/R) Bullfinches (50x60cm-20x24in) s.d.1940 (S.KR 38000)
£3931	$7076	(19-Nov-91 GO.G178/R) Squirrel (91x97cm-36x38in) s.d.24 (S.KR 41000)
£3985	$7292	(11-May-92 NOR.S14/R) Ducks landing (45x66cm-18x26in) s.d.1933 (S.KR 42000)
£4602	$8284	(23-Nov-91 SO.S609/R) Winterlandscape with hare (48x64cm-19x25in) s.d.39 (S.KR 48000)
£4730	$8562	(19-May-92 AB.S4915/R) Black grouse in tree, winter (137x93cm-54x37in) s.d.1934 (S.KR 50000)
£4744	$8681	(11-May-92 NOR.S16/R) Jays (55x74cm-22x29in) s.d.1944 (S.KR 50000)
£5313	$9723	(12-May-92 GO.G176) Herring-gulls on rock (56x88cm-22x35in) s.d.1943 (S.KR 56000)
£6321	$11188	(5-Nov-91 BA.S169/R) Fox by snow cowered fence (90x140cm-35x55in) s.d.1944 (S.KR 67000)
£989	*$1760*	*(28-Oct-91 AB.S408) Fox and black-cock in winter (28x43cm-11x17in) s. W/C (S.KR 10500)*

STOOTER, Cornelis Leonardsz (circle) (?-1655) Dutch

£1400	$2450	(25-Feb-92 PH11) Mountainous landscape with three figures on mound by torrent (72x112cm-28x44in) panel

STORCH, Anton (1892-1979) Austrian

£537	$929	(3-Oct-91 D.V203/R) Fishing boats (60x77cm-24x30in) s.indis.d.59 board (A.S 11000)
£589	*$1119*	*(25-Jun-92 D.V654/R) Strandbad Kritzendorf, study for poster (42x29cm-17x11in) s.d.29 mixed media (A.S 12000)*

STORCH, F (1805-1883) Danish

£1675	$2982	(28-Apr-92 RAS.K80/R) Italian fisherman and his family by water's edge (63x45cm-25x33in) s.d.1861 (D.KR 19000)
£3700	$6328	(10-Mar-92 RAS.K133/R) Nymphs dancing around Cupid (79x92cm-31x36in) s.i.d.1840 (D.KR 41000)

STORCH, Frederik (1805-1883) Danish

£496	$894	(19-Nov-91 RAS.K159/R) Young Italian woman with water jug (42x24cm-17x9in) s. (D.KR 5500)
£573	$1020	(28-Apr-92 RAS.K486) Summer landscape with Dannebrog (43x54cm-17x21in) s.d.1868 (D.KR 6500)
£669	$1244	(16-Jun-92 RAS.K251) Portrait of Sofie Margrethe Henriette Skibsted (66x51cm-26x20in) s.d.1858 oval (D.KR 7500)
£1764	$3139	(28-Apr-92 RAS.K143/R) Little girl resting in wood after picking berries (91x78cm-36x31in) (D.KR 20000)
£2646	$4709	(28-Apr-92 RAS.K472/R) Young girl putting flowers in basket (98x71cm-39x28in) (D.KR 30000)

STORCK, Abraham (c.1635-c.1710) Dutch

£3510	$6424	(14-May-92 BU.S143/R) The harbour in Livorno (78x62cm-31x24in) bears sig. (S.KR 30000)
£19000	$36480	(8-Jul-92 S142/R) Views in the harbour of Amsterdam (26x29cm-10x11in) s. pair
£23256	$40000	(14-Oct-91 H.C8/R) Canal scene with men loading ferry (56x48cm-22x19in) s.d.1690 panel
£26000	$49920	(10-Jul-92 C2/R) Italianate ports with gentry, pilgrims and stevedores by fountain and with shipping by church (80x68cm-31x27in) one s. pair
£29825	$53684	(22-Nov-91 SA.A1502/R) Amsterdam Harbour (59x74cm-23x29in) indis.s.d. (DM 85000)
£62000	$108500	(1-Apr-92 S14/R) Capriccio Mediterranean harbour scene (132x200cm-52x79in) s.d.1679

STORCK, Abraham (circle) (c.1635-c.1710) Dutch

£2389	$4324	(21-May-92 L.K145/R) Dutch fleet on the Ij near Amsterdam (67x84cm-26x33in) i. (DM 7000)
£4000	$7280	(10-Dec-91 PH201/R) Port scene with ships moored alongside quay and seamen rowing ashore (54x71cm-21x28in) bears sig.

STORCK, Abraham (studio) (c.1635-c.1710) Dutch

£4073	$7536	(10-Jun-92 ZZ.F53) La rade d'un port Hollandais par temps calme (61x80cm-24x31in) bears sig. (F.FR 40000)

STORCK, Abraham (studio) (c.1635-c.1710) Dutch-cont.
£10200 $18156   (30-Oct-91 S3/R) River scene in Amsterdam (81x112cm-32x44in) canvas on panel

STORCK, Abraham (style) (c.1635-c.1710) Dutch
£612 $1089   (29-Oct-91 VN.R291/R) Shipping in harbour (58x79cm-23x31in) (D.FL 2000)
£2048 $3706   (21-May-92 L.K146) Seascapes with shipping (21x27cm-8x11in) panel pair (DM 6000)
£2348 $4250   (22-May-92 S.BM20/R) Promenade at the harbourside Medena (33x41cm-13x16in) i.verso canvas on panel
£2623 $4696   (12-Nov-91 SY.AM132/R) Figures unloading cargo in Italianate harbour (74x65cm-29x26in) (D.FL 8500)
£14000 $24500   (3-Apr-92 C137/R) Mediterranean harbour scenes, with cattle drovers on bridge and elegant couple by portico (48x63cm-19x25in) one indist.s pair

STORCK, Jacob (circle) (17th C) Dutch
£2732 $4672   (18-Mar-92 D.V378/R) Southern harbour landscape (56x68cm-22x27in) (A.S 55000)

STORER, Charles (1817-1907) American
£608 $1100   (5-Dec-91 GRO.B441/R) Roses in vase (91x61cm-36x24in) s.d.1907

STORER, Inez (20th C) American
£588 $1000   (23-Oct-91 B.SF3810/R) Signal (122x144cm-48x57in) s.d.65 mixed media assemblage board

STORER, Johann Christoph (1611-1671) Swiss
£5113 $9254   (3-Dec-91 SY.MI217/R) Sansone che distrugge il tempio (253x158cm-100x62in) (I.L 11000000)

STORK, Jan (19th C) ?
£897 $1606   (16-Jan-92 D.V29/R) Frozen canal landscape (18x24cm-7x9in) s. panel (A.S 18000)

STORM, Juan (20th C) Uruguayan?
£618 $1100   (28-Oct-91 GC.M21) Escena de Puerto (50x72cm-20x28in) s.d.57 board
£618 $1100   (28-Oct-91 GC.M20/R) Naturaleza muerta (64x90cm-25x35in) s.d.1957
£820 $1500   (4-Jun-92 GOM.M63) Estancia El Taruman (89x116cm-35x46in) s.d.
£1156 $2000   (30-Sep-91 GC.M13/R) Un camino es Ilusion (89x116cm-35x46in) s.d.90

STORMONT, Howard Gull (fl.1884-1923) British
£750 $1283   (12-Mar-92 CSK85/R) The valley of poppies (25x43cm-10x17in) s. s.i.verso pencil W/C
£1400 $2380   (24-Oct-91 CSK41) Punting on Clevedon Reach (41x66cm-16x26in) s.d.1890 pencil W/C htd.bodycol.

STORRIER, Tim (1949-) Australian
£2564 $4564   (28-Apr-92 CH.ME149) Matches (152x122cm-60x48in) st.sig. s.verso (A.D 6000)
£726 $1293   (27-Apr-92 J.M83 a) Australia (57x75cm-22x30in) s.d.84 W/C (A.D 1700)
£2115 $3806   (24-Nov-91 SY.S145/R) Door (50x40cm-20x16in) s.i.d.1988 mixed media board (A.D 4800)
£3419 $6085   (27-Apr-92 J.M95) Shank, dream and axe - still life (96x146cm-38x57in) s.i.d. W/C (A.D 8000)
£8150 $14670   (24-Nov-91 SY.S382/R) Point to Point (135x198cm-53x78in) s.i.d.1987 mixed media canvas (A.D 18500)

STORRS, John (1885-1956) American
£3846 $7000   (28-May-92 CH.NY258/R) Three people abstract (25x30cm-10x12in) init. s.d.45 verso canvasboard

STORSTEIN, Aage (1900-1983) Norwegian
£965 $1795   (18-Jun-92 GWP.O99/R) The old garden at Froen Manor house (46x64cm-18x25in) s.d.41 i.verso panel (N.KR 11000)
£1404 $2611   (15-Jun-92 B.O151/R) View towards Krok, Holmsbu (38x46cm-15x18in) s. panel (N.KR 16000)
£1754 $3263   (15-Jun-92 B.O150/R) Autumn landscape (51x72cm-20x28in) s.d.44 (N.KR 20000)
£2391 $4353   (14-Dec-91 BU.O63/R) Pine trees, Holmsbu (49x65cm-19x26in) s.d.40 (N.KR 27000)
£3158 $5874   (18-Jun-92 GWP.O100/R) Sketch for embellishment (66x200cm-26x79in) s.d.38 (N.KR 36000)
£6497 $11175   (10-Oct-91 BU.O36/R) Family idyl (67x88cm-26x35in) s.d.39 s.i.d.verso (N.KR 74000)

STORTENBEKER, Pieter (1828-1898) Dutch
£489 $866   (5-Nov-91 SY.AM475) Cows in meadow (28x52cm-11x20in) s. W/C (D.FL 1600)

STORY, George H (1835-1923) American
£1488 $2500   (14-Aug-91 B.P55/R) Whitehead, Cushing's Island in Casco Bay (23x28cm-9x11in) s.
£2432 $4500   (10-Jun-92 CE.NY261/R) Costume party (76x51cm-30x20in) s. canvas on masonite
£11050 $20000   (5-Dec-91 SY.NY21/R) Portrait of Abraham Lincoln (51x46cm-20x18in) s.

STOSKOPFF, Sebastien (attrib) (1597-1657) German
£5408 $9572 (10-Feb-92 GL.P38/R) Vanite au bougeoir et au livre (49x58cm-19x23in) (F.FR 53000)

STOSKOPFF, Sebastien (circle) (1597-1657) German
£9684 $18012 (18-Jun-92 SY.MO222/R) Vanite aux livres et sablier (58x77cm-23x30in) (F.FR 95000)

STOSSEL, Oskar (1879-?) Austrian
£741 $1298 (19-Feb-92 D.V160/R) The red bridge (62x50cm-24x20in) s. (A.S 15000)

STOTHARD, Thomas (1755-1834) British
£6500 $11635 (11-Nov-91 S540) Portland vase - studies front and back W/C two one frame

STOTT, William R S (fl.1905-1934) British
£740 $1325 (14-Jan-92 SWS264/R) The ferry (49x39cm-19x15in) s.indis.d.1935 board
£950 $1805 (23-Jun-92 CG726/R) Harlequin (91x61cm-36x24in) s.d.1920
£1000 $1740 (15-Apr-92 PHL63/R) Piccadilly Circus (25x35cm-10x14in) s.i.d.99 col.wash htd white

STOUT, Myron (1908-1987) American
£37989 $68000 (13-Nov-91 CH.NY151/R) Hierophant (96x76cm-38x30in)

STOWELL, Flaxney (19/20th C) ?
£5000 $9150 (15-May-92 CBS194) Castletown from Qualtroughs yard (43x56cm-17x22in) s.d.1904 W/C

STOWER, Willy (1864-1931) German
£559 $968 (25-Mar-92 KM.K1761) View from bridge of escorting ship (56x40cm-22x16in) s.i.d.1912 W/C (DM 1600)

STRAATEN, Bruno van (jnr) (1812-1887) Dutch
£669 $1164 (17-Sep-91 CH.AM364) Hunter and his dog on snowy path and skaters on frozen waterway (44x57cm-17x22in) (D.FL 2200)

STRAATEN, Johannes Josephus Ignatius van (19th C) Dutch
£2265 $4122 (14-Dec-91 BOD.P756/R) Hunting still life with dead rabbit and horn in landscape (90x76cm-35x30in) s. (DM 6500)

STRACHAN, C (1865-1929) British
£760 $1353 (24-Jan-92 MAX321/R) The pet calf (18x25cm-7x10in) s. W/C
£800 $1424 (24-Jan-92 MAX319/R) Two ladies with black cat outside cottage (18x25cm-7x10in) s. W/C
£1500 $2670 (24-Jan-92 MAX320/R) The lame duck (18x25cm-7x10in) s. W/C

STRACHAN, Claude (1865-1929) British
£500 $915 (15-May-92 CBS234) Mother and children with ducks and chickens outside cottage (36x28cm-14x11in) s. W/C
£500 $895 (5-May-92 SWS188/R) A break from the harvest (24x35cm-9x14in) s. W/C bodycol.
£580 $1061 (14-May-92 B295/R) Wayside cottages (18x26cm-7x10in) s. W/C
£720 $1289 (5-May-92 SWS224/R) Village in Warwickshire (18x26cm-7x10in) s. indist.i.verso W/C over pencil htd bodycol.
£750 $1328 (6-Nov-91 S264) Watching the ducks (17x26cm-7x10in) s. W/C htd bodycol
£760 $1315 (4-Sep-91 RBB797) View of thatched cottages at Broughton Hackett, Worcester (15x33cm-6x13in) s. i.mount W/C
£1900 $3439 (20-May-92 B219/R) The ferry (27x43cm-11x17in) s. W/C
£1900 $3382 (29-Oct-91 C74/R) Feeding the chickens (29x46cm-11x18in) s. W/C htd bodycol.
£1900 $3249 (13-Mar-92 C22/R) Streatley Mill (30x47cm-12x19in) s. i.verso W/C htd.white
£2200 $3850 (27-Feb-92 KING278) Thatched cottages with figures by stream (61x122cm-24x48in) s. W/C
£2200 $3850 (24-Sep-91 SWO2) Thatched cottage and garden (20x30cm-8x12in) s. W/C
£2400 $4104 (13-Mar-92 C21/R) Worcestershire cottage (30x47cm-12x19in) s. i.verso W/C htd.bodycol
£2500 $4475 (14-Jan-92 SWS64/R) Village street. By the cottage door (18x26cm-7x10in) s. WC bodycol pair
£2800 $4900 (1-Apr-92 B151/R) Young girl and geese by cottage (18x27cm-7x11in) s. W/C bodycol pair
£3600 $6300 (24-Sep-91 SWO3) Thatched cottage and garden (20x30cm-8x12in) s. W/C

STRACHAN, David Edgar (1919-1970) British
£553 $979 (26-Apr-92 SY.ME5) Still life (28x33cm-11x13in) s.indist.d. board (A.D 1300)

STRACKE, Louis (1856-1934) Dutch
£3161 $5500 (10-Sep-91 BG.M683/R) Tow nude children playing amongst tapestries, carpets and tiger skin (89x180cm-35x71in) canvas on board

STRACKLECKY, Wandalin (1855-1917) Polish
£1465 $2490 (24-Oct-91 D.V147/R) Hunting party with dogs (25x48cm-10x19in) s.d.1880 (A.S 30000)

STRADONE, Giovanni (1911-) Italian
£1112 $1980   (29-Nov-91 F.F163) Fuoco d'artificio (25x35cm-10x14in) s.i.d.1969
     (I.L 2400000)
£1610 $2881   (14-Nov-91 F.M53/R) Campagna (28x39cm-11x15in) s.i.verso (I.L 3500000)
£1840 $3293   (14-Nov-91 F.M18/R) Casimiro (55x40cm-22x16in) s.i.d.1953verso board
     (I.L 4000000)
£2041 $3736   (12-May-92 F.R190/R) Paesaggio romano del Soratte (30x40cm-12x16in)
     s.i.d.1964verso (I.L 4500000)
£3224 $5868   (9-Dec-91 CH.R93/R) Periferia Romana (70x50cm-28x20in) s.i.d.1959verso
     (I.L 7000000)
£4568 $7948   (14-Apr-92 F.M228/R) Via Salaria (40x50cm-16x20in) s.i.d.1945verso
     (I.L 10000000)
£6124 $11207   (12-May-92 F.R215/R) Ragazzo con chitarra (100x70cm-39x28in)
     s.i.d.1959verso (I.L 13500000)

STRAET, Jan van der (attrib) (1523-1605) Flemish
£559 $1000   (15-Jan-92 CH.NY126/R) Good Samaritan (16x23cm-6x9in) black chk pen wash
     htd white

STRAHN, Peter Josef (1904-) German
£969 $1841   (24-Jun-92 KM.K1274) Shepherd girl with goats (60x50cm-24x20in) s.
     (DM 2800)

STRAIN, Daniel (fl.1870-1890) American
£1250 $2250   (22-Nov-91 S.BM38/R) Scene in Morocco (61x91cm-24x36in) s.i.d.1883

STRAKA, Josef (1864-1946) Austrian
£1562 $2702   (3-Oct-91 D.V226/R) Traunsee landscape with jetty (40x50cm-16x20in) s.
     (A.S 32000)

STRAKHOV, Piotr (1921-) Russian
£728 $1275   (5-Apr-92 ARC.P117/R) Le verre de the (50x55cm-20x22in) s.verso board
     (F.FR 7000)
£973 $1752   (27-Jan-92 ARC.P220/R) Les fleurs bleues (80x64cm-31x25in) s. (F.FR 9500)

STRALEN, Antoni van see VERSTRALEN, Anthonie

STRAND, Svein (1934-) Norwegian
£2195 $3775   (10-Oct-91 BU.O125/R) Seated woman (93x68cm-37x27in) s.d.1956
     (N.KR 25000)

STRANG, Ray C (1893-1957) American
£811 $1500   (10-Jun-92 CE.NY333/R) Desert traveller with donkey (68x91cm-27x36in) s.
     board

STRANG, William (1859-1921) British
£1200 $2148   (13-Nov-91 WI1161/R) Allegory of Motherhood (50x40cm-20x16in) s.d.1918
£4500 $7740   (6-Mar-92 C18/R) Boy reading on harbour's edge (46x53cm-18x21in)

STRANGE, Frederick (?) Australian
£5983 $10650   (28-Apr-92 CH.ME213/R) Launceston from Windmill Hill (28x51cm-11x20in)
     s.i.d.1858 W/C (A.D 14000)

STRANOVER, Tobias (1684-1735) Czechoslovakian
£3550 $6247   (11-Apr-92 AT.P131/R) Nature morte avec oiseau et grappe de raisin
     (30x35cm-12x14in) panel (F.FR 35000)
£5525 $10000   (22-May-92 SY.NY233/R) Ducks, pheasant and other birds in landscape
     (93x138cm-37x54in) s.
£6250 $11063   (5-Nov-91 GF.L2025/R) Still life with peaches and grapes
     (48x38cm-19x15in) (S.FR 16000)
£8840 $16000   (21-May-92 CH.NY194/R) Parrot perched on ring, swags grapes and flowers
     above urn with fruit on stone ledge (140x128cm-55x50in) shaped top
£15180 $27780   (14-May-92 BU.S145/R) Still life of parrot and fruit in landscape
     (80x112cm-31x44in) s. (S.KR 160000)

STRANOVER, Tobias (attrib) (1684-1735) Czechoslovakian
£8500 $14960   (8-Apr-92 S115/R) Still life of parrots on perch with grapes
     (65x54cm-26x21in) panel

STRANOVER, Tobias (circle) (1684-1735) Czechoslovakian
£950 $1663   (27-Feb-92 CSK176) Pear, apples and a plum with cob nuts in a landscape
     (30x39cm-12x15in)

STRANOVER, Tobias (style) (1684-1735) Czechoslovakian
£1204 $2156   (6-May-92 GD.B1242/R) Still life of peaches in basket with figs, grapes
     and vine leaves (45x64cm-18x25in) (S.FR 3300)

STRANSKY, Ferdinand (1904-) Austrian
£3476 $6187   (28-Nov-91 D.V227/R) Factory in the snow (73x93cm-29x37in) s.d.65
     (A.S 70000)
£437 $778   (28-Apr-92 D.V250) Rooftops, view from Rennerhof (25x33cm-10x13in)
     s.i.d.74verso chl (A.S 9000)
£548 $982   (15-Jan-92 D.V186/R) Nude seated (40x29cm-16x11in) s.d.60 tempera gouache
     (A.S 11000)

STRANSKY, Ferdinand (1904-) Austrian-cont.
£794 $1414   *(28-Nov-91 D.V206/R) Man and woman (50x39cm-20x15in) s.d.52 brush indian ink (A.S 16000)*

STRASSER, Margarethe (1885-?) Austrian
£976 $1689   (3-Oct-91 D.V96/R) Pot of azalea and vase with flowers (66x56cm-26x22in) s. (A.S 20000)

STRASSER, Roland (1892-1974) Austrian
£2488 $4428   (25-Nov-91 W.T1871/R) Balinese farmer and horse (71x58cm-28x23in) s. (C.D 5000)
£4128 $7555   (1-Jun-92 W.T1232/R) Legong temple dancer with orchestra (89x61cm-35x24in) s. s.verso (C.D 9000)
£4587 $8394   (1-Jun-92 W.T1231/R) Temple dancer, Bali (99x60cm-39x24in) s. s.verso (C.D 10000)
£5046 $9234   (1-Jun-92 W.T1233/R) Balinese man and fighting cock (102x69cm-40x27in) s. s.verso (C.D 11000)
£5224 $9299   (25-Nov-91 W.T1870/R) Balinese dancer (94x50cm-37x20in) s.i. (C.D 10500)
£5275 $9654   (1-Jun-92 W.T1230/R) Pitjai, the Legong, Bali 1920 (97x51cm-38x20in) s. (C.D 11500)
£3980 $7085   *(25-Nov-91 W.T1778/R) Villager, Bali (57x23cm-22x9in) s. i.verso chl (C.D 8000)*

STRAUBINGER, Klaus (1839-?) German
£813 $1422   (3-Apr-92 BM.B572) Autumn landscape (80x100cm-31x39in) (DM 2300)
£919 $1608   (3-Apr-92 BM.B573) Bunch of field flowers (80x100cm-31x39in) mono (DM 2600)

STRAUCH, Lorenz (1554-1630) German
£850 $1547   (13-Dec-91 C148) Portrait of gentleman in black coat with white lace collar (10cm-4ins circular) mono.d.1604 copper

STRAUS, Meyer (1831-1905) American
£3158 $6000   (24-Jun-92 B.SF6280/R) Grazing cattle (104x178cm-41x70in) s. canvas on board

STRAYER, Paul (1885-?) American
£787 $1400   (2-Nov-91 IH.NY198/R) Elk collapses at tree and hunter. Approaching wolves with ax (53x38cm-21x15in) s.d.1915 and 1914 two

STREATFIELD, Rev Thomas (1777-1840) British
£620 $1091   *(7-Apr-92 C34/R) South front of Wilton House and Palladian Bridge (20x30cm-8x12in) i.verso pen W/C*

STREBEL, Fritz (1920-) Swiss
£1065 $1980   (19-Jun-92 ZOF.Z2104/R) Group of figures (83x101cm-33x40in) i.stretcher (S.FR 2800)
£1137 $2036   (15-Nov-91 ZOF.Z1897) L'ombra della sera (120x90cm-47x35in) mono.d.79 i.verso (S.FR 2900)

STRECKENBACH, M T (1865-1936) German
£1783 $3049   (19-Mar-92 N.M2847) Flowers in vase (55x61cm-22x24in) s. (DM 5100)

STRECKER, Paul (1900-1950) German
£683 $1242   (30-May-92 VG.B963/R) Landscape, South of France (34x68cm-13x27in) s. board (DM 2000)

STRECKFUSS, Wilhelm (1817-1896) German
£550 $935   *(25-Oct-91 BM.B844/R) Coastal landscape with beached fishing boat (24x35cm-9x14in) W/C (DM 1600)*

STREECK, Hendrik van (1659-1719) Dutch
£15000 $28800   (7-Jul-92 PH33/R) Still life with earthenware ewer, bowl charcoal, tobacco and clay pipe on ledge (36x26cm-14x10in) s. panel

STREECK, Jurriaen van (1632-1687) Dutch
£13374 $24208   (7-Dec-91 CH.MO29/R) Nature morte avec un citron et des peches sur un plat (51x42cm-20x17in) s. panel oval (F.FR 130000)

STREECK, Jurriaen van (style) (1632-1687) Dutch
£6000 $11520   (10-Jul-92 C178/R) Peeled lemon and roll of pepper in bowl, with oyster, roemer and orange on drpaed ledge (36x30cm-14x12in) panel
£10000 $19200   (8-Jul-92 S254/R) Still life of oysters, fruit and vessels on draped table (57x81cm-22x32in) panel

STREEFKERK, Carl August (1894-?) Dutch
£520 $905   (14-Apr-92 SY.AM219) View of the Nicolaaskerk in Amsterdam (58x98cm-23x39in) s. (D.FL 1700)

STREET, Robert (1796-1865) American
£852 $1550   (13-Dec-91 DOU.M2) Ancestral portrait (61x53cm-24x21in)
£852 $1550   (13-Dec-91 DOU.M3) Ancestral portrait (61x76cm-24x30in)
£1667 $3000   (11-Jan-92 S.BM243) Sentinel - watch dog guarding child sleeping in landscape (64x76cm-25x30in) s.i.d.1835 i.verso

STREETON, Sir Arthur Ernest (1867-1943) Australian

£2979	$5272	(26-Apr-92 SY.ME493/R) Portrait of young boy (24x25cm-9x10in) s. canvas on board (A.D 7000)
£6923	$13223	(19-Jul-92 SY.ME1/R) Yachts and headland (9x15cm-4x6in) i.verso panel (A.D 18000)
£7042	$11761	(19-Aug-91 SY.ME268 a/R) Corfe Castle (28x43cm-11x17in) init. (A.D 15000)
£7930	$14273	(24-Nov-91 SY.S356/R) Summer field (29x44cm-11x17in) init. canvas on board (A.D 18000)
£10638	$18830	(26-Apr-92 SY.ME292/R) Mixed blooms in silver vase (59x47cm-23x19in) s.d.36 canvasboard (A.D 25000)
£11702	$20713	(26-Apr-92 SY.ME484/R) Yorkshire (36x40cm-14x16in) s. (A.D 27500)
£12903	$22452	(16-Sep-91 CH.ME78/R) View up harbour from Little Sirius Cove (18x16cm-7x6in) s.d.95 panel (A.D 28000)
£15859	$28546	(24-Nov-91 SY.S413/R) Vase of pink and yellow roses (58x48cm-23x19in) s.
£16129	$28065	(16-Sep-91 CH.ME118/R) Leafy June (24x18cm-9x7in) init. i.verso panel (A.D 35000)
£16239	$28906	(28-Apr-92 CH.ME189/R) Venice (28x59cm-11x23in) s. (A.D 38000)
£16901	$28225	(19-Aug-91 SY.ME325/R) Macedon Seventy Miles away, 1925 (62x75cm-24x30in) s. (A.D 36000)
£19231	$34231	(28-Apr-92 CH.ME181/R) Grey day, Melbourne (19x65cm-7x26in) s. (A.D 45000)
£19718	$32930	(19-Aug-91 SY.ME256/R) Road to Ranges (21x13cm-8x5in) s. board (A.D 42000)
£22026	$39207	(26-Nov-91 J.M133/R) Valley after rain (49x75cm-19x30in) s. (A.D 50000)
£25000	$44500	(28-Nov-91 C95/R) Banksias against bay (20x66cm-8x26in) s. with i.verso panel
£26923	$51423	(19-Jul-92 SY.ME12/R) Summer idyll (21x26cm-8x10in) s.d.1895 panel (A.D 70000)
£27000	$48060	(28-Nov-91 C21/R) Kosciusko (51x77cm-20x30in) s. i.stretcher
£29915	$53248	(28-Apr-92 CH.ME170/R) The last of the messmates (62x75cm-24x30in) s. i.verso (A.D 70000)
£34188	$60855	(27-Apr-92 J.M74/R) Lime kiln, Lilydale (49x75cm-19x30in) s.d.35 (A.D 80000)
£34361	$61163	(26-Nov-91 J.M20/R) Mernda Hill (63x75cm-25x30in) s. (A.D 78000)
£50000	$95500	(19-Jul-92 SY.ME30/R) Observatory, Millers Point, Sydney (19x45cm-7x18in) s. panel (A.D 130000)
£385	$685	(27-Apr-92 J.M1082) Carisbrook, Isle of Wight (22x33cm-9x13in) s.i.d.1906 pencil (A.D 900)
£685	$1275	(15-Jun-92 MGS.S103) Dhows and Nile village (15x22cm-6x9in) init. W/C (A.D 1700)
£1008	$1875	(15-Jun-92 MGS.S109) Villiers Britoniuux France (29x45cm-11x18in) s.i.d.1918 W/C (A.D 2500)
£1198	$2085	(17-Sep-91 JRL.S314) Dhows of Nile (14x21cm-6x8in) init. W/C (A.D 2600)
£1282	$2282	(27-Apr-92 J.M289) Near Government House, Melbourne (18x24cm-7x9in) W/C (A.D 3000)
£2553	$4519	(26-Apr-92 SY.ME341/R) Battersea Bridge (16x24cm-6x9in) s. W/C (A.D 6000)
£3052	$5096	(19-Aug-91 SY.ME253/R) Windsor Great Park (35x50cm-14x20in) s. W/C (A.D 6500)
£4930	$8232	(19-Aug-91 SY.ME234) River Thames (22x30cm-9x12in) s. W/C (A.D 10500)

STREHBLOW, Heinrich (1862-?) Austrian

£18000	$32040	(27-Nov-91 S159/R) Ladies embroidering in workshop (85x125cm-33x49in) s.d.1892

STREICHMAN, Yehezkel (1906-) Israeli

£4324	$8000	(9-Jun-92 GG.TA446/R) Reclining woman (60x75cm-24x30in) s.d.36 board
£4865	$9000	(9-Jun-92 GG.TA445/R) Reclining woman (55x74cm-22x29in) s.d.45
£432	$800	(8-Jun-92 GG.TA264/R) Untitled (22x30cm-9x12in) s. pastel
£532	$1000	(5-Jan-92 GG.TA392/R) Vase and flowers (32x23cm-13x9in) s.d.1981 W/C
£638	$1200	(5-Jan-92 GG.TA391/R) Landscape (25x35cm-10x14in) s. mixed media
£649	$1200	(8-Jun-92 GG.TA263/R) Vase of flowers on window sill (37x45cm-15x18in) s.d.91 W/C mixed media
£973	$1800	(9-Jun-92 GG.TA295/R) Untitled (69x49cm-27x19in) s.d.1966 mixed media
£1027	$1900	(8-Jun-92 GG.TA262/R) Flowers (49x35cm-19x14in) s. W/C pencil
£1596	$3000	(5-Jan-92 GG.TA388/R) Trees (59x89cm-23x35in) s.d.1972 W/C
£1649	$3100	(5-Jan-92 GG.TA387/R) Head of woman (62x47cm-24x19in) s.d.1961 mixed media
£1915	$3600	(5-Jan-92 GG.TA389/R) Landscape (70x100cm-28x39in) s.d.1951 W/C mixed media

STREITENFELD, Ludwig (1849-1930) Austrian

£625	$1094	(29-Sep-91 AG.W16) Garden (60x45cm-24x18in) s. W/C board (P.Z 12000000)

STREITT, Franciszek (1839-1890) Polish

£756	$1315	(21-Sep-91 SA.A1789/R) Courting couple in landscape (25x19cm-10x7in) s.d.1886 panel (DM 2200)
£1408	$2366	(28-Aug-91 KH.K187/R) Street scene in Munich, two boys smoking (37x26cm-15x10in) s. (D.KR 16000)
£1568	$2854	(11-Dec-91 N.M606/R) Young girl with lilies of the valley talking to monk in landscape (56x46cm-22x18in) s. (DM 4500)
£1698	$3006	(25-Apr-92 SO.S381/R) Wandering musicians (51x76cm-20x30in) s.d.1873 (S.KR 18000)

STREMPEL, Horst (1904-1975) German
£1024 $1853   (23-May-92 GB.B7277) View of Hofkirche, Dresden (114x76cm-45x30in) mono.d.1949 board (DM 3000)

STRETTON, Philip Eustace (fl.1884-1919) British
£550 $946   (8-Oct-91 PH152) Portrait of Nancie - a terrier (26x37cm-10x15in) s. i.d.20.1.1886 panel
£950 $1701   (5-May-92 SWS314/R) Water spaniel (38x33cm-15x13in) s.d.16 board
£2300 $4117   (14-Jan-92 SWS186/R) Jock, favourite Jack Russell. Study of hed of Staffordshire bull terrier (29x23cm-11x9in) s.d.1896 and 1898 canvas on board oval pair
£4200 $7266   (26-Mar-92 LE242) Long haired terrier reclining by a barrel kennel (48x76cm-19x30in)
£6011 $11000   (5-Jun-92 SY.NY275/R) His master's coat (76x63cm-30x25in) s.d.1922
£8200 $15170   (12-Jun-92 C204/R) Border terrier puppy (50x76cm-20x30in) s.d.1884

STREVENS, John (1902-) British
£550 $941   (17-Mar-92 SWS1167) The red dress (45x34cm-18x13in) s.i.verso
£750 $1343   (5-May-92 SWS450) Jeanne (44x34cm-17x13in) s.
£800 $1536   (28-Jul-92 SWS430/R) Julie (44x34cm-17x13in) s.
£1050 $1880   (14-Jan-92 SWS276/R) Lady Helen (44x34cm-17x13in) s. s.i.verso

STRICH-CHAPELL, Walter (1877-1960) German
£2234 $3887   (17-Sep-91 FN.S2575/R) Phlox and larkspur in vase (81x71cm-32x28in) s. (DM 6500)

STRIDH, Hans (1893-1957) Swedish
£604 $1087   (19-Nov-91 GO.G179) Town scene, Boras (60x47cm-24x19in) s.d.36 (S.KR 6300)

STRIEFFLER, Marie (1917-1987) German
£859 $1512   (11-Apr-92 AW.H2316/R) Landscape with garden (59x56cm-23x22in) s.d.1981 (DM 2500)
£1443 $2540   (11-Apr-92 AW.H2315/R) Summer flowers in vase (76x59cm-30x23in) s.d.1973 (DM 4200)
£1644 $2827   (11-Oct-91 AW.H3102/R) Bunch of summer flowers in blue vase (76x58cm-30x23in) s. (DM 4800)
£2055 $3534   (11-Oct-91 AW.H3101/R) View from studio to flowering garden, spring (59x76cm-23x30in) s. i.stretcher (DM 6000)

STRINDBERG, August (1849-1912) Swedish
£96500 $174664   (19-May-92 AB.S4280/R) Coastal landscape on fire-screen (100x70cm-39x28in) (S.KR 1020000)
£430000 $799800   (17-Jun-92 S323/R) Inferno, 1901 (100x70cm-39x28in) s.indist.i.

STRINGA, Francesco (attrib) (1635-1709) British
£926 $1676   (19-May-92 GF.L2415/R) Putto carrying tower (49x31cm-19x12in) (S.FR 2500)

STRISIK, Paul (1918-) American
£1429 $2500   (22-Feb-92 YFA.M185/R) Rockport Docks (51x76cm-20x30in) s.

STROEBEL, Johann Anthonie Balthasar (1821-1905) Dutch
£970 $1716   (22-Apr-92 CH.AM85) An elegant lady with a maid and pets in an interior (23x17cm-9x7in) s. panel (D.FL 3200)
£1273 $2253   (22-Apr-92 CH.AM93) Conversation of kitchenmaids (20x17cm-8x7in) s.d.55 panel (D.FL 4200)
£1667 $2950   (22-Apr-92 CH.AM84) Mother and child in a courtyard watching a cooper at work (54x42cm-21x17in) s.d.58 (D.FL 5500)
£2424 $4291   (22-Apr-92 CH.AM83/R) Jacob van Campen revealing his plan for the Amsterdam-City Hall (49x63cm-19x25in) s. (D.FL 8000)
£3060 $5600   (5-Feb-92 KH.K125/R) The visit - Dutch interior with figures (82x111cm-32x44in) s.d.1885 (D.KR 34000)

STROEBEL, Johann Anthonie Balthasar and TEN KATE, Herman (19th C) Dutch
£2752 $4899   (30-Oct-91 CH.AM223/R) Beggars in entrance hall of patrician's house (50x39cm-20x15in) s.d.83 panel (D.FL 9000)

STROELY, Peter Eduard see STROHLING, Peter Eduard

STROHER, Friedrich Karl (1876-?) German
£5155 $8969   (17-Sep-91 FN.S2577/R) Blacksmith Jakobs in his workshop (77x63cm-30x25in) s. (DM 15000)

STROHLING, Peter Eduard (1768-1826) Russian
£3500 $6720   (10-Jul-92 C196/R) Bacchus and Ariadne (65x55cm-26x22in) copper
£870 $1565   (21-Nov-91 SY.G8/R) Portrait of lady wearing turban and low-cut dress (8x?cm-3x?in) min. oval gilt-metal mount wood frame (S.FR 2200)
£2200 $3916   (27-Nov-91 C196/R) Lady seated on mossy bank in landscape (8x?cm-3x?in) min.s.gilt-metal wood frame octagonal

STROHOFER, Hans (1885-1961) Austrian
£1730 $3028   (19-Feb-92 D.V47/R) Standing female nude (40x28cm-16x11in) mono.d.06 paper on board (A.S 35000)

STROM, Charles W (1886-1967) Norwegian
£487 $887   (9-Dec-91 B.O112/R) Interior with bureau (68x55cm-27x22in) s. (N.KR 5500)
£1019 $1854   (14-Dec-91 BU.O18/R) Seated woman (97x72cm-38x28in) s.d.12 (N.KR 11500)

STROM, Halfdan (1863-1949) Norwegian
£658 $1224   (15-Jun-92 B.O152/R) View towards Akershus Castle (20x30cm-8x12in) s.
                (N.KR 7500)
£2368 $4405   (15-Jun-92 B.O153/R) Farmer's wife and two children (95x75cm-37x30in)
                s.d.1912 (N.KR 27000)

STROMEYER, Helene Marie (1834-1924) German
£822 $1414   (8-Oct-91 ZEL.L1736/R) Bunch of roses in vase (42x54cm-17x21in) s.d.1918
                panel (DM 2400)
£3265 $5680   (21-Sep-91 SA.A1930/R) Bush roses by fountain (64x86cm-25x34in) s.d.1907
                (DM 9500)

STROMME, Olav (1909-1978) Norwegian
£526 $979   (15-Jun-92 B.O155/R) Towards the mountain (45x50cm-18x20in) s. panel
                (N.KR 6000)
£570 $1061   (15-Jun-92 B.O157/R) From the theatre (33x24cm-13x9in) s.d.56 panel
                (N.KR 6500)
£709 $1255   (15-Feb-92 BU.O132) Composition (50x68cm-20x27in) s. (N.KR 8000)
£746 $1387   (15-Jun-92 B.O156/R) From the Chinese Opera (27x22cm-11x9in) s.d.58 panel
                (N.KR 8500)
£797 $1451   (9-Dec-91 B.O114/R) Composition with figures, religious scene
                (38x46cm-15x18in) s. panel (N.KR 9000)
£802 $1388   (23-Mar-92 B.O125/R) Theatre scene from 'Queen Elisabeth'
                (33x24cm-13x9in) panel (N.KR 9000)
£834 $1435   (10-Oct-91 BU.O14/R) Coastal landscape with pine tree (58x47cm-23x19in)
                s.d.53 (N.KR 9500)
£966 $1661   (7-Oct-91 B.O132/R) Black horizon, red signs (65x73cm-26x29in) s. panel
                (N.KR 11000)
£1317 $2265   (7-Oct-91 B.O131/R) View from Volvat (50x70cm-20x28in) s. (N.KR 15000)
£1550 $2821   (14-Dec-91 BU.O9/R) View of a town (54x65cm-21x26in) s.d.58 panel
                (N.KR 17500)

STRONG, Ray Stanford (1905-) American
£737 $1400   (24-Jun-92 B.SF6361/R) California vista (61x122cm-24x48in) s.
£737 $1400   (24-Jun-92 B.SF6363/R) Hillside landscape (56x71cm-22x28in) s. masonite
£842 $1600   (24-Jun-92 B.SF6360/R) California hillside (61x122cm-24x48in) s. board

STROUT, C (?) ?
£2700 $4536   (15-Aug-91 B404/R) Kate of London, Capt. T. Harper, off Lizard, 1892
                (52x77cm-20x30in) s.i. board

STROZZI, Bernardo (1581-1644) Italian
£1642 $2940   (6-May-92 GD.B659/R) Christ and the Apostles having meal in Emmaus
                (120x158cm-47x62in) (S.FR 4500)

STROZZI, Bernardo (attrib) (1581-1644) Italian
£1500 $2610   (13-Apr-92 S151/R) Study of arm (27x13cm-11x5in) black chk

STROZZI, Bernardo (school) (1581-1644) Italian
£2486 $4500   (20-May-92 D.NY89) Madonna and Child (58x74cm-23x29in)

STROZZI, Bernardo (style) (1581-1644) Italian
£1200 $2184   (26-May-92 PH100) St. Francis (120x89cm-47x35in)
£1400 $2520   (21-Nov-91 CSK111/R) The Triumph of David (76x63cm-30x25in)
£2356 $4500   (16-Jul-92 SY.NY196/R) Portrait of bearded man (63x50cm-25x20in)
£11000 $19250   (1-Apr-92 S82/R) Allegory of Vanity (159x128cm-63x50in)

STRUDEL, Peter (attrib) (1660-1714) Austrian
£2484 $4247   (18-Mar-92 D.V345/R) Two putti with flowers by fountain (81x72cm-32x28in)
                (A.S 50000)

STRUNKE, Laris (20th C) Scandinavian
£1044 $1910   (13-May-92 BU.S195/R) White beaches (69x101cm-27x40in) s.verso
                (S.KR 11000)

STRUTT and CLARK (19th C) ?
£2400 $4224   (10-Apr-92 K378) Welsh mountain landscape - young girl and dog resting by
                stile, cattle (74x97cm-29x38in) s.d.1869

STRUTT, Alfred William (1856-1924) British
£34000 $62900   (12-Jun-92 C196/R) A watched pot never boils (82x115cm-32x45in) s.
£580 $1050   (19-May-92 PH66) Friend of the chase (55x40cm-22x16in) s. W/C gouache
£1277 $2260   (26-Apr-92 SY.ME218) Going like wind (63x38cm-25x15in) s. gouache W/C
                (A.D 3000)
£1277 $2260   (26-Apr-92 SY.ME221/R) Keen as mustard (63x38cm-25x15in) s.i. gouache W/C
                (A.D 3000)
£2700 $4833   (5-May-92 SWS258/R) Ready money (55x89cm-22x35in) s. s.i.d.1920 stretcher
                W/C pencil
£7000 $11900   (22-Oct-91 C100/R) Hunt (48x88cm-19x35in) s. W/C

STRUTT, Arthur John (1819-1888) British
£1300 $2223 (12-Mar-92 CSK303/R) The Roman Campagna (29x46cm-11x18in) s.d.1886
£3500 $6125 (23-Sep-91 PHB37/R) An Italian villa and viaduct (54x74cm-21x29in) s.d.1866
£4500 $7695 (19-Mar-92 B127/R) The Falls at Tivoli (58x76cm-23x30in) s.i.d.1855

STRUTT, Arthur John (circle) (1819-1888) British
£1400 $2604 (18-Jun-92 B46/R) Paestum (37x54cm-15x21in)

STRUTT, Jacob George (1790-1864) British
£600 $1146 (16-Jul-92 CSK190) Tivoli (30x25cm-12x10in) s. board
£1130 $1944 (8-Oct-91 ZEL.L1737/R) Shepherd and sheep on path with view of Bay of Naples, evening (17x13cm-7x5in) s.d.1840 panel (DM 3300)
£1473 $2533 (8-Oct-91 ZEL.L1738/R) Shepherd and cattle in river landscape with fortified bridge (17x26cm-7x10in) s. panel (DM 4300)

STRUTT, William (1826-1915) British
£769 $1369 (27-Apr-92 J.M1201) After the chase (16x24cm-6x9in) board (A.D 1800)
£5106 $9038 (26-Apr-92 SY.ME293/R) Goats in cornfield (72cm-28ins circular) s. (A.D 12000)
£5800 $10034 (4-Sep-91 BT315/R) Pilgrimage to Canterbury in the 14th Century (36x147cm-14x58in) s.d.1868

STRUTZEL, Otto (1855-1930) German
£550 $957 (19-Sep-91 N.M2823/R) In the Jachenau (24x31cm-9x12in) s. canvas on board (DM 1600)
£734 $1256 (18-Mar-92 N.M658) Group of houses and trees (18x24cm-7x9in) d.1879verso paper on board (DM 2100)
£906 $1649 (11-Dec-91 N.M608/R) Moor landscape in the foothills of the Alps, spring (35x52cm-14x20in) i.stretcher (DM 2600)
£1031 $1887 (2-Jun-92 FN.S2770/R) Winter in the suburb (34x46cm-13x18in) s.d.1887 (DM 3000)
£1399 $2420 (28-Mar-92 BOD.P1033) Ox-drawn cart in field landscape (26x31cm-10x12in) mono canvas on board (DM 4000)
£1546 $2691 (18-Sep-91 N.M717/R) Farmstead (29x40cm-11x16in) mono.i.d.1887 (DM 4500)
£2787 $5073 (11-Dec-91 N.M607/R) Peasant and horses ploughing (32x43cm-13x17in) s.d.86 panel (DM 8000)
£4651 $8000 (17-Oct-91 SY.NY270/R) Bluehender apfelbaum (108x151cm-43x59in) s.d.1914
£7560 $13155 (18-Sep-91 N.M716/R) Shepherdess with sheep in moor landscape, possibly Murnauer Moos (75x100cm-30x39in) s. (DM 22000)

STRUWER, Ardy (1939-) Swedish
£515 $906 (11-Apr-92 FAL.M396/R) Paradise Birdie-nam-nam (40x30cm-16x12in) s.d.1969 acrylic (S.KR 5400)
£696 $1225 (11-Apr-92 FAL.M395/R) 'Vanessa Atalanta 1968 ripsa' (53x64cm-21x25in) acrylic (S.KR 7300)
£1316 $2315 (11-Apr-92 FAL.M394/R) '1970-71, Menton' (98x71cm-39x28in) s. acrylic (S.KR 13800)

STRUYKEN, Peter (1939-) Dutch
£3030 $5485 (19-May-92 CH.AM223/R) Structure 1, 67 (140x140cm-55x55in) s.i.d.67 verso perspex board diamond shape (D.FL 10000)

STRY, Abraham van (attrib) (18/19th C) Dutch
£994 $1709 (7-Mar-92 CH.AM254/R) Sportsman accosting peasant girl observed by old woman (39x31cm-15x12in) panel (D.FL 3200)
£3211 $5587 (14-Apr-92 SY.AM335/R) Woman in kitchen, with children playing beyond (65x80cm-26x31in) panel (D.FL 10500)
£3591 $6500 (22-May-92 SY.NY298/R) Extensive landscape with two shepherds conversing possibly Laban and Jacob (101x146cm-40x57in)

STRY, Abraham van (circle) (18/19th C) Dutch
£800 $1360 (22-Oct-91 S239) Cattle in field (28x30cm-11x12in) panel

STRY, Abraham van (style) (18/19th C) Dutch
£980 $1784 (11-Dec-91 ZZ.B168) Shepherdess and young boy in landscape minding cattle and sheep (97x79cm-38x31in)
£6600 $11484 (13-Sep-91 C35/R) Connoisseur seated in interior studying sketch by van Stry (65x55cm-26x22in) i. panel
£8000 $14000 (27-Feb-92 CSK145) Huntsman with hounds on track in river landscape (228x165cm-90x65in)

STRY, Jacob van (1756-1815) Dutch
£4938 $8938 (5-Dec-91 SY.MO328/R) Scene pastorale dans un paysage (77x108cm-30x43in) panel (F.FR 48000)
£12000 $21840 (10-Dec-91 PH67/R) Landscape with horseman and figures on path winding through trees by lake (69x94cm-27x37in) s. panel
£1006 $1800 (15-Jan-92 CH.NY162/R) Seated old man (25x21cm-10x8in) s. black chk wash W/C
£1029 $1862 (5-Dec-91 SY.MO31/R) Paysan vu de dos (36x23cm-14x9in) s. blk.chk. (F.FR 10000)

STRY, Jacob van (style) (1756-1815) Dutch
£1543 $2762 (12-Nov-91 SY.AM100) Kitchen maid emptying mouse trap (33x24cm-13x9in) panel (D.FL 5000)

STRY, Jacob van (style) (1756-1815) Dutch-cont.
£3000 $5250   (27-Feb-92 CSK144 a/R) A drover watering cattle on an estuary (55x79cm-22x31in)

STRYDONCK, Guillaume van (1861-1937) Belgian
£510 $872   (21-Mar-92 KV.L334) Nude at a wash basin (43x48cm-17x19in) s.d.1924 canvas on board (B.FR 30000)

STRYJENSKA, Zofia (1894-1976) Polish
£484 $880   (15-Dec-91 REM.W43) In a bourgeois house (40x56cm-16x22in) s. ink (P.Z 9500000)
£916 $1667   (15-Dec-91 REM.W44) Laying flower wreaths (40x49cm-16x19in) s. temp gouache (P.Z 18000000)
£1308 $2264   (8-Sep-91 REM.W37) Girl with pitcher (97x62cm-38x24in) s. gouache (P.Z 25000000)
£1569 $2699   (13-Oct-91 REM.W27) Love-making (90x70cm-35x28in) s.gouache (P.Z 30000000)

STUART, Charles (19th C) British
£520 $926   (21-Jan-92 SWS1049) Croft in Highlands (76x127cm-30x50in) s.
£880 $1522   (26-Mar-92 CSK138) Still life of grapes, plums, pear, peach and urn in draped landscape (51x41cm-20x16in) s.
£1050 $1827   (16-Apr-92 PHX378/R) Kelp gatherers (61x127cm-24x50in) s.
£3200 $5856   (3-Jun-92 S201/R) Still life with fruit (76x63cm-30x25in) bears.init.i.

STUART, Ernest (fl.1889-1903) British
£440 $770   (3-Apr-92 BW421) Coastal scene (74x51cm-29x20in) s. W/C

STUART, Gilbert (1755-1828) American
£1930 $3300   (21-Mar-92 W.W141/R) Portrait of gentleman in white wig (76x64cm-30x25in)
£3500 $6265   (15-Nov-91 C179/R) Portrait of Sir William Kirkpatrick, wearing coat and cravat (74x61cm-29x24in)
£6760 $12100   (14-Nov-91 GRO.B11/R) Portrait of Maria Cornelia Durant - Ritchie (74x61cm-29x24in)
£50000 $95500   (17-Jul-92 C9/R) Portrait of John Gell, Admiral of the White standing on the shore (240x148cm-94x58in)

STUART, Gilbert (attrib) (1755-1828) American
£1835 $3156   (7-Oct-91 CH.E203/R) Portrait of John Crone of Byblox, son of Daniel Crone and Aphra Johnson (71x60cm-28x24in) painted oval (E.P 2000)
£5384 $9530   (7-Nov-91 D.V374/R) Portrait of young gentleman (76x63cm-30x25in) (A.S 110000)

STUART, Raymond J (20th C) American
£1011 $1800   (2-Nov-91 IH.NY103/R) Boy plays harmonica as he is licked by calf (61x81cm-24x32in) s.d.1945
£2388 $4250   (2-Nov-91 IH.NY102/R) Boy in cowboy clothes riding pig (66x46cm-26x18in) s.

STUBBS, George (1724-1806) British
£191257 $350000   (5-Jun-92 SY.NY29/R) Mr Ogilvy's racehorse Trentham at Newmarket with jockey up (101x132cm-40x52in) s.d.1771

STUBBS, George (circle) (1724-1806) British
£5882 $10529   (15-Nov-91 GK.Z5026/R) Bay horse in wooded landscape (100x125cm-39x49in) (S.FR 15000)

STUBBS, George and BARRET, George (snr) (18th C) British
£95000 $181450   (15-Jul-92 S89/R) A horse frightened by a lion (68x108cm-27x43in)

STUBBS, W P (1842-1909) American
£919 $1700   (10-Jun-92 CE.NY1/R) Clipper ship in storm (61x91cm-24x36in) s.

STUBBS, William P (1842-1909) American
£1176 $2000   (6-Aug-91 RB.HY110/R) Portrait of ship Tempest at sea (61x91cm-24x36in) s.
£1286 $2250   (31-Mar-92 MOR.P112) The American schooner Lottie K Friend in moderate seas (61x89cm-24x35in) s.
£2941 $5000   (6-Aug-91 RB.HY280/R) Portrait of bark Taria Topan, passing lighthouse, pilot schooner beyond (56x91cm-22x36in) s.
£3088 $5250   (6-Aug-91 RB.HY231/R) Portrait of American 4-masted schooner off coast (66x107cm-26x42in) s.
£4118 $7000   (6-Aug-91 RB.HY270/R) Schooner Jeanie Lippitt running for home (66x107cm-26x42in) s.

STUBER, Dedrick B (1878-1954) American
£1067 $1900   (26-Nov-91 MOR.P136) Landscape - sunrise (30x41cm-12x16in) s.
£2825 $5000   (12-Feb-92 B.SF514/R) Sheltering trees (63x76cm-25x30in) s.

STUBNER, Robert Emil (1874-1931) German
£8000 $14240   (26-Nov-91 PH30/R) Before the mirror (104x87cm-41x34in) s.d.1916

STUCK, Franz von (1863-1928) German
£3500 $6510   (19-Jun-92 C95/R) Faun und Bacchusknabe (32x32cm-13x13in) s. board octagonal

STUCK, Franz von (1863-1928) German-cont.
£3521	$6373	(3-Dec-91 FN.S2488) Portrait of young lady in landscape (33cm-13ins circular) s.d.1892 (DM 10000)
£5600	$9576	(20-Mar-92 C30/R) Portrait of lady seated holding book (93x93cm-37x37in) s.d.1918
£7500	$12825	(20-Mar-92 C29/R) Portrait of Olga Oberhummer s.d.1908 panel oval
£9500	$16245	(20-Mar-92 C28/R) Knabe mit Trauben (76x69cm-30x27in) s.d.1903 panel
£16151	$30041	(20-Jun-92 BM.B1080 a/R) Dionysos (59x49cm-23x19in) s. panel (DM 47000)
£26000	$48360	(19-Jun-92 C96/R) Tanzende Salome (48x25cm-19x10in) s. panel
£423	$765	(4-Dec-91 DO.H3410) Male nude seen from behind, study for Fruhlingszug (50x33cm-20x13in) s. pencil (DM 1200)
£1923	$3327	(25-Mar-92 KM.K1762/R) Boy as apple thief (24x33cm-9x13in) s. pen wash (DM 5500)
£6200	$10602	(20-Mar-92 C27/R) Portrait of lady standing wearing feather hat (90x52cm-35x20in) s.d.1910 pastel board
£13736	$25000	(28-May-92 SY.NY124/R) Ideal head (53x46cm-21x18in) s.d.1902 pencil oil panel

STUCKELBERG, Ernst (1831-1903) Swiss
£1275	$2308	(5-Dec-91 SY.Z33/R) Study for Romeo and Juliet (35x25cm-14x10in) s.i.d.1867verso canvas on board (S.FR 3200)
£4887	$8944	(4-Jun-92 SY.Z351/R) Portrait of Elisabeth Sengenwald-Burckhardt (45x33cm-18x13in) s.d.1874 (S.FR 13000)
£784	$1404	(15-Nov-91 ZOF.Z1898/R) Caritas (181x70cm-71x28in) chl (S.FR 2000)

STUCKELBERGER, Wilhelm (1867-1926) Swiss
£475	$884	(19-Jun-92 ZOF.Z2106/R) Dragoon in field s.d.1894 W/C (S.FR 1250)

STUEMPFIG, Walter (1914-1970) American/German
£1117	$2000	(14-Nov-91 CE.NY282/R) By docks (30x46cm-12x18in) with letter
£1977	$3500	(5-Nov-91 BG.M771/R) Pozzioli (56x71cm-22x28in) s.d.1951

STUHLMANN, Heinrich (1803-1886) German
£717	$1291	(30-Jan-92 RAS.V683) Old man and boy outside Southern town (36x30cm-14x12in) (D.KR 8000)

STUHLMULLER, Karl (1858-1930) German
£7422	$13137	(5-Nov-91 GF.L2156/R) Cattle market in Bavarian village (34x56cm-13x22in) s.i. board (S.FR 19000)
£11847	$21561	(11-Dec-91 N.M611/R) Yard of Birgmannbrau, market day in Dachau (37x59cm-15x23in) s. panel (DM 34000)
£19429	$34000	(19-Feb-92 CH.NY68/R) Cattle market (34x58cm-13x23in) s. panel

STULL, Henry (1851-1913) American
£1093	$2000	(5-Jun-92 SY.NY167/R) Bay racehorse with jockey up (62x74cm-24x29in) s.d.1902
£3403	$6500	(3-Jul-92 S.W3083/R) Don Alonz - bay racehorse with jockey up (51x71cm-20x28in) s.d.1892

STULL, Henry (attrib) (1851-1913) American
£659	$1200	(13-Dec-91 S.W2616/R) White horse in stable (46x61cm-18x24in) bears sig.d.1881
£1236	$2200	(30-Oct-91 D.NY57) Chestnut thoroughbred with jockey up (41x61cm-16x24in)

STUMPF, Wilhelm (1873-1928) German
£2577	$4485	(21-Sep-91 SA.A1928/R) Still life with field flowers and flowering branches (80x60cm-31x24in) s.d.1906 (DM 7500)

STURGESS, John (19th C) British
£1000	$1720	(5-Mar-92 D110/R) Enthusiasts (25x33cm-10x13in) s. i.verso

STURGESS, John (attrib) (19th C) British
£600	$1086	(4-Dec-91 RBB880) Three racehorses with jockey up galloping on the Downs (20x3cm-8x1in) bears sig.d.1869 metal panel

STURGESS, R W (1890-1932) Australian
£881	$1568	(26-Nov-91 J.M823) Spooning for mullet (29x37cm-11x15in) s. W/C (A.D 2000)

STURGESS, Reginald Ward (1890-1932) Australian
£1496	$2662	(27-Apr-92 J.M173 a/R) Sailing in light wind (23x30cm-9x12in) s. board (A.D 3500)
£1250	$2388	(29-Jun-92 AAA.S118) Cattle at the stream (38x49cm-15x19in) s. W/C (A.D 3200)

STURM, George (1855-1923) Dutch
£6667	$11800	(22-Apr-92 CH.AM242/R) The wedding of Peleus and Thetis (333x493cm-131x194in) s.d.1892 canvas oval (D.FL 22000)

STURM, Helmut (1932-) German
£2399	$4343	(3-Dec-91 AB.S5160/R) Composition (53x33cm-21x13in) s. panel (S.KR 25000)
£3413	$6212	(25-May-92 WK.M1183/R) Composition (53x33cm-21x13in) s. s.i.d.1965verso panel (DM 10000)
£5461	$9939	(26-May-92 KF.M1289/R) Abgeschirmte Hantierung (96x84cm-38x33in) mono.d.1978 oil tempera cotton (DM 16000)

STURM, Helmut (1932-) German-cont.
£23208	$42239	(26-May-92 KF.M1288/R) Composition with masks (119x153cm-47x60in) s.d.1959verso (DM 68000)
£887	$1615	(26-May-92 KF.M1293) Composition (29x34cm-11x13in) s.d.1985 mixed media (DM 2600)
£1195	$2174	(26-May-92 KF.M1294/R) Composition with blue oval (36x46cm-14x18in) s.d. mixed media (DM 3500)
£1195	$2174	(25-May-92 WK.M1185/R) Untitled (55x68cm-22x27in) i.verso gouache board (DM 3500)
£1365	$2485	(25-May-92 WK.M1184/R) Composition (46x36cm-18x14in) s.d.1977 mixed media board (DM 4000)
£1536	$2795	(26-May-92 KF.M1291/R) Composition (54x72cm-21x28in) s.d.1979 gouache board (DM 4500)
£1536	$2795	(26-May-92 KF.M1290/R) Composition with white lines (42x29cm-17x11in) s.d.1975 collage gouache (DM 4500)
£10210	$18173	(26-Nov-91 KF.M1073/R) Composition (90x100cm-35x39in) s.d.1963 mixed media (DM 29200)

STURSA, Jan (1880-1925) Czechoslovakian
£499	$892	(15-Jan-92 D.V84/R) Female nude picking up cloth (20x18cm-8x7in) s.d.1920 pencil W/C (A.S 10000)

STURZENEGGER, Hans (1875-1943) Swiss
£2191	$3966	(5-Dec-91 SY.Z120/R) Ticino landscape (46x61cm-18x24in) mono (S.FR 5500)

STUTTERHEIM, Lodewyk Philippus (1873-1943) Dutch
£864	$1512	(18-Feb-92 CH.AM79) View of Kortenhoef with peasants on path along canal (40x60cm-16x24in) s. (D.FL 2800)

STYKA, Adam (1890-c.1970) French
£1018	$1853	(15-Dec-91 REM.W45) Lane in Cairo (23x19cm-9x7in) s. board (P.Z 20000000)
£1124	$2000	(22-Jan-92 SY.NY315/R) Grazing along banks of Nile (65x81cm-26x32in) s.
£3672	$6500	(5-Nov-91 BG.M755/R) Warm embrace (79x64cm-31x25in) s.
£4396	$8000	(27-May-92 CH.NY16/R) Two Ouled Nails Dancers (55x68cm-22x27in) s.

STYKA, Jan (1858-1925) French
£571	$1000	(18-Feb-92 CE.NY158) Officer on horseback stopping to speak with soldier (117x138cm-46x54in) s.d.
£763	$1389	(15-Dec-91 REM.W46) Young woman with lilac (110x36cm-43x14in) s. (P.Z 15000000)
£778	$1400	(22-Nov-91 S.BM52/R) Portrait of elegant young woman in green (76x61cm-30x24in) s.i.d.1905 oval
£10991	$19014	(8-Sep-91 REM.W38) Hussar on horseback (210x200cm-83x79in) s. (P.Z 210000000)
£513	$913	(3-Nov-91 PSA.W17) Portrait of Alexander Biergel (33x28cm-13x11in) s. pencil crayon (P.Z 10000000)

STYKA, Tade (1889-1954) French
£750	$1305	(11-Sep-91 MMB283/R) Portrait of a young woman, head and shoulder (61x48cm-24x19in) s. panel oval
£1095	$1993	(14-Dec-91 BA.S111) Nude model (63x81cm-25x32in) (S.KR 11500)
£2222	$4022	(19-May-92 GF.L2171/R) Lioness waiting for prey (100x125cm-39x49in) s.d.1908 (S.FR 6000)

STYLE, J M (19th C) British
£1284	$2286	(30-Oct-91 CH.AM102) Children on stair case (104x69cm-41x27in) s.d.1887 (D.FL 4200)

STYLE, Jane M (19th C) British
£1481	$2681	(20-May-92 GK.Z5076) Children seated and sleeping in entrance of house (104x69cm-41x27in) s. (S.FR 4000)

SU RENSHAN (1813-1859) Chinese
£847	$1500	(7-Nov-91 B.SF1257/R) Zhongkui and demons (79x42cm-31x17in) s. ink

SUAREZ, Antonio (1923-) Spanish
£525	$935	(21-Jan-92 DUR.M466/R) Florero (35x25cm-14x10in) s. canvas laid down on canvas (S.P 95000)
£608	$1082	(21-Jan-92 DUR.M465/R) Manzanas (25x35cm-10x14in) s.d.78 paper laid down on canvas (S.P 110000)
£736	$1266	(7-Oct-91 ANS.M176/R) Manzanas (25x30cm-10x12in) s.d.1975 i.verso (S.P 135000)

SUBLEYRAS, Pierre (1699-1749) French
£1296	$2346	(19-May-92 GF.L2417/R) St Basilius celebrating mass with Emperor Valerius (27x19cm-11x7in) i. i.verso panel (S.FR 3500)

SUBLEYRAS, Pierre (circle) (1699-1749) French
£5500	$10010	(11-Dec-91 S208/R) Saint Peter baptising Centurion Cornelius (71x47cm-28x19in)

SUBLEYRAS, Pierre (studio) (1699-1749) French
£4000	$7120	(1-Nov-91 C63/R) Saint Joseph and Christ Child (220x175cm-87x69in)

SUCH, William T (fl.1847-1857) British
£3800 $6726   (6-Nov-91 S46/R) The woodcock's haunt (91x122cm-36x48in) s.d.1856

SUCHODOLSKI, Janvier (1797-1875) Polish
£3138 $5398   (13-Oct-91 REM.W28) Unveiling of statue of John III Sobieski
                (70x104cm-28x41in) s. (P.Z 60000000)

SUCHY, Adalbert (1783-1849) Austrian
£437 $778   (29-Apr-92 D.V733/R) Portrait of young man in Roman costume (8x6cm-3x2in)
                min.s. W/C oval (A.S 9000)
£3500 $6230   (27-Nov-91 C198/R) Portraits of Johann Peter. Wife Josephine. Daughter
                Henriette (9x?cm-4x?in) min.s.d.1831,1827 3 on leather travelling case

SUCHY, Vladimir (1923-) Czechoslovakian
£745 $1326   (29-Nov-91 D.V79/R) Oskar Kokoschka (140x100cm-55x39in) s.d.87
                (A.S 15000)

SUDAYKIN, Serge (20th C) ?
£400 $720   (20-Nov-91 B57/R) The suitors (72x98cm-28x39in) s.i.d.1928 W/C bodycol

SUDDABY, Rowland (1912-1973) British
£600 $1044   (17-Sep-91 PH101/R) Window scene (51x41cm-20x16in) s.d.41
£1300 $2249   (2-Oct-91 S203/R) Fishing village, Cornwall (41x48cm-16x19in) s.indis.d.
£420 $802   (16-Jul-92 B125) Cottage by country lane (37x53cm-15x21in) s.d.44 W/C

SUETIN, Nikolai Mikhailovich (1897-1954) Russian
£580 $1056   (30-May-92 VG.B939/R) Composition (17x11cm-7x4in) s.d.1920 pencil
                (DM 1700)

SUEUR, Eustache le (attrib) (1617-1655) French
£700 $1218   (13-Apr-92 S216) Deposition (17x19cm-7x7in) black chk squared
£719 $1294   (22-Nov-91 AGS.P107) Etudes de moines vus de dos (29x18cm-11x7in) pierre
                noire stumping htd.white chamois paper (F.FR 7000)

SUEUR, Eustache le (circle) (1617-1655) French
£5233 $9000   (10-Oct-91 SY.NY33/R) Perseus with Pegasus before King Cepheus
                (49x65cm-19x26in) panel

SUEUR, Eustache le (style) (1617-1655) French
£2389 $4324   (21-May-92 L.K85/R) The Finding of Moses (48x38cm-19x15in) (DM 7000)

SUEUR, Louis le (1746-1803) French
£509 $931   (15-May-92 AT.P164) Renard dans un poulailler (36x27cm-14x11in) s.d.1790
                black chk pen wash (F.FR 5000)
£782 $1400   (15-Jan-92 CH.NY98/R) Farmhouse with tree (20x28cm-8x11in) with i.verso
                red chk

SUGAI, Kumi (1919-) Japanese
£756 $1316   (17-Sep-91 RAS.K62) Bleu et rouge (20x41cm-8x16in) s. (D.KR 8500)
£15000 $25950   (26-Mar-92 S39/R) Hare (93x73cm-37x29in) s.d.1960 s.d.60 verso
£17143 $30000   (27-Feb-92 CH.NY3/R) Untitled (115x26cm-45x10in) s. s.d.1954verso
£18156 $32500   (14-Nov-91 SY.NY291/R) Okina (146x114cm-57x45in) s. s.d.56 verso
£1789 $3256   (10-Dec-91 RAS.K103/R) Composition (46x26cm-18x10in) s.d.56 gouache .
                (D.KR 20000)
£1800 $3096   (17-Oct-91 S126/R) Untitled (68x46cm-27x18in) s.d.62 ink W/C Japanese
                paper

SUGHI, Alberto (1928-) Italian
£2043 $3636   (29-Apr-92 F.F18/R) Un uomo e una donna (100x70cm-39x28in) s.i.d.1969
                cardboard on canvas (I.L 4500000)
£2138 $3870   (3-Dec-91 F.R166/R) Donna al caffe (37x24cm-15x9in) s. canvas board
                (I.L 4600000)
£2497 $4444   (29-Apr-92 F.F165/R) Adolescente allo specchio (50x35cm-20x14in) s.
                (I.L 5500000)

SUHR, V Bloch (19th C) ?
£485 $863   (28-Apr-92 RAS.K306) Near 'Slukefter' (36x59cm-14x23in) s.d.1896
                (D.KR 5500)

SUHRLANDT, Carl (1828-1919) German
£3825 $7000   (5-Jun-92 SY.NY70/R) In the kennel (49x67cm-19x26in) s.d.1885

SUKDOLSKY-SVOBODA (19th C) Austrian
£1600 $2736   (17-Mar-92 PH65/R) Elegant lady (110x73cm-43x29in) s.d.1885 pastel

SUKER, Arthur (1857-?) British
£485 $863   (26-Nov-91 J.M1048) Cliffs at Cornwall (60x39cm-24x15in) init. W/C
                (A.D 1100)
£789 $1500   (26-Jun-92 WOL.C435/R) Autumn in Perthshire, Scotland (53x79cm-21x31in)
                s. W/C board
£1100 $1969   (15-Jan-92 BT90/R) Early morning on the west coast of Sark
                (46x69cm-18x27in) s. W/C

SUKHOROVSKY, Martsely Gavrilovich (1840-1908) Russian
£3321 $6077   (14-May-92 BU.S200/R) The milkmaid (88x67cm-35x26in) s.d.1904
(S.KR 35000)

SULLIVAN, Luke (1705-1771) British
£850 $1462   (4-Mar-92 C51/R) Officer, wearing gold-bordered scarlet uniform
(3x?cm-1x?in) min. mono.d. bracelet clasp frame garnets oval

SULLIVAN, S (19/20th C) British
£500 $915   (5-Feb-92 CSK267) Argument (46x61cm-18x24in) s.d.1885 s.i.d.1885 verso

SULLIVAN, William Holmes (?-1908) British
£7000 $12460   (27-Apr-92 PHB239/R) Fairy dance (52x68cm-20x27in) s.d.1882 W/C

SULLIVANT, Thomas S (1854-1926) American
£618 $1100   (2-May-92 IH.NY108/R) The birth of libel (33x51cm-13x20in) s. pen ink

SULLY, Robert Matthew (1803-1855) American
£2179 $3900   (14-Nov-91 CE.NY40) Portrait of Chief Justice John Marshall
(30x20cm-12x8in) s.i.d.1832 pencil ink

SULLY, Thomas (1783-1872) American/British
£691 $1250   (21-May-92 S.W2953/R) Landscape with rock foundation (13x18cm-5x7in)
paper on canvas
£2747 $5000   (28-May-92 CH.NY15/R) Spanish mother (51x43cm-20x17in)
£7735 $14000   (6-Dec-91 CH.NY16/R) Mrs Thomas Fitzgerald (76x62cm-30x24in) init.d.1858
verso
£13260 $24000   (6-Dec-91 CH.NY8/R) Portrait of William Brown (76x63cm-30x25in)
£18713 $32000   (12-Mar-92 CH.NY11/R) Mother and child (91x71cm-36x28in)
£60773 $110000   (6-Dec-91 CH.NY5/R) Life study of the Marquis de Lafayette
(55x48cm-22x19in)
£8840 $16000   (6-Dec-91 CH.NY13/R) Gypsy maidens (42x36cm-17x14in) init.d.1839 W/C

SULLY, Thomas (attrib) (1783-1872) American/British
£909 $1600   (8-Apr-92 D.NY70) Portrait of Miss Mary Adams (76x61cm-30x24in)

SULTAN, Altoon (20th C) American
£1117 $2000   (12-Nov-91 CE.NY99/R) Hudson River Mansion Annandale on Hudson, NY
(35x71cm-14x28in) s.d.78 i.stretcher

SULTAN, Donald (1951-) American
£5028 $9000   (14-Nov-91 SY.NY254/R) Black eggs Nov 1 1985 (155x122cm-61x48in)
init.d.1985 chl
£5587 $10000   (7-May-92 SY.NY213 a/R) Untitled (32x31cm-13x12in) init.d.1978 tile
plaster tar wood
£8380 $15000   (14-Nov-91 SY.NY336/R) Yellow lemon, March 21, 1989 (32x32cm-13x13in)
init.d. oil tar tile on wood
£8380 $15000   (14-Nov-91 SY.NY248/R) Lemons and egg, Jan.13, 1986 (152x122cm-60x48in)
init.d.1986 chl
£8571 $15000   (25-Feb-92 SY.NY225/R) Black lemons (152x122cm-60x48in) init.i.d.1985 chl
£9827 $17000   (3-Oct-91 SY.NY137/R) Lemon and eggs (152x122cm-60x48in) init.i.d.Mayb 15
1986 chl.
£13966 $25000   (7-May-92 SY.NY195/R) Four apples, three pears and lemon
(32x32cm-13x13in) s.d.1986 s.d.1985 v. oil spackle tar tiele wood
£13966 $25000   (14-Nov-91 SY.NY228/R) Forest fire July 10, 1984 (244x244cm-96x96in)
init.d.1984 latex tar vinyl tile masonite

SUMNER, Maud (1902-1985) South African
£1193 $2076   (13-Apr-92 SY.J349/R) Still life with fruit in bowl (60x45cm-24x18in) s.
(SA.R 6000)
£1310 $2320   (4-Nov-91 SY.J332/R) Crocuses in flower pot (44x36cm-17x14in) s. canvas
on board (SA.R 6500)
£1543 $2623   (21-Oct-91 SY.J378/R) Hout Bay (72x90cm-28x35in) s. (SA.R 7500)
£1815 $3212   (4-Nov-91 SY.J333/R) Crocuses in flower pot (36x44cm-14x17in) s. canvas
on board (SA.R 9000)
£2218 $3925   (4-Nov-91 SY.J335/R) Silence and space (117x82cm-46x32in) s. (SA.R 11000)
£4374 $7610   (13-Apr-92 SY.J348/R) Lilac on orange stool (73x53cm-29x21in) s.
(SA.R 22000)
£565 $999   (4-Nov-91 SY.J113/R) Landscape with river and trees (46x61cm-18x24in) s.
W/C (SA.R 2800)
£636 $1107   (13-Apr-92 SY.J347/R) Cornflowers and poppies (46x63cm-18x25in) s. W/C
pen (SA.R 3200)
£706 $1249   (4-Nov-91 SY.J336/R) River scene with church spire (44x59cm-17x23in) s.
pen W/C (SA.R 3500)
£766 $1356   (4-Nov-91 SY.J337/R) Spring flowers in white jug (54x37cm-21x15in) s. pen
W/C (SA.R 3800)
£1111 $1900   (12-Mar-92 SY.J426/R) Royal visit, Adderley Street, Cape Town
(60x46cm-24x18in) s.d.47 W/C (SA.R 5500)

SUNDBLOM, Haddon Hubbard (1899-) American
£2247 $4000   (2-Nov-91 IH.NY110/R) Daniel Bone at the Cumberland Gap
(84x102cm-33x40in) s.
£13812 $25000   (5-Dec-91 SY.NY93/R) Sunny afternoon (76x107cm-30x42in) s.

SUNDSTROM, Alf (1888-1961) Swedish
£664 $1142   (19-Oct-91 UA.U358) Early spring (65x100cm-26x39in) s.d.1918 (S.KR 7000)

SUNYER, Joachim (1875-1956) Spanish
£10944 $19480   (29-Oct-91 BRO.B373/R) El desnudo de la calle de Hermosilla
                             (61x50cm-24x20in) s.d.23 (S.P 2000000)

SUPANCHICH, Konrad von (1858-1935) Hungarian
£874 $1555   (28-Apr-92 D.V95/R) Southern harbour with amphitheatre (89x82cm-35x32in)
                          s.i.d.1918 (A.S 18000)

SUPPANTSCHITSCH, Max (1865-1953) Austrian
£565 $972   (8-Oct-91 ZEL.L1742/R) Donkey with cart on woodland path with country
                          estate beyond, spring (56x68cm-22x27in) s. (DM 1650)
£1600 $2848   (28-Nov-91 CSK189) Venetian backwater (44x59cm-17x23in) s. canvas board
£1986 $3535   (28-Nov-91 D.V73/R) Kahlenberg seen from Cobenzl (19x28cm-7x11in) s.
                          board (A.S 40000)
£971   *$1728*   *(29-Apr-92 D.V628/R) Village view (35x30cm-14x12in) s. W/C (A.S 20000)*

SURAND, Gustave (1860-?) French
£416   *$728*   *(30-Mar-92 ZZ.F65 b) L'Elephant (30x47cm-12x19in) s. W/C (F.FR 4000)*

SURBEK, Victor (1885-1975) Swiss
£2148 $3888   (20-May-92 GK.Z5120/R) The artist's sister (33x27cm-13x11in)
                          mono.i.d.1909 (S.FR 5800)
£2157 $3667   (23-Oct-91 GD.B736/R) Brienzersee landscape (31x54cm-12x21in) s. canvas
                          over panel (S.FR 5500)
£5138 $9249   (19-Nov-91 GS.B3272) Calypso Bay, Malta (105x140cm-41x55in) s.
                          (S.FR 13000)
£395   *$711*   *(19-Nov-91 GS.B3274/R) View of Jungfrau (50x71cm-20x28in) s. chl*
                          (S.FR 1000)
£474   *$854*   *(19-Nov-91 GS.B3273) Bielersee landscape with Petersinsel*
                          (37x54cm-15x21in) s. indian ink over pencil (S.FR 1200)

SURDI, Luigi (1897-1959) Italian
£1023 $1851   (3-Dec-91 F.R227) Nei pressi di San Pietro (50x64cm-20x25in) s.d.1921
                          s.i.verso board on panel (I.L 2200000)
£1116 $2019   (3-Dec-91 F.R163) Via dei Fori Imperiali. Natura morta con frutta s. one
                          board one panel pair (I.L 2400000)
£1117 $2000   (13-Nov-91 B.SF2243/R) Still life with cabbage, onions, bottle of wine,
                          pitcher and copper jug (61x102cm-24x40in) s.

SUREDA, Andre (1872-1930) French
£2439 $4244   (13-Apr-92 AT.P214) Scene d'interieur (66x71cm-26x28in) s. panel
                          (F.FR 24000)

SURGELOOSE, Constant de (fl.1840) Belgian
£3997 $7434   (16-Jun-92 SY.B305/R) Portrait of Joseph Josse de Weweirne
                          (158x120cm-62x47in) s.d.1840 (B.FR 240000)

SURIKOV, Vasilii Ivanovich (1848-1916) Russian
£7500 $13350   (28-Nov-91 S510/R) Portrait study of cossack officer in summer uniform
                          (34x25cm-13x10in) s.i. canvas on board

SURO, D (20th C) ?
£4536 $8029   (7-Nov-91 AT.P65/R) Composition numerique (61x30cm-24x12in) s.i.d.1954
                          board three panels (F.FR 45000)

SURREY, Philip Henry (1910-) Canadian
£457 $836   (14-May-92 SY.T131) Autumn night, St. Andrew's, N.B (20x14cm-8x6in) sig.
                          d.1964 verso board (C.D 1000)
£800 $1416   (6-Nov-91 SY.T110) Deli lunch counter, Montreal (14x19cm-6x7in) s. board
                          (C.D 1600)
£1142   *$2089*   *(14-May-92 SY.T201/R) Cafe de la Madeleine s. d.1965 verso W/C pencil*
                          (C.D 2500)

SURTEES, John (1817-1915) British
£600 $1092   (10-Dec-91 AG309/R) Girls gathering kindling by lake (36x74cm-14x29in) s.

SURTEL, Paul (20th C) ?
£612 $1138   (17-Jun-92 I.N81) Chapelle a Volonne (32x41cm-13x16in) s. board
                          (F.FR 6000)

SURVAGE, Leopold (1879-1968) French
£3208 $5934   (12-Jun-92 ARC.P21/R) Pecheur et nu rose (81x60cm-32x24in) s.d.66
                          (F.FR 31500)
£7855 $13982   (28-Oct-91 GL.P204/R) Le soleil (80x65cm-31x26in) s.d.1957 (F.FR 78000)
£8000 $13840   (24-Mar-92 C32/R) Paysage cubiste (55x50cm-22x20in) s.
£14184 $25674   (24-May-92 GL.P50/R) Baigneuses (65x54cm-26x21in) s.d.24 (F.FR 140000)
£28659 $51013   (28-Nov-91 FB.P28/R) L'homme dans la ville (81x100cm-32x39in) s.
                          (F.FR 280000)
£503   *$900*   *(9-May-92 CE.NY111/R) Dessin strie (46x38cm-18x15in) s.d.67 pen*
£593   *$1073*   *(22-May-92 EA.Z104) Two figures (44x28cm-17x11in) s.d.1932 indian ink*
                          st.studio (S.FR 1600)

SURVAGE, Leopold (1879-1968) French-cont.

£619	$1070	(27-Mar-92 PPB.P68/R) Maisons et feuilles (5x6cm-2x2in) s.d.49 casein panel (F.FR 6000)
£835	$1420	(22-Oct-91 C.A303) Composition (16x26cm-6x10in) s.d.1937 W/C (B.FR 50000)
£977	$1857	(24-Jun-92 GL.P168/R) Les oiseaux (11x7cm-4x3in) s.d.1942 caseine panel (F.FR 9500)
£1186	$2051	(23-Mar-92 GL.P154/R) Paysage a la feuille (10x11cm-4x4in) s.d.1948 W/C wood (F.FR 11500)
£1249	$2185	(5-Apr-92 ZZ.F270/R) Personnage (29x19cm-11x7in) s.d.1933 pencil dr (F.FR 12000)
£1337	$2421	(4-Dec-91 LD.P29/R) Femme a la cruche (19x11cm-7x4in) mono. studio st.verso Indian ink htd.gouache (F.FR 13000)
£2134	$3713	(14-Apr-92 CSC.P36/R) Profil a la ville (13x10cm-5x4in) s.d.55 caseine panel (F.FR 21000)
£2284	$3974	(14-Apr-92 F.M178/R) Composizione (55x55cm-22x22in) s.d.1956 casein panel (I.L 5000000)
£2483	$4495	(23-May-92 KV.L425/R) La mer (24x34cm-9x13in) s.d.49 W/C (B.FR 150000)
£3252	$5659	(16-Apr-92 FB.P39/R) Rythme bleu (37x32cm-15x13in) s.studio st. mixed media (F.FR 32000)
£5500	$9955	(3-Dec-91 C176/R) Le couple aux feuilles (24x19cm-9x7in) s.d.35 gouache

SUS, Gustav Konrad (1823-1881) German

| £1031 | $1887 | (2-Jun-92 FN.S2771/R) Chickenyard with hens and chicks feeding before open barn door (23x19cm-9x7in) s. board (DM 3000) |

SUSENIER, Abraham (attrib) (1620-1664) Dutch

| £4420 | $8000 | (22-May-92 SY.NY125/R) Still life with roemer, grapes and lemon on ledge with butterflies (41x36cm-16x14in) |

SUSS, Josef (19th C) Austrian

| £2800 | $4956 | (13-Feb-92 CSK155/R) Classical beauty (98x49cm-39x19in) s. |

SUSTERMANS (1597-1681) Flemish

| £5100 | $9741 | (14-Jul-92 DR384/R) Isabella, in brocade dress (152x99cm-60x39in) |

SUSTERMANS, Justus (1597-1681) Flemish

| £5424 | $9818 | (18-May-92 SY.MI222/R) La Maddalena (170x91cm-67x36in) (I.L 12000000) |
| £10000 | $19200 | (10-Jul-92 C60/R) Portrait of Matthias de' Medici, wearing armour and holding baton (70x57cm-28x22in) |

SUSTERMANS, Justus (after) (1597-1681) Flemish

| £2700 | $4698 | (15-Apr-92 PHL190/R) Portrait of Prince of Denmark in armour (70x51cm-28x20in) i.verso |

SUSTERMANS, Justus (attrib) (1597-1681) Flemish

| £6592 | $11602 | (11-Apr-92 AT.P25/R) Sainte Martye a mi-corps (84x63cm-33x25in) (F.FR 65000) |

SUSTERMANS, Justus (style) (1597-1681) Flemish

| £4000 | $7000 | (27-Feb-92 CSK233/R) Portrait of a lady, wearing a black dress trimmed with lace (208x133cm-82x52in) |
| £4982 | $9218 | (8-Jun-92 CH.R767/R) Ritratto di giovane in armatura (73x60cm-29x24in) in oval (I.L 11000000) |

SUSTRIS, Friedrich (1540-1599) Dutch

| £33520 | $60000 | (16-Jan-92 CH.NY99/R) Adoration of shepherds (115x96cm-45x38in) |

SUSTRIS, Friedrich (attrib) (1540-1599) Dutch

| £2535 | $4462 | (11-Apr-92 AT.P32/R) La Crucifixion (42x29cm-17x11in) panel (F.FR 25000) |

SUSTRIS, Lambert (c.1515-1568) Dutch

| £1813 | $3245 | (7-May-92 CH.AM154/R) Raising of Lazarus (82x87cm-32x34in) panel (D.FL 6000) |
| £33149 | $60000 | (22-May-92 SY.NY82/R) Birth of Virgin (76x104cm-30x41in) |

SUSTRIS, Lambert (circle) (c.1515-1568) Dutch

| £850 | $1547 | (10-Dec-91 PH104/R) Portrait of man, in jacket and collar (61x45cm-24x18in) |

SUTCLIFFE, J (19th C) British

| £1400 | $2688 | (29-Jul-92 B152/R) A family group (127x101cm-50x40in) s.d.1860 |

SUTCLIFFE, John (19th C) British

| £900 | $1539 | (12-Mar-92 CSK258/R) At the spring (51x71cm-20x28in) s. |

SUTER, Jakob (1805-1874) Swiss

| £1200 | $2052 | (18-Mar-92 S50/R) The Mer de Glace from Mount Anvers, Switzerland (17x24cm-7x9in) s.d.1829 W/C |
| £2593 | $4693 | (19-May-92 GF.L2642/R) View of South Italian town before gigantic rock (64x85cm-25x33in) s.d.1842 W/C paper on canvas (S.FR 7000) |

SUTER, Willy (1918-) ?

| £902 | $1615 | (15-Nov-91 ZOF.Z1901) Rocky landscape (66x92cm-26x36in) s.d.56 (S.FR 2300) |

SUTHERLAND, Graham (1903-1980) British

£22951	$42000	(11-May-92 CH.NY57/R) Portrait of Douglas Cooper (130x81cm-51x32in) s.d.9.ii.67
£30000	$54300	(4-Dec-91 S183/R) Woods (55x46cm-22x18in) s.d.3.III.62 verso
£60000	$106200	(8-Nov-91 C228/R) Tonnelle de Vine (51x97cm-20x38in) s.d.1947 i.verso pencil oil panel
£850	$1556	(14-May-92 C176/R) Welsh landscape (9x11cm-4x4in) s.d.1944 W/C bodycol pen pencil
£1250	$2163	(2-Oct-91 S84/R) Ostrich (25x20cm-10x8in) s.i.d.76 pen ink W/C three
£1500	$2595	(25-Mar-92 S77/R) Landscape (12x18cm-5x7in) init.i.d.1941 crayon pen brush indian ink wash
£1600	$2832	(8-Nov-91 C227/R) Study for Pinnacles (20x16cm-8x6in) s.i.d.50 gouache
£1750	$3238	(11-Jun-92 C27/R) Landscape form (32x25cm-13x10in) init.d.71 pencil wax crayon W/C double-sided
£1800	$3186	(10-Feb-92 B16/R) Untitled composition (51x51cm-20x20in) s.d.1976 gouache W/C chl
£2200	$3806	(25-Mar-92 S76/R) Tree roots (20x30cm-8x12in) init.d.1949 mixed media paper laid down on card
£2800	$5096	(12-Dec-91 CSK279) Thorn cross in oval (28x22cm-11x9in) init.d.'59 gouache W/C brush ink pencil chl.
£2800	$4956	(10-Feb-92 B149) Vegetable form with setting sun (35x28cm-14x11in) s.d.1974 W/C pastel pen
£3000	$5550	(11-Jun-92 C22/R) Study for portrait of 13th Earl of Airlie (42x37cm-17x15in) pencil W/C bodycol pair
£3279	$6000	(11-May-92 CH.NY58/R) Portrait of Douglas Cooper (31x25cm-12x10in) s.d. W/C pencil ballpoint pen paper on board
£3400	$6290	(11-Jun-92 C24/R) palm opening (28x19cm-11x7in) init.d.64 oil gouache paper
£3400	$6290	(11-Jun-92 C23/R) Study for Coventry Cathedral Tapestry (25x21cm-10x8in) init. pencil W/C bodycol double-sided
£3800	$6574	(25-Mar-92 S84/R) The captive - animal form (27x24cm-11x9in) s.indist.i.d.1963 gouache pastel indian ink
£4100	$7585	(11-Jun-92 C19/R) Study for self-portrait (34x25cm-13x10in) init. i.d.1977 verso pencil
£4500	$8595	(1-Jul-92 S225/R) The forest (26x25cm-10x10in) inits. oil W/C gouache over pencil
£5000	$9250	(11-Jun-92 C20/R) Study for portrait of Sir Winston Churchill (13x13cm-5x5in) init.d.1954 pencil ink htd white tracing paper
£5500	$10175	(11-Jun-92 C25/R) Articulated forms (22x28cm-9x11in) s.d.1948 pencil col.crayon W/C bodycol gouache
£7000	$12110	(25-Mar-92 S81/R) Woman in a cornfield (18x16cm-7x6in) s.i.d.1950label oil gouache pencil chl. card
£7500	$12975	(25-Mar-92 S78/R) Gower landscape (38x47cm-15x19in) s.d.1941 W/C wax crayon pen indian ink
£9200	$16652	(4-Dec-91 S186/R) Shipwreck (36x24cm-14x9in) s.d.1978 gouache W/C pastel pencil paper board

SUTHERLAND, Robert Lewis (?-1932) British

£800	$1344	(26-Aug-91 S994/R) Out from school (38x56cm-15x22in) s.

SUTHERS, L (19/20th C) British

£600	$1098	(7-Feb-92 BW364) Feeding time (43x33cm-17x13in) s.

SUTTER, Ray (1920-1988) French

£869	$1590	(8-Feb-92 CSC.P4) Torrent (62x115cm-24x45in) (F.FR 8500)

SUTTON, John (?) British?

£2465	$4461	(3-Dec-91 FN.S2489/R) Schooner Prince de Neufchatel followed by English frigate in the Channel (61x91cm-24x36in) s.d.1813 i.verso (DM 7000)

SUTTON, Philip (1928-) British

£800	$1464	(14-May-92 C75/R) Cristina in red and black blouse (105x105cm-41x41in) s.i.verso i.stretcher

SUVEE, Joseph Benoit (1743-1807) Flemish

£618	$1057	(20-Mar-92 ZZ.F2) Vue d'une tour en ruine et des personnages (45x33cm-18x13in) i. sanguine (F.FR 6000)

SUZOR-COTE, Marc-Aurele de Foy (1867-1937) Canadian

£750	$1328	(6-Nov-91 SY.T265) Vieille constructions, Fuentarabia, Espagne (15x22cm-6x9in) s.d.1907 verso panel (C.D 1500)
£1461	$2659	(26-May-92 JOY.T105/R) Woman in red (26x21cm-10x8in) s.d.1906 panel (C.D 3200)
£2941	$5441	(9-Jun-92 FB.M40/R) Un coin du bois St-Michel, Nicolet (30x35cm-12x14in) s. (C.D 6500)
£1500	$2655	(6-Nov-91 SY.T56/R) Seated nude (24x19cm-9x7in) s.d.1925 red conte crayon (C.D 3000)
£15982	$29087	(26-May-92 JOY.T32/R) Entre nous, paysans Normands (71x89cm-28x35in) s. col.chk canvas (C.D 35000)

SVABINSKY, Max (1873-1962) Czechoslovakian

£586	$1008	(10-Oct-91 D.V280/R) River landscape with mother child and dog (31x40cm-12x16in) s.d.1926 W/C (A.S 12000)
£741	$1298	(19-Feb-92 D.V22/R) Would you like a cigarette (90x60cm-35x24in) mono. pastel board (A.S 15000)

SVANBERG, Max Walter (1912-) Swedish
£381 $671 (11-Apr-92 FAL.M400/R) *What a completely delightful evening* (66x55cm-26x22in) s.d.57 W/C tablecloth (S.KR 4000)
£399 $694 (13-Apr-92 AB.S417) Figure composition with yellow background (26x18cm-10x7in) s. W/C (S.KR 4200)
£2460 $4452 (19-May-92 AB.S5329/R) Imaginary female figure (69x29cm-27x11in) s.d.61 W/C (S.KR 26000)

SVARSTAD, Anders C (1869-1943) Norwegian
£797 $1451 (9-Dec-91 B.O115/R) Mountain landscape (66x97cm-26x38in) s. (N.KR 9000)

SVEINSDOTTIR, Juliana (1889-?) Icelandic
£1779 $3096 (17-Sep-91 RAS.K691/R) Icelandic landscape (65x75cm-26x30in) s.d.57 (D.KR 20000)

SVENDSEN, Svend (1864-?) Norwegian
£595 $1000 (28-Aug-91 MFA.C170) Snowscene (51x41cm-20x16in) s.
£632 $1100 (11-Sep-91 D.NY87) Mountainous river landscape in winter (76x102cm-30x40in) s.
£857 $1500 (28-Sep-91 YFA.M228/R) Blue winter day (56x71cm-22x28in) s.

SVENSSON, Christian Fredrik (1834-1909) Swedish
£527 $949 (19-Nov-91 GO.G181) Seascape with sailing vessel (38x70cm-15x28in) s. (S.KR 5500)
£1440 $2606 (3-Dec-91 AB.S4670/R) Seascape with sailship in rough seas (62x92cm-24x36in) s.d.1894 (S.KR 15000)

SVENSSON, Gunnar (1892-1977) Swedish
£570 $991 (13-Apr-92 AB.S257) Still life of plant and apples (59x72cm-23x28in) s. (S.KR 6000)
£779 $1355 (13-Apr-92 AB.S256) Tulips and bowl of fruit on table (99x59cm-39x23in) s. (S.KR 8200)

SVENSSON, Gustaf (1893-1957) Swedish
£678 $1207 (28-Oct-91 AB.S227) View from the National Museum, Stockholm in winter (55x72cm-22x28in) s.d.1942 (S.KR 7200)

SVENSSON, Roland (1910-) Swedish
£950 $1652 (13-Apr-92 AB.S420) *Coastal landscape with beach huts, Spirckopp* (40x29cm-16x11in) s. W/C (S.KR 10000)

SVERTSCHKOFF, Nicolas Gregorovitch (1817-1898) Russian
£1488 $2648 (1-Dec-91 HOR.H19/R) Troika in flight, winter (37x46cm-15x18in) s. (F.M 11500)
£24000 $42720 (28-Nov-91 S440/R) Return from bear hunt (114x187cm-45x74in) s.

SVETLANOV, Maxim (?) ?
£465 $888 (21-Jul-92 JRL.S9) Life of a woman (59x49cm-23x19in) s. (A.D 1200)

SVIPDAG, Elin (1905-1987) Swedish
£763 $1359 (27-Nov-91 BU.S28/R) The shout without an echo (82x100cm-32x39in) s.d.1955 (S.KR 8000)

SWAANSWIJK, Lubertus Jacobus see LUCEBERT

SWABIAN SCHOOL, 16th C German
£2484 $4247 (18-Mar-92 D.V301/R) Portrait of father with son and coat of arms (67x51cm-26x20in) panel (A.S 50000)

SWAHN, Ragnar (1882-1964) Swedish
£566 $1002 (25-Apr-92 SO.S601/R) Kalmar Palace (79x104cm-31x41in) s. (S.KR 6000)

SWAINE, Francis (1740-1782) British
£1600 $2880 (9-Jan-92 B294) British frigates in heavy seas before an approaching storm (21x30cm-8x12in)
£2200 $4070 (11-Jun-92 CSK193/R) Men of War in stiff breeze (48x63cm-19x25in)
£6000 $11460 (17-Jul-92 C140/R) British men-o-war and fishing boats in stiff breeze. Fishing boats moored in river estuary (15x20cm-6x8in) s. board pair

SWAINE, Francis (attrib) (1740-1782) British
£1124 $2000 (22-Jan-92 SY.NY384/R) British frigate under sail (35x43cm-14x17in)

SWAINE, Francis (circle) (1740-1782) British
£4000 $7240 (20-May-92 S30/R) British squadron off Gibraltar (63x89cm-25x35in)

SWAINE, Francis (style) (1740-1782) British
£2000 $3400 (21-Oct-91 H264) Moonlit coastal scene with fort, man-o'-war firing salute and other shipping and figures (91x112cm-36x44in)

SWAISH, Frederick George (fl.1920s) British
£680 $1210 (28-Nov-91 B110) Head study of young girl (20x15cm-8x6in) s.d.1919 panel

SWAN, Cuthbert Edmund (1870-1931) British
£750 $1343 (14-Nov-91 CSK343) Lion cubs with snake (18x25cm-7x10in) s. board
£1350 $2565 (23-Jun-92 PH107) Puma and cubs (63x126cm-25x50in) s.d.1905

SWAN, Cuthbert Edmund (1870-1931) British-cont.
£680 $1142 *(27-Aug-91 SWS1761/R) A tiger (17x35cm-7x14in) s. W/C*

SWAN, Douglas (1935-) German
£724 $1318 (25-May-92 CH.R50/R) Black wave (100x80cm-39x31in) s. i.d.1960verso
        (I.L 1600000)

SWANE, Christine (1876-1960) Danish
£500 $874 (1-Apr-92 KH.K225) Christmas cactus in flower (31x42cm-12x17in) init.
        (D.KR 5500)
£641 $1115 (17-Sep-91 RAS.K692) Still life (30x40cm-12x16in) init.d.1951 (D.KR 7200)
£1604 $2759 (16-Oct-91 KH.K78/R) Still life of flowers and blue jug on table
        (65x58cm-26x23in) init.d.1945 (D.KR 18000)
£542 $926 *(12-Mar-92 RAS.K734) Still life of blue bottle and fruit*
        (47x60cm-19x24in) init.d.1948 pencil W/C (D.KR 6000)

SWANE, Sigurd (1879-1973) Danish
£500 $874 (1-Apr-92 KH.K232) Autumn landscape by the fjord (72x84cm-28x33in) init.
        (D.KR 5500)
£552 $960 (17-Sep-91 RAS.K694) Landscape near Gryde Mill (70x70cm-28x28in)
        init.d.25 (D.KR 6200)
£704 $1218 (2-Sep-91 BU.K84/R) Old buildings in Skagen town (77x83cm-30x33in)
        init.d.31 (D.KR 8000)
£730 $1269 (17-Sep-91 RAS.K693/R) Sunset over bare orchard (101x89cm-40x35in)
        init.d.33 (D.KR 8200)
£954 $1669 (1-Apr-92 KH.K233) Tulips in a vase (50x36cm-20x14in) init. (D.KR 10500)
£3090 $5500 (22-Jan-92 SY.NY433/R) In country (44x58cm-17x23in) s.d.1904

SWANENBURGH, Jacob Isaacsz (circle) (1571-1638) Flemish
£1165 $2109 (20-May-92 CSC.P7) Le jugement dernier (22x16cm-9x6in) copper
        (F.FR 11500)

SWANEVELT, Herman van (1600-1655) Dutch
£2974 $5442 (16-May-92 F.L9/R) Paesaggio con figure (50x74cm-20x29in) (S.FR 8000)
£1553 $2764 *(25-Nov-91 CH.AM108/R) Italianate wooded landscape with herdsmen by*
        village (25x36cm-10x14in) pen wash (D.FL 5000)
£1863 $3317 *(25-Nov-91 CH.AM109/R) Roman ruins near the Palatine (13x19cm-5x7in) pen*
        wash (D.FL 6000)
£2514 $4500 *(15-Jan-92 CH.NY139/R) River landscape with Venus and Adonis*
        (20x23cm-8x9in) mono. black chk wash vellum

SWANWICK, Betty (1915-1989) British
£800 $1392 *(19-Sep-91 B93/R) Dog's dance (51x61cm-20x24in) W/C bodycol over pencil*

SWANWICK, Harold (1866-1929) British
£4000 $6960 (12-Sep-91 CSK177) 'Ah, Whoa-Whup' (91x61cm-36x24in) s.d.1891 s.i.verso
£3524 $6273 *(26-Nov-91 J.M34/R) To a well earned rest (59x104cm-23x41in) s. W/C*
        (A.D 8000)

SWANZY, Mary (1882-1978) Irish
£1091 $1887 (2-Oct-91 A.D52) Tree (23x18cm-9x7in) s. board (E.P 1200)
£1500 $2610 (18-Sep-91 CG146/R) Cafe in wood (23x18cm-9x7in) board
£1776 $3072 (25-Mar-92 A.D178) Fishermen, Kilkeel, Co. Down (30x43cm-12x17in) s.
        board (E.P 1900)
£1800 $3132 (18-Sep-91 CG147/R) Donegal coast (29x38cm-11x15in) s. canvas on board
£2778 $5056 (11-Dec-91 A.D90/R) Tropical grasses (56x51cm-22x20in) i.verso (E.P 3000)
£4727 $8178 (2-Oct-91 A.D94) Sleeping gardener (20x25cm-8x10in) s. board (E.P 5200)
£10909 $18873 (2-Oct-91 A.D164/R) Banana grove (76x56cm-30x22in) s. (E.P 12000)

SWART VAN GRONINGEN, Jan (circle) (c.1495-1560) Dutch
£5500 $9790 (29-Oct-91 PH52/R) The Flagellation, St Augusting and St Jerome triptych
        panel

SWART, Corstiaan Hendrikus de (1818-1897) Dutch
£3364 $5988 (30-Oct-91 CH.AM38/R) Skaters on frozen river and faggott gatherer by
        farmhouses, winter (77x100cm-30x39in) s.d.1837 (D.FL 11000)

SWARTZ, Johan David (after) (1678-c.1729) Swedish
£1183 $2140 (19-May-92 AB.S4298/R) Portrait of Karl XII wearing blue uniform
        (82x61cm-32x24in) (S.KR 12500)

SWARTZ, Johan David (attrib) (1678-c.1729) Swedish
£996 $1713 (19-Oct-91 UA.U348/R) Karl XII (83x70cm-33x28in) (S.KR 10500)

SWEBACH (studio) (18/19th C) French
£1301 $2276 (30-Mar-92 ZZ.F16) Chasse a courre (36x53cm-14x21in) panel (F.FR 12500)

SWEBACH, Bernard Edouard (1800-1870) French
£4406 $7930 (27-Jan-92 CSC.P24/R) Halte de cavaliers (25x33cm-10x13in) (F.FR 43000)
£6352 $11434 (27-Jan-92 CSC.P25/R) Le depart pour le marche (27x35cm-11x14in) s.
        (F.FR 62000)
£7645 $14220 (18-Jun-92 SY.MO73/R) Scene de course (30x61cm-12x24in) panel
        (F.FR 75000)
£14604 $25704 (10-Apr-92 AGS.P21/R) L'arrivee des courses (33x41cm-13x16in) s.d.18..
        (F.FR 144000)

SWEBACH, Bernard Edouard (1800-1870) French-cont.
£22936 $42661   (19-Jun-92 CN.P68/R) L'ecurie de la Maison du roi Louis XVIII, son ecuyer et le cheval du roi (24x33cm-9x13in) s.d.1819 (F.FR 225000)
£1114 $2017   (22-May-92 BL.P19/R) Scene de chasse a courre (14x26cm-6x10in) s. W/C (F.FR 11000)

SWEBACH, Bernard Edouard (attrib) (1800-1870) French
£1427 $2654   (18-Jun-92 SY.MO430/R) La Fete Foraine et la Tarantelle pen wash two (F.FR 14000)

SWEBACH-DESFONTAINES, Jacques Francois (1769-1823) French
£619 $1070   (27-Mar-92 CN.P22) Caravane (23x35cm-9x14in) s.d.1786 blk.chk.pen wash (F.FR 6000)

SWEBACH-DESFONTAINES, Jacques Francois (attrib) (1769-1823) French
£815 $1475   (19-May-92 GF.L2422/R) Hunting party by fountain (35x49cm-14x19in) panel (S.FR 2200)

SWEBACH-DESFONTAINES, Jacques Francois (circle) (1769-1823) French
£2400 $4200   (3-Apr-92 C36/R) Extensive landscape with army on march and cavalry officers (30x40cm-12x16in) panel

SWEBACH-DESFONTAINES, Jacques Francois (school) (1769-1823) French
£3779 $6500   (9-Oct-91 CH.NY100/R) Traveller and soldiers on horseback before inn (36x43cm-14x17in) panel

SWEDLUND, Pelle (1865-1947) Swedish
£482 $833   (28-Mar-92 UA.U440) Sunset over mountains (26x41cm-10x16in) s.d.97 panel (S.KR 5000)

SWEERTS, Jeronimus (attrib) (1603-1636) Dutch
£1813 $3227   (28-Nov-91 BU.S82/R) Still life of spring flowers in vase (22x18cm-9x7in) bears sig. panel (S.KR 19000)

SWEERTS, Michiel (1624-1664) Dutch
£1045 $1850   (24-Apr-92 DOU.M1) The lace maker (13x43cm-5x17in)
£5556 $10056   (19-May-92 GF.L2026/R) Portrait of young gentleman (84x66cm-33x26in) (S.FR 15000)

SWEERTS, Michiel (attrib) (1624-1664) Dutch
£2593 $4693   (19-May-92 GF.L2406/R) Before the card game (48x37cm-19x15in) panel (S.FR 7000)

SWEET, Walter H (?) British
£620 $1104   (29-Oct-91 SWS343/R) Cornish harbour (62x48cm-24x19in) s. mounted as firescreen
£1000 $1780   (29-Nov-91 T330/R) Fisherfolk by West Country harbour (64x48cm-25x19in) s. W/C
£1200 $2304   (29-Jul-92 CSK90/R) Two Newlyn scenes. Harbour, Mousehole (50x29cm-20x11in) s.i. pencil W/C htd.white three

SWIERZYNSKI, Saturnin (1820-1883) Polish
£865 $1575   (15-Dec-91 REM.W47) Tatras landscape (38x31cm-15x12in) s. (P.Z 17000000)

SWIESZEWSKI, Alexander (1839-1895) Polish
£1095 $1917   (3-Apr-92 BM.B716/R) View of Kufstein with figures (22x32cm-9x13in) s. panel (DM 3100)

SWIFT, John Warkup (1815-1869) British
£1400 $2534   (20-May-92 S24/R) To the rescue (35x53cm-14x21in) s.
£1849 $3106   (28-Aug-91 KH.K189/R) Seascapes with sailship off the coast (45x63cm-18x25in) s.d.1854 pair (D.KR 21000)
£4200 $7560   (22-Nov-91 C101/R) Approaching harbour. Fishing boats off rocky coast (46x63cm-18x25in) s. one d.1854 pair

SWIMBERGHE, Gilbert (1927-) Belgian
£1242 $2248   (23-May-92 KV.L320) Composition (80x70cm-31x28in) s. (B.FR 75000)

SWINNERTON, James G (1875-1941) American
£1117 $2000   (14-Nov-91 CE.NY285/R) Coming storm (35x46cm-14x18in) s. panel

SWINSTEAD, George Hillyard (1860-1926) British
£1450 $2581   (30-Apr-92 T105) Portrait of beer girl - Fomona Northcott (36x25cm-14x10in) s.i.d.99
£2616 $4500   (17-Oct-91 SY.NY315/R) Following ducklings (61x51cm-24x20in) s.
£5500 $9460   (4-Mar-92 S160/R) April showers (61x51cm-24x20in) s.

SWISS SCHOOL (?) Swiss
£1931 $3301   (12-Mar-92 GK.Z84) Hunting trophy with game and rifle, wooded landscape with ruin beyond (178x118cm-70x46in) c.1800 (S.FR 5000)

SWISS SCHOOL, 17th C
£2907 $5000   (10-Oct-91 SY.NY170/R) William Tell shooting the apple from his son's head (87x117cm-34x46in) panel

SWISS SCHOOL, 18th C
£3519 $6369   (19-May-92 GF.L2241/R) Diana bathing (105x127cm-41x50in) (S.FR 9500)
£10288 $18621   (5-Dec-91 SY.MO138/R) Vues des alpes (39x52cm-15x20in) pair (F.FR 100000)

SWISS SCHOOL, 19th C
£431   *$733*   *(23-Oct-91 GD.B667/R) Lausanne (24x35cm-9x14in) W/C (S.FR 1100)*
£2464   *$4435*   *(21-Nov-91 BL.P15) Vue des rochers de Lourley et de la peche de saumons*
      (33x48cm-13x19in) gouache (F.FR 24000)

SWISS SCHOOL, 20th C
£1176 $2000   (23-Oct-91 GD.B676/R) Coastal landscape (60x92cm-24x36in) indis.s.
      (S.FR 3000)

SWOBODA VON WIKINGEN, Emmerich Alexius (1849-1920) Austrian
£880 $1479   (27-Aug-91 RAS.K451/R) A Turk on his verandah (107x75cm-42x30in) s.d.1858
      (D.KR 10000)
£1056 $1775   (27-Aug-91 RAS.K455/R) Zobeide's monument by Tigris, Bagdad
      (90x120cm-35x47in) s. (D.KR 12000)

SWOBODA, Gerhard (1924-) Austrian
£874   *$1556*   *(25-Nov-91 WK.M971/R) Seefahrt in den Gewassern des Konigreiches Bohemia*
      (41x81cm-16x32in) s.i.d.1972/73 oil indian ink pen panel (DM 2500)

SWOBODA, Josef Cestmir (1889-?) American
£917 $1633   (30-Oct-91 CH.AM107) Stream in snowy forest (90x90cm-35x35in) s.d.33
      (D.FL 3000)

SWOBODA, Josefine (1861-1924) Austrian
£909 $1618   (29-Nov-91 ZEL.L1110/R) Portrait of girl with bare breast before white
      wall (80x64cm-31x25in) s. (DM 2600)
£571   *$1000*   *(21-Feb-92 BG.M132/R) The Holy Family (58x58cm-23x23in) s.d.1908 W/C*

SWOBODA, Rudolf (elder) (1819-1859) Austrian
£1939 $3529   (27-May-92 D.V565/R) Cattle grazing in landscape (32x40cm-13x16in)
      s.d.1852 (A.S 40000)
£2506 $4536   (5-Dec-91 D.V137) Cattle grazing on Alpine pastures with Dachstein range
      beyond (68x94cm-27x37in) s. (A.S 50000)

SWOBODA, Rudolf (younger) (1859-1914) Austrian
£741 $1298   (20-Feb-92 D.V324/R) Stable interior (63x79cm-25x31in) rem.sig.
      (A.S 15000)
£2500 $4450   (27-Nov-91 S146/R) Young lady in Japanese costume (30x18cm-12x7in)
      s.d.1894 cardboard

SWORD, James Brade (1839-1915) American
£2023 $3500   (6-Sep-91 S.BM166/R) A New Hampshire Fishing excursion (51x76cm-20x30in)
      s.i.d.1875

SWYNCOP, Charles (1895-1970) Belgian
£911 $1648   (23-May-92 KV.L322) Still life of flowers (78x67cm-31x26in) mono.
      (B.FR 55000)
£1078 $1973   (12-May-92 C.A308/R) A Spanish beauty (100x80cm-39x31in) s.d.1920
      (B.FR 65000)

SWYNNERTON, Annie (1844-1933) British
£1174 $1960   (19-Aug-91 SY.ME187/R) Portrait of Honourable Colwyn E.A. Philipps, son
      of Viscount St David (83x80cm-33x31in) s.verso (A.D 2500)
£2600 $4602   (6-Nov-91 S145/R) Blossom time (61x51cm-24x20in) s.d.1888

SYBERG, Fritz (1862-1939) Danish
£660 $1109   (27-Aug-91 RAS.K517) Summer landscape with elderflowers (50x70cm-20x28in)
      mono. (D.KR 7500)
£661 $1170   (23-Apr-92 RAS.V1017/R) Late summer landscape with farm (56x66cm-22x26in)
      mono. (D.KR 7500)
£661 $1123   (8-Aug-91 RAS.V1072/R) Wooded landscape (71x104cm-28x41in) mono.d.1930
      (D.KR 7500)
£716 $1302   (10-Dec-91 RAS.K271) Summer landscape (70x96cm-28x38in) mono. (D.KR 8000)
£1114 $1916   (15-Oct-91 RAS.K266) Winter landscape with farmhouses and poplars
      (65x86cm-26x34in) mono.d.1906 (D.KR 12500)
£1726 $3020   (1-Apr-92 KH.K281/R) Workers in the field (135x175cm-53x69in) mono.d.1931
      (D.KR 19000)
£490   *$858*   *(1-Apr-92 KH.K244) Fields in winter (50x65cm-20x26in) mono.d.1917 W/C*
      (D.KR 5400)
£527   *$944*   *(6-May-92 KH.K294) Italian church (77x106cm-30x42in) mono.d.1912 i.verso*
      (D.KR 6000)

SYCHKOV, Th (19/20th C) Russian
£3429 $6000   (20-Feb-92 SY.NY246/R) Friends (82x60cm-32x24in) s.d.1930

SYCHRA, Vladimir (1903-) Czechoslovakian
£745 $1326   (29-Nov-91 D.V80/R) Still life with lemon (35x45cm-14x18in) s.d.51 panel
      (A.S 15000)
£912 $1642   (23-Nov-91 N.M385/R) Oriental female fortune teller in landscape
      (30x58cm-12x23in) s.d.1941 (DM 2600)

SYER, John (1815-1885) British
£600 $1098   (5-Feb-92 CSK298) Mumbles, South Wales (24x39cm-9x15in) s.d.1860
                 s.i.stretcher verso
£1300 $2314   (28-Apr-92 S143/R) Angler in the Highlands (102x151cm-40x59in) s.d.84
£1987 $3596   (19-May-92 AB.S4382/R) Park landscape with family in summer
                 (127x107cm-50x42in) s.d.65 (S.KR 21000)
*£700 $1211   (25-Mar-92 PHI471/R) Near Ffestiniog (37x62cm-15x24in) s.d.78 W/C
                 htd.bodycol*

SYER, John C (c.1846-1913) British
£580 $986   (9-Aug-91 T109) River landscape with angler (76x127cm-30x50in) s.d.82
£1000 $1830   (15-May-92 CBS183) Scarborough (76x127cm-30x50in) s.d.1870
£1500 $2685   (5-May-92 SWS325/R) Eventide, Criccieth (74x124cm-29x49in) s.d.1878

SYKES, George (1863-?) British
£700 $1204   (16-Oct-91 PHL225/R) Figures before Wharfe near Bolton Abbey
                 (84x113cm-33x44in) s.

SYKES, Henry (19th C) British
£620 $1066   (16-Oct-91 PHL207/R) Cottage garden (26x34cm-10x13in) s. col.wash
*£2000 $3440   (16-Oct-91 PHL180/R) Portrait of Spanish girl (65x40cm-26x16in) s.
                 col.wash*

SYKES, John Gutteridge (1866-?) British
£400 $712   (28-Nov-91 L289) Horse and chickens before farm buildings
                 (38x28cm-15x11in) s. W/C
£500 $875   (27-Feb-92 L185/R) Farm cart and horse on a wooded track
                 (25x36cm-10x14in) s.

SYLVESTER, Frederick Oakes (1869-1915) American
£565 $1000   (10-Nov-91 LIT.L190) Boats at dock (30x36cm-12x14in) s.d.97
£1436 $2600   (2-Dec-91 S.SL294/R) River landscape at dusk (53x48cm-21x19in) s.d.1913

SYME, Eveline W (1888-?) Australian
*£485 $863   (26-Nov-91 J.M1093) Spanish hillside (33x23cm-13x9in) s.d.1929 W/C
                 (A.D 1100)*

SYMONS, George Gardner (1863-1930) American
£734 $1300   (12-Feb-92 B.SF530/R) New England landscape with trees (10x15cm-4x6in)
                 init. estate st.verso board
£734 $1300   (12-Feb-92 B.SF528/R) New England landscape with houses (10x15cm-4x6in)
                 init. estate st.verso board
£988 $1700   (20-Oct-91 HG.C6) Indian lake (61x76cm-24x30in) s. board
£1445 $2500   (29-Mar-92 MY.F110/R) California forest (30x41cm-12x16in) s. panel
£1554 $2750   (12-Feb-92 B.SF521/R) Country landscape with stream (16x22cm-6x9in) s.
                 estate st.verso board
£1554 $2750   (12-Feb-92 B.SF529/R) California landscape (10x15cm-4x6in) init. estate
                 st.verso board
£1579 $3000   (23-Jun-92 MOR.P61) Snow trail (18x25cm-7x10in) init. board
£1857 $3250   (31-Mar-92 MOR.P130) Winter river (20x25cm-8x10in) s. board
£3846 $7000   (28-May-92 BG.M467/R) Sunburnt fields (61x76cm-24x30in) s.
£5714 $10000   (21-Feb-92 BG.M125/R) Autumnal river landscape with figure and cart
                 (76x91cm-30x36in) s.
£9143 $16000   (26-Sep-91 CH.NY75/R) Winter twilight (64x76cm-25x30in) s.

SYMONS, William Christian (1845-1911) British
£2300 $4209   (15-May-92 TE408/R) Suggestion (112x86cm-44x34in) s.d.1882

SYS, Maurice (1880-1972) Belgian
£9697 $17552   (21-May-92 SY.AM88/R) Zomeravond in de Braakman (90x126cm-35x50in) s.
                 s.i.d.1911stretcher (D.FL 32000)
£9938 $17193   (24-Mar-92 VN.R91/R) Saling boats in winter river landscape
                 (80x100cm-31x39in) s. (D.FL 32000)

SZANTHO, Maria (1898-) Hungarian
£520 $941   (21-May-92 CSK263) Young beauty (79x58cm-31x23in) s. panel
£580 $1050   (21-May-92 CSK272) Reclining female nude (33x99cm-13x39in) s.d. board
£600 $1038   (26-Mar-92 CSK82) Reclining female nude (61x88cm-24x35in) s.
£606 $1073   (22-Apr-92 ZZ.F142) Jeune femme au masque (60x80cm-24x31in) s.
                 (F.FR 6000)
£700 $1239   (13-Feb-92 CSK148) Standing female nude holding ewer (100x34cm-39x13in)
                 s. board
£700 $1211   (3-Oct-91 CSK185) Music hath charms (79x58cm-31x23in) s.
£750 $1358   (21-May-92 CSK260/R) Ballerinas (70x85cm-28x33in) s.d.
£752 $1361   (5-Dec-91 D.V111) Young beauty (80x60cm-31x24in) s. (A.S 15000)
£1000 $1730   (3-Oct-91 CSK229/R) Susanne and the elders (99x69cm-39x27in) s. board
£1100 $1991   (21-May-92 CSK266/R) Reclining female nude (55x80cm-22x31in) s.
£1199 $2062   (8-Oct-91 ZEL.L1744/R) Female nude wearing gold headband with coins
                 (100x70cm-39x28in) s. (DM 3500)
£1243 $2200   (5-Nov-91 CE.NY64/R) Gypsy. Two ballerinas s. two
£1300 $2353   (21-May-92 CSK267) Reclining beauty (75x128cm-30x50in) s.
£1367 $2364   (3-Oct-91 D.V216/R) Girl with violin (86x69cm-34x27in) s. (A.S 28000)
£1400 $2478   (13-Feb-92 CSK142/R) A reclining beauty (65x110cm-26x43in) s.
£1565 $2801   (5-May-92 ZEL.L1564/R) Portrait of young woman with bare breasts
                 (79x59cm-31x23in) s. board (DM 4600)

SZANTHO, Maria (1898-) Hungarian-cont.
£1600 $2896   (21-May-92 CSK268/R) Reclining beauty (105x76cm-41x30in) s. panel
£1900 $3249   (18-Mar-92 S62/R) A young beauty (76x56cm-30x22in) s.
£1977 $3460   (19-Feb-92 D.V169/R) Girl with lute (79x60cm-31x24in) s. (A.S 40000)

SZCZYGLINSKI, Henryk (1881-1944) Polish
£523 $905   (8-Sep-91 REM.W39) Mansion entrance (25x29cm-10x11in) s. board
(P.Z 10000000)

SZENES, Arpad (1897-1985) French
£4209 $7577   (20-Nov-91 CN.P219/R) Composition cubiste (40x80cm-16x31in) s.
(F.FR 41000)

SZERBAKOW, Fedor (1911-) German?
£707 $1237   (3-Apr-92 BM.B574/R) Moor landscape near Worpswede (60x81cm-24x32in) s.
panel (DM 2000)

SZERDAHELYI, B (?) ?
£750 $1298   (26-Mar-92 CSK3) Still life of roses and daisies in vase
(99x79cm-39x31in) s.

SZINYEI MERSE, Pal von (1845-1920) Hungarian
£2747 $4945   (21-Nov-91 D.V113/R) Mountain landscape (27x36cm-11x14in) s. board
(A.S 55000)
£8000 $14880   (17-Jun-92 S389/R) Wild rose bush by field (58x73cm-23x29in) s.d.1904

SZONGOTT, Jakob (1876-?) Hungarian
£1162 $2069   (30-Oct-91 CH.AM111) Gypsies outside barn (90x125cm-35x49in) s.
(D.FL 3800)

SZULE, M (?) ?
£1400 $2478   (13-Feb-92 CSK159) In the artist's studio (79x60cm-31x24in) s.

SZURCSIK, Jozsef (20th C) Hungarian
£454 $781   (14-Oct-91 AT.P166) Venus (70x100cm-28x39in) mono.d.1988 mixed media
paper pasted on panel (F.FR 4500)
£605 $1041   (14-Oct-91 AT.P165/R) Megalomanie (70x100cm-28x39in) pastel (F.FR 6000)

SZUSIKOWSKI (?) ?
£1083 $1949   (19-Nov-91 RAS.K175/R) Young Italian boy with grapes (58x48cm-23x19in) s.
(D.KR 12000)

SZYK, Arthur (1894-) Polish
£663 $1214   (12-May-92 C.A311) Praying in the synagogue (28x41cm-11x16in) s. gouache
(B.FR 40000)
£663 $1214   (12-May-92 C.A310) The Jewish banker (39x28cm-15x11in) mono. gouache
(B.FR 40000)
£903 $1625   (19-Nov-91 RAS.K529) Moses changing a stick to a snake (29x40cm-11x16in)
init.i. gouache (D.KR 10000)

SZYMANOVSKI, Waclaw (1859-1930) Polish
£2015 $3648   (3-Dec-91 AB.S4757/R) Interior with man and woman by window
(64x79cm-25x31in) s.d.86 (S.KR 21000)

SZYSKOWITZ, Rudolf (1905-1976) Austrian
£3724 $6629   (28-Nov-91 D.V242/R) Ennstal landscape (53x71cm-21x28in) mono.d.1949
(A.S 75000)

SZYSZLO, Fernando de (1925-) Peruvian
£8287 $15000   (18-May-92 CH.NY172/R) Mar de Lurin (100x100cm-39x39in) s. acrylic canvas
£8333 $15000   (19-Nov-91 CH.NY64/R) Mar de lurin (150x150cm-59x59in) s.d.1987 i.verso
acrylic
£8840 $16000   (18-May-92 CH.NY178/R) Pasajeros (120x120cm-47x47in) s. i.d.78 verso
acrylic canvas
£8840 $16000   (19-May-92 SY.NY67/R) Inkarri (119x119cm-47x47in) s. i.d.68verso acrylic
panel
£10000 $18000   (19-Nov-91 CH.NY86/R) Recinto (150x150cm-59x59in) acrylic
£10556 $19000   (18-Nov-91 SY.NY183/R) Puka Wamani (152x122cm-60x48in) s. i.d.68verso
acrylic panel
£13260 $24000   (18-May-92 CH.NY179/R) Mar de Lurin (150x120cm-59x47in) s. i.d.88 verso
acrylic canvas

TAAFFE, Philip (1955-) American
£1486 $2600   (27-Feb-92 CE.NY264/R) Untitled (56x86cm-22x34in) s.d.1987 oil enamel
£1429 $2500   (27-Feb-92 CE.NY261/R) Untitled (42x55cm-17x22in) s.d.88 verso W/C
gouache wax
£1676 $3000   (9-May-92 CE.NY191/R) Untitled (42x55cm-17x22in) s.d.88verso W/C gouache
wax
£1788 $3200   (9-May-92 CE.NY194/R) Untitled (48x61cm-19x24in) s.d.1986verso graphite
set of three
£3143 $5500   (27-Feb-92 CH.NY83/R) Untitled (56x86cm-22x34in) s.verso oil enamel paper

TAAFFE, Philip (1955-) American-cont.
£3911 $7000   (5-May-92 CH.NY178/R) Untitled (47x93cm-19x37in) s.d.1987verso col.crayon
£3911 $7000   (5-May-92 CH.NY108/R) Braided arcs (35x43cm-14x17in) s.id.1988verso
     acrylic enamel silkscreen canvas
£5714 $10000   (27-Feb-92 CH.NY93/R) Green form (61x51cm-24x20in) s.i.d.1985-86verso
     acrylic paper collage canvas
£47486 $85000   (5-May-92 CH.NY14/R) Nativity red white (165x228cm-65x90in)
     s.i.d.1986verso acrylic silkscreen on canvas

TABAKOVA, Elena (1919-) Russian
£541 $947   (5-Apr-92 ARC.P148/R) Les coqelicots (49x69cm-19x27in) s. board
     (F.FR 5200)
£593 $1038   (5-Apr-92 ARC.P150/R) Vassilsourk (47x66cm-19x26in) s.d.48 (F.FR 5700)
£594 $1057   (25-Nov-91 ARC.P126/R) Nature morte aux fruits (99x74cm-39x29in) s.
     (F.FR 5800)
£798 $1421   (25-Nov-91 ARC.P124/R) Dans les champs (33x49cm-13x19in) s. (F.FR 7800)
£921 $1640   (25-Nov-91 ARC.P123/R) La sieste (85x95cm-33x37in) s. (F.FR 9000)
£922 $1660   (27-Jan-92 ARC.P223/R) Les coquelicots (80x70cm-31x28in) s.d.57
     (F.FR 9000)

TABAR, Francois Germain Leopold (attrib) (1818-1869) French
£893 $1500   (12-Aug-91 SG.M600) Landscape with water in forest clearing with
     buildings (51x64cm-20x25in) s.

TABARY, F (?) ?
£2646 $4709   (28-Apr-92 RAS.K318/R) Nude model resting (73x60cm-29x24in) s. pastel
     (D.KR 30000)

TABER, Lincoln (?) ?
£800 $1528   (16-Jul-92 B65) Reversed canvas (40x35cm-16x14in)

TABER, Sarah A (1844-1928) American
£632 $1200   (25-Jun-92 BG.M498/R) Mountainous riverfall landscape with boats,
     figures, animals and houses (41x61cm-16x24in) i.verso

TABUCHI, Yasse (1921-) Japanese
£1423 $2604   (13-May-92 BU.S197/R) 'Les fruits de nulle part' (80x100cm-31x39in)
     s.d.1966 (S.KR 15000)

TACK, Augustus Vincent (1870-1949) American
£4945 $9000   (28-May-92 CH.NY177/R) Portrait of woman with red rose (101x73cm-40x29in)

TADINI, Emilio (1927-?) Italian
£1840 $3293   (14-Nov-91 F.M16/R) Il lampo e la candela (46x55cm-18x22in) s.i.verso
     (I.L 4000000)
£2299 $3977   (28-Mar-92 F.L123) Trofeo del turista (80x100cm-31x39in) d.1983 acrylic
     (S.FR 6000)
£3449 $6174   (14-Nov-91 F.M84/R) Figura (81x66cm-32x26in) s.i.d.1978 acrylic
     (I.L 7500000)
£4111 $7153   (14-Apr-92 F.M224/R) Museo dell'uomo (100x81cm-39x32in) s.i.d.1974verso
     acrylic (I.L 9000000)
£9198 $16464   (14-Nov-91 F.M137/R) Film (200x290cm-79x114in) s.i.d.1977verso acrylic
     (I.L 20000000)

TAEUBER-ARP, Sophie (1889-1943) Swiss
£20339 $36000   (5-Nov-91 CH.NY1/R) No. 10 (21x13cm-8x5in) st. num.191619 verso pencil
     gouache
£35000 $66850   (1-Jul-92 S175/R) Composition a motifs d'oiseaux (39x28cm-15x11in) studio
     st. gouache W/C over pencil

TAFURI, Raffaele (1857-1929) Italian
£16860 $29000   (17-Oct-91 SY.NY98/R) Il Giovane Cacciatore (96x70cm-38x28in) s.i.

TAG, Willy (1886-?) German
£1675 $3200   (16-Jul-92 SY.NY416/R) Horses and cart in landscape (48x67cm-19x26in) s.

TAGLIABUE, Carlo Costantino (1880-?) Italian
£998 $1857   (16-Jun-92 F.M7) Notturno a Santa Maria del Campo a Rapallo
     (110x100cm-43x39in) s.d.1927 i.d.verso (I.L 2200000)

TAHOMA, Quincy (1921-1956) American
£973 $1800   (14-Jun-92 S.BM161) Charge (48x38cm-19x15in) s.d.47 gouache
£1189 $2200   (14-Jun-92 S.BM190/R) Untitled (51x30cm-20x12in) s. gouache
£1366 $2500   (8-Feb-92 S.BM134/R) Hunter (46x56cm-18x22in) s. gouache

TAIBO, German (19/20th C) ?
£819 $1408   (16-Oct-91 FER.M124/R) Rio Mino (31x22cm-12x9in) s.i. W/C (S.P 150000)

TAILLANDIER, Yvon (1926-) French
£515 $881   (19-Mar-92 CSC.P67/R) Taillandier Lines (30x36cm-12x14in) mono. acrylic
     panel (F.FR 5000)
£541 $947   (5-Apr-92 R.P209/R) Voyage a Laval (51x65cm-20x26in) s. acrylic paper
     laid down on canvas (F.FR 5200)
£618 $1057   (18-Mar-92 LT.P134) Taillandier - Land (65x50cm-26x20in) s. acrylic paper
     (F.FR 6000)

TAILLANDIER, Yvon (1926-) French-cont.

£865	$1548	(17-Nov-91 R.P188/R) Grande centaurosse amelioree (92x65cm-36x26in) s.d.90 acrylic (F.FR 8500)
£1092	$1867	(21-Mar-92 AT.P49/R) Outre-couleur no.12 (130x162cm-51x64in) s.d.6 septembre 1987 acrylic (F.FR 10600)
£1854	$3170	(18-Mar-92 LT.P133/R) Admirateurs de l'unique automobilel d'Auricilia (202x200cm-80x79in) s.i. acrylic (F.FR 18000)

TAIT, Arthur Fitzwilliam (1819-1905) American

£1243	$2250	(21-May-92 GRO.B77/R) Good doggie (36x56cm-14x22in) s.i.d.94 s.i.d.verso
£3324	$6250	(18-Dec-91 SY.NY43/R) Spaniel and Canvas Back Duck (31x41cm-12x16in) s.d.92
£4000	$7000	(26-Sep-91 CH.NY40/R) Trespassers (56x36cm-22x14in) s.d.86 s.i.d.1886-87 verso
£4286	$7500	(28-Sep-91 YFA.M229/R) The twins (41x61cm-16x24in) s.d.1891 s.i.d.verso
£4455	$7975	(14-Nov-91 GRO.B78/R) Spring head - April (46x69cm-18x27in) s.i.d.93 s.i.d.1893 verso
£4598	$8000	(15-Apr-92 SY.NY35/R) Young quail (20x25cm-8x10in) s.d.1863 s.d.1863 num.233 verso board
£5000	$8500	(25-Oct-91 S.W2750/R) Quail chicks (20x25cm-8x10in) s.d.1866 s.i.d.1866 num.491 verso board
£5223	$9350	(14-Nov-91 GRO.B79/R) Motherly care (30x46cm-12x18in) s.i.d.1900 s.d.1900 verso
£5263	$9000	(21-Mar-92 W.W152/R) Chicks (25x36cm-10x14in) s.d.1865 s.i.d.1865 num.397 verso board
£7182	$13000	(4-Dec-91 D.NY37/R) Well retrieved (25x36cm-10x14in) s.d.1886
£8287	$15000	(6-Dec-91 CH.NY100/R) Chicks and Delft bowl (25x35cm-10x14in) s.i.d.90 panel
£9615	$17500	(28-May-92 CH.NY52/R) Maternal affection (23x32cm-9x13in) s.d.1859 board
£11494	$20000	(20-Sep-91 DM.D2014/R) Chickens feeding (64x74cm-25x29in) s.d.1870
£23204	$42000	(6-Dec-91 CH.NY93/R) Buck and doe (73x56cm-29x22in) s.d.1878
£120879	$220000	(28-May-92 CH.NY43/R) Flushed - ruffed grouse shooting (61x92cm-24x36!n) s.d.57
£302198	$550000	(28-May-92 CH.NY104/R) Trappers following the trail - at fault (91x127cm-36x50in) s.d.1851

TAIT, Arthur Fitzwilliam and HART, James MacDougal (19th C) American

£5198	$9200	(10-Nov-91 LIT.L84) Buck at Raquet Lake (36x56cm-14x22in) s. panel

TAIT, Bess Norris see NORRIS, Bessie

TAJAR, Ziona (1900-1988) Israeli

£1556	$2800	(6-Jan-92 GG.TA442/R) Safed, mountain vacation (50x65cm-20x26in) s. i.d.1965verso
£6667	$12000	(6-Jan-92 GG.TA441/R) Jerusalem, ascent to Mount Zion (38x55cm-15x22in) s. s.i.d.1927verso
£378	*$700*	*(8-Jun-92 GG.TA110/R) Landscape (35x50cm-14x20in) s. W/C*
£532	*$1000*	*(5-Jan-92 GG.TA400/R) Ha'ari Synagogue in Safed (53x40cm-21x16in) s. W/C gouache*
£957	*$1800*	*(5-Jan-92 GG.TA399/R) Bathers on the beach of Tel Aviv (48x36cm-19x14in) s.d.1934 W/C*

TAKASHIMA, Y (20th C) Japanese/American

£785	$1500	(3-Jul-92 S.W3894/R) Tabletop still life of peaches with porcelain plate (33x46cm-13x18in) s. s.i.verso board

TAKUSH, M (fl.1833-1837) British

£1000	*$1760*	*(9-Apr-92 S201/R) Portaits of Samuel and Elizabeth Takush (9x?cm-4x?in) min. s.i.d.1833 verso enamel ormolu frm two rec*

TAL COAT (1905-1985) French

£669	*$1210*	*(6-Dec-91 GL.P264) Autoportrait (48x31cm-19x12in) s. lead pencil (F.FR 6500)*

TAL COAT, Pierre (1905-1985) French

£1249	$2185	(5-Apr-92 ZZ.F197/R) Promenade a la campagne (38x56cm-15x22in) s. (F.FR 12000)
£1317	$2384	(20-May-92 I.N180/R) Promenade a la campagne (56x38cm-22x15in) s. (F.FR 13000)
£1575	$2741	(16-Apr-92 FB.P44/R) Nature morte (11x22cm-4x9in) s. d.1941verso panel (F.FR 15500)
£3064	$5363	(21-Feb-92 LC.P58/R) Nature morte (38x55cm-15x22in) s. (F.FR 30000)
£4230	$7190	(27-Oct-91 P.V1/R) Sans titre (33x41cm-13x16in) mono. (F.FR 42000)
£9774	$17690	(6-Dec-91 GL.P291/R) Violine (146x114cm-57x45in) s. (F.FR 95000)
£10062	$18111	(22-Nov-91 PIC.P51/R) En Bretagne a Doelan, la bolee de cidre (96x69cm-38x27in) (F.FR 98000)
£13581	$23360	(12-Oct-91 GL.P35 b/R) Horreurs de la guerre (95x127cm-37x50in) s. (F.FR 135000)
£15594	$26821	(12-Oct-91 GL.P29/R) Eclats noirs dans le rouge (113x146cm-44x57in) init. (F.FR 155000)
£17606	$30282	(12-Oct-91 GL.P27/R) Lumiere affleurante (97x130cm-38x51in) s. (F.FR 175000)
£557	*$1009*	*(21-May-92 CC.P8) Autoportrait (22x18cm-9x7in) s.d.1975 crayon dr (F.FR 5500)*

TAL COAT, Pierre (1905-1985) French-cont.
£659 $1192   (21-May-92 CC.P6/R) Autoportrait (39x25cm-15x10in) mono. crayon (F.FR 6500)
£667 $1201   (19-Nov-91 FB.P123/R) Sans titre (40x30cm-16x12in) s.d.48 ink wash (F.FR 6500)
£875 $1497   (22-Mar-92 I.N70/R) Sans titre (42x49cm-17x19in) s.d.1982 W/C (F.FR 8500)
£1228 $2186   (1-Dec-91 I.N89/R) Sans titre (52x66cm-20x26in) s. chl. (F.FR 12000)
£1543 $2793   (6-Dec-91 GL.P268) Sans titre (65x50cm-26x20in) init. ink wash (F.FR 15000)

TALBOYS, Agnes Augusta (fl.1920) British
£2300 $4140   (28-Jan-92 OT672/R) The last move (49x75cm-19x30in) s.

TALCOTT, Allen Butler (1867-1908) American
£2072 $3750   (22-May-92 S.BM129/R) The point - a landscape (61x76cm-24x30in) s.d.1902

TALKESSY, Valer (?) ?
£550 $995   (21-May-92 CSK160) Mixed flowers in painted vases (60x80cm-24x31in) s.

TALLANT, Richard H (1853-1934) American
£944 $1700   (22-Nov-91 E.EDM888/R) Northwest landscape (61x91cm-24x36in) s.d.89

TALLON, Desmond C (?) British
£900 $1728   (28-Jul-92 SWS149) The Classics (49x75cm-19x30in) s. board

TALLONE, Cesare (1853-1919) Italian
£1582 $2864   (18-May-92 SY.MI106) Studio di testa maschile (61x43cm-24x17in) s.d.1877 (I.L 3500000)

TALLONE, Guido (1894-1967) Italian
£2101 $3656   (14-Apr-92 F.M23/R) Vaso di fiori (90x75cm-35x30in) s. (I.L 4600000)
£2284 $3974   (14-Apr-92 F.M90/R) Paesaggio di Granvigna (50x60cm-20x24in) s.i.d.1950 (I.L 5000000)
£3017 $5671   (19-Dec-91 F.M131/R) Venezia, Rio della Croce (69x90cm-27x35in) s.d.1956 s.i.d.verso (I.L 6500000)

TALMAGE, Algernon (1871-1939) British
£500 $850   (22-Oct-91 SWS375) Harvest-time (46x61cm-18x24in) s.d.06
£1150 $2047   (23-Jan-92 CSK144) Bathing pool, Ilfracombe (53x66cm-21x26in) s.d.1902
£2000 $3400   (22-Oct-91 SWS400/R) Trafalgar Square (77x118cm-30x46in) s.d.07
£3800 $6574   (2-Oct-91 S57/R) Wounded horses returning from the front, France (77x109cm-30x43in) s.i.d.18
£5000 $9150   (15-May-92 TE421/R) Figures in square by night (61x76cm-24x30in)

TALON (?) ?
£1530 $2800   (3-Jun-92 D.NY92) Venetian views (46x64cm-18x25in) s. pair

TAMAGNI, Vincenzo (attrib) (1492-1530) Italian
£2800 $5376   (7-Jul-92 C7/R) Sheet of studies with nudes and figures on horseback (29x21cm-11x8in) pen

TAMAYO, Rufino (1899-1991) Mexican
£27624 $50000   (19-May-92 SY.NY64/R) Cabeza (30x25cm-12x10in) s.d.0-72 oil sand
£38889 $70000   (18-Nov-91 SY.NY51/R) Paisaje con luna (24x36cm-9x14in) s.d.0-47 canvas laid down on board
£41667 $75000   (19-Nov-91 CH.NY5/R) Esfera Flotante (35x51cm-14x20in) s.d.70 oil sand
£77348 $140000   (19-May-92 SY.NY21/R) Naturaleza muerta (49x49cm-19x19in) s.d.30
£138122 $250000   (19-May-92 SY.NY14/R) Bodegon (41x51cm-16x20in) s.d.28 s.i.verso
£154696 $280000   (19-May-92 SY.NY25/R) Nido de Pajaros (77x60cm-30x24in) s.d.0-45
£176796 $320000   (19-May-92 SY.NY57/R) La rubia del Antifaz (100x81cm-39x32in) s.d.0-78 oil sand
£188889 $340000   (18-Nov-91 SY.NY53/R) Personaje en rojo (130x97cm-51x38in) s.d.0-75 i.d.verso acrylic sand
£204420 $370000   (19-May-92 SY.NY48/R) Hombre con brazos cruzados (97x130cm-38x51in) s.d.0-78
£266667 $480000   (18-Nov-91 SY.NY34/R) Pareja (96x129cm-38x51in) s.d.68 oil sand
£361111 $650000   (19-Nov-91 CH.NY12/R) Atormentado (101x76cm-40x30in) s.d.48
£375000 $675000   (18-Nov-91 SY.NY27/R) Ritmo Obrero (75x101cm-30x40in) s.d.35
£486111 $875000   (18-Nov-91 SY.NY14/R) Retrato de Olga (121x86cm-48x34in) s.d.41
£2762 $5000   (19-May-92 SY.NY136/R) Caballo (15x23cm-6x9in) s. graphite pastel
£3333 $6000   (19-Nov-91 CH.NY121 a/R) Figura (33x25cm-13x10in) s.d.66 pencil crayon
£5278 $9500   (19-Nov-91 CH.NY194/R) Cabeza Pre-Colombina (33x26cm-13x10in) s.d.72 W/C pencil
£6077 $11000   (18-May-92 CH.NY162/R) Hombre (33x25cm-13x10in) s.d.67 pencil crayon sold with book
£8287 $15000   (19-May-92 SY.NY110/R) Mujeres (26x21cm-10x8in) s.d.31 gouache
£9444 $17000   (19-Nov-91 CH.NY121 b/R) Rostro (25x33cm-10x13in) s.d.67 pencil crayon
£10556 $19000   (19-Nov-91 CH.NY122/R) Bailarinas (39x28cm-15x11in) s. one d.39 gouache two
£11111 $20000   (18-Nov-91 SY.NY144/R) Personaje (30x25cm-12x10in) s.d.0-66 graphite col.pencil
£11602 $21000   (19-May-92 SY.NY131/R) Guerrero (36x46cm-14x18in) s.d.0-60 graphite pastel
£14365 $26000   (18-May-92 CH.NY1/R) Sandias (25x33cm-10x13in) s.d.68 crayon pencil
£16575 $30000   (18-May-92 CH.NY163/R) Mujer con Rebozo (30x22cm-12x9in) gouache

1790

TAMAYO, Rufino (1899-1991) Mexican-cont.
£17680	*$32000*	*(18-May-92 CH.NY87/R) Mujer con Baston (24x18cm-9x7in) s.d.42 gouache*
		pencil
£19444	*$35000*	*(18-Nov-91 SY.NY50/R) Cargador (43x35cm-17x14in) s.d.44 gouache*
£22222	*$40000*	*(18-Nov-91 SY.NY48/R) Mujer (23x15cm-9x6in) s. W/C*
£30387	*$55000*	*(19-May-92 SY.NY24/R) Banistas (63x47cm-25x19in) s. gouache paper mounted*
		on board

TAMBURI, Orfeo (1910-?) Italian
£1949	$3664	(19-Dec-91 F.M54) Case a Parigi (31x20cm-12x8in) s. (I.L 4200000)
£2043	$3636	(29-Apr-92 F.F176/R) Natura morta (45x55cm-18x22in) s.d.1935
		(I.L 4500000)
£2284	$3974	(14-Apr-92 F.M25/R) La saracinesca (66x82cm-26x32in) s.d.1963
		(I.L 5000000)
£3563	$6199	(14-Apr-92 F.M219/R) Rose appassite (45x40cm-18x16in) s.d.1941
		(I.L 7800000)
£4536	$8301	(12-May-92 F.R236/R) Paesaggio urbano (55x45cm-22x18in) s.d.1948
		(I.L 10000000)
£5337	$10034	(19-Dec-91 F.M179/R) Paesaggio mediterraneo (46x55cm-18x22in) s.d.1949
		s.verso (I.L 11500000)
£12066	$22685	(19-Dec-91 F.M143/R) La casa di Apollinaire (77x158cm-30x62in) s.d.1957
		(I.L 26000000)
£726	*$1293*	*(29-Apr-92 F.F34/R) Case (27x21cm-11x8in) s.d.1960 tempera mixed media*
		(I.L 1600000)
£772	*$1374*	*(29-Apr-92 F.F21) Giardino (23x32cm-9x13in) s.d.1953 W/C paper on canvas*
		(I.L 1700000)

TAMBURINI, Arnaldo (1843-?) Italian
£500	$855	(17-Mar-92 SWS1234) The Monk's cockerel (30x24cm-12x9in) s.i.
£1902	$3519	(8-Jun-92 CH.R548/R) Spadaccino e frate ubriaco (46x34cm-18x13in)
		s.d.1877 (I.L 4200000)
£2000	$3420	(18-Mar-92 S186/R) Tasting the cream. The Cellarer (30x24cm-12x9in) s.
		one i. pair
£3398	$6049	(29-Apr-92 D.V780/R) The bagpiper (37x24cm-15x9in) s.d.1879 (A.S 70000)

TAMBURINI, Giovanni Maria (?-1660) Italian
| £1100 | *$2002* | *(10-Dec-91 C144/R) The Port of Bologna (14x24cm-6x9in) i. red chk.ink* |

TAMM, Franz Werner (1658-1724) German
£24709	$42500	(10-Oct-91 SY.NY114/R) Still lifes (69x56cm-27x22in)
£31098	$55976	(19-Nov-91 F.R174/R) Vaso di fiori con rose. Vaso di fiori con boules de
		neige (50x65cm-20x26in) pair (I.L 67000000)
£32990	$57072	(26-Mar-92 PIC.P15/R) Bouquet de fleurs dans une urne devant un paysage
		(94x117cm-37x46in) (F.FR 320000)

TAMM, Franz Werner (circle) (1658-1724) German
£2584	$4728	(12-May-92 SY.AM138/R) White rabbit beside fruit (31x46cm-12x18in)
		(D.FL 8500)
£3916	$6931	(7-Nov-91 D.V360/R) Garlands of flowers (45x55cm-18x22in) pair
		(A.S 80000)

TAMM, Franz Werner (style) (1658-1724) German
| £4000 | $7280 | (11-Dec-91 S186/R) Still life of mixed fruit accompanied by pair doves |
| | | (48x64cm-19x25in) |

TAMM, Franz Werner and MARATTA, Carlo (attrib) (17th C) German/Italian
| £15897 | $27183 | (18-Mar-92 D.V60/R) Two women and putto decorating stone bust with |
| | | flowers in park (160x115cm-63x45in) (A.S 320000) |

TANA-KALEYA (?) ?
| £937 | $1639 | (5-Apr-92 R.P178) L'une et l'autre (120x80cm-47x31in) s. paper laid down |
| | | on canvas (F.FR 9000) |

TANABE, Takao (1926-) Canadian
| £550 | $1007 | (2-Jun-92 R.T575/R) Rock face (65x65cm-26x26in) s.d.60 i.stretcher |
| | | acrylic canvas (C.D 1200) |

TANAKA, Akira (?) ?
| £2472 | $4227 | (18-Mar-92 PIC.P97/R) Le couple assis (89x130cm-35x51in) s. (F.FR 24000) |

TANAKA, Yasushi (1886-?) Japanese
| £12648 | $22514 | (29-Nov-91 GAB.G2887) Nu au bord de l'eau (64x168cm-25x66in) s. |
| | | (S.FR 32000) |

TANCREDI (1927-1964) Italian
£8679	$15101	(14-Apr-92 F.M135/R) Composizione n.22 (70x100cm-28x39in) s.d.1952
		tempera canvasboard (I.L 19000000)
£17625	$30490	(28-Mar-92 F.L114/R) Polvere d'erba (90x115cm-35x45in) s.i.d.1957verso
		(S.FR 46000)
£19959	$36525	(12-May-92 F.R221/R) Composizione (91x123cm-36x48in) s.d.1954
		(I.L 44000000)
£20367	$37067	(25-May-92 CH.R79/R) Composizione astratta (90x115cm-35x45in) s.
		s.d.58verso (I.L 45000000)
£24969	$44444	(29-Apr-92 F.F289/R) Senza titolo (70x101cm-28x40in) d.1960
		(I.L 55000000)

TANCREDI (1927-1964) Italian-cont.

£33364	$59388	(26-Nov-91 SY.MI214/R) Composizione (137x176cm-54x69in) s.d.56 s.d.verso tempera (I.L 72000000)
£33930	$61413	(3-Dec-91 F.R255/R) Composizione (126x170cm-50x67in) s.d.1954verso faesite (I.L 73000000)
£2497	$4444	(29-Apr-92 F.F290/R) Senza titolo (31x21cm-12x8in) s. oil mixed media (I.L 5500000)
£4402	$7836	(26-Nov-91 SY.MI133/R) Matto Flaccido (38x30cm-15x12in) s.i.d.60 W/C pencil (I.L 9500000)
£4634	$8248	(26-Nov-91 SY.MI131/R) Facezie (41x33cm-16x13in) s.d.60 mixed media (I.L 10000000)
£6507	$11778	(3-Dec-91 F.R246/R) Composizione (68x98cm-27x39in) s.d.1952 mixed media cardboard (I.L 14000000)
£8751	$15926	(9-Dec-91 CH.R121/R) Composizione (70x100cm-28x39in) s. mixed media (I.L 19000000)
£9136	$15896	(14-Apr-92 F.M246/R) Senza titolo (68x50cm-27x20in) d.1960/1961 mixed media collage canvas (I.L 20000000)

TANGUY, Yves (1900-1955) French

£127119	$225000	(6-Nov-91 SY.NY40/R) Le Prodigue ne revient Jamais I (28x23cm-11x9in) s.d.43
£127119	$225000	(6-Nov-91 SY.NY43/R) Le Prodigue ne revient Jamais IV (28x23cm-11x9in) s.d.43
£127119	$225000	(6-Nov-91 SY.NY41/R) Le Prodigue ne revient Jamais II (28x23cm-11x9in) s.d.43
£127119	$225000	(6-Nov-91 SY.NY42/R) Le Prodigue ne revient Jamais III (28x23cm-11x9in) s.d.43
£140387	$251292	(13-Nov-91 CD.P14/R) Title unknown (50x71cm-20x28in) s.d.43 (F.FR 1380000)
£1366	$2500	(13-May-92 SY.NY215/R) Bacchanale (20x11cm-8x4in) s. gouache pencil W/C
£5979	$10344	(23-Mar-92 GL.P146 b/R) Composition surrealiste (20x16cm-8x6in) s.d.1926 i. W/C ink (F.FR 58000)

TANNER, Henry Ossawa (1859-1937) American

| £2762 | $5000 | (6-Dec-91 CH.NY145/R) Feeding sheep (26x41cm-10x16in) mono. |

TANNING, Dorothea (20th C) American

| £3107 | $5500 | (5-Nov-91 CE.NY226/R) Soeurs (61x29cm-24x11in) s. s.d.1953verso |
| £1433 | $2609 | (30-May-92 VG.B966/R) Paysage essouffle. Figure study (28x32cm-11x13in) s.d.1962 collage board gouache double-sided (DM 4200) |

TANOBE, Miyuki (20th C) Canadian

| £1122 | $2020 | (19-Nov-91 FP.M163) Pizzeria (40x51cm-16x20in) s. s.d.74 verso (C.D 2300) |
| £1010 | $1768 | (25-Sep-91 EA.M473) Demain c'est la St. Jean Baptiste (25x30cm-10x12in) s.d.1990 verso nihonga panel (C.D 2000) |

TANOUX, Adrien Henri (1865-1923) French

£1600	$2800	(18-Feb-92 CE.NY98/R) Tailor shop (100x74cm-39x29in) s.d.1889
£1966	$3500	(28-Apr-92 PO.BA18) Escena galante (256x335cm-101x132in) s.d.1889
£2527	$4549	(19-Nov-91 RAS.K49/R) Mother nursing baby (120x84cm-47x33in) s. (D.KR 28000)
£2708	$4630	(12-Mar-92 RAS.V997/R) Two seated women on railway station, one nursing a baby (120x84cm-47x33in) s. (D.KR 30000)
£2907	$5000	(15-Oct-91 CE.NY390) A picnic in the fields (100x73cm-39x29in) s.d.1909
£3226	$5710	(8-Nov-91 CN.P49/R) Portrait de jeune garcon (147x89cm-58x35in) s.d.1901 (F.FR 32000)

TANSEY, Mark (20th C) American

£7821	$14000	(6-May-92 CH.NY244/R) Untitled (44x54cm-17x21in) s.d.79 board after Rubens
£39106	$70000	(12-Nov-91 CH.NY66 a/R) Study for action painting II (102x147cm-40x58in)
£122905	$220000	(5-May-92 CH.NY65/R) The myth of depth (99x226cm-39x89in) s.i.d.1984verso

TANZIO DA VARALLO, Antonio d'Enrico (1575-1635) Italian

| £2235 | $4000 | (14-Jan-92 SY.NY57/R) Sheet of studies of lower half of standing draped figure (20x15cm-8x6in) red chk |

TAPIES, Antonio (1923-) Spanish

£8147	$15071	(13-Jun-92 AT.P10) Horizon (124x80cm-49x31in) s. acrylic paper (F.FR 80000)
£20471	$36438	(30-Nov-91 FB.P16/R) Cinq franges noires (73x50cm-29x20in) s.verso oil sable (F.FR 200000)
£20597	$35221	(17-Mar-92 FB.P58/R) Bleu et plastique (132x117cm-52x46in) s.verso card laid down on canvas (F.FR 200000)
£25567	$44231	(29-Mar-92 P.V40/R) Sinuos lateral (100x81cm-39x32in) s.verso (F.FR 248000)
£28000	$48440	(26-Mar-92 S37/R) Claredad (92x65cm-36x26in) s.verso oil sand canvas
£35000	$66850	(2-Jul-92 S44/R) Composition with brown matter (60x73cm-24x29in) s.d.1956verso oil sand
£35754	$64000	(6-May-92 CH.NY277/R) Figure 8 (46x39cm-18x15in) s.d.1963 verso oil sand canvas
£110000	$210100	(2-Jul-92 S48/R) Tres manchas sobre espacio gris (146x89cm-57x35in) s.d.1957verso oil sand
£2576	$4662	(21-May-92 SY.AM286/R) Mancha (32x45cm-13x18in) s. W/C pencil (D.FL 8500)

TAPIES, Antonio (1923-) Spanish-cont.

£2879	$5211	(21-May-92 SY.AM368/R) Untitled (22x18cm-9x7in) s. pastel crayon card on canvas (D.FL 9500)
£3939	$7130	(21-May-92 SY.AM225/R) Petite corde (55x33cm-22x13in) s.verso wax rope collage canvas (D.FL 13000)
£4424	$8316	(17-Dec-91 BRO.B338/R) Autoretrat i llunes (19x16cm-7x6in) ink (S.P 800000)
£6912	$12994	(17-Dec-91 BRO.B429/R) Dibuix (21x17cm-8x7in) ink (S.P 1250000)
£8046	$13920	(23-Mar-92 AB.L152/R) Jambe (61x43cm-24x17in) s. grease chk indian ink (S.FR 21000)
£8191	$14908	(25-May-92 WK.M1194/R) Composition (48x64cm-19x25in) s.d.1962 gouache chl (DM 24000)
£9677	$18192	(17-Dec-91 BRO.B361) Personatge (40x25cm-16x10in) s.d.1949 Indian ink (S.P 1750000)
£10000	$17300	(26-Mar-92 C62/R) The bread in the boat (54x38cm-21x15in) s. pencil wash ink col.crayon chl.
£11000	$18920	(17-Oct-91 C18/R) Collage de Pavel y Cordel (76x56cm-30x22in) s. collage rope card ink col.crayon
£13000	$23660	(29-May-92 C472/R) Forme accroupie (75x55cm-30x22in) s. oil composition
£13000	$22360	(17-Oct-91 S40/R) Senod con manchas negras I rosas (39x57cm-15x22in) s. wax crayon pencil ink
£16293	$30143	(13-Jun-92 AT.P9/R) Irregular (59x59cm-23x23in) s.verso mixed media panel (F.FR 160000)
£23368	$42763	(2-Jun-92 L.K977/R) Ochre et graphisme (52x66cm-20x26in) s. indian ink wash acrylic chk (DM 68000)
£32000	$55040	(17-Oct-91 C26/R) Sac colle sur toile (116x81cm-46x32in) s.verso oil paper bag composition oil canvas
£32000	$58240	(29-May-92 C464/R) Small ochre and black with diagonal (50x51cm-20x20in) s.d.1963verso oil composition canvas
£33520	$60000	(14-Nov-91 SY.NY299/R) Diagonal relief (56x47cm-22x19in) s.d.1962 verso mixed media canvas
£35000	$63700	(29-May-92 C469/R) Efecte de Cos en Relleu (195x232cm-77x91in) s.verso mixed media fabric on canvas
£38229	$65755	(8-Oct-91 CC.P35/R) Marro Fosc (50x61cm-20x24in) s.d.1961 verso mixed media canvas (F.FR 380000)
£40000	$76400	(2-Jul-92 C35/R) Square (81x99cm-32x39in) s.verso oil composition board
£50000	$90500	(5-Dec-91 C22/R) Platter collage (76x55cm-30x22in) s. oil composition plate canvas
£89385	$160000	(14-Nov-91 SY.NY301/R) M Blanc (199x139cm-78x55in) s.verso enamel acrylic cardboard on linen
£97236	$173081	(30-Nov-91 FB.P32/R) Diptyque (81x201cm-32x79in) mixed media panel (F.FR 950000)
£98000	$178360	(29-May-92 C468/R) Wood on earth (162x195cm-64x77in) s.i.verso sand pigment wood on board
£540000	$934200	(26-Mar-92 S56/R) White, string and triangle (130x195cm-51x77in) s.verso acrylic pencil string canvas

TAPIRO Y BARO, Jose (1830-1913) Spanish

£1538	$2800	(26-May-92 CE.NY239/R) Holding a tambourine (38x28cm-15x11in) s.i. W/C
£2000	$3840	(28-Jul-92 RG2481) Young woman washing clothes (36x25cm-14x10in) s.i. W/C
£2800	$4844	(4-Oct-91 C119/R) The herb seller (39x26cm-15x10in) s. W/C
£10286	$18000	(18-Feb-92 CE.NY203/R) Tangerian beauty (66x47cm-26x19in) s.i. W/C paperboard

TAPPERT, Georg (1880-1957) German

£3671	$6535	(30-Nov-91 VG.B1012/R) Munkmarsch, Sylt (40x50cm-16x20in) s.d.34 (DM 10500)
£80000	$144800	(2-Dec-91 C21/R) In der Garderobe (53x50cm-21x20in) s. i.d.1913verso
£420	$747	(30-Nov-91 VG.B101/R) Figures in street (22x20cm-9x8in) indian ink pen wash (DM 1200)
£423	$765	(4-Dec-91 DO.H3417/R) Female seated holding head (22x14cm-9x6in) s. indian ink over pencil (DM 1200)
£612	$1089	(25-Nov-91 WK.M987/R) Squatting female nude seen from behind (16x12cm-6x5in) s.d.1913 W/C indian ink pen (DM 1750)
£683	$1242	(30-May-92 VG.B971/R) Reclining female nude (14x32cm-6x13in) s. W/C pen (DM 2000)
£687	$1271	(12-Jun-92 HN.H800/R) Betty getting undressed (26x11cm-10x4in) s. indian ink pen wash (DM 2000)
£760	$1414	(19-Jun-92 G.Z34/R) Snake charming (33x25cm-13x10in) s.d.1929 W/C indian ink (S.FR 2000)
£1049	$1867	(30-Nov-91 VG.B1013/R) Betty standing (33x20cm-13x8in) W/C ink over pencil (DM 3000)

TAPPESER, Heinz (1888-1942) German?

£614	$1118	(27-May-92 PH.DU180) Southern landscape (100x119cm-39x47in) (DM 1800)

TAPPESER, Rainer (20th C) ?

£524	$934	(25-Nov-91 WK.M2065/R) Flecken aus der Reihe shina moji (130x195cm-51x77in) s.i.d.1981-82stretcher (DM 1500)

TARANCZEWSKI, Waclaw (1903-1987) Polish

£1806	$3234	(17-Nov-91 REM.W28) Still life in red (60x75cm-24x30in) s. (P.Z 35000000)
£523	$905	(8-Sep-91 REM.W40) Still life with pitcher (50x65cm-20x26in) s. pastel (P.Z 10000000)

TARAVAL, Guillaume (1701-1750) French
£1518 $2778   *(14-May-92 BU.S68/R) Baby Jesus carrying the cross and treading on a snake (45x33cm-18x13in) mono. panel (S.KR 16000)*

TARAVAL, Guillaume (circle) (1701-1750) French
£2941 $5382   *(14-May-92 BU.S69/R) Night - sleeping Putti and Cupid in landscape (70x86cm-28x34in) (S.KR 31000)*

TARAVAL, Guillaume (style) (1701-1750) French
£5203 $9418   *(19-May-92 AB.S4383/R) Afrodite on dolphin with Eros with shell (115x160cm-45x63in) (S.KR 55000)*

TARAVAL, Hugues (1729-1785) French
£2333 $4105   *(11-Apr-92 AT.P93/R) La mere comblee (16x21cm-6x8in) wood (F.FR 23000)*
£4144 $7500   *(21-May-92 CH.NY168/R) Portrait of boy, in waistcoat and jacket and hat (43x36cm-17x14in)*

TARBELL, Edmund C (1862-1938) American
£6433 $11000   *(18-Mar-92 GRO.B66/R) Portrait of William A. Gaston (112x91cm-44x36in) s.d.22*

TARBET, J A Henderson (?-1938) British
£700 $1267   *(4-Dec-91 S201/R) Loch Achray, Ben Venue (51x68cm-20x27in) s.*
£750 $1275   *(7-Aug-91 ZZ.B32) Edinburgh from the Links (39x50cm-15x20in) s. W/C*
£1800 $3204   *(28-Apr-92 S201/R) Edinburgh from the Golf Links (36x48cm-14x19in) s. W/C*

TARENGHI, Enrico (1848-?) Italian
£618 $1100   *(22-Jan-92 SY.NY514/R) Reading litany (78x53cm-31x21in) s. W/C*

TARKAY, Itzchak (1935-) Yugoslavian/Israeli
£3531 $6250   *(6-Nov-91 D.NY115/R) Autumn, ladies in cafe (68x80cm-27x31in) s.*

TARKHOFF, Nicolas (1871-1930) Russian
£5882 $10000   *(23-Oct-91 GD.B1299/R) Paysage l'ile de France (19x57cm-7x22in) s. board (S.FR 15000)*
£7843 $14039   *(15-Nov-91 GK.Z5259/R) Chrysanthemums in blue vase (41x33cm-16x13in) s. (S.FR 20000)*

TARR, James (1905-) British
£700 $1281   *(14-May-92 C177/R) Chess players (56x76cm-22x30in) s.i.stretcher*
£2000 $3660   *(5-Jun-92 C82/R) Rubbish and rhubarb (63x76cm-25x30in) s.i.verso*

TARRANT, Margaret W (1888-1959) British
£2800 $5348   *(13-Jul-92 PH125/R) Fairies midst the sweet peas (33x18cm-13x7in) s.d.1920 W/C htd white*

TASSAERT, Octave (1800-1874) French
£968 $1801   *(18-Jun-92 SY.MO497/R) Le denicheur d'oiseaux endormi. Le reve du Pacha (28x37cm-11x15in) pen wash chl double-sided (F.FR 9500)*

TASSAERT, Pierre (attrib) (?-1693) Flemish
£2035 $3500   *(9-Oct-92 CH.NY50/R) Portrait of lady, as shepherdess (83x65cm-33x26in) s.d.*

TASSEL, Jean (1608-1667) French
£3347 $5890   *(11-Apr-92 AT.P77/R) Tobie et l'Ange (65x81cm-26x32in) (F.FR 33000)*
£6179 $11617   *(18-Dec-91 AT.P168/R) Adam et Eve (100x81cm-39x32in) (F.FR 60000)*

TASSEL, Jean (circle) (1608-1667) French
£1100 $1925   *(25-Feb-92 PH67/R) Charity (51x33cm-20x13in) fragment*

TASSI, Agostino (attrib) (1565-1644) Italian
£1412 $2527   *(15-Nov-91 GK.Z5105) River landscape with fishermen and ruins beyond (62x91cm-24x36in) (S.FR 3600)*
£3636 $6545   *(19-Nov-91 GS.B3670) View of estuary in Meditarranean landscape with figures (61x188cm-24x74in) (S.FR 9200)*

TASSI, Agostino (circle) (1565-1644) Italian
£4200 $7476   *(1-Nov-91 C3/R) Mediterranean rocky coast with boats moored below Watchtower (56x110cm-22x43in) mono.*

TASSI, Agostino (style) (1565-1644) Italian
£1000 $1920   *(9-Jul-92 CSK263) Figures in ruinous coastal landscape (25x33cm-10x13in) panel*
£3700 $6660   *(22-Nov-91 SWS176/R) A shipwreck by the coast (91x131cm-36x52in)*

TATAFIORE, Ernesto (1943-) Italian
£526 $947   *(19-Nov-91 L.K1146) A Robespiere David (50x34cm-20x13in) s. chl pencil htd.white (DM 1500)*
£1073 $1856   *(23-Mar-92 AB.L166/R) Untitled (56x57cm-22x22in) s. pencil mixed media paper on fabriano (S.FR 2800)*
£1341 $2320   *(23-Mar-92 AB.L164/R) Les souvenirs (56x76cm-22x30in) s.i. gouache collage fabriano (S.FR 3500)*

1794

TATHAM, A J (20th C) British
£500 $950 (24-Jun-92 PHI505/R) Bowl of tiger lilies (52x70cm-20x28in) s.d.1923 W/C
£500 $950 (24-Jun-92 PHI506) Dogs resting before bowl of summer flowers (52x70cm-20x28in) s. W/C

TATLIN, Vladimir (1885-1953) Russian
£1456 $2519 (28-Mar-92 F.L60/R) Signora con cappello (46x29cm-18x11in) d.1940 pencil (S.FR 3800)
£4215 $7291 (28-Mar-92 F.L72/R) Progetto di costume di un comico del XVIII secolo (61x44cm-24x17in) d.1935 pencil W/C (S.FR 11000)

TATO (1896-1968) Italian
£594 $1033 (14-Apr-92 F.M1) Guglie del Brenta (18x23cm-7x9in) panel (I.L 1300000)
£865 $1548 (17-Nov-91 FB.P97) Nature morte a la tasse de cafe (20x27cm-8x11in) s. peinture a l'essence (F.FR 8500)
£1382 $2515 (9-Dec-91 CH.R94/R) Bosco (104x80cm-41x31in) s. (I.L 3000000)

TAUBE, Eugen (1860-1913) Finnish
£1802 $3279 (11-Dec-91 HOR.H115) Sailing in moonlight (29x39cm-11x15in) s.d.1893 (F.M 14000)
£2458 $4375 (1-Dec-91 HOR.H221) Waterfall (30x39cm-12x15in) s.d.1895 (F.M 19000)
£2717 $4836 (1-Dec-91 HOR.H225) Reflections (50x30cm-20x12in) s. (F.M 21000)
£2781 $4895 (12-Apr-92 HOR.H230/R) Moonlit seascape with boats (32x48cm-13x19in) s. (F.M 22000)
£3881 $6908 (1-Dec-91 HOR.H222) Boat on the beach (47x27cm-19x11in) s. (F.M 30000)

TAUBES, Frederick (1900-1981) American
£508 $900 (12-Feb-92 B.SF599/R) Boy in blue (127x91cm-50x36in) s.
£957 $1800 (18-Dec-91 SY.NY423/R) George Washington Bridge (50x61cm-20x24in) s.
£2527 $4750 (18-Dec-91 SY.NY246/R) Setting the table (88x127cm-35x50in) s.

TAUNAY, Nicolas Antoine (1755-1830) French
£1649 $2854 (27-Mar-92 CN.P36/R) Paysage au porteur d'eau (27x23cm-11x9in) i.verso (F.FR 16000)
£2840 $4998 (11-Apr-92 AT.P116/R) Paysage rocheux a la cascade (32x41cm-13x16in) (F.FR 28000)
£7202 $13035 (3-Dec-91 CN.P48/R) L'aurore - depart pour les champs. Le crepuscule - danse de paysans (24x32cm-9x13in) pair (F.FR 70000)
£30864 $55864 (7-Dec-91 CH.MO54/R) Le Charlatan (37x43cm-15x17in) s. panel (F.FR 300000)

TAUNAY, Nicolas Antoine (attrib) (1755-1830) French
£1221 $2185 (17-Nov-91 FB.P127) Le chemin (24x32cm-9x13in) panel (F.FR 12000)
£2672 $4596 (6-Mar-92 ARC.P30/R) Le tombeau de Jean-Jacques Rousseau a Ermenonville (37x48cm-15x19in) panel (F.FR 26000)
£5525 $10000 (21-May-92 CH.NY89/R) Tropical landscape with villagers seated by riverbank and unloading canoe (37x53cm-15x21in) panel

TAUNAY, Nicolas Antoine (circle) (1755-1830) French
£3800 $6764 (1-Nov-91 C61/R) Crowd watching acrobats perform in grounds of chateau (27x20cm-11x8in) i. panel
£4200 $7644 (11-Dec-91 S97/R) Italianate landscape with figures and animals on road (29x44cm-11x17in) bears sig.

TAUZIN, Louis (fl.1867-1914) French
£903 $1543 (12-Mar-92 RAS.V998/R) Young woman seated with goat by wheelbarrow of wild flowers (55x46cm-22x18in) s. (D.KR 10000)

TAVANNES, Henri de (circle) (17/18th C) French
£5534 $9850 (29-Nov-91 GAB.G3046/R) L'Apotheose d'Hercule (65x121cm-26x48in) (S.FR 14000)

TAVELLA, C A and MAGNASCO, A (school) (17/18th C) Italian
£2616 $4500 (9-Oct-91 CH.NY53/R) Monks parying in landscape (93x126cm-37x50in) canvas on board

TAVELLA, Carlo Antonio (1668-1738) Italian
£10929 $18689 (18-Mar-92 D.V53/R) Wooded river landscape with travellers resting (155x126cm-61x50in) (A.S 220000)
£800 $1456 (10-Dec-91 C157/R) The Penitent Magdalen in a landscape (36x27cm-14x11in) ink oval
£1788 $3200 (15-Jan-92 CH.NY35/R) Farmyard with peasants and animals (39x28cm-15x11in) black chk pen

TAVENRAAT, Johannes (1809-1881) Dutch
£699 $1210 (25-Mar-92 KM.K1463/R) Dutch landscape with figures on frozen river (14x18cm-6x7in) s. panel (DM 2000)

TAVERNIER, Andrea (1858-1932) Italian
£3021 $5166 (19-Mar-92 F.M43/R) Val Savaranche (33x23cm-13x9in) panel (I.L 6500000)
£6678 $12154 (10-Dec-91 F.R210/R) Bosco (29x37cm-11x15in) s. (I.L 14500000)

TAVERNIER, Armand (1899-1991) Belgian
£2168 $3817 (7-Apr-92 C.A233/R) Winter landscape in Rinse (40x30cm-16x12in) s. (B.FR 130000)

TAYE, de (?) ?
£1504 $2556   (22-Oct-91 GM.B627) Nu et Nenuphars s. mixed media canvas (B.FR 90000)

TAYLER, Albert Chevallier (1862-1925) British
£520 $993   (15-Jul-92 B107) Portrait of gentleman (90x69cm-35x27in) s.
£899 $1600   (22-Jan-92 SY.NY486/R) Portrait of Sir Edward James Poynter, P.R.A (51x41cm-20x16in) s.indist.d.
£18000 $32940   (5-Jun-92 C23/R) Sisters (106x169cm-42x67in) s.d.1905

TAYLER, David (20th C) British
£520 $894   (15-Oct-91 B128/R) Diamond Smugglers by Ian Fleming (37x28cm-15x11in) s. gouache

TAYLER, John Frederick (1802-1889) British
£450 $815   (19-May-92 SWS489) Sporting party (23x33cm-9x13in) init.d.1880 bears i.verso W/C pencil
£460 $819   (29-Nov-91 T197) Hunting scene (23x33cm-9x13in) s.init.d.1873 W/C
£650 $1190   (6-Feb-92 DLY311) Gone to ground (23x33cm-9x13in) init.d.1873 W/C
£1000 $1780   (28-Apr-92 S174/R) Bringing down the kye (48x73cm-19x29in) i.verso W/C

TAYLER, John Frederick (attrib) (1802-1889) British
£520 $894   (16-Oct-91 PHL41) Study of huntsman holding two horses, with hound at side (38x26cm-15x10in) pencil col.wash htd white

TAYLOR, Charles (19th C) British
£1000 $1720   (10-Oct-91 L286) Sailing barges under full sail in English Channel with shipping beyond (38x71cm-15x28in) s. W/C
£2500 $4425   (15-Feb-92 TA.B403) Marine scenes (38x76cm-15x30in) s. W/C pair

TAYLOR, Charles (jnr) (fl.1841-1883) British
£420 $756   (27-Jan-92 PH57) Dutch fishing boat in Channel (37x54cm-15x21in) W/C
£550 $968   (6-Apr-92 PH71) Shipping off the coast (25x72cm-10x28in) W/C htd white
£6100 $11285   (12-Jun-92 TE605/R) Yachts and paddle steamer off the coast. Yachts and steamship offcoastline (38x74cm-15x29in) s.W/C bodycol.pair

TAYLOR, Ernest Archibald (20th C) British
£650 $1164   (13-Nov-91 CG640) Cottages in a Galloway landscape (60x80cm-24x31in) s.

TAYLOR, Frederick Bourchier (1906-1987) Canadian
£1220 $2195   (19-Nov-91 FP.M162) Belmont Street, Montreal (61x76cm-24x30in) s.d.53 s.d.1953 verso (C.D 2500)

TAYLOR, Henry Fitch (1853-1925) American
£517 $900   (15-Sep-91 JRB.C99/R) Woman resting (18x20cm-7x8in) init.d.88 W/C

TAYLOR, Henry King (19th C) British
£1800 $3258   (20-May-92 S43/R) Shipping off French harbour (61x106cm-24x42in) s.

TAYLOR, J (19th C) British
£686 $1200   (1-Mar-92 LIT.L268) Marine scene (56x91cm-22x36in) s. board

TAYLOR, Leonard Campbell (1874-?) British
£650 $1242   (23-Jul-92 CSK177/R) Pitch Hill from Wykehurst Farm, Ewhurst (33x44cm-13x17in) s.i.d.1917verso
£4242 $7509   (22-Apr-92 CH.AM195/R) June roses (24x15cm-9x6in) s.i.d.23 panel (D.FL 14000)

TAYLOR, Maeve (20th C) Irish
£550 $1024   (17-Jun-92 A.D155) Snow on Broadmeadow (51x61cm-20x24in) s. (E.P 600)

TAYLOR, Stephen (attrib) (19th C) British
£700 $1225   (27-Feb-92 B183/R) Still life of a dead hare, pheasant, partridges and others in a landscape (75x91cm-30x36in) bears sig.

TAYLOR, Thomas (19th C) British?
£480 $816   (22-Oct-91 SWS40/R) View of Warwick Castle (36x46cm-14x18in) s.d.1802 W/C over pencil

TCHAOUSS, Viktor (1940-) Russian
£772 $1397   (6-Dec-91 ARC.P38) Nature morte au sammovar (100x81cm-39x32in) s. (F.FR 7500)

TCHEBAKOV, Nikita (1914-1968) Russian
£508 $884   (13-Apr-92 ARC.P188/R) Les achats (49x71cm-19x28in) s. board (F.FR 5000)
£1016 $1768   (13-Apr-92 ARC.P186/R) Le journal illustre (49x70cm-19x28in) s. (F.FR 10000)

TCHEKHLOV, Vladimir (1956-) Russian
£1019 $1896   (17-Jun-92 ARC.P156/R) Derniere neige (55x40cm-22x16in) s. (F.FR 10000)

TCHELITCHEV, Pavel (1898-1957) American/Russian
£4624 $8000   (6-Sep-91 S.BM302/R) Still life, fruit (71x58cm-28x23in) s.
£8939 $16000   (9-May-92 CE.NY145/R) Still life with pears (65x54cm-26x21in) s.
£11000 $19030   (25-Mar-92 S170/R) Portrait of a Spahi holding a fan (100x81cm-39x32in) s.d.1931

TCHELITCHEV, Pavel (1898-1957) American/Russian-cont.

£447	$800	(9-May-92 CE.NY53/R) Portrait of man (41x30cm-16x12in) s.d.35 pencil brush sepia ink paper on board
£450	$815	(2-Dec-91 CSK89/R) Les Jardins de Luxembourg, Paris (49x32cm-19x13in) st.sig.i.verso gouache
£595	$1100	(12-Jun-92 SY.NY94/R) Study for hide and seek (29x20cm-11x8in) s.d.38 pen
£600	$1086	(2-Dec-91 CSK86/R) Tete de clown (27x21cm-11x8in) st.sig.verso wash
£629	$1100	(28-Feb-92 SY.NY96/R) White ship (32x49cm-13x19in) s.d.1925 verso gouache
£750	$1358	(2-Dec-91 CSK87/R) L'acrobat (17x10cm-7x4in) st.sig.i.verso wash
£757	$1400	(12-Jun-92 SY.NY105/R) Standing male nudes (35x27cm-14x11in) W/C pair
£782	$1400	(9-May-92 CE.NY184/R) Autumn leaves (27x21cm-11x8in) s.d.39 pen col.ink gouache ink wash
£900	$1647	(4-Jun-92 CSK38) Portrait of Boris Kochno (44x28cm-17x11in) st.sig.verso num.168 brush ink
£971	$1700	(28-Feb-92 SY.NY66/R) Dames corps de ballet - costume design for concerto i. gouache fabric two sheets
£1017	$1750	(12-Oct-91 SY.NY68/R) Le prince - costume design for concerto (36x19cm-14x7in) i. gouache pencil
£1017	$1750	(12-Oct-91 SY.NY67/R) Femmes corps de ballet - costume design for concerto (29x37cm-11x15in) i. gouache pencil paper fabric swatch attached
£1081	$2000	(12-Jun-92 SY.NY95/R) Leaf children (21x27cm-8x11in) pen brush India ink
£1130	$2000	(7-Nov-91 SY.NY4/R) Three figures (27x21cm-11x8in) s.d.31 India ink ink wash
£1163	$2000	(12-Oct-91 SY.NY69/R) La Reine - costume design for concerto (36x28cm-14x11in) i. gouache pencil indian ink
£1163	$2000	(12-Oct-91 SY.NY70/R) L'ami de Prince - costume design for concerto (36x20cm-14x8in) i. gouache pencil paper fabric swatches attach
£1337	$2300	(12-Oct-91 SY.NY73/R) Figure studies (25x35cm-10x14in) one s. one init. ink wash pair
£1412	$2500	(7-Nov-91 SY.NY8/R) Space composition (35x25cm-14x10in) s.d.XII/52 pastel
£1514	$2800	(12-Jun-92 SY.NY97/R) Skull (27x21cm-11x8in) s.indis.d. pen India ink wash
£1571	$2750	(28-Feb-92 SY.NY70) Un dame blonde - costume design for Concerto i. gouache two sheets
£1695	$3000	(7-Nov-91 SY.NY3/R) Circus performers (26x21cm-10x8in) s.d.32 ink wash
£1800	$3348	(16-Jun-92 S91/R) Costume design for dancer (33x22cm-13x9in) s. W/C pencil htd.gouache
£1857	$3250	(28-Feb-92 SY.NY15/R) Study of male nude (56x44cm-22x17in) st.sig.verso pencil crayon tissue
£1857	$3250	(28-Feb-92 SY.NY68/R) Terpischore - costume design for Apollon Musagete i. pen gouache two sheets
£1977	$3400	(12-Oct-91 SY.NY74/R) Head and figure studies (35x25cm-14x10in) one s.d.1950 num.II one s.d.37 chk ink pair
£1977	$3400	(12-Oct-91 SY.NY75/R) Figure studies and study of hands with apples (28x22cm-11x9in) one s.indist.i.d.1946 indian ink wash ink pair
£2471	$4250	(12-Oct-91 SY.NY76/R) Seated Moorish boy with fan (64x49cm-25x19in) st.sig.verso gouache
£2800	$5348	(29-Jun-92 CSK72/R) Costume design - archer (40x33cm-16x13in) i.d.22 W/C bodycol htd gold paint collage card
£3143	$5500	(28-Feb-92 SY.NY69/R) Polyhymnia, Calliope and Apollo - costume designs for Apollon Masagete i. pen gouache fabric two sheets
£3143	$5500	(28-Feb-92 SY.NY67) Hommes corps de ballet - costume design for Concerto i. gouache fabric two sheets
£3198	$5500	(12-Oct-91 SY.NY77/R) Study of man. Leaf children (28x22cm-11x9in) one s.d.31 one s.d.39 Indian ink wash pair
£3488	$6000	(12-Oct-91 SY.NY78/R) Robert (21x27cm-8x11in) st.sig.verso gouache board
£3514	$6500	(12-Jun-92 SY.NY104/R) Male nude torso (55x48cm-22x19in) s.d.1929 verso gouache
£4000	$7000	(28-Feb-92 SY.NY14/R) Study for one who fell (65x50cm-26x20in) s.verso gouache
£5000	$8650	(25-Mar-92 S169/R) Portrait de Robert Cluzan (65x50cm-26x20in) st.sig.verso pastel
£5500	$9460	(16-Oct-91 S57/R) Portrait. Nude (33x24cm-13x9in) s. pen ink W/C gouache double-sided

TCHERNORITSKY, Valery (1961-) Russian

£510	$948	(17-Jun-92 ARC.P5/R) Les poupees (65x46cm-26x18in) s. (F.FR 5000)
£535	$968	(6-Dec-91 ARC.P2/R) La femme au chale (49x65cm-19x26in) s. (F.FR 5200)
£561	$1043	(17-Jun-92 ARC.P1/R) Pres de l'entree (65x50cm-26x20in) s. (F.FR 5500)
£617	$1117	(6-Dec-91 ARC.P8/R) La conversation (54x65cm-21x26in) s. (F.FR 6000)
£709	$1284	(20-May-92 ARC.P5/R) Bouquet jaune et rouge (80x40cm-31x16in) s. (F.FR 7000)
£714	$1327	(17-Jun-92 ARC.P2/R) Sur le canape (60x73cm-24x29in) s. (F.FR 7000)
£720	$1303	(6-Dec-91 ARC.P9 a/R) A la datcha (65x54cm-26x21in) s. (F.FR 7000)
£762	$1326	(13-Apr-92 ARC.P134/R) Dans l'atelier du peintre (73x50cm-29x20in) s. (F.FR 7500)
£823	$1490	(6-Dec-91 ARC.P9/R) Avant le dejeuner (60x60cm-24x24in) s. (F.FR 8000)
£874	$1583	(6-Dec-91 ARC.P5) Au salon (80x65cm-31x26in) s. (F.FR 8500)
£912	$1650	(20-May-92 ARC.P6/R) Chrysanthemes et jonquilles (80x40cm-31x16in) s. (F.FR 9000)
£921	$1640	(25-Nov-91 ARC.P133/R) Le modele prefere (73x60cm-29x24in) s. (F.FR 9000)
£965	$1680	(13-Apr-92 ARC.P132/R) Sur les Grands Boulevards (90x39cm-35x15in) s. (F.FR 9500)
£965	$1680	(13-Apr-92 ARC.P133/R) Lumieres de Paris (90x39cm-35x15in) s. (F.FR 9500)

TCHERNORITSKY, Valery (1961-) Russian-cont.

£977	$1769	(6-Dec-91 ARC.P1/R) Au parc (55x46cm-22x18in) s. (F.FR 9500)
£1008	$1825	(6-Dec-91 ARC.P10/R) Dans le jardin du Luxembourg (45x55cm-18x22in) s. (F.FR 9800)
£1013	$1834	(20-May-92 ARC.P4/R) Le cafe du matin (55x46cm-22x18in) s. (F.FR 10000)
£1070	$1991	(17-Jun-92 ARC.P4/R) Nu au miroir (81x65cm-32x26in) s. (F.FR 10500)
£1132	$2048	(6-Dec-91 ARC.P6/R) Les rideaux bleus (61x46cm-24x18in) s. (F.FR 11000)
£1270	$2210	(13-Apr-92 ARC.P129/R) Au salon (100x73cm-39x29in) s. (F.FR 12500)
£1286	$2328	(6-Dec-91 ARC.P4/R) Lumiere du matin (60x72cm-24x28in) s. (F.FR 12500)
£1474	$2564	(13-Apr-92 ARC.P135/R) La violoniste (73x54cm-29x21in) s. (F.FR 14500)
£1474	$2564	(13-Apr-92 ARC.P128/R) En attendant (46x38cm-18x15in) s. (F.FR 14500)
£1520	$2751	(20-May-92 ARC.P1/R) La fenetre bleue (91x73cm-36x29in) s. (F.FR 15000)
£1778	$3095	(13-Apr-92 ARC.P131/R) Odalisque (100x38cm-39x15in) s. (F.FR 17500)
£1824	$3301	(20-May-92 ARC.P3/R) La seductrice (55x46cm-22x18in) s. (F.FR 18000)
£2033	$3537	(13-Apr-92 ARC.P130/R) Nu assis (100x40cm-39x16in) s. (F.FR 20000)
£2243	$4171	(17-Jun-92 ARC.P3/R) Lumiere du soir (100x73cm-39x29in) s. (F.FR 22000)
£2837	$5135	(20-May-92 ARC.P2/R) Jeune femme au chapeu noir (81x60cm-32x24in) s. (F.FR 28000)
£3252	$5659	(13-Apr-92 ARC.P136/R) Les tulipes (50x81cm-20x32in) s. (F.FR 32000)

TCHERNYCHEV, Mikhail (1908-) Russian

£554	$970	(24-Sep-91 ARC.P114/R) Nature morte sur le buffet (79x100cm-31x39in) s. verso (F.FR 5500)

TCHOUIKOV, Yevgeni (1924-) Russian

£536	$917	(13-Mar-92 ARC.P191/R) Les jeunes pecheurs (33x57cm-13x22in) s. (F.FR 5200)

TCHOUKOV, Nikolai (1923-) Russian

£520	$911	(5-Apr-92 ARC.P114/R) La riviere Snov (40x59cm-16x23in) s. (F.FR 5000)
£655	$1147	(24-Sep-91 ARC.P25/R) Sur le banc (85x96cm-33x38in) s. (F.FR 6500)
£655	$1147	(24-Sep-91 ARC.P23/R) Devant la barriere (59x80cm-23x31in) s. (F.FR 6500)
£706	$1235	(24-Sep-91 ARC.P21/R) La petite Tania (64x49cm-25x19in) s. (F.FR 7000)
£1109	$1941	(24-Sep-91 ARC.P24/R) Sur le bord de la fenetre (76x54cm-30x21in) s. (F.FR 11000)
£2621	$4587	(24-Sep-91 ARC.P25 b/R) Chez Grand-pere (110x140cm-43x55in) s. (F.FR 26000)

TCHOUMAKOFF, Theodore (1823-1911) Russian

£1353	$2367	(5-Apr-92 ZZ.F30/R) Portrait de jeune fille (36x27cm-14x11in) s. panel (F.FR 13000)

TCHOUPRINA, Nikolai (1928-) Russian

£768	$1366	(25-Nov-91 ARC.P1/R) Bouquet d'automne (70x100cm-28x39in) s. (F.FR 7500)
£768	$1366	(25-Nov-91 ARC.P3) Au bord de la mer (32x70cm-13x28in) s. board (F.FR 7500)
£839	$1494	(25-Nov-91 ARC.P4/R) Jour de canicule (60x43cm-24x17in) s. (F.FR 8200)
£1029	$1862	(6-Dec-91 ARC.P143/R) Les bouquets composes (66x87cm-26x34in) s. (F.FR 10000)

TCHUBANOV, Boris (1946-) Russian

£1126	$2004	(25-Nov-91 ARC.P33/R) En plein air (70x49cm-28x19in) s. (F.FR 11000)
£1223	$2275	(17-Jun-92 ARC.P108/R) Roman d'amour (73x54cm-29x21in) s. (F.FR 12000)
£1321	$2299	(13-Apr-92 ARC.P174) La favorite des enfants (46x38cm-18x15in) s. (F.FR 13000)
£1484	$2642	(25-Nov-91 ARC.P36) Les jeux sur le sable (55x46cm-22x18in) s. (F.FR 14500)
£1595	$2886	(6-Dec-91 ARC.P173/R) Le miroir ovale (59x60cm-23x24in) s. (F.FR 15500)
£1638	$2915	(25-Nov-91 ARC.P35/R) Le soir sur le quai (78x50cm-31x20in) s. (F.FR 16000)
£1791	$3188	(25-Nov-91 ARC.P31/R) Le nouveau cadeau (64x50cm-25x20in) s. (F.FR 17500)
£1824	$3301	(20-May-92 ARC.P125) Sur le pont (55x46cm-22x18in) s. (F.FR 18000)
£1824	$3301	(20-May-92 ARC.P129/R) Au jardin (60x73cm-24x29in) s. (F.FR 18000)
£1829	$3183	(13-Apr-92 ARC.P172/R) Les petits voiliers (46x38cm-18x15in) s. (F.FR 18000)
£1880	$3271	(13-Apr-92 ARC.P175/R) Promenade du dimanche (73x60cm-29x24in) s. (F.FR 18500)
£1955	$3538	(6-Dec-91 ARC.P174/R) Dans le chambre de maman (54x64cm-21x25in) s. (F.FR 19000)
£2027	$3668	(6-Dec-91 ARC.P172/R) Intimite (55x38cm-22x15in) s. (F.FR 19700)
£2263	$4097	(6-Dec-91 ARC.P175/R) La partie de croquet (65x54cm-26x21in) s. (F.FR 22000)
£2263	$4097	(6-Dec-91 ARC.P171/R) La femme en blanc (65x46cm-26x18in) s. (F.FR 22000)
£2456	$4373	(25-Nov-91 ARC.P30/R) La jeune letrice (61x46cm-24x18in) s. (F.FR 24000)
£2533	$4585	(20-May-92 ARC.P127) Pendant les vacances (55x46cm-22x18in) s. (F.FR 25000)
£2559	$4555	(25-Nov-91 ARC.P32/R) La jeune pianiste (55x46cm-22x18in) s. (F.FR 25000)
£2610	$4646	(25-Nov-91 ARC.P34/R) Dans le jardin du Luxembourg (49x61cm-19x24in) s. (F.FR 25500)
£2984	$5400	(6-Dec-91 ARC.P168) Premier jour de vacances (46x38cm-18x15in) s. (F.FR 29000)
£3040	$5502	(20-May-92 ARC.P126/R) Les jeunes estivantes (81x65cm-32x26in) s. (F.FR 30000)
£3058	$5688	(17-Jun-92 ARC.P106/R) Avant l'escale (73x91cm-29x36in) s. (F.FR 30000)

TCHUBANOV, Boris (1946-) Russian-cont.
£3086 $5586   (6-Dec-91 ARC.P167/R) Le matin au bord de la mer (73x60cm-29x24in) s.
                  (F.FR 30000)
£3201 $5570   (13-Apr-92 ARC.P173/R) Le matin dans la veranda (81x60cm-32x24in) s.
                  (F.FR 31500)
£3242 $5868   (20-May-92 ARC.P130/R) Sur la jetee (60x73cm-24x29in) s. (F.FR 32000)
£3303 $5747   (13-Apr-92 ARC.P170/R) Le soir a la campagne (66x80cm-26x31in) s.
                  (F.FR 32500)
£3343 $6052   (20-May-92 ARC.P131/R) Promenade en gondole (100x81cm-39x32in) s.
                  (F.FR 33000)
£3498 $6331   (6-Dec-91 ARC.P169/R) Deux soeurs (81x65cm-32x26in) s. (F.FR 34000)
£4255 $7702   (20-May-92 ARC.P128/R) La conversation (81x60cm-32x24in) s. (F.FR 42000)
£5081 $8841   (13-Apr-92 ARC.P171/R) Dans le jardin des Tuileries (54x65cm-21x26in) s.
                  (F.FR 50000)
£5268 $9536   (20-May-92 ARC.P124/R) En croisiere (92x73cm-36x29in) s. (F.FR 52000)

TCVETKOV, Viktor (1920-) Russian
£907 $1588   (24-Sep-91 ARC.P203/R) L'Hermitage (130x130cm-51x51in) s. (F.FR 9000)
£1019 $1896   (17-Jun-92 ARC.P94/R) Le jeune berger (58x67cm-23x26in) s. (F.FR 10000)
£1937 $3602   (17-Jun-92 ARC.P96/R) Le chef d'orchestre (124x100cm-49x39in) s.
                  (F.FR 19000)

TCVETKOVA, Valentina (1917-) Russian
£1586 $2824   (25-Nov-91 ARC.P180/R) Au bord de la mer (70x100cm-28x39in) s.
                  (F.FR 15500)

TEBBITT, Henri (1852-1926) Australian
£441 $784   (26-Nov-91 J.M464) Across bridge (70x98cm-28x39in) s. W/C (A.D 1000)

TEDESCHI, Pietro (1750-1805) Italian
£1461 $2600   (22-Jan-92 SY.NY84/R) Visitation (65x50cm-26x20in) s.d.1787 verso copper

TEED, Douglas Arthur (1864-1929) American
£862 $1500   (20-Sep-91 DM.D149/R) Wooded landscape (51x76cm-20x30in) s.d.1920
£872 $1500   (18-Oct-91 DM.D2246/R) Dutch village (28x43cm-11x17in) s.d.1919
£1412 $2500   (5-Nov-91 BG.M761/R) Courtyard scene with fountain, pillars and pottery
                  (102x84cm-40x33in) s.d.1925
£1676 $3000   (15-Nov-91 DM.D2012/R) Market scene with merchants in courtyard and woman
                  presenting tray (66x91cm-26x36in) s.d.26
£1754 $3000   (13-Mar-92 DM.D1006/R) Galleon (56x46cm-22x18in) s.d.1924
£1836 $3250   (14-Feb-92 DM.D2007/R) Market scene (51x61cm-20x24in)
£1977 $3500   (5-Nov-91 DM.M760/R) Village scene with flower market (102x84cm-40x33in)
                  s.d.1924-5
£2047 $3500   (13-Mar-92 DM.D2014/R) Mosque and market scene (61x97cm-24x38in) s.d.1920
£2339 $4000   (13-Mar-92 DM.D2016/R) Pewabic pottery vases (58x89cm-23x35in) s.
£10526 $18000   (13-Mar-92 DM.D2015/R) Nude dancer (142x112cm-56x44in) s.d.1927

TEERLINK, Abraham (attrib) (1776-1857) Dutch
£608 $1058   (17-Sep-91 CH.AM368) Italianate mountainous landscape with cowherd
                  resting and cattle in meadow (35x47cm-14x19in) s.i.d.1823 (D.FL 2000)

TEGNER, Christian Martin (1803-1881) Danish
£794 $1413   (28-Apr-92 RAS.K180) Chalet near Bakhammer mountain (46x57cm-18x22in) s.
                  i.d.1838verso (D.KR 9000)

TEGTMEIER, Wilhelm (1895-1968) German
£1767 $3092   (3-Apr-92 BM.B564/R) Pygmalion (74x88cm-29x35in) s.i.d.1950 panel
                  (DM 5000)

TEIBLER, Georg (1854-1911) Austrian
£1246 $2231   (16-Jan-92 D.V41) Rheintochter mit dem Schatz der Nibelungen
                  (42x53cm-17x21in) s.d.1904 panel (A.S 25000)

TEICHER, Louis (20th C) ?
£832 $1597   (6-Jul-92 HC.P63/R) Cafe dans les souks de Jerusalem (38x46cm-15x18in) s.
                  (F.FR 8000)

TEIXIDOR, Modest (?) Spanish
£520 $946   (11-Dec-91 FER.M112/R) La noche de un boulevard parisino (18x32cm-7x13in)
                  s. panel (S.P 95000)

TEJEO, Rafael (1798-1856) Spanish
£1800 $3438   (2-Jul-92 D132/R) The Good Samaritan (89x86cm-35x34in) s.
£9421 $16487   (20-Feb-92 EP.M17/R) Retrato de una nina sentada en un jardin
                  (80x119cm-31x47in) s.d.1842 (S.P 1700000)
£41752 $77240   (12-Jun-92 ARC.P66/R) Le combat des Centaures et des Lapithes
                  (88x119cm-35x47in) s. (F.FR 410000)

TELARIK, A (?) ?
£1247 $2182   (19-Feb-92 DUR.M765/R) Leyendo la carta (52x41cm-20x16in) s. (S.P 225000)

TELBIN, William (snr) (1815-1873) British
£1300 $2483   (29-Jun-92 PHB156/R) Eastern landscape (45x70cm-18x28in) W/C bodycol

TELEMAQUE, Herve (1937-) Haitian

£1751	$2994	(19-Mar-92 CSC.P69/R) Crochet (42x33cm-17x13in) s.i.d.1977verso acrylic (F.FR 17000)
£2000	$3460	(26-Mar-92 C23) Contamination verte (60x60cm-24x24in) s.i.d.1970verso
£3601	$6842	(26-Jun-92 FB.P86/R) Le large, avec trou (100cm-39ins circular) mono. s.i.d.1976verso acrylic (F.FR 35000)
£4630	$8796	(26-Jun-92 FB.P63/R) Le rouleau, avec Cornette (99cm-39ins circular) s.d.1974verso acrylic (F.FR 45000)
£4928	$8871	(19-Nov-91 FB.P227/R) Voute (99cm-39ins circular) s.i.d.1974verso acrylic (F.FR 48000)
£7202	$13035	(5-Dec-91 BG.P79/R) Il se demande si les gens (97x130cm-38x51in) s.i.d.1968verso (F.FR 70000)
£10235	$18219	(30-Nov-91 FB.P80/R) Vacancies (175x200cm-69x79in) s.d.1975verso (F.FR 100000)
£1237	*$2140*	*(23-Mar-92 CC.P29) Sans titre (103x68cm-41x27in) s. gouache felt (F.FR 12000)*

TELFER, William Walker (1907-) British

£850	$1539	(4-Dec-91 S253/R) Still life of bottle, fruit and pot plant (33x25cm-13x10in) s. board

TELIGA, Stanley Frederick de (1924-) Australian

£605	$1125	(21-Jun-92 SY.ME12/R) Under way, lake Burley Griffin (134x94cm-53x37in) s.d.1979 s.i.d.verso acrylic nylon canvas (A.D 1500)
£711	$1216	(17-Mar-92 JRL.S251) Bulk ore carrier (181x140cm-71x55in) s.d.82 (A.D 1600)

TELKESSY, Valeria (1870-?) Hungarian

£565	$999	(4-Nov-91 SY.J233/R) Still life with flowers (58x78cm-23x31in) s. (SA.R 2800)
£850	$1471	(3-Oct-91 CSK143) A lady in a summer garden (64x79cm-25x31in) s.

TELLA, Jose Garcia (1905-1983) Spanish

£801	$1441	(19-Nov-91 FB.P124/R) Chateau avec soleil rouge (54x73cm-21x29in) s.d.65 panel (F.FR 7800)

TELLAECHE, Julian de (20th C) Spanish

£15280	$26281	(16-Oct-91 FER.M266/R) El grumete de rojo (71x84cm-28x33in) s. (S.P 2800000)

TELLES, Sergio (20th C) French?

£1008	$1784	(10-Nov-91 ZZ.F263/R) Paris, rue Animee (21x30cm-8x12in) s. panel (F.FR 10000)

TEMPEL, Abraham van den (attrib) (1622-1672) Dutch

£4297	$7605	(5-Nov-91 GF.L2375/R) Portrait of Henriette Maria of France (118x89cm-46x35in) (S.FR 11000)

TEMPESTA, Antonio (1555-1630) Italian

£850	$1479	(13-Apr-92 S6/R) St. James the Great. St. Thomas (20x11cm-8x4in) bear mono. num.132 133 pen wash over chk pair
£1900	$3648	(8-Jul-92 PH215/R) Marcus Curtius leaping into abyss (27x22cm-11x9in) i. pen wash over black chk
£5000	$8700	(14-Apr-92 C96/R) Battle scene (36x52cm-14x20in) chk pen wash htd.white

TEMPESTA, Antonio (after) (1555-1630) Italian

£7463	$13284	(25-Nov-91 W.T2030/R) Israelites scattering men. Joseph telling his dreams. Destruction of Pharaoh's horses (42x54cm-17x21in) set of three marble panels (C.D 15000)

TEMPESTA, Antonio (circle) (1555-1630) Italian

£785	$1500	(16-Jul-92 SY.NY24 a/R) Wild boar hunt (26x33cm-10x13in) init. pen India ink

TEMPESTA, Antonio (style) (1555-1630) Italian

£25000	$43750	(1-Apr-92 S99/R) Turks hunting lions. Moors hunting leopards (97x133cm-38x52in) pair

TEMPESTA, Pieter Mullier see MULIER, Pieter (younger)

TEMPLE, Hans (1857-1931) Austrian

£728	$1296	(29-Apr-92 D.V896/R) Soldiers receiving pay (27x21cm-11x8in) s. panel (A.S 15000)
£825	$1469	(29-Apr-92 D.V832) Portrait of gentleman (24cm-9ins circular) s.d.902 board (A.S 17000)
£989	$1730	(20-Feb-92 D.V449/R) Portrait of lady (121x99cm-48x39in) s.d.909 (A.S 20000)

TEMPLE, Richard (19th C) British

£10500	$17850	*(23-Oct-91 S199/R) Temple of Olympian Zeus and Acropolis. Athens from Mount Anchesmus (23x38cm-9x15in) s.d.1816 pen W/C over pencil pair*

TEMPLIN, Bernhard (1894-1971) German

£1365	$2485	(27-May-92 PH.DU70/R) Still life of flowers, fruit and wine glass (60x70cm-24x28in) s. (DM 4000)

TEN BERGE, Bernardus Gerardus (1825-1875) Dutch
£1667 $2950   (22-Apr-92 CH.AM110/R) Wooded landscape with a peasant conversing with an artist (78x110cm-31x43in) s.d.1860 (D.FL 5500)

TEN CATE (19/20th C) Dutch
£613 $1123   (5-Feb-92 FB.P233) Peniche a quai (46x37cm-18x15in) s.d.85 pastel chl. (F.FR 6000)

TEN CATE, Hendrik Gerrit (1803-1856) Dutch
£3416 $6081   (26-Nov-91 VN.R23/R) Sailing ships in a harbour (25x31cm-10x12in) s.d.1841 panel (D.FL 11000)
£5810 $10110   (14-Apr-92 SY.AM252/R) Landscape with figures on frozen river (28x36cm-11x14in) s.d.1839 panel (D.FL 19000)

TEN CATE, Johannes (1859-1896) Dutch
£1064 $1926   (20-May-92 I.N181) Paysage de neige (27x41cm-11x16in) s. pastel canvas (F.FR 10500)
£2141 $3725   (14-Apr-92 SY.AM99/R) Two women working in fields (45x38cm-18x15in) s. (D.FL 7000)
£765 $1361   (30-Oct-91 CH.AM367/R) Farewell to father (36x26cm-14x10in) s. pencil W/C htd.white (D.FL 2500)

TEN CATE, Siebe Johannes (1858-1908) Dutch
£1083 $1852   (12-Mar-92 RAS.V930/R) View from Dordrecht (38x47cm-15x19in) s.d.1902 (D.KR 12000)
£997 $1824   (13-May-92 LC.P22) L'entree du port du Havre (30x38cm-12x15in) s. pastel gouache (F.FR 9800)
£1078 $1940   (22-Nov-91 PIC.P15) Overschee (33x25cm-13x10in) s.d.1905 pastel (F.FR 10500)

TEN COMPE, Jan (1713-1761) Dutch
£18023 $31000   (10-Oct-91 SY.NY89/R) A view of castle Persijn, near Wassenaar, Holland (27x37cm-11x15in) s.d.1749

TEN HOVEN, H (19/20th C) Dutch
£550 $946   (16-Oct-91 CSK264) Barges on river town (55x85cm-22x33in) s.
£600 $1026   (17-Mar-92 PH29) Flower market, Amsterdam (55x85cm-22x33in) s.

TEN KATE, C (19th C) Dutch
£703 $1224   (14-Apr-92 SY.AM368) Landscape with shepherd and cattle (32x42cm-13x17in) s.d.1846 panel (D.FL 2300)

TEN KATE, Herman (1822-1891) Dutch
£734 $1306   (30-Oct-91 CH.AM262) Declaration of love (20x18cm-8x7in) indis.s.d. panel (D.FL 2400)
£838 $1500   (13-Nov-91 B.SF2238/R) The chemist (49x37cm-19x15in) cradled panel
£2171 $3800   (18-Feb-92 CE.NY80/R) Good smoke (16x23cm-6x9in) s.d.1857 panel
£2200 $3938   (14-Jan-92 SWS210/R) Visitor (26x34cm-10x13in) s. panel
£4557 $7928   (14-Apr-92 SY.AM76/R) The artist's studio (24x33cm-9x13in) s.d.1874 panel (D.FL 14900)
£734 $1299   (5-Nov-91 SY.AM319/R) Receiving Burgomaster (24x17cm-9x7in) s. W/C (D.FL 2400)
£917 $1633   (30-Oct-91 CH.AM343) The card players (17x23cm-7x9in) s. pen W/C (D.FL 3000)
£1223 $2177   (30-Oct-91 CH.AM342 a/R) The investigation (19x31cm-7x12in) s. pen W/C (D.FL 4000)
£1468 $2598   (5-Nov-91 SY.AM94/R) Travellers in tavern (22x33cm-9x13in) s. W/C (D.FL 4800)
£1835 $3266   (30-Oct-91 CH.AM322/R) Les Romains de la Decadence (28x48cm-11x19in) s.i.d.1849 W/C pencil (D.FL 6000)
£1970 $3486   (22-Apr-92 CH.AM261/R) In the tavern (25x36cm-10x14in) s.d.1863 ink W/C htd.white (D.FL 6500)
£2061 $3647   (22-Apr-92 CH.AM262/R) The brawl (23x35cm-9x14in) s. ink W/C htd.white (D.FL 6800)

TEN KATE, Herman (after) (1822-1891) Dutch
£900 $1728   (28-Jul-92 SWS391/R) A glass of wine (56x65cm-22x26in)

TEN KATE, Herman and STROEBEL, Johann Anthonie Balthasar (19th C) Dutch
£2752 $4899   (30-Oct-91 CH.AM223/R) Beggars in the entrance hall of patrician's house (50x39cm-20x15in) s.d.83 panel (D.FL 9000)

TEN KATE, Jan Jacob Lodewijk (1850-1929) Dutch
£6000 $10260   (20-Mar-92 C4/R) Fisherfolk gathered on beach with boat landing in gale (99x226cm-39x89in) s.i.d.49

TEN KATE, Johan Mari (1831-1910) Dutch
£1070 $1894   (5-Nov-91 SY.AM215) Farmyard (39x52cm-15x20in) s. panel (D.FL 3500)
£5200 $9412   (21-May-92 CSK130/R) Pet rabbits (44x60cm-17x24in) s.
£11000 $19580   (27-Nov-91 S25/R) Artist at rest by easel (33x44cm-13x17in) s. panel
£1150 $2105   (6-Feb-92 T160/R) Winter woodland scene with faggot gatherers (51x43cm-20x17in) s. W/C
£1500 $2670   (26-Nov-91 PH78/R) The day's bag (24x35cm-9x14in) s. W/C
£2000 $3720   (17-Jun-92 S350/R) Snowball fight (25x34cm-10x13in) s. W/C
£2800 $5068   (22-May-92 C202/R) Day's catch (26x36cm-10x14in) s. W/C card

TEN KATE, Johan Mari (1831-1910) Dutch-cont.
£3400 $5814   (18-Mar-92 S48/R) Flying the kite (43x58cm-17x23in) s. W/C

TEN KATE, Marie (?) Dutch?
£5046 $8780   (14-Apr-92 SY.AM23/R) The little fishermen (35x50cm-14x20in) s.
                      (D.FL 16500)

TENGELER, Johannes Willem (1746-1811) Dutch
£1600 $3072   (9-Jul-92 CSK309/R) Coastal landscape with fishing boats moored in calm
                      (63x79cm-25x31in) s.d.1806

TENIERS (style) (17th C) Flemish
£1300 $2275   (27-Feb-92 B91) The Village dispute (76x63cm-30x25in)
£4332 $7798   (19-Nov-91 RAS.K417/R) Peasants merrymaking (69x86cm-27x34in)
                      (D.KR 48000)

TENIERS, Abraham (1629-1670) Flemish
£16255 $30885   (26-Jun-92 AT.P107/R) Les singes patissiers. Les singes cuisiniers
                      (17x24cm-7x9in) pair (F.FR 158000)

TENIERS, Abraham (attrib) (1629-1670) Flemish
£10299 $19361   (18-Dec-91 AT.P45/R) Paysan regardant des signes qui jouent
                      (18x23cm-7x9in) panel (F.FR 100000)

TENIERS, Abraham (school) (1629-1670) Flemish
£1457 $2549   (1-Apr-92 CSC.P22/R) Paysage troglodyte anime de lavandieres
                      (42x63cm-17x25in) (F.FR 14000)

TENIERS, David (after) (17th C) Flemish
£773 $1400   (19-May-92 CE.NY317) Boors smoking and drinking in tavern
                      (41x56cm-16x22in) panel
£800 $1400   (27-Feb-92 CSK202) The card players (28x23cm-11x9in) panel
£1321 $2299   (13-Apr-92 AT.P60) Joueurs de cartes dans une auberge (29x42cm-11x17in)
                      panel (F.FR 13000)
£1800 $3456   (9-Jul-92 CSK175/R) Tavern interior with peasant reading letter
                      (41x30cm-16x12in) panel
£2687 $4864   (3-Dec-91 AB.S4758/R) Landscape with wanderers by lake (77x123cm-30x48in)
                      bears mono. (S.KR 28000)
£3071 $5559   (3-Dec-91 AB.S4759/R) Inn interior with figures (46x63cm-18x25in) panel
                      (S.KR 32000)

TENIERS, David (attrib) (17th C) Flemish
£6179 $11617   (18-Dec-91 AT.P151/R) Scene de tabagie (24x34cm-9x13in) panel
                      (F.FR 60000)

TENIERS, David (circle) (17th C) Flemish
£1200 $2196   (14-May-92 TL47/R) Figures around table eating and drinking
                      (38x28cm-15x11in) panel
£1408 $2549   (4-Dec-91 DO.H2956/R) Landscape with peasants playing before tavern
                      (37x52cm-15x20in) mono. panel (DM 4000)
£1573 $2800   (30-Oct-91 D.NY93) Country wedding (61x51cm-24x20in)
£2491 $4510   (21-May-92 L.K147/R) Smoker sleeping (24x16cm-9x6in) mono panel (DM 7300)
£2572 $4887   (26-Jun-92 AT.P83/R) Kermesse pres d'une auberge (63x80cm-25x31in)
                      (F.FR 25000)

TENIERS, David (elder) (1582-1649) Flemish
£13000 $22750   (1-Apr-92 S34/R) Paul and Barnabas at Lystra (54x81cm-21x32in) panel

TENIERS, David (school) (17th C) Flemish
£1524 $2652   (13-Apr-92 AT.P61/R) Scene de sabbat (22x28cm-9x11in) panel (F.FR 15000)
£4321 $8210   (24-Jun-92 CSC.P20/R) L'arracheur de dents (44x33cm-17x13in) panel
                      (F.FR 42000)
£6687 $12706   (26-Jun-92 AT.P106/R) La tentation de St.Antoine (24x35cm-9x14in) panel
                      (F.FR 65000)

TENIERS, David (style) (17th C) Flemish
£750 $1313   (27-Feb-92 CSK199) The cobbler (57x46cm-22x18in)
£800 $1440   (21-Nov-91 CSK189) Boors smoking in tavern interior (34x27cm-13x11in)
                      panel
£828 $1423   (16-Oct-91 KM.K1005) The alchemist (26x36cm-10x14in) panel (DM 2400)
£850 $1632   (9-Jul-92 CSK194) The bottle seller (38x31cm-15x12in)
£950 $1824   (9-Jul-92 CSK269/R) Peasants outside inn (30x43cm-12x17in)
£950 $1691   (31-Oct-91 B116) Group of Topers outside country tavern (58x71cm-23x28in)
                      bears sig.
£951 $1721   (4-Dec-91 DO.H2957/R) Village landscape, winter (40x29cm-16x11in) mono.
                      panel (DM 2700)
£970 $1727   (27-Apr-92 BU.K70/R) Interior of inn with figures (82x109cm-32x43in)
                      (D.KR 11000)
£1000 $1920   (9-Jul-92 CSK191/R) Peasants playing skittles (15x20cm-6x8in) panel
£1022 $1900   (19-Jun-92 S.BM327) Simple pleasures - view of fishing village by
                      moonlight (33x58cm-13x23in) panel
£1048 $2002   (3-Jul-92 SD.P92) Kermesse (23x34cm-9x13in) panel (F.FR 10200)
£1200 $2304   (9-Jul-92 CSK176/R) Figures in tavern (25x32cm-10x13in) copper
£1568 $2854   (12-Dec-91 L.K180) Peasant dancing before tavern and church tower beyond
                      (18x28cm-7x11in) mono. panel (DM 4500)

TENIERS, David (style) (17th C) Flemish-cont.

£1751	$3291	(18-Dec-91 AT.P160/R) Un seigneur et des paysans pres d'un chateau (23x28cm-9x11in) panel (F.FR 17000)
£1934	$3500	(19-May-92 CE.NY335/R) Couple drinking and peasants warming themselves by fire in tavern (38x53cm-15x21in) bears mono. panel
£2091	$3805	(12-Dec-91 L.K181) Soldiers plundering village (31x37cm-12x15in) mono. panel (DM 6000)
£2703	$4622	(12-Mar-92 GK.Z81) Peasants merrymaking in tavern (32x47cm-13x19in) copper (S.FR 7000)
£4181	$7610	(11-Dec-91 N.M367/R) Village scene with peasants merrymaking and view of river landscape (103x142cm-41x56in) (DM 12000)
£13374	$24208	(7-Dec-91 CH.MO18/R) Une fete villageoise (68x111cm-27x44in) panel (F.FR 130000)

TENIERS, David (younger) (1610-1690) Flemish

£2200	$3850	(1-Apr-92 S104/R) Peasants gambling in interior (43x59cm-17x23in) panel
£3333	$5667	(23-Oct-91 GD.B1303/R) Kitchen interior with servant girl sleeping and men conversing beyond (45x60cm-18x24in) s. panel (S.FR 8500)
£11000	$19140	(15-Apr-92 C126/R) Boor smoking in interior with old woman by brazier (29x21cm-11x8in) s.
£26000	$47320	(10-Dec-91 PH58/R) Allegory of winter (17x12cm-7x5in) mono. panel
£27000	$49140	(12-Dec-91 B57/R) Landscapes with travellers on sandy track (20x33cm-8x13in) mono. panel pair
£43000	$75250	(26-Feb-92 MMB253/R) Interior of inn with figures playing backgammon (33x43cm-13x17in) s.

TENIERS, David (younger-after) (1610-1690) Flemish

| £2135 | $3843 | (19-Nov-91 F.R40) Scena d'interno (43x57cm-17x22in) panel (I.L 4600000) |
| £2200 | $3828 | (13-Sep-91 C145/R) Boors playing cards in inn (49x72cm-19x28in) with sig.indist.d. panel |

TENIERS, David (younger-attrib) (1610-1690) Flemish

£741	$1341	(19-May-92 GF.L2678/R) Rustungsteile und Partisane (28x33cm-11x13in) panel (S.FR 2000)
£4200	$7350	(1-Apr-92 S151/R) Temptation of Saint Anthony (15x21cm-6x8in) bears sig. panel
£7692	$13154	(18-Mar-92 N.M455/R) Peasants dancing before tavern in river landscape (59x73cm-23x29in) (DM 22000)
£15963	$30010	(18-Dec-91 AT.P46/R) Singes pres d'un brasero (19x24cm-7x9in) panel (F.FR 155000)

TENIERS, David (younger-circle) (1610-1690) Flemish

£1698	$3039	(14-Nov-91 CH.AM97) The Mystic Marriage of St Catherine (53x65cm-21x26in) panel after Paolo Veronese (D.FL 5500)
£2718	$5028	(8-Jun-92 CH.R728/R) Fumatore di pipa (17x12cm-7x5in) panel (I.L 6000000)
£2920	$5226	(6-May-92 GD.B1265/R) Village in river landscape (47x68cm-19x27in) (S.FR 8000)
£3000	$5460	(10-Dec-91 PH181/R) Travellers conversing on path near river (26x36cm-10x14in)
£4000	$7280	(10-Dec-91 PH230/R) Interior with figures feasting and celebrating (61x120cm-24x47in) bears sig.d.
£6077	$11000	(22-May-92 SY.NY163/R) Witches practicing necromancy with imps and demons looking on (48x54cm-19x21in) panel
£11480	$20550	(7-May-92 CH.AM114/R) Temptation of Saint Anthony (55x70cm-22x28in) copper (D.FL 38000)

TENIERS, David (younger-school) (1610-1690) Flemish

£1543	$2900	(17-Dec-91 BG.M691/R) Figures playing cards in a tavern (25x28cm-10x11in) s. panel
£3867	$7000	(21-May-92 CH.NY152/R) Interior with boor holding jug and another lighting pipe (22x16cm-9x6in) bears mono. panel
£4630	$8796	(26-Jun-92 AT.P84/R) Villageois attables devant l'auberge (65x86cm-26x34in) bears mono. panel (F.FR 45000)

TENIERS, David (younger-studio) (1610-1690) Flemish

| £2482 | $4493 | (22-May-92 LD.P67) La tentation de Saint-Antoine (42x57cm-17x22in) panel (F.FR 24500) |
| £10000 | $18200 | (13-Dec-91 C35/R) Soldiers at cards in guardroom (48x64cm-19x25in) mono.d.1644 copper |

TENIERS, David (younger-style) (1610-1690) Flemish

£730	$1300	(22-Jan-92 SY.NY207) Peasants gathered outside tavern (43x31cm-17x12in)
£750	$1373	(12-May-92 SWS815) Landscape with peasants outside inn (29x42cm-11x17in)
£820	$1476	(22-Nov-91 SWS67/R) Interior with card players (29x23cm-11x9in) bears sig.d.1643 panel
£926	$1657	(12-Nov-91 SY.AM157) Peasants on country road (20x26cm-8x10in) panel (D.FL 3000)
£950	$1710	(22-Nov-91 SWS84) Peasants in a kitchen interior (32x43cm-13x17in) panel
£1173	$2052	(18-Feb-92 CH.AM255) Boors playing cards in barn (24x32cm-9x13in) with sig. panel (D.FL 3800)
£1300	$2275	(28-Feb-92 C56/R) Two peasants outside a thatched cottage, landscape beyond (14x20cm-6x8in) mono. panel
£1300	$2379	(12-May-92 H362/R) Kitchen interior (51x69cm-20x27in)
£1348	$2400	(22-Jan-92 SY.NY205/R) Peasants bowling outside tavern (48x63cm-19x25in) i.

TENIERS, David (younger-style) (1610-1690) Flemish-cont.
£1500	$2625	(28-Feb-92 C85) The Temptation of Saint Anthony (43x37cm-17x15in)
£1900	$3477	(12-May-92 SWS746/R) Falconer. Fisherman (18x14cm-7x6in) copper pair
£1987	$3398	(18-Mar-92 D.V388/R) Peasants resting near fortified castle (82x72cm-32x28in) mono. canvas on panel (A.S 40000)
£2037	$3646	(12-Nov-91 SY.AM161) Peasant carrying sack on his back (29x23cm-11x9in) panel (D.FL 6600)
£2225	$4250	(16-Jul-92 SY.NY79/R) Backgammon players (55x75cm-22x30in)
£2315	$4144	(14-Nov-91 CH.AM17/R) Boor at table in inn (34x40cm-13x16in) mono. panel (D.FL 7500)
£2500	$4450	(30-Oct-91 S46) Poetry. Plenty (42x23cm-17x9in) bears mono. pair
£3141	$6000	(16-Jul-92 SY.NY80/R) Peasants in an interior (47x64cm-19x25in) panel
£3200	$6144	(10-Jul-92 PH54/R) Winter landscape with skaters on village pond (29x49cm-11x19in) pair
£4012	$7182	(12-Nov-91 SY.AM191/R) Old man seducing kitchen maid (44x63cm-17x25in) panel (D.FL 13000)
£9945	$18000	(22-May-92 SY.NY154/R) Monkey barbershop and monkey tavern (71x105cm-28x41in) panel pair
£10288	$18621	(7-Dec-91 CH.MO12/R) Les Singes Cuisines (25x35cm-10x14in) panel (F.FR 100000)

TENIERS, David and D'ARTHOIS, Jacques (attrib) (17th C) Flemish
| £3038 | $5377 | (11-Feb-92 GM.B158/R) Paysage anime de personnages (52x82cm-20x32in) (B.FR 180000) |

TENNANT, Dorothy (1855-1926) British
| £1900 | $3268 | (11-Oct-91 C111/R) Nude seated in wooded lake landscape (19x14cm-7x6in) s.d.1885 s.i.d.verso panel |

TENNANT, John F (1796-1872) British
£1000	$1910	(29-Jun-92 PHB167) Cattle beside river at sunset (56x92cm-22x36in) s.d.1848
£2300	$4002	(11-Sep-91 PHL113/R) Fisherfolk tending lobster pots on beach - thought to be Herne Bay (52x80cm-20x31in) s.d.1839
£2700	$5184	(28-Jul-92 SWS370/R) Early morning near Henley (36x52cm-14x20in) s.d.1843
£4467	$7595	(25-Oct-91 BM.B847/R) View of coastal town with fishermen returning with catch (87x126cm-34x50in) s.d.1829 (DM 13000)
£5000	$9550	(15-Jul-92 S74/R) Lhangattoc Rocks, S Wales (59x89cm-23x35in) s.
£5100	$9741	(17-Jul-92 C176/R) Fishermen mending their nets (48x71cm-19x28in) s.d.1830

TEPLER, Samuel (1918-) Israeli
| £585 | $1100 | (5-Jan-92 GG.TA221/R) Seated boy (80x65cm-31x26in) s.d.1956 |

TEPPER, Saul (1899-1987) American
£1292	$2300	(2-Nov-91 IH.NY183/R) Woman at tailor shop (64x91cm-25x36in) s. monochrome oil
£2247	$4000	(2-May-92 IH.NY156/R) Couple at doorway to dentist's office (76x91cm-30x36in) s.d.1926
£2669	$4750	(2-May-92 IH.NY74/R) Shipboard duel with swords (53x102cm-21x40in) s.

TER MEULEN, Frans Pieter (1843-1927) Dutch
£459	$839	(1-Jun-92 W.T1380) Evening sky (53x78cm-21x31in) s. (C.D 1000)
£1866	$3321	(25-Nov-91 W.T1967/R) Shepherd and flock (74x95cm-29x37in) s. (C.D 3750)
£780	*$1405*	*(19-Nov-91 FP.M131/R) Loading sand (38x61cm-15x24in) s. W/C (C.D 1600)*
£917	*$1596*	*(14-Apr-92 SY.AM114/R) Woman with cattle on path (38x59cm-15x23in) s. W/C (D.FL 3000)*

TERA, Teppo (1935-) Finnish
| £5304 | $9441 | (1-Dec-91 HOR.H226/R) Caroleans arriving (50x61cm-20x24in) s.d.1972 (F.M 41000) |

TERAN, Frederico Ferrandiz (attrib) (?) ?
| £1421 | $2600 | (3-Jun-92 D.NY93/R) Padre by well (23x33cm-9x13in) panel |

TERBORCH, Gerard (1617-1681) Dutch
| £41667 | $74583 | (12-Nov-91 SY.AM31/R) Portrait of man standing in interior (68x57cm-27x22in) panel (D.FL 135000) |

TERBORCH, Gerard (after) (1617-1681) Dutch
£917	$1578	(7-Oct-91 CH.E221/R) Lady seated playing lute (48x39cm-19x15in) (E.P 1000)
£1517	$2700	(22-Jan-92 SY.NY147/R) Interior with lady and maid (49x37cm-19x15in) panel
£6000	$10680	(1-Nov-91 C103/R) Lady washing hands in bedchamber attended by maid (53x42cm-21x17in)

TERBORCH, Gerard (attrib) (1617-1681) Dutch
| £20442 | $37000 | (22-May-92 SY.NY215/R) Young men drinking in tavern (30x36cm-12x14in) panel |

TERBORCH, Gerard (circle) (1617-1681) Dutch
| £2155 | $3750 | (16-Sep-91 B.SF2010/R) Elegant company in mountainous setting (42x36cm-17x14in) |

TERBORCH, Gerard (style) (1617-1681) Dutch
£1200 $2196   (12-May-92 SWS676) Concert (24x20cm-9x8in) arched top
£15000 $28800   (10-Jul-92 C142/R) Young lady having hair combed by maid
                           (57x47cm-22x19in)

TERBORCH, Gesina (attrib) (1663-1690) Dutch
£628 $1200   (16-Jul-92 SY.NY151 a/R) Figures in an interior (31x24cm-12x9in) canvas
                           on masonite

TERECHKOVITCH, Costia (1902-1978) French
£5587 $10000   (9-May-92 CE.NY59/R) La danseuse (81x54cm-32x21in) s. board on canvas
£7194 $12374   (4-Mar-92 AT.P207/R) Femme au chapeau fleuri (56x33cm-22x13in) s.d.43
                           panel (F.FR 70000)
£1117 $2000   (9-May-92 CE.NY147/R) Femme debout (58x35cm-23x14in) s. W/C gouache
                           pencil
£1296 $2346   (20-May-92 GK.Z5014/R) Place a Bayonne, Paris (42x55cm-17x22in) s. W/C
                           (S.FR 3500)

TERENTIEV, Vladimir (1932-) Russian
£764 $1398   (3-Jun-92 ARC.P70/R) La maison rouge (78x100cm-31x39in) board (F.FR 7500)
£916 $1677   (3-Jun-92 ARC.P72/R) L'automne (99x77cm-39x30in) board (F.FR 9000)
£1230 $2213   (27-Jan-92 ARC.P122/R) Le jardin en fleurs (113x126cm-44x50in) s.verso
                           (F.FR 12000)
£1434 $2582   (27-Jan-92 ARC.P123/R) Pres du lac (81x100cm-32x39in) s. board
                           (F.FR 14000)
£1477 $2702   (3-Jun-92 ARC.P69/R) Pres de la riviere (98x102cm-39x40in) s.verso
                           (F.FR 14500)
£2037 $3727   (3-Jun-92 ARC.P73/R) L'automne dans les environs de Moscou
                           (164x190cm-65x75in) (F.FR 20000)
£2152 $3873   (27-Jan-92 ARC.P121/R) Le premier Mai (106x167cm-42x66in) s.verso
                           (F.FR 21000)
£3586 $6455   (27-Jan-92 ARC.P120/R) Sous bois en automne (222x235cm-87x93in) s.
                           (F.FR 35000)

TERLIKOWSKI, Vladimir de (1873-1951) Polish
£1118 $1945   (14-Apr-92 ZZ.F21/R) Bouquet aux fleurs rouge (55x38cm-22x15in) s.
                           (F.FR 11000)

TERLINDEN, Felix (1836-1912) Belgian
£2600 $4628   (26-Nov-91 PH101) Woman seated in garden (50x35cm-20x14in) s.

TERNANTE-LEMAIRE, Amedee de (19th C) French
£2361 $4251   (18-Nov-91 AT.P379) La place du marche (47x77cm-19x30in) s. (F.FR 23000)

TERNI, A L (?) Italian
£1453 $2500   (15-Oct-91 CE.NY406/R) The return home (68x105cm-27x41in) s.
£1569 $2699   (13-Oct-91 REM.W31) Town in the Bay of Naples (54x69cm-21x27in) s.
                           (P.Z 30000000)

TERRAIRE, Clovis (19/20th C) French
£4651 $8000   (17-Oct-91 SY.NY164/R) Le vacher dans la region Lyonnaise
                           (124x230cm-49x91in) s.d.1905

TERRIER, Jean Michel (20th C) French
£520 $998   (6-Jul-92 HC.P90/R) Khazak (42x53cm-17x21in) mixed media gold silver
                           mineral pigments (F.FR 5000)

TERRUELLA, Joaquim (1891-1957) Spanish
£766 $1394   (11-Dec-91 FER.M111/R) Arboleda en la montana (27x23cm-11x9in) s. panel
                           (S.P 140000)
£1860 $3312   (29-Oct-91 BRO.B359) Jardin en otono (50x61cm-20x24in) s. (S.P 340000)
£3871 $7277   (17-Dec-91 BRO.B385/R) Vista de Girona, con el Onyar y la catedral
                           (60x73cm-24x29in) s.d.43 (S.P 700000)

TERRUSO, Saverio (1939-) Italian
£1518 $2716   (14-Nov-91 F.M20) Fiori (50x70cm-20x28in) s. (I.L 3300000)
£1671 $3141   (19-Dec-91 F.M42) Processione (50x70cm-20x28in) s. s.i.verso
                           (I.L 3600000)
£1931 $3457   (14-Nov-91 F.M36/R) Anna (70x50cm-28x20in) s. s.i.d.1979verso
                           (I.L 4200000)

TERRY, Henry (fl.1879-1920) British
£400 $716   (14-Jan-92 SWS68/R) Pillar of the connenticle (39x28cm-15x11in) s.
                           s.i.verso W/C
£600 $1020   (22-Oct-91 SWS189/R) Grandpa's little friend (35x44cm-14x17in) s.d.1886
                           W/C over pencil

TERVAKORPI (?) Scandinavian?
£507 $897   (6-Nov-91 HOR.H130) Breakers (45x66cm-18x26in) s. (F.M 3600)

TERWESTEN, Matheus (1670-1757) Dutch
£3867 $7000   (22-May-92 SY.NY234/R) Time revealing truth (125x100cm-49x39in)
£5587 $10000   (17-Jan-92 SY.NY166/R) Time revealing truth (125x100cm-49x39in)

TERWESTEN, Matheus and VERBRUGGEN, Gaspar Pieter II (17/18th C) Dutch/Flemish
£10500 $19110   (11-Dec-91 S113/R) Putti adorning classical urn with festoons of fruit and flowers (82x114cm-32x45in) bears sig.

TESI, Mauro Antonio (1730-1766) Italian
£782 $1400   (15-Jan-92 CH.NY46/R) Design for ornamental acanthus spray, portrait man. Architectural study (27x17cm-11x7in) black chk pen wash lead double-sided

TESI, Mauro Antonio (attrib) (1730-1766) Italian
£1100 $1914   (13-Apr-92 S237/R) Three designs for vases (17x28cm-7x11in) pen wash

TESSARI, Romolo (1868-?) Italian
£4802 $8500   (25-Apr-92 YFA.M286/R) St. Mark's Square, Venice (58x74cm-23x29in) s.

TESSIER, Louis (style) (1719-1781) French
£1700 $3060   (22-Nov-91 SWS172/R) Still life of astronomical instruments upon a ledge (34x117cm-13x46in)

TESSITORE, Giuseppe Raffaele (1861-?) Italian
£834 $1442   (24-Mar-92 CH.R118 c) Piccolo venditore di fragole davanti alla chiesa del Carmine (42x16cm-17x6in) s.d.1902 (I.L 1800000)

TESTA, Pietro (1611-1650) Italian
£955 $1700   (1-Nov-91 PO.BA27) Alegoria (31x21cm-12x8in) s. Indian ink dr

TESTA, Pietro (attrib) (1611-1650) Italian
£2800 $5096   (11-Dec-91 PH263/R) Drovers in mountain landscape (16x21cm-6x8in) i. pen wash

TESTAS, Willem de Famars (1834-1896) Dutch
£489 $866   (5-Nov-91 SY.AM106) Street scene in El Kab (32x24cm-13x9in) s.d.1859 W/C (D.FL 1600)
£917 $1624   (5-Nov-91 SY.AM146/R) Street scene in Oriental city (12x17cm-5x7in) s.d.65 W/C (D.FL 3000)

TESTU, Pierre (19/20th C) French
£865 $1582   (17-May-92 T.B211/R) Sur la Greve avant la peche (49x65cm-19x26in) s.d.1893 (F.FR 8500)

TETAR VAN ELVEN, Jan Baptist (1805-1889) Dutch
£578 $1005   (17-Sep-91 CH.AM539) Figures in the aisle of a church (50x35cm-20x14in) s. panel (D.FL 1900)

TETAR VAN ELVEN, P (19th C) Dutch
£2058 $3909   (22-Jun-92 AT.P40) Les lavandieres (30x54cm-12x21in) s. panel (F.FR 20000)

TETAR VAN ELVEN, Pierre Henri Theodore (1828-1908) Dutch
£1155 $1987   (12-Oct-91 CH.AM196) View of Lake Como with hooded boats off bank (53x68cm-21x27in) s. (D.FL 3800)
£1520 $2644   (17-Sep-91 CH.AM500/R) View in Amsterdam with figures near stagecoach on quay along canal (22x29cm-9x11in) s.d.1850 i. verso panel (D.FL 5000)
£4620 $8316   (18-Nov-91 AT.P382/R) La priere sur l'ile de Philae (97x133cm-38x52in) s. (F.FR 45000)

TETERINE, Victor (1922-1991) Russian
£619 $1058   (13-Mar-92 ARC.P180/R) Le paysane urbain (67x82cm-26x32in) s.d.50 (F.FR 6000)
£866 $1584   (3-Jun-92 ARC.P184/R) Les champs du Caucase (44x72cm-17x28in) s. (F.FR 8500)
£1018 $1864   (3-Jun-92 ARC.P187/R) Le couvent de Sainte Trinite (79x86cm-31x34in) s. (F.FR 10000)
£1069 $1957   (3-Jun-92 ARC.P185/R) Les vignes en automne (59x95cm-23x37in) s. (F.FR 10500)
£1935 $3541   (3-Jun-92 ARC.P186/R) Les oliviers Foros (69x90cm-27x35in) s. (F.FR 19000)

TETMAYER, Wlodzimierz (1862-1923) Polish
£1450 $2725   (21-Dec-91 HO.P5) The Scythmen attack in the Raclawice Battle (20x89cm-8x35in) (P.Z 28000000)
£5208 $9114   (29-Sep-91 AG.W17) Grasshoppers (95x82cm-37x32in) s. (P.Z 100000000)

TEUBER, Hermann (1894-1985) German
£550 $935   (25-Oct-91 BM.B1112/R) View of farmhouse (33x45cm-13x18in) s.d.1957 W/C (DM 1600)
£764 $1367   (15-Nov-91 KM.K680) Lake Garda, morning (31x45cm-12x18in) s. W/C (DM 2200)

TEUPKEN, Dirk Antoon (jnr) see TOPKE, Dirk Antoon (jnr)

TEUTRE, P du (?) ?
£526 $1000   (24-Jun-92 D.NY79) Mother and daughter (56x46cm-22x18in) s.

TEWBANK, T (19th C) ?
£624 $1073   (15-Oct-91 RAS.K270) The protectress - small girl with pigeon
                            (65x65cm-26x26in) s.d.1860 (D.KR 7000)

TEXIER, Richard (1955-) French
£409 $748   *(5-Feb-92 FB.P233 a) Une toute petite intuition (76x53cm-30x21in)*
                            s.i.d.87 mixed media panel (F.FR 4000)
£2047 $3644   *(1-Dec-91 I.N79/R) Les deux axes de la tourmente (130x130cm-51x51in)*
                            s.d.1985/86 i.verso oil mixed media canvas (F.FR 20000)
£2266 $3874   *(19-Mar-92 CSC.P101/R) Sans titre (65x81cm-26x32in) s.verso mixed media*
                            canvas (F.FR 22000)
£2305 $4150   *(2-Feb-92 CSC.P150/R) Petite mecanique celeste (65x80cm-26x31in)*
                            mono.i.d.12 nov 89 mixed media paper on canvas (F.FR 22500)
£2817 $4845   *(8-Oct-91 CC.P78/R) Re (114x146cm-45x57in) s.i. verso mixed media canvas*
                            (F.FR 28000)

THACKERAY, Jane (?) British?
£540 $983   (10-Dec-91 SWS12) Peasants on mountain path (27x38cm-11x15in) s. board

THADEN, Barbara (20th C) ?
£617 $1117   (2-Dec-91 CC.P51/R) Sternen Himmel (130x140cm-51x55in) s.i.d.1985verso
                            acrylic (F.FR 6000)

THAMM, Adolf (1859-1925) German
£3878 $7058   (27-May-92 D.V598/R) Taufers in Sudtirol (42x61cm-17x24in) s. (A.S 80000)
£6993 $12098   (25-Mar-92 KM.K1466/R) View of Capri with figures conversing in garden
                            (73x108cm-29x43in) s.d.93 (DM 20000)

THANNENBERG (20th C) Austrian?
£902 $1633   (5-Dec-91 D.V248) Yellow roses on white drape (35x51cm-14x20in) s. board
                            (A.S 18000)

THARP, Charles Julian Theodore (1878-?) British
£1450 $2494   (3-Mar-92 SWS1630/R) Gathering roses (100x75cm-39x30in) indist.s.d.

THARRATS, Juan Jose (1918-) Spanish
£838 $1500   (9-May-92 CE.NY178/R) Centre galactique (61x50cm-24x20in) s.
                            s.i.d.67verso
£387 $728   *(17-Dec-91 BRO.B328) Composicion (22x32cm-9x13in) s. mixed media*
                            (S.P 70000)
£762 $1326   *(16-Apr-92 FB.P176/R) Composition (50x65cm-20x26in) s.d.60 mixed media*
                            crumpled paper (F.FR 7500)
£793 $1451   *(13-May-92 FER.M205/R) Composicion tricolor (38x55cm-15x22in) s.*
                            s.d.1968-71 mixed media (S.P 145000)
£2460 $4181   *(24-Oct-91 DUR.M1007/R) O policroma (148x114cm-58x45in) s. s.i.d.1973*
                            mixed media canvas (S.P 450000)

THAULOW, Fritz (1847-1906) Norwegian
£665 $1177   (15-Feb-92 BU.O136) Foutain (29x37cm-11x15in) i.verso (N.KR 7500)
£2286 $4000   (18-Feb-92 CE.NY325/R) Impression of Oslo (30x39cm-12x15in) init. panel
£2546 $4379   (7-Oct-91 B.O134/R) French landscape (38x45cm-15x18in) init. (N.KR 29000)
£2971 $5200   (18-Feb-92 CE.NY318/R) Winter in Oslo (46x56cm-18x22in) init.
£3345 $5620   (28-Aug-91 KH.K193/R) Cattle by farmhouse, Brittany (36x46cm-14x18in) s.
                            (D.KR 38000)
£3662 $6225   (6-Aug-91 UL.T234) French street scene (35x27cm-14x11in) (N.KR 42000)
£4000 $7240   (22-May-92 C29/R) Farmhouse by moonlight, Arques-la-Bataille near Dieppe
                            (60x81cm-24x32in) s. canvas on board
£4200 $7602   (22-May-92 C31/R) Winter street scene, Montreuil (61x46cm-24x18in) s.d.
£6909 $12574   (14-Dec-91 BU.O53/R) Harbour in France (35x46cm-14x18in) s.d.75
                            (N.KR 78000)
£7024 $12081   (7-Oct-91 B.O133/R) Winter at Vindern (72x53cm-28x21in) s. panel
                            (N.KR 80000)
£11000 $19910   (22-May-92 C30/R) Dieppe (65x92cm-26x36in) init.
£11429 $20000   (20-Feb-92 SY.NY103/R) Mill stream (39x56cm-15x22in) s.
£11842 $22026   (18-Jun-92 GWP.O102/R) River landscape, Normandy (73x60cm-29x24in) s.
                            i.verso paper on canvas (N.KR 135000)
£12264 $21953   (7-May-92 RAS.S54/R) River landscape with pigeons (65x81cm-26x32in) s.
                            (S.KR 130000)
£14047 $25004   (29-Oct-91 UL.T234 c/R) Transporting ice (60x73cm-24x29in) (N.KR 160000)
£14912 $27737   (18-Jun-92 GWP.O101/R) Spring in Montreuille (66x46cm-26x18in) s.d.94
                            (N.KR 170000)
£16038 $28708   (7-May-92 RAS.S25/R) Summer landscape with ducks, Beaulieu 1903
                            (65x81cm-26x32in) s. (S.KR 170000)
£16571 $29000   (19-Feb-92 CH.NY84/R) Freight train, dusk (64x81cm-25x32in) s. canvas on
                            board
£16571 $29000   (20-Feb-92 SY.NY102/R) Collecting water at river's edge (61x74cm-24x29in)
                            s.
£16981 $30396   (7-May-92 RAS.S55/R) Autumn river landscape (46x55cm-18x22in) s.
                            (S.KR 180000)
£26339 $45303   (10-Oct-91 BU.O93/R) French river landscape (65x92cm-26x36in) s.d.95
                            (N.KR 300000)
£27458 $49973   (10-Dec-91 UL.T228/R) Landscape, Normandy (65x80cm-26x31in) (N.KR 310000)
£36315 $66094   (10-Dec-91 UL.T227/R) Near the Madeleine church, Paris 1895
                            (62x51cm-24x20in) (N.KR 410000)

THAULOW, Fritz (1847-1906) Norwegian-cont.
£42142	$75013	(29-Oct-91 UL.T233/R) Autumn day in France (82x100cm-32x39in) (N.KR 480000)
£989	$1800	(13-Dec-91 S.W2850/R) Stream in winter (81x109cm-32x43in) s. pastel
£3424	$5889	(10-Oct-91 BU.O29/R) River landscape with trees (67x100cm-26x39in) s.d.90 pastel (N.KR 39000)
£3672	$6500	(13-Feb-92 S.W2693/R) Horse drawn carts in winter (20x30cm-8x12in) s. pastel
£6800	$12104	(29-Nov-91 C76/R) River landscape with moored boat (65x58cm-26x23in) s. pastel paper laid down on canvas
£15058	$27405	(14-Dec-91 BU.O49/R) Spring thaw (56x95cm-22x37in) s. pastel paper on canvas (N.KR 170000)

THAYER, Abbott H (1849-1921) American
£536	$900	(28-Aug-91 MFA.C149/R) Flower study (23x36cm-9x14in) s.

THEAKER, Harry George (1873-1954) British
£1800	$3078	(13-Mar-92 C56/R) Young maiden with pan and cupid in wild garden (55x36cm-22x14in) s. pencil W/C
£5600	$9912	(6-Nov-91 S319/R) When a queen, long dead, was young (45cm-18ins circular) s. W/C

THEAULON, Etienne (1739-1780) French
£4630	$8380	(5-Dec-91 SY.MO281/R) Offrande a Venus (46x55cm-18x22in) (F.FR 45000)

THEDY, Marc (1858-1924) German
£1050	$1880	(14-Jan-92 SWS216/R) The solo performance (38x49cm-15x19in) s. panel

THEGERSTROM, Robert (1857-1919) Swedish
£2170	$3841	(5-Nov-91 BA.S173/R) Waterlilies on pond (49x33cm-19x13in) s. (S.KR 23000)

THELANDER, P G (1936-) Scandinavian
£573	$1019	(27-Nov-91 BU.S86) Untitled (15x20cm-6x8in) s. (S.KR 6000)
£1518	$2778	(13-May-92 BU.S201/R) Open bag (79x65cm-31x26in) s. (S.KR 16000)
£3036	$5556	(13-May-92 BU.S200/R) Monsieur Jean I (130x105cm-51x41in) s. (S.KR 32000)
£3036	$5556	(13-May-92 BU.S198/R) Monsieur Jean II (140x210cm-55x83in) s. (S.KR 32000)
£4459	$8160	(13-May-92 BU.S199/R) Fly agaric (61x40cm-24x16in) s. (S.KR 47000)
£17176	$30573	(27-Nov-91 BU.S13/R) Japan I (130x105cm-51x41in) s. (S.KR 180000)

THELEN-RUDEN, Friedrich von (1836-?) Austrian
£1456	$2592	(29-Apr-92 D.V819/R) Sale (50x40cm-20x16in) s.d.870 (A.S 30000)

THEOTOKOPOULOS, Domenikos see GRECO, El

THERIAT, Charles James (1860-?) American
£500	$865	(3-Oct-91 CSK166) An Arab tribesman in a desert landscape (23x38cm-9x15in)
£600	$1086	(21-May-92 CSK186) Snake charmers (54x37cm-21x15in)
£600	$1038	(3-Oct-91 CSK158) A hunter with dogs in a desert landscape (56x109cm-22x43in)
£850	$1471	(3-Oct-91 CSK163) An Arab village (36x46cm-14x18in) s.d.19
£1150	$1990	(3-Oct-91 CSK161/R) The snake charmers (53x36cm-21x14in)
£1200	$2076	(3-Oct-91 CSK164) Rocks at El Kantara, Algeria (38x58cm-15x23in) s.d.1901
£1200	$2076	(3-Oct-91 CSK154/R) Portrait of the artist (46x36cm-18x14in)
£1421	$2600	(3-Jun-92 D.NY94/R) Assemblage in Biskra Courtyard, Algeria (51x66cm-20x26in) s.i.
£1600	$2768	(3-Oct-91 CSK165/R) The vegetable seller (46x36cm-18x14in) s.d.95
£1600	$2848	(28-Nov-91 CSK135/R) Crossing the desert (79x124cm-31x49in) s.d.95
£1700	$3026	(28-Nov-91 CSK132) Arab in interior. Arab woman at loom set of four
£2000	$3560	(28-Nov-91 CSK140) Camel saddlery set of five
£2100	$3633	(3-Oct-91 CSK156/R) The goose herder (43x53cm-17x21in) s.d.95
£2200	$3916	(28-Nov-91 CSK136/R) Arabs before ruin. Desert landscapes set of three
£2400	$4272	(28-Nov-91 CSK145/R) Venetian backwater. Venetian courtyards (55x37cm-22x15in) set of three
£2400	$4272	(28-Nov-91 CSK128/R) Bedouin encampment. Desert landscape. Arabs in street (46x61cm-18x24in) set of three
£2400	$4152	(3-Oct-91 CSK167/R) At El Kantara (46x53cm-18x21in)
£2600	$4628	(28-Nov-91 CSK141/R) Arabs at rest by town wall (67x123cm-26x48in) s.d.90
£3200	$5696	(28-Nov-91 CSK143/R) Leading the herd (94x142cm-37x56in) s.d.97
£3200	$5696	(28-Nov-91 CSK138) Tending the herd (82x149cm-32x59in) s.d.92
£3600	$6408	(28-Nov-91 CSK146/R) Lesson from Grampa (91x112cm-36x44in)
£5400	$9612	(28-Nov-91 CSK147/R) Portrait of elegant beauty wearing bonnet. Study of female nude (46x38cm-18x15in) two

THERKILDSEN, Agnete (20th C) Danish
£617	$1116	(20-May-92 KH.K186) Composition (76x80cm-30x31in) init.d.86verso (D.KR 7000)

THERKILDSEN, Michael (1850-1925) Danish
£750	$1334	(28-Apr-92 RAS.K263/R) Watering place on the heath (71x109cm-28x43in) init.d.02 (D.KR 8500)
£903	$1625	(19-Nov-91 RAS.K317/R) Horses in field (43x60cm-17x24in) init. (D.KR 10000)

THERKILDSEN, Michael (1850-1925) Danish-cont.
£948	$1669	(12-Apr-92 HOR.H33) Cattle grazing (40x61cm-16x24in) s.d.1905 (F.M 7500)
£981	$1825	(16-Jun-92 RAS.K314/R) Frightened horses (109x152cm-43x60in) init. (D.KR 11000)
£1075	$1891	(12-Apr-92 HOR.H34/R) Out riding (37x52cm-15x20in) s.d.1910 (F.M 8500)

THERRIEN, Robert (20th C) American
| £1117 | $2000 | *(12-Nov-91 CE.NY134/R) Weigh, blue keystone (9x9cm-4x4in) gouache paper on book cover* |

THERY, John (20th C) ?
| £824 | $1409 | (18-Mar-92 LT.P107/R) Sans titre (81x65cm-32x26in) s. acrylic (F.FR 8000) |

THESLEFF, Ellen (1869-1954) Finnish
| £822 | $1446 | *(12-Apr-92 HOR.H231) Head of boy (20x15cm-8x6in) s.d.1915 crayon (F.M 6500)* |

THEUERKAUF, Gottlob (1831-1911) German
| £497 | $854 | *(11-Oct-91 AW.H1327/R) View of Burg Spangenberg (27x42cm-11x17in) s.i.d.1870 W/C over pencil (DM 1450)* |

THEVENET, Jacques (1891-?) French
| £712 | $1275 | (13-Nov-91 PIC.P86) L'etang dans la Nievre (50x64cm-20x25in) s.d.44 board (F.FR 7000) |
| £865 | $1548 | (13-Nov-91 PIC.P88) Les quais, l'Institut sous la neige (50x64cm-20x25in) s. panel (F.FR 8500) |

THEVENET, Jean (1800-1867) French
| £666 | $1239 | *(16-Jun-92 SY.B328) Portrait of a lady (14x10cm-6x4in) indis.s. W/C oval (B.FR 40000)* |

THEVENET, Louis (1874-1930) Belgian
£848	$1536	(19-May-92 CH.AM140) Village by a river (32x26cm-13x10in) s.d.15 board (D.FL 2800)
£1168	$2055	(7-Apr-92 C.A234) Still life (40x50cm-16x20in) s. (B.FR 70000)
£4010	$6817	(22-Oct-91 C.A304/R) Still life with piano (52x62cm-20x24in) s. (B.FR 240000)

THEWENETI, Lorenzo (1797-1878) British
| £2400 | $4128 | *(4-Mar-92 C69/R) Lady, seated in crimson dress with gauze sleeves, scarf in hair (12x?cm-5x?in) min. s. gilt-metal mount red leather case rec.* |

THEYNET, Max (1875-1949) Swiss
| £471 | $800 | (23-Oct-91 GD.B744/R) Neuenburgersee with rowing boat by shore (60x70cm-24x28in) s. board (S.FR 1200) |

THEYS, Ivan (1936-) Belgian
£1173	$2135	(11-Dec-91 CH.AM134) Couple (81x100cm-32x39in) s.d.85 (D.FL 3800)
£1529	$2615	(21-Mar-92 KV.L287) Two figures (40x50cm-16x20in) s. d.1970 verso (B.FR 90000)
£2566	$4645	(7-Dec-91 KV.L440/R) De vrijheid ontvoerd (200x129cm-79x51in) s. s.i.d.1983 verso (B.FR 150000)
£4333	$7453	(12-Oct-91 KV.L434/R) The idol (200x160cm-79x63in) s.d.1986 verso (B.FR 260000)
£596	$1079	*(23-May-92 KV.L326) Dancers (51x35cm-20x14in) s.d.85 gouache collage (B.FR 36000)*

THEYS, P (19th C) Belgian
| £1465 | $2490 | (24-Oct-91 D.V174/R) The wood transport (28x44cm-11x17in) s.indis.d. panel (A.S 30000) |

THIALIER, Raymond (1913-) French
| £9869 | $17567 | (30-Oct-91 QWA.P7/R) Le marche (146x97cm-57x38in) s. (F.FR 98000) |

THIBESART, Raymond (1874-?) French
| £872 | $1500 | (12-Oct-91 SY.NY30/R) Summer landscape with haystacks (27x41cm-11x16in) s. |
| £989 | $1730 | (5-Apr-92 ZZ.F180/R) Arbres en fleurs sur la colline (33x46cm-13x18in) s. (F.FR 9500) |

THIBON DE LIBIAN, Valentin (1889-1931) Argentinian
£3226	$6000	(16-Jun-92 RO.BA92) El paisaje (20x30cm-8x12in) panel
£22472	$40000	(1-Nov-91 PO.BA43) Mademoiselle Papillon (66x88cm-26x35in) s.
£80645	$150000	(16-Jun-92 RO.BA39) Antes de la Funcion (55x74cm-22x29in)

THIEBAUD, Wayne (1920-) American
£33520	$60000	(7-May-92 SY.NY284/R) Hillside (91x91cm-36x36in) s.d.1968
£39106	$70000	(14-Nov-91 SY.NY356/R) Boxes (31x25cm-12x10in) s.d.1963
£111732	$200000	(12-Nov-91 CH.NY36/R) Shelf pies (61x46cm-24x18in) s.d.61 i.stretcher
£12291	$22000	*(6-May-92 CH.NY364/R) Seated woman (74x58cm-29x23in) s.d.1985 d.1985 verso chl*

THIEL, Ewald (1855-?) German
| £692 | $1315 | *(24-Jun-92 KM.K1278/R) Interior with figures, Schloss Waldeck (41x30cm-16x12in) s. W/C (DM 2000)* |

THIELE, Alexander (1924-) German
£526	$900	(13-Mar-92 WOL..C480) Ducks in marshes (41x61cm-16x24in) s.
£584	$1069	(2-Jun-92 FN.S2774) Ducks in pond landscape (40x61cm-16x24in) s. (DM 1700)
£619	$1052	(25-Oct-91 BM.B965/R) Wannsee open air restaurant (50x60cm-20x24in) s. i.verso (DM 1800)
£632	$1080	(13-Mar-92 FN.S2989) Munich beer garden (50x60cm-20x24in) s. i.verso (DM 1800)
£982	$1680	(13-Mar-92 FN.S2990) Ducks by pond (41x60cm-16x24in) s. (DM 2800)

THIELE, Anton (1838-1902) Danish
£1012	$1701	(27-Aug-91 RAS.K554/R) Mother and daughter with flowers comforted (77x58cm-30x23in) s.d.1885 (D.KR 11500)

THIELE, Otto (1870-?) German
£819	$1483	(23-May-92 GB.B7291) Flower market, Berlin (60x48cm-24x19in) s. board (DM 2400)
£848	$1484	(3-Apr-92 BM.B717/R) Village view, winter (75x102cm-30x40in) s. (DM 2400)

THIELEN, Jan Philips van (1618-1667) Flemish
£16000	$28000	(1-Apr-92 S53/R) Baroque cartouche containing bust of woman adorned with bouquets of flowers (86x61cm-34x24in) s.indist.d.

THIELEN, Jan Philips van (attrib) (1618-1667) Flemish
£5000	$9100	(11-Dec-91 S183/R) Still life of flowers decorating part of cartouche (42x32cm-17x13in) canvas on panel fragment

THIELEN, Jan Philips van (circle) (1618-1667) Flemish
£2300	$4025	(25-Feb-92 PH100/R) Swag of flowers with roses, tulips and ivy attached to brass hooks (30x45cm-12x18in)

THIELEN, Jan Philips van (style) (1618-1667) Flemish
£6000	$10920	(11-Dec-91 S150/R) Still life of flowers in vase on table (38x30cm-15x12in)

THIELEN, Jan Philips van and WILLEBOIRTS, Thomas (attrib) (17th C) Flemish
£5523	$9500	(10-Oct-91 SY.NY206/R) The Madonna and child with infant Saint John Baptist in stone cartouche (105x77cm-41x30in)

THIELER, Fred (20th C) German
£3860	$6947	(19-Nov-91 L.K1153/R) Composition (65x50cm-26x20in) s.d.58 board (DM 11000)
£5802	$10560	(30-May-92 VG.B375/R) Composition red black (50x65cm-20x26in) s.d.1958 s.d.verso board (DM 17000)
£6826	$12423	(25-May-92 WK.M1224/R) Composition (68x96cm-27x38in) s.d.1958 s.i.d.verso acrylic board on panel (DM 20000)
£8532	$15529	(25-May-92 WK.M1225/R) Composition (68x96cm-27x38in) s.d.1959 s.i.d.verso acrylic board on panel (DM 25000)
£14860	$26451	(25-Nov-91 WK.M999/R) Accents in white (89x145cm-35x57in) s.d.1959 s.i.d.verso (DM 42500)
£9000	*$16290*	*(5-Dec-91 C10/R) Untitled (95x65cm-37x26in) s.d.64 oil gouache W/C torn paper*
£13986	*$24895*	*(30-Nov-91 VG.B355/R) Composition (210x160cm-83x63in) s.i.d.1981verso mixed media canvas double-sided (DM 40000)*
£17065	*$31058*	*(25-May-92 WK.M1226/R) Out in space (150x130cm-59x51in) s.d.1966 s.i.d.verso mixed media fabric collage (DM 50000)*
£23776	*$42322*	*(30-Nov-91 VG.B354/R) Untitled (150x124cm-59x49in) s.d.1960 mixed media over paper collage canvas (DM 68000)*

THIEM, Paul (1858-1922) German
£1049	$1794	(18-Mar-92 N.M659/R) Pond landscape, autumn (112x133cm-44x52in) s.d.1917 (DM 3000)

THIEME, Anthony (1888-1954) American/Dutch
£552	$1000	(21-May-92 S.W2444) Beach cottages, Florida (30x41cm-12x16in) s. canvas on board
£686	$1200	(31-Mar-92 MOR.P18) Corner market (20x25cm-8x10in) s. canvasboard
£702	$1250	(3-May-92 LIT.L10) Harbour scene (20x38cm-8x15in) s.
£889	$1600	(24-Nov-91 JRB.C133/R) French market (23x36cm-9x14in) board
£895	$1700	(28-Jun-92 LIT.L151) Punta Jorge, Laguna de Atitlan, Guatemala (64x76cm-25x30in) s.
£1111	$2000	(24-Nov-91 JRB.C180/R) North Easter (64x76cm-25x30in) s.
£1111	$1900	(13-Mar-92 S.BM268/R) The breakers (76x91cm-30x36in) s. s.st.studio i.verso
£1345	$2300	(12-Mar-92 MFA.C87) Mexican village (64x76cm-25x30in) s.
£1379	$2400	(15-Sep-91 JRB.C69/R) Port scene (30x41cm-12x16in) s. artist's board with pastel portrait s.i.
£1437	$2500	(15-Apr-92 SY.NY145/R) Summer in Vermont (50x61cm-20x24in) s. masonite
£1512	$2600	(20-Oct-91 HG.C12) Harbour scene (61x76cm-24x30in) s.
£1579	$2700	(22-Mar-92 LIT.L215) Italian fishing fleet (30x41cm-12x16in) s. board
£1628	$2800	(14-Oct-91 H.C156/R) Harbor scene (61x76cm-24x30in) s.
£1886	$3300	(23-Sep-91 S.SL260) Harbour scene (81x81cm-32x32in) s. sketch verso
£2023	$3500	(6-Sep-91 S.BM276/R) Custom House Tower (69x56cm-27x22in)
£2235	$4000	(14-Nov-91 CE.NY322/R) Lilac time (65x77cm-26x30in) s.i.verso

THIEME, Anthony (1888-1954) American/Dutch-cont.
£2339	$4000	(13-Mar-92 S.BM267/R) Fishing boats at the pier, Rockport (64x76cm-25x30in) s.
£2471	$4200	(11-Aug-91 LIT.L103) Sunny day (51x61cm-20x24in) s.
£2542	$4500	(25-Apr-92 YFA.M287/R) Morning breeze (76x64cm-30x25in) s.
£2632	$4500	(12-Mar-92 CH.NY186/R) Evening, Florida (63x76cm-25x30in) s. st.sig.verso
£2793	$5000	(14-Nov-91 CE.NY347/R) Seminole Indian village (46x91cm-18x36in) s. i.verso
£2933	$5250	(15-Nov-91 DM.D2009/R) Aniles Street, St Augustine, Florida (61x74cm-24x29in) s.
£3911	$7000	(14-Nov-91 CE.NY283/R) Blossoms, Rockport (76x91cm-30x36in) s.
£4094	$7000	(12-Mar-92 CH.NY188/R) Old Rockport (77x92cm-30x36in) s. i.verso
£4094	$7000	(11-Mar-92 SY.NY79/R) Autumn fields (63x76cm-25x30in) sa. i.st.verso
£5249	$9500	(4-Dec-91 D.NY89/R) Italian wharf, Gloucester (76x91cm-30x36in) with sig. i.verso
£8571	$15000	(26-Sep-91 CH.NY97/R) Morning light near Charleston, South Carolina (76x91cm-30x36in) s. s.i.verso
£497	*$900*	*(21-May-92 GRO.B96/R) Motif no 1 (48x76cm-19x30in) s. W/C*
£2024	*$3400*	*(28-Aug-91 MFA.C256/R) Bahamas (51x71cm-20x28in) s. W/C*

THIERAT, Melitine (19/20th C) French
£466	*$867*	*(16-Jun-92 SY.B298) Woman seated on Gothic chair (21x12cm-8x5in) s.d.1902 gouache (B.FR 28000)*

THIERFELDER, Vivian (1929-) Canadian
£769	*$1346*	*(17-Feb-92 HO.ED29/R) Rondo (33x33cm-13x13in) s.d.1977 W/C (C.D 1600)*

THIERY (19th C) French
£1128	$2019	(19-Jan-92 CSC.P132) Scene orientale (32x24cm-13x9in) s.d.75 (F.FR 11000)

THILEN, Ada (1852-1933) Finnish
£673	$1197	(1-Dec-91 HOR.H228) Reeds on beach (22x33cm-9x13in) s. (F.M 5200)

THIOLE, A (19th C) ?
£744	$1346	(3-Dec-91 SY.MI125) Montagne innevate (53x73cm-21x29in) s.d.1898 (I.L 1600000)

THIOLLET, Alexandre (1824-1895) French
£1800	$3186	(14-Feb-92 C30/R) The donkey boy (35x28cm-14x11in) s. panel
£2600	$4446	(17-Mar-92 PH135/R) Figures in landscape (26x24cm-10x9in) s.

THIRION, Victor Charles (1833-1878) French
£3976	$7037	(5-Nov-91 SY.AM50/R) Little shepherdess (137x75cm-54x30in) s.d.1878 (D.FL 13000)

THIRTLE, John (1777-1839) British
£4800	*$8448*	*(9-Apr-92 S58/R) Devil's Tower, Norwich (20x28cm-8x11in) W/C over pencil*

THIRY, Leonard (1500-1550) Flemish
£700	*$1344*	*(8-Jul-92 PH139/R) Study of head of woman, hair arranged in elaborate plaits (24x18cm-9x7in) i. black chk htd white*

THIVET, Yvonne (20th C) French
£1027	$1848	(18-Nov-91 AT.P380) L'oasis (60x73cm-24x29in) s.d.1921 (F.FR 10000)

THOL, Hendrick Otto von (1859-1902) Dutch
£524	$907	(25-Mar-92 KM.K1469) Dutch landscape with figures working in field (20x35cm-8x14in) indis.s. canvas on panel (DM 1500)

THOLEN, Willem Bastiaan (1860-1931) Dutch
£546	$1000	(4-Jun-92 GOM.M13) Pueblo de Pescadores (40x44cm-16x17in) s.
£765	$1330	(14-Apr-92 SY.AM253) Landscape at dusk with man in boat (38x58cm-15x23in) s.d.94 (D.FL 2500)
£1223	$2128	(14-Apr-92 SY.AM261/R) View of Rhenen with the Cunera-Tower (30x51cm-12x20in) s. panel (D.FL 4000)
£1672	$2909	(17-Sep-91 CH.AM415) A view on the Kampveersche toren, Veere (28x43cm-11x17in) s.d.08 canvas laid down on panel (D.FL 5500)
£2141	$3725	(14-Apr-92 SY.AM116/R) Woody lake (75x65cm-30x26in) s. (D.FL 7000)
£8869	$15431	(14-Apr-92 SY.AM106/R) Men towing boats in canal (46x51cm-18x20in) (D.FL 29000)
£11621	$20685	(30-Oct-91 CH.AM13/R) View of jetty of Enkhuizen with sailing vessels and fishermen on quay (64x93cm-25x37in) s.d.1901 (D.FL 38000)
£13065	$23256	(29-Oct-91 PH.T27/R) Windmills, Giethoorn (92x149cm-36x59in) s. (C.D 26000)
£550	*$980*	*(30-Oct-91 CH.AM303) Blacksmith in forge (17x25cm-7x10in) s. W/C bodycol htd.white (D.FL 1800)*
£909	*$1609*	*(22-Apr-92 CH.AM327/R) Schokland (34x50cm-13x20in) s. W/C (D.FL 3000)*
£979	*$1742*	*(30-Oct-91 CH.AM349) Workers in sandpit (36x55cm-14x22in) s. col.chk htd.white (D.FL 3200)*
£1468	*$2554*	*(14-Apr-92 SY.AM65/R) Street scene (36x47cm-14x19in) s. W/C (D.FL 4800)*

THOLEN, Willem Bastiaan and VOERMAN, Jan (19th C) Dutch
£1809	$3220	(29-Oct-91 PH.T19/R) Bringing home cows (40x63cm-16x25in) s. (C.D 3600)

THOLER, Raymond (1859-?) French
£526 $1000   (24-Jun-92 D.NY80) Still life of peaches, plums, cherries, berries and figs before cruche (53x74cm-21x29in) s.

THOLSTRUP, Anne (20th C) Danish
£529 $957   (20-May-92 KH.K192) Composition (130x100cm-51x39in) init. (D.KR 6000)

THOM, James C (1785-?) British
£1038 $1900   (16-May-92 HG.C256/R) Lesson in cookery (33x23cm-13x9in) s. panel

THOM, James Crawford (1835-1898) American
£552 $1000   (24-May-92 LIT.L60) Boy on pony in snowstorm (36x46cm-14x18in) s.
£847 $1500   (14-Feb-92 DM.D2027/R) Sheep and children s.
£1229 $2200   (14-Nov-91 CE.NY190/R) Pink and white roses (30x24cm-12x9in) init. board

THOMA, Hans (1839-1924) German
£2799 $5094   (26-May-92 KF.M430/R) Dachs hounds (62x74cm-24x29in) mono.d.1885 (DM 8200)
£2891 $5175   (5-May-92 ZEL.L1565/R) Crucifixion (49x34cm-19x13in) mono board (DM 8500)
£3253 $5596   (8-Oct-91 ZEL.L1748/R) Woman beneath group of trees in lake landscape, evening (33x45cm-13x18in) mono.d.1887 board (DM 9500)
£59441 $105804   (25-Nov-91 WK.M1003/R) Lauterbrunner Tal (159x135cm-63x53in) mono.d.1904 (DM 170000)
£479   *$825*   *(11-Oct-91 AW.H1329/R) The fight against dishonesty 1914 and earlier (24x17cm-9x7in) s.i. indian ink pen over pencil (DM 1400)*
£825   *$1435*   *(18-Sep-91 N.M281/R) Black Forest landscape near Bernau (21x27cm-8x11in) mono.i. pencil wash htd.white sold with poem (DM 2400)*
£1199   *$2062*   *(11-Oct-91 AW.H1330/R) Female nude lying on rock in sea (23x31cm-9x12in) mono.d.1891 chk W/C (DM 3500)*

THOMA, Hans (attrib) (1839-1924) German
£1648 $3000   (28-May-92 SY.NY247/R) Harvest (89x121cm-35x48in) s.d.1878

THOMA, Hans (circle) (1839-1924) German
£2637 $4536   (8-Oct-91 ZEL.L1747/R) Boy playing flute seated by the edge of wood (122x101cm-48x40in) (DM 7700)

THOMA, Josef (1828-1899) Austrian
£599 $1083   (3-Dec-91 FN.S2183) Moonlit mountainous river landscape (62x40cm-24x16in) s. (DM 1700)
£627 $1141   (11-Dec-91 N.M613/R) Landscape with palm trees by water and Arabic town beyond (42x68cm-17x27in) s. (DM 1800)
£687 $1196   (21-Sep-91 SA.A1830/R) View of village in mountain village (19x26cm-7x10in) s. (DM 2000)
£781 $1383   (5-Nov-91 GF.L2510/R) Cottage by mountain stream (45x55cm-18x22in) s.d.1857 (S.FR 2000)
£1236 $2163   (20-Feb-92 D.V493/R) Mountain range (37x58cm-15x23in) s.d.1879 (A.S 25000)
£1254 $2283   (12-Dec-91 L.K703) River landscape with farmhouse and mountain range beyond (51x76cm-20x30in) s. (DM 3600)
£1384 $2422   (20-Feb-92 D.V492/R) View of Swiss glacier (37x58cm-15x23in) s.d.1879 (A.S 28000)
£1696 $3221   (24-Jun-92 KM.K1279/R) Landscape near Bozen with peasants driving cattle across wooden bridge (70x94cm-28x37in) s. (DM 4900)
£1895 $3240   (13-Mar-92 FN.S2992/R) Kochelsee landscape with hunter and dog on path (68x105cm-27x41in) s. (DM 5400)
£2343 $4053   (25-Mar-92 KM.K1470) Grundelsee landscape with figures in rising thunderstorm, Salzkammergut (69x106cm-27x42in) s. (DM 6700)
£3497 $5979   (18-Mar-92 N.M662/R) Mountain lake landscape with farmhouse and figures (52x74cm-20x29in) s. (DM 10000)
£4895 $8371   (18-Mar-92 N.M661/R) Stag and deer by torrent (105x79cm-41x31in) s. (DM 14000)

THOMA-HOEFELE, Carl (1866-1923) Swiss
£1745 $3123   (16-Jan-92 D.V18/R) Still life of cherries (31x48cm-12x19in) s.i. (A.S 35000)
£1835 $3266   (30-Oct-91 CH.AM178/R) Pfingstrosen und Porzellan (77x89cm-30x35in) s. s.i.verso (D.FL 6000)

THOMAS, Felix (1815-1875) French
£1848 $3326   (18-Nov-91 AT.P368/R) La sentinelle devant les ruines de Ninive (28x45cm-11x18in) s. (F.FR 18000)

THOMAS, George Housman (1824-1868) British
£560   *$1002*   *(15-Jan-92 BT72/R) Cavalry (30x46cm-12x18in) s.i.d.1861 W/C*

THOMAS, Gerard (school) (1663-1720) Flemish
£3629 $6423   (6-Nov-91 LT.P70/R) L'atelier de sculpture (118x101cm-46x40in) (F.FR 36000)
£4611 $8299   (27-Jan-92 CSC.P38/R) L'atelier de sculpture (118x101cm-46x40in) (F.FR 45000)

THOMAS, Henri Joseph (1878-1972) Belgian
£850 $1453   (21-Mar-92 KV.L289) Nu a la draperie rouge (27x35cm-11x14in) s. panel (B.FR 50000)

THOMAS, Henri Joseph (1878-1972) Belgian-cont.
£2500 $4300   (12-Oct-91 KV.L378/R) The seamstress (40x32cm-16x13in) s. (B.FR 150000)

THOMAS, Henry (19/20th C) ?
£5970 $10925   (12-May-92 C.A314/R) La toilette (73x60cm-29x24in) s. (B.FR 360000)

THOMAS, Howard (1899-?) American
£774 $1300   (14-Aug-91 B.P80/R) Belle Vernon Bridge, Pennsylvania (41x51cm-16x20in)
s. board

THOMAS, M (?) ?
£863 $1553   (23-Nov-91 SO.S625/R) Woman with roses (78x40cm-31x16in) s.d.1890
(S.KR 9000)

THOMAS, Melina (19th C) French
£1013 $1834   (22-May-92 LD.P68) Anne Boleyn prisonniere dans la Tour de Londres se
confesse a l'archeveque de Cantorbery (80x64cm-31x25in) s.d.
(F.FR 10000)

THOMAS, Robert Strickland (1787-1853) British
£4600 $8740   (24-Jun-92 DR187/R) Coastal scenes with fishermen (28x35cm-11x14in) one
s.d.1836 pair

THOMAS, T (19th C) British
£2000 $3560   (1-Nov-91 MAI619) Landscape with drovers and sheep s.

THOMAS, Thomas (19th C) British
£620 $1135   (14-May-92 CSK240) By the ford (46x61cm-18x24in) s.
£1400 $2562   (14-May-92 CSK199/R) Wooded river landscapes with figures by mill. Cattle
watering (51x76cm-20x30in) s. pair
£1550 $2976   (5-Aug-92 RBB572/R) Lane near Dinmore (48x58cm-19x23in) s.

THOMAS, William Cave (1820-?) British
£550   *$1018*   *(11-Jun-92 CSK128/R) The tired fisherboy (36x25cm-14x10in) s.d.66 pencil
W/C htd.white*

THOMASSE, Adolphe (1850-1930) French
£1561   *$2732*   *(30-Mar-92 ZZ.F151/R) Les chiens de Cirque (35x66cm-14x26in) gouache
(F.FR 15000)*

THOMASSIN, Desire (1858-1933) Austrian
£2768 $5260   (27-Jan-92 FN.L1170) Fishing boats off the Dutch coast (42x50cm-17x20in)
s. board (DM 8000)
£4225 $7648   (3-Dec-91 FN.S2492/R) Hungarian farmhouse with girl and geese by stream
(41x54cm-16x21in) s. board (DM 12000)
£5498 $9567   (17-Sep-91 FN.S2584/R) Snow covered landscape with stream near farmhouse
and children (65x94cm-26x37in) s. (DM 16000)

THOMASSIN, Desire (attrib) (1858-1933) Austrian
£2448 $4185   (18-Mar-92 N.M663/R) Village scene with peasants at dawn in winter
(53x74cm-21x29in) i. (DM 7000)

THOMASSIN, Pauline (19th C) ?
£1032 $1920   (16-Jun-92 SY.B287/R) Portrait of little girl with pigeon
(86x68cm-34x27in) s.i. (B.FR 62000)

THOMASSIN, Sophie (20th C) Hungarian
£555   *$955*   *(14-Oct-91 AT.P21) Sans titre (67x50cm-26x20in) s.d.1991 mixed media
panel (F.FR 5500)*

THOME, Verner (1878-?) Finnish
£1552   *$2763*   *(1-Dec-91 HOR.H232) Begonias (34x26cm-13x10in) s.d.1922 (F.M 12000)*
£2655   *$4673*   *(12-Apr-92 HOR.H233/R) Yacht race (40x51cm-16x20in) s.d.1930 (F.M 21000)*
£5310   *$9345*   *(12-Apr-92 HOR.H232) Still life (42x45cm-17x18in) s.d.1908 (F.M 42000)*
£670   *$1179*   *(12-Apr-92 HOR.H234) Drying the sails (34x50cm-13x20in) s.d.1912 W/C
(F.M 5300)*

THOMKINS, Andre (20th C) ?
£1417   *$2438*   *(16-Oct-91 G.Z120/R) Halten am Alten (18x12cm-7x5in) s.i.d.1974 indian
ink pen pencil (S.FR 3600)*

THOMON, Thomas de (1754-1813) French
£1433   *$2595*   *(21-May-92 L.K341/R) Town near Rome (21x27cm-8x11in) s.verso pen pencil
board (DM 4200)*

THOMOPOULOS, Epaminondas (1878-1974) Greek
£800 $1448   (2-Dec-91 CSK85/R) The young shepherdesses (49x61cm-19x24in) s.
canvasboard

THOMPSON, Cephas Giovanni (1809-1888) American
£838 $1500   (14-Nov-91 CE.NY32/R) Portrait of young man (71x57cm-28x22in) s. panel

THOMPSON, E (19/20th C) ?
£441   *$785*   *(28-Apr-92 RAS.K709/R) Shipsportrait 'Valdemar Seir Faaborg'
(25x38cm-10x15in) s.d.1901 gouache (D.KR 5000)*

HOMPSON, Edward H (1866-1949) British
£400 $764   *(30-Jun-92 SWS1746) Scene in the Lake District (30x45cm-12x18in) s. W/C*
£460 $851   *(10-Jun-92 HAR437) Cloudy June (20x43cm-8x17in) s. W/C*
£540 $923   *(16-Mar-92 LW1838) View of Derwent Water (30x51cm-12x20in) s. W/C*
£960 $1642   *(16-Mar-92 LW1839/R) View of Double Dry stone bridge at Grange in Borrowdale (43x61cm-17x24in) W/C*

HOMPSON, G H (19th C) British
£800 $1376   (4-Mar-92 S50/R) Sunrise - Arundel Tower, Southampton (35x46cm-14x18in) s.d.83 i.stretcher

HOMPSON, Jacob (1806-1879) British
£1250 $2125   (7-Aug-91 WAW333/R) Four trout on rock with foliage and river in background (21x26cm-8x10in) s.d.1848 panel

HOMPSON, Leslie P (1880-1963) American
£1676 $3000   (14-Nov-91 CE.NY81/R) Summer picnic (77x128cm-30x50in)

HOMPSON, Michel (1921-) French
£790 $1430   (20-May-92 I.N182/R) La foule (100x100cm-39x39in) s. acrylic canvas (F.FR 7800)
£1613 $2790   (6-Oct-91 BG.P49/R) Nature morte (130x164cm-51x65in) s.d.1953 (F.FR 16000)

HOMPSON, Sydney Lough (1877-1973) British
£1791 $3206   (6-May-92 DS.W93) Old doorway, South of France (39x31cm-15x12in) s. i.verso (NZ.D 6000)
£3086 $5586   (4-Dec-91 DS.W166) Washing at the fountain, Brittany (30x90cm-12x35in) s. (NZ.D 10000)
£4500 $8190   (12-Dec-91 CSK92) Concarneau, a group of fisherfolk (45x56cm-18x22in) s.
£5075 $9084   (6-May-92 DS.W52) Washing at the fountain, Brittany (31x39cm-12x15in) s. i.verso (NZ.D 17000)
£12346 $22346   (4-Dec-91 DS.W38/R) Street scene in Southern France (79x62cm-31x24in) s. (NZ.D 40000)
£3284 $5878   *(6-May-92 DS.W26/R) Street in Brittany (48x37cm-19x15in) s. gouache (NZ.D 11000)*

HOMPSON, Thomas (1775-1852) American
£3000 $5340   (1-May-92 PHE20 a) Barque off the coast at Dover (55x85cm-22x33in) s. indist.d.1809verso

HOMPSON, Thomas John (1877-1917) Canadian
£620 $1184   (21-Jul-92 JRL.S86) Ulysses tormented by the sirens (159x117cm-63x46in) s. acrylic (A.D 1600)
£891 $1703   (21-Jul-92 JRL.S156) Penelope beset by the Suitors (177x83cm-70x33in) acrylic (A.D 2300)
£969 $1851   (21-Jul-92 JRL.S157) The Feeding of the 5000 (180x120cm-71x47in) s. acrylic (A.D 2500)
£4457 $8514   (21-Jul-92 JRL.S158) Annunciation, distant town (84x131cm-33x52in) s. board (A.D 11500)

HOMPSON, William (19th C) British
£2000 $3560   (31-Oct-91 B174/R) Portrait of William Warboys holding cricket bat. Portrait of brother, Thomas, holding bow and arrow (61x50cm-24x20in) s.d.1836 pair

HOMPSON, William John (1771-1845) British
£900 $1602   *(27-Nov-91 C240/R) Portrait of lady in dress with lace shawl (7x?cm-3x?in) min. gold frame oval*

HOMSEN, August Carl Wilhelm (1813-1886) Danish
£714 $1327   (16-Jun-92 RAS.V881/R) Wooded landscape with deer by lake (82x123cm-32x48in) s.d.1875 (D.KR 8000)
£3846 $7000   (27-May-92 CH.NY67/R) Sunday afternoon outing (55x45cm-22x18in) mono.d.1898

HOMSON, Carl Christian Frederik Jakob (1847-1912) Danish
£1764 $3139   (28-Apr-92 RAS.K148/R) By a sick-bed (88x70cm-35x28in) mono.d.83 (D.KR 20000)

HOMSON, George (1860-1939) British
£3500 $6405   (5-Jun-92 C3/R) The Monument (76x56cm-30x22in) s.d.1897

HOMSON, Horatio (fl.1884-1906) British
£680 $1170   (11-Oct-91 PHE106) Yorkhill Wharf on the Clyde (51x76cm-20x30in) s.

HOMSON, Hugh (1860-1920) British
£400 $696   *(17-Sep-91 SWS185/R) 'As if I had addressed myself wholly to him' (30x20cm-12x8in) s.d.1903 ink W/C*
£600 $1044   *(17-Sep-91 SWS186/R) 'What do you follow me for' (27x20cm-11x8in) s.d.12 ink pencil wash*

HOMSON, John Murray (1885-?) British
£1300 $2184   (26-Aug-91 S862/R) Litter of puppies (61x91cm-24x36in) s.

THOMSON, Keith (1934-) American?
£366 $659   (18-Nov-91 HO.ED27) Hillside (51x71cm-20x28in) W/C (C.D 750)

THOMSON, Tom (1877-1917) Canadian
£27397 $50137   (14-May-92 SY.T74/R) Forest interior (20x25cm-8x10in) estate st. panel (C.D 60000)
£34247 $62329   (26-May-92 JOY.T100 b) Hillside on Big Cauchon Lake, Algonquin Park (21x26cm-8x10in) studio st.verso panel (C.D 75000)
£42289 $75274   (26-Nov-91 JOY.T75/R) Island 182, Split Rock group, Georgian Bay (21x26cm-8x10in) studio st. s.i.verso panel (C.D 85000)
£43532 $77488   (26-Nov-91 JOY.T25/R) Algonquin Park (21x29cm-8x11in) studio st. board (C.D 87500)
£47500 $84075   (6-Nov-91 SY.T80/R) Pine trees at sunset (27x21cm-11x8in) s. board (C.D 95000)
£47500 $84075   (6-Nov-91 SY.T88/R) Northern lake (20x25cm-8x10in) s. panel (C.D 95000)
£79909 $146233   (14-May-92 SY.T66/R) Woodland interior, winter (22x26cm-9x10in) estate st. board (C.D 175000)
£86758 $157900   (26-May-92 JOY.T85/R) Nocturne (40x45cm-16x18in) (C.D 190000)

THOMSON, William (1927-1990) British
£550 $1051   (16-Jul-92 B185/R) Reflection (152x152cm-60x60in) s.d.1979

THONY, Eduard (1866-1950) German
£874 $1512   (25-Mar-92 KM.K1763) Die Kaiserjager (32x25cm-13x10in) mono.d.1915 pastel (DM 2500)
£1119 $1992   (25-Nov-91 WK.M1002/R) Prozess Lucie Berlin (42x26cm-17x10in) mixed media paper on board (DM 3200)
£1220 $2220   (11-Dec-91 N.M272/R) At the race court (21x24cm-8x9in) mono.i.d.1897 indian ink (DM 3500)

THONY, Wilhelm (1888-1949) Austrian
£2181 $3970   (26-May-92 D.V107/R) A breath of ... (25x20cm-10x8in) s. pen indian ink (A.S 45000)
£3151 $5734   (26-May-92 D.V106/R) Cafe Stefanie (20x28cm-8x11in) pen brush indian ink col.pencil (A.S 65000)
£3476 $6187   (28-Nov-91 D.V165/R) On the bridge (17x22cm-7x9in) s. pen brush indian ink wash (A.S 70000)
£4847 $8822   (26-May-92 D.V108/R) Landscape with figure (24x31cm-9x12in) s. W/C (A.S 100000)

THORBJORNSEN, G C (19th C) Norwegian
£630 $1097   (14-Sep-91 BU.O344) 'Laurvigen' (37x53cm-15x21in) s. gouache (N.KR 7200)
£3012 $5481   (10-Dec-91 UL.T229/R) 'Laurvigen' W/C gouache (N.KR 34000)

THORBURN, A (1860-1935) British
£550 $995   (6-Dec-91 K452/R) Sketch of Gooseander (20x30cm-8x12in) W/C

THORBURN, Archibald (1860-1935) British
£417 $700   (28-Aug-91 MFA.C268) Bird (10x10cm-4x4in) s.d.1923 W/C htd white
£950 $1596   (26-Aug-91 S928) Head of a stag (25x33cm-10x13in) d.Sept.27.01 W/C
£1050 $1869   (21-Jan-92 SWS1353/R) Hare and blackgame in snow (35x25cm-14x10in) s. W/C bodycol grisaille arched top
£1050 $1838   (25-Feb-92 C34/R) Warbler (19x13cm-7x5in) init. pencil W/C htd white
£1300 $2405   (12-Jun-92 C58) Study of a hare (17x21cm-7x8in) init. pencil W/C htd.white
£1350 $2363   (25-Feb-92 C88/R) Lilford, Pinetum - to fore Wattled and Crowned Crane and Stork and pelicans (25x18cm-10x7in) s. en grisaille
£1400 $2450   (25-Feb-92 C92/R) Terns (33x24cm-13x9in) s. W/C en grisaille
£1500 $2625   (25-Feb-92 C96/R) Water Rail. Spotted Crake. Sun birds (10x14cm-4x6in) two init. pencil W/C bodycol three one mount
£1650 $2888   (26-Sep-91 KING342) Oyster catchers (23x30cm-9x12in) s. W/C
£1900 $3383   (27-Nov-91 B154/R) Golden eagle (23x30cm-9x12in) s.i. W/C
£2000 $3360   (26-Aug-91 S926/R) Pheasants in snow (14x18cm-6x7in) s. W/C
£2400 $4032   (26-Aug-91 S899/R) Common buzzard (28x18cm-11x7in) s.d.1925 W/C htd bodycol.
£2800 $4984   (29-Oct-91 C152/R) A little crake (23x32cm-9x13in) s. W/C htd white
£3000 $5550   (12-Jun-92 C56/R) Study of a cockatoo (26x21cm-10x8in) s.d.1906 pencil W/C htd.bodycol.
£3200 $5696   (28-Apr-92 S207/R) Four grouse in Highland landscape (30x44cm-12x17in) s. W/C htd white bodycol.
£3500 $6125   (25-Feb-92 C91/R) Grey Plover. Redshank. Knot. Ruff (8x10cm-3x4in) one s. all i. pencil pen W/C four one frame
£3500 $6125   (25-Feb-92 C110/R) Eagle owl at dusk (24x18cm-9x7in) s.d.1910 pencil W/C htd white
£3700 $6660   (21-Nov-91 WA129/R) Jack Snipe (18x28cm-7x11in) s.d.1929 W/C
£4500 $7875   (25-Feb-92 C97/R) Mallard (23x16cm-9x6in) s.d.1905 i.verso pencil W/C bodycol
£4500 $7560   (26-Aug-91 S932/R) Pair of Golden Eagles (21x13cm-8x5in) s.d.1900 W/C htd bodycol.
£4800 $8400   (25-Feb-92 C99/R) Widgeon swimming (23x16cm-9x6in) s.d.1905 i.verso pencil W/C bodycol
£5000 $8750   (25-Feb-92 C156/R) Partridges in stubble (18x26cm-7x10in) s.d.1931 pencil W/C bodycol
£5500 $9845   (13-Nov-91 CG554/R) Mallard rising (34x55cm-13x22in) s.d.1926 W/C htd.bodycol.

THORBURN, Archibald (1860-1935) British-cont.

£	$	Description
£5500	$9845	(13-Nov-91 CG557/R) A black cock on a branch (55x45cm-22x18in) s. W/C htd.white
£5500	$9625	(25-Feb-92 C160/R) Blackcock (24x17cm-9x7in) s. pencil W/C bodycol
£5700	$10260	(21-Nov-91 WA130/R) Snipe (18x28cm-7x11in) s.d.1929 W/C
£5800	$9744	(26-Aug-91 S896/R) Curlew sandpiper, knot and dunlin in winter (20x28cm-8x11in) s.d.1926 W/C htd bodycol.
£6000	$10500	(25-Feb-92 C169/R) Cock Grouse in flight (18x29cm-7x11in) s.d.1903 pencil W/C htd white
£6000	$10500	(25-Feb-92 C164/R) Grouse coming down wind (37x54cm-15x21in) s.d.1901 i.verso pencil W/C htd white
£6000	$10740	(13-Nov-91 CG556/R) A snipe drumming (55x35cm-22x14in) s.d.1927 W/C htd.white
£6200	$10788	(17-Sep-91 SWS189/R) Robin in winter (27x18cm-11x7in) s.d.1930 W/C bodycol.
£6300	$11025	(25-Feb-92 C113/R) Barn owl (37x27cm-15x11in) s.d.1929 i.verso pencil W/C bodycol
£6500	$11375	(25-Feb-92 C100/R) Garganey (24x16cm-9x6in) s.d.1906 i.verso pencil W/C bodycol
£7000	$12250	(25-Feb-92 C157/R) Snipe at water's edge (18x27cm-7x11in) s.d.1929 pencil W/C bodycol
£7104	$13000	(5-Jun-92 SY.NY317/R) November - Woodcock (59x52cm-23x20in) s.d.1907 W/C
£7500	$13125	(25-Feb-92 C168/R) Snipe at water's edge (15x19cm-6x7in) s.d.1921 pencil W/C bodycol
£7500	$12600	(26-Aug-91 S933/R) Snipe (27x18cm-11x7in) s.d.1910 W/C htd white
£7500	$13425	(13-Nov-91 CG553/R) Widgeon rising (33x55cm-13x22in) s.d.1926 W/C htd.white
£7500	$13125	(25-Feb-92 C165/R) Red-legged Partridge and covey of grey partridges by corn stooks (23x37cm-9x15in) init. pencil W/C htd white
£8000	$14240	(28-Apr-92 S225/R) Redstart, white-spotted bluethroat, whinchat and other birds (54x40cm-21x16in) s.i.d.1913 W/C bodycol.
£8000	$14240	(28-Apr-92 S228/R) Starlings, nutcracker, jay, chough and other birds (54x40cm-21x16in) s.i.d.1913 W/C bodycol.
£8000	$14240	(28-Apr-92 S227/R) Waxwing, flycatchers, golden oriole and other birds (54x40cm-21x16in) s.i.d.1913 W/C bodycol.
£8500	$14280	(26-Aug-91 S905/R) Greyhen in flight (47x64cm-19x25in) init.d.1889 W/C htd bodycol.
£10000	$17500	(25-Feb-92 C161/R) Grey partridges at edge of field (18x27cm-7x11in) s.d.1916 W/C htd white
£10000	$18500	(12-Jun-92 C64/R) Swerving from the guns - red grouse in flight over moorland (56x77cm-22x30in) s.d.1911 pencil W/C htd.white
£12000	$20160	(26-Aug-91 S922/R) Partridge in flight (43x77cm-17x30in) s.d.1900 W/C
£12000	$21720	(4-Dec-91 S169 a) Peregrin falcon and prey (75x54cm-30x21in) s.d.1889 W/C htd bodycol
£14000	$25060	(13-Nov-91 CG552/R) A covey of English partridge flying over a covey of French partridge (34x55cm-13x22in) s.d.1926 W/C htd.bodycol.
£15000	$26250	(25-Feb-92 C161 a/R) Snipe in snow (18x28cm-7x11in) s.d.1929 pencil W/C bodycol
£15000	$26700	(28-Apr-92 S205/R) Bustards at sunrise (47x74cm-19x29in) s.d.1894 W/C
£16500	$28875	(25-Feb-92 C94/R) Widgeon at low tide (53x74cm-21x29in) s.d.1899 pencil W/C bodycol
£18000	$32220	(13-Nov-91 CG551/R) A cock and two hen pheasants in a woodland (35x55cm-14x22in) s.d.1926 W/C htd.bodycol.
£20000	$36200	(4-Dec-91 S169/R) Greenland or Gyr falcon (75x54cm-30x21in) s.d.1899 W/C htd white
£21000	$36750	(25-Feb-92 C159/R) Partridges in flight (44x76cm-17x30in) s.d.1902 pencil W/C bodycol
£25000	$43750	(25-Feb-92 C158/R) Blackgame (36x55cm-14x22in) s.d.1928 pencil W/C htd white
£30000	$52500	(25-Feb-92 C171/R) Partridge amongst stubble (53x74cm-21x29in) s.d.1900 pencil W/C bodycol
£30000	$55500	(12-Jun-92 C62/R) Red grouse packing (56x76cm-22x30in) s.d.1911 pencil W/C htd bodycol.
£40000	$70000	(25-Feb-92 C162/R) Clearing after rain - Red Grouse amongst heather (53x76cm-21x30in) s.d.1920 pencil W/C bodycol

THOREN, Esaias (1901-1981) Swedish

£	$	Description
£493	$903	(12-May-92 GO.G185) Line composition with eye (22x27cm-9x11in) s. panel (S.KR 5200)
£576	$1042	(3-Dec-91 AB.S5165/R) Planetarium (64x53cm-25x21in) s.d.1980 panel (S.KR 6000)
£616	$1059	(8-Mar-92 BU.M319) Ornamental plan (24x33cm-9x13in) s.d.1951 (S.KR 6400)
£1068	$1858	(17-Sep-91 RAS.K113/R) Underwater landscape (38x46cm-15x18in) s. masonite (D.KR 12000)
£1184	$1978	(25-Aug-91 BU.M488) Meeting with Spain (61x51cm-24x20in) s.d.1955 panel (S.KR 12600)
£1536	$2779	(3-Dec-91 AB.S5164/R) The cliff of eyes (38x46cm-15x18in) s. panel (S.KR 16000)
£2044	$3658	(16-Nov-91 FAL.M359/R) Composition with lemons (46x53cm-18x21in) s. panel (S.KR 21500)
£2879	$5211	(3-Dec-91 AB.S5163/R) The table - composition (83x118cm-33x46in) s.d.1963 (S.KR 30000)
£3455	$6253	(3-Dec-91 AB.S5162/R) Red and green mask (40x50cm-16x20in) s.d.32 (S.KR 36000)

THOREN, Esaias (1901-1981) Swedish-cont.
£3784 $6850   (19-May-92 AB.S5331/R) Pictures in six panels (80x64cm-31x25in) s.d.1951 panel (S.KR 40000)

THOREN, Otto von (1828-1889) Austrian
£1200 $2076   (4-Oct-91 C81/R) The storm (34x52cm-13x20in) s.
£1504 $2722   (5-Dec-91 D.V110) Riders (28x46cm-11x18in) s. panel (A.S 30000)
£436 $750   *(12-Oct-91 DU.E511) Pausing for a drink before the battle (20x23cm-8x9in) s.d.1840 graphite W/C gouache*

THORENFELD, A (1839-1907) Danish
£617 $1099   (28-Apr-92 RAS.K612) Landscape from Troense, Tasinge (43x64cm-17x25in) mono.d.73 (D.KR 7000)

THORN, Diana (?) ?
£1073 $1900   (9-Nov-91 W.W121/R) Polo (46x61cm-18x24in) s.i. panel

THORNAM, Emmy (1852-1935) Danish
£778 $1416   (12-Dec-91 RAS.V794) Still life of blue and white flowers (53x44cm-21x17in) s. (D.KR 8700)
£1529 $2661   (14-Apr-92 SY.AM210/R) Still life with geraniums (58x45cm-23x18in) s. (D.FL 5000)
£3000 $5430   (22-May-92 C8/R) White and blue cineraria (52x44cm-20x17in) s.

THORNAM, Ludovica (1853-1896) Danish
£903 $1625   (19-Nov-91 RAS.K140/R) Interior with girl peeling carrots (65x50cm-26x20in) s.d.1895 (D.KR 10000)

THORNBERY, William A see THORNLEY, William

THORNE, Alfred (1850-1916) Swedish
£569 $1042   (12-May-92 GO.G186) Street scene in winter (16x10cm-6x4in) s.d.1885 panel (S.KR 6000)
£760 $1322   (13-Apr-92 AB.S260) Road by lake, Hallstahammar (55x69cm-22x27in) s. (S.KR 8000)
£1179 $2087   (25-Apr-92 SO.S608/R) Summer landscape (36x60cm-14x24in) s. (S.KR 12500)
£1509 $2672   (25-Apr-92 SO.S607/R) Trangforsen 1905 (37x60cm-15x24in) s. (S.KR 16000)
£2075 $3674   (25-Apr-92 SO.S606/R) Boy on beach (53x37cm-21x15in) s.d.1890 (S.KR 22000)
£2207 $3995   (3-Dec-91 AB.S4671/R) Spring landscape with croft and women working (37x62cm-15x24in) s.d.1884 (S.KR 23000)

THORNE, J R (?) ?
£600 $1098   (5-Feb-92 ZZ.B86) Grecian maidens in interior (72x92cm-28x36in) s.

THORNE-WAITE, Robert see WAITE, Robert Thorne

THORNELEY, C (fl.1858-1898) British
£1300 $2470   (24-Jun-92 DR114) Mount St. Michael. Fisherfolk on beach (25x41cm-10x16in) one indist.s. pair

THORNELEY, Charles (fl.1858-1898) British
£554 $1052   (24-Jun-92 KM.K1281) Sailing ship and rowing boat before harbour entrance (25x20cm-10x8in) s. panel one of pair (DM 1600)
£588 $1118   (24-Jun-92 KM.K1280) Sailing ship and rowing boat in choppy seas (25x20cm-10x8in) s. panel one of pair (DM 1700)
£950 $1710   (22-Nov-91 C76/R) Sunrise on the Essex Coast (25x41cm-10x16in) bears sig. bears sig.verso
£3200 $5376   (15-Aug-91 B414/R) Spiritsail barge in River Medway. Coastal craft and fishermen, Margate (20x41cm-8x16in) indist.s. pair

THORNELEY, Charles (attrib) (fl.1858-1898) British
£3500 $6300   (22-Nov-91 C111/R) Fisherfolk unloading catch at end of day. Returning home with catch (28x46cm-11x18in) bears sig.d.1874 board oval pair

THORNEYCROFT, Sir William Hamo see THORNYCROFT, Hamo

THORNHILL, Sir James (attrib) (1675-1734) British
£800 $1432   (13-Nov-91 S187/R) The Judgement of Paris (32x24cm-13x9in)

THORNLEY, Hubert (19th C) British
£520 $998   (29-Jul-92 PHC384/R) Harbour scene with shipping (24x39cm-9x15in) s.
£900 $1728   (28-Jul-92 SWS368) Coastal scene with fisherfolk (25x39cm-10x15in) s.
£1300 $2496   (28-Jul-92 SWS361) Whitby, evening (25x20cm-10x8in) s. panel
£2500 $4500   (22-Nov-91 C57/R) Sunrise low tide, Scarborough. Shipping off Whitby (36x30cm-14x12in) s. pair

THORNLEY, William (19/20th C) British
£900 $1629   (20-May-92 S203/R) Sunset, old hulks and shipping (35x30cm-14x12in) s. i.verso
£900 $1629   (20-May-92 S228/R) Fishing boats at low tide (35x61cm-14x24in) s.
£950 $1691   (28-Apr-92 PH79) Bringing in catch, moonlight (34x29cm-13x11in) s.
£1100 $2035   (9-Jun-92 AG350/R) Sunrise Cromer. St. Michael's Mount (29x19cm-11x7in) s. pair
£1250 $2288   (5-Feb-92 CSK282) Evening calm (28x24cm-11x9in) s.

HORNLEY, William (19/20th C) British-cont.
£1646 $2798   (21-Oct-91 SY.J314) Wind against tide - hay barge near Gravesend (39x59cm-15x23in) s. (SA.R 8000)
£1800 $3456   (28-Jul-92 SWS364/R) The quayside. Busy estuary (34x29cm-13x11in) s. pair
£1800 $3258   (20-May-92 S204/R) Shipping, mouth of the Thames (40x56cm-16x22in) s. i.stretcher
£2100 $3528   (15-Aug-91 B408) Scarborough (20x30cm-8x12in) s.i. board pair
£2900 $5220   (9-Jan-92 B283/R) Fishing vessles off a coastline (25x41cm-10x16in) pair
£4500 $8100   (22-Nov-91 C40/R) Fishermen on beach below Mont St Michel (61x91cm-24x36in) s.
£4970 $8648   (13-Apr-92 SY.J254/R) Scarborough. On Medway (34x29cm-13x11in) s. pair (SA.R 25000)
£515   *$881*   (22-Mar-92 LT.P131) Canal a Venise (24x34cm-9x13in) s. W/C gouache (F.FR 5000)
£1034   *$1840*   (27-Nov-91 BL.P195) Paris, la Seine a l'ancien Trocadero (34x50cm-13x20in) s. W/C (F.FR 10100)

HORNLEY, William (circle) (19/20th C) British
£1200 $2292   (17-Jul-92 C168/R) Shipyard on a Thames reach (40x76cm-16x30in) indis.s.

HORNTON, H (19th C) British
£1000   *$1790*   (14-Jan-92 SWS1/R) The clerk of the course (35x27cm-14x11in) s.d.1835 s.i.d.verso W/C over pencil

HORNYCROFT, Theresa G (1853-?) British
£1300 $2301   (6-Nov-91 S221/R) Dawn at Bethlehem (89x190cm-35x75in) s. arched top
£3400 $6018   (6-Nov-91 S210/R) Flower maidens (140x340cm-55x134in) curved top

HORP, William Eric (1901-?) British
£450   *$806*   (14-Jan-92 PH110) Moonlight on sea (37x48cm-15x19in) s. pastel

HORPE, Lesbia (1919-) Australian
£617   *$1098*   (26-Nov-91 J.M1001) Botanical gardens (48x61cm-19x24in) s. canvas on board (A.D 1400)

HORRESTRUP, Christian (1823-1892) Danish
£686   *$1200*   (18-Feb-92 CE.NY72 a) Meeting by church (40x35cm-16x14in) s.d.1864

HORS, J (19th C) British
£639 $1067   (25-Aug-91 BU.M264) Wooded landscape (53x44cm-21x17in) s. (S.KR 6800)
£1650 $3152   (16-Jul-92 HB624/R) Huntsman, fisherman and worker by wood (89x69cm-35x27in) s.
£2750 $4730   (4-Mar-92 CBB28) In the shadow of the Wrekin (18x14cm-7x6in) s.

HORS, Joseph (19th C) British
£500   *$860*   (8-Oct-91 PH109) River scene in Holland (17x29cm-7x11in) s. i.verso panel
£520   *$926*   (1-Nov-91 BW390) Rural scene with farmstead, figure and sheep (18x25cm-7x10in)
£580   *$986*   (7-Aug-91 CSK458) View in Nottinghamshire (23x36cm-9x14in) s.i.d.1868verso board
£800 $1416   (6-Nov-91 S43/R) Bromsgrove (23x33cm-9x13in) s.i.
£994 $1700   (13-Mar-92 WOL.C412/R) Figures in country landscape (74x109cm-29x43in) s.
£995 $1771   (25-Nov-91 W.T1917/R) English landscapes with old cottages and figures (18x26cm-7x10in) s. board pair (C.D 2000)
£1149 $2000   (13-Sep-91 S.W2853/R) Outside cottage. Tending flock (41x64cm-16x25in) pair
£1200 $2088   (12-Sep-91 CSK131) Country road (25x36cm-10x14in) s.
£1350 $2322   (11-Oct-91 K500) Lone traveller on wooded country lane (15x20cm-6x8in) s.
£1371 $2400   (23-Sep-91 S.SL77) A view near Dorking, Surrey (51x76cm-20x30in) s.
£1450 $2596   (14-Jan-92 SWS144/R) Figure in country landscape (25x35cm-10x14in) s. panel
£1800 $3060   (24-Oct-91 CSK110/R) The Old Mill, Solihull (56x91cm-22x36in) s.
£1800 $3294   (3-Jun-92 S111/R) Riverside path (40x61cm-16x24in) s.
£1829 $3200   (18-Feb-92 CE.NY127/R) Fishing by stone bridge (51x61cm-20x24in) s.
£2000 $3660   (7-Feb-92 K523/R) Country landscape with pond, willow trees, tudor cottages and figure (30x43cm-12x17in) s.
£2400 $4272   (28-Nov-91 B160/R) Figure beside pond and cottages beyond (30x46cm-12x18in) s. pair
£2500 $4575   (3-Jun-92 S74/R) Calm before the storm (76x127cm-30x50in) s.
£3179 $5500   (29-Mar-92 MY.F52/R) Near Watson, Warwickshire (91x132cm-36x52in) s.
£3600 $6408   (28-Apr-92 PH122/R) View in Surrey (51x76cm-20x30in) s.
£3800 $7030   (12-Jun-92 C146/R) Near Weston, Warwickshire (92x133cm-36x52in) s.

HORS, Joseph (attrib) (19th C) British
£1440 $2750   (16-Jul-92 SY.NY507/R) Wood gatherers by a stream (78x101cm-31x40in) s.

HORVALDSEN, Bertel (1770-1844) Danish
£423   *$731*   (2-Sep-91 BU.K2/R) Classical figures. Mother and child (12x19cm-5x7in) pencil double-sided (D.KR 4800)

HRANE, Ragnhild (1853-1913) Scandinavian
£1250 $2100   (13-Aug-91 AG261/R) Small girl at bedroom doorway watching her mother descend stairs (61x36cm-24x14in) s.d.1891

THRASH, Dox (20th C) American
£718 $1300   (24-May-92 JRB.C55/R) Cloria (48x30cm-19x12in) s.d.1946 i.verso canvasboard

THRASHER, Leslie (1889-1936) American
£1826 $3250   (2-May-92 IH.NY187/R) Man toasting nurse and baby (51x41cm-20x16in) s.
£1826 $3250   (2-Nov-91 IH.NY89/R) Tattooed man swallowing sword (51x41cm-20x16in)

THULDEN, Theodor van (1606-1669) Dutch
£14903 $25484   (18-Mar-92 D.V100/R) Madonna with Child (89x65cm-35x26in) panel (A.S 300000)

THULDEN, Theodor van (attrib) (1606-1669) Dutch
£4023 $7000   (13-Sep-91 S.W2869/R) Judgment of Virginia (117x124cm-46x49in)

THULDEN, Theodor van (style) (1606-1669) Dutch
£850 $1530   (21-Nov-91 CSK11) Madonna and Child (58x48cm-23x19in)

THUMA, Marilyn (20th C) American
£1117 $2000   (13-Nov-91 B.SF2820/R) Abstraction (30x23cm-12x9in) init. pastel

THUNMAN, Olof (1879-1944) Swedish
£560 $963   (19-Oct-91 UA.U401/R) Winter in the field (33x41cm-13x16in) s. (S.KR 5900)
£1021 $1767   (28-Mar-92 UA.U506/R) Breakers by the coast (30x46cm-12x18in) s. (S.KR 10600)
£597 $1033   (28-Mar-92 UA.U507) Working by the coalmine (34x35cm-13x14in) s.indist.d. Indian ink (S.KR 6200)
£750 $1289   (19-Oct-91 UA.U402) Swans, Malaren (41x55cm-16x22in) s. Indian ink W/C (S.KR 7900)

THURBER, James (20th C) American
£1011 $1800   (2-Nov-91 IH.NY142/R) Man and dog sleep as woman longs to go out (20x25cm-8x10in) s. pencil
£2107 $3750   (2-May-92 IH.NY113/R) Man's head with four marginal dogs (23x20cm-9x8in) s. pastel

THURMAN, Peder (1839-1919) Norwegian
£1337 $2313   (23-Mar-92 B.O129/R) Mill house near waterfall (100x75cm-39x30in) s. (N.KR 15000)

THURMANN, Oystein (1925-1989) Norwegian
£664 $1209   (14-Dec-91 BU.O74/R) Fishing harbour, St. Tropez (46x65cm-18x26in) s.d.49 i.verso (N.KR 7500)

THYGESEN, Rudolf (1880-?) Norwegian
£1495 $2631   (7-Apr-92 UL.T235/R) Landscape (59x72cm-23x28in) s. panel (N.KR 17000)
£1667 $3100   (18-Jun-92 GWP.O105/R) Coastal landscape (51x53cm-20x21in) init.d.16 (N.KR 19000)
£2371 $4077   (7-Oct-91 B.O135/R) Still life of flowers (64x62cm-25x24in) init. (N.KR 27000)
£2546 $4379   (7-Oct-91 B.O136/R) Town scene (60x73cm-24x29in) init.d.29 (N.KR 29000)
£2807 $5221   (15-Jun-92 B.O167/R) Landscape with house by road (56x65cm-22x26in) mono. (N.KR 32000)
£5268 $9061   (10-Oct-91 BU.O54/R) June sunshine (85x80cm-33x31in) init.d.11 s.i.verso (N.KR 60000)
£6579 $12237   (15-Jun-92 B.O166/R) Mid summer night (99x165cm-39x65in) init.d.36 (N.KR 75000)

THYS, Kathy (1936-) Swiss
£547 $980   (6-May-92 GD.B1271/R) Coiffeur (30x30cm-12x12in) s. (S.FR 1500)

TIAN YANYUN (20th C) Chinese
£3328 $5825   (30-Mar-92 CH.HK397/R) Ladies with horses (37x22cm-15x9in) i. ink W/C four scrolls (HK.D 45000)

TIBALDI, Domenico (attrib) (1541-1583) Italian
£1022 $1829   (6-May-92 GD.B1529/R) Kneeling woman seen from behind and child (40x26cm-16x10in) i. pencil (S.FR 2800)

TIBALDI, Pellegrino (1527-1596) Italian
£13966 $25000   (14-Jan-92 SY.NY86/R) Study for figure of Aeolus (29x18cm-11x7in) bears i. red chk

TIBBETS, J van (19th C) ?
£1951 $3395   (19-Sep-91 D.V212/R) Still life of fruit (47x70cm-19x28in) s.d.1877 (A.S 40000)

TIBBITS, William (1837-1906) Australian
£684 $1217   (28-Apr-92 CH.ME164/R) Newton, Daylesford, and the Plant of the Victorian Goldmining Company (34x71cm-13x28in) s.d.1901 W/C (A.D 1600)
£1542 $2744   (26-Nov-91 J.M40/R) No. 2 Adelaide Street, Armadale, Victoria (30x44cm-12x17in) s.i. W/C (A.D 3500)
£3846 $6846   (28-Apr-92 CH.ME260/R) Creswick (24x39cm-9x15in) s.i. W/C (A.D 9000)

TIBBLE, Geoffrey (1909-?) British
£3400 $5950   (27-Sep-91 C136/R) Three women (76x63cm-30x25in) s. i. stretcher
£4000 $7080   (7-Nov-91 C91/R) The band (63x76cm-25x30in) s. d.Jan '49verso

TICHO, Anna (?) Israeli
£486 $900   (8-Jun-92 GG.TA162/R) Woman wearing head-kerchief (61x41cm-24x16in) s. chl
£532 $1000   (5-Jan-92 GG.TA220/R) Old woman (59x38cm-23x15in) pen
£611 $1100   (6-Jan-92 GG.TA413) Landscape (9x13cm-4x5in) s. pastel

TIDEMAND, Adolph (1814-1876) Norwegian
£1844 $3171   (7-Oct-91 B.O138/R) The artist's brother Emil Tidemand (27x24cm-11x9in) s.d.1844 (N.KR 21000)
£1974 $3671   (18-Jun-92 GWP.O106/R) Portrait of man (42x37cm-17x15in) s. paper on panel (N.KR 22500)
£3743 $6476   (23-Mar-92 B.O134/R) The artist's wife, Claudine (55x47cm-22x19in) s.i.d.1843 (N.KR 42000)
£4534 $7707   (6-Aug-91 UL.T236/R) Sailship 1833 (24x29cm-9x11in) (N.KR 52000)

TIDEMAND, Adolph Claudius (1854-1919) Norwegian
£526 $979   (15-Jun-92 B.O169/R) Portrait of woman (51x65cm-20x26in) (N.KR 6000)
£526 $979   (15-Jun-92 B.O170/R) Portrait of man (65x51cm-26x20in) (N.KR 6000)

TIECHE, Adolphe (1877-1957) Swiss
£627 $1067   (23-Oct-91 GD.B748/R) Schloss Schuls-Tarasp (58x76cm-23x30in) s. (S.FR 1600)
£902 $1533   (23-Oct-91 GD.B747/R) Engadin landscape with deserted farmhouses (70x95cm-28x37in) (S.FR 2300)

TIEDJEN, W (1881-1950) German
£655 $1160   (6-Nov-91 N.M1165/R) Peasant and two horses in field (55x75cm-22x30in) s.d.13 (DM 1900)

TIEDJEN, Willy (1881-1950) German
£874 $1512   (25-Mar-92 KM.K1471/R) Cattle grazing in landscape, autumn (60x80cm-24x31in) s. (DM 2500)
£1329 $2272   (18-Mar-92 N.M664/R) Sheep outside stable (55x75cm-22x30in) s. (DM 3800)
£1644 $2827   (8-Oct-91 ZEL.L1751/R) Turkey and chickens (31x49cm-12x19in) s.d.1917 board (DM 4800)

TIEL, Quiryn Martinus Adrianus van (1900-1967) Dutch
£788 $1426   (21-May-92 SY.AM57/R) Golgotha (72x75cm-28x30in) s.d.38 s.i.d.verso (D.FL 2600)
£1273 $2304   (21-May-92 SY.AM64/R) View of the Oude Schans (80x100cm-31x39in) s. i.stretcher (D.FL 4200)
£2273 $4114   (21-May-92 SY.AM112) Staande vrouw met haan (160x90cm-63x35in) s.d.51 (D.FL 7500)
£3333 $6033   (21-May-92 SY.AM56/R) Straatzanger (103x93cm-41x37in) s. (D.FL 11000)
£455 $823   (21-May-92 SY.AM177) Still life (55x43cm-22x17in) oil gouache (D.FL 1500)
£497 $860   (24-Mar-92 VN.R92/R) Man on horseback (57x42cm-22x17in) s. W/C (D.FL 1600)

TIELEMANS, Louis (1826-1856) Belgian
£999 $1858   (16-Jun-92 SY.B293/R) Pipe smoker by an inn (27x21cm-11x8in) s.d.1859 panel (B.FR 60000)

TIELENS, Alexandre (1868-1959) Belgian
£769 $1400   (26-May-92 CE.NY82/R) Chrysanthemums in a stein (61x45cm-24x18in) s.

TIELING, Lodewyck (17th C) ?
£2222 $3978   (12-Nov-91 SY.AM241/R) Flight into Egypt (19x25cm-7x10in) s. panel (D.FL 7200)

TIEPOLO, Giovanni Battista (1696-1770) Italian
£2200 $3828   (14-Apr-92 C143/R) Studies of hands (19x25cm-7x10in) chk
£2800 $5320   (24-Jun-92 DR72/R) Study of standing young man, seen from behind (20x12cm-8x5in) bears mono. ink wash over chk
£3168 $5766   (28-May-92 F.M81) Studio di tre figure per l'Ascensione di Cristo (35x23cm-14x9in) ink sepia (I.L 7000000)
£4000 $7280   (10-Dec-91 C167/R) Caricature of a man (19x11cm-7x4in) i. ink wash
£5086 $9308   (15-May-92 AT.P141/R) Femme sur des nuages (23x16cm-9x6in) pen wash (F.FR 50000)
£5500 $10010   (10-Dec-91 C166/R) Caricature of a gentleman (17x11cm-7x4in) i. ink wash
£6500 $12480   (7-Jul-92 C203/R) Oriental youth in cloak and hat (24x13cm-9x5in) chk pen wash
£6704 $12000   (15-Jan-92 CH.NY41/R) Study of man seen di sotto in su (28x19cm-11x7in) num.99 pen wash
£7500 $13050   (14-Apr-92 C139/R) Caricature of man in coat and tricorne seen from behind (19x10cm-7x4in) pen wash corners cut
£9000 $17280   (7-Jul-92 C201/R) Two figures seen from below, study for ceiling (16x23cm-6x9in) pen wash
£9000 $17280   (6-Jul-92 S89/R) Caricature of a cleric (18x12cm-7x5in) pen wash
£9500 $16530   (14-Apr-92 C140/R) Caricature of gentleman in profile holding tricorne (16x11cm-6x4in) pen wash corners cut
£11000 $21120   (7-Jul-92 C202/R) Studies of heads of bearded men (28x21cm-11x8in) chk

TIEPOLO, Giovanni Battista (1696-1770) Italian-cont.
£19009	$34596	(28-May-92 F.M82/R) Testa di vecchio (31x20cm-12x8in) sanguine (I.L 42000000)
£19914	$36243	(28-May-92 F.M72/R) Scipione e lo schiavo (51x37cm-20x15in) pen ink squared (I.L 44000000)
£27155	$49423	(28-May-92 F.M73/R) Sacrificio di Ifigenia. Testa e busto di giovane uomo, figure diverse (43x55cm-17x22in) pen ink W/C pencil double-sided (I.L 60000000)
£28000	$53760	(7-Jul-92 C200/R) Winged Deity and other figures in the clouds (29x21cm-11x8in) chk pen wash
£34000	$65280	(6-Jul-92 S164/R) The Holy Family adored by Saints Sebastian and Francis (43x29cm-17x11in) pen over chk.

TIEPOLO, Giovanni Battista (circle) (1696-1770) Italian
| £37543 | $67952 | (21-May-92 L.K150/R) Old bearded oriental man (64x49cm-25x19in) (DM 110000) |

TIEPOLO, Giovanni Battista (style) (1696-1770) Italian
£750	$1313	(27-Feb-92 CSK2) The Assumption of the Virgin (104x65cm-41x26in) arched top
£4000	$7680	(9-Jul-92 CSK52/R) Madonna and Child (83x69cm-33x27in)
£5814	$10000	(10-Oct-91 SY.NY160/R) Faith, Hope and Charity. Allegory of Justice (60x63cm-24x25in) pair

TIEPOLO, Giovanni Domenico (1727-1804) Italian
£44693	$80000	(17-Jan-92 SY.NY78/R) Saint Joseph and the Christ Child (39x31cm-15x12in)
£2149	$3826	(29-Nov-91 ARC.P3/R) Hercule et Cacus (26x18cm-10x7in) s. wash double-sided sketch verso (F.FR 21000)
£3600	$6264	(13-Apr-92 S366/R) Studies of putti and angels with musical instruments and heads two men (20x28cm-8x11in) s. pen wash
£3992	$7105	(29-Nov-91 ARC.P1/R) Benediction d'un eveque (19x28cm-7x11in) s. pen wash (F.FR 39000)
£4190	$7500	(14-Jan-92 SY.NY123/R) Group of flying cherubs (17x24cm-7x9in) s. pen wash corners cut
£7000	$13440	(7-Jul-92 C40/R) Centaur with nymph (25x31cm-10x12in) s. chk pen wash
£9794	$16943	(27-Mar-92 CN.P23/R) Centaure et satyres (18x27cm-7x11in) blk.chk.pen wash (F.FR 95000)
£37709	$67500	(14-Jan-92 SY.NY95/R) Swing (30x42cm-12x17in) s.d.1791 pen wash

TIEPOLO, Giovanni Domenico (attrib) (1727-1804) Italian
| £16760 | $30000 | (17-Jan-92 SY.NY165/R) Head of the Madonna (56x32cm-22x13in) |

TIEPOLO, Lorenzo (1736-1776) Italian
| £3631 | $6500 | (15-Jan-92 CH.NY42/R) Beheading of Saint John the Baptist (40x28cm-16x11in) red chk pen wash htd white |

TIFFIN, Sheila (?) British
| £1400 | $2394 | (11-Mar-92 B78/R) Children playing on beach before St Michael's Mount, Cornwall (101x127cm-40x50in) s. |

TIGLIO, Marcos (1903-1976) Argentinian
£1111	$2000	(20-Nov-91 V.BA101) Nina con flor (24x31cm-9x12in) d.1935
£2907	$5000	(9-Oct-91 RO.BA44/R) Flores (69x59cm-27x23in) s.d.57
£3073	$5500	(6-May-92 V.BA105) Naturaleza muerta (35x44cm-14x17in)
£6180	$11000	(1-Nov-91 PO.BA61) Iglesia del Espiritu Santo (56x71cm-22x28in) s.d.51 board
£7303	$13000	(1-Nov-91 PO.BA60) Pan casero (62x71cm-24x28in) board

TIKHMENOV, E (20th C) Russian
| £1000 | $1860 | (16-Jun-92 S30/R) Hunting scene with borzoi dogs (39x67cm-15x26in) s. |

TIKKANEN, Henrik (1924-1984) Finnish
| £392 | $690 | (12-Apr-92 HOR.H235) From Helsingfors (24x35cm-9x14in) s. W/C Indian ink (F.M 3100) |

TILBORCH, Gillis van (c.1625-1678) Flemish
£6000	$11520	(10-Jul-92 C159 a/R) Peasants by watermill (102x131cm-40x52in)
£7407	$13259	(14-Nov-91 CH.AM111/R) Village kermesse (78x117cm-31x46in) (D.FL 24000)
£100000	$192000	(8-Jul-92 S64/R) Large company feasting outside house (197x267cm-78x105in) s.

TILBORCH, Gillis van (circle) (c.1625-1678) Flemish
| £1600 | $2800 | (27-Feb-92 CSK249) Rebecca and Eliezer at the well (48x60cm-19x24in) |

TILBORCH, Gillis van and FYT, Jan (circle) (17th C) Flemish
| £18700 | $32538 | (13-Sep-91 C164/R) Peasant woman and laden donkey on way to market (175x226cm-69x89in) |

TILIUS, Jan (1660-1719) Italian
| £5918 | $10476 | (10-Feb-92 GL.P27/R) Le joueur de trompette (37x30cm-15x12in) s.d.1686 panel (F.FR 58000) |

TILKE, Max (1869-?) German
| £1394 | $2537 | (11-Dec-91 N.M614/R) Donkeys before Spanish house (75x105cm-30x41in) s.d.1899 (DM 4000) |

TILKE, Max (1869-?) German-cont.
£2577 $4794   (20-Jun-92 BM.B973 a/R) Andalusian gypsies (98x128cm-39x50in) s.d.1902 (DM 7500)

TILL, Johan (1827-1894) Austrian
£3500 $6230   (27-Nov-91 S137/R) Summer (68x94cm-27x37in) s.i.

TILLBERG, Peter (1946-) Swedish
£946 $1712   (19-May-92 AB.S5334/R) The bed (103x128cm-41x50in) s.d.68 (S.KR 10000)

TILLEMANS, Peter (circle) (1684-1734) Flemish
£1850 $3367   (11-Dec-91 MMB236/R) The stag hunt (48x66cm-19x26in)

TILLEMANS, Peter (style) (1684-1734) Flemish
£980 $1882   (8-Jul-92 S218) Horseman at rest beside inn (21x32cm-8x13in) canvas on panel
£3960 $6890   (13-Sep-91 C47/R) Rhenish landscape with horseman taking directions from peasants. Village landscape with packmule an (46x59cm-18x23in) pair
£4600 $8096   (10-Apr-92 C130/R) View of Chiswick from the river Thames (16x73cm-6x29in) paper on board

TILLER, Lars (1924-) Norwegian
£1025 $1773   (23-Mar-92 B.O135/R) Blue ocean (38x57cm-15x22in) s.d.66 (N.KR 11500)

TILLOU, Serge (1928-) French?
£705 $1255   (30-Oct-91 QWA.P187) La ferme (73x60cm-29x24in) s. (F.FR 7000)

TILSON, Joe (1928-?) British
£1500 $2775   (11-Jun-92 C80/R) Labyrinthos, Troy Dance (152x122cm-60x48in) s.i.d.1974 verso panel
£1507 $2623   (14-Apr-92 F.M11/R) Rock dance (50x40cm-20x16in) s.i.d.1974verso oil relief panel (I.L 3300000)
£1700 $3009   (8-Nov-91 C274/R) Collage 10/W 1961 (122x153cm-48x60in) s.i.d.1961verso wood oil mixed media collage
£2400 $4104   (11-Mar-92 B20/R) Setting for scene III, act 1, The Revengers Tragedy (34x79cm-13x31in) s.i. W/C gouache over pencil sold with another
£7280 $12594   (28-Mar-92 F.L109/R) Page 3, Snow White and the Black dwarf (84x52cm-33x20in) d.1960 silkscreen on canvas on panel (S.FR 19000)

IMLIN, William M (1893-1943) South African
£565 $999   (4-Nov-91 SY.J92/R) Gossip (17x14cm-7x6in) s.i.d.42 W/C (SA.R 2800)
£1590 $2767   (13-Apr-92 SY.J295/R) Enchanted forest (49x64cm-19x25in) s.i. W/C (SA.R 8000)
£2982 $5189   (13-Apr-92 SY.J296/R) Building of fairy city, Gold Workers' Guild (74x50cm-29x20in) s.d.1939 pen W/C (SA.R 15000)

IMMERMAHN (1942-) Swiss
£912 $1633   (6-May-92 GD.B1274/R) Enemy of nature (68x48cm-27x19in) s.d.81 panel (S.FR 2500)

IMMERMANS, Jean (1899-1986) Belgian
£535 $909   (22-Oct-91 GM.B257) Rochers au bord de la mer (83x105cm-33x41in) s. (B.FR 32000)

IMMERMANS, Louis (1846-1910) French
£864 $1563   (3-Dec-91 AB.S4761/R) Seascape with steam ship (50x91cm-20x36in) s. (S.KR 9000)
£1387 $2650   (3-Jul-92 GL.P177) Barques au bord de la riviere (49x65cm-19x26in) s. (F.FR 13500)
£2000 $3500   (18-Feb-92 CE.NY287/R) Port of Bruges (61x50cm-24x20in) s.
£3189 $6060   (22-Jun-92 AT.P91/R) Bretagne - retour des pecheurs, 1908 (50x65cm-20x26in) s.d.1908 (F.FR 31000)
£3226 $5645   (5-Apr-92 CSC.P106/R) Le port de Bruges (61x50cm-24x20in) s. (F.FR 31000)

IMOFEIEV, Alexandre (1921-) Russian
£527 $954   (20-May-92 ARC.P147) Le cargo rouge (44x65cm-17x26in) s. board (F.FR 5200)
£1064 $1926   (20-May-92 ARC.P145/R) La chapeau blanc (35x48cm-14x19in) s. board (F.FR 10500)

IMYN, William (20th C) ?
£897 $1606   (15-Jan-92 D.V52/R) Leopards (81x101cm-32x40in) s. panel (A.S 18000)

INDALL, C Lyall (?) Australian?
£705 $1255   (26-Nov-91 J.M770 a) Nude (40x53cm-16x21in) s. pastel (A.D 1600)

INDALL, Charles E S (1863-1951) Australian
£469 $895   (29-Jun-92 AAA.S119) Harbour Wharves (25x35cm-10x14in) s. W/C (A.D 1200)
£617 $1098   (26-Nov-91 J.M17) Balmain, N.S.W (24x34cm-9x13in) s. W/C (A.D 1400)

INDLE, David (1932-) British
£550 $941   (1-Aug-91 CSK22) Buckets and cranes (81x61cm-32x24in) s.d.59
£900 $1719   (16-Jul-92 B111) Rotherhithe (66x61cm-26x24in) s.d.59
£1800 $3150   (27-Sep-91 C84/R) Still life with Lobster (30x40cm-12x16in) s.d.1957 i. verso board

TING, Walasse (1929-) Chinese

£623	$1084	(18-Sep-91 KH.K77) Sam Francis sit in jet (60x73cm-24x29in) s.d.63verso (D.KR 7000)
£1023	$1780	(18-Sep-91 KH.K91/R) Composition (37x49cm-15x19in) st.sig. acrylic paper on canvas (D.KR 11500)
£1290	$2245	(17-Sep-91 RAS.K38/R) I think of you (40x51cm-16x20in) s.d.86 acrylic (D.KR 14500)
£1423	$2477	(17-Sep-91 RAS.K37/R) Composition (100x120cm-39x47in) s.d.62verso (D.KR 16000)
£1968	$3581	(10-Dec-91 RAS.K26/R) Green mountain side nobody see to much orchids (101x132cm-40x52in) s.d.70verso (D.KR 22000)
£2166	$3704	(12-Mar-92 RAS.K638/R) I am drunk take me to bed (51x76cm-20x30in) s.d.74verso (D.KR 24000)
£2555	$4625	(20-May-92 KH.K200/R) Do you love me (87x112cm-34x44in) s.d.83verso acrylic (D.KR 29000)
£3008	$5113	(22-Oct-91 C.A328/R) A southern beauty (62x88cm-24x35in) s.verso acrylic (B.FR 180000)
£3578	$6512	(10-Dec-91 RAS.K281 a/R) Catch me a butterfly (81x106cm-32x42in) s.d.76verso (D.KR 40000)
£4715	$8205	(17-Sep-91 RAS.K42/R) I have a springtime on bed (127x178cm-50x70in) s.i.d.77verso acrylic (D.KR 53000)
£970	$1755	(19-May-92 CH.AM354) Woman with fan (36x47cm-14x19in) st.sig. W/C (D.FL 3200)
£1083	$1863	(12-Oct-91 KV.L298/R) Two women with fans (18x28cm-7x11in) s. W/C on ricepaper (B.FR 65000)
£1698	$3090	(11-Dec-91 CH.AM404 a) Composition with two women, cat, horse and fishes (89x96cm-35x38in) s. brush ink W/C (D.FL 5500)
£2669	$4697	(7-Apr-92 C.A237/R) Lady with a fan (48x59cm-19x23in) s. W/C (B.FR 160000)
£3939	$7130	(19-May-92 CH.AM310/R) Oriental girls with parrot and grasshopper (176x96cm-69x38in) W/C (D.FL 13000)

TINGUELY, Jean (1925-1991) Swiss

£17391	$30957	(29-Nov-91 GAB.G3205/R) Sans titre (49x48cm-19x19in) s.d.1990 paper (S.FR 44000)
£822	$1570	(3-Jul-92 GL.P178/R) Untitled (29x21cm-11x8in) s. collage gouache felt-pen dr (F.FR 8000)
£1426	$2637	(13-Jun-92 AT.P42/R) Hommage a Yves Klein s. collage (F.FR 14000)
£1600	$2752	(17-Oct-91 C76/R) Hommage a Yves Klein (30x42cm-12x17in) s.num.46/100 collage feather sellotape pen
£1900	$3287	(26-Mar-92 S101/R) Untitled (70x50cm-28x20in) s.d.72 felt-tip pen ball point collage print
£1938	$3508	(20-May-92 KH.K138/R) Composition (25x32cm-10x13in) s.d.1988 acrylic W/C gouache (D.KR 22000)
£2527	$4321	(12-Mar-92 RAS.K630/R) Composition (25x31cm-10x12in) s.i. oil acrylic collage cardboard (D.KR 28000)
£2546	$4633	(15-Dec-91 P.V68) C'etait bien de te revoir -- et a bientot (21x30cm-8x12in) s. collage mixed media (F.FR 25000)
£2575	$4403	(21-Mar-92 AT.P112/R) Sans titre (45x63cm-18x25in) s.num.XV/XX red feather collage (F.FR 25000)
£2789	$5048	(4-Dec-91 G.219/R) Chere Huguette, Maier, merci - salutations (34x44cm-13x17in) s.d.1968 W/C collage (S.FR 7000)
£3000	$5190	(26-Mar-92 C48/R) Untitled (24x30cm-9x12in) s.d.1966 pen crayon wool transfer paper collage
£3021	$5136	(27-Oct-91 P.V73/R) E No 11 (50x65cm-20x26in) s.i.d.1978 crayon lithograph sheet (F.FR 30000)
£3150	$5417	(16-Oct-91 G.Z87/R) Caro Eddy, Salut Niki Lauda ... Regazzoni (21x29cm-8x11in) s. mixed media W/C ball point felt tip (S.FR 8000)
£3249	$5556	(12-Mar-92 RAS.K629/R) Composition (23x37cm-9x15in) s.d.1986 i. oil acrylic collage cardboard (D.KR 36000)
£5200	$8996	(26-Mar-92 S23/R) Hulten (71x53cm-28x21in) s.d.1972 felt-tip pen ball point pencil collage
£6000	$10380	(26-Mar-92 S5/R) Le Monstre dans la foret (58x80cm-23x31in) W/C felt-tip pen ball point pencil
£6145	$11000	(12-Nov-91 CE.NY178/R) Untitled (20x20cm-8x8in) s.d.88 acrylic W/C col.felt tip paper collage
£7263	$13000	(12-Nov-91 CE.NY177/R) Untitled (22x30cm-9x12in) s.d.83 acrylic ball-point mixed media collage
£8077	$15346	(25-Jun-92 GK.B689/R) Metaharmonie (30x40cm-12x16in) s.i.d.1989 bodycol indian ink (S.FR 21000)
£10769	$20462	(25-Jun-92 GK.B688/R) Freie Metaharmonie (41x59cm-16x23in) s.i.d.1989 bodycol oil collage (S.FR 7000)
£11765	$20000	(23-Oct-91 GD.B749/R) Composition (29x39cm-11x15in) s.d.90 mixed media collage (S.FR 30000)

TINTORE, Simone del (attrib) (17th C) Italian

£16201	$29000	(17-Jan-92 SY.NY69/R) Still life of grapes, funghi, quinces, pears and other fruits (65x91cm-26x36in)

TINTORETTO (16/17th C) Italian

£27624	$50000	(21-May-92 CH.NY30/R) Allegory of Prudence (144x107cm-57x42in)
£93923	$170000	(21-May-92 CH.NY18/R) Toilet of Venus (115x103cm-45x41in)
£1900	$3458	(10-Dec-91 C109) Study of a standing nude (29x14cm-11x6in) i. blk.chk.lead pen ink

TINTORETTO (after) (16/17th C) Italian
£880 $1479   (27-Aug-91 RAS.K610) Woman reading (94x73cm-37x29in) (D.KR 10000)

TINTORETTO (style) (16/17th C) Italian
£1348 $2400   (22-Jan-92 SY.NY62/R) Susannah and Elders (29x37cm-11x15in)
£2486 $4500   (20-May-92 D.NY76) Portrait of doge (112x89cm-44x35in)

TINTORETTO, Domenico (1560-1635) Italian
£7459 $13500   (22-May-92 SY.NY263/R) Portrait of man (55x51cm-22x20in)
£11765 $21059   (15-Nov-91 GK.Z5107/R) Flight to Egypt (78x90cm-31x35in) (S.FR 30000)
£15663 $27724   (7-Nov-91 D.V4/R) Portrait of cardinal (132x110cm-52x43in) (A.S 320000)
£85000 $154700   (11-Dec-91 S26/R) Lamentation (51x75cm-20x30in)

TINTORETTO, Domenico (attrib) (1560-1635) Italian
£22000 $40040   (13-Dec-91 C230/R) Portrait of bearded gentleman wearing fur-trimmed
     black costume (102x81cm-40x32in)

TINTORETTO, Domenico (studio) (1560-1635) Italian
£2235 $4000   (13-Nov-91 B.SF2122 a/R) Adoration of the Magi (109x96cm-43x38in)
£3867 $7000   (22-May-92 SY.NY274/R) Portrait of cardinal, standing beside table with
     crucifix (110x103cm-43x41in) i.

TINTORETTO, Domenico (style) (1560-1635) Italian
£3500 $6370   (11-Dec-91 S212/R) Portrait of Venetian senator (74x66cm-29x26in)
£1000 $1920   (7-Jul-92 C297/R) Battle scene (28x39cm-11x15in) chk wash htd white

TINTORETTO, Jacopo (1518-1594) Italian
£10814 $20330   (18-Dec-91 AT.P10/R) Tete de donateur (40x30cm-16x12in) (F.FR 105000)

TINTORETTO, Jacopo (after) (1518-1594) Italian
£3360 $6047   (19-Nov-91 GS.B3643) Crucifixion (50x121cm-20x48in) (S.FR 8500)
£5435 $10055   (8-Jun-92 CH.R720/R) San Rocco risana gli appestati (98x232cm-39x91in)
     (I.L 12000000)

TINTORETTO, Jacopo (attrib) (1518-1594) Italian
£54000 $98280   (13-Dec-91 C256/R) Portrait of Tommaso Contarini in armour and holding a
     baton (169x103cm-67x41in) i.
*£3400 $5916   (13-Apr-92 S265) Reclining female figure (12x27cm-5x11in) bears i. black
     chk*

TINTORETTO, Jacopo (circle) (1518-1594) Italian
£1200 $2304   (10-Jul-92 C256/R) Portrait of bearded man (60x43cm-24x17in) with
     indist.i.verso canvas on panel

TINTORETTO, Jacopo (school) (1518-1594) Italian
£7735 $14000   (21-May-92 CH.NY169/R) Portrait of Ecclesiastic (65x53cm-26x21in)

TINTORETTO, Jacopo (studio) (1518-1594) Italian
£5874 $10396   (7-Nov-91 D.V3/R) Portrait of Senator Girolamo Grimani (115x87cm-45x34in)
     (A.S 120000)
£16575 $30000   (21-May-92 CH.NY35/R) Portrait of Doge Girolamo Priuli (88x68cm-35x27in)

TINTORETTO, Jacopo (style) (1518-1594) Italian
£800 $1536   (10-Jul-92 C230) Portrait of bearded man, as Saint Paul (70x53cm-28x21in)
£2000 $3840   (10-Jul-92 C257/R) Portrait of bearded man, right hand resting on volume
     of Aristotle (103x87cm-41x34in) i.
£3453 $6250   (22-May-92 SY.NY225/R) Susannah and Elders (49x103cm-19x41in)
£6079 $11125   (12-May-92 SY.AM142/R) Samson and Delilah (93x121cm-37x48in) (D.FL 20000)
£14000 $24500   (1-Apr-92 S27/R) Holy Family (118x132cm-46x52in)

TIPLADY, John (1938-) Australian
£705 $1255   (26-Nov-91 J.M89) Low tide (44x59cm-17x23in) s.d.89 (A.D 1600)
£766 $1425   (15-Jun-92 MGS.S115) Market at Albi, France (45x60cm-18x24in) s.
     (A.D 1900)

TIRATELLI, Aurelio (1842-1900) Italian
£6500 $11570   (29-Nov-91 C112/R) Harvesters in cornfield. Moving to fresh pastures
     (17x36cm-7x14in) s. pair
£7200 $12744   (14-Feb-92 C101/R) In Allegra Compagnia (41x74cm-16x29in) s.i.
£9500 $17670   (18-Jun-92 B66/R) Italian farmyard (51x77cm-20x30in) s.i. panel

TIREN, Johan (1853-1911) Swedish
*£1368 $2421   (5-Nov-91 BA.S246/R) Young Lapplander asleep with reindeer and dog
     (28x21cm-11x8in) s.d.95 Indian ink wash (S.KR 14500)*
£1509 $2672   (5-Nov-91 BA.S245/R) Watering place (46x65cm-18x26in) s. W/C (S.KR 16000)
*£5758 $10422   (3-Dec-91 AB.S4672/R) Lapplander fallen off his sleigh, sunny winter
     landscape (34x53cm-13x21in) s. W/C htd white (S.KR 60000)*
*£10886 $18833   (28-Mar-92 UA.U441/R) Lapplanders watching flock of reindeer
     (75x130cm-30x51in) s.d.1903 W/C htd white (S.KR 113000)*

TIREN, Nils (1885-1935) Swedish
*£472 $835   (5-Nov-91 BA.S247/R) Winter hare (27x35cm-11x14in) s.d.1920 W/C htd white
     (S.KR 5000)*

TIRIBACCO (19/20th C) Italian
£492 $900   (16-May-92 HG.C149) Cardinal and parrot (33x28cm-13x11in) s.

TIRINNANZI, Nino (1923-) Italian
£741 $1320   (29-Nov-91 F.F74/R) Prete (9x7cm-4x3in) mono s.verso board (I.L 1600000)

TIRONI, Francesco (attrib) (?-1800) Italian
£12155 $22000   (21-May-92 CH.NY139/R) Piazza San Marco, Venice (52x84cm-20x33in) canvas
                on panel
£14000 $24500   (28-Feb-92 C149/R) The Zattere from the Giudecca, Venice
                (53x81cm-21x32in)

TIRONI, Francesco (circle) (?-1800) Italian
£2700 $5184   (10-Jul-92 PH70/R) Venice - view of Grand Canal and Rialto Bridge from
                north (37x57cm-15x22in)
£3000 $5400   (22-Nov-91 SWS220/R) Venice, Santa Maria della salute (33x45cm-13x18in)
£4325 $7396   (20-Mar-92 ZZ.F39/R) Vue du Palais des Doges a Venice (63x106cm-25x42in)
                (F.FR 42000)
£5400 $9720   (22-Nov-91 SWS3/R) Views of Rome (40x28cm-16x11in) pair
£16310 $30336   (20-Jun-92 CH.MO18/R) Vues de Venise (54x89cm-21x35in) pair (F.FR 160000)

TIRONI, Francesco (style) (?-1800) Italian
£7000 $12250   (3-Apr-92 C4/R) Grand Canal, Venice looking from Santa Maria della Carita
                to Bacino San Marco (44x125cm-17x49in)

TISCHBEIN, Anton (1730-1804) German
£2500 $4450   (30-Oct-91 S97) Portrait of lady (26x21cm-10x8in)

TISCHBEIN, Heinrich (style) (?) ?
£1200 $2100   (3-Apr-92 C109) Portrait of lady, said to be Wilhelmina, Grafin von
                Gravenitz (68x51cm-27x20in) with i.stretcher

TISCHBEIN, Johann Friedrich August (1750-1812) German
£1500 $2625   (3-Apr-92 C78/R) Personification of Faith - veiled maiden holding chalice
                (100x75cm-39x30in)
£4811 $8371   (18-Sep-91 N.M453/R) Johann Fridrich Stoll von Berneck in mountain
                landscape (113x82cm-44x32in) s.d.1802 (DM 14000)

TISCHBEIN, Johann Heinrich (circle) (18th C) German
£4800 $8400   (3-Apr-92 C129/R) Woman holding letter by candlelight (116x145cm-46x57in)

TISCHBEIN, Johann Heinrich (elder) (1722-1789) German
£17422 $31707   (12-Dec-91 L.K185 a/R) Portrait of Landgraf Carl von Hessen-Kassel in
                pilgrim's clothes (73x60cm-29x24in) (DM 50000)
*£1951 $3551   (12-Dec-91 L.K482/R) Family of Landgraf Friedrich II of Hessen-Kassel
                (42x32cm-17x13in) s.i.d.1772 pen wash painted with W.Ch.Mayr (DM 5600)*

TISCHBEIN, Johann Heinrich (style) (18th C) German
£1057 $1893   (7-May-92 CH.AM10) Brutus swearing revenge as Lucretia swoons
                (65x80cm-26x31in) (D.FL 3500)

TISCHBEIN, Johann Heinrich Wilhelm (1751-1829) German
£19368 $36024   (18-Jun-92 SY.MO47/R) Penelope et Ulysse (66x88cm-26x35in) s.d.1802
                (F.FR 190000)
*£1600 $3072   (8-Jul-92 PH70/R) Portrait of Maria Carolina of Austria. Queen Maria
                Luisa. Queen of Sardegna (24x20cm-9x8in) i. ink htd red chk three*

TISCHLER-WEBER, Anna (1881-1955) Yugoslavian
£997 $1785   (15-Jan-92 D.V28/R) Still life with fruit, bunch of flowers and chianti
                bottle (47x66cm-19x26in) s.d.1938 board (A.S 20000)

TISIO, Benvenuto da Garofalo (1481-1559) Italian
£90000 $172800   (10-Jul-92 C44/R) Holy Family with Saint Elizabeth and infant Saint John
                the Baptist, in wooded, river landscape (31x27cm-12x11in) panel

TISIO, Benvenuto da Garofalo (attrib) (1481-1559) Italian
£10497 $19000   (22-May-92 SY.NY138/R) Virgin and Child with Saints Roch and Sebastian
                (36x29cm-14x11in) panel

TISSOT, James Jacques Joseph (1836-1902) French
£9156 $16389   (17-Nov-91 FB.P169/R) Scene de la vie du Christ (64x82cm-25x32in) s.
                (F.FR 90000)
£24673 $41944   (21-Oct-91 ARC.P20/R) Le rendez-vous secret (61x46cm-24x18in) s.
                (F.FR 245000)
£110000 $203500   (12-Jun-92 C117/R) Le retour de l'enfant prodique (115x205cm-45x81in)
                s.d.1862
£150000 $277500   (12-Jun-92 C116/R) Une Veuve (68x49cm-27x19in) s.d.1868
£160000 $272000   (25-Oct-91 C48/R) Type of beauty, portrait of Mrs Kathleen Newton
                (59x46cm-23x18in) s.
£168605 $290000   (17-Oct-91 SY.NY114 a/R) Portrait de femme a l'eventail
                (88x118cm-35x46in) s.
*£2191 $3900   (22-Jan-92 SY.NY295/R) Figure of Christ (19x10cm-7x4in) s. W/C pencil
*£3800 $6536   (4-Mar-92 S325/R) Study for 'At Rifle Range'. Study of troubadour and
                troubadour's head (41x26cm-16x10in) pencil double-sided*
£40698 $70000   (17-Oct-91 SY.NY71/R) On river (34x23cm-13x9in) W/C

TITCOMB, William Holt Yates (1858-1930) British
£5000 $8900   (28-Nov-91 L360/R) The Church in Cornwall - Rogation Day Procession (89x168cm-35x66in) s.

TITIAN (c.1488-1576) Italian
£6800000 $12376001   (13-Dec-91 C85/R) Venus and Adonis (160x196cm-63x77in) painted with studio

TITIAN (after) (c.1488-1576) Italian
£800 $1536   (9-Jul-92 CSK344) Danae (43x61cm-17x24in)
£860 $1531   (21-Jan-92 SWS1006) Dinae (39x53cm-15x21in)
£1500 $2625   (2-Apr-92 CSK21/R) Madonna and Child (67x84cm-26x33in)
£2000 $3640   (12-Dec-91 B33/R) Venus and organist (103x148cm-41x58in)
£2692 $4765   (7-Nov-91 D.V226/R) Allegory of love (24x59cm-9x23in) paper on panel (A.S 55000)
£3800 $6802   (11-Nov-91 S492/R) Mystic marriage of St. Catherine (72x94cm-28x37in)
£6600 $11484   (13-Sep-91 C163/R) Danae (124x176cm-49x69in)
£9935 $16990   (18-Mar-92 D.V204/R) Danae (122x172cm-48x68in) (A.S 200000)
£1500 $2685   (11-Nov-91 S626/R) Sacred and Profane Love (23x56cm-9x22in) W/C after Titian

TITIAN (school) (c.1488-1576) Italian
£760 $1414   (18-Jun-92 DOL.Z235/R) The Three Kings (108x91cm-43x36in) (S.FR 2000)

TITIAN (style) (c.1488-1576) Italian
£730 $1300   (22-Jan-92 SY.NY103/R) Portrait of pope, probably Julius II (64x49cm-25x19in)
£899 $1600   (22-Jan-92 SY.NY63/R) Entombment (79x99cm-31x39in)
£950 $1691   (29-Oct-91 PH85) The Madonna and Child with Saints Stephen, Jerome and Maurice (41x55cm-16x22in)
£1842 $3500   (25-Jun-92 BG.M510/R) Sacred and profane love (79x183cm-31x72in)
£2568 $4418   (8-Oct-91 ZEL.L1516/R) Adoration of the Child in landscape, evening (104x122cm-41x48in) (DM 7500)
£2787 $5073   (12-Dec-91 L.K187/R) Holy Family with infant St John in mountainous landscape (65x84cm-26x33in) (DM 8000)
£17442 $30000   (10-Oct-91 SY.NY6/R) Entombment (137x210cm-54x83in)

TITO, Ettore (1859-1941) Italian
£2195 $3820   (19-Sep-91 D.V88/R) Peasant seated holding glass of wine (39x26cm-15x10in) s. (A.S 45000)
£3254 $5889   (3-Dec-91 SY.MI48) Paesaggio (25x52cm-10x20in) s. panel (I.L 7000000)
£11155 $20191   (3-Dec-91 SY.MI47/R) Bambini che passeggiano in riva a un lago (94x68cm-37x27in) s. (I.L 24000000)
£14738 $26823   (12-Dec-91 F.M64/R) Ali d'Italia (133x68cm-52x27in) s. panel (I.L 32000000)
£55185 $98781   (14-Nov-91 CH.R218) Donne di pescatori (113x140cm-44x55in) s. (I.L 120000000)

TITO, Santi di (1536-1603) Italian
£1600 $3072   (7-Jul-92 C152/R) Prudence and Faith flanking blank armorial cartouche. Standing figure (18x34cm-7x13in) i. i.verso chk pen wash double-sided
£13000 $22620   (14-Apr-92 C95/R) Execution of St John the Baptist (33x22cm-13x9in) i. chk pen wash htd.white

TITO, Santi di (circle) (1536-1603) Italian
£3315 $6000   (21-May-92 CH.NY217/R) Portrait of Prince Alphonso Gesualdi, seated, on red velvet cushion (87x66cm-34x26in) i.d.MDLXXXXVI mono.

TITUS-CARMEL, Gerard (20th C) ?
£1545 $2642   (19-Mar-92 CSC.P105/R) Le casque de Nikko, theorie du printemps, no.10 (132x100cm-52x39in) s.i.d.83 Indian ink pastel board (F.FR 15000)
£2546 $4633   (15-Dec-91 P.V77/R) Nuits-nuit noire no.3 (73x92cm-29x36in) s.i.d.1984 (F.FR 25000)
£554 $959   (4-Oct-91 CSC.P53) Objet (23x31cm-9x12in) s.i. crayon collage (F.FR 5500)
£1010 $1788   (24-Apr-92 CN.P208/R) Eclat Chrome 1 (80x121cm-31x48in) mixed media (F.FR 10000)

TIXIER DE LADOULE, P V (19th C) ?
£420 $752   (11-Nov-91 PH37) Portrait of Colonel P.S.Webb (8x?cm-3x?in) min.s.d.1826 gilt metal mount

TJAPALTJARRI, Billy Stockman see STOCKMAN, Billy

TJAPANDTI, Tim Payunka (20th C) Australian
£1037 $1804   (17-Sep-91 JRL.S454/R) Dingo dreaming (181x121cm-71x48in) acrylic canvas (A.D 2250)

TJERNED, Leif (1942-) Scandinavian
£588 $1076   (13-May-92 BU.S202/R) Woman in a flash (120x100cm-47x39in) s.d.1989 panel (S.KR 6200)
£1193 $2123   (27-Nov-91 BU.S36/R) Torso (130x100cm-51x39in) s. acrylic collage (S.KR 12500)

TOBEEN, Felix-Elie (1880-?) French

£866	$1575	(11-Dec-91 ZZ.F68/R) Roses et oeillets (24x18cm-9x7in) s. panel (F.FR 8500)

TOBEY, Mark (1890-1976) American

£2793	$5000	(13-Nov-91 CH.NY140/R) Baroque (13x18cm-5x7in) s.d.60 tempera paper
£7500	$12900	(17-Oct-91 C13/R) White writing (21x68cm-8x27in) s.d.53 tempera board
£10000	$17300	(26-Mar-92 S15/R) Untitled (97x47cm-38x19in) s.d.1969 tempera paper
£10615	$19000	(13-Nov-91 CH.NY132/R) Threaded plane (38x32cm-15x13in) s.d.59 tempera paper mounted vellum
£16760	$30000	(13-Nov-91 CH.NY144/R) Other places, other spaces (82x61cm-32x24in) s.d.67 tempera
£25098	$43169	(12-Oct-91 F.L244/R) Venise B (79x40cm-31x16in) s.d.62 tempera paper laid down on canvas (S.FR 64000)
£30726	$55000	(6-May-92 CH.NY291/R) In grass No. II (45x40cm-18x16in) s.d.58 d.1958 verso tempera board
£463	$792	(18-Mar-92 LT.P81) Sans titre (35x12cm-14x5in) s.d.61 Indian ink collage (F.FR 4500)
£1700	$2924	(17-Oct-91 C12) Untitled (14x11cm-6x4in) s.d.66 monotype gouache
£4600	$7912	(17-Oct-91 C10/R) Ballet (30x21cm-12x8in) s.d.65 tempera ink board
£4634	$8248	(26-Nov-91 SY.MI181/R) Paesaggio (16x22cm-6x9in) s.d.67 oil mixed media (I.L 10000000)
£5028	$9000	(6-May-92 CH.NY280/R) Apparitions (45x30cm-18x12in) s.d.54 tempera W/C
£6704	$12000	(14-Nov-91 SY.NY302/R) Chinese grocery (13x20cm-5x8in) s.d.57 ink gouache
£8380	$15000	(6-May-92 CH.NY290/R) Pavanne (48x61cm-19x24in) s.d.52 pen col.chk paper on board
£11173	$20000	(7-May-92 SY.NY242/R) World dust (62x46cm-24x18in) s.d.54 gouache
£15686	$26980	(12-Oct-91 F.L243/R) Sumi (69x51cm-27x20in) Indian ink chamois paper (S.FR 40000)

TOBIAS, Ben (c.1901-1985) Canadian

£560	$980	(27-Feb-92 L561) Figures walking on Penzance Promenade before Mount's Bay (41x51cm-16x20in) s.d.1960
£600	$1068	(28-Nov-91 L117) Punch and Judy Show, Cornwall (38x48cm-15x19in) s.i.d.1957 canvas laid on board
£640	$1139	(28-Nov-91 L118) St. Ives, Cornwall (38x48cm-15x19in) s.i.d.1957 canvas laid on board
£650	$1157	(28-Nov-91 L116) Mousehole, figures on harbourside with village beyond (38x48cm-15x19in) s.i.d.1957 canvas laid on board
£650	$1157	(28-Nov-91 L120/R) St. Ives Harbour (38x48cm-15x19in) s.i.d.1957 canvas laid on board
£680	$1210	(28-Nov-91 L119) Cornwall - figures and beach umbrellas (48x58cm-19x23in) s.i.d.1975 canvas laid on board
£700	$1246	(28-Nov-91 L121/R) Cornwall - figures on beach, bathing tents and boats offshore (38x48cm-15x19in) s.i.d.1957 canvas laid on board
£800	$1376	(11-Oct-91 PHE98 a) The Frumans Eve of Passover (39x49cm-15x19in) s.i.d.1961 canvas laid down
£950	$1634	(11-Oct-91 PHE142 a) Frumans by the sea (39x49cm-15x19in) s.i.d.1961 canvas laid down
£1200	$2064	(10-Oct-91 L46) Penzance, figures on the promenade (38x51cm-15x20in) s.d.1960 canvas on board
£1200	$2064	(10-Oct-91 L45/R) St Ives, boats in harbour and figures on quayside and beach (41x51cm-16x20in) s.d.1959

TOBIASSE, Theo (1927-) Israeli

£838	$1600	(3-Jul-92 S.W3825) L'oiseau et les deux poires (36x23cm-14x9in) s.
£1351	$2297	(6-Aug-91 UL.T238) Venetian scene (15x21cm-6x8in) (N.KR 15500)
£2000	$3440	(16-Oct-91 S122/R) L'homme qui fait le tour de la ville (33x41cm-13x16in) s.i.d.67
£2971	$5200	(26-Sep-91 SY.I101/R) La vache blanche (22x16cm-9x6in) s.i.d.64
£3381	$6086	(27-Jan-92 GL.P81/R) La Seine a Paris (24x33cm-9x13in) s.i. (F.FR 33000)
£5143	$9000	(28-Feb-92 SY.NY183/R) View of Paris along Seine (38x46cm-15x18in) s.i.d.74
£5143	$9000	(28-Feb-92 SY.NY182/R) View of Notre Dame (33x41cm-13x16in) s.i.d.74
£5307	$9500	(9-May-92 CE.NY127/R) Le sacrifice d'Isaac (70x70cm-28x28in) s.i.d.68
£5595	$10239	(17-May-92 GL.P245/R) La danseuse et l'homme en noir (40x40cm-16x16in) s.i. (F.FR 55000)
£5714	$10000	(25-Feb-92 SY.NY132/R) L'orange et la bohilloire fleurie (79x63cm-31x25in) s.d.61
£6000	$10320	(16-Oct-91 S84/R) Mon village, une pomme et un bateau (38x46cm-15x18in) s.i.
£6145	$11000	(9-May-92 CE.NY129/R) La petite lumiere qui rechauffe le passe (60x73cm-24x29in) s.i.d.71
£6215	$11000	(5-Nov-91 CE.NY236/R) Lumiere de Venise (38x46cm-15x18in) s.i.d.75 oil paper collage canvas
£6395	$11000	(12-Oct-91 SY.NY168/R) Le berger et l'enfant (66x53cm-26x21in) s.d.62
£6857	$12000	(28-Feb-92 SY.NY194/R) Le fou qui danse sur une chevre (65x81cm-26x32in) s.
£6857	$12000	(28-Feb-92 SY.NY192/R) Nous sommes sortis du meme fleur profond (51x70cm-20x28in) s.d.76 board
£7297	$13500	(12-Jun-92 SY.NY207/R) L'Enfance de Jacob (55x46cm-22x18in) s.d.80
£9143	$16000	(26-Sep-91 SY.I100/R) La Menorah du Grand Canal (46x55cm-18x22in) s.i.d.66
£12429	$22000	(5-Nov-91 CE.NY184/R) Les joueurs de flute (81x100cm-32x39in) s.i.d.61

TOBIASSE, Theo (1927-) Israeli-cont.

£791	$1400	(5-Nov-91 CE.NY183/R) Les amoureux (28x22cm-11x9in) s.i.d.89 pencil col.chk
£937	$1639	(5-Apr-92 ZZ.F257/R) La serenade (27x21cm-11x8in) s. pastel (F.FR 9000)
£1622	$3000	(12-Jun-92 SY.NY206/R) L'Ombre orangee du desir (25x34cm-10x13in) s.d.80 mixed media
£2747	$5026	(17-May-92 GL.P9/R) Le don de la Thora (48x63cm-19x25in) s. gouache (F.FR 27000)
£3672	$6500	(5-Nov-91 CE.NY181/R) Fleur de silence pour un homme seul (70x51cm-28x20in) s.i. oil col.wax crayon pencil paper collage
£4028	$6848	(24-Oct-91 CSC.P57/R) Le cheval qui faisait rire l'enfant (49x68cm-19x27in) s.i. mixed media (F.FR 40000)
£4269	$7598	(29-Nov-91 GAB.G2896 a) Ou sont tous ces lieux qui sont entres dans notre vie (51x67cm-20x26in) s.d.1970 mixed media paper laid down (S.FR 10800)
£4273	$7819	(17-May-92 GL.P247/R) Les annees Ezra et Nehemie (51x70cm-20x28in) s.i. pastel paper on canvas (F.FR 42000)
£4857	$8500	(27-Feb-92 CE.NY76/R) Oiseau egare dans la lumiere du temps (70x102cm-28x40in) s. acrylic col.wax crayons paper collage
£9040	$16000	(5-Nov-91 CE.NY121/R) Les chanteurs des rues (65x54cm-26x21in) s.i.d.74 paper collage oil canvas

TOCQUE, Louis (1696-1772) French

£16575	$30000	(22-May-92 SY.NY70/R) Portrait of Monsieur Bouret seated and reading letter (139x109cm-55x43in) s.

TOCQUE, Louis (attrib) (1696-1772) French

£994	$1699	(18-Mar-92 D.V254/R) Portrait of gentleman wearing powdered wig (74x60cm-29x24in) (A.S 20000)
£1667	$2800	(12-Aug-91 SG.M572) Femme...Louis XV (99x74cm-39x29in)

TOCQUE, Louis (circle) (1696-1772) French

£3027	$5207	(16-Oct-91 AT.P107/R) Portrait d'un gentilhomme tenant un livre (81x65cm-32x26in) (F.FR 30000)

TOCQUE, Louis (style) (1696-1772) French

£2200	$3850	(27-Feb-92 CSK239/R) Portrait of lady, in gold brocade dress (70x57cm-28x22in)

TODD, H G (1847-1898) British

£1250	$2263	(6-Dec-91 K553/R) Still life study of silver cream jug and mixed fruit on ledge (41x33cm-16x13in) s.d.1878

TODD, Henry George (1847-1898) British

£650	$1125	(25-Mar-92 PHI549) Still life of grapes and peach on stone ledge (25x20cm-10x8in) s.d.1893
£1450	$2625	(5-Dec-91 HB754) Still life study of fruit, nuts and silver goblet on table (30x25cm-12x10in) s.d.1876
£1600	$2880	(19-Nov-91 PH124/R) Still life with fruit (20x26cm-8x10in) s.d.1884
£1900	$3477	(12-May-92 H341) Still lifes of fruit (25x20cm-10x8in) s.d.1891 pair
£2000	$3800	(23-Jun-92 PH211/R) Grapes and pears on marble ledge. Grapes and peaches on marble ledge (25x20cm-10x8in) s.d.1896 pair
£4000	$7080	(6-Nov-91 CB145/R) Still life of grapes, apples and other fruit on marble ledge by window (43x36cm-17x14in) s.d.1892

TODD, Ralph (fl.1880-1929) British

£400	$712	(28-Nov-91 L170/R) Rusty anchors on foreshore before Newlyn Pier (33x23cm-13x9in) s.verso
£600	$1086	(19-May-92 PH96) Fast falls the eventide (38x27cm-15x11in) s. i.verso W/C
£1000	$1750	(27-Feb-92 L347) Study of girl with pink blouse holding fish basket (36x25cm-14x10in) s. W/C
£1150	$2013	(27-Feb-92 L348) The broken net (38x25cm-15x10in) s.d.1886 W/C
£1200	$2232	(19-Jun-92 HC321) Interior with old lady in white frilled cap, seated at table (28x36cm-11x14in) s. W/C
£1200	$2076	(3-Oct-91 DLY170/R) Letter from abroad (38x28cm-15x11in) s. W/C
£1300	$2223	(13-Mar-92 C6/R) Tales of grandfather (50x36cm-20x14in) s.i. pencil W/C
£2200	$4026	(4-Jun-92 DLY181/R) Mounts Bay fisherwoman (53x36cm-21x14in) s. W/C
£2600	$4966	(23-Jul-92 T292) Cottage interior with old lady arranging vase of daffodils (28x38cm-11x15in) s.

TODE, Knut Gustaf Waldemar (1859-1900) Swedish

£2958	$5265	(28-Nov-91 BU.S38/R) Young lady with parasol (63x44cm-25x17in) s.d.1883 (S.KR 31000)

TODESCHINI, Giambattista (1857-1938) Italian

£771	$1435	(16-Jun-92 F.M43) Il verziere, Milano (28x35cm-11x14in) s. panel (I.L 1700000)

TODHUNTER, Francis Augustus (1884-1963) American

£526	$1000	(24-Jun-92 B.SF6309/R) Ranch at Alto (61x76cm-24x30in) s.
£565	$1000	(12-Feb-92 B.SF538/R) Cemetery (61x76cm-24x30in) s.
£579	$1100	(24-Jun-92 B.SF6308/R) Silveria Ranch (61x76cm-24x30in) st.stretcher
£684	$1300	(24-Jun-92 B.SF6311/R) Spring at Greenbrae (61x76cm-24x30in) s. st.stretcher
£734	$1300	(12-Feb-92 B.SF536/R) Avella's ranch (61x76cm-24x30in) indist.s. d.46 verso

1828

TODHUNTER, Francis Augustus (1884-1963) American-cont.
£1412 $2500 (12-Feb-92 B.SF537/R) Marin Cove (61x76cm-24x30in) artist's st.verso
£737 *$1400* *(24-Jun-92 B.SF6315/R) View across bay (48x58cm-19x23in) s. W/C*

TOEPFFER-STILKE, Ada (20th C) ?
£1384 $2422 (19-Feb-92 D.V88/R) Garden before farmhouse (48x45cm-19x18in) mono.i.verso panel (A.S 28000)

TOEPUT, Lodewyk (1550-1603) Flemish
£2407 $4357 (19-May-92 GF.L2348/R) The meeting of St Francis and St Dominic (84x88cm-33x35in) (S.FR 6500)
£4895 $8664 (7-Nov-91 D.V18/R) Elegant party in garden palais (41x74cm-16x29in) panel (A.S 100000)

TOEPUT, Lodewyk (attrib) (1550-1603) Flemish
£11620 $21032 (5-Dec-91 F.M121/R) Tavola imbandita con figura femminile (81x101cm-32x40in) (I.L 25000000)

TOEPUT, Lodewyk (circle) (1550-1603) Flemish
£3058 $5688 (20-Jun-92 CH.MO37/R) Paysage avec une ville fortifiee dans le lointain (36x57cm-14x22in) panel (F.FR 30000)
£3500 $6125 (28-Feb-92 C135) An amorous duet in a wood (101x111cm-40x44in)

TOESCHI, G (19/20th C) ?
£7429 $13000 (19-Feb-92 CH.NY100/R) Flirtation (57x40cm-22x16in) s.d.1876

TOESCHI, Giovanni (19th C) Italian
£2400 $4152 (4-Oct-91 C192/R) The introduction (49x62cm-19x24in) s.d.1864

TOFANO, Edouardo (1838-1920) Italian
£994 $1700 (21-Mar-92 W.W39/R) Study of woman in fancy dress (20x13cm-8x5in) s. panel
£2717 $4700 (6-Sep-91 S.BM149/R) Portrait of a young woman with a bouquet (25x18cm-10x7in) s. panel
£3895 $6894 (7-Nov-91 F.M6/R) Signora napoletana (18x12cm-7x5in) s. i.verso panel (I.L 8500000)
£1900 *$3249* *(18-Mar-92 S190/R) Portrait of a pensive lady (34x26cm-13x10in) s. W/C*
£2356 *$4500* *(16-Jul-92 SY.NY580/R) A pensive moment (66x48cm-26x19in) s. W/C*

TOFANO, Sergio (20th C) Italian
£1174 *$2101* *(7-May-92 CH.R358) Bonaventura (43x32cm-17x13in) mixed media (I.L 2600000)*

TOFFOLI, Louis (1907-) French
£8637 $15114 (5-Apr-92 ZZ.F193/R) Le pecheur assis (73x52cm-29x20in) s. (F.FR 83000)
£8914 $16045 (2-Feb-92 ZZ.F202/R) Amoureux sur la plage (73x92cm-29x36in) s. (F.FR 87000)
£10786 $19092 (10-Nov-91 ZZ.F217/R) Les mariachis (60x92cm-24x36in) s. i.verso (F.FR 107000)
£1411 *$2498* *(10-Nov-91 ZZ.F264/R) Le marechal-ferrant (26x20cm-10x8in) s. W/C (F.FR 14000)*
£1844 *$3320* *(2-Feb-92 ZZ.F226/R) Le train (31x42cm-12x17in) s. chl. (F.FR 18000)*

TOFT, Peter (1825-1901) Danish
£7222 *$13000* *(19-Nov-91 CH.NY214/R) View of Mexico City (50x67cm-20x26in) s.s.i.d.89 s.i.d.verso W/C gouache*

TOGORES, Jose de (1893-1970) Spanish
£877 $1579 (23-Nov-91 N.M304/R) Famille sur la plage (33x41cm-13x16in) mono. (DM 2500)
£2138 $3805 (26-Nov-91 BRO.B364) Jeux (50x73cm-20x29in) s. (S.P 390000)
£2212 $4158 (17-Dec-91 BRO.B359) Composition (46x65cm-18x26in) s.d.928 (S.P 400000)
£2514 $4600 (4-Jun-92 GOM.M36/R) El Zapatero (65x81cm-26x32in) s.
£38064 $67754 (28-Apr-92 EP.M3/R) Autorretrato (108x65cm-43x26in) s.d.920 (S.P 7000000)
£2736 *$4870* *(29-Oct-91 BRO.B364/R) Pajaros (92x73cm-36x29in) s. gouache paper laid down on canvas (S.P 500000)*

TOIT, Paul du and WELZ, Jean (20th C) South African
£2087 $3632 (13-Apr-92 SY.J350/R) Pink rose in water glass (30x24cm-12x9in) s.d.1045 verso panel (SA.R 10500)

TOJETTI, Virgilio (1851-1901) American
£2941 $5000 (25-Oct-91 S.W2782) Unrequited love (61x46cm-24x18in) s.d.1896
£10857 $19000 (20-Feb-92 SY.NY87 a/R) Bambina con bambola (48x67cm-19x26in) s.i.

TOKAREV, Wietcheslav (1917-) Russian
£5572 $10086 (20-May-92 ARC.P25/R) Jour de fete (35x47cm-14x19in) s. board (F.FR 55000)

TOKAREVA, Alexandra (1926-) Russian
£514 $931 (6-Dec-91 ARC.P55/R) Nu de dos (49x36cm-19x14in) s. board (F.FR 5000)
£598 $1022 (13-Mar-92 ARC.P61) Bouquet de lilas (63x87cm-25x34in) s. (F.FR 5800)
£661 $1149 (13-Apr-92 ARC.P45/R) En plein ete (60x50cm-24x20in) s. (F.FR 6500)
£722 $1234 (13-Mar-92 ARC.P60/R) Les fleurs des champs (93x99cm-37x39in) s.d. (F.FR 7000)

TOKAREVA, Alexandra (1926-) Russian-cont.
£773	$1322	(13-Mar-92 ARC.P59/R) Les iris (95x81cm-37x32in) s. (F.FR 7500)
£825	$1410	(13-Mar-92 ARC.P58/R) Les pivoines (100x100cm-39x39in) s. (F.FR 8000)
£921	$1640	(25-Nov-91 ARC.P145/R) Ludmila (130x70cm-51x28in) s. (F.FR 9000)
£965	$1680	(13-Apr-92 ARC.P42/R) L'anniversaire d'Aline (65x85cm-26x33in) s. (F.FR 9500)
£1433	$2551	(25-Nov-91 ARC.P144/R) Le reveil (65x94cm-26x37in) s. (F.FR 14000)
£1842	$3279	(25-Nov-91 ARC.P146/R) Nature morte au melon (82x101cm-32x40in) s. (F.FR 18000)

TOL, Dominicus van (1635-1676) Dutch
£4948	$8561	(26-Mar-92 PIC.P30/R) La dentelliere et la marchande de volailles (33x28cm-13x11in) s. panel (F.FR 48000)

TOL, Dominicus van (after) (1635-1676) Dutch
£994	$1699	(18-Mar-92 D.V410/R) The pulled out tooth (31x26cm-12x10in) metal (A.S 20000)

TOL, Dominicus van (attrib) (1635-1676) Dutch
£12000	$21840	(13-Dec-91 C152/R) Old woman plucking duck, seated man by fire nearby (52x40cm-20x16in) panel

TOL, Dominicus van (style) (1635-1676) Dutch
£5500	$10010	(13-Dec-91 C151/R) Fiddler at casement holding wine glass and decanter (33x27cm-13x11in) panel

TOLE, Charles (?) ?
£648	$1173	(4-Dec-91 DS.W47) Landscape with boat sheds (47x57cm-19x22in) (NZ.D 2100)

TOLEDANA, S (?) ?
£620	$1122	(21-May-92 CSK169/R) Mixed flowers in glass vase by peach and grapes on ledge (34x27cm-13x11in) s. board

TOLEDO, Francisco (1940-) Mexican
£4444	$8000	(19-Nov-91 CH.NY145/R) La ciguena (29x29cm-11x11in) i. s.verso canvas on board
£10000	$18000	(19-Nov-91 CH.NY49/R) Pez (54x65cm-21x26in) s. s.d.62verso oil sand burlap
£15470	$28000	(18-May-92 CH.NY139/R) El circo (97x130cm-38x51in) s.d.61 i.verso oil sand burlap
£30556	$55000	(18-Nov-91 SY.NY65/R) Nuevo mapa de Juchitan (87x115cm-34x45in) i. oil sand canvas laid down on masonite
£66298	$120000	(19-May-92 SY.NY52/R) El mago inexperto (75x88cm-30x35in) s.i.verso oil sand
£105556	$190000	(18-Nov-91 SY.NY52/R) El chivo equivocado (102x127cm-40x50in) s.i.verso oil sand
£1381	$2500	(19-May-92 SY.NY204/R) Pajaro rosado (20x27cm-8x11in) s. ink gouache
£1852	$3352	(6-Dec-91 GL.P280/R) Composition (42x44cm-17x17in) gouache W/C ink (F.FR 18000)
£2500	$4500	(18-Nov-91 SY.NY167/R) Pareja y pescado (38x46cm-15x18in) s. gouache
£2572	$4655	(6-Dec-91 GL.P279/R) Composition (42x44cm-17x17in) gouache W/C ink (F.FR 25000)
£2762	$5000	(18-May-92 CH.NY161/R) Payasos (23x25cm-9x10in) s.d.63 gouache pen
£3039	$5500	(18-May-92 CH.NY137/R) Mascara (28x34cm-11x13in) s. gouache gold leaf
£3198	$5500	(12-Oct-91 SY.NY198/R) Jester. Figure with pet (63x48cm-25x19in) s. pen indian ink wash W/C gouache board pair
£4144	$7500	(19-May-92 SY.NY137/R) Untitled (23x33cm-9x13in) s. gouache sand
£4420	$8000	(18-May-92 CH.NY141/R) Cocodrilo, Sapos y Tortugas (25x33cm-10x13in) s. gouache pen sepia ink
£5000	$9000	(18-Nov-91 SY.NY124/R) Garzas (28x38cm-11x15in) s. W/C gouache
£5000	$9000	(18-Nov-91 SY.NY125/R) Mapa de Juchitan (28x38cm-11x15in) s. gouache
£5081	$8841	(15-Apr-92 PLF.P107/R) Le cerf et le chien (46x65cm-18x26in) s. W/C ink (F.FR 50000)
£8287	$15000	(19-May-92 SY.NY138/R) El que perdio la tijeras (33x23cm-13x9in) s. gouache W/C ink
£11050	$20000	(18-May-92 CH.NY142/R) En Esta Esquina (55x37cm-22x15in) s. mixed meida amate paper
£12778	$23000	(18-Nov-91 SY.NY122/R) Matriz (54x75cm-21x30in) s. ink W/C gouache
£13260	$24000	(19-May-92 SY.NY152/R) Desinfectando (39x45cm-15x18in) s. W/C graphite
£16667	$30000	(19-Nov-91 CH.NY63/R) La soledad (74x56cm-29x22in) s. gouache
£22099	$40000	(18-May-92 CH.NY42/R) Tortuga con pistachos (60x80cm-24x31in) s. mixed media collage pistacho shells paper
£23481	$42500	(19-May-92 SY.NY63/R) La bomba de Flit (56x76cm-22x30in) s. W/C gouache
£25000	$45000	(19-Nov-91 CH.NY43/R) Mujer del calendario (93x52cm-37x20in) s. wash gouache chl sanguine wax crayon collage
£27624	$50000	(18-May-92 CH.NY39/R) Autorretrato (40x50cm-16x20in) s. mixed media linen on masonite

TOLKOUNOV, Nikolai (1917-) Russian
£512	$911	(25-Nov-91 ARC.P14) Sur le perron (135x90cm-53x35in) s. (F.FR 5000)
£512	$911	(25-Nov-91 ARC.P13/R) Dans le Jardin (95x75cm-37x30in) s. (F.FR 5000)
£669	$1210	(6-Dec-91 ARC.P195/R) Le feu d'artifice (60x50cm-24x20in) s. (F.FR 6500)
£870	$1549	(25-Nov-91 ARC.P11/R) Parmi les buissons (104x140cm-41x55in) s. (F.FR 8500)

TOLKOUNOV, Nikolai (1917-) Russian-cont.
£1279 $2277   (25-Nov-91 ARC.P10/R) La petite jardiniere (90x70cm-35x28in) s.
                   (F.FR 12500)

TOLLMANN, Gunther (1926-1990) German
£5614 $10105   *(23-Nov-91 N.M306/R) Untitled (118x158cm-46x62in) s.d.1979 collage canvas*
                   (DM 16000)

TOLLMANN, Markus (1963-) German
£4561 $8211   (23-Nov-91 N.M307/R) Portrait of Beatrice (100x74cm-39x29in) s. acrylic
                   (DM 13000)

TOLNAY, Akos (1861-?) Hungarian
£501 $907   (5-Dec-91 D.V112) Daily life in the country (65x55cm-26x22in) s.
                   (A.S 10000)

TOLSTOY, Alexander (1895-1969) Swedish
£819 $1458   (28-Oct-91 AB.S234) Portrait of girl in national costume
                   (40x32cm-16x13in) s. (S.KR 8700)

TOM, Jan Bedys (1813-1894) Dutch
£917 $1596   (14-Apr-92 SY.AM334/R) Landscape with cattle (53x74cm-21x29in) s. panel
                   (D.FL 3000)

TOM-PETERSEN, Peter (1861-1926) Danish
£485 $863   (28-Apr-92 RAS.K470) Street scene, Standgade in Helsingor
                   (47x62cm-19x24in) s. (D.KR 5500)
£490 $843   (15-Oct-91 RAS.K210) Helsingor harbour (65x50cm-26x20in) s. (D.KR 5500)
£528 $887   (27-Aug-91 RAS.K528) Timber yard (42x56cm-17x22in) s.d.1906 (D.KR 6000)
£673 $1192   (11-Feb-92 RAS.K268/R) From Wilders Plads (36x46cm-14x18in) s.
                   (D.KR 7500)
£704 $1204   (12-Mar-92 RAS.V1003/R) Town scene from Aeroskobing (48x52cm-19x20in)
                   s.d.1917 (D.KR 7800)
£1054 $1888   (6-May-92 KH.K166/R) From the King's Garden (39x55cm-15x22in) s.
                   (D.KR 12000)
£1054 $1888   (6-May-92 KH.K169/R) From Caritas well, Nytorv, winter morning
                   (43x31cm-17x12in) s. (D.KR 12000)
£1350 $2471   (5-Feb-92 KH.K101/R) Street scene, Vognmagergade (43x34cm-17x13in) s.
                   (D.KR 15000)
£1406 $2517   (6-May-92 KH.K168/R) From Nybrogade, towards Nicolaj Church
                   (45x55cm-18x22in) s.d.97 (D.KR 16000)

TOMA, Gioacchino (1836-1891) Italian
£3171 $5866   (8-Jun-92 CH.R655/R) Bambina sul seggiolone (27x21cm-11x8in)
                   (I.L 7000000)

TOMANECK, Joseph (1889-?) American
£1214 $2100   (29-Mar-92 MY.F173/R) Tending the piglets (51x41cm-20x16in) s.verso
£4420 $8000   (24-May-92 JRB.C135/R) The fawn (160x160cm-63x63in) s.d.28

TOMASO, Rico (1898-1985) American
£899 $1600   (2-May-92 IH.NY60/R) Woman playing violin, men enthralled
                   (71x107cm-28x42in) s.
£2528 $4500   (2-May-92 IH.NY84/R) Family sitting on back porch (86x71cm-34x28in) s.

TOMBA, Casimiro (1857-1929) Italian
£2618 $5000   (16-Jul-92 SY.NY583/R) The flirtatious cavalier (62x45cm-24x18in) s.

TOMEA, Fiorenzo (1910-1960) Italian
£726 $1293   (29-Apr-92 F.F196/R) Autoritratto (11x7cm-4x3in) s.verso panel
                   (I.L 1600000)
£1856 $3490   (19-Dec-91 F.M34/R) Fiori in vaso (23x25cm-9x10in) s.d.1937verso board
                   (I.L 4000000)
£2263 $4119   (26-May-92 SY.MI49/R) Candele (40x50cm-16x20in) s. s.i.d.1942verso panel
                   (I.L 5000000)
£3219 $5762   (14-Nov-91 F.M28/R) Paesaggio a Zoppe (50x40cm-20x16in) s. (I.L 7000000)
£4171 $7424   (26-Nov-91 SY.MI19/R) Lanterne (40x49cm-16x19in) s.init.d.1952verso
                   board (I.L 9000000)
£4799 $9119   (23-Jun-92 F.M134/R) Natura morta con frutta (40x50cm-16x20in) s.
                   s.d.1942verso (I.L 10500000)

TOMEC, Heinrich (1863-1928) Austrian
£2055 $3700   (19-Nov-91 GS.B3669/R) Schloss Schonbrunn near Vienna, autumn
                   (65x80cm-26x31in) s. (S.FR 5200)

TOMESCU, Aida (?) Australian
£711 $1216   (17-Mar-92 JRL.S238) Panspermie (120x120cm-47x47in) init.d.88 (A.D 1600)
£800 $1368   (17-Mar-92 JRL.S241) Aida Plai II (182x213cm-72x84in) (A.D 1800)
£844 $1444   (17-Mar-92 JRL.S240) Locunu (182x213cm-72x84in) s.d.89 (A.D 1900)
£889 $1520   (17-Mar-92 JRL.S239) Seed papadia (180x210cm-71x83in) s.d.89 verso
                   (A.D 2000)

TOMINETTI, Achille (1848-1917) Italian
£5198 $9409   (18-May-92 SY.MI116/R) Veduta di Intra (92x67cm-36x26in) s.
                   (I.L 11500000)

TOMINZ, Alfredo (1854-1936) Italian
£13500 $24030   (26-Nov-91 PH67/R) The morning ride (70x45cm-28x18in) s.d.01

TOMKINS, William (1730-1792) British
£2234 $3887   (18-Sep-91 N.M454/R) Farmhouse by woodland pond and figures
                   (57x65cm-22x26in) s.d.1761 (DM 6500)

TOMKINS, William (style) (1730-1792) British
£6318 $11372   (19-Nov-91 RAS.K116/R) Romantic landscape with sheep grazing by ruins
                    (80x132cm-31x52in) (D.KR 70000)

TOMLIN, Bradley Walker (20th C) ?
£6857 $12000   (27-Feb-92 CH.NY19/R) Number 21 (41x48cm-16x19in)

TOMMASI, Adolfo (1851-1933) Italian
£1594 $2854   (6-May-92 B.P102/R) Vineyards (15x20cm-6x8in) s.indist.d. board
£5000 $8550   (18-Mar-92 S181/R) Figures in a park (31x58cm-12x23in) s.
£6042 $10937   (3-Dec-91 SY.MI144/R) Paese (22x34cm-9x13in) s.i.d.1880 panel
                   (I.L 13000000)

TOMMASI, Adolfo (attrib) (1851-1933) Italian
£1380 $2470   (14-Nov-91 CH.R160) Paesaggio con contadina (34x18cm-13x7in) i. canvas on
                   panel (I.L 3000000)

TOMMASI, Ludovico (1866-1941) Italian
£2671 $4862   (12-Dec-91 F.M15/R) Figure sedute in riva al mare (27x45cm-11x18in) s.
                   board (I.L 5800000)
£5200 $9204   (14-Feb-92 C110/R) Un libro interessante (37x27cm-15x11in) s. panel
£7358 $13171   (14-Nov-91 CH.R175/R) Bambini al campo (31x44cm-12x17in) s.d.97 canvas on
                   board (I.L 16000000)

TOMMASI, Publio de (1849-?) Italian
£3524 $6273   (26-Nov-91 J.M253/R) Courtship (70x45cm-28x18in) s.i. (A.D 8000)
£7489 $13330   (26-Nov-91 J.M58/R) Celebration (60x90cm-24x35in) s.i. (A.D 17000)
£10117 $18110   (14-Nov-91 CH.R155/R) Alla taverna (55x81cm-22x32in) s.d.1890
                    (I.L 22000000)
£2203 $3921   (26-Nov-91 J.M46/R) Story (49x73cm-19x29in) s.i. W/C (A.D 5000)

TOMMASI, Publio de (attrib) (1849-?) Italian
£1357 $2591   (21-Jul-92 JRL.S215/R) Interior scene (28x38cm-11x15in) (A.D 3500)

TOMMASINI, C (1927-) ?
£1813 $3227   (30-Oct-91 QWA.P71/R) Mascherata (100x100cm-39x39in) s. (F.FR 18000)

TOMMASO (?) Italian
£80111 $145000   (21-May-92 CH.NY10/R) Venus and Adonis (93x210cm-37x83in)

TOMSON, Clifton (1775-1828) British
£1493 $2657   (25-Nov-91 W.T1935/R) Bay racehorse and hound in paddock
                   (61x75cm-24x30in) s.d.1802 (C.D 3000)

TONELLI, Giorgio (20th C) Italian
£5097 $9073   (26-Nov-91 SY.MI23/R) Dentro la citta (60x50cm-24x20in) s.
                   s.init.d.1987verso panel (I.L 11000000)

TONGE, Lammert van der (1871-1937) Dutch
£917 $1679   (1-Jun-92 W.T1386/R) Girl with earthenware bowl (20x15cm-8x6in) s. panel
                  (C.D 2000)

TONGEREN, Jan van (20th C) Dutch
£1698 $3090   (11-Dec-91 CH.AM85) Still life with milkjug, bowl and box on table
                   (55x70cm-22x28in) s.d.1967 (D.FL 5500)
£2576 $4662   (19-May-92 CH.AM36/R) Still life of boxes and jugs on draped table
                   (66x91cm-26x36in) s.d.1963 (D.FL 8500)

TONIOLO, Leopoldo (1833-1908) Italian
£7715 $14350   (16-Jun-92 F.M297/R) Capricci infantili (114x176cm-45x69in) s.
                    (I.L 17000000)

TONNANCOUR, Jacques de (1917-) Canadian
£1194 $2125   (26-Nov-91 JOY.T51) Landscape (30x40cm-12x16in) s.d.60 board (C.D 2400)
£3980 $7085   (26-Nov-91 JOY.T60/R) Woman in black sweater (80x60cm-31x24in)
                   s.d.3.11.53 (C.D 8000)

TOOKER, George (1920-) American
£31429 $55000   (25-Sep-91 SY.NY103/R) White wall (61x46cm-24x18in) s. tempera gessoed
                    panel
£38674 $70000   (5-Dec-91 SY.NY112/R) Un ballo in maschera (56x76cm-22x30in) s. egg
                    tempera gessoed cardboard

TOORENVLIET, Jacob (1635-1719) Dutch
£1165 $2109   (20-May-92 CSC.P6) Portrait d'homme (12x17cm-5x7in) s. copper
                   (F.FR 11500)
£2675 $4895   (12-May-92 SY.AM145/R) Kitchenmaid holding roemer (30x22cm-12x9in) s.
                   (D.FL 8800)

TOORENVLIET, Jacob (1635-1719) Dutch-cont.
£3867	$7000	(22-May-92 SY.NY244/R) Amorous couple drinking in interior (37x29cm-15x11in) panel
£9000	$16380	(13-Dec-91 C155/R) Banquet on terrace (61x72cm-24x28in)
£1604	$2903	(21-May-92 L.K343/R) Peasants smoking and drinking (20x31cm-8x12in) ochre (DM 4700)

TOORENVLIET, Jacob (attrib) (1635-1719) Dutch
| £3086 | $5525 | (12-Nov-91 SY.AM186/R) Huntsman teasing dog with pheasant (25x21cm-10x8in) (D.FL 10000) |

TOORENVLIET, Jacob (circle) (1635-1719) Dutch
| £1500 | $2880 | (10-Jul-92 C163/R) Woman, holding wineglass (23x19cm-9x7in) panel |

TOORENVLIET, Jacob (style) (1635-1719) Dutch
| £973 | $1780 | (12-May-92 SY.AM44/R) Dentist conducting examination (35x28cm-14x11in) (D.FL 3200) |

TOOROP, Charley (1891-1955) Dutch
| £8485 | $15358 | (21-May-92 SY.AM48/R) Tree (100x80cm-39x31in) s.d.1910 (D.FL 28000) |

TOOROP, Jan Th (1858-1928) Dutch
£5000	$9050	(20-May-92 GK.Z5006) Two ladies in flower field (26x35cm-10x14in) s.d.1902 panel (S.FR 13500)
£424	$768	(19-May-92 CH.AM124) Portrait of Dr Prinsen Jzn (51x45cm-20x18in) a.d.1915 chk. (D.FL 1400)
£455	$823	(19-May-92 CH.AM94) Old man supported by helping hands on a bridge (11x19cm-4x7in) s.i.d.1907 pen crayon wash (D.FL 1500)
£463	$843	(11-Dec-91 CH.AM221) St Franciscus en de Apostel'poorten (14x14cm-6x6in) s.i.d.1913 pencil pen col.crayons (D.FL 1500)
£500	$870	(19-Sep-91 B103) Christ alone can redeem us (15x28cm-6x11in) s.i.indist.d. chl
£703	$1245	(5-Nov-91 SY.AM202) Moored bomschuit on beach (18x20cm-7x8in) s. W/C black chk (D.FL 2300)
£988	$1798	(11-Dec-91 CH.AM230) Een kind voor het Sander Instituut (8x13cm-3x5in) s.i.d.1912 pencil W/C postcard (D.FL 3200)
£1235	$2247	(11-Dec-91 CH.AM220) Italie (18x11cm-7x4in) s.i.d.1925 pencil W/C (D.FL 4000)
£1364	$2468	(19-May-92 CH.AM125) Visscherij - a sketch (11x20cm-4x8in) s.i. pencil crayon (D.FL 4500)
£1376	$2450	(30-Oct-91 CH.AM294 a/R) View of village with windmill by bridge (19x32cm-7x13in) s. pencil wash W/C (D.FL 4500)
£1515	$2742	(19-May-92 CH.AM148/R) Village street scene (13x13cm-5x5in) s.d.1917 pencil W/C (D.FL 5000)
£1529	$2706	(5-Nov-91 SY.AM155/R) In garden (11x15cm-4x6in) s.i.d.1908 pastel pencil (D.FL 5000)
£1829	$3402	(16-Jun-92 VN.R295/R) Anglers on a quay (20x15cm-8x6in) s. W/C (D.FL 6000)
£1835	$3248	(5-Nov-91 SY.AM267/R) Religion (20x14cm-8x6in) s.i. pencil black chk (D.FL 6000)
£2006	$3651	(11-Dec-91 CH.AM229) Crucifixion (19x26cm-7x10in) s.d.1912 W/C pen (D.FL 6500)
£2160	$3932	(11-Dec-91 CH.AM227/R) Farmer and cow on path (13x18cm-5x7in) s.indis.i.d.1906 pencil col.crayons (D.FL 7000)
£2424	$4388	(19-May-92 CH.AM150/R) Veere (22x28cm-9x11in) s.i.d.1909 pencil chk. (D.FL 8000)
£2424	$4388	(19-May-92 CH.AM146/R) Maria - Lente (16x10cm-6x4in) s.d.1926 pencil W/C htd.white (D.FL 8000)
£2424	$4388	(19-May-92 CH.AM152/R) Seated girl (29x23cm-11x9in) s.d.1884 pencil W/C (D.FL 8000)
£3364	$5954	(5-Nov-91 SY.AM122/R) River scene (11x15cm-4x6in) s.i.d.1916 W/C (D.FL 11000)
£4128	$7307	(5-Nov-91 SY.AM85/R) Swan Lake (14x14cm-6x6in) s. Indian ink (D.FL 13500)
£10802	$19660	(11-Dec-91 CH.AM228/R) Portrait of Anna Smulders reading (21x19cm-8x7in) s.i.d.1905 pencil (D.FL 35000)
£14679	$25982	(5-Nov-91 SY.AM66/R) Portrait of wife, Annie Hall (20x27cm-8x11in) s.i.d.1895 mixed media (D.FL 48000)
£14679	$25541	(14-Apr-92 SY.AM341/R) Het Verleden. Het Heden. De Toekomst (30x40cm-12x16in) one s.d.1902 pencil col.crayon three (D.FL 48000)
£16049	$29210	(11-Dec-91 CH.AM259/R) Tete d'une Anglaise, Lady H (41x32cm-16x13in) s.i.d.1895 pencil (D.FL 52000)

TOOVEY, Dora (20th C) Australian
| £1154 | $2054 | (27-Apr-92 J.M118/R) Sydney harbour (29x37cm-11x15in) s. canvas on board (A.D 2700) |

TOPFFER, Wolfgang Adam (1766-1847) Swiss
£1098	$1867	(23-Oct-91 GD.B750/R) Lac Leman with snow covered mountain range beyond (33x77cm-13x30in) (S.FR 2800)
£1900	$3287	(4-Oct-91 C80/R) Rocky landscape with lake beyond (21x29cm-8x11in) mono.d.1812 paper on board
£408	$758	(18-Jun-92 SY.MO444) Paysans dans la campagne (12x19cm-5x7in) ink wash (F.FR 4000)
£752	$1376	(4-Jun-92 SY.Z329/R) Promenade a la campagne (20x25cm-8x10in) pencil wash indian ink (S.FR 2000)

TOPHAM, Frank William Warwick (1838-1929) British
£2200 $3784   (11-Oct-91 C122/R) Morning of the Festival - Central Italy (55x77cm-22x30in) s.d.1876
£3200 $5504   (11-Oct-91 C47/R) The flower garland (107x76cm-42x30in) s.d.1900

TOPKE, D A (jnr) (1828-1859) Dutch
£1600 $2896   (20-May-92 S76/R) The snow Robert off the coast (49x67cm-19x26in) s.i.d.1846 W/C pen over pencil
£2000 $3620   (20-May-92 S70/R) Courier Van Noord Holland, Kapitein M.F.Schaap (52x70cm-20x28in) s.i.d.1845 W/C pen

TOPKE, D A (snr) (1801-1845) Dutch
£2100 $3801   (20-May-92 S77/R) Mary, Newcastle, Capt M.G.Hutchenson, entering the Texel (52x70cm-20x28in) s.i.d.1838 i.verso W/C pen over pencil

TOPKE, Dirk Antoon (jnr) (1828-1859) Dutch
£1212 $2145   (22-Apr-92 CH.AM265) The Brig - Henrica - off the coast (52x71cm-20x28in) s.d.1859 pencil ink W/C htd.white (D.FL 4000)

TOPOLSKI, Feliks (1907-1989) Polish
£550 $1018   (9-Jun-92 RG2338) Portrait of Bernard Shaw (66x91cm-26x36in) s.i.d.43

TOPOR, Roland (1938-) French
£802 $1460   (12-Dec-91 SY.AM311/R) Untitled (24x35cm-9x14in) s.d.1976 W/C ink (D.FL 2600)

TOPPELIUS, Woldemar (1858-1936) Russian
£1770 $3115   (12-Apr-92 HOR.H239) Stones on beach (36x28cm-14x11in) s.d.1907 (F.M 14000)
£2070 $3684   (1-Dec-91 HOR.H234/R) Foaming seas (28x39cm-11x15in) s.d.1930 (F.M 16000)
£2216 $3833   (28-Mar-92 UA.U474/R) Summer in the skerries (45x70cm-18x28in) s.d.1918 (S.KR 23000)

TOPTANOW, K (19/20th C) Russian
£608 $1132   (19-Jun-92 G.Z129/R) River landscape, winter (38x61cm-15x24in) s.d.1915 gouache (S.FR 1600)

TORAL, Cristobal (20th C) Spanish
£30000 $54600   (29-May-92 C437 a/R) Still life (81x89cm-32x35in) s.

TORDI, Sinibaldo (1876-1955) Italian
£1300 $2249   (4-Oct-91 C194/R) The centre of attention (36x58cm-14x23in) s.
£1600 $2736   (17-Mar-92 PH244) Welcome to the ball (43x65cm-17x26in) s.d.1923

TORELLI (?) ?
£3330 $5827   (3-Apr-92 ZZ.F68/R) Vue de parc s'ouvrant sur la mer (178x306cm-70x120in) s.d.1924 (F.FR 32000)

TORGERSEN, Thorvald (1862-?) Norwegian
£1316 $2447   (15-Jun-92 B.O175/R) Children fishing (58x68cm-23x27in) s.d.1929 (N.KR 15000)
£2193 $4079   (15-Jun-92 B.O174/R) Picking cloud-berries (69x99cm-27x39in) s.d.05 (N.KR 25000)

TORGGLER, Erich (1899-1938) Austrian
£1562 $2702   (3-Oct-91 D.V236) Still life with tea jug and apple (46x46cm-18x18in) s. (A.S 32000)

TORHAMN, Gunnar (1894-1955) Swedish
£2589 $4660   (23-Nov-91 SO.S627/R) Fishermen seated by harbour (44x54cm-17x21in) s. panel (S.KR 27000)

TORHAMN, Ingegerd (1898-?) Swedish
£949 $1736   (13-May-92 BU.S206/R) Lines (33x41cm-13x16in) init. panel (S.KR 10000)
£953 $1678   (11-Apr-92 FAL.M407/R) 'Splitter' (50x60cm-20x24in) s.verso panel (S.KR 10000)
£1233 $2257   (13-May-92 BU.S205/R) Burst substance (52x105cm-20x41in) init. panel (S.KR 13000)
£1423 $2604   (13-May-92 BU.S204/R) Beams and reflexes (116x39cm-46x15in) init. panel (S.KR 15000)

TORKILDSEN, Trygve (1899-1984) Norwegian
£746 $1387   (15-Jun-92 B.O176/R) Summer by Upper Eiker (65x85cm-26x33in) s.i.d.42 (N.KR 8500)

TORNA, Oscar (1842-1894) Swedish
£3643 $6558   (23-Nov-91 SO.S632/R) Landscape with cattle and trees (50x72cm-20x28in) s. (S.KR 38000)
£3974 $7192   (19-May-92 AB.S4281/R) Summer landscape with trees and children on beach (38x55cm-15x22in) s.d.1887 (S.KR 42000)

TORNAI, Gyula (1861-1928) Hungarian
£700 $1211   (3-Oct-91 CSK146) A harem beauty (66x145cm-26x57in) s.
£856 $1516   (5-Nov-91 SY.AM469) Moroccan woman (54x45cm-21x18in) s.i. panel (D.FL 2800)

TORNAI, Gyula (1861-1928) Hungarian-cont.
£1942 $3456   (29-Apr-92 D.V802/R) The medicine man (73x44cm-29x17in) s.d.1902 panel (A.S 40000)
£2500 $4450   (27-Nov-91 S122/R) At shrine (85x60cm-33x24in) s.d.1907 panel
£8725 $15880   (27-May-92 D.V614/R) Temptation (155x118cm-61x46in) s.d.1885 (A.S 180000)
£11000 $19580   (27-Nov-91 S121/R) In harem (142x211cm-56x83in) s.

TORNAU, Karl Wilhelm Gustav (1820-1864) Austrian
£977 $1660   (24-Oct-91 D.V62/R) Breeding bull in landscape (25x32cm-10x13in) s.d.1847 panel (A.S 20000)

TORNEMAN, Axel (1880-1925) Swedish
£2642 $4728   (7-May-92 RAS.S79/R) Lonely (50x66cm-20x26in) s.d.1913 (S.KR 28000)
£3795 $6945   (11-May-92 NOR.S60/R) Nude dancer (211x105cm-83x41in) s.d.1915 (S.KR 40000)
£5693 $10417   (11-May-92 NOR.S58/R) The blue room (103x72cm-41x28in) s.d.1918 (S.KR 60000)
£11385 $20835   (11-May-92 NOR.S65/R) Autumn hunt (196x152cm-77x60in) s.d.1920 (S.KR 120000)
£30361 $55560   (11-May-92 NOR.S51/R) Etude d'un portrait (80x59cm-31x23in) (S.KR 320000)
£37951 $69450   (11-May-92 NOR.S37/R) Cafe at night 1 (180x200cm-71x79in) s.i.d.1906 (S.KR 400000)

TORNIG, Oscar (?) Belgian?
£1191 $2145   (19-Nov-91 GM.B567) Coucher de soleil (34x56cm-13x22in) s. (B.FR 70000)

TORNOE, Wenzel (1844-1907) Danish
£628 $1112   (11-Feb-92 RAS.K11 a) Crow by it's nest (134x77cm-53x30in) s.d.1903 (D.KR 7000)
£747 $1337   (6-May-92 KH.K16/R) Interior with old woman carding wood (56x41cm-22x16in) (D.KR 8500)
£748 $1294   (2-Sep-91 BU.K75/R) Hamlet (147x109cm-58x43in) (D.KR 8500)
£1264 $2274   (19-Nov-91 RAS.K166/R) Having failed - nude woman with empty net (134x77cm-53x30in) s.d.1903 (D.KR 14000)
£1411 $2511   (28-Apr-92 RAS.K483/R) A mishap - interior with two children (49x40cm-19x16in) init. (D.KR 16000)
£1762 $3119   (23-Apr-92 RAS.V918) Italian coastal landscape with figures (151x208cm-59x82in) (D.KR 20000)
£2025 $3401   (27-Aug-91 RAS.K553/R) Interior with mother feeding gruel to baby (100x80cm-39x31in) s. (D.KR 23000)
£2708 $4630   (12-Mar-92 RAS.V1004/R) Visiting the grandparents (73x52cm-29x20in) s. (D.KR 30000)

TORNQUIST, Jorrit (1938-) Austrian
£481 $880   (2-Jun-92 L.K1005) Opus (50x50cm-20x20in) s.verso acrylic (DM 1400)

TORR, Helen (1886-1967) American
£1600 $2800   (26-Sep-91 CH.NY288/R) Still life (26x31cm-10x12in)
£8840 $16000   (5-Dec-91 SY.NY101/R) Flower rhythm (29x22cm-11x9in) panel mounted on metal

TORRALLARDONA, Carlos (1913-1986) Argentinian
£573 $1100   (4-Aug-92 V.BA108) El taller (44x30cm-17x12in)
£718 $1250   (19-Sep-91 V.BA103) Billares (37x45cm-15x18in) d.1968
£778 $1400   (20-Nov-91 V.BA102) Rincon de tango (42x62cm-17x24in) mixed media

TORRE, Andre (20th C) French
£561 $1043   (17-Jun-92 I.N8) La Sainte-Victoire (33x41cm-13x16in) s. (F.FR 5500)
£601 $1119   (17-Jun-92 I.N22) Le mas (46x55cm-18x22in) s. (F.FR 5900)
£3229 $5554   (20-Oct-91 I.N42) Saint-Paul-de-Vence (55x46cm-22x18in) s. (F.FR 32000)

TORRE, Carlos de la (1856-1832) Argentinian
£625 $1200   (4-Aug-92 V.BA40) Paisaje (12x21cm-5x8in) 41

TORRE, Enrico della (1931-) Italian
£1012 $1811   (14-Nov-91 F.M22/R) Costruzione (45x32cm-18x13in) s. s.i.d.1986verso oil collage canvas (I.L 2200000)

TORRE, Flaminio (1621-1661) Italian
£19890 $36000   (21-May-92 CH.NY94/R) Sibyl (87x75cm-34x30in)

TORRE, Giulio del (1856-1932) Italian
£1700 $3009   (14-Feb-92 C107/R) Un Utile Passatempo (40x24cm-16x9in) s. panel
£1829 $3200   (18-Feb-92 CE.NY215/R) Dressing doll (21x27cm-8x11in) s.i.d.04 panel
£1835 $3266   (30-Oct-91 CH.AM81/R) The broken bowl (26x21cm-10x8in) s.i. panel (D.FL 6000)
£2600 $4602   (14-Feb-92 C106/R) Un pasto frugale (21x16cm-8x6in) s.d.1893

TORREANO, John (20th C) ?
£872 $1500   (12-Oct-91 SY.NY376/R) Space painting (83x83cm-33x33in) s.d.1973 oil glass jewels canvas on panel

TORREGIANI, Bartolomeo (?-1675) Italian
£3333 $5700   (17-Mar-92 JRL.S132/R) Landscape with ruins and men (72x60cm-28x24in) (A.D 7500)

ORREGIANI, Bartolomeo (?-1675) Italian-cont.
£1000 $1920   (7-Jul-92 C32/R) Wooded landscape with figures crossing bridge. Four
                  figures in wood (25x39cm-10x15in) i.d.1677 chk pen wash double-sided

ORREGIANI, Bartolomeo (style) (?-1675) Italian
£3100 $5580   (22-Nov-91 SWS149) Mountainous landscape (114x145cm-45x57in)

ORRENT, Evelino (19th C) ?
£977 $1857   (26-Jun-92 CSC.P28) Le joueur de guitare (46x61cm-18x24in) s. pastel
                  (F.FR 9500)

ORRES AGUERO, Leopoldo (1924-) Argentinian
£1111 $2000   (20-Nov-91 V.BA104) Figura (60x40cm-24x16in) d.1958

ORRES, Antonio de (1666-c.1754) Mexican
£19444 $35000   (18-Nov-91 SY.NY1/R) Virgen de Guadalupe (196x132cm-77x52in) s.d.1729

ORRES, Augusto (1913-) Uruguayan
£587 $1045   (25-Nov-91 GC.M71) Escollera (49x60cm-19x24in) s.
£963 $1715   (25-Nov-91 GC.M69) Arboles y casas (59x70cm-23x28in) s.
£1067 $1900   (28-Oct-91 GC.M32) Tren Elevado en Nueva York (50x70cm-20x28in) s. board
£1348 $2400   (28-Oct-91 GC.M33) Calle Rincon (42x52cm-17x20in) s. board

ORRES, Horacio (20th C) South American
£874 $1600   (4-Jun-92 GOM.M43/R) Objeto No.2 (43x36cm-17x14in) s.d.1950 board
£1505 $2800   (17-Jun-92 CAS.M18) Naturaleza muerta (68x82cm-27x32in)
£2204 $4100   (17-Jun-92 CAS.M22/R) Catedral de Notre Dame (61x74cm-24x29in)
£3064 $5300   (30-Sep-91 GC.M31/R) Fragata en Puerto (70x87cm-28x34in) s.d.1947
£4194 $7800   (17-Jun-92 CAS.M23/R) Catedral de Chartres (150x90cm-59x35in)

ORRES-GARCIA, Joaquin (1874-1949) Uruguayan
£11013 $19714   (14-Nov-91 ANS.M69/R) Rincon de Bruselas (35x47cm-14x19in) s.
                  (S.P 2000000)
£12155 $22000   (18-May-92 CH.NY114/R) Sail boat (32x38cm-13x15in) s.d.1922
£15470 $28000   (18-May-92 CH.NY89/R) La Piazza della Signoria (35x45cm-14x18in)
                  init.d.23 board on panel
£16575 $30000   (18-May-92 CH.NY47/R) Hombre con sombrero (38x41cm-15x16in) init.d.40
                  board
£16667 $30000   (19-Nov-91 CH.NY60/R) Canal in Venice (26x40cm-10x16in) board on panel
£18132 $33000   (11-Dec-91 RO.BA5/R) Calle con Capilla (34x43cm-13x17in) inits.
£41667 $75000   (19-Nov-91 CH.NY10/R) Dos figuras constructivas (42x53cm-17x21in)
                  init.d.46 board
£66667 $120000   (19-Nov-91 CH.NY17/R) Constructivo con objetos deformados
                  (52x41cm-20x16in) s.d.37 masonite
£490 $871   (30-Nov-91 VG.B1022/R) Spanish street scene (24x32cm-9x13in) s.d.1919
                  col.chk pencil (DM 1400)
£1000 $1830   (4-Jun-92 CSK73) Figures outside grocer's shop (23x31cm-9x12in) s.d.1919
                  col.chk
£6667 $12000   (18-Nov-91 SY.NY171/R) Caballo (13x14cm-5x6in) inits.d.33 graphite ink
                  W/C
£9722 $17500   (18-Nov-91 SY.NY170/R) Dibujo constructivo (16x11cm-6x4in) inits.d.33
                  graphite ink W/C
£60773 $110000   (18-May-92 CH.NY50/R) Composicion constructiva (46x55cm-18x22in) s.d.31
                  tempera gessoe panel

TORRIGLIA, Giovanni Battista (attrib) (1858-?) Italian
£1744 $3000   (15-Oct-91 CE.NY323/R) Amusing the baby (93x63cm-37x25in) s.

TORRINI, E (19th C) Italian
£5500 $9955   (22-May-92 C228/R) Serenade (81x61cm-32x24in) s.

TORRINI, Pietro (1852-1920) Italian
£922 $1650   (14-Nov-91 GRO.B31/R) Musician (30x25cm-12x10in) s.
£1774 $3157   (30-Oct-91 CH.AM80/R) A painted smile (45x35cm-18x14in) s. (D.FL 5800)
£2846 $5066   (29-Nov-91 GAB.G2178 a) La querelle d'amour (60x90cm-24x35in) s.
                  (S.FR 7200)
£3429 $6000   (20-Feb-92 SY.NY275/R) New coat of paint (61x81cm-24x32in) s.i.

TORSLEFF, August (1884-) Danish
£542 $975   (19-Nov-91 RAS.K310) Model looking herself in mirror (76x53cm-30x21in) s.
                  pastel (D.KR 6000)

TORSTEINSON, Torstein L (1876-1966) Norwegian
£3333 $6200   (15-Jun-92 B.O177/R) Still life of fruit and jugs on table
                  (72x92cm-28x36in) s.d.1932verso (N.KR 38000)

TOSI, Arturo (1871-1956) Italian
£4526 $8237   (26-May-92 SY.MI64/R) Cupole (40x32cm-16x13in) s. (I.L 10000000)
£4887 $8845   (4-Dec-91 KH.K141/R) Ulivi sul lago (50x60cm-20x24in) s. (D.KR 54000)
£4977 $9009   (4-Dec-91 KH.K142/R) Fiori (50x40cm-20x16in) s. plywood (D.KR 55000)
£6208 $11113   (14-Nov-91 F.M30/R) Paesaggio bergamasco (30x40cm-12x16in) s.
                  (I.L 13500000)
£6256 $11135   (29-Nov-91 F.F171/R) Paesaggio a Rovetta (50x60cm-20x24in) s.d.1942
                  (I.L 13500000)
£6336 $11532   (26-May-92 SY.MI161/R) Ulivi sul lago (50x60cm-20x24in) s. (I.L 14000000)

TOSI, Arturo (1871-1956) Italian-cont.
£7818 $13994   (14-Nov-91 F.M81/R) Natura morta (30x40cm-12x16in) s. (I.L 17000000)
£8354 $15705   (19-Dec-91 F.M209/R) Paesaggio con alberi (32x41cm-13x16in) s.
         (I.L 18000000)
£22397 $42555   (23-Jun-92 F.M150/R) Baita (100x120cm-39x47in) s. (I.L 49000000)

TOSINI, Michele (attrib) (1503-1577) Italian
£7000 $12250   (31-Mar-92 PH55/R) Holy Family with infant St. John the Baptist
         (110x87cm-43x34in) panel
£8287 $15000   (22-May-92 SY.NY215 a/R) Portrait of magistrate (110x84cm-43x33in) i.
         panel
£13372 $23000   (10-Oct-91 SY.NY121/R) The Madonna and Child with the infant Saint John
         the Baptist (84x66cm-33x26in)

TOTT, Alois (1870-C1907) Austrian
£1582 $2768   (20-Feb-92 D.V526/R) Summer landscape with farmhouse and castle ruin
         (24x35cm-9x14in) s.d.1899 W/C (A.S 32000)

TOTVANIAN, A (20th C) Polish
£568 $1016   (17-Nov-91 REM.W29) By the pool in a park (38x22cm-15x9in) s. panel
         (P.Z 11000000)

TOUDOUZE, Adele Anais (1822-1899) French
£586 $1008   (10-Oct-91 D.V352/R) Portrait of young girl with dog in landscape
         (13x14cm-5x6in) min.s. W/C paper oval (A.S 12000)

TOULMOUCHE, Auguste (1829-1890) French
£1923 $3500   (28-May-92 SY.NY178/R) Portrait of woman (14x13cm-6x5in) s.d.1879
£2857 $5000   (20-Feb-92 SY.NY157/R) Proposal (48x39cm-19x15in) s.d.1866
£3234 $5757   (1-Dec-91 HOR.H21/R) Lady wearing red dress (62x44cm-24x17in) s.d.1868
         (F.M 25000)
£3380 $6050   (14-Nov-91 GRO.B100/R) Young lady - reverie (46x30cm-18x12in) s.d.1887
£5870 $11036   (16-Dec-91 AGS.P26/R) Femme devant sa Psyche (90x54cm-35x21in) s.d.1889
         (F.FR 57000)
£17582 $32000   (27-May-92 CH.NY21/R) La Toilette (90x53cm-35x21in) s.d.1889

TOULOUSE-LAUTREC (1864-1901) French
£1078 $1973   (12-May-92 GM.B492) Le divan japonais s. poster (B.FR 65000)

TOULOUSE-LAUTREC, Henri de (1864-1901) French
£32000 $61120   (1-Jul-92 S111/R) Femme en priere (73x60cm-29x24in) s.d.82
£33898 $60000   (7-Nov-91 SY.NY108/R) Portrait de la femme de la maison de la Rue
         d'Amboise (28x24cm-11x9in) paper on canvas
£112994 $200000   (5-Nov-91 CH.NY37/R) Vieillard a Celeyran (55x46cm-22x18in) st.mono.
£368852 $675000   (13-May-92 SY.NY68/R) Madame Juliette Pascal (56x51cm-22x20in)
£1200 $2172   (2-Dec-91 CSK29/R) Etudes de juristes (15x24cm-6x9in) pencil
£1230 $2250   (14-May-92 SY.NY103/R) Le bourdelles, substitut (11x9cm-4x4in) st.mono.i.
         pen paper on board
£1353 $2367   (30-Mar-92 ZZ.F106/R) Rhinoceros (12x20cm-5x8in) studio st.sig. pen
         craft-paper (F.FR 13000)
£1500 $2715   (2-Dec-91 CSK49/R) Monsieur Paul Viaud (12x9cm-5x4in) st.mono. pencil
£1848 $3326   (19-Nov-91 FB.P93/R) Croquis de cheval. Traits de crayon (31x20cm-12x8in)
         bears st.mono. blue crayon double-sided (F.FR 18000)
£2012 $3461   (12-Oct-91 SY.MO3/R) Personnages (17x27cm-7x11in) st.mono. black conte
         crayon (F.FR 20000)
£2158 $4122   (1-Jul-92 FB.P2 a) Ou va-t-elle (17x11cm-7x4in) ink dr (F.FR 21000)
£2571 $4500   (28-Feb-92 SY.NY7/R) Une loge au theatre (22x20cm-9x8in) pen sepia ink
£4000 $7000   (28-Feb-92 SY.NY4/R) Chevaux, lad et chien. Graffiti (15x20cm-6x8in)
         graphite double-sided
£4000 $7000   (28-Feb-92 SY.NY3/R) Chevaux (20x31cm-8x12in) st.mono. pen graphite
£4266 $7765   (30-May-92 VG.B113/R) Tete de femme de profil, etude de Mary Hamilton
         (11x9cm-4x4in) pencil (DM 12500)
£5107 $8938   (24-Feb-92 ARC.P18/R) Le jockey (15x20cm-6x8in) bears st.init. lead
         pencil (F.FR 50000)
£5200 $8944   (16-Oct-91 S5/R) Presentation (22x33cm-9x13in) st.mono pencil paper on
         board
£8500 $15385   (4-Dec-91 S114/R) Chien Maltais (26x17cm-10x7in) st. pencil
£33898 $60000   (6-Nov-91 CH.NY108/R) Femme assise (48x39cm-19x15in) s.i. chl
£50000 $90500   (3-Dec-91 S27/R) La femme au chien (56x42cm-22x17in) init. brush indian
         ink wash
£983607 $1800000   (12-May-92 CH.NY121/R) Cavaliers se rendant au Bois de Boulogne
         (85x54cm-33x21in) s. gouache board

TOUR-DONAS, Marthe see DONAS, Marthe

TOURNACHON, Gaspard Felix (1820-1910) French
£510 $948   (18-Jun-92 SY.MO516/R) Au bal masque (27x20cm-11x8in) s.d.1853 pencil chl
         W/C htd gouache (F.FR 5000)

TOURNEMINE, Charles Emile de (1812-1872) Italian
£1945 $3462   (29-Nov-91 ARC.P25/R) Enfants dans la barque (23x34cm-9x13in) panel
         (F.FR 19000)

TOURNIER, Nicolas (circle) (16/17th C) French
£5093 $9116   (12-Nov-91 SY.AM79/R) St Peter and St Paul (53x70cm-21x28in) (D.FL 16500)

TOURNIER, Nicolas (circle) (16/17th C) French-cont.
£5587 $10000   (17-Jan-92 SY.NY193/R) Christ betrayed by Judas (53x89cm-21x35in) panel

TOURNY, Leon Auguste (1835-?) French
£474 $900   (26-Jun-92 WOL.C447) Sailboats (25x41cm-10x16in) s.i.d.1901

TOUSSAINT, F (1873-1955) Belgian
£1535 $2885   (18-Dec-91 GM.B4046) Femme accoudee (41x32cm-16x13in) s. board (B.FR 90000)
£1705 $3205   (18-Dec-91 GM.B4108/R) Portrait de femme a l'Ombrelle (46x37cm-18x15in) s. board (B.FR 100000)

TOUSSAINT, Fernand (1873-1955) Belgian
£767 $1350   (7-Apr-92 C.A241) The pigsty (38x46cm-15x18in) s. board (B.FR 46000)
£856 $1524   (30-Oct-91 CH.AM54) Wooded landscape with steamtrain (37x46cm-15x18in) s. board (D.FL 2800)
£1056 $1817   (7-Oct-91 RY.P113/R) Pont-a-Damme (65x80cm-26x31in) s. (F.FR 10500)
£1821 $3296   (23-May-92 KV.L404/R) La robe blanche (33x27cm-13x11in) s. board (B.FR 110000)
£2506 $4261   (22-Oct-91 C.A307) Reverie (46x37cm-18x15in) s. board (B.FR 150000)
£3086 $5617   (11-Dec-91 CH.AM250/R) Still life with flowers in vase (44x36cm-17x14in) s. board (D.FL 10000)
£4800 $8928   (17-Jun-92 S347/R) Portrait of woman in brown hat (45x37cm-18x15in) s. canvasboard
£8821 $15789   (19-Jan-92 CSC.P129/R) Jeune femme au bouquet (82x65cm-32x26in) s. (F.FR 86000)
£12000 $21360   (29-Nov-91 C62/R) At the Opera (99x80cm-39x31in) s.
£1001 $1761   (7-Apr-92 C.A240/R) Small bridge in Brugge (50x60cm-20x24in) s. mixed media (B.FR 60000)

TOUSSAINT, Louis (1826-?) German
£3984 $7250   (28-May-92 SY.NY250 a/R) Wo ist hotel (65x53cm-26x21in) s.d.1879

TOWERS, S (1862-1943) British
£500 $890   (1-Nov-91 BW397) Figure and horses on lane through woods (48x36cm-19x14in) s. W/C
£580 $1003   (4-Oct-91 BW389) Young lady under archway near a thatched cottage (41x30cm-16x12in) s. W/C

TOWN, Harold (1924-1991) Canadian
£634 $1148   (2-Dec-91 R.T221/R) Portrait of Joy Carroll (48x35cm-19x14in) s.d.48 (C.D 1300)

TOWNE, C (18/19th C) British
£1650 $3053   (12-Jun-92 K516/R) Wooded landscape with cattle and sheep and figures (61x76cm-24x30in)

TOWNE, Charles (18/19th C) British
£500 $880   (10-Apr-92 C160/R) Newfoundland dog in winter landscape (9x11cm-4x4in) init. panel
£950 $1815   (14-Jul-92 DR441/R) Landscape with cattle (25x33cm-10x13in) s. panel
£2466 $4241   (8-Oct-91 ZEL.L1756/R) Landscape with view of Bilton Abbey and cows watering in pond, evening (57x76cm-22x30in) i.verso (DM 7200)
£3200 $5696   (31-Oct-91 B183/R) Landscape with goats and sheep, ruin and mountainous river landscape beyond (12x17cm-5x7in) panel pair
£39617 $72500   (5-Jun-92 SY.NY16/R) William Yates of Springfield on his favourite roadster (99x121cm-39x48in)

TOWNE, Charles (attrib) (18/19th C) British
£500 $840   (27-Aug-91 EH714) Grazing cattle with windmill in middle ground (18x13cm-7x5in) canvas laid down

TOWNE, Charles (style) (18/19th C) British
£1200 $2136   (21-Jan-92 PH68) Shepherd on donkey herding flock, cottage beyond (45x53cm-18x21in)

TOWNE, Francis (1740-1816) British
£3200 $5632   (9-Apr-92 S108/R) Cattle watering in classical landscape (18x25cm-7x10in) pen W/C over pencil
£4000 $7160   (12-Nov-91 C88/R) In the grounds of Rydal Hall (23x16cm-9x6in) s.i.verso pencil ink wash
£5500 $9845   (12-Nov-91 C11/R) Edinburgh Castle (17x25cm-7x10in) s.i.d.August 14th 1811verso pencil W/C
£5800 $10382   (12-Nov-91 C14/R) Windsor Castle from the play grounds at Eton College (17x51cm-7x20in) s.i.d.Sept 12th 1811verso pencil pen W/C
£6000 $10740   (12-Nov-91 C9/R) Durham (17x51cm-7x20in) s.i.d.August 9thverso pencil W/C
£6500 $11635   (12-Nov-91 C8/R) Durham (71x51cm-28x20in) s.i.d.August 7th 1811verso pencil W/C
£8500 $15215   (12-Nov-91 C10/R) Edinburgh Castle and Calton Hill (17x51cm-7x20in) s.i.d.August 13th 1811verso pencil W/C
£12500 $22375   (12-Nov-91 C15/R) Windsor Castle from Fellows' Eyot (17x51cm-7x20in) s.i.d.Sept 12th 1811verso pencil pen W/C
£22000 $39380   (14-Nov-91 S68/R) Lake Coniston, Lancashire (15x47cm-6x19in) pen over pencil W/C

TOWNLEY, Charles (1746-1800) British
£13661 $25000   (5-Jun-92 SY.NY18/R) Storm, groom and horse (91x121cm-36x48in) s.d.1797

TOWNSEND, William (1909-) British
£950 $1815   (16-Jul-92 B186/R) Hop alleys (63x70cm-25x28in) s.

TOWNSHEND, Geoffrey K (1888-1969) Australian
£594 $1039   (23-Sep-91 AAA.S126) Country cottage (33x43cm-13x17in) s. W/C (A.D 1300)

TOWNSHEND, James A (?-1949) British
£400 $684   (17-Mar-92 JRL.S103) Stroll in English country garden (35x25cm-14x10in)
           s. W/C (A.D 900)

TOYEN, Marie Germinova (1902-1980) Czechoslovakian
£972 $1731   (27-Nov-91 AT.P66) Sans titre (18x13cm-7x5in) s.d.39 wash htd.colour two
           in same frame (F.FR 9500)

TOZER, H Spernon (20th C) British
£800 $1448   (20-May-92 BT181/R) Cottage interior (23x33cm-9x13in) s.d.1899
£1100 $1892   (4-Mar-92 S182/R) Surrey kitchen, near Farnham, Surrey. Kitchen at
           Woolpack Inn, Surrey (20x25cm-8x10in) one s.d.1885 both
           s.indist.i.verso pair
£710 $1235   (11-Sep-91 PHL15/R) My model (26x35cm-10x14in) s.d.1920 col.wash
£800 $1424   (29-Oct-91 C69/R) Reading the news (20x28cm-8x11in) s.d.1913 pencil W/C
£800 $1424   (29-Oct-91 C68/R) Game of draughts (20x28cm-8x11in) s.d.1918 pencil W/C
£880 $1531   (15-Apr-92 PHL60) Fireside chat (25x33cm-10x13in) s.d.1930 col.wash

TOZZI, Mario (1895-?) Italian
£9268 $16497   (29-Nov-91 F.F169/R) Paesaggio notturno (44x81cm-17x32in) s.d.1912
           (I.L 20000000)
£16556 $29634   (14-Nov-91 F.M88/R) La casetta rosa (55x45cm-22x18in) s.d.1966
           s.i.d.verso (I.L 36000000)
£50280 $95532   (23-Jun-92 F.M179/R) Il gioco della dama (118x75cm-46x30in) s.d.1962
           (I.L 110000000)
£2675 $4842   (4-Dec-91 LD.P30/R) Visage de femme (53x30cm-21x12in) s.d.30 Indian ink
           (F.FR 26000)

TRABALLESI, Giuliano (1724-1812) Italian
£12268 $22450   (16-May-92 F.L73/R) Orfeo ed Euridice negli inferi (100x80cm-39x31in)
           (S.FR 33000)

TRACHEL, Ercole (1820-1872) French
£1340 $2292   (11-Mar-92 CJ.N109/R) Le Paillon a Nice (21x36cm-8x14in) s. W/C
           (F.FR 13000)

TRACHSEL, Albert (1863-1929) Swiss
£1880 $3440   (4-Jun-92 SY.Z368/R) Paysage de Reve, Vallee du Petit Bernard pres Geneve
           (56x73cm-22x29in) s. (S.FR 5000)
£471 $842   (15-Nov-91 ZOF.Z1907) Landscape (24x32cm-9x13in) s. W/C (S.FR 1200)
£677 $1238   (4-Jun-92 SY.Z361/R) Carnations (34x28cm-13x11in) s. pastel (S.FR 1800)
£752 $1376   (4-Jun-92 SY.Z367/R) Le Saleve (25x35cm-10x14in) W/C pencil (S.FR 2000)
£902 $1651   (4-Jun-92 SY.Z364/R) Spring landscape (27x36cm-11x14in) s. W/C
           (S.FR 2400)
£977 $1789   (4-Jun-92 SY.Z369/R) Spielgerten near Lenk, Berner Oberland
           (29x44cm-11x17in) s. W/C (S.FR 2600)
£1316 $2408   (4-Jun-92 SY.Z409/R) Landscape (23x34cm-9x13in) s. W/C (S.FR 3500)

TRACY, Liam (1934-) Irish
£909 $1573   (2-Oct-91 A.D211) Flower sellers, Grafton Street (41x51cm-16x20in) s.
           (E.P 1000)

TRAFFELET, Fritz (1897-1954) Swiss
£2213 $3984   (19-Nov-91 GS.B3289) Grauholzsoldaten mit Zweispitz (73x50cm-29x20in) s.
           (S.FR 5600)
£876 $1568   (6-May-92 GD.B2414) Militardefile (27x42cm-11x17in) s.d.1934 indian ink
           pen W/C (S.FR 2400)

TRAGARDH, Carl (1861-1899) Swedish
£859 $1529   (28-Nov-91 BU.S39/R) French town (28x35cm-11x14in) s. panel (S.KR 9000)
£962 $1655   (8-Mar-92 BU.M41) Pig (32x40cm-13x16in) s.d.90 panel (S.KR 10000)
£759 $1306   (19-Oct-91 UA.U361) Flowering study (72x56cm-28x22in) s. W/C (S.KR 8000)

TRAIES, Frank D (19th C) British
£1900 $3306   (18-Sep-91 PHS568/R) Still life of flowers and fruit on table
           (74x66cm-29x26in) s.d.1853

TRAIES, William and Frank D (19th C) British
£8000 $14320   (15-Jan-92 BT216/R) The Vale of the Teign, Devon (91x130cm-36x51in)
           s.d.1853 i.verso

TRAILL, Jessie Constance Alicia (1881-1967) Australian
£35242 $62731   (26-Nov-91 J.M10/R) The tea gardens (67x122cm-26x48in) s. canvas on board
           (A.D 80000)

TRAIN, Edward (19th C) British
£600 $1140   (23-Jun-92 CG673) Figures at head of Loch Awe with Kilchurn Castle beyond (33x46cm-13x18in) s.d.1850
£720 $1224   (5-Aug-91 WW77) Highlanders in landscape (69x85cm-27x33in) s.d.1869
£750 $1313   (25-Sep-91 CSK245) Figures on a track in winter (23x33cm-9x13in) s.d.1855 board
£800 $1432   (5-May-92 SWS356/R) Village in winter (32x42cm-13x17in) s.d.1860
£900 $1548   (3-Mar-92 AG248/R) Highlanders at waterfall (66x83cm-26x33in) s.d.1869
£920 $1647   (14-Jan-92 SWS141/R) Winter landscape (30x44cm-12x17in) s.
£1400 $2352   (26-Aug-91 S801/R) Highland loch (43x62cm-17x24in) s.d.1853

TRAMEAU (20th C) French
£1230 $2213   (27-Jan-92 GL.P190) Nu assis (60x73cm-24x29in) s.d.1937 (F.FR 12000)

TRAMPEDACH, Kurt (1943-) Danish
£534 $929   (17-Sep-91 RAS.K149) Portrait (90x120cm-35x47in) s.d.69verso (D.KR 6000)
£667 $1161   (17-Sep-91 RAS.K152) Portrait (60x80cm-24x31in) canvas on panel (D.KR 7500)
£1351 $2324   (4-Mar-92 KH.K230/R) Self portrait (75x55cm-30x22in) s.d.77-78verso plywood (D.KR 15000)

TRANKELL, Bo (1942-) Scandinavian
£1431 $2548   (27-Nov-91 BU.S42/R) Mother and child (81x92cm-32x36in) init. (S.KR 15000)
£1992 $3646   (13-May-92 BU.S207/R) Nude by spring (175x168cm-69x66in) (S.KR 21000)

TRAPPES, Francis M (19th C) British
£580 $998   (16-Oct-91 ZZ.B100) The Keeper's Cottage (51x92cm-20x36in) mono.d.1879 i.verso

TRAPPES, Francis M and BRADLEY, Basil (19th C) British
£7000 $12530   (13-Nov-91 CG558/R) The road from the moors (51x91cm-20x36in) mono.d.1878 s.i.d.verso

TRAQUAIR, Phoebe Anne (1852-1936) Irish
£10000 $17000   (25-Oct-91 C58/R) The New Creation (58x49cm-23x19in) mono.d.1887 canvas on panel

TRAUB, Gustav (1885-?) German
£825 $1452   (11-Apr-92 AW.H2363/R) View of Black Forest farmhouse in June (75x100cm-30x39in) s. i.d.1944verso board (DM 2400)
£859 $1512   (11-Apr-92 AW.H2362/R) Black Forest view (100x135cm-39x53in) s. s.i.d.1944verso board (DM 2500)

TRAUT, Wolfgang (1486-1520) German
£5155 $8969   (18-Sep-91 N.M455/R) The Assumption of the Virgin Mary (65x82cm-26x32in) part of altar panel (DM 15000)

TRAUTMANN, Johann Georg (1713-1769) German
£1394 $2537   (11-Dec-91 N.M372/R) Flight to Egypt (19x15cm-7x6in) panel (DM 4000)
£702 $1263   (22-Nov-91 SA.A1501/R) Riverside town on fire at night (16x21cm-6x8in) bodycol (DM 2000)

TRAUTMANN, Johann Georg (circle) (1713-1769) German
£1543 $2701   (18-Feb-92 CH.AM246/R) Packhorse at trough and donkey stealing hay from its saddle-bag (48x36cm-19x14in) panel (D.FL 5000)

TRAVERS, H (?) ?
£698 $1200   (15-Oct-91 CE.NY402/R) A side entrance (55x46cm-22x18in) s.d.1899

TRAVERSE, Charles de la (1726-1780) French
£431 $776   (22-Nov-91 AGS.P138) La bergere taquine (21x14cm-8x6in) pen Indian ink wash (F.FR 4200)
£856 $1455   (25-Oct-91 AT.P98) Hercule (30x21cm-12x8in) pen wash traces blk.crayon (F.FR 8500)

TRAVERSI, Gaspare (?-1769) Italian
£55000 $100100   (13-Dec-91 C94/R) Peasant woman and her son resting with an old beggar (82x98cm-32x39in)

TRAVERSI, Gaspare (circle) (?-1769) Italian
£2300 $4094   (29-Oct-91 PH143/R) Portrait of an architect seated in his library (99x84cm-39x33in) canvas laid down on board

TRAVI, Antonio (attrib) (1608-1665) Italian
£11155 $20191   (4-Dec-91 CH.R156/R) Capriccio di rovine barocche con urna antica, cavaliere ed altre figure (88x132cm-35x52in) (I.L 24000000)

TRAVI, Antonio (circle) (1608-1665) Italian
£5800 $11136   (7-Jul-92 PH161/R) Travellers resting at base of rocky pass, with two riders and horses (80x116cm-31x46in)

TRAWOGER, Ernst (1955-) Austrian
£727 $1323   (26-May-92 D.V358/R) Untitled (60x46cm-24x18in) s.d.1986verso (A.S 15000)

TRAWOGER, Ernst (1955-) Austrian-cont.
£485 $882   (26-May-92 D.V359/R) Untitled (53x45cm-21x18in) s.d.87verso indian ink
                            gouache (A.S 10000)
£489 $870   (31-Oct-91 D.V207/R) Untitled (53x45cm-21x18in) s.d.87verso indian ink
                            gouache (A.S 10000)

TRAYER, Jules (1824-1908) French
£608 $1132   (19-Jun-92 G.Z132/R) Le repos (33x23cm-13x9in) s. W/C (S.FR 1600)

TREBILCOCK, Paul (1902-1981) American
£3448 $6000   (15-Sep-91 JRB.C96/R) Venus in Orvieto (97x122cm-38x48in) s.

TREBUTIEN, Etienne Leon (1902-1981) French
£2600 $4498   (3-Oct-91 CSK131) Roses, peaches, a basket of rasberries and other fruit
                            by an urn (99x79cm-39x31in) s. canvas laid down on board

TRECCANI, Ernesto (1920-) Italian
£1040 $1851   (29-Oct-91 BRO.B308) Amore (81x65cm-32x26in) s.i.d.1987 (S.P 190000)
£1584 $2883   (25-May-92 CH.R66/R) Vegetazione (54x70cm-21x28in) s.d.1970 (I.L 3500000)

TREGANZA, Ruth C Robinson (1887-?) American
£971 $1700   (3-Apr-92 S.W2462) Farm in pastoral landscape (64x76cm-25x30in) s.

TREMERIE, Carolus (1858-1945) Belgian
£2152 $3896   (23-May-92 KV.L332) Begijnhof under the snow (130x120cm-51x47in) s.
                            (B.FR 130000)

TREMOLIERE, Pierre Charles (1703-1739) French
£750 $1305   (13-Apr-92 S376) View of park with balustrade by lake (27x32cm-11x13in)
                            s.d.1734 black white chk

TREMOLIERE, Pierre Charles (attrib) (1703-1739) French
£7000 $12740   (10-Dec-91 PH10/R) Nymph and satyr (64x113cm-25x44in)

TREMOLIERE, Pierre Charles (circle) (1703-1739) French
£2141 $3982   (19-Jun-92 ARC.P86/R) L'Amour porteur de torches. L'Amour porteur de
                            gerbes (122x98cm-48x39in) oval pair (F.FR 21000)

TRENKWALDER, Elmar (1959-) Austrian
£831 $1479   (31-Oct-91 D.V217/R) Untitled (92x69cm-36x27in) s.d.84verso mixed media
                            canvas (A.S 17000)

TRENNERY, Horace Hurtle (1899-1958) Australian
£1111 $1978   (27-Apr-92 J.M120/R) Settlers cottage, Woodside SA (23x24cm-9x9in) s.
                            canvas on board (A.D 2600)
£5991 $10424   (16-Sep-91 CH.ME159/R) Seascape (54x59cm-21x23in) s. (A.D 13000)
£10599 $18442   (16-Sep-91 CH.ME83/R) Pink road - Thomas Martin's farm (42x54cm-17x21in)
                            s. canvasboard (A.D 23000)

TRENTIN, Angelo (1850-1912) Austrian
£752 $1361   (5-Dec-91 D.V114) Lake landscape with figures (24x37cm-9x15in) s.d.1881
                            (A.S 15000)

TRESHAM, Henry (attrib) (1751-1814) British
£1400 $2464   (8-Apr-92 S189/R) Condemnation of Bushy (182x133cm-72x52in)

TREVELYAN, Julian (1910-1988) British
£900 $1692   (18-Dec-91 C159/R) The watermill (35x46cm-14x18in) s.i.d.1928stretcher
£1900 $3477   (14-May-92 C151/R) Richmond Bridge (23x28cm-9x11in) s.d.55 board
£3000 $5490   (14-May-92 C31/R) Self-portrait (91x75cm-36x30in) s.d.65 s.i.stretcher
£3500 $6020   (6-Mar-92 C99/R) Standing figure with ace of clubs (93x65cm-37x26in)
                            s.d.33
£4000 $6960   (19-Sep-91 CSK211/R) Cottages on Tresco (51x61cm-20x24in) s.d.45
£5500 $9735   (8-Nov-91 C223/R) The main line (18x20cm-7x8in) s.d.44 panel
£580 $1009   (19-Sep-91 B89/R) Picnic - bather by river (21x22cm-8x9in) s.d.53 W/C
                            bodycol pen
£650 $1242   (16-Jul-92 B150) Chicken farm (36x54cm-14x21in) s.d.29 W/C over pencil

TREVI (20th C) Italian?
£417 $742   (29-Nov-91 F.F119) Composizione (35x32cm-14x13in) s.d.1963 ink acrylic
                            cardboard (I.L 900000)

TREVISAN, A (19/20th C) Italian
£457 $800   (3-Apr-92 S.W1977/R) Grand Canal, Venice (30x48cm-12x19in) s. W/C

TREVISANI, Francesco (1656-1746) Italian
£11173 $20000   (17-Jan-92 SY.NY131/R) Mystic marriage of Saint Catherine
                            (107x84cm-42x33in)

TREVISANI, Francesco (attrib) (1656-1746) Italian
£1950 $3744   (10-Jul-92 C268/R) Hercules and Omphale (49x61cm-19x24in)
£8599 $15651   (28-May-92 F.M133/R) Ritratto di architetto (116x91cm-46x36in)
                            (I.L 19000000)

TREVISANI, Francesco (circle) (1656-1746) Italian
£1800	$3150	(3-Apr-92 C85/R) Madonna and Child (54x42cm-21x17in)
£4200	$7308	(15-Apr-92 C161/R) St Joseph with the Christ Child (64x49cm-25x19in)
£4651	$8000	(10-Oct-91 SY.NY66/R) Martyrdom of male saint (96x57cm-38x22in)

TREVISANI, Francesco (school) (1656-1746) Italian
£1657	$3000	(21-May-92 CH.NY216/R) Terpsichore (62x74cm-24x29in)

TREVISANI, Francesco (studio) (1656-1746) Italian
£1400	$2548	(10-Dec-91 PH227/R) Penitent Magdalen (97x76cm-38x30in)

TREVISANI, Francesco (style) (1656-1746) Italian
£1077	$1906	(7-Nov-91 D.V229/R) The Mourning of Christ (32x32cm-13x13in) (A.S 22000)
£1900	$3477	(12-May-92 SWS775/R) Christ comforted by angel at Gethsemane (97x83cm-38x33in)
£2500	$4550	(13-Dec-91 C252/R) Sophonisba presented with the poisoned chalice (99x136cm-39x54in)
£2914	$5099	(30-Mar-92 ZZ.F47/R) La Vierge a l'enfant avec le petit Saint Jean Baptiste (127x95cm-50x37in) (F.FR 28000)
£3072	$5560	(21-May-92 L.K154/R) Holy Family with infant St John (101x79cm-40x31in) (DM 9000)

TREVITHICK, James Garland (19/20th C) British?
£2200	$4004	(28-May-92 C94/R) Fishing boats in Auckland harbour (22x40cm-9x16in) s.i.d.1883 board

TREZZINI, Angiolo (1827-1904) Italian
£1714	$3000	(18-Feb-92 CE.NY232/R) Peasant woman on snowy hillside (59x46cm-23x18in) s.
£5438	$9299	(19-Mar-92 F.M5/R) Figura di popolana di fronte al mare (44x38cm-17x15in) s. (I.L 11700000)

TRIEBEL, Carl and RENTZELL, August von (19th C) German
£2062	$3588	(17-Sep-91 FN.S2587/R) Animals and figures resting in mountain landscape, thunderstorm rising (70x96cm-28x38in) s. (DM 6000)
£2168	$3750	(6-Sep-91 S.BM131/R) Genre scene with young shepherd (69x97cm-27x38in) s.
£4530	$8244	(11-Dec-91 WE.MU144/R) Cattle and children in high mountain landscape (69x97cm-27x38in) s. (DM 13000)

TRIER, A (fl.1879-1903) British
£4000	$7000	(20-Feb-92 SY.NY267/R) Still life with peonies on table (79x58cm-31x23in) indist.s.

TRIER, Hann (1915-) German
£4124	$7629	(11-Jun-92 HN.H454/R) Assel (41x33cm-16x13in) s.d.1961 s.i.d.verso (DM 12000)
£11684	$21381	(2-Jun-92 L.K1007/R) Macchia (116x87cm-46x34in) s.d.1969 i.d.verso acrylic (DM 34000)
£13333	$24000	(19-Nov-91 L.K1162/R) Ricercare III (97x129cm-38x51in) s.d.69 acrylic (DM 38000)
£13746	$25155	(2-Jun-92 L.K1006) Schwanken II (100x65cm-39x26in) mono.d.1958 s.i.d.verso (DM 40000)
£17014	$30455	(15-Nov-91 KM.K686/R) Zodiacus Leo (158x119cm-62x47in) s.d.67 s.i.verso tempera (DM 49000)
£751	$1367	(30-May-92 VG.B974/R) Composition (24x18cm-9x7in) mono.s.i.d.1965 col.chk (DM 2200)
£2061	$3730	(21-May-92 SY.AM210/R) Untitled (72x50cm-28x20in) s.d.59 W/C (D.FL 6800)
£3093	$5722	(11-Jun-92 HN.H455/R) Design for poster for Kunstverein Koln (65x50cm-26x20in) d.1958 i.verso gouache (DM 9000)

TRIGT, Hendrik Albert van (1829-1899) Dutch
£2105	$3600	(13-Mar-92 FN.S2993 a/R) Sardinian shepherd boy playing flute (96x72cm-38x28in) s.i. (DM 6000)

TRIMOLET, Edma (attrib) (1801-1878) French
£687	$1196	(18-Sep-91 N.M720/R) Kitchen interior with female servant working (32x46cm-13x18in) i. (DM 2000)

TRINDALL, Gordon Lyall (1886-?) Australian
£1068	$1902	(28-Apr-92 CH.ME232/R) Child with goat (48x41cm-19x16in) s. board (A.D 2500)

TRINER, Heinrich (1796-1873) Swiss
£370	$670	(19-May-92 GF.L2828) View of Wilhelm Tell's birth house (24x31cm-9x12in) s.i. W/C (S.FR 1000)

TRIPP, Wilson B Evan (1896-?) American
£881	$1550	(9-Apr-92 FA.PH687) Boxing match at Sharkey's (61x91cm-24x36in) s.

TRISCOTT, Samuel Peter Rolt (1846-1925) American
£1111	$2000	(24-Nov-91 JRB.C28/R) Landscapes (13x33cm-5x13in) s.d.75 and 89 W/C pair

TRISTRAM, John W (1872-1938) Australian
£769	$1369	(27-Apr-92 J.M257/R) Clair de Lune (28x29cm-11x11in) s.d.1919 W/C (A.D 1800)

TRISTRAM, John W (1872-1938) Australian-cont.
£529	$941	(26-Nov-91 J.M188/R) Headland (25x36cm-10x14in) s.d.1928 W/C (A.D 1200)
£661	$1176	(26-Nov-91 J.M187) Nocturne (28x18cm-11x7in) s.d.1920 W/C (A.D 1500)

TRIVIDIC, Pierre le (1898-1960) French
£1270	$2210	(19-Apr-92 ZZ.F27/R) Peniches amarrees (54x62cm-21x24in) s. gouache (F.FR 12500)

TROCCOLI, Giovanni Battista (1882-1940) Italian/American
£678	$1200	(25-Apr-92 YFA.M288/R) Still life (64x51cm-25x20in) s. mono.

TROGER, Paul (1698-1762) Austrian
£1660	$2839	(12-Mar-92 GK.Z4) Ecce homo (68x50cm-27x20in) (S.FR 4300)
£1200	$2184	(10-Dec-91 C249/R) Saint John the Baptist (30x19cm-12x7in) ink
£1228	$2100	(13-Mar-92 FN.S1985/R) Angel making music (27x20cm-11x8in) s. pencil htd.white (DM 3500)
£2235	$4000	(14-Jan-92 SY.NY138/R) St. Joseph with infant Christ (19x21cm-7x8in) bears i. pen black chk stumping htd white

TROGER, Paul (attrib) (1698-1762) Austrian
£5185	$9385	(19-May-92 GF.L2418/R) The Marriage of Mary and Joseph. The Death of St Joseph (66x39cm-26x15in) pair (S.FR 14000)

TROGER, Paul (studio) (1698-1762) Austrian
£2484	$4247	(18-Mar-92 D.V401/R) The resurrection of Lazarus (70x47cm-28x19in) (A.S 50000)

TROILI, Uno (1815-1875) Swedish
£476	$867	(14-Dec-91 BA.S115) Theodor Sack, cellist and winemerchants (S.KR 5000)

TROKES, Heinz (1913-) German
£1280	$2445	(4-Jul-92 BOD.P655) 5 vereinzelte and 1 Zange (25x20cm-10x8in) s.d.53 i.verso (DM 3700)
£2405	$4402	(2-Jun-92 L.K1009) Blickfeld (77x80cm-30x31in) s.d.1965 i.verso (DM 7000)
£4688	$8297	(5-Nov-91 GF.L2226/R) African trails (75x80cm-30x31in) s. i.d.1961verso tempera (S.FR 12000)
£481	$847	(10-Apr-92 KM.K567) Earth in space (30x24cm-12x9in) s. pen over W/C board (DM 1400)
£751	$1359	(23-May-92 GB.B7301) Geometric composition (51x66cm-20x26in) s.d.1948 W/C (DM 2200)
£1014	$1734	(21-Mar-92 WK.M615/R) Turmbauten (50x61cm-20x24in) s.d.1975 W/C over pen (DM 2900)
£1031	$1753	(26-Oct-91 WK.M714/R) Lines (48x63cm-19x25in) s.d.1962 i.d.verso gouache (DM 3000)
£1049	$1867	(25-Nov-91 WK.M1025/R) Blue hand (55x70cm-22x28in) s.d.1967 i.d.verso W/C gouache (DM 3000)

TROMBADORI, Francesco (1886-?) Italian
£2553	$4799	(19-Dec-91 F.M229/R) Paese (48x65cm-19x26in) s. (I.L 5500000)
£3021	$5468	(3-Dec-91 F.R160/R) Nudo femminile (30x15cm-12x6in) s. oil board on canvas (I.L 6500000)
£3249	$6107	(19-Dec-91 F.M185/R) Marina (40x50cm-16x20in) s. (I.L 7000000)
£4416	$7992	(3-Dec-91 F.R2645/R) Santa Maria del Popolo (40x50cm-16x20in) s. panel (I.L 9500000)

TROMBETI, U (19th C) Italian
£920	$1646	(14-Nov-91 CH.R232 a) Scorcio di Venezia (38x23cm-15x9in) s. (I.L 2000000)

TROMETTA, Nicolo (16/17th C) Italian
£2100	$3654	(13-Apr-92 S8/R) Body of St. Francis attended by followers with Jerome touching stigmata (37x22cm-15x9in) pen wash htd white black chk

TROMP, Jan Zoetelief (1872-1947) Dutch
£2654	$4750	(6-May-92 D.NY71/R) Mother and child in interior (56x41cm-22x16in) s. canvas on board
£3823	$6651	(14-Apr-92 SY.AM161/R) Children on hay-wagon (28x42cm-11x17in) s. (D.FL 12500)
£4893	$8514	(14-Apr-92 SY.AM172/R) Children with goats in field (29x40cm-11x16in) s. (D.FL 16000)
£5523	$9500	(16-Oct-91 CH.NY224/R) The daisy chain (40x56cm-16x22in) s.
£7339	$12771	(14-Apr-92 SY.AM135/R) The pet goat (23x33cm-9x13in) s. (D.FL 24000)
£8939	$16000	(6-May-92 D.NY72/R) Wildflowers (30x41cm-12x16in) s.
£11621	$20220	(14-Apr-92 SY.AM108/R) Playing children on beach (39x54cm-15x21in) s. (D.FL 38000)
£12538	$21817	(14-Apr-92 SY.AM262/R) In the fields (38x48cm-15x19in) s. (D.FL 41000)
£12844	$22734	(5-Nov-91 SY.AM41/R) Children in dunes (34x49cm-13x19in) s. (D.FL 42000)
£13761	$24495	(30-Oct-91 CH.AM213 a/R) Flowers for mother (50x60cm-20x24in) s. (D.FL 45000)
£15902	$28306	(30-Oct-91 CH.AM184 b/R) Beach pleasure (40x56cm-16x22in) s. (D.FL 52000)

TROOD, William Henry Hamilton (1848-1899) British
£522	$950	(13-Dec-91 S.W2871) Plough horses (56x46cm-22x18in) s.
£1150	$1955	(22-Oct-91 SWS295/R) Bitter cry (45x35cm-18x14in) s.d.1884

TROOD, William Henry Hamilton (1848-1899) British-cont.
£10000 $17900   (14-Jan-92 B245/R) Uncorking the bottle (41x56cm-16x22in) s.d.1887 board pair

TROOST, Cornelis (1697-1750) Dutch
£14525 $26000   (14-Jan-92 SY.NY105/R) View through open woodland with seated gentleman reading, dog at feet (45x60cm-18x24in) s. gouache
£14907 $26534   (25-Nov-91 CH.AM173 a/R) Corps de Garde with officers playing cards (29x41cm-11x16in) s.d.1744 bodycol (D.FL 48000)

TROOST, Cornelis (attrib) (1697-1750) Dutch
£1493 $2731   (12-May-92 GM.B242) Rencontre, le soir (64x46cm-25x18in) (B.FR 90000)

TROOST, Sara (1731-1803) Dutch
£667 $1140   (13-Mar-92 FN.S2994) 17th century tavern interior with figures (20x30cm-8x12in) s. panel (DM 1900)

TROOST, Willem (18/19th C) Dutch
£7200 $13824   (6-Jul-92 S93/R) Fantasy Rhine landscape (37x49cm-15x19in) s. gouache

TROST, Friedrich (1844-1922) German
£500 $855   (17-Mar-92 PH62) In the park (27x34cm-11x13in) s.d.09 board

TROTTER, Alexander Mason (1891-1946) British
£1200 $2136   (30-Apr-92 CG890/R) The Cab Stand, Waverley Station, Edinburgh (23x29cm-9x11in) s. canvas board

TROTTER, Newbold Hough (1827-1898) American
£559 $1000   (14-Nov-91 CE.NY105/R) Cow and calf (31x43cm-12x17in) s.d.1862 s.i. num.61 verso

TROTTI, Giovanni Battista (circle) (1555-1619) Italian
£9000 $16380   (10-Dec-91 PH155/R) Madonn and Child (86x63cm-34x25in) panel

TROTZIG, Ulf (1925-) Norwegian
£522 $909   (13-Apr-92 AB.S261) La nef de fous (48x67cm-19x26in) s. (S.KR 5500)

TROUILLZ, Clovis (1889-?) French
£13225 $24201   (14-May-92 BG.P67/R) La Robe Ecarlate (54x73cm-21x29in) s. s.i.verso (F.FR 130000)
£1169 $2034   (16-Apr-92 FB.P40/R) Le Roie de Bamboula il en grande tenue (32x25cm-13x10in) s.i.d.1909 W/C Indian ink (F.FR 11500)

TROUILLEBERT (style) (19th C) French
£2469 $4395   (28-Apr-92 RAS.K599) Romantic river landscape (74x115cm-29x45in) (D.KR 28000)

TROUILLEBERT, P D (1829-1900) French
£3204 $5736   (17-Nov-91 LL.LH44 a) Nu au coussin (33x56cm-13x22in) (F.FR 31500)

TROUILLEBERT, Paul Desire (1829-1900) French
£934 $1700   (26-May-92 CE.NY272/R) Wooded landscape (23x15cm-9x6in) s. board
£2941 $5000   (11-Aug-91 LIT.L49) River landscape (43x56cm-17x22in) s.
£3650 $6533   (6-May-92 GD.B1291/R) The old mill (32x36cm-13x14in) indis.s. (S.FR 10000)
£4800 $8208   (18-Mar-92 S116/R) Windy day by the sea (21x26cm-8x10in) s.
£5143 $9000   (20-Feb-92 SY.NY167/R) Fortuna (43x34cm-17x13in) s.
£5155 $8969   (18-Sep-91 N.M721/R) Lake landscape with washerwomen and castle amongst trees (32x46cm-13x18in) s. (DM 15000)
£5967 $11337   (26-Jun-92 AGS.P22/R) Le repos sous l'arbre (40x54cm-16x21in) s. (F.FR 58000)
£6857 $12000   (19-Feb-92 CH.NY44/R) Chateau de Thouars (29x41cm-11x16in) s.
£6996 $13292   (26-Jun-92 AGS.P21/R) Maisons au bord d'une riviere (32x48cm-13x19in) s. (F.FR 68000)
£7377 $13279   (2-Feb-92 ZZ.F58/R) Bord de Loire a Saumur (28x41cm-11x16in) s. (F.FR 72000)
£8147 $15071   (10-Jun-92 ZZ.F46/R) Paysage anime (55x46cm-22x18in) s. (F.FR 80000)
£8791 $16000   (28-May-92 SY.NY153/R) A la sortie du village (38x56cm-15x22in) s. d.1893 verso
£9143 $16000   (20-Feb-92 SY.NY26/R) Mill house (46x56cm-18x22in) s.
£9469 $16571   (5-Apr-92 ZZ.F55/R) Barque au bord de la riviere (32x41cm-13x16in) s. (F.FR 91000)
£10526 $18947   (23-Nov-91 N.M312/R) Une ferme pres de Barbizon (33x41cm-13x16in) s. (DM 30000)
£11500 $19665   (18-Mar-92 S117/R) Fishermen in a river landscape (41x59cm-16x23in) s.
£12157 $20667   (23-Oct-91 GD.B1308/R) Wooded river landscape with figures (33x46cm-13x18in) s. (S.FR 31000)
£18000 $32040   (27-Nov-91 S210/R) View of Romarantin in Loire Valley (37x55cm-15x22in) s.

TROUILLEBERT, Paul Desire (attrib) (1829-1900) French
£791 $1423   (19-Nov-91 GS.B3673/R) Wooded lake landscape with fishermen and boat (19x27cm-7x11in) (S.FR 2000)

TROUSSARD, H G (1896-?) French
£749 $1311   (30-Mar-92 ZZ.F30) Jeune garcon (88x115cm-35x45in) s.d.1926 (F.FR 7200)

TROVA, Ernest (1927-) American
£1257 $2200   (27-Feb-92 CE.NY186/R) Study for falling man no.82 (170x170cm-67x67in)
                s.d.63 verso acrylic graphite canvas

TROXLER, Georges Alfons (1901-1990) Swiss
£532 $990   (19-Jun-92 ZOF.Z2116) Moor landscape near Muri (50x69cm-20x27in)
                i.d.70verso (S.FR 1400)
£608 $1132   (19-Jun-92 ZOF.Z2117/R) View of Zofingen seen from Heiternplatz
                (46x55cm-18x22in) s.d.1962 i.verso (S.FR 1600)
£647 $1158   (15-Nov-91 ZOF.Z1910) Hallwilersee with view of Seengen, Brestenberg
                (45x57cm-18x22in) s. i.d.72verso (S.FR 1650)

TROY, Francois de (1645-1730) French
£10000 $19100   (15-Jul-92 S18/R) Portrait of James Edward Stuart,The Old Pretender
                (71x55cm-28x22in) painted oval
£2243 $4171   (20-Jun-92 CH.MO227/R) Etude de mains de femme tenant un eventail
                (28x45cm-11x18in) black white chk (F.FR 22000)
£2514 $4500   (14-Jan-92 SY.NY115/R) Study of young boy writing at table
                (46x33cm-18x13in) bears num.3 red chk htd white squared black chk

TROY, Francois de (attrib) (1645-1730) French
£2220 $3818   (16-Oct-91 AT.P101/R) Portrait d'un gentilhomme (81x65cm-32x26in) oval
                (F.FR 22000)

TROY, Francois de (circle) (1645-1730) French
£5000 $9100   (13-Dec-91 C209/R) Vertumnus and Pomona (75x124cm-30x49in)

TROY, Francois de (style) (1645-1730) French
£1500 $2625   (28-Feb-92 C101/R) Portrait of a young nobleman, half length, wearing
                armour (75x61cm-30x24in) oval
£4800 $8400   (3-Apr-92 C43/R) Portrait of lady, wearing grey bodice and blue wrap
                (81x65cm-32x26in) oval

TROY, Jean Francois de (1679-1752) French
£6687 $12104   (7-Dec-91 CH.MO52/R) La Resurrection (63x34cm-25x13in) canvas laid down
                on board (F.FR 65000)
£142712 $265443   (18-Jun-92 SY.MO50/R) Pan et Syrinx (90x73cm-35x29in) s.d.1733
                (F.FR 1400000)

TROY, Jean Francois de (attrib) (1679-1752) French
£22518 $40082   (29-Nov-91 ARC.P37/R) Suzanne et les vieillards (96x133cm-38x52in)
                (F.FR 220000)

TROY, Jean Francois de (circle) (1679-1752) French
£18538 $31699   (20-Mar-92 ZZ.F23/R) Diane et ses nymphes (98x135cm-39x53in)
                (F.FR 180000)

TROY, Mary (?) Australian
£881 $1586   (19-Nov-91 JRL.S259/R) Terrace (142x154cm-56x61in) s. (A.D 2000)

TROYER, Prosper de (1880-1961) Belgian?
£2649 $4795   (23-May-92 KV.L480/R) The bath (142x79cm-56x31in) s.d.25 panel
                (B.FR 160000)

TROYON, Constant (1810-1865) French
£1027 $1858   (3-Dec-91 C.A298) Cattle watering (66x55cm-26x22in) s. (B.FR 60000)
£1700 $3026   (27-Nov-91 S209/R) Meadow landscape (29x60cm-11x24in) s. panel
£2035 $3500   (10-Oct-91 FA.PH924/R) Cow in golden field (58x74cm-23x29in) bears estate
                st.
£2424 $4291   (22-Apr-92 CH.AM174/R) Bull in a sunlit meadow (47x55cm-19x22in)
                (D.FL 8000)
£2645 $4734   (13-Nov-91 PIC.P87/R) Chasseur et ses trois chiens (25x37cm-10x15in) s.
                panel (F.FR 26000)
£2675 $5082   (26-Jun-92 AGS.P23/R) Le chemin de la ferme (25x20cm-10x8in) s. panel
                (F.FR 26000)
£2857 $5000   (19-Feb-92 CH.NY37/R) Cows in landscape (38x46cm-15x18in) init.
£3000 $5310   (14-Feb-92 C24/R) Milking time (91x73cm-36x29in) s.
£5202 $9000   (6-Sep-91 S.BM123/R) Herder with cattle (53x79cm-21x31in) s.
£5495 $10000   (27-May-92 CH.NY159/R) Vaches a la Mare (68x92cm-27x36in)
£5519 $9878   (14-Nov-91 CH.R7/R) Paesaggio con mucche all'abbeverata (14x32cm-6x13in)
                s. panel (I.L 12000000)
£7692 $14000   (27-May-92 CH.NY160/R) Mill stream with fishermen (43x51cm-17x20in) s.
                panel
£8000 $14000   (20-Feb-92 SY.NY22/R) Watering horses (51x62cm-20x24in) s.
£8242 $15000   (27-May-92 CH.NY158/R) Catle grazing in landscape (49x71cm-19x28in)
                s.d.1857 panel
£497 $850   (21-Mar-92 W.W11/R) Farmers tending oxen (23x30cm-9x12in) s. W/C pencil
£1023 $1852   (22-May-92 LD.P6) Boulevard a Paris (23x30cm-9x12in) crayon chl pastel
                (F.FR 10100)
£1660 $2838   (11-Mar-92 LGB.P136) Bergere et troupeau (22x27cm-9x11in) s. pastel
                canvas (F.FR 16100)

TROYON, Constant (attrib) (1810-1865) French
£780 $1413   (3-Dec-91 R.T204/R) Cows grazing near cottage (65x91cm-26x36in) s.d.1856 (C.D 1600)
£850 $1454   (17-Mar-92 PH112/R) Study of bull in landscape (42x52cm-17x20in) panel

TRUANAS (20th C) ?
£831 $1437   (26-Mar-92 DUR.M955/R) Honfleur (60x72cm-24x28in) s. s.i.d.1983verso (S.P 150000)

TRUBNER, Wilhelm (1851-1917) German
£962 $1693   (11-Apr-92 AW.H775/R) Standing female nude leaning against tree (78x42cm-31x17in) board (DM 2800)
£1718 $2990   (18-Sep-91 N.M724/R) Portrait of gentleman (43x35cm-17x14in) s.d.1886 i.verso (DM 5000)
£1852 $3352   (19-May-92 GF.L2146/R) Die Kellnerin Zenzi (51x40cm-20x16in) mono (S.FR 5000)
£3976 $7076   (30-Oct-91 CH.AM160/R) Peasant girl standing in Chiemsee landscape (64x45cm-25x18in) init. (D.FL 13000)

TRUE, David (20th C) ?
£930 $1600   (12-Oct-91 SY.NY327/R) Symmetry and Ethiopian (69x91cm-27x36in) s.d.80 verso oil pencil prepared board
£1744 $3000   (12-Oct-91 SY.NY320/R) Savannah sea (137x198cm-54x78in)
£1078 $1800   (25-Aug-91 JRB.C97) Untitled (66x99cm-26x39in) W/C ink acrylic gesso

TRUELSEN, Mathias Jacob Theodore (1836-1900) European
£1264 $2274   (19-Nov-91 RAS.K528/R) Ships portrait of 'Mary Elisabeth Anderson of Suisun' (38x64cm-15x25in) s.i. W/C (D.KR 14000)

TRUFFAUT, Fernand (20th C) French
£424 $751   (24-Apr-92 CN.P146) Trouville, le port (36x51cm-14x20in) s. W/C gouache (F.FR 4200)

TRULSSON, Anders (1874-1911) Swedish
£760 $1361   (16-Nov-91 FAL.M362/R) 'Old Ludvig' - original from Tosterup (84x66cm-33x26in) s.d.94 (S.KR 8000)

TRUMAN, J (?) British?
£1214 $2160   (29-Apr-92 D.V766/R) Horse in stable (51x66cm-20x26in) s.d.1866 (A.S 25000)

TRUPHEME, Auguste Joseph (1836-1898) French
£2974 $5324   (19-Jan-92 CSC.P131) La lecon de chant (50x61cm-20x24in) s. (F.FR 29000)

TRUPHEMUS, Jacques (20th C) French
£2520 $4461   (10-Nov-91 ZZ.F206/R) Place animee a Paris (65x30cm-26x12in) s.d.1957 (F.FR 25000)
£3429 $6000   (28-Feb-92 SY.NY187/R) Nue dans un interieur (38x46cm-15x18in) s.d.60 s.num.13C verso

TRUPPE, Karl (1887-1959) Austrian
£893 $1519   (25-Oct-91 BM.B966/R) Still life with pipe and matches (21x21cm-8x8in) s. panel (DM 2600)
£2184 $3888   (28-Apr-92 D.V138/R) Still life with fruit (52x46cm-20x18in) (A.S 45000)
£2234 $3887   (18-Sep-91 N.M725/R) Young peasant woman wearing costume (63x53cm-25x21in) s.d.1942 board (DM 6500)
£2407 $4357   (19-May-92 GF.L2569/R) Red curls (40x44cm-16x17in) s.d.1940 board (S.FR 6500)

TRUSTTUM, Philip (1940-) New Zealander
£3333 $6033   (4-Dec-91 DS.W16/R) Garden series (83x63cm-33x25in) s.d.73 (NZ.D 10800)
£3436 $5739   (21-Aug-91 DS.W45/R) Cherry tree - from Garden Series (136x131cm-54x52in) board (NZ.D 10000)

TRUSZ, Ivan (1869-1940) Russian
£523 $905   (8-Sep-91 REM.W41) River landscape (33x48cm-13x19in) s. board (P.Z 10000000)
£1099 $1901   (7-Sep-91 AL.W6) The Dnieper Bends near Kiev (69x97cm-27x38in) s. panel (P.Z 21000000)

TRYON, Dwight W (1849-1925) American
£1193 $2100   (9-Apr-92 FA.PH701/R) Harbour view (28x38cm-11x15in) s.d.1889 panel

TSAI YIN-TANG (1909-) Chinese
£13908 $23783   (22-Mar-92 SY.TA61/R) Pei-T'Ou Park (38x45cm-15x18in) s.d.1958 (T.D 605000)

TSCHAGGENY, Frederic (1851-1921) Belgian
£1173 $2052   (18-Feb-92 CH.AM172) A gipsy girl (105x72cm-41x28in) s. (D.FL 3800)

TSCHANG-YEUL KIM (1929-) Korean
£1754 $3158   (23-Nov-91 N.M159) Gouties d'eau (100x100cm-39x39in) s.d.1973 s.i.d.verso (DM 5000)

TSCHARNER, Johann Wilhelm von (1886-1946) Swiss
£980 $1667   (23-Oct-91 GD.B757/R) House with garden (53x72cm-21x28in) s. (S.FR 2500)
£1128 $2064   (4-Jun-92 SY.Z400/R) Still life with glass (22x35cm-9x14in) s.
                 (S.FR 3000)
£1176 $2106   (15-Nov-91 GK.Z5358) Basle autumn fair (81x73cm-32x29in) s. s.i.stretcher
                 (S.FR 3000)
£1504 $2752   (4-Jun-92 SY.Z439/R) View from the window (61x85cm-24x33in) s.
                 (S.FR 4000)
£4511 $8256   (4-Jun-92 SY.Z438/R) Still life with bread and onions (59x73cm-23x29in)
                 s. (S.FR 12000)

TSCHUMI, Otto (1904-1985) Swiss
£8029 $14372   (6-May-92 GD.B1294/R) Demenagement (33x64cm-13x25in) s.d.50 (S.FR 22000)
£460   *$795*   *(23-Mar-92 AB.L63/R) Self portrait (30x21cm-12x8in) s.d.63 pencil*
                 (S.FR 1200)
£2115   *$4019*   *(25-Jun-92 GK.B702) A Carcia Lorea (26x36cm-10x14in) s.i.d.1943 W/C*
                 bodycol over indian ink (S.FR 5500)
£3846   *$7308*   *(25-Jun-92 GK.B703) The street (31x24cm-12x9in) s. s.i.d.1969verso W/C*
                 over pencil (S.FR 10000)

TSINGOS, Thanos (1914-1965) Greek
£815 $1517   (15-Jun-92 GL.P75) Fleurs sur fond bleu (35x24cm-14x9in) s.d.1960
                 (F.FR 8000)
£1169 $2034   (13-Apr-92 GL.P97/R) Fleurs (24x33cm-9x13in) s.d.1956 hardboard
                 (F.FR 11500)
£1208 $2151   (28-Oct-91 GL.P181) Fleur blanche eclatee (55x46cm-22x18in) s. panel
                 (F.FR 12000)
£1321 $2299   (13-Apr-92 GL.P96) Fleurs (65x81cm-26x32in) s.d.1960 (F.FR 13000)
£1356 $2400   (5-Nov-91 CE.NY228/R) Boats (60x92cm-24x36in) s.
£1410 $2510   (28-Oct-91 GL.P180/R) Oiseaux monochromes (60x73cm-24x29in) s.d.1957
                 (F.FR 14000)
£1427 $2654   (15-Jun-92 GL.P74) Fleurs rouges (34x41cm-13x16in) s. paper laid down on
                 panel (F.FR 14000)
£1626 $2829   (14-Apr-92 ZZ.F8/R) Composition aux fleurs (92x72cm-36x28in) s.
                 (F.FR 16000)
£1626 $2829   (14-Apr-92 ZZ.F9/R) Fond sous-marin (73x100cm-29x39in) s.d.60
                 (F.FR 16000)
£2039 $3792   (15-Jun-92 GL.P72/R) Le port (90x116cm-35x46in) s.d.1959 (F.FR 20000)
£2115 $3764   (28-Oct-91 GL.P178 b/R) Nature morte aux fruits de mer (60x73cm-24x29in)
                 s.d.1960 (F.FR 21000)
£2342 $4263   (11-Dec-91 ZZ.F134/R) Fleurs des champs (89x116cm-35x46in) s. d.59verso
                 (F.FR 23000)

TSIREH, Awa (1895-1955) American
£865   *$1600*   *(14-Jun-92 S.BM242/R) Shalako (36x13cm-14x5in) s. gouache board*
£1189   *$2200*   *(14-Jun-92 S.BM238/R) Herder (20x28cm-8x11in) s. gouache*

TSUJI, H (20th C) Japanese
£549 $1000   (13-Dec-91 S.W2249) Mount Fuji (71x91cm-28x36in) s. i.d.1938 verso

TUBBECKE, Paul (1848-1924) German
£632 $1080   (13-Mar-92 FN.S2995) Washing drying on line before farmhouse
                 (25x30cm-10x12in) s. i.verso board (DM 1800)
£2613 $4756   (11-Dec-91 N.M619/R) Mill by stream and washerwoman (61x81cm-24x32in)
                 s.i.d.1895 i.stretcher (DM 7500)

TUBKE, Werner (1929-) ?
£1053   *$1895*   *(19-Nov-91 L.K1165/R) Male and female nudes (39x48cm-15x19in) s.d.1973*
                 chk (DM 3000)

TUCEK, Karl (1889-?) Austrian
£1172 $2074   (5-Nov-91 GF.L2766/R) Still life (62x70cm-24x28in) s. (S.FR 3000)

TUCK, Marie (1872-?) Australian
£705 $1255   (26-Nov-91 J.M1208) Feeding seagulls (24x60cm-9x24in) (A.D 1600)
£1322 $2352   (26-Nov-91 J.M294/R) In orchard (45x60cm-18x24in) s. (A.D 3000)

TUCKER, Albert (1914-) Australian
£470 $837   (27-Apr-92 J.M749) Portrait of Mrs Manders (28x24cm-11x9in) s.d.24
                 i.d.1888verso (A.D 1100)
£1462 $2792   (19-Jul-92 SY.ME7/R) Ibis (34x24cm-13x9in) s.d.64 paper on board
                 (A.D 3800)
£1496 $2662   (27-Apr-92 J.M122/R) Brolga in bush (24x37cm-9x15in) s.d.63 board
                 (A.D 3500)
£2304 $4009   (16-Sep-91 CH.ME143 a) Lasseter (51x41cm-20x16in) s. (A.D 5000)
£3846 $6846   (27-Apr-92 J.M211/R) Parrots in flight (40x50cm-16x20in) s. canvas on
                 board (A.D 9000)
£4405 $7930   (19-Nov-91 JRL.S353/R) Parrots in the bush (65x75cm-26x30in) s. board
                 (A.D 10000)
£7489 $13480   (24-Nov-91 SY.S398/R) Parrots amongst trees (55x70cm-22x28in) s. board
                 (A.D 17000)

TUCKER, Allen (1866-1939) American
£838 $1500   (13-Nov-91 B.SF2643/R) Summer landscape (51x41cm-20x16in) s. board
£1034 $1800   (15-Apr-92 SY.NY104/R) Washing day (41x51cm-16x20in) s. s.d.25 stretcher

TUCKER, Allen (1866-1939) American-cont.
£1130 $2000   (22-Apr-92 D.NY93) Great Elm (51x61cm-20x24in) s.d.1917 i.stretcher
£3041 $5200   (13-Mar-92 S.BM224/R) Cherry trees (64x76cm-25x30in) s. i.verso

TUCKER, Arthur (1864-1929) British
£400 $768   (29-Jul-92 CSK114) Feeding the chickens (22x28cm-9x11in) s. pencil W/C

TUCKER, Edward (c.1830-1909) British
£450 $810   (9-Jan-92 B252) Fishing smacks off St Michaels Mount (23x36cm-9x14in) W/C scratching out
£480 $816   (22-Oct-91 SWS137/R) Fishermen rowing out (28x48cm-11x19in) s.d.1847 W/C gum arabic
£480 $859   (14-Nov-91 CSK115) Windermere from Brentfell (25x41cm-10x16in) s. W/C htd.white
£600 $1068   (27-Nov-91 B199) Alnwick Castle, Northumberland (27x43cm-11x17in) s. W/C
£600 $1020   (22-Oct-91 SWS138) Sailing vessels on lake (35x53cm-14x21in) s. W/C
£850 $1462   (4-Mar-92 S224) Thames (17x33cm-7x13in) s.i. W/C
£900 $1584   (6-Apr-92 PH64) Off Dover (26x43cm-10x17in) s. W/C scratching out

TUCKER, Frederick (fl.1880-1915) British
£400 $716   (16-Jan-92 B231/R) River flowing from mountainous landscape (76x127cm-30x50in) s. W/C hld white

TUCKER, James W (1898-1972) British
£4800 $8496   (7-Nov-91 C75/R) The homecoming (85x117cm-33x46in) s. i.verso tempera

TUCKER, John Wallace (circle) (18/19th C) British
£2400 $4080   (22-Oct-91 S260/R) Fisherfolk and boats on beach. River estuary with boats (23x28cm-9x11in) pair

TUCKER, Tudor St George (1862-1906) British
£855 $1521   (27-Apr-92 J.M287/R) Portrait (14x11cm-6x4in) init.d.1896 board (A.D 2000)

TUCKERMAN, Ernest (?) ?
£950 $1625   (18-Mar-92 CSK332) The salon door (61x51cm-24x20in) init. panel
£1200 $2052   (18-Mar-92 CSK333) Dandelions, poppies and dried flowers in vase with Japanese doll on table (66x53cm-26x21in) init. panel

TUCKSON, John Anthony (1921-1973) Australian
£645 $1200   (21-Jun-92 SY.ME104/R) Black and white lattice (76x102cm-30x40in) gouache (A.D 1600)
£2203 $3965   (24-Nov-91 SY.S526/R) Blue head (74x54cm-29x21in) board (A.D 5000)
£565 $1050   (21-Jun-92 SY.ME81) Black, red and yellow abstract (50x38cm-20x15in) gouache (A.D 1400)
£605 $1125   (21-Jun-92 SY.ME13) Green head (51x38cm-20x15in) gouache (A.D 1500)
£1210 $2250   (21-Jun-92 SY.ME95) Untitled (178x76cm-70x30in) chl (A.D 3000)
£1322 $2379   (24-Nov-91 SY.S389) Lovers No.13 (51x76cm-20x30in) gouache (A.D 3000)
£11064 $19583   (26-Apr-92 SY.ME394/R) Black, white, yellow XO (122x122cm-48x48in) PVA hardboard (A.D 26000)

TUDELA, Martinez (19th C) Spanish
£2400 $4248   (14-Feb-92 C82/R) Reclining nude (20x25cm-8x10in) s.i.verso board

TUDGAY, F J (fl.1863-1876) ?
£2857 $5000   (19-Feb-92 CH.NY158/R) Clipper ship Macedon off Dover coast (51x76cm-20x30in) s.

TUDGAY, Francis (19th C) British
£2800 $5348   (17-Jul-92 C124/R) Blackwall frigates in stiff breeze (65x88cm-26x35in)

TUDGAY, I (19th C) British
£2857 $5000   (19-Feb-92 CH.NY159/R) On open seas (61x94cm-24x37in) s.d.1860

TUERENHOUT, Jef van (1926-) Belgian
£1086 $1846   (22-Oct-91 C.A1038/R) The rider (80x45cm-31x18in) s.d.1953 (B.FR 65000)
£2335 $4110   (7-Apr-92 C.A268/R) Les vilains nains (99x70cm-39x28in) s. dr. (B.FR 140000)
£5795 $10488   (23-May-92 KV.L505/R) Nude with parrot (120x80cm-47x31in) s. gouache (B.FR 350000)

TUGEL, Otto (1892-1973) German
£893 $1662   (20-Jun-92 BM.B778/R) Landscape with houses (77x61cm-30x24in) s. (DM 2600)
£976 $1776   (14-Dec-91 BOD.P760) View of town (76x60cm-30x24in) s. (DM 2800)
£601 $1051   (3-Apr-92 BM.B570/R) Winter landscape (46x64cm-18x25in) s.d.1947 W/C (DM 1700)

TUKE, Henry Scott (1858-1929) British
£500 $915   (6-Feb-92 T80/R) Portrait of young man (28x20cm-11x8in) s. card
£2500 $4325   (3-Oct-91 DLY254/R) Venice (18x25cm-7x10in) init.i.d.1899 panel
£3600 $6228   (3-Oct-91 DLY253/R) Mackeral fishing, Falmouth Bay (25x36cm-10x14in) init.d.1900 board
£550 $1007   (6-Feb-92 DLY233) Liner at anchor off Falmouth (25x36cm-10x14in) W/C
£650 $1092   (15-Aug-91 B189/R) Fishing smacks at evening (14x21cm-6x8in) s.d.1899 W/C

1848

TUKE, Henry Scott (1858-1929) British-cont.
£740	$1280	(4-Sep-91 BT12 a) Fisherman (18x10cm-7x4in) init.d.1889 W/C
£850	$1556	(6-Feb-92 DLY232/R) Rowing away from fishing boat (25x36cm-10x14in) W/C
£900	$1602	(27-Apr-92 PHB211 b) Venetian lagoon with gondolas (17x26cm-7x10in) s.indist.d.1900 W/C
£900	$1665	(9-Jun-92 ZZ.B3) Fishing vessels at anchor in Falmouth harbour (28x18cm-11x7in) s. W/C
£980	$1754	(5-May-92 SWS256/R) Barges on the Thames (24x34cm-9x13in) s.d.1909 W/C
£1400	$2408	(10-Oct-91 L91/R) Five masted sailing vessel at anchor (23x33cm-9x13in) W/C
£1550	$2775	(5-May-92 SWS290/R) Vessels moored in calm estuary (24x34cm-9x13in) s.d.1904 W/C pencil
£2000	$3500	(27-Sep-91 C57/R) The Port of St Tropez (37x26cm-15x10in) s.d.1928 W/C
£2400	$4152	(4-Sep-91 BT193/R) French barque at anchor in Falmouth harbour (28x43cm-11x17in) s.d.1923 W/C
£5500	$9625	(27-Sep-91 C74/R) The bathers (28x44cm-11x17in) s.d.1922 W/C
£5500	$9955	(20-May-92 BT121/R) Getting canvas on her (36x25cm-14x10in) s.d.1914 W/C

TUNNARD, John (1900-1971) British
| £17500 | $31500 | (20-Nov-91 S175/R) Focal point (122x153cm-48x60in) s.d.43 board |

TUNNICLIFFE, Charles Frederick (1901-) British
£10000	$17500	(25-Feb-92 C50/R) Swan and cygnets (87x105cm-34x41in)
£700	$1225	(25-Feb-92 C38/R) Pair of mallards (39x57cm-15x22in) s. studio st.verso pencil W/C htd white
£750	$1313	(25-Feb-92 C46/R) Lapwings and redshanks (29x41cm-11x16in) s. st.verso pencil black chk W/C bodycol
£800	$1400	(25-Feb-92 C47) Domestic pigeon (25x28cm-10x11in) i. st.verso pencil col.chk W/C htd white
£820	$1435	(31-Mar-92 RJ176) Preliminary drawing of black headed gull and crow (46x56cm-18x22in) s. gouache W/C
£850	$1632	(28-Jul-92 SWS70/R) August stoat (36x63cm-14x25in) s. W/C pencil
£950	$1663	(25-Feb-92 C41/R) Herring gulls with young. Collared doves (36x48cm-14x19in) s. st.verso pencil black chk W/C htd white pair
£1000	$1810	(21-May-92 B174/R) Emperor geese (42x66cm-17x26in) s. pencil W/C
£1100	$1925	(25-Feb-92 C49/R) Racing pigeon (30x24cm-12x9in) i. st.verso pencil black chk W/C bodycol
£1100	$1925	(25-Feb-92 C45/R) Oystercatchers (35x47cm-14x19in) s. st.verso pencil W/C bodycol tracing paper
£1200	$2100	(25-Feb-92 C42/R) Shelduck with young (46x74cm-18x29in) s. pencil black chk W/C htd white
£1400	$2450	(25-Feb-92 C40/R) Great Crested Grebes with young (39x56cm-15x22in) s. pencil W/C bodycol
£1500	$2625	(25-Feb-92 C120/R) Barn owl in tree with artist's house beyond (41x53cm-16x21in) s. pencil col.chk wash
£1600	$2960	(12-Jun-92 C57/R) A Blue Hungarian Pigeon (28x24cm-11x9in) i. pencil W/C bodycol.
£1800	$3456	(28-Jul-92 SWS49/R) Roaring stag (42x66cm-17x26in) s. W/C pencil
£1800	$3456	(28-Jul-92 SWS48/R) Welsh pony stallion (35x50cm-14x20in) s. W/C pencil
£2000	$3500	(25-Feb-92 C48/R) Pigeon (25x28cm-10x11in) i. st.verso pencil W/C green chk htd white
£3000	$5760	(28-Jul-92 SWS68/R) Goosanders alarmed (34x70cm-13x28in) s. W/C pencil
£3000	$5250	(25-Feb-92 C104/R) Short-eared owl (39x57cm-15x22in) s. pencil W/C
£3100	$5952	(28-Jul-92 SWS62/R) Fighting stags (41x68cm-16x27in) s. W/C pencil
£5100	$9792	(28-Jul-92 SWS66/R) Great horse (42x59cm-17x23in) s. W/C pencil
£8000	$14800	(12-Jun-92 C59/R) Winter sun (45x62cm-18x24in) s. pencil W/C

TUNOLD, Bernt (1877-1946) Norwegian
| £3030 | $5242 | (23-Mar-92 B.O136/R) Landscape from Selje (75x100cm-30x39in) s. (N.KR 34000) |

TUOHY, Patrick (1894-1930) British
| £3738 | $6467 | (25-Mar-92 A.D138/R) The artist's model (99x74cm-39x29in) (E.P 4000) |
| £514 | $889 | (25-Mar-92 A.D44) Portrait of Douglas Hyde (23x18cm-9x7in) s. pencil study (E.P 550) |

TUPKE-GRANDE, Helene (1876-?) German
| £2921 | $5082 | (21-Sep-91 SA.A536/R) Ducks in pond (57x68cm-22x27in) s. (DM 8500) |

TUPY, Wilhelm (1875-1972) Austrian
| £544 | $952 | (19-Feb-92 D.V159/R) Girl wearing Sunday costume (51x41cm-20x16in) s. (A.S 11000) |

TURCATO, Giulio (1912-) Italian
£1859	$3365	(3-Dec-91 F.R150) Arcipelago (40x50cm-16x20in) s. oil sand (I.L 4000000)
£2092	$3786	(3-Dec-91 F.R181) Arcipelago (50x70cm-20x28in) s.verso oil sand (I.L 4500000)
£2224	$3959	(29-Nov-91 F.F133/R) Senza titolo (50x70cm-20x28in) s. oil sand (I.L 4800000)
£2284	$3974	(14-Apr-92 F.M157/R) Composizione (42x62cm-17x24in) s. oil sand (I.L 5000000)
£2556	$4627	(3-Dec-91 F.R156) Cangiante in verde (53x72cm-21x28in) s. oil sand (I.L 5500000)
£2785	$5235	(19-Dec-91 F.M174/R) Ritratto di donna (70x40cm-28x16in) s.d.1953 (I.L 6000000)

TURCATO, Giulio (1912-) Italian-cont.

£2942 $5354   (25-May-92 CH.R64/R) Cangiante (100x80cm-39x31in) s. s.i.verso oil sand canvas (I.L 6500000)

£3486 $6310   (3-Dec-91 F.R207) Composizione (30x40cm-12x16in) s. (I.L 7500000)
£3634 $6250   (12-Oct-91 SY.NY132/R) Abstract landscape (59x39cm-23x15in) s. board
£4526 $8237   (26-May-92 SY.MI132/R) Paesaggio (50x56cm-20x22in) s. (I.L 10000000)
£4990 $9131   (12-May-92 F.R203/R) Senza titolo (81x129cm-32x51in) s. i.verso oil sand (I.L 11000000)

£5105 $9597   (19-Dec-91 F.M155/R) Composizione (120x60cm-47x24in) oil sand (I.L 11000000)

£6678 $12154   (9-Dec-91 CH.R85/R) Composizione con pesci e fiori (50x70cm-20x28in) s. (I.L 14500000)

£8228 $15632   (23-Jun-92 F.M139/R) Labirintico (60x81cm-24x32in) s. (I.L 18000000)
£9296 $16825   (3-Dec-91 F.R266/R) Senza titolo (50x70cm-20x28in) s. panel (I.L 20000000)

£10658 $18971   (26-Nov-91 SY.MI187/R) Paesaggio (64x80cm-25x31in) s. (I.L 23000000)
£1448 $2636   (26-May-92 SY.MI93/R) Fabrica (48x33cm-19x13in) s. W/C (I.L 3200000)
£1905 $3487   (12-May-92 F.R110) Collage (50x70cm-20x28in) s.verso oil collage canvas (I.L 4200000)

£5801 $10906   (19-Dec-91 F.M215/R) Senza titolo (70x100cm-28x39in) s. oil collage canvas (I.L 12500000)

TURCHI, Alessandro (1578-1649) Italian

£3500 $6125   (28-Feb-92 C131/R) The Holy Family with Saint Francis (18x14cm-7x6in) copper

£8840 $16000   (22-May-92 SY.NY221/R) Procris and Cephalus (187x265cm-74x104in)
£28807 $52140   (5-Dec-91 SY.MO155/R) Mars et Venus. Le Triomphe de Neptune (42x34cm-17x13in) pair slate painted with circle pair (F.FR 280000)

TURCHI, Alessandro (style) (1578-1649) Italian

£1600 $2880   (21-Nov-91 C63) Bathsheba at her toilet (145x96cm-57x38in)
£7000 $12740   (10-Dec-91 PH138/R) Hercules and Omphale (82x94cm-32x37in)

TURIN SCHOOL (?) Italian

£2200 $4026   (12-May-92 SWS753/R) Landscape with Rebecca and Eliezer at well (59x90cm-23x35in) c.1700

TURIN SCHOOL, 18th C Italian

£2058 $3724   (5-Dec-91 SY.MO378/R) Paysage (53x63cm-21x25in) (F.FR 20000)
£5086 $9308   (13-May-92 LC.P10/R) Portrait d'un gentilhomme devant un fond d'architecture (130x97cm-51x38in) (F.FR 50000)

TURKISH SCHOOL, 19th C

£2600 $4420   (23-Oct-91 S35/R) Genealogical tree of the Ottoman Sultans from Usman I to Abdul Majid I (92x73cm-36x29in) i.

TURLAND, George (?) British

£580 $998   (10-Oct-91 L260/R) Fishing vessels before Smeatons Pier, St Ives, Cornwall (61x76cm-24x30in) s.

TURNER DE LONDE, William (19th C) Irish

£3000 $5220   (18-Sep-91 CG61/R) View of Limerick town from across River Shannon (42x56cm-17x22in) W/C htd bodycol

TURNER OF OXFORD, William (1789-1862) British

£28000 $53480   (17-Jul-92 C23/R) Extensive wooded landscape, with distant view of town (89x157cm-35x62in)
£580 $1003   (4-Sep-91 PHK73/R) On the Wye (50x67cm-20x26in) i.verso W/C over pencil
£1500 $2640   (6-Apr-92 PH31/R) An Oxfordshire landscape (26x43cm-10x17in) s. W/C htd white

TURNER, A (?) British

£1000 $1720   (11-Oct-91 K475/R) Embankment with Westminster Bridge and Houses of Parliament (30x43cm-12x17in) s. W/C

TURNER, Alfred M (1852-1932) British

£1148 $2100   (17-May-92 DU.E1044/R) Sister's new dress (94x71cm-37x28in) s.d.1885

TURNER, Charles Henry (1848-?) American

£690 $1200   (15-Apr-92 SY.NY87/R) Summer landscape in Catskills (36x51cm-14x20in) s.

TURNER, Charles Yardley (1850-1919) American

£503 $900   (13-Nov-91 B.SF2794/R) Plainsmen (69x145cm-27x57in) init.d.1912
£3315 $6000   (4-Dec-91 D.NY16/R) Harvest meal (76x114cm-30x45in) s.d.1883

TURNER, Claridge (fl.1882-1893) British

£650 $1125   (1-Oct-91 SWS1741) Fern gatherer (90x70cm-35x28in) s.d.82

TURNER, Daniel (fl.1782-1817) British

£1400 $2506   (13-Nov-91 S186/R) View of London from the Thames with Palace of Westminster and Abbey (22x32cm-9x13in) panel

TURNER, Francis Calcraft (c.1782-1846) British

£620 $1079   (11-Sep-91 MMB315) Hounds in full cry (46x61cm-18x24in) s.

TURNER, George (1843-1910) British

£840	$1470	(26-Sep-91 HB510) Midsummer cottage (20x28cm-8x11in) s.i.d.1890
£1300	$2236	(4-Mar-92 DR210) Near Stanton-by-Bridge, Derbyshire (30x51cm-12x20in) s.d.1873
£1400	$2520	(19-Nov-91 PH94/R) Summer scene near Knowle Hills, Derbyshire (35x53cm-14x21in) s. s.i.d.1877verso
£1400	$2478	(6-Nov-91 S52/R) Ogwyn Valley, North Wales (30x49cm-12x19in) s. s.i.d.1892verso
£1453	$2500	(7-Mar-92 LAE.L116/R) Feeding the ducks near Derbyshire (41x61cm-16x24in) s.d.1897
£1700	$3145	(11-Jun-92 CSK129/R) Devonshire's pleasant hills (34x53cm-13x21in) s. panel
£3000	$5310	(6-Nov-91 S34/R) Alton Manor, Derbyshire (30x45cm-12x18in) s.
£3000	$5250	(23-Sep-91 PHB45/R) A Derbyshire lane (49x74cm-19x29in) s. canvas laid down
£3198	$5500	(15-Oct-91 CE.NY22/R) The Trent near Ingleby (61x102cm-24x40in) s.d.1875
£3500	$6265	(14-Jan-92 SWS177/R) Derbyshire lane (29x44cm-11x17in) s.indis.d.94
£4000	$7120	(27-Apr-92 PHB300/R) Quiet spot for perch, near Barrow-on-Trent (46x76cm-18x30in) s.d.77 i.verso
£6800	$11560	(22-Oct-91 SWS298/R) In woods near Matlock (49x75cm-19x30in) s.i. s.d.1897 verso

TURNER, James Alfred (19/20th C) Australian

£1221	$2038	(19-Aug-91 SY.ME102/R) In yard. Broken fence (18cm-7ins circular) init. oil on tin plates pair (A.D 2600)
£1542	$2744	(26-Nov-91 J.M280/R) Taking break (18cm-7ins circular) board (A.D 3500)
£1542	$2744	(26-Nov-91 J.M277/R) Filling the billy (18cm-7ins circular) init. board (A.D 3500)
£1900	$3230	(22-Oct-91 C106/R) Horse and cart at ford (15x30cm-6x12in) s.d.1905 board
£2423	$4313	(26-Nov-91 J.M242/R) Watering horses (34x24cm-13x9in) s.d.1907 (A.D 5500)
£2564	$4564	(28-Apr-92 CH.ME187/R) Flooded track (14x45cm-6x18in) s. i.verso board (A.D 6000)
£3419	$6085	(27-Apr-92 J.M161/R) Sheep pen (20x40cm-8x16in) s.d.1901 canvas on board (A.D 8000)
£3632	$6466	(27-Apr-92 J.M320) Out of range (25x32cm-10x13in) s.d.1888 (A.D 8500)
£3756	$6272	(19-Aug-91 SY.ME265/R) Australian landscape - Bush track (29x45cm-11x18in) s.d.1905 board (A.D 8000)
£4405	$7841	(26-Nov-91 J.M38/R) Across creek (22x29cm-9x11in) s.d.1898 board (A.D 10000)
£4681	$8285	(26-Apr-92 SY.ME489/R) Harvesting (25x43cm-10x17in) s.d. canvas on board (A.D 11000)
£4846	$8722	(24-Nov-91 SY.S420/R) Bullock team (20x36cm-8x14in) s.d.1904 canvas on board (A.D 11000)
£5128	$9128	(28-Apr-92 CH.ME228/R) Returning home (34x69cm-13x27in) s.d.1896 board (A.D 12000)
£6410	$11410	(28-Apr-92 CH.ME144/R) Harvesting (27x87cm-11x34in) s.d.1883 board (A.D 15000)
£9251	$16467	(26-Nov-91 J.M9/R) Yarding the colt (33x50cm-13x20in) s.d.1887 (A.D 21000)
£9390	$15681	(19-Aug-91 SY.ME312/R) Before rain (24x44cm-9x17in) s.d.1891 (A.D 20000)
£9692	$17251	(26-Nov-91 J.M28/R) Gleam after gloom (52x75cm-20x30in) s.d.1907 (A.D 22000)
£88106	$158590	(24-Nov-91 SY.S470/R) Fighting for home (83x124cm-33x49in) s.d.1886 (A.D 200000)

TURNER, John Davenall (1900-1980) Canadian

£1346	$2356	(17-Feb-92 HO.ED39/R) On top of Sulpher Mountain (61x76cm-24x30in) s. i.verso board (C.D 2800)

TURNER, Joseph Mallord William (1775-1851) British

£1400	$2506	(14-Nov-91 S11/R) Windsor Catle, Berkshire (13x21cm-5x8in) pencil
£1430	$2731	(16-Jul-92 S21/R) Old cottage at Hartfield, Sussex (21x13cm-8x5in) i. pencil
£2300	$4393	(14-Jul-92 C21/R) Figures at entrance to rocky gorge (18x22cm-7x9in) with i.verso pencil wash
£5000	$8950	(14-Nov-91 S102/R) Knaresborough Castle, Yorkshire (7x12cm-3x5in) W/C over pencil
£8000	$15280	(14-Jul-92 C23/R) Gateway, Rochester (20x26cm-8x10in) pencil wash
£11000	$21010	(14-Jul-92 C86/R) Studies of heads of birds - Guinea fowl. Red-brested Merganser. Smew (16x14cm-6x6in) pencil W/C three
£12500	$23875	(14-Jul-92 C24/R) Dover (24x19cm-9x7in) s.d.1794 pencil W/C
£15000	$26400	(9-Apr-92 S45/R) Ramsgate harbour from sea (18x28cm-7x11in) W/C over pencil
£17000	$29920	(9-Apr-92 S71/R) Castle in Val d'Aosta, Italy (14x19cm-6x7in) W/C over pencil pen blue chk
£18286	$32000	(19-Feb-92 CH.NY167/R) Careg Cennen Castle near Llandilo, South Wales (46x59cm-18x23in) s.i.verso W/C over pencil board
£52000	$91520	(9-Apr-92 S59/R) Inverness, from across River Ness (9x16cm-4x6in) W/C over pencil
£70000	$123200	(9-Apr-92 S56/R) Wolf's hope - from Bride of Lammermoor (10x15cm-4x6in) W/C over pencil
£220000	$420200	(14-Jul-92 C85/R) Splugen Pass (29x45cm-11x18in) i. pencil W/C

TURNER, Joseph Mallord William (after) (1775-1851) British
£750 $1388   (9-Jun-92 RG2389) Extensive landscape with figures and trees in foreground and rainbow (61x74cm-24x29in)
£750 $1373   (3-Jun-92 ZZ.B192) Stonehenge, Wiltshire (74x97cm-29x38in)
£847 $1499   (4-Nov-91 SY.J211/R) The Sun of Venice going to sea (59x69cm-23x27in) bears sig. (SA.R 4200)
£1350 $2336   (25-Mar-92 PHI544) Capriccio classical scene at sunset (61x107cm-24x42in)
£4974 $9500   (16-Jul-92 SY.NY529/R) Rouen (87x112cm-34x44in)

TURNER, Joseph Mallord William (attrib) (1775-1851) British
£917 $1679   (1-Jun-92 W.T1321/R) Stangate Creek on the Medway (16x23cm-6x9in) W/C (C.D 2000)
£395 $700   (9-Nov-91 W.W91/R) Dardanelles (23x33cm-9x13in) W/C
£395 $700   (9-Nov-91 W.W90/R) Beyrout - Syria (23x33cm-9x13in) W/C
£400 $764   (13-Jul-92 PH29/R) Langdale Pike (15x22cm-6x9in) W/C

TURNER, Joseph Mallord William (circle) (1775-1851) British
£2484 $4247   (18-Mar-92 D.V332/R) The dead white horse (27x45cm-11x18in) panel (A.S 50000)
£3000 $5280   (8-Apr-92 S224/R) Enchanted castle (69x89cm-27x35in)

TURNER, Joseph Mallord William (style) (1775-1851) British
£1150 $1967   (17-Mar-92 SWS1107/R) The Temple of Jupiter Panelinius (57x82cm-22x32in)

TURNER, Joseph Mallord William and GIRTIN, Thomas (19th C) British
£1500 $2640   (7-Apr-92 C107/R) Arona, Lago Maggiore (15x24cm-6x9in) i.verso pencil W/C
£3000 $5280   (7-Apr-92 C106/R) Radicofani in Tuscany (15x24cm-6x9in) i.verso pencil W/C

TURNER, R (19/20th C) ?
£600 $1044   (12-Sep-91 CSK149/R) Loading the hay cart (71x91cm-28x36in) s.

TURNER, Ross Sterling (1847-1915) American
£500 $900   (24-Nov-91 JRB.C5/R) Venice street scene (48x36cm-19x14in) s.d.89 linen

TURNER, W H (19/20th C) British
£1200 $2052   (12-Mar-92 CSK140/R) Dark bay hunter in landscape (31x43cm-12x17in) s.d.1853

TURNER, William Eddowes (19th C) British
£1200 $2052   (12-Mar-92 CSK132) Mare and foal with sheep beside stable (30x38cm-12x15in) s.d.1865

TURNER, William Lakin (1867-1936) British
£1750 $3028   (4-Sep-91 PHK80) Mountain valley, West Coniston (92x71cm-36x28in) s.d.1900 s.i.verso

TURPIN DE CRISSE, Lancelot Theodore (1782-1859) French
£5144 $9774   (26-Jun-92 AT.P90/R) La Tour de Philippe le Bel au port du Rhone (32x24cm-13x9in) mono.d.1818 (F.FR 50000)
£8239 $15489   (18-Dec-91 AT.P119/R) Vue de la chambre des deputes a Paris. Vue du Luxembourg a Paris (42x67cm-17x26in) pen sepia htd.white two (F.FR 80000)

TURTIAINEN, Jorma (1939-) Finnish
£531 $935   (12-Apr-92 HOR.H241) The farm (54x47cm-21x19in) s.d.1989 (F.M 4200)

TURVILLE, Serge de (1924-) French
£662 $1199   (19-May-92 AB.S5335/R) La plage de Cagnes (130x162cm-51x64in) s.d.63 (S.KR 7000)

TURY, Gyula (1866-1932) Hungarian
£752 $1361   (5-Dec-91 D.V250) Path along the wall (31x21cm-12x8in) s.d.1907 panel (A.S 15000)

TUSCAN SCHOOL, 14th C Italian
£9259 $16759   (19-May-92 GF.L2669/R) Crucifixion (31x26cm-12x10in) panel (S.FR 25000)

TUSCAN SCHOOL, 16th C Italian
£2699 $5128   (23-Jun-92 D.V25/R) Angelo annunciante (160x110cm-63x43in) (A.S 55000)
£4688 $8297   (5-Nov-91 GF.L2321/R) The Sacrifice of Abraham (77x61cm-30x24in) panel (S.FR 12000)
£5961 $10194   (18-Mar-92 D.V1/R) Madonna with Child (70x51cm-28x20in) panel (A.S 120000)

TUSCAN SCHOOL, 17th C Italian
£1808 $3273   (18-May-92 SY.MI208) Conversione di S.Paolo (6x22cm-2x9in) marble (I.L 4000000)
£2625 $4778   (28-May-92 F.M6) Maddalena confortata dagli angeli (201x144cm-79x57in) (I.L 5800000)

TUSCAN SCHOOL, 18th C Italian
£2789 $5048   (4-Dec-91 CH.R18) Flora (96x75cm-38x30in) (I.L 6000000)

TUSCAN SCHOOL, 19th C Italian
£2882 $4928   (19-Mar-92 F.M48) Dintorni di San Miniato al Monte, Firenze (17x24cm-7x9in) panel (I.L 6200000)

TUSQUETS Y MAIGNON, R (1839-1904) Italian
£547 $996   (27-May-92 DUR.M923/R) Marina (41x31cm-16x12in) bears sig.d.1873 (S.P 100000)

TUSQUETS Y MAIGNON, Ramon (1839-1904) Italian
£3325 $5819   (18-Feb-92 DUR.M5/R) Pastora con su rebano (26x33cm-10x13in) s.d.1888 panel (S.P 600000)

TUTRIN, Alexandre (1951-) Russian
£533 $959   (27-Jan-92 ARC.P205/R) La sieste sous la veranda (65x92cm-26x36in) s. board (F.FR 5200)
£615 $1107   (27-Jan-92 ARC.P206/R) Les lilas (100x100cm-39x39in) s. (F.FR 6000)

TUTTLE, Richard (1941-) American
£6485   *$11802*   *(25-May-92 WK.M1248/R) Overlap piece no 4 (51x175cm-20x69in) s.i.d.1989verso W/C (DM 19000)*
£48110   *$88041*   *(2-Jun-92 L.K1013/R) 40 days (23x31cm-9x12in) s.i.d.1989verso ball point pen W/C set of 40 (DM 140000)*

TUXEN, Laurits (1853-1927) Danish
£484 $813   (27-Aug-91 RAS.K530/R) A bedouin (35x28cm-14x11in) init.i.d.91 (D.KR 5500)
£485 $863   (28-Apr-92 RAS.K315) Seascape with sailship in rough seas (27x40cm-11x16in) init.d.80 (D.KR 5500)
£490 $843   (15-Oct-91 RAS.K282) Portrait of Director Holger Petersen (84x52cm-33x20in) init.d.06 sketch (D.KR 5500)
£631 $1124   (25-Nov-91 BU.K18/R) Landscape from Alhambra, Spain (53x72cm-21x28in) s.d.02 (D.KR 7000)
£794 $1413   (27-Apr-92 BU.K47/R) Fisherfamily on beach (27x41cm-11x16in) init.d.1883 (D.KR 9000)
£926 $1648   (28-Apr-92 RAS.K313/R) Nude studies of woman and man, Bonnats studio, Paris (72x59cm-28x23in) (D.KR 10500)
£1058 $1884   (28-Apr-92 RAS.K308/R) Nude studies of woman and man, Bonnats studio, Paris (81x65cm-32x26in) (D.KR 12000)
£1160 $2157   (16-Jun-92 RAS.K106/R) The artist's self portrait (60x50cm-24x20in) init.d.1908 (D.KR 13000)
£1232 $2070   (27-Aug-91 RAS.K54/R) French fisherfamily on the beach (32x44cm-13x17in) init.i.d.83 (D.KR 14000)
£1264 $2161   (12-Mar-92 RAS.V1007/R) View of the sea near Skagen (40x74cm-16x29in) init.d.09 panel (D.KR 14000)
£1320 $2218   (27-Aug-91 RAS.K34/R) Orpheus and Eurydike (87x112cm-34x44in) (D.KR 15000)
£1323 $2354   (28-Apr-92 RAS.K514/R) Mother nad her two children with thatched houses in background (62x80cm-24x31in) s. (D.KR 15000)
£1661 $2939   (11-Feb-92 RAS.K3/R) Garden in bloom, summer (20x29cm-8x11in) init. wood panel (D.KR 18500)
£2888 $4939   (12-Mar-92 RAS.V1006/R) Young woman wearing white dress on beach (33x50cm-13x20in) s.d.15 (D.KR 32000)
£7489 $13256   (23-Apr-92 RAS.V919/R) Nude woman in sunshine (45x37cm-18x15in) (D.KR 85000)
£7937 $14127   (28-Apr-92 RAS.K6/R) Summer's day on the beach (46x65cm-18x26in) init.d.08 (D.KR 90000)

TUZINA, Gunter (1951-) ?
£5119 $9317   (25-May-92 WK.M1250/R) Young people like to dream (115x75cm-45x30in) s.i.d.1982verso acrylic hessian (DM 15000)
£1706   *$3106*   *(25-May-92 WK.M1249/R) First picture (59x40cm-23x16in) s.i.d.1981 acrylic pencil panel (DM 5000)*

TVERMOES, Jenny (19th C) ?
£2437   *$4167*   *(10-Mar-92 RAS.K156/R) Nude girl with thin drapery (150x70cm-59x28in) s.i.d.1896 pastel (D.KR 27000)*

TVETER, Kare (1922-) Norwegian
£704 $1238   (8-Apr-92 GWP.O144) Blue landscape (50x61cm-20x24in) s. (N.KR 8000)

TWACHTMAN, John Henry (1853-1902) American
£3005 $5500   (16-May-92 HG.C150/R) Country road with farm buildings (23x33cm-9x13in) s. board
£32967 $60000   (28-May-92 CH.NY143/R) Horseneck Falls (76x63cm-30x25in)
£82418 $150000   (28-May-92 CH.NY156/R) Tiger lilies (76x63cm-30x25in)

TWEDDLE, Isabel Hunter (?) Australian?
£769 $1369   (27-Apr-92 J.M124/R) Still life (60x49cm-24x19in) mono. board (A.D 1800)

TWEEDIE, William Menzies (attrib) (1828-1878) British
£1031 $1887   (3-Jun-92 DO.H2039/R) Sailing ships before the English Coast (62x74cm-24x29in) (DM 3000)

TWELVETREES, Charles (20th C) American
£1264   *$2250*   *(2-May-92 IH.NY189/R) Skating baby, waving (61x51cm-24x20in) s. gouache*

TWOMBLY, Cy (1929-?) American
£2458 $4400 (9-May-92 CE.NY363/R) Untitled (29x25cm-11x10in) s.d.1961 blue ball-point pen red crayon
£21494 $38260 (30-Nov-91 FB.P47/R) Composition (57x57cm-22x22in) s.d.86verso paper (F.FR 210000)
£17341 *$30000* *(3-Oct-91 SY.NY92/R) Untitled (28x35cm-11x14in) graphite vellum*
£18000 *$34380* *(2-Jul-92 C58/R) Orpheus (100x70cm-39x28in) s.i.d.1975 verso oil wax crayon paper on canvas*
£75000 $143250 (2-Jul-92 S53 a/R) Venus in Menfi (96x141cm-38x56in) s.i.d.1960 oil pencil canvas
£105000 $200550 (2-Jul-92 C51/R) Untitled (79x100cm-31x39in) s. oil pencil col.crayons canvas
£237430 $425000 (6-May-92 SY.NY48/R) Leda and the swan (194x203cm-76x80in) s.i.d.1960verso oil crayon pencil canvas
£300000 $543000 (5-Dec-91 C18/R) Rome (123x99cm-48x39in) s.d.1963 oil pencil canvas
£335196 $600000 (5-May-92 CH.NY43/R) Untitled (201x262cm-79x103in) oil crayon canvas
£474860 $850000 (13-Nov-91 SY.NY54/R) Untitled (173x216cm-68x85in) s.d.1968 verso oil graphite canvas
£837989 $1500000 (6-May-92 SY.NY33/R) Untitled (200x240cm-79x94in) s. s.d.1969verso oil house paint crayon canvas

TWORKOV, Jack (1900-1982) American
£10056 $18000 (14-Nov-91 SY.NY292/R) Related to Barrier (101x58cm-40x23in) s. s.d.63 verso
£36313 $65000 (13-Nov-91 SY.NY22/R) Queen II (178x94cm-70x37in) s.d.75 verso

TYDEN, Nils (1889-1976) Swedish
£8159 $14932 (14-May-92 BU.S72/R) View of Old part of Stockholm (121x139cm-48x55in) s.d.1926 (S.KR 86000)

TYLER, James Gale (1855-1931) American
£514 $900 (22-Feb-92 YFA.M196/R) Seascape (25x36cm-10x14in) s.
£593 $1050 (10-Nov-91 LIT.L37) Cup trials at New port - Jay boat of America's Cup coming in to Newport (76x61cm-30x24in) s.
£643 $1100 (13-Mar-92 S.BM218/R) The squall (43x36cm-17x14in) s.
£694 $1200 (24-Mar-92 GRO.B51/R) Moonlit sail (76x64cm-30x25in) s.
£819 $1400 (13-Mar-92 DM.D2032/R) Harbour scene (30x48cm-12x19in) s.d.1895
£1463 $2750 (18-Dec-91 SY.NY107/R) Clipper ship at sea (63x76cm-25x30in) s.d.1918
£2254 $3900 (6-Sep-91 S.BM185/R) Yacht off rocky cliffs (36x30cm-14x12in) s.d.1884 board
£3333 $5900 (9-Nov-91 W.W202/R) Sailing off a rocky coast (51x76cm-20x30in) s.
£3352 $6000 (14-Nov-91 CE.NY265/R) Going to windward (38x56cm-15x22in) s.d.1902
£537 *$950* *(25-Apr-92 YFA.M292/R) Yacht race (25x46cm-10x18in) s. W/C*

TYLER, William R (1825-1896) American
£1862 $3500 (18-Dec-91 SY.NY82/R) The breakers (55x96cm-22x38in) s.

TYNDALE, T N (19/20th C) British
£600 $1086 (5-Dec-91 LE544/R) Cottage in floral garden setting, being Mary Arden's house (15x23cm-6x9in) s. W/C
£620 $1122 (5-Dec-91 LE543/R) Cottages with country lane alongside, figures to foreground (23x15cm-9x6in) s. W/C

TYNDALE, Thomas Nicholson (19/20th C) British
£1300 $2327 (14-Jan-92 SWS65/R) Surrey cottage (32x23cm-13x9in) s. W/C

TYNDALE, Walter (1855-1943) British
£2800 *$4956* *(6-Nov-91 S244/R) El Gamaleia (38x28cm-15x11in) s. W/C*

TYNDALL, Peter (20th C) Australian
£2016 $3750 (21-Jun-92 SY.ME101/R) Person looks at work of art (168x46cm-66x18in) d.1978 i.verso acrylic (A.D 5000)

TYRAHN, Georg (1860-1917) German
£1375 $2515 (2-Jun-92 FN.S2778/R) Two girls seated in field winding flower wreaths (48x64cm-19x25in) s.i.d.1904 (DM 4000)

TYROLEAN SCHOOL, 15th C Austrian
£11050 $20000 (21-May-92 CH.NY50/R) Saints Christopher and George (92x62cm-36x24in) panel

TYROLEAN SCHOOL, 18th C Austrian
£2484 $4247 (18-Mar-92 D.V389/R) Adoration of the Shepherds (168x79cm-66x31in) arched top (A.S 50000)

TYSSENS, A (18th C) ?
£1980 $3445 (13-Sep-91 C24) Wagonner on riverside track, ruin beyond. Herdsmen watering cattle (21x27cm-8x11in) panel pair

TYSZBLAT, Michel (1936-) French
£1540 $2772 (19-Nov-91 FB.P273/R) Personnage (160x112cm-63x44in) s.d.85 (F.FR 15000)

TYTGAT, Edgard (1879-1957) Belgian
£4106 $7432 (7-Dec-91 KV.L402/R) Jeune fille (81x65cm-32x26in) s.d.1931 (B.FR 240000)

TYTGAT, Edgard (1879-1957) Belgian-cont.
£6683	$11362	(22-Oct-91 C.A309/R) Young woman in blue dress (81x65cm-32x26in) s.d.1932 (B.FR 400000)
£520	$952	(5-Feb-92 ZZ.B202) Caldos dos Rainha (33x49cm-13x19in) s.d.1936 W/C
£919	$1562	(22-Oct-91 C.A311/R) Puppet theatre (18x22cm-7x9in) W/C pair (B.FR 55000)
£1170	$1988	(22-Oct-91 C.A310/R) My room in Kerkepanne (36x51cm-14x20in) s.d.1939 W/C (B.FR 70000)
£1970	$3565	(21-May-92 SY.AM83/R) Caldas da Rainha, blinde muzikant (35x51cm-14x20in) s.d.1936 W/C (D.FL 6500)

TYTGAT, Medard (1871-1948) Belgian
| £434 | $739 | (22-Oct-91 C.A312/R) Junon (60x45cm-24x18in) s.d.1907 dr. (B.FR 26000) |

TZORTZOGLOU, Gergios (1954-) Hungarian
£605	$1041	(14-Oct-91 AT.P7) Lignes brisees (60x50cm-24x20in) s.d.91 canvas laid down on panel (F.FR 6000)
£706	$1215	(14-Oct-91 AT.P5) Lignes brisees (40x40cm-16x16in) s.i.d.90 canvas laid down on panel (F.FR 7000)
£807	$1388	(14-Oct-91 AT.P8) Lignes brisees (70x50cm-28x20in) s.d.91 canvas laid down on panel (F.FR 8000)
£807	$1388	(14-Oct-91 AT.P6) Lignes brisees (22x26cm-9x10in) s.d.90 mixed mediaa (F.FR 8000)

UBAC, Raoul (1910-1985) Belgian
£40692	$72838	(17-Nov-91 GL.P39/R) Groupe (195x97cm-77x38in) init. (F.FR 400000)
£1283	$2310	(22-Nov-91 ZZ.F86) Composition (44x55cm-17x22in) s. gouache slate (F.FR 12500)
£1486	$2674	(2-Feb-92 CSC.P92) Labyrinthe (24x25cm-9x10in) Indian ink (F.FR 14500)
£2626	$4491	(19-Mar-92 CSC.P18/R) Tete (85x60cm-33x24in) mono.d.46 pastel (F.FR 25500)
£5035	$8560	(27-Oct-91 P.V3/R) Composition (50x66cm-20x26in) s.d.1954 mixed media paper laid down on canvas (F.FR 50000)

UBEDA, Augustin (1925-) Spanish
£703	$1300	(12-Jun-92 SY.NY221/R) Still life (59x73cm-23x29in) s.
£1021	$1788	(23-Feb-92 FE.P134) Composition (92x73cm-36x29in) (F.FR 10000)
£1229	$2200	(9-May-92 CE.NY181/R) Naturaleza muerta (46x63cm-18x25in) s.
£1341	$2400	(9-May-92 CE.NY182/R) Composicion con dos figuras (51x74cm-20x29in) s.
£1366	$2500	(16-May-92 HG.C36/R) Ceremonial figures (64x79cm-25x31in) s.
£2033	$3537	(15-Apr-92 PLF.P108) La crucifixion (65x81cm-26x32in) s. canvas laid down on panel (F.FR 20000)
£2541	$4421	(15-Apr-92 PLF.P109/R) Composition abstraite (60x81cm-24x32in) s. (F.FR 25000)
£3107	$5500	(5-Nov-91 CE.NY234/R) Las floras se oyen pasar (81x100cm-32x39in) s. s.i.verso
£3672	$6500	(5-Nov-91 CE.NY221/R) Musique (155x130cm-61x51in) s. s.i.verso
£5247	$9865	(3-Jan-92 DUR.M7/R) Don Quijote encuentra a Dulcinea en un pueblo encantado (114x143cm-45x56in) s. s.i.verso (S.P 950000)

UBERBRUCK, Wilhelm (1884-?) German
| £791 | $1384 | (20-Feb-92 D.V411/R) Girl reading (75x90cm-30x35in) s. (A.S 16000) |

UBERFELDT, Jan Braet van (1807-1894) Dutch
| £950 | $1824 | (9-Jul-92 B177) Portrait of gentleman, holding gloves in hand, seated, landscape beyond (105x86cm-41x34in) s.d.1838 |

UBERTINI, Francesco (1494-1557) Italian
| £54311 | $98846 | (28-May-92 F.M138/R) Il trionfo del Tempo (32x25cm-13x10in) panel (I.L 120000000) |

UBERTINI, Francesco (style) (1494-1557) Italian
| £2880 | $5500 | (16-Jul-92 SY.NY227/R) Portrait of young lady in elaborate headdress (63x50cm-25x20in) panel |
| £4000 | $7280 | (13-Dec-91 C253/R) The Three Fates (41x27cm-16x11in) panel |

UCHERMANN, Karl (1855-1940) Norwegian
| £624 | $1079 | (23-Mar-92 B.O138/R) A Pekinese (66x54cm-26x21in) s.d.1921 (N.KR 7000) |
| £966 | $1661 | (7-Oct-91 B.O141/R) Fish (100x67cm-39x26in) s.d.03 (N.KR 11000) |

UDEMANS, Willem (1723-1797) Dutch
| £2584 | $4444 | (12-Oct-91 CH.AM196 a) Frigate 't Huys Om offshore, man-o-war and other shipping in stiff breeze (47x64cm-19x25in) s.d.1774 panel (D.FL 8500) |

UDEN, Lucas van (1595-1672) Flemish
£4077	$7584	(20-Jun-92 CH.MO42/R) Paysage anime de figures (11x16cm-4x6in) mono. copper (F.FR 40000)
£4339	$7463	(16-Oct-91 AT.P54/R) Chevrier au bord des ruines avec son troupeau (26x42cm-10x17in) panel (F.FR 43000)
£5961	$10194	(18-Mar-92 D.V88/R) River landscape with peasants and village (61x81cm-24x32in) (A.S 120000)

UDEN, Lucas van (1595-1672) Flemish-cont.
£15000 $26100 (15-Apr-92 C117/R) Landscape with peasants returning from the fields by chapel (109x164cm-43x65in)
£15331 $27902 (12-Dec-91 L.K191/R) Flemish landscape with Christ healing the Blind (43x65cm-17x26in) i.d.1647 panel (DM 44000)
£864 $1547 *(12-Nov-91 SY.AM272/R) Landscape with figures among trees by lake (14x21cm-6x8in) bears sig. pen wash over chk (D.FL 2800)*

UDEN, Lucas van (circle) (1595-1672) Flemish
£1662 $2974 (7-May-92 CH.AM81/R) Wooded outcrop with faggot gatherers and peasants working by stream (74x61cm-29x24in) (D.FL 5500)
£2467 $4514 (14-May-92 BU.S146/R) Landscape with shepherds (57x77cm-22x30in) (S.KR 26000)
£5612 $9934 (10-Feb-92 GL.P2/R) Paysage d'hiver au coucher de soleil (79x107cm-31x42in) (F.FR 55000)

UECHTRITZ-STEINKIRCH, Ulrich V (1881-?) German
£968 $1627 (28-Aug-91 KH.K214) Marina, Wannsee, Berlin (60x95cm-24x37in) s. (D.KR 11000)

UECKER, Gunther (20th C) German
£699 *$1245 (25-Nov-91 WK.M1029/R) Composition (28x20cm-11x8in) s. felt tip pen (DM 2000)*
£37543 $68328 (29-May-92 VG.B91/R) Gespaltenes Feld (180x180cm-71x71in) s.i.d.1987verso nails oilpaint canvas on panel (DM 110000)

UFER, Walter (1876-1936) American
£20950 $37500 (13-Nov-91 B.SF2709/R) Zuni women carrying water (51x41cm-20x16in) s.

UGOLINO DI NERIO (14th C) Italian
£46961 $85000 (21-May-92 CH.NY26/R) Saint Andrew (72x41cm-28x16in) tempera gold ground panel

UGOLINO DI NERIO (studio) (14th C) Italian
£110000 $200200 (10-Dec-91 PH78/R) Crucifixion (64x40cm-25x16in) panel gold ground

UHLIG, Max (1937-) German
£912 $1642 (23-Nov-91 N.M314/R) Landscape (50x97cm-20x38in) s.d.1984 W/C (DM 2600)
£2105 $3789 (23-Nov-91 N.M313/R) Landscape near Penzlin (66x147cm-26x58in) s.d.1981 (DM 6000)
£444 $803 *(23-May-92 GB.B7310) Abstract composition (32x70cm-13x28in) s. indian ink pen (DM 1300)*
£962 $1761 *(2-Jun-92 L.K1019/R) Portrait J B (71x61cm-28x24in) s.d.1987 W/C (DM 2800)*
£2730 $4969 *(30-May-92 VG.B415/R) Katharinenberg (80x180cm-31x71in) s.i.d.1986verso mixed media canvas (DM 8000)*
£4895 $8713 *(30-Nov-91 VG.B419/R) Tempelberg Kruckow (55x150cm-22x59in) s. s.i.d.1982verso mixed media canvas (DM 14000)*

UHLMAN, Fred (20th C?) ?
£620 $1097 (5-Nov-91 CD549/R) Winter, New York (38x53cm-15x21in) s.
£800 $1528 (16-Jul-92 B104) Cemetiere de St Barnabas (56x73cm-22x29in) s.
£1000 $1730 (2-Oct-91 S87/R) San Gimignano (27x38cm-11x15in) board
£1800 $3114 (2-Oct-91 S83/R) Winter in Wales (46x61cm-18x24in) s. s.i.verso

UHLMANN, Hans (1900-1975) German
£1297 *$2347 (23-May-92 GB.B7315/R) Composition (53x34cm-21x13in) s.d.1948 W/C indian ink brush double-sided (DM 3800)*
£1538 *$2738 (30-Nov-91 VG.B1024/R) Four figures (35x50cm-14x20in) s.d.1948 indian ink (DM 4400)*
£2867 *$5103 (30-Nov-91 VG.B1026/R) Group (44x59cm-17x23in) s.d.1951 s.verso indian ink brush W/C (DM 8200)*
£3147 *$5601 (30-Nov-91 VG.B1025/R) Two figures (56x35cm-22x14in) s.d.1948 indian ink brush bodycol wash (DM 9000)*

UHRDIN, Sam (1886-1964) Swedish
£522 $898 (19-Oct-91 UA.U364) Woman in profile (42x32cm-17x13in) s.d.1917 (S.KR 5500)

UJAVARY, F (1898-?) Hungarian
£900 $1557 (3-Oct-91 CSK57) A country farmstead (61x79cm-24x31in) s.

UJHAZY, Ferenc (1827-1921) Hungarian
£501 $907 (5-Dec-91 D.V117) Alpine flowers (30x20cm-12x8in) s. panel (A.S 10000)
£501 $907 (5-Dec-91 D.V116) Alpine flowers (30x20cm-12x8in) s. panel (A.S 10000)

ULBRICHT, Johann Philipp and BAUER, Philipp Jakob (19th C) German
£2823 $4940 (25-Sep-91 CSC.P31/R) Canal gele avec patineurs devant un chateau (61x74cm-24x29in) s. both artists d.1823 copper (F.FR 28000)

ULBRICHT, John (1926-) Cuban
£2046 $3703 (20-May-92 ANS.M114/R) Paisaje (81x100cm-32x39in) s. s.d.1990verso (S.P 375000)

ULFSTEN, Nicolai Martin (1854-1895) Norwegian
£2674 $4626   (23-Mar-92 B.O139/R) Landscape with boats (70x53cm-28x21in) s.i.d.1878
                      (N.KR 30000)

ULIANOFF, Vsevolod (1880-1940) American?
£579 $1100   (24-Jun-92 B.SF6460/R) View from brick fence (44x58cm-17x23in) s. board

ULLMAN, Sigfrid (1886-1960) Swedish
£767 $1381   (19-Nov-91 GO.G189) Landscape from Kloveron, Marstrand (64x76cm-25x30in)
                      s.d.36 (S.KR 8000)

ULMANN, Charles (19th C) ?
£1667 $3000   (22-Nov-91 S.BM49/R) Surveying grounds (51x119cm-20x47in) s.i.d.1862

ULNITZ, E C (19/20th C) ?
£812 $1462   (19-Nov-91 RAS.K169/R) Dahlias in vase (67x60cm-26x24in) s.d.1912
                      (D.KR 9000)

ULP, Clifford (1885-1957) American
£1011 $1800   (26-Jan-92 LIT.L65) Deer in snowy wooded landscape (71x91cm-28x36in) s.

ULRICH, Charles Frederic (1858-1908) American
£920 $1600   (15-Apr-92 SY.NY40/R) Friedl. *Portrait study of lady (39x35cm-15x14in)
                      one init.i.d. pencil wht chk red chk board pair*

ULRICH, Friedrich (1750-1808) German
£1536 $2750   (13-Nov-91 B.SF2111/R) Horsemen at blacksmith's forge (43x53cm-17x21in)
                      s.

ULRICH, Hermann (1904-1961) Austrian
£485 $864   (29-Apr-92 D.V704/R) *View of Klosterneuburg (37x27cm-15x11in) s.i. W/C
                      (A.S 10000)*

ULRICH, Hugo (18/19th C) ?
£501 $852   (22-Oct-91 GM.B489) Rathaus Breslau (70x94cm-28x37in) s. (B.FR 30000)

ULRICH, Johann (1798-1877) Swiss
£3195 $5848   (4-Jun-92 SY.Z317/R) The Rhinefalls (54x81cm-21x32in) s.d.1866
                      (S.FR 8500)

ULVING, Even (1863-1952) Norwegian
£490 $848   (23-Mar-92 B.O141/R) Rowing boat at anchor (26x33cm-10x13in) s.
                      (N.KR 5500)
£570 $1061   (15-Jun-92 B.O179/R) Autumn day, Helgeland (32x49cm-13x19in) s.
                      (N.KR 6500)
£610 $1037   (6-Aug-91 UL.T242) Grey day, Vrengen (45x60cm-18x24in) (N.KR 7000)
£702 $1305   (18-Jun-92 GWP.O241/R) Summer evening (30x47cm-12x19in) s. (N.KR 8000)
£834 $1435   (7-Oct-91 B.O144/R) Coastal view (48x75cm-19x30in) s. (N.KR 9500)
£834 $1485   (29-Oct-91 UL.T240/R) Old cottage, Gudvangen (46x65cm-18x26in)
                      (N.KR 9500)
£834 $1435   (7-Oct-91 B.O143/R) Gathering firewood (41x61cm-16x24in) s. (N.KR 9500)
£878 $1563   (29-Oct-91 UL.T238/R) The old bathing house, Asgardstrand
                      (48x70cm-19x28in) (N.KR 10000)
£974 $1773   (9-Dec-91 B.O125/R) Summer landscape (40x65cm-16x26in) s. i.verso
                      (N.KR 11000)
£1070 $1850   (23-Mar-92 B.O140/R) Landscape from North of Norway (36x54cm-14x21in) s.
                      (N.KR 12000)
£1099 $1935   (8-Apr-92 GWP.O72/R) View of Nettuno, Italy (64x49cm-25x19in) s.
                      s.i.d.1906verso (N.KR 12500)
£1240 $2257   (9-Dec-91 B.O124/R) Mooring the boat (42x66cm-17x26in) s. (N.KR 14000)
£1592 $2785   (25-Feb-92 UL.T244) From Kviteseid (70x100cm-28x39in) (N.KR 18000)
£1756 $3020   (7-Oct-91 B.O142/R) Interior with open fireplace (61x81cm-24x32in) s.
                      (N.KR 20000)
£1771 $3224   (9-Dec-91 B.O126/R) Landscape from Bronnoysund (42x67cm-17x26in) s.
                      i.d.1887verso (N.KR 20000)
£1860 $3385   (10-Dec-91 UL.T232/R) Landscape from Nordland (40x59cm-16x23in)
                      (N.KR 21000)
£1930 $3589   (18-Jun-92 GWP.O107/R) Two women in garden (40x59cm-16x23in) s.
                      (N.KR 22000)
£1970 $3762   (21-Jul-92 UL.T221/R) The old sawmill in Asgardstrand (75x100cm-30x39in)
                      (N.KR 22000)
£2303 $4191   (9-Dec-91 B.O118/R) View from Asgardstrand (72x100cm-28x39in) s.
                      (N.KR 26000)
£2476 $4332   (25-Feb-92 UL.T245/R) View of 'Verden's Ende,' Tjome (60x80cm-24x31in)
                      (N.KR 28000)
£2639 $4644   (7-Apr-92 UL.T236/R) Interior (75x101cm-30x40in) s. (N.KR 30000)
£2657 $4836   (10-Dec-91 UL.T234/R) Landscape from Nordland (60x90cm-24x35in)
                      (N.KR 30000)

ULYSSE, J (1835-1887) ?
£676 $1184   (5-Apr-92 CSC.P105) Gentilhomme venant de la cave (21x15cm-8x6in) s.
                      panel (F.FR 6500)

UMBRIAN SCHOOL, 14th C Italian
£14903 $25484 (18-Mar-92 D.V247/R) St Michael killing the dragon (198x131cm-78x52in) chk tempera casein W/C transferred on canvas (A.S 300000)

UMBRIAN SCHOOL, 15th C Italian
£13333 $24133 (19-May-92 GF.L2009/R) Crucifixion and saints triptych panel rounded top (S.FR 36000)

UMBRIAN SCHOOL, 16th C Italian
£5249 $9500 (21-May-92 CH.NY243/R) Saint Louis of Toulouse (17cm-7ins circular) tempera gold ground panel part predella
£7182 $13000 (22-May-92 SY.NY180/R) Madonna and child enthroned with saints Francis, Clare and Bernard (194x173cm-76x68in)

UMGELTER, Hermann Ludwig (1891-1962) German
£697 $1262 (3-Dec-91 FN.S2498) Woodland with sun spots (75x59cm-30x23in) s. (DM 1980)
£1053 $1800 (13-Mar-92 FN.S2997) Snow covered Feuerbach landscape, evening (58x73cm-23x29in) s. (DM 3000)
£1158 $1980 (13-Mar-92 FN.S2999) Feuerbach landscape in late autumn (44x34cm-17x13in) s. board (DM 3300)
£1268 $2294 (3-Dec-91 FN.S2497/R) Peasant women putting up corn stooks (59x75cm-23x30in) s. (DM 3600)
£1404 $2400 (13-Mar-92 FN.S2996/R) Feuerbacher Tal landscape in early spring, evening (75x75cm-30x30in) s. i.verso (DM 4000)
£1754 $3000 (13-Mar-92 FN.S3000/R) Feuerbach, early spring (55x46cm-22x18in) s. board (DM 5000)
£515 $897 (17-Sep-91 FN.S2588) Black Forest landscape with view of Schauinsland near Freiburg (34x47cm-13x19in) s.i.d.1950 W/C (DM 1500)

UNBEREIT, Paul (1884-1937) German/Austrian
£802 $1452 (5-Dec-91 D.V118) Weissenkirchen in the Wachau (16x22cm-6x9in) s. board (A.S 16000)
£2427 $4320 (28-Apr-92 D.V98/R) Early spring (53x78cm-21x31in) s.d.1910 (A.S 50000)
£582 $1059 (27-May-92 D.V666/R) Farmhouse with well (35x50cm-14x20in) s. W/C (A.S 12000)

UNCETA Y LOPEZ, Marcelino de (1836-1905) Spanish
£800 $1488 (16-Jun-92 PH95) Aragones on mule, Zaragoza, Spain (29x22cm-11x9in) s. board en grisaille
£2200 $3982 (21-May-92 CSK253/R) In courtyard (17x12cm-7x5in) s.d.1890 panel

UNCINI, Giuseppe (1929-) Italian
£3629 $6641 (12-May-92 F.R222/R) Dimora delle cose (58x98cm-23x39in) s.d.1980verso cement polychrome panel (I.L 8000000)

UNDERHILL, Frederick Charles (19th C) British
£550 $1073 (15-Jan-92 CSK205/R) Children by stream carrying flowers and corn, with harvesters beyond (30x46cm-12x18in) s.indist.i.verso
£700 $1274 (11-Dec-91 B126) The blind piper (112x87cm-44x34in)

UNDERHILL, W (19th C) British
£1300 $2496 (7-Aug-92 BW420 a/R) After the days shoot (76x64cm-30x25in) s.

UNDERWOOD, Leon (1890-1975) British
£1200 $2292 (16-Jul-92 B66) The paddock (35x30cm-14x12in)
£400 $716 (14-Jan-92 SWS92/R) Peter (25x21cm-10x8in) s.d.1922 pen ink chk

UNGER, Hans (1872-1936) German
£627 $1141 (13-Dec-91 BM.B854/R) View of grotto, Capri (40x55cm-16x22in) s. i.verso board (DM 1800)
£699 $1210 (25-Mar-92 KM.K1485) Portrait of Mrs Unger (75x63cm-30x25in) s. (DM 2000)
£767 $1395 (13-Dec-91 BM.B855/R) Female nude standing in landscape (121x65cm-48x26in) s. i.verso (DM 2200)

UNGERER, Tomi (?) ?
£449 $800 (2-Nov-91 IH.NY128/R) Man repairing vase as elephant appears at door (38x43cm-15x17in) ink W/C

UNOVIS SCHOOL (20th C) Russian
£2600 $4472 (16-Oct-91 S64/R) Composition with red. Composition with blue (15x12cm-6x5in) pencil gouache two

UNSELD, Albert (1879-?) German
£1056 $1912 (3-Dec-91 FN.S1846/R) Southern landscape (70x90cm-28x35in) s.d.1946 s.i.d.verso (DM 3000)

UNTERBERGER, Franz Richard (1838-1902) Belgian
£597 $1063 (25-Nov-91 W.T1872 a) Coastal scene with fishermen (39x69cm-15x27in) s. (C.D 1200)
£1284 $2273 (5-Nov-91 SY.AM357/R) Street in south Italian town (35x30cm-14x12in) s. panel (D.FL 4200)
£8000 $14240 (29-Nov-91 C29/R) Wedding party boarding boat (81x112cm-32x44in) s.d.64
£11000 $19030 (4-Oct-91 C158/R) Marina Piccola, Capri (82x66cm-32x26in) s.
£15116 $26000 (16-Oct-91 CH.NY231/R) Road in Pompei, Italy (44x38cm-17x15in) s. panel

UNTERBERGER, Franz Richard (1838-1902) Belgian-cont.
£19000	$32490	(18-Mar-92 S80/R) Rocca d'Amalfi (81x69cm-32x27in) s. i.verso
£19000	$33820	(29-Nov-91 C95/R) La Giudecca with San Giorgio Maggiore, Venice (81x70cm-32x28in) s.
£20000	$37200	(17-Jun-92 S395/R) View of Bay of Naples (58x110cm-23x43in) s. s.i.verso
£23256	$40000	(16-Oct-91 CH.NY230/R) Ile de Capri (67x93cm-26x37in) s. i. verso
£25000	$44500	(27-Nov-91 S109/R) Vietri sul mare, looking towards Salerno (77x127cm-30x50in) s.
£38000	$67640	(29-Nov-91 C94/R) Grand Canal with Santa Maria della Salute beyond, Venice (84x71cm-33x28in) s.
£44674	$77732	(21-Sep-91 SA.A1742/R) Torre del Greco, Naples (92x154cm-36x61in) s. s.verso (DM 130000)
£48000	$82080	(20-Mar-92 C53/R) Fondamenta Zorzi, Campiello S.Barbara, Venice (131x111cm-52x44in) s. s.i.verso

UNTERBERGER, Franz Richard (style) (1838-1902) Belgian
| £1000 | $1810 | (21-May-92 CSK151/R) Dutch coastal town with figures on quayside (69x104cm-27x41in) bears sig.d.1881 |

UNTERBERGER, Michelangelo (1695-1758) Austrian
| £3925 | $7458 | (23-Jun-92 D.V118/R) Crucifixion (122x91cm-48x36in) (A.S 80000) |

UNTERBERGER, Michelangelo (circle) (1695-1758) Austrian
| £4651 | $8000 | (9-Oct-91 CH.NY30/R) Immaculate Conception (67x43cm-26x17in) |

UPHOFF, Carl Emil (1885-) German
| £1237 | $2164 | (3-Apr-92 BM.B576/R) View of Teufelsmoor (93x114cm-37x45in) s. i.verso (DM 3500) |

UPPER RHINE SCHOOL (?) German
| £21000 | $38220 | (13-Dec-91 C103/R) Saint Cathering and Saint George (36x20cm-14x8in) c.1500 panel pair |

UPRKA, Joza (1861-?) Czechoslovakian
| £993 | $1768 | (29-Nov-91 D.V3/R) Maratice girl (27x18cm-11x7in) mono. panel (A.S 20000) |

URBAN, L (19/20th C) ?
| £522 | $950 | (26-May-92 CE.NY96/R) The violin player (47x31cm-19x12in) s. |

URCULO, Eduardo (1938-) Spanish
£4147	$7797	(16-Dec-91 ANS.M81/R) La cortina verde (100x110cm-39x43in) s.d.78 s.i.verso (S.P 750000)
£491	*$845*	*(16-Oct-91 FER.M175/R) Perplejidad (25x33cm-10x13in) s.d.65 mixed media (S.P 90000)*
£498	*$936*	*(16-Dec-91 ANS.M221/R) Pareja (24x32cm-9x13in) s.d.65 gouache (S.P 90000)*

URDAL, Atle (1913-1988) Norwegian
| £707 | $1238 | (25-Feb-92 UL.T242/R) Figure composition (50x60cm-20x24in) panel (N.KR 8000) |
| £841 | $1531 | (14-Dec-91 BU.O7/R) Landscape (75x61cm-30x24in) s.d.50 panel (N.KR 9500) |

URDIN, Kiro (?) ?
| £11515 | $20842 | (19-May-92 CH.AM269/R) Le medicin (50x61cm-20x24in) s.i. (D.FL 38000) |

UREN, John C (1845-1932) British
£400	*$704*	*(9-Apr-92 B14/R) Kelp gatherers at St Michael's Mount (29x49cm-11x19in) s. W/C*
£450	*$824*	*(4-Jun-92 DLY163/R) Fishing cove (18x30cm-7x12in) s. W/C*
£590	*$1033*	*(27-Feb-92 L246/R) Fishing boats beached before St Michael's Mount, Cornwall (36x53cm-14x21in) s. W/C*

URGELL Y INGLADA, Modesto (1839-1919) Spanish
£4104	$7305	(29-Oct-91 BRO.B368/R) Grupo de figuras con banderas en una calle de pueblo (69x38cm-27x15in) s. (S.P 750000)
£4104	$7305	(29-Oct-91 BRO.B322/R) Paisaje. Luz crepuscular (46x73cm-18x29in) s. (S.P 750000)
£410	*$726*	*(12-Feb-92 ANS.M43/R) Carta autografa con ilustraciones (31x21cm-12x8in) s. ink dr (S.P 74000)*

URGELL, Ricardo (1874-1924) Spanish
| £2298 | $4091 | (29-Oct-91 BRO.B285/R) Paisaje otonal. Dia gris (84x54cm-33x21in) s. (S.P 420000) |
| £4925 | $8766 | (29-Oct-91 BRO.B349/R) Bailadora (179x141cm-70x56in) s. (S.P 900000) |

URI, Aviva (1927-1989) Israeli
| *£541* | *$1000* | *(8-Jun-92 GG.TA121/R) Trees (53x38cm-21x15in) s. pencil* |

URIARTE, Carlos (1910-) Argentinian
| £1354 | $2600 | (4-Aug-92 V.BA110) Playa (60x80cm-24x31in) |

URQUHART, Murray (1880-1972) British
| £776 | $1327 | (12-Mar-92 RAS.K757/R) By the town gate at night (93x120cm-37x47in) s. (D.KR 8600) |
| £800 | $1400 | (23-Sep-91 PHB28/R) Bridge and Beauty - Foxhounds (38x48cm-15x19in) s.i.d.1921 |

URSO, Antonio (1964-) ?
£509 $942   (10-Jun-92 LD.P131/R) Le petit genie a la plume jaune, W27
(136x97cm-54x38in) s. (F.FR 5000)

URSULA (1921-) German
£378 $665   (10-Apr-92 KM.K573) Traum-Fussball, sudlich (48x64cm-19x25in) s.d.1970
col.pencil (DM 1100)

URUETA, Cordelia (1908-) Mexican
£13812 $25000   (18-May-92 CH.NY193/R) Piramide (120x101cm-47x40in) s.d.89 s.i.d.verso

URY, Lesser (1861-1931) German
£2448 $4357   (30-Nov-91 VG.B112/R) Dutch canal landscape (13x16cm-5x6in) s.d.1892
board on board (DM 7000)
£8741 $15559   (28-Nov-91 SY.BE56/R) Poplars (21x21cm-8x8in) s. panel (DM 25000)
£17483 $31119   (30-Nov-91 VG.B135/R) Fountain by fence in farmstead (78x96cm-31x38in)
s.d.88 (DM 50000)
£17747 $32300   (30-May-92 VG.B136/R) Trees by lake shore (34x53cm-13x21in) s. (DM 52000)
£29189 $54000   (8-Jun-92 GG.TA124/R) Boulevard in Berlin (33x25cm-13x10in) s.
£38596 $66000   (13-Mar-92 FN.S2614/R) Pond by the edge of the wood (40x52cm-16x20in) s.
(DM 110000)
£1024 $1853   (23-May-92 GB.B7319) Portrait of bearded Jew (47x36cm-19x14in) s.
(DM 3000)
£1049 $1867   (30-Nov-91 VG.B1036/R) Head of woman (28x21cm-11x8in) s. chl paper on
board (DM 3000)
£2439 $4439   (11-Dec-91 WE.MU250/R) Wooded river landscape (33x51cm-13x20in) s.d.1890
chk (DM 7000)
£2797 $4979   (30-Nov-91 VG.B1035/R) Beach (49x36cm-19x14in) s.d.1891 pastel board
(DM 8000)
£3072 $5560   (23-May-92 GB.B7318/R) Self portrait (45x29cm-18x11in) s. chl (DM 9000)
£3136 $5707   (11-Dec-91 WE.MU251/R) View through window (55x40cm-22x16in) s.twice chk
(DM 9000)
£3322 $5913   (30-Nov-91 VG.B114/R) Farmstead in landscape (32x49cm-13x19in) s.d.1912
chk chl (DM 9500)
£3357 $5875   (3-Apr-92 N.M.B947/R) Avenue (48x62cm-19x24in) s.d.24 pastel board
(DM 9500)
£3497 $6224   (30-Nov-91 VG.B109/R) Moses in the mountains (32x21cm-13x8in) s.i.d. chl
htd.white paper on board (DM 10000)
£6826 $12423   (30-May-92 VG.B135/R) Bowl with fruit (35x50cm-14x20in) s. pastel board
(DM 20000)
£6993 $12098   (25-Mar-92 KM.K1486/R) Prophets conversing on mountain (29x21cm-11x8in)
s. pastel board (DM 20000)
£9441 $16804   (30-Nov-91 VG.B138/R) Gentleman reading newspaper in cafe (16x10cm-6x4in)
s.d.1889 indian ink brush htd.white (DM 27000)
£10526 $18947   (23-Nov-91 N.M316/R) Thunderstorm in mountain lake landscape
(35x48cm-14x19in) s.d.1893 pastel board (DM 30000)
£11702 $22000   (5-Jan-92 GG.TA152/R) Tessiner Dorf (35x49cm-14x19in) s.d.1893 pastel
£11888 $21161   (28-Nov-91 SY.BE1/R) Tree trunks by the lake (49x35cm-19x14in) s. pastel
board (DM 34000)
£12587 $22406   (30-Nov-91 VG.B136/R) Brandenburg lake landscape (49x32cm-19x13in)
s.d.1888 W/C bodycol over pencil (DM 36000)
£12969 $23604   (30-May-92 VG.B134/R) Windmill (35x25cm-14x10in) s. pastel board on board
(DM 38000)
£14685 $26140   (29-Nov-91 VG.B5/R) Gentleman in coffee shop reading the newspaper
(50x31cm-20x12in) s.d.1920 chl chk paper on board (DM 42000)
£18771 $34164   (29-May-92 VG.B10/R) Kemperplatz (27x42cm-11x17in) s.i. pastel board
(DM 55000)
£19795 $36027   (30-May-92 VG.B133/R) Wooded Mark lake landscape (48x35cm-19x14in) s.
pastel board (DM 58000)
£24000 $42000   (26-Sep-91 SY.16/R) Street in Berlin (34x49cm-13x19in) s. pastel
£25597 $46587   (27-May-92 PH.DU71/R) Berlin-Unter den Linden (34x49cm-13x19in) s. pastel
board (DM 75000)
£39860 $70951   (29-Nov-91 VG.B6/R) Unter den Linden with Brandenburger Tor after rain,
evening (25x17cm-10x7in) pastel over pencil paper on board (DM 114000)
£43706 $77797   (30-Nov-91 VG.B139/R) Rainy street scene, Berlin (35x49cm-14x19in) s.
pastel chk board (DM 125000)

USELLINI, Gian Filippo (1903-1971) Italian
£4599 $8232   (14-Nov-91 F.M130/R) Fuga (40x70cm-16x28in) s.d.1965 (I.L 10000000)

USHER, R W (20th C) ?
£460 $819   (1-May-92 BW387/R) Laying the nets s.d.1927 W/C

UTH, Max (1863-1914) German
£900 $1593   (13-Feb-92 CSK127/R) Girl in village street (74x84cm-29x33in) s.
£3004 $5256   (3-Apr-92 BM.B948/R) Angler standing by stream (70x70cm-28x28in) s.
(DM 8500)

UTHAUG, Jorleif (1911-1990) Norwegian
£709 $1255   (15-Feb-92 BU.O150) Fragment (93x85cm-37x33in) s. panel (N.KR 8000)
£1935 $3405   (8-Apr-92 GWP.O74/R) Man with glass and bottle (120x120cm-47x47in)
s.d.1988 (N.KR 22000)

UTRECHT SCHOOL, 17th C (-) Flemish
£1826 $3213   (11-Apr-92 AT.P49/R) La toilette de Ninon (44x27cm-17x11in) s.verso panel
                    (F.FR 18000)

UTRECHT, Adriaen van (1599-1653) Flemish
£22000 $42240   (8-Jul-92 S18/R) Garland of fruit and nuts (84x120cm-33x47in) bears
                    sig.d.1643
£85000 $163200   (10-Jul-92 C12/R) Gamekeeper with punt gun and maidservant, holding up
                    dead hare in larder with various seafood (154x199cm-61x78in) s.d.1639

UTRECHT, Adriaen van (attrib) (1599-1653) Flemish
£7037 $12737   (19-May-92 GF.L2398/R) Animals in landscape (101x131cm-40x52in)
                    (S.FR 19000)

UTRECHT, Adriaen van (circle) (1599-1653) Flemish
£12000 $21360   (1-Nov-91 C148/R) Swag of mixed fruit and hazelnuts (70x76cm-28x30in)
                    with sig.d.1657 canvas on panel
£12346 $22099   (12-Nov-91 SY.AM38/R) Maid working in kitchen with game on table and
                    religious scene beyond (170x206cm-67x81in) (D.FL 40000)

UTRILLO, Lucie Valore see VALORE, Lucie

UTRILLO, Maurice (1883-1955) French
£8475 $15000   (6-Nov-91 CH.NY303/R) Plante dans un pot de tercuite (36x28cm-14x11in) s.
                    board
£17065 $31058   (25-May-92 WK.M1262/R) La Butte Pinson a Montmagny (40x33cm-16x13in) s.
                    canvas on board (DM 50000)
£27322 $50000   (14-May-92 SY.NY265/R) Rue de l'Abreuvoir a Montmartre (30x36cm-12x14in)
                    s.i.
£28902 $50000   (2-Oct-91 SY.NY86/R) Moulin de Sannois (21x22cm-8x9in) s. panel
£33881 $60986   (22-Nov-92 PIC.P24/R) Village de Bretagne (60x73cm-24x29in) s. board laid
                    down on canvas (F.FR 330000)
£35000 $63350   (3-Dec-91 C1268/R) Sannois (24x33cm-9x13in) s.i.
£35519 $65000   (14-May-92 SY.NY340/R) L'Eglise de Droue (46x55cm-18x22in) s.i.d.1936
£38000 $72580   (1-Jul-92 S200/R) Le Lapin Agile (52x75cm-20x30in) s. paper laid down on
                    cradled panel
£42000 $80220   (30-Jun-92 C176/R) Le lapin agile a Montmartre (38x46cm-15x18in) s.i.
£45714 $80000   (25-Feb-92 CH.NY67/R) Le moulin de Sannois (22x33cm-9x13in) s.
                    s.i.stretcher
£48632 $88024   (24-May-92 GL.P65/R) Le maquis de Montmartre (25x33cm-10x13in) s.d.1941
                    paper laid down on canvas (F.FR 480000)
£49133 $85000   (2-Oct-91 SY.NY87/R) Paysage sous la neige (38x55cm-15x22in) s.d.1935
£50847 $90000   (6-Nov-91 CH.NY289/R) Montmartre (61x50cm-24x20in) s.i.
£54000 $93420   (25-Mar-92 S67/R) Lac du Vivier et chateau de Florac - Isere
                    (64x54cm-25x21in) s.d.1928 i.verso
£54645 $100000   (14-May-92 SY.NY268/R) Le Moulin de la Galette (34x49cm-13x19in) s. paper
                    on panel
£57377 $105000   (13-May-92 CH.NY257/R) Place Saint-Pierre a Montmartre (45x54cm-18x21in)
                    s.
£59322 $105000   (7-Nov-91 SY.NY222/R) Le moulin de la Galette a Montmartre
                    (38x46cm-15x18in) s.i.
£62000 $107260   (25-Mar-92 S62/R) La Place du Tertre (46x61cm-18x24in) s. i.stretcher
£62842 $115000   (13-May-92 CH.NY245/R) Place du Tertre a Montmartre (50x61cm-20x24in) s.
£76503 $140000   (14-May-92 SY.NY269/R) L'Eglise de Maillane, Bouches-du-Rhone
                    (65x81cm-26x32in) s.d.1930 s.i.d.verso
£80000 $144800   (3-Dec-91 C257/R) Bourg la Reine (38x55cm-15x22in) s.i.d.1935
£97143 $170000   (25-Feb-92 SY.NY19/R) La maison de Mimi Pinson Rue du Mont-Cenis
                    (52x75cm-20x30in) s.
£110000 $210100   (30-Jun-92 S31/R) La Grand Rue a Montrouge (60x81cm-24x32in) s.
£130000 $235300   (3-Dec-91 S47/R) La Place du Tertre et le Sacre-Coeur (60x73cm-24x29in)
                    s.d.1922
£451977 $800000   (6-Nov-91 SY.NY24/R) Rue Muller a Montmartre (82x61cm-32x24in) s. cradled
                    panel
£2505 $4584   (3-Feb-92 SD.P225) Le Moulin de la Galette (30x41cm-12x16in) s.
                    col.crayons (F.FR 24500)
£4561 $7800   (13-Mar-92 FN.S2615/R) Pot plant on draped table (22x17cm-9x7in) s.
                    col.chk gouache paper on board (DM 13000)
£13238 $24491   (12-Jun-92 AT.P24/R) Le moulin de la Galette (39x50cm-15x20in) s. gouache
                    board (F.FR 130000)
£14500 $24940   (16-Oct-91 S82/R) Paysage a la Lessive (38x50cm-15x20in) s. gouache card
£24000 $41280   (16-Oct-91 S78/R) La Rue Norvins au printemps (35x31cm-14x12in) s.
                    gouache
£24590 $45000   (14-May-92 SY.NY153/R) Scene de rue (24x34cm-9x13in) s. W/C gouache
£24590 $45000   (13-May-92 SY.NY58/R) Eglise sous la neige (24x34cm-9x13in) s.d.1922
                    gouache
£25329 $45846   (24-May-92 GL.P61/R) Chemin d'Argenteuil (24x31cm-9x12in) s.d.1923
                    gouache (F.FR 250000)
£32787 $60000   (14-May-92 SY.NY154/R) Eglise Saint Michel a Limoges (62x42cm-24x17in)
                    s.i.d.1934 gouache
£38191 $64161   (16-Aug-91 ZZ.F41/R) Le bal du Moulin de la Galette (23x31cm-9x12in) s.
                    gouache (F.FR 380000)
£50865 $91048   (17-Nov-91 GL.P4/R) Montmartre (38x28cm-15x11in) s.i. gouache
                    (F.FR 500000)

UTTER, Andre (1886-1948) French
£616 $1109   (20-Nov-91 CN.P221) La pinede a Fontvieille (50x61cm-20x24in) s.
                            (F.FR 6000)
£657 $1162   (24-Apr-92 CN.P192) Arlequinade (55x47cm-22x19in) s. i.verso (F.FR 6500)

UTTER, Andre (attrib) (1886-1948) French
£954 $1670   (3-Apr-92 BM.B949/R) Female nude seated (81x65cm-32x26in) indis.s.
                            (DM 2700)

UTZ, Thornton (1915-) American
£843 $1500   (2-Nov-91 IH.NY106/R) Family opening Christmas presents by tree
                            (41x58cm-16x23in) s.i. board

UVA, Cesare (19th C) Italian
£1812 $3352   (9-Jun-92 F.R86) Ritorno dalla scampagnata (27x43cm-11x17in) s. tempera
                            cardboard (I.L 4000000)
£1200 $2124   (13-Feb-92 CSK55/R) Neapolitan folk on carriage in campagna
                            (27x44cm-11x17in) s.i. bodycol.
£1800 $3186   (13-Feb-92 CSK52/R) Peasants resting by lake on Neapolitan shore.
                            Figures, horse and cart (37x56cm-15x22in) s. bodycol. pair

UVA, Cesare (attrib) (19th C) Italian
£820 $1460   (27-Nov-91 B3/R) Roman Amphitheatre, Taormina (58x88cm-23x35in) gouache

UWINS, Thomas (1782-1857) British
£497 $865   (13-Apr-92 SY.J255/R) Italian women and child in courtyard
                            (30x38cm-12x15in) board (SA.R 2500)
£820 $1402   (12-Mar-92 CSK298) Neapolitan mother and child (39x32cm-15x13in) s.
                            i.verso board
£7000 $12810   (3-Jun-92 S178/R) Young Neapolitans returning from the Fests of St
                            Antonio (76x63cm-30x25in)

UWINS, Thomas (circle) (1782-1857) British
£1550 $2775   (14-Jan-92 SWS125/R) Rustic contentment (70x90cm-28x35in)

UYTEWAEL, Joachim (studio) (1566-1638) Dutch
£15000 $27300   (10-Dec-91 PH225/R) Meeting of David and Abigail (107x147cm-42x58in)

UYTEWAEL, Joachim (style) (1566-1638) Dutch
£7500 $14400   (8-Jul-92 S188/R) The Meeting of David and Abigail (64x74cm-25x29in)
                            bears i.d.1600

UYTEWAEL, Pieter (1596-1660) Dutch
£7000 $13440   (8-Jul-92 S260/R) Diana (57cm-22ins circular) panel

UYTTENBROECK, Moses van (1590-1648) Dutch
£7509 $13590   (21-May-92 L.K156/R) Two nymphs bathing (49x39cm-19x15in) panel
                            (DM 22000)

UZELAC, Milivoy (1897-1950) Yugoslavian
£635 $1130   (29-Nov-91 D.P82/R) Yola et Henri (60x45cm-24x18in) s. W/C collage board
                            (F.FR 6200)

V G (?) ?
£1200 $2136   (28-Nov-91 CSK207/R) The shepherd. The pipe smoker (61x47cm-24x19in)
                            init.d.1838 and 1842 pair

V S (?) ?
£2400 $4272   (28-Nov-91 S441/R) Winter sleigh (26x30cm-10x12in) indist.s. panel

VA, Barry le (1941-) American
£4469 $8000   (14-Nov-91 SY.NY174/R) Drawing interruptions - blocked structures no.6 -
                            combined 2 perspective (122x184cm-48x72in) s.d. ink pencil chl
                            paintstick tracing paper

VAA, Dyre (1903-1980) Norwegian
£1009 $1876   (18-Jun-92 GWP.O108/R) November evening, Totakk lake, Rauland
                            (75x90cm-30x35in) s. s.i.d.1942verso, sketch verso (N.KR 11500)

VAAMONDE, Joaquin (c.1872-?) Spanish
£600 $1032   (16-Oct-91 FER.M62/R) Nina pensativa (37x37cm-15x15in) s.d.1890 sanguine
                            dr (S.P 110000)
£982 $1689   (16-Oct-91 FER.M64/R) Invierno, calentandose junto a la lumbre
                            (39x30cm-15x12in) s.i.d.1890 chl dr oval (S.P 180000)

VAARBERG, Johannes Christoffel (1825-1871) Dutch
£1468 $2598   (5-Nov-91 SY.AM193) Children before child welfare board
                            (80x106cm-31x42in) (D.FL 4800)

VAARDT, Jan van der (1647-1721) Dutch
£4360 $7500   (10-Oct-91 SY.NY20/R) Mountainous southern landscape with figures by a stream (75x62cm-30x24in) s.

VAARDT, Jan van der (attrib) (1647-1721) Dutch
£1180 $2100   (22-Jan-92 SY.NY125/R) Portrait of lady (126x103cm-50x41in)

VAARDT, Jan van der (circle) (1647-1721) Dutch
£4600 $8096   (8-Apr-92 S155/R) Portrait of lady, seated holding flower. Portrait of Gentleman in style of Henri Gascars (124x99cm-49x39in) pair

VAARULA, Olavi (1927-1989) Finnish
£822 $1446   (12-Apr-92 HOR.H243) Wandering (50x40cm-20x16in) s. (F.M 6500)
£506   *$890*   *(12-Apr-92 HOR.H245) On the road (47x48cm-19x19in) s.d.1982-83 mixed media (F.M 4000)*

VACCARO, A (17th C) Italian
£453 $838   (9-Jun-92 F.R39) Il ciabattino (30x20cm-12x8in) s. canvasboard (I.L 1000000)

VACCARO, Andrea (?1598-1670) Italian
£4800 $8736   (12-Dec-91 B26/R) Diana and her nymphs surprised by Actaeon (101x128cm-40x50in)
£7901 $14302   (3-Dec-91 SY.MI202/R) Madonna col bambino (111x80cm-44x31in) (I.L 17000000)
£19337 $35000   (21-May-92 CH.NY31/R) Judith holding head of Holofernes, accompanied by maidservant (126x101cm-50x40in)

VACCARO, Andrea (attrib) (17th C) Italian
£1744 $3000   (10-Oct-91 SY.NY180/R) Ecstasy of Saint Francis (61x47cm-24x19in)
£3455 $6012   (13-Apr-92 AT.P46/R) Judith et la servante (96x72cm-38x28in) (F.FR 34000)

VACCARO, Andrea (studio) (c.1598-1670) Italian
£1000 $1750   (25-Feb-92 PH42) Head of shepherdess (37cm-15ins circular) panel

VACHER, Charles (1818-1883) British
£1100   *$1881*   *(13-Mar-92 C35/R) Thebes (35x91cm-14x36in) s.i.d.1863 pencil W/C*
£1400   *$2492*   *(31-Oct-91 D104/R) Bay of Naples (56x124cm-22x49in) s. W/C htd white*
£2766   *$4896*   *(26-Apr-92 SY.ME228/R) Sunrise at Thebes during inundation of Nile (54x131cm-21x52in) s.i.d.1873 s.i.verso W/C (A.D 6500)*

VADDER, Lodewyk de (1605-1655) Flemish
£2160 $3867   (14-Nov-91 CH.AM138/R) Travellers on path near pond (55x85cm-22x33in) init. (D.FL 7000)
£5800 $11136   (7-Jul-92 PH165/R) Extensive landscape with figures conversing on path by pond (60x85cm-24x33in)
£8000 $14240   (1-Nov-91 C124/R) Wooded hillside with peasants on path passing hunting party (47x67cm-19x26in) panel transferred canvas
£800   *$1456*   *(10-Dec-91 C235/R) An extensive wooded landscape with a distant farm (29x48cm-11x19in) blk.chk.wash*

VADDER, Lodewyk de (attrib) (1605-1655) Flemish
£1100 $2002   (26-May-92 PH138/R) Shepherd minding flock from hill overlooking extensive valley (42x53cm-17x21in)
£4444 $8044   (19-May-92 GF.L2407/R) Wooded river landscape with farmhouse and figures (23x33cm-9x13in) panel (S.FR 12000)
£989   *$1730*   *(3-Apr-92 AGS.P208) Paysage boise avec chemin (19x32cm-7x13in) mono. pen blk.crayon wash (F.FR 9500)*

VAERTEN, Jan (1909-1980) Belgian?
£2815 $5094   (23-May-92 KV.L438/R) Jumping horse (100x81cm-39x32in) s.d.51 (B.FR 170000)
£434   *$739*   *(22-Oct-91 C.A952) Unshakable (100x69cm-39x27in) s.d.1965 mixed media (B.FR 26000)*

VAES, Walter (1882-?) Belgian
£2673 $4545   (22-Oct-91 C.A953/R) Still life with herrings (27x35cm-11x14in) s. panel (B.FR 160000)

VAGH WEINMANN, Elemer (1906-) Hungarian
£1093 $1912   (5-Apr-92 ZZ.F209/R) Vase de fleurs (82x65cm-32x26in) s. (F.FR 10500)

VAGH WEINMANN, Maurice (1899-?) Hungarian
£1160 $1996   (20-Oct-91 I.N246) La fete foraine (60x74cm-24x29in) s. (F.FR 11500)

VAGH WEINMANN, Nandor (1897-?) French
£728 $1275   (5-Apr-92 ZZ.F211/R) Paysage de neige (38x46cm-15x18in) s. panel (F.FR 7000)
£832 $1457   (5-Apr-92 ZZ.F152/R) Maisons du Pays Basque (60x80cm-24x31in) s. panel (F.FR 8000)
£843 $1475   (5-Apr-92 ZZ.F224/R) Village sous la neige (60x80cm-24x31in) s. panel (F.FR 8100)

VAGUIN, Alexandre (?) Russian
£618 $1162   (18-Dec-91 LGB.P211/R) Equipage (50x65cm-20x26in) s.d.1991 (F.FR 6000)

VAILLANT, Wallerant (1623-1677) Dutch
£11500 $22080   (7-Jul-92 PH48/R) Still life of dead game, with bowl asparagus on table with cat (105x105cm-41x41in) s.d.1652
£1000 $1920   (7-Jul-92 C89/R) Portrait of the Marquis de Mondejar in armour with sash (58x45cm-23x18in) chk

VAILLANT, Wallerant (attrib) (1623-1677) Dutch
£1016 $1798   (5-Nov-91 GF.L2083/R) Portrait of young fayence painter (66x52cm-26x20in) (S.FR 2600)

VAINIO, Niilo (1927-) Finnish
£1940 $3454   (1-Dec-91 HOR.H239) Waxwings on branch (41x36cm-16x14in) s. (F.M 15000)

VAISMAN, Meyer (1960-) American
£10615 $19000   (13-Nov-91 CH.NY302/R) Filler (183x183cm-72x72in) process inks canvas over plywood panel
£22346 $40000   (14-Nov-91 SY.NY185/R) Uffizi portrait (188x345cm-74x136in) process inks canvas

VAJDA, Zsigmond (1860-1931) Hungarian
£2200 $3982   (21-May-92 CSK232/R) At cabaret (73x61cm-29x24in) s. board
£2800 $4984   (27-Nov-91 S142/R) Lady at toilette (139x101cm-55x40in) s.

VALADIE, Johny (20th C) French?
£954 $1660   (13-Apr-92 SY.J274/R) Le fauteuil rouge (72x54cm-28x21in) s.d.67 s.i.d.67 verso (SA.R 4800)

VALADON, Suzanne (1865-1938) French
£1114 $2017   (18-May-92 AT.P39) La toilette (15x15cm-6x6in) s. pencil dr (F.FR 11000)
£2497 $4645   (19-Jun-92 ARC.P24/R) Femme peintre (61x37cm-24x15in) s.d.1927 Indian ink wash sanguine (F.FR 24500)
£3480 $6194   (27-Nov-91 BL.P196/R) Jeune femme en rouge dans un paysage (29x22cm-11x9in) s. gouache (F.FR 34000)

VALAPERTA, Francesco (1836-1908) Italian
£1475 $2640   (14-Nov-91 GRO.B39) Caught with letter (48x33cm-19x13in) s.

VALDEN, L (17th C) Dutch
£730 $1307   (6-May-92 GD.B1298/R) Snow covered river landscape with skaters (41x61cm-16x24in) s. panel (S.FR 2000)

VALDES LEAL (younger) (17th C) Spanish
£10814 $20330   (18-Dec-91 AT.P14/R) Saint Michel terrasant les dragons (112x79cm-44x31in) (F.FR 105000)

VALDES LEAL, Juan de (attrib) (1622-1690) Spanish
£3141 $6000   (16-Jul-92 SY.NY43/R) Immaculate Conception (73x58cm-29x23in)

VALDES LEAL, Juan de (circle) (1622-1690) Spanish
£3800 $6916   (10-Dec-91 PH5/R) Mystic marriage of St. Catherine (203x144cm-80x57in)
£32000 $55680   (15-Apr-92 C151/R) King David. Zacchaeus. St Longinus. Centurion of Guard at Resurrection (189x102cm-74x40in) mono.i. i.verso set of four

VALDES LEAL, Juan de (style) (1622-1690) Spanish
£1900 $3325   (27-Feb-92 CSK13/R) The penitent Magdalene (90x72cm-35x28in)

VALDES, Manuel (1942-) Spanish
£13000 $23660   (29-May-92 C474/R) El bano (149x149cm-59x59in) s.d.88verso burlap

VALDIVIA, Victor (1897-?) ?
£2000 $3400   (22-Oct-91 C8/R) Gaucho herding cattle (86x114cm-34x45in) s.

VALENCIA, Manuel (1856-1935) American
£571 $1000   (31-Mar-92 MOR.P56) Cows in landscape (51x66cm-20x26in) s. board
£2895 $5500   (24-Jun-92 B.SF6251/R) Native American women in Yosemite (127x76cm-50x30in) s.

VALENCIAN SCHOOL (?) Spanish
£1296 $2346   (19-May-92 GF.L2357/R) Beheading of St John the Baptist (55x82cm-22x32in) panel (S.FR 3500)
£88667 $155168   (20-Feb-92 EP.M3/R) La Virgen con el Nino, con cuatro vinetas de Santas (185x119cm-73x47in) c.1400 tempera gold ground panel (S.P 16000000)

VALENCIENNES, Pierre Henri de (attrib) (1750-1819) French
£1019 $1896   (18-Jun-92 SY.MO242/R) Paysage boise (29x25cm-11x10in) paper laid down on canvas (F.FR 10000)

VALENCIENNES, Pierre Henri de (circle) (1750-1819) French
£1800 $3240   (21-Nov-91 C75/R) Mountainous coastal landscape with peasants by creek near castle (69x93cm-27x37in)

VALENKAMPH, Theodor Victor Carl (1868-1924) American
£514 $900   (22-Feb-92 YFA.M199/R) Fishing beach (20x28cm-8x11in) s.
£1064 $2000   (18-Dec-91 SY.NY79/R) Clipper ship (55x81cm-22x32in) s.d.1904

VALENKAMPH, Theodor Victor Carl (1868-1924) American-cont.
£2000 $3400   (6-Aug-91 RB.HY259/R) On run - large full-rigged ship crashing through waves (61x91cm-24x36in) s.

VALENTA, Rudolf (1929-) German?
£874 $1556   (25-Nov-91 WK.M1041/R) Construction (80x45cm-31x18in) s.i.d.1990 collage paper on board (DM 2500)

VALENTI, Italo (1912-) Italian
£5569 $10470   (19-Dec-91 F.M128/R) Due figure (100x80cm-39x31in) s.d.1952 i.verso (I.L 12000000)
£711 $1281   (22-Nov-91 EA.Z32) Untitled (12x21cm-5x8in) s.d.1965 W/C (S.FR 1800)
£927 $1650   (26-Nov-91 SY.MI89) Composizione (50x67cm-20x26in) s.i.a.1956 gouache (I.L 2000000)

VALENTIN (?) French
£490 $847   (25-Mar-92 KM.K1487) Rhine landscape with figures near Dusseldorf (60x80cm-24x31in) s. (DM 1400)

VALENTIN, Jean de see BOULOGNE, Valentin de

VALENTINE, J (19/20th C) ?
£520 $931   (14-Jan-92 B225/R) A Sealyham Terrier (23x33cm-9x13in) s. W/C

VALENTINI, A (?) Italian
£453 $838   (9-Jun-92 F.R64) I pupari (30x40cm-12x16in) s. (I.L 1000000)

VALENTINI, Gottardo (1820-1884) Italian
£3224 $5868   (12-Dec-91 F.M11/R) Contadini con pecore nei pressi del Lago di Fucino (67x97cm-26x38in) s.d.1855 i.verso (I.L 7000000)

VALENTINI, R (19th C) Italian
£1313 $2245   (12-Mar-92 GK.Z111) View of Venice with gondolieri (37x57cm-15x22in) s. (S.FR 3400)

VALENTINO, Gian Domenico (17th C) Italian
£942 $1800   (3-Jul-92 S.W3071/R) Kitchen interior (48x66cm-19x26in)
£4200 $7350   (31-Mar-92 PH126/R) Kitchen interior with copper utensils strewn before hearth, cat nearby (36x45cm-14x18in)

VALENTINO, Gian Domenico (style) (17th C) Italian
£1650 $2871   (13-Sep-91 C113/R) Scullery with cat on chair by open stove (64x79cm-25x31in)

VALERI, Silvestro (1814-1902) Italian
£800 $1368   (17-Mar-92 PH231/R) Figure on donkey in North African landscape (46x32cm-18x13in) s.i. W/C

VALERO, Ricardo (?) ?
£664 $1247   (17-Dec-91 DUR.M52/R) Maja fumando (42x26cm-17x10in) s. panel (S.P 120000)

VALETTE, Pierre Adolphe (1876-1942) French
£500 $870   (19-Sep-91 CSK144) Mrs Andrea Valette reading in red jacket (81x63cm-32x25in) s. i.verso
£800 $1392   (19-Sep-91 CSK151/R) Summer still life on table in garden (76x61cm-30x24in) s. board
£1000 $1740   (19-Sep-91 CSK172/R) Cattle grazing by river (61x76cm-24x30in) s.d.1913
£1000 $1740   (19-Sep-91 CSK143/R) Young girl with Japanese doll (61x51cm-24x20in) s.d.19 panel
£1100 $1914   (19-Sep-91 CSK141/R) Still life with pears and teapot (50x65cm-20x26in) s. canvas on board
£3500 $6090   (19-Sep-91 CSK147/R) Artist's son Tita (76x62cm-30x24in) s.d.1915

VALINDER, Knut (1909-) Swedish
£665 $1157   (13-Apr-92 AB.S265) Ducks landing - coastal landscape (40x59cm-16x23in) s. (S.KR 7000)
£772 $1374   (28-Oct-91 AB.S238) Spring landscape with pair of pheasants by stones (44x74cm-17x29in) s. (S.KR 8200)

VALIRA, C de (19th C) Continental
£1600 $2800   (18-Feb-92 CE.NY259/R) On Mediterranean (52x104cm-20x41in) s.d.1873

VALK, Hendrik (1930-) Dutch
£515 $932   (21-May-92 SY.AM374) Spaanse Danseressen (57x52cm-22x20in) init.d.72 s.i.d.verso board (D.FL 1700)

VALK, Hendrik de (fl.1693-1717) Dutch
£15116 $26000   (10-Oct-91 SY.NY107/R) Interior with rowdy school children at their lessons, adults beyond (71x101cm-28x40in)

VALK, J M van der (?) Dutch?
£814 $1400   (16-Oct-91 D.NY99) Bringing the passenger aboard (28x36cm-11x14in) indist.s.i. panel

VALKENBORCH, Frederick van (1570-1623) Flemish
£6000 $10680   (1-Nov-91 C129/R) Sack of Troy (40x58cm-16x23in) mono.d.95
£22657 $42595   (18-Dec-91 AT.P34/R) L'exploitation d'une mine de fer (30x42cm-12x17in)
                     copper (F.FR 220000)

VALKENBORCH, Frederick van (attrib) (1570-1623) Flemish
£4835 $9187   (24-Jun-92 CSC.P47/R) La conversation sur le chemin forestier
                     (58x56cm-23x22in) panel (F.FR 47000)

VALKENBORCH, Frederick van (circle) (1570-1623) Flemish
£19368 $36024   (18-Jun-92 SY.MO109/R) Construction de la Tour de Babel (31x40cm-12x16in)
                     copper (F.FR 190000)

VALKENBORCH, Frederick van (style) (1570-1623) Flemish
£926 $1657   (14-Nov-91 CH.AM38) Bathers in wood with peasants dancing beyond
                     (21cm-8ins circular) panel (D.FL 3000)

VALKENBORCH, Gillis van (circle) (c.1570-1622) Flemish
£3000 $5340   (1-Nov-91 C102/R) Solomon supervising construction of Temple at Jerusalem
                     (71x102cm-28x40in)

VALKENBORCH, Lucas van (1535-1597) Flemish
£1411 $2498   (6-Nov-91 LT.P42) Paysage avec ermite lisant (13cm-5ins circular) panel
                     (F.FR 14000)

VALKENBORCH, Lucas van (circle) (1535-1597) Italian
£50000 $96000   (10-Jul-92 C206/R) German city with knights jousting in palace garden
                     (21x40cm-8x16in) panel

VALKENBORCH, Lucas van (style) (1535-1597) Flemish
£750 $1313   (27-Feb-92 CSK153) An extensive landscape with farm buildings with
                     travellers on a path (22x29cm-9x11in) panel

VALKENBURG, Dirk (1675-1727) Dutch
£11111 $20111   (19-May-92 GF.L2064/R) Hunting still lifes of dead rabbits, birds,
                     dahlias and fruit (88x69cm-35x27in) rem.sig. i.verso pair (S.FR 30000)

VALKENBURG, Dirk (attrib) (1675-1727) Dutch
£11069 $20035   (19-May-92 AB.S4385/R) Landscape with gun, dog and dead game
                     (173x220cm-68x87in) (S.KR 117000)

VALKENBURG, Hendrik (1826-1896) Dutch
£897 $1614   (30-Jan-92 RAS.V687/R) Two smartly dressed young boys on country road
                     (64x82cm-25x32in) s. (D.KR 10000)
£2599 $4627   (30-Oct-91 CH.AM126/R) Cottage interior with mother sewing and two
                     children at table (52x65cm-20x26in) s.d.84 (D.FL 8500)
£917 $1633   *(30-Oct-91 CH.AM298) Cottage interior with peasant woman peeling potatoes*
                     (37x50cm-15x20in) init. W/C htd.white (D.FL 3000)
£1294 $2302   *(25-Nov-91 W.T1836/R) Sunlit cottage interior and young woman sewing*
                     (35x47cm-14x19in) s.d.1879 W/C (C.D 2600)
£3364 $5853   *(14-Apr-92 SY.AM35/R) Mother and child (41x56cm-16x22in) s. W/C*
                     (D.FL 11000)

VALLATI (attrib) (?) Italian
£621 $1100   (13-Feb-92 S.W1870) Hounds attacking boar (18x25cm-7x10in) bears sig. ink
                     wash

VALLAYER-COSTER, Anne (1744-1818) French
£11317 $20484   (5-Dec-91 SY.MO171 a/R) Faunesse et enfants bacchants (15x28cm-6x11in)
                     s.d.1773 (F.FR 110000)

VALLAYER-COSTER, Anne (attrib) (1744-1818) French
£4077 $7584   (20-Jun-92 CH.MO55/R) Nature morte avec des peches, des raisins, un vase
                     et une prune (24x30cm-9x12in) (F.FR 40000)

VALLAYER-COSTER, Anne (circle) (1744-1818) French
£3198 $5500   (9-Oct-91 CH.NY129/R) Basket of apricots and greengages on stone ledge
                     draped with linen cloth (45x55cm-18x22in)

VALLAYER-COSTER, Anne and PREVOST, Jean Louis (circle) (18th C) French
£3704 $6704   (19-May-92 GF.L2109/R) Still life of roses and lily of the valley
                     (38x32cm-15x13in) panel (S.FR 10000)

VALLDEPERAS, Eusebio (1827-?) Spanish
£2187 $4002   (13-May-92 FER.M112/R) Alegoria del Invierno y la Primavera
                     (98x78cm-39x31in) s.d.1865 (S.P 400000)

VALLE (?) ?
£1019 $1815   (29-Nov-91 F.F55) Tramonto a Premusa (70x60cm-28x24in) s. s.verso panel
                     (I.L 2200000)

VALLE, Angelo della (1852-1903) Argentinian
£109551 $195000   (1-Nov-91 PO.BA31) Patrulla en la Pampa (48x79cm-19x31in) s.

VALLE, Pietro della (19th C) Italian
£7818 $13994   (14-Nov-91 CH.R124/R) Paesaggio marino con figure danzanti
   (63x95cm-25x37in) s.d.1855 (I.L 17000000)

VALLEE, Etienne Maxime (19th C) French
£1520 $2600   (21-Mar-92 W.W9/R) Peasant woman gathering brush near country brook
   (36x46cm-14x18in) s. panel
£1714 $3033   (10-Nov-91 ZZ.F124/R) Nu dans la foret (48x65cm-19x26in) s. (F.FR 17000)

VALLEE, Ludovic (20th C) French
£2907 $5000   (12-Oct-91 SY.NY25/R) Le matin au parc (63x80cm-25x31in) s.

VALLEJO, Boris (1941-) ?
£730 $1300   (2-Nov-91 IH.NY149/R) Montage of murdered woman and evil characters
   (69x43cm-27x17in) s. acrylic canvasboard

VALLEJO, Don Francisco Antonio (fl.1752-1784) Mexican
£16575 $30000   (19-May-92 SY.NY1/R) Virgen de Guadalupe (92x54cm-36x21in) s.d.1781

VALLES, Lorenzo (1830-1910) Spanish
£2186 $3717   (22-Oct-91 DUR.M13/R) Perugia, Procesion Via Apia (27x17cm-11x7in) s.
   panel (S.P 400000)

VALLES, Roman (1923-) Spanish
£657 $1169   (29-Oct-91 BRO.B281) Impulso gestual monocromo (73x100cm-29x39in) s.d.61
   acrylic (S.P 120000)
£1051 $1975   (17-Dec-91 BRO.B377) Signos gestuales (98x130cm-39x51in) s.frame acrylic
   (S.P 190000)

VALLET, Edouard (1876-1929) Swiss
£3360 $5980   (29-Nov-91 GAB.G2898/R) Temple de Saturne, Rome s.d.05 (S.FR 8500)
£11067 $19700   (29-Nov-91 GAB.G2900/R) Printemps a Vercorin s.d.1926 (S.FR 28000)
£15625 $27656   (5-Nov-91 GF.L2262/R) La premiere neige a Grangis (54x65cm-21x26in)
   s.d.1912 i.stretcher (S.FR 40000)
£1255   *$2246*   *(15-Nov-91 ZOF.Z1914/R) Trinite (8x14cm-3x6in) i. indan ink pen sold with*
   original etching (S.FR 3200)
£1502   *$2674*   *(29-Nov-91 GAB.G2901/R) Le recueillement (30x47cm-12x19in) s.d.1908 W/C*
   (S.FR 3800)
£2941   *$5000*   *(23-Oct-91 GD.B762/R) Head of girl (18x23cm-7x9in) s. pastel (S.FR 7500)*

VALLET, Jean Emile (?-1899) French
£2198 $4000   (28-May-92 SY.NY209/R) Beaux arts ball at Paris Opera, 1897
   (69x84cm-27x33in) s.d.97 pair

VALLGREN, Ville (1855-1940) Scandinavian
£683 $1202   (12-Apr-92 HOR.H246/R) Palms (26x30cm-10x12in) s.i.d.1908 (F.M 5400)

VALLIN, Jacques Antoine (attrib) (1760-1831) French
£2263 $4097   (3-Dec-91 CN.P54/R) Allegorie de la Fidelite (23x17cm-9x7in) (F.FR 22000)
£3532 $6075   (16-Oct-91 AT.P137/R) Allegorie de l'ete (32x40cm-13x16in) (F.FR 35000)

VALLMAN, Uno (1913-) Swedish
£522 $909   (13-Apr-92 AB.S267) Lappland winter landscape with mountain birches
   (26x35cm-10x14in) s.d.1965 (S.KR 5500)
£550 $1007   (12-May-92 GO.G187) Floating timber, Alfta (61x50cm-24x20in) s. panel
   (S.KR 5800)
£631 $1123   (28-Oct-91 AB.S240) Northern summer landscape from Lappland
   (45x37cm-18x15in) s. (S.KR 6700)
£736 $1302   (25-Apr-92 SO.S625/R) Street cafe in town (37x45cm-15x18in) s.d.1981
   (S.KR 7800)
£759 $1389   (13-May-92 BU.S210/R) Southern landscape with riders and figures
   (55x65cm-22x26in) s.d.1952 (S.KR 8000)
£779 $1355   (13-Apr-92 AB.S266) Cat and ornament (49x60cm-19x24in) s.d.1957 panel
   (S.KR 8200)
£377   *$670*   *(28-Oct-91 AB.S415) Reindeer in mountain landscape (48x60cm-19x24in)*
   s.d.1954 pastel (S.KR 4000)
£550   *$946*   *(19-Oct-91 UA.U365) Sunset at Rano (51x65cm-20x26in) s.d.1967 mixed media*
   panel (S.KR 8000)

VALLOIS, Paul Felix (19th C) French
£1923 $3500   (27-May-92 CH.NY198/R) Laundry day in a French village (48x94cm-19x37in)
   s.d.01 canvas on board

VALLOTTON, Felix (1865-1925) Swiss
£2037 $3687   (19-May-92 GF.L2283/R) Sous-bois (21x45cm-8x18in) s.d.1903 board
   (S.FR 5500)
£2252 $4008   (27-Nov-91 AT.P199) Nu de dos (14x9cm-6x4in) bears studio st.verso canvas
   laid down on board (F.FR 22000)
£8989 $15730   (26-Feb-92 CK.P84) Houlgate (21x27cm-8x11in) bears st.verso panel
   (F.FR 88000)
£39841 $72112   (5-Dec-91 SY.Z104/R) L'etoffe jaune (81x65cm-32x26in) s.d.13
   (S.FR 100000)
£1535   *$2733*   *(27-Nov-91 AT.P67) Sauvons Rome et la France (25x18cm-10x7in) init.*
   Indian ink (F.FR 15000)

VALLOTTON, Felix (1865-1925) Swiss-cont.
£3984 $7211   (5-Dec-91 SY.Z71/R) Guernsey landscape (19x29cm-7x11in) mono.d.1907 W/C
     (S.FR 10000)

VALLS, Ernesto (1891-1941) ?
£5056 $9000   (22-Jan-92 SY.NY537/R) Women collecting water at fountain
     (130x100cm-51x39in) s.
£14535 $25000   (17-Oct-91 SY.NY125/R) Ninos Jugando en la playa (80x100cm-31x39in) s.

VALMIER, Georges (1885-1937) French
£26749 $50823   (24-Jun-92 GL.P204/R) Place de village (69x95cm-27x37in) s.d.1925
     (F.FR 260000)
£6364 $11518   (21-May-92 SY.AM148/R) Untitled (15x11cm-6x4in) s. gouache paper collage
     (D.FL 21000)
£10526 $18947   (21-Nov-91 L.K486/R) Femme assise (28x20cm-11x8in) s. gouache collage
     (DM 30000)

VALOIS, J C (18/19th C) Dutch
£916 $1704   (16-Jun-92 SY.B240) Portrait of Maurits von Nagell and his wife Anna
     (55x45cm-22x18in) s. W/C gum arabic (B.FR 55000)

VALORE, Lucie (1878-1965) Swiss
£1571 $2750   (28-Feb-92 SY.NY207/R) House with red trees (46x56cm-18x22in) s. s.d.1948
     stretcher

VALPA, A la (19th C) ?
£4811 $8900   (13-Jun-92 WK.M342/R) Italian coastal landscape with shipping
     (51x105cm-20x41in) s.d.1861 (DM 14000)

VALSTAD, Otto (1862-?) Norwegian
£1671 $2941   (7-Apr-92 UL.T237) From a cabinet-maker's workshop, 1903
     (90x70cm-35x28in) (N.KR 19000)

VALTAT, Louis (1869-1952) French
£1360 $2311   (27-Oct-91 LT.P76/R) Le jete de fleurs (15x24cm-6x9in) mono. panel
     (F.FR 13500)
£1410 $2397   (27-Oct-91 LT.P70/R) Fleurs rouges et mauves (10x17cm-4x7in) st.sig.
     (F.FR 14000)
£1644 $2828   (4-Mar-92 AT.P209) Vase de fleurs (8x10cm-3x4in) init. panel (F.FR 16000)
£1722 $3118   (19-May-92 FB.P42/R) Les poissons (21x32cm-8x13in) st.sig. (F.FR 17000)
£1842 $3279   (27-Nov-91 AT.P200) Composition aux fleurs (38x35cm-15x14in) bears studio
     st. paper laid down on board (F.FR 18000)
£2881 $5214   (6-Dec-91 GL.P195/R) Nature morte aux fruits (24x33cm-9x13in) st.init.
     (F.FR 28000)
£3040 $5502   (19-May-92 FB.P39/R) Le mas et les oliviers (26x41cm-10x16in) mono.
     (F.FR 30000)
£3498 $6331   (4-Dec-91 CB.P106/R) L'heure du the (27x37cm-11x15in) st.mono.
     (F.FR 34000)
£3842 $6916   (2-Feb-92 ZZ.F91/R) Nature morte aux fruits (24x34cm-9x13in) st.init.
     (F.FR 37500)
£4000 $7000   (29-Sep-91 LIT.L305) Woman with purple dress (28x23cm-11x9in)
£4520 $8000   (5-Nov-91 CE.NY20/R) Les coquelicots (22x23cm-9x9in)
£4863 $8802   (19-May-92 FB.P48/R) Maison aux volets rouges, Versailles
     (47x62cm-19x24in) st.sig. board (F.FR 48000)
£4863 $8802   (19-May-92 FB.P38/R) La pendule directoire et bouquet de fleurs
     (40x47cm-16x19in) mono. (F.FR 48000)
£5066 $9169   (19-May-92 FB.P46/R) Suzanne Valtat assise (44x56cm-17x22in) st.sig.
     board (F.FR 50000)
£5167 $9353   (19-May-92 FB.P49/R) Les ormeaux (38x55cm-15x22in) mono. (F.FR 51000)
£5268 $9536   (19-May-92 FB.P47/R) Chemin fleuri (40x51cm-16x20in) st.sig. board
     (F.FR 52000)
£6000 $10380   (24-Mar-92 C57/R) Bouquet de fleurs (21x22cm-8x9in) st.init.
£6890 $12470   (19-May-92 FB.P44/R) Les tomates et coupe de fruits aux prunes et raisins
     (39x50cm-15x20in) st.sig. board (F.FR 68000)
£8571 $15000   (25-Feb-92 SY.NY17/R) L'enfant au costume marin bleu (73x60cm-29x24in) s.
£8571 $15000   (25-Feb-92 CH.NY31/R) Giroflees, cruche marron (61x38cm-24x15in) s.
£8916 $16138   (19-May-92 FB.P51/R) Paysage (65x81cm-26x32in) mono. (F.FR 88000)
£9497 $17000   (9-May-92 CE.NY13/R) Vase de fleurs (46x38cm-18x15in) st.init.
£12220 $22607   (12-Jun-92 AT.P27/R) Vase de soucis et pommes (65x81cm-26x32in) s.
     (F.FR 120000)
£13407 $23731   (5-Nov-91 ZZ.F125/R) Jeune femme assise (92x74cm-36x29in) s.
     (F.FR 133000)
£15000 $28650   (30-Jun-92 C175/R) Vase bleu, tulipes et draperie (50x73cm-20x29in) s.
£15000 $27150   (3-Dec-91 C265/R) Fleurs d'Amandier (81x65cm-32x26in) s.
£15847 $29000   (14-May-92 SY.NY319/R) Les bouquets de fleurs (42x44cm-17x17in) st.init.
£16393 $30000   (13-May-92 CH.NY215/R) Les deux bouquets (60x72cm-24x28in) st.sig.
£16601 $29549   (29-Nov-91 GAB.G3209/R) Paysage d'Antheor (54x64cm-21x25in) s.
     (S.FR 42000)
£19250 $34843   (19-May-92 FB.P40/R) Suzanne Valtat au jardin (73x92cm-29x36in) st.sig.
     (F.FR 190000)
£19429 $34000   (25-Feb-92 SY.NY80/R) Vase de tulipes (60x73cm-24x29in) s.
£20765 $38000   (13-May-92 CH.NY220/R) Vase, tulipes et fleurs blanches (55x46cm-22x18in)
     s.
£21143 $37000   (25-Feb-92 SY.NY14/R) Femme au chat et livres (67x51cm-26x20in) s. panel
£32787 $60000   (14-May-92 SY.NY249/R) Les coquelicots (73x92cm-29x36in) s.

VALTAT, Louis (1869-1952) French-cont.
£459	$853	(18-Jun-92 CB.P24 b) Deux femmes au bord d'un quai (21x32cm-8x13in) st.mono. W/C (F.FR 4500)
£1008	$1784	(8-Nov-91 LGB.P110/R) Paysage de Provence (25x32cm-10x13in) studio st. W/C (F.FR 10000)
£1644	$2828	(4-Mar-92 AT.P95/R) Scene de rue (31x43cm-12x17in) init. ink wash (F.FR 16000)
£4215	$7291	(28-Mar-92 F.L44/R) Marina (25x33cm-10x13in) s. pencil W/C (S.FR 11000)

VALTER, Frederick E (19/20th C) British
£503	$900	(11-Nov-91 GC.M16/R) Escena de establo (41x61cm-16x24in) s.
£400	$688	(16-Oct-91 CSK148) Shire horses and cattle in farmyard (32x46cm-13x18in) s.d.1927 pencil W/C
£500	$925	(12-Jun-92 K509/R) Cattle resting at evening (30x64cm-12x25in) s. W/C
£520	$894	(3-Mar-92 AG203/R) When the day is done (25x43cm-10x17in) s.d.1927 W/C
£600	$1146	(13-Jul-92 PH111) Sheep and ducks in Worcestershire meadows (45x68cm-18x27in) s.d.1919 W/C
£900	$1566	(11-Sep-91 MMB192/R) A farm yard scene (41x58cm-16x23in) s.d.1910

VALTER, H (fl.1854-1864) British
£680	$1231	(5-Dec-91 HB736) Extensive seascape with shipping and figure off Dutch coast (51x81cm-20x32in) s.

VALTER, Henry (fl.1854-1864) British
£1300	$2314	(29-Nov-91 T340) Shore scenes with figures and boats (30x46cm-12x18in) s. W/C pair

VALTER, Karel (1909-) Czechoslovakian
£993	$1768	(29-Nov-91 D.V189/R) Near the cobwebs (105x115cm-41x45in) s.d.87 (A.S 20000)
£993	$1768	(29-Nov-91 D.V185/R) In the meadow (105x115cm-41x45in) s.d.84 (A.S 20000)

VANAISE, Gustaaf (1854-1902) Belgian
£911	$1648	(23-May-92 KV.L343) Les photographies (58x43cm-23x17in) s. (B.FR 55000)

VANBERGER, Rubin (20th C) ?
£2273	$4000	(8-Apr-92 D.NY73) Floral still life (102x76cm-40x30in) s.

VANCELLS, Joaquin (1866-1942) Spanish
£712	$1295	(27-May-92 DUR.M929/R) Marina (18x30cm-7x12in) s. panel (S.P 130000)
£4562	$8576	(17-Dec-91 BRO.B366/R) Paisaje con pinar (70x111cm-28x44in) s.d.97 (S.P 825000)

VANDENBRANDEN, Guy (20th C) Belgian
£668	$1136	(22-Oct-91 C.A976) Composition (90x90cm-35x35in) s. panel (B.FR 40000)
£752	$1278	(22-Oct-91 C.A975) Composition (122x91cm-48x36in) s.d.1973 verso panel (B.FR 45000)

VANDERBANK, John (18th C) British
£1200	$2292	(15-Jul-92 S118/R) Portrait of a gentleman in blue coat (124x100cm-49x39in)
£6180	$11000	(22-Jan-92 SY.NY123/R) Portrait of lady (127x102cm-50x40in)

VANDERBANK, John (circle) (18th C) British
£2200	$4026	(15-May-92 TE353) Portrait of young boy in red coat (76x64cm-30x25in)

VANDERCAM, Serge (1924-) Danish
£500	$929	(16-Jun-92 SY.B362/R) Odense 63/2 (98x70cm-39x28in) s.d.1962 paper (B.FR 30000)
£1001	$1761	(7-Apr-92 C.A615) Christ (109x72cm-43x28in) s. gouache (B.FR 60000)

VANDERCAMMEN, Edmond (1901-1980) Belgian
£3080	$5574	(7-Dec-91 KV.L412/R) Les ombres (54x72cm-21x28in) s. panel (B.FR 180000)

VANDERLICK, Armand (1897-1985) Belgian
£1253	$2130	(22-Oct-91 C.A318) Woman with a lamp (50x73cm-20x29in) s.d.1974 (B.FR 75000)
£2005	$3409	(22-Oct-91 C.A317) Cabins on the beach (80x60cm-31x24in) s. (B.FR 120000)
£2815	$5094	(23-May-92 KV.L489/R) Woman in brown (100x80cm-39x31in) s. (B.FR 170000)
£3229	$5521	(21-Mar-92 KV.L480/R) Beach cabins (54x65cm-21x26in) s. (B.FR 190000)
£3593	$6503	(7-Dec-91 KV.L485/R) Woman in a white blouse (76x57cm-30x22in) s.d.51 (B.FR 210000)
£5500	$9460	(12-Oct-91 KV.L409/R) Woman in blue (110x99cm-43x39in) s.d.55 (B.FR 330000)
£401	$682	(22-Oct-91 C.A316/R) Beach scene (48x32cm-19x13in) s.d.1978 W/C (B.FR 24000)

VANDERLYN, John (1775-1852) American
£1600	$2720	(23-Oct-91 S273/R) Three hunters at Niagara Falls (53x79cm-21x31in) s. W/C over pencil htd white

VANDERMEER, Jan (19/20th C) ?
£1204	$2083	(25-Mar-92 CH.R60) Veduta di un borgo fiammingo adiacente ad un corso d'acqua (48x74cm-19x29in) (I.L 2600000)

VANDEVERDONCK, Franz (19th C) Belgian
£877 $1500   (13-Mar-92 WOL.C420 a/R) Ram, ewe and lamb in landscape (18x25cm-7x10in)
          s.d.1889 panel
£950 $1767   (16-Jun-92 SWS243/R) Poultry in landscape (18x23cm-7x9in) s.d.1870
          indis.i.verso panel

VANGI, Giuliano (1931-) Italian
£1498 $2667   (29-Apr-92 F.F111/R) Figura (75x54cm-30x21in) s.d.1978 pencil cardboard
          (I.L 3300000)

VANLOO, Carle see LOO, Carle van

VANMOUR, Jan Baptiste (1671-1737) Flemish
£3800 $6460   (23-Oct-91 S28/R) Turkish lady holding pipe (29x23cm-11x9in)
£4004 $7207   (18-Nov-91 AT.P378/R) Femme brodant (35x26cm-14x10in) (F.FR 39000)
£12500 $21250   (23-Oct-91 S26/R) Sultana with black eunuch (34x29cm-13x11in)
£12500 $21250   (23-Oct-91 S25/R) Sultan with horse and page in the second court of the
          Seraglio (34x30cm-13x12in)

VANMOUR, Jan Baptiste (attrib) (1671-1737) Flemish
£5000 $8500   (23-Oct-91 S27/R) Zulaf Baltadgi, page des Princes Enfermes
          (33x24cm-13x9in) i. i.verso

VANMOUR, Jan Baptiste (style) (1671-1737) Flemish
£2600 $4420   (23-Oct-91 S77/R) Turk in landscape. Turkish lady at the water's edge
          (29x23cm-11x9in) pair
£3800 $6460   (23-Oct-91 S213 a) Portrait of Sultan (39x28cm-15x11in) i.

VANNI, Francesco (c.1563-1610) Italian
£513 $924   (22-Nov-91 AGS.P139) Vision de Sait Francois (18x14cm-7x6in) blk.crayon
          sanguine (F.FR 5000)
£1200 $2184   (11-Dec-91 PH287/R) Studies of an infant (18x25cm-7x10in) i. chk
£2800 $5376   (7-Jul-92 C157/R) Christ (24x12cm-9x5in) chk top corners cut

VANNI, Giuseppe Florenzo (18th C) Italian
£1500 $2880   (6-Jul-92 S95/R) Bird of Paradise (36x24cm-14x9in) W/C

VANNI, Sam (1908-) Finnish
£9185 $16349   (1-Dec-91 HOR.H242/R) Composition (65x100cm-26x39in) s.d.1957 (F.M 71000)

VANNINI, Ottavio (attrib) (1585-1643) Italian
£1400 $2688   (6-Jul-92 S26/R) Female nude. Coat of arms (24x19cm-9x7in) chk htd.white
          double-sided

VANNUCCI, Pietro (circle) (1445-1523) Italian
£19547 $35381   (5-Dec-91 SY.MO349/R) Vierge a l'enfant entre deux Saints
          (54x57cm-21x22in) tempera panel gold sheet (F.FR 190000)

VANNUCCI, Pietro (studio) (1445-1523) Italian
£55233 $95000   (9-Oct-91 CH.NY199/R) Madonna and Child enthroned with Saints Sebastian,
          John the Baptist, Peter and Roch, landscape beyon (205x204cm-81x80in)

VANNUCCI, Pietro (style) (1445-1523) Italian
£1300 $2379   (12-May-92 SWS.613/R) Holy Family (62x42cm-24x17in) panel
£8000 $14000   (31-Mar-92 PH15/R) Resurrection (32x59cm-13x23in) canvas on panel

VANNUTELLI, Scipione (1834-1894) Italian
£2557 $4500   (10-Apr-92 DM.D2011/R) Drawing room scene with man reading woman letter
          (61x43cm-24x17in)

VANTONGERLOO, Frans (20th C) Belgian
£617 $1123   (12-Dec-91 SY.AM145/R) Blossoming trees (25x35cm-10x14in) s. mono.d.1919
          cardboard (D.FL 2000)

VANVITELLI, Gaspare see WITTEL, Gaspar van

VARGA, Ferenc (1908-) Hungarian
£877 $1579   (23-Nov-91 N.M318/R) Composition en gris (39x62cm-15x24in) s.d.1956 panel
          (DM 2500)

VARGAS RUIZ, Guillermo (1910-) Spanish
£498 $897   (29-Jan-92 FER.M237) Paisaje en malvas (11x18cm-4x7in) s. panel
          (S.P 90000)
£547 $1001   (13-May-92 FER.M84/R) Escena de Fragonard (17x24cm-7x9in) s.d.67 tablex
          (S.P 100000)
£1659 $3119   (17-Dec-91 DUR.M99/R) Descansando (29x48cm-11x19in) s. (S.P 300000)

VARGAS, Alberto (20th C) American
£14045 $25000   (2-Nov-91 IH.NY20/R) Portrait bust of woman with flower petals
          (33x33cm-13x13in) s.i. W/C

VARGAS, Mario (20th C) Spanish?
£811 $1467   (20-May-92 I.N188) Deux personnages (92x73cm-36x29in) s. (F.FR 8000)
£1009 $1736   (20-Oct-91 I.N238) L'enfant (55x46cm-22x18in) s. mixed media panel
          (F.FR 10000)

VARGAS, Mario (20th C) Spanish?-cont.

| £1110 | $1909 | (20-Oct-91 I.N237/R) Le petit chat (46x55cm-18x22in) s. mixed media panel (F.FR 11000) |
| £1124 | $1966 | (23-Feb-92 I.N226/R) La detente (46x55cm-18x22in) s. mixed media (F.FR 11000) |

VARLEY, Cornelius (1781-1873) British

| £750 | $1305 | (12-Sep-91 CSK13/R) An Irish cart (23x33cm-9x13in) s.i.d.1848 pen wash |
| £1800 | $3222 | (14-Nov-91 S10) Snowdon and the Pass of Llanberis, Wales (32x48cm-13x19in) i. wash over pencil |

VARLEY, Edgar J (?-1888) British

| £500 | $895 | (5-May-92 SWS117/R) West view of Bosham Church and quay, Sussex (17x37cm-7x15in) s.d.1866 i.d.verso W/C htd bodycol.gum arabic |
| £950 | $1701 | (11-Nov-91 PH170/R) View of Twickenham Church from Ham House, Petersham, Richmond, Surrey (9x17cm-4x7in) s.d.1874 i.d.verso W/C |

VARLEY, Frederick Horsman (1881-1969) British/Canadian

£2927	$5268	(19-Nov-91 FP.M186/R) Artists, Whycogomah (29x38cm-11x15in) s. s.d.1953 verso board (C.D 6000)
£4146	$7505	(2-Dec-91 R.T274/R) Sunset near Kaslo, B.C (30x41cm-12x16in) s. i.verso canvasboard (C.D 8500)
£8458	$15055	(26-Nov-91 JOY.T21/R) Mountain Lake, B.C. Sketch of mountains (30x37cm-12x15in) s. panel double-sided (C.D 17000)
£450	$797	(6-Nov-91 SY.T67) Pear tree (29x23cm-11x9in) s. st.verso pencil (C.D 900)
£746	$1328	(26-Nov-91 JOY.T185/R) River bend, Doon (18x24cm-7x9in) s. col.crayons wash (C.D 1500)

VARLEY, John (1778-1842) British

£750	$1433	(15-Jul-92 S203/R) Figures on path in landscape (25x33cm-10x13in) board
£540	$967	(5-May-92 SWS95) Wooded valley with distant mountain (9x13cm-4x5in) W/C
£580	$1038	(11-Nov-91 PH101/R) Morpeth Tower, Northumberland (10x13cm-4x5in) W/C
£605	$1071	(4-Nov-91 SY.J209/R) River landscape with abbey ruin (15x22cm-6x9in) s. W/C (SA.R 3000)
£700	$1253	(14-Nov-91 S113) Travellers passing cottage (9x13cm-4x5in) s.d.1831 W/C htd.bodycol gum arabic
£740	$1258	(22-Oct-91 SWS86/R) Caernarvon Castle (7x12cm-3x5in) W/C pencil
£766	$1356	(4-Nov-91 SY.J210/R) River landscape with figure and barge (23x32cm-9x13in) s. W/C (SA.R 3800)
£800	$1432	(12-Nov-91 C62 a) Figures by a lake beneath trees. Italianate landscape. Landscape study at sunset pencil W/C gum arabic one oval three same mount
£1050	$1848	(9-Apr-92 S113) Figures by river, windmill beyond (11x16cm-4x6in) s. W/C
£1200	$2112	(6-Apr-92 PH29/R) River scene with castle (25x51cm-10x20in) s.d.1841 W/C bodycol.varnish
£1265	$2416	(16-Jul-92 S126/R) Travellers by cottage, river beyond (24x18cm-9x7in) s. W/C over pencil
£1500	$2685	(12-Nov-91 C107/R) Fishing boat on the Thames (15x20cm-6x8in) s.d.1831 pencil W/C
£2000	$3820	(1-Jul-92 B5) Cattle watering by stone bridge near ruined abbey (14x20cm-6x8in) s. W/C
£2200	$3872	(9-Apr-92 S120/R) On Thames near Windsor, Berkshire (19x32cm-7x13in) s.d.1842 W/C htd bodycol gum arabic
£2700	$5157	(1-Jul-92 B4/R) View on the Thames towards Chiswick (14x21cm-6x8in) s. W/C
£3100	$5456	(6-Apr-92 PH10/R) Quie. ackwater (24x32cm-9x13in) s. W/C
£6000	$10740	(14-Nov-91 S106/R) Richmond Hill, Surrey (25x37cm-10x15in) W/C over pencil htd.bodycol

VARLEY, John (attrib) (1778-1842) British

| £500 | $955 | (14-Jul-92 DR349) San Sebastian, Spain (25x52cm-10x20in) W/C |

VARLEY, John (jnr) (?-1899) British

| £4800 | $8160 | (23-Oct-91 S249/R) Temple of Philae on the Nile (49x75cm-19x30in) s. s.i.d.1879verso |
| £5800 | $9860 | (22-Oct-91 SWS285/R) Azabu, Tokio. Akabane and part of Shiba Park (27x33cm-11x13in) s.d.91 i.verso panel pair |

VARLIN (1900-) Swiss

£12030	$22015	(4-Jun-92 SY.Z422/R) Promenade des Anglais in Nizza (33x41cm-13x16in) (S.FR 32000)
£20677	$37838	(4-Jun-92 SY.Z407/R) Promenade des Anglais in Nizza (49x80cm-19x31in) s. (S.FR 55000)
£20677	$37838	(4-Jun-92 SY.Z393/R) Horse drawn coaches (39x55cm-15x22in) s. s.verso (S.FR 55000)
£20884	$39262	(19-Dec-91 F.M198/R) Uomo in poltrona (118x107cm-46x42in) s. (I.L 45000000)
£21053	$38526	(4-Jun-92 SY.Z413/R) Jetty at the Burkliplatz in Zurich (42x45cm-17x18in) s. canvas on pavatex (S.FR 56000)
£46154	$87692	(26-Jun-92 GK.B145 a/R) Portrait of Friedrich Durrenmatt (200x140cm-79x55in) s. i.d.1962verso (S.FR 120000)

VARNI, Antonio (c.1840-1908) Italian

| £6186 | $10950 | (7-Nov-91 F.M6870/R) Marina con ciminiere. Contadine sulla riva canvas on board pair (I.L 13500000) |

VARO, Remedios (1900-1963) Spanish
£220994 $400000   (18-May-92 CH.NY44/R) Vuelo magico (86x105cm-34x41in) s.d.1956 oil mother-of-pearl masonite
£305556 $550000   (19-Nov-91 CH.NY45/R) Microcosmos or Determinismo (94x89cm-37x35in) s. tempera masonite

VAROTARI, Alessandro (attrib) (1588-1648) Italian
£5000 $9600   (8-Jul-92 S122/R) Judith with the head of Holofernes (115x98cm-45x39in)

VAROTARI, Alessandro (school) (1588-1648) Italian
£1816 $3232   (28-Apr-92 F.R39) Sant'Orsola (80x65cm-31x26in) (I.L 4000000)

VAROTARI, Alessandro (style) (1588-1648) Italian
£1500 $2700   (21-Nov-91 C100/R) Madonna and Child on plinth with town in landscape beyond (81x69cm-32x27in)

VARRIALE, W Stella (1927-) American
£925 $1600   (2-Oct-91 D.NY95) Rehearsal break (51x102cm-20x40in) s.

VARRONE, Johann (1832-1910) Austrian
£3393 $6175   (27-May-92 D.V518/R) Royal hunting castle near Murzsteg (106x107cm-42x42in) s.indis.i.d.1889 (A.S 70000)
£3486 $5961   (19-Mar-92 F.M25/R) Ponte su un torrente (53x64cm-21x25in) s. panel (I.L 7500000)

VARVARESSOS, Vicki (1950-) Australian
£1244 $2128   (17-Mar-92 JRL.S260) New curl how to get it how to keep it (161x180cm-63x71in) s.d.77 verso (A.D 2800)

VASARELY, Victor (1908-) Hungarian
£762 $1326   (16-Apr-92 FB.P193/R) Transparence VII (25x21cm-10x8in) s. (F.FR 7500)
£1714 $3000   (27-Feb-92 CE.NY191/R) Zoeld blue/yellow (101x101cm-40x40in) s. s.d.71 num.2/8 verso luran metal
£1931 $3360   (16-Apr-92 FB.P167/R) Immat (29x28cm-11x11in) s. i.verso board (F.FR 19000)
£2286 $4000   (27-Feb-92 CE.NY189/R) Zett S.Z. green/Violet (101x101cm-40x40in) s. s.d.71 num.1/4 verso luran metal
£3631 $6500   (9-May-92 CE.NY348/R) AXO-IX (105x105cm-41x41in) s.i.d.1975verso
£3800 $6536   (17-Oct-91 S73/R) Quaser-R (54x54cm-21x21in) s. s.d.1968 verso tempera cardboard
£4525 $8190   (4-Dec-91 KH.K16/R) Composition (30x49cm-12x19in) s.d.47 (D.KR 50000)
£4800 $8256   (17-Oct-91 S104/R) Titkos (80x80cm-31x31in) s. s.d.1965 verso tempera board
£5500 $9460   (17-Oct-91 S105/R) Sende (50x50cm-20x20in) s. s.d.1967 verso tempera board
£5587 $10000   (12-Nov-91 CE.NY86/R) AXO-IX (105x105cm-41x41in) s.i.d.1975verso
£5758 $10422   (3-Dec-91 AB.S5167/R) Vonal-BIP-I (52x52cm-20x20in) s. d.1968verso tempera panel (S.KR 60000)
£6857 $12000   (25-Feb-92 SY.NY180/R) Ond-BV (48x48cm-19x19in) s. s.i.d.1968verso acrylic board
£7338 $13355   (25-May-92 WK.M1264/R) Andro-Neg (37x53cm-15x21in) s. s.i.d.1957verso panel (DM 21500)
£8939 $16000   (9-May-92 CE.NY349/R) Katoltar (100x100cm-39x39in) s. s.i.d.1973verso acrylic
£9128 $16613   (25-May-92 ZZ.F88/R) Negyes (100x100cm-39x39in) s. s.d.1987verso (F.FR 90000)
£9282 $17450   (19-Dec-91 F.M159/R) Ortiz (31x34cm-12x13in) s.d.1952 panel (I.L 20000000)
£9394 $17003   (21-May-92 SY.AM317/R) Akos (86x81cm-34x32in) s. s.i.d.1960/89 i.verso (D.FL 31000)
£10606 $19197   (21-May-92 SY.AM323/R) Monnca (100x100cm-39x39in) s. s.i.d.1986verso (D.FL 35000)
£11173 $20000   (6-May-92 CH.NY382/R) Jell (165x160cm-65x63in) s. s.d.1968 verso acrylic canvas
£12358 $21133   (19-Mar-92 CSC.P49/R) 2759 K.S.T. (91x91cm-36x36in) s.d.1973/74 acrylic (F.FR 120000)
£14000 $25340   (5-Dec-91 C25/R) Palota (166x126cm-65x50in) s. i.d.1957verso
£14617 $25433   (14-Apr-92 F.M245/R) Pengoe - P (80x80cm-31x31in) s.d.1967 acrylic masonite (I.L 32000000)
£15000 $25800   (17-Oct-91 C57 a/R) VP-119 (260x130cm-102x51in) s. s.i.d.1971 verso acrylic canvas
£15779 $29665   (19-Dec-91 F.M216/R) Kelet (60x60cm-24x24in) s. s.i.verso panel (I.L 34000000)
£16000 $27520   (17-Oct-91 S107/R) Ion-neu (193x210cm-76x83in) s.d.1973 verso acrylic canvas
£18156 $32500   (14-Nov-91 SY.NY335/R) Sende (200x200cm-79x79in) s.d.1967 verso
£25000 $45250   (5-Dec-91 S44/R) Oeta (194x129cm-76x51in) s. s.d.1956-58 verso
£30000 $57300   (2-Jul-92 S19/R) Souzon (130x97cm-51x38in) s.i.d.1950verso
£1838   *$3124*   *(22-Oct-91 C.A322) Composition (60x45cm-24x18in) s. collage (B.FR 110000)*
£2371   *$4102*   *(23-Mar-92 CC.P31/R) Contrefonds indian ink three dr in same mount (F.FR 23000)*
£3429   *$6000*   *(25-Feb-92 SY.NY183/R) Axo-ter (40x30cm-16x12in) s. paper collage on board*
£6084   *$11316*   *(19-Jun-92 G.Z23/R) Sedul (55x47cm-22x19in) s.d.1976 s.i.d.verso collage (S.FR 16000)*

VASARI, Andrea (?) Italian
£1200 $2124   (13-Feb-92 CSK229/R) Lake Como (41x61cm-16x24in) s. i.verso

VASARI, Giorgio (1511-1574) Italian
£1200 $2184   (10-Dec-91 C121/R) Saint Francis receiving the Stigmata (13x11cm-5x4in)
     ink wash
£24000 $43680   (10-Dec-91 C120/R) God the father flanked by angels and putti
     (28x42cm-11x17in) i. blk.chk.ink wash squared paper

VASARI, Giorgio (attrib) (1511-1574) Italian
£5490 $9827   (15-Nov-91 GK.Z5110/R) The Conversion of St Paul (66x56cm-26x22in) panel
     (S.FR 14000)

VASARI, Giorgio (circle) (1511-1574) Italian
£9654 $16799   (15-Apr-92 CB.P3) Adorations des bergers (88x60cm-35x24in) panel round
     top (F.FR 95000)
£1620 $2900   (14-Jan-92 SY.NY158/R) Soldiers on horseback leaving walled town, other
     soldiers to fore (27x20cm-11x8in) bears i. pen wash over black chk htd
     white
£2500 $4350   (13-Apr-92 S277/R) Group of standing saints, primarily bishops, with
     putti above (27x25cm-11x10in) pen wash htd white top corners rounded

VASARRI, Emilio (19/20th C) Italian
£18023 $31000   (17-Oct-91 SY.NY81/R) Ladies of Pompeii (88x152cm-35x60in) s.

VASILOVSKY, Sergei Ivanovich (1854-1917) Russian
£569 $1042   (14-May-92 BU.S201/R) White house with thatched roof (21x30cm-8x12in) s.
     panel (S.KR 6000)
£1200 $2232   (16-Jun-92 S22/R) Thatched cottage in the Kharkov region (23x36cm-9x14in)
     s.i. init.verso board

VASLET, Lewis (1770-1808) British
£5000 $8800   (8-Apr-92 S46/R) Portrait of Eizabeth Maria Chevallier (42x33cm-17x13in)
£1100 $1969   (11-Nov-91 S530) Portrait of Miss Beatrice Hester Decima Syke. Miss
     Elizabeth Sykes, sister (25x20cm-10x8in) pastel oval pair

VASNETSOV, Viktor Mikhaelovich (1848-1919) Russian
£583 $1037   (29-Apr-92 D.V521/R) Girl with sledge (29x21cm-11x8in) s.d.1891 chk
     (A.S 12000)

VASQUEZ DIAZ, Daniel (1882-1969) Spanish
£51335 $92402   (22-Nov-91 PIC.P7/R) La Promenade (50x65cm-20x26in) s. (F.FR 500000)

VASQUEZ, Carlos (1869-1944) Spanish
£3320 $5678   (17-Mar-92 FER.M144/R) Alegoria de la Guerra Civil (200x130cm-79x51in) s.
     (S.P 600000)
£465 $847   (11-Dec-91 FER.M7/R) Tertulia de damas al borde del mar (44x33cm-17x13in)
     s. chl dr (S.P 85000)

VASSILIEFF, Danila (1899-1958) Australian
£2660 $4707   (26-Apr-92 SY.ME467) White victory (44x56cm-17x22in) s. board (A.D 6250)
£5066 $9119   (24-Nov-91 SY.S455/R) Gossiping on corner (42x44cm-17x17in) s. i.d.1949
     verso board (A.D 11500)
£513 $913   (28-Apr-92 CH.ME114) Blue eyes (34x26cm-13x10in) W/C (A.D 1200)
£684 $1217   (28-Apr-92 CH.ME13) Landscape of yellow field (26x40cm-10x16in) gouache
     (A.D 1600)

VASSILIEFF, Marie (1894-1955) Russian
£407 $745   (13-May-92 LC.P31) La coquette (27x21cm-11x8in) studio st. chl
     (F.FR 4000)
£763 $1396   (13-May-92 LC.P30/R) Le modele a la poitrine nue (29x22cm-11x9in) studio
     st. chl (F.FR 7500)
£1220 $2122   (14-Apr-92 ZZ.F66/R) Danseuse aux quatre visages (45x30cm-18x12in) s. W/C
     (F.FR 12000)

VASSILIEFF, Pjotr (1909-) Russian
£676 $1217   (27-Jan-92 ARC.P189/R) Promenade a Venise (47x68cm-19x27in) s.verso
     (F.FR 6600)

VASSILIEV, Ivan (1930-) Russian
£509 $932   (3-Jun-92 ARC.P161/R) Le paysage d'hiver (40x54cm-16x21in) s. (F.FR 5000)
£515 $881   (13-Mar-92 ARC.P7/R) La petite cour (57x28cm-22x31in) s. (F.FR 5000)
£560 $1025   (3-Jun-92 ARC.P162/R) Le cirque de St.Petersbourg (43x52cm-17x20in) s.
     (F.FR 5500)
£567 $970   (13-Mar-92 ARC.P4/R) Pres du jardin d'ete (41x59cm-16x23in) s.
     (F.FR 5500)
£605 $1058   (24-Sep-91 ARC.P209/R) Rue animee, St Petersbourg (42x60cm-17x24in) s.
     (F.FR 6000)
£670 $1146   (13-Mar-92 ARC.P5/R) Sur la Fontanka (41x58cm-16x23in) s. (F.FR 6500)
£692 $1267   (3-Jun-92 ARC.P160/R) L'ile Vassilievski (46x52cm-18x20in) s. (F.FR 6800)
£713 $1304   (3-Jun-92 ARC.P158/R) Village lacustre (35x42cm-14x17in) s. (F.FR 7000)
£728 $1275   (5-Apr-92 ARC.P2/R) L'eglise de St Pantaleon (44x50cm-17x20in) s.
     (F.FR 7000)
£733 $1342   (3-Jun-92 ARC.P159/R) La Fontanka (41x58cm-16x23in) s. (F.FR 7200)
£770 $1348   (5-Apr-92 ARC.P3/R) La Neva enhiver (40x58cm-16x23in) s. (F.FR 7400)

VASSILIEV, Ivan (1930-) Russian-cont.
£773	$1322	(13-Mar-92 ARC.P8) Les fleurs d'Ukraine (79x50cm-31x20in) s. (F.FR 7500)
£832	$1457	(5-Apr-92 ARC.P4) Le petit parc, St Petersbourg (43x52cm-17x20in) s. (F.FR 8000)
£957	$1675	(5-Apr-92 ARC.P5/R) La rive de Fontanka (41x53cm-16x21in) s.verso (F.FR 9200)
£1041	$1821	(5-Apr-92 ARC.P7/R) La riviere Karpovka (41x50cm-16x20in) s. (F.FR 10000)
£1602	$2804	(5-Apr-92 ARC.P6/R) Vue de la Fontanka (41x59cm-16x23in) s. (F.FR 15400)

VASSINE, Viktor (1919-) Russian
£527	$954	(20-May-92 ARC.P50/R) Vue du balcon (118x98cm-46x39in) s. (F.FR 5200)
£659	$1192	(20-May-92 ARC.P48) Au bord du canal (60x80cm-24x31in) s. (F.FR 6500)
£711	$1238	(13-Apr-92 ARC.P69/R) Une journee ensoleilee (89x64cm-35x25in) s. (F.FR 7000)
£894	$1556	(13-Apr-92 ARC.P68) Les fleurs du jardin (74x98cm-29x39in) s. (F.FR 8800)
£915	$1591	(13-Apr-92 ARC.P70/R) Macha et ses nouveaux livres (133x94cm-52x37in) s. (F.FR 9000)
£917	$1706	(17-Jun-92 ARC.P78/R) Le carroussel (36x69cm-14x27in) s. board (F.FR 9000)
£968	$1801	(17-Jun-92 ARC.P82/R) La terrasse (70x98cm-28x39in) s. (F.FR 9500)
£1013	$1834	(20-May-92 ARC.P47/R) Le remorqueur a quai (69x89cm-27x35in) s. (F.FR 10000)
£1016	$1768	(13-Apr-92 ARC.P67/R) Matine de fete (94x133cm-37x52in) s. (F.FR 10000)
£1169	$2034	(13-Apr-92 ARC.P15/R) Au bord du canal (77x90cm-30x35in) s. (F.FR 11500)
£1169	$2034	(13-Apr-92 ARC.P13/R) Derniers rayons de soleil (48x73cm-19x29in) s. (F.FR 11500)
£1223	$2275	(17-Jun-92 ARC.P81/R) Le pecheur (70x80cm-28x31in) s. (F.FR 12000)
£1244	$2313	(17-Jun-92 ARC.P83/R) La Grande Roue (98x79cm-39x31in) s. (F.FR 12200)
£1317	$2384	(20-May-92 ARC.P51/R) La marchande d'ombrelles (76x117cm-30x46in) s. (F.FR 13000)
£1372	$2387	(13-Apr-92 ARC.P16/R) L'automne au bord de la mer (59x79cm-23x31in) s. (F.FR 13500)
£1778	$3095	(13-Apr-92 ARC.P12/R) Plage de Crimee (48x73cm-19x29in) s. (F.FR 17500)
£2287	$3979	(13-Apr-92 ARC.P14/R) La table rouge (80x65cm-31x26in) s. (F.FR 22500)
£2330	$4218	(20-May-92 ARC.P46/R) Midi en Crimee (100x141cm-39x56in) s. (F.FR 23000)
£2548	$4740	(17-Jun-92 ARC.P77/R) Voiliers a Sebastopol (79x119cm-31x47in) s. (F.FR 25000)
£3040	$5502	(20-May-92 ARC.P49/R) Lilas et roses (100x110cm-39x43in) s. (F.FR 30000)
£3364	$6257	(17-Jun-92 ARC.P80/R) Les marins (110x149cm-43x59in) s. (F.FR 33000)

VASSTROM, Eric (1887-1958) Finnish?
| £492 | $875 | (1-Dec-91 HOR.H244) From Helsingfors (46x38cm-18x15in) s.d.1946 (F.M 3800) |
| £992 | $1766 | (25-Nov-91 BU.K37/R) Stalls at Helsinki market (46x55cm-18x22in) s.d.1930 (D.KR 11000) |

VASTAGH, Geza (1866-1919) Hungarian
£479	$825	(8-Oct-91 ZEL.L1761/R) Two lions (52x73cm-20x29in) s. panel (DM 1400)
£900	$1629	(21-May-92 CSK182/R) Lion (63x112cm-25x44in) s.
£1400	$2478	(13-Feb-92 CSK172) Portrait of young girl holding sunflower (136x78cm-54x31in) s.d.indist.188..
£8200	$14186	(4-Oct-91 C76 f/R) Head of lion (102x84cm-40x33in) s.d.1892
£13000	$22490	(4-Oct-91 C93/R) Portrait of boy seated on sofa draped with lion skin (150x84cm-59x33in) s.d.1895

VASZARY, Janos (1867-1939) Hungarian
| £1066 | $1941 | (26-May-92 D.V124/R) Strandbad (55x74cm-22x29in) s. (A.S 22000) |

VATIN, E (19th C) ?
| £1685 | $3000 | (30-Oct-91 D.NY11/R) Portrait of girl with blue ribbon in hair. Boy with ruffled collar (43x36cm-17x14in) s.d.1891 one d.1869 pastel pair oval |

VAUDOYER, Laurent Thomas (1756-1846) French
£473	$857	(6-Dec-91 ARC.P108) Etude pour un kiosque (23x14cm-9x6in) i. pierre noire (F.FR 4600)
£514	$931	(6-Dec-91 ARC.P91/R) Projet de prison (22x17cm-9x7in) i. pierre noire pen W/C (F.FR 5000)
£566	$1024	(6-Dec-91 ARC.P89/R) Arc de Triomphe (17x29cm-7x11in) i. pierre noire pen wash W/C (F.FR 5500)
£617	$1117	(6-Dec-91 ARC.P84) Projet de Laiterie (29x17cm-11x7in) i. pierre noire wash W/C (F.FR 6000)
£617	$1117	(6-Dec-91 ARC.P100) Porjet de Cathedrale (30x20cm-12x8in) i. pierre noire pen wash W/C (F.FR 6000)
£617	$1117	(6-Dec-91 ARC.P105) Projet de moument commemoratif (29x14cm-11x6in) i. pierre noire pen wash W/C (F.FR 6000)
£662	$1225	(12-Jun-92 ARC.P188) Detail de la porte du temple de Vesta a Tivoli (92x63cm-36x25in) st. pen black crayon indian ink (F.FR 6000)
£669	$1210	(6-Dec-91 ARC.P106) Projet pour un temple (28x17cm-11x7in) i. pierre noire pen wash W/C (F.FR 6500)
£874	$1583	(6-Dec-91 ARC.P218/R) Etudes de ruines antiques i. pierre noire pen wash two (F.FR 8500)
£947	$1713	(6-Dec-91 ARC.P71) Releves de baignoires antiques (29x20cm-11x8in) i. pierre noire pen wash (F.FR 9200)
£1080	$1955	(6-Dec-91 ARC.P188) Releve de ruines (26x14cm-10x6in) i. pierre noire W/C (F.FR 10500)

VAUDOYER, Laurent Thomas (1756-1846) French-cont.

£1183	$2141	(6-Dec-91 ARC.P83) Colonne Commemorative (28x20cm-11x8in) i. pierre noire pen wash W/C (F.FR 11500)
£1183	$2141	(6-Dec-91 ARC.P87) Projet pour une salle de concert (32x19cm-13x7in) i. pierre noire pen wash W/C (F.FR 11500)
£1235	$2235	(6-Dec-91 ARC.P88) Projet d'horloge (14x8cm-6x3in) pierre noire wash (F.FR 12000)
£1286	$2328	(6-Dec-91 ARC.P94/R) Projet de monument commemoratif (22x14cm-9x6in) i. pierre noire wash (F.FR 12500)
£1543	$2793	(6-Dec-91 ARC.P193) Etudes de rochers i. pierre noire W/C two (F.FR 15000)
£1852	$3352	(6-Dec-91 ARC.P95/R) Maison d'un cosmopolite (31x19cm-12x7in) pierre noire pen indian ink (F.FR 18000)
£1955	$3538	(6-Dec-91 ARC.P49 a) Releve d'un plan de Palais Romain (18x25cm-7x10in) i. pierre noire (F.FR 19000)
£1955	$3538	(6-Dec-91 ARC.P86/R) Projet de decoration d'une facade (18x23cm-7x9in) i. pierre noire wash (F.FR 19000)
£2521	$4562	(6-Dec-91 ARC.P93/R) Colombier avec laiterie en dessous (27x18cm-11x7in) i. pierrre noire wash W/C (F.FR 24500)
£2778	$5028	(6-Dec-91 ARC.P75) Medaille i. pierre noire pen wash two (F.FR 27000)

VAUDOYER, Leon (1803-1872) French

| £494 | $894 | (6-Dec-91 ARC.P238) Projet pour une place des victoires a Paris (77x48cm-30x19in) d.27 bJuillet 1825 crayon pen W/C (F.FR 4800) |

VAUGHAN, Keith (1912-) British

£600	$1044	(19-Sep-91 CSK197) Tree figure (29x20cm-11x8in) panel
£600	$1044	(19-Sep-91 CSK201/R) Lovers (28x21cm-11x8in) studio st.verso pencil
£650	$1131	(19-Sep-91 CSK262) Green and red landscape with figure (29x20cm-11x8in) board
£2600	$4680	(20-Nov-91 S50/R) Green landscape with buildings (46x39cm-18x15in) board
£3600	$6480	(20-Nov-91 S23/R) Figures in green and orange (27x37cm-11x15in) s.d.48 board
£3800	$6840	(20-Nov-91 S49/R) High Easter (61x51cm-24x20in) s.i.d.1972 verso
£4500	$8100	(20-Nov-91 S44/R) Two figures by water (44x39cm-17x15in) board
£6200	$11160	(20-Nov-91 S24/R) Figures by sea (39x46cm-15x18in) canvas on board
£6500	$11700	(20-Nov-91 S51/R) Horizontal figure (102x122cm-40x48in) s. init.d.1968 verso
£7000	$12600	(20-Nov-91 S57/R) Standing figure (122x102cm-48x40in) s.i.d.1970/72 verso
£7000	$12950	(11-Jun-92 C10/R) Black Purbeck landscape (117x86cm-46x34in) s.i.d.1964 verso
£8000	$14400	(20-Nov-91 S52/R) Ganemede (127x102cm-50x40in) s.i.d.1962 verso
£8500	$15045	(8-Nov-91 C291/R) Garden (102x91cm-40x36in) s.i.d.1975verso
£10500	$18900	(20-Nov-91 S53/R) High Easter (102x91cm-40x36in) s.i.d.1967 verso
£11000	$19800	(20-Nov-91 S54/R) Group of figures (102x91cm-40x36in) s.i.d.1964 verso
£12000	$21600	(20-Nov-91 S47/R) Farm in Sussex (93x172cm-37x68in) board
£17000	$30600	(20-Nov-91 S55/R) Sixth assembly of figures (114x127cm-45x50in) s.i.d.1962 verso
£480	$902	(18-Dec-91 C184/R) Reclining figure (18x15cm-7x6in) s.d.65 gouache col.crayons
£800	$1376	(5-Mar-92 CSK179/R) November landscape (14x18cm-6x7in) s. W/C bodycol
£900	$1647	(14-May-92 C49/R) Burning fields (47x38cm-19x15in) gouache
£950	$1682	(8-Nov-91 C230) Green and blue landscape (28x35cm-11x14in) s.d.58 pencil gouache
£1200	$2196	(14-May-92 C10/R) Self-portrait (53x35cm-21x14in) i.d.1932 black crayon htd white
£1200	$2160	(20-Nov-91 S10/R) Man and fossils (12x19cm-5x7in) i.d.1942 studio st. pen wash
£1800	$3240	(20-Nov-91 S33/R) Slade studies - No.12 - hooded figure. No.7, figure nolding object (13x10cm-5x4in) two s.d.63 pencil gouache crayon W/C four
£1900	$3420	(20-Nov-91 S34/R) Slade studies - No.8. Landscape with figures. No.27, group figures (14x10cm-6x4in) s.i.d. pencil gouache crayon three
£1900	$3420	(20-Nov-91 S32/R) Figure (66x57cm-26x22in) i.d.1960 verso black chk
£2000	$3600	(20-Nov-91 S12/R) Figure studies. Reclining nude. Model. Double portrait study. Two boys (13x28cm-5x11in) two s.d. i.d. d. pencil pen W/C gouache five
£2000	$3600	(20-Nov-91 S38) Figures stretching and sitting (34x28cm-13x11in) one s.d.69 one s.d.70 gouache wax resist pair
£2000	$3600	(20-Nov-91 S21/R) Studies (29x23cm-11x9in) studio st. i.verso pencil four
£2100	$3780	(20-Nov-91 S11/R) Two figures by shore (18x13cm-7x5in) with studio st. s.i.verso pen wash htd white
£2200	$3894	(8-Nov-91 C204/R) Foreshore with three figures (14x17cm-6x7in) s.d.52 gouache brush ink
£2200	$3960	(20-Nov-91 S17/R) Portrait of young man. Self-portrait (19x14cm-7x6in) s.d.42 i.d.1942 pen W/C wax resist pencil four
£3200	$5664	(5-Nov-91 PH40/R) Oyster fishermen 2 (27x37cm-11x15in) s.d.48 i.verso gouache Indian ink
£3200	$5760	(20-Nov-91 S37/R) Group of figures and bathers under moon (52x41cm-20x16in) gouache crayon pair
£3500	$6300	(20-Nov-91 S19/R) Blast furnace series (30x23cm-12x9in) s. one d.50 pen W/C col.chk htd gouache three
£4800	$8640	(20-Nov-91 S13/R) Figure studies, including standing figures, boys, nude with hand on hip. (24x17cm-9x7in) s.d. s.i.d. pen W/C gouache pastel pencil ten

VAUGHAN, Keith (1912-) British-cont.
£40000 $72000   (20-Nov-91 S35/R) Erotic fantasies (46x40cm-18x16in) i. gouache board
                    fifty-two sheets

VAUTHIER, Pierre (1845-1916) French
£1815 $3212   (10-Nov-91 ZZ.F112/R) Bord de riviere (48x65cm-19x26in) s. (F.FR 18000)

VAUTHRIN, Ernest Germain (20th C) French
£1137 $1933   (23-Oct-91 GD.B1315/R) Rochefort sur Mer with shipping (46x55cm-18x22in)
                    s. (S.FR 2900)
£1180 $2160   (17-May-92 T.B360/R) Thoniers et barques sous voiles en Bretagne
                    (46x100cm-18x39in) s.d.1942 (F.FR 11600)

VAUTIER, Ben see BEN

VAUTIER, Benjamin (19/20th C) German/Swiss
£811 $1467   (20-May-92 FB.P51) Bla bla bla je t'aime bla (60x120cm-24x47in) acrylic
                    canvas (F.FR 8000)
£4024 $6922   (12-Oct-91 GL.P54/R) Vie (73x92cm-29x36in) s.i.d.1964verso (F.FR 40000)
£7904 $13753   (18-Sep-91 N.M736/R) Brother and sister eating on bench with dog jumping
                    up (35x33cm-14x13in) s.d.1894 (DM 23000)
£9400 $17203   (4-Jun-92 SY.Z348/R) Peasants playing cards in pub during mass caught by
                    their wives (61x86cm-24x34in) s.d.62 canvas on pavatex (S.FR 25005)
£11278 $20639   (4-Jun-92 SY.Z347/R) Peasant women conversing in interior
                    (53x66cm-21x26in) s.d.94 (S.FR 30000)
£493 $892   (4-Dec-91 DO.H2960) Two Black Forest girls (14x9cm-6x4in) s. W/C over
                    pencil (DM 1400)
£853 $1544   (21-May-92 L.K345/R) Happy family (23x18cm-9x7in) mono pencil htd.white
                    (DM 2500)
£1712 $2910   (24-Oct-91 CSC.P50/R) Art (40x40cm-16x16in) s. mixed media panel
                    (F.FR 17000)

VAUTIER, Benjamin (elder) (1829-1898) German
£2964 $5277   (29-Nov-91 GAB.G2181/R) Les paysannes au coin du feu (52x43cm-20x17in)
                    s.d.1885 (S.FR 7500)

VAUTIER, J C (19/20th C) ?
£524 $1000   (3-Jul-92 S.W2747/R) Baghdad (25x36cm-10x14in) s.

VAUTIER, Otto (1863-1919) Swiss
£1020 $1825   (15-Nov-91 GK.Z5359) Young woman seated at morning toilet
                    (55x38cm-22x15in) s. (S.FR 2600)
£3137 $5333   (23-Oct-91 GD.B765/R) Jeune fille au violon (70x92cm-28x36in) s.
                    (S.FR 8000)
£870 $1548   (29-Nov-91 GAB.G2182/R) Couple d'amoureux (72x55cm-28x22in) s.
                    (S.FR 2200)
£941 $1600   (23-Oct-91 GD.B769/R) Standing nude (62x32cm-24x13in) s. gouache
                    (S.FR 2400)

VAUZATTE (19th C) French?
£2158 $4122   (1-Jul-92 FB.P32/R) Reunion au Chateau de Roucy (32x41cm-13x16in) gouache
                    (F.FR 21000)

VAUZELLE, Jean Lubin (1776-?) French
£1540 $2772   (21-Nov-91 BL.P20/R) Vue d'une ville d'Espagne (26x39cm-10x15in) s. pen
                    W/C (F.FR 15000)
£2400 $4368   (10-Dec-91 C218/R) The Palais Jacques Coeur, Bourges (30x44cm-12x17in) s.
                    blk.chk.ink W/C

VAVRA, Frank (1898-1967) American
£1117 $2000   (13-Nov-91 B.SF2736/R) Aspen (91x76cm-36x30in) s.

VAZ, Oscar (1909-1987) Argentinian
£661 $1150   (19-Sep-91 V.BA109) Ocre gris (26x32cm-10x13in)
£894 $1600   (6-May-92 V.BA111) Bruma boquense (28x33cm-11x13in)
£917 $1650   (20-Nov-91 V.BA108) Barcos (26x32cm-10x13in) d.1961
£989 $1800   (11-Dec-91 RO.BA443) Ribera Marplatense (60x50cm-24x20in) s. s.i.verso
£1075 $2000   (16-Jun-92 RO.BA91) Barcazas (31x45cm-12x18in)
£1149 $2000   (19-Sep-91 V.BA107) Ocaso (40x50cm-16x20in)
£1341 $2400   (6-May-92 V.BA109) Grises del rio (40x50cm-16x20in)
£1344 $2500   (16-Jun-92 RO.BA90) Manana de sol (32x45cm-13x18in) panel
£1685 $3000   (1-Nov-91 PO.BA65) El patron de la lancha (67x77cm-26x30in) s.
£1686 $2900   (9-Oct-91 RO.BA580) Placidez (50x60cm-20x24in) s.d.56
£2299 $4000   (19-Sep-91 V.BA108/R) Atardecer en Barracas (70x80cm-28x31in)
£2500 $4500   (20-Nov-91 V.BA109/R) Barca del Delta (70x90cm-28x35in) d.1962
£3495 $6500   (16-Jun-92 RO.BA73) Puerto (60x80cm-24x31in)
£3837 $6600   (9-Oct-91 RO.BA398) Niebla del Riachuelo (67x77cm-26x30in) s.d.53
£4167 $8000   (4-Aug-92 V.BA112/R) Descarga de la madera (70x90cm-28x35in)

VAZINE, Dimitri (1917-) Russian
£528 $920   (13-Apr-92 ARC.P39) Le square en hiver (44x78cm-17x31in) s. (F.FR 5200)
£1067 $1857   (13-Apr-92 ARC.P36/R) Pierre Le Grand sur le chantier de St Petersbourg
                    (50x98cm-20x39in) s. (F.FR 10500)

VAZQUEZ DIAZ, Daniel (1881-1969) Spanish
£816 $1452   (28-Apr-92 DUR.M574/R) Dos figuras (31x22cm-12x9in) s.d.1929 pencil dr
        (S.P 150000)

VAZQUEZ, Antonio (c.1485-1563) Spanish
£42000 $76440   (29-May-92 C310/R) Christ on the Cross embracing St Bernard with Sts
        Sebastian and others (187x169cm-74x67in) oil gold panel painted arched
        tops altar piece

VECCHIA, Pietro della (1605-1678) Italian
£5424 $9818   (18-May-92 SY.MI288/R) Un filosofo (109x90cm-43x35in) (I.L 12000000)
£6485 $11737   (21-May-92 L.K100/R) Two philosophers conversing (46x37cm-18x15in)
        (DM 19000)
£23204 $42000   (21-May-92 CH.NY27/R) Feast of Esther (81x141cm-32x56in)

VECCHIA, Pietro della (attrib) (1605-1678) Italian
£1453 $2500   (9-Oct-91 CH.NY166/R) High Priest holding censor and book
        (76x62cm-30x24in)
£2033 $3537   (13-Apr-92 AT.P39/R) La lecon d'arithmetique (40x52cm-16x20in)
        (F.FR 20000)
£2337 $4276   (2-Jun-92 FN.S2676/R) St Hieronymus in hermitage and view of hilly
        landscape (26x41cm-10x16in) panel (DM 6800)

VECELLIO, Francesco (attrib) (1483-1559) Italian
£10497 $19000   (22-May-92 SY.NY11/R) Flight into Egypt (77x90cm-30x35in)

VECELLIO, Orazio (attrib) (1525-1576) Italian
£3680 $6992   (23-Jun-92 D.V208/R) Portrait of gentleman, possibly Sebastiano Venier
        who defeated the Turks (105x78cm-41x31in) (A.S 75000)
£16000 $28000   (1-Apr-92 S38/R) Madonna and child with infant Saint John the Baptist in
        landscape (52x71cm-20x28in)

VEDDER, Elihu (1836-1923) American
£914 $1600   (26-Sep-91 CH.NY64/R) Labyrinth (16x22cm-6x9in) init. chl pastel paper on
        board

VEDEL, Herman (1875-1948) Danish
£993 $1768   (28-Nov-91 D.V72/R) Two experienced women (42x49cm-17x19in) mono.d.1907
        (A.S 20000)

VEDOVA, Emilio (1919-) Italian
£2098 $3734   (25-Nov-91 WK.M1051/R) Composition (25x34cm-10x13in) s.d.1951 indian ink
        W/C (DM 6000)
£5200 $8944   (17-Oct-91 S39/R) Untitled (34x48cm-13x19in) s.d.1953 ink gouache
£8599 $15651   (25-May-92 CH.R82/R) Senza titolo (28x41cm-11x16in) s.verso mixed media
        (I.L 19000000)
£22699 $40404   (29-Apr-92 F.F279/R) Il pescatore (130x60cm-51x24in) d.1946 paper collage
        on panel (I.L 50000000)

VEEN, Otto van (attrib) (1556-1629) Flemish
£2907 $5000   (10-Oct-91 SY.NY175/R) Madonna and child with Joseph, the infant St John
        Baptist and an angel (21x16cm-8x6in) panel

VEEN, Otto van (circle) (1556-1629) Flemish
£800 $1400   (31-Mar-92 PH51/R) Head of Christ (53x43cm-21x17in) panel
£4500 $8640   (10-Jul-92 C158/R) Crucifixion (107x76cm-42x30in) panel

VEEN, Otto van (style) (1556-1629) Flemish
£1235 $2210   (14-Nov-91 CH.AM79) Adoration of the Shepherds (135x193cm-53x76in) i.
        (D.FL 4000)
£1900 $3325   (28-Feb-92 C50) The Virgin and Child (76x64cm-30x25in) oval

VEEN, Pieter van (circle) (1610-1662) Dutch
£2900 $5568   (7-Jul-92 PH226/R) Ceres and Proserpine feted by putti (84x140cm-33x55in)

VEEN, Rochus van (?-1706) Dutch
£1916 $3488   (12-Dec-91 L.K485/R) Dead song birds (11x18cm-4x7in) W/C set of four
        (DM 5500)

VEERENDAEL, Nicolaes van see   VERENDAEL, Nicolas van

VEGA Y MUNOZ, Pedro de (1840-1868) Spanish
£600 $1026   (17-Mar-92 PH211) The flower seller (45x30cm-18x12in) s. W/C

VEGA, Jorge de la (1930-1971) Argentinian
£7778 $14000   (19-Nov-91 CH.NY147/R) Los ritos (146x114cm-57x45in) s.d.61 s.d.verso
        s.i.d.stretcher

VEILLON, Auguste-Louis (1834-1890) Swiss
£2734 $4840   (5-Nov-91 GF.L2261/R) Monch and Jungfrau (40x65cm-16x26in) s. (S.FR 7000)

VEIT, Johannes (1790-1854) German
£524 $907   (25-Mar-92 KM.K1701/R) Portrait of girl wearing hair in plaited bun
        (8x6cm-3x2in) min.s. W/C (DM 1500)

VEITER, Josef (attrib) (1819-1902) Austrian
£736 $1398   (25-Jun-92 D.V499/R) Mountain village with smithy (48x63cm-19x25in)
                 (A.S 15000)

VEITH, Eduard (1856-1925) Austrian
£1900 $3382   (26-Nov-91 PH146/R) The hunter's favourite (18x24cm-7x9in) s. panel
£2200 $3916   (27-Nov-91 S118/R) Allegory of Plenty (140x169cm-55x67in) s.i.
£10000 $18600   (17-Jun-92 S402/R) Violet procession on Kahlenberg (134x150cm-53x59in)
                 s.i.

VELA ZANETTI, Jose (20th C) Spanish
£2463 $4483   (26-May-92 DUR.M71/R) Gavilla (65x81cm-26x32in) s.d.72 (S.P 450000)

VELASCO, Jose Maria (1840-1912) Mexican
£276243 $500000   (18-May-92 CH.NY9/R) Valle de Mexico (43x61cm-17x24in) s.d.1887
£1222222 $2200000   (18-Nov-91 SY.NY7/R) Valle de Mexico (76x106cm-30x42in) s.d.1888
£4696 $8500   (18-May-92 CH.NY120/R) Estudio de Pies (32x49cm-13x19in) s.d.1864 chl
                      pencil

VELASCO, Luis de (circle) (?-1606) Spanish
£4200 $7644   (29-May-92 C305/R) The Visitation (66x51cm-26x20in) panel

VELASQUEZ (after) (17th C) Spanish
£1045 $1860   (25-Nov-91 W.T2051) L'infanta Margherita (10x8cm-4x3in) paper (C.D 2100)

VELASQUEZ, Diego Rodriguez de Silva y (after) (1599-1660) Spanish
£765 $1400   (3-Jun-92 D.NY82) Pope Innocent X (61x76cm-24x30in) oval
£12291 $22000   (16-Jan-92 CH.NY115/R) Portrait of artist (78x57cm-31x22in)

VELASQUEZ, Diego Rodriguez de Silva y (circle) (1599-1660) Spanish
£28000 $50960   (29-May-92 C321/R) Portrait of Juan de Pareja (82x70cm-32x28in)

VELASQUEZ, Diego Rodriguez de Silva y (style) (1599-1660) Spanish
£1573 $2800   (22-Jan-92 SY.NY177/R) Infanta Margarita (42x33cm-17x13in) panel
£5376 $10000   (19-Jun-92 S.BM218/R) Portrait of lady of court (196x107cm-77x42in)

VELASQUEZ, Jose Antonio (1906-) South American
£1714 $3000   (28-Feb-92 SY.NY250/R) Iglesia (54x69cm-21x27in) s.d.1958

VELAY, Amedee Joseph (19th C) French
£859 $1495   (18-Sep-91 N.M737/R) Old mill by waterfall (37x35cm-15x14in) s. (DM 2500)

VELAZQUEZ (after) (?) Spanish
£899 $1600   (22-Jan-92 D.NY9) Portrait of Spanish nobleman (18x13cm-7x5in) i.verso
                 panel
£1300 $2275   (3-Apr-92 C99) Equestrian portrait of Don Balthasar Carlos as boy
                 (42x34cm-17x13in) canvas on board
£2000 $3560   (1-Nov-91 S365/R) Portrait of Infanta Maria Theresa of Spain
                 (73x60cm-29x24in)

VELAZQUEZ, Eugenio Lucas (1817-1870) Spanish
£1091 $1975   (20-May-92 ANS.M70/R) Retrato de dama (47x33cm-19x13in) (S.P 200000)
£2969 $5225   (9-Apr-92 ANS.M137/R) El regreso de la pesca (13x20cm-5x8in) board on
                 panel (S.P 540000)
£4379 $7969   (26-May-92 DUR.M87/R) Huyendo (75x48cm-30x19in) indist.s. (S.P 800000)
£7500 $13650   (29-May-92 C356/R) Bull fight (24x34cm-9x13in) paper
£8208 $15595   (23-Jun-92 DUR.M30/R) La familia del pescador (46x37cm-18x15in)
                 (S.P 1500000)
£10953 $20920   (2-Jul-92 ANS.M117/R) El entierro del Quijote (30x44cm-12x17in) s.
                 (S.P 2000000)
£13216 $23656   (14-Nov-91 ANS.M77/R) Acampada (30x42cm-12x17in) tin (S.P 2400000)
£553 $984   (21-Jan-92 DUR.M127/R) Madre e hija (25x28cm-10x11in) W/C (S.P 100000)
£873 $1502   (16-Oct-91 FER.M100/R) Reunion de los mayores (18x20cm-7x8in) s.d.1862
                 W/C (S.P 160000)
£1040 $1892   (11-Dec-91 FER.M137/R) Interior de una catedral (19x13cm-7x5in) s. W/C
                 (S.P 190000)

VELDE, Adriaen van de (1636-1672) Dutch
£5000 $8750   (1-Apr-92 S155/R) Shepherd and shepherdess with animals in classical
                 landscape (50x38cm-20x15in)
£9317 $16584   (25-Nov-91 CH.AM80/R) Study of reclining nude (17x27cm-7x11in) chk
                 (D.FL 30000)

VELDE, Adriaen van de (attrib) (1636-1672) Dutch
£13408 $24000   (17-Jan-92 SY.NY30 a/R) Wooded landscape with a watermill and two figures
                 (53x41cm-21x16in) panel

VELDE, Adriaen van de (circle) (1636-1672) Dutch
£1500 $2700   (21-Nov-91 C30) Wooded landscape with peasant mother seated by tree and
                 cattle watering (21x28cm-8x11in) panel
£2778 $5028   (19-May-92 GF.L2059/R) Pastoral landscape (59x72cm-23x28in) (S.FR 7500)

VELDE, Adriaen van de (style) (1636-1672) Dutch
£846 $1514   (7-May-92 CH.AM63) Shepherd boy with sheep, goats and cattle by pond,
                 Italianate landscape (35x44cm-14x17in) panel (D.FL 2800)

VELDE, Adriaen van de (style) (1636-1672) Dutch-cont.
£1500	$2625	(27-Feb-92 B76/R) Shepherdess and her lover with sheep and cattle in a wooded landscape (35x41cm-14x16in)
£3040	$5562	(12-May-92 SY.AM127/R) Travellers in winter landscape (40x45cm-16x18in) (D.FL 10000)

VELDE, Bram van (1895-1981) Dutch
£1235	$2247	(11-Dec-91 CH.AM312/R) Longinus piercing the side of Christ (73x54cm-29x21in) (D.FL 4000)
£3333	$6033	(19-May-92 CH.AM201/R) Still life of flowers in stoneware pot (90x65cm-35x26in) s. (D.FL 11000)
£25915	$45091	(15-Apr-92 PLF.P113/R) Nature morte (73x92cm-29x36in) s. (F.FR 255000)
£14815	*$26963*	*(11-Dec-91 CH.AM321/R) Untitled (63x48cm-25x19in) gouache (D.FL 48000)*
£21127	*$36338*	*(12-Oct-91 GL.P20/R) Sans titre (90x56cm-35x22in) gouache paper laid down on canvas (F.FR 210000)*
£91650	*$169552*	*(12-Jun-92 AT.P41/R) Composition (117x124cm-46x49in) gouache paper laid down on canvas (F.FR 900000)*

VELDE, Esaias van de (1587-1630) Dutch
£3704	$6630	(14-Nov-91 CH.AM107/R) Baptism of the Eunuch (13x19cm-5x7in) indis.s. panel (D.FL 12000)
£10929	$18689	(18-Mar-92 D.V85/R) Wooded landscape with two riders (48x64cm-19x25in) panel (A.S 220000)
£17869	$31093	(17-Sep-91 FN.S2589/R) Skirmish in dune landscape. Shepherds and cattle near gallows (14cm-6ins circular) s.d.1625 panel pair (DM 52000)
£95000	$182400	(10-Jul-92 C1/R) Wooded landscape with cottage by bridge and travellers on track (33x49cm-13x19in) s.d.1624 panel
£3500	*$6720*	*(6-Jul-92 S63/R) Village street in the dunes with cart (20x31cm-8x12in) s.d.1628 chk wash*
£25309	*$45302*	*(12-Nov-91 SY.AM283/R) Village in winter (18x30cm-7x12in) s.d.1628 chk wash htd.white (D.FL 82000)*

VELDE, Geer van (1898-) Dutch
£8642	$15728	(11-Dec-91 CH.AM319/R) Abstract composition (28x53cm-11x21in) init. (D.FL 28000)
£9091	$16455	(19-May-92 CH.AM241/R) Le Musicien (83x32cm-33x13in) init. (D.FL 30000)
£11561	$20000	(2-Oct-91 SY.NY33/R) Woman with vase of flowers (46x38cm-18x15in) init.
£12121	$21939	(19-May-92 CH.AM250/R) Abstract Composition (50x50cm-20x20in) init. (D.FL 40000)
£13238	$24094	(11-Dec-91 ZZ.F135/R) Trois personnages a l'interieur bleu (81x100cm-32x39in) s. (F.FR 130000)
£13918	$24077	(29-Mar-92 P.V28/R) Composition (80x48cm-31x19in) mono. (F.FR 135000)
£22636	$38934	(12-Oct-91 GL.P28/R) Composition (100x80cm-39x31in) s. (F.FR 225000)
£29321	$53364	(12-Dec-91 SY.AM206/R) Interieur-exterieur 1950 (100x100cm-39x39in) init. s.d.50 verso (D.FL 95000)
£32193	$55372	(12-Oct-91 GL.P30/R) Gouter sur la terrasse (80x100cm-31x39in) s. (F.FR 320000)
£1223	*$2275*	*(15-Jun-92 GL.P4/R) Personnage dans un interieur (17x17cm-7x7in) init. gouache (F.FR 12000)*
£2160	*$3932*	*(11-Dec-91 CH.AM439/R) Interior with girl at table (14x18cm-6x7in) pen gouache (D.FL 7000)*
£3636	*$6582*	*(19-May-92 CH.AM205/R) Abstract composition (27x20cm-11x8in) init. gouache (D.FL 12000)*
£3831	*$6627*	*(4-Oct-91 CSC.P22/R) Composition (32x27cm-13x11in) mono. W/C (F.FR 38000)*
£3939	*$7130*	*(19-May-92 CH.AM249/R) Le peintre (25x21cm-10x8in) init. gouache (D.FL 13000)*

VELDE, Hanny Vander (1883-?) American
£471	$900	(17-Jul-92 DM.D45/R) Still life with flowers (76x91cm-30x36in) s.

VELDE, Jan van de II (c.1593-1641) Dutch
£11801	*$21006*	*(25-Nov-91 CH.AM120/R) Road leading through village with swineherd resting by cross (18x31cm-7x12in) i. pen wash (D.FL 38000)*
£24224	*$43118*	*(25-Nov-91 CH.AM119/R) Ruined tower by bridge over river near town (14x41cm-6x16in) pen W/C (D.FL 78000)*

VELDE, Pieter van de (1634-1687) Flemish
£4500	$8100	(21-Nov-91 C5/R) Dutch wydschip off jetty in calm. Dutch man-of-war firing salute off fort (14x22cm-6x9in) one init. panel pair
£7202	$13683	(26-Jun-92 AT.P27/R) Galere ottomane sortant d'un port (83x121cm-33x48in) (F.FR 70000)
£12041	$20831	(25-Mar-92 CH.R83/R) Porto con velieri e dignitari cinesi in una scialuppa (97x133cm-38x52in) s.d. (I.L 26000000)

VELDE, Pieter van de (attrib) (1634-1687) Flemish
£1769	$3096	(1-Apr-92 CSC.P9) Navires par gros temps (20x28cm-8x11in) mono. (F.FR 17000)
£2422	$4602	(24-Jun-92 KM.K971/R) Seascape with battle scene (46x62cm-18x24in) (DM 7000)

VELDE, Pieter van de (style) (1634-1687) Flemish
£2000	$3500	(28-Feb-92 C28) Shipping in breezy weather offshore (26x36cm-10x14in) panel

VELDE, Willem van de (elder) (1611-1693) Dutch

£2174	$3870	(25-Nov-91 CH.AM156/R) Study of ship (22x25cm-9x10in) lead wash (D.FL 7000)
£2329	$4146	(25-Nov-91 CH.AM158/R) Eendracht and other Dutch men-o-war setting sail (25x56cm-10x22in) i. chk wash partly made up (D.FL 7500)
£2329	$4146	(25-Nov-91 CH.AM159/R) Dutch men-o-war at sea in calm and two yachts (23x40cm-9x16in) lead wash two joined sheets (D.FL 7500)
£75000	$136500	(13-Dec-91 C26/R) Zeeland man-of-war in calm off jetty (69x91cm-27x36in) init. panel

VELDE, Willem van de (school) (17/18th C) Dutch

£4842	$8134	(27-Aug-91 RAS.K198/R) Naval battle between English and Dutch fleet (87x120cm-34x47in) panel (D.KR 55000)

VELDE, Willem van de (younger) (1633-1707) Dutch

£864	$1547	(12-Nov-91 SY.AM334) Shipping off the coast with town on the horizon (9x32cm-4x13in) chk wash (D.FL 2800)
£894	$1600	(15-Jan-92 CH.NY153/R) English two-decker preparing to anchor (22x34cm-9x13in) with i. black lead
£1350	$2592	(8-Jul-92 PH73/R) Figures watching fleet of boats from shore (22x42cm-9x17in) W/C over black chk
£3400	$6086	(11-Nov-91 S657/R) Dutch fleet at sea (25x46cm-10x18in) wash over black chk
£3416	$6081	(25-Nov-91 CH.AM160/R) Dutch men-o-war at sea in calm (10x46cm-4x18in) init.i. lead wash two joined sheets (D.FL 11000)
£3727	$6634	(25-Nov-91 CH.AM161/R) Dutch men-o-war at sea (20x47cm-8x19in) i. lead wash (D.FL 12000)
£7821	$14000	(15-Jan-92 CH.NY151/R) Fleet of ships (23x83cm-9x33in) black chk pen wash

VELDE, Willem van de (younger-after) (1633-1707) Dutch

£1250	$2400	(10-Jul-92 C102) Dutch shipping offshore (42x56cm-17x22in)
£1852	$3315	(12-Nov-91 SY.AM67/R) Sketch of burning of the Royal James at the Battle of Solebay (28x45cm-11x18in) i. (D.FL 6000)

VELDE, Willem van de (younger-style) (1633-1707) Dutch

£880	$1531	(13-Sep-91 C103) Ships foundering offshore in storm (99x111cm-39x44in)
£1500	$2700	(21-Nov-91 CSK160) Man-o-war firing salute in calm (167x192cm-66x76in)
£1638	$2833	(28-Mar-92 UA.U405/R) Naval engagement off Chatham 1666 (42x65cm-17x26in) panel (S.KR 17000)
£2870	$5137	(7-May-92 CH.AM66/R) Calm amd storm - English men-o'-war at anchor in estuary and in gale (20cm-8ins circular) panel pair (D.FL 9500)
£8025	$14364	(14-Nov-91 CH.AM134/R) Smalship and other shipping in choppy seas (48x42cm-19x17in) (D.FL 26000)

VELDE, van de (17th C) Dutch

£833	$1600	(30-Jul-92 E.EDM352/R) Dutch shipping near shore (36x48cm-14x19in) i. panel

VELDEN, Petrus van der (1837-1915) Dutch

£1031	$1722	(21-Aug-91 DS.W56/R) Man chopping (73x50cm-29x20in) chl (NZ.D 3000)

VELICKOVIC, Vladimir (1935-) Yugoslavian

£6890	$12470	(20-May-92 FB.P29 a) L'Orateur no.2 (250x170cm-98x67in) s.d.1968 (F.FR 68000)
£8551	$14708	(8-Oct-91 CC.P58/R) L'homme qui saute, fig.I (195x195cm-77x77in) s.i.d.1974 verso (F.FR 85000)
£915	$1591	(13-Apr-92 GL.P99/R) Le marcheur (76x56cm-30x22in) s.d.20/12/1978 Indian ink (F.FR 9000)
£915	$1591	(13-Apr-92 GL.P100/R) Le aut en longueur (76x56cm-30x22in) s.d.11/12/1978 Indian ink (F.FR 9000)
£916	$1677	(3-Jun-92 CSC.P104) Untitled (100x65cm-39x26in) s.d.1989 mixed media gouache (F.FR 9000)
£1339	$2289	(22-Mar-92 I.N41/R) Chronoposte (87x67cm-34x26in) s.d.1989 mixed media craft-paper (F.FR 13000)
£1986	$3614	(15-Dec-91 P.V58) L'homme qui saute (74x106cm-29x42in) s.i.d.10/6/79 mixed media (F.FR 19500)
£2156	$3881	(19-Nov-91 FB.P259/R) Mouvements fig. XXX14 s.i.d.19.9.1982 ink (F.FR 21000)

VELIER, E (19/20th C) ?

£3846	$7000	(27-May-92 CH.NY27/R) By the sea (51x37cm-20x15in) s.d.1885

VELIM, Anton (1892-1954) Austrian

£1068	$1901	(28-Apr-92 D.V143/R) Still life with fruit (50x50cm-20x20in) double-sided (A.S 22000)

VELLANI, Francesco and RUBBIANI, Felice (18th C) Italian

£18785	$34000	(22-May-92 SY.NY35/R) Still life of flowers in vase, fruit and grapes and antique frieze (83x143cm-33x56in) s.d.34

VELLAY (?) ?

£669	$1150	(12-Oct-91 SY.NY45/R) Section d'or (55x46cm-22x18in) s.d.1935 gouache pen gold foil

VELTEN, H (20th C) ?
£551 $998   (5-Dec-91 D.V138) Still life of fishes (74x101cm-29x40in) s. (A.S 11000)

VELTEN, Wilhelm (1847-1929) Russian
£1916 $3488   (11-Dec-91 N.M640/R) Little girl with white rabbit on bench before farmhouse (35x31cm-14x12in) s. (DM 5500)
£1930 $3474   (22-Nov-91 SA.A1698/R) The ride with the mail coach (16x24cm-6x9in) s. panel (DM 5500)
£2265 $4122   (11-Dec-91 N.M638/R) Horses grazing beneath trees (37x50cm-15x20in) s. panel (DM 6500)
£2385 $4150   (14-Apr-92 SY.AM292/R) Poultry in yard (22x27cm-9x11in) s.i. panel (D.FL 7800)
£2465 $4461   (3-Dec-91 FN.S2500/R) Ambush with musketeers stopping horse-drawn cart in wooded landscape (23x32cm-9x13in) s. panel (DM 7000)
£2509 $4566   (11-Dec-91 N.M637/R) Soldier and woman drinking before tent (12x16cm-5x6in) s. panel (DM 7200)
£2787 $5073   (11-Dec-91 N.M636/R) Woman with cart presenting drink to soldier riding on road (16x24cm-6x9in) s. panel (DM 8000)
£4225 $7648   (3-Dec-91 FN.S2499/R) Village raid in river landscape with figures (33x26cm-13x10in) s.i. panel (DM 12000)
£6620 $12049   (11-Dec-91 N.M635/R) Elegant party with horses arriving at Schloss Lustheim (16x23cm-6x9in) s. panel (DM 19000)
£7451 $12667   (23-Oct-91 GD.B1317/R) Horse with plough and figures in Bavarian landscape, early spring (13x23cm-5x9in) s.i. panel (S.FR 19000)
£8000 $14160   (14-Feb-92 C53/R) The refreshment (36x46cm-14x18in) s.i. panel

VELTZ, Ivan (20th C) Russian
£1233 $2257   (14-May-92 BU.S202/R) Frozen watercourse at sunset (36x43cm-14x17in) s.d.1920 panel (S.KR 13000)

VELZEN, Johannes Petrus van (1816-1853) Dutch
£2424 $4291   (22-Apr-92 CH.AM112) Winterlandscape with skaters on a frozen river and peasants on snowy path (82x68cm-32x27in) s. (D.FL 8000)

VEN, Paul van der (1892-) Dutch
£909 $1609   (22-Apr-92 CH.AM42) View of the Prinsegracht, Amsterdam, with a moored boat (81x126cm-32x50in) s. (D.FL 3000)

VENANT, Francois (circle) (1592-1636) Dutch
£2000 $3500   (25-Feb-92 PH98/R) Meeting of Abraham and Melchizedek (57x59cm-22x23in) panel

VENARD, Claude (1913-) French
£540 $925   (21-Mar-92 W.W103/R) Le phare, la nuit (46x56cm-18x22in) s.
£698 $1200   (12-Oct-91 SY.NY191/R) Still life on table (38x46cm-15x18in) s.
£800 $1528   (29-Jun-92 CSK141/R) Nature morte au fond rouge (33x41cm-13x16in) s.
£894 $1600   (9-May-92 CE.NY99/R) Nature morte aux pasteques (54x65cm-21x26in) s.
£1000 $1710   (12-Mar-92 B90) Blue and white composition with nude (73x60cm-29x24in) s.
£1170 $2000   (21-Mar-92 W.W107/R) La plage (46x56cm-18x22in) s.
£1453 $2600   (9-May-92 CE.NY96/R) Port Croix (97x116cm-38x46in) s.
£1600 $2800   (28-Feb-92 SY.NY180/R) Nature morte (100x100cm-39x39in) s.
£1616 $2861   (26-Apr-92 FE.P48) Montmartre (81x65cm-32x26in) s. (F.FR 16000)
£1695 $3000   (5-Nov-91 CE.NY212/R) Nature morte au poisson (75x75cm-30x30in) s.
£1714 $3000   (28-Feb-92 SY.NY181/R) Rooftops of Paris (96x129cm-38x51in) s.
£1977 $3500   (5-Nov-91 CE.NY239/R) Nature morte au poisson (100x100cm-39x39in) s.
£1977 $3500   (5-Nov-91 CE.NY211/R) Les oliviers noirs (100x100cm-39x39in) s.d.63
£2105 $3789   (23-Nov-91 N.M323/R) Bistro (100x100cm-39x39in) s. s.i.d.1972 stretcher (DM 6000)
£2567 $4620   (19-Nov-91 FB.P27/R) Le Port (100x100cm-39x39in) s. panel (F.FR 25000)
£2707 $4737   (23-Feb-92 FE.P94) L'entree du Port (60x120cm-24x47in) s.d.70 (F.FR 26500)
£2971 $5348   (2-Feb-92 CSC.P43 b/R) Port de peche (82x100cm-32x39in) s. (F.FR 29000)
£3125 $5531   (10-Nov-91 ZZ.F232/R) Pichet sur en entablement fleuri (75x75cm-30x30in) s. (F.FR 31000)
£3200 $5440   (23-Oct-91 MMB270/R) Poissons (89x160cm-35x63in) s.d.54
£3500 $5985   (12-Mar-92 B88) Le compotier (76x76cm-30x30in) s.
£4032 $6976   (6-Oct-91 BG.P185/R) L'arlequin (146x114cm-57x45in) s.d.1955 (F.FR 40000)
£1086   *$1900*   *(27-Feb-92 CE.NY79/R) Interieur. L'estaminet (30x70cm-12x28in) s. oil wax crayon pencil pair*
£2053   *$3696*   *(19-Nov-91 FB.P66/R) Nature morte (103x145cm-41x57in) s. mixed media canvas (F.FR 20000)*

VENET, Bernar (1941-) French
£1744   *$3121*   *(19-Jan-92 CC.P36/R) Cercle et trace d'un arc (130x98cm-51x39in) i. graphite (F.FR 17000)*
£1955   *$3538*   *(2-Dec-91 CC.P48/R) Ligne indeterminee no.5 (77x96cm-30x38in) s.i.d.1984 collage crayon (F.FR 19000)*
£2561   *$4611*   *(2-Feb-92 CSC.P179/R) Undetermined line (93x80cm-37x31in) s.i.d.87 graphite lead pencil (F.FR 25000)*
£3364   *$6257*   *(15-Jun-92 GL.P19/R) Ligne indeterminee (75x100cm-30x39in) s.d.1990 crayon (F.FR 33000)*

VENETIAN SCHOOL (?) Italian
£2700 $4860   (22-Nov-91 SWS200/R) Figures by classical ruins (92x111cm-36x44in) c.1800

VENETIAN SCHOOL (?) Italian-cont.

£3951	$7151	(3-Dec-91 SY.MI206) Ritratto di gentiluomo (100x75cm-39x30in) c.1600 (I.L 8500000)
£4000	$7000	(27-Feb-92 CSK247/R) The Rialto Bridge, Venice. The Bacino di San Marco (34x47cm-13x19in) two
£4587	$8532	(18-Jun-92 SY.MO294/R) Adoration des Mages (108x143cm-43x56in) c.1700 (F.FR 45000)
£5000	$8750	(28-Feb-92 C19/R) Portrait of Tita Bodussi (118x94cm-46x37in) c.1722 6 i.
£5345	$9675	(3-Dec-91 SY.MI248/R) Cristo nella casa di Simone (25x36cm-10x14in) c.1700 (I.L 11500000)
£5424	$9818	(18-May-92 SY.MI251) Paesaggio (74x114cm-29x45in) c.1800 (I.L 12000000)
£14500	$26535	(14-May-92 TL58/R) Supper at Emmaus (97x196cm-38x77in)
£16725	$30272	(18-May-92 SY.MI214/R) Baccanale (198x290cm-78x114in) c.1700 (I.L 37000000)
£60000	$109200	(11-Nov-91 S81/R) Sleeping Venus with satyr (115x168cm-45x66in) c.1700

VENETIAN SCHOOL, 16th C Italian

£1500	$2730	(10-Dec-91 PH123/R) Portrait of lady, wearing string pearls (33x25cm-13x10in) panel
£1852	$3352	(19-May-92 GF.L2440/R) Portrait of bearded man (48x38cm-19x15in) (S.FR 5000)
£2351	$4254	(18-May-92 SY.MI243) Madonna col Bambino e S.Giovannino (51x42cm-20x17in) panel (I.L 5200000)
£2880	$5500	(16-Jul-92 SY.NY142/R) The Holy Family (44x59cm-17x23in) panel
£2937	$5198	(7-Nov-91 D.V10/R) Portrait of noble lady with dog (111x97cm-44x38in) (A.S 60000)
£3086	$5586	(5-Dec-91 SY.MO362/R) L'annonciation (47x35cm-19x14in) panel (F.FR 30000)
£3168	$5766	(28-May-92 F.M41) San Gerolamo (64x79cm-25x31in) (I.L 7000000)
£4500	$7830	(15-Apr-92 C157/R) The Resurrection (23x25cm-9x10in) panel
£4526	$8237	(28-May-92 F.M47) Madonna col Bambino, santi e donatore (55x84cm-22x33in) panel (I.L 10000000)
£5000	$8900	(1-Nov-91 C21/R) Madonna and child with Saint Catherine and male saint (35x45cm-14x18in) panel
£5578	$10095	(5-Dec-91 F.M135/R) Andata al Calvario (66x98cm-26x39in) (I.L 12000000)
£6972	$12619	(5-Dec-91 F.M109/R) Sacra Famiglia con San Giovannino (34x46cm-13x18in) panel (I.L 15000000)
£7500	$13650	(11-Dec-91 S211/R) Madonna and Child with four male saints, archangel Michael and donor (84x126cm-33x50in)
£7901	$14302	(5-Dec-91 F.M69) Madonna col Bambino San Gerolamo e San Domenico (90x110cm-35x43in) (I.L 17000000)
£7945	$14141	(28-Apr-92 F.R26/R) Adorazione dei pastori (57x43cm-22x17in) copper (I.L 17500000)
£8011	$14500	(22-May-92 SY.NY122/R) Portrait of lady (89x72cm-35x28in)
£8800	$15664	(30-Oct-91 S164/R) Christ on the road to Calvary (42x78cm-17x31in) panel
£2730	*$4942*	*(22-May-92 GB.B5428/R) Sacrifice (24x35cm-9x14in) pen wash (DM 8000)*

VENETIAN SCHOOL, 17th C Italian

£1816	$3232	(28-Apr-92 F.R33) Venere e Adone (43x67cm-17x26in) (I.L 4000000)
£2092	$3786	(5-Dec-91 F.M76) Allegoria della Carita (131x91cm-52x36in) (I.L 4500000)
£2344	$4148	(5-Nov-91 GF.L2064/R) Senator with son (132x101cm-52x40in) (S.FR 6000)
£2360	$4200	(22-Jan-92 D.NY92/R) Joseph and brothers (102x137cm-40x54in)
£2749	$5250	(16-Jul-92 SY.NY52/R) Adoration of the Magi (86x109cm-34x43in)
£3100	$5270	(23-Oct-91 LJ266) View of St. Marks Square with elegant figures and gondola in foreground (50x71cm-20x28in) panel
£3198	$5500	(10-Oct-91 SY.NY61/R) Portrait of a woman (91x80cm-36x31in)
£4641	$8355	(19-Nov-91 F.R87/R) Allegoria della Ricchezza (110x161cm-43x63in) (I.L 10000000)
£6395	$11000	(9-Oct-91 CH.NY149/R) Portrait of astronomer, seated beside table with globe of constellations (140x146cm-55x57in)
£12000	$21480	(11-Nov-91 S474/R) Rest on Flight into Egypt (38x87cm-15x34in)

VENETIAN SCHOOL, 18th C Italian

£1468	$2599	(7-Nov-91 D.V231/R) Salomon offering to the Gods (90x65cm-35x26in) canvas on panel (A.S 30000)
£1991	$3624	(28-May-92 F.M20) San Giovannino (50x74cm-20x29in) (I.L 4400000)
£2000	$3560	(31-Oct-91 B56) Figures dining at table in loggia (81x102cm-32x40in)
£2037	$3707	(28-May-92 F.M66) Ritratto di gentiluomo (69x58cm-27x23in) (I.L 4500000)
£2369	$4453	(18-Dec-91 AT.P137/R) La predication de Saint Jean Baptiste (71x105cm-28x41in) i.verso (F.FR 23000)
£2520	$4461	(6-Nov-91 LT.P68) Allegorie des Arts (33x26cm-13x10in) (F.FR 25000)
£2622	$4484	(18-Mar-92 N.M468/R) Travellers resting by stream and village beyond (50x40cm-20x16in) painted oval (DM 7500)
£2962	$5390	(11-Dec-91 N.M376/R) Personification of prudence with mirror and snake (100x74cm-39x29in) (DM 8500)
£3249	$5848	(19-Nov-91 F.R157) Paesaggio con cascata (53x70cm-21x28in) (I.L 7000000)
£3330	$5728	(16-Oct-91 AT.P18/R) L'Incredulite de Saint Thomas (113x143cm-44x56in) (F.FR 33000)
£3671	$6498	(7-Nov-91 D.V244/R) View from Chiesa di San Giorgio to Riva degli Schiavoni and Doge's Palace (64x83cm-25x33in) (A.S 75000)
£3718	$6730	(5-Dec-91 F.M82) Paesaggio fluviale con ponte e figure (136x118cm-54x46in) (I.L 8000000)
£4089	$7483	(16-May-92 F.L3/R) Paesaggio con pastori e armenti. Paesaggio con figure in riva a un fiume (45x63cm-18x25in) pair (S.FR 11000)
£4200	$7644	(10-Dec-91 PH102/R) Martyrdom of saint (67x72cm-26x28in)

VENETIAN SCHOOL, 18th C Italian-cont.

£4405	$7797	(7-Nov-91 D.V36/R) Venetian ladies attending party of monkeys in castle park (34x45cm-13x18in) (A.S 90000)
£4405	$7797	(7-Nov-91 D.V247/R) The Finding of Moses (52x67cm-20x26in) (A.S 90000)
£4416	$7992	(5-Dec-91 F.M45) Interno con figure in maschera (67x94cm-26x37in) (I.L 9500000)
£4533	$8295	(4-Jun-92 F.M233) Le figlie di Lot (123x163cm-48x64in) (I.L 10000000)
£5424	$9818	(18-May-92 SY.MI250/R) Battaglia (71x131cm-28x52in) (I.L 12000000)
£5578	$10095	(3-Dec-91 SY.MI231/R) Paesaggi con rovine (41x60cm-16x24in) gouache paper on canvas pair (I.L 12000000)
£5967	$10800	(5-Dec-91 SY.MO317/R) Vue du Grand Canal a Venise avec l'eglise de la Carita … (80x115cm-31x45in) (F.FR 58000)
£6255	$11447	(4-Jun-92 F.M234) Scena di battaglia. Dopo la battaglia (92x115cm-36x45in) pair (I.L 13800000)
£6498	$11696	(19-Nov-91 F.R133/R) Prospettiva architettonica (122x95cm-48x37in) pair (I.L 14000000)
£6563	$11944	(28-May-92 F.M24) Agar nel deserto (136x113cm-54x44in) (I.L 14500000)
£8599	$15651	(28-May-92 F.M83/R) Marina in burrasca (66x113cm-26x44in) pair (I.L 19000000)
£10397	$18818	(18-May-92 SY.MI209/R) Nature morte con fiori (70x54cm-28x21in) oval pair (I.L 23000000)
£11213	$20856	(18-Jun-92 SY.MO113/R) Tete d'Oriental (58x47cm-23x19in) (F.FR 110000)
£11301	$20454	(18-May-92 SY.MI204/R) Nature morte con fiori (70x54cm-28x21in) pair oval (I.L 25000000)
£12544	$22829	(12-Dec-91 L.K193/R) Southern landscape with figures and man pointing to inscription (50x77cm-20x30in) (DM 36000)
£24465	$45505	(18-Jun-92 SY.MO215/R) Le sommeil d'Endymion. Le triomphe de Neptune (54x72cm-21x28in) pair (F.FR 240000)
£25309	$45302	(12-Nov-91 SY.AM69/R) Capriccio with classical buildings and ruins (80x97cm-31x38in) (D.FL 82000)
£30810	$51761	(27-Aug-91 RAS.K193/R) Esther and Ahasverus (130x108cm-51x43in) (D.KR 350000)
£55791	$101540	(25-May-92 ARC.P38/R) Scene de Carnaval, le concert (90x129cm-35x51in) style of Carpioni (F.FR 550100)

VENETIAN SCHOOL, 19th C Italian

£1963	$3750	(16-Jul-92 SY.NY287/R) View of the Doge's Palace, Venice (36x57cm-14x22in)
£2200	$3916	(30-Oct-91 S135/R) The island of San Michele, Venice (54x80cm-21x31in)
£3000	$5460	(11-Dec-91 S135/R) Venice, Santa Maria della Salute (18x28cm-7x11in)
£5200	$9256	(30-Oct-91 SY.S136/R) Bucintoro returning to Molo on Ascension Day. Regatta at Grand Canal (47x73cm-19x29in) canvas on panel pair
£9080	$16162	(28-Apr-92 F.R69) Veduta del Ponte di Rialto. Veduta di Piazza San Marco (63x92cm-25x36in) pair (I.L 20000000)

VENETO SCHOOL (?) Italian

£2107	$3750	(22-Jan-92 SY.NY198/R) Pastoral landscape with sheep, cows, figures and valley beyond (74x100cm-29x39in) c.1700

VENETO SCHOOL, 15th C Italian

£24862	$45000	(22-May-92 SY.NY12/R) Virgin and Child (43x32cm-17x13in) panel

VENETO SCHOOL, 18th C Italian

£2907	$5000	(10-Oct-91 SY.NY99/R) Landscape with figures by a river waiting for a ferry, tower on far shore (33x50cm-13x20in)
£16575	$30000	(22-May-92 SY.NY199/R) Harbour scene with classical ruins and figures (57x107cm-22x42in)

VENETO-DALMATIAN SCHOOL (?) Italian

£4541	$7810	(16-Oct-91 AT.P1/R) L'Adoration des Mages (75x101cm-30x40in) c.1500 panel (F.FR 45000)

VENIUS, Otto (1556-1629) Italian

£3049	$5305	(13-Apr-92 AT.P105/R) Portrait d'enfant sur un lit (34x29cm-13x11in) d.1584 panel (F.FR 30000)

VENIUS, Otto (attrib) (1556-1629) Italian

£3055	$5591	(3-Jun-92 HC.P11) Vierge a l'Enfant (69x54cm-27x21in) panel (F.FR 30000)

VENNE, Adolf van der (1828-1911) Austrian

£1443	$2511	(17-Sep-91 FN.S2590/R) View of Gaisalm with shepherd boy and animals (34x30cm-13x12in) s. panel (DM 4200)
£1714	$3000	(18-Feb-92 CE.NY136) Gypsy wagon (28x46cm-11x18in) s.d.1888
£2972	$5142	(25-Mar-92 KM.K1489/R) Figures conversing by the edge of wood (87x130cm-34x51in) s. (DM 8500)

VENNE, Adriaen Pietersz van de (1589-1662) Dutch

£1111	$2011	(19-May-92 GF.L2411/R) Wilhelm Tell and Gessler (33x85cm-13x33in) (S.FR 3000)
£2210	$4000	(22-May-92 SY.NY253/R) Cavaliers making merry on horseback outside tent (34x44cm-13x17in) panel
£4633	$7923	(12-Mar-92 GK.Z40/R) Woman stealing peasant's money while dentist is pulling out his tooth (41x32cm-16x13in) panel (S.FR 12000)
£6000	$11520	(8-Jul-92 S211/R) Guile leads to wealth (41x32cm-16x13in) i. panel
£6800	$11900	(28-Feb-92 C67/R) A chimney sweep (28x22cm-11x9in) i. panel

VENNE, Adriaen Pietersz van de (attrib) (1589-1662) Dutch
£1600　　$2720　　(22-Oct-91 S247/R) Chimney sweep (28x23cm-11x9in) i. panel

VENNE, Adriaen Pietersz van de (style) (1589-1662) Dutch
£900　　$1575　　(2-Apr-92 CSKI10) Quarrel in tavern (41x56cm-16x22in) canvas on board

VENNE, Fritz van der (19/20th C) German
£1306　　$2272　　(19-Sep-91 N.M2832/R) Peasant with hay cart (26x34cm-10x13in) s. canvas
　　　　　　　　　on board (DM 3800)
£1761　　$3187　　(3-Dec-91 FN.S2501/R) Hungarian wedding procession riding on horses in
　　　　　　　　　puszta landscape (50x70cm-20x28in) s.i. (DM 5000)

VENNE, Pseudo van de (17th C) Belgian
£6173　　$11728　　(26-Jun-92 AGS.P54/R) Le remouleur ambulant (73x87cm-29x34in)
　　　　　　　　　(F.FR 60000)

VENNEMAN, Charles (1802-1875) Flemish
£3429　　$6000　　(18-Feb-92 CE.NY59/R) Frolicking peasants (39x49cm-15x19in) s. panel

VENTAYOL, Juan (20th C) Uruguayan?
£983　　$1700　　(30-Sep-91 GC.M4/R) Fachada y Sol (120x90cm-47x35in) s. fibre

VENTNOR, Arthur (fl.1896-1926) British
£1429　　$2500　　(18-Feb-92 CE.NY157) Frugal tea (23x28cm-9x11in) s.

VENTOSA, Josep (1897-1982) Spanish?
£2433　　$4574　　(17-Dec-91 BRO.B428) Afueras de la Estacion. Manresa (54x73cm-21x29in)
　　　　　　　　　s.d.43 s.i.d.verso (S.P 440000)

VENTURA DI MORO (circle) (15th C) Italian
£4000　　$7280　　(13-Dec-91 C237/R) Madonna and Child with Saints Catherine, Nicholas,
　　　　　　　　　Jerome and Anthony (67x42cm-26x17in) panel

VENTURE, T M (circle) (18th C) French
£1000　　$1730　　(24-Mar-92 CG807/R) Bust portrait of a girl (19x16cm-7x6in) canvas laid
　　　　　　　　　down on panel

VENTUROLI, Angelo (attrib) (1749-1821) Italian
£387　　$701　　(6-Dec-91 GB.B5688/R) Altar design (34x22cm-13x9in) pen wash (DM 1100)

VENUSTI, Marcello (attrib) (c.1515-1579) Italian
£13000　　$24960　　(7-Jul-92 PH47/R) Resurrection (31x16cm-12x6in) panel arched top

VENUSTI, Marcello (style) (c.1515-1579) Italian
£2800　　$5012　　(11-Nov-91 S493/R) Annunciation to Virgin with donor (38x28cm-15x11in)
　　　　　　　　　panel

VERA, Cristino de (1931-) Spanish
£1636　　$3043　　(16-Jun-92 EP.M58/R) Paisaje (80x100cm-31x39in) s. (S.P 300000)
£2290　　$4260　　(16-Jun-92 EP.M61/R) Despedida (102x72cm-40x28in) s. (S.P 420000)

VERA, F (?) Spanish
£3404　　$6331　　(16-Jun-92 F.M248/R) L'ora del the (54x24cm-21x9in) s.d.1899 panel
　　　　　　　　　(I.L 7500000)

VERBEECK, Francois Xavier Henri (1686-1755) Flemish
£1852　　$3315　　(12-Nov-91 SY.AM214/R) Elegant company in astronomer's study
　　　　　　　　　(64x76cm-25x30in) bears sig. (D.FL 6000)

VERBEECK, Pieter Cornelisz (1610-1654) Dutch
£4144　　$7500　　(22-May-92 SY.NY150/R) Horse and sleeping dog in grotto (20x17cm-8x7in)
　　　　　　　　　s. panel

VERBEET, Gijsbertha (1838-1916) Dutch
£728　　$1296　　(29-Apr-92 D.V773/R) Still life with glass (30x25cm-12x10in) indis.s.
　　　　　　　　　panel (A.S 15000)
£4286　　$7500　　(20-Feb-92 SY.NY199/R) Still life with fruit on marble ledge
　　　　　　　　　(78x63cm-31x25in) s.d.1854 panel

VERBOECKHOVEN, Eugene (1798-1881) Belgian
£522　　$925　　(9-Nov-91 W.W16/R) Sheep in a meadow (18x23cm-7x9in) s. panel
£800　　$1488　　(17-Jun-92 S278/R) Sheep in barn (19x20cm-7x8in) s. panel
£1000　　$1820　　(10-Dec-91 SWS295/R) The young shepherd (10x13cm-4x5in) board
£1053　　$1895　　(22-Nov-91 SA.A1593/R) Cattle and sheep grazing (24x33cm-9x13in) panel
　　　　　　　　　(DM 3000)
£1423　　$2604　　(12-May-92 GO.G236) Country scene with girl milking cow (50x45cm-20x18in)
　　　　　　　　　s.d.1825 panel (S.KR 15000)
£1481　　$2593　　(18-Feb-92 CH.AM304/R) Sheep in forest (34x26cm-13x10in) s. panel
　　　　　　　　　(D.FL 4800)
£1833　　$3300　　(22-Nov-91 S.BM26 a/R) Spring lambs - pasture view (28x36cm-11x14in) s.
　　　　　　　　　panel
£1951　　$3532　　(3-Dec-91 R.T906/R) Sheep and poultry in pasture (14x18cm-6x7in) s.d.1875
　　　　　　　　　panel (C.D 4000)
£2198　　$4000　　(13-Dec-91 S.BM449) Sheep and lamb at rest (43x61cm-17x24in) s. panel

VERBOECKHOVEN, Eugene (1798-1881) Belgian-cont.

£2600	$4420	(22-Oct-91 SWS342/R) Group of sheep by tree (17x20cm-7x8in) s.d.1835 panel
£3413	$6212	(27-May-92 PH.DU148/R) Goat, sheep with lamb and hen in a stall (17x24cm-7x9in) s. panel (DM 10000)
£3415	$6180	(3-Dec-91 R.T95/R) Barn interior with sheep and poultry tending young (30x40cm-12x16in) s.d.1878 s.i.d.verso (C.D 7000)
£3655	$6250	(13-Mar-92 S.BM165/R) Manger with sheep, lambs and hens (53x79cm-21x31in) s.d.1870
£3704	$6481	(18-Feb-92 CH.AM303/R) Cow standing in pond (67x55cm-26x22in) s.d.1859 panel (D.FL 12000)
£3780	$6918	(2-Jun-92 FN.S2781/R) Domestic animals resting in shade of rock in hilly landscape (68x56cm-27x22in) s.d.1829 panel (DM 11000)
£4500	$8370	(17-Jun-92 S277/R) Cattle and sheep in summer pasture (86x110cm-34x43in) s.d.1826
£4945	$9000	(11-Dec-91 RO.BA55/R) Berger avec brebis et moutons (54x67cm-21x26in) s.
£5498	$10062	(2-Jun-92 FN.S2782/R) Sheep, lamb and goats in landscape, evening (57x78cm-22x31in) s.d.1841 panel (DM 10000)
£6044	$11000	(28-May-92 SY.NY227/R) Sheep gathered in barn (56x77cm-22x30in) s.d.1870 panel
£6500	$11765	(22-May-92 C196/R) Grey stallion with dog (19x16cm-7x6in) s.d.1844 panel
£8621	$14828	(16-Oct-91 KM.K1422) Sheep and lambs in landscape (59x80cm-23x31in) s.d.1859 panel (DM 25000)
£16484	$30000	(28-May-92 SY.NY23/R) Guarding flock by coast (71x110cm-28x43in) s.d.1867
£445	$805	(3-Dec-91 C.A347) Cattle (46x60cm-18x24in) s.d.1866 W/C (B.FR 26000)
£608	$1100	(21-May-92 GRO.B21/R) Winter day in Holland (13x18cm-5x7in) s.d.1840 W/C htd.white board
£756	$1300	(15-Oct-91 CE.NY71) Sheep and poultry grazing in a landscape (29x48cm-11x19in) s.d.1870 chl.white chk.

VERBOECKHOVEN, Eugene (attrib) (1798-1881) Belgian

| £2571 | $4500 | (18-Feb-92 CE.NY193/R) Four sheep and two rabbits in barn (70x61cm-28x24in) s.d.1878 |

VERBOECKHOVEN, Eugene (circle) (1798-1881) Belgian

| £950 | $1634 | (15-Oct-91 CSK622) Ewes and a lamb in a landscape (13x16cm-5x6in) with sig.d.1864 panel |

VERBOECKHOVEN, Eugene (style) (1798-1881) Belgian

| £1100 | $1991 | (21-May-92 CSK133/R) Cattle and sheep in barn (32x48cm-13x19in) bears sig. panel |

VERBOECKHOVEN, Eugene and CAMPOTOSTO, Henry (19th C) Belgian

| £14500 | $25810 | (29-Nov-91 C44/R) Children with sheep and chickens in wooded landscape (66x87cm-26x34in) s.d.1879 panel |

VERBOECKHOVEN, Eugene and DAIWAILLE, Alexander Joseph (19th C) Belgian

| £5932 | $10500 | (6-Nov-91 D.NY21/R) Peasants leading herds to watering hole (43x54cm-17x21in) s.i.verso board |

VERBOECKHOVEN, Eugene and JONGHE, Jan Baptiste de (19th C) Belgian

| £1000 | $1860 | (17-Jun-92 S282/R) Hunters resting in wood (43x61cm-17x24in) s.d.1846 wash |

VERBOECKHOVEN, Eugene and KEELHOFF, Frans (19th C) Belgian

£4286	$7500	(18-Feb-92 CE.NY138/R) Sheep and cattle grazing (67x108cm-26x43in) s.indist.i.
£6000	$11160	(17-Jun-92 S276/R) Shepherd with flock by mill (69x111cm-27x44in) s.
£10857	$19000	(19-Feb-92 CH.NY131/R) Country road (68x107cm-27x42in) s.d.1868 s.

VERBOECKHOVEN, Eugene and KLOMBEEK, Johann Bernard (19th C) Belgian

| £10000 | $18600 | (19-Jun-92 C9/R) Wooded landscape with drovers, cattle and sheep on path (92x122cm-36x48in) s.d.1872 |

VERBOECKHOVEN, Eugene and KOEKKOEK, Marinus Adrianus (19th C) Belgian

| £5814 | $10000 | (17-Oct-91 SY.NY235/R) Landscape with cattle (42x60cm-17x24in) s. |

VERBOECKHOVEN, Eugene and SCHELFHOUT, Andreas (19th C) Belgian/Duch

| £19697 | $34864 | (22-Apr-92 CH.AM223/R) Winterscene with peasant on a snowy path, a skater and other figures (53x70cm-21x28in) s.both artists panel (D.FL 65000) |

VERBOECKHOVEN, Louis (1802-1889) Belgian

£560	$1014	(21-May-92 CSK154) Fishing boat in swell (14x20cm-6x8in) s.
£1600	$2848	(26-Nov-91 PH89/R) Fishing boats off coast (24x32cm-9x13in) s. panel
£1625	$2942	(7-Dec-91 KV.L345) Marine (9x13cm-4x5in) s. panel pair (B.FR 95000)
£2000	$3720	(17-Jun-92 S297/R) Still life of flowers and fruit (71x58cm-28x23in) s.d.82
£2076	$3945	(24-Jun-92 KM.K1296/R) Sailing ships in choppy seas (54x76cm-21x30in) s. (DM 6000)
£2200	$4202	(17-Jul-92 C119/R) Dutch pinks and barges off the coast (45x68cm-18x27in) s.
£2577	$4304	(21-Aug-91 DS.W193 a) Untitled s. (NZ.D 7500)
£3670	$6385	(14-Apr-92 SY.AM144/R) Watching the vessels (38x71cm-15x28in) s. panel (D.FL 12000)

VERBOECKHOVEN, Louis (1802-1889) Belgian-cont.
£4587	$7982	(14-Apr-92 SY.AM80/R) Sailing vessels (40x65cm-16x26in) s. panel (D.FL 15000)
£10500	$18690	(27-Nov-91 S6/R) Fishing vessels by shore (93x128cm-37x50in) s.d.1830
£12000	$22320	(17-Jun-92 S270/R) Shipping in stormy sea. Fishing boats in harbour (46x61cm-18x24in) s. panel pair

VERBOOM, Adriaen (1628-1670) Dutch
£4587	$8532	(18-Jun-92 SY.MO172/R) Paysage avec bergers (96x80cm-38x31in) s. (F.FR 45000)

VERBOOM, Adriaen (style) (1628-1670) Dutch
£1500	$2625	(28-Feb-92 C119) Extensive river landscape with horseman and peasants (30x37cm-12x15in) panel

VERBRUGGE, Emile (1856-?) Belgian
£613	$1103	(19-Nov-91 GM.B306/R) Interieur d'artiste peintre (22x27cm-9x11in) s. wood (B.FR 36000)
£832	$1457	(5-Apr-92 ZZ.F27/R) Canal dans la ville (46x33cm-18x13in) s. panel (F.FR 8000)

VERBRUGGEN (style) (17/18th C) Dutch/Flemish
£850	$1632	(9-Jul-92 B179) Still life of mixed flowers in stone vase, landscape beyond (135x98cm-53x39in)

VERBRUGGEN, Gaspar Pieter (17/18th C) Flemish
£3779	$6500	(9-Oct-91 CH.NY78/R) Mixed flowers (69x55cm-27x22in)

VERBRUGGEN, Gaspar Pieter (attrib) (17/18th C) Flemish
£3039	$5500	(22-May-92 SY.NY236/R) Portrait of young girl holding bouquet of flowers (84x70cm-33x28in)
£5000	$8900	(29-Oct-91 PH125/R) Garland of flowers surrounding a head of Christ. Garland of flowers surrounding a head of the Virgin (123x91cm-48x36in) pair

VERBRUGGEN, Gaspar Pieter (style) (17/18th C) Flemish
£950	$1653	(19-Sep-91 TL357) Still life of mythological figure within garland of flowers (54x43cm-21x17in)
£2000	$3500	(27-Feb-92 CSK174) Carnations, morning glory and other flowers in an urn (56x47cm-22x19in)
£3488	$6000	(10-Oct-91 SY.NY204/R) Still life of flowers in a vase (73x61cm-29x24in)
£4974	$9500	(16-Jul-92 SY.NY277/R) Still life of flowers (107x86cm-42x34in)
£6077	$11000	(22-May-92 SY.NY235/R) Still life of mixed flowers in vase with birds in landscape (113x72cm-44x28in)

VERBRUGGEN, Gaspar Pieter II (1664-1730) Flemish
£11000	$20020	(13-Dec-91 C172/R) Tulips, honeysuckle, peony, rose and other flowers in ornate vase (80x65cm-31x26in) s.
£11100	$19092	(16-Oct-91 AT.P52/R) Fleurs ornant un vase de pierre orne d'un mascaron (121x92cm-48x36in) (F.FR 110000)
£14330	$25507	(29-Nov-91 ARC.P31/R) Vase de fleurs sur un entablement avec un perroquet (103x84cm-41x33in) (F.FR 140000)
£14500	$26390	(10-Dec-91 PH47/R) Still life of mixed flowers in glass bowls on stone ledge (81x64cm-32x25in)
£15000	$28800	(8-Jul-92 S34/R) Still life of flowers in sculpted urn (117x101cm-46x40in) bears sig.
£19767	$34000	(10-Oct-91 SY.NY162/R) Putti and flowers with portraits possibly of William III and Mary (160x103cm-63x41in) both i. pair

VERBRUGGEN, Gaspar Pieter II (attrib) (1664-1730) Flemish
£5500	$9790	(30-Apr-92 CG877/R) Girl in classical dress with grapes and flowers (26x35cm-10x14in)

VERBRUGGEN, Gaspar Pieter II (style) (1664-1730) Flemish
£1050	$1869	(31-Oct-91 B106) Still life of mixed flowers in basket (50x80cm-20x31in)
£1500	$2670	(30-Oct-91 S7/R) Still life of flowers with parrot and fruit in garden (112x80cm-44x31in)
£1900	$3325	(28-Feb-92 C89) Garland of flowers surrounding medallion of Venus and Cupid (55x46cm-22x18in)
£3000	$5400	(21-Nov-91 C158/R) Spring flowers in vase with butterfly, caterpillar and beetle on ledge (96x70cm-38x28in) bears sig.

VERBRUGGEN, Gaspar Pieter II and TERWESTEN, Matheus (17/18th C) Flemish/Dutch
£10500	$19110	(11-Dec-91 S113/R) Putti adorning classical urn with festoons of fruit and flowers (82x114cm-32x45in) bears sig.

VERBRUGGEN, Jan (18th C) Dutch
£4181	$7610	(12-Dec-91 L.K195/R) Coastal landscape with three Dutch war ships (46x64cm-18x25in) panel (DM 12000)

VERBRUGGHE, Charles (1877-1974) Belgian
£513	$924	(20-Nov-91 CN.P190 b) Bouquet de fleurs dans un vase (60x49cm-24x19in) s. panel (F.FR 5000)
£521	$954	(5-Feb-92 FB.P239) La Place Clichy (33x46cm-13x18in) s. i.verso hardboard (F.FR 5100)

VERBRUGGHE, Charles (1877-1974) Belgian-cont.
£1844 $3320   (2-Feb-92 ZZ.F144/R) Le pont de l'Hydromel a Bruges le matin
                 (60x73cm-24x29in) s. i.verso (F.FR 18000)

VERBUECKEN, J (19th C) Continental
£4188 $8000   (16-Jul-92 SY.NY475/R) Still life with grapes and shellfish
                 (101x77cm-40x30in) s.d.1870

VERBURGH, Cornelis Gerrit (19th C) Dutch
£1407 $2490   (5-Nov-91 SY.AM258/R) Figures by lighthouse of Katwijk (38x47cm-15x19in)
                 s.d.1832 panel (D.FL 4600)
£8800 $16368   (17-Jun-92 S286/R) Figures and skaters in frozen landscape
                 (60x79cm-24x31in) s.d.1840 panel

VERBURGH, Dionys (1655-1722) Dutch
£3000 $5250   (31-Mar-92 PH119/R) Travellers gathered round fountain before ruined
                 castle by river valley (52x57cm-20x22in) panel
£3021 $5408   (7-May-92 CH.AM90/R) Travellers on sandy road, valley beyond
                 (64x54cm-25x21in) init. panel (D.FL 10000)
£4321 $7735   (14-Nov-91 CH.AM139/R) View of village by torrent with travellers on road
                 and hilltop castle (30x44cm-12x17in) init. panel (D.FL 14000)
£5556 $9944   (14-Nov-91 CH.AM154/R) View of valley with shepherds by classical ruins
                 (73x108cm-29x43in) s. panel (D.FL 18000)
£8840 $16000   (22-May-92 SY.NY170 a/R) Travellers resting on mountain road by fountain,
                 extensive landscape with winding river beyond (88x120cm-35x47in)
                 indist.mono.

VERBURGH, Dionys (circle) (1655-1722) Dutch
£2000 $3840   (10-Jul-92 C130/R) Extensive landscape with stag hunt (64x77cm-25x30in)

VERBURGH, Dionys (style) (1655-1722) Dutch
£1705 $2967   (13-Sep-91 C161/R) Italianate landscape with peasants under tree, bridge
                 beyond (33x38cm-13x15in)
£1914 $3425   (12-Nov-91 SY.AM156/R) Figures by fountain in Italianate landscape
                 (55x79cm-22x31in) (D.FL 6200)

VERBURGH, Gerardus Johannes (1775-1864) Dutch
£1114 $2005   (19-Nov-91 F.R38/R) Paesaggio con pastori presso una fontana
*   (38x48cm-15x19in) s. W/C (I.L 2400000)*

VERBURGH, Medard (1886-1957) Belgian
£1671 $2840   (22-Oct-91 C.A323/R) Landscape (50x60cm-20x24in) s. (B.FR 100000)

VERBURGH, Rutger (1678-?) Belgian
£6500 $12415   (21-Jul-92 PH250/R) Peasants gathered on frozen river beside bridge at
                 foot of castle (52x66cm-20x26in) panel

VERCAMMEN, Waut (1938-) Belgian
£919 $1562   (22-Oct-91 C.A1043) Mona Lisa (100x100cm-39x39in) s.verso (B.FR 55000)

VERCELLI, Giulio Romano (1871-1951) Italian
£907 $1660   (12-May-92 F.R155) Sul limitare del bosco (38x49cm-15x19in) s. s.verso
                 board (I.L 2000000)

VERDE RUBIO, Ricardo (19th C) Spanish
£1247 $2207   (12-Feb-92 ANS.M78/R) Rocas de Javea (33x41cm-13x16in) s. (S.P 225000)
£6500 $11830   (29-May-92 C384/R) Break for lunch (88x130cm-35x51in) s.d.99 s.i.verso

VERDIER, Francois (1651-1730) French
£407 $754   (12-Jun-92 ARC.P189) Trois scenes d'histoire ancienne (16x28cm-6x11in)
*   black crayon htd white (F.FR 4000)*
£714 $1327   (20-Jun-92 CH.MO221/R) Quo Vadis (33x24cm-13x9in) red white chk
*   (F.FR 7000)*
£815 $1517   (19-Jun-92 ARC.P73/R) Hercule combattant le lion de Nemee
*   (27x36cm-11x14in) black chk wash htd white (F.FR 8000)*

VERDIER, Francois (attrib) (1651-1730) French
£444 $803   (21-May-92 L.K350) Venus and Adonis (26x40cm-10x16in) indian ink pen
*   board (DM 1300)*
£906 $1649   (12-Dec-91 L.K488) Oriental scenes (29x54cm-11x21in) chk htd.white two
*   (DM 2600)*

VERDIER, Marcel Antoine (1817-1856) French
£3488 $6000   (9-Oct-91 RO.BA11) Jeune femme tenant des fleurs contre sa poitrine
                 (92x73cm-36x29in) s.

VERDILHAN, Andre (20th C) French
£1332 $2398   (2-Feb-92 ZZ.F146/R) Vase de fleurs devant le port de Marseille
                 (46x55cm-18x22in) s. (F.FR 13000)

VERDILHAN, Mathieu (1875-1928) French
£5572 $10086   (20-May-92 I.N190/R) Rue de village (93x62cm-37x24in) s. (F.FR 55000)
£11329 $19372   (22-Mar-92 LT.P54/R) Animation sur un pont Provencal (59x71cm-23x28in) s.
                 (F.FR 110000)

VERDILHAN, Mathieu (1875-1928) French-cont.
£12860 $24434   (22-Jun-92 AT.P125/R) Le pavillon de l'Afrique Occidentale francaise a
l'Exposition Coloniale de Marseille en 1906 (82x94cm-32x37in) s.
(F.FR 125000)
£1019 $1896   (17-Jun-92 I.N84) Garconnet assis (32x25cm-13x10in) crayon dr
(F.FR 10000)
£1080 $2052   (22-Jun-92 AT.P111) La promenade (24x32cm-9x13in) s. pastel (F.FR 10500)

VERDOEL, Adriaan (attrib) (1620-1695) Dutch
£2800 $4900   (28-Feb-92 C53/R) Solomon's idolatry (66x84cm-26x33in)

VERDONCK, Cornelis (18th C) Dutch
£6853 $12129   (7-Nov-91 D.V135/R) Rhine landscape with vineyards and fortified castle
(32x39cm-13x15in) panel one of pair (A.S 140000)

VERDUN, Raymond (1873-1954) French
£667 $1193   (19-Jan-92 CSC.P134) Paysage (46x60cm-18x24in) (F.FR 6500)

VERDUSSEN, Jan Peeter (1700-1763) Flemish
£1931 $3360   (13-Apr-92 AT.P77) Scene de cabaret et de pillage (40x57cm-16x22in)
(F.FR 19000)
£8935 $15546   (21-Sep-91 SA.A1706/R) Army soldiers besieging town. Soldiers withdrawing
pair (DM 26000)
£12346 $22346   (5-Dec-91 SY.MO273/R) Scenes de bataille (49x69cm-19x27in) pair
(F.FR 120000)
£40000 $72800   (10-Dec-91 PH27/R) Battle scene between Turks and Austrians. Battle scene
between Turks and Russians (72x93cm-28x37in) s. pair

VERDUSSEN, Jan Peeter (circle) (1700-1763) Flemish
£4400 $7612   (25-Mar-92 PHI594/R) Elegant gentleman mounting horse from stable block
in riding school (51x71cm-20x28in)

VERDUSSEN, Paul (1868-1945) Belgian
£2762 $5000   (21-May-92 S.W2894) River view (69x147cm-27x58in) s.

VERDYEN, Eugene (19/20th C) Belgian
£828 $1498   (23-May-92 KV.L377) Winter's morning (74x54cm-29x21in) s. paper on panel
(B.FR 50000)

VEREECKE, Armand (1912-1990) Belgian
£567 $998   (7-Apr-92 C.A644) Mirage futuriste (80x100cm-31x39in) s. (B.FR 34000)

VERELST (style) (?) ?
£1950 $3393   (15-Apr-92 PHL134/R) Portrait of child, seated on cushion, with dog in
landscape (88x74cm-35x29in)

VERELST, Cornelis (attrib) (1667-1734) Dutch
£8140 $14000   (9-Oct-91 CH.NY186/R) Flowers in glass vase on ledge (51x41cm-20x16in)
pair

VERELST, Herman (circle) (c.1641-1690) Dutch
£9000 $16110   (15-Nov-91 C7/R) Portrait of boy, with dog. Portrait of girl, seated with
basket flowers on lap, with pet lamb (127x96cm-50x38in) pair

VERELST, Johannes (1648-?) Dutch
£2128 $3766   (26-Apr-92 SY.ME220/R) Portrait of man of property and wife
(112x81cm-44x32in) one s.d. 1729 pair (A.D 5000)

VERELST, Pieter (c.1618-1668) Dutch
£2200 $4224   (8-Jul-92 S169/R) Portrait of lady (80x65cm-31x26in) mono
£8000 $14000   (1-Apr-92 S135/R) Portrait of gentleman holding gloves (84x68cm-33x27in)
s. panel
£111732 $200000   (17-Jan-92 SY.NY26/R) Elegant couples drinking in an interior
(44x36cm-17x14in) s.

VERELST, Pieter (circle) (c.1618-1668) Dutch
£1543 $2762   (14-Nov-91 CH.AM36/R) The Five Senses - boors smoking and drinking in inn
(30x30cm-12x12in) (D.FL 5000)

VERELST, Simon (1644-1721) Dutch
£24000 $42720   (30-Oct-91 S191/R) Still life of flowers in glass vase on ledge
(76x63cm-30x25in)

VERELST, Simon (after) (1644-1721) Dutch
£4968 $8495   (18-Mar-92 D.V356/R) Bunch of flowers on stone table (64x78cm-25x31in)
(A.S 100000)

VERELST, Simon (circle) (1644-1721) Dutch
£1800 $3240   (22-Nov-91 SWS231/R) Portrait said to be of Louis de Kerouaille, Duchess
of Portsmouth (73x61cm-29x24in)
£2400 $4272   (29-Oct-91 PH73/R) Still life of peonies in a vase with a peach and
butterfly on a plinth (44x31cm-17x12in)

VERELST, Simon (style) (1644-1721) Dutch
£4000 $7120   (30-Oct-91 S8/R) Still life of flowers in vase on pedestal
     (76x63cm-30x25in) bears sig.
£8500 $14875   (28-Feb-92 C150/R) Roses, Morning Glory and other flowers in sculpted urn
     on ledge (98x76cm-39x30in)

VERENDAEL, Frans (1659-1747) Flemish
£3477 $5946   (18-Mar-92 D.V357/R) Bunch of flowers in vase (56x44cm-22x17in)
     (A.S 70000)

VERENDAEL, Nicolas van (1640-1691) Flemish
£35000 $60900   (15-Apr-92 C3/R) Roses and other flowers with butterfly on wheat in vase
     on stone ledge (44x33cm-17x13in)
£35000 $60900   (15-Apr-92 C4/R) Roses, tulip and other flowers in glass vase on stone
     ledge (44x33cm-17x13in)

VERENDAEL, Nicolas van (attrib) (1640-1691) Flemish
£4630 $8796   (26-Jun-92 AT.P103/R) Guirlande de fleurs retenue par des rubans bleus
     (50x70cm-20x28in) (F.FR 45000)

VERETSHCHAGIN (19th C) Russian
£1100 $2046   (16-Jun-92 S28/R) Fighting cossacks (31x47cm-12x19in) s. board

VERETSHCHAGIN, Piotr (1836-1886) Russian
£15000 $27900   (16-Jun-92 S75/R) Nizhny Novgorod (77x105cm-30x41in) s.

VERETSHCHAGIN, Vassily Petrovich (1835-1909) Russian
£1347 $2318   (8-Mar-92 BU.M390) Old man wearing fur hat (17x14cm-7x6in) s. panel
     (S.KR 14000)

VERETSHCHAGIN, Vassily Vasilievich (1842-1904) Russian
£2087 $3820   (14-May-92 BU.S203/R) Lone pine (56x22cm-22x9in) init. panel (S.KR 22000)
£2144 $3688   (13-Oct-91 REM.W33) Fatally wounded (76x65cm-30x26in) (P.Z 41000000)

VEREY, Arthur (19th C) British
£2000 $3440   (11-Oct-91 C90/R) Mowing clover (76x127cm-30x50in) s.

VERGETAS, Louis (1882-?) French
£471 $800   (23-Oct-91 GD.B1318) Retraite aux flambeaux (54x45cm-21x18in) s. board
     (S.FR 1200)

VERGNES, R (20th C) French
£615 $1107   (2-Feb-92 ZZ.F180/R) Bouquet de fleurs (65x54cm-26x21in) s. (F.FR 6000)

VERGOS (15th C) Spanish
£2183 $3754   (16-Oct-91 FER.M191/R) Moises (224x50cm-88x20in) panel (S.P 400000)

VERGOS, Pablo (?-1495) Spanish
£44053 $77974   (7-Nov-91 D.V21/R) The death of St Ludwig of Tolosa (158x194cm-62x76in)
     oil tempera gold ground panel (A.S 900000)

VERHAECHT, Tobias (1561-1631) Flemish
£4743 $8443   (29-Nov-91 GAB.G3109/R) Paysage de la vallee du Rhin (57x83cm-22x33in)
     (S.FR 12000)
£13500 $24570   (13-Dec-91 C114/R) Mountainous landscape with travellers on winding track
     in gorge (32x42cm-13x17in) panel
£1491   *$2653*   *(25-Nov-91 CH.AM11/R) View of Rome with Torre delle Milizie and Trajan's
     Column beyond (17x23cm-7x9in) i. chk pen wash (D.FL 4800)*
£1863   *$3317*   *(25-Nov-91 CH.AM100/R) Travellers on road in wooded river landscape with
     castle and town (17x38cm-7x15in) ink wash (D.FL 6000)*
£2640   *$4699*   *(25-Nov-91 CH.AM99/R) Travellers on road near farm in wooded hilly
     landscape with castle (21x32cm-8x13in) i. pen wash (D.FL 8500)*

VERHAECHT, Tobias (attrib) (1561-1631) Flemish
£7500 $13650   (13-Dec-91 C126/R) The conversion of Saint Paul (116x168cm-46x66in)

VERHAECHT, Tobias (circle) (1561-1631) Flemish
£11000 $20020   (13-Dec-91 C113/R) Pyramus and Thisbe, Rape of Europa, Mercury and Argus
     and other mythological scenes (5x10cm-2x4in) copper fifteen in one
     frame

VERHAEGEN, Fernand (1884-1976) Belgian
£1105 $1889   (21-Mar-92 KV.L346) Les Gilles de Binche le Matin (35x40cm-14x16in) s.
     board (B.FR 65000)
£2053 $3716   (7-Dec-91 KV.L457/R) Tulips (70x59cm-28x23in) s. board (B.FR 120000)

VERHAERT, Dirck (17th C) Dutch
£1800 $3150   (28-Feb-92 C64) Imaginary coastal town with clocktower (63x47cm-25x19in)
     init. panel
£2778 $4972   (14-Nov-91 CH.AM163/R) Travellers resting near ruined tower in Italianate
     landscape (47x36cm-19x14in) init. panel (D.FL 9000)

VERHAERT, Dirck (attrib) (17th C) Dutch
£2640 $4594   (13-Sep-91 C88/R) Italianate wooded river landscape with drovers and
     cattle on track (76x91cm-30x36in) panel

VERHAERT, Piet (1852-1908) Flemish
£1023 $1923   (17-Dec-91 GM.B854/R) Dans le dunes a Knocke (32x48cm-13x19in) s. (B.FR 60000)

VERHAS, Frans (c.1827-1897) Belgian
£6977 $12000   (16-Oct-91 CH.NY214/R) The green kimono (61x39cm-24x15in) s.d.1876 st.artist's seal verso panel

VERHAS, Theodor (1811-1872) German
£582   *$1001*   *(11-Oct-91 AW.H1362/R) View of Worms Cathedral (19x13cm-7x5in) pencil wash (DM 1700)*
£925   *$1590*   *(11-Oct-91 AW.H1361/R) Ruins of Kloster Limburg with view of Bad Durkheim (20x27cm-8x11in) mono. pencil indian ink wash htd.white (DM 2700)*
£1438   *$2474*   *(11-Oct-91 AW.H1359/R) Courtyard of Schloss Heidelberg (22x29cm-9x11in) mono. wash indian ink pencil htd.white (DM 4200)*
£1541   *$2651*   *(11-Oct-91 AW.H1358/R) View of Schloss Heidelberg and garden (23x29cm-9x11in) s. wash indian ink pencil htd.white (DM 4500)*

VERHEGGEN, Hendrik Frederik (1809-1883) Dutch
£515 $891   (7-Sep-91 CH.AM198) A mountain landscape with a peasant herding cattle across a bridge neara waterfall (39x49cm-15x19in) s. (D.FL 1700)
£1376 $2450   (30-Oct-91 CH.AM20) Peasant woman feeding chickens on farmyard (33x44cm-13x17in) s. (D.FL 4500)

VERHEYDEN, Francois (1806-1889) Belgian
£829 $1500   (22-May-92 S.BM35/R) Le Belge (20x18cm-8x7in) s. panel
£8140 $14000   (17-Oct-91 SY.NY242/R) Young flower sellers (99x78cm-39x31in) s.d.1865

VERHEYDEN, Isidore (1848-1905) Belgian
£800 $1376   (12-Oct-91 KV.L347) Staketsel with fishing boats (45x61cm-18x24in) studio st. (B.FR 48000)
£842 $1440   (13-Mar-92 FN.S3001) Cattle grazing before farmhouse amongst trees (54x71cm-21x28in) s.i.d.1901 (DM 2400)
£919 $1562   (22-Oct-91 C.A1051) Portrait of Maria Verheyden (111x83cm-44x33in) s.d.1889 (B.FR 55000)
£1251 $2202   (7-Apr-92 C.A269) Winter landscape (50x35cm-20x14in) s. (B.FR 75000)
£1500 $2715   (22-May-92 C201/R) Pansies in glass vase with nasturtiums (45x34cm-18x13in) s.d.73 panel
£5970 $10925   (12-May-92 C.A359/R) Farm at the edge of a forest (71x99cm-28x39in) s.d.1898 (B.FR 360000)

VERHEYEN, Jan Hendrik (1778-1846) Dutch
£4500 $8010   (27-Nov-91 S1/R) Figures near church (46x59cm-18x23in) s.d.1810 panel
£6272 $11415   (12-Dec-91 L.K711/R) View of Dutch town with church and canal with boat (33x26cm-13x10in) s.d.1822 panel (DM 18000)

VERHEYEN, Jan Hendrik (circle) (1778-1846) Dutch
£2300 $4094   (27-Nov-91 S33/R) Capriccio scene of canal (38x45cm-15x18in) panel

VERHOESEN, Albertus (1806-1881) Dutch
£500 $905   (19-May-92 SWS124) Cattle resting (17x23cm-7x9in) s.d.1872 panel
£612 $1064   (14-Apr-92 SY.AM44) Poultry in yard (14x18cm-6x7in) s.d.1845 panel (D.FL 2000)
£1061 $1835   (7-Sep-91 CH.AM200) Grazing cows in a meadow near a fence aand a pollard-willow (28x34cm-11x13in) s. panel (D.FL 3500)
£1064 $1851   (17-Sep-91 CH.AM530) A chicken yard with hens, a cockerel, and a turkey among architecturalruins (13x17cm-5x7in) s. panel (D.FL 3500)
£1300 $2314   (26-Nov-91 PH90) Still life with copper pot, earthenware jugs and basket in barn interior (31x40cm-12x16in) s.d.1847
£1300 $2353   (21-May-92 CSK136/R) Cockerell and chickens in landscape (33x45cm-13x18in) s.d.1860 panel
£1376 $2450   (30-Oct-91 CH.AM263) Poultry in landscape (18x23cm-7x9in) s.d.1877 panel (D.FL 4500)
£1487 $2692   (3-Dec-91 SY.MI115) Nature morte con pavoni e pollame (13x17cm-5x7in) s.d.1870 panel (I.L 3200000)
£1800 $3438   (29-Jun-92 PHB182) Peacock with poultry (19x24cm-7x9in) s.d.1875 panel pair

VERHOEVEN-BALL, Adrien Joseph (1824-1882) Belgian
£8000 $14640   (15-May-92 TE416/R) Peter Paul Rubens in studio of Frans Snyders (76x91cm-30x36in) s.d.1872 i.verso

VERHULST (?) ?
£767 $1334   (14-Apr-92 GM.B666/R) Marine (143x200cm-56x79in) (B.FR 46000)

VERKOLJE, Jan (1650-1693) Dutch
£679   *$1215*   *(12-Nov-91 SY.AM342) Elegant couple about to mount horses with staircase and terrace behind (20x24cm-8x9in) i.verso pen wash (D.FL 2200)*

VERKOLJE, Nicolaes (attrib) (1673-1746) Dutch
£1354 $2437   (19-Nov-91 RAS.K405/R) Caritas Romana (60x76cm-24x30in) (D.KR 15000)
£3800 $6650   (3-Apr-92 C91/R) Venus with Helen and Paris (48x48cm-19x19in)

VERKOLJE, Nicolaes (circle) (1673-1746) Dutch
£2000 $3840   (10-Jul-92 C164/R) Young woman sewing in interior (32x27cm-13x11in)

VERKOLJE, Nicolaes (circle) (1673-1746) Dutch-cont.
£3300 $5775   (31-Mar-92 PH93/R) Two children arguing over bowl of fruit in draped
                  stone window arch (52x41cm-20x16in)

VERLAT, C M M (1824-1890) Belgian
£667 $1167   (24-Sep-91 GM.B658) Musee Plantin (54x66cm-21x26in) (B.FR 40000)

VERLAT, Charles Michel Maria (1824-1890) Belgian
£1600 $2848   (28-Nov-91 CSK110) Little girl with smooth-coated pinscher
                  (183x147cm-72x58in) s.d.1868 panel

VERLEY, Olivier Suire (20th C) French?
£756 $1323   (25-Sep-91 CC.P7) Marais o'Arts (60x73cm-24x29in) (F.FR 7500)
£1008 $1764   (25-Sep-91 CC.P6) Saint-Clement des Baleines (65x81cm-26x32in)
                  (F.FR 10000)
£1109 $1941   (25-Sep-91 CC.P5) Le carenage (50x65cm-20x26in) (F.FR 11000)

VERLINDE, Claude (20th C) ?
£2490 $4308   (23-Mar-92 AB.L115/R) La ville (97x130cm-38x51in) s. s.i.verso
                  (S.FR 6500)
*£418 $760   (11-Dec-91 ZZ.F128) Le village de la folie (19x24cm-7x9in) s. lead pencil
                  (F.FR 4100)*
*£611 $1112   (11-Dec-91 ZZ.F132/R) Personnage au haut de forme (65x38cm-26x15in) s.
                  lead pencil Indian ink wash (F.FR 6000)*

VERMEER OF HAARLEM, Jan (younger) (1656-1705) Dutch
£2653 $4696   (10-Feb-92 GL.P5/R) Troupeau dans un paysage au soleil couchant
                  (33x41cm-13x16in) s.d.1678 (F.FR 26000)

VERMEER, Barent (17th C) Dutch
£17065 $30887   (21-May-92 L.K163/R) Still life of peaches, plums, pears and other fruit
                    on stone ledge (64x76cm-25x30in) (DM 50000)

VERMEHREN, Frederik (1822-1910) Danish
£1364 $2292   (27-Aug-91 RAS.K170/R) Farmer cutting a cudgel (37x21cm-15x8in) s.d.1853
                  (D.KR 15500)

VERMEHREN, Gustav (1863-1931) Danish
£551 $998   (5-Dec-91 D.V252) Landscape with farmhouse and windmill beyond
                  (28x39cm-11x15in) mono. (A.S 11000)
£579 $996   (15-Oct-91 RAS.K286/R) Interior with old man peeling potatoes
                  (43x49cm-17x19in) s.d.1919 (D.KR 6500)
£835 $1494   (6-May-92 KH.K17) Girl sewing outside a white painted farmhouse
                  (53x46cm-21x18in) s. (D.KR 9500)
£852 $1534   (30-Jan-92 RAS.V690/R) Cottage interior with man smoking pipe s.d.1923
                  (D.KR 9500)

VERMEHREN, Sophus (1866-1950) Danish
£485 $858   (23-Apr-92 RAS.V926) Interior with old man filling his pipe
                  (66x49cm-26x19in) s. (D.KR 5500)
£587 $1056   (19-Nov-91 RAS.K288/R) Interior with young girl looking in mirror
                  (48x49cm-19x19in) s. (D.KR 6500)
£852 $1534   (30-Jan-92 RAS.V691/R) Interior with girl reading (51x48cm-20x19in) s.
                  (D.KR 9500)

VERMEHREN, Yelva (?) ?
£1073 $1867   (19-Sep-91 D.V108/R) Flowers in glass pot (55x48cm-22x19in) s.
                  (A.S 22000)

VERMEIR, Alfons (20th C) Belgian?
£545 $987   (21-May-92 SY.AM79) Landscape (70x80cm-28x31in) board (D.FL 1800)
£617 $1123   (11-Dec-91 CH.AM52) View on harbour with boat along quai
                  (60x80cm-24x31in) s. (D.FL 2000)

VERMEULEN, A T (?) Dutch
£1000 $1830   (15-May-92 TE393) Candlelight market (51x41cm-20x16in) s. panel

VERMEULEN, Andreas Franciscus (circle) (1821-1884) Dutch
£1200 $2136   (28-Nov-91 B103/R) Candlelit market (69x54cm-27x21in) panel

VERMEULEN, Andries (1763-1814) Dutch
£1162 $2022   (14-Apr-92 SY.AM180/R) Candlelit scenes (26x21cm-10x8in) s. panel pair
                  (D.FL 3800)
£4696 $8500   (21-May-92 CH.NY1/R) Traveller conversing with shepherd on riverbank,
                  figures and town beyond (28x43cm-11x17in) s. panel
£11000 $19580   (1-Nov-91 C131/R) Winter landscape with skaters and kolf players by
                    windmill (35x51cm-14x20in) s. panel
£33721 $58000   (9-Oct-91 CH.NY1/R) Winter landscape with figures skating, horse-drawn
                    sleigh, windmill beyond (85x110cm-33x43in) s.d.1798
*£506 $900   (30-Oct-91 D.NY92) Frozen waterway near windmill with skaters and other
                  peasants (38x48cm-15x19in) s. W/C*

VERMEULEN, Andries (after) (18/19th C) Dutch
£780 $1443   (12-Jun-92 TE619/R) Skaters on a lke by a village (36x51cm-14x20in)

VERMEULEN, Andries (circle) (18/19th C) Dutch
£1200 $2100   (27-Feb-92 CSK132) Horse-drawn sleigh on frozen moat with skaters
(14x16cm-6x6in) panel

VERMEULEN, Andries (style) (18/19th C) Dutch
£3400 $5950   (3-Apr-92 C145/R) Winter landscape with skaters and sleigh on frozen
waterway (38x52cm-15x20in) panel

VERMEYEN, Jan Cornelisz (1500-1559) Dutch
£9259 $16759   (5-Dec-91 SY.MO259/R) Portrait d'homme (60x49cm-24x19in) panel
(F.FR 90000)

VERNA, Claudio (1937-) Italian
£510 $907   (29-Nov-91 F.F60) Composizione (55x76cm-22x30in) s.d.1990 mixed media
cardboard (I.L 1100000)

VERNAY, Francois (1821-1896) French
£527 $928   (6-Apr-92 GGL.L6/R) Paysage au soleil couchant (28x69cm-11x27in) s.
chl.htd.gouache W/C (F.FR 5200)

VERNER, Elizabeth O'Neill (1884-?) American
£1879 $3250   (6-Sep-91 S.BM192/R) A View of Charleston, St Michael's Episcopal Church
(43x33cm-17x13in) s. pastel panel
£2361 $4250   (22-Nov-91 S.BM69/R) Pipe smoking (33x28cm-13x11in) s. pastel canvasboard
£2527 $4750   (18-Dec-91 SY.NY197/R) The flower seller (22x22cm-9x9in) s. pastel linen
on board

VERNER, Frederick Arthur (1836-1928) Canadian
£457 $836   (14-May-92 SY.T1) Village at dusk (21x33cm-8x13in) s.d.1898 W/C
(C.D 1000)
£480 $845   (10-Apr-92 K200) Wooded landscape with sheep grazing in foreground
(51x69cm-20x27in) s.d.1889 W/C
£550 $974   (6-Nov-91 SY.T227) View of farmyard with thatched cottage
(25x36cm-10x14in) s.d.1896 W/C (C.D 1100)
£600 $1068   (31-Oct-91 D100/R) Herd of buffalo (33x51cm-13x20in) s.d.1900 W/C bodycol
£822 $1504   (14-May-92 SY.T69 a) Tending flock (43x72cm-17x28in) s.d.1890 W/C
(C.D 1800)
£878 $1580   (18-Nov-91 HO.ED89/R) Untitled - boy near stream (22x32cm-9x13in) s. W/C
(C.D 1800)
£900 $1593   (6-Nov-91 SY.T224/R) Anne Hathaway's cottage (25x51cm-10x20in)
s.indist.d. W/C (C.D 1800)
£2488 $4428   (25-Nov-91 W.T1582/R) Grazing buffalo (30x60cm-12x24in) s. W/C (C.D 5000)

VERNERT, Leon Job (19th C) ?
£493 $897   (27-May-92 DUR.M373/R) Paisaje al anochecer (56x107cm-22x42in) s.d.1866
(S.P 90000)

VERNET, Carle (1758-1836) French
£504 $856   (24-Oct-91 D.P4) Cavalier (27x19cm-11x7in) s. W/C pen (F.FR 5000)
£661 $1210   (15-May-92 AT.P219) La chasse a courre - le Bat-l'eau (35x47cm-14x19in)
black chk htd white (F.FR 6500)
£1511 $2750   (28-May-92 SY.NY173/R) Startled horses in stable (41x59cm-16x23in) pen
wash
£3189 $5773   (3-Dec-91 CN.P22/R) Entree des Francais a Milan (24x35cm-9x14in) s.
pierre noire pen wash (F.FR 31000)
£4000 $7120   (27-Nov-91 S192/R) Battle scene by Italian port (23x35cm-9x14in) s.
pencil pen wash htd white bodycol
£5133 $9240   (22-Nov-91 AGS.P140) Les preparatifs d'une course de chevaux
(27x52cm-11x20in) pen (F.FR 50000)

VERNET, Horace (1789-1863) French
£6000 $11160   (17-Jun-92 S441/R) Cavalry officer. Soldiers in moonlight. Soldier
resting by tree. Cavalry officer preparing for atta (31x23cm-12x9in)
two init. four

VERNET, Horace (style) (1789-1863) French
£2300 $4002   (19-Sep-91 TL428) Harbour view with fisherfolk (76x91cm-30x36in)

VERNET, Jean Antoine (attrib) (1716-1775) French
£2062 $3773   (2-Jun-92 FN.S2784/R) Three master in heavy seas before harbour with
lighthouse on rock beyond (76x147cm-30x58in) (DM 6000)

VERNET, Jean Jacques (circle) (?) French
£2528 $4500   (30-Oct-91 D.NY48) Travellers looking out on inland waterway
(61x76cm-24x30in)

VERNET, Joseph (1714-1789) French
£4587 $8532   (18-Jun-92 SY.MO163/R) Vue de la Cote Mediterraneenne avec pecheurs
(16x12cm-6x5in) copper oval (F.FR 45000)
£7076 $12383   (1-Apr-92 CSC.P21/R) Paysage avec baigneuses (40x48cm-16x19in)
(F.FR 68000)
£12232 $22752   (18-Jun-92 SY.MO55/R) Coucher de soleil (21x25cm-8x10in) s. panel
(F.FR 120000)
£35678 $66361   (18-Jun-92 SY.MO62/R) Combat naval (86x130cm-34x51in) s.d.1786
(F.FR 350000)

VERNET, Joseph (1714-1789) French-cont.

£38187	$70647	(10-Jun-92 ZZ.F60/R) Cavaliers sur un pont effrayes par l'orage (88x132cm-35x52in) s. indist.d.17.. (F.FR 375000)
£61728	$111728	(5-Dec-91 SY.MO174/R) Vue d'un port Mediterraneen (51x73cm-20x29in) s.d.1775 (F.FR 600000)
£782123	$1400000	(17-Jan-92 SY.NY72/R) Morning landscape with fishermen. A calm sea in moonlight (303x260cm-119x102in) s.d.1778 pair
£507	$917	(22-May-92 LD.P57/R) Pont sur un fleuve avec roue de moulin (13x25cm-5x10in) black chk wash paper laid down on board (F.FR 5000)
£1134	$1962	(27-Mar-92 CN.P15/R) Paysage anime de lavandieres (18x25cm-7x10in) blk.chk.ink (F.FR 11000)
£1733	$3223	(19-Jun-92 CN.P26/R) Trois hommes au pied d'un arbre (36x25cm-14x10in) s. ink (F.FR 17000)

VERNET, Joseph (attrib) (1714-1789) French

£1527	$2780	(11-Dec-91 LD.P37/R) Paysage de campagne avec un pont (33x39cm-13x15in) paper laid down on board (F.FR 15000)
£3086	$5586	(5-Dec-91 SY.MO304/R) Vue de port (29x37cm-11x15in) (F.FR 30000)
£3177	$5750	(20-May-92 D.NY102) Fishermen standing near rock formation (64x81cm-25x32in)
£4420	$8000	(22-May-92 S.BM12/R) Quiet port at sunset (99x137cm-39x54in)
£4972	$9000	(22-May-92 S.BM13/R) Landing at port (99x135cm-39x53in)
£7437	$13460	(4-Dec-91 CH.R118/R) Burrasca con scena di naufragio (72x110cm-28x43in) (I.L 16000000)
£9296	$16825	(3-Dec-91 SY.MI209/R) Veduta di marina tempestosa (63x91cm-25x36in) (I.L 20000000)

VERNET, Joseph (circle) (1714-1789) French

£1518	$2778	(14-May-92 BU.S147/R) Shipwreck by coastal cliffs (52x69cm-20x27in) panel (S.KR 16000)
£1800	$3456	(10-Jul-92 PH28/R) Mediterranean port scene with figures resting on shore opposite town (32x46cm-13x18in)
£2200	$4180	(23-Jun-92 CG652) Italianate landscape with anglers and sailors on rocky shore (86x111cm-34x44in)
£4070	$7000	(9-Oct-91 CH.NY119/R) Shipping in storm with figures drawing in boat (98x137cm-39x54in)
£6522	$11609	(29-Nov-91 GAB.G3111/R) Scene de port Mediterraneen au clair de lune (58x94cm-23x37in) (S.FR 16500)
£8239	$15489	(18-Dec-91 AT.P65/R) Le matin (54x80cm-21x31in) bears sig.d.1767 (F.FR 80000)
£8239	$15489	(18-Dec-91 AT.P192/R) La jeune Napolitaine a la peche (46x74cm-18x29in) bears sig. (F.FR 80000)

VERNET, Joseph (school) (1714-1789) French

£1628	$2800	(13-Oct-91 H.C29/R) Mountain river scene with dam and castle (30x38cm-12x15in) panel
£1798	$3200	(30-Oct-91 D.NY17) View of Mediterranean port with figures brawling (53x69cm-21x27in)
£1860	$3200	(13-Oct-91 H.C28/R) Harbour scene with sailing crafts (30x38cm-12x15in) panel
£2907	$5000	(9-Oct-91 CH.NY159/R) Mountainous landscape with fisherfolk in pool below waterfall (78x51cm-31x20in)
£3913	$7357	(18-Dec-91 AT.P194/R) Rivage mediterraneen par mer agitee (75x98cm-30x39in) (F.FR 38000)
£5249	$9500	(21-May-92 CH.NY207/R) Evening - fisherfolk on rocky outcrop. Storm with ships in distress (49x69cm-19x27in) pair
£5802	$10443	(19-Nov-91 F.R115/R) Burrasca di mare (100x109cm-39x43in) (I.L 12500000)

VERNET, Joseph (studio) (1714-1789) French

£468	$819	(3-Apr-92 AGS.P212) La jeune Napolitaine a la peche (29x44cm-11x17in) blk.chk.htd.white (F.FR 4500)

VERNET, Joseph (style) (1714-1789) French

£1000	$1780	(29-Oct-91 PH21) Sailors trying to salvage their boat off a rocky coastline in stormy seas (45x70cm-18x28in)
£1000	$1800	(21-Nov-91 C2) Mediterranean harbour scene (12x18cm-5x7in) panel
£1312	$2256	(16-Oct-91 AT.P121) Pecheurs dans un paysage mediterraneen (32x40cm-13x16in) (F.FR 13000)
£1587	$2825	(27-Apr-92 BU.K65/R) Romantic landscape with figures resting (71x90cm-28x35in) i.verso (D.KR 18000)
£2800	$4900	(28-Feb-92 C139) Harbour entrance at sunset with fishermen in foreground (79x95cm-31x37in)
£3900	$7020	(22-Nov-91 SWS215/R) A harbour scene (75x99cm-30x39in) bears init.
£5500	$9570	(13-Sep-91 C149/R) Mediterranean coastal scene, with fishermen hauling in nets at dawn (43x64cm-17x25in)
£5740	$10275	(7-May-92 CH.AM27/R) Dawn and sunset - Mediterranean views with fisherfolk at work in calm and storm (41x73cm-16x29in) pair (D.FL 19000)
£10800	$19224	(30-Oct-91 S183/R) Mediterranean harbour scene at sunset (96x120cm-38x47in)

VERNET, Jules (1792-1843) French

£1333	$2280	(13-Mar-92 FN.S367/R) Portrait of Pierre Tattet. Portrait of Anne Tattet (9x8cm-4x3in) min.s.d.1837 gouache ivory oval (DM 3800)

VERNET, Jules (style) (1792-1843) French
£4775 $8500   (22-Jan-92 SY.NY228/R) Harbour in mist at dawn (63x102cm-25x40in)

VERNIER, Emile Louis (1829-1887) French
£1519 $2750   (21-May-92 GRO.B58/R) Harvest scene (41x61cm-16x24in) s.

VERNIER, Jules (1862-?) French
£4024 $6922   (7-Oct-91 CSC.P157/R) Nymphes s.d.1893 (F.FR 40000)

VERNON, Arthur Langley (fl.1871-1922) British
£680 $1210   (21-Jan-92 PH150/R) Walk in garden (61x45cm-24x18in) s.d.80 84
£950 $1653   (18-Sep-91 PHS561) Milkmaid with basket of eggs (61x38cm-24x15in) s.
£950 $1758   (11-Jun-92 CSK237) In the rose garden (25x17cm-10x7in) s.d.83
£1500 $2670   (21-Jan-92 PH142/R) Palm reader (53x36cm-21x14in) s.d.80

VERNON, Emile (19/20th C) British
£2205 $3924   (27-Apr-92 BU.K26/R) Young lady with garland of flowers in her hair (72x54cm-28x21in) s.d.1901 (D.KR 25000)
£3800 $7296   (28-Jul-92 SWS415/R) Auburn beauty. Brunette beauty (37x25cm-15x10in) s. pair
£32161 $57246   (29-Oct-91 PH.T148/R) Young girl with kittens (63x53cm-25x21in) s.d.1919 (C.D 64000)

VERNON, Emile (after) (19/20th C) British
£750 $1440   (28-Jul-92 SWS402/R) Young lady amongst roases (58x43cm-23x17in) paper on canvas

VERNON, Florence (fl.1881-1904) British
£4000 $7400   (12-Jun-92 C194/R) The fairy haunt (46x30cm-18x12in) s.

VERNON, Paul (19th C) French
£7143 $12929   (22-May-92 LD.P21) La mare en foret (21x27cm-8x11in) s. panel (F.FR 70500)

VERNON, W H (1820-1909) British
£650 $1138   (25-Sep-91 HUN2) Cattle watering by a stream beneath Dunster Castle (51x74cm-20x29in)

VERON, Alexandre Rene (1826-1897) French
£1507 $2592   (8-Oct-91 ZEL.L1763/R) Figures and donkey before mill in hilly wooded Ardennes landscape (24x32cm-9x13in) s. panel (DM 4400)
£1702 $3080   (4-Dec-91 NA.BA13) Nocturne, paysage a la riviere (53x64cm-21x25in) s.d.82 panel
£2060 $3872   (18-Dec-91 PR.P68/R) Les rochers a Fontainebleau (31x37cm-12x15in) studio st. board (F.FR 20000)

VERONE (20th C) ?
£1195 $2163   (4-Dec-91 G.Z79/R) Please, don't touch my flowers (59x60cm-23x24in) s. (S.FR 3000)
£1811 $3115   (16-Oct-91 G.Z82/R) Le chat de Cleopatre (92x73cm-36x29in) s. (S.FR 4600)

VERONESE (16th C) Italian
£88398 $160000   (21-May-92 CH.NY15/R) Portrait of young man, wearing striped costume with ruff, gold chain around neck (51x40cm-20x16in)
£21788 $39000   (14-Jan-92 SY.NY24/R) Studies of Rebecca and Eliezar at well (12x10cm-5x4in) pen wash

VERONESE (after) (16th C) Italian
£3230 $5750   (22-Jan-92 D.NY83/R) Holy Family (51x69cm-20x27in)

VERONESE (style) (16th C) Italian
£1200 $2184   (26-May-92 PH164) Mystic marriage of St. Catherine (58x52cm-23x20in) panel
£1404 $2500   (22-Jan-92 D.NY91) Rebecca at well (86x114cm-34x45in)

VERONESE SCHOOL, 15th C Italian
£22099 $40000   (22-May-92 SY.NY5/R) Cupid and Psyche (30cm-12ins circular) tempera panel

VERONESE SCHOOL, 17th C Italian
£3700 $6660   (22-Nov-91 SWS55/R) Joseph and Potiphar's wife (147x110cm-58x43in)
£5525 $10000   (22-May-92 SY.NY177/R) Adoration of shepherds (55x55cm-22x22in) slate

VERONESE SCHOOL, 18th C Italian
£3173 $5806   (4-Jun-92 F.M227/R) Giuditta con la testa di Oloferne (43x35cm-17x14in) slate (I.L 7000000)

VERONESE, Bonifazio or PITATI, Bonfazio see BONIFAZIO DI PITATI

VERONESE, Paolo (1528-1588) Italian
£104322 $178390   (18-Mar-92 D.V43/R) Queen of Cyprus presenting crown to Doge of Venice in 1489 (162x350cm-64x138in) painted with Benedetto and Carletto Caliari (A.S 2100000)
£223464 $400000   (16-Jan-92 CH.NY38/R) Saint Catherine of Alexandria in prison, Holy Ghost above (116x84cm-46x33in)

VERONESE, Paolo (after) (1528-1588) Italian
£2400 $4272   (29-Oct-91 PH117) Saints Mark and Marceliano brought to a marriage
                       (145x231cm-57x91in)
£3632 $6465   (28-Apr-92 F.R30/R) Cena in casa di Simone (250x280cm-98x110in)
                       (I.L 8000000)

VERONESE, Paolo (circle) (1528-1588) Italian
£3200 $5824   (10-Dec-91 PH233/R) Adoration of Kings (58x58cm-23x23in)

VERONESE, Paolo (school) (1528-1588) Italian
£4282 $7750   (20-May-92 D.NY68) Minerva (117x91cm-46x36in)

VERONESE, Paolo (style) (1528-1588) Italian
£1173 $2099   (14-Nov-91 CH.AM14/R) Christ and the Centurion (48x83cm-19x33in)
                       (D.FL 3800)
£2491 $4609   (8-Jun-92 CH.R747/R) Allegoria (153x101cm-60x40in) in oval (I.L 5500000)
£14500 $25375   (1-Apr-92 S231/R) Assembly of Gods (84x124cm-33x49in)

VERONESI, Luigi (1908-) Italian
£13902 $24745   (26-Nov-91 SY.MI165/R) Organico n.28 (106x65cm-42x26in) s.d.61
                       s.i.d.verso (I.L 30000000)
*£788 $1402   (29-Nov-91 F.F32) Senza titolo (34x23cm-13x9in) s.d.1972 indian ink
                       cardboard (I.L 1700000)*

VERPILLEUX, Emile Antoine (1888-1964) British
£1400 $2548   (12-Dec-91 CSK88/R) The sheep auction (51x76cm-20x30in) s.d.1914

VERPOORTEN, Oscar (1895-1948) Belgian
£564 $1032   (12-May-92 C.A388) Scene on the Scheld (50x50cm-20x20in) s. panel
                       (B.FR 34000)
£1658 $3035   (12-May-92 C.A387/R) Scene on the Scheld (90x125cm-35x49in) s.
                       (B.FR 100000)

VERROCCHIO, Andrea (style) (15th C) Italian
£2500 $4500   (21-Nov-91 CSK205) Boy giving money to gypsy mother and child
                       (72cm-28ins circular)

VERSCHAFFELT, Edouard (1874-?) French?
£9446 $17002   (18-Nov-91 AT.P383) La diseuse de bonne aventure (51x66cm-20x26in) s.
                       (F.FR 92000)

VERSCHUIER, Lieve (1630-1686) Dutch
£3395 $6077   (14-Nov-91 CH.AM20/R) States yacht moored in Dutch harbour at night with
                       herdsman and cattle (36x49cm-14x19in) mono. panel (D.FL 11000)

VERSCHURING, Hendrik (1627-1690) Dutch
£8000 $14000   (1-Apr-92 S238/R) Southern landscape with hunting party by villa
                       (43x60cm-17x24in) s. panel
*£4077 $7584   (20-Jun-92 CH.MO256/R) Une armee donnant l'assaut au pied d'une colline
                       (36x45cm-14x18in) s.d.1662 wash (F.FR 40000)*

VERSCHURING, Hendrik (after) (1627-1690) Dutch
£2222 $4022   (19-May-92 GF.L2410/R) Lady riding on horse (59x46cm-23x18in) panel
                       (S.FR 6000)

VERSCHURING, Hendrik (attrib) (1627-1690) Dutch
£6173 $11049   (12-Nov-91 SY.AM207/R) Young lady at dressing table with dog
                       (26x20cm-10x8in) indis.s. panel (D.FL 20000)

VERSCHUUR, Wouter (19/20th C) Dutch
£1488 $2842   (4-Jul-92 BOD.P657) Portrait of horse and cat (18x14cm-7x6in) s. panel
                       (DM 4300)
£4500 $8010   (26-Nov-91 PH9/R) Saddling the horses (26x38cm-10x15in) s. panel
£8500 $14535   (17-Mar-92 PH5/R) Horse with dog and poultry in stable interior
                       (21x29cm-8x11in) s. panel
£1600 $2896   (21-May-92 CSK7/R) Halt at inn (30x40cm-12x16in) s.d.1832 pencil pen W/C

VERSCHUUR, Wouter (jnr) (1841-1936) Dutch
£1529 $2661   (14-Apr-92 SY.AM41/R) Two horses in stable (17x21cm-7x8in) s.d.64 panel
                       (D.FL 5000)
£2446 $4330   (5-Nov-91 SY.AM23/R) Construction of railway (23x36cm-9x14in) s.d.67
                       panel (D.FL 8000)
£6200 $11036   (28-Nov-91 B157/R) Horses in stable (18x25cm-7x10in) s. bears sig.l.verso
                       panel

VERSCHUUR, Wouter (style) (19/20th C) Dutch
£912 $1568   (12-Oct-91 CH.AM197) Peasant family and grey horse by barn in wooded
                       hilly landscape (67x80cm-26x31in) canvas on panel (D.FL 3000)

VERSTAPPEN, Martin (1773-1853) Belgian
£1520 $2751   (23-May-92 G.SB498/R) Paysage de campagne avec cavalier et paysanne et
                       son ane en chemin (44x58cm-17x23in) s.d.1807 (F.FR 15000)

VERSTER, Floris (1861-1927) Dutch
£18519 $33704   (11-Dec-91 CH.AM252/R) Flower still life with hortensias and nasturtium in glass vases (74x56cm-29x22in) s.d.94 (D.FL 60000)

VERSTRAETEN, Edmond (1870-1956) Belgian
£3086 $5617   (11-Dec-91 CH.AM291/R) Landscape with haystacks (40x101cm-16x40in) mono.d.1915 (D.FL 10000)

VERSTRAETEN, J (19th C) ?
£700 $1267   (19-May-92 SWS10/R) Souvenir de Normandie (33x46cm-13x18in) s.d.1869 s.i.verso

VERSTRALEN, Anthonie (1594-1641) Dutch
£24474 $43319   (7-Nov-91 D.V157/R) Skaters in winter landscape (24x31cm-9x12in) panel (A.S 500000)
£27778 $49722   (12-Nov-91 SY.AM89/R) Skaters in winter landscape (21x32cm-8x13in) panel (D.FL 90000)

VERSTRALEN, Anthonie (attrib) (1594-1641) Dutch
£2018 $3471   (16-Oct-91 AT.P51/R) Paysage de riviere gelee (17x13cm-7x5in) panel (F.FR 20000)

VERTANGEN, Daniel (1598-1684) Dutch
£3528 $6245   (6-Nov-91 LT.P67/R) Diane decouvrant la gorssesse de Callisto (31x40cm-12x16in) s. panel (F.FR 35000)
£9119 $16687   (12-May-92 SY.AM131/R) Gathering of gods (39x47cm-15x19in) s. panel (D.FL 30000)

VERTANGEN, Daniel (circle) (1598-1684) Dutch
£2035 $3500   (9-Oct-91 CH.NY87/R) Nymphs sleeping by rocky outcrop while satyr approaches, cattle beyond (33x47cm-13x19in) panel

VERTANGEN, Daniel (style) (1598-1684) Dutch
£950 $1739   (12-May-92 SWS806/R) Two putti with dog in landscape (18x23cm-7x9in) bears init. panel

VERTES, Marcel (1895-1961) French
£756 $1300   (14-Oct-91 H.C85) Reclining woman (25x41cm-10x16in) s.
£420 $726   (25-Mar-92 KM.K1767) Lady with dog on path in park (21x19cm-8x7in) s. W/C pen (DM 1200)
£654 $1125   (12-Oct-91 SY.MO207) Chat du jardin (41x33cm-16x13in) s. pencil (F.FR 6500)
£1811 $3115   (12-Oct-91 SY.MO206/R) Oedipe et le sphinx (38x56cm-15x22in) s.i. pencil (F.FR 18000)
£4024 $6922   (12-Oct-91 SY.MO177) Dessins erotiques (24x40cm-9x16in) two s. i. ball point pen four (F.FR 40000)

VERTIN, Petrus Gerardus (1819-1893) Dutch
£700 $1239   (13-Feb-92 CSK118) Figures in Dutch street (30x23cm-12x9in) s.d.55 panel
£912 $1587   (17-Sep-91 CH.AM502) A view of a town in winter with several skaters and sledges ona frozen canal (16x20cm-6x8in) s.d.91 (D.FL 3000)
£1000 $1860   (16-Jun-92 PH21/R) Dutch street scene (44x34cm-17x13in) s.d.55
£1455 $2575   (22-Apr-92 CH.AM132) View of Amsterdaam with the Dome of the former Lutehran church beyond (22x17cm-9x7in) s.d.90 panel (D.FL 4800)
£2128 $3702   (17-Sep-91 CH.AM501/R) Summer view of canal in a town with a vegetable stall, church beyond (41x53cm-16x21in) s.d.89 (D.FL 7000)
£2141 $3789   (5-Nov-91 SY.AM93/R) Street scene in winter (25x19cm-10x7in) s.d.79 paper (D.FL 7000)
£9500 $17670   (19-Jun-92 C4/R) Dutch street scene (41x47cm-16x19in) s.d.60

VERTUNNI, Achille (1826-1897) Italian
£471 $900   (3-Jul-92 S.W2738) Roman ruin, campagna (20x13cm-8x5in) paper
£1111 $1923   (24-Mar-92 CH.R7) Paesaggio lacustre (15x27cm-6x11in) panel (I.L 2400000)
£1111 $1923   (24-Mar-92 CH.R9) Paesaggio fluviale al tramonto (15x27cm-6x11in) s. panel (I.L 2400000)
£2456 $4200   (12-Mar-92 MFA.C131) Figures overlooking bay (51x41cm-20x16in) s.
£4077 $7542   (9-Jun-92 F.R178/R) Campagna al tramonto (23x54cm-9x21in) s. (I.L 9000000)
£4631 $8012   (24-Mar-92 CH.R27/R) Bufali in un paesaggio paludoso (45x92cm-18x36in) s. (I.L 10000000)
£6571 $11500   (20-Feb-92 SY.NY291/R) Paestum (101x202cm-40x80in) s.i.

VERVEER, Elchanon Leonardus (1826-1900) Dutch
£1067 $1974   (13-Jun-92 CH.AM194) Waiting for the fishing fleet to return (20x26cm-8x10in) s. panel (D.FL 3500)

VERVEER, S L (1813-1876) Dutch
£915 $1701   (16-Jun-92 VN.R300) Beach scene (19x24cm-7x9in) panel (D.FL 3000)

VERVEER, Salomon Leonardus (1813-1876) Dutch
£2599 $4523   (14-Apr-92 SY.AM254/R) Dutch village with figures by dike (20x16cm-8x6in) s. panel (D.FL 8500)
£3976 $6917   (14-Apr-92 SY.AM164/R) Townsfolk on market square (22x19cm-9x7in) s. panel (D.FL 13000)

VERVEER, Salomon Leonardus (1813-1876) Dutch-cont.
£4281 $7450   (14-Apr-92 SY.AM304/R) Figures on waterfront, city beyond
      (36x53cm-14x21in) s.d.61 (D.FL 14000)
£21407 $37248   (14-Apr-92 SY.AM221/R) Capriccio view of a Jewish quarter
      (45x37cm-18x15in) s.d.58 panel (D.FL 70000)

VERVISCH, Godfried (1930-) Belgian
£1882 $3406   (7-Dec-91 KV.L351) Village street (80x120cm-31x47in) s.d.1966
      (B.FR 110000)
£546 $989   *(23-May-92 KV.L383) Composition (54x73cm-21x29in) s. gouache pastel*
      (B.FR 33000)

VERVLOET, Frans (1795-1872) Dutch
£3636 $6436   (22-Apr-92 CH.AM160/R) Church interior, with an officer and elegant
      gentlemen conversing (62x53cm-24x21in) s.i.d.1820 panel (D.FL 12000)

VERVOORT, M (fl.1820-1826) Flemish
£3800 $6764   (27-Nov-91 S17/R) Two cockerels (78x89cm-31x35in) s.d.1821

VERWEE, Alfred Jacques (1838-1895) Belgian
£1838 $3124   (22-Oct-91 GM.B618/R) Vaches au Pre (70x93cm-28x37in) s. (B.FR 110000)

VERWEE, Louis Pierre (1807-1877) Belgian
£1339 $2423   (19-May-92 JRL.S100) Landscape with sheep (62x91cm-24x36in) s. (A.D 3200)
£2700 $4806   (26-Nov-91 PH6/R) Shepherd with flock in landscape (39x55cm-15x22in) s.
      panel

VERWEER, Abraham (?-1650) Dutch
£14815 $26519   (12-Nov-91 SY.AM20/R) Shipping off Fort Rammekens (96x133cm-38x52in) s.
      (D.FL 48000)

VERWEY, Kees (1900-) Dutch
£3636 $6582   (19-May-92 CH.AM161/R) Still life of nasturtiums (45x58cm-18x23in) s.
      (D.FL 12000)
£3636 $6582   (19-May-92 CH.AM147/R) Young ballerina (50x32cm-20x13in) s. (D.FL 12000)
£5152 $9324   (19-May-92 CH.AM196/R) Flower still life (45x60cm-18x24in) s.
      (D.FL 17000)
£36364 $65818   (19-May-92 CH.AM163/R) Dream horse (150x125cm-59x49in) s.d.56
      (D.FL 120000)
£1173 $2135   *(11-Dec-91 CH.AM209) Jeanne, wife of the artist reading (33x26cm-13x10in)*
      s.d.68 W/C (D.FL 3800)
£2006 $3651   *(11-Dec-91 CH.AM215 a) Boulevard des Italiens, Paris (63x49cm-25x19in)*
      s.i.d.22 W/C (D.FL 6500)
£2160 $3932   *(11-Dec-91 CH.AM208) Still life with flowers in vase and apple on plate*
      (23x33cm-9x13in) s.d.78 gouache (D.FL 7000)
£3030 $5485   *(19-May-92 CH.AM159/R) Still life of flowers (66x47cm-26x19in) s.d.74 W/C*
      (D.FL 10000)
£3395 $6179   *(11-Dec-91 CH.AM210/R) Still life with flowers (53x43cm-21x17in) s.d.65*
      W/C (D.FL 11000)
£5556 $10111   *(11-Dec-91 CH.AM215/R) Still life with flowers in vase (62x46cm-24x18in)*
      s.d.72 W/C (D.FL 18000)

VERWILT, Francois (1620-1691) Dutch
£11268 $20394   (3-Dec-91 FN.S2504/R) Flight to Egypt in arcadian landscape with
      fortification on rock (118x166cm-46x65in) s. (DM 32000)

VERWORNER, Ludolf (1867-1927) German
£1289 $2346   (11-Dec-91 N.M641/R) Young couple playing draughts on table before window
      (56x78cm-22x31in) s.i.d.1891 (DM 3700)
£1697 $3088   (27-May-92 D.V611/R) The game of draughts (55x77cm-22x30in) s.d.91
      (A.S 35000)

VESAAS, Oystein (1883-1969) Norwegian
£891 $1542   (23-Mar-92 B.O142/R) Summer landscape (73x60cm-29x24in) s.d.1942 panel
      (N.KR 10000)

VESIN, Jaroslav Fr Julius (1859-1915) Bulgarian
£3484 $6341   (11-Dec-91 N.M642/R) Bulgarian horse market (120x160cm-47x63in)
      s.i.d.1900 (DM 10000)
£6641 $11754   (5-Nov-91 GF.L2160/R) Fox hunting, winter (69x120cm-27x47in) s.i.d.1913
      (S.FR 17000)

VESPIGNANI, Renzo (1924-) Italian
£6033 $11342   (19-Dec-91 F.M151/R) Giardino a Bracciano (98x138cm-39x54in) s.d.1966
      (I.L 13000000)
£14409 $26079   (3-Dec-91 F.R175/R) Vallo Prenestino (75x100cm-30x39in) s.d.1956
      (I.L 31000000)
£2108 $3753   *(27-Nov-91 F.M287/R) Figura femminile (50x30cm-20x12in) s.d.1951 ink W/C*
      (I.L 4550000)
£4568 $7948   *(14-Apr-92 F.M174/R) Gasometro (70x101cm-28x40in) s.d.1963 mixed media*
      (I.L 10000000)

VESTER, Willem (1824-1871) Dutch
£826 $1461   (5-Nov-91 SY.AM380) Figures on frozen canal (15x23cm-6x9in) s.d.1863
      board (D.FL 2700)

VESTER, Willem (1824-1871) Dutch-cont.
£1896 $3299   (14-Apr-92 SY.AM7/R) Wooded landscape with cows on path (30x48cm-12x19in)
             s. panel (D.FL 6200)

VESTIER, Antoine (1740-1824) French
£7200 $12600   (31-Mar-92 PH90/R) Portrait of lady, wearing silk dress decorated with
             roses (65x53cm-26x21in) oval
£5937   *$10567*   *(29-Nov-91 ARC.P113/R) Tete de jeune femme en costume de la Premiere
             Republique (39x31cm-15x12in) pierre noire stumping htd.white
             (F.FR 58000)*

VESTIER, Antoine (attrib) (1740-1824) French
£1170 $2000   (21-Mar-92 W.W4/R) Portrait of young woman in blue dress
             (91x74cm-36x29in)
£6977 $12000   (9-Oct-91 CH.NY17/R) Portrait of lady said to be Princesse de Lamballe,
             standing by tree (79x62cm-31x24in) i. oval

VESTIER, Antoine (school) (1740-1824) French
£1798 $3200   (30-Oct-91 D.NY95) Portrait of elegant lady (89x66cm-35x26in)

VETELET, Theodore Felix (1860-?) French
£988   *$1759*   *(29-Nov-91 GAB.G2185) Demoiselle dans un paysage (46x38cm-18x15in) s.
             (S.FR 2500)*

VETH, Jan (1864-1925) Dutch
£4281 $7578   (5-Nov-91 SY.AM183/R) Portrait of painter Max Liebermann
             (65x51cm-26x20in) s.d.1904 (D.FL 14000)

VETSCH, Christian (20th C) Swiss?
£510 $913   (15-Nov-91 ZOF.Z338/R) Departing to the alpine pastures (35x60cm-14x24in)
             s.d.1979 pavatex (S.FR 1300)
£784 $1404   (15-Nov-91 ZOF.Z337/R) Departing to the alpine pastures
             (25x130cm-10x51in) s.d.1984 pavatex (S.FR 2000)

VETTER, Charles (1858-?) German
£619 $1076   (18-Sep-91 N.M738/R) Residenz, Munich (62x45cm-24x18in) s.d.1921
             i.stretcher (DM 1800)
£1100 $1881   (17-Mar-92 PH87) Interior, Munchner Residenz (62x45cm-24x18in) s.
£1394 $2537   (11-Dec-91 WE.MU204/R) In der Residenz (55x45cm-22x18in) (DM 4000)
£1400 $2604   (16-Jun-92 PH20/R) Busy street scene, winter (40x32cm-16x13in) s.d.1907
£5575 $10146   (12-Dec-91 L.K712) Merry party in Cafe Annast, Odeonsplatz, Munich
             (45x80cm-18x31in) s. (DM 16000)

VEYRASSAT, Jules Jacques (1828-1893) French
£2700 $4806   (26-Nov-91 PH52/R) Loading haycarts (26x34cm-10x13in) s. panel
£2941 $5000   (23-Oct-91 GD.B1321/R) Peasant forcing heavy loaded horse-drawn cart
             uphill on woodland path (27x45cm-11x18in) s.d.1881 board (S.FR 7500)
£3357 $6009   (13-Nov-91 PIC.P91/R) Charrette attelee (17x25cm-7x10in) s.d.68 panel
             (F.FR 33000)
£3488 $6000   (16-Oct-91 CH.NY40/R) The country girl (55x50cm-22x20in) s.d.64
£3538 $6191   (5-Apr-92 CSC.P107/R) La moisson (25x46cm-10x18in) s.d.57 panel
             (F.FR 34000)
£6166 $11778   (1-Jul-92 FB.P67/R) Le dejeuner (64x100cm-25x39in) s.d.1857 (F.FR 60000)
£7293 $13200   (4-Dec-91 NA.BA4) La charrete de foin (51x77cm-20x30in) s.
£16000 $28480   (29-Nov-91 C23/R) The harvesters' return (61x102cm-24x40in) s.d.1879
£461   *$825*   *(14-Nov-91 GRO.B27) Crossing stream (25x30cm-10x12in) s. W/C paper on
             board*
£565   *$1016*   *(20-Nov-91 CN.P66) Le chevalet (6x10cm-2x4in) s. W/C (F.FR 5500)*
£706   *$1249*   *(10-Nov-91 ZZ.F4/R) Chevaux dans le sous bois (20x29cm-8x11in) s. W/C
             (F.FR 7000)*

VEZELAY, Paule (20th C) ?
£1500 $2565   (11-Mar-92 S155/R) Introduction (22x27cm-9x11in) s.d.1931 verso
£8500 $15300   (20-Nov-91 S178/R) Eugene Goossens and Richard Tauber rehearsing at
             Prince's Theatre,Bristol (80x99cm-31x39in) d.1925
£400   *$684*   *(12-Mar-92 B104) Balancing forms (21x27cm-8x11in) pencil col.crayons*

VEZIN, Charles (1858-?) American
£1387 $2400   (6-Sep-91 S.BM280/R) Manhattan (30x41cm-12x16in) s. masonite
£2976 $5000   (28-Aug-91 MFA.C110/R) New York harbour (66x76cm-26x30in) s.

VEZIN, Frederick (19/20th C) British
£1000 $1780   (28-Nov-91 CSK174/R) The proposal (60x80cm-24x31in) s.indis.i.verso

VEZIN, Frederik (1859-?) American
£519 $986   (24-Jun-92 KM.K1295) Hermann, portrait of two year old boy with doll
             (50x40cm-20x16in) s.d.1924 (DM 1500)

VIALAT, Laurent (20th C) French
£615 $1064   (6-Oct-91 E.LA127) St Mammes - effet de soleil (38x55cm-15x22in) s.
             (F.FR 6100)
£1272 $2200   (2-Oct-91 D.NY97) Pont Croix (46x56cm-18x22in) s. s.i.verso

VIALLAT, Claude (1936-) French
£915	$1591	(14-Apr-92 CSC.P85) Empreintes vertes et roses (100x65cm-39x26in) acrylic paper (F.FR 9000)
£915	$1591	(14-Apr-92 CSC.P84) Empreintes bleues et blanches (100x65cm-39x26in) acrylic paper (F.FR 9000)
£1731	$3168	(3-Jun-92 CSC.P185/R) Bas de pantalon I, 1979 (55x51cm-22x20in) acrylic canvas (F.FR 17000)
£2163	$3698	(19-Mar-92 CSC.P84/R) Empreinte acrylic paper triptych (F.FR 21000)
£4990	$9131	(3-Jun-92 CSC.P184/R) Portiere peinte (77x206cm-30x81in) acrylic fabric (F.FR 49000)
£1016	$1768	(16-Apr-92 FB.P265/R) Empreintes (61x85cm-24x33in) mixed media (F.FR 10000)
£1321	$2299	(16-Apr-92 FB.P245/R) Empreintes (65x97cm-26x38in) W/C (F.FR 13000)
£7209	$12327	(21-Mar-92 AT.P70/R) Sans titre (213x134cm-84x53in) print tarpaulin (F.FR 70000)
£8258	$14038	(27-Oct-91 P.V88/R) Sans titre (224x235cm-88x93in) Mauler mordant colours canvas book (F.FR 82000)

VIALLE, B (?) ?
£1091	$1975	(20-May-92 ANS.M131/R) Pareja de bodegones (56x73cm-22x29in) s. two (S.P 200000)

VIANELLI, Achille (1803-1894) Italian
£820	$1460	(28-Nov-91 CSK13) Villa Dackenhausen et Port de Castellamare (25x38cm-10x15in) s.d.1842 pencil wash
£1290	$2347	(12-Dec-91 F.M10/R) Veduta di Napoli (23x33cm-9x13in) s.d.1888 W/C (I.L 2800000)
£2529	$4527	(14-Nov-91 CH.R99) Veduta del golfo di Napoli (22x31cm-9x12in) s. W/C (I.L 5500000)
£4689	$8722	(18-Jun-92 SY.MO427/R) Piazza della Rotunda (29x46cm-11x18in) s.d.1837 ink wash (F.FR 46000)

VIANELLO, Cesare (19th C) Italian?
£1600	$2736	(19-Mar-92 B73/R) St Mark's, Venice (85x62cm-33x24in) s.
£1628	$2914	(17-Nov-91 FB.P101) La marchande de fleurs (46x55cm-18x22in) s. (F.FR 16000)

VIANELLO, Giovanni (1873-1926) Italian
£2891	$5175	(5-May-92 ZEL.L1571/R) Canale Grande with Rialto Bridge (70x99cm-28x39in) s. (DM 8500)

VIANI, Giovanni Maria (1636-1700) Italian
£928	$1605	(27-Mar-92 CN.P6/R) Etude de mains (25x20cm-10x8in) i. blk.white chk.sanguine (F.FR 9000)

VIANI, Lorenzo (1882-1936) Italian
£511	$925	(3-Dec-91 F.R130/R) Mensa dei poveri (36x24cm-14x9in) ink (I.L 1100000)
£927	$1650	(26-Nov-91 SY.MI127) Ritratto (29x20cm-11x8in) s. pencil indian ink (I.L 2000000)
£1854	$3299	(27-Nov-91 F.M220) Peritucco (26x18cm-10x7in) s. ink W/C pencil (I.L 4000000)
£5569	$10470	(19-Dec-91 F.M204/R) Personaggi della Ruche, Parigi (65x48cm-26x19in) s. pastel pencil (I.L 12000000)

VIARD, Georges (fl.1831-1848) French
£3575	$6256	(24-Feb-92 CSC.P29/R) Nature morte a la perruche et au verre de cerise (54x40cm-21x16in) s.d.1860 (F.FR 35000)

VIAU, Domingo (1884-1964) Argentinian
£603	$1050	(19-Sep-91 V.BA110) Plaza (45x37cm-18x15in)

VIBERT, J G (1840-1902) French
£624	$1093	(30-Mar-92 ZZ.F35) Portrait d'Eugene Buttura (106x65cm-42x26in) s. (F.FR 6000)

VIBERT, Jean Georges (1840-1902) French
£1648	$3000	(27-May-92 CH.NY42/R) A pinch of snuff (41x31cm-16x12in) s.d.67 panel
£20000	$37200	(19-Jun-92 C86/R) The carpet seller (70x93cm-28x37in) s.i.d.1871
£21978	$40000	(27-May-92 CH.NY53/R) The diet (73x58cm-29x23in) s. panel
£854	$1537	(19-Nov-91 FP.M103/R) Arranging flowers (35x24cm-14x9in) s. W/C (C.D 1750)
£1163	$2000	(15-Oct-91 CE.NY297) Carmen (34x29cm-13x11in) s.d.1872 W/C paperboard

VICENTE, Eduardo (?) Spanish?
£3557	$6473	(11-Dec-91 FER.M173/R) Pareja bailando (100x80cm-39x31in) s. (S.P 650000)
£465	$850	(13-May-92 FER.M86/R) Cabrero (64x49cm-25x19in) s. W/C (S.P 85000)

VICENTE, Esteban (1904-) Spanish
£2743	$4800	(27-Feb-92 CE.NY155 a/R) Untitled (41x30cm-16x12in) s.verso

VICENTINO, Andrea see MICHIELI, Andrea dei

VICENZINO, Giuseppe (17/18th C) Italian
£8178	$14967	(16-May-92 F.L59/R) Nature morte con fiori (35x55cm-14x22in) pair (S.FR 22000)

VICENZINO, Giuseppe (17/18th C) Italian-cont.
£18000 $32040   (1-Nov-91 C16/R) Mixed flowers in basket on draped table
(68x107cm-27x42in)

VICENZINO, Giuseppe (circle) (17/18th C) Italian
£32000 $56000   (3-Apr-92 C128/R) Mixed flowers with mixed fruit and vegetables on rocky
ledges (116x145cm-46x57in) pair

VICKERS, A H (fl.1853-1907) British
£580 $1015   (3-Apr-92 BW205) Standon Abbey (30x61cm-12x24in) s.

VICKERS, Alfred (19th C) British
£680 $1163   (12-Mar-92 CSK181) Figures beside riverside cottage in landscape
(25x35cm-10x14in) s.
£750 $1283   (12-Mar-92 CSK177/R) Eton College from the Thames (21x30cm-8x12in)
s.d.1879
£1100 $2013   (5-Feb-92 CSK285) On Isis, near Oxford (24x37cm-9x15in) s.
£3523 $6200   (9-Apr-92 FA.PH625/R) Babbicomb Bay (18x36cm-7x14in) s. board
£13000 $22360   (11-Oct-91 C119/R) Windsor Castle from the Brocas Meadows
(62x95cm-24x37in) s.d.1854

VICKERS, Alfred (snr) (1786-1868) British
£1000 $1750   (23-Sep-91 PHB46/R) Bray on the Thames (26x36cm-10x14in) s.indist.d. i.
verso
£1600 $3056   (21-Jul-92 PH281/R) Extensive river landscape with fishing vessels before
town (18x31cm-7x12in) s. board
£2300 $4393   (21-Jul-92 PH280/R) Sandown Bay, Isle of Wight (25x39cm-10x15in)
s.i.d.1854 verso
£2500 $4775   (21-Jul-92 PH279/R) Figures angling and cattle before cottage in wooded
river landscape (70x101cm-28x40in) s.d.1864

VICKERS, Alfred Gomersal (1810-1837) British
£650 $1242   (14-Jul-92 C142/R) Budapest and River Danube (16x22cm-6x9in) with i.
pencil W/C

VICKERS, Alfred H (fl.1853-1907) British
£500 $930   (18-Jun-92 B70) River landscape with cottages (24x44cm-9x17in) s.
£615 $1100   (13-Nov-91 B.SF2180/R) Extensive river landscape (41x81cm-16x32in) s.
£1000 $1720   (3-Mar-92 SWS1571/R) Near Shipley, Kent, Edenbridge (34x54cm-13x21in)
s.i.indist.d. pair
£1000 $1850   (11-Jun-92 CSK110) Distant view of Canterbury (50x76cm-20x30in)
s.i.d.1888 verso
£1300 $2223   (16-Mar-92 LW1844/R) Extensive river landscape with figures, cottages,
boats and mountains (46x81cm-18x32in) s.
£1900 $3382   (28-Apr-92 PH129/R) River landscapes (21x41cm-8x16in) pair

VICTORIAN SCHOOL (19th C) British
£800 $1440   (29-Jan-92 RBB922/R) Portrait of girl with corn sheaf and dog standing in
landscape (86x64cm-34x25in)
£2200 $3982   (18-May-92 HS340/R) Study of three masted sailing ship - East African, in
open seas (55x75cm-22x30in) init.d.95
£3300 $5676   (4-Mar-92 RBB894/R) Seascape with man-of-war sailing ship and early
paddle steamer, rough sea (119x168cm-47x66in) i.verso

VICTORICA, Miguel Carlos (1884-1955) Argentinian
£930 $1600   (9-Oct-91 RO.BA578) Capilla de San Antonio, Cordoba (23x30cm-9x12in) s.
£1802 $3100   (9-Oct-91 RO.BA396) Flores (30x40cm-12x16in) s.
£1823 $3500   (4-Aug-92 V.BA114/R) Paisaje (20x22cm-8x9in)
£2809 $5000   (1-Nov-91 PO.BA41) Paisaje de Toledo (25x30cm-10x12in) s. board
£3226 $6000   (16-Jun-92 RO.BA18) Capilla de San Antonio (28x36cm-11x14in)
£3226 $6000   (16-Jun-92 RO.BA28) Cordoba (29x34cm-11x13in)
£3371 $6000   (1-Nov-91 PO.BA39) Iglesia de San Francisco (66x53cm-26x21in) s. board
£4494 $8000   (1-Nov-91 PO.BA40) Iglesia de Notre Dame (28x34cm-11x13in)
£10674 $19000   (1-Nov-91 PO.BA38) La modelo (139x110cm-55x43in) d.1940
£11236 $20000   (1-Nov-91 PO.BA38) Descendimiento (103x65cm-41x26in) s.d.1953
£690 $1200   (19-Sep-91 V.BA111) Cabeza (50x38cm-20x15in) d.1951 coaldust

VICTORS, Jacobus (1640-1705) Dutch
£2712 $4909   (18-May-92 SY.MI296) Natura morta con piccioni (40x48cm-16x19in)
(I.L 6000000)

VICTORS, Jacobus (attrib) (1640-1705) Dutch
£3058 $5688   (19-Jun-92 ARC.P103) Nature morte aux lievre, pigeon, noix et couteau sur
un entablement (83x59cm-33x23in) s. panel (F.FR 30000)

VICTORS, Jacobus (circle) (1640-1705) Dutch
£1173 $2099   (14-Nov-91 CH.AM112/R) Poultry in yard near pond and mansion beyond
(49x41cm-19x16in) indis.s. panel (D.FL 3800)

VICTORS, Jan (1620-1676) Dutch
£17132 $30323   (7-Nov-91 D.V108/R) Village wedding (70x101cm-28x40in) s. (A.S 350000)

VICTORS, Jan (circle) (1620-1676) Dutch
£5500 $10010   (13-Dec-91 C150/R) Washerwoman and her daughter in scullery
(59x68cm-23x27in) bears sig.

VICTORS, Jan (school) (1620-1676) Dutch
£2875 $5175   (21-Nov-91 BL.P47/R) Samson et Dalila (108x131cm-43x52in) bears sig.
                           (F.FR 28000)

VICTORS, Jan (style) (1620-1676) Dutch
£1600 $2928   (12-May-92 SWS744/R) Vertumnus and Pomona (76x90cm-30x35in)
£1900 $3420   (21-Nov-91 CSK123) Milkmaid with cattle at work and boy with dog on canal
                           bank (81x65cm-32x26in)

VICTORYNS, Anthonie (1612-1655) Flemish
£2500 $4800   (8-Jul-92 S246) Boors in interior (24x33cm-9x13in) panel

VICTORYNS, Anthonie (attrib) (1612-1655) Flemish
£5500 $9790   (30-Oct-91 S101/R) Peasants drinking in barn (39x55cm-15x22in) panel

VIDAL, A (?) ?
£1047 $2000   (3-Jul-92 S.W3824) Gondoliers along Venetian canal (36x51cm-14x20in) s.

VIDAL, Louis (1754-?) French
£4115 $7819   (26-Jun-92 AT.P125/R) Bouquet de fleurs dans un vase en verre
                           (27x21cm-11x8in) (F.FR 40000)
£4634 $8713   (18-Dec-91 AT.P195/R) Trophee au coq, au panier d'oeufs et aux pigeons
                           (77x58cm-30x23in) s. panel (F.FR 45000)
£9302 $16000   (10-Oct-91 SY.NY159/R) Still life of flowers and fruit in a landscape
                           with birds and a weasel (71x103cm-28x41in) s. panel

VIDAR, Frede (20th C) ?
£2107 $3750   (26-Jan-92 JRB.C7/R) The Piper Plays at Plainfield (64x76cm-25x30in) s.

VIEGERS, Bernard (1886-1947) Dutch
£4070 $7000   (16-Oct-91 CH.NY235/R) The ferry near Vollenhove, Holland
                           (57x79cm-22x31in) s.

VIEIRA DA SILVA, Maria Helena (1908-1992) French
£4500 $7785   (26-Jun-92 C10) Untitled (11x15cm-4x6in) mono.
£4624 $8000   (3-Oct-91 SY.NY25/R) Untitled (13x22cm-5x9in) s. i.d.1967stretcher
£11000 $21010   (2-Jul-92 S11/R) Disjoindre (57x30cm-22x12in) s.d.72 tempera paper laid
                           down on canvas
£12000 $20760   (26-Mar-92 C9/R) Untitled (18x15cm-7x6in) s.i.d.1966stretcher
£36598 $63314   (29-May-92 P.V42/R) Composition (46x55cm-18x22in) s. (F.FR 355000)
£37261 $63343   (24-Oct-91 CSC.P84/R) Cite lacustre (55x46cm-22x18in) s.d.77
                           (F.FR 370000)
£95000 $164350   (26-Mar-92 S38/R) Composition (54x74cm-21x29in) s.d.48
£924 $1663   *(19-Nov-91 FB.P182/R) Sans titre (10x12cm-4x5in) mono. ink wash*
                           (F.FR 9000)
£3279 $6000   *(13-May-92 CH.NY329/R) Composition (15x13cm-6x5in) s. ball-point pen over*
                           gouache paper on board
£7847 $13497   (8-Oct-91 CC.P3/R) Lisbonne (20x30cm-8x12in) s.i.d.1948 W/C (F.FR 78000)
£8025 $14605   *(11-Dec-91 CH.AM427/R) Abstract composition (23x17cm-9x7in) W/C*
                           (D.FL 26000)
£13720 $23872   *(15-Apr-92 PLF.P115/R) Composition bleue (33x49cm-13x19in) s.d.77 gouache*
                           (F.FR 135000)
£14841 $26418   *(30-Nov-91 FB.P15/R) Ville (37x55cm-15x22in) s. gouache (F.FR 145000)*
£39448 $74162   *(19-Dec-91 F.M161/R) Senza titolo (70x70cm-28x28in) s.d.1956 gouache*
                           board (I.L 85000000)

VIEN, Joseph Marie (1716-1809) French
£2474 $4280   (27-Mar-92 CN.P39/R) Allegorie de la Prudence (14x20cm-6x8in) paper laid
                           down on canvas (F.FR 24000)
£203874 $379205   (18-Jun-92 SY.MO64/R) La toilette d'une jeune mariee dans le costume
                           antique (100x135cm-39x53in) s.d.1777 (F.FR 2000000)
£559 $1000   *(15-Jan-92 CH.NY80/R) Ruins on Palatine Hill, Rome (16x22cm-6x9in) with*
                           i. num.93 black chk

VIEN, Joseph Marie (style) (1716-1809) French
£1009 $1736   (16-Oct-91 AT.P148) Portrait d'un rabbin (72x59cm-28x23in) d.1780 oval
                           (F.FR 10000)

VIENNESE SCHOOL (?) Austrian
£2235 $3823   (18-Mar-92 D.V319/R) Portrait of Austrian family and dog
                           (73x56cm-29x22in) c.1800 (A.S 45000)
£5961 $10194   (18-Mar-92 D.V328/R) Child with canary (76x58cm-30x23in) c.1800
                           (A.S 120000)

VIERA, Petrona (?) Uruguayan?
£1098 $1900   (30-Sep-91 GC.M28/R) Playa Malvin (26x26cm-10x10in) s.d.1931
£1329 $2300   (30-Sep-91 GC.M27/R) Quinta de Castro (25x26cm-10x10in) s. board

VIERTEL, Carl (1772-1834) Danish
£1054 $1888   (6-May-92 KH.K209/R) Portrait of Nina Catharine Paulsen (41x34cm-16x13in)
                           s.d.1819 (D.KR 12000)

VIETINGHOFF, Egon Alexis von (1903-?) German
£988 $1779   (19-Nov-91 GS.B3300) Still life of soup plate with lemons, knife and egg
                           cups (38x46cm-15x18in) s.d.1932 i.stretcher canvas on panel (S.FR 2500)

VIGEE, Louis (1715-1767) French
£1600 $2912   (11-Dec-91 PH144/R) *Portrait of gentleman in blue jacket* (61x50cm-24x20in) *pastel oval*

VIGEE, Louis (attrib) (1715-1767) French
£2803 $5214   (19-Jun-92 CN.P17/R) *Portrait d'homme* (61x50cm-24x20in) *pastel* (F.FR 27500)

VIGEE-LEBRUN, Marie Louise Elisabeth (1755-1842) French
£46296 $83796   (7-Dec-91 CH.MO42/R) *Portrait de Philippine-Marie-Helene de France* (77x61cm-30x24in) *oval* (F.FR 450000)
£90726 $160585   (7-Nov-91 AT.P73/R) *Les enfants de France* (116x96cm-46x38in) (F.FR 900000)
£150000 $273000   (13-Dec-91 C63/R) *Portrait of Angelica Catalani singing at a pianoforte* (122x91cm-48x36in) s.i.d.1806
£152905 $284404   (18-Jun-92 SY.MO69/R) *Portrait de la Comtesse Maria-Theresa Kinsky* (81x64cm-32x25in) *oval* (F.FR 1500000)
£300000 $546000   (11-Dec-91 S76/R) *Portrait of Countess Catherine Vladimirowna Apraxina* (112x94cm-44x37in) s.d.1796
£9781 $17118   (3-Apr-92 AGS.P218/R) *Portrait de Mademoiselle de Pont, niece du Comte de Coetlosquet* (40x31cm-16x12in) s.d.1818 *pastel* (F.FR 94000)
£34000 $59160   (14-Apr-92 C169/R) *Portrait of Louisa, Queen of Prussia with pearl necklace* (51x41cm-20x16in) *pastel*
£46000 $80040   (14-Apr-92 C168/R) *Portrait of Louisa, Princess Radziwill in velvet dress and lace collar* (59x42cm-23x17in) *pastel*
£70000 $127400   (11-Dec-91 S79/R) *Portrait of Aglae de Polignac, Duchesse de Guiche* (80x64cm-31x25in) s.d.1784 *pastel oval*

VIGEE-LEBRUN, Marie Louise Elisabeth (after) (1755-1842) French
£1080 $1900   (8-Apr-92 D.NY74) *Self-portrait* (99x79cm-39x31in) i.verso
£1350 $2322   (5-Mar-92 D83/R) *Portrait of artist at work* (94x81cm-37x32in)
£1404 $2500   (22-Jan-92 SY.NY58/R) *Self-portrait of artist with daughter* (98x76cm-39x30in)
£1542 $2775   (24-Nov-91 SY.S249/R) *Self-portrait* (24x20cm-9x8in) i.verso (A.D 3500)
£2107 $3750   (22-Jan-92 SY.NY60/R) *Self-portrait. Madame Vigee Le Brun* (102x83cm-40x33in) *pair*
£2320 $4200   (21-May-92 CH.NY167/R) *Portrait of artist* (101x81cm-40x32in)
£3500 $6300   (21-Nov-91 CSK243/R) *Portrait of the artist* (99x76cm-39x30in)
£5500 $10560   (10-Jul-92 C193/R) *Portrait of Queen Marie Antoinette of France, holding rose in landscape* (117x89cm-46x35in)

VIGEE-LEBRUN, Marie Louise Elisabeth (attrib) (1755-1842) French
£4073 $7250   (22-Jan-92 D.NY36/R) *Portrait of Martin van Nieuwenhove, praying to Madonna and Child* (46x66cm-18x26in) *copper diptych after Hans Memling*

VIGEE-LEBRUN, Marie Louise Elisabeth (circle) (1755-1842) French
£1512 $2676   (6-Nov-91 LT.P33/R) *Portrait presume de Monsieur Landry de Saint-Aubin* (73x60cm-29x24in) *oval* (F.FR 15000)

VIGEE-LEBRUN, Marie Louise Elisabeth (style) (1755-1842) French
£709 $1284   (23-May-92 G.SB498 b/R) *La fillette a la pelote de laine* (43x34cm-17x13in) (F.FR 7000)
£3200 $5824   (10-Dec-91 PH118/R) *Peace and Abundance* (97x130cm-38x51in)

VIGIL, Romando (1902-) American
£973 $1800   (14-Jun-92 S.BM214/R) *Untitled* (53x56cm-21x22in) s. W/C ink wash

VIGIL, Thomas (1889-1960) American
£486 $900   (14-Jun-92 S.BM71/R) *Tesuque snake dancers* (20x25cm-8x10in) s. gouache

VIGNALI, Jacopo (school) (1592-1664) Italian
£3488 $6000   (9-Oct-91 CH.NY63/R) *Hagar and angel* (168x216cm-66x85in)

VIGNET, Henri (1857-1920) French
£1099 $2100   (16-Jul-92 SY.NY410/R) *Street scene in Rouen* (45x32cm-18x13in) s.i.

VIGNOLES, Andre (?) ?
£520 $889   (17-Mar-92 PH150/R) *Summer landscape* (54x73cm-21x29in) s.
£975 $1756   (19-Nov-91 FB.P100/R) *Nature morte a la toile de paysage* (114x146cm-45x57in) s.d.61 (F.FR 9500)

VIGNON, Claude (1593-1670) French
£3500 $6230   (29-Oct-91 PH103/R) *St. Anthony* (89x116cm-35x46in)
£8380 $15000   (17-Jan-92 SY.NY160/R) *King Solomon worshipping the false idols of Baal* (76x77cm-30x30in) s.d.1626

VIGNON, Claude (circle) (1593-1670) French
£800 $1536   (10-Jul-92 C202 a/R) *Young man wearing ornate gilt plumed helmet and classical costume* (10cm-4ins circular) panel

VIGNON, Victor (1847-1909) French
£1545 $2904   (16-Dec-91 AGS.P28/R) *La sortie de l'ecole* (19x27cm-7x11in) init. (F.FR 15000)
£2314 $3980   (11-Oct-91 HC.P41/R) *Vue de la Seine* (16x29cm-6x11in) s.d.1874 (F.FR 23000)

VIGNON, Victor (1847-1909) French-cont.
£3074	$5533	(2-Feb-92 ZZ.F61/R) Bord de Seine, Paris (16x30cm-6x12in) s. d.1874 (F.FR 30000)
£3429	$6000	(28-Feb-92 SY.NY28/R) Spring landscape (32x41cm-13x16in) s.
£4942	$8500	(12-Oct-91 SY.NY18/R) Eglise de Jonay Le Comte (46x55cm-18x22in) s.d.85
£5000	$9550	(1-Jul-92 S133/R) La route en hiver (42x37cm-17x15in) s.
£5714	$10000	(25-Feb-92 CH.NY7/R) Village de l'Ile de France (55x81cm-22x32in) s.
£9734	$17520	(2-Feb-92 ZZ.F98/R) Eglise et village de Jouay-le-Comte (46x55cm-18x22in) s.d.1885 (F.FR 95000)

VIGNY, Sylvain (1902-1970) French
| £807 | $1388 | (20-Oct-91 I.N50) L'entree du port (47x64cm-19x25in) s. paper (F.FR 8000) |

VIGO, Abraham R (1893-1957) Argentinian
| £559 | $1000 | (6-May-92 V.BA113) Paisaje (56x70cm-22x28in) |

VIIRILA, Reino (1901-) Finnish
| £582 | $1036 | (1-Dec-91 HOR.H247) Red roof (50x61cm-20x24in) s.d.1952 (F.M 4500) |
| £704 | $1246 | (6-Nov-91 HOR.H141) Mountain birches (50x73cm-20x29in) s.d.1953 (F.M 5000) |

VIKE, Harald (1906-) Norwegian/Australian
£855	$1521	(27-Apr-92 J.M240 a) Reclining nude (46x58cm-18x23in) s. (A.D 2000)
£1709	$3043	(27-Apr-92 J.M262 a) Evening in Capricornia, Bowen (90x105cm-35x41in) s. canvas on board (A.D 4000)
£441	*$784*	*(26-Nov-91 J.M1087) At Elwood (32x40cm-13x16in) s. mixed media (A.D 1000)*

VIKHAGEN, Havard (1952-) Norwegian
| £658 | $1133 | (7-Oct-91 B.O145/R) Stormy weather (113x146cm-44x57in) (N.KR 7500) |

VIKSTEN, Hans (1926-1987) Swedish
£668	$1189	(27-Nov-91 BU.S23/R) Composition (120x99cm-47x39in) s.d.1965 (S.KR 7000)
£710	$1284	(19-May-92 AB.S5336/R) The hospital (108x90cm-43x35in) s.d.66 (S.KR 7500)
£763	$1359	(27-Nov-91 BU.S39/R) Joy of life (120x120cm-47x47in) s.d.1965 (S.KR 8000)
£949	$1736	(13-May-92 BU.S216/R) 'Handelserymd' (89x115cm-35x45in) s.d.1967 (S.KR 10000)

VILA ARUFAT, Antonio (1896-1989) Spanish
| £2765 | $5198 | (17-Dec-91 BRO.B422) Estudi, nino comiendo sopa (55x46cm-22x18in) s.d.1964 mono.i.d.verso (S.P 500000) |

VILA PUIG, Joan (1892-1963) Spanish
| £1607 | $2845 | (12-Feb-92 ANS.M121/R) Paisaje con pueblo (46x55cm-18x22in) s. (S.P 290000) |

VILA Y PRADES, Julio (1873-1930) Spanish
£1355	$2547	(16-Dec-91 ANS.M121/R) Dama paseando con su perro (29x16cm-11x6in) s.i. panel (S.P 245000)
£1786	$3000	(1-Sep-91 PO.BA19) Contemplando el becerro (100x151cm-39x59in) s.
£1966	$3500	(1-Nov-91 PO.BA19) Playa (36x51cm-14x20in) s.
£4105	$7471	(26-May-92 DUR.M36/R) Romeria (38x46cm-15x18in) s. (S.P 750000)
£6541	$11251	(7-Oct-91 ANS.M98/R) A la orilla del mar (40x55cm-16x22in) s. (S.P 1200000)
£8242	$15000	(27-May-92 CH.NY231/R) Boats in the harbour at St Tropez (60x90cm-24x35in) s.

VILA, J (?) ?
| £492 | $900 | (13-May-92 FER.M63/R) Vista de San Francisco el Grande desde el Manzanares (35x43cm-14x17in) s. panel (S.P 90000) |

VILA-PUIG, Juan (1890-1963) Spanish
| £3874 | $6624 | (17-Mar-92 FER.M146/R) Paisaje del Pirineo catalan, Salardu (60x73cm-24x29in) s. (S.P 700000) |
| £3874 | $6624 | (17-Mar-92 FER.M147/R) Paisaje del Pirineo catalan, Santiga (60x73cm-24x29in) s. s.i.verso (S.P 700000) |

VILAR, J (19th C) Spanish
| £927 | $1594 | (7-Oct-91 ANS.M190/R) Paisaje con casas (90x47cm-35x19in) s. (S.P 170000) |
| £981 | $1688 | (7-Oct-91 ANS.M191/R) Paisaje (90x47cm-35x19in) s. (S.P 180000) |

VILARO, Carlos Paez (20th C) Uruguayan
| £877 | $1500 | (21-Mar-92 W.W65/R) Velorio en Palermo (71x99cm-28x39in) s.d.55 s.verso board |

VILATO, Javier (1921-) French
£1220	$2122	(16-Apr-92 FB.P104/R) Tot le matin (55x46cm-22x18in) s. d.VII 59verso (F.FR 12000)
£1304	$2322	(29-Nov-91 GAB.G2952/R) Figure (60x72cm-24x28in) s. d.II 68 V 68verso (S.FR 3300)
£1626	$2829	(16-Apr-92 FB.P127/R) Le barrage (73x60cm-29x24in) s. d.VII 59verso (F.FR 16000)

VILIMEK, Johann (1860-?) Austrian
| £629 | $1120 | (29-Nov-91 ZEL.L1113/R) Still life of Japanese doll, Satsuma porcelain and vase on table (66x51cm-26x20in) s.d.1930 (DM 1800) |

VILLA, Aleardo (1865-1906) Italian
£3900 $6942   (21-Jan-92 SWS932/R) Market day (100x155cm-39x61in) s.d.85
£4183 $7153   (19-Mar-92 F.M110/R) Ritratto di giovane uomo a cavallo con Alano
     (70x100cm-28x39in) s. (I.L 9000000)

VILLA, Emile (19th C) French
£1149 $2000   (11-Sep-91 D.NY91) Portrait of woman in fancy headpiece thought to be
     Natohalie Bertholet (28x20cm-11x8in) s.

VILLA, Hernando (20th C) American
£474 $900   (24-Jun-92 B.SF6407/R) Crashing waves (24x34cm-9x13in) s. W/C
£1184 $2250   (24-Jun-92 B.SF6404/R) Sailing along coast (57x48cm-22x19in) s.d.9.48 W/C

VILLAAMIL, Jenaro Perez see PEREZ DE VILLAAMIL, Genaro

VILLACRES, Cesar A (20th C) South American
£791 $1400   (13-Feb-92 S.W2697/R) View of the Seine at dusk (61x91cm-24x36in)
     s.d.1957
£800 $1400   (28-Feb-92 SY.NY162/R) Place Clichy (51x61cm-20x24in) s.

VILLALOBOS MASTER (15th C) Spanish
£10773 $19500   (22-May-92 SY.NY126/R) Flight into Egypt (71x71cm-28x28in) oil tempera
     panel

VILLANI, Gennaro (1885-) Italian
£544 $1006   (8-Jun-92 CH.R677) Bambini nell'aia (13x19cm-5x7in) s. board
     (I.L 1200000)
£1019 $1763   (24-Mar-92 CH.R133) Nel parco (47x40cm-19x16in) s. canvas on board
     (I.L 2200000)

VILLANUEVA, Rafael (1932-) Spanish
£610 $1079   (12-Feb-92 ANS.M110/R) Esquema de poder (75x53cm-30x21in) s.d.1985
     (S.P 110000)

VILLEBOIS, Pierre (18th C) French
£14418 $27106   (18-Dec-91 AT.P62/R) Concert sur la terrase d'un palais (73x91cm-29x36in)
     s.d.741 (F.FR 140000)

VILLEGAS Y CORDERO, Jose (1848-1922) Spanish
£1364 $2347   (16-Oct-91 FER.M220/R) El seminarista (53x32cm-21x13in) s.d.89
     (S.P 250000)
£3000 $5340   (27-Nov-91 S360/R) Feeding poultry in backstreet (70x39cm-28x15in) s.
£3600 $6228   (4-Oct-91 C124/R) The letter (24x18cm-9x7in) s. panel
£12791 $22000   (17-Oct-91 SY.NY121/R) Bathers at Biarritz (16x25cm-6x10in) s.i. panel
£13684 $24904   (26-May-92 DUR.M28/R) En la playa (15x24cm-6x9in) s. panel (S.P 2500000)
£32796 $55753   (24-Mar-92 DUR.M29/R) Carmen (126x87cm-50x34in) s.d.1907 (S.P 6000000)
£36021 $63037   (18-Feb-92 DUR.M12/R) Baile andaluz (43x74cm-17x29in) s. (S.P 6500000)
£116279 $200000   (16-Oct-91 CH.NY170/R) Afternoon by the sea, Biarritz (62x90cm-24x35in)
     s.d.1906
£1117 $2000   (13-Nov-91 B.SF2242/R) Papal audience (47x65cm-19x26in) s. W/C
£1742 $3100   (22-Jan-92 SY.NY542/R) Afternoon nap (45x28cm-18x11in) s. W/C
£2189 $3985   (26-May-92 DUR.M30/R) La siesta (44x26cm-17x10in) s. W/C (S.P 400000)
£2463 $4483   (26-May-92 DUR.M29/R) La audiencia (44x66cm-17x26in) s. W/C (S.P 450000)
£3955 $7000   (6-Nov-91 D.NY37/R) Traje de Luces (85x51cm-33x20in) s. W/C

VILLEGAS, Jose (?) Spanish
£3826 $6505   (22-Oct-91 DUR.M28/R) Venecia (45x72cm-18x28in) s. (S.P 700000)

VILLEGLE, Jacques de la (1926-) French
£2320 $4013   (29-Mar-92 P.V99/R) Rue de la Perle (81x104cm-32x41in) s. s.i.d.70verso
     torn posters canvas (F.FR 22500)
£3141 $5685   (21-May-92 CC.P97) Passage Villemot (110x85cm-43x33in) s.d.1964verso torn
     posters canvas (F.FR 31000)
£3608 $6242   (29-Mar-92 P.V98/R) Boulevard de la Bastille (70x87cm-28x34in)
     s.d.1968verso torn posters canvas (F.FR 35000)

VILLEGOS, F (19th C) Spanish
£743 $1300   (18-Feb-92 CE.NY263) Sip of wine (55x68cm-22x27in) s.

VILLELIA, Moises (1928-) Spanish
£410 $731   (29-Oct-91 BRO.B279) Composicion simetrica (65x50cm-26x20in) s.d.73 mixed
     media collage (S.P 75000)

VILLENEUVE, Arthur (1910-) Canadian
£976 $1756   (19-Nov-91 FP.M155) Alcan (79x103cm-31x41in) s.d.61 (C.D 2000)

VILLENEUVE, L (?) French
£1646 $3128   (22-Jun-92 AT.P92/R) Les chatons (31x46cm-12x18in) s. panel (F.FR 16000)

VILLEON, Emmanuel de la (1858-1944) French
£1695 $3000   (5-Nov-91 CE.NY4/R) Barque sur la riviere (31x39cm-12x15in) s. panel
£1921 $3400   (9-Nov-91 W.W42/R) Paysage d'automne (25x20cm-10x8in) s. panel
£2371 $4102   (23-Mar-92 CC.P9) Quedeville. Sous-bois. Les roses a Vienne panel one
     paper three (F.FR 23000)

VILLEON, Emmanuel de la (1858-1944) French-cont.

£3162	$5628	(29-Nov-91 GAB.G3168/R) Les genets et Mont Salvar (38x46cm-15x18in) s. (S.FR 8000)
£3593	$6468	(19-Nov-91 FB.P52/R) Rue du village en Suisse (60x45cm-24x18in) s.d.1895 (F.FR 35000)
£3755	$6684	(29-Nov-91 GAB.G3169/R) Coin de parc a Salvar (46x37cm-18x15in) s. panel (S.FR 9500)
£5138	$9146	(29-Nov-91 GAB.G2777/R) Dernieres fleurs d'automne (55x46cm-22x18in) s.d.1905 (S.FR 13000)
£5149	$9681	(18-Dec-91 PR.P99/R) Le peintre dans la campagne (46x55cm-18x22in) s. (F.FR 50000)
£5645	$9992	(10-Nov-91 ZZ.F178/R) Chemin ombrage (50x62cm-20x24in) s. (F.FR 56000)
£6110	$11120	(15-Dec-91 T.B239/R) Coucher de soleil (33x46cm-13x18in) s. panel (F.FR 60000)
£8539	$16224	(24-Jun-92 FB.P96/R) Bord d'etang a l'automne (126x160cm-50x63in) s. (F.FR 83000)
£9486	$16885	(29-Nov-91 GAB.G3167/R) Riviere de la Cannerie (73x60cm-29x24in) s. (S.FR 24000)
£1524	*$2606*	*(22-Mar-92 LT.P137) Paysage aux environs de Grenoble (22x27cm-9x11in) s. W/C (F.FR 14800)*

VILLERET, Francois Etienne (1800-1866) French

£412	*$704*	*(22-Mar-92 LT.P173) Place de la Concorde (8x13cm-3x5in) mono. W/C (F.FR 4000)*
£433	*$740*	*(22-Mar-92 LT.P175) La Madeleine (8x13cm-3x5in) mono. W/C (F.FR 4200)*
£453	*$775*	*(22-Mar-92 LT.P174) Les Champs-Elysees (8x13cm-3x5in) mono. W/C (F.FR 4400)*
£645	*$1129*	*(3-Apr-92 AGS.P219/R) La cathedrale d'anvers (22x16cm-9x6in) s.d.1832 W/C pen (F.FR 6200)*
£1075	*$1957*	*(25-May-92 ARC.P58) La Place de la Concorde (13x18cm-5x7in) s. W/C (F.FR 10600)*
£1745	*$3142*	*(22-Mar-92 AGS.P145/R) Arc de Triomphe. Les Invalides (12x9cm-5x4in) W/C gouache two (F.FR 17000)*

VILLERET, Francois Etienne (attrib) (1800-1866) French

| *£765* | *$1422* | *(18-Jun-92 SY.MO477/R) Place Vendome (14x10cm-6x4in) W/C htd gouache (F.FR 7500)* |

VILLERS, Jacob de (1616-1667) Dutch

| £10299 | $19361 | (18-Dec-91 AT.P35/R) Paysage a la cascade (85x150cm-33x59in) mono. (F.FR 100000) |

VILLERS, Jacob de (attrib) (1616-1667) Dutch

| £4360 | $7500 | (9-Oct-91 CH.NY75/R) Alpine landscape with traveller on path in foreground (112x84cm-44x33in) |

VILLERS, Maximilien (1760-1836) French

| *£1221* | *$2101* | *(10-Oct-91 D.V328/R) Jules de Castellana as boy with drum in garden (8cm-3ins circular) min. W/C gouache (A.S 25000)* |

VILLEVALDE, Bogdan Pavlovich (1818-1903) Russian

| £2800 | $4984 | (28-Nov-91 S412/R) Officer and soldiers of artillery regiment in park at Gatchina (67x96cm-26x38in) s. |

VILLEVIELLE, Leon (1826-1863) French

| £790 | $1375 | (17-Sep-91 CH.AM455) A huntsman and his dog on a wooded bank of the Seine (35x30cm-14x12in) s. (D.FL 2600) |

VILLODAS DE LA TORRE, Ricardo de (1846-1904) Spanish

£665	$1177	(12-Feb-92 ANS.M144/R) Ecce Homo (46x38cm-18x15in) s. (S.P 120000)
£438	*$797*	*(26-May-92 DUR.M103/R) El mercado (26x21cm-10x8in) s. W/C (S.P 80000)*
£493	*$897*	*(26-May-92 DUR.M126/R) El afilador (20x29cm-8x11in) s. W/C (S.P 90000)*

VILLON, Jacques (1875-1963) French

£1856	$3210	(23-Mar-92 GL.P191 b) Evasion (26x34cm-10x13in) s.i.d.1957 tracing paper (F.FR 18000)
£2442	$4200	(12-Oct-91 SY.NY60/R) Portrait of man (24x20cm-9x8in) d.1942 verso
£2825	$5000	(6-Nov-91 CH.NY316/R) Crane, memento mori (24x18cm-9x7in) s.d.33
£8500	$14705	(24-Mar-92 C74/R) Le pigeon a la tasse (33x24cm-13x9in) s. s.i.d.48verso
£11864	$21000	(7-Nov-91 SY.NY158/R) Celestial globes (38x46cm-15x18in) s.d.25
£17341	$30000	(2-Oct-91 SY.NY63 a/R) Jardin a Bernay (38x46cm-15x18in) s. s.d.47 verso
£18000	$31140	(24-Mar-92 C75/R) Caliban (65x54cm-26x21in) s.d.39 s.i.verso
£69176	$123825	(17-Nov-91 GL.P19/R) Mon ame est une infante (80x60cm-31x24in) s. i.d.48verso (F.FR 680000)
£455	*$814*	*(7-May-92 LGB.P154) Crucifixion (42x31cm-17x12in) s. pen (F.FR 4500)*
£457	*$796*	*(13-Apr-92 GL.P17) Le visiteur (29x24cm-11x9in) s.d.1895 W/C (F.FR 4500)*
£773	*$1322*	*(11-Mar-92 LGB.P138) Nu debout, de dos (26x20cm-10x8in) s. pen (F.FR 7500)*
£2277	*$4167*	*(13-May-92 BU.S217/R) Composition (17x22cm-7x9in) s. W/C gouache (S.KR 24000)*
£3000	*$5730*	*(29-Jun-92 CSK24/R) La conversation (27x21cm-11x8in) s.d.95 W/C*
£8000	*$14000*	*(25-Feb-92 SY.NY7/R) Le negre en bonne fortune (30x36cm-12x14in) s. gouache ink wash pencil*

VILLORESI (20th C) Italian
£999 $1778   (29-Apr-92 F.F170/R) Stazione con luce verde e azzurra (40x50cm-16x20in)
       s. s.i.verso (I.L 2200000)

VILLORESI, Franco (20th C) Italian
£731 $1272   (14-Apr-92 F.M18) Paesaggio invernale (46x60cm-18x24in) s.d.1955
       (I.L 1600000)
£743 $1396   (19-Dec-91 F.M53) Figure sotto la pioggia (40x50cm-16x20in) s.d.1952
       (I.L 1600000)
£1487 $2692   (3-Dec-91 F.R229/R) La citta d'inverno (45x55cm-18x22in) s.d.1954
       (I.L 3200000)

VIN, Paul van der (1823-1887) Belgian
£1882 $3406   (3-Dec-91 C.A328/R) Village fair (50x80cm-20x31in) s. (B.FR 110000)

VINAY, Jean (1907-1978) French
£831 $1504   (18-May-92 AT.P157) Le vapeur a Bougival (65x81cm-26x32in) s. s.d.54verso
       (F.FR 8200)

VINCENT (?) ?
£1200 $2196   (2-Jun-92 S694) Henriette Jeane Armaude Andre du Homme seated by urn in
       landscape (10cm-4ins circular) min.s.d.1803 framed

VINCENT, Francois Andre (1746-1816) French
£2240 $4145   (12-Jun-92 ARC.P193/R) Jeune garcon pensif (21x21cm-8x8in) pen wash
       (F.FR 22000)
£5086 $9308   (15-May-92 AT.P221/R) Tete de jeune homme (37x28cm-15x11in) crayons
       (F.FR 50000)
£69317 $128930   (18-Jun-92 SY.MO68/R) Esquisse pour la lecon de labourage
       (60x49cm-24x19in) oil pencil canvas (F.FR 680000)

VINCENT, Francois Andre (attrib) (1746-1816) French
£1628 $2979   (15-May-92 AT.P220/R) Un ange portant une tiare (41x53cm-16x21in)
       sanguine (F.FR 16000)
£1751 $2994   (20-Mar-92 ZZ.F3) Paysage avec cascade (30x45cm-12x18in) sanguine
       (F.FR 17000)

VINCENT, George (1796-c.1831) British
£1600 $3056   (21-Jul-92 PH278/R) Figures with horse, dog and sheep at stream before
       cottages (48x66cm-19x26in)
£4500 $7920   (10-Apr-92 C143/R) Wooded river landscape with figures, sailing barges
       and old tower beyond (65x79cm-26x31in)
£11500 $21965   (15-Jul-92 S66/R) View of the Needles, Isle of Wight, from Christchurch
       (29x39cm-11x15in) s. i.verso panel

VINCENT, Harry A (1864-1931) American
£3911 $7000   (13-Nov-91 B.SF2668/R) Ships in harbour (71x91cm-28x36in) s.
£714 $1200   (14-Aug-91 B.P178/R) Dock scene (58x48cm-23x19in) s. W/C

VINCENT, Jean (20th C) French?
£2661 $4737   (27-Nov-91 CB.P48/R) Tigres (74x100cm-29x39in) s.d.1936 (F.FR 26000)

VINCENT, Rene (1879-1936) French
£454 $781   (20-Oct-91 PLF.P83 b/R) Peugeot, premier au Gd Prix touriste de l'Acf
       (30x24cm-12x9in) studio st. crayon htd.W/C tracing paper (F.FR 4500)

VINCENT, W (?) British?
£600 $1032   (4-Mar-92 ZZ.B181) Fishing boats in choppy coastal waters
       (61x101cm-24x40in) s.

VINCENZINA, Giuseppe (circle) (18th C) Italian
£2000 $3500   (31-Mar-92 PH37) Still life of flowers in basket (47x64cm-19x25in)

VINCHE, Lionel (1936-) Belgian
£770 $1393   (3-Dec-91 C.A484) Hand in hand with a fruit bowl (100x140cm-39x55in)
       s.d.1987 verso (B.FR 45000)

VINCK, Franz (1827-1903) Belgian
£1167 $2030   (14-Apr-92 GM.B639/R) La confidence (50x40cm-20x16in) s. (B.FR 70000)
£2294 $4197   (1-Jun-92 W.T1239/R) Venetian noblewoman with attendants being greeted at
       palazza (51x40cm-20x16in) s. panel (C.D 5000)

VINCK, Joseph (1900-1979) Belgian
£668 $1136   (22-Oct-91 C.A1078/R) Working in the fields (62x80cm-24x31in) s.d.1914
       (B.FR 40000)
£1671 $2840   (22-Oct-91 C.A1077/R) Landscape (67x106cm-26x42in) s.d.1925 (B.FR 100000)

VINCKEBOONS, David (1576-1629) Flemish
£5800 $11136   (7-Jul-92 PH122/R) Distributing bread to poor (29x43cm-11x17in) panel
£15116 $26000   (10-Oct-91 SY.NY9/R) Elegant huntsmen chasing stags on a wooded riverbank
       (28x51cm-11x20in) panel
£28000 $50960   (13-Dec-91 C119/R) Young pickpocket at work as two labourers watch a
       birdnester (26x33cm-10x13in) panel

VINCKEBOONS, David (style) (1576-1629) Flemish
£900 $1620   (21-Nov-91 CSK150) Elegant figures on woodland path by river with ducks
and stocks (29x20cm-11x8in) panel
£1650 $3168   (9-Jul-92 B128) Sportsman shooting duck and other figures in wooded
landscape (25x47cm-10x19in) panel
£2315 $4144   (14-Nov-91 CH.AM53) Bandits gathered around fire in grotto
(20x27cm-8x11in) panel (D.FL 7500)

VINE OF COLCHESTER, J (1809-1867) British
£1650 $2838   (4-Mar-92 RBB981/R) Study of Durham ox standing in landscape
(58x71cm-23x28in) s.d.1843

VINE OF COLCHESTER, John (1809-1867) British
£850 $1556   (5-Feb-92 CSK199) Long-horn bull in landscape (42x52cm-17x20in) s.

VINEA, Francesco (1845-1902) Italian
£1460 $2613   (6-May-92 GD.B1319/R) Adone vinto (25x17cm-10x7in) s.i. panel (S.FR 4000)
£1702 $3250   (16-Jul-92 SY.NY586/R) Peasants on stone steps (15x9cm-6x4in) s.i. panel
£3164 $5727   (18-May-92 SY.MI81) Fanciulla con cane (21x15cm-8x6in) s. panel
(I.L 7000000)
£4775 $8500   (22-Jan-92 SY.NY521/R) Portrait of lady (74x62cm-29x24in) s.
£4833 $8844   (16-May-92 F.L101/R) Gentiluomo in costume del settecento con levriero
(49x37cm-19x15in) s. (S.FR 13000)
£4918 $9000   (17-May-92 DU.E1114/R) Lady in pink silk taking tea in the garden
(46x38cm-18x15in) s.i.
£6557 $12000   (17-May-92 DU.E1115/R) Young woman with kitten and canary
(46x38cm-18x15in) s.
£17442 $30000   (17-Oct-91 SY.NY86/R) Visit (82x149cm-32x59in) s.d.1881

VINES, Hernando (1904-) Spanish
£1093 $2001   (13-May-92 FER.M206/R) Mujer tumbada leyendo (18x23cm-7x9in) s. panel
(S.P 200000)
£1107 $1993   (28-Jan-92 EP.M59/R) Figura (19x24cm-7x9in) s.d.31 board (S.P 200000)
£1232 $2241   (26-May-92 DUR.M70/R) Nocturno (24x19cm-9x7in) s. board (F.FR 25000)
£2541 $4421   (15-Apr-92 PLF.P112) Femme nue (50x40cm-20x16in) s.d.47 (F.FR 25000)
£3590 $6750   (3-Jan-92 DUR.M8/R) Puerto pesquero (53x38cm-21x15in) s. (S.P 650000)
£6921 $12458   (28-Jan-92 EP.M66/R) Pueblo (54x65cm-21x26in) s. (S.P 1250000)

VINES, Roberto (19/20th C) Spanish
£5429 $9500   (20-Feb-92 SY.NY319/R) Retrato de Nina (122x90cm-48x35in) s.d.1919 canvas
on masonite

VINIEGRA Y LASSO, Salvador (1862-1915) Spanish
£2765 $5198   (16-Dec-91 ANS.M102/R) Fiesta marinera (60x110cm-24x43in) s. (S.P 500000)

VINJUM, Johannes (1930-1991) Norwegian
£877 $1632   (15-Jun-92 B.O185/R) Horse jumping (38x43cm-15x17in) s. panel
(N.KR 10000)
£1667 $3100   (15-Jun-92 B.O184/R) View towards Beitelen, Sognefjord (56x79cm-22x31in)
s. panel (N.KR 19000)

VINNE, Vincent Jansz van der (1736-1811) Dutch
£4500 $8190   (11-Dec-91 S94/R) Landscape with figures on road flanked by canal
enclosing farmstead (35x45cm-14x18in) s. panel

VINNE, Vincent Laurensz van der I (1629-1702) Dutch
£4688 $8297   (5-Nov-91 GF.L2048/R) Vanitas still life (39x35cm-15x14in) s.i. panel
(S.FR 12000)

VINNE, Vincent Laurensz van der II (1686-1742) Dutch
£3600 $6300   (31-Mar-92 PH101/R) Travellers on country path (29x37cm-11x15in) s. panel

VINNEN, Carl (1863-1922) German
£2234 $3887   (21-Sep-91 SA.A1987/R) Worpswede cottage winter (44x54cm-17x21in)
(DM 6500)
£5155 $8969   (21-Sep-91 SA.A535/R) Road lined with birch trees, autumn
(55x44cm-22x17in) i.verso (DM 15000)
£9278 $17258   (20-Jun-92 BM.B779/R) Church of Worpswede in snow covered landscape
(105x136cm-41x54in) s.d.1891 (DM 27000)

VINOGRADOFF, Sergei Arssenietitsch (1869-1938) Russian
£1500 $2670   (28-Nov-91 S519/R) Corner of drawing room (55x46cm-22x18in) s.d.1924
£2800 $5208   (16-Jun-92 S47/R) Tales of war (86x96cm-34x38in) s.d.1915
£3000 $5580   (16-Jun-92 S72/R) In the orchard (62x74cm-24x29in) s.d.1926 i.stretcher
£7000 $13020   (16-Jun-92 S48/R) Summer contemplation (75x62cm-30x24in) s.
£10000 $17800   (28-Nov-91 S406/R) On Volga (89x143cm-35x56in) s.

VINSON, A (20th C) French
£520   *$911*   *(5-Apr-92 ZZ.F221/R) Bouquet de fleurs (82x63cm-32x25in) s. pastel*
(F.FR 5000)

VINTON, John Rogers (1801-1847) American
£8380 $15000   (6-May-92 B.P173/R) Justenuggee Chupko surveying ruins Sugar House near
New Smyrna, Florida (28x38cm-11x15in) s.d.1843 verso

VIOLA (?) ?
£1700 $3077   (6-Dec-91 TE581) The tame dove. Playing with grandpa (48x69cm-19x27in) s. pair

VIOLA, Giovanni Battista (attrib) (1576-1662) Italian
£1007 $1712   (24-Oct-91 D.P21/R) Les apprets du repas pres de la cascade (49x65cm-19x26in) (F.FR 10000)

VIOLA, Giovanni Battista (style) (1576-1662) Italian
£3951 $7231   (12-May-92 SY.AM117/R) Figures in Italianate landscape, town beyond (56x40cm-22x16in) (D.FL 13000)

VIOLA, Manuel (1919-1987) Spanish
£574 $1051   (13-May-92 FER.M94/R) Velero en verde (25x20cm-10x8in) s. tablex (S.P 105000)
£601 $1101   (13-May-92 FER.M96/R) Pelea de gallos (25x21cm-10x8in) s. tablex (S.P 110000)
£601 $1101   (13-May-92 FER.M95/R) Barco velero (24x18cm-9x7in) s. tablex (S.P 110000)
£800 $1456   (29-May-92 C447/R) Sin titulo (55x33cm-22x13in)
£990 $1742   (9-Apr-92 ANS.M164/R) Composicion en azul (46x38cm-18x15in) s. (S.P 180000)
£1244 $2339   (16-Dec-91 ANS.M152/R) Composicion en negro (30x24cm-12x9in) s. canvas on tablex (S.P 225000)
£1915 $3639   (23-Jun-92 DUR.M503/R) Composicion (74x61cm-29x24in) s. (S.P 350000)
£1940 $3433   (12-Feb-92 ANS.M107/R) Pelea de gallos (54x45cm-21x18in) s. panel (S.P 350000)
£2423 $4337   (14-Nov-91 ANS.M60/R) Untitled (70x100cm-28x39in) s. (S.P 440000)

VIOLLET LE DUC, Victor (1848-1901) French
£1711 $3097   (3-Dec-91 C.A359) The Forest of Champagne (55x73cm-22x29in) s. (B.FR 100000)
£1711 $3097   (3-Dec-91 C.A360) Adams Island (50x73cm-20x29in) s. (B.FR 100000)

VIONNET, Charles (19/20th C) French
£611 $1112   (13-Dec-91 ZZ.F37) Pecheur au quai de la ligne en Avignon (27x41cm-11x16in) s. panel (F.FR 6000)
£2138 $3892   (13-Dec-91 ZZ.F36) La procession a Villeneuve les Avignon (65x105cm-26x41in) s. (F.FR 21000)

VIONOJA, Veikko (1909-) Finnish
£1707 $3004   (12-Apr-92 HOR.H249) Tulips at Christmas (55x45cm-22x18in) s.d.1948 (F.M 13500)
£3752 $6678   (1-Dec-91 HOR.H251) Winter in the park (66x80cm-26x31in) s. (F.M 29000)
£10746 $18913   (12-Apr-92 HOR.H2548/R) Farmyard in winter (94x74cm-37x29in) s.d.1956 (F.M 85000)

VIRGIKOVSKI, Edvard (1928-) Russian
£528 $920   (13-Apr-92 ARC.P80/R) Place du Palais a Saint-Petersbourg (39x59cm-15x23in) s. (F.FR 5200)
£566 $1024   (6-Dec-91 ARC.P191/R) Le pont Kirov sur la Neva (18x27cm-7x11in) s. board (F.FR 5500)
£614 $1093   (25-Nov-91 ARC.P203) Jour d'hiver (39x94cm-15x37in) s. (F.FR 6000)
£645 $1148   (25-Nov-91 ARC.P204/R) Village sous la neige (50x70cm-20x28in) s. (F.FR 6300)
£665 $1184   (25-Nov-91 ARC.P202) Jour du soeil (24x34cm-9x13in) s. board (F.FR 6500)
£926 $1676   (6-Dec-91 ARC.P190/R) Concert improvise (49x73cm-19x29in) s. (F.FR 9000)
£965 $1680   (13-Apr-92 ARC.P79/R) La Fontanka (52x77cm-20x30in) s. (F.FR 9500)
£977 $1769   (6-Dec-91 ARC.P188/R) Le passage a niveau (44x80cm-17x31in) s. (F.FR 9500)
£1014 $1846   (27-May-92 GL.P100/R) Noel (80x84cm-31x33in) s. (F.FR 10000)
£1029 $1862   (6-Dec-91 ARC.P187/R) Nuit blanche - St Petersbourg (19x28cm-7x11in) s. board (F.FR 10000)
£1075 $1913   (25-Nov-91 ARC.P200/R) La grande place (50x80cm-20x31in) s. (F.FR 10500)
£1169 $2034   (13-Apr-92 ARC.P78/R) Quai de la Neva (28x36cm-11x14in) s. (F.FR 11500)
£1399 $2533   (6-Dec-91 ARC.P186/R) Nuit blanche sur la Neva (26x40cm-10x16in) s. (F.FR 13600)
£1440 $2607   (6-Dec-91 ARC.P189/R) Jeux d'hiver (69x91cm-27x36in) s. (F.FR 14000)

VIRGIN, Gottfrid (1831-1876) Swedish
£604 $1087   (19-Nov-91 GO.G197) Woman in national costume with children and cat (32x26cm-13x10in) s.d.1865 (S.KR 6300)

VIRY, Paul Alphonse (19th C) French
£5429 $9500   (19-Feb-92 CH.NY51/R) Proposal (76x63cm-30x25in) s.d.76 panel

VISCONTI, Adolfo Ferraguti (1850-1924) Italian
£900 $1593   (13-Feb-92 CSK92) The approaching storm (79x102cm-31x40in) s.

VISENTINI, Antonio (circle) (1688-1782) Italian
£14000 $24920   (1-Nov-91 C9/R) Architectural capricci with figures (22x30cm-9x12in) pair

VISEUX, Claude (1927-) French
£504 $882   (25-Sep-91 CC.P19) Composition (64x50cm-25x20in) d.1956 paper (F.FR 5000)
£461 $830   (2-Feb-92 CSC.P154) Machine - Sculpture (64x49cm-25x19in) s.d.69 mixed media (F.FR 4500)

VISKI, Janos (1891-) Polish
£520 $967   (18-Jun-92 CSK225) The wedding party (76x99cm-30x39in)

VISO, Nicola (18th C) Italian
£7500 $13125   (1-Apr-92 S88/R) River landscape with peasants and animals
                             (76x127cm-30x50in)

VISPRE, Francis Xavier (attrib) (c.1730-1790) French/British
£9774 $18570   (26-Jun-92 AGS.P56/R) Sucrier d'argent, corbeille de peches, raisins sur
                             entablement de marbre (49x65cm-19x26in) (F.FR 95000)

VISSCHER, Cornelis de (1619-1662) Dutch
£1242 $2211   (25-Nov-91 CH.AM88/R) Child crying holding bowl and spoon (13x11cm-5x4in)
                             s. chk vellum sold with copy by A.Delfos (D.FL 4000)

VITALI, Candido (attrib) (1680-1753) Italian
£2900 $5568   (7-Jul-92 PH115/R) Still life of dead birds in landscape
                             (76x114cm-30x45in)

VITALI, Candido (circle) (1680-1753) Italian
£4972 $9000   (21-May-92 CH.NY99 a/R) Basket of mixed fruit on ground with jugs of wine
                             and bird, in landscape (67x91cm-26x36in)

VITALI, E (?) ?
£546 $1000   (5-Feb-92 D.NY88) Watering stream (53x36cm-21x14in) s. W/C

VITO, Camillo de (19th C) Italian
£1900 $3287   (4-Oct-91 C148/R) Eruzione del 1833 (44x66cm-17x26in) s.i. bodycol
£3400 $5882   (4-Oct-91 C149/R) Torre del Greco distrutta dall'Eruzione del 1794
                             (43x65cm-17x26in) s.i.bodycol
£3800 $6764   (27-Nov-91 S313/R) Vesuvius erupting at night (30x42cm-12x17in) s.
                             gouache pair

VITO, Camillo de (attrib) (19th C) Italian
£9500 $18145   (14-Jul-92 DR361/R) Veduta di Napoli dalle parte di Mergallina.
                             Neapolitan views (27x41cm-11x16in) gouache five

VITO, Michele de (?) Italian
£385 $700   (26-May-92 CE.NY234) Costume de Civita Vecchia, Provincia Contado di
                             Molise (20x15cm-8x6in) s.i. W/C
£4300 $7654   (27-Nov-91 B11/R) Aquajolo di Strada (30x20cm-12x8in) s.i.W/C sold with
                             eight other pictures

VITO, de (?) Italian
£4000 $6800   (23-Oct-91 S89/R) Napoli da Posillipo. Napoli dal Carmine. S.Lucia a mare
                             in Napoli (19x25cm-7x10in) s.i. gouache set of three

VIUDES, Vincente (1916-) ?
£578 $1000   (25-Mar-92 D.NY76) Light and Shadow (84x102cm-33x40in) s.

VIVANCOS, Miguel Garcia (20th C) Spanish
£527 $954   (18-May-92 AT.P161) Un coin de Gotem, pays Basque (38x55cm-15x22in) s.
                             s.d.1956verso (F.FR 5200)
£1013 $1834   (18-May-92 AT.P160) L'eglise St.Germain, Auxerre (55x46cm-22x18in)
                             s.d.12-8-54 (F.FR 10000)

VIVAR, Juan Correa de see   CORREA DE VIVAR, Juan

VIVARINI, Antonio (style) (c.1415-c.1484) Italian
£4696 $8500   (20-May-92 D.NY56) The Risen Christ. Virgin Mary. Angel one arched two
                             tondi panel three in one frame

VIVIAN, J (19th C?) British?
£550 $1018   (11-Jun-92 CSK247) On the Rhine (31x55cm-12x22in) s.
£3600 $6912   (28-Jul-92 SWS420/R) The Grand Canal, Venice (60x105cm-24x41in) s.
£5200 $8892   (12-Mar-92 CSK309/R) Grand Canal with Bacino di San Marco. Grand Canal at
                             Ca'Labia (46x82cm-18x32in) s. pair

VIVIAN, John (19th C) British?
£4200 $8064   (29-Jul-92 PHC366/R) View of the Lagoon, Venice (86x114cm-34x45in) s.

VIVIANI, Antonio (attrib) (1560-1620) Italian
£1958 $3465   (7-Nov-91 D.V274/R) Rest on the Flight to Egypt (17x14cm-7x6in) copper
                             (A.S 40000)

VIVIANI, Giuseppe (1898-1965) Italian
£6810 $12121   (29-Apr-92 F.F159/R) Marinai in barca (41x58cm-16x23in) s. (I.L 15000000)
£8172 $14545   (29-Apr-92 F.F161/R) Il poeta (51x70cm-20x28in) s.d.1963 (I.L 18000000)
£9080 $16162   (29-Apr-92 F.F164/R) Composizione (41x59cm-16x23in) s.d.1936 board
                             (I.L 20000000)
£2043 $3636   (29-Apr-92 F.F158/R) La chitarra (16x21cm-6x8in) s. st.sig.verso pencil
                             (I.L 4500000)
£2088 $3717   (29-Apr-92 F.F154/R) Statuina sul mare (31x39cm-12x15in) s.d.1948
                             sanguine (I.L 4600000)

VIVIANI, Giuseppe (1898-1965) Italian-cont.

£2179	$3879	(29-Apr-92 F.F156/R) Campanello, cardo, foglia e battistero (29x34cm-11x13in) s.d.1944 pen W/C (I.L 4800000)
£2270	$4040	(29-Apr-92 F.F155/R) Cocomero a fette (22x32cm-9x13in) s.d.1944 pen W/C (I.L 5000000)
£2270	$4040	(29-Apr-92 F.F157/R) Dolci e bambola (32x44cm-13x17in) s.d.1944 pen W/C (I.L 5000000)
£2270	$4040	(29-Apr-92 F.F153/R) L'aquilone (23x32cm-9x13in) s.d.1952 pencil (I.L 5000000)
£7264	$12929	(29-Apr-92 F.F163/R) Autoritrtto con la gamba ortopedica (33x27cm-13x11in) s.d.1957 gouache board (I.L 16000000)
£7718	$13737	(29-Apr-92 F.F160/R) Madonna della rosa (58x41cm-23x16in) s.d. st.sig.verso gouache canvas (I.L 17000000)
£8172	$14545	(29-Apr-92 F.F162/R) Il cane (75x57cm-30x22in) s.d.1962 gouache st.sig.lithography verso (I.L 18000000)

VIVIANI, Raoul (1883-1965) Italian

| £604 | $1094 | (3-Dec-91 SY.Ml138) Paesaggio lacustre (59x79cm-23x31in) s. (I.L 1300000) |

VIZKELETI, W E (1819-1895) Hungarian

£500	$855	(17-Mar-92 PH100) Market scene (61x91cm-24x36in) s.
£604	$1100	(26-May-92 CE.NY368) Marketplace (50x70cm-20x28in) s.
£1000	$1810	(21-May-92 CSK246/R) Gypsy dancer (99x140cm-39x55in) s.

VIZZINI, Andrea (?) Italian

| £2043 | $3636 | (29-Apr-92 F.F218/R) Luna rossa (60x50cm-24x20in) s.i.verso oil mixed media panel (I.L 4500000) |
| £3707 | $6599 | (29-Nov-91 F.F161 f) La luna nera (65x95cm-26x37in) s. s.d.1985/86verso mixed media panel (I.L 8000000) |

VLAANDEREN, Karel van (1903-1983) Belgian

| £795 | $1438 | (23-May-92 KV.L375) Woodland scene (60x70cm-24x28in) st.sig.d.1973 panel (B.FR 48000) |

VLAMINCK, Maurice de (1876-1958) French

£515	$968	(16-Dec-91 AT.P46/R) Le hameau (74x92cm-29x36in) s. (F.FR 5000)
£536	$1007	(16-Dec-91 AT.P45/R) Le hameau aux toits rouges (73x92cm-29x36in) s. (F.FR 5200)
£1133	$2130	(16-Dec-91 AT.P39/R) Village sous la neige (61x74cm-24x29in) s. (F.FR 11000)
£20367	$37678	(12-Jun-92 AT.P26/R) Nature morte (54x73cm-21x29in) s. (F.FR 200000)
£21469	$38000	(6-Nov-91 CH.NY295/R) Falaises au bord de la mer (60x73cm-24x29in) s.
£21469	$38000	(6-Nov-91 CH.NY319/R) Rue de village (36x45cm-14x18in) s.
£23000	$43930	(1-Jul-92 S186/R) Le couvert (60x81cm-24x32in) s.
£23855	$42462	(28-Nov-91 BU.S108/R) Park landscape (73x60cm-29x24in) s. (S.KR 250000)
£26000	$44980	(25-Mar-92 S69/R) La sortie du village (30x50cm-12x20in) s.
£32203	$57000	(6-Nov-91 CH.NY304/R) Vase de fleurs (46x38cm-18x15in) s.
£33000	$59730	(4-Dec-91 S172/R) La ferme aux deux arbres (54x65cm-21x26in) s.
£34286	$60000	(25-Feb-92 SY.NY18/R) Maison au bord de riviere (33x43cm-13x17in) s.
£34623	$64053	(12-Jun-92 AT.P28/R) Le hameau aux toits rouges (73x92cm-29x36in) s. (F.FR 340000)
£39548	$70000	(7-Nov-91 SY.NY154/R) Portrait de femme au chapeau en plume (65x49cm-26x19in) s.
£42000	$72660	(25-Mar-92 S66/R) Vase de fleurs (55x46cm-22x18in) s.
£42770	$79124	(12-Jun-92 AT.P25/R) Vase de fleurs (73x54cm-29x21in) s. (F.FR 420000)
£45198	$80000	(6-Nov-91 CH.NY288/R) Paysage d'automne (54x65cm-21x26in) s.
£47814	$87500	(14-May-92 SY.NY333/R) Nature morte aux fleurs (80x65cm-31x26in) s.
£50000	$90500	(3-Dec-91 C253/R) Sous le arbres (56x65cm-22x26in) s.
£56000	$106960	(30-Jun-92 C209/R) Paysage tempetueux (60x73cm-24x29in) s.
£58000	$110780	(1-Jul-92 S196/R) Maisons dans la campagne (60x73cm-24x29in) s.
£73770	$135000	(14-May-92 SY.NY334/R) Paysage en neige (81x100cm-32x39in) s.
£80564	$136959	(24-Oct-91 CSC.P24/R) Le vase Louis Philippe (73x54cm-29x21in) s. (F.FR 800000)
£99415	$170000	(13-Mar-92 DM.D2008/R) La table de cuisine (81x117cm-32x46in) s. d.1932stretcher
£400000	$724000	(2-Dec-91 C15/R) Guillaume Apollinaire au Bord de la Seine (54x65cm-21x26in) s.
£2396	$4456	(19-Jun-92 ARC.P22/R) Le hameau (17x23cm-7x9in) s. match dr (F.FR 23500)
£4098	$7500	(13-May-92 CH.NY262/R) Rue de Valmondois (38x46cm-15x18in) s. brush Indian ink
£4201	$7561	(2-Feb-92 ZZ.F150/R) Paysage (35x43cm-14x17in) s. Indian ink (F.FR 41000)
£9446	$17002	(22-Nov-91 PIC.P23/R) Maisons dans la campagne (38x45cm-15x18in) s. gouache (F.FR 92000)
£10169	$18000	(6-Nov-91 CH.NY176/R) Le village (30x39cm-12x15in) s. W/C pen india ink
£13171	$23840	(24-May-92 GL.P4/R) Pommiers en fleurs (46x61cm-18x24in) s. gouache W/C paper laid down on board (F.FR 130000)
£51852	$93852	(20-May-92 GK.Z5017/R) Village enneige (44x51cm-17x20in) s. gouache (S.FR 140000)

VLASBECK, P H (?) ?

| £524 | $907 | (25-Mar-92 KM.K1495) Elderly gentlemen wearing 17th century costumes in German interior (71x81cm-28x32in) s. (DM 1500) |

VLASOV, Arseni (1914-) Russian
| £504 | $882 | (24-Sep-91 ARC.P211/R) Nature morte aux pivoines (100x130cm-39x51in) s. verso (F.FR 5000) |

£605 $1058 (24-Sep-91 ARC.P212/R) La partie de peche (80x100cm-31x39in) s. (F.FR 6000)

£655 $1147 (24-Sep-91 ARC.P210/R) Le parc du chateau (99x130cm-39x51in) s. (F.FR 6500)

VLASSELAER, Julien (1907-1982) Belgian
£911 $1648 (23-May-92 KV.L376) Seated nude in hat with flowers (110x75cm-43x30in) s.d.32 (B.FR 55000)

VLASSOV, Vladimir (1927-) Russian
£557 $1009 (20-May-92 ARC.P77/R) Scene villageoise (60x50cm-24x20in) s. tempera board (F.FR 5500)

£588 $1064 (20-May-92 ARC.P78/R) La petite jetee (30x42cm-12x17in) s. board (F.FR 5800)

£659 $1192 (20-May-92 ARC.P76/R) Vacances a la mer (23x32cm-9x13in) s. (F.FR 6500)

VLASSOVA, Klara (1926-) Russian
£514 $931 (6-Dec-91 ARC.P23/R) Au coucher du soleil (75x120cm-30x47in) s. (F.FR 5000)

£557 $1009 (20-May-92 ARC.P231) Au square (67x87cm-26x34in) s. (F.FR 5500)

VLEUGHELS, Nicolas (1668-1737) French
£8025 $14364 (12-Nov-91 SY.AM176/R) Nymph spied by satyrs (80x164cm-31x65in) (D.FL 26000)

VLEUGHELS, Nicolas (attrib) (1668-1737) French
£2937 $5198 (7-Nov-91 D.V299/R) The Wedding of Canaan (35x45cm-14x18in) after Tintoretto (A.S 60000)

£3500 $6720 (8-Jul-92 S113/R) Figures by fountain (15x24cm-6x9in) panel

VLIEGER, Simon de (1600-1653) Dutch
£194444 $348056 (14-Nov-91 CH.AM156/R) Amsterdam man-of-war and other shipping in stiff breeze (75x114cm-30x45in) indis.s. panel (D.FL 630000)

£2174 $3870 (25-Nov-91 CH.AM122/R) Cottage in wooded landscape with peasant by gate (14x20cm-6x8in) init. chk wash (D.FL 7000)

VLIEGER, Simon de (style) (1600-1653) Dutch
£3600 $6408 (30-Oct-91 S22/R) Figures disembarking from ferry on the river Maas (110x179cm-43x70in)

VLIET, Hendrik Cornelisz van der (1611-1675) Dutch
£18519 $35185 (26-Jun-92 AT.P16/R) Interieur d'eglise en Hollande (46x33cm-18x13in) panel (F.FR 180000)

VLIET, Hendrik Cornelisz van der (attrib) (1611-1675) Dutch
£3315 $6000 (21-May-92 CH.NY151/R) Church interior with elegant figures and workman carving inscription (50x43cm-20x17in) canvas on panel

£4969 $8845 (25-Nov-91 CH.AM140/R) Nave of the Nieuwe Kerk in Delft looking west (18x28cm-7x11in) pen (D.FL 16000)

VLIET, Willem van der (attrib) (1584-1642) Dutch
£2000 $3500 (31-Mar-92 PH30/R) Portrait of man, turned to right, wearing jacket, right hand to chest (75x59cm-30x23in) panel

VLIST, Leendert van der (1894-1962) Dutch
£1284 $2235 (14-Apr-92 SY.AM206) The Magere Brug in Amsterdam (38x58cm-15x23in) s. (D.FL 4200)

VOERMAN, Jan (1857-1941) Dutch
£2599 $4523 (14-Apr-92 SY.AM163/R) View of the Ijssel (53x74cm-21x29in) s. panel (D.FL 8500)

VOERMAN, Jan (jnr) (1890-) Dutch
£617 $1123 (12-Dec-91 SY.AM3/R) Landscape with Scheveningen in distance (39x69cm-15x27in) mono. (D.FL 2000)

VOERMAN, Jan (snr) (1857-1941) Dutch
£788 $1395 (22-Apr-92 CH.AM43/R) Tjalks on the river Issel with Hattem beyond, at sunset (42x52cm-17x20in) (D.FL 2600)

£1553 $2764 (26-Nov-91 VN.R127/R) River landscape (47x66cm-19x26in) s. pastel (D.FL 5000)

VOERMAN, Jan and THOLEN, Willem Bastiaan (19th C) Dutch
£1809 $3220 (29-Oct-91 PH.T19/R) Bringing home cows (40x63cm-16x25in) s. (C.D 3600)

VOET, Jacob Ferdinand (1639-c.1700) Flemish
£1468 $2525 (7-Oct-91 CH.E240) Portrait of Princess Maria Beatrice of Modena, holding red carnation (71x61cm-28x24in) (E.P 1600)

£6173 $11728 (26-Jun-92 AT.P35/R) Portrait de Maria Hortensia Biscia del Drago (71x59cm-28x23in) (F.FR 60000)

£7692 $14692 (15-Jul-92 CH.S750/R) Portrait of lady, in pink dress, trimmed with lace (72x56cm-28x22in) painted oval (A.D 20000)

VOET, Jacob Ferdinand (circle) (1639-c.1700) Flemish
£2800 $5012   (15-Nov-91 C159/R) Portrait of gentleman, in velvet cloak with jewelled clasp and jabot (75x62cm-30x24in) i.verso painted oval

VOET, Jacob Ferdinand (style) (1639-c.1700) Flemish
£1047 $2000   (16-Jul-92 SY.NY265/R) Portrait of nobleman (73x58cm-29x23in)

VOGEL VON VOGELSTEIN, Carl Christian (1788-1868) German
£2200 $4092   (17-Jun-92 S372/R) Portrait of lady in costume (47x40cm-19x16in) bears sig.d.1843 s.d.1843 verso board
£651   *$1119*   *(11-Oct-91 AW.H1364/R) Portrait of girl seated (28x20cm-11x8in) s. indian ink pen wash (DM 1900)*

VOGEL, C (19th C) ?
£1803 $3210   (25-Nov-91 BU.K67/R) Portrait of an Italian woman (49x42cm-19x17in) s.d.1843 cardboard (D.KR 20000)

VOGEL, Cornelis Jan de (1824-1879) Flemish
£6143 $11181   (27-May-92 PH.DU42/R) Heath landscape (80x120cm-31x47in) s. (DM 18000)

VOGEL, Hugo (1854-1934) German
£1569 $2667   (23-Oct-91 GD.B1325/R) The painter and his family (145x122cm-57x48in) s. after Cornelius de Vos (S.FR 4000)

VOGEL, Hy (20th C) American
£368   *$700*   *(25-Jun-92 BG.M257) Jimmy Stewart (30x23cm-12x9in) s. mixed media*
£395   *$750*   *(25-Jun-92 BG.M259) Jimmy Durante (30x23cm-12x9in) s. mixed media*
£447   *$850*   *(25-Jun-92 BG.M300) Bob Hope, Sophie Tucker and Eddie Cantor (30x69cm-12x27in) s. mixed media triptych*
£474   *$900*   *(25-Jun-92 BG.M301) Herbert Marshall, Danny Thomas and Gloria Swanson (30x69cm-12x27in) s. mixed media triptych*
£526   *$1000*   *(25-Jun-92 BG.M305) Bobby Layne, Judy Garland and van Patrick (30x69cm-12x27in) s. mixed media triptych*
£632   *$1200*   *(25-Jun-92 BG.M288/R) Alfred Hitchcock (30x23cm-12x9in) s. mixed media*

VOGEL, Johannes Gysbert (17/19th C) German/Dutch
£612 $1064   (14-Apr-92 SY.AM406) Sheep on a heath (53x81cm-21x32in) s.d.69 (D.FL 2000)
£667 $1140   (13-Mar-92 FN.S3002) Wooded lake landscape at sunset (45x65cm-18x26in) s.d.1900 (DM 1900)
£1973 $3531   (5-May-92 ZEL.L1572/R) Alpine landscape with figures and goats (46x68cm-18x27in) s.d.1864 (DM 5800)

VOGEL, Ludwig (1788-1879) Swiss
£677   *$1238*   *(4-Jun-92 SY.Z330/R) In Mariahilf near Freiburg (21x27cm-8x11in) i. pencil htd.white (S.FR 1800)*
£1004   *$1717*   *(12-Mar-92 GK.Z394/R) Appenzell peasant interior with figures working (19x23cm-7x9in) sepia pen wash (S.FR 2600)*

VOGEL, Ludwig (attrib) (1788-1879) Swiss
£684   *$1273*   *(19-Jun-92 ZOF.Z2125/R) Battle of Murten (28x44cm-11x17in) (S.FR 1800)*

VOGEL, Max (?) German?
£800 $1384   (3-Oct-91 CSK222) On the terrace (61x91cm-24x36in) s.

VOGEL, Willy (20th C) German
£697 $1268   (13-Dec-91 BM.B545) Evening (80x60cm-31x24in) s. i.d.1979verso (DM 2000)

VOGELAER, Karel van (circle) (1653-1695) Dutch
£2736 $5006   (12-May-92 SY.AM54/R) Still life of flowers in basket set on ledge (61x75cm-24x30in) (D.FL 9000)

VOGELAER, Karel van (style) (1653-1695) Dutch
£6077 $11000   (21-May-92 CH.NY248/R) Flowers wrapped around stick, sculpted ewer and classical ruins (89x120cm-35x47in)

VOGELER, Heinrich (1872-1942) German
£853   *$1544*   *(23-May-92 GB.B7345/R) Impression aus dem Kaukasus (22x17cm-9x7in) s.d.1923 pen over pencil (DM 2500)*
£1408   *$2549*   *(6-Dec-91 GB.B7215/R) Cotton, poster design (22x29cm-9x11in) i. gouache (DM 4000)*

VOGELS, Guillaume (1836-1896) Belgian
£4587 $8119   (5-Nov-91 SY.AM169/R) Horse-drawn carriages in snow (35x48cm-14x19in) s. (D.FL 15000)
£5500 $9460   (12-Oct-91 KV.L374/R) Le Bucheron (82x56cm-32x22in) s. (B.FR 330000)

VOGLER, Hermann (1859-?) German
£5714 $10000   (20-Feb-92 SY.NY242/R) In park (80x126cm-31x50in) s.d.91

VOGLER, Paul (1852-1904) French
£1750 $3133   (14-Jan-92 SWS230/R) La Place Clichy a Paris (31x29cm-12x11in) s.i.d.1870verso panel
£2055 $3535   (6-Mar-92 ARC.P36/R) Pecheuses au bord de la greve (35x26cm-14x10in) panel (F.FR 20000)

VOGLER, Paul (1852-1904) French-cont.
£3186 $5480   (6-Mar-92 ARC.P37/R) La rencontre des pecheurs (35x26cm-14x10in) panel
                    (F.FR 31000)
£1145   *$2003*   *(5-Apr-92 ZZ.F111/R) Fleuve anime au soleil couchant (55x77cm-22x30in) s.*
                    pastel (F.FR 11000)

VOGT, Adolf (1843-1871) American
£1000 $1730   (3-Oct-91 CSK83/R) A study of an Ox (79x66cm-31x26in) s.

VOGT, J L (19th C) German
£1306 $2272   (21-Sep-91 SA.A1719/R) Still life with dandelion in water glass
                    (35x26cm-14x10in) s.d.1814 metal panel (DM 3800)

VOIGT, Bruno (1912-1989) German
£410 $745   (30-May-92 VG.B987/R) Spring is coming (37x32cm-15x13in) mono.d.1932 pen
                    (DM 1200)
£490 $871   (30-Nov-91 VG.B1049/R) Verlorene (47x30cm-19x12in) mono.d.1933 pen indian
                    ink brush (DM 1400)
£769 $1369   (30-Nov-91 VG.B1048/R) Schlotbaron (48x33cm-19x13in) mono.d.1932 pen wash
                    spray technique (DM 2200)
£1160 $2112   (30-May-92 VG.B986/R) Pub interior in Weimar (46x37cm-18x15in)
                    mono.d.1932 W/C pen (DM 3400)

VOIGT, David (1944-) Australian
£641 $1141   (27-Apr-92 J.M728) Hidden places through forest journeys
                    (99x150cm-39x59in) s. (A.D 1500)

VOIGT, Richart Otto (1895-1971) German
£915 $1657   (3-Dec-91 FN.S1915/R) Lupins in terracotta vase (75x60cm-30x24in)
                    s.i.d.1950stretcher (DM 2600)

VOIGT, W (?) ?
£775 $1402   (7-Dec-91 WK.M495/R) Car racing (76x122cm-30x48in) d.1932 board (DM 2200)

VOILLEMOT, Charles (1823-1893) French
£760 $1414   (19-Jun-92 ZOF.Z1625/R) The love letter (40x27cm-16x11in) s. (S.FR 2000)
£4625 $8834   (1-Jul-92 FB.P58/R) Jeune femme nue au nid (102x76cm-40x30in) s.
                    (F.FR 45000)

VOIRIN, Leon-Joseph (1833-1887) French
£1731 $3203   (10-Jun-92 ZZ.F47) Scene intimiste au parc (40x32cm-16x13in) s.
                    (F.FR 17000)

VOIS, Arie de (circle) (1631-1680) Flemish
£6202 $11040   (28-Nov-91 BU.S64/R) Soldiers smoking (89x80cm-35x31in) (S.KR 65000)

VOIS, Arie de (style) (1631-1680) Flemish
£1600 $2912   (13-Dec-91 C153) Music party at draped arched casement (28x22cm-11x9in)
                    panel
£3160 $5878   (19-Jun-92 CN.P65/R) Le repos du chasseur (41x35cm-16x14in) bears mono.
                    panel (F.FR 31000)

VOLAIRE, Pierre Jacques (1729-1802) French
£48000 $84000   (31-Mar-92 PH102/R) Sir William Hamilton and others watching eruption of
                    Mount Vesuvius (31x51cm-12x20in) s.
£50279 $90000   (16-Jan-92 CH.NY67/R) Bay of Naples with Mount Vesuvius erupting and
                    figures in foreground (69x105cm-27x41in) s.
£100000 $192000   (10-Jul-92 C23/R) Baia with Temples of Venus and Diana from fortress.
                    Fortress Don Pedro de Toledo from Campi Flegrei (73x128cm-29x50in) pair
£580   *$1114*   *(8-Jul-92 PH133/R) Study of man leaning on high table (18x11cm-7x4in)*
                    black chk
£8380   *$15000*   *(14-Jan-92 SY.NY99/R) Fishermen on coast (53x65cm-21x26in) one s. pastel*
                    paper on canvas pair

VOLAIRE, Pierre Jacques (attrib) (1729-1802) French
£6116 $11376   (20-Jun-92 CH.MO61/R) Vue du Vesuve en eruption (31x52cm-12x20in)
                    (F.FR 60000)
£7500 $13125   (3-Apr-92 C3/R) Dawn-calm with fishermen in rocky inlet. Evening-calm
                    with fishermen hauling in nets (39x47cm-15x19in) pair

VOLCKER, Johann Wilhelm (1812-1873) German
£5500 $9790   (27-Nov-91 S134/R) Still life of flowers on marble edge (44x34cm-17x13in)
                    s.

VOLKERS, Emil (1831-1905) German
£687 $1202   (30-Mar-92 ZZ.F149) Cheval selle (23x31cm-9x12in) s.d.1904 panel
                    (F.FR 6600)
£836 $1522   (13-Dec-91 BM.B732/R) Portrait of horse (25x32cm-10x13in) s.
                    indis.i.verso (DM 2400)
£966 $1661   (16-Oct-91 KM.K1427) Horse and dog (32x42cm-13x17in) s.d.1868 (DM 2800)

VOLKERT, Edward Charles (1871-1935) American
£683 $1250   (9-Feb-92 LIT.L202) Spring pasture (20x28cm-8x11in) s. board
£1667 $2900   (15-Apr-92 SY.NY102/R) Farmer Sterling in field. Woodlot
                    (30x41cm-12x16in) one s. one s. s.d.1932 verso board panel pair

VOLKERT, Hans (1878-?) Austrian?
£388 $691 (28-Apr-92 D.V5/R) Heads of two children (23x23cm-9x9in) s. pencil chk (A.S 8000)

VOLKHART, Max (1848-1935) German
£962 $1780 (13-Jun-92 WK.M370/R) Salome dancing before Herodes (76x99cm-30x39in) s.i. (DM 2800)
£1800 $3114 (4-Oct-91 C76 c/R) On the balcony (54x38cm-21x15in) s.

VOLKMANN, Hans Richard von (1860-1927) German
£954 $1670 (3-Apr-92 BM.B720/R) Wooded landscape, possibly Dachauer Moos (25x43cm-10x17in) s.d.1926 board (DM 2700)
£1557 $2974 (4-Jul-92 BOD.P666/R) Wooded landscape (24x42cm-9x17in) s.d.1926 panel (DM 4500)
£1787 $3145 (11-Apr-92 AW.H790/R) Eifel landscape, autumn (65x94cm-26x37in) s. (DM 5200)
£2389 $4348 (27-May-92 PH.DU149/R) View across Bad Schachen and Bodensee of Santis (46x79cm-18x31in) s.i.d.1925 (DM 7000)
£2528 $4500 (22-Jan-92 SY.NY258/R) Summer landscape (65x95cm-26x37in) s.d.1920

VOLKMAR, Antonie (1827-?) German
£15000 $26700 (29-Nov-91 C39/R) Emigration to America (112x190cm-44x75in) s.d.1860

VOLKMAR, Charles (1841-1914) American
£546 $1000 (15-May-92 S.BM104/R) The drink (71x43cm-28x17in) s.
£1429 $2500 (26-Sep-91 CH.NY38/R) Grazing at water's edge (119x89cm-47x35in) s.

VOLKOV, Efim Efimovich (1844-1920) Russian
£759 $1389 (14-May-92 BU.S204/R) Peasant girl in birch grove (31x25cm-12x10in) s.d.1877 (S.KR 8000)

VOLKOV, Viktor (1941-) Russian
£508 $884 (13-Apr-92 ARC.P5/R) Les bouquets de roses (65x100cm-26x39in) s. hardboard (F.FR 5000)
£530 $986 (17-Jun-92 ARC.P200/R) Escalier fleuri en Crimee (80x60cm-31x24in) s. (F.FR 5200)
£559 $973 (13-Apr-92 ARC.P2) Nature morte sur un plateau (100x110cm-39x43in) s. (F.FR 5500)
£669 $1210 (6-Dec-91 ARC.P106/R) Fleurs et ombrelle (100x95cm-39x37in) s. hardboard (F.FR 6500)
£693 $1289 (17-Jun-92 ARC.P199/R) Roses et raisins (85x100cm-33x39in) s. (F.FR 6800)
£915 $1591 (13-Apr-92 ARC.P4/R) Nature morte d'automne (85x100cm-33x39in) s. (F.FR 9000)
£1016 $1768 (13-Apr-92 ARC.P1/R) L'ombrelle rouge (85x100cm-33x39in) s. (F.FR 10000)
£1955 $3538 (6-Dec-91 ARC.P108/R) Les roses (70x80cm-28x31in) s. (F.FR 19000)

VOLL, Christoph (1897-1939) German
£378 $665 (11-Apr-92 AW.H2383) Portrait of woman seated (48x37cm-19x15in) s. (DM 1100)

VOLLERDT, Johann Christian (1708-1769) German
£1500 $2625 (25-Feb-92 PH69/R) Travellers conversing on path by moonlight (21x31cm-8x12in) s. panel
£4031 $7296 (3-Dec-91 AB.S4762/R) Mountainous landscape with figures (46x31cm-18x12in) s. (S.KR 42000)
£8741 $14948 (18-Mar-92 N.M472/R) River landscape with shipping and peasant family resting on path (28x38cm-11x15in) s.d.1756 panel (DM 25000)
£10000 $19200 (8-Jul-92 S105/R) River landscape (33x43cm-13x17in) s. panel
£10615 $19000 (17-Jun-92 SY.NY153/R) Winter mountainous landscape with skaters on a frozen river (38x57cm-15x22in) s.d.1762
£18994 $34000 (17-Jan-92 SY.NY84/R) Landscapes with Manor House by river, and with figures and farmhouse on hill by river (59x75cm-23x30in) indist.s. one d.1760 pair

VOLLERDT, Johann Christian (attrib) (1708-1769) German
£3754 $6795 (21-May-92 L.K170/R) River landscape with travellers resting (18x22cm-7x9in) panel (DM 11000)
£4057 $7140 (11-Apr-92 AT.P65/R) Patineurs dans un paysage d'hiver (21x30cm-8x12in) s. (F.FR 40000)
£6500 $11830 (10-Dec-91 PH103/R) Rhineland winter landscape with skaters (35x45cm-14x18in) bears init.d.1631

VOLLERDT, Johann Christian (circle) (1708-1769) German
£2210 $4000 (21-May-92 CH.NY246/R) Figures in mountainous river landscape with town beyond (44x54cm-17x21in)
£2400 $4320 (21-Nov-91 CSK115/R) Peasants on path beneath hilltop castle (25x32cm-10x13in) panel
£3500 $6685 (21-Jul-92 PH233/R) Peasants conversing beside woodland bridge, Rhineland landscape and landscape (36x45cm-14x18in) pair
£5000 $9100 (13-Dec-91 C195/R) Rhenish landscapes in winter and summer (23x36cm-9x14in) panel pair
£20000 $35000 (28-Feb-92 C71/R) Shepherds in extensive Italianate landscapes with ducks and herons (57x75cm-22x30in) pair

VOLLERDT, Johann Christian (style) (1708-1769) German
£2300 $4140   (22-Nov-91 SWS153/R) A wooded river landscape (71x92cm-28x36in)

VOLLMER, Adolf Friedrich (1806-1875) German
£1637 $2800   (13-Mar-92 WOL.C810/R) Still life of fruit. Still life of flowers
                    (38x25cm-15x10in) s. pair

VOLLMER, Grace Libby (1884-1977) American
£1130 $2000   (12-Feb-92 B.SF588/R) Sunflowers (61x51cm-24x20in) s. board

VOLLMERING, Joseph (1810-1887) American
£829 $1500   (4-Dec-91 D.NY13/R) Keene Valley, Adirondacks (41x56cm-16x22in)

VOLLON, Alexis (1865-1945) French
£1070 $1991   (18-Jun-92 CB.P75 b) Le marche a Avallon (27x35cm-11x14in) s.d.1922 panel
                    (F.FR 10500)
£47674 $82000   (16-Oct-91 CH.NY58/R) Pierrot, Colombine et Polichinelle
                    (240x209cm-94x82in) s.

VOLLON, Antoine (1833-1900) French
£1124 $2000   (22-Jan-92 SY.NY350/R) Still life with copper pots (63x85cm-25x33in) s.
£1512 $2600   (15-Oct-91 CE.NY218/R) Still life with fruit, chinese bowl and a beer
                    stein on a tble (23x16cm-9x6in) s. panel
£1800 $3078   (17-Mar-92 PH114) River landscape (27x40cm-11x16in) s.i.
£3976 $7076   (30-Oct-91 CH.AM255/R) Violets in reeded basket on forest floor
                    (45x55cm-18x22in) s.d.72 panel (D.FL 13000)
£6857 $12000   (19-Feb-92 CH.NY34/R) French farming village (46x56cm-18x22in) s.

VOLLON, Jacques Antoine (1894-?) French
£1885 $3600   (30-Jun-92 PO.BA4) Naturaleza muerta con ollas (22x28cm-9x11in) s.

VOLMAR, Georg (1770-1831) German
£791 $1423   (19-Nov-91 GS.B3301) Wooded landscape with shepherd scene
                    (38x32cm-15x13in) s. panel (S.FR 2000)

VOLODIMIROV, Nikolai (1910-) Russian
£564 $1014   (27-Jan-92 ARC.P128/R) Les paniers de champignons (60x81cm-24x32in) s.
                    (F.FR 5500)

VOLODINE, Mikhail (1912-1987) Russian
£608 $1100   (20-May-92 ARC.P68) La robe rouge (70x50cm-28x20in) s. board (F.FR 6000)
£628 $1137   (20-May-92 ARC.P67/R) Danse folklorique (45x73cm-18x29in) s. (F.FR 6200)
£762 $1326   (13-Apr-92 ARC.P190/R) Terrasse en ete (74x100cm-29x39in) s. oil tempera
                    board (F.FR 7500)
£1064 $1926   (20-May-92 ARC.P69/R) Le vase de porcelaine (70x80cm-28x31in) s.
                    (F.FR 10500)

VOLPATO, Giorgio (?) Italian
*£3500 $5950   (23-Oct-91 S88/R) Paestum (35x49cm-14x19in) one s. pen W/C three sold
                    with 2 views of ruins*

VOLPATO, Giovanni and DUCROS, Abraham Louis Rodolphe (18th C) Italian/French
*£3800 $6460   (23-Oct-91 S100) Gardens of the Villa Pamphilji, Rome (51x73cm-20x29in)
                    s. W/C bodycol over etched line*

VOLPE, Alessandro la (1820-1887) Italian
£1900 $3382   (28-Nov-91 CSK90/R) The ferry (135x269cm-53x106in) s.d.81
£3200 $5472   (17-Mar-92 PH225) Ferry crossing river (53x106cm-21x42in) s.d.81
£4529 $8380   (9-Jun-92 F.R65/R) Veduta di Amalfi (36x67cm-14x26in) s. (I.L 10000000)
£5122 $9271   (3-Dec-91 R.T222/R) Mediterranean coastal view with fishing boats
                    (52x104cm-20x41in) s. (C.D 10500)
£10000 $17100   (17-Mar-92 PH224/R) Bringing home the catch, Sorrento (51x104cm-20x41in)
                    s.

VOLPE, Vincenzo (1855-1929) Italian
£2022 $3600   (1-Nov-91 PO.BA2) Partiendo para la escuela (62x102cm-24x40in) s.

VOLSCHENK, Jan E A (1853-1936) South African
£645 $1142   (4-Nov-91 SY.J252/R) Residence near Riversdale (15x24cm-6x9in) s.d.1917
                    s.i.d.1917verso (SA.R 3200)
£782 $1329   (21-Oct-91 SY.J338) Rocks (14x17cm-6x7in) s.d.1914 board (SA.R 3800)
£800 $1520   (23-Jun-92 PH73) Mountains near ladysmith, South Africa (18x27cm-7x11in)
                    s. i.verso board
£806 $1427   (4-Nov-91 SY.J251/R) Die Aasvogelberg from near Albertina
                    (18x44cm-7x17in) s.d.1911 s.i.d.verso (SA.R 4000)
£909 $1555   (12-Mar-92 SY.J392) Autumn under Drakenstein Mountains, Franschhoek
                    (25x34cm-10x13in) s.d.1932 s.i.d.verso (SA.R 4500)
£1034 $1799   (13-Apr-92 SY.J299/R) Last glow, Karroo (25x45cm-10x18in) s.d.1920
                    s.i.d.1920 verso (SA.R 5200)
£1789 $3113   (13-Apr-92 SY.J298/R) Field of Aloes, Riversdale (25x40cm-10x16in)
                    s.d.1912 s.i.d.1912 verso (SA.R 9000)

VOLTERRA, Daniele da (circle) (1509-1566) Italian
£3220 $5539   (15-Oct-91 CH.R74/R) Compianto sul Cristo morto (162x107cm-64x42in) panel
                    (I.L 7000000)

VOLTI, Antoniucci (1915-1990) French
£757 $1400   (12-Jun-92 SY.NY159/R) Crouching female nude (41x31cm-16x12in) s.d.1971 chk.
£1107 $1992   (2-Feb-92 ZZ.F211/R) Nu assis (65x50cm-26x20in) s.d.1988 pastel (F.FR 10800)

VOLTZ, Friedrich (1817-1886) German
£519 $991   (4-Jul-92 BOD.P667) Calf in field (22x26cm-9x10in) s.mono canvas on board (DM 1500)
£1203 $2201   (2-Jun-92 FN.S2788/R) Cow and calf in stable interior (25x22cm-10x9in) mono canvas on panel (DM 3500)
£1203 $2093   (17-Sep-91 FN.S2591/R) Cow grazing (30x33cm-12x13in) s. board (DM 3500)
£1434 $2451   (18-Mar-92 N.M678/R) View of Karwendel range and Zugspitze with Walchensee (22x32cm-9x13in) s. paper on panel (DM 4100)
£1496 $2677   (16-Jan-92 D.V58/R) Stable interior (13x20cm-5x8in) s. i.d.1851verso board (A.S 30000)
£1500 $2595   (3-Oct-91 CSK60/R) Cattle watering at a stream (15x33cm-6x13in) with sig. panel
£1706 $3089   (21-May-92 L.K494/R) Mountain landscape with stream (24x35cm-9x14in) s. panel (DM 5000)
£2749 $4784   (18-Sep-91 N.M741/R) Hay harvest in the foothills of the Alps (19x30cm-7x12in) s. board (DM 8000)
£3136 $5707   (13-Dec-91 BM.B733/R) Alpine landscape with shepherds by pond, evening (31x42cm-12x17in) s. board (DM 9000)
£5155 $8969   (18-Sep-91 N.M740/R) Shepherdess with kid, sheep and cow in stable (66x64cm-26x25in) s.d.1850 (DM 15000)
£6272 $11415   (11-Dec-91 N.M643/R) Cows and shepherd couple with dog in lake landscape (15x39cm-6x15in) s. paper on panel (DM 18000)
£10239 $18532   (21-May-92 L.K493/R) Wooded landscape with goats on rocky outcrop (71x56cm-28x22in) s. (DM 30000)
£12000 $21000   (20-Feb-92 SY.NY34 a/R) Watering hole (32x64cm-13x25in) s.d.1876 cradled panel
£14035 $25263   (22-Nov-91 SA.A1603/R) Cattle and goats grazing in high mountain landscape (66x61cm-26x24in) s.d.1866 (DM 40000)
£15358 $27952   (27-May-92 PH.DU44/R) Ducks and cows near angler in boat on a lake (20x45cm-8x18in) s.d.1870 (DM 45000)
£17544 $30000   (13-Mar-92 FN.S3003/R) Cattle watering in ford and shepherd girl in wooded landscape (31x64cm-12x25in) s.i.d.1876 panel (DM 50000)
£27491 $50309   (2-Jun-92 FN.S2786/R) Cattle watering in wooded lake landscape and thunderstorm rising (42x103cm-17x41in) s.d.1878 panel (DM 80000)
£41237 $71753   (18-Sep-91 N.M739/R) Shepherd with cows watering in lake landscape (36x86cm-14x34in) s.d.1869 (DM 120000)
£431 $772   (12-Nov-91 GF.L5157) Two girls with goats and cows (19x25cm-7x10in) s. pencil (S.FR 1100)

VOLTZ, Friedrich (circle) (1817-1886) German
£2300 $4071   (13-Feb-92 CSK110/R) Cattle by river in landscape (69x122cm-27x48in)

VOLTZ, Ludwig (1825-1911) German
£1399 $2420   (25-Mar-92 KM.K1496) Cattle watering in lake landscape with thunderstorm rising (25x48cm-10x19in) s. (DM 4000)
£2439 $4439   (11-Dec-91 WE.MU143/R) Cows watering in pond landscape (15x34cm-6x13in) s. panel (DM 7000)

VOLZ, Hermann (1814-1894) German
£3436 $5979   (17-Sep-91 FN.S2593/R) Travelling merchant showing antique statues in tavern interior (41x33cm-16x13in) s.d.1884 i.d.verso (DM 10000)

VONCK, Elias (attrib) (1605-1652) Dutch
£559 $1000   (13-Jan-92 CE.NY204) Game on a ledge (28x36cm-11x14in) canvas laid down on panel

VONCK, Jan (1630-?) Dutch
£1824 $3337   (12-May-92 SY.AM62/R) Still life of partidge and songbirds on ledge (34x26cm-13x10in) s. panel (D.FL 6000)
£6145 $11000   (16-Jan-92 CH.NY69/R) Song birds on stone ledge, watched by dog below (71x55cm-28x22in) s.d.1660 panel

VONCK, Jan (attrib) (1630-?) Dutch
£1698 $3039   (14-Nov-91 CH.AM192/R) Dead partridges, songbirds with gun and basket on draped ledge (54x74cm-21x29in) bears sigd.1663 (D.FL 5500)

VONNOH, Robert (1858-1933) American
£5220 $9500   (28-May-92 CH.NY142/R) Springtime (50x61cm-20x24in) indis.s.

VONTILLIUS, Jeppe (?) Scandinavian
£487 $887   (25-May-92 RAS.K217) Seated woman wearing brown suit (95x49cm-37x19in) init.i.d.1958 (D.KR 5500)

VOORDEN, August Willem van (1881-1921) Dutch
£2484 $4298   (24-Mar-92 VN.R94/R) Sailing ship on the Maas with Rotterdam Harbour beyond (56x96cm-22x38in) s. (D.FL 8000)
£1223 $2128   (14-Apr-92 SY.AM257/R) Men loading horse-cart, Rotterdam in distance (42x63cm-17x25in) s. W/C (D.FL 4000)

VOORHOUT, Johannes (1647-1723) Dutch
£1934 $3500   (21-May-92 CH.NY159/R) Crowning with thorns (77x63cm-30x25in) s.
£2649 $4795   (19-May-92 AB.S4386/R) Zeus and Kallisto (110x91cm-43x36in) s.
                              (S.KR 28000)
£3071 $5559   (3-Dec-91 AB.S4763/R) Zeus and Kallistro (110x91cm-43x36in) s.
                              (S.KR 32000)

VOORT, Cornelis van der (attrib) (1576-1624) Flemish
£6116 $11376   (20-Jun-92 CH.MO28/R) Portrait d'une dame de qualite (108x76cm-43x30in)
                              d.1607 panel (F.FR 60000)

VOORZAAT, Theo (20th C) Dutch
£988 $1798   (11-Dec-91 CH.AM150) Still life with doll (25x25cm-10x10in) s.d.78
                              (D.FL 3200)

VORDEMBERGE, Friedrich (1897-1980) German
£521 $932   (15-Nov-91 KM.K701 a) Lilies and marguerites in glass (52x37cm-20x15in)
*   s. wax crayons htd.white board (DM 1500)*
£550 $1006   (3-Jun-92 L.K455) Still life with pumpkin, plums and grapes
*   (50x68cm-20x27in) s. W/C (DM 1600)*
£632 $1137   (21-Nov-91 L.K497/R) White house with stairs (78x53cm-31x21in) s.
*   s.i.d.1968verso W/C pastel bodycol (DM 1800)*

VORDEMBERGE-GILDEWART (1899-1963) German
£420 $726   (28-Mar-92 BOD.P1039) Composition with red rhombus (60x45cm-24x18in) s.
                              (DM 1200)

VORGANG, Paul (1860-1927) German
£662 $1205   (13-Dec-91 BM.B734/R) Lake landscape, Mark (28x44cm-11x17in) s. canvas on
                              board (DM 1900)

VOROBIEFF, Maria see MAREVNA, Marie

VOROBIOVA, Nadejda (1924-) Russian
£689 $1247   (20-Nov-92 ARC.P87/R) Les champignons (89x74cm-35x29in) s. (F.FR 6800)
£823 $1490   (6-Dec-91 ARC.P44/R) Retour de l'ecole (50x61cm-20x24in) s. (F.FR 8000)
£977 $1769   (6-Dec-91 ARC.P41/R) Les vacances a la campagne (94x102cm-37x40in) s.
                              (F.FR 9500)

VOS, Cornelis de (1585-1651) Flemish
£7000 $12740   (11-Dec-91 S107/R) Portrait of lady, said to be Jeanne de Blois
                              (118x90cm-46x35in)
£17132 $30323   (7-Nov-91 D.V117/R) The Finding of Moses (173x259cm-68x102in) mono.
                              (A.S 350000)

VOS, Cornelis de (attrib) (1585-1651) Flemish
£4200 $7350   (28-Feb-92 C4/R) The Judgement of Paris (50x65cm-20x26in) copper

VOS, Cornelis de (circle) (1585-1651) Flemish
£1200 $2184   (10-Dec-91 PH132/R) Portrait of gentleman, wearing black hat
                              (60x49cm-24x19in)
£3315 $6000   (21-May-92 CH.NY160/R) Portrait of gentleman, standing, in costume with
                              ruff (108x85cm-43x33in) i.d.1634

VOS, F (?) ?
£528 $913   (24-Mar-92 VN.R95) Entre roses (50x60cm-20x24in) s.d.1897 pastel
*   (D.FL 1700)*

VOS, Hubert (1855-1935) American
£6630 $12000   (6-Dec-91 CH.NY128/R) The knitting room (82x151cm-32x59in) s.d.89 pastel
*   canvas*

VOS, Jan de IV (1593-?) Dutch
£11000 $20020   (10-Dec-91 PH31/R) Extensive view of Dutch town with windmill, several
                              figures on path (73x107cm-29x42in) panel

VOS, Maria (1824-1906) Dutch
£1040 $1840   (5-Nov-91 SY.AM150/R) Carrots and jugs by well (24x33cm-9x13in) s.d.1857
                              panel (D.FL 3400)

VOS, Martin de (1532-1603) Flemish
£11858 $21107   (29-Nov-91 GAB.G3112/R) Le paradis terrestre (48x71cm-19x28in)
                              (S.FR 30000)
£450 $819   (11-Dec-91 PH138/R) Christ blessing the little children (30x44cm-12x17in)
*   pen wash*
£650 $1183   (11-Dec-91 PH6/R) Cimon and Pero (30x24cm-12x9in) s.d.1581 pen wash
*   htd.white*
£700 $1344   (8-Jul-92 PH277/R) Sacrifice with attendants (18x15cm-7x6in) s. pen wash
£1500 $2610   (13-Apr-92 S263/R) Holofernes before King Nabuchodonosor of Assyrians
*   (19x27cm-7x11in) s.d.1587 pen wash*
£1733 $3223   (20-Jun-92 CH.MO201/R) Saint Luc (34x27cm-13x11in) chk pen wash htd white
*   (F.FR 17000)*
£2500 $4800   (6-Jul-92 S73/R) Esdras and the Angel on Mount Sion (18x28cm-7x11in)
*   s.d.1582 pen wash*

VOS, Martin de (1532-1603) Flemish-cont.
£7136 $13272   (20-Jun-91 CH.MO255/R) L'ete (18x24cm-7x9in) init.d.1593 i. black chk ink wash (F.FR 70000)

VOS, Martin de (circle) (1532-1603) Flemish
£1300 $2275   (25-Feb-92 PH56/R) St Benedict praying in landscape. St Hilarian praying in landscape (23x43cm-9x17in) glass pair
£2800 $5376   (10-Jul-92 PH43/R) Christ and woman of Samaria (36x27cm-14x11in) panel
£3200 $5600   (28-Feb-92 C35/R) The Prophet Habakkuk giving sustenance to Daniel in the Lion's Den (97x149cm-38x59in) panel

VOS, Martin de (school) (1532-1603) Flemish
£8380 $15000   (16-Jan-92 CH.NY83/R) Paul and Barnabas at Lystra (76x109cm-30x43in) panel

VOS, Martin de (studio) (1532-1603) Flemish
£1007 $1712   (25-Oct-91 AT.P139) L'Exode (19x26cm-7x10in) i. pen wash (F.FR 10000)

VOS, Martin de (style) (1532-1603) Flemish
£1698 $3039   (14-Nov-91 CH.AM27/R) The Annunciation (113x87cm-44x34in) panel (D.FL 5500)

VOS, Paul de (1596-1678) Flemish
£3027 $5207   (16-Oct-91 AT.P50) Chiens se disputant un morceau de viande (105x152cm-41x60in) (F.FR 30000)

VOS, Paul de (attrib) (1596-1678) Flemish
£4651 $8000   (9-Oct-91 CH.NY26/R) Monkey and fox in landscape (97x178cm-38x70in)
£5523 $9500   (9-Oct-91 CH.NY24/R) Two monkeys picking fruit from tree (97x178cm-38x70in)
£6395 $11000   (9-Oct-91 CH.NY23/R) Two hunting dogs chasing hares in landscape (97x178cm-38x70in)
£9884 $17000   (9-Oct-91 CH.NY25/R) Three dogs chasing hare in landscape (97x178cm-38x70in)

VOS, Paul de (studio) (17th C) Flemish
£2591 $4509   (13-Apr-92 AT.P62) Herons et renard (101x127cm-40x50in) (F.FR 25500)

VOS, Paul de (studio) and WILDENS, Jan (17th C) Flemish
£4400 $7832   (30-Oct-91 S166/R) Hounds chasing foxes in landscape (174x242cm-69x95in)

VOS, Paul de (style) (17th C) Flemish
£3800 $7296   (9-Jul-92 CSK314/R) Lion attacking leopard, with lioness and cub feeding on deer (141x222cm-56x87in)
£4012 $7182   (14-Nov-91 CH.AM196/R) Italianate landscape with cockerel attacking spaniel (131x171cm-52x67in) (D.FL 13000)
£13000 $23140   (30-Oct-91 S94/R) Leopards and lions (172x233cm-68x92in)

VOS, Simon de (attrib) (1603-1676) Flemish
£1031 $1887   (2-Jun-92 FN.S2790) Salome presenting the head of St John the Baptist to King Herodes (46x61cm-18x24in) (DM 3000)
£2800 $4900   (28-Feb-92 C36/R) The Penitent Magdalen (64x48cm-25x19in) panel

VOS, Simon de (style) (1603-1676) Flemish
£4400 $7656   (13-Sep-91 C123/R) Merry company (29x39cm-11x15in) panel

VOS, Vincent de (1829-1875) Belgian
£993 $1708   (8-Oct-91 ZEL.L1764/R) Dogs with broken bowl (17x25cm-7x10in) s. panel (DM 2900)
£1047 $2000   (16-Jul-92 SY.NY481/R) La toilette du chien (24x17cm-9x7in) s.d. panel
£3825 $7000   (5-Jun-92 SY.NY183/R) The wicker basket (51x69cm-20x27in) s.d.68

VOSMAER, Daniel (17th C) Dutch
£2128 $3894   (12-May-92 SY.AM94/R) Aftermath of explosion of powder magazine at Delft (82x99cm-32x39in) s.i. (D.FL 7000)
£6122 $10837   (10-Feb-92 GL.P28/R) L'explosion de la poudriere de delft en 1654 (91x128cm-36x50in) i. (F.FR 60000)

VOSS, Jan (1936-) German
£3846 $6846   (26-Nov-91 KF.M1115/R) Le petit chasseur (60x73cm-24x29in) s.d.1965 (DM 11000)
£5783 $10062   (18-Sep-91 KH.K72/R) L'Ange gardiene surmene (100x65cm-39x26in) s.d.64 (D.KR 65000)
£5872 $10217   (18-Sep-91 KH.K45/R) Bonne anniversaire (81x100cm-32x39in) s.d.65 (D.KR 66000)
£6306 $10847   (4-Mar-92 KH.K122 g/R) Composition (114x162cm-45x64in) s.d.78 acrylic (D.KR 70000)
£7930 $14352   (20-May-92 KH.K140/R) Composition (146x114cm-57x45in) s.d.87 acrylic (D.KR 90000)
£8188 $14575   (30-Nov-91 FB.P46/R) Eclipse partielle (114x162cm-45x64in) s.d.72 (F.FR 80000)
£8874 $16150   (30-May-92 VG.B381/R) Somnambules (96x146cm-38x57in) s.i.d.1971verso (DM 26000)
£15125 $26317   (18-Sep-91 KH.K9/R) Composition (195x115cm-77x45in) paper on canvas (D.KR 170000)

VOSS, Jan (1936-) German-cont.

£1057	$1914	(20-May-92 KH.K26/R) Dunkle Ahnung (24x33cm-9x13in) s.d.85 oil W/C crayon collage (D.KR 12000)
£1068	$1858	(18-Sep-91 KH.K32/R) Spielmaterial (24x33cm-9x13in) s.d.85 W/C crayon collage (D.KR 12000)
£1722	$3118	(21-May-92 CC.P78/R) Untitled (66x100cm-26x39in) s.d.1981 crayon ink (F.FR 17000)
£4895	$8469	(28-Mar-92 BOD.P1040) Horses (200x130cm-79x51in) mixed media (DM 14000)
£6539	$11247	(12-Oct-91 GL.P88/R) Sans titre (153x114cm-60x45in) s.d.1985 gouache W/C collage paper laid canvas (F.FR 65000)

VOSS, Karl Leopold (1856-1921) German

£515	$897	(18-Sep-91 N.M743) Lake Chiemsee banks (30x40cm-12x16in) s. i.verso canvas on board (DM 1500)
£1203	$2093	(18-Sep-91 N.M742) Palace garden, Dachau (26x32cm-10x13in) s.d.1921 i.d.verso board (DM 3500)
£515	$897	(18-Sep-91 N.M287/R) Young lady wearing bonnet and parasol (31x22cm-12x9in) gouache W/C board (DM 1500)

VOSTELL, Wolf (1932-) German

£773	$1338	(23-Mar-92 CC.P101/R) Tauromaquia con quadrado de oro 4 (35x50cm-14x20in) s.d.1989 crayon gold sheet (F.FR 7500)
£1890	$3459	(2-Jun-92 L.K1027/R) Untitled (73x101cm-29x40in) s.d.1986 gouache col.chk indian ink board (DM 5500)
£4190	$7500	(13-Nov-91 SY.NY128/R) Psychogrammen (49x65cm-19x26in) s.d.64 oil crayon chl solvent ball point pen

VOSTERMAN, Johannes (?1643-1699?) Flemish

| £5500 | $9790 | (30-Oct-91 S53) River landscapes (10x15cm-4x6in) metal pair |

VOTOIX, L (20th C) French

| £526 | $925 | (9-Apr-92 FA.PH577) At the races (46x53cm-18x21in) s.i. |

VOUET, Simon (1590-1649) French

| £2123 | $3800 | (15-Jan-92 CH.NY66/R) Head of old woman, veiled, in profile to left (14x13cm-6x5in) with i. black white chk |

VOUET, Simon (after) (1590-1649) French

| £939 | $1700 | (19-May-92 CE.NY323) Lot and daughters (84x71cm-33x28in) |
| £4200 | $7350 | (3-Apr-92 C153/R) Hercules and Omphale (75x57cm-30x22in) painted oval |

VOUET, Simon (attrib) (1590-1649) French

| £16760 | $30000 | (17-Jan-92 SY.NY161/R) Helen presenting to Menelus the cup with the draught of Queen Polydamna (100x81cm-39x32in) |

VOUET, Simon (circle) (1590-1649) French

£1223	$2275	(18-Jun-92 SY.MO149/R) Lucrece se poignardant (30x22cm-12x9in) slate (F.FR 12000)
£30581	$56881	(18-Jun-92 SY.MO24/R) Vierge a l'Enfant (73x61cm-29x24in) (F.FR 300000)
£6500	$11310	(14-Apr-92 C151/R) Esther before Ahasuerus (38x27cm-15x11in) chk wash htd.white

VOUET, Simon (style) (1590-1649) French

£800	$1440	(21-Nov-91 CSK59) Rest on the Flight into Egypt (76x63cm-30x25in)
£906	$1622	(7-May-92 CH.AM62) Crucifixion (43x33cm-17x13in) panel (D.FL 3000)
£2447	$4332	(7-Nov-91 D.V369/R) St John the Baptist (75x54cm-30x21in) (A.S 50000)
£3000	$5220	(15-Apr-92 C149/R) Salvator Mundi (35x27cm-14x11in) panel
£7000	$12250	(3-Apr-92 C130/R) Allegory of Public Felicity (166x129cm-65x51in)

VOULLEMIER, Anne Nicole (1796-1886) French

| £926 | $1676 | (3-Dec-91 CN.P42/R) Portrait presume du Prince de Joinville (46x38cm-18x15in) (F.FR 9000) |

VOWE, Paul Gerhart (1874-?) German

| £525 | $918 | (18-Feb-92 CH.AM290/R) Portrait of a young lady seated, in a hat (64x51cm-25x20in) s. board (D.FL 1700) |

VOYET, Jacques (20th C) French?

| £1947 | $3700 | (25-Jun-92 BG.M62/R) Bound game cock (74x99cm-29x39in) s. |

VOYSEY, Charles Francis Annesley (1857-1941) British

| £2600 | $4758 | (5-Feb-92 C9/R) Designs for coachman's cottage at Colwall, Malvern for J.W. Wilson, M.P (56x79cm-22x31in) s.d.1908 ink W/C pencil three linen four |

VRANCX, Sebastian (1573-1647) Flemish

£1067	$1900	(22-Jan-92 D.NY61) Abraham and Melchisadek (51x30cm-20x12in) i.verso
£5556	$9944	(14-Nov-91 CH.AM201/R) Battle between officer Breaute and Gerard Abrahamsz at Vught, 1600 (25x37cm-10x15in) panel (D.FL 18000)
£6383	$11681	(12-May-92 SY.AM11/R) Cavalry battle (58x84cm-23x33in) panel (D.FL 21000)
£10000	$17500	(1-Apr-92 S89/R) Landscape with cavalry battle (45x62cm-18x24in) s. panel

VRANCX, Sebastian (attrib) (1573-1647) Flemish

| £31768 | $57500 | (22-May-92 SY.NY26/R) Landscape with deerhunt. Landscape with two lovers presented with flowers (182x279cm-72x110in) pair |

VRANCX, Sebastian (circle) (1573-1647) Flemish
£3500 $6265   (13-Nov-91 CG571/R) An ambush (58x84cm-23x33in) panel

VRANCX, Sebastian (style) (1573-1647) Flemish
£1650 $2871   (13-Sep-91 C146/R) Highwaymen holding up travellers on wooded track (25x35cm-10x14in) panel

VRANCX, Sebastian and MOMPER, Frans de (17th C) Flemish
£12155 $22000   (22-May-92 SY.NY137/R) Village with two men fixing wheel of cart and other townsfolk (62x86cm-24x34in)

VREEDENBURGH, Cornelis (1880-1946) Dutch
£1835 $3358   (3-Jun-92 R.T100/R) Dutch landscape with farmer milking (40x60cm-16x24in) s. (C.D 4000)
£3757 $6500   (6-Sep-91 S.BM136/R) Putting up the Sails (61x91cm-24x36in) s.
£5810 $10110   (14-Apr-92 SY.AM185/R) Het Singel with the Lutheran Church in Amsterdam (80x100cm-31x39in) s.d.1918 (D.FL 19000)

VRIENDT, Frans Floris de see FLORIS, Frans

VRIES, Abraham de (attrib) (1590-c.1662) Dutch
£5000 $8750   (3-Apr-92 C69/R) Portrait of bearded gentleman, said to be Vicomte de la Bouviere (91x73cm-36x29in) with i.verso panel

VRIES, Catharina Julia de (1813-1883) Dutch
£700 $1239   (13-Feb-92 CSK79) Still life of hanging partridge, with grapes and pomegranite on ledge (44x35cm-17x14in) init.

VRIES, Emanuel de (1816-1875) Dutch
£3333 $5900   (22-Apr-92 CH.AM123/R) Shipping an anchor in a calm near a jetty, village beyond (35x43cm-14x17in) s.d.1841 panel (D.FL 11000)

VRIES, Hubert de (20th C) Belgian?
£564 $1032   (12-May-92 C.A85) Fishing port (95x120cm-37x47in) s.verso (B.FR 34000)
£667 $1174   (7-Apr-92 C.A428) Still life (70x70cm-28x28in) s.d.1965 (B.FR 40000)

VRIES, Michiel de (?-c.1702) Dutch
£4800 $9216   (10-Jul-92 C126/R) River landscape with fishermen in boat, hamlet nearby (73x57cm-29x22in) s.d.1653 panel

VRIES, Paul Vredeman de (1567-c.1630) Flemish
£14000 $24500   (1-Apr-92 S30/R) Palace courtyard with David and Bathsheba (98x133cm-39x52in)

VRIES, Paul Vredeman de (attrib) (1567-c.1630) Dutch
£3477 $5946   (18-Mar-92 D.V352/R) Interior of gothic church (53x64cm-21x25in) (A.S 70000)

VRIES, Paul Vredeman de (circle) (1567-c.1630) Dutch
£3040 $5562   (12-May-92 SY.AM90/R) Feast in courtyard of palace (32x47cm-13x19in) panel (D.FL 10000)

VRIES, Paul Vredeman de (style) (1567-c.1630) Dutch
£4000 $7000   (1-Apr-92 S129/R) Church interior (58x45cm-23x18in) bears seal verso. panel
£7000 $12460   (30-Oct-91 S5/R) Christ in the house of Martha and Mary (42x66cm-17x26in) init. panel

VRIES, Roelof van (1631-1681) Dutch
£4630 $8287   (12-Nov-91 SY.AM71/R) Horseman on forest path (68x53cm-27x21in) panel (D.FL 15000)
£5525 $10000   (21-May-92 CH.NY115/R) Wooded landscapes with travellers and huntsmen on paths (32x24cm-13x9in) s. panel pair
£6826 $12355   (21-May-92 L.K172/R) Landscape with bridge and thatched house amongst trees (41x53cm-16x21in) s. panel (DM 20000)

VRIES, Roelof van (style) (1631-1681) Dutch
£800 $1536   (10-Jul-92 C125 a) Wooded landscape with child outside cottage by stream (57x46cm-22x18in) panel
£2200 $4026   (12-May-92 SWS606/R) Wooded landscape with fisherman (36x31cm-14x12in) bears sig. panel
£2235 $3823   (18-Mar-92 D.V379/R) Riverside village (40x32cm-16x13in) panel (A.S 45000)

VROLYK, Adrianus Jacobus (1834-1862) Dutch
£3400 $5814   (18-Mar-92 S9/R) Landscape with cows by a river (47x66cm-19x26in) s.indist.d. panel

VROLYK, Jan (1845-1894) Dutch
£486 $836   (12-Oct-91 CH.AM200) Cows in meadow (18x14cm-7x6in) s. panel (D.FL 1600)

VROMANS, Isaak (1655-1719) Dutch
£1900 $3420   (21-Nov-91 CSK252/R) Forest floor still life with snake, lizard and butterflies (62x46cm-24x18in) panel

VROMANS, Isaak (1655-1719) Dutch-cont.
£8500 $15300   (21-Nov-91 CSK253/R) Forest floor still life with toads, dragonfly and other insects (64x53cm-25x21in) s.

VROOM, Cornelis Hendriksz (1591-1661) Dutch
£21000 $40320   (8-Jul-92 S49/R) Wooded river landscape with horsemen and fowler (35x47cm-14x19in) panel

VROOM, Hendrik Cornelisz (1566-1640) Dutch
£1955 $3500   (13-Nov-91 B.SF2132/R) Old oak trees in extensive landscape (74x57cm-29x22in) d.1607 cradled panel

VROOM, Hendrik Cornelisz (style) (1566-1640) Dutch
£3704 $6630   (12-Nov-91 SY.AM65/R) Shipping on choppy sea (29x40cm-11x16in) panel (D.FL 12000)
£8000 $14000   (1-Apr-92 S91/R) Shipping on choppy sea (29x40cm-11x16in) panel

VUAGNAT, Francois (1910-) French
£941 $1685   (15-Nov-91 ZOF.Z1917) River landscape (40x29cm-16x11in) s. i.verso (S.FR 2400)

VUCHT, Gerrit van (1610-1699) Dutch
£2500 $4450   (30-Oct-91 S68/R) Still life of glassware and silver ware on table with bread and ham (18x12cm-7x5in) panel
£5556 $9944   (12-Nov-91 SY.AM125/R) Still life of ham, fruit, bottles and violin on partly draped table (40x32cm-16x13in) panel (D.FL 18000)

VUCHT, Jan van der (1603-1637) Dutch
£6996 $12663   (3-Dec-91 CN.P70/R) Interieur d'une eglise renaissance (26x35cm-10x14in) s. panel (F.FR 68000)

VUILLARD, Edouard (1868-1940) French
£9000 $17190   (1-Jul-92 S126/R) Nu dans l'atelier (24x24cm-9x9in) st.inits. board
£20000 $34600   (24-Mar-92 C10/R) Le soir au jardin (24x33cm-9x13in) thinned oil board
£22951 $42000   (13-May-92 CH.NY241/R) La lecture dans le petit salon - Madame Hessel au chateau des Clayes (46x38cm-18x15in) st.sig. paper on canvas
£27119 $48000   (6-Nov-91 CH.NY276/R) Madame Vuillard a table (31x28cm-12x11in) st.sig.
£37572 $65000   (2-Oct-91 SY.NY30/R) Nature morte aux prunes (19x24cm-7x9in) s.
£38251 $70000   (14-May-92 SY.NY247/R) Vase de fleurs (36x43cm-14x17in) st.sig. board
£95000 $181450   (30-Jun-92 S21/R) La chambre verte - Mme.Vuillard et Annette, rue Truffaut (44x42cm-17x17in) st.sig. board
£197740 $350000   (5-Nov-91 CH.NY38/R) Le chocolat (31x36cm-12x14in) init. board on panel
£231156 $388342   (16-Aug-91 ZZ.F127/R) Madame Hessel dans son interieur (37x60cm-15x24in) s. board (F.FR 2300000)
£914 $1600   (28-Feb-92 SY.NY1/R) Two figures in landscape (11x15cm-4x6in) st.init. graphite
£1163 $2000   (12-Oct-91 SY.NY10/R) Seated woman (11x18cm-4x7in) with st.init. pencil
£1279 $2200   (10-Oct-91 FA.PH803/R) Bouquet de fleurs devant la fenetre (20x10cm-8x4in) st.init. pencil
£1500 $2595   (25-Mar-92 S15/R) Portrait de femme assise (21x12cm-8x5in) st.init. pencil
£2326 $4000   (12-Oct-91 SY.NY11 a/R) Portrait of Marie Vuillard. Two figures (26x23cm-10x9in) pastel joined paper double-sided
£2419 $4282   (10-Nov-91 ZZ.F193/R) Table devant la fenetre (11x11cm-4x4in) st.init. pastel chl. (F.FR 24000)
£2722 $4818   (10-Nov-91 ZZ.F191/R) La terrasse (11x15cm-4x6in) st.init. pastel chl.chk. (F.FR 27000)
£4500 $7785   (24-Mar-92 C2/R) Femme assise sur fond rouge (24x12cm-9x5in) st.studio pastel
£4918 $9000   (14-May-92 SY.NY104/R) Scene de ville. Homme en chemise, de dos, feuilletant un livre (11x16cm-4x6in) st.init. pastel crayon sanguine double-sided
£6780 $12000   (7-Nov-91 SY.NY110/R) Jeune femme au bouquet de fleurs (37x19cm-15x7in) with st.sig. pastel chl
£8436 $15270   (4-Dec-91 CB.P49) Madame Bernheim dans son salon (20x12cm-8x5in) st.init. drawing (F.FR 82000)
£8571 $15000   (25-Feb-92 SY.NY8/R) Femme dans un interieur (24x32cm-9x13in) st.init. pastel crayon
£9381 $16230   (23-Mar-92 GL.P102 b/R) La buvette au Mont-Dore (142x99cm-56x39in) st.sig. pastel (F.FR 91000)
£9827 $17000   (2-Oct-91 SY.NY12/R) Madame Hessel dans le jardin a Vaucresson (24x31cm-9x12in) with st.sig. pastel
£10929 $20000   (13-May-92 SY.NY23/R) Portrait of Madame Vuillard (21x12cm-8x5in) st.init. pencil
£13714 $24000   (25-Feb-92 CH.NY29/R) La robe noire (74x45cm-29x18in) st.sig. chl peinture colle canvas
£15000 $25800   (16-Oct-91 S6/R) Portrait de femme (26x21cm-10x8in) s. pastel
£21469 $38000   (7-Nov-91 SY.NY111/R) Le pot vert (25x32cm-10x13in) s. pastel
£24590 $45000   (13-May-92 SY.NY24/R) La couturiere (19x25cm-7x10in) indian ink pencil
£24717 $46468   (16-Dec-91 AGS.P6/R) Paysage au grand chene (32x23cm-13x9in) s. pastel (F.FR 240000)
£25714 $45000   (25-Feb-92 SY.NY11/R) Petite maison a Saint-Jacut (50x65cm-20x26in) st.sig. distemper paper on canvas
£27322 $50000   (13-May-92 SY.NY5/R) Le mannequin (23x28cm-9x11in) s. chl

VUILLARD, Edouard (1868-1940) French-cont.
| £36000 | $68760 | (1-Jul-92 S129/R) Etang au chateau des Clayes (23x26cm-9x10in) s. pastel pencil |

£109290 $200000 (12-May-92 CH.NY129/R) Le banc, square Vintimille (65x54cm-26x21in) s. paper on canvas

£314208 $575000 (13-May-92 SY.NY79/R) Madame Hessel dans son salon (100x55cm-39x22in) st.sig. peinture a la colle paper on canvas

VUILLARD, Edouard (style) (1868-1940) French
£2963 $5363 (19-May-92 GF.L2564/R) View of Banlieue with Seine, Paris (51x62cm-20x24in) bears sig. board (S.FR 8000)

VUILLEFROY, Felix Dominique de (1841-?) French
£1132 $2150 (26-Jun-92 CSC.P130) La fermiere (38x55cm-15x22in) s. (F.FR 11000)

VUILLERMET, Charles Francois (1849-1918) Swiss
£549 $933 (23-Oct-91 GD.B780) Wood clearing with figures (27x40cm-11x16in) s.d.76 (S.FR 1400)

VUILLERMOZ, Louis (1923-) French?
£464 $798 (20-Oct-91 LT.P142) l'ile de Raguenes a Pont-Aven (56x75cm-22x30in) s. i.verso W/C (F.FR 4600)

£505 $868 (20-Oct-91 LT.P122/R) Bateaux Amarres, la Varenne (66x103cm-26x41in) s. W/C (F.FR 5000)

£555 $955 (20-Oct-91 LT.P132) Sur la Plage de Lanroz (66x103cm-26x41in) s. i.verso W/C (F.FR 5500)

£656 $1128 (20-Oct-91 LT.P8/R) Le parc Saint Maur en hiver (103x66cm-41x26in) s.i.d.85 W/C (F.FR 6500)

VUORI, Ilmari (1898-1975) Finnish
£704 $1246 (6-Nov-91 HOR.H146) Summer jobs (55x66cm-22x26in) s.d.1947 (F.M 5000)

VYSEKAL, Edouard Antonin (1890-1939) American
£1017 $1800 (12-Feb-92 B.SF611/R) Luvena in mandarin costume (30x22cm-12x9in) init. board

£2260 $4000 (12-Feb-92 B.SF590/R) Still life (32x44cm-13x17in) s.
£6215 $11000 (12-Feb-92 B.SF545/R) Sunshine and laundry (46x58cm-18x23in) s.
£395 $750 (24-Jun-92 B.SF6503/R) Kutrina (27x20cm-11x8in) s. W/C
£508 $900 (12-Feb-92 B.SF608/R) Poplars (37x53cm-15x21in) s. W/C
£734 $1300 (12-Feb-92 B.SF612/R) Neighbouring houses (37x55cm-15x22in) s.d.39 W/C
£904 $1600 (12-Feb-92 B.SF615/R) Hollywood (41x53cm-16x21in) s. W/C
£1017 $1800 (12-Feb-92 B.SF614/R) Silverlake Blvd (36x48cm-14x19in) s. gouache

VYSEKAL, Luvena (1873-1954) American
£621 $1100 (12-Feb-92 B.SF610/R) Neighbour children (25x34cm-10x13in) s.
£1554 $2750 (12-Feb-92 B.SF609/R) Ruth and baby Nell (25x36cm-10x14in)

VYTLACIL, Vaclav (1892-?) American
£647 $1100 (25-Oct-91 S.W2825) Mountain landscape in autumn (28x36cm-11x14in) s.d.15 board

W A C (?) ?
£1020 $1754 (4-Mar-92 RBB970/R) Study of dead salmon (61x122cm-24x48in) mono.d.1860

W H W (?) ?
£600 $1146 (20-Jul-92 WW60) Hawking party with dismounted rider and horse (21x28cm-8x11in) init.i. panel

WAAGE, Carl (1820-?) ?
£748 $1338 (16-Jan-92 D.V138/R) Village with ice skaters on lake (18x24cm-7x9in) s. panel (A.S 15000)

WAAGEN, Adalbert (1833-1898) German
£1237 $2153 (17-Sep-91 FN.S2594) View of Berchtesgaden with peasant girls crossing bridge over torrent (31x44cm-12x17in) s. i.verso board (DM 3600)

£3399 $6119 (19-Nov-91 GS.B3678/R) Mountain landscape near Berchtesgaden (70x56cm-28x22in) s.d.1871 (S.FR 8600)

WAAGSTEIN, Joen (1879-1949) Scandinavian
£509 $890 (1-Apr-92 KH.K266) Houses by the fjord, Faroe Islands (47x64cm-19x25in) s.d.1928 (D.KR 5600)

WAARDEN, Jan van der (19/20th C) Dutch
£729 $1255 (12-Oct-91 CH.AM201) Wooded landscape with figures by farm (29x37cm-11x15in) init.d.1855 panel (D.FL 2400)

£18500 $34410 (19-Jun-92 C11/R) Peaches, melons and grapes with sweet peas and poppies on stone ledge (92x77cm-36x30in) s.i. panel

WACHENHUSEN, Fritz (1859-1925) German
£4848 $8582 (22-Apr-92 CH.AM216/R) View of the Volendam harbour with fisherfolk on a quay (134x213cm-53x84in) s.d.94 (D.FL 16000)

WACHTEL, Elmer (1864-1929) American
£1826	$3250	(26-Nov-91 MOR.P55) Landscape (36x46cm-14x18in) s.
£2895	$5500	(23-Jun-92 MOR.P109) Alpine glow, Sierra Nevada (36x46cm-14x18in) s.
£7910	$14000	(12-Feb-92 B.SF525/R) Convict Lake (41x51cm-16x20in) s.
£857	$1500	(31-Mar-92 MOR.P80 a) Harbour scene (231x38cm-91x15in) s. W/C
£1130	$2000	(12-Feb-92 B.SF489/R) Boathouse (16x37cm-6x15in) s. W/C
£1836	$3250	(12-Feb-92 B.SF495/R) Mission San Juan Capistrano (29x43cm-11x17in) s. W/C

WACHTEL, Marion K (1876-1954) American
£2684	$4750	(12-Feb-92 B.SF578/R) Woman in flower garden (30x25cm-12x10in) s. canvas on board
£9040	$16000	(12-Feb-92 B.SF526/R) Long Lake (61x81cm-24x32in) s.
£1000	$1900	(23-Jun-92 MOR.P106 a) Girl in blue apron (41x28cm-16x11in) s.d.1896 W/C

WACHTER, Eberhard (1762-1852) German
£1742	$3171	(11-Dec-91 N.M646/R) Herakles bei der Pythia in Delphi (74x84cm-29x33in) i.verso (DM 5000)

WACKER, Rudolf (1893-1939) Austrian
£399	$714	(15-Jan-92 D.V87/R) Two sculptures (29x21cm-11x8in) mono.d.22 chk (A.S 8000)
£499	$892	(15-Jan-92 D.V88/R) Mother and child (28x22cm-11x9in) mono.d.22 pencil (A.S 10000)
£684	$1190	(12-Sep-91 D.V239) Female figure after model in Museum fur Volkerkunde (27x19cm-11x7in) indis.i.d.21 pencil (A.S 14000)
£684	$1190	(12-Sep-91 D.V242) Fire god, Mus. Mexico (26x19cm-10x7in) indis.i.d.21 pencil (A.S 14000)
£733	$1275	(12-Sep-91 D.V240) Wall with masks after model in Museum fur Volkerkunde (28x22cm-11x9in) mono.d.22 pencil (A.S 15000)
£879	$1530	(12-Sep-91 D.V241) Standing female figure after model in Museum fur Volkerkunde (27x21cm-11x8in) mono.d.22 pencil (A.S 18000)
£993	$1768	(28-Nov-91 D.V127/R) Mother and child (33x25cm-13x10in) mono. pencil (A.S 20000)
£1490	$2651	(28-Nov-91 D.V128/R) Man and woman (29x19cm-11x7in) mono.d. pencil (A.S 30000)
£1738	$3093	(28-Nov-91 D.V129/R) Mother and child (31x16cm-12x6in) mono.d. chk (A.S 35000)

WADE, Robert A (?) ?
£513	$913	(27-Apr-92 J.M365) The Olgas (12x20cm-5x8in) s. W/C (A.D 1200)

WADHAM, W Joseph (1864-?) Australian
£755	$1315	(13-Apr-92 SY.J37/R) Welsh lane (56x85cm-22x33in) s.d.1911 W/C (SA.R 3800)

WADSWORTH, Edward (1889-1949) British
£150000	$274500	(13-May-92 S58/R) The Cattewater, Plymouth Sound (63x89cm-25x35in) s. tempera board
£10000	$18300	(13-May-92 S57/R) Study for the Bexhill Mural (54x73cm-21x29in) s.d.1935 W/C gouache

WAEL, Cornelis de (1592-1667) Flemish
£20000	$38400	(8-Jul-92 S318/R) Cavalry and musketeers resting by river (101x153cm-40x60in)
£34000	$65280	(8-Jul-92 S85/R) Battle in landscape with distant city (128x194cm-50x76in) bears i.verso

WAEL, Cornelis de (attrib) (1592-1667) Flemish
£2863	$5095	(28-Nov-91 BU.S78/R) Party of Orientals and Europeans (53x66cm-21x26in) (S.KR 30000)
£3200	$6144	(7-Jul-92 PH191/R) Figures gathered to watch dentist at work in town square (33x59cm-13x23in)
£7099	$12707	(14-Nov-91 CH.AM155/R) Military encampment with soldiers merrymaking and ruins on hilltop beyond (66x124cm-26x49in) (D.FL 23000)

WAEL, Cornelis de (circle) (1592-1667) Flemish
£1800	$3456	(10-Jul-92 PH52/R) Street scene with militia evicting peasants (64x80cm-25x31in)

WAENERBERG, Thorsten (1846-1917) Scandinavian
£3793	$6675	(12-Apr-92 HOR.H250) Windy day (30x45cm-12x18in) s.d.1890 (F.M 30000)
£4398	$7829	(1-Dec-91 HOR.H256) Cliffs (40x57cm-16x22in) s. (F.M 34000)
£4528	$8060	(1-Dec-91 HOR.H257) Steep shore (40x29cm-16x11in) s.d.1884 (F.M 35000)
£7245	$12895	(1-Dec-91 HOR.H255/R) Whirling water (39x57cm-15x22in) s.d.1894 (F.M 56000)
£8926	$15889	(1-Dec-91 HOR.H254) Landscape from Hogland (63x92cm-25x36in) s.d.1892 (F.M 67000)

WAGEMAKER, Jaap (1906-) Dutch
£1667	$3017	(19-May-92 CH.AM381/R) A still life (64x81cm-25x32in) s.i. (D.FL 5500)
£1152	$2084	(19-May-92 CH.AM366/R) Abstract composition (57x45cm-22x18in) s.d.58 collage mixed media (D.FL 3800)
£2121	$3839	(19-May-92 CH.AM366 a) Abstract composition (60x45cm-24x18in) s.d.57 collage mixed media (D.FL 7000)

WAGENBAUER, Max Josef (1774-1829) German
£21678 $38587   (26-Nov-91 KF.M272/R) Path in hilly landscape with shepherd and cattle
(50x62cm-20x24in) mono.i. copper (DM 62000)

WAGENSCHOEN, Franz Xaver (1726-1790) Austrian
£4630 $8287   (12-Nov-91 SY.AM110/R) Venus watching Mars forge armour for Aeneas
(71x92cm-28x36in) (D.FL 15000)

WAGNER, A (20th C) German
£617 $1080   (18-Feb-92 CH.AM287) Still life with lobster and fish on table by window
(86x70cm-34x28in) s. (D.FL 2000)

WAGNER, Adolf (1884-1962) ?
£2200 $3982   (22-May-92 C168/R) Ganymede (70x70cm-28x28in) bodycol canvas pair

WAGNER, Cornelis (1870-1956) German
£524 $907   (25-Mar-92 KM.K1503) River landscape with ship (32x45cm-13x18in) s.d.35
paper (DM 1500)
£524 $907   (25-Mar-92 KM.K1506) River landscape in Norwegian highlands with
flowering heath (45x65cm-18x26in) s.d.1901 (DM 1500)
£902 $1533   (23-Oct-91 GD.B1330/R) Steam ships and fishing boats on the Elbe
(41x50cm-16x20in) mono. (S.FR 2300)

WAGNER, Franz (1857-?) German
£602 $1089   (5-Dec-91 D.V140) Fountain in Vierwaldstatter See landscape
(25x27cm-10x11in) s.d.74 board (A.S 12000)

WAGNER, Fred (1864-?) American
£663 $1200   (24-May-92 JRB.C114/R) Portrait of Hortense Ferne (99x124cm-39x49in)

WAGNER, Fritz (1896-1939) German
£769 $1315   (19-Mar-92 N.M2853/R) Monk in his study (40x35cm-16x14in) s.i. (DM 2200)
£1310 $2200   (1-Sep-91 PO.BA23) Taberna con personajes (28x29cm-11x11in) s. panel
£1444 $2613   (3-Dec-91 FN.S2509/R) Dutch interior with figures playing dice at table
(70x86cm-28x34in) s.i. (DM 4100)
£1546 $2830   (2-Jun-92 FN.S2791/R) Music lesson (61x51cm-24x20in) s.i. (DM 4500)
£3265 $5680   (17-Sep-91 FN.S2596/R) Dutch merchants in 17th century costume seated at
table hearing news (65x80cm-26x31in) s.i. (DM 9500)
£3400 $6052   (26-Nov-91 PH15/R) Captivating story (58x79cm-23x31in) s.i.

WAGNER, Hans Joachim (20th C) German
£859 $1572   (2-Jun-92 FN.S2792/R) View of Venice lagoon with shipping and dome of
S.Maria de la Salute (66x97cm-26x38in) canvas on panel (DM 2500)

WAGNER, Jacob (1852-1898) American
£1031 $1753   (25-Oct-91 BM.B860/R) Dutch harbour with figures and rising thunderstorm
(53x80cm-21x31in) s. (DM 3000)

WAGNER, Karl (19/20th C) Austrian/German
£1220 $2122   (19-Sep-91 D.V52/R) Harbour scene, evening (73x99cm-29x39in) s.
(A.S 25000)

WAGNER, Paul Hermann (1852-?) German
£2321 $4201   (21-May-92 L.K496/R) Shepherd boy with geese and dog by pond
(49x60cm-19x24in) s. panel (DM 6800)
£2448 $4185   (18-Mar-92 N.M679/R) Brother and sister in Upper Bavarian costume
(66x50cm-26x20in) s.i. (DM 7000)

WAGNER, Theodor (19/20th C) ?
£572 $1098   (6-Jul-92 HC.P25) Nature morte au Hareng (33x55cm-13x22in) s. (F.FR 5500)
£1031 $1794   (21-Sep-91 SA.A1954/R) On the way to school (24x19cm-9x7in) s. (DM 3000)

WAGNER, Volker (1959-) German?
£512 $932   (25-May-92 WK.M1285/R) Number composition (76x88cm-30x35in)
s.i.d.1989verso panel (DM 1500)

WAGNER-HOHENBERG, Josef (1870-?) German
£1034 $1779   (16-Oct-91 KM.K1431/R) Clergyman seated in study (33x40cm-13x16in) s.
(DM 3000)

WAGREZ, Jacques (1846-1908) French
£849 $1503   (5-Nov-91 BA.S180/R) Girl wearing velvet dress (47x36cm-19x14in) s.d.1882
(S.KR 9000)

WAHL, Johann Salomon (1689-1765) Danish
£880 $1479   (27-Aug-91 RAS.K311/R) Portrait of Christina Louise (78x62cm-31x24in)
(D.KR 10000)
£1852 $3296   (28-Apr-92 RAS.K131/R) Portrait of Else de Junge (80x62cm-31x24in)
s.i.d.1724verso (D.KR 21000)

WAHLBERG, Alfred (1834-1906) Swedish
£575 $1019   (25-Apr-92 SO.S618/R) Coastal landscape, Uppsala (31x43cm-12x17in) s.
(S.KR 6100)
£576 $1042   (3-Dec-91 AB.S4678/R) Rocky landscape (27x36cm-11x14in) s.d.59 panel
(S.KR 6000)

WAHLBERG, Alfred (1834-1906) Swedish-cont.
£672	$1216	(3-Dec-91 AB.S4676/R) Wooded landscape with sunset over water (27x41cm-11x16in) s. panel (S.KR 7000)
£771	$1333	(28-Mar-92 UA.U406) Nature study from Bohuslan (27x35cm-11x14in) s.d.1862 (S.KR 8000)
£1536	$2779	(3-Dec-91 AB.S4677/R) Landscape with punt by lakeside, moonlight (18x27cm-7x11in) s.d.83 panel (S.KR 16000)
£2642	$4728	(7-May-92 RAS.S15/R) Bords de riviere, effet de soleil couchant (29x42cm-11x17in) s. panel (S.KR 28000)
£2657	$4861	(12-May-92 GO.G188/R) Coastal landscape (55x70cm-22x28in) s.i.d.1899 (S.KR 28000)

WAHLBERG, Ulf (?) ?
£816	$1476	(3-Dec-91 AB.S5168/R) Composition (100x81cm-39x32in) s. (S.KR 8500)
£1139	$2083	(13-May-92 BU.S209/R) Interior (65x81cm-26x32in) s.d.82 (S.KR 12000)
£441	$799	*(3-Dec-91 AB.S5169/R) Crashed cars in gravel-pit (21x15cm-8x6in) s.d.85 W/C collage (S.KR 4600)*

WAHLBERGSON, Erik (1808-1865) Swedish
£695	$1224	(12-Apr-92 HOR.H35) Blowing bubbles (40x32cm-16x13in) s.d.1858 (F.M 5500)

WAHLBOM, Carl (1810-1858) Swedish
£2751	$5035	(14-May-92 BU.S76/R) Parading Swedish cavalry during the 30years war (50x77cm-20x30in) s.d.1849 (S.KR 29000)

WAHLE, Friedrich (1863-1927) German
£697	$1268	(11-Dec-91 N.M649) Two gentlemen conversing in hallway (39x30cm-15x12in) s. board (DM 2000)

WAHLQVIST, Ehrnfried (1815-1895) Swedish
£776	$1404	(19-May-92 AB.S4287/R) Winter landscape with figures by farm and water (35x49cm-14x19in) s. (S.KR 8200)
£1325	$2397	(19-May-92 AB.S4286/R) Night scene with church and figures by torchlight (58x83cm-23x33in) s.d.1858 (S.KR 14000)

WAHLSTROM, Charlotte (1849-1924) Swedish
£522	$955	(17-May-92 BU.M455) Sunny haze over coastal landscape (100x75cm-39x30in) s.d.1917 (S.KR 5500)
£550	$1007	(12-May-92 GO.G189) Wooded tarn (30x53cm-12x21in) s. (S.KR 5800)
£664	$1215	(12-May-92 GO.G191) Heath landscape (40x56cm-16x22in) s. (S.KR 7000)
£946	$1712	(19-May-92 AB.S4289/R) Summer landscape with trees by water (59x50cm-23x20in) s. (S.KR 10000)
£1328	$2431	(12-May-92 GO.G190) Lake landscape with a resplendent tree s.d.1920 (S.KR 14000)
£2460	$4452	(19-May-92 AB.S4288/R) Swedish wooded landscape with goats and woman with faggots (76x136cm-30x54in) s.d.84 (S.KR 26000)

WAIDMANN, Pierre (1860-1937) French
£857	$1500	(18-Feb-92 CE.NY267/R) Dans la Vosges (47x61cm-19x24in) s.i.verso
£1012	$1750	(28-Mar-92 UA.U407) Dutch canal scene (66x94cm-26x37in) s. (S.KR 10500)
£1230	$2213	(2-Feb-92 ZZ.F8/R) Promeneuse aubord de l'estuaire (91x65cm-36x26in) s. (F.FR 12000)

WAIJO, A (?) ?
£489	$890	(11-Dec-91 HOR.H128) Street scene in Paris (74x62cm-29x24in) s.d.1956 (F.M 3800)

WAILAND, Friedrich (1821-1904) Austrian
£583	$1037	*(29-Apr-92 D.V734/R) Portrait of lady wearing white dress (8x6cm-3x2in) min.s.d.57 W/C in leather case (A.S 12000)*
£879	$1512	*(10-Oct-91 D.V343/R) Portrait of young lady wearing white dress with red trimming (12x9cm-5x4in) min.s.i.d.1868 oval (A.S 18000)*

WAILLY, Charles de (1729-1798) French
£12291	*$22000*	*(14-Jan-92 SY.NY62/R) Interior of celestial palace (31x44cm-12x17in) pen wash*

WAIN, Louis (1860-1939) British
£410	*$722*	*(10-Apr-92 K456/R) Bath time (33x23cm-13x9in) s. W/C*
£420	*$764*	*(11-Dec-91 CSK91) A moment's rest (18x25cm-7x10in) s. col.chks.htd.bodycol.*
£420	*$777*	*(11-Jun-92 B30/R) Stitch in time (21x10cm-8x4in) s. pencil ink*
£450	*$797*	*(13-Feb-92 B249/R) The little nipper (36x27cm-14x11in) s.i. gouache monochrome*
£480	*$874*	*(11-Dec-91 CSK88) We little kittens will prepare you your dinner (38x28cm-15x11in) s.i. pencil pen htd.white*
£520	*$946*	*(11-Dec-91 CSK82/R) Three studies of cats - sadness, joy and expectation s. ink three in same mount*
£520	*$952*	*(14-May-92 B155/R) More milk (22x17cm-9x7in) s. W/C bodycol*
£620	*$1128*	*(11-Dec-91 CSK84) Looking in the shop windows (18x23cm-7x9in) s.i. pencil*
£650	*$1183*	*(11-Dec-91 CSK80/R) I's for Isobel, an imp of a kitten (25x20cm-10x8in) s.i. pencil ink W/C htd.white*
£700	*$1253*	*(5-May-92 SWS257/R) A laughing cat (23x17cm-9x7in) s. col.crayons*
£720	*$1260*	*(1-Apr-92 B153) Study of seated tabby cat (28x17cm-11x7in) s. gouache*
£850	*$1522*	*(5-May-92 SWS286/R) 'Simple Simon' (29x23cm-11x9in) s. gouache*

WAIN, Louis (1860-1939) British-cont.
£900 $1638 (11-Dec-91 CSK90/R) Club news (53x36cm-21x14in) s.i. pencil pen
£950 $1729 (11-Dec-91 CSK89/R) The cat marching band. The freethinker
          (38x28cm-15x11in) s.i. pencil ink two
£1200 $2184 (11-Dec-91 CSK96/R) Miss Cat and Master Puss. Strutting tom cat. Played
          (38x28cm-15x11in) s.i. pencil pen three
£1250 $2275 (11-Dec-91 CSK85/R) Speak, sardines, speak. An extra tasty glass
          (38x28cm-15x11in) s.i. pencil ink htd.white two
£1250 $2275 (11-Dec-91 CSK106) Stage memories (43x25cm-17x10in) s.i. pencil ink
£3000 $5760 (10-Jul-92 CSK42/R) Prima Donna of night (51x33cm-20x13in) s. pencil
          bodycol

WAINEWRIGHT, Thomas Francis (19th C) British
£500 $925 (11-Jun-92 CSK7/R) Sheep in winter landscape (20x30cm-8x12in) s.i.d.1861
          pencil W/C

WAINEWRIGHT, Thomas Francis and PEARSON, Cornelius (19th C) British
£475 $879 (9-Jun-92 FB.M210) Cattle watering near river bend (21x40cm-8x16in)
          s.i.d.1876 W/C (C.D 1050)
£550 $1018 (11-Jun-92 CSK8) Sheep resting by a river (20x41cm-8x16in) s.d.1878
          pencil W/C htd. white

WAINWRIGHT, John (19th C) British
£1300 $2314 (28-Apr-92 S218/R) Blackgame and songbirds (71x93cm-28x37in) s.d.1864

WAIS, Alfred (1905-) German
£3265 $5974 (2-Jun-92 FN.S2415/R) Path in landscape with thatched houses
          (59x83cm-23x33in) s.d.1943 panel (DM 9500)
£550 $1006 (2-Jun-92 FN.S2414/R) Inn valley in fog (36x50cm-14x20in) s.d.1959 W/C
          (DM 1600)

WAITE, Edward Wilkins (fl.1878-1927) British
£3600 $6660 (11-Jun-92 CSK137/R) A wayside inn (30x45cm-12x18in) s.i.
£4400 $8448 (28-Jul-92 SWS378/R) Autumn glow (42x54cm-17x21in) s.
£5800 $9976 (4-Mar-92 S116/R) Outside Dolphin, Betchworth, Surrey. Geese in country
          lane (31x46cm-12x18in) s. pair
£8000 $13760 (11-Oct-91 C99/R) The brook he loved (55x43cm-22x17in) s.d.1892
£9000 $15390 (13-Mar-92 C102/R) The old watermill (51x76cm-20x30in) s.
£10000 $18300 (3-Jun-92 S56/R) May, Fittleworth, Sussex (51x76cm-20x30in) s.

WAITE, James Clarke (19th C) British
£2800 $5180 (12-Jun-92 C217/R) The new bonnet (40x51cm-16x20in) s.

WAITE, Robert Thorne (1842-1935) British
£3600 $6192 (4-Mar-92 S43/R) Haymaking (30x40cm-12x16in) s.
£500 $955 (1-Jul-92 B41/R) Cattle and sheep in a field at evening (12x35cm-5x14in)
          s. W/C
£800 $1424 (21-Jan-92 SWS1292) Parham Park, Sussex (63x100cm-25x39in) i.verso W/C
          over pencil
£960 $1670 (13-Sep-91 MAX323/R) The Downs in autumn (36x51cm-14x20in) s. W/C
£1600 $2848 (27-Nov-91 B196) The Downs in autumn (36x53cm-14x21in) s.i.verso W/C
£2500 $4475 (14-Jan-92 SWS90/R) Norwich Cathedral (31x74cm-12x29in) s. s.i.verso W/C
£2800 $4760 (23-Oct-91 MMB216/R) Crossing ford near Arundel (66x104cm-26x41in) s. W/C

WAITT, Richard (18th C) British
£3400 $5984 (8-Apr-92 S157/R) Portrait of Alexander Brodie of Brodie
          (72x60cm-28x24in) i. painted oval

WAKELIN, Roland Shakespeare (1887-?) Australian
£460 $833 (19-May-92 JRL.S43) Bridge (22x29cm-9x11in) s.d.56 board (A.D 1100)
£661 $1189 (24-Nov-91 SY.S22) Light on hill (24x30cm-9x12in) s.d.1958 board
          (A.D 1500)
£700 $1246 (28-Nov-91 C44/R) Landscape (14x20cm-6x8in) s.d.1921 paper on board
£830 $1452 (30-Mar-92 AAA.S94) NSW landscape (34x44cm-13x17in) s. board (A.D 1900)
£855 $1547 (2-Dec-91 AAA.S118) Still life (35x55cm-14x22in) s. board (A.D 2000)
£881 $1586 (24-Nov-91 SY.S202/R) Landscape (14x16cm-6x6in) s.d.22 board (A.D 2000)
£1057 $1903 (24-Nov-91 SY.S226/R) Still life - with jar, book and fruit
          (34x24cm-13x9in) s.d.1935 canvas on board (A.D 2400)
£1367 $2611 (29-Jun-92 AAA.S90) Judy sewing (55x45cm-22x18in) s. board (A.D 3500)
£1447 $2561 (26-Apr-92 SY.ME312) Cloudy morning, Skillion, Terrigal (39x45cm-15x18in)
          s.d.54 canvasboard (A.D 3400)
£1498 $2696 (24-Nov-91 SY.S436/R) Rest and recreation (41x53cm-16x21in) s.d.1950
          board (A.D 3400)
£1549 $2587 (19-Aug-91 SY.ME53/R) Deserted house. Unfinished still life
          (50x37cm-20x15in) s.d.1936 i.verso board double-sided (A.D 3300)
£1800 $3204 (28-Nov-91 C42/R) Still life (28x16cm-11x6in) s.d.1920 board
£2340 $4143 (26-Apr-92 SY.ME496/R) Still life (39x49cm-15x19in) s.d.1928 canvasboard
          (A.D 5500)
£2555 $4599 (24-Nov-91 SY.S260/R) De Mestre's House (34x44cm-13x17in) s.d.1943 board
          (A.D 5800)
£2800 $4984 (28-Nov-91 C41/R) Beach and houses (11x17cm-4x7in) s.d.1918 board
£2817 $4704 (19-Aug-91 SY.ME306/R) Cityscape (41x54cm-16x21in) s. board (A.D 6000)
£2979 $5272 (26-Apr-92 SY.ME325/R) Still life with fruit, vase and bottle, 1944
          (53x44cm-21x17in) s. board (A.D 7000)

WAKELIN, Roland Shakespeare (1887-?) Australian-cont.

£3600	$6408	(28-Nov-91 C46/R) Descriptive sketch in Lincoln's Inn Fields (30x19cm-12x7in) s.d.1923 i.verso board
£4500	$8010	(28-Nov-91 C48/R) Valley of Yarra, Heidelberg, Victoria (53x74cm-21x29in) s.d.51 canvas on board
£4846	$8626	(26-Nov-91 J.M5/R) Landscape with horses (41x54cm-16x21in) s.d.27 board (A.D 11000)
£5128	$9128	(28-Apr-92 CH.ME5/R) Yachts on Sydney Harbour (79x99cm-31x39in) s.d.65 board (A.D 12000)
£6809	$12051	(26-Apr-92 SY.ME384/R) Swanston Street, Melbourne (62x74cm-24x29in) s.d.1951 board (A.D 16000)
£8000	$14240	(28-Nov-91 C43/R) Boathouses (26x31cm-10x12in) s.d.1920 board

WAKHEVITCH, Georges (1907-?) French

£1554	$2750	(7-Nov-91 SY.NY45/R) El Amor Brujo -two three-fold screens (178x182cm-70x72in)
£904	*$1600*	*(7-Nov-91 SY.NY49/R) Beauty and the Beast - design for the decor (53x72cm-21x28in) s. gouache paper laid down on board*
£1186	*$2100*	*(7-Nov-91 SY.NY44/R) El amor Brujo - two costume designs for gypsies (38x62cm-15x24in) W/C on same mount*

WALBOURN, E (19/20th C) British

£650	$1157	(1-Nov-91 MAI615) Study of girl st.studio
£950	$1691	(1-Nov-91 MAI610) Farmyard scene with chicks s.

WALBOURN, Ernest (1872-?) British

£508	$900	(9-Nov-91 W.W111/R) Summer's day (25x38cm-10x15in) st.mono. panel
£850	$1556	(3-Jun-92 S85/R) Cottages (27x40cm-11x16in) s. board
£977	$1700	(11-Sep-91 D.NY93) Gathering strays in from meadow (41x61cm-16x24in) s.
£2000	$3440	(11-Oct-91 C21/R) Turning the hay, near Epping, Essex (41x61cm-16x24in) s. board
£2100	$3906	(18-Jun-92 CSK263/R) After church (51x61cm-20x24in) s.
£2137	$3803	(27-Apr-92 J.M321) Figures in a vegetable garden (90x128cm-35x50in) s. (A.D 5000)
£2400	$4224	(10-Apr-92 K505/R) Wooded river landscapes - lady by punt and swans. Lady feeding ducks (38x56cm-15x22in) s. pair
£2400	$4440	(11-Jun-92 CSK213/R) Sussex farmstead (50x76cm-20x30in) s.
£2800	$5180	(9-Jun-92 LW1805) Mountain river landscape with figures harvesting hay on far bank (102x152cm-40x60in) s.
£4500	$8460	(19-Dec-91 C187/R) Feeding the doves (51x76cm-20x30in) s.
£5000	$8600	(11-Oct-91 C88/R) Encounter on the road (61x91cm-24x36in) s.
£5500	$10175	(12-Jun-92 C125/R) A stroll in the garden (91x60cm-36x24in) s.
£8500	$15980	(19-Dec-91 C185/R) By the river (51x76cm-20x30in) s.

WALBOURNE, Sidney (?) British?

£1000	$1700	(24-Oct-91 CSK100) A tranquil river (61x91cm-24x36in) s.

WALCH, Charles (1896-1948) French

£1464	$2533	(27-Mar-92 PPB.P76) Sur le jardin (33x45cm-13x18in) s. panel (F.FR 14200)
£3242	$5868	(20-May-92 I.N199/R) Personnages et fleurs (34x47cm-13x19in) s. panel (F.FR 32000)
£3889	$6883	(22-Apr-92 ZZ.F152/R) Bouquet dans la cour de ferme (65x54cm-26x21in) s. (F.FR 38500)
£8745	*$16615*	*(24-Jun-92 GL.P222/R) Composition decorative au bouquet (120x240cm-47x94in) s. gouache paper laid down on canvas (F.FR 85000)*

WALCH, Paul Johann (1881-1958) German

£481	$895	(20-Jun-92 BM.B976/R) Still life of asters with jug (70x79cm-28x31in) s. (DM 1400)

WALCH, Thomas (1867-1831) Austrian

£1718	$3144	(2-Jun-92 FN.S2794/R) Young peasant woman holding flowers seated on rock in alpine landscape (49x57cm-19x22in) s. panel (DM 5000)

WALCKIERS, G (1831-1891) Belgian

£4433	$8334	(18-Dec-91 GM.B4145) Ancien Palais de Justice (144x195cm-57x77in) s. (B.FR 260000)
£5456	$10257	(18-Dec-91 GM.B4101) Place du Petit Sablon, Bruxelles (80x112cm-31x44in) s. (B.FR 320000)

WALCOT, William (1874-1943) British

£420	*$760*	*(19-May-92 SWS318/R) Figures in city square (21x29cm-8x11in) s. gouache*
£500	*$870*	*(12-Sep-91 CSK51) Figures in grounds of castle (25x36cm-10x14in) s.i.verso pencil W/C bodycol.*
£2000	*$3420*	*(16-Mar-92 LW1849) Scene in poolof London with cargo ships at quayside (41x74cm-16x29in) s.d.1924 W/C gum arabic over pencil*
£2300	*$4094*	*(30-Apr-92 CG838/R) The Opera House, Paris (15x22cm-6x9in) s. pencil W/C*
£2600	*$4810*	*(12-Jun-92 C21/R) Wellington Arch at Constitution Hill (41x54cm-16x21in) s. pencil W/C gum arabic*
£2900	*$4959*	*(16-Mar-92 LW1846) View of Egyptian temple with artist at work to fore (51x69cm-20x27in) s.d.1928 W/C over pencil gum arabic*
£3100	*$5301*	*(16-Mar-92 LW1847/R) View of Egyptian temple at Edfou, with figures in foreground (51x69cm-20x27in) s.d.1928 W/C over pencil gum arabic*
£3731	*$6642*	*(25-Nov-91 W.T1819/R) Restoration to front facade, Westminster Abbey (48x56cm-19x22in) s. W/C (C.D 7500)*

WALCOT, William (1874-1943) British-cont.
£4200 $7182   *(16-Mar-92 LW1848/R) Buildings in Trafalgar Square with figures and buses in foreground (43x58cm-17x23in) s.d.1934 W/C over pencil*

WALDAU, A (19th C) ?
£1580 $2750   (15-Apr-92 B.SF3504/R) Portrait of Madame Dubarry (36x30cm-14x12in) s.d.

WALDE, Alfons (1891-1958) Austrian
£6000 $10320   (16-Oct-91 S38/R) Hauser im Gebirge (22x24cm-9x9in) s.i.verso board
£9500 $16340   (16-Oct-91 S41/R) Hauser in Winterlandschaft (43x33cm-17x13in) board
£10801 $19659   (11-Dec-91 WE.MU264/R) On the way to church (26x28cm-10x11in) board (DM 31000)
£11498 $20927   (11-Dec-91 WE.MU265/R) Meeting (26x29cm-10x11in) board (DM 33000)
£12000 $20640   (16-Oct-91 S39/R) Palmbretzen (26x28cm-10x11in) mono.d.1912 board
£13000 $22360   (16-Oct-91 S37/R) Sonntag (28x26cm-11x10in) mono.d.1912 board
£14000 $24080   (16-Oct-91 S40/R) Kirchgang am Palmsonntag (25x28cm-10x11in) s. board
£17378 $30933   (28-Nov-91 D.V160/R) Farmhouse in mountain landscape (33x51cm-13x20in) s.i.verso board (A.S 350000)
£18943 $33908   (15-Jan-92 D.V92/R) Mountain farmhouse (36x32cm-14x13in) s. board (A.S 380000)
£19753 $35951   (12-Dec-91 SY.AM55/R) Sommer in Tirol (38x28cm-15x11in) s. d.1935 verso cardboard (D.FL 64000)
£30000 $51900   (25-Mar-92 S173/R) Tiroler dorf (60x42cm-24x17in) s. board
£37239 $66286   (28-Nov-91 D.V161/R) Aurach near Kitzbuhel (56x44cm-22x17in) s.d.34 i.verso board (A.S 750000)
£1845   *$3283*   *(28-Apr-92 D.V197/R) Seven fir trees (11x14cm-4x6in) W/C (A.S 38000)*
£2184   *$3888*   *(28-Apr-92 D.V196/R) Flowers (26x25cm-10x10in) gouache pencil (A.S 45000)*
£4500   *$7785*   *(25-Mar-92 S171/R) Schifahrer (10x10cm-4x4in) s. pencil gouache*

WALDE, Martin (1957-) Austrian
£440 $783   *(31-Oct-91 D.V83/R) Untitled (49x70cm-19x28in) s.d.87 mixed media collage (A.S 9000)*
£489 $870   *(31-Oct-91 D.V164/R) Untitled (70x50cm-28x20in) s.d.85 mixed media (A.S 10000)*

WALDECK, H (19/20th C) Austrian
£620 $1111   (6-May-92 GD.B1328/R) Nymph with fawn (50x24cm-20x9in) s. panel (S.FR 1700)

WALDEN, Lionel (1861-1933) American
£1287 $2200   (12-Mar-92 MFA.C115) Open sea (66x97cm-26x38in) s.

WALDENBURG, Alfred von (1847-1915) German
£1031 $1887   (2-Jun-92 FN.S2795/R) Chiemsee landscape with figures in boat (90x160cm-35x63in) mono.d.1875 (DM 3000)

WALDHAUSER, Ernst (20th C) Austrian
£679   *$1235*   *(27-May-92 D.V663/R) Hotel Mariahilf, Vienna (34x42cm-13x17in) s. W/C (A.S 14000)*

WALDMULLER, Ferdinand Georg (1793-1865) Austrian
£2195 $3973   (3-Dec-91 R.T164/R) Picking cherries (61x46cm-24x18in) s. canvas on board (C.D 4500)
£12118 $22055   (27-May-92 D.V562/R) Girl wearing red shoulder wrap (52x43cm-20x17in) s.d.1821verso (A.S 250000)
£12207 $20752   (24-Oct-91 D.V76/R) Portrait of painter Ferdinand Mallitsch (17x14cm-7x6in) s.d.1853 panel (A.S 250000)
£52265 $95122   (11-Dec-91 N.M651/R) Path with farmhouse near Weissenbach and Hinterbruhl near Vienna (30x39cm-12x15in) (DM 150000)
£125436 $228293   (11-Dec-91 N.M650/R) Grapes in silver vessel on marble ledge (48x38cm-19x15in) s.d.1841 panel (DM 360000)
£157343 $269056   (18-Mar-92 N.M680/R) Mother and children looking at pictures in peasant interior (55x44cm-22x17in) s.d.1856 panel (DM 450000)

WALDMULLER, Ferdinand Georg (circle) (1793-1865) Austrian
£1400 $2604   (18-Jun-92 B152) Kitchen interior with mother and child (38x31cm-15x12in)

WALDORP, Antonie (1803-1866) Dutch
£486 $846   (17-Sep-91 CH.AM608) Fishermen in a boat (22x28cm-9x11in) with sig. panel (D.FL 1600)
£585 $1060   (3-Dec-91 R.T93/R) Dutch smalchip and other vessels offshore (45x60cm-18x24in) s.indis.d. (C.D 1200)
£650 $1164   (5-May-92 SWS399/R) Dutch courtyard, winter (23x18cm-9x7in) s.
£2584 $4495   (17-Sep-91 CH.AM428/R) A fishing smack setting off in a stiff breeze, other shipping beyond (65x92cm-26x36in) s.d.1841 (D.FL 8500)
£3000 $5310   (14-Feb-92 C47/R) On the Maas, near Dordrecht (41x60cm-16x24in) s. panel
£8571 $15000   (19-Feb-92 CH.NY132/R) Capture of Den Briel (92x171cm-36x67in) s.d.1862

WALDSTEIN, Maria Anna Grafin (1763-1808) Austrian
£971 $1728   (29-Apr-92 D.V909/R) Park landscape (17x25cm-7x10in) i.verso metal (A.S 20000)

WALENN, F (19/20th C) ?
£4000 $7120   (27-Nov-91 S261/R) Nudes on beach (114x94cm-45x37in) s.d.1914

WALES, James (attrib) (1748-1795) British
£600 $1146   (14-Jul-92 C160/R) Kailasa (47x49cm-19x19in) indist.i. pencil W/C

WALFORD, Howard (1864-1950) British
£480 $902   (19-Dec-91 C25/R) Glory of summer (36x27cm-14x11in) s. i.verso pencil W/C
                      htd white

WALISZEWSKI, Zygmunt (1897-1936) Polish
£7634 $13895   (15-Dec-91 REM.W48) Don Quixote in a cage (63x51cm-25x20in) gouache
                      (P.Z 150000000)

WALKE, Ann (fl.1909-1940) British
£1000 $1830   (6-Feb-92 DLY272/R) Children playing (61x74cm-24x29in) s.

WALKER and WEEKS (20th C) American
£468 $800   (13-Mar-92 WOL.C66) Tudor style multi-use building Cleveland Heights,
                      Ohio (46x71cm-18x28in) s. W/C pencil
£497 $850   (13-Mar-92 WOL.C63/R) Architectural rendering of the Bond Clothiers
                      Building (28x43cm-11x17in) W/C
£643 $1100   (13-Mar-92 WOL.C62/R) Interior design, Indiana War Memorial
                      (64x10cm-25x4in) pen
£1462 $2500   (13-Mar-92 WOL.C61/R) Grand foyer, Severence Hall (76x15cm-30x6in) s. W/C
                      pencil

WALKER, Dame Ethel (1867-1951) British
£900 $1692   (18-Dec-91 C173/R) Female nude study. Young couple embracing beneath tree
                      (35x26cm-14x10in) s. panel double-sided
£950 $1596   (16-Aug-91 K557) French market scene with gendarme and other figures
                      (25x30cm-10x12in) s.
£950 $1691   (29-Oct-91 SWS151/R) Comedienne (60x49cm-24x19in) i.verso
£1100 $1925   (27-Sep-91 C99/R) Seascape (62x73cm-24x29in) s.i. stretcher
£1100 $1947   (7-Nov-91 C46/R) Moontide (50x61cm-20x24in)
£1250 $2188   (27-Sep-91 C108/R) Portrait of a Lady (76x63cm-30x25in)
£2885 $5510   (19-Jul-92 SY.ME40/R) Still life of flowers (50x40cm-20x16in) s.
                      (A.D 7500)

WALKER, Eaton (?) British?
£500 $865   (4-Sep-91 BT272/R) The Comedian (33x28cm-13x11in) s.

WALKER, Edward (1879-?) British
£650 $1112   (18-Mar-92 CSK310) Courtyard in the Alhambra Palace, Granada
                      (23x18cm-9x7in) s.d.1913 board

WALKER, Francis S (1872-1916) American
£896 $1594   (25-Nov-91 W.T1906/R) Day dreams (39x31cm-15x12in) indis.s.verso
                      (C.D 1800)

WALKER, Frederick (1840-1875) British
£400 $684   (13-Mar-92 C75/R) Cosy couple (8x10cm-3x4in) mono.s.i. pen ink

WALKER, Horatio (1858-1938) Canadian
£697 $1240   (26-Nov-91 JOY.T277) Chickens (22x30cm-9x12in) panel (C.D 1400)
£3250 $5753   (6-Nov-91 SY.T186/R) Hippocrene (70x90cm-28x35in) s.d.1919 (C.D 6500)
£5970 $10627   (25-Nov-91 W.T1571/R) Collecting the milk, I'lle d'Orleans
                      (56x41cm-22x16in) s. board (C.D 12000)
£647 $1151   (26-Nov-91 JOY.T196/R) Plovers (24x33cm-9x13in) init. W/C (C.D 1300)

WALKER, James Alexander (?-1898) British
£1685 $3000   (22-Jan-92 SY.NY500/R) Portrait of cavalryman (24x18cm-9x7in) s. panel

WALKER, John (1939-) British
£1106 $1958   (26-Apr-92 SY.ME401/R) Untitled abstract (61x45cm-24x18in) s.d.1985 verso
                      (A.D 2600)

WALKER, John Crampton (1890-1942) British
£3670 $6826   (15-Jun-92 AD.D67) Malahide Estuary. Pastuarage (18x25cm-7x10in) i.verso
                      one s. pair (E.P 4000)

WALKER, John Eaton (fl.1855-1866) British
£600 $1092   (10-Dec-91 SWS291/R) Bathers by Egyptian ruins (59x49cm-23x19in) s. oval
£800 $1336   (22-Aug-91 CSK157/R) Preparing Moses for the Fair (33x43cm-13x17in)
                      s.i.verso

WALKER, John Hanson (1844-1933) British
£2800 $5180   (12-Jun-92 C128/R) Dora Garton nee Chevalier (75x62cm-30x24in) s.i.d.

WALKER, John Law (1899-) American
£847 $1500   (12-Feb-92 B.SF501/R) Light wine (102x91cm-40x36in) s.d.32

WALKER, R Hollands (19/20th C) British
£400 $764   (1-Jul-92 B121) A summer's day (28x49cm-11x19in) s. W/C
£1000 $1830   (3-Jun-92 S245/R) Fishing. Gathering flowers (19x32cm-7x13in) s. W/C
                      htd.bodycol.

WALKER, Robert (1607-1658?) British
£230000 $404800   (10-Apr-92 C12/R) Portrait of John Evelyn the diarist at table leaning on skull (88x64cm-35x25in) i.

WALKER, Robert (after) (1607-1658) British
£1400 $2380   (22-Oct-91 S225) Portrait of Oliver Cromwell, wearing armour (72x58cm-28x23in)
£1500 $2640   (8-Apr-92 S146/R) Portrait of Oliver Cromwell, standing, wearing armour and holding baton (126x101cm-50x40in)

WALKER, Robert (circle) (1607-1658) British
£1731 $3306   (15-Jul-92 CH.S757/R) Portrait of gentleman, wearing armour (80x58cm-31x23in) feigned cartouche (A.D 4500)
£3400 $6086   (13-Nov-91 S133/R) Portrait of lady holding black scarf (74x62cm-29x24in)

WALKER, William Aiken (1839-1921) American
£1215 $2200   (4-Dec-91 D.NY30/R) Cotton picker (20x10cm-8x4in) init. i.verso board
£1800 $3348   (18-Jun-92 B122/R) A southern homestead (14x29cm-6x11in) s. board
£2128 $4000   (18-Dec-91 SY.NY65/R) Coastal beach (15x43cm-6x17in) s.d.1905 board
£2200 $3762   (19-Mar-92 B130/R) Wash day (16x31cm-6x12in) s. board
£2459 $4500   (16-May-92 HG.C205/R) By cotton field (25x33cm-10x13in) s. board
£2652 $4800   (6-Dec-91 CH.NY95/R) Beach at Ponce Park, Florida (16x45cm-6x18in) init.
£2660 $5000   (18-Dec-91 SY.NY63/R) Plantation house along the coast (17x24cm-7x9in) s.d.1870
£2660 $5000   (18-Dec-91 SY.NY62/R) Cotton pickers (15x31cm-6x12in) s. board
£2778 $5000   (22-Nov-91 S.BM68/R) Sharecroppers' cabin (15x30cm-6x12in) s. i.verso board
£2926 $5500   (18-Dec-91 SY.NY64/R) Cabin scene (23x31cm-9x12in) s. board
£3039 $5500   (4-Dec-91 D.NY29/R) Cottonfield (15x30cm-6x12in) init. board
£3191 $6000   (18-Dec-91 SY.NY61/R) Cabin scene (15x31cm-6x12in) s. board
£3216 $5500   (11-Mar-92 SY.NY13/R) Picking cotton by cabin (15x30cm-6x12in) s. panel
£3509 $6000   (11-Mar-92 SY.NY12/R) Cabin scene (15x30cm-6x12in) s. panel
£3771 $6750   (6-May-92 D.NY11/R) Sharecroppers before their fields (30x15cm-12x6in) s. i.verso board
£3801 $6500   (11-Mar-92 SY.NY14/R) Cotton pickers in field (23x31cm-9x12in) s. board
£4330 $7750   (6-May-92 D.NY14/R) Daily chores (23x30cm-9x12in) s. i.verso board
£4386 $7500   (11-Mar-92 SY.NY15/R) Cotton picker with possum (31x16cm-12x6in) s. panel
£4678 $8000   (12-Mar-92 CH.NY74/R) Full baskets (20x10cm-8x4in) init. board pair
£4972 $9000   (6-Dec-91 CH.NY94/R) Palms at Ponce Park, Florida (17x46cm-7x18in) init.
£5714 $10000   (26-Sep-91 NY26/R) Wash day (23x30cm-9x12in) init. board
£49724 $90000   (6-Dec-91 CH.NY101/R) The wagon's empty (37x61cm-15x24in) init.

WALKER, William Eyre (1847-1930) British
£700 $1246   (29-Oct-91 C99/R) Herding sheep near Kinlochewe, Loch Maree (32x50cm-13x20in) s. s.i.d.1873verso pencil W/C
£1500 $2670   (29-Oct-91 C100/R) Study on the Greta (42x66cm-17x26in) s.i.d.1882 pencil W/C

WALKOWITZ, Abraham (1880-1965) Russian
£3297 $6000   (28-May-92 CH.NY236/R) The bather (45x61cm-18x24in) s. canvasboard
£405 $750   (10-Jun-92 CE.NY519) Swirling female figure (28x18cm-11x7in) s.d.1915 pencil W/C
£532 $1000   (18-Dec-91 SY.NY336/R) Figures in landscape (43x57cm-17x22in) s. W/C pencil
£726 $1300   (14-Nov-91 CE.NY388) Dense crowd (25x20cm-10x8in) s.d.1909 pencil W/C
£1006 $1800   (14-Nov-91 CE.NY420) Coloured abstraction (40x32cm-16x13in) s. W/C
£1871 $3200   (12-Mar-92 CH.NY256/R) Abstract forms (26x17cm-10x7in) s.d.1932 pen ink pencil
£2456 $4200   (12-Mar-92 CH.NY225/R) Bathers (25x35cm-10x14in) s. W/C pencil

WALL, William Coventry (1810-1886) American
£574 $1050   (9-Feb-92 LIT.L369) Winter scene near Pittsburgh (48x69cm-19x27in) s.d.1846

WALLACE, H Frank (1881-1962) British
£659 $1200   (26-May-92 CE.NY155) The outcast (38x53cm-15x21in) s. W/C gouache paperboard
£750 $1320   (8-Apr-92 CSK52) Hinds and stag on hill (36x52cm-14x20in) s. bodycol

WALLACE, J (19/20th C) British
£1000 $1910   (16-Jul-92 CG593) Portrait of Alex Herd standing with driver (6x3cm-2x1in) init.d.1897 pencil W/C

WALLACE, John (19/20th C) British
£900 $1512   (13-Aug-91 AG230/R) Watermill by moonlight (54x82cm-21x32in) s.d.1893
£1900 $3192   (26-Aug-91 S979) Village street (45x61cm-18x24in) s.d.1893 pair

WALLACE, R Craig (19/20th C) British
£950 $1663   (27-Feb-92 L386) Figures amongst rock pools (38x53cm-15x21in) s.verso
£2300 $4117   (14-Jan-92 SWS268/R) Ketch Albyn on the Firth of Clyde (75x62cm-30x24in) s.i.d.1939verso

WALLANDER, Alf (1862-1914) Swedish
£569 $1042   (12-May-92 GO.G192) Street scene with vegetable stall (48x28cm-19x11in) s.i. (S.KR 6000)

WALLANDER, Josef Wilhelm (1821-1888) Swedish
£949 $1736   (14-May-92 BU.S105/R) Costumes from Osteraker, Sodermanland
                   (27x21cm-11x8in) W/C (S.KR 10000)

WALLAT, Paul (1879-?) German
£722 $1256   (21-Sep-91 SA.A1969/R) Quiet part of Rostock harbour (71x81cm-28x32in) s.
                   (DM 2100)

WALLEN, Gustaf Teodor (1860-1948) Swedish
£2109 $3797   (19-Nov-91 GO.G191) Coastal landscape with fisherboys (42x59cm-17x23in)
                   s. (S.KR 22000)

WALLER, Samuel Edmund (1850-1903) British
£1000 $1720   (8-Oct-91 PH129) First time in the ring (97x71cm-38x28in) s.d.1894

WALLET, Albert-Charles (1852-1918) French
£815 $1475   (19-May-92 GF.L2543/R) Two peasant women conversing (59x73cm-23x29in) s.
                   canvas on panel (S.FR 2200)

WALLET, Taf (1902-) Belgian
£3229 $5521   (21-Mar-92 KV.L353/R) Marine (80x90cm-31x35in) s. (B.FR 190000)

WALLIN, David (1876-1957) Swedish
£607 $1111   (12-May-92 GO.G193) Breakers near Marstrand (57x70cm-22x28in) s. panel
                   (S.KR 6400)
£660 $1169   (25-Apr-92 SO.S622/R) Hovs Hallar (47x55cm-19x22in) s.d.1948 panel
                   (S.KR 7000)
£755 $1336   (25-Apr-92 SO.S620/R) Woman and child (52x64cm-20x25in) s. (S.KR 8000)

WALLIN, Ellis (1888-1972) Swedish
£584 $1039   (28-Oct-91 AB.S249) View towards Riddarholmen, Stockholm
                   (69x139cm-27x55in) s.d.36 (S.KR 6200)
£474 $868   (12-May-92 GO.G294) Summer's day, Grundsund (42x62cm-17x24in) s.d.31
                   gouache (S.KR 5000)

WALLIS, Alfred (1855-1942) British
£1400 $2394   (12-Mar-92 B43) Train entering tunnel (20x12cm-8x5in) s. card
£1500 $2685   (14-Jan-92 PH171/R) Ship and lighthouse (15x21cm-6x8in) oil over pencil
£1900 $3629   (14-Jul-92 DR285/R) Ship (21x35cm-8x14in) s. pencil oil board
£2400 $4248   (5-Nov-91 PH45/R) Six boats (24x30cm-9x12in) s. oil over pencil
£2500 $4275   (12-Mar-92 B41/R) Steamer (15x22cm-6x9in) card
£3000 $5730   (14-Jul-92 DR284/R) Three masted ship. Three ships entering harbour
                   (15x30cm-6x12in) pencil oil board shaped pair
£5800 $9976   (6-Mar-92 C73/R) Cottages and trees (47x57cm-19x22in) cardboard
£500 $855   (12-Mar-92 B42) Schooner and lighthouse (4x11cm-2x4in) W/C pencil card
£1000 $1810   (6-Dec-91 TE520) Fishing boats returning to harbour (25x36cm-10x14in) s.
                   crayon
£1100 $1991   (6-Dec-91 TE521) Boats in harbour. Three-master ship (25x36cm-10x14in) s.
                   col.crayon double-sided
£2000 $3440   (6-Mar-92 C74/R) Lighthouse and ships. Sailing ship (26x37cm-10x15in) s.
                   col.crayons double-sided
£2300 $3956   (6-Mar-92 C75/R) Ships entering harbour (25x36cm-10x14in) s. crayon

WALLIS, Captain James (1785-1858) Australian
£24000 $40800   (22-Oct-91 C93/R) Newcastle, New South Wales, looking towards Prospect
                   Hill (45x68cm-18x27in) panel

WALLIS, Henry (1830-1916) British
£5500 $10230   (19-Jun-92 C81/R) The pharmacy (43x59cm-17x23in) init. W/C

WALLIS, Hugh (fl.1894-1922) British
£1278 $2250   (6-Apr-92 B.LA2363/R) Portrait of woman (38x40cm-15x16in) s.d.1900 pastel
                   gilt

WALLIS, Raymond (?) Australian?
£563 $941   (19-Aug-91 SY.ME93) Old toll house, breakwater, Geelong (14x26cm-6x10in)
                   s.d.1920 board (A.D 1200)

WALLMANN, Carl (19th C) German?
£4530 $8244   (11-Dec-91 N.M652/R) Shepherd with cattle in wooded river landscape with
                   gothic church ruin (95x136cm-37x54in) s.d.1812 (DM 13000)

WALLNER, Thure (1888-1965) Swedish
£713 $1276   (16-Nov-91 FAL.M365/R) Seabirds swimming in the skerries (24x33cm-9x13in)
                   s. panel (S.KR 7500)
£913 $1626   (28-Oct-91 AB.S254) Spring landscape with young gull by stones
                   (19x32cm-7x13in) s. panel (S.KR 9700)
£943 $1670   (25-Apr-92 SO.S629/R) Swans swimming (20x18cm-8x7in) s. panel
                   (S.KR 10000)
£950 $1652   (13-Apr-92 AB.S272) Mountain landscape with hare in heather
                   (35x27cm-14x11in) s. panel (S.KR 10000)
£1088 $1969   (19-May-92 AB.S4293/R) Osprey by nest (37x29cm-15x11in) s. (S.KR 11500)
£1177 $2095   (28-Oct-91 AB.S255) Winter landscape with pair of yellow hammers
                   (21x34cm-8x13in) s. panel (S.KR 12500)

WALLNER, Thure (1888-1965) Swedish-cont.
£1177 $2095   (28-Oct-91 AB.S253) Fox by pine tree in wood (34x31cm-13x12in) s. panel
     (S.KR 12500)
£1183 $2140   (19-May-92 AB.S4292/R) Cat on rock in wooded landscape (35x27cm-14x11in)
     s. panel (S.KR 12500)
£1365 $2430   (28-Oct-91 AB.S252) Hare leaping among heather (35x27cm-14x11in) s. panel
     (S.KR 14500)
£1392 $2519   (3-Dec-91 AB.S4682/R) Seagull with catch on rocky stones
     (35x26cm-14x10in) s. panel (S.KR 14500)
£1425 $2479   (13-Apr-92 AB.S273) Summer landscape with fox with catch
     (54x45cm-21x18in) s. panel (S.KR 15000)
£1792 $3173   (5-Nov-91 BA.S184/R) Ducks (24x35cm-9x14in) s. panel (S.KR 19000)
£1918 $3452   (23-Nov-91 SO.S643/R) Fox by fence (23x34cm-9x13in) s. panel (S.KR 20000)
£4319 $7817   (3-Dec-91 AB.S4681/R) Female mallard swimming with young by reeds
     (64x81cm-25x32in) s.d.1924 (S.KR 45000)
£5943 $10520   (25-Apr-92 SO.S627/R) Wooded landscape with eagle and hare
     (63x91cm-25x36in) s. (S.KR 63000)
£6711 $12081   (19-Nov-91 GO.G193/R) Winter with cat catching rat (75x82cm-30x32in) s.
     (S.KR 70000)

WALLS, William (1860-?) British
£2000 $3560   (1-May-92 PHE61/R) Two leopards fighting (90x120cm-35x47in) s.
£3000 $5040   (26-Aug-91 S885/R) Loch Duich, mares and foals (45x61cm-18x24in) s.
     s.i.label verso board

WALMSLEY, Thomas (1763-1806) British
£3400 $5984   (8-Apr-92 S229/R) Moonlit coastal landscape with buildings burning
     (68x114cm-27x45in)

WALRAVEN, Jan (1827-?) Dutch
£1000 $1780   (28-Nov-91 CSK157) Under arrest (43x33cm-17x13in) s. panel
£1400 $2492   (28-Nov-91 B119/R) Feeding the rabbits (36x28cm-14x11in) s. panel

WALS, Gottfried (style) (c.1600-c.1640) German
£2760 $4748   (15-Oct-91 CH.R43/R) Capriccio con il tempio di Venere (37x52cm-15x20in)
     (I.L 6000000)

WALSCAPELLE, Jacob van (1644-1727) Dutch
£30387 $55000   (22-May-92 SY.NY26 a/R) Still life of mixed flowers, stalk wheat in glass
     vase on stone ledge, with insects (69x56cm-27x22in) init.

WALSER, Karl (1877-1943) Swiss
£1642 $2940   (6-May-92 GD.B1330/R) Music, design for wall painting (95x122cm-37x48in)
     s. panel (S.FR 4500)

WALSH DE SERRANT, Ludovic (1965-) ?
£763 $1396   (13-May-92 LC.P57/R) Run away to west, to meet Bizzar (106x134cm-42x53in)
     s.d. (F.FR 7500)

WALSH, T (19th C) British
£646   *$1202*   *(19-Jun-92 G.Z167/R) Full cry (27x43cm-11x17in) s.d.1878 W/C (S.FR 1700)*

WALTENSPERGER, Charles (1870-1931) American
£508 $900   (14-Feb-92 DM.D2029/R) Shepherdess, child and sheep (33x38cm-13x15in) s.
£565 $1000   (14-Feb-92 DM.D2030/R) Harbour scene (28x36cm-11x14in) s. board
£565 $1000   (14-Feb-92 DM.D2032/R) Children with swans (23x30cm-9x12in) s.
£615 $1100   (15-Nov-91 DM.D2126/R) Morning sunlight, Gloucester Harbour
     (25x33cm-10x13in) s. i.verso board
£904 $1600   (14-Feb-92 DM.D2028/R) Dutch woman with child (41x33cm-16x13in) s.
£1356 $2400   (14-Feb-92 DM.D2031/R) Woman with kettle (51x41cm-20x16in) s.

WALTER, E (19th C) British
£893 $1555   (21-Sep-91 SA.A1926/R) Still life of flowers (40x30cm-16x12in) s. panel
     (DM 2600)

WALTER, Emma (19th C) British
£1600   *$2848*   *(27-Nov-91 B127/R) Still life of fruit and flowers on marble ledge*
     (53x67cm-21x26in) s. W/C

WALTER, Joseph (1783-1856) British
£800 $1400   (27-Feb-92 B212/R) Figures unloading from a beached vessel, lighthouse
     beyond (30x41cm-12x16in) s.

WALTER, Martha (1876-1976) American
£1371 $2400   (26-Sep-91 CH.NY62/R) French family (23x28cm-9x11in) s. board
£3488 $6000   (12-Oct-91 DU.E88/R) Dark eyed child (53x43cm-21x17in) panel
£8242 $15000   (27-May-92 SY.NY69/R) Trouville (37x46cm-15x18in) s. board
£8791 $16000   (28-May-92 CH.NY165/R) By the water's edge (35x46cm-14x18in) s. board
£22099 $40000   (5-Dec-91 SY.NY68/R) Overhead trestle, Bass Rocks, Massachusetts
     (102x81cm-40x32in) s.

WALTERS, Emile (1893-?) American
£1006 $1800   (13-Nov-91 B.SF2734/R) Summer storm (64x77cm-25x30in) s.

WALTERS, G S (19th C) British
£950 $1625   (1-Aug-91 RBB540/R) Fishing boats off Ramsgate (30x48cm-12x19in) s.d. W/C

WALTERS, George Stanfield (1838-1924) British
£1250 $2375   (24-Jun-92 PHI554) Yarmouth Harbour (20x30cm-8x12in) s. panel
£1450 $2436   (15-Aug-91 B416/R) Fishing smack in swell, frigate beyond
              (38x56cm-15x22in) s.d.1883 indist.i.verso
£400 $716   (15-Jan-92 BT101) Fishing boats off the coast (25x41cm-10x16in) s. W/C
£520 $920   (11-Feb-92 PH121) Calm weather, Holland (31x48cm-12x19in) s. W/C htd
              white
£580 $1009   (9-Sep-91 PH73/R) Sailing vessels in a calm sea off the coast
              (23x34cm-9x13in) s. W/C
£600 $1044   (14-Apr-92 CSK85) Misty evening Southampton Water (25x35cm-10x14in) s.i.
              pencil W/C htd white
£650 $1157   (27-Nov-91 B129) Old sheds and herring boats at Great Yarmouth
              (24x34cm-9x13in) s. W/C
£720 $1318   (14-May-92 CSK141) Dutch barges at the entrance to harbour
              (30x51cm-12x20in) s.d.1876 pencil W/C htd.white
£1000 $1750   (1-Apr-92 B77/R) The Giudecca, Venice (23x56cm-9x22in) s. W/C
£1000 $1740   (12-Sep-91 CSK67/R) Trawlers running into Ramsgate. Fishing boats at
              mouth of Dutch river s. pencil W/C htd white two

WALTERS, John (19th C) British
£1600 $2880   (22-Nov-91 C12 a) Harbour of Ilfracombe with view of the wreck of
              Concordia, 4-2-1796 (43x63cm-17x25in) s.i.d.1796 pencil W/C

WALTERS, R (?) ?
£634 $1173   (8-Jun-92 CH.R503) Ai limitari del bosco (50x75cm-20x30in) s.
              (I.L 1400000)

WALTERS, Samuel (1811-1882) British
£850 $1428   (15-Aug-91 B412 b) Men-o'-War and fishing smacks in rough seas
              (14x19cm-6x7in) indist.mono. panel
£2000 $3440   (5-Mar-92 D120/R) Sailing ship anchored in cove, with fishing fleet in
              coastal waters (64x104cm-25x41in) s.
£4200 $8022   (17-Jul-92 C142/R) The Stacks off the Giant's Causeway (76x114cm-30x45in)
              s.d.1861
£30000 $54000   (22-Nov-91 C112/R) The Star of the East hove-to for pilot
              (84x130cm-33x51in) s.d.1854

WALTERS, Wes (1928-) Australian
£1322 $2352   (26-Nov-91 J.M460) Reclining nude (89x120cm-35x47in) s.d.91 (A.D 3000)
£1586 $2855   (24-Nov-91 SY.S110/R) Female nude seated on white chair (74x59cm-29x23in)
              s.d.91 (A.D 3600)

WALTHER, Ernst Hermann (1858-1945) German
£2048 $3727   (27-May-92 PH.DU40/R) In deep thought (50x35cm-20x14in) s.d.84 (DM 6000)

WALTHER, Gustav (1828-1904) German
£2600 $4836   (17-Jun-92 S371/R) Lady by orange tree (71x59cm-28x23in) s.d.1864

WALTHER, Karl (1905-) German
£859 $1589   (13-Jun-92 WK.M372/R) View from Viktualienmarkt to Sparkassenstrasse
              (50x61cm-20x24in) (DM 2500)

WALTHER, V K (19/20th C) ?
£490 $871   (29-Nov-91 ZEL.L1119/R) Iron foundry (48x61cm-19x24in) s. (DM 1400)

WALTON, Constance (?-1960) British
£1300 $2314   (28-Apr-92 S281/R) Roses (36x35cm-14x14in) s. s.i.verso W/C
£1500 $2715   (4-Dec-91 S338/R) Roses in bowl (34x44cm-13x17in) s. W/C
£3000 $5040   (26-Aug-91 S1013/R) Roses in blue and white vase (49x67cm-19x26in) s. W/C
              htd bodycol.

WALTON, Edward Arthur (1860-1922) British
£1100 $1991   (4-Dec-91 S362/R) Fishing the stream (18x24cm-7x9in) s. board
£7000 $12460   (30-Apr-92 CG893/R) Day's work ended (91x66cm-36x26in) s.

WALTON, John W (19th C) British
£930 $1600   (14-Oct-91 H.C32/R) First trial by jury (117x173cm-46x68in) s.d.1881

WANDESFORDE, Juan B (1817-1902) American
£1447 $2750   (24-Jun-92 B.SF6257/R) Clear Lake near Lakeport landing (36x51cm-14x20in)
              s.

WANE, R (19th C) ?
£600 $1050   (17-Feb-92 HS194) News from abroad - study of young girl seated at well
              reading letter (75x50cm-30x20in) s.d.1883 W/C

WANE, Richard (1852-1904) British
£700 $1267   (6-Dec-91 CBS219) At Port St.Mary (30x48cm-12x19in) s. i.verso W/C

WANG DAWEN (1942-) Chinese
£2589 $4530   (30-Mar-92 CH.HK166/R) Lotus (68x79cm-27x31in) s.d.1985 ink W/C scroll
              (HK.D 35000)

WANG HUI (1632-1717) Chinese
£1271 $2250   (7-Nov-91 B.SF1213/R) Mountain landscape (?x51cm-?x20in) s.d.1706 ink
                colour fan

WANG PAN-YUAN (1912-) Chinese
£27816 $47566 (22-Mar-92 SY.TA53/R) Sailing (72x60cm-28x24in) s. (T.D 1210000)
£7586 $12972 (22-Mar-92 SY.TA78/R) Greeting mountain (39x54cm-15x21in) seal W/C
                (T.D 330000)

WANG YISHI (1939-) Chinese
£3328 $5825   (30-Mar-92 CH.HK317/R) Melon shed by Lotus pond (68x68cm-27x27in)
                s.d.1991 ink W/C scroll (HK.D 45000)

WANG ZHEN (1866-1938) Chinese
£1036 $1812   (30-Mar-92 CH.HK358/R) Monk (129x38cm-51x15in) s.i.d.1919 ink W/C hanging
                scroll (HK.D 14000)

WANGENSTEN, Wilhelm (1884-1962) Norwegian
£660 $1161   (8-Apr-92 GWP.O155) Summer in the skerries (60x73cm-24x29in) s. panel
                (N.KR 7500)
£880 $1548   (8-Apr-92 GWP.O75/R) Young woman (114x104cm-45x41in) s. (N.KR 10000)

WANING, Cornelis Anthony van (1861-1929) Dutch
£528 $913   (24-Mar-92 VN.R99/R) Sailing ships in river landscape (80x142cm-31x56in)
                s.d.1908 (D.FL 1700)

WANING, Martin van (1889-) Dutch
£765 $1353   (5-Nov-91 SY.AM123) View of Dordrecht (75x140cm-30x55in) s. panel
                (D.FL 2500)

WANKEL, Charlotte (1888-1969) Norwegian
£890 $1548   (18-Sep-91 KH.K87/R) Portrait (83x56cm-33x22in) mono.d.32 (D.KR 10000)

WANSART, Adolphe (1873-1954) Belgian
£1656 $2997   (23-May-92 KV.L385/R) La Fontaine D'Amour - Villa des Cedres
                (73x92cm-29x36in) s.d.1919 panel (B.FR 100000)

WANSLEBEN, Arthur (1861-1917) German
£699 $1210   (25-Mar-92 KM.K1508) Lower Rhine landscape with cattle grazing
                (36x46cm-14x18in) s. (DM 2000)

WAPPERS, Gustave (1803-1874) Belgian
£745 $1267   (23-Oct-91 GD.B1332/R) Die spanische Furie (67x80cm-26x31in) s.
                (S.FR 1900)
£7143 $13000 (28-May-92 SY.NY231/R) Peter the Great at Zaardam (103x129cm-41x51in)
                s.d.1836

WARB, Nicolaas (1906-) Dutch
£1235 $2346   (24-Jun-92 GL.P248) Solidarite (33x46cm-13x18in) s.d.1952verso panel
                (F.FR 12000)
£432 $821   (24-Jun-92 GL.P249) Untitled (68x48cm-27x19in) gouache (F.FR 4200)

WARBURG, Sophie Elisabeth see WARB, Nicolaas

WARD OF HULL, John (1798-1849) British
£9000 $16110 (13-Nov-91 S9/R) The barque Columbine in calm waters off the coast
                (23x35cm-9x14in) panel
£30000 $57300 (15-Jul-92 S4/R) HMS Queen sailing out of Portsmouth Harbour
                (32x49cm-13x19in) s.

WARD, Charles (20th C) British
£2400 $4128   (11-Oct-91 C17/R) At the blacksmith's (63x88cm-25x35in) s.d.1862

WARD, Edmund F (1892-1991) American
£532 $1000   (18-Dec-91 SY.NY313/R) The swimming hole (45x61cm-18x24in) s.
£588 $1000   (27-Oct-91 LIT.L209) Illustration - Purchase of White Plains 1683
                (61x91cm-24x36in) s. estate st.verso
£588 $1000   (27-Oct-91 LIT.L205) Illustration - ballet scene - male and female in
                Arabian dress (76x64cm-30x25in) s. estate st.verso board
£706 $1200   (27-Oct-91 LIT.L191) Illustrative fantasy scene - Headless Horseman with
                witches and elves (91x91cm-36x36in) estate st.verso
£730 $1300   (2-May-92 IH.NY51/R) Woman embracing girl amidst luggage
                (66x79cm-26x31in) s.d.11 grisaile board
£745 $1400   (18-Dec-91 SY.NY357/R) The fussilade (71x101cm-28x40in) s. s.i.verso
£1000 $1700   (27-Oct-91 LIT.L227) Rainy Sunday (51x61cm-20x24in) s. estate st.verso
                board
£1765 $3000   (27-Oct-91 LIT.L167) Out - powerful scene of boxer counted by referee
                (51x61cm-20x24in) s. estate st.verso board

WARD, Edward Matthew (1816-1879) British
£4945 $9000   (11-Dec-91 RO.BA266) Eve of St.Bartholomew (130x158cm-51x62in) s.
£95000 $175750 (12-Jun-92 C109/R) The last parting of Marie Antoinette and her son
                (122x183cm-48x72in) s.d.1856

WARD, Edward Matthew (attrib) (1816-1879) British
£1050 $1880   (5-May-92 SWS424/R) Christmas (25x30cm-10x12in)
£1600 $2720   (23-Oct-91 B80/R) The Dandy (58x86cm-23x34in)

WARD, Fred (?) Australian?
£5333 $9120   (17-Mar-92 JRL.S257) Untitled (120x150cm-47x59in) s. acrylic canvas
              (A.D 12000)

WARD, H (?) British
£420   *$739*   *(6-Apr-92 WW95) Salisbury cathedral from old mill at Harnham*
              (35x49cm-14x19in) s.d.1876 W/C htd white

WARD, James (1769-1859) British
£1400 $2688   (9-Jul-92 B58/R) Stag hunt (71x102cm-28x40in)
£3000 $5730   (15-Jul-92 S200/R) Figures by a campfire (61x81cm-24x32in) i.
£3039 $5500   (4-Dec-91 NA.BA24/R) Chestnut bay with dog in stable (50x61cm-20x24in)
              s.s.
£4000 $7120   (1-Nov-91 S440/R) Shepherd sleeping by goats and sheep. Feeding pigs
              (29x37cm-11x15in) s. pair
£800   *$1432*   *(14-Nov-91 S70) Stonehenge (14x28cm-6x11in) pen W/C over pencil*

WARD, James (circle) (19th C) British
£850 $1615   (23-Jun-92 PH105/R) Two Irish wolfhounds in landscape (41x34cm-16x13in)
              panel

WARD, John (1917-) British
£420   *$731*   *(17-Sep-91 PH118/R) A view of Lower Regent Street (25x33cm-10x13in)*
              s.i.d.1962 pen col.washes

WARD, John (1948-) Canadian
£731 $1337   (14-May-92 SY.T107/R) Approaching car (38x47cm-15x19in) s. d.1982 verso
              acrylic canvas (C.D 1600)

WARD, Martin Theodore (1799-1874) British
£880 $1514   (16-Oct-91 PHL337/R) Terrier and wasp (19x15cm-7x6in) board
£900 $1629   (21-May-92 B176) At the cottage door (23x28cm-9x11in) s.

WARD, Martin Theodore (circle) (1799-1874) British
£750 $1283   (12-Mar-92 CSK141/R) Chestnut hunter in landscape (16x20cm-6x8in) board

WARD, Mary K (19th C) British
£800   *$1360*   *(23-Oct-91 S211/R) View of the Golden Horn (33x51cm-13x20in) s.d.1873 W/C*
              over pencil

WARD, S (attrib) (?) ?
£900 $1557   (6-Sep-91 BW411) Christopher Columbus expounding to Isabella and
              Ferdinand (41x53cm-16x21in)

WARD, Sir Leslie (1851-1922) British
£420   *$802*   *(14-Jul-92 DR378) Study of Lieutenant General George Higginson*
              (13x14cm-5x6in) W/C
£500   *$955*   *(14-Jul-92 DR377) Portrait of Lieutenant General George Higginson*
              (30x19cm-12x7in) s. W/C sold with print

WARD, Vernon (1905-) British
£520 $926   (21-Jan-92 SWS917) Swans nesting (44x49cm-17x19in) s. i.verso
£520 $894   (18-Oct-91 T100/R) Swans on river bank (46x51cm-18x20in) s.
£600 $1032   (5-Mar-92 CSK36/R) Oyster Catchers - summer display (41x51cm-16x20in)
              i.stretcher
£900 $1611   (5-May-92 SWS482/R) Oyster catchers (39x49cm-15x19in) s.
£1250 $2238   (5-May-92 SWS455/R) Still life of mimosa, tulips and freesias in vase
              (69x60cm-27x24in) s.
£2100 $3654   (15-Apr-92 PHL138/R) Spring blooms in bowl on console table
              (62x74cm-24x29in) s.

WARD-THOMPSON, Ramon (1941-) New Zealander
£622 $1064   (17-Mar-92 JRL.S68) Wood pile (57x73cm-22x29in) s. board (A.D 1400)
£667 $1140   (16-Mar-92 MGS.S107) Gore Cove Sydney Harbour (45x60cm-18x24in) s.
              (A.D 1500)
£1204 $2070   (14-Oct-91 MGS.S202) Early snowfall (59x89cm-23x35in) s. canvas on board
              (A.D 2600)

WARDLE, Arthur (1864-1947) British
£629 $1100   (23-Sep-91 S.SL254) Woman with dog in a landscape (51x36cm-20x14in)
              s.d.1898
£700 $1246   (1-Nov-91 MAI600) Otter hunting s.
£750 $1305   (19-Sep-91 CSK60/R) Young girl by river (25x35cm-10x14in) init. panel
£800 $1376   (4-Mar-92 S84/R) Lion with kill (45x61cm-18x24in) s.
£880 $1575   (5-May-92 SWS313/R) Study of bulldog (38x29cm-15x11in) s.d.1903 paper
£900 $1665   (11-Jun-92 CSK162) Good companions (36x26cm-14x10in) s. paper on panel
£980 $1872   (16-Jul-92 CSK195/R) Spaniel holding pheasant (62x51cm-24x20in) s.d.1900
£1050 $1838   (25-Sep-91 CSK316) Two collies (41x33cm-16x13in) s. board
£1475 $2700   (5-Jun-92 SY.NY204/R) Lions on the African plain (40x81cm-16x32in)
£1600 $2736   (12-Mar-92 CSK243/R) Lion on rock (46x61cm-18x24in) s.
£1900 $3629   (16-Jul-92 CSK194/R) Hidden out of sight (75x55cm-30x22in) s.

WARDLE, Arthur (1864-1947) British-cont.

£2100	$3612	(8-Oct-91 PH157) Picking up the scent (66x46cm-26x18in) s.
£2732	$5000	(5-Jun-92 SY.NY213/R) An Irish wolfhound (22x30cm-9x12in) s. board
£3552	$6500	(5-Jun-92 SY.NY212/R) A Jack Russell terrier (40x50cm-16x20in) s.
£4000	$6880	(4-Mar-92 S150/R) Jaguar and macaw (51x76cm-20x30in) s.
£5491	$9500	(6-Sep-91 S.BM247/R) Working a hedgerow (41x51cm-16x20in) s. i. verso
£7000	$11760	(26-Aug-91 S882/R) Spaniels flushing mallard (46x61cm-18x24in) s.
£8743	$16000	(5-Jun-92 SY.NY214/R) A King charles spaniel (56x35cm-22x14in) s.
£9400	$16168	(4-Mar-92 S151/R) Leopards drinking (51x76cm-20x30in) s.
£11000	$20130	(3-Jun-92 S123/R) The deer stalker (101x127cm-40x50in) s.
£12000	$20520	(13-Mar-92 C141/R) Tigers at dusk (66x81cm-26x32in) s.
£400	$760	(24-Jun-92 DR71) Leopard with pheasant (29x42cm-11x17in) s. pastel
£727	$1250	(10-Oct-91 FA.PH682/R) Rabbit hunt (20x38cm-8x15in) pencil wash
£900	$1647	(3-Jun-92 S297/R) Two Scotties (34x24cm-13x9in) s. pastel
£1100	$1969	(14-Jan-92 B221/R) A Bulldog in a barn (12x19cm-5x7in) s. W/C
£1163	$2000	(15-Oct-91 CE.NY434/R) Across the desert (40x61cm-16x24in) s.i. pastel col.chks. paperboard
£1200	$2148	(14-Jan-92 B219/R) Scotties in a landscape (12x19cm-5x7in) s. W/C
£1700	$3009	(6-Nov-91 S311/R) Lying in wait (26x35cm-10x14in) s. col.chk
£2459	$4500	(5-Jun-92 SY.NY220/R) Left in charge (53x39cm-21x15in) s. W/C gouache
£2600	$4602	(6-Nov-91 S304/R) Tiger (27x39cm-11x15in) s. col.chk

WARGH, Carl (1938-) Finnish

£592	$1047	(6-Nov-91 HOR.H147) Beach (57x76cm-22x30in) s.d.1988 W/C (F.M 4200)

WARHOL, Andy (1930-1986) American

£3086	$5586	(2-Dec-91 CC.P44/R) Fish (25x20cm-10x8in) s.d.verso acrylic serigraph (F.FR 30000)
£4218	$7635	(2-Dec-91 CC.P43/R) Monkey (25x20cm-10x8in) s.d.1983verso acrylic serigraph (F.FR 41000)
£4527	$8193	(2-Dec-91 CC.P42/R) Roll over mouse (28x35cm-11x14in) s.d.1983verso acrylic serigraph canvas (F.FR 44000)
£6286	$11000	(25-Feb-92 SY.NY164/R) Untitled (13x13cm-5x5in) init.d.64verso acrylic
£41899	$75000	(12-Nov-91 CH.NY19/R) Minestrone soup (23x15cm-9x6in) s.stretcher oil metallic paint
£52941	$90000	(23-Oct-91 B.SF3772/R) Campbell's Tomato Soup (51x41cm-20x16in) s.d.62verso
£386	$695	(22-Nov-91 SA.A464/R) 20 Christmas angels wish Bob Jones a merry Christmas (30x22cm-12x9in) i. felt tip pen (DM 1100)
£456	$821	(22-Nov-91 SA.A465) Merry Christmas Bob Jones (30x22cm-12x9in) felt tip pen (DM 1300)
£526	$947	(22-Nov-91 SA.A466/R) And merry Christmas Mr Jones (30x22cm-12x9in) i. felt tip pen (DM 1500)
£601	$1058	(11-Apr-92 AW.H2390) Fool and fox conversing (42x56cm-17x22in) s.mono. indian ink brush (DM 1750)
£862	$1500	(15-Sep-91 JRB.C212/R) Blue shoe (20x25cm-8x10in) s. letterpress ink W/C
£920	$1600	(15-Sep-91 JRB.C226/R) Judy Garland's shoe (25x20cm-10x8in) s. letterpress ink W/C
£1471	$2500	(23-Oct-91 B.SF3774/R) Blue shoe (25x20cm-10x8in) s. letterpress hand-painted ink W/C
£1546	$2675	(29-Mar-92 P.V79) Birth of Venus (24x36cm-9x14in) s.i.d.1984 assemblage sewn photos (F.FR 15000)
£1618	$2750	(23-Oct-91 B.SF3775/R) Two cherubs (20x25cm-8x10in) s. letterpress hand-painted ink W/C
£2353	$4000	(23-Oct-91 B.SF3776/R) Cherub picking flowers (20x25cm-8x10in) s. letterpress hand-painted ink W/C
£2869	$5164	(2-Feb-92 CSC.P184/R) Jeune homme de profil (43x33cm-17x13in) s. Indian ink (F.FR 28000)
£3073	$5500	(6-May-92 CH.NY388/R) Shadow (28x36cm-11x14in) s.d.1979 diamond dust polymer silkscreen canvas
£3824	$6500	(23-Oct-91 B.SF3777/R) Four flowers (13x13cm-5x5in) indist.s.verso synthetic polymer acrylic canvas
£4469	$8000	(7-May-92 SY.NY313/R) Shadow (36x38cm-14x15in) s.i.d.1979 synthetic polymer paint diamond dust
£4800	$8304	(26-Mar-92 S100/R) Cecil Beaton (56x36cm-22x14in) s. ink W/C collage
£5000	$8650	(26-Mar-92 S84/R) Speedboat (20x25cm-8x10in) s.d.83 verso polymer silkscreen canvas
£6704	$12000	(7-May-92 SY.NY335/R) Heart (36x28cm-14x11in) s.i. synthetic polymer silkscreen canvas
£8380	$15000	(7-May-92 SY.NY308/R) flower (13x13cm-5x5in) s.i.d.65 synthetic polymer paint silkscreen
£8380	$15000	(6-May-92 CH.NY304/R) Flowers (13x13cm-5x5in) s.d.64 v. synthetic polymer silkscreen canvas
£8380	$15000	(6-May-92 CH.NY315/R) Soup can (67x57cm-26x22in) s.d.85 v. synthetic polymer silkscreen canvas
£8380	$15000	(14-Nov-91 SY.NY376/R) Dollar sign (25x20cm-10x8in) s.i.d.82 v.synthetic polymer silkscreen canvas
£9249	$16000	(3-Oct-91 SY.NY88/R) Guns (51x51cm-20x20in) s.i.d.81 synthetic polymer paint silkscreen
£10049	$17485	(14-Apr-92 F.M233/R) Vesuvius (80x100cm-31x39in) s. serigraph (I.L 22000000)
£10615	$19000	(14-Nov-91 SY.NY354/R) Double one dollar bill (22x25cm-9x10in) s.d.62 v.synthetic polymer silkscreen canvas
£11176	$19000	(23-Oct-91 B.SF3773/R) Linda Cossey (102x102cm-40x40in) silkscreen on canvas

WARHOL, Andy (1930-1986) American-cont.

£12571	$22000	(25-Feb-92 SY.NY173/R) Untitled (142x107cm-56x42in) s.d.84 synthetic polymer silkscreen on canvas
£15000	$25950	(26-Mar-92 S83/R) Untitled (51x76cm-20x30in) s.overlap acrylic silkscreen canvas
£23464	$42000	(6-May-92 CH.NY342/R) Untitled (54x62cm-21x24in) s. silkscreen synthetic polymer dollar bills
£25140	$45000	(7-May-92 SY.NY327/R) Shadows (193x133cm-76x52in) s. diamond dust synthetic polymer paint canvas
£27933	$50000	(7-May-92 SY.NY303 a/R) Flowers (56x56cm-22x22in) synthetic polymer paint silkscreen canvas
£30347	$52500	(3-Oct-91 SY.NY65/R) Jackie (51x41cm-20x16in) s.d.64 synthetic polymer silkscreen canvas
£30726	$55000	(14-Nov-91 SY.NY345/R) Flowers (61x61cm-24x24in) s.d.64 v. synthetic polymer silkscreen canvas
£34637	$62000	(12-Nov-91 CH.NY34/R) Flowers (61x61cm-24x24in) s.d.64 silkscreen ink synthetic polymer canvas
£36313	$65000	(14-Nov-91 SY.NY387/R) One Red Marilyn - reversal series (51x40cm-20x16in) st.sig. v. synthetic polymer silkscreen canvas
£39106	$70000	(13-Nov-91 CH.NY250/R) Knives (180x125cm-71x49in) s.verso silkscreen ink synthetic polymer canvas
£50279	$90000	(6-May-92 SY.NY56/R) Mao (66x56cm-26x22in) s.d.72 synthetic polymer silkscreen on canvas
£51429	$90000	(25-Feb-92 SY.NY168/R) Shadow (193x132cm-76x52in) s.d.1978verso synth.polymer silkscreen canvas
£53073	$95000	(14-Nov-91 SY.NY363/R) Self-portrait (57x57cm-22x22in) synthetic polymer silkscreen canvas
£69832	$125000	(6-May-92 CH.NY343/R) Marilyn - reversal series (91x71cm-36x28in) s.d.86 silkscreen synthetic polymer canvas
£81006	$145000	(7-May-92 SY.NY313 a/R) Four gold-black Marilyns - reversal series (91x71cm-36x28in) st.sig. synthetic polymer paint silkscreen
£83799	$150000	(13-Nov-91 SY.NY45/R) Mao (127x107cm-50x42in) init.d.73 v. syn. polymer silkscreen canvas
£84000	$160440	(2-Jul-92 C56/R) Little race riot (76x84cm-30x33in) s.overlap synthetic polymer canvas
£100559	$180000	(12-Nov-91 CH.NY46/R) Mao (128x107cm-50x42in) st. silkscreen ink synthetic polymer canvas
£115000	$219650	(2-Jul-92 S37 a/R) Colored Campbell's soup can (92x61cm-36x24in) s.d.65verso silkscreen acrylic canvas
£178771	$320000	(13-Nov-91 SY.NY42/R) Red Jackie (101x101cm-40x40in) synthetic polymer silkscreen handpaint canvas
£212291	$380000	(6-May-92 SY.NY26/R) 16 Jackies (204x163cm-80x64in) s.synthetic polymer ink silkscreen on canvas
£293296	$525000	(6-May-92 SY.NY39/R) Most wanted men no 11, John Joseph H (124x198cm-49x78in) s.verso synthetic polymer silkscreen on canvas
£1061453	$1900000	(5-May-92 CH.NY46/R) 210 Coca-Cola bottles (210x267cm-83x105in) s.d.62verso silkscreen ink synthetic polymer

WARLING, Elisabeth (1858-1915) Swedish

£771	$1333	(28-Mar-92 UA.U409/R) Evening fishing (14x24cm-6x9in) s. panel (S.KR 8000)

WARNBERGER, Simon (1769-1847) German

£512	$932	(26-May-92 KF.M440) In the English Garden (23x18cm-9x7in) s.verso pen chk pencil wash double-sided (DM 1500)

WARNER, Everett L (1877-1963) American

£1637	$2800	(12-Mar-92 CH.NY213/R) Winter morning (66x81cm-26x32in) s. masonite

WARNER, Nell Walker (1891-1970) American

£632	$1200	(23-Jun-92 MOR.P122) House in mountain landscape (41x51cm-16x20in) s.
£904	$1600	(12-Feb-92 B.SF473/R) Boats along seashore (41x51cm-16x20in) s.

WARNOLF, Bertil (1950-) Swedish

£946	$1712	(19-May-92 AB.S5339/R) Matches - diptych (55x240cm-22x94in) s.d.1979 (S.KR 10000)

WAROQUIER, Henry de (1881-1970) French

£760	$1375	(18-May-92 AT.P158) Nu (55x38cm-22x15in) s. mono.verso board (F.FR 7500)
£1304	$2322	(29-Nov-91 GAB.G2908) Vue de Venise (33x41cm-13x16in) s. mono.verso (S.FR 3300)
£1600	$3056	(29-Jun-92 CSK26/R) Vue de ville (73x60cm-29x24in) s. init.num.2166 verso board
£1778	$3218	(20-May-92 GK.Z5077) View of Lake Como (61x79cm-24x31in) s.d.1912 board (S.FR 4800)
£2000	$3500	(28-Feb-92 SY.NY113/R) Venice (65x81cm-26x32in) s.i. init.num.verso
£2203	$3965	(2-Feb-92 CSC.P64/R) L'homme deux (44x28cm-17x11in) s.d.1939 painted under glass (F.FR 21500)
£11202	$20387	(12-Dec-91 CSC.P397/R) Etude pour la tragedie (71x106cm-28x42in) s.i.d.1937 panel (F.FR 110000)
£498	$910	(12-May-92 C.A87) Sailing boats (22x27cm-9x11in) s. W/C (B.FR 30000)
£1648	$2818	(22-Mar-92 I.N73/R) L'apocalypse blanche (37x28cm-15x11in) s.d.1917 gouache (F.FR 16000)
£1800	$3132	(19-Sep-91 B104/R) Eastern tip of L'Ile aux Moines at low tide (26x95cm-10x37in) s.i.d.1910 W/C bodycol

WARREN, Alan (1919-) Australian

£523	$999	(21-Jul-92 JRL.S230) Animals in abstract landscape (73x98cm-29x39in) s.d.50 (A.D 1350)
£684	$1217	(27-Apr-92 J.M199) Seated nude (91x65cm-36x26in) s.d.70 board (A.D 1600)
£812	$1445	(27-Apr-92 J.M51) Sunset (65x91cm-26x36in) s.d.60 board (A.D 1900)
£1068	$1902	(27-Apr-92 J.M258/R) Studio nude (86x119cm-34x47in) s.d.70 board (A.D 2500)
£1282	$2282	(27-Apr-92 J.M135/R) Reclining nude on sun lounge (85x119cm-33x47in) s.d.71 board (A.D 3000)
£1282	$2282	(27-Apr-92 J.M127/R) Suburban rooftops (65x91cm-26x36in) s.d.60 board (A.D 3000)

WARREN, Barbara (20th C) Irish?

£455	$786	(2-Oct-91 A.D69) Two standing figures (91x51cm-36x20in) s. (E.P 500)
£602	$1095	(11-Dec-91 A.D112) Galway fishermen. Houses in landscape (56x46cm-22x18in) s. double-sided (E.P 650)

WARREN, Edmund George (1834-1909) British

£520	*$926*	*(21-Jan-92 SWS1232) Fisherfolk on rocky shore (29x57cm-11x22in) s.d.1868 W/C gouache over pencil*
£4000	*$7080*	*(6-Nov-91 S253/R) The way to the village (25x35cm-10x14in) s.d.1866 W/C htd.bodycol*

WARSHAW, Howard (1920-) American

£706	$1200	(23-Oct-91 B.SF3744/R) Potatoes (19x29cm-7x11in) s.d.45

WARSHAWSKY, Abel George (1883-1962) American

£597	$1050	(9-Apr-92 FA.PH787) Late April in the French countryside (53x43cm-21x17in) s. board
£1184	$2250	(23-Jun-92 MOR.P59) Figures in a street (33x41cm-13x16in) s. board
£1189	$2200	(10-Jun-92 CE.NY309/R) California coast scene (39x48cm-15x19in) s. panel
£1271	$2250	(12-Feb-92 B.SF449/R) Red barn (41x51cm-16x20in) s. canvasboard
£1397	$2500	(13-Nov-91 B.SF2782/R) Woman of Finisterre (65x53cm-26x21in) s.

WARSHAWSKY, Alexander (1887-1945) American

£1322	$2300	(15-Apr-92 SY.NY159/R) Old Aloes (66x81cm-26x32in) s.

WARSINSKI, Richard (1937-) ?

£615	$1057	(7-Oct-91 B.O146/R) Composition in grey and green (154x104cm-61x41in) s. (N.KR 7000)
£1949	$3547	(14-Dec-91 BU.O89/R) Nirvana (118x100cm-46x39in) s.i. paper (N.KR 22000)
£3512	$6040	(10-Oct-91 BU.O59/R) Untitled (116x96cm-46x38in) s. paper (N.KR 40000)

WASHINGTON, Georges (1827-1910) French

£3730	$6602	(5-Nov-91 ZZ.F130/R) Cavaliers arabes (50x61cm-20x24in) s. (F.FR 37000)
£6000	$10380	(4-Oct-91 C127/R) Arab cavalry fording stream (50x61cm-20x24in) s.
£12195	$21220	(13-Apr-92 AT.P212/R) Halte des cavaliers a la fontaine (73x92cm-29x36in) s. (F.FR 120000)
£13182	$24783	(16-Dec-91 BG.P113/R) L'arret a l'oasis (114x145cm-45x57in) s. (F.FR 128000)
£16427	$29569	(18-Nov-91 AT.P384/R) Le retour des cavaliers (67x97cm-26x38in) s. (F.FR 160000)

WASILEWSKI, Czeslaw (20th C) Polish

£555	*$1000*	*(24-Nov-91 AG.W16) Sleighing (23x49cm-9x19in) s. W/C (P.Z 11000000)*

WASKE, Erich (1889-) German

£481	$837	(19-Sep-91 N.M2836/R) Cloudy mountainous landscape (66x61cm-26x24in) i.verso (DM 1400)

WASKE, Felix (1942-) Austrian

£876	*$1586*	*(4-Dec-91 G.Z1281/R) Familie Tatoo I (49x70cm-19x28in) s.i.d.1968 col.pencil (S.FR 2200)*

WASLEY, F (fl.1880-1914) British

£680	*$1170*	*(6-Mar-92 BW384) Venetian view (36x25cm-14x10in) s. W/C*

WASLEY, Frank (fl.1880-1914) British

£650	$1177	(20-May-92 S227/R) Fishing boats at dusk (61x91cm-24x36in) s.
£900	$1539	(12-Mar-92 CSK290/R) Fishing boats off jetty. Shipping off rocky coast (76x56cm-30x22in) s.
£900	$1512	(15-Aug-91 B391) Unloading catch (41x61cm-16x24in) s.
£1100	$1914	(12-Sep-91 CSK182/R) Coastal landscape with fisherfolk and beached fishing vessels at sunset (61x107cm-24x42in) s.
£420	*$802*	*(1-Jul-92 B49) Coastal scene (54x73cm-21x29in) s. W/C*
£480	*$845*	*(6-Apr-92 PH100) Entrance to the Grand Canal, Venice (24x44cm-9x17in) s. W/C bodycol.*
£513	*$913*	*(27-Apr-92 J.M312) Morning mists (24x54cm-9x21in) s. W/C (A.D 1200)*
£600	*$1032*	*(3-Mar-92 SWS1755) The Victoria Tower, London (43x24cm-17x9in) s. W/C gouache over pencil*
£620	*$1184*	*(16-Jul-92 CSK134) Houses of Parliament from Thames (24x55cm-9x22in) s. W/C bodycol*
£660	*$1135*	*(16-Oct-91 PHL95) Coming to anchor, North Sea fishing off Robin Hood's Bay (27x37cm-11x15in) s.verso col.wash htd white bodycol*

WASLEY, Frank (fl.1880-1914) British-cont.
£1550 $2806   *(21-May-92 KING452) On the lagoon, Venice, St Georges (36x51cm-14x20in)*
                       s. W/C

WASMANN, Friedrich (attrib) (1805-1886) German
£847 $1517   (16-Jan-92 D.V67/R) Portrait of little girl (31x38cm-12x15in) (A.S 17000)

WASMULLER, J H (19th C) American
£857 $1500   (21-Feb-92 BG.M147) Barbazon landscape (69x102cm-27x40in)

WASSENBERGH, Jan Abel (1689-1750) Dutch
£3081 $5176   (27-Aug-91 RAS.K201/R) Diana and Endymion (118x127cm-46x50in) indist.sig.
                       i.d.1735 (D.KR 35000)
£3200 $6144   (7-Jul-92 PH136/R) Holy Family (48x39cm-19x15in) s.

WATELET, C J (1867-1954) Belgian
£509 $871   (10-Mar-92 GM.B391/R) Portrait de femme (100x80cm-39x31in) s.
                       (B.FR 30000)

WATELIN, Louis (1838-1907) French
£572 $1002   (5-Apr-92 ZZ.F47/R) Paysage a la mare (27x33cm-11x13in) s. (F.FR 5500)
£601 $1100   (7-Jun-92 LIT.L125 a) Cows grazing (56x74cm-22x29in) s.
£5900 $10798   (17-May-92 T.B364) Paysage anime breton - l'Anse de Benodet et Ste Marine
                       (104x165cm-41x65in) s.d.1872 (F.FR 58000)

WATERHOUSE, John William (1849-1917) British
£10000 $17100   (19-Mar-92 B136/R) A study for A Naiad (29x24cm-11x9in) canvas laid down
                       on board
£32000 $54400   (25-Oct-91 C29/R) Flora (102x68cm-40x27in) i.stretcher
£80000 $136000   (25-Oct-91 C31/R) Miranda, the Tempest (100x138cm-39x54in) s.d.1916

WATERLOO, Anthonie (1609-1690) Flemish
£497   *$884*   *(25-Nov-91 CH.AM144) Wooded rocky landscape with travellers on road*
                       (28x29cm-11x11in) i.verso chk wash htd.white (D.FL 1600)
£600   *$1092*   *(11-Dec-91 PH13/R) Wooded landscape (28x21cm-11x8in) chk htd white*
£3395   *$6077*   *(12-Nov-91 SY.AM313/R) River bank with dense trees and broken branches*
                       (41x32cm-16x13in) chk wash (D.FL 11000)
£14500   *$27840*   *(6-Jul-92 S3/R) Pnaoramic landscape with tavern amongst trees*
                       (15x18cm-6x7in) chk wash pen htd.white

WATERLOO, Anthonie (attrib) (1609-1690) Flemish
£838   *$1500*   *(15-Jan-92 CH.NY146/R) House above series of arched recesses*
                       (16x19cm-6x7in) black chk wash

WATERLOW, Sir Ernest Albert (1850-1919) British
£500 $930   (18-Jun-92 CSK246) River in Berkshire (30x51cm-12x20in) s.d.1877
£4200 $7896   (19-Dec-91 C105/R) Winter landscape with flock of sheep by farm
                       (76x102cm-30x40in) s.
£400   *$684*   *(12-Mar-92 CSK62) The old man at Corniston (20x43cm-8x17in) init.d.75*
                       pencil W/C htd.white
£850   *$1462*   *(4-Mar-92 S255/R) Berkshire cottage (17x25cm-7x10in) s. s.i.verso W/C htd*
                       bodycol

WATERMAN, Marcus (1834-1914) American
£877 $1500   (13-Mar-92 S.BM192/R) Hens and rooster (13x20cm-5x8in) mono.d.1859
                       i.verso
£2047 $3500   (12-Mar-92 CH.NY98/R) The merchant and the genie (102x56cm-40x22in) s.

WATERS, Billie (1896-1979) British
£1800 $3114   (2-Oct-91 S207/R) Olives in Anacapri (41x51cm-16x20in) s. s.i.verso

WATERS, G S (?) British
£680   *$1190*   *(19-Feb-92 HAR384) On the Guidecca Canal, Venice (23x56cm-9x22in) s.*

WATERS, George W (1832-1912) American
£608 $1100   (5-Dec-91 GRO.B429/R) Landscape with cattle (43x71cm-17x28in) s.

WATERS, Maynard (1938-) Australian
£430 $821   (29-Jun-92 AAA.S76) Balloon aloft (41x51cm-16x20in) s. board (A.D 1100)
£470 $851   (2-Dec-91 AAA.S138) The picnic races (46x61cm-18x24in) s. board
                       (A.D 1100)
£655 $1146   (30-Mar-92 AAA.S77) Balmain morning (46x51cm-18x20in) s. board (A.D 1500)
£776 $1358   (23-Sep-91 AAA.S134) Street scene, Balmain (46x61cm-18x24in) s. board
                       (A.D 1700)
£1197 $2166   (2-Dec-91 AAA.S870) From Balmain (76x122cm-30x48in) s. (A.D 2800)

WATKINS, B Colles (1833-1891) Irish
£1200 $2148   (11-Nov-91 S594/R) Portrush, Ireland (16x26cm-6x10in) s.i.stretcher
£2336 $4042   (25-Mar-92 A.D31/R) West of Ireland mountain landscape with donkey and
                       farmer (23x33cm-9x13in) s.d.18700 canvas laid on board (E.P 2500)

WATKINS, Frank (fl.1880-1889) British
£580 $986   (5-Aug-91 WW81) Interior of kitchen with cooks preparing banquet
                       (51x63cm-20x25in) s.
£1000 $1780   (28-Nov-91 B61/R) Kitchen interior (52x63cm-20x25in) s.

WATKINS, Franklin Chenault (1894-1972) American
£973 $1800   (10-Jun-92 CE.NY540/R) Blue bench (60x75cm-24x30in) s.
£550 $979   (29-Oct-91 C108/R) Temple Bar, looking East (44x40cm-17x16in) s. pencil W/C htd white

WATKINS, J (19th C) British
£1481 $2681   (19-May-92 GF.L2204/R) Portrait of horse with view of landscape (47x61cm-19x24in) s.d.1873 (S.FR 4000)

WATKINS, John Samuel (1886-1942) Australian
£617 $1110   (24-Nov-91 SY.S26/R) Dee Why (29x37cm-11x15in) s.d.1924 canvasboard (A.D 1400)
£851 $1506   (26-Apr-92 SY.ME28/R) Cove (24x29cm-9x11in) s. canvas on board (A.D 2000)

WATROUS, Harry W (1857-1940) American
£1649 $3100   (18-Dec-91 SY.NY259/R) Kwan-Yin (50x45cm-20x18in) s.
£7263 $13000   (6-May-92 D.NY24/R) The parakeet ring (41x48cm-16x19in) s.

WATSON, Alfred S (19/20th C) British
£420 $752   (14-Nov-91 B182/R) Richmond Bridge, midwinter (18x27cm-7x11in) s.d.1908 W/C
£720 $1289   (14-Nov-91 B181/R) Richmond Bridge, early evening (36x53cm-14x21in) s.d.1908 W/C

WATSON, Arthur (19th C) British
£519 $918   (5-Nov-91 BA.S186/R) In the rosegarden (30x20cm-12x8in) s.d.1895 (S.KR 5500)

WATSON, C E (20th C) British
£1100 $1914   (10-Sep-91 RG2273) Mountainous Scottish loch scene with Highland cattle in foreground (33x43cm-13x17in) s.indist.d.
£2000 $3360   (26-Aug-91 S818/R) Highland calves by Loch Restil (35x46cm-14x18in) s.d.1911 s.i.verso

WATSON, Charles A (1857-1923) American
£843 $1500   (2-May-92 W.W103/R) Sunset, Baltimore Harbour (41x76cm-16x30in) s. s.d.1897 i.stretcher

WATSON, Dawson (1864-1939) American
£1170 $2200   (18-Dec-91 SY.NY121/R) The hunter (170x131cm-67x52in) s.d.1891

WATSON, George Spencer (1869-1934) British
£560 $980   (27-Sep-91 C101/R) Evening (76x102cm-30x40in) i.

WATSON, Homer Ransford (1855-1936) Canadian
£746 $1328   (25-Nov-91 W.T1596/R) Winter forest scene (30x41cm-12x16in) s. board (C.D 1500)
£1370 $2507   (14-May-92 SY.T57) After rain (35x45cm-14x18in) s.d.90 d.stretcher (C.D 3000)
£2750 $4868   (6-Nov-91 SY.T222/R) Toward evening (44x60cm-17x24in) s. (C.D 5500)
£3234 $5756   (26-Nov-91 JOY.T34/R) Brook oak (63x77cm-25x30in) s. canvas on board (C.D 6500)
£3653 $6648   (26-May-92 JOY.T118/R) Rural home (85x120cm-33x47in) s. canvas on board (C.D 8000)

WATSON, Jessie N (1870-1963) American
£474 $900   (23-Jun-92 MOR.P50 a) California landscape (36x43cm-14x17in) s.i.d.49 paper

WATSON, John (early 20th C) British?
£600 $1056   (10-Apr-92 K525/R) Still life study of mixed fruit, withblack and gilded vase on marble ledge (46x33cm-18x13in) s.

WATSON, John Dawson (1832-1892) British
£600 $1068   (29-Oct-91 C71/R) The model-maker (35x27cm-14x11in) inits.d.1867 pencil W/C bodycol.

WATSON, R (18th C) British
£2528 $4500   (22-Jan-92 SY.NY511/R) Highland sheep and cattle (61x93cm-24x37in) s.d.1894 pair

WATSON, Raymond (20th C) British
£450 $788   (25-Feb-92 C74) Shag on rocky coast (32x26cm-13x10in) s. pencil W/C bodycol

WATSON, Robert (19th C) British
£750 $1388   (11-Jun-92 CSK157) Sheep in Highland landscape (91x61cm-36x24in) s.
£800 $1360   (22-Oct-91 SWS280/R) Highland cattle by loch (47x73cm-19x29in) s.d.1882
£900 $1566   (15-Apr-92 PHL126) Cattle by loch in Highland landscape (30x45cm-12x18in) s.d.1891
£1006 $1800   (6-May-92 B.P90/R) Highland cattle (41x61cm-16x24in) s.d.1898
£1300 $2327   (11-Nov-91 HS354/R) Highland sheep and lambs on rocky outcrop with river and loch beyond (50x75cm-20x30in) s.d.1906
£1397 $2500   (6-May-92 B.P89/R) Highland sheep (41x61cm-16x24in) s.d.1898

WATSON, Robert (19th C) British-cont.
£1413	$2530	(14-Nov-91 GRO.B22/R) Shepherd with flock in Highland landscape (51x76cm-20x30in) s.d.1906
£1800	$3258	(5-Dec-91 CG301/R) Highland cattle in glen (76x127cm-30x50in) s.d.1904
£6500	$11635	(12-Nov-91 CHAP310/R) Highland cattle by stream. Sheep on rocky outcrop (61x89cm-24x35in) s.d.1916 pair

WATSON, Samuel (1818-1867) Irish
£1028	$1779	(25-Mar-92 A.D93) View of the Lee from Curracupaun, from nature (33x25cm-13x10in) s.i.d.March 1843verso (E.P 1100)

WATSON, Thomas J (1847-1912) British
£2600	$4368	(26-Aug-91 S844/R) Highland cattle watering (61x91cm-24x36in) s.d.1903

WATSON, Walter J (1879-?) British
£2600	$4628	(28-Apr-92 S189/R) Loch Lyon, Perthshire. Highland river (41x66cm-16x26in) s.d.1931 pair
£2900	$4930	(23-Oct-91 MMB345/R) On Lledr, N. Wales (41x66cm-16x26in) s.d.1908 s.i.verso
£4400	$7568	(4-Mar-92 S153/R) On Llugwy, North Wales. On Glaslyn, North Wales (41x66cm-16x26in) s.d.1921 s.i.verso pair

WATSON, William (19/20th C) British
£1100	$1848	(26-Aug-91 S843/R) Sheep in the Highlands (33x48cm-13x19in) s.d.1895
£1200	$2052	(12-Mar-92 CSK221) Highland cattle watering beside burn (61x91cm-24x36in) s.d.1889
£1651	$3022	(3-Jun-92 R.T155/R) Highland sheep and young (61x91cm-24x36in) s.d.1878 (C.D 3600)
£2747	$5000	(28-May-92 SY.NY277/R) By Highland streams - Glen Dochart, Perthshire (62x92cm-24x36in) s.d.1907 s.verso
£3100	$5549	(5-May-92 SWS426/R) Spring in the Highlands (40x55cm-16x22in) s.d.1884
£3297	$6000	(28-May-92 SY.NY291/R) Sheep grazing in Highlands (84x67cm-33x26in) s.d.1903

WATSON, William (attrib) (19/20th C) British
£1488	$2500	(12-Aug-91 SG.M599) The Collie and mountain sheep (61x91cm-24x36in) s.

WATSON, William Peter (?-1932) British
£950	$1625	(17-Mar-92 SWS1203/R) Feeding the doves (75x44cm-30x17in) s.

WATSON, William Stewart (?) British
£1800	$3024	(26-Aug-91 S850/R) The meeting of Dr.Samuel Johnson and James Boswell with Flora Macdonald (79x109cm-31x43in) s.i.verso

WATT, Alison (1965-) British
£920	$1674	(29-May-92 PHG98) Self portrait (38x28cm-15x11in) s.d.87 acrylic paper
£5000	$8550	(11-Mar-92 S189/R) Bute bathers (137x101cm-54x40in) s.
£1100	*$2002*	*(29-May-92 PHG93) Two girls (28x20cm-11x8in) s. pastel gouache*

WATT, Miss Linnie (fl.1875-1908) British
£520	$910	(26-Sep-91 KING361) Mother and children on beach (30x64cm-12x25in) s.
£700	$1295	(11-Jun-92 CSK252/R) In the churchyard (31x48cm-12x19in) s. board
£950	$1663	(26-Sep-91 KING364) Woodland path in France with figures (28x41cm-11x16in) s.
£980	$1715	(26-Sep-91 KING362) On the Pincio (23x33cm-9x13in) s.i.verso canvas on board
£1050	$1838	(26-Sep-91 KING367) Harbour at Concarneau with figures (30x46cm-12x18in) s.i.
£1100	$1925	(26-Sep-91 KING365) Orchard in Brittany with figures (30x43cm-12x17in) s.
£1150	$2013	(26-Sep-91 KING363) French street scene with figures (46x33cm-18x13in) s.
£1150	$2013	(26-Sep-91 KING366) At Guingamp (33x46cm-13x18in) s.i.verso
£1450	$2538	(26-Sep-91 KING371) Taking the pig to market (53x38cm-21x15in) s.
£1500	$2625	(26-Sep-91 KING369) Children gathering flowers on hillside (33x48cm-13x19in) s.
£1650	$2888	(26-Sep-91 KING368) At the fair in Concarneau (30x48cm-12x19in) s.i.
£1850	$3238	(26-Sep-91 KING370) Flower market in Brittany (46x36cm-18x14in) s.

WATTEAU (18/19th C) French
£1300	$2327	(13-Nov-91 WI1165) Fete champetre figures in courtly costume in arcadian landscape (10x11cm-4x4in)
£1300	$2353	(6-Dec-91 CBS277) The garden fete (64x81cm-25x32in)

WATTEAU (after) (18/19th C) French
£1337	$2421	(3-Dec-91 CN.P64/R) Les jaloux (64x86cm-25x34in) (F.FR 13000)

WATTEAU DE LILLE, Louis Joseph (1731-1798) French
£3200	*$6144*	*(7-Jul-92 C64/R) Studies of figures and animals (23x38cm-9x15in) chk two*

WATTEAU, Francois L J (1758-1823) French
£1030	$1936	(18-Dec-91 AT.P209/R) Une petite marchande de legumes (15x13cm-6x5in) panel (F.FR 10000)

WATTEAU, Jean Antoine (1684-1721) French
£7200 $12600   (3-Apr-92 C46/R) Elegant company out-of-doors with marriage discussed. Elegant company, with arrival of Bridal couple (27x35cm-11x14in) panel pair
£8000 $15360   (7-Jul-92 C53/R) Woman seen from behind with left arm extended (13x9cm-5x4in) chk
£10614 $18574   (3-Apr-92 AGS.P220/R) Deux etudes de femmes (13x17cm-5x7in) sanguine blk.chk. (F.FR 102000)
£19553 $35000   (15-Jan-92 CH.NY75/R) Studies of head of woman and man blowing, in profile to right (15x20cm-6x8in) red black chk after Rubens
£78212 $140000   (15-Jan-92 CH.NY73/R) Three ladies in profile to right, one seated holding reins (17x22cm-7x9in) with i. red chk
£122905 $220000   (15-Jan-92 CH.NY74/R) Studies of two girls' heads (13x19cm-5x7in) col.chk

WATTEAU, Jean Antoine (after) (1684-1721) French
£950 $1710   (22-Nov-91 SWS139/R) Le Pierrot content (66x95cm-26x37in)
£1200 $2136   (29-Oct-91 PH10) La cascade (47x36cm-19x14in)

WATTEAU, Jean Antoine (circle) (1684-1721) French
£17000 $30940   (11-Dec-91 S73/R) La dance (80x100cm-31x39in)

WATTEAU, Jean Antoine (style) (1684-1721) French
£4800 $8400   (3-Apr-92 C47/R) Fete Champetre (81x108cm-32x43in)

WATTER, Josef (1838-1913) German
£378 $658   (18-Sep-91 N.M290) Couple entering gondola leaving for Kythera (32x25cm-13x10in) pencil htd.white (DM 1100)

WATTEVILLE, Felicie de (1795-?) French
£635 $1092   (10-Oct-91 D.V325/R) Portrait of young woman wearing black hat and shawl (8x6cm-3x2in) min.s. oval (A.S 13000)

WATTIER, Charles Emile (1800-1868) French
£661 $1210   (15-May-92 AT.P225) Jeune couple dans un parc (20x25cm-8x10in) s. black chk sanguine htd white (F.FR 6500)

WATTS, Frederick William (1800-1862) British
£850 $1615   (23-Jun-92 PH66/R) Fishing boats on continental estuary with castle beyond (17x22cm-7x9in) s.verso board
£1100 $1892   (4-Mar-92 S18/R) Crossing bridge (17x22cm-7x9in) board
£1800 $3222   (13-Nov-91 S217/R) Landscape with cottages (12x18cm-5x7in) board
£2100 $4011   (21-Jul-92 PH284/R) Barge on river, cottage beyond (24x34cm-9x13in) board
£3000 $5730   (15-Jul-92 S195/R) Cattle on Hampstead Heath (24x36cm-9x14in) panel
£4000 $7160   (13-Nov-91 S80/R) Heath scene with windmill and sheep, Hampstead (44x59cm-17x23in) s.i.d. 1843 paper on canvas
£4500 $7920   (8-Apr-92 S92/R) Landscapes with cottages (11x17cm-4x7in) three i.verso board four
£5500 $9845   (13-Nov-91 S83/R) River landscape with fishermen and distant village (54x72cm-21x28in)
£6400 $11456   (13-Nov-91 S192/R) Beach scenes (14x19cm-6x7in) paper set of four
£6400 $12224   (15-Jul-92 S197/R) Beach scenes (10x16cm-4x6in) card pair
£6500 $12415   (21-Jul-92 PH267/R) Figures and cattle before church in Forest of Dean (47x67cm-19x26in) panel
£8500 $15215   (13-Nov-91 S82/R) River landscape with figures by inn (43x70cm-17x28in) s.
£23000 $43930   (15-Jul-92 S68/R) Cattle and horses by a lock in landscape with village beyond (49x73cm-19x29in)

WATTS, Frederick William (attrib) (1800-1862) British
£917 $1679   (3-Jun-92 R.T148/R) River view with horse team and countrymen traversing bridge (30x46cm-12x18in) i.verso (C.D 2000)

WATTS, George Frederick (1817-1904) British
£1400 $2520   (19-Nov-91 PH63/R) Orpheus and Eurydice (61x102cm-24x40in)

WATTS, J T (1853-1930) British
£850 $1471   (6-Sep-91 BW410) Autumnal woodland scene with peasants on pathway (28x38cm-11x15in) s. board

WATTS, James T (1853-1930) British
£900 $1593   (6-Nov-91 S53) Autumnal woodland scene with pheasant (30x41cm-12x16in) s. panel

WAUER, William (20th C) ?
£2730 $4942   (23-May-92 GB.B7370/R) Senat, Berlin (60x178cm-24x70in) s.d.1948 (DM 8000)

WAUGH, Frederick J (1861-1940) American
£615 $1100   (13-Nov-91 B.SF2843/R) Veteran of Monterey (36x51cm-14x20in) s.
£773 $1400   (22-May-92 S.BM145/R) Coming day (56x74cm-22x29in) s. canvasboard
£967 $1750   (7-Dec-91 LAE.L85) Surf and rocks (53x66cm-21x26in) s. masonite
£1117 $2100   (18-Dec-91 SY.NY329/R) The Road to Nowhere (77x76cm-30x30in) ds.i.
£1189 $2200   (10-Jun-92 CE.NY411/R) Rocky coast (71x96cm-28x38in) s.
£1420 $2500   (9-Apr-92 FA.PH793) Breaking surf (61x76cm-24x30in) s.
£1838 $3400   (10-Jun-92 CE.NY352/R) Crashing waves (56x72cm-22x28in) s.

WAUGH, Frederick J (1861-1940) American-cont.
£2235	$4000	(14-Nov-91 CE.NY160/R) Moonlight (63x76cm-25x30in) s. s.i.num.26 verso canvasboard
£2571	$4500	(26-Sep-91 CH.NY80/R) Breaking waves (63x76cm-25x30in) s.
£4678	$8000	(11-Mar-92 SY.NY41/R) Seascape (91x122cm-36x48in) s. masonite
£5220	$9500	(28-May-92 CH.NY170/R) The Channel (91x122cm-36x48in) s.
£5882	$10000	(11-Aug-91 LIT.L133) Old Wharves, Gloucester (64x76cm-25x30in) s. s.d.1910 verso
£6433	$11000	(11-Mar-92 SY.NY40/R) Early morn (63x76cm-25x30in) s.

WAUGH, Hal (?-1941) Australian
£427	$774	(2-Dec-91 AAA.S91) Bullock team (22x31cm-9x12in) s. W/C (A.D 1000)

WAUTERS, Alex (1899-1965) Belgian
£816	$1395	(21-Mar-92 KV.L359) Boat (58x74cm-23x29in) mono. panel (B.FR 48000)
£2039	$3487	(21-Mar-92 KV.L477/R) Petite grue aux gants blancs (35x23cm-14x9in) s. canvas on unalit (B.FR 120000)
£1500	$2580	(12-Oct-91 KV.L355) Peasant in a punt on the Leie II (66x99cm-26x39in) s. W/C (B.FR 90000)

WAUTERS, Camille (1856-1919) Belgian
£4775	$8500	(27-Apr-92 S.SL520/R) Female nude figure with red hair and shawl draped around hips (191x109cm-75x43in) s.d.1890

WAXSCHLUNGER, Johann Georg (18th C) German
£1365	$2485	(27-May-92 PH.DU90/R) Still life of dead birds and animals (78x100cm-31x39in) mono. (DM 4000)

WAY, Andrew John Henry (1826-1888) American
£8516	$15500	(28-May-92 CH.NY41/R) A gourmet's delight (25x30cm-10x12in) init. board
£9714	$17000	(25-Sep-91 SY.NY5/R) Still life with oysters (25x36cm-10x14in) s.d.72

WAY, C (?) ?
£450	$788	(1-Apr-92 ZZ.B58) View of Lausanne (49x73cm-19x29in) s.i. W/C

WAY, Charles Jones (1834-1919) British
£633	$1172	(9-Jun-92 FB.M24/R) Picking berries near river (58x48cm-23x19in) s.d.1865 W/C (C.D 1400)
£667	$1133	(23-Oct-91 GD.B784/R) Full moon above landscape with snow covered mountain range beyond (37x73cm-15x29in) s.d.1866 W/C (S.FR 1700)
£796	$1417	(25-Nov-91 W.T1580/R) Rocky mountain vista (70x48cm-28x19in) s.d.1885 W/C (C.D 1600)

WAYLEN, James (attrib) (fl.1834-1838) British
£4200	$7434	(6-Nov-91 S114/R) Family portrait (113x158cm-44x62in) indis.s.d.

WEATHERHEAD, William Harris (1843-1903) British
£1600	$2960	(12-Jun-92 C218/R) Crossing the stream (59x90cm-23x35in) s.indis.d.

WEATHERILL, George (1810-1890) British
£400	$688	(16-Oct-91 PHL73) Fishing vessels off Whitby in calm, at sunset (11x20cm-4x8in) s. col.wash
£450	$855	(24-Jun-92 PHI531) View of Whitby from the shore (13x23cm-5x9in) s. W/C
£460	$800	(15-Apr-92 PHL62) Paddle steamer and fishing vessels in calm seas off Whitby (14x24cm-6x9in) s. col.wash
£500	$850	(24-Oct-91 RS33) Vessels off Whitby (15x23cm-6x9in) s. W/C
£512	$927	(21-May-92 L.K354) Shipping near rocky coast (11x20cm-4x8in) s. W/C (DM 1500)
£1050	$1995	(24-Jun-92 PHI530/R) Leaving Whitby Harbour by moonlight (11x20cm-4x8in) s. i.verso W/C
£1500	$2730	(11-Dec-91 PHL43/R) Numerous sailing vessels in the harbour at Whitby by moonlight (9x13cm-4x5in) col.washes
£1900	$3477	(15-May-92 TE323) Coastal village near Whitby (10x18cm-4x7in) s. W/C
£2500	$4575	(15-May-92 TE324) Shipping off coast, near Whitby (10x20cm-4x8in) s. W/C
£2600	$4758	(15-May-92 TE321/R) Fishing boats entering harbour (10x20cm-4x8in) s. W/C
£2600	$4758	(15-May-92 TE322/R) Whitby harbour (15x25cm-6x10in) s. W/C
£3000	$5160	(16-Oct-91 PHL72/R) Fishing boats by quay before swivel bridge at Whitby (11x18cm-4x7in) s. pencil col.wash htd white
£3700	$6364	(16-Oct-91 PHL125/R) Whitby harbour by moonlight (11x20cm-4x8in) s. pencil col.wash
£6000	$10320	(4-Mar-92 S193/R) Whitby (26x42cm-10x17in) s. W/C

WEATHERSTONE, Alfred C (fl.1888-1929) British
£490	$858	(26-Feb-92 PHL165) On the terrace (36x25cm-14x10in) s. col.washes

WEAVER, Thomas (1774-1843) British
£2200	$3872	(10-Apr-92 C169/R) Huntsman on chestnut hunter and horse at stable door in landscape (77x101cm-30x40in) indis.i.
£3700	$6734	(12-Dec-91 B94/R) Chestnut mare and foal (63x76cm-25x30in) s.d.1813

WEAVER, Thomas (circle) (1774-1843) British
£1200	$2112	(8-Apr-92 S212/R) Favourite cow, bred by John Downer, owned by Thomas Collins, landscape (39x54cm-15x21in)

WEBB, B (19th C) British
£750 $1358   (5-Dec-91 CSK143/R) Deer freightened by storm in highland landscape (77x114cm-30x45in) s.d.65

WEBB, Byron (19th C) British
£2778 $5000   (8-Jan-92 D.NY95) The bribe (76x102cm-30x40in)

WEBB, C M (1830-1895) British
£826 $1461   (5-Nov-91 SY.AM460) Farmyard (45x81cm-18x32in) s.d.1890 (D.FL 2700)

WEBB, Charles Meer (1830-1895) British
£640 $1100   (10-Oct-91 FA.PH692/R) Alchemist (61x53cm-24x21in) s.d.1864
£1337 $2300   (17-Oct-91 SY.NY293/R) Chess game (53x62cm-21x24in) s.d.1864
£1600 $2832   (13-Feb-92 CSK197/R) The winning move (66x82cm-26x32in) s.

WEBB, James (1825-1895) British
£520 $894   (8-Oct-91 PH90) Evening, North Wales (15x25cm-6x10in) s.i.d.1877verso panel
£1395 $2665   (21-Jul-92 JRL.S193/R) Zandvoort (68x98cm-27x39in) init. board (A.D 3600)
£1500 $2745   (14-May-92 TL60/R) On the Rotter (36x51cm-14x20in) s.d.1878 i.verso panel
£2000 $3440   (4-Mar-92 S9/R) On Rotter, Holland (30x56cm-12x22in) s.d.1876x77 s.i.d.verso
£3000 $5640   (19-Dec-91 C132/R) Castle of Beauvine, Dinant, Belgium (60x91cm-24x36in) s.d.77 s.i.d.verso
£3297 $6000   (28-May-92 SY.NY283/R) Fishing boats at low tide (63x93cm-25x37in) s.d.70 s.indist.i.verso
£3800 $7144   (19-Dec-91 C133/R) Heidelburg (65x102cm-26x40in) s.
£4000 $7160   (5-May-92 SWS417/R) Littlehampton (100x125cm-39x49in) s.i.d.86-7
£4400 $7568   (4-Mar-92 S2/R) On Scheldt (18x27cm-7x11in) s.d.75 s.i.d.verso panel
£5000 $9400   (19-Dec-91 C136/R) A bit in Holland (23x32cm-9x13in) s.i.d.83 panel
£5800 $10034   (26-Mar-92 RB651) The shrimpers (48x58cm-19x23in) s.
£6000 $10200   (23-Oct-91 S230/R) View of Constantinople (43x78cm-17x31in) s. mono.i.d.1873-4
£8791 $16000   (28-May-92 SY.NY275/R) Bamborough Castle (76x127cm-30x50in) indist.s.
£10465 $18000   (17-Oct-91 SY.NY289/R) Rotterdam, Holland (76x127cm-30x50in) s.i.
£16000 $28320   (6-Nov-91 S19/R) Mount Orgeuil Castle, Jersey (91x142cm-36x56in) s.d.1862
£25076 $44385   (5-Nov-91 SY.AM76/R) View of Cologne (183x275cm-72x108in) s.d.1870 (D.FL 82000)
£440 $757   *(6-Mar-92 BW395) Venetian canal scene (36x53cm-14x21in) s. W/C*

WEBB, James (style) (1825-1895) British
£1300 $2314   (21-Jan-92 PH85) Low tide (46x71cm-18x28in) bears sig.
£1600 $2896   (20-May-92 S229/R) Pulling in nets. Heavy swell (51x76cm-20x30in) bear sig. pair
£1600 $2784   (14-Apr-92 CSK161/R) Fisherfolk on beach with town beyond (51x76cm-20x30in) with sig.

WEBB, Josephine (?) Irish
£1101 $2048   (17-Jun-92 A.D20) Nude in front of mirror (53x36cm-21x14in) s. board (E.P 1200)

WEBB, Kenneth (?) British
£459 $853   (15-Jun-92 AD.D57) Bulloch Harbour (64x76cm-25x30in) s. (E.P 500)
£495 $921   (15-Jun-92 AD.D79) Bog cut Clifden (99x41cm-39x16in) s. (E.P 540)

WEBB, W B (?) ?
£1400 $2380   (22-Oct-91 SWS320/R) Fishing boats off pier. Pulling in lobster pots (28x49cm-11x19in) s. pair

WEBB, William (fl.1819-1850) British
£36000 $68760   (15-Jul-92 S98/R) Favourite hunters, property of Richard 1st Earl Howe (132x166cm-52x65in) s.

WEBB, William Edward (1862-1903) British
£950 $1739   (15-May-92 CBS185) Boats in harbour (23x33cm-9x13in) s.
£1100 $1947   (6-Nov-91 S74/R) St Mary's Gate, Manchester, Saturday morning (36x25cm-14x10in) s.
£1150 $2013   (27-Feb-92 L65/R) Unloading the catch on the Lancashire coast (30x46cm-12x18in) s.
£1150 $1978   (4-Mar-92 S8/R) Beached fishing boats (25x35cm-10x14in) s.
£1600 $2848   (21-Jan-92 PH77/R) Low tide (48x76cm-19x30in) s.
£1900 $3477   (15-May-92 CBS184) Off Lancashire coast (28x43cm-11x17in) s. i.verso
£2000 $3820   (17-Jul-92 C163/R) Fishermen with nets near a coastal town (48x76cm-19x30in) s.
£2209 $3800   (15-Oct-91 CE.NY400/R) The River at King's Lynn, Norfolk (41x61cm-16x24in) s. i. verso
£2900 $4930   (22-Oct-91 SWS302/R) Busy harbour (54x95cm-21x37in) s.
£3000 $5490   (15-May-92 CBS219) Estuary scene with boats and windmill (41x53cm-16x21in) s.
£3550 $6177   (16-Sep-91 CHAP101/R) Cornish fishing village near Penzance (56x97cm-22x38in) s.
£3600 $6048   (15-Aug-91 B390/R) Windy day, Peel harbour (61x91cm-24x36in) s. i.verso
£3800 $6878   (20-May-92 S59/R) Off North Shields (61x91cm-24x36in) s. s.i.stretcher
£4600 $8326   (6-Dec-91 CBS258) Peel Harbour and Castle (76x51cm-30x20in) s.

WEBB, William Edward (1862-1903) British-cont.
£5000 $9000   (22-Nov-91 C78) Quayside fishmarket, Peel Harbour, Isle of Man
           (56x97cm-22x38in) s.indis.d.89
£5800 $10498   (6-Dec-91 CBS257) Peel Harbour s.
£5800 $10498   (6-Dec-91 CBS259/R) Harbour scene (56x97cm-22x38in) s.
£7000 $12600   (19-Nov-91 PH32/R) The East Indiaman Witch of the Sea off Table Bay
           (50x75cm-20x30in) init.
£1000   *$1710*   *(12-Mar-92 CSK64/R) Fisherfolk on the shore at Peel. Unloading day's*
           catch near Prawle Point (28x20cm-11x8in) s.i. pencil W/C htd.bodycol
           pair
£1750   *$3203*   *(15-May-92 CBS192) Unloading catch at Peel. Near Prawle Point, South*
           Devon (28x23cm-11x9in) s. W/C pair

WEBB, William Edward (attrib) (1862-1903) British
£720 $1282   (28-Nov-91 PHX520) Low water, Peel (13x18cm-5x7in) indis.s.i.stretcher

WEBBER, Wesley (1841-1914) American
£774 $1300   (14-Aug-91 B.P180/R) Late Evening sail (76x69cm-30x27in) s.
£2973 $5500   (10-Jun-92 CE.NY163/R) Shepherd with flock in stormy landscape
           (46x127cm-18x50in) s.

WEBBER, Wesley (attrib) (1841-1914) American
£885 $1700   (4-Aug-92 RB.HY100/R) View of Boston Harbour (61x112cm-24x44in)

WEBER, Alfred Charles (1862-1922) French
£1127 $1950   (29-Mar-92 MY.F74/R) Cardinal with dog begging (30x23cm-12x9in) s. panel

WEBER, Andreas Paul (1893-1980) German
£420   *$726*   *(27-Mar-92 GRA.B2948/R) The wood gatherer (43x37cm-17x15in) s.mono.i. pen*
           (DM 1200)
£475   *$860*   *(4-Dec-91 DO.H3456/R) Bilanz des Opiumkrieges in Britische Bilder*
           (30x45cm-12x18in) mono.s.i. indian ink pen (DM 1350)
£514   *$884*   *(11-Oct-91 AW.H3190/R) Self portrait as Eulenspiegel (28x24cm-11x9in)*
           s.i.d.64 i.verso (DM 1500)
£687   *$1168*   *(25-Oct-91 BM.B1118/R) Der Tod in der Kiepe (41x34cm-16x13in) s. indian*
           ink (DM 2000)
£687   *$1168*   *(25-Oct-91 BM.B1119/R) Riders (43x56cm-17x22in) s. indian ink (DM 2000)*

WEBER, Arnaud (19th C) French
£1964   *$3338*   *(24-Oct-91 D.P5/R) Bouquet de fleurs (56x43cm-22x17in) s. gouache vellum*
           (F.FR 19500)

WEBER, C (19/20th C) American
£1300 $2301   (13-Feb-92 CSK185) The lute player (86x66cm-34x26in) s.d.1870 oval

WEBER, Carl (1850-1921) American
£734 $1300   (9-Nov-91 W.W184/R) Rocky gorge (86x61cm-34x24in) s.
£785 $1350   (10-Oct-91 FA.PH872) Deer by forest stream (86x51cm-34x20in) s.
£520   *$900*   *(29-Mar-92 MY.F156/R) Old homestead (33x66cm-13x26in) s. W/C board*

WEBER, Evarist Adam (1887-?) German
£1111 $2011   (19-May-92 GF.L2598/R) Eternal snow (79x100cm-31x39in) s. (S.FR 3000)

WEBER, Joseph (1803-1881) German
£1761 $3187   (4-Dec-91 DO.H2964/R) Portrait of Philipp Artaria (44x33cm-17x13in)
           s.i.d.1832verso (DM 5000)

WEBER, Kurt (1893-1964) Austrian
£2991 $5354   (15-Jan-92 D.V162/R) Woman drinking absinth. Landscape (70x100cm-28x39in)
           board double-sided (A.S 60000)
£499   *$892*   *(15-Jan-92 D.V201/R) Untitled (84x60cm-33x24in) gouache (A.S 10000)*

WEBER, M (?) ?
£1571 $3000   (16-Jul-92 SY.NY432/R) Young woman examining a string of pearls
           (64x25cm-25x10in) s.d.83

WEBER, Maria (19th C) German
£1272 $2200   (6-Sep-91 S.BM146/R) Woman with a parasol (56x28cm-22x11in) s.i.d.1883
           panel

WEBER, Max (1881-1961) American
£1776 $3250   (6-Jun-92 LAE.L116/R) Sailors and girls in bar-room (53x71cm-21x28in)
           s.d.39
£13714 $24000   (25-Sep-91 SY.NY111/R) Discourse (63x76cm-25x30in) s.d.1950
£1264   *$2300*   *(15-Dec-91 LIT.L232) Two women (18x13cm-7x5in) s. W/C pen cardboard*
£13187 $24000   (27-May-92 SY.NY99/R) Soloist at Wanamaker's (74x47cm-29x19in) s.d.1910
           gouache board three joined sheets

WEBER, Mili (1891-1978) Swiss
£684   *$1273*   *(19-Jun-92 ZOF.Z2130/R) S'Buebli mit sim Fruchtli (13x12cm-5x5in) mono.*
           i.verso W/C (S.FR 1800)

WEBER, Otis S (19th C) American
£4034 $7100   (9-Apr-92 FA.PH813/R) Paddlewheeler J. Putnam Bradlee (66x107cm-26x42in)
           s.

WEBER, Otto (1832-1888) German
£1573 $2691   (18-Mar-92 N.M681/R) Figures collecting beechnuts and cattle grazing
(43x66cm-17x26in) s. (DM 4500)
£1600 $2976   (16-Jun-92 SWS306/R) Peasants with cattle on the campagna
(37x73cm-15x29in) s.

WEBER, Paul (1823-1916) German
£893 $1555   (19-Sep-91 N.M2837) Young ox (29x19cm-11x7in) s.d.1876 i.verso board
(DM 2600)
£904 $1700   (18-Dec-91 SY.NY45/R) Rural river landscape (35x43cm-14x17in) s.
£941 $1712   (12-Dec-91 L.K722) Shepherd and flock in southern mountain landscape
(40x80cm-16x31in) s. (DM 2700)
£979 $1674   (18-Mar-92 N.M682/R) Wooded landscape with farmhouses (41x65cm-16x26in)
st.sig. (DM 2800)
£1399 $2490   (26-Nov-91 KF.M274/R) Willow trees by stream (16x25cm-6x10in) st.sig.
board (DM 4000)
£1404 $2400   (13-Mar-92 FN.S3006) Wooded Alpine lake landscape with figures in boat
(21x29cm-8x11in) s. canvas on board (DM 4000)
£4444 $8044   (19-May-92 GF.L2118/R) Pond landscape in evening glow (58x94cm-23x37in)
s. (S.FR 12000)
£5233 $9000   (10-Oct-91 FA.PH726/R) Forest stream (137x178cm-54x70in) s.d.1859
£6173 $10988   (28-Apr-92 RAS.K319) Landscape from Chiemsee in Bayern (40x34cm-16x13in)
s.d.1869 (D.KR 70000)
£6969 $12683   (11-Dec-91 N.M653/R) Alpine landscape with shepherds feeding goats
(70x113cm-28x44in) s.i.d.1872 (DM 20000)

WEBER, Rudolf (1872-?) Austrian
£989 $1730   (19-Feb-92 D.V92/R) Houses by canal (70x100cm-28x39in) s. (A.S 20000)
£1097 $1963   (15-Jan-92 D.V73/R) Alpine pasture with view of Dachstein
(85x120cm-33x47in) s.d.1902 (A.S 22000)
£3460 $6055   (20-Feb-92 D.V458/R) Sailing boats at jetty (90x128cm-35x50in) s.d.1899
i.verso (A.S 70000)
£3476 $6187   (28-Nov-91 D.V15/R) Lower Austrian landscape (76x96cm-30x38in) s.d.1900
(A.S 70000)
*£782 $1344   (10-Oct-91 D.V271/R) Landscape with hillside castle (62x48cm-24x19in)
s.d.1905 mixed media (A.S 16000)*

WEBER, Sarah S Stilwell (1878-1939) American
£2639 $4750   (22-Nov-91 S.BM156/R) Lady with leopards (102x76cm-40x30in) s.

WEBER, Theodore (1838-1907) French
£632 $1137   (19-Nov-91 RAS.K387) Vessels off Dover (32x50cm-13x20in) s. (D.KR 7000)
£650 $1183   (10-Dec-91 SWS138/R) The rescue (59x90cm-23x35in) s.
£684 $1239   (3-Dec-91 C.A376) Marine (29x20cm-11x8in) s. (B.FR 40000)
£1300 $2262   (12-Sep-91 CSK179/R) Shipping in swell off jetty (33x51cm-13x20in) s.
£1900 $3363   (13-Feb-92 CSK134/R) Fishing boats returning home (75x62cm-30x24in) s.
s.i.indist.stretcher
£2088 $3800   (26-May-92 CE.NY59/R) Entering rough seas (55x86cm-22x34in) s.
£2300 $4163   (20-May-92 S218/R) Unloading the catch (86x134cm-34x53in) s.
£2400 $4104   (17-Mar-92 PH148/R) Shipping off St Ives (57x86cm-22x34in) s.
£2679 $4500   (1-Sep-91 PO.BA3) Costa con botes (31x54cm-12x21in) s.
£2794 $4750   (25-Oct-91 S.W2788) Fishing boat on rough seas (86x58cm-34x23in) s.

WEBER, Werner (1892-?) Swiss
£1020 $1733   (23-Oct-91 GD.B790/R) La Cartuja de Valldemosa, Mallorca
(63x50cm-25x20in) s.d.27 i.verso panel (S.FR 2600)

WEBER, Willy (1895-1959) German
£582 $1001   (11-Oct-91 AW.H3219) Hay harvest on the Krautinsel, Chiemsee
(24x29cm-9x11in) board (DM 1700)

WEBERG, Wilhelm (1910-) Scandinavian
£918 $1661   (19-May-92 AB.S5340/R) View from the artist's studio, Sodermalm,
Stockholm (56x67cm-22x26in) s. (S.KR 9700)
£1727 $3127   (3-Dec-91 AB.S5170/R) Spring (67x100cm-26x39in) s. (S.KR 18000)

WEBSTER (?) British
*£600 $1110   (9-Jun-92 RG2388) Interior scene with figures playing chess
(61x43cm-24x17in) s. W/C*

WEBSTER, C (19th C) British
£2200 $3982   (20-May-92 S225/R) Fishermen in the mist (61x107cm-24x42in) s.

WEBSTER, Charles (19th C) British
£980 $1646   (15-Aug-91 B334) Moonlit river scene (61x107cm-24x42in) s.i.verso

WEBSTER, E Ambrose (1869-1935) American
£3161 $5500   (15-Sep-91 JRB.C143/R) Volunteer firemen - Provincetown Towers
(102x163cm-40x64in) s.d.32
£4023 $7000   (15-Sep-91 JRB.C142/R) Rocks - Bermuda (76x102cm-30x40in) s.d.16

WEBSTER, George (19th C) British
£4000 $7640   (17-Jul-92 C115/R) Dutch fishing boats and English man-o-war at mouth of
river estuary (32x41cm-13x16in) s.
£4300 $7740   (9-Jan-92 B314/R) Vessels off the Dutch coast (63x76cm-25x30in) s.

WEBSTER, Thomas (1800-1886) British
£984 $1800   (3-Jun-92 D.NY98) Truant (53x102cm-21x40in) mono.d.1872
£1500 $2580   (4-Mar-92 S111/R) Violet seller (42x24cm-17x9in) s.d.1844 panel arched
                    top
£1963 $3750   (3-Jul-92 S.W3129/R) Disruption outside school room (53x102cm-21x40in)
                    s.d.1872

WEBSTER, Thomas (circle) (1800-1886) British
£900 $1647   (15-May-92 TE405) Cottage interior (28x38cm-11x15in) bears sig.d.

WEBSTER, Walter Ernest (1878-1959) British
£850 $1488   (27-Feb-92 L101/R) Fashions (56x69cm-22x27in) i.verso
£1400 $2520   (20-Nov-91 B22/R) Portrait of young lady seated by toys (61x51cm-24x20in)
                    s.
£1500 $2745   (4-Jun-92 CSK113/R) Cherie and Wong (56x68cm-22x27in)
£560   *$1002*   *(11-Nov-91 PH208/R) The pink fan (30x41cm-12x16in) s. W/C*
£1800   *$3240*   *(27-Jan-92 PH117) Pensive (55x40cm-22x16in) s. W/C*

WECHLEN, Hans van (1537-?) Flemish
£75000 $131250   (1-Apr-92 S57/R) Wedding scene (38x53cm-15x21in) mono. panel

WECKBRODT, Ferdinand (1838-1902) Austrian
£631   *$1123*   *(29-Apr-92 D.V659/R) Brucke im Wiental (26x31cm-10x12in) s. W/C*
                    (A.S 13000)

WECKMAN, Jan Kenneth (1946-) Finnish
£1896   *$3338*   *(12-Apr-92 HOR.H251) Composition (193x140cm-76x55in) s. mixed media*
                    (F.M 15000)

WEDDIGE, Carl (1815-1862) Dutch
£2599 $4627   (30-Oct-91 CH.AM222/R) Candle lit interior with mother and child in
                    cradle by fireside (51x48cm-20x19in) s.d.1857 panel (D.FL 8500)

WEDEL, Nils (1897-1967) Swedish
£1248   *$2258*   *(3-Dec-91 AB.S5172/R) Composition with blue back-ground (35x42cm-14x17in)*
                    s. gouache (S.KR 13000)

WEDELIN, Erik (1850-1881) Swedish
£2767 $4926   (28-Nov-91 BU.S40/R) Autumn landscape (47x68cm-19x27in) s.d.1875
                    (S.KR 29000)

WEDER, Jakob (1906-) ?
£1961 $3510   (15-Nov-91 GK.Z5782/R) Composition after choral by J.S.Bach
                    (100x70cm-39x28in) i. (S.FR 5000)

WEDIG, Gotthardt de (1583-1641) German
£27624 $50000   (22-May-92 SY.NY104/R) Still life with fruit, bread, wine with plates,
                    glasses and jug on table (44x62cm-17x24in) panel

WEEDON, Augustus Walford (1838-1908) British
£620   *$1116*   *(27-Jan-92 PH33) Resting from harvest (35x51cm-14x20in) s. W/C over*
                    pencil

WEEDON, Fiona (1954-) British
£750 $1373   (3-Feb-92 B7/R) Contemplation of night (168x168cm-66x66in) init.
£850 $1556   (3-Feb-92 B8) Blooms in winter (168x168cm-66x66in) s.

WEEKES, Henry (jnr) (fl.1880's) British
£900 $1548   (15-Oct-91 GA149) Spaniel and retriever looking over bag of dead game
                    (61x91cm-24x36in) s.d.1873
£2000 $3760   (19-Dec-91 C155/R) Gundogs with day's bag (61x91cm-24x36in)
                    s.d.indist.1873

WEEKES, Herbert William see WEEKES, William

WEEKES, William (fl.1864-1904) British
£1200 $2136   (30-Oct-91 HUN1) Calf and swans (20x33cm-8x13in)
£1450 $2494   (8-Oct-91 PH154) Portrait of a terrier (34x27cm-13x11in) s.d.79 board
£1789 $3113   (13-Apr-92 SY.J253/R) Companions waiting (28x19cm-11x7in) s. panel
                    (SA.R 9000)
£1955 $3500   (13-Nov-91 B.SF2210/R) Love's call. Guilty (29x20cm-11x8in) s. panel pair
£2400 $4296   (5-May-92 SWS429/R) Our member of the Commons (26x36cm-10x14in) s. board
£3600 $6192   (4-Mar-92 S95/R) Farmyard gossip (43x33cm-17x13in) s.
£3800 $6840   (19-Nov-91 PH118/R) Pigs resting in straw (20x29cm-8x11in) s. panel
£6000 $11280   (19-Dec-91 C149/R) The disputed gate (51x76cm-20x30in) s.

WEEKS, Edwin Lord (1849-1903) American
£556 $1000   (22-Nov-91 S.BM37/R) Moor at prayer (41x30cm-16x12in) with i.verso
£585 $1000   (12-Mar-92 MFA.C216) Arabian horse (51x56cm-20x22in) s.
£667 $1200   (22-Nov-91 S.BM33/R) Study of man in grey - young man on horseback
                    (43x28cm-17x11in) num.153 verso canvasboard
£4360 $7500   (17-Oct-91 SY.NY145/R) Fording stream (51x76cm-20x30in) s.
£5278 $9500   (22-Nov-91 S.BM35/R) Boy with monkeys (46x56cm-18x22in) s.i. num.58 verso

WEEKS, John (?) New Zealander?
£1015 $1817   (6-May-92 DS.W27/R) Fertassa, Morocco (18x23cm-7x9in) s. pastel
        (NZ.D 3400)

WEELE, Herman Johannes van der (1852-1930) Dutch
£612 $1083   (5-Nov-91 SY.AM444) Farmer ploughing (68x89cm-27x35in) s. (D.FL 2000)
£1702 $3250   (16-Jul-92 SY.NY479/R) Herding sheep along s stream (66x90cm-26x35in) s.

WEENIX (school) (17/18th C) Dutch
£2992 $5445   (25-May-92 ARC.P59) Natures mortes au gibier (73x60cm-29x24in) pair
        (F.FR 29500)

WEENIX, Jan (style) (1640-1719) Dutch
£5000 $8900   (1-Nov-91 S371/R) Still life of game in extensive landscape
        (100x127cm-39x50in)

WEENIX, Jan Baptist (1621-1663) Dutch
£9302 $16000   (10-Oct-91 SY.NY123/R) Harbour scene with a merchant and slaves below a
        statue of Neptune (107x140cm-42x55in) s.
£9774 $17887   (4-Jun-92 SY.Z557/R) Partridge hanging (50x39cm-20x15in) s. (S.FR 26000)
£30769 $52615   (18-Mar-92 N.M474/R) Black servant boy presenting fruit to lady with dog
        (142x120cm-56x47in) s. i.stretcher (DM 88000)

WEENIX, Jan Baptist (attrib) (1621-1663) Dutch
£1031 $1887   (2-Jun-92 FN.S2797/R) Peasant woman and child with sheep before ruin in
        wooded river landscape (27x38cm-11x15in) panel (DM 3000)
£4200 $7560   (21-Nov-91 C36/R) Still life of dead game with hare, partridge and wader
        on stone ledge (77x66cm-30x26in) s.d.1648

WEENIX, Jan Baptist (style) (1621-1663) Dutch
£2569 $4625   (19-Nov-91 GS.B3680/R) Hunting still life in landscape (76x93cm-30x37in)
        (S.FR 6500)

WEENIX, Jan Baptist and HAAGEN, Joris van der (17th C) Dutch
£11856 $20510   (26-Mar-92 PIC.P7/R) Scene de chasse a courre dans une foret
        (91x91cm-36x36in) panel (F.FR 115000)

WEERT, Anna de (1867-1950) Belgian
£1000 $1720   (12-Oct-91 KV.L89) View from the window (31x24cm-12x9in) mono.
        (B.FR 60000)
£1933 $3460   (17-Nov-91 FB.P208) Le village (22x41cm-9x16in) s.d.Octobre 1919verso
        (F.FR 19000)
£1987 $3596   (23-May-92 KV.L115/R) De kraanlei te Gent (40x50cm-16x20in) s.d.1910
        (B.FR 120000)
£2667 $4587   (12-Oct-91 KV.L87) View of Aix les Bains (34x41cm-13x16in) s.verso board
        (B.FR 160000)
£7333 $12613   (12-Oct-91 KV.L380/R) Country path in June (34x50cm-13x20in) s.d.1905
        (B.FR 440000)
£1105 $1889   (21-Mar-92 KV.L106) Sakramentsdag (88x70cm-35x28in) s.d.1903 chk pastel
        (B.FR 65000)

WEGENER, Gerda (1885-1940) Danish
£623 $1084   (17-Sep-91 RAS.K708) Portrait of lady (50x36cm-20x14in) s.d.1925
        i.d.versp cardboard (D.KR 7000)
£1063 $1934   (25-May-92 RAS.K146/R) Two graces with baskets of flowers
        (73x59cm-29x23in) s.d.1928 (D.KR 12000)
£4606 $8199   (27-Nov-91 AT.P204/R) La parisienne (157x80cm-62x31in) s. i.d.1921verso
        (F.FR 45000)
£705 $1198   (8-Aug-91 RAS.V999/R) Venetian canal view with carnival figures and
        gondola (35x28cm-14x11in) s.d.1920 W/C (D.KR 8000)
£728 $1296   (28-Apr-92 D.V70/R) La Fuite du Sapajon (29x21cm-11x8in) s. pencil indian
        ink htd.white (A.S 15000)
£748 $1339   (5-May-92 ZEL.L1183/R) Portrait of young woman (73x47cm-29x19in) s.d.1911
        ochre (DM 2200)
£865 $1600   (12-Jun-92 SY.NY86/R) The bouquet (32x26cm-13x10in) s. W/C graphite
£903 $1543   (12-Mar-92 RAS.K582) Strand-Matinee (37x29cm-15x11in) s. i.verso Indian
        ink pencil W/C (D.KR 10000)
£1006 $1730   (13-Oct-91 SY.MO232/R) Nue dans le style fauve (34x17cm-13x7in) s. crayon
        (F.FR 10000)
£1068 $1858   (17-Sep-91 RAS.K707) Nude model seen from behind (77x36cm-30x14in)
        init.d.1922 W/C gouache (D.KR 12000)
£1230 $2213   (2-Feb-92 ZZ.F218/R) Elegantes sur le balcon (65x55cm-26x22in) s. W/C
        gouache chl. (F.FR 12000)
£1405 $2600   (12-Jun-92 SY.NY88/R) La Petite Modele (35x27cm-14x11in) s.d.1922 W/C
        pencil
£1490 $2651   (28-Nov-91 D.V124/R) Female nude and black boy with white cat
        (23x15cm-9x6in) s.i. mixed media (A.S 30000)
£3568 $6636   (19-Jun-92 ARC.P36/R) Florence, odalisques aux corbeilles de fruits
        (61x49cm-24x19in) s. W/C (F.FR 35000)
£5664 $9686   (18-Mar-92 ARC.P11/R) Elegante tenant une statuette d'Eros
        (90x71cm-35x28in) s. W/C gouache (F.FR 55000)
£5870 $10038   (18-Mar-92 ARC.P10/R) Elegante (90x71cm-35x28in) s.d.1928 W/C gouache
        (F.FR 57000)

WEGENER, M (?) ?
£987 $1776   (30-Jan-92 RAS.V688/R) View from Langlinie with figures walking
                        (53x79cm-21x31in) s. (D.KR 11000)

WEGER, Marie (1882-?) American
£578 $1000   (29-Mar-92 MY.F130/R) Phlox (64x48cm-25x19in) s. canvas on board

WEGMAN, William (1943-) American
£3073 $5500   (12-Nov-91 CE.NY166/R) Airplane (41x59cm-16x23in) s.verso
£4469 $8000   (14-Nov-91 SY.NY337/R) Travelling salesman on barren soil
                        (28x46cm-11x18in)
£514   *$900*   *(27-Feb-92 CE.NY198/R) Before after (22x28cm-9x11in) brush ink*
£670   *$1200*   *(9-May-92 CE.NY256/R) Oh, about 2.30 (22x28cm-9x11in) init.d.73verso*
                        graphite
£782   *$1400*   *(9-May-92 CE.NY254/R) No solicitors (21x23cm-8x9in) init.d.76verso W/C*
                        graphite
£800   *$1400*   *(27-Feb-92 CE.NY200/R) Right place wrong time. Wrong place wrong time*
                        (22x28cm-9x11in) init.d.74 verso graphite pair
£1117   *$2000*   *(9-May-92 CE.NY255/R) Two norsemen with weapons (34x27cm-13x11in) paper*
                        collage on photograph
£1371   *$2400*   *(27-Feb-92 CE.NY237/R) Neighbour's yard (89x61cm-35x24in) s.d.1987*
                        col.chk lithography

WEGMAYR, Sebastian (1776-1857) Austrian
£485   *$864*   *(29-Apr-92 D.V582/R) Bunch of flowers (23x18cm-9x7in) s.d.1828 W/C*
                        (A.S 10000)

WEGNER, Erich (1899-) German
£915   *$1657*   *(6-Dec-91 GB.B7235/R) Couple in cafe. Wooded hilly landscape*
                        (35x25cm-14x10in) s. W/C (DM 2600)

WEGUELIN, John Reinhard (1849-1927) British
£800   *$1480*   *(11-Jun-92 CSK26/R) Spring blossoms and youth (38x51cm-15x20in) s.d.1904*
                        W/C htd white
£1900   *$3572*   *(19-Dec-91 C15/R) A pastoral (37x54cm-15x21in) s.d.1905 s.i.verso pencil*
                        W/C htd white

WEHRINGER, Herbert (1926-) German
£483 $830   (16-Oct-91 KM.K1436) Peasant folk on the way to church, spring
                        (10x15cm-4x6in) s. panel (DM 1400)
£483 $830   (16-Oct-91 KM.K1437) River landscape with rowing boat and village beyond
                        (10x15cm-4x6in) s. panel (DM 1400)
£509 $916   (22-Nov-91 SA.A1822) Wooded landscape (8x12cm-3x5in) s. i.verso panel
                        (DM 1450)
£509 $916   (22-Nov-91 SA.A1596/R) Landscape with view of village, spring
                        (8x12cm-3x5in) s.i. i.verso panel (DM 1450)
£517 $890   (16-Oct-91 KM.K1438) Frozen river landscape with figures, evening
                        (10x15cm-4x6in) s. panel (DM 1500)
£632 $1137   (22-Nov-91 SA.A1766/R) Figures collecting brushwood in frozen moor
                        landscape (12x20cm-5x8in) s.i. i.verso panel (DM 1800)
£704 $1275   (3-Dec-91 FN.S2521/R) Bavarian landscape with village and Zugspitz range
                        beyond (37x46cm-15x18in) s.i. panel (DM 2000)
£737 $1326   (22-Nov-91 SA.A1630/R) Moor landscape in autumn (17x29cm-7x11in) s.i.
                        i.verso panel (DM 2100)
£962 $1674   (21-Sep-91 SA.A1939/R) Going hunting (23x39cm-9x15in) s.i. panel
                        (DM 2800)
£1154 $1996   (25-Mar-92 KM.K1511) Wooded landscape with pond (36x65cm-14x26in) s.
                        panel (DM 3300)

WEIBEL, Jakob Samuel (c1771-1846) Swiss
£1036   *$1875*   *(4-Dec-91 G.Z1287/R) Golattentor in Bern (27x39cm-11x15in) s. W/C*
                        (S.FR 2600)

WEICHMANN, Thomas (19th C) ?
£1048   *$1856*   *(4-Nov-91 SY.J220/R) Canal scene (68x54cm-27x21in) s.d.1894 (SA.R 5200)*

WEIDEL, Anton (fl.1838-1843) Austrian
£3739 $6692   (16-Jan-92 D.V85/R) Portrait of girl wearing white dress
                        (42x33cm-17x13in) s.d.1847 panel (A.S 75000)

WEIDEMANN, Friedrich Wilhelm (1668-1750) German
£7394 $13384   (6-Dec-91 GB.B5635/R) Friedrich Wilhelm I, King of Prussia
                        (62x55cm-24x22in) (DM 21000)

WEIDEMANN, Jakob (1923-) Norwegian
£570 $1061   (15-Jun-92 B.O196/R) Winter landscape (27x35cm-11x14in) s.d.42 panel
                        (N.KR 6500)
£753 $1370   (14-Dec-91 BU.O66/R) Composition (35x50cm-14x20in) s.i.d.67 paper
                        (N.KR 8500)
£931 $1685   (3-Dec-91 AB.S5174/R) Coastal town (22x33cm-9x13in) s.d.45 panel
                        (S.KR 9700)
£1317 $2265   (7-Oct-91 B.O150/R) Composition (35x27cm-14x11in) s. panel (N.KR 15000)
£1404 $2611   (18-Jun-92 GWP.O112/R) Composition (43x61cm-17x24in) s.d.68 paper
                        (N.KR 16000)

WEIDEMANN, Jakob (1923-) Norwegian-cont.
£2456	$4568	(15-Jun-92 B.O189/R) Composition - self portrait (45x37cm-18x15in) s.d.72 paper on panel (N.KR 28000)
£2634	$4530	(7-Oct-91 B.O148/R) Composition (54x65cm-21x26in) s. panel (N.KR 30000)
£2639	$4644	(7-Apr-92 UL.T239/R) Landscape 1955 (50x60cm-20x24in) (N.KR 30000)
£3387	$5859	(23-Mar-92 B.O145/R) Winter's day 1956 (61x70cm-24x28in) s.d.56 (N.KR 38000)
£3509	$6526	(15-Jun-92 B.O190/R) Crocus (50x40cm-20x16in) i.d.84verso (N.KR 40000)
£4214	$7248	(7-Oct-91 B.O147/R) Any luck tonight.. (81x65cm-32x26in) s.d.42 panel (N.KR 48000)
£7018	$13053	(18-Jun-92 GWP.O111/R) Sunset over the sea (200x160cm-79x63in) s.d.66 s.i.verso (N.KR 80000)
£8795	$15479	(7-Apr-92 UL.T240/R) The student 1952 (100x81cm-39x32in) (N.KR 100000)
£9804	$16961	(23-Mar-92 B.O144/R) L'Ancolie (120x100cm-47x39in) s.d.75verso (N.KR 110000)
£19737	$36711	(15-Jun-92 B.O187/R) Impression on nature (160x160cm-63x63in) s.d.85 (N.KR 225000)

WEIDINGER, Franz Xaver (1890-1972) Austrian
£878	$1520	(3-Oct-91 D.V241/R) Winter landscape (25x33cm-10x13in) board (A.S 18000)
£1068	$1901	(28-Apr-92 D.V233/R) View of village (41x50cm-16x20in) mono board (A.S 22000)
£442	$839	(25-Jun-92 D.V606) Farmhouse by the edge of the wood (34x47cm-13x19in) s. W/C (A.S 9000)
£736	$1398	(25-Jun-92 D.V605) Attersee with Schafberg (26x39cm-10x15in) s.i.verso W/C (A.S 15000)

WEIDNER, Willem Frederik (1817-1850) Dutch
£1376	$2436	(5-Nov-91 SY.AM395) Still life with flowers on ledge (33x24cm-13x9in) s.d.1841 panel (D.FL 4500)

WEIE, Edvard (1879-1943) Danish
£797	$1451	(25-May-92 RAS.K187) Still life of pots, jar and fruit (35x41cm-14x16in) init. (D.KR 9000)
£1499	$2668	(27-Apr-92 BU.K77/R) Nude study (61x42cm-24x17in) init. (D.KR 17000)
£1783	$3066	(16-Oct-91 KH.K107/R) Interior with the artist Marius Hammann by lamplight (132x105cm-52x41in) init. (D.KR 20000)
£2906	$5086	(1-Apr-92 KH.K262/R) At sunrise, Christianso ca.1917-18 (42x52cm-17x20in) (D.KR 32000)
£4011	$6898	(16-Oct-91 KH.K96/R) Coastal landscape, Bornholm (48x62cm-19x24in) (D.KR 45000)
£9083	$15895	(1-Apr-92 KH.K210/R) Lady in garden (97x102cm-38x40in) init. (D.KR 100000)
£20890	$36558	(1-Apr-92 KH.K76/R) Langelinie picture (64x81cm-25x32in) (D.KR 230000)
£22624	$40950	(4-Dec-91 KH.K27/R) Nature morte (73x73cm-29x29in) (D.KR 250000)

WEIGHT, Carel (1908-) British
£1200	$2136	(28-Apr-92 RG2559) He's seen the demon rider (41x48cm-16x19in) s.
£1200	$2184	(12-Dec-91 CSK137) Box on a spring morning (35x45cm-14x18in)
£1400	$2436	(19-Sep-91 B60) Figures walking by river (63x76cm-25x30in)
£1800	$3294	(4-Jun-92 CSK148/R) Road up - tea-break (22x28cm-9x11in) s. canvasboard
£1800	$3186	(7-Nov-91 C97/R) A dispute in the shrubbery (16x21cm-6x8in) s. board
£2100	$3612	(6-Mar-92 C132/R) Spencer Park (28x35cm-11x14in) s. s.i.d.1987verso board
£2500	$4425	(7-Nov-91 C100/R) Terpiscorah song and dance (53x38cm-21x15in) board squared
£2600	$4732	(12-Dec-91 CSK111/R) Hydrangea (77x65cm-30x26in)
£2800	$5124	(5-Jun-92 C83/R) Windermere (24x40cm-9x16in) board
£3000	$5490	(14-May-92 C131/R) Sunday afternoon (51x61cm-20x24in) s. board
£4500	$8235	(5-Jun-92 C99/R) Three women (122x123cm-48x48in) s.
£4500	$8235	(13-May-92 S68/R) The bagsnatcher (122x122cm-48x48in) s. board
£4800	$8448	(6-Apr-92 WW33/R) Irish girl (61x51cm-24x20in)
£6000	$10440	(19-Sep-91 B61/R) Norfolk nativity (71x91cm-28x36in)
£6200	$11346	(5-Jun-92 C85/R) Nightfall (122x94cm-48x37in) s.i.verso board
£6500	$11310	(19-Sep-91 B62/R) Nursery piece (63x68cm-25x27in)
£8000	$13760	(6-Mar-92 C131/R) Pygmalion (71x91cm-28x36in) s.i.frame
£9000	$16470	(13-May-92 S71/R) Walham Green, Evening (61x91cm-24x36in) s. s.i.verso
£11000	$19800	(20-Nov-91 S197/R) For children, the witches are here (212x113cm-83x44in) s.
£15000	$26550	(7-Nov-91 C96/R) The Thames at Hammersmith (63x76cm-25x30in) s.i.verso

WEIGHT, H A (19th C) British
£1050	$1900	(5-Dec-91 GRO.B464/R) Coriander (43x53cm-17x21in) s.d.84

WEILAND, James G (1872-?) American
£536	$900	(28-Aug-91 MFA.C55 a) Woman holding green parasol (61x51cm-24x20in) s.
£595	$1000	(28-Aug-91 MFA.C55 c/R) Woman in white (61x51cm-24x20in) s.
£804	$1350	(28-Aug-91 MFA.C55 b/R) Woman in white by water (61x51cm-24x20in) s. board

WEILAND, Johannes (1856-1909) Dutch
£621	$1106	(26-Nov-91 VN.R130/R) Man in rowing boat on a canal before a house (42x27cm-17x11in) s. panel (D.FL 2000)
£714	$1236	(24-Mar-92 VN.R102/R) Still life of fruit on tin plate (34x47cm-13x19in) s. (D.FL 2300)

WEILAND, Johannes (1856-1909) Dutch-cont.
£917 $1624   (5-Nov-91 SY.AM194) Interior with woman mending (56x43cm-22x17in) s.
                     (D.FL 3000)
£1529 $2706   (5-Nov-91 SY.AM52/R) Old woman by fire (54x38cm-21x15in) s. (D.FL 5000)
£2600 $4836   (17-Jun-92 S296/R) Still life with flowers (46x33cm-18x13in) s. canvas on
                     panel

WEILER, Max (1910-) Austrian
£485 $864   (28-Apr-92 D.V340) The lighthouse of Kampen (9x14cm-4x6in)
                     mono.indis.i.d. W/C chk (A.S 10000)

WEINBERGER, Friedrich (19th C) German?
£687 $1258   (2-Jun-92 FN.S2804/R) View of Schloss Lierheim (27x37cm-11x15in) s.d.1836
                     W/C (DM 2000)

WEINDORF, Arthur (1885-?) American
£636 $1100   (6-Sep-91 S.BM317/R) Jazz (64x109cm-25x43in) s.d.1926 board

WEINER, Lawrence (1940-) American
£8380 $15000   (13-Nov-91 SY.NY112/R) One steel I beam placed up on a boundary and
                     allowed to rest (22x32cm-9x13in) s.i. felt tip marker

WEINGART, Joachim (1895-1942) Polish
£1616 $2861   (22-Apr-92 ZZ.F152 b) Femme au buste nu (73x60cm-29x24in) s. (F.FR 16000)
£663 $1174   (12-Feb-92 GL.P105) Coupe de fruits et banjo (64x49cm-25x19in) s. gouache
                     board (F.FR 6500)

WEINSTEIN, Debora (1956-) Canadian
£412 $704   (21-Mar-92 AT.P80/R) Sans titre (100x100cm-39x39in) s.d.1990verso mixed
                     media (F.FR 4000)

WEIR, Harrison William (1824-1906) British
£2600 $4628   (27-Nov-91 B155/R) Grouse on moorland. Pointer and setter
                     (33x49cm-13x19in) s.d.1865 W/C bodycol two

WEIR, J Alden (1852-1919) American
£1160 $2100   (4-Dec-91 D.NY7) View of West Point, New York (10x20cm-4x8in) s.i.d.1871
                     s.i.verso board
£16592 $29700   (14-Nov-91 GRO.B116/R) Studio tea (114x81cm-45x32in) s.d.1888 canvas on
                     masonite
£1136 $2000   (12-Apr-92 LIT.L223) Roses (23x33cm-9x13in) s. W/C graphite

WEIROTTER, Franz Edmund (1730-1771) Austrian
£1490 $2548   (18-Mar-92 D.V172/R) Fire raging in river landscape at night
                     (17x25cm-7x10in) panel (A.S 30000)

WEIROTTER, Franz Edmund (circle) (1730-1771) Austrian
£2484 $4247   (18-Mar-92 D.V173/R) Fire raging in landscape at night (39x57cm-15x22in)
                     panel (A.S 50000)

WEIS, John Ellsworth (1892-?) American
£898 $1500   (20-Aug-91 RB.HY40/R) Village street scene 1933 (64x76cm-25x30in) s.d.33

WEISBUCH, Claude (1927-) French
£3502 $5988   (18-Mar-92 LT.P54/R) Sur la Piste (54x65cm-21x26in) s. (F.FR 34000)
£4000 $7000   (27-Feb-92 CE.NY64/R) Femme nue (129x96cm-51x38in) s.
£4286 $7500   (27-Feb-92 CE.NY85/R) La chute du cheval (150x150cm-59x59in) s.
£4494 $7865   (26-Feb-92 CK.P87/R) Cavalier (50x61cm-20x24in) s. acrylic (F.FR 44000)

WEISE, Alexander (1883-?) Russian
£915 $1657   (3-Dec-91 FN.S2522) Snow covered Kochelsee landscape with village
                     (28x41cm-11x16in) s. board (DM 2600)

WEISE, Karl (?) ?
£484 $813   (27-Aug-91 RAS.K537) Harem woman seated on steps (80x65cm-31x26in) s.
                     panel (D.KR 5500)
£800 $1384   (3-Oct-91 CSK213) In the library (76x66cm-30x26in) s.

WEISER, Joseph Emanuel (1847-1911) German
£1031 $1794   (18-Sep-91 N.M745/R) Scientist in laboratory (30x22cm-12x9in) s. panel
                     (DM 3000)

WEISGERBER, Carl (19th C) German
£1024 $1863   (27-May-92 PH.DU187/R) In the circus tent (40x50cm-16x20in) s. (DM 3000)

WEISMANN, Jacques (1878-?) French
£816 $1452   (28-Apr-92 DUR.M986/R) Mujer con abanico (92x73cm-36x29in) s.
                     (S.P 150000)

WEISS, B (?) ?
£909 $1555   (19-Mar-92 N.M2858/R) Threemaster in stormy seas (75x96cm-30x38in)
                     s.d.1843 panel (DM 2600)

WEISS, Bartholomaus Ignaz (c.1740-1814) German
£1027 $1767   (11-Oct-91 AW.H1019/R) *St John the Evangelist and St John the Baptist.*
     The Damned (19x15cm-7x6in) pen wash over ochre double-sided (DM 3000)

WEISS, Johann Baptist (1812-1879) German
£756 $1315   (17-Sep-91 FN.S2606) Shipping in choppy sea with thunderstorm rising
     (41x65cm-16x26in) s. (DM 2200)
£1117 $2000   (13-Nov-91 B.SF2324/R) Shipping in rough waters (60x41cm-24x16in) s.
     panel

WEISS, Johannes (1810-?) Swiss
£1259 $2279   (19-May-92 GF.L2597/R) Portrait of Oberstleutnant von Waldkirch
     (82x64cm-32x25in) s.i.d.1838verso (S.FR 3400)

WEISS, Jose (1859-?) British
£596 $1091   (1-Jun-92 W.T1339/R) On the River Arun, Sussex (36x51cm-14x20in) s.
     (C.D 1300)
£600 $1050   (19-Feb-92 B50/R) Summer landscape (81x122cm-32x48in) s.
£600 $1056   (8-Apr-92 CSK288) Wooded river landscape at sunset (61x91cm-24x36in) s.
£688 $1259   (1-Jun-92 W.T1338/R) The elms in the artist's garden (36x51cm-14x20in) s.
     (C.D 1500)
£860 $1565   (11-Dec-91 PHL125) Cattle by a river in a sunlit wooded landscape
     (61x91cm-24x36in) s.
£872 $1500   (15-Oct-91 CE.NY67/R) A riverbank (25x46cm-10x18in) s. panel
£917 $1679   (1-Jun-92 W.T1337/R) Sussex lane (50x75cm-20x30in) s. (C.D 2000)
£1105 $2100   (22-Jun-92 SG.M644) Summer landscape (36x51cm-14x20in) s.
£1200 $2124   (13-Feb-92 CSK99) Wooded river landscape with angler in punt
     (41x61cm-16x24in) s.
£2424 $4411   (27-May-92 D.V537/R) River landscape, spring (61x92cm-24x36in) s.
     (A.S 50000)

WEISS, Paul (1888-?) Swiss
£1301 $2238   (11-Oct-91 AW.H3224/R) Lady seen from behind seated on chair in park
     (74x56cm-29x22in) s. board (DM 3800)

WEISS, Peter (1916-) Swedish?
£759 $1389   (13-May-92 BU.S213/R) Red cottage (30x39cm-12x15in) s. cardboard
     (S.KR 8000)

WEISS, Rudolf Johann (1846-?) Swiss
£1486 $2600   (18-Feb-92 CE.NY281/R) Arab marketplace (9x13cm-4x5in) s. panel
£29070 $50000   (16-Oct-91 CH.NY99/R) Nubian guard (177x96cm-70x38in) s.

WEISS, Rudolph (1869-?) Czechoslovakian
£620 $1104   (28-Nov-91 CSK153) Young beauty (46x38cm-18x15in) s.

WEISS, Wojciech (1875-1950) Polish
£1047 $1811   (8-Sep-91 REM.W43) Girl with sickle (45x32cm-18x13in) s. board
     (P.Z 20000000)
£1294 $2433   (21-Dec-91 PSA.W22) Portrait of Fela (76x60cm-30x24in) s. (P.Z 25000000)
£1308 $2249   (13-Oct-91 REM.W32) After harvesting (50x65cm-20x26in) s. (P.Z 25000000)
£1497 $2679   (17-Nov-91 REM.W30) Nude (34x47cm-13x19in) s. (P.Z 29000000)
£1570 $2716   (8-Sep-91 REM.W42) View of the Barbican and Florian Gate from artist's
     window (47x62cm-19x24in) s. board (P.Z 30000000)

WEISSBERG, Leon (1893-?) Polish
£924 $1663   (19-Nov-91 FB.P96/R) Nature morte (46x55cm-18x22in) s. (F.FR 9000)
£1526 $2792   (17-May-92 GL.P223/R) Bouquet (35x27cm-14x11in) s. board on canvas
     (F.FR 15000)

WEISSBORT, George (20th C) ?
£1300 $2223   (1-Aug-91 CSK28) Still life with grapes and pewter tankard on draped
     table (49x59cm-19x23in) s.d.1982 masonite

WEISSENBRUCH (19th C) Dutch
£2732 $5000   (16-May-92 HG.C147) Interior with woman knitting (20x36cm-8x14in) s.
     panel

WEISSENBRUCH, Hendrik Johannes see WEISSENBRUCH, Jan Hendrik

WEISSENBRUCH, Jan (1822-1880) Dutch
£2446 $4355   (30-Oct-91 CH.AM322 a) *River landscape with sailors in moored vessels by*
     farmhouse (26x35cm-10x14in) s.d.66 pen ink W/C htd.white (D.FL 8000)
£3939 $6973   (22-Apr-92 CH.AM338/R) *Elegant figures strolling on a quay, Dordrecht*
     (35x52cm-14x20in) s. ink W/C (D.FL 13000)

WEISSENBRUCH, Jan Hendrik (1824-1903) Dutch
£909 $1609   (22-Apr-92 CH.AM40/R) Birches (40x28cm-16x11in) s. canvas laid down on
     panel (D.FL 3000)
£2324 $4044   (14-Apr-92 SY.AM287/R) Polder landscape with sailing boats, village
     beyond (23x34cm-9x13in) s. (D.FL 7600)
£2981 $5307   (26-Nov-91 VN.R132) Wooded landscape (20x32cm-8x13in) s. board
     (D.FL 9600)
£3400 $5814   (17-Mar-92 PH38/R) Cottage in river landscape (34x50cm-13x20in) s.d.90
     paper on canvas

WEISSENBRUCH, Jan Hendrik (1824-1903) Dutch-cont.

£4006	$7250	(21-May-92 GRO.B28/R) Near Hilversum (25x41cm-10x16in) s. canvas on panel
£4281	$7621	(30-Oct-91 CH.AM212 b) Polder landscape (39x29cm-15x11in) s. panel (D.FL 14000)
£41284	$73073	(5-Nov-91 SY.AM111/R) Gezicht op de benoordenhoutseweg, Hague (41x75cm-16x30in) s. (D.FL 135000)
£1376	$2450	(30-Oct-91 CH.AM304/R) River landscape with farmers in rowing boat (26x38cm-10x15in) s. pencil W/C htd.white (D.FL 4500)
£1677	$2985	(26-Nov-91 VN.R133) Sailing ship and windmill in polder landscape (16x14cm-6x6in) s. W/C (D.FL 5400)
£3364	$5988	(30-Oct-91 CH.AM354/R) Farmhouse in river landscape (22x30cm-9x12in) s. W/C (D.FL 11000)
£6468	$11512	(25-Nov-91 W.T1832/R) Canalside village with figures on the tow path (33x49cm-13x19in) s. W/C (C.D 13000)
£8257	$14367	(14-Apr-92 SY.AM33/R) Polder landscape with peasant pushing rowing boat (34x45cm-13x18in) s. W/C (D.FL 27000)

WEISSENBRUCH, Willem (1864-1941) Dutch

£703	$1245	(5-Nov-91 SY.AM125) Polder landscape with farm (33x49cm-13x19in) s. (D.FL 2300)
£1034	$1799	(13-Apr-92 SY.J264/R) House on canal (20x15cm-8x6in) s. panel (SA.R 5200)
£1100	$1913	(17-Sep-91 FN.S2607/R) Dutch river landscape with drawbridge and windmills (28x42cm-11x17in) s. (DM 3200)
£741	$1296	(18-Feb-92 CH.AM201/R) Cows in farm yard (35x45cm-14x18in) s. blk.chk.W/C htd.white (D.FL 2400)

WEISSENKIRCHNER, Hans Adam (1646-1695) Austrian

£559	$996	(26-Nov-91 KF.M181) Allegorical death bed scene (20x27cm-8x11in) pen wash over chk (DM 1600)

WEISSER, Charles Louis Auguste (1864-?) French

£800	$1448	(21-May-92 CSK101) Milking time (114x161cm-45x63in) s.

WEIXLBAUM, Michel (style) (1790-1824) Austrian

£751	$1359	(22-May-92 L.K1113) Portrait of Joseph Graf von Berlichingen (6x5cm-2x2in) min. oval (DM 2200)

WELCH, Denton (1915-1948) British

£1500	$2595	(2-Oct-91 S179/R) Flower-head. Male nude at the hop garden, Platt (51x32cm-20x13in) board double-sided
£1700	$2941	(2-Oct-91 S178/R) Fox-gloves, teazels, dahlias and daisies in greek vase (79x55cm-31x22in) s. board
£3000	$5190	(2-Oct-91 S182/R) Dog in garden. Factory (72x61cm-28x24in) board double-sided

WELCH, Mabel R (20th C) American

£565	$1000	(10-Nov-91 LIT.L109) Midsummer's morning (51x61cm-20x24in) s.

WELCH, Thaddeus (1844-1919) American

£500	$950	(23-Jun-92 MOR.P11) Cows grazing in landscape (28x43cm-11x17in) s. board
£2105	$4000	(24-Jun-92 B.SF6271/R) Tending cows (46x75cm-18x30in) s.d.1881
£3947	$7500	(24-Jun-92 B.SF6272/R) Grazing by sea (51x91cm-20x36in) s.d.94

WELLER, Theodor Leopold (1802-1880) German

£15200	$25992	(20-Mar-92 C61/R) The festival (82x67cm-32x26in) s.d.1845
£986	$1785	(6-Dec-91 GB.B6062/R) Nude boy seated (54x37cm-21x15in) pencil wash (DM 2800)

WELLIVER, Neil (1929-) American

£14857	$26000	(27-Feb-92 CE.NY178/R) Reflection (183x183cm-72x72in) s.

WELLS, F (?) ?

£1100	$1848	(26-Aug-91 S861/R) Setters in the Highlands (41x61cm-16x24in) s. pair

WELLS, George (fl.1842-1888) British

£1900	$3249	(12-Mar-92 CSK265/R) The courtship (65x53cm-26x21in) s.d.1852
£2800	$4788	(12-Mar-92 CSK207/R) The woodland stream (122x96cm-48x38in) s.

WELLS, John (1907-) British

£900	$1638	(12-Dec-91 CSK150) Journey into space (53x61cm-21x24in) s.i.d.1947verso masonite
£1200	$2124	(8-Nov-91 C244/R) Abstract composition (25x41cm-10x16in) s.d.1962-86verso gesso-prepared board
£700	$1204	(10-Oct-91 L55/R) Abstract (23x33cm-9x13in) s.d.1968 pencil W/C chk
£800	$1416	(11-Feb-92 PH122) Village street (31x48cm-12x19in) s. W/C ink pair

WELLS, John Sanderson see SANDERSON-WELLS, John

WELLS, William (1842-1880) British

£3100	$5518	(1-May-92 PHE48/R) Feeding the ducks (34x44cm-13x17in) s.

WELLS, William Page Atkinson (1871-1923) British

£1400	$2492	(30-Apr-92 CG911/R) The orchard (25x35cm-10x14in) s. board
£2500	$4475	(13-Nov-91 CG623/R) The potato gatherers (35x46cm-14x18in) s.
£3000	$5370	(13-Nov-91 CG637/R) Feeding the hens (34x41cm-13x16in) s.

WELLS, William Page Atkinson (1871-1923) British-cont.
£3500	$5880	(26-Aug-91 S1020/R) Harvest (51x71cm-20x28in) s.
£4200	$7602	(4-Dec-91 S310/R) Carting kale (49x59cm-19x23in) s.
£5000	$8900	(30-Apr-92 CG907/R) Teignmouth, Devon (82x102cm-32x40in) s.
£6000	$11460	(16-Jul-92 CG606/R) Westward Ho (30x41cm-12x16in) s. panel

WELTI, Albert (1862-1912) Swiss
£1022	*$1829*	*(6-May-92 GD.B1541/R) Study for wall painting (30x40cm-12x16in) col.chk double-sided (S.FR 2800)*
£1880	$3440	(4-Jun-92 SY.Z362/R) River landscape (17x20cm-7x8in) st.studio verso pastel (S.FR 5000)
£1912	$3461	(5-Dec-91 SY.Z57/R) Wooded landscape (14x20cm-6x8in) pastel (S.FR 4800)
£2191	$3966	(5-Dec-91 SY.Z56/R) Landscape beneath cloudy sky (21x19cm-8x7in) pastel (S.FR 5500)
£2191	$3966	(5-Dec-91 SY.Z58/R) Hilly landscape (19x21cm-7x8in) pastel (S.FR 5500)
£2390	$4327	(5-Dec-91 SY.Z55/R) Farmhouse (14x20cm-6x8in) pastel (S.FR 6000)

WELY, Jacques (1873-1910) French
| £1200 | $2232 | (16-Jun-92 PH123/R) Petite amie (50x61cm-20x24in) s. |

WELZ, Jean (1900-1975) South African
£5645	$9992	(4-Nov-91 SY.J319/R) Girl in interior (40x30cm-16x12in) s.d.54 board (SA.R 28000)
£5964	$10378	(13-Apr-92 SY.J351/R) Artist's studio, Langerug, Worcester (46x60cm-18x24in) s.d.53 canvasboard (SA.R 30000)
£11089	$19627	(4-Nov-91 SY.J318/R) Two nudes (44x34cm-17x13in) s.d.53twice canvasboard (SA.R 55000)

WELZ, Jean and TOIT, Paul du (20th C) South African
| £2087 | $3632 | (13-Apr-92 SY.J350/R) Pink rose in water glass (30x24cm-12x9in) s.d.1945 verso panel (SA.R 10500) |

WEMAIRE, Pierre (1913-) Belgian
£709	$1290	(25-May-92 RAS.K73) Avant les Collages (60x73cm-24x29in) s.d.68 (D.KR 8000)
£1246	$2167	(18-Sep-91 KH.K46/R) Le charme conquerant (65x54cm-26x21in) s. (D.KR 14000)
£3559	$6192	(17-Sep-91 RAS.K2/R) PArfois violent (97x130cm-38x51in) s.d.76 i.verso (D.KR 40000)

WENCKE, Sophie (1874-1963) German
| £687 | $1168 | (25-Oct-91 BM.B639/R) Landscape near Worpswede, evening (43x73cm-17x29in) s. (DM 2000) |

WENDLBERGER, Wenzel Hermann (1882-?) German
| £839 | $1452 | (25-Mar-92 KM.K1518) Still life of flowers with apple and plums (60x46cm-24x18in) s. (DM 2400) |

WENDLING (19th C) ?
| £4281 | $7963 | (20-Jun-92 CH.MO105/R) Jeune femme regardant des bijoux (90x117cm-35x46in) s.d.1835 (F.FR 42000) |

WENDT, William (1865-1946) American
£1404	$2500	(26-Nov-91 MOR.P120 a) California coastal (30x41cm-12x16in) s. canvasboard
£2368	$4500	(24-Jun-92 B.SF6423/R) California sycamores (41x61cm-16x24in)
£4678	$8000	(13-Mar-92 WOL.C451/R) Valley landscape (51x91cm-20x36in) s.
£7018	$12000	(11-Mar-92 SY.NY39/R) Landscape with figures fishing (61x76cm-24x30in) s.
£8000	$14000	(31-Mar-92 MOR.P106) Winter landscape, Sierra (51x76cm-20x30in) s.
£10734	$19000	(12-Feb-92 B.SF524/R) Rushing onward (63x76cm-25x30in) s.
£11299	$20000	(12-Feb-92 B.SF523/R) Rock, San Luis Obispo (76x91cm-30x36in) s.d.1940
£15537	$27500	(12-Feb-92 B.SF474/R) California landscape (71x91cm-28x36in) s.

WENGLEIN, Joseph (1845-1919) German
£1988	$3459	(14-Apr-92 SY.AM401) Watering cattle at sunset (13x31cm-5x12in) s.d.1876 i.verso paper laid down on panel (D.FL 6500)
£3801	$6500	(13-Mar-92 S.BM163/R) A drink from the river, landscape with cows (25x36cm-10x14in) s.d.01 board
£6873	$11959	(18-Sep-91 N.M747/R) Moor landscape with hunter and dog by water (75x58cm-30x23in) s.d.1889 (DM 20000)
£10105	$18390	(11-Dec-91 N.M656/R) Moor landscape with huntsman and dog, autumn (60x53cm-24x21in) s. (DM 29000)
£10309	$17938	(18-Sep-91 N.M746/R) Moor landscape near Tolz (100x141cm-39x56in) s. i.stretcher (DM 30000)
£524	*$934*	*(26-Nov-91 KF.M276) Two wood workers on mountain path (24x19cm-9x7in) W/C over pencil (DM 1500)*

WENGLEIN, Joseph (circle) (1845-1919) German
| £1568 | $2854 | (11-Dec-91 N.M545/R) Murnauer Moos landscape with figures gathering peat (25x48cm-10x19in) (DM 4500) |

WENICOF, R (19th C) Russian
| £599 | $1083 | (3-Dec-91 FN.S2523/R) Siberian fur hunters in sleigh threatened by wolves in moonlit landscape (67x87cm-26x34in) s.d.1886 (DM 1700) |

WENK, Albert (1863-1934) German
£629 $1076   (18-Mar-92 N.M684) Coastal landscape with lighthouse and boats in choppy sea (80x120cm-31x47in) s.i. (DM 1800)
£944 $1614   (19-Mar-92 N.M2859/R) Terrace above rocky coast (101x89cm-40x35in) s.i. (DM 2700)
£2297 $4019   (3-Apr-92 BM.B724/R) Sunset near Capri (124x140cm-49x55in) s.d.1911 (DM 6500)

WENNERBERG, Brynolf (1823-1894) Swedish
£2265 $4122   (11-Dec-91 N.M658/R) Young soldier with four girls (40x32cm-16x13in) mono. (DM 6500)

WENNERBERG, Gunnar (1863-1914) Swedish
£777 $1407   (3-Dec-91 AB.S4683/R) Flowers (34x75cm-13x30in) s.d.1907 (S.KR 8100)
£1852 $3222   (13-Apr-92 AB.S274) Welcome beautiful morning - nude man among the birches (198x106cm-78x42in) s.d.1900 (S.KR 19500)

WENNERWALD, Emil (1859-1934) Danish
£542 $975   (19-Nov-91 RAS.K326) Road behind Husum (95x125cm-37x49in) s.d.1903 (D.KR 6000)
£807 $1453   (30-Jan-92 RAS.V689/R) Autumn wood with magpies and crows (76x101cm-30x40in) s.d.1882 (D.KR 9000)
£847 $1517   (16-Jan-92 D.V72/R) Hilly lake landscape (48x71cm-19x28in) s.d.1906 (A.S 17000)
£1074 $1857   (3-Oct-91 D.V68/R) Autumn landscape (45x64cm-18x25in) s. (A.S 22000)
£1456 $2592   (29-Apr-92 D.V809/R) Summer landscape (64x99cm-25x39in) s.d.1898 (A.S 30000)

WENNING, Pieter (1873-1921) South African
£5040 $8921   (4-Nov-91 SY.J259/R) The Location Church near Pretoria (24x37cm-9x15in) canvas on board (SA.R 25000)

WENNING, Ype (1879-1959) Dutch
£547 $952   (17-Sep-91 CH.AM211) The Wisse Watje, Leeuwarden (33x43cm-13x17in) s.i. verso (D.FL 1800)

WENTORF, Carl (1863-1914) Danish
£7042 $11831   (27-Aug-91 RAS.K159/R) Northern light - young coupe watching sunset from a verandah (79x94cm-31x37in) s.d.1910-13 (D.KR 80000)

WENTWORTH, D F (1850-?) American
£1638 $2900   (10-Nov-91 LIT.L47) Springtime, cows in pasture (61x91cm-24x36in) s.

WENTZEL, Gustav (1859-1927) Norwegian
£709 $1255   (15-Feb-92 BU.O154) Farm (39x69cm-15x27in) s. (N.KR 8000)
£891 $1542   (23-Mar-92 B.O148/R) A farm (35x60cm-14x24in) s. (N.KR 10000)
£921 $1713   (15-Jun-92 B.O197/R) Winter landscape (35x60cm-14x24in) s. (N.KR 10500)
£1159 $2004   (23-Mar-92 B.O147/R) Winter landscape, Asker (35x60cm-14x24in) s. (N.KR 13000)
£1580 $2718   (7-Oct-91 B.O152/R) Green landscape (35x60cm-14x24in) s. (N.KR 18000)
£1756 $3020   (7-Oct-91 B.O151/R) Winter landscape (50x70cm-20x28in) s. (N.KR 20000)
£3947 $7342   (18-Jun-92 GWP.O114/R) Summer evening near Bondivann in Asker (90x130cm-35x51in) s. (N.KR 45000)
£6157 $10836   (8-Apr-92 GWP.O77/R) The card players 1890-92 (96x140cm-38x55in) s. (N.KR 70000)

WENZEL, A E (20th C) ?
£829 $1559   (16-Dec-91 ANS.M162/R) Hay que morir para renacer (150x200cm-59x79in) s.d.1945 (S.P 150000)

WEREFKIN, Marianne von (1870-1938) Russian
£9630 $17430   *(20-May-92 GK.Z5016/R) Die Judenschenke (42x59cm-17x23in) (S.FR 26000)*

WERENSKIOLD, Erik Theodor (1855-1938) Norwegian
£850 $1624   (21-Jul-92 UL.T224) Portrait of young woman (54x44cm-21x17in) (N.KR 9500)
£1756 $3020   (7-Oct-91 B.O154/R) Boy getting dressed (100x60cm-39x24in) init. (N.KR 20000)
£1800 $3186   (13-Feb-92 CSK98/R) Norwegian village (61x81cm-24x32in) init.d.90
£22427 $39472   (8-Apr-92 GWP.O78/R) Woman reading (32x40cm-13x16in) init.d.1881 panel (N.KR 255000)
£400 $732   *(6-Feb-92 B.O281) Landscape with horses and boys running (70x93cm-28x37in) init.d.1902 chl dr (N.KR 4500)*
£550 $957   *(19-Sep-91 TL456) An itinerant family (6x11cm-2x4in) init. pen sketch*
£620 $1128   *(14-Dec-91 BU.O192) Peasant family (7x12cm-3x5in) s. pen (N.KR 7000)*
£660 $1109   *(28-Aug-91 KH.K296) Edvard Grieg walking in the mountains (79x87cm-31x34in) init.d.1902 chl (D.KR 7500)*
£1097 $1888   *(10-Oct-91 BU.O66/R) Frozen brook (64x46cm-25x18in) s.i. chl dr (N.KR 12500)*

WERFF, Adriaen van der (after) (1659-1722) Dutch
£3729 $6750   (22-May-92 SY.NY123/R) Susannah and Elders (62x49cm-24x19in) bears i. panel

WERFF, Adriaen van der (attrib) (1659-1722) Dutch
£926 $1676   (19-May-92 GF.L2403/R) Woman praying (30x24cm-12x9in) panel (S.FR 2500)

WERFF, Adriaen van der (school) (1659-1722) Dutch
£1050 $1900   (22-May-92 S.BM22/R) Banishment of Hagar and Ishmael (48x38cm-19x15in)

WERFF, Adriaen van der (style) (1659-1722) Dutch
£1500 $2625   (2-Apr-92 CSK38/R) Lot and daughters (44x34cm-17x13in) panel
£1698 $3039   (14-Nov-91 CH.AM22) Peace triumphant over War (95x85cm-37x33in)
                 (D.FL 5500)
£4907 $9128   (16-Jun-92 EP.M12/R) Escena mitologica (43x35cm-17x14in) panel
                 (S.P 900000)

WERFF, Pieter van der (1665-1722) Dutch
£1568 $2854   (11-Dec-91 N.M378/R) Portrait of lady. Portrait of gentleman and view of
                 park landscape (49x40cm-19x16in) s.d.1700 one s.d.1705 pair (DM 4500)
£3500 $6125   (1-Apr-92 S84/R) Adam and Eve in Garden of Eden (47x40cm-19x16in) s.
                 panel
£4972 $9000   (22-May-92 SY.NY214/R) Infant Hercules wrestling with snakes. Infant
                 Bacchus (26x30cm-10x12in) copper pair
£5000 $9600   (10-Jul-92 C141/R) Portrait of nobleman, wearing breastplate. Portrait of
                 wife, in cloak (68x51cm-27x20in) with init.verso copper oval pair

WERGELAND, Oscar (1844-1910) Scandinavian
£2195 $3775   (10-Oct-91 BU.O85/R) Fishing with trailing line (76x92cm-30x36in) s.
                 (N.KR 25000)
£4429 $8060   (10-Dec-91 UL.T240) Idyl by the water-pump (62x44cm-24x17in) (N.KR 50000)

WERKNER, Turi (1949-) Austrian
£679 $1235   (26-May-92 D.V289/R) Untitled (79x134cm-31x53in) s.i.d.1977verso felt tip
                 pen (A.S 14000)

WERNER, A F (?) ?
£523 $951   (12-Dec-91 N.M2851/R) Parade scene in Wimpfen (28x14cm-11x6in) s. panel
                 (DM 1500)

WERNER, Anton Alexander von (1843-1915) German
£418 $761   (12-Dec-91 L.K493) Rider before house and man, woman and child in doorway
                 (21x30cm-8x12in) mono.d.1867 pencil indian ink pen wash (DM 1200)

WERNER, Carl (1808-1894) German
£500 $890   (28-Nov-91 CSK15) Tambourine girl above Italian coast (43x33cm-17x13in)
                 s.d.1861 pencil W/C
£720 $1303   (3-Dec-91 AB.S4764/R) Renaissance interior with man reading
                 (73x52cm-29x20in) s.d.1862 W/C (S.KR 7500)
£1250 $2200   (6-Apr-92 WW153) Bridge of Sighs, Venice (56x40cm-22x16in) s.d.1854 W/C
                 over pencil
£1300 $2353   (21-May-92 CSK94) Carnival, Rome, on Via del Corso (27x22cm-11x9in)
                 s.d.1839 pencil W/C htd white
£2105 $3600   (13-Mar-92 FN.S3014/R) View of Cairo (30x52cm-12x20in) s.i.d.1865 W/C
                 (DM 6000)
£2105 $3600   (13-Mar-92 FN.S3015/R) Carthago (27x45cm-11x18in) s.d.1877 W/C (DM 6000)
£2160 $3910   (3-Dec-91 CN.P7/R) Vue ideale de l'entree du cloitre de la Villa Rufolo a
                 Ravello (28x23cm-11x9in) s.d.1840 W/C (F.FR 21000)
£2650 $5088   (28-Jul-92 SWS282/R) The Rialto Bridge (42x63cm-17x25in) i.d.1853 pen W/C
                 over pencil htd.bodycol.
£6000 $10380   (4-Oct-91 C129/R) Arab figures in coffee house (20x29cm-8x11in) s.d.1870
                 pencil W/C
£7800 $14118   (22-May-92 C219 b/R) Egyptian souk (50x34cm-20x13in) s.d.1868 pencil W/C
                 htd white

WERNER, Clemens (20th C) German
£697 $1268   (11-Dec-91 WE.MU104/R) By the edge of the village (41x51cm-16x20in) s.i.
                 paper on board (DM 2000)

WERNER, Gosta (1909-1989) Swedish
£2562 $4688   (13-May-92 BU.S214/R) In memory of Paul Ronnback and the vessel Idalla
                 (101x81cm-40x32in) s.d.1967 (S.KR 27000)

WERNER, Louis (1824-1901) French
£2000 $3440   (4-Mar-92 S128) Portrait of James Johnston, aged 17. Portrait of Agnes
                 Johnston, aged 13 (71x51cm-28x20in) bear i.verso pair

WERNER, Theodor (1886-1969) German
£1203 $2093   (17-Sep-91 FN.S2097) Lake Constance landscape (50x38cm-20x15in) s.d.1918
                 board (DM 3500)
£1706 $3106   (30-May-92 VG.B992/R) Konstruktiv fliessend (31x21cm-12x8in) s.d.1955
                 tempera over pencil (DM 5000)
£1748 $3112   (26-Nov-91 KF.M1123/R) Composition Z 2 (47x34cm-19x13in) s.d.1967 i.verso
                 tempera pencil board (DM 5000)
£2168 $3859   (26-Nov-91 KF.M1122/R) Untitled (68x48cm-27x19in) s.i.d.1962 oil pencil
                 (DM 6200)
£2457 $4472   (26-May-92 KF.M1378/R) Composition (42x59cm-17x23in) s.d.1956 tempera
                 (DM 7200)
£512 $932   (26-May-92 KF.M1379) Composition with blue (11x16cm-4x6in) mono.d.1956
                 pastel indian ink pencil (DM 1500)
£962 $1761   (2-Jun-92 FN.S2416/R) Composition (42x33cm-17x13in) s.d.1948 gouache
                 pencil (DM 2800)

WERNER, Theodor (1886-1969) German-cont.

£1263	$2298	(26-May-92 KF.M1380/R) Composition (69x45cm-27x18in) s.d.1957 pencil pastel (DM 3700)
£3413	$6212	(26-May-92 KF.M1377/R) Composition (36x51cm-14x20in) s.i.d.1950verso mixed media (DM 10000)
£4895	$8713	(30-Nov-91 VG.B339/R) Composition no.12 (43x62cm-17x24in) s.d.1955 tempera spray technique over pencil (DM 14000)
£7692	$13692	(30-Nov-91 VG.B351/R) Composition 7/58 (73x51cm-29x20in) s.d.1958 oil over pencil (DM 22000)
£7692	$13692	(30-Nov-91 VG.B337/R) Improvisation no 2 (80x99cm-31x39in) s.d.1948 s.i.d.verso W/C gouache pencil (DM 22000)
£9091	$16182	(30-Nov-91 VG.B338/R) Composition no 3 (99x80cm-39x31in) s.d.1948 W/C gouache pencil paper on board (DM 26000)

WERRO, Roland (1926-) Swiss

| £438 | $784 | (6-May-92 GD.B1348) Geometric composition (71x75cm-28x30in) s.d.1958 (S.FR 1200) |

WERTHEIMER, Gustave (1847-1904) Austrian

| £2160 | $4105 | (26-Jun-92 CSC.P131/R) Portraits d'elegants au bord de la mer (100x81cm-39x32in) s.d.1882 (F.FR 21000) |
| £3689 | $6750 | (16-May-92 HG.C216/R) Lorelei (173x112cm-68x44in) s. |

WERTMULLER, Adolf Ulrik (attrib) (1751-1811) Swedish

| £2541 | $4421 | (13-Apr-92 AT.P123/R) Portrait de femme a la coiffe de dentelle (64x55cm-25x22in) oval (F.FR 25000) |

WESSEL-FOUGSTEDT, Erik (1915-) Scandinavian

| £480 | $869 | (3-Dec-91 AB.S5175/R) Houses by the harbour (60x73cm-24x29in) s.d.52 (S.KR 5000) |

WESSEL-ZUMLOH, Irmgart (1907-) German

| £1399 | $2490 | (25-Nov-91 WK.M1085/R) Peach (100x90cm-39x35in) s.d.1975 s.i.d.verso (DM 4000) |
| £1399 | $2490 | (25-Nov-91 WK.M1084/R) Wrapped up vessels (90x140cm-35x55in) s.d.1973/76 s.i.d.verso (DM 4000) |

WESSELMANN, Tom (1931-) American

£7429	$13000	(25-Feb-92 SY.NY166/R) Study for Mel's model (24x22cm-9x9in) s.i.d.83verso
£8000	$14000	(25-Feb-92 SY.NY170/R) Study for reclining stockinged nude (16x39cm-6x15in) s.i.d.81verso canvas on board
£13966	$25000	(14-Nov-91 SY.NY348/R) Smoker study - 27 (25x20cm-10x8in) s.d.67
£17143	$30000	(27-Feb-92 CH.NY28/R) Study for bedroom painting, no 2 (25x36cm-10x14in)
£2432	$4500	(12-Jun-92 SY.NY297/R) Nude (9x22cm-4x9in) s.d.89 pencil on ragboard
£3080	$5544	(19-Nov-91 FB.P243/R) Study for bedroom blonde with lavender wallpaper (23x25cm-9x10in) s.d.85 liquitex bristol (F.FR 30000)
£3631	$6500	(6-May-92 CH.NY389/R) Beautiful Kate no.15 (9x22cm-4x9in) s.d.81 num.15 s.d.1983 verso graphite acrylic
£3631	$6500	(6-May-92 CH.NY332/R) Banner nude (9x11cm-4x4in) s.d.74 num.4 liquitex graphite bristol board
£4190	$7500	(14-Nov-91 SY.NY385/R) Study for Marilyn in bed (16x31cm-6x12in) s.d.84 liquitex Bristol board
£4190	$7500	(7-May-92 SY.NY314/R) Open-ended nude drawing edition no.109 (10x23cm-4x9in) s.d.80 num.109 pencil liquitex board
£6704	$12000	(6-May-92 CH.NY387/R) Study for blonde Monica in half-slip (43x48cm-17x19in) s.d.86 liquitex graphite bristol board
£16763	$29000	(3-Oct-91 SY.NY79/R) Study for the bedroom painting no.51 (101x151cm-40x59in) s.d.1982 liquitex
£117318	$210000	(13-Nov-91 SY.NY42 a/R) Still life No.21 (122x152cm-48x60in) acrylic collage board recorded tape

WESSMAN, Bjorn (1949-) Scandinavian

£499	$903	(3-Dec-91 AB.S5177/R) Landscape composition over text (46x52cm-18x20in) s. paper (S.KR 5200)
£946	$1712	(19-May-92 AB.S5342/R) Torso (171x150cm-67x59in) s.d.1985verso (S.KR 10000)
£378	$685	(19-May-92 AB.S5343/R) Nymph (114x90cm-45x35in) s.d.86 W/C (S.KR 4000)

WEST, Benjamin (1738-1820) British

| £440 | $840 | (16-Jul-92 S70) Study of male nude (12x21cm-5x8in) s.d.1784 i.verso pen two joined sheets |

WEST, Benjamin (after) (1738-1820) British

£1596	$3000	(18-Dec-91 SY.NY8/R) The Battle of La Hogue (81x104cm-32x41in)
£1826	$3342	(14-May-92 SY.T89/R) Death of General Wolfe (53x71cm-21x28in) metal (C.D 4000)
£2398	$4100	(1-Aug-91 E.EDM770/R) Death of General Wolfe (122x130cm-48x51in)
£3961	$6655	(27-Aug-91 RAS.K188/R) William Penn's agreement with the indians (68x92cm-27x36in) (D.KR 45000)

WEST, Edgar (19th C) British

| £410 | $759 | (9-Jun-92 LW1746/R) Mountainous coastal scene with figures and boats before bay (66x99cm-26x39in) s. W/C |
| £560 | $969 | (4-Sep-91 BT96/R) Dutch fishing boats in Torbay (48x66cm-19x26in) s. W/C |

WEST, Edgar (19th C) British-cont.
£1400 $2408   (4-Mar-92 S250/R) Looking across Severn Valley (70x122cm-28x48in) s. W/C htd bodycol

WEST, Franz (1947-) Austrian
£582 $1059   (26-May-92 D.V303/R) Untitled (22x36cm-9x14in) s. dispersion board (A.S 12000)
£782 $1392   (31-Oct-91 D.V149/R) Opinion 76 (62x90cm-24x35in) s.i.d.76 W/C collage (A.S 16000)
£880 $1566   (31-Oct-91 D.V148/R) Untitled (61x90cm-24x35in) s.d.1975 W/C collage (A.S 18000)
£1066 $1941   (26-May-92 D.V302/R) Untitled (29x22cm-11x9in) d.1981 gouache newspaper (A.S 22000)

WEST, M P (19th C) British
£6000 $10920   (28-May-92 C5/R) Boy of Bermuda. Girl of Bermuda (53x42cm-21x17in) one s.i. one s.d.verso pair

WEST, Richard Whately (1848-1905) British
£880 $1531   (12-Sep-91 CSK174) Irish country house with castellated turret (35x53cm-14x21in) s.stretcher verso

WEST, Samuel (19th C) British
£5000 $8950   (14-Jan-92 SWS163/R) The daisy chain, portrait of James K. Brown's children (140x105cm-55x41in) s. i.verso arch topped

WESTALL, Richard (1765-1836) British
£10000 $17900   (11-Nov-91 S547/R) Eloisa (192x145cm-76x57in)
£14271 $26544   (20-Jun-92 CH.MO95 b/R) Un troupeau attaque par des lions, Episode de l'Histoire d'Achille (115x158cm-45x62in) s.d.1809 panel (F.FR 140000)
£1100 $1936   (10-Apr-92 K474/R) Mother reading book to three children, floral terrace background (41x36cm-16x14in) W/C

WESTALL, Richard (attrib) (1765-1836) British
£416 $774   (16-Jun-92 SY.B300) Fidelity (26x20cm-10x8in) W/C (B.FR 25000)

WESTBERG, Victoria (1859-1941) Swedish
£472 $835   (5-Nov-91 BA.S187/R) Snowcowered glen (52x75cm-20x30in) s.d.1900 (S.KR 5000)

WESTCHILOFF, Constantin (1877-1945) Russian
£611 $1130   (10-Jun-92 ZZ.F49) Vagues deferlant sur la falaise (60x49cm-24x19in) (F.FR 6000)
£389 $700   (23-Nov-91 YFA.M302/R) Russian village in winter (46x61cm-18x24in) s. pastel

WESTENBERG, Pieter George (1791-1873) Dutch
£1682 $2994   (30-Oct-91 CH.AM145) View of the Y, Amsterdam in winter (35x43cm-14x17in) s.d.1860 panel (D.FL 5500)

WESTENDORP-OSIECK, Betsy (1880-1968) Dutch
£606 $1097   (21-May-92 SY.AM145/R) Vaas met bloemen (51x47cm-20x19in) s. i.d.1929verso cardboard (D.FL 2000)
£1852 $3241   (18-Feb-92 CH.AM3) Peaches and cherries (45x55cm-18x22in) s. (D.FL 6000)

WESTERBEEK, Cornelis (1844-1903) Dutch
£520 $920   (5-Nov-91 SY.AM356/R) Milking time (36x45cm-14x18in) s.d.95 (D.FL 1700)
£600 $1068   (26-Nov-91 PH81) Sheep in winter landscape (32x51cm-13x20in) s.d.92
£686 $1200   (21-Feb-92 BG.M139) Three cows at watering hole (56x107cm-22x42in) s.indis.d.
£734 $1306   (30-Oct-91 CH.AM257) Shepherdess and flock in heathland (50x80cm-20x31in) s.d.96 (D.FL 2400)
£750 $1335   (26-Nov-91 PH105) Cattle in summer landscape (54x81cm-21x32in) s.d.95
£807 $1397   (24-Mar-92 VN.R103/R) Cows in polder landscape (40x60cm-16x24in) s.d.85 (D.FL 2600)
£1314 $2300   (22-Feb-92 YFA.M206/R) Bringing in flock (51x79cm-20x31in) s.
£1389 $2431   (18-Feb-92 CH.AM81/R) River landscape with cows and windmill in distance (70x112cm-28x44in) s.d.92 (D.FL 4500)
£1407 $2505   (29-Oct-91 PH.T23/R) Bringing home flock (58x99cm-23x39in) s.d.96 (C.D 2800)
£1437 $2500   (14-Sep-91 LAE.L236/R) Landscape with cows (38x58cm-15x23in) s.d.1885
£1437 $2500   (13-Sep-91 S.W2860/R) Cows in marshy landscape (61x99cm-24x39in) s.
£1500 $2670   (28-Nov-91 B158/R) Shepherd and sheep in landscape (61x100cm-24x39in) s.d.99
£1529 $2706   (5-Nov-91 SY.AM198/R) Polder landscape with cows on hazy day (45x70cm-18x28in) s.d.89 (D.FL 5000)
£1651 $2923   (5-Nov-91 SY.AM25/R) Polder landscape with cows on waterfront (58x98cm-23x39in) s.d.96 (D.FL 5400)
£2600 $4628   (30-Apr-92 CG884/R) To new pastures (75x100cm-30x39in) s.d.96
£2600 $4498   (4-Oct-91 C68/R) Shepherdess with flock (61x99cm-24x39in) s.d.99

WESTERBEEK, Cornelis (jnr) (1873-1917) Dutch
£912 $1568   (12-Oct-91 CH.AM203/R) Shepherd and flock on track in wooded moorland (60x100cm-24x39in) s. (D.FL 3000)

WESTERHOLM, Victor (1860-1919) Finnish
£2908 $5118   (12-Apr-92 HOR.H254/R) Summer evening (25x35cm-10x14in) s. (F.M 23000)
£7585 $13350   (12-Apr-92 HOR.H253) Cold day (34x50cm-13x20in) s.i.d.1917 (F.M 60000)
£8926 $15889   (1-Dec-91 HOR.H260) Coastal landscape with sailship in bay
                 (36x59cm-14x23in) s.d.1906 (F.M 69000)
£18963 $33375   (12-Apr-92 HOR.H252/R) Cattle in birch grove (135x64cm-53x25in) s.d.1900
                 (F.M 150000)

WESTERIK, Jacobus (1924-) Dutch
£463   *$843*   *(11-Dec-91 CH.AM123) Composition (14x14cm-6x6in) s.d.74 W/C pen ink*
                 (D.FL 1500)

WESTERMARCK, Helena (1857-1938) Finnish
£25917 $45613   (12-Apr-92 HOR.H255/R) The needlework (63x79cm-25x31in) s.d.1887
                 (F.M 205000)

WESTMAN, Edvard (1865-1917) Swedish
£1338 $2342   (25-Sep-91 HOR.H111) Harvesting (31x40cm-12x16in) s.d.1898 (F.M 9500)

WESTPFAHL, Conrad (1891-1976) German
£385   *$685*   *(25-Nov-91 WK.M1089) Wooded landscape (39x46cm-15x18in) s.indis.d.1924*
                 gouache W/C (DM 1100)

WESTWOOD, Bryan (1930-) Australian
£565 $1050   (21-Jun-92 SY.ME42) Duck and crow (87x89cm-34x35in) board (A.D 1400)
£1709 $3043   (27-Apr-92 J.M137/R) Two more mallards from Joe (92x92cm-36x36in) s.
                 (A.D 4000)
£2128 $3766   (26-Apr-92 SY.ME377/R) Jockey with saddle (135x74cm-53x29in) init.
                 (A.D 5000)

WET, Gerrit de (1616-1674) Dutch
£2037 $3687   (19-May-92 GF.L2082/R) Samson and Delila (57x80cm-22x31in) rem.sig. panel
                 (S.FR 5500)

WET, Jacob Jacobsz de (1640-1697) Dutch
£2778 $5028   (19-May-92 GF.L2084/R) Esther before Akasver (80x107cm-31x42in)
                 (S.FR 7500)

WET, Jacob de (1610-1671) Dutch
£915 $1591   (13-Apr-92 AT.P68/R) Laissex venir a moi les petits enfants
                 (42x35cm-17x14in) panel (F.FR 9000)
£2200 $3916   (31-Oct-91 B78/R) Offering of Abigail before David (77x110cm-30x43in)
                 panel
£2800 $4900   (28-Feb-92 C108) The crossing of the Red Sea (59x84cm-23x33in) panel
£2941 $5176   (11-Apr-92 AT.P68/R) Le retour de Tobie (41x53cm-16x21in) panel
                 (F.FR 29000)
£3198 $5500   (10-Oct-91 SY.NY104/R) Joseph greeting his father Jacob and their family
                 as they enter Egypt (60x83cm-24x33in) s.
£3229 $5522   (18-Mar-92 D.V372/R) Jewish wedding (60x84cm-24x33in) panel (A.S 65000)
£3333 $6033   (19-May-92 GF.L2389/R) Das Opfer Manoahs (55x42cm-22x17in) panel
                 (S.FR 9000)

WET, Jacob de (attrib) (1610-1671) Dutch
£1057 $1893   (7-May-92 CH.AM38) Lamentation (54x42cm-21x17in) panel (D.FL 3500)

WET, Jacob de (circle) (1610-1671) Dutch
£7558 $13000   (10-Oct-91 SY.NY203/R) Joseph sold into slavery. Joseph revealing himself
                 to his brothers (59x83cm-23x33in) panel pair

WET, Jacob de (style) (1610-1671) Dutch
£780 $1498   (9-Jul-92 CSK315) An entourage (77x60cm-30x24in) panel
£1400 $2688   (9-Jul-92 CSK316/R) Infant Bacchus disporting with putti
                 (107x82cm-42x32in)
£1800 $3456   (9-Jul-92 CSK75/R) Joseph and his brothers taking leave of their father
                 Jacob (104x118cm-41x46in)
£2111 $3821   (3-Dec-91 AB.S4765/R) Landscape with figures by Noah's Ark
                 (59x77cm-23x30in) panel (S.KR 22000)
£4257 $7706   (19-May-92 AB.S4389/R) Dancing around the golden calf (76x110cm-30x43in)
                 panel (S.KR 45000)

WETHERBEE, George Faulkner (1851-1920) American
£1223 $2177   (29-Oct-91 VN.R308) De pianoles (80x65cm-31x26in) s. (D.FL 4000)

WETLESEN, Wilhelm (1871-1925) Norwegian
£1404 $2611   (18-Jun-92 GWP.O116/R) From Lillehammer (66x51cm-26x20in) init.d.1904
                 i.verso (N.KR 16000)

WETTERWIK, C H (1910-1949) Scandinavian
£694 $1200   (28-Mar-92 UA.U511/R) River landscape, Fyrisan (56x69cm-22x27in) s.
                 (S.KR 7200)

WEX, Adalbert (1867-?) German
£756 $1315   (18-Sep-91 N.M748/R) Angler in valley by mountain stream
                 (42x60cm-17x24in) s. (DM 2200)

WEX, Adalbert (1867-?) German-cont.
£871 $1585   (11-Dec-91 WE.MU292) River landscape, autumn evening (60x80cm-24x31in) s. i.verso (DM 2500)

WEX, Willibald (1831-1892) German
£1328 $2351   (5-Nov-91 GF.L2491/R) Lake landscapes (32x56cm-13x22in) s. panel pair (S.FR 3400)

WEXELSEN, Christian Delphin (1830-1883) Norwegian
£1583 $2786   (8-Apr-92 GWP.O79/R) Landscape with cows (38x58cm-15x23in) s.indist.d.1872 (N.KR 18000)

WEYDE, van der (jnr) (19th C) ?
£2088 $3800   (28-May-92 CH.NY3/R) Buffalo hunt (11x18cm-4x7in) s.d.1858 pen brush ink wash

WEYDEN, Harry van der (1868-?) American
£500 $890   (30-Apr-92 T136) Coastal scene at dusk (36x56cm-14x22in) s. board
£664 $1175   (5-Nov-91 GF.L2504/R) River landscape (37x46cm-15x18in) s.d.1913 canvas on board (S.FR 1700)
£1031 $1794   (21-Sep-91 SA.A1986/R) Coastal landscape, evening (19x32cm-7x13in) s. (DM 3000)

WEYDEN, Rogier van der (style) (1399-1464) Flemish
£9556 $17297   (21-May-92 L.K174/R) Descent from the Cross (48x35cm-19x14in) panel (DM 28000)
£12500 $24000   (10-Jul-92 C214/R) Virgin and child with two music-making angels in rose garden (72x57cm-28x22in) panel

WEYER, Hermann (attrib) (17th C) German
£1301 $2238   (11-Oct-91 AW.H893/R) Diana discovering indiscretion of Callisto. Figure study (17x20cm-7x8in) indian ink pen htd white wash double-sided (DM 3800)

WEYER, Jacob (c.1620-1670) German
£8500 $14875   (3-Apr-92 C35/R) Cavalrymen and infantrymen storming burning town (52x70cm-20x28in) init. panel

WEYER, Jacob (style) (c.1620-1670) German
£6154 $11754   (15-Jul-92 CH.S772/R) Cavalry skirmish (99x123cm-39x48in) (A.D 16000)

WEYER, Matthias (?-1690) German
£3000 $5460   (11-Dec-91 PH71/R) Mounted soldier in conversation with companion in encampment (20x32cm-8x13in) i. chk pen wash

WEYERMAN, Jacob Christoph (1698-1757) Dutch?
£8362 $15220   (11-Dec-91 N.M379/R) Hunting party in wooded landscape with view of riverside town (113x158cm-44x62in) s.d.1733 (DM 24000)

WEYLER, Jean Baptiste (1747-1791) French
£450 $774   (4-Mar-92 C23/R) Nobleman, in blue-grey coat, open shirt and powdered hair in queue (4x?cm-2x?in) min. engraved init.verso gilt frame oval
£1150 $1978   (4-Mar-92 C7/R) Lady, in decollete blue dress, with blue ribbon in upswept powdered hair (4x?cm-2x?in) min. gold mount lid box st.florettes oval

WEYTS, Petrus Cornelius (attrib) (1799-1855) Flemish
£1117 $2000   (15-Nov-91 RB.HY60/R) Arno of Sunderland Capt. Michael Young, passing Flushing, 1852 (53x71cm-21x28in) paper applied glass

WHAITE, Henry Clarence (1828-1912) British
£1000 $1810   (4-Dec-91 S122/R) Strength of hills (147x101cm-58x40in) s. s.i.stretcher

WHAITE, James (19th C) British
£1150 $2047   (28-Nov-91 L334/R) Continental market before cathedral (36x23cm-14x9in) s.
£400 $712   (21-Jan-92 SWS1233) Figures unloading boats at jetty by loch (44x74cm-17x29in) s. W/C
£1100 $1903   (24-Mar-92 PHC321/R) Sheep on sunlit hillside (27x40cm-11x16in) s. W/C

WHAITE, T (19th C) British
£500 $890   (28-Nov-91 B33/R) Artful dodger (41x66cm-16x26in) s.i.d.1878verso board

WHALE, John Hicks (attrib) (1829-1905) Canadian?
£685 $1253   (14-May-92 SY.T207) View of Niagara Falls (70x90cm-28x35in) (C.D 1500)

WHALE, Robert Reginald (1805-1887) Canadian
£1891 $3365   (26-Nov-91 JOY.T217/R) View of Hamilton (27x35cm-11x14in) (C.D 3800)

WHARTON, Philip Fishbourne (1841-1880) American
£474 $900   (25-Jun-92 BG.M497/R) Forest glade with young girl carrying water bucket and hunter with dog (56x69cm-22x27in) s.d.1876

WHATLEY, Henry (1824-1901) British
£780 $1427   (6-Feb-92 DLY199/R) Fisherfolk (43x66cm-17x26in) s. W/C

WHEATLEY, Francis (1747-1801) British
£2200	$4202	(15-Jul-92 S207) View in Dublin Bay (43x62cm-17x24in) s.
£6704	$12000	(16-Jan-92 CH.NY19/R) Mother and children gathering twigs by farmhouse. Mother pouring milk children in interior (36x28cm-14x11in) s.d.1794 pair
£11050	$20000	(22-May-92 SY.NY91/R) Portrait of Miss Fridiswede Moore, later the Hon. Mrs Robert Henry Southwell (74x61cm-29x24in) s.d.1782 painted oval
£15000	$26850	(15-Nov-91 C42/R) Soldier's return (49x38cm-19x15in) s.d.1785
£55866	$100000	(17-Jan-92 SY.NY81/R) Portrait of Robert and Anne Campbell, with their daughter Elizabeth Mary (102x114cm-40x45in)

WHEATLEY, Francis (circle) (1747-1801) British
£2294	$3945	(7-Oct-91 CH.E209/R) Portrait of lady, standing, holding parasol, St. Michael's Mount beyond (71x58cm-28x23in) (E.P 2500)

WHEELER (?) British
£2500	$4450	(27-Nov-91 C265/R) Portrait of William Morris. His wife (7x?cm-3x?in) min. gilt-metal mount oval two leather case

WHEELER, Alfred (1852-1932) British
£1900	$3477	(3-Jun-92 S116/R) Bulldogs (30x33cm-12x13in) s.d.1916 board pair
£2000	$3580	(14-Jan-92 PH71) Before start, Newmarket (49x60cm-19x24in) s. after Sir Alfred Munnings
£2000	$3840	(28-Jul-92 SWS80/R) Hounds' heads (27x47cm-11x19in) s.d.1889 board
£2186	$4000	(5-Jun-92 SY.NY198/R) The last fence. The finish (25x40cm-10x16in) s.d.1896 pair
£2732	$5000	(5-Jun-92 SY.NY43 a/R) Ladas, a dark brown racehorse with jockey up (50x61cm-20x24in) s.i.
£4372	$8000	(5-Jun-92 SY.NY87/R) Calling the hounds. End of the day (50x61cm-20x24in) 1 s. pair

WHEELER, Charles Arthur (1881-) Australian
£485	$863	(26-Nov-91 J.M11) Farmlet over river (29x38cm-11x15in) s. board (A.D 1100)
£684	$1217	(27-Apr-92 J.M157/R) At Barwon Heads (21x28cm-8x11in) s. board (A.D 1600)
£962	$1712	(28-Apr-92 CH.ME107) Carting hay (55x80cm-22x31in) s. (A.D 2250)
£2553	$4519	(26-Apr-92 SY.ME483/R) Rock pool (59x79cm-23x31in) s. i.verso (A.D 6000)

WHEELER, John Arnold (1821-1903) British
£600	$1068	(28-Nov-91 B35/R) Horse in stable (46x61cm-18x24in) s.d.1902
£700	$1239	(6-Nov-91 S90/R) Donkey and dog in barn (38x51cm-15x20in) s.
£850	$1522	(14-Jan-92 B246/R) A Golden Retriever in a landscape (35x40cm-14x16in) s. board
£1200	$2220	(11-Jun-92 CSK170/R) Over the stone wall. At the river (21x31cm-8x12in) mono. board pair
£1200	$2076	(25-Mar-92 PH586/R) The Grey, Bedouin, and dog in stable interior (63x77cm-25x30in) s.i.d.1868
£2200	$3828	(12-Sep-91 CSK206) Gone away. Full cry. Over the ditch. The kill (30x41cm-12x16in) mono. set of four
£2235	$4000	(13-Nov-91 B.SF2194/R) Full cry (46x61cm-18x24in) s.
£3000	$5280	(8-Apr-92 S140/R) Lord Worcester on grey hunter Beckford followed by hound (33x44cm-13x17in)
£3800	$6802	(15-Nov-91 C148/R) General Gough, with escort of 3rd Light Dragoons, receiving surrender of Sikh chiefs, 1845 (76x111cm-30x44in) s.

WHEELER, John Arnold (attrib) (1821-1903) British
£1600	$2736	(13-Mar-92 C132/R) Fox hounds (41x51cm-16x20in)

WHEELER, M E (?) British?
£590	$1127	(3-Jul-92 BW408) Still life study depicting two vases of flowers, ornamental figure etc (91x91cm-36x36in) s.

WHEELWRIGHT, J Hadwen (19th C) British
£1000	$1790	(15-Nov-91 C105/R) Huntsmen crossing stream (26x34cm-10x13in) s.indist.d. panel

WHEELWRIGHT, Roland (1870-1955) British
£4144	$7500	(21-May-92 GRO.B70/R) Startled by the hunt (76x127cm-30x50in) s.
£12000	$20520	(13-Mar-92 C153/R) The dinner hour (102x153cm-40x60in) s. s.i.verso

WHEELWRIGHT, W H (19th C) British
£546	$1000	(5-Jun-92 SY.NY156/R) A coach and four (24x34cm-9x13in) s.d.85 W/C

WHICHELO, C John M (?-1865) British
£1600	$2864	(11-Nov-91 S568/R) High Alps from Ouchy, Geneva (41x61cm-16x24in) s.d.1847 W/C

WHICHELO, Henry Mayle (fl.1818-1845) British
£1450	$2494	(3-Mar-92 H301/R) Figures and horse and cart by timbered cottage (46x61cm-18x24in) s.d.1832

WHISSON, Kenneth Roland (1927-) Australian
£6057	$10903	(24-Nov-91 SY.S527/R) Country sleep, 1980 (99x119cm-39x47in) (A.D 13750)
£6573	$10977	(19-Aug-91 SY.ME324/R) Tailor (85x108cm-33x43in) s.i.d.1974 board (A.D 14000)

WHISSON, Kenneth Roland (1927-) Australian-cont.
£363 $675   (21-Jun-92 SY.ME143) Television (35x52cm-14x20in) s.d.1976 ink (A.D 900)
£404 $716   (26-Apr-92 SY.ME145) Untitled- figures (30x40cm-12x16in) s.i.verso crayon
               (A.D 950)

WHISTLER, James Abbott McNeill (1834-1903) American
£11050 $20000   (6-Dec-91 CH.NY133/R) A Venetian courtyard (30x20cm-12x8in) chl pastel

WHISTLER, Rex (1905-1944) British
£3600 $6480   (20-Nov-91 S160/R) Peaches and tapestry in the dining room no 3 Foro
               Romano (25x35cm-10x14in) s.i.d.1929 canvasboard
£4600 $8280   (20-Nov-91 S161/R) Dahlias in antique urn (48x35cm-19x14in)
£450 $860   (16-Jul-92 B38) Lady golfer (22x17cm-9x7in) pen wash
£1400 $2520   (20-Nov-91 S168/R) Bosco sacro, G.B. sketching (16x25cm-6x10in) i.d. pen
               W/C
£2400 $4320   (20-Nov-91 S166/R) Chimneypiece design for 5, Belgrave Square
               (37x23cm-15x9in) pencil pen W/C htd.white gold
£2800 $5040   (20-Nov-91 S164/R) Study for the Tate Gallery Mural (19x26cm-7x10in) pen
               W/C squared for transfer
£3000 $5400   (20-Nov-91 S165/R) Castel Gandolfo from Lake Albano (16x25cm-6x10in)
               s.i.d.1928 i.verso pen W/C
£3600 $6480   (20-Nov-91 S163/R) Designs for the Port Lympne Mural (11x28cm-4x11in)
               pencil pen W/C htd.white two

WHITAKER, George (1834-1874) British
£560 $1002   (5-May-92 SWS116/R) The Skerries, Start Point, Devon (59x119cm-23x47in)
               s.d.1865 W/C htd gouache scratching out

WHITAKER, George William (1841-1916) American
£643 $1100   (13-Mar-92 S.BM194) Still life with melons and summer fruits
               (8x15cm-3x6in) s. canvas on board
£690 $1200   (15-Apr-92 SY.NY33/R) Still life with fruit (61x86cm-24x34in) s.d.93
£833 $1500   (22-Nov-91 S.BM62 d/R) Twilight mist - landscape with cattle by pool
               (74x91cm-29x36in) s.d.1902

WHITCOMB, Jon (1906-1988) American
£506 $900   (2-Nov-91 IH.NY68/R) Woman admiring her smile in hand-held mirror
               (36x23cm-14x9in) s. gouache
£618 $1100   (2-May-92 IH.NY80/R) Woman kissing soldier, pink chair in background
               (30x36cm-12x14in) s. gouache

WHITCOMBE, Thomas (1760-c.1824) British
£3200 $5376   (15-Aug-91 B417/R) Lord Howe's action, 1794 (18x27cm-7x11in)
£4500 $7560   (15-Aug-91 B398/R) Indiaman in two positions off Walmer Castle, Kent
               (91x148cm-36x58in)
£5500 $9845   (13-Nov-91 S5/R) HMS Brunswick, HMS George and other shipping in Plymouth
               Sound (42x59cm-17x23in) indis.i.stretcher
£10929 $20000   (5-Jun-92 SY.NY241/R) The HCS Canton leaving The Downs - 1796
               (66x99cm-26x39in) i.verso
£12000 $21720   (20-May-92 S68/R) Man of war off the coast (61x91cm-24x36in) init.d.1797
£18000 $32580   (20-May-92 S67/R) Men of war at sea (91x126cm-36x50in) s.d.1787
£28000 $50680   (20-May-92 S28/R) Naval battle (91x137cm-36x54in)

WHITE, Arthur (1865-1953) British
£620 $1085   (27-Feb-92 L342) Norway Lane, St Ives (43x33cm-17x13in) s. board

WHITE, Edith (1855-1946) American
£737 $1400   (24-Jun-92 B.SF6318/R) Violets (25x36cm-10x14in) s.d.1909

WHITE, Ethelbert (1891-1972) British
£750 $1305   (17-Sep-91 PH18) The pink house (53x63cm-21x25in) s. i. verso
£800 $1528   (16-Jul-92 B75/R) Figures beneath tree with rolling landscape and farm
               buildings beyond (51x61cm-20x24in) s. board
£850 $1454   (11-Mar-92 B208/R) Cows grazing in pastoral landscape (81x102cm-32x40in)
               s.
£1100 $1881   (12-Mar-92 B50/R) An Iberian landscape with cottages and figures
               (55x65cm-22x26in) s.
£420 $752   (14-Jan-92 SWS96/R) Bridge over the Burn, Co Down (26x34cm-10x13in) s.
               chk W/C
£500 $855   (1-Aug-91 CSK74) Beeches (32x37cm-13x15in) s. W/C bodycol.

WHITE, Gabriella Antoinette (fl.1880-1915) American
£702 $1200   (21-Mar-92 W.W186/R) Still life with lemonade (36x61cm-14x24in) s.d.09

WHITE, George (?-1732) British
£1053 $2000   (26-Jun-92 WOL.C428/R) Portrait of Annie Palmer (89x71cm-35x28in)

WHITE, George Harlow (1817-1888) Canadian/British
£550 $1056   (29-Jul-92 PHC340/R) View of Whitby (43x97cm-17x38in) s.i.verso

WHITE, H C (20th C) American
£909 $1600   (12-Apr-92 LIT.L147) Wooded landscape (41x61cm-16x24in) s.d.1914 panel

WHITE, J (1851-1933) British
£400 $728   (13-Dec-91 CBB260) Coastal scene (18x25cm-7x10in) s. W/C

WHITE, J Talmage (19th C) ?
£1500 $2565   (12-Mar-92 CSK306) The Temples at Paestum (84x190cm-33x75in) s.d.1861

WHITE, John (1851-1933) British
£500 $925   (11-Jun-92 T101) Cottage by the sea at Seaton (25x33cm-10x13in)
      s.i.d.1906 panel
£600 $1098   (6-Feb-92 T73) Figures and dog on woodland path (51x91cm-20x36in)
      s.d.1876
£950 $1758   (11-Jun-92 T950/R) The North Path, Croft Beach, near Saunton Sands
      (20x36cm-8x14in) s.i. panel
£1600 $3056   (23-Jul-92 T80/R) Morning light, Coverack, Cornwall (30x41cm-12x16in)
      i.d.1891 verso
£2000 $3640   (11-Dec-91 MMB300/R) Weed for the plots (76x102cm-30x40in) s.d.1903
      s.i.verso
£3200 $5568   (19-Sep-91 TL430) Welcome (62x99cm-24x39in) s.d.1896
£650 $1190   (6-Feb-92 T244) Farmstead by river with figures (28x46cm-11x18in) s. W/C
£700 $1281   (6-Feb-92 T269) Beer headland (18x28cm-7x11in) s.i. W/C
£800 $1480   (11-Jun-92 T225) Farrington Hill Road near Exeter (36x25cm-14x10in) s.i.
£880 $1522   (1-Oct-91 SWS1887/R) Boys by rock pool (17x52cm-7x20in) s. W/C
£1250 $2225   (29-Nov-91 T217) Beer Beach (18x28cm-7x11in) s. W/C
£1500 $2565   (19-Mar-92 T170/R) Horse and cart at Peak Hill, Sidmouth
      (36x53cm-14x21in) s.d.1902 W/C
£1500 $2670   (30-Apr-92 T250/R) Branscombe cottage with figure and donkey - church
      beyond (46x30cm-18x12in) s. W/C
£1500 $2565   (19-Mar-92 T122) Sheep on the cliffs at Beer Head (28x46cm-11x18in) s.
      W/C
£1650 $2822   (19-Mar-92 T140/R) Dartmouth (36x25cm-14x10in) s.i.d.92 W/C
£1700 $2958   (16-Apr-92 PHX288/R) Getting ready for market, Georgenympton, nr. South
      Molton (46x28cm-18x11in) s.i.verso W/C
£1800 $3294   (6-Feb-92 T400/R) Sun setting above Branscombe, Devon (18x53cm-7x21in)
      s.i. W/C
£1800 $3150   (1-Apr-92 B70) On the cliff path (27x37cm-11x15in) s. gouache
£1900 $3363   (6-Nov-91 S262/R) Feeding the ducks, Corfe (25x35cm-10x14in) s.d.1894
      gouache
£1900 $3382   (30-Apr-92 T243) Shepherd and sheep by seaside farm, Branscombe
      (25x36cm-10x14in) s. W/C
£2100 $3654   (19-Sep-91 TL520) Minding the geese (34x24cm-13x9in) s.d.97 W/C
      htd.gouache
£2100 $3885   (11-Jun-92 T300/R) Kings Nympton, N.Devon (28x46cm-11x18in) s. W/C
£2200 $3938   (5-May-92 SWS174/R) Seatown, Dorset (28x45cm-11x18in) s. W/C gouache
£2200 $4070   (11-Jun-92 T295) Fishing boats and figures on Beer Beach
      (25x36cm-10x14in) s. W/C
£2300 $3979   (6-Sep-91 T201) The encampment (28x46cm-11x18in) s. W/C
£2600 $4966   (1-Jul-92 B91/R) Returning home (35x53cm-14x21in) s. gouache
£2600 $4810   (11-Jun-92 T330/R) Childhood days, Clovelly (28x46cm-11x18in) s.i. W/C
£2700 $4806   (29-Nov-91 T320/R) Fishing boats near Breakwater (25x36cm-10x14in) s. W/C
£2800 $5180   (11-Jun-92 T350/R) Mother and children by mill stream (28x46cm-11x18in)
      s. gouache
£3100 $5301   (19-Mar-92 T260/R) Fisher of Clovelly (36x53cm-14x21in) s. W/C
£3500 $6230   (30-Apr-92 T350/R) Unloading the catch on Beer Beach (33x51cm-13x20in)
      s.d.1932 W/C

WHITE, Orrin A (1883-1969) American
£947 $1800   (23-Jun-92 MOR.P80) Coastal scene (25x30cm-10x12in) s. board
£1067 $1900   (26-Nov-91 MOR.P81) San Miguel de Allende (46x36cm-18x14in) s. masonite
£1124 $2000   (26-Nov-91 MOR.P70 b) Cathedral in Mexico (61x61cm-24x24in) s.
£1676 $3000   (14-Nov-91 CE.NY331/R) High Sierra stream (51x61cm-20x24in) s.
£4211 $8000   (23-Jun-92 MOR.P72) Landscape (64x76cm-25x30in) s.
£9551 $17000   (26-Nov-91 MOR.P55 a) Coastal - Monterey (46x61cm-18x24in) s.
£787 $1400   (26-Nov-91 MOR.P33) Coastal scene (28x38cm-11x15in) s. gouache

WHITE, Robert (1645-1703) British
£698 $1200   (10-Oct-91 FA.PH853) Still life with lemons (30x41cm-12x16in) s. masonite
£1210 $2311   (16-Jul-92 S58/R) Portrait of Charles Seymour, 6th Duke of Somerset
      (13x9cm-5x4in) i. pencil stump vellum

WHITEHEAD, Frederick (1853-1938) British
£900 $1719   (2-Jul-92 D157/R) West Cliff, Portland looking towards Priory Corner
      (28x51cm-11x20in) s. i.verso
£1438 $2474   (8-Oct-91 ZEL.L1780/R) River landscape near Moreton, Dorset
      (40x61cm-16x24in) s.d.1899 i.verso (DM 4200)
£3200 $6112   (20-Jul-92 WW30/R) Mallard over mere (61x91cm-24x36in) s.

WHITELEY, Brett (1939-1992) Australian
£1234 $2184   (26-Apr-92 SY.ME390) Watsons Bay (23x43cm-9x17in) init.d.1959 board
      (A.D 2900)
£1382 $2406   (17-Sep-91 JRL.S486) Typhoid injection (64x78cm-25x31in) s.d.59 board
      (A.D 3000)
£1617 $2862   (26-Apr-92 SY.ME310) Corner of Hunter and Phillip Street
      (40x50cm-16x20in) s.i.d.1959 (A.D 3800)
£3524 $6344   (24-Nov-91 SY.S440) Study for swim (60x100cm-24x39in) s.i.d.1980
      (A.D 8000)
£6383 $11298   (26-Apr-92 SY.ME374/R) Cheetah (152x152cm-60x60in) s.i.d.1965 paper on
      board (A.D 15000)

WHITELEY, Brett (1939-1992) Australian-cont.

£13617	$24102	(26-Apr-92 SY.ME328/R) Honey in rain (82x101cm-32x40in) s.i. s.i.d.1983 verso oil glass eye plywood (A.D 32000)
£15859	$28546	(24-Nov-91 SY.S487/R) Two vases, 1976-77 (71x76cm-28x30in) s.d.1976 mono. s.i.d.verso (A.D 36000)
£16129	$28065	(16-Sep-91 CH.ME131/R) Nude (122x172cm-48x68in) board (A.D 35000)
£855	$1521	(27-Apr-92 J.M58/R) Landscape (12x20cm-5x8in) st.init. mixed media (A.D 2000)
£1709	$3043	(27-Apr-92 J.M175) Sketch of a garden (54x74cm-21x29in) s.i.d.78 ink (A.D 4000)
£1762	$3172	(24-Nov-91 SY.S154) Peter-the-Head from Leeds...off to Marrakesh (56x76cm-22x30in) i.d.16/6/67 mixed media (A.D 4000)
£2350	$4184	(27-Apr-92 J.M79 a) Tangier postcard (55x76cm-22x30in) mixed media (A.D 5500)
£3846	$6846	(27-Apr-92 J.M91/R) The crow (76x76cm-30x30in) s.d.83 i.verso oil collage (A.D 9000)
£4701	$8368	(27-Apr-92 J.M96) Watego Bay (54x75cm-21x30in) s.d.89 W/C collage (A.D 11000)
£9390	$15681	(19-Aug-91 SY.ME319/R) Startled heron (157x130cm-62x51in) s.d.1984 st.mono. mixed media paper on board (A.D 20000)
£11915	$21089	(26-Apr-92 SY.ME305/R) Gardenia and Lino-block scroll (91x91cm-36x36in) s. s.i.d.1976 verso oil linocut canvas (A.D 28000)
£14085	$23521	(19-Aug-91 SY.ME309/R) Oberon landscape (120x90cm-47x35in) s.d.1982 mixed media canvas (A.D 30000)
£14097	$25374	(24-Nov-91 SY.S478/R) Two hearts of Australia (81x68cm-32x27in) s. mixed media board (A.D 32000)
£56338	$94085	(19-Aug-91 SY.ME301/R) Dive, Bondi (168x122cm-66x48in) s.i.d.1988 oil collage board (A.D 120000)

WHITESIDE, B (19/20th C) American

| £1230 | $2250 | (5-Jun-92 SY.NY280/R) Polo match, Palm Springs (83x74cm-33x29in) s. board |

WHITFORD, Richard (19th C) British

| £2600 | $4966 | (29-Jun-92 PHB163/R) Three prize Leicester border ewes (45x61cm-18x24in) s.d.1889 |
| £2800 | $4900 | (27-Feb-92 B188/R) Portrait of a sheep and a shepherd (44x54cm-17x21in) pair |

WHITLEY, Kate Mary (c.1860-1920) British

| £1600 | $2960 | (12-Jun-92 C16 a) Still life of dead game, lemons, jug and basin (50x73cm-20x29in) init.d.1878 pencil W/C bodycol. |

WHITMORE, Coby (1913-) American

| £1011 | $1800 | (2-Nov-91 IH.NY204/R) Couple kissing in the snow, she in snowshoes (23x64cm-9x25in) s. board |
| £618 | $1100 | (2-Nov-91 IH.NY60/R) Girl lying in bed (20x38cm-8x15in) s. gouache |

WHITTAKER, John Barnard (1836-?) American

| £950 | $1700 | (14-Nov-91 CE.NY104/R) Cobbler's shop (54x43cm-21x17in) s. |

WHITTAKER, Marion (?) ?

| £1000 | $1830 | (13-May-92 WI1075/R) Milking time, view of village street, spring, milkmaid and cattle (51x127cm-20x50in) s. |

WHITTLE, Thomas (19th C) British

£599	$1083	(3-Dec-91 FN.S2529) Wooded hilly landscape with peasant boy and dog, evening (35x46cm-14x18in) s.d.1882 (DM 1700)
£880	$1584	(30-Jan-92 GSP433) Landscape with cottage, figures, sheep and ducks (41x61cm-16x24in) s.d.1885
£1050	$1785	(22-Oct-91 SWS270/R) Lock on Medway, near Maidstone (33x52cm-13x20in) s.d.1883 s.i.d.1884 stretcher
£1450	$2784	(28-Jul-92 SWS316/R) On a country lane. The valley stream (20x25cm-8x10in) s.i.d.1863 verso 1 panel 2 board pair

WHITTREDGE, Worthington (1820-1910) American

£1695	$3000	(13-Feb-92 S.W2816/R) The Campagna seen from the Via Appia (10x18cm-4x7in) s.d.1857 i.verso board
£2000	$3640	(28-May-92 C30/R) Shaded brook (34x27cm-13x11in) s.d.1862 board
£4945	$9000	(13-Dec-91 S.W2601/R) Evening service (89x122cm-35x48in) s.
£11050	$20000	(6-Dec-91 CH.NY24/R) Happy as a King (92x122cm-36x48in)
£49451	$90000	(27-May-92 SY.NY41/R) Along Platte River, Colorado (49x76cm-19x30in) s.

WHORF, John (1903-1959) American

£2762	$5000	(5-Dec-91 FA.PH583/R) Trout water (36x53cm-14x21in) s. W/C
£4678	$8000	(13-Mar-92 S.BM311/R) Montparnesse, nuit blanche (30x41cm-12x16in) s. W/C
£13187	$24000	(28-May-92 CH.NY193/R) Brroklyn Bridge from the Brooklyn Navy Yard (52x63cm-20x25in) s.
£372	$700	(5-Jan-92 LIT.L333) Stream in winter (36x51cm-14x20in) s. W/C
£532	$1000	(18-Dec-91 SY.NY366/R) Backyard in spring (58x36cm-23x14in) s. W/C
£722	$1300	(24-Nov-91 JRB.C116/R) The dock (43x58cm-17x23in) s. W/C
£838	$1500	(6-May-92 D.NY26/R) Courtyard pool (36x53cm-14x21in) s. W/C
£872	$1500	(10-Oct-91 FA.PH913/R) Active coast (36x46cm-14x18in) s. W/C
£919	$1700	(10-Jun-92 CE.NY488/R) In park, Copley Square Boston (24x28cm-9x11in) s. W/C paperboard

WHORF, John (1903-1959) American-cont.
£1124 $2000   (2-May-92 W.W98/R) Dock scene, Provincetown, Massachusetts
                  (36x53cm-14x21in) s. W/C
£1170 $2000   (13-Mar-92 S.BM300/R) Bather in landscape. Bather standing on beach
                  (56x38cm-22x15in) s.i. W/C gouache double-sided
£1302 $2500   (31-Jul-92 E.EDM34/R) Friendship Sloop at dock (36x51cm-14x20in) s. W/C
£1754 $3000   (13-Mar-92 S.BM261/R) Road to the beach, winter (36x56cm-14x22in) s.i.
                  W/C graphite
£2326 $4000   (13-Oct-91 H.C6/R) Street scene with figures and horses (36x48cm-14x19in)
                  s. W/C
£2381 $4000   (14-Aug-91 B.P68/R) The hunter (36x53cm-14x21in) s. W/C
£2395 $4000   (20-Aug-91 RB.HY93/R) After the bath (53x38cm-21x15in) s. W/C gouache
£3714 $6500   (25-Sep-91 SY.NY90/R) Winter waterfront, New York (54x76cm-21x30in) s.
                  W/C

WHYMPER, Charles (1853-1941) British
£4200 $7056   (26-Aug-91 S925/R) A poacher (25x36cm-10x14in) init. W/C htd bodycol.

WHYMPER, Josiah Wood (1813-1903) British
£800 $1440   (27-Jan-92 PH60/R) Near Hindhead (31x48cm-12x19in) s.d.1876 W/C

WHYTE, Duncan McGregor (1866-1953) British
£550 $963   (23-Sep-91 PHB49) Sunny morning - tiree (46x61cm-18x24in) s.d.1941 i.
                  verso
£650 $1177   (4-Dec-91 S316/R) Sunny morning, Tiree (46x61cm-18x24in) s.d.1941

WIBERG, Harald (1908-1986) Swedish
£815 $1467   (23-Nov-91 SO.S649/R) Wooded landscape (43x29cm-17x11in) s.d.1939 panel
                  (S.KR 8500)
£1899 $3305   (13-Apr-92 AB.S277/R) Autumn landscape with hunter and dog
                  (52x64cm-20x25in) s.d.1949 (S.KR 20000)
£2119 $3771   (28-Oct-91 AB.S258/R) Badgers in wooded glade, summer (45x54cm-18x21in)
                  s.d.1943 panel (S.KR 22500)
£2264 $4008   (5-Nov-91 BA.S188/R) Ringed plovers (55x65cm-22x26in) s.d.1946
                  (S.KR 24000)
£2310 $3973   (8-Mar-92 BU.M238) Badger, summer morning (64x54cm-25x21in) s.d.1945
                  (S.KR 24000)
£2502 $4304   (8-Mar-92 BU.M237) Goshawk hunting hare (50x60cm-20x24in) s.d.1946
                  (S.KR 26000)
£760 $1322   (13-Apr-92 AB.S428) Blackbird on fence, Falsterbo (23x31cm-9x12in)
                  s.i.d.1974 W/C (S.KR 8000)
£1415 $2505   (5-Nov-91 BA.S250/R) Female elk by snowcovered field (29x40cm-11x16in)
                  s.d.1965 gouache (S.KR 15000)

WICART, Nicolaas (1748-1815) Dutch
£559 $995   (25-Nov-91 CH.AM210/R) View of the village of Pernis on the river Maas
                  (16x25cm-6x10in) i. pen wash (D.FL 1800)
£870 $1548   (25-Nov-91 CH.AM214) View of Deel on the Waal. View of Zeyp on the Yssel
                  (12x43cm-5x17in) s.i. s.i.verso pen W/C wash pair (D.FL 2800)
£994 $1769   (25-Nov-91 CH.AM215) View of Loenen on the Vecht. View of Mourik on the
                  Lek (12x43cm-5x17in) s.i. s.i.verso pen W/C wash pair (D.FL 3200)

WICHBERG, H (19th C) Danish
£1988 $3518   (5-Nov-91 SY.AM31/R) Flowers in basket (51x65cm-20x26in) s.d.1852
                  (D.FL 6500)

WICHERA, Raimund von (1862-1925) Austrian
£551 $998   (5-Dec-91 D.V141) Portrait of girl (56x35cm-22x14in) s.i.d.1895
                  (A.S 11000)
£1456 $2592   (29-Apr-92 D.V746/R) Still life of flowers and wine decanter with glasses
                  (52x75cm-20x30in) s.i. (A.S 30000)

WICHMAN, Erich (1890-1929) Dutch
£545 $987   (21-May-92 SY.AM174/R) Portrait of Mr Somer (54x45cm-21x18in) (D.FL 1800)
£818 $1481   (21-May-92 SY.AM136/R) Sinterklaas en Zwarte Piet (50x70cm-20x28in)
                  init.i.d.27 (D.FL 2700)
£909 $1645   (21-May-92 SY.AM59/R) Portrait (48x34cm-19x13in) s.init.d.26 s.i.d.verso
                  (D.FL 3000)

WICHMANN, Adolf (1820-1866) German
£10309 $18866   (2-Jun-92 FN.S2810/R) Young man seated reading to elegant party in wooded
                  landscape (100x138cm-39x54in) (DM 30000)

WICHMANN, Johannes (1854-?) German
£700 $1344   (28-Jul-92 SWS409/R) Plaiting her hair (29x22cm-11x9in) s.d.1872 panel

WICHMANN-ELMQUIST, Erna (1869-1929) German
£376 $688   (4-Jun-92 SY.Z601/R) Roses (40x43cm-16x17in) s. W/C (S.FR 1000)
£639 $1170   (4-Jun-92 SY.Z602/R) Autumn leaves (53x62cm-21x24in) s. W/C (S.FR 1700)

WICHT, John von (20th C) American
£1222 $2200   (24-Nov-91 JRB.C326/R) Blue symphony (102x127cm-40x50in) s.

WICKMAN, Carl Johan (fl.1747-1795) Swedish
£2716 $4862 (12-Nov-91 SY.AM118/R) Portrait of Christian Jens Klarup. Portrait of
Lenor Jensd Biering (76x61cm-30x24in) i.verso pair (D.FL 8800)

WICKSTEAD, Philip (attrib) (fl.1763-1786) British
£3200 $5824 (28-May-92 C6/R) Mr. Butler and daughter Mary fishing in Jamaica
(17x21cm-7x8in) with i.verso panel

WIDDAS, R D (1826-1885) British
£1600 $2784 (12-Sep-91 CSK256/R) Picnickers on hillside overlooking river estuary
(76x112cm-30x44in) s.d.1869

WIDERBACK, Gusten (1878-1970) Swedish
£482 $833 (28-Mar-92 UA.U514) Savja river and Uppsala (32x28cm-13x11in) s. paper
(S.KR 5000)
£530 $917 (28-Mar-92 UA.U513) Vaksala church, summer (41x50cm-16x20in) s.
(S.KR 5500)
£569 $979 (19-Oct-91 UA.U406) Vaksala church (39x50cm-15x20in) s. (S.KR 6000)
£597 $1033 (28-Mar-92 UA.U515) Church in Uppland (46x53cm-18x21in) s. panel
(S.KR 6200)
£901 $1550 (19-Oct-91 UA.U405) Vaksala parish (47x54cm-19x21in) s. (S.KR 9500)
£983 $1700 (28-Mar-92 UA.U512/R) Evening light over Uppsale (55x72cm-22x28in) s.
(S.KR 10200)

WIDERBERG, Frans (?) Norwegian
£1231 $2167 (8-Apr-92 GWP.O80/R) Meteor (43x60cm-17x24in) s.indist.d.16.5.76
(N.KR 14000)

WIDFORSS, Gunnar M (1874-1934) American
£3421 $6500 (24-Jun-92 B.SF6261/R) Yosemite Valley in winter (33x41cm-13x16in)
s.d.1925 W/C
£3509 $6000 (13-Mar-92 B.BM252/R) Grand Canyon (33x46cm-13x18in) s. i.verso W/C
£4211 $8000 (24-Jun-92 B.SF6268/R) Grand Canyon (47x36cm-19x14in) s. W/C
£4749 $8500 (14-Nov-91 CE.NY330/R) Snowy mountains (103x76cm-41x30in) s.d.1926 W/C
gouache paperboard

WIDGERY, Frederick John (1861-1942) British
£550 $979 (28-Nov-91 PHX533) Black Tor, Dartmoor (36x74cm-14x29in) s.
£900 $1602 (28-Nov-91 PHX525/R) The estuary of the Gannel, Newquay
(71x107cm-28x42in) s.
£1650 $2855 (4-Sep-91 BT295/R) The Exe Estuary. Picking flowers in dunes
(25x74cm-10x29in) both s. one mono. pair
£400 $712 (29-Nov-91 T199) Sheep grazing on Dartmoor (36x53cm-14x21in) s. W/C
£400 $692 (4-Sep-91 BT81) On Dartmoor (25x36cm-10x14in) s. gouache
£420 $735 (25-Sep-91 CSK68) Exeter Cathedral from the Bishop's Palace
(41x61cm-16x24in) s.d.81 i. verso pencil W/C htd.white
£440 $761 (4-Sep-91 BT172) High Tor, Dartmoor (48x71cm-19x28in) s.d.1904 gouache
£500 $865 (4-Sep-91 BT158) Bellever Tor, Dartmoor (28x46cm-11x18in) s. gouache
£500 $915 (6-Feb-92 PHF143/R) Near Lizard, Cornwall - extensive coastal landscape
(74x125cm-29x49in) s.i. gouache
£500 $895 (15-Jan-92 BT58) West Mill Tor, Dartmoor (58x89cm-23x35in) s.i. gouache
£520 $905 (9-Sep-91 PH105) A moorland stream (37x52cm-15x20in) s. W/C gouache
£540 $934 (4-Sep-91 BT125/R) Steperton Tor (33x51cm-13x20in) s. W/C
£550 $941 (12-Mar-92 B68/R) The lizard, Cornwall (75x124cm-30x49in) s.i. W/C
bodycol
£600 $1068 (28-Nov-91 PHX367/R) Dartmoor pool (48x74cm-19x29in) s. bodycol
£680 $1176 (4-Sep-91 BT131/R) Dartmoor (28x46cm-11x18in) s. gouache
£720 $1246 (4-Sep-91 BT173) Fistral Bay, Newquay (48x74cm-19x29in) s.i. gouache
£720 $1375 (13-Jul-92 PH121/R) Blue skies over Dartmoor (40x101cm-16x40in) s.
gouache
£1150 $2197 (16-Jul-92 PHX302) Summer Dartmoor landscape with sheep grazing. Moorland
landscape (28x79cm-11x31in) s. bodycol pair

WIDGERY, William (1822-1893) British
£500 $890 (28-Nov-91 PHX531) Figures on Dartmoor bridge, probably Fingle Bridge
(30x43cm-12x17in) s.
£630 $1166 (11-Jun-92 T98) River landscape with figures and castle (20x46cm-8x18in)
s. board
£650 $1112 (17-Mar-92 SWS1150/R) Cottagers returning home (29x44cm-11x17in) s. board
£1250 $2238 (5-May-92 SWS360/R) Cattle watering at sunset (102x152cm-40x60in) s.
£640 $1088 (9-Aug-91 T27) River landscape with cattle (43x71cm-17x28in) s. W/C
£800 $1384 (4-Sep-91 BT115/R) Cattle on moors. Moorland pool (23x71cm-9x28in) s.
gouache pair

WIDHOPFF, D O (1867-1933) French
£578 $1035 (5-May-92 ZEL.L1582/R) Portrait of young lady standing (48x33cm-19x13in)
s.d.1903 (DM 1700)

WIEDERHOLD, Carl (1865-1961) German
£3800 $7068 (17-Jun-92 S396/R) In park in Hanover (39x45cm-15x18in) s.d.1914 i.verso
cardboard

WIEDH, Leonard (1866-1938) Swedish
£510 $877 (8-Mar-92 BU.M174) Coastal landscape (75x127cm-30x50in) s. (S.KR 5300)

WIEDH, Leonard (1866-1938) Swedish-cont.
| £659 | $1173 | (28-Oct-91 AB.S261) Evening sun in the skerries (59x89cm-23x35in) s. (S.KR 7000) |
| £774 | $1369 | (25-Apr-92 SO.S632/R) Seascape with sailingvessel in rough seas (70x126cm-28x50in) s. (S.KR 8200) |

WIEGAND, Charmion von (1899-) American
| *£2586* | *$4500* | *(15-Apr-92 SY.NY260/R) Counterpoint II (22x20cm-9x8in) init.d.1947 s.i.d.1947 verso collage board* |

WIEGAND, Gustave (1870-1957) American
£506	$900	(2-May-92 W.W90/R) Moonlight on Lake Sunapee, New Hampshire (25x20cm-10x8in) s. board
£514	$900	(3-Apr-92 S.W2010) Morning in spring (51x41cm-20x16in) s. i.verso
£904	$1600	(22-Apr-92 D.NY95) Flowering crabs beside lake (30x41cm-12x16in) s. i.verso board
£920	$1600	(15-Apr-92 SY.NY99/R) Golden days, Mount Kearsarge, New Hampshire (76x91cm-30x36in) s.
£1149	$2000	(15-Apr-92 SY.NY100/R) Red Maples - autumn rubies. Apple blossoms (77x93cm-30x37in) s. pair

WIEGERS, Jan (1893-1959) Dutch
£926	$1685	(11-Dec-91 CH.AM5) Portrait of the sculptor Frits Sieger (61x45cm-24x18in) s.d.47 (D.FL 3000)
£988	$1798	(12-Dec-91 SY.AM130/R) Still life (33x46cm-13x18in) s.d.44 (D.FL 3200)
£1818	$3291	(19-May-92 CH.AM51/R) Reclining nude (54x74cm-21x29in) s.d.32 (D.FL 6000)
£2160	$3932	(11-Dec-91 CH.AM96/R) Nude standing (68x52cm-27x20in) s.d.39 (D.FL 7000)
£4012	$7302	(12-Dec-91 SY.AM120/R) Still life with basket (68x53cm-27x21in) init. s.d.1953 verso (D.FL 13000)
£4545	$8227	(19-May-92 CH.AM160/R) Still life with fruit and flowers in vase (80x100cm-31x39in) s.d.41 (D.FL 15000)
£7407	$13481	(11-Dec-91 SY.AM95/R) Twents landschap (75x60cm-30x24in) s. (D.FL 24000)
£1790	*$3258*	*(12-Dec-91 SY.AM123/R) Design for Russian ballet - Igor (31x45cm-12x18in) s.d.52 gouache (D.FL 5800)*

WIEGHORST, Olaf (1899-1988) American
£5028	$9000	(13-Nov-91 B.SF2716/R) Watching over herd (51x77cm-20x30in) s. s.i.d.1929 verso
£7182	$13000	(5-Dec-91 SY.NY51/R) Moonlight camp (63x76cm-25x30in) s.
£33333	$60000	(10-Jan-92 DM.D2002/R) Navajo land (71x97cm-28x38in) s.
£670	*$1200*	*(14-Nov-91 CE.NY316) Before rodeo (35x28cm-14x11in) s. pen pencil*

WIEGMAN, Gerard (1875-1964) Dutch
| £590 | $1021 | (24-Mar-92 VN.R104) Harbour scene (59x69cm-23x27in) s. (D.FL 1900) |

WIEGMAN, Matthieu (1886-1971) Dutch
£926	$1685	(11-Dec-91 CH.AM4) Flower still life with hortensias (40x27cm-16x11in) s. board (D.FL 3000)
£1212	$2194	(19-May-92 CH.AM99) Village in the mountains (60x75cm-24x30in) s. (D.FL 4000)
£1481	$2696	(12-Dec-91 SY.AM2) Zonnebloemen (73x60cm-29x24in) s. (D.FL 4800)
£1515	$2742	(19-May-92 CH.AM145 a) Still life of flowers (100x80cm-39x31in) s. (D.FL 5000)
£1818	$3291	(19-May-92 CH.AM132) Village square (73x60cm-29x24in) s. (D.FL 6000)
£2315	$4213	(11-Dec-91 CH.AM36) View on church in village, France (60x73cm-24x29in) s. (D.FL 7500)

WIEHL, Hermann (20th C) German?
| £997 | $1824 | (2-Jun-92 FN.S2419/R) Black Forest landscape (60x76cm-24x30in) s. panel (DM 2900) |
| £1930 | $3474 | (23-Nov-91 N.M333/R) Winter landscape (60x75cm-24x30in) mono. panel (DM 5500) |

WIELAND, Hans Beat (1867-1945) Swiss
£549	$933	(23-Oct-91 GD.B519/R) Female nude standing beside window (53x45cm-21x18in) mono.indis.d. board (S.FR 1400)
£889	$1609	(19-May-92 GF.L2627/R) An der Grimsel (50x59cm-20x23in) s.d.1934 i.verso panel (S.FR 2400)
£1394	$2524	(5-Dec-91 SY.Z93/R) Sunshine landscape (58x72cm-23x28in) s. s.i.d.1930verso (S.FR 3500)
£2256	$4128	(4-Jun-92 SY.Z415/R) View from the Simplon (45x50cm-18x20in) s.i.d.1913verso (S.FR 6000)
£4706	$8000	(23-Oct-91 GD.B802/R) Splungenpost, mail sledge arriving in snow covered landscape (54x63cm-21x25in) s. i.d.1928verso (S.FR 12000)
£588	*$1000*	*(23-Oct-91 GD.B803/R) Winter landscape near Arosa (58x76cm-23x30in) s.d.28 W/C (S.FR 1500)*

WIEMKEN, Walter Kurt (1907-1940) Swiss
£1594	$2884	(5-Dec-91 SY.Z141/R) Two fishes (29x38cm-11x15in) board (S.FR 4000)
£3759	$6880	(4-Jun-92 SY.Z405/R) Self portrait (30x22cm-12x9in) board (S.FR 10000)
£2874	*$4971*	*(23-Mar-92 AB.L121/R) Couple with dogs beneath sun (22x21cm-9x8in) mono mixed media (S.FR 7500)*
£3008	*$5504*	*(4-Jun-92 SY.Z374/R) Landscape with castle, Ticino (39x27cm-15x11in) mono.d.26 W/C chl indian ink pen (S.FR 8000)*

WIERINGEN, Cornelis Claesz van (1580-1633) Dutch
£3800 $6612   (13-Apr-92 S121/R) Small sailing vessel off Dutch coast. Landscape sketch
         with trees, birds (7x12cm-3x5in) pen wash black chk double-sided
£6200 $11904   (6-Jul-92 S62/R) Shipping approaching derelict quayside (12x17cm-5x7in)
         pen

WIERINGEN, Cornelis Claesz van (school) (1580-1633) Dutch
£7735 $14000   (21-May-92 CH.NY111/R) Man-of-war and other ships on rocky coast.
         Shipping off coastal village (39x70cm-15x28in) indist.init. pair

WIERUSZ-KOWALSKI, Alfred von (1849-1915) Polish
£1170 $2000   (21-Mar-92 W.W16/R) Soldier on horseback (41x51cm-16x20in) estate
         sig.verso
£3308 $6021   (15-Dec-91 REM.W17) Horse drawn cart (42x66cm-17x26in) s. (P.Z 65000000)
£5177 $9732   (21-Dec-91 PSA.W7) Sledge (43x63cm-17x25in) s. (P.Z 100000000)
£7317 $13317   (12-Dec-91 L.K724/R) Horse-drawn carts with peasant party, evening
         (24x31cm-9x12in) indis.s. (DM 21000)

WIERUSZ-KOWALSKI, Anton von (style) (?) ?
£1400 $2380   (23-Oct-91 S184/R) Greek dancing with swords (75x100cm-30x39in)

WIESE, Theo (?) German
£2160 $3932   (11-Dec-91 WE.MU57/R) The River Isar with view of church
         (76x101cm-30x40in) s.i. (DM 6200)

WIESENDANGER, Dan (1915-) American
£442 $840   (24-Jun-92 B.SF6530/R) What say Leger (76x61cm-30x24in) s. board

WIESENTHAL, Franz (1856-1938) Hungarian
£1595 $2855   (16-Jan-92 D.V106/R) The broken wheelbarrow (76x61cm-30x24in) s.d.1893
         (A.S 32000)

WIETHASE, Edgard (1881-1965) Belgian
£434 $739   (22-Oct-91 C.A1090) Horses in a paddock (43x67cm-17x26in) s.d.1961 W/C
         (B.FR 26000)
£500 $881   (7-Apr-92 C.A662) Jument et poulain (43x55cm-17x22in) s. W/C (B.FR 30000)

WIGAND, Balthasar (1771-1846) Austrian
£3000 $5160   (4-Mar-92 C27/R) View of Palais Auersperg from side of Glacis
         (?x22cm-?x9in) min. s.card set cover wood box shaped book rec

WIGDAHL, A G (1830-1914) Norwegian
£790 $1406   (29-Oct-91 UL.T236 f/R) Olav Kyrresgate, Bergen 1903 (80x65cm-31x26in)
         (N.KR 9000)

WIGGERS, Dirk (1866-1933) Dutch
£608 $1058   (17-Sep-91 CH.AM252) Avondstemming Holleweg, Limburg (48x66cm-19x26in) s.
         i.d.1895 label blk.chk.pastel (D.FL 2000)

WIGGINS, Carleton (1848-1932) American
£677 $1300   (31-Jul-92 E.EDM82/R) Spring ploughing (76x91cm-30x36in) s.
£1044 $1900   (15-Dec-91 LIT.L252) White birches in the forest (61x36cm-24x14in) init.
         board
£1463 $2750   (18-Dec-91 SY.NY68/R) On the Chester Meadows (68x101cm-27x40in) s.d.79
£3509 $6000   (12-Mar-92 CH.NY85/R) Evening row, Long Island (61x92cm-24x36in) s.
         s.i.verso

WIGGINS, Guy (1883-1962) American
£599 $1000   (20-Aug-91 RB.HY282/R) Rockport St. (30x41cm-12x16in) s. board
£1433 $2450   (22-Mar-92 LIT.L118) Winter morning, Madison Square (23x30cm-9x12in)
         board
£2326 $4000   (12-Oct-91 DU.E87/R) Chrysler building (36x30cm-14x12in) s. panel
£2730 $4750   (15-Apr-92 SY.NY153/R) Summer afternoon, Essex Conn (51x61cm-20x24in) s.
£2762 $5000   (4-Dec-91 D.NY84/R) Farm in winter, Kent (51x61cm-20x24in) s.i.verso
£2793 $5000   (13-Nov-91 B.SF2686/R) New York winter (41x30cm-16x12in) s. canvasboard
£2825 $5000   (9-Nov-91 W.W266/R) The rabbit hunter (76x64cm-30x25in) s.i.verso
£2890 $5000   (8-Sep-91 LIT.L156) City snow scene (30x41cm-12x16in) s. board
£2973 $5500   (10-Jun-92 CE.NY513 a/R) Carriages at Plaza (51x61cm-20x24in) s.
£2982 $5100   (22-Mar-92 LIT.L144) Boat near drawbridge (66x76cm-26x30in) s.
£4190 $7500   (13-Nov-91 B.SF2685/R) Wall Street storm (30x41cm-12x16in) s. canvasboard
£4767 $8200   (7-Mar-92 LAE.L168/R) Farm in winter, Kent (51x61cm-20x24in) s.i.verso
£5525 $10000   (6-Dec-91 CH.NY194/R) Entrance to the Plaza (40x30cm-16x12in) s.
         canvasboard
£6286 $11000   (26-Sep-91 CH.NY169/R) Winter weather on Fifth Avenue (30x41cm-12x16in)
         s. s.i.verso canvasboard
£6857 $12000   (26-Sep-91 CH.NY168/R) Looking down Avenue from Plaza, winter
         (30x41cm-12x16in) s. s.i.verso canvasboard
£7558 $13000   (10-Oct-91 FA.PH919/R) Saint Patrick's Cathedral (61x51cm-24x20in) s.
£8242 $15000   (27-May-92 SY.NY116/R) Clock tower, Harkness Memorial, New Haven
         (76x63cm-30x25in) s. indist.s.verso
£8380 $15000   (6-May-92 D.NY29/R) Wall street winter (61x51cm-24x20in) s. s.i.verso
£10440 $19000   (27-May-92 SY.NY115/R) Winter's day along Nassau Street (61x51cm-24x20in)
         s.
£10819 $18500   (11-Mar-92 SY.NY76/R) Swing shift going on (102x127cm-40x50in) s.
         s.d.1943 verso

WIGGINS, Guy (1883-1962) American-cont.
£10857 $19000   (25-Sep-91 SY.NY87/R) Chicago blizzard (63x76cm-25x30in) s.
£12088 $22000   (28-May-92 CH.NY159/R) Washington's Birthday, New York (40x30cm-16x12in)
         s. s.i.d.1927 verso
£14035 $24000   (11-Mar-92 SY.NY77/R) Old Trinity in winter (76x63cm-30x25in) s.
£19231 $35000   (28-May-92 CH.NY160/R) Double-decker bus in winter (64x76cm-25x30in) s.

WIGLEY, James (1918-) Australian
£598 $1065   (27-Apr-92 J.M354) *Interior with figure (25x16cm-10x6in) s. mixed media*
         (A.D 1400)

WIIK, Maria (1853-1928) Finnish
£1798 $3254   (19-May-92 AB.S4390/R) Still life of a bunch of currants (14x20cm-6x8in)
         s. panel (S.KR 19000)
£5433 $9671   (1-Dec-91 HOR.H263) Girl on fence (26x20cm-10x8in) s. (F.M 42000)
£14877 $26481   (1-Dec-91 HOR.H262/R) Sick boy (50x62cm-20x24in) s.d.1894 (F.M 115000)

WIJNBERG, Nicolaas (1918-) Dutch
£1111 $2022   (11-Dec-91 CH.AM45/R) Cote d'Azur (46x55cm-18x22in) s.d.47 s.i.d.verso
         board (D.FL 3600)

WIJNGAARDEN, Theo van (1874-1952) Dutch
£590 $1050   (26-Nov-91 VN.R136) Man on horseback on a towpath (21x30cm-8x12in) s.
         panel (D.FL 1900)
£612 $1089   (29-Oct-91 VN.R313) Interior with female figure at table
         (42x60cm-17x24in) s. (D.FL 2000)

WIJNGAERDT, Piet van (1873-1964) Dutch
£543 $950   (18-Feb-92 CE.NY323) Cottages by riverbank (41x61cm-16x24in) s.
£586 $1067   (11-Dec-91 CH.AM23) Het jaagdpad (68x80cm-27x31in) s. i.verso (D.FL 1900)
£586 $1067   (11-Dec-91 CH.AM30) Mowing time at the farm (70x81cm-28x32in) s.
         (D.FL 1900)
£636 $1152   (21-May-92 SY.AM16) Chrysanten (75x100cm-30x39in) s. s.i.verso
         (D.FL 2100)
£788 $1426   (19-May-92 CH.AM2) Chrysanthemums (78x67cm-31x26in) s. (D.FL 2600)
£788 $1426   (19-May-92 CH.AM46) Molen (58x70cm-23x28in) s. (D.FL 2600)
£909 $1645   (21-May-92 SY.AM24/R) Road in Brabant (85x100cm-33x39in) s. s.i.verso
         (D.FL 3000)
£912 $1587   (17-Sep-91 CH.AM14) A still life of tulips in a vase on a ledge
         (60x50cm-24x20in) s. (D.FL 3000)
£926 $1685   (11-Dec-91 CH.AM34) Roode amaryllis (87x78cm-34x31in) s. s.i.verso
         (D.FL 3000)
£970 $1755   (19-May-92 CH.AM52) Brabant peasant woman, Heeze (90x120cm-35x47in) s.
         (D.FL 3200)
£988 $1798   (11-Dec-91 CH.AM3) Farmers interior (70x82cm-28x32in) s. (D.FL 3200)
£1111 $2022   (12-Dec-91 SY.AM11/R) Still life with carnations (72x61cm-28x24in) s.
         (D.FL 3600)
£1333 $2413   (21-May-92 SY.AM143/R) De Groententuin (80x80cm-31x31in) s. (D.FL 4400)

WIJNVELD, B (1820-1902) Dutch
£1300 $2301   (13-Feb-92 CSK187/R) Rest in the wood (112x147cm-44x58in) s.

WIKBERG, Nils (1907-1971) Finnish
£543 $967   (1-Dec-91 HOR.H264) *Winter's day (54x44cm-21x17in) s.d.1964 gouache*
         (F.M 4200)

WIKELES, Isaac van (attrib) (18th C) Dutch
£7042 $12113   (11-Oct-91 HC.P19/R) La porte Saint-Martin (34x46cm-13x18in) panel
         (F.FR 70000)

WILBUR, Arthur Rutherford (19/20th C) Canadian?
£639 $1163   (26-May-92 JOY.T230/R) Sail boats at sunset, New Brunswick
         (44x77cm-17x30in) s.d.1902 (C.D 1400)

WILCKENS, August (1870-1939) German
£1579 $2937   (15-Jun-92 B.O199/R) Kitchen interior (76x60cm-30x24in) s.d.03
         (N.KR 18000)

WILCOCK, George Barrell (1811-1852) British
£1600 $3056   (21-Jul-92 PH276/R) Figures before cottage in wooded river landscape
         (46x61cm-18x24in)

WILCOX, Frank Nelson (1887-1964) American
£526 $1000   (26-Jun-92 WOL.C146/R) *Shoreline (48x74cm-19x29in) s.d.52 W/C pencil*

WILD, Ernst (1924-1985) German
£2560 $4659   (26-May-92 KF.M1386/R) Black dream, transmitting station in the sea
         (140x239cm-55x94in) s.indis.d.1968 i.stretcher (DM 7500)

WILD, Frank Percy (1861-?) British
£580 $1108   (14-Jul-92 DR253) Corner of canal, Gyldenscroft (20x41cm-8x16in) s.i.

WILDA, Charles (1854-1907) Austrian
£20000 $34200   (20-Mar-92 C52/R) At the water's edge (91x67cm-36x26in) s.d.1897
£32000 $59520   (19-Jun-92 C87/R) The fortune teller (58x81cm-23x32in) s.d.1894

WILDAY, Charles (19th C) British?
£500 $895   (14-Nov-91 CSK84/R) The Hansom Cab (15x23cm-6x9in) s.d.1853 W/C

WILDE, Frans de (19th C) ?
£7558 $13000   (17-Oct-91 SY.NY240/R) Bloemenruil (102x71cm-40x28in) s.d.1884
£7849 $13500   (17-Oct-91 SY.NY241/R) Winterpret (102x71cm-40x28in) s.d.1884

WILDE, H (?) American?
£1250 $2200   (8-Apr-92 D.NY77) Patient pup (61x51cm-24x20in) s.d.81

WILDENRADT, Johann Peter (1861-1904) Danish
£505 $864   (12-Mar-92 RAS.V1011) Street scene with woman and small boy, Helsingor
     (71x55cm-28x22in) s.d.1882 (D.KR 5600)

WILDENS, Jan (1586-1653) Flemish
£7056 $12349   (25-Sep-91 CSC.P28/R) Paysage anime avec paysans et bergers
     (65x101cm-26x40in) (F.FR 70000)
£20576 $39095   (26-Jun-92 AT.P25/R) Paysage de foret avec le depart pour la chasse
     (116x183cm-46x72in) (F.FR 200000)
£32000 $56960   (30-Oct-91 S167/R) Wooded landscape with huntsmen and dogs
     (122x214cm-48x84in) s.d.1615
£2778 $4972   (12-Nov-91 SY.AM305/R) View along village street with peasants flailing
     corn (19x28cm-7x11in) pen wash right hand bottom corner cut (D.FL 9000)
£3395 $6077   (12-Nov-91 SY.AM247/R) Mountainous river landscape with peasants
     harvesting grapes (27x34cm-11x13in) pen wash (D.FL 11000)

WILDENS, Jan (attrib) (1586-1653) Flemish
£5384 $9530   (7-Nov-91 D.V306/R) Landscape with shepherds by waterfall
     (88x114cm-35x45in) (A.S 110000)
£2400 $4176   (13-Apr-92 S246/R) Italianate harbourside scene (29x43cm-11x17in) pen
     wash

WILDENS, Jan and SNYDERS, Frans (attrib) (17th C) Flemish/Dutch
£11500 $20125   (28-Feb-92 C155/R) Hounds attacking a wolf over a dead buck
     (171x25cm-67x10in)

WILDENS, Jan and SNYDERS, Frans (style) (17th C) Flemish/Dutch
£5500 $10560   (10-Jul-92 C119/R) Wolf and hounds fighting over dead buck
     (262x296cm-103x117in)

WILDENS, Jan and VOS, Paul de (studio) (17th C) Flemish
£4400 $7832   (30-Oct-91 S166/R) Hounds chasing foxes in landscape (174x242cm-69x95in)

WILDER (?) ?
£743 $1300   (18-Feb-92 CE.NY221) Grand Canal, Venice (51x44cm-20x17in) s. W/C
     paperboard

WILDER, Andre (1871-1965) French
£1434 $2582   (2-Feb-92 ZZ.F113/R) Pont de Pierre pres du village (46x55cm-18x22in) s.
     (F.FR 14000)

WILDER, Tom (?) American?
£1163 $2000   (20-Oct-91 HG.C35) Beach scene (71x86cm-28x34in) s.

WILDING (?) ?
£1300 $2223   (18-Mar-92 B75/R) View of Hammersmith Bridge (49x74cm-19x29in) s. pair

WILDING, R T (attrib) (20th C) British
£460 $819   (29-Oct-91 SWS462) Harbour mouth (37x61cm-15x24in) W/C htd bodycol

WILES, Irving Ramsey (1861-1948) American
£862 $1500   (15-Apr-92 SY.NY74 a) Connoisseur (132x95cm-52x37in) s.d.1916
£2210 $4000   (21-May-92 S.W2909/R) Reclining nude on lakebank (20x36cm-8x14in) s.
     i.stretcher
£6250 $11000   (12-Apr-92 LIT.L153) Purple kimono (71x61cm-28x24in) s.
£10440 $19000   (28-May-92 CH.NY130/R) Idle moments (38x43cm-15x17in) s. s.i.verso
£13187 $24000   (28-May-92 CH.NY164/R) Scallopers, Peconic Bay (51x67cm-20x26in) s.
£15385 $28000   (27-May-92 SY.NY75/R) Enchanted pool (69x100cm-27x39in) s.
£49724 $90000   (6-Dec-91 CH.NY160/R) In the garden (66x50cm-26x20in) s.
£730 $1300   (2-Nov-91 IH.NY84/R) Crew race, women in boat (48x36cm-19x14in) s.
     gouache en grisaille
£2143 $3600   (14-Aug-91 B.P162/R) In the hills (41x25cm-16x10in) s.i. W/C

WILES, Lemuel (1826-1905) American
£541 $1000   (10-Jun-92 CE.NY204) Melrose Abbey (44x30cm-17x12in) s.i.d.1883 s.i.verso

WILFORD, Loran (1892-?) American
£526 $900   (12-Mar-92 MFA.C170) Seated Indian girl by pots (61x51cm-24x20in) s.
     board

WILHELM, Paul (1886-1965) German
£2273 $4045   (28-Nov-91 SY.BE43/R) Lupins and poppies with watering can
     (51x63cm-20x25in) s. (DM 6500)

WILHELMSON, Carl (1866-1928) Swedish
£1246 $2244   (23-Nov-91 SO.S651/R) The chappel 1918 (59x77cm-23x30in) s. (S.KR 13000)
£2589 $4660   (19-Nov-91 GO.G195) Coastal landscape with water reflections
     (22x27cm-9x11in) s. panel (S.KR 27000)
£2925 $5176   (5-Nov-91 BA.S189/R) Reclining model (20x57cm-8x22in) s. paper on panel
     (S.KR 31000)
£5177 $9319   (19-Nov-91 GO.G196/R) Town landscape with sailing vessel
     (41x33cm-16x13in) s. panel (S.KR 54000)
£14421 $26391   (14-May-92 BU.S78/R) After work (80x63cm-31x25in) s. (S.KR 152000)

WILHJELM, Johannes (1868-1938) Danish
£485 $863   (28-Apr-92 RAS.K321) Ponte Vecchio in Florenze (45x59cm-18x23in)
     init.d.24 (D.KR 5500)
£903 $1625   (19-Nov-91 RAS.K249/R) Joy of motherhood (62x76cm-24x30in) init.
     (D.KR 10000)
£1700 $3077   (19-May-92 SWS11/R) Children on beach (52x63cm-20x25in) init.d.18
£3610 $6498   (19-Nov-91 RAS.K87/R) Girls on an outing in the woods (70x93cm-28x37in)
     s.d.18 (D.KR 40000)

WILKE, Paul Ernst (1894-1972) German
£515 $876   (25-Oct-91 BM.B649/R) Morning sun over the Hamme (60x70cm-24x28in) s.
     i.d.1943verso (DM 1500)
£584 $1087   (20-Jun-92 BM.B785/R) Summer sun in Weddewarden (40x50cm-16x20in) s.
     i.verso (DM 1700)
£687 $1278   (20-Jun-92 BM.B784/R) Finkenwerder fishing boats (80x60cm-31x24in) s.
     i.verso (DM 2000)
£756 $1406   (20-Jun-92 BM.B783/R) Granatkutter in Burhave (100x70cm-39x28in) s.
     i.d.1937verso (DM 2200)
£756 $1406   (20-Jun-92 BM.B782/R) Fishing cutter in harbour s. i.verso board
     (DM 2200)
£825 $1534   (20-Jun-92 BM.B781/R) Farmhouses in autumn sunshine (49x60cm-19x24in) s.
     i.d.1940verso board (DM 2400)
£1166 $2041   (3-Apr-92 BM.B585/R) Hallig Langeness (80x100cm-31x39in) s.i. (DM 3300)

WILKIE (style) (?) British
£1000 $1820   (12-Dec-91 B97) Adoration of the Magi (85x63cm-33x25in)

WILKIE, Sir David (1785-1841) British
£995 $1771   (25-Nov-91 W.T1927/R) South German interior with rural figures and child
     musicians (37x55cm-15x22in) s.d.1806 (C.D 2000)
£5000 $8950   (13-Nov-91 S89/R) Sketch for the highland whisky still (14x20cm-6x8in)
     s.d.1817verso panel
£750   *$1320*   *(9-Apr-92 S57) Studies of figures in tavern (25x37cm-10x15in) i.d.1806*
     pen pencil
£2400   *$4584*   *(14-Jul-92 C109/R) Scene from Peveril of Peak. Scene from Quentin Durward*
     (18x23cm-7x9in) i. pen wash pair

WILKIE, Sir David (after) (1785-1841) British
£4000 $7160   (14-Nov-91 CSK232/R) The blind fiddler (56x76cm-22x30in) bears sig.d.1806
     panel

WILKIE, Sir David (attrib) (1785-1841) British
£1152 $2200   (16-Jul-92 SY.NY509/R) The bad shilling (38x46cm-15x18in) panel

WILKIE, Sir David (style) (1785-1841) British
£950 $1653   (11-Sep-91 MMB337/R) Scene outside a country post office
     (43x61cm-17x24in) indist.s.

WILKINSON, Arthur (?) Australian?
£460   *$796*   *(24-Mar-92 PHC336/R) Harvesters in coastal landscape (33x50cm-13x20in) s.*
     W/C
£560   *$1075*   *(28-Jul-92 SWS256) The cottage (37x27cm-15x11in) s. W/C htd.bodycol.*
£750   *$1388*   *(11-Jun-92 CSK49/R) Labourer and his family at cottage gate*
     (30x46cm-12x18in) s. pencil W/C htd.white
£900   *$1602*   *(28-Apr-92 RG2440) Cottage garden scenes with figures (28x38cm-11x15in)*
     s. W/C pair
£950   *$1672*   *(6-Apr-92 PH118/R) Sussex homestead (29x39cm-11x15in) s. W/C bodycol.*
£1000   *$1720*   *(4-Mar-92 S254/R) Sewing by cottage door. Preparing to go out*
     (27x39cm-11x15in) s. W/C htd white pair
£1000   *$1760*   *(6-Apr-92 PH119/R) Fishermen's cottages, Cornwall (29x39cm-11x15in) s.*
     W/C bodycol.

WILKINSON, Arthur Stanley (c.1860-c.1930) British
£500   *$860*   *(15-Oct-91 GA168) Road to sea, Porthallon, Cornwall - summer scene*
     (43x28cm-17x11in) s. W/C
£516   *$862*   *(19-Aug-91 SY.ME175) Hillside farm, Hampshire (37x54cm-15x21in) s. W/C*
     htd bodycol (A.D 1100)
£950   *$1653*   *(12-Sep-91 CSK62) Old Hampshire cottage (28x38cm-11x15in) s. pencil W/C*
     htd white
£1000   *$1710*   *(13-Mar-92 C12) Mother and child by cottage door. In the cottage garden*
     (37x27cm-15x11in) s. pencil W/C htd.white pair
£1000   *$1710*   *(13-Mar-92 C15/R) Cottage garden with mother and child standing by the*
     door (35x53cm-14x21in) s. pencil W/C bodycol

WILKINSON, John B (19th C) Canadian
£2195 $3951   *(19-Nov-91 FP.M37/R) Sleighing on snow cone, Montmorency Falls, Quebec (21x29cm-8x11in) s. W/C (C.D 4500)*

WILKINSON, Norman (1878-1971) British
£800 $1344   (15-Aug-91 B320/R) Coming into port (41x61cm-16x24in) s.
£900 $1557   (25-Mar-92 PHS563/R) Las Palmas, The Canary Islands (43x58cm-17x23in) s.
£1000 $1740   (15-Apr-92 PHL154/R) Sailing barges on river estuary (28x38cm-11x15in) s. panel
£2900 $5017   (25-Mar-92 PHS562/R) Near Hythe (43x61cm-17x24in) s.
£560 $997   *(29-Nov-91 T246) River landscape with fishermen in boat (15x30cm-6x12in) s. W/C*
£900 $1620   *(27-Jan-92 PH142) Royal yacht reviewing fleet (23x35cm-9x14in) s. W/C htd white*

WILKS, Maurice C (1911-1983) British
£650 $1105   (22-Oct-91 SWS386/R) Bogland, Connemara, evening (39x49cm-15x19in) s. bears i.verso
£741 $1348   (11-Dec-91 A.D60 a) Rocky coastal landscape (20x30cm-8x12in) s. board (E.P 800)
£800 $1392   (18-Sep-91 CG204/R) Coast at Ballycastle, Co. Antrim (41x51cm-16x20in) s. i.verso
£818 $1415   (2-Oct-91 A.D144) Easterly wind, North Channel, North Antrim (36x46cm-14x18in) s. (E.P 900)
£818 $1415   (2-Oct-91 A.D124) Rocky coastal landscape (20x30cm-8x12in) s. board (E.P 900)
£850 $1522   (14-Jan-92 SWS251/R) Curragh, Atlantic Drive, Co.Donegal (40x45cm-16x18in) s.
£880 $1690   (30-Jul-92 GSP555) White Park Bay, Co. Antrim (43x48cm-17x19in) s.
£900 $1566   (18-Sep-91 CG172/R) Feeding chickens by farmhouses, Tyrella, Mourne mountains beyond (30x41cm-12x16in) s. canvasboard
£900 $1647   (6-Feb-92 DLY274) Kyle More Lake, Connemara (51x61cm-20x24in) s. i.verso
£972 $1769   (11-Dec-91 A.D156) Spring morning, Glendun, Co.Antrim (51x41cm-20x16in) s. s.i.verso (E.P 1050)
£1000 $1740   (18-Sep-91 CG201) Incoming tide, Melmore Head (51x61cm-20x24in) s.
£1121 $1940   (25-Mar-92 A.D141) Slieve Bignian, Mourne Mountains, Co. Down (33x43cm-13x17in) s. (E.P 1200)
£1200 $2088   (18-Sep-91 CG203/R) Children by Lough Fee, Connemara (36x45cm-14x18in) s. i.verso
£1215 $2102   (25-Mar-92 A.D47) Morning light, Roundstone (36x43cm-14x17in) s. (E.P 1300)
£1267 $2344   (9-Jun-92 FB.M91) At Roundstone, Connemara (40x51cm-16x20in) s. (C.D 2800)
£1273 $2202   (2-Oct-91 A.D168) Early morning, Lackagh River, Co. Donegal (41x51cm-16x20in) s. (E.P 1400)
£1400 $2506   (16-Nov-91 TA.B1) Killarney. Creeslough, County Donegal (25x20cm-10x8in) s. pair
£1402 $2425   (25-Mar-92 A.D148) At Forrglass, Connemara (41x51cm-16x20in) s. (E.P 1500)
£1402 $2425   (25-Mar-92 A.D136) Landscape, near Cliften, Connemra, Co.Galway (38x74cm-15x29in) s. (E.P 1500)
£1425 $2722   (23-Jul-92 T100/R) Cottages near Cliveden, Connemara (46x61cm-18x24in) s.i.
£1495 $2587   (25-Mar-92 A.D78) Rough seas, Dooney Cove, Atlantic Drive, Co.Donegal (41x99cm-16x39in) s. (E.P 1600)
£1500 $2610   (18-Sep-91 CG206/R) Corragh Atlantic Drive, Co. Donegal (63x76cm-25x30in) s.
£1560 $2854   (1-Jun-92 W.T1312/R) Peaceful morning, Connemara, Co Galway (51x61cm-20x24in) s. (C.D 3400)
£1651 $3072   (17-Jun-92 A.D143) In Credagh Wood, Cushendun (41x51cm-16x20in) s. (E.P 1800)
£2018 $3754   (15-Jun-92 AD.D84) Errislenon, Connemara, Co Galway (46x61cm-18x24in) s. (E.P 2200)
£2100 $3570   (22-Oct-91 SWS385/R) Roundstone, County Galway. Mourne Mountains, County Down (34x44cm-13x17in) s. pair
£2100 $3654   (17-Sep-91 PH112/R) Curraghs in sunlit cove, Country Kerry (51x61cm-20x24in) s. i. verso
£2600 $4524   (18-Sep-91 CG205/R) Farmyard in West of Ireland (61x76cm-24x30in) s.
£2752 $5119   (17-Jun-92 A.D57/R) On Dun River, Cushendun, Co. Antrim (51x61cm-20x24in) s. (E.P 3000)
£2778 $4861   (17-Feb-92 AD.D45/R) Autumn day, Bloody Foreland, Co. Donegal (56x69cm-22x27in) s.i.verso (E.P 3000)
£4545 $7864   (2-Oct-91 A.D177/R) Old farm, Brablagh, Cushendun (36x46cm-14x18in) s. (E.P 5000)
£407 $741   *(11-Dec-91 A.D120) McCormick's Farm (25x61cm-10x24in) s. W/C (E.P 440)*

WILKS, Maxwell (1944-) Australian
£485 $863   (26-Nov-91 J.M207) Fencers (54x70cm-21x28in) s.d.90 (A.D 1100)
£617 $1098   (26-Nov-91 J.M137) Unloading sugar from Lake Barine (75x89cm-30x35in) s.d.87 (A.D 1400)

WILL, Frank see FRANK WILL

WILL, G (19/20th C) ?
£769 $1400   (26-May-92 CE.NY247/R) Rapallo (33x46cm-13x18in) s.i.d.1900

WILLAERT, Arthur (1875-?) Belgian
£750 $1358   (2-Dec-91 CSK134/R) Voiliers au coucher du soleil (85x116cm-33x46in) s.

WILLAERT, Ferdinand (1823-1905) Belgian
£5464 $9889   (23-May-92 KV.L475/R) Zierikzee (70x96cm-28x38in) s. (B.FR 330000)

WILLAERT, Joseph (20th C) ?
£728 $1319   (23-May-92 KV.L390) Interior (179x120cm-70x47in) s.d.1973 (B.FR 44000)

WILLAERTS, Abraham (1603-1669) Dutch
£8642 $15469   (12-Nov-91 SY.AM91/R) Fishermen dividing out catch on sea shore
    (53x82cm-21x32in) s. panel (D.FL 28000)

WILLAERTS, Isaac (1620-1693) Dutch
£2469 $4420   (14-Nov-91 CH.AM16/R) Fisherman displaying wares on the beach with ruined
    tower on jetty beyond (20x26cm-8x10in) s.d.1638 panel (D.FL 8000)

WILLAERTS, Isaac and ORMEA, Willem (17th C) Dutch
£5093 $9116   (12-Nov-91 SY.AM16/R) Fishermen bringing catch ashore (39x53cm-15x21in)
    init. panel (D.FL 16500)

WILLCOCK, George Barrell (1811-1852) British
£920 $1766   (28-Jul-92 SWS313/R) Near Lapford, Devon (33x44cm-13x17in)
£1279 $2200   (15-Oct-91 CE.NY236/R) Fingal Mill (51x61cm-20x24in) s.i.

WILLCOCK, George Barrell (attrib) (1811-1852) British
£1700 $3111   (7-Feb-92 K499/R) Washing sheep (48x58cm-19x23in)

WILLE, August von (1829-1887) German
£1379 $2372   (16-Oct-91 KM.K1442/R) Moonlit Rhine landscape with view of customs tower
    and tavern (21x26cm-8x10in) s. panel (DM 4000)
£3833 $6976   (12-Dec-91 L.K725/R) St Hubertus falling on his knees meeting the white
    stag in forest (131x99cm-52x39in) s. (DM 11000)
£6061 $10727   (22-Apr-92 CH.AM214/R) Rhenish valley with a ferry and a moored vessel. A
    moonlit river-valley (25x48cm-10x19in) s.d.1880 two (D.FL 20000)

WILLE, Clara von (1838-1883) German
£4842 $8134   (27-Aug-91 RAS.K162/R) Dachshunds playing about (52x51cm-20x20in)
    s.d.1868 (D.KR 55000)

WILLE, Fritz von (1860-1941) German
£2028 $3508   (25-Mar-92 KM.K1523) Rhine landscape with Burg Katz near St Goar and
    shipping (28x44cm-11x17in) i.d.1915 (DM 5800)
£2218 $4038   (27-May-92 PH.DU21/R) Eifel landscape (15x20cm-6x8in) s.d.25 board
    (DM 6500)
£2502 $4304   (8-Mar-92 BU.M412) Alpine landscape (60x80cm-24x31in) s. (S.KR 26000)
£3276 $5634   (16-Oct-91 KM.K1450/R) Eifel landscape with lake (21x36cm-8x14in) s.d.88
    panel (DM 9500)
£4138 $7117   (16-Oct-91 KM.K1447/R) Snowy Eifel landscape with view of Totenmaar
    (80x100cm-31x39in) s.d.1940 (DM 12000)
£4181 $7610   (12-Dec-91 L.K726/R) Thaw in Eifel landscape with stream
    (50x60cm-20x24in) mono.d.82 (DM 12000)
£4181 $7610   (12-Dec-91 L.K728/R) Eifel landscape with Schloss Hamm in spring
    (50x60cm-20x24in) s.d.33 (DM 12000)
£4196 $7259   (25-Mar-92 KM.K1522/R) View of farmhouse in Eifel landscape
    (80x60cm-31x24in) s.d.84 (DM 12000)
£4483 $7710   (16-Oct-91 KM.K1449/R) Flowering Eifel landscape with view of village
    (60x80cm-24x31in) s. (DM 13000)
£4498 $8547   (24-Jun-92 KM.K1311/R) Eifel landscape with view of Totenmaar at
    Mosenberg (60x80cm-24x31in) s. (DM 13000)
£5517 $9490   (16-Oct-91 KM.K1448/R) Eifel landscape with view of Reifferscheid
    (60x80cm-24x31in) s. (DM 16000)
£5517 $9490   (16-Oct-91 KM.K1446/R) Hilly Eifel landscape with view of Reifferscheid
    (50x60cm-20x24in) s. (DM 16000)
£7067 $12367   (3-Apr-92 BM.B737/R) Burg Reichenstein (51x62cm-20x24in) s. (DM 20000)
£8191 $14826   (21-May-92 L.K500/R) Rhine landscape with view of Hammerstein and
    Hammersteinerwerth (85x111cm-33x44in) s.d.1900 (DM 24000)
£11419 $21696   (24-Jun-92 KM.K1310/R) Landscape near Mosenberg, Eifel
    (125x150cm-49x59in) s.d.07 (DM 33000)

WILLE, Johann Georg (1715-1808) German
*£1400 $2688   (7-Jul-92 C236/R) Kiln at Vernon with washerwomen and cottage beyond
    (23x34cm-9x13in) s.d.1761 chk*
*£1500 $2880   (7-Jul-92 C237/R) House with seated peasant woman at Sceaux-les-Chartreux
    (20x28cm-8x11in) s.d.1766 chk wash*

WILLE, Pierre-Alexandre (1748-1821) French
£1397 $2500   (14-Jan-92 SY.NY167/R) Head of old man (23x18cm-9x7in) s.d.1792 pen

WILLEBOIRTS, Thomas (1614-1654) Flemish
£1200 $2100   (31-Mar-92 PH73/R) St. Francis of Assisi (202x77cm-80x30in)

WILLEBOIRTS, Thomas (circle) (1614-1654) Flemish
£3600 $6912   (10-Jul-92 PH60/R) Venus and Cupid (148x111cm-58x44in)

WILLEBOIRTS, Thomas and THIELEN, Jan Philips van (attrib) (17th C) Flemish
£5523 $9500   (10-Oct-91 SY.NY206/R) The Madonna and child with infant Saint John
                Baptist in stone cartouche (105x77cm-41x30in)

WILLEBRANT, James (1950-) Australian
£599 $1042   (16-Sep-91 CH.ME106) Poolscape (131x168cm-52x66in) s. s.i.d.1987 verso
                (A.D 1300)

WILLEMS, Florent (1823-1905) Belgian
£4163 $7744   (16-Jun-92 SY.B283/R) Lady with her dog (54x44cm-21x17in) s. panel
                (B.FR 250000)

WILLEMSENS, Abraham (after) (fl.1627-1672) Flemish?
£2469 $4420   (14-Nov-91 CH.AM40/R) Italianate landscape with beggar boy offered milk
                by milkmaid (104x120cm-41x47in) (D.FL 8000)

WILLETT, Arthur (1868-?) British
£400 $724   *(19-May-92 PH50) Stream amidst the silver birches (51x68cm-20x27in) s.*
                W/C bodycol
£480 $869   *(19-May-92 SWS468/R) Falmer, Sussex (28x43cm-11x17in) s.i.verso W/C over*
                pencil htd.bodycol
£500 $890   *(29-Oct-91 C113) Figures and horse on path, Ashdown Forest*
                (26x20cm-10x8in) s.i.verso pencil W/C htd white
£620 $1085   *(25-Sep-91 RB729) Patcham Hanger, near Brighton (53x36cm-21x14in)*
£850 $1573   *(10-Jun-92 WAW315) Hamlet in the countryside (30x64cm-12x25in) s. W/C*

WILLIAM, S (?) ?
£500 $890   (28-Nov-91 B126) Forest clearing (39x60cm-15x24in) s. panel

WILLIAMS OF NORWICH, William (fl.1758-1797) British
£4000 $7160   (15-Nov-91 C44/R) Cottager's return (92x75cm-36x30in) s.d.

WILLIAMS OF PLYMOUTH, William (1808-1895) British
£950 $1691   (28-Nov-91 B31/R) Wooded river scene (36x49cm-14x19in) s.i.d.1890

WILLIAMS, A (?) ?
£1500 $2715   (6-Dec-91 BW390) Still life study of flowers on ledge (61x51cm-24x20in)
                s.

WILLIAMS, Albert (19th C) British
£550 $1001   (12-Dec-91 CSK239/R) Still life with pink roses and a porcelain figurine
                (40x51cm-16x20in) s.
£620 $1104   (28-Apr-92 RG2397) Still life study of pink roses in vase
                (38x48cm-15x19in) s.
£650 $1125   (3-Sep-91 CHAP304/R) Still life of christmas roses, daphne and other
                spring flowers (41x25cm-16x10in) s.
£800 $1384   (3-Sep-91 CHAP303/R) Still life of hybrid tea roses in a porcelain jug
                (38x36cm-15x14in) s.
£1550 $2682   (3-Sep-91 CHAP305) Still life of azaleas, irises and aquilegias
                (76x64cm-30x25in) s.
£2600 $4498   (3-Sep-91 CHAP306/R) Still life of peonies and other summer flowers in a
                porcelain vase (64x76cm-25x30in) s.

WILLIAMS, Alexander (1846-1930) British
£5800 $10092   (18-Sep-91 CG109/R) When boats come home, Skerries Beach, evening
                (61x91cm-24x36in) s.d.1889 with i.verso

WILLIAMS, Alfred Walter (1824-1905) British
£600 $1116   (18-Jun-92 B154) Surrey-distant and far away (49x75cm-19x30in) s.d.1882
£1600 $2848   (28-Apr-92 PH130/R) Working the fields (46x77cm-18x30in) s.d.1854

WILLIAMS, Caroline F (1836-1921) British
£1600 $2832   (6-Nov-91 S15/R) Margate, night (27x48cm-11x19in) s.i.stretcher

WILLIAMS, Edward (1782-1855) British
£4500 $8595   (15-Jul-92 S67/R) River landscape with children sitting on a riverbank
                (57x79cm-22x31in) s.
£5500 $9460   (11-Oct-91 C20/R) Landscape with figures (63x76cm-25x30in) s.i.verso
                panel
£14000 $25060   (13-Nov-91 S71/R) Fishermen unloading catch in estuary (60x86cm-24x34in)
                s. panel

WILLIAMS, Edward (attrib) (1782-1855) British
£2400 $4080   (22-Oct-91 S273/R) Wooded landscape with figures on path
                (48x61cm-19x24in)
£3300 $5808   (6-Apr-92 WW58) On Stour (46x62cm-18x24in) pair

WILLIAMS, Edward Charles (1807-1881) British
£1100 $1881   (18-Mar-92 CSK306) River estuary at sunset (38x61cm-15x24in) i.verso
£1200 $2292   (17-Jul-92 C86/R) Moonlight on the River Yare (49x61cm-19x24in) s.
£1429 $2500   (21-Feb-92 BG.M252/R) Figures and animals in river landscape
                (61x51cm-24x20in) s.
£2094 $4000   (16-Jul-92 SY.NY520/R) Along the Upper Thames (61x106cm-24x42in) s.d.67
£3500 $6580   (19-Dec-91 C196/R) The mill. Children fishing at pool (21x25cm-8x10in)
                pair

WILLIAMS, Edward Charles (1807-1881) British-cont.
| £5500 | $9460 | (4-Mar-92 S26/R) Gypsies by way (51x71cm-20x28in) |
| £6400 | $12160 | (24-Jun-92 DR144/R) On Thames, Haymaking, with figures fishing from punt (61x108cm-24x43in) i.d.1850 |

WILLIAMS, Edward Charles (attrib) (1807-1881) British
£1300	$2262	(12-Sep-91 CSK125/R) Wooded landscape with children and dog on track (46x61cm-18x24in)
£1440	$2750	(16-Jul-92 SY.NY517/R) Figures in wooded grove (66x88cm-26x35in) bears.sig.
£1644	$2827	(8-Oct-91 ZEL.L1794/R) Cows watering in wooded river landscape, autumn (50x61cm-20x24in) (DM 4800)
£1998	$3596	(21-Nov-91 D.V32/R) Two young anglers (61x51cm-24x20in) (A.S 40000)

WILLIAMS, Edward Charles (circle) (1807-1881) British
| £1500 | $2685 | (5-May-92 SWS370/R) Figures on country path near cottage. Cattle watering by cottage (29x45cm-11x18in) pair |

WILLIAMS, Edward Charles (style) (1807-1881) British
| £1500 | $2595 | (26-Mar-92 CSK148) River landscape with figures and cattle resting on bank, windmill beyond (46x63cm-18x25in) |

WILLIAMS, Edward Charles and SHAYER, William (19th C) British
| £5400 | $10368 | (28-Jul-92 SWS373/R) A roadside inn (74x92cm-29x36in) |
| £13000 | $23790 | (3-Jun-92 S38/R) Near Wantage, Berkshire (77x128cm-30x50in) s.d.51 |

WILLIAMS, Edward Charles and SHAYER, William (snr) (19th C) British
| £9000 | $15840 | (8-Apr-92 S99/R) landscape with cattle watering (70x90cm-28x35in) s. |

WILLIAMS, Ellen (1790-?) British
| £463 | $843 | (11-Dec-91 A.D34) The fisher boy (91x71cm-36x28in) s.d.1842 (E.P 500) |

WILLIAMS, Emmett (1925-) American
| £429 | $777 | (21-May-92 F.M243) Lichtskulptur, first state (99x69cm-39x27in) s.i.d.1989 tempera collage on cardboard (I.L 950000) |
| £620 | $1128 | (25-May-92 RAS.K109) Escape by moonlight (56x77cm-22x30in) s.d.1981 gouache airbrush (D.KR 7000) |

WILLIAMS, Evelyn (1929-) British
| £620 | $1097 | (5-Nov-91 PH162/R) The attic room (79x135cm-31x53in) chl. |

WILLIAMS, Frederick (fl.1827) British?
| £1200 | $2148 | (14-Nov-91 S167) The Palace of Necessidade, near Lisbon, Portugal (30x46cm-12x18in) s.i.d.1826verso W/C over pencil htd.bodycol |

WILLIAMS, Frederick Ballard (1871-1956) American
£726	$1300	(13-Nov-91 B.SF2651/R) Music in afternoon (63x76cm-25x30in) s.
£773	$1400	(21-May-92 S.W2987) Autumn view (30x45cm-12x18in) s.
£820	$1500	(6-Jun-92 LAE.L117/R) Women in interior of forest (64x76cm-25x30in) s.
£950	$1700	(13-Nov-91 B.SF2652/R) Seven maidens (102x127cm-40x50in)
£2299	$4000	(13-Sep-91 S.W2873/R) Afternoon light (76x114cm-30x45in) s. i.verso

WILLIAMS, Frederick Dickenson (1829-1915) British
£575	$1000	(13-Sep-91 DOU.M8) Landscape with village, aquaduct, people (137x89cm-54x35in)
£661	$1150	(13-Sep-91 DOU.M10) Landscape, trees, river (137x86cm-54x34in)
£782	$1400	(14-Nov-91 CE.NY179/R) Cottage path (46x66cm-18x26in) s.d.1876
£1878	$3400	(4-Dec-91 D.NY24/R) Outing in forest of Fontainebleau (30x46cm-12x18in) s.d.1875
£7778	$14000	(22-Nov-91 S.BM62 a/R) View of Boston - first block of Columbus Avenue and Boston-Providence railroad station (46x76cm-18x30in) s.i.d.1868

WILLIAMS, Frederick Ronald (1927-1982) Australian
£11915	$21089	(26-Apr-92 SY.ME278/R) Landscape (96x65cm-38x26in) s. (A.D 28000)
£25532	$45191	(26-Apr-92 SY.ME327/R) Wattles at Dunmoochin (87x87cm-34x34in) s. (A.D 60000)
£28634	$51542	(24-Nov-91 SY.S448/R) Landscape with wattles (88x88cm-35x35in) s. d.1969 verso (A.D 65000)
£40598	$72265	(28-Apr-92 CH.ME245/R) Botanist's garden (101x101cm-40x40in) s. i.d.1975verso (A.D 95000)
£5957	$10545	(26-Apr-92 SY.ME270/R) Upwey landscape, 1965-66 (34x54cm-13x21in) s. gouache (A.D 14000)
£6608	$11894	(24-Nov-91 SY.S378/R) Burnt blackboys (55x73cm-22x29in) s. gouache (A.D 15000)
£9362	$16570	(26-Apr-92 SY.ME381/R) Waterpond in landscape, 1966 (72x54cm-28x21in) s. gouache (A.D 22000)
£9787	$17323	(26-Apr-92 SY.ME474/R) Upwey landscape (54x72cm-21x28in) s. gouache (A.D 23000)

WILLIAMS, George Augustus (1814-1901) British
| £664 | $1149 | (25-Mar-92 KM.K1525) Rider and dog in landscape (27x40cm-11x16in) s. (DM 1900) |
| £850 | $1454 | (12-Mar-92 CSK185/R) Wooded river landscape with angler on bank (36x61cm-14x24in) mono. |

WILLIAMS, George Augustus (1814-1901) British-cont.

£1000	$1900	(23-Jun-92 PH204/R) Sunset on the upper stretches of the Thames (40x66cm-16x26in)
£1100	$1892	(4-Mar-92 S20/R) Cowherd's rest (35x51cm-14x20in) mono.
£1800	$3348	(18-Jun-92 B64/R) Winter landscape with mill and figures (44x67cm-17x26in)
£3000	$5340	(28-Nov-91 B188 c) Spring, view in Surrey (41x61cm-16x24in) mono. i.verso
£5500	$9460	(11-Oct-91 C163/R) Ice cart - hazy winter morning (61x101cm-24x40in) mono.d.1859

WILLIAMS, George Augustus and HERRING, John Frederick (jnr) (19th C) British

| £3500 | $6405 | (3-Jun-92 S39/R) Outside a country inn (55x91cm-22x36in) s.bears sig. of Herring |

WILLIAMS, Harry Hughes (?) British

| £1225 | $2328 | (25-Jun-92 ME1) Riverbank scene with trees to background and ruin by bank (53x74cm-21x29in) s.verso |

WILLIAMS, Haynes (19th C) British

| £500 | $860 | (16-Oct-91 CSK222) La Gitana (33x25cm-13x10in) s. s.i.verso board oval |

WILLIAMS, Henry (19th C) British

| £1408 | $2366 | (27-Aug-91 RAS.K494/R) Roman lady and her little girl by an altar (50x41cm-20x16in) s.d.1834 (D.KR 16000) |

WILLIAMS, Hugh Grecian (1773-1829) British

£750	$1343	(12-Nov-91 C80/R) *Dancing figures overlooking the Bay of Naples (51x63cm-20x25in) pencil W/C*
£800	$1408	(9-Apr-92 S64/R) *Milkmaid. Boy fishing by rocky stream (65x51cm-26x20in) s.d.1816 W/C over pencil htd bodycol pair*
£1300	$2210	(23-Oct-91 S7/R) *Acropolis from the Theseum (45x68cm-18x27in) W/C over pencil htd gum arabic bodycol*
£3000	$5370	(13-Nov-91 CG616/R) *A view of Edinburgh and the Pentlands (75x131cm-30x52in) pencil W/C htd.bodycol scratching out*
£12000	$20400	(23-Oct-91 S192/R) *Acropolis (63x98cm-25x39in) W/C over pencil htd.bodycol gum arabic*
£15500	$26350	(23-Oct-91 S191/R) *Acropolis, Athens (44x63cm-17x25in) W/C over pencil*

WILLIAMS, John Haynes (1836-1908) British

| £1800 | $3096 | (4-Mar-92 S165/R) Spanish water carrier (61x51cm-24x20in) s. |

WILLIAMS, John L Scott (1897-1976) American

| £421 | $750 | (2-May-92 IH.NY87/R) Couple in Arbor (51x48cm-20x19in) s. chl |

WILLIAMS, Kyffin (1918-) British

£720	$1253	(17-Sep-91 PH150/R) Coast at St.David's (71x61cm-28x24in) init.
£1300	$2483	(16-Jul-92 B190/R) Storm at Trer Addur (76x76cm-30x30in) init.
£1300	$2483	(16-Jul-92 B189/R) The old gypsy lady (127x76cm-50x30in) init.

WILLIAMS, Mary Belle (19/20th C) American

| £621 | $1100 | (12-Feb-92 B.SF441/R) Still life with persimmons (51x61cm-20x24in) s. |

WILLIAMS, Micah (1782-1837) American

| £2312 | $4000 | (8-Sep-91 LIT.L78) Portrait of gentleman (64x53cm-25x21in) pastel backed with original newspaper d.1825 |

WILLIAMS, Paul A (1934-) American

£511	$900	(10-Apr-92 DM.D2002/R) Crossing bay (30x41cm-12x16in) s.
£526	$900	(21-Mar-92 W.W258/R) Whispers of spring (25x30cm-10x12in) s. s.i.verso board
£537	$950	(9-Nov-91 W.W336/R) Vanilla and friends (20x25cm-8x10in) s. i.verso
£568	$1000	(10-Apr-92 DM.D2003/R) Les fleurs (51x41cm-20x16in) s.
£574	$1050	(7-Jun-92 LIT.L137) The gang at the beach (28x36cm-11x14in) s.
£575	$1000	(20-Sep-91 DM.D2034/R) Mon chocolat (46x36cm-18x14in) s.
£608	$1100	(24-May-92 LIT.L122) Friends (30x41cm-12x16in) s.
£618	$1100	(2-May-92 W.W119/R) Children's tea (23x28cm-9x11in) s. board
£621	$1100	(14-Feb-92 DM.D2002/R) Tinka II (23x30cm-9x12in) s. board
£765	$1300	(11-Aug-91 LIT.L94) Rowing (36x46cm-14x18in) s.
£773	$1400	(24-May-92 LIT.L96) Garden cottage (41x51cm-16x20in) s. s.i.verso
£795	$1400	(12-Apr-92 LIT.L87) Summer rapture (51x41cm-20x16in) s.
£847	$1500	(14-Feb-92 DM.D2003/R) Blooming flowers (30x25cm-12x10in) s. board
£925	$1600	(8-Sep-91 LIT.L167) Summer charm (36x46cm-14x18in) s.
£938	$1650	(12-Apr-92 LIT.L212) Summer enchantment (51x61cm-20x24in) s.
£1006	$1750	(20-Sep-91 DM.D2032/R) Orange bicycle (30x23cm-12x9in) s.
£1038	$1900	(9-Feb-92 LIT.L267) By beautiful sea (36x46cm-14x18in) s.
£1093	$2000	(7-Jun-92 LIT.L183) Bittersweet bicycle (46x61cm-18x24in) s.
£1324	$2250	(11-Aug-91 LIT.L56) Blue velvet (41x30cm-16x12in) s.
£1379	$2400	(15-Sep-91 H.C784/R) Tinka and friends (28x36cm-11x14in) s.

WILLIAMS, Penry (1798-1885) British

| £2300 | $3910 | (24-Oct-91 CSK178/R) Italian peasants in a landscape (38x61cm-15x24in) s.i.d.1860 i. verso |

WILLIAMS, Penry (attrib) (1798-1885) British

| £1023 | $1851 | (3-Dec-91 SY.MI109) Paesaggio con fiume (45x66cm-18x26in) (I.L 2200000) |

WILLIAMS, R E (?) British
£620 $1079   (19-Sep-91 TL500) Dandy - a favourite (90x67cm-35x26in) i.verso

WILLIAMS, Rhys (1894-1976) Australian
£617 $1110   (24-Nov-91 SY.S28) Gun pit, Bradley's Head (38x48cm-15x19in) s. i.verso
       canvasboard (A.D 1400)
£1150 $2047   (28-Nov-91 C28/R) North Head, Sydney Harbour (51x76cm-20x30in) s. canvas
       on masonite

WILLIAMS, Terrick (1860-1937) British
£620 $1073   (25-Mar-92 PHS568/R) On the Dutch coast (23x33cm-9x13in) s.d.99 i.verso
£750 $1343   (14-Jan-92 SWS258/R) St Jacques, Dieppe (26x40cm-10x16in) s.i.d.1899verso
£800 $1400   (27-Sep-91 C60/R) Dover from the sea (26x40cm-10x16in) s. canvasboard
£1000 $1790   (14-Jan-92 PH107) On Loch Fynne (18x26cm-7x10in) s. s.i.verso panel
£1100 $1903   (25-Mar-92 PHS567/R) Canal on the Gindecca, Venice (28x43cm-11x17in)
       s.i.d.1894verso
£1200 $2064   (10-Oct-91 L106/R) Unloading boat on quayside before harbour
       (23x41cm-9x16in) s.
£2460 $4379   (28-Nov-91 L306/R) Coming into Plymouth Harbour (15x23cm-6x9in) s. board
£3800 $6726   (5-Nov-91 PH92/R) Under the trees (25x35cm-10x14in) s.d.1902 i.verso
£4800 $8304   (2-Oct-91 S7/R) Mending nets, Milford Haven (40x66cm-16x26in) s.
£400 $684   (11-Mar-92 B248) Lake Lucerne (24x28cm-9x11in) s. pastel

WILLIAMS, Virgil (19th C) ?
£4211 $8000   (24-Jun-92 B.SF6266/R) Landscape with indians (46x76cm-18x30in) s.

WILLIAMS, W (19th C) British
£600 $1098   (7-Feb-92 BW370) Extensive landscape with cottages and figures
       (25x46cm-10x18in) s.
£698 $1200   (16-Oct-91 D.NY100) Eastern mother carrying her child in a basket
       (48x36cm-19x14in) s.
£1600 $2960   (12-Jun-92 C138/R) Morning on the Topsham Marshes (38x61cm-15x24in) s.i.

WILLIAMS, Walter (19th C) British
£600 $1068   (21-Jan-92 PH101) On Exminster marshes (21x32cm-8x13in) s.i.verso canvas
       on board
£750 $1343   (14-Nov-91 CSK223/R) Snowdon from Llwyn-y-groes, North Wales
       (15x23cm-6x9in) init.d.1868 s.i.verso
£850 $1522   (5-May-92 SWS380/R) Approach of evening (29x39cm-11x15in)
       indist.i.stretcher
£1200 $2040   (7-Aug-91 CSK397) River estuary with distant castle. Moonlit river
       estuary (15x23cm-6x9in) init. pair
£1500 $2595   (26-Mar-92 RB613) Country scenes with blackberry pickers, lake and
       beached boat (13x20cm-5x8in) s.d.1881 pair
£1700 $2924   (4-Mar-92 S17/R) Paths in mountains (16x11cm-6x4in) init.d.1867 oval pair
£1900 $3287   (25-Mar-92 PHS581/R) Estuary landscape at sunset with figures, cattle,
       moored ship and cottage (48x79cm-19x31in) s.i.d.1850
£1900 $3306   (15-Apr-92 PHL116/R) Figures on wooded hillside overlooking lake. River
       landscape (22x17cm-9x7in) init.d.1876 board pair
£2800 $4788   (19-Mar-92 B100) Figures on a path in a summer landscape
       (36x56cm-14x22in) s.
£3400 $6222   (7-Feb-92 K496/R) Summer landscapes - figures by wooden gate and on
       valley lane by church and cottages (36x28cm-14x11in) s. pair
£6500 $11895   (3-Jun-92 S91/R) Rural scenes (24x19cm-9x7in) init. six

WILLIAMS, Walter (attrib) (19th C) British
£1800 $3078   (12-Mar-92 CSK190) Mountainous lake landscape with figures on track
       (61x91cm-24x36in)

WILLIAMS, Walter Heath (19th C) British
£1700 $3009   (6-Nov-91 S50/R) Harvest time (45x66cm-18x26in)
£3800 $7030   (12-Jun-92 C137/R) Scenes in Sussex (30x61cm-12x24in) pair

WILLIAMS, Warren (1863-1918) British
*£440 $845   (29-Jul-92 PHC315) The Beaver Fall, Betws-y-Coed (35x52cm-14x20in) s.i.
       W/C*
£480 $840   (19-Feb-92 HAR388) Mountain stream (36x51cm-14x20in) s.
*£500 $875   (31-Mar-92 RJ161) Conway Valley with sheep in foreground
       (36x25cm-14x10in) s. W/C*
£520 $936   (27-Jan-92 PH147) In Snowdonia (28x43cm-11x17in) s. W/C
*£520 $910   (19-Feb-92 HAR387) Highland lake with sheep in the foreground
       (25x46cm-10x18in) s.*
£540 $929   (3-Mar-92 AG187) Conway village and harbour (25x36cm-10x14in) s. W/C
*£580 $1114   (28-Jul-92 RJ159) Anglesey coastal scene with yacht (20x56cm-8x22in)
       s.d.1900*
£600 $1110   (9-Jun-92 AG203/R) Master foxhounds leading field (24x38cm-9x15in) s. W/C
*£620 $1079   (15-Apr-92 HAR445) Highland landscape with sheep grazing
       (33x51cm-13x20in) s. W/C*
*£780 $1490   (30-Jun-92 RJ140/R) Llyn Mymbyr with Snowdon Horsehoe and sheep in
       foreground (25x46cm-10x18in) s. W/C*
*£800 $1368   (12-Mar-92 CSK19) Preparing the fishing boats for sea (41x71cm-16x28in)
       s. W/C*
*£870 $1523   (31-Mar-92 RJ128) Coastal scene near Deganwy, sailing boats near shore
       (25x36cm-10x14in) s. W/C*

WILLIAMS, Warren (1863-1918) British-cont.

£900	$1728	(29-Jul-92 PHC314) View of Westshore towards Penmaenmawr (24x35cm-9x14in) s. W/C pair
£920	$1665	(4-Dec-91 ME1) Haven under the Hill, Pwllheli - coastal cottages with figures by boat (25x36cm-10x14in) s.i. W/C
£940	$1795	(30-Jun-92 RJ188) Snowdonia river with bridge and figure (25x36cm-10x14in) s. W/C
£950	$1815	(30-Jun-92 RJ174) Rocky beach scene at West shore Llandudno, looking towards Penmaenmawr (25x36cm-10x14in) W/C
£950	$1653	(11-Sep-91 ME381) Cottage at Cemaes Bay with woman and chickens in foreground (30x51cm-12x20in) s. W/C
£950	$1682	(6-Nov-91 S258/R) Belaugh, on the Broads, Norfolk (37x61cm-15x24in) s. s.i.verso W/C htd.white
£1000	$1740	(11-Sep-91 ME365) Anglesey coastal scene with fisherfolk and boats (25x36cm-10x14in) s. i.label verso W/C
£1000	$1920	(29-Jul-92 PHC313/R) View at Tal-y-Cafn (34x55cm-13x22in) s. W/C
£1075	$1860	(24-Mar-92 PHC344/R) Figures on shore (37x62cm-15x24in) s. W/C
£1340	$2559	(30-Jun-92 RJ194) Shore scene at Black Rocks, Deganwy (30x56cm-12x22in) s. W/C
£1480	$2590	(31-Mar-92 RJ169) Snowdon form Pen-y-Gwryd (28x43cm-11x17in) s. W/C
£1500	$2685	(5-May-92 SWS233/R) Gathering clouds on Snowdon, Bettws-y-Coed (25x35cm-10x14in) s. W/C pair
£1500	$2625	(31-Mar-92 RJ167) Conway and harbour (25x36cm-10x14in) s. W/C
£1600	$3056	(30-Jun-92 RJ158/R) Conway estuary beach scene, with numerous boats and Deganwy and Orme (30x48cm-12x19in) s. W/C
£1750	$3133	(14-Jan-92 SWS43/R) River landscapes in Snowdonia (33x51cm-13x20in) s. W/C htd.bodycol pair

WILLIAMSON, Frederick (19th C) British

£1500	$2640	(6-Apr-92 PH72) Sheep in Dorset hills (22x35cm-9x14in) s. W/C htd white

WILLIAMSON, John (1826-1885) American

£811	$1500	(10-Jun-92 CE.NY226/R) Marshy landscape (20x38cm-8x15in) s.d.63
£1351	$2500	(10-Jun-92 CE.NY217/R) Palisades, Hudson River (20x27cm-8x11in) init. i.verso board
£2542	$4500	(9-Nov-91 W.W319/R) River landscape (61x76cm-24x30in) mono.d.66 board
£17582	$32000	(28-May-92 CH.NY59/R) Bolton's Landing, Lake George (77x127cm-30x50in) mono.d.78

WILLIAMSON, W H (1820-1883) British

£1500	$2745	(3-Jun-92 S2/R) St Michael's Mount. After a storm (30x61cm-12x24in) s.indis.d. pair

WILLIAMSON, William Henry (1820-1883) British

£700	$1267	(6-Dec-91 CBS217) Seascape (23x33cm-9x13in) s.d.1856
£720	$1289	(14-Jan-92 SWS169/R) Off Scarborough (29x49cm-11x19in) s.i.d.1865stretcher

WILLIG, Carl (fl.1928-1930) British

£480	$821	(11-Mar-92 B333) Head study of old woman (31x23cm-12x9in) s.d.1928 pencil

WILLIGEN, Claes Jansz van der (1630-1676) Dutch

£926	$1657	(12-Nov-91 SY.AM231) Aeneas and Anchises fleeing Troy (33x42cm-13x17in) s. panel (D.FL 3000)
£1296	$2320	(14-Nov-91 CH.AM44) Mother and child conversing with traveller on forest path (24x29cm-9x11in) s. panel (D.FL 4200)
£4420	$8000	(22-May-92 SY.NY278/R) Man crossing wooden bridge, village and mountainous landscape beyond (63x49cm-25x19in) s. panel

WILLINK, Carel (1900-1979) Dutch

£5758	$10421	(19-May-92 CH.AM189/R) Portrait of George Fernberg (47x34cm-19x13in) s.d.42 (D.FL 19000)
£15152	$27424	(19-May-92 CH.AM188/R) Rossinilaan, Hilversum (64x50cm-25x20in) s.d.46 (D.FL 50000)
£21605	$39321	(12-Dec-91 SY.AM59/R) Standing female nude (147x78cm-58x31in) s.d.1929 (D.FL 70000)
£24691	$44938	(11-Dec-91 CH.AM280/R) Landscape in Bormis (97x78cm-38x31in) s.d.1928 (D.FL 80000)
£1364	$2468	(21-May-92 SY.AM119/R) Study for Zebra's in Zwarte Rotskloof (59x46cm-23x18in) s.d.59 chl chk (D.FL 4500)
£1852	$3241	(18-Feb-92 CH.AM112 a/R) A seated nude (47x41cm-19x16in) s.d.6 Dec 1926 pencil (D.FL 6000)
£2727	$4936	(21-May-92 SY.AM120/R) Untitled (63x45cm-25x18in) s.d.50 col.chk (D.FL 9000)

WILLIS, A V (19th C) British?

£2459	$4500	(5-Jun-92 SY.NY218/R) Over the fence (27x45cm-11x18in) s.d.65

WILLIS, Charles (20th C) British

£600	$1056	(8-Apr-92 CSK211) Exciting news (60x81cm-24x32in) s.i.verso
£1300	$2210	(22-Oct-91 SWS289/R) Happy birthday to you (49x67cm-19x26in) s. i.verso

WILLIS, Henry Brittan (1810-1884) British

£2286	$4000	(18-Feb-92 CE.NY133/R) Dolgelly, North Wales (57x89cm-22x35in) s.d.55

WILLIS, Henry Brittan (1810-1884) British-cont.
£560 $1075   (29-Jul-92 PHC283) The Pool near Midhurst, Sussex (19x31cm-7x12in)
                   s.indis.d. W/C

WILLIS, Henry Brittan and JENKINS, Joseph John (19th C) British
£800 $1536   (28-Jul-92 SWS250/R) Highland rovers (46x65cm-18x26in) s.d.1857

WILLIS, J (?) British
£570 $1043   (12-May-92 H353) Drawing room interior with lady seated at table
                   (46x36cm-18x14in)

WILLIS, T (20th C) American
£529 $900   (6-Aug-91 RB.HY102/R) Portrait of steam-yacht Taniwha (41x81cm-16x32in)
                   s.

WILLIS, William Alexander (1799-1862) British
£3000 $5100   (23-Oct-91 S299/R) Boat camp of HMS Cruizer, Swan River (25x40cm-10x16in)
                   i.d.1830 pen W/C over pencil

WILLMANN, Michael Lukas (1630-1706) Austrian
£1564 $2800   (15-Jan-92 CH.NY170/R) Death of Priam (21x30cm-8x12in) black lead pen
                   wash

WILLROIDER, Josef (1838-1915) Austrian
£2100 $3591   (17-Mar-92 PH76) Alpine chalet in summer landscape (27x38cm-11x15in) s.
                   canvasboard
£2265 $4122   (11-Dec-91 N.M660/R) Tree lined river landscape (25x35cm-10x14in) s.
                   canvas on panel (DM 6500)
£2962 $5390   (11-Dec-91 N.M661/R) Corn harvest in the foothills of the Alps
                   (23x32cm-9x13in) s. paper (DM 8500)
£7666 $13951   (11-Dec-91 N.M659/R) Maria Worth, Worthersee (22x30cm-9x12in) s. panel
                   (DM 22000)
£378 $658   (18-Sep-91 N.M292) Landscape with peasants on path through fields near
                   Bad Villach (28x40cm-11x16in) s.i.d.1880 pencil htd.white (DM 1100)
£523 $951   (12-Dec-91 L.K495) Landscape with riverside mill (31x48cm-12x19in) s.
                   pencil (DM 1500)

WILLROIDER, Ludwig (1845-1910) German
£1375 $2392   (18-Sep-91 N.M751/R) Rocks and trees (56x32cm-22x13in) s. canvas on board
                   (DM 4000)
£1684 $2880   (13-Mar-92 FN.S3019/R) Peasant girl on path through fields, late summer
                   (25x40cm-10x16in) mono. (DM 4800)
£1916 $3488   (12-Dec-91 L.K730) Carinthia landscape (24x33cm-9x13in) board (DM 5500)
£2613 $4756   (12-Dec-91 L.K729) Landscape with cattle by stream (17x25cm-7x10in) s.
                   panel (DM 7500)
£5185 $9385   (19-May-92 GF.L2122/R) Shepherd with sheep and cattle in autumnal
                   landscape (51x68cm-20x27in) s.d.1908 (S.FR 14000)

WILLUMS, Olaf Abrahamsen (1886-1967) Norwegian
£527 $906   (7-Oct-91 B.O156/R) Peonies (38x46cm-15x18in) s.d.50 panel (N.KR 6000)

WILLUMSEN, J F (1863-1958) Danish
£28507 $51597   (4-Dec-91 KH.K21/R) Washerwomen by river, Nice (84x106cm-33x42in)
                   init.d.1919 i.verso (D.KR 315000)
£727 $1272   (1-Apr-92 KH.K272) Scene from Salome, The Royal Theatre (36x44cm-14x17in)
                   s.d.1919 W/C (D.KR 8000)
£1181 $2066   (1-Apr-92 KH.K231/R) Negro girl from Martinique (62x48cm-24x19in)
                   init.d.1918 pastel (D.KR 13000)

WILLUMSEN, Jens Ferdinand (1863-1958) Danish
£3000 $5430   (22-May-92 C40/R) Mother's vision (221x221cm-87x87in) d.1909

WILMARTH, Christopher (1943-1987) American
£1143 $2000   (25-Feb-92 SY.NY200/R) Edges of the nine clearings (38x106cm-15x42in)
                   init.d.75 W/C graphite
£1397 $2500   (9-May-92 CE.NY320/R) Edge of long straight stray (77x56cm-30x22in)
                   s.init.i.d.1978 W/C graphite

WILMS, Joseph (1814-1892) German
£1500 $2700   (22-Nov-91 S.BM51/R) Still life with fruit, wine and nuts
                   (33x36cm-13x14in) s.d.1871

WILNER, Marie (1910-) American
£638 $1200   (18-Dec-91 SY.NY291/R) Bears at the zoo (76x101cm-30x40in) s.

WILS, Wilhelm (1880-?) Danish
£713 $1226   (16-Oct-91 KH.K288) Spanish variety dancer (108x80cm-43x31in) s.
                   (D.KR 8000)

WILSON (?) British
£1099 $2000   (26-May-92 CE.NY115/R) Extensive river town (50x81cm-20x32in) s.d.1871

WILSON, A (?) British
£560 $1070   (1-Jul-92 B151/R) Flower covered thatched cottage with two children on
                   way in (48x70cm-19x28in) s.d.1887

WILSON, Charles Edward (19th C) British
£975	$1775	(10-Dec-91 HAR614) Village children (28x23cm-11x9in) s. W/C
£2000	$3580	(5-May-92 SWS264/R) The playful kitten (35x26cm-14x10in) s. W/C over pencil
£4200	$7518	(14-Jan-92 SWS103/R) Bubbles (20cm-8ins circular) s. W/C over pencil
£6000	$10740	(14-Jan-92 SWS102/R) Playful kitten (20cm-8ins circular) s. W/C over pencil
£6200	$11470	(12-Jun-92 C51/R) A bit of gossip (52x35cm-20x14in) s.d.1903 pencil W/C
£7000	$12530	(13-Nov-91 ELR255) In sweet springtime (30x25cm-12x10in) s.d.1889 W/C bodycol
£7500	$13725	(3-Jun-92 S272/R) The young pipe player (38x28cm-15x11in) s.i. verso W/C

WILSON, Chester (19th C) British
| £1000 | $1750 | (23-Sep-91 HS381/R) The letter - interior with figures in 17th century costume (90x70cm-35x28in) s.d.1873 |
| £1900 | $3306 | (12-Sep-91 CSK234/R) Feeding the rabbits (61x51cm-24x20in) s.d.1874 |

WILSON, David Forrester (1873-?) British
| £650 | $1157 | (28-Apr-92 S199/R) Ewe and lamb (40x51cm-16x20in) s. |

WILSON, Dora Lynell (1883-1946) Australian
£556	$989	(27-Apr-92 J.M1217) Fruit stall and news stand, Melbourne (29x39cm-11x15in) s. (A.D 1300)
£598	$1065	(27-Apr-92 J.M1144) Collins Street (50x39cm-20x15in) s. canvas on board (A.D 1400)
£711	$1216	(17-Mar-92 JRL.S83) Still life (34x37cm-13x15in) s. board (A.D 1600)
£939	$1568	(19-Aug-91 SY.ME105/R) Church (31x34cm-12x13in) s.d.1926 canvas on board (A.D 2000)

WILSON, Eric (1915-1946) Australian
£855	$1521	(27-Apr-92 J.M1215) Guns at the Castle, Edinburgh (28x45cm-11x18in) s. board (A.D 2000)
£5727	$10308	(24-Nov-91 SY.S326/R) Perugia (40x20cm-16x8in) s.i.d.39 board (A.D 13000)
£396	$706	(26-Nov-91 J.M619) Devon Exeter hills (9x15cm-4x6in) i. mixed media (A.D 900)

WILSON, Francis Vaux (1874-1938) American
| £618 | $1100 | (2-May-92 IH.NY69/R) Woman wearing blue scarf standing outdoors (43x43cm-17x17in) s. gouache |

WILSON, Frank Avray (1914-) British
| £1200 | $2220 | (11-Jun-92 C49/R) Red abstract (64x76cm-25x30in) s.d.67 panel |

WILSON, H (?) British
| £732 | $1324 | (3-Dec-91 R.T121/R) Idle moment (51x77cm-20x30in) s. i.verso (C.D 1500) |

WILSON, Hart (?) ?
| £500 | $950 | (26-Jun-92 WOL.C934 a) The Feast of Bacchus (170x119cm-67x47in) s. pastel |

WILSON, J (?) British
| £800 | $1448 | (20-May-92 S48) Rowing boat (76x127cm-30x50in) |

WILSON, J C (19th C) British
| £1200 | $2256 | (19-Dec-91 C114/R) Artillery Practice (26x34cm-10x13in) s.i.verso |

WILSON, John (1774-1855) British
| £2000 | $3480 | (14-Apr-92 CSK138/R) Off coast of Brittany, entrance to Saint Briac (42x67cm-17x26in) s. |

WILSON, John James (1818-1875) British
| £600 | $1080 | (22-Nov-91 SWS2273) Cattle and sheep in a landscape (36x48cm-14x19in) s. |

WILSON, John James (attrib) (1818-1875) British
| £1100 | $1980 | (22-Nov-91 C107/R) Calm waters (15x20cm-6x8in) indis.init. paper on panel |

WILSON, Lawrence W (19/20th C) New Zealander
£507	$908	(6-May-92 DS.W55) Bob's Cove, Lake Wakatipu (29x44cm-11x17in) s.i.d.1886 (NZ.D 1700)
£1306	$2181	(21-Aug-91 DS.W64) Lake Hawea Otago N.Z (49x74cm-19x29in) s.i. (NZ.D 3800)
£746	$1336	(6-May-92 DS.W54) Lake Manapouri from Monument Arm (24x47cm-9x19in) s.i. pastel (NZ.D 2500)
£896	$1603	(6-May-92 DS.W8) Head of the Waimakariri River, West Coast Road (27x36cm-11x14in) s.i. W/C (NZ.D 3000)

WILSON, M B (19th C) American
| £785 | $1500 | (3-Jul-92 S.W3135/R) Under full sail (69x91cm-27x36in) s.d.1879 canvas on board |

WILSON, Ray (1906-1972) American
| £424 | $750 | (12-Feb-92 B.SF633/R) Houses in morning (38x57cm-15x22in) s. W/C |
| £960 | $1700 | (12-Feb-92 B.SF632/R) Southern Pacific railroad. Street scene (38x52cm-15x20in) s. W/C double-sided |

WILSON, Richard (1714-1782) British
£6000 $10560   (8-Apr-92 S74/R) Landscape with view of St. Pauls (28x36cm-11x14in)
£990 $1891   (16-Jul-92 S95/R) Figures in italianate landscape (15x19cm-6x7in) i.
   pencil chk

WILSON, Richard (after) (1714-1782) British
£2200 $3762   (12-Mar-92 CSK155/R) Boys fishing on wooded riverbank with ruins
   overlooking stone bridge (102x127cm-40x50in)

WILSON, Richard (attrib) (1714-1782) British
£476 $867   (14-Dec-91 BA.S122/R) River landscape with figures and ruins
   (67x58cm-26x23in) (S.KR 5000)
£540 $950   (8-Apr-92 D.NY79) View of Italian landscape (74x91cm-29x36in)
£720 $1231   (17-Mar-92 OT598/R) Italianate lake landscape with figure by the shore
   (43x56cm-17x22in)

WILSON, Richard (circle) (1714-1782) British
£733 $1400   (16-Jul-92 SY.NY130/R) Figures in landscape at daybreak (43x53cm-17x21in)
£950 $1805   (23-Jun-92 PH58) Figures in lake landscape (46x56cm-18x22in)
£950 $1701   (13-Nov-91 CG525/R) Figures in a forest clearing (38x49cm-15x19in)
£1100 $2101   (14-Jul-92 DR448/R) Classical landscape with figures (41x52cm-16x20in)
£2100 $3759   (13-Nov-91 CG512/R) Dolbadarn Castle, North Wales (37x49cm-15x19in)
£2200 $3938   (15-Nov-91 C50/R) Bridge at Rimini (61x76cm-24x30in)
£4800 $8448   (10-Apr-92 C146/R) The white monk (44x58cm-17x23in) i.verso

WILSON, Richard (school) (1714-1782) British
£3481 $6266   (19-Nov-91 F.R121/R) Le cascatelle di Tivoli con la villa di Mecenate
   (42x72cm-17x28in) (I.L 7500000)

WILSON, Richard (studio) (1714-1782) British
£1400 $2492   (30-Apr-92 CG871/R) View of Tivoli with figures resting (74x91cm-29x36in)
   mono.
£5000 $8900   (30-Apr-92 CG870/R) Summit of Cader Idris, Llyn-y-Cau (51x76cm-20x30in)

WILSON, Richard (style) (1714-1782) British
£880 $1505   (18-Mar-92 CSK201/R) River landscape with goat herd (117x155cm-46x61in)
£1000 $1790   (13-Nov-91 CG570/R) Figures resting by a ruined temple (62x76cm-24x30in)
   mono.d.1776
£1900 $3648   (9-Jul-92 B37) View of Castelgondolfo with figures in foreground
   (35x43cm-14x17in) pair
£2300 $4393   (2-Jul-92 D163/R) Figures beside classical ruins with river and landscape
   beyond (79x107cm-31x42in)

WILSON, Ronald York (1907-) Canadian
£547 $974   (26-Nov-91 JOY.T244/R) Tribute (75x100cm-30x39in) s.d.75 acrylic canvas
   (C.D 1100)
£917 $1679   (1-Jun-92 W.T1105 a) Toloca market (122x203cm-48x80in) s. i.verso board
   (C.D 2000)

WILSON, Scottie (1889-1972) British
£922 $1660   (27-Jan-92 GL.P39/R) Composition (38x28cm-15x11in) s. ink col.crayons
   (F.FR 9000)
£1029 $1862   (6-Dec-91 GL.P252) Composition (38x28cm-15x11in) s. ink col.crayons
   (F.FR 10000)
£1029 $1862   (6-Dec-91 GL.P248) Composition (38x28cm-15x11in) s. ink col.crayons
   (F.FR 10000)
£1127 $2029   (27-Jan-92 GL.P36) Composition (38x28cm-15x11in) s. ink col.crayons
   (F.FR 11000)
£1132 $2048   (6-Dec-91 GL.P249) Composition (38x28cm-15x11in) s. ink col.crayons
   (F.FR 11000)
£1230 $2213   (27-Jan-92 GL.P35) Composition (38x28cm-15x11in) ink (F.FR 12000)
£1309 $2330   (28-Oct-91 GL.P151) Sans titre (38x28cm-15x11in) s. ink col.crayons
   (F.FR 13000)
£1337 $2421   (6-Dec-91 GL.P251/R) Composition (38x28cm-15x11in) s. ink col.crayons
   (F.FR 13000)
£1410 $2510   (28-Oct-91 GL.P152) Sans titre (38x28cm-15x11in) s. ink col.crayons
   (F.FR 14000)
£1410 $2510   (28-Oct-91 GL.P155/R) Sans titre (38x28cm-15x11in) s. ink col.crayons
   (F.FR 14000)
£1511 $2689   (28-Oct-91 GL.P154/R) Sans titre (37cm-15ins circular) ink col.crayons
   (F.FR 15000)
£1543 $2793   (6-Dec-91 GL.P250/R) Composition (38x28cm-15x11in) s. ink col.crayons
   (F.FR 15000)
£1543 $2793   (6-Dec-91 GL.P253) Composition (56x38cm-22x15in) s. ink col.crayons
   (F.FR 15000)
£1610 $2769   (12-Oct-91 GL.P2/R) Sans titre (38x56cm-15x22in) s. ink col.crayons
   (F.FR 16000)
£1611 $2868   (28-Oct-91 GL.P153/R) Sans titre (38x28cm-15x11in) s. ink col.crayons
   (F.FR 16000)
£1646 $2979   (6-Dec-91 GL.P247/R) Composition (56x38cm-22x15in) ink col.crayons
   (F.FR 16000)
£1811 $3115   (12-Oct-91 GL.P1/R) Sans titre (38x28cm-15x11in) s. ink col.crayons
   (F.FR 18000)
£1955 $3538   (6-Dec-91 GL.P254/R) Composition (42x25cm-17x10in) s. ink col.crayons
   (F.FR 19000)

WILSON, Scottie (1889-1972) British-cont.
£2012 $3461   (12-Oct-91 GL.P4/R) Sans titre (56x38cm-22x15in) s. ink col.crayons (F.FR 20000)
£2012 $3461   (12-Oct-91 GL.P3/R) Sans titre (55x37cm-22x15in) s. ink col.crayons (F.FR 20000)
£2012 $3461   (12-Oct-91 GL.P5/R) Mind picture (38x44cm-15x17in) s. ink col.crayons (F.FR 20000)
£2014 $3585   (28-Oct-91 GL.P156/R) Sans titre (60x43cm-24x17in) s. ink col.crayons cut and pasted paper (F.FR 20000)

WILSON, Sol (20th C) American
£865 $1600   (10-Jun-92 CE.NY433/R) Torn sail (117x102cm-46x40in) s.

WILSON, Thomas Fairbairn (attrib) (19th C) British
£2800 $4928   (10-Apr-92 C174/R) Minna, four year old Shorthorn bull in meadow (61x76cm-24x30in) i.d.1822

WILSON, Thomas Walter (19th C) British
£1163 $2000   (15-Oct-91 CE.NY384/R) Westgate on the sea (43x71cm-17x28in) s.d.1876

WILSON, W Reynolds (20th C) American
£526 $925   (9-Apr-92 FA.PH754) The pose (117x86cm-46x34in)

WILSON, W Yates (20th C) British?
£750 $1365   (11-Dec-91 B105 a/R) Hanging the Christmas decorations (61x51cm-24x20in) s.

WILT, Hans (1867-1917) Austrian
£2234 $3977   (28-Nov-91 D.V4/R) Der Schone Brunnen in Schonbrunn (100x135cm-39x53in) s.d.1910 (A.S 45000)

WILT, Thomas van der (1659-1733) Dutch
£3800 $6650   (28-Feb-92 C8/R) The sacrifice of Iphigenia (48x62cm-19x24in) s.

WILT, Thomas van der (attrib) (1659-1733) Dutch
£1296 $2346   (19-May-92 GF.L2408/R) Elegant party in interior (56x47cm-22x19in) panel (S.FR 3500)

WIMMER, Konrad (1844-1905) German
£4181 $7610   (11-Dec-91 N.M663/R) Moonlit landscape with cattle watering (22x46cm-9x18in) s. (DM 12000)
£4878 $8878   (11-Dec-91 N.M662/R) Hunter in winter landscape (49x78cm-19x31in) s. (DM 14000)

WIMPERIS, E M (1835-1900) British
£400 $724   (6-Dec-91 BW367) Surrey landscape (25x33cm-10x13in) s. W/C
£640 $1139   (1-Nov-91 BW380/R) Extensive landscape with cottage and sheep in foreground (23x36cm-9x14in) mono.d.99 W/C

WIMPERIS, Edmund Morison (1835-1900) British
£580 $1009   (12-Sep-91 CSK155/R) On the Arun (36x51cm-14x20in) init.d.89 indist.i.verso
£800 $1424   (28-Apr-92 S147/R) Bridge in the Highlands (61x91cm-24x36in) s.d.92
£1550 $2697   (13-Sep-91 HC1/R) Peat gatherers (28x48cm-11x19in) s.
£3800 $7220   (23-Jun-92 CG698/R) Wooded landscape with shepherd driving sheep by ford, village beyond (61x91cm-24x36in) init.d.1900
£4500 $8010   (28-Apr-92 PH58/R) Glebe stream, Danbury, Essex (161x116cm-63x46in) s.d.92
£8000 $14640   (3-Jun-92 S47/R) Watering the team. Footbridge (76x61cm-30x24in) init.d.90 pair
£400 $696   (9-Sep-91 PH116) Herding sheep (30x50cm-12x20in) init.d.85 W/C over pencil
£400 $708   (7-Nov-91 PHC648) View in Stirlingshire (54x81cm-21x32in) W/C
£500 $875   (17-Feb-92 HS230/R) Extensive landscape with figures conversing beside pool, windmill beyond (37x60cm-15x24in) s.d.73 W/C
£650 $1131   (11-Sep-91 ME350) Landscape with sheep in foreground (48x74cm-19x29in) init.d.78 W/C
£700 $1337   (13-Jul-92 PH58) Near Studland, Dorset (24x34cm-9x13in) init.d.86 W/C
£740 $1354   (6-Feb-92 T136) Sheep in meadow (23x36cm-9x14in) init.d.99 W/C
£800 $1432   (5-May-92 SWS194/R) Yorkshire landscape. By the mill stream (34x52cm-13x20in) init.d.98 W/C over pencil pair

WINCHELL, Paul (20th C) American
£877 $1500   (13-Mar-92 WOL.C132) Reclining female nude (58x74cm-23x29in)
£1170 $2000   (13-Mar-92 WOL.C127) The bath (66x81cm-26x32in)

WINCK, Johann Amandus (1748-1817) German
£40698 $70000   (10-Oct-91 SY.NY149/R) Still life of fruit, butterflies, snails and insects on a marble ledge (49x38cm-19x15in) init.
£83799 $150000   (16-Jan-92 CH.NY3/R) Still life of mixed fruit in porcelain bowls with birds and insects (30x42cm-12x17in) one s.d.1802 one init. copper pair

WINCK, Johann Christian Thomas (1738-1797) German
£8362 $15220   (11-Dec-91 N.M380/R) Adoration of the Shepherds (35x25cm-14x10in) one of pair (DM 24000)

WINCK, Johann Christian Thomas (1738-1797) German-cont.
£12544 $22829   (11-Dec-91 N.M381/R) Adoration of the Kings (35x25cm-14x10in) one of pair
                            (DM 36000)

WINCK, Joseph Gregor (1710-1781) German
£3601 $6517   (5-Dec-91 SY.MO310/R) Musicien au verre de vin (48x36cm-19x14in) s.verso
                            (F.FR 35000)

WINDER, D H (fl.1880-1920) British
£850 $1471   (24-Mar-92 PHC415/R) Derwentwater (44x69cm-17x27in) s.d.1903

WINDHAGER, Franz (1879-?) Austrian
£900 $1602   (26-Nov-91 PH136) Refreshment in the park (20x26cm-8x10in) s. panel
£1212 $2206   (26-May-92 D.V77/R) The preparations (58x90cm-23x35in) s.d.1921 panel
                            (A.S 25000)

WINDMAIER, Anton (1840-1896) German
£1047 $2000   (16-Jul-92 SY.NY412/R) Sunset over rural landscape (50x75cm-20x30in)
                            s.d.1875
£1546 $2691   (17-Sep-91 FN.S2613/R) Ox-drawn cart with workmen on woodland path
                            (37x48cm-15x19in) s. (DM 4500)
£2680 $4718   (11-Apr-92 AW.H820/R) Covered wagon in landscape with farmhouse on rainy
                            day (14x34cm-6x13in) s. panel (DM 7800)

WINDMAIER, Anton (attrib) (1840-1896) German
£702 $1200   (13-Mar-92 FN.S3020/R) Peasants returning on frozen stream by cottages,
                            evening (40x60cm-16x24in) panel (DM 2000)

WINDO, Bruce (20th C) British
*£520 $894   (15-Oct-91 B144/R) Secret Adversary by Agatha Christie (37x27cm-15x11in)
                            gouache*

WINDT, Chris van der (1877-1952) Dutch
*£2121 $3755   (22-Apr-92 CH.AM328/R) Farmyard with a peasant working in front of
                            haystacks (45x72cm-18x28in) s.d.1906 W/C htd.white (D.FL 7000)*
*£2752 $4789   (14-Apr-92 SY.AM10/R) Farm on waterfront (33x57cm-13x22in) s.d.1906 W/C
                            (D.FL 9000)*

WINGATE, Sir James Lawton (1846-1924) British
£488 $883   (3-Dec-91 R.T122/R) Summer sunset Fairlee (36x51cm-14x20in) (C.D 1000)
£550 $979   (28-Apr-92 S139) Village street (41x51cm-16x20in) s.
£800 $1432   (13-Nov-91 CG644) Culloden Moor (35x51cm-14x20in) s.
£800 $1424   (30-Apr-92 CG917) Sheep on a drove road (56x92cm-22x36in) s.d.1873
£7000 $12460   (30-Apr-92 CG883/R) Wanderers (57x77cm-22x30in) s.d.78

WINGERT, Edward Oswald (1864-?) American
£528 $950   (24-Nov-91 JRB.C84/R) Phiox (30x33cm-12x13in) s. board

WINGHE, Jeremias van (1578-1645) German
£15444 $26409   (12-Mar-92 GK.Z77/R) Still life of fruit in bowls, roemer with wine,
                            bread and jug on table (42x56cm-17x22in) mono. (S.FR 40000)

WINKLER, Ralf see PENCK, A R

WINT, Peter de (1784-1849) British
*£3000 $5280   (8-Apr-92 S71/R) Landscape with traveller approaching village
                            (23x32cm-9x13in) board*
*£4000 $7040   (8-Apr-92 S72/R) View of river running below cliffs, probably Dovedale,
                            Derbyshire (28x44cm-11x17in) board*
£470 $799   (6-Aug-91 OT358) Figures in forest glade (36x26cm-14x10in) W/C
*£900 $1719   (14-Jul-92 C40) Figures in boat below Newark Castle, Northamptonshire
                            (33x41cm-13x16in) pencil W/C*
*£1200 $2136   (27-Nov-91 B72/R) The North Archway Tower, East Bergholt Church
                            (34x46cm-13x18in) W/C*
*£1400 $2506   (14-Nov-91 S91/R) Buildings by country road (28x39cm-11x15in) W/C over
                            pencil*
£1540 $2941   (16-Jul-92 S128/R) Docks and mallow (16x25cm-6x10in) W/C over pencil
*£2200 $3872   (9-Apr-92 S117/R) Syon House from River Thames (29x46cm-11x18in) W/C over
                            pencil*
*£2700 $4752   (7-Apr-92 C143/R) Ornamental Garden fountain surrounded by trees
                            (29x24cm-11x9in) pencil W/C*
*£3000 $5280   (9-Apr-92 S122/R) Goodrich Castle on the Wye, Herefordshire
                            (26x36cm-10x14in) W/C gum arabic*
£3000 $5280   (9-Apr-92 S107/R) Gypsies by bank (14x23cm-6x9in) W/C over pencil
£3300 $6303   (16-Jul-92 S142/R) Harvesters at work (30x39cm-12x15in) W/C over pencil
£3500 $6265   (12-Nov-91 C84/R) Figures by a cottage gate (11x15cm-4x6in) pencil W/C
£4000 $7640   (14-Jul-92 C42/R) Wooded landscape (28x37cm-11x15in) W/C
*£5500 $9845   (14-Nov-91 S159/R) Knaresborough, Yorkshire (45x61cm-18x24in) i.verso w/c
                            over pencil htd.bodycol*
*£8000 $14320   (14-Nov-91 S136/R) Castle Rising Norfolk (32x49cm-13x19in)
                            s.indis.i.verso W/C over pencil*
£10500 $18480   (9-Apr-92 S81/R) Shamblands (32x48cm-13x19in) i.verso W/C over pencil

WINT, Peter de (attrib) (1784-1849) British
£700 $1232   (6-Apr-92 WW17/R) Harvesting (36x46cm-14x18in)

WINTER, Alice Beach (1877-?) American
| £1333 | $2400 | (24-Nov-91 JRB.C183/R) Girl in garden (61x51cm-24x20in) s. |
| £500 | $850 | (27-Oct-91 LIT.L247) Girl with umbrella (71x41cm-28x16in) s. W/C chl |

WINTER, Andrew (1893-1958) American
£595	$1000	(14-Aug-91 B.P62/R) Monhegan (56x71cm-22x28in) s.
£726	$1300	(6-May-92 B.P139/R) House on Maine Coast (30x46cm-12x18in) s. canvasboard
£1285	$2300	(6-May-92 B.P135/R) Coastal Maine (76x102cm-30x40in) s.

WINTER, Charles Allan (1869-1942) American
| £1261 | $2270 | (23-Nov-91 YFA.M310) Monhegan (51x61cm-20x24in) s.d.32 |

WINTER, Fritz (1905-1976) German
£1168	$2138	(2-Jun-92 L.K1049) Untitled (25x18cm-10x7in) s.d.1961 (DM 3400)
£1512	$2797	(11-Jun-92 HN.H499/R) Composition (15x19cm-6x7in) s.i.d.1959 tempera paper (DM 4400)
£1787	$3306	(11-Jun-92 HN.H502/R) Composition (17x22cm-7x9in) s.d.1961 tempera (DM 5200)
£1924	$3387	(10-Apr-92 KM.K597 a/R) Composition (49x70cm-19x28in) s.d.64 paper (DM 5600)
£2281	$4105	(23-Nov-91 N.M337/R) Untitled composition in green red white (17x24cm-7x9in) s.d.1960 paper (DM 6500)
£2474	$4577	(11-Jun-92 HN.H500/R) Composition (13x18cm-5x7in) s.d.1959 tempera oil paper (DM 7200)
£2474	$4577	(11-Jun-92 HN.H501/R) Composition (15x15cm-6x6in) tempera oil paper (DM 7200)
£2632	$4737	(19-Nov-91 L.K1215/R) Figurine (70x50cm-28x20in) mono.i.d.1929 board pencil study verso (DM 7500)
£2982	$5368	(23-Nov-91 N.M335/R) Untitled (19x18cm-7x7in) s.d.1959 paper (DM 8500)
£3147	$5601	(26-Nov-91 KF.M1128/R) Untitled (50x70cm-20x28in) s.d.1954 paper (DM 9000)
£3147	$5601	(26-Nov-91 KF.M1129/R) Untitled (50x70cm-20x28in) s.d.1955 paper (DM 9000)
£3436	$6357	(11-Jun-92 HN.H503/R) Untitled (62x35cm-24x14in) s.d.1964 indian ink brush (DM 10000)
£3860	$6947	(23-Nov-91 N.M336/R) Untitled (18x19cm-7x7in) s.d.1959 paper (DM 11000)
£6873	$12715	(11-Jun-92 HN.H498/R) Grun sich erwarmend (50x70cm-20x28in) s.i.d.1953 tempera oil paper (DM 20000)
£6873	$12577	(2-Jun-92 L.K1048/R) After red (50x70cm-20x28in) s.d.1953 s.i.d.verso board (DM 20000)
£7605	$14144	(19-Jun-92 G.Z7/R) The darkness (49x72cm-19x28in) mono.d.1932 paper (S.FR 20000)
£8874	$16150	(25-May-92 WK.M1315/R) Untitled (61x43cm-24x17in) s.d.1972 board (DM 26000)
£16783	$29874	(30-Nov-91 VG.B350/R) Das rot (50x70cm-20x28in) s.d.1953 board (DM 48000)
£19931	$36474	(2-Jun-92 L.K1047/R) Black stains (74x100cm-29x39in) s.d.1954 s.i.d.verso board on canvas (DM 58000)
£20000	$34600	(26-Mar-92 C37/R) Rote Mitte (90x80cm-35x31in) s.d.66 i.verso
£20478	$37270	(30-May-92 VG.B338/R) Landscape (60x70cm-24x28in) s.d.1965 s.i.d.1965 (DM 60000)
£21000	$38010	(5-Dec-91 C14/R) Linien Zwischen Rot und Blau (45x61cm-18x24in) s.d.53 i.verso
£25773	$47165	(2-Jun-92 L.K1050/R) Red vertical (90x80cm-35x31in) s.d.67 s.i.d.verso (DM 75000)
£27972	$49790	(28-Nov-91 SY.BE76/R) With red line (90x80cm-35x31in) s.d.66 s.i.d.verso (DM 80000)
£40000	$72400	(5-Dec-91 C12/R) Wandlung (136x145cm-54x57in) s.d.53 i.verso
£563	$1020	(6-Dec-91 GB.B7242) Untitled (20x18cm-8x7in) mono.d.1975 col.felt tip pen (DM 1600)
£632	$1137	(19-Nov-91 L.K1222) Composition (20x18cm-8x7in) mono.d.1975 col.felt tip pen (DM 1800)
£751	$1367	(25-May-92 WK.M1317/R) Composition (19x18cm-7x7in) mono.d.1975 col.felt tip pen (DM 2200)
£853	$1553	(30-May-92 VG.B997/R) Untitled (17x26cm-7x10in) mono.i. chk vellum (DM 2500)
£1024	$1863	(30-May-92 VG.B998/R) Untitled (16x25cm-6x10in) mono.i. chk vellum (DM 3000)
£1092	$1988	(26-May-92 KF.M1390/R) Composition with yellow, orange and purple (20x18cm-8x7in) mono.d.1975 felt tip pen (DM 3200)
£1474	$2653	(19-Nov-91 L.K1218) Untitled (43x61cm-17x24in) s.d.29 graphite (DM 4200)
£1536	$2795	(30-May-92 VG.B335/R) Untitled (29x21cm-11x8in) mono.d.1932 mixed media (DM 4500)
£1570	$2857	(26-May-92 KF.M1391/R) Shapes with blue, red and orange (20x18cm-8x7in) mono.d.1975 (DM 4600)
£2343	$4170	(25-Nov-91 WK.M1101/R) Composition (16x17cm-6x7in) s.d.1959 mixed media (DM 6700)
£2982	$5368	(19-Nov-91 L.K1219/R) Composition (50x71cm-20x28in) s.d.1954 indian ink brush board (DM 8500)
£3322	$5913	(30-Nov-91 VG.B332/R) Untitled (29x21cm-11x8in) mono.d.1932 oil wax (DM 9500)
£3333	$6000	(19-Nov-91 L.K1216/R) Abstract composition (17x24cm-7x9in) s.d.60 oil indian ink (DM 9500)
£3509	$6316	(19-Nov-91 L.K1217/R) Abstract composition (17x24cm-7x9in) s.d.60 oil indian ink (DM 10000)

WINTER, Fritz (1905-1976) German-cont.
£4811 $8804   (2-Jun-92 L.K1051) Untitled (59x39cm-23x15in) s.d.1965 gouache oil paint
                  board (DM 14000)
£5578 $10096   (4-Dec-91 G.Z120/R) Composition (49x69cm-19x27in) s.d.1953 mixed media
                  (S.FR 14000)
£7168 $12759   (30-Nov-91 VG.B346/R) Composition (50x69cm-20x27in) s.d.1951 oil col.chk
                  board (DM 20500)
£8874 $16150   (30-May-92 VG.B339/R) Composition (48x61cm-19x24in) s.d.1950 oil gouache
                  paper on board (DM 26000)
£13993 $25468   (26-May-92 KF.M1389/R) Grosse Bewegung (49x70cm-19x28in) s.d.1949 mixed
                  media board (DM 41000)
£38462 $68462   (26-Nov-91 KF.M1127/R) Forces of the earth (29x21cm-11x8in) mono.d.1944
                  mixed media (DM 110000)

WINTER, Gillis de (1650-1720) Flemish
£29369 $51982   (7-Nov-91 D.V145/R) Villagers merrymaking in landscape (42x50cm-17x20in)
                  (A.S 600000)

WINTER, Gillis de (circle) (1650-1720) Flemish
£2572 $4887   (26-Jun-92 AT.P101/R) Un marchand de legumes. Un marchand de volailles
                  (24x33cm-9x13in) pair (F.FR 25000)

WINTER, William Arthur (1909-) Canadian
£457 $831   (26-May-92 JOY.T177/R) Afternoon play (40x50cm-16x20in) s. board
                  (C.D 1000)
£683 $1229   (18-Nov-91 HO.ED43) Bass fisherman (41x51cm-16x20in) board (C.D 1400)
£685 $1247   (26-May-92 JOY.T5/R) Children playing on city street (55x70cm-22x28in) s.
                  (C.D 1500)
£822 $1496   (26-May-92 JOY.T255/R) Paper boys (40x50cm-16x20in) s.d.70 canvasboard
                  (C.D 1800)

WINTER, William Tatton (1855-1928) British
£470 $790   (27-Aug-91 SWS1755) Hankley Common (33x44cm-13x17in) s. W/C pencil
£950 $1682   (13-Feb-92 B170) A drover and sheep on a heath (63x46cm-25x18in) s. W/C
£1000 $1710   (12-Mar-92 CSK49/R) Returning home (56x74cm-22x29in) s. pencil W/C
                  htd.white

WINTER-SHAW, Arthur (1869-1948) British
£498 $886   (25-Nov-91 W.T1886) By the meadow gate (30x46cm-12x18in) s. (C.D 1000)
£800 $1480   (11-Jun-92 CSK110) Herdswoman with cattle (30x45cm-12x18in) s.

WINTERHALTER, Franz Xavier (1806-1873) German
£3027 $5207   (16-Oct-91 AT.P143/R) Portrait de Napoleon III (37x28cm-15x11in) canvas
                  laid down on cut board (F.FR 30000)
£35000 $62300   (27-Nov-91 S163/R) Portrait of lady (130x98cm-51x39in) s.i.d.1860 oval
£82578 $140383 (21-Oct-91 ARC.P10/R) Portrait de fillette a la rose (94x73cm-37x29in)
                  s.d.1840 (F.FR 820000)

WINTERHALTER, Franz Xavier (after) (1806-1873) German
£1000 $1710   (18-Mar-92 CSK180/R) The serenaders (231x180cm-91x71in)

WINTERHALTER, Franz Xavier (studio) (1806-1873) German
£4077 $7584   (20-Jun-92 CH.MO97/R) Portrait de Napoleon III (195x137cm-77x54in)
                  (F.FR 40000)

WINTERHALTER, Hermann (1808-1891) German
£27291 $51308   (16-Dec-91 AGS.P27/R) Portrait de Madame Alfred Andre (86x68cm-34x27in)
                  s.d.1859 oval (F.FR 265000)

WINTERHALTER, Joseph (younger-attrib) (1743-1807) German
£2208 $4195   (23-Jun-92 D.V117/R) Apotheosis of St Francis (62x48cm-24x19in)
                  (A.S 45000)

WINTERLIN, Anton (1805-1894) Swiss
£3725 $6333   (23-Oct-91 GD.B807/R) Alpine landscape with mill by torrent and
                  farmhouses (72x93cm-28x37in) mono.d.1874 (S.FR 9500)
£4444 $8044   (19-May-92 GF.L2588/R) Chamonix valley with Glacier de Bois
                  (62x74cm-24x29in) mono.d.1871 i.verso (S.FR 12000)
£1195 $2163   (5-Dec-91 SY.Z16/R) Wooded landscape with stream (31x45cm-12x18in)
                  mono.d.1838 pencil W/C (S.FR 3000)
£2925 $5265   (19-Nov-91 GS.B4715/R) Unterseen with view of Jungfrau and shepherd with
                  animals (46x66cm-18x26in) mono. W/C (S.FR 7400)
£3755 $6759   (19-Nov-91 GS.B4714/R) Urnersee landscape with Urirotstock and
                  Fronalpstock s. W/C (S.FR 9500)

WINTERLIN, Anton (attrib) (1805-1894) Swiss
£3802 $7072   (19-Jun-92 ZOF.Z2135/R) View of Arth on the Zugersee at night
                  (41x60cm-16x24in) i.verso paper on canvas (S.FR 10000)

WINTERS, Michael J (1943-) Australian
£684 $1238   (2-Dec-91 AAA.S146) The edge, Coogee (91x122cm-36x48in) s. (A.D 1600)

WINTERS, Robin (20th C) American?
£2235 $4000   (7-May-92 SY.NY214/R) Another inadequate gift (183x152cm-72x60in)
                  s.d.1986 verso acrylic pencil metal canvas

WINTERS, Terry (1949-) American
£15363 $27500   (14-Nov-91 SY.NY229/R) Botanical subject No. 4 (122x91cm-48x36in)
  s.d.1982 stretcher linen
£17877 $32000   (13-Nov-91 CH.NY239/R) Untitled (107x67cm-42x26in) s.d.1983verso linen
£27933 $50000   (13-Nov-91 SY.NY74/R) Stamina I (152x213cm-60x84in) linen
£3911 $7000   (5-May-92 CH.NY116/R) N (29x39cm-11x15in) s.i.d.1987verso gouache
  graphite
£4749 $8500   (5-May-92 CH.NY114/R) P (28x37cm-11x15in) s.i.d.1987verso gouache
£9143 $16000   (25-Feb-92 SY.NY224/R) Untitled (105x75cm-41x30in) chl

WIRBEL, Veronique (20th C) French?
£2884 $4931   (22-Mar-92 I.N66/R) La, peut-etre la nuit... (146x114cm-57x45in) s.d.1989
  acrylic (F.FR 28000)

WIRGMAN, C A (19th C) British?
£3800 $6498   (16-Mar-92 LW1822) Two Chinese peasant girls and Mongol boy
  (23x13cm-9x5in) s. W/C htd bodycol three
£4200 $7182   (16-Mar-92 LW1821/R) Studies of Japanese Geisha girls (28x18cm-11x7in) s.
  W/C htd bodycol three

WIRGMAN, T Blake (1848-1925) British
£3000 $5310   (6-Nov-91 S163/R) Portrait of Mis Agatha Cox, later Lady Hamo Thornycorft
  (112x86cm-44x34in) s.d.1884

WIRTANEN, Kaapo (1886-1959) Finnish?
£569 $1001   (12-Apr-92 HOR.H261) The child (36x29cm-14x11in) s. (F.M 4500)
£632 $1113   (12-Apr-92 HOR.H260) Coastal meadow (32x40cm-13x16in) s. (F.M 5000)
£930 $1645   (6-Nov-91 HOR.H156) Water-lilies (55x46cm-22x18in) s.d.1938 (F.M 6600)
£970 $1727   (1-Dec-91 HOR.H268) Summer day (38x46cm-15x18in) s.d.1945 (F.M 7500)
£1094 $1991   (11-Dec-91 HOR.H131) Light and shadow (53x64cm-21x25in) s.d.1921
  (F.M 8500)
£1268 $2244   (6-Nov-91 HOR.H155) Birches on the beach (82x65cm-32x26in) s. (F.M 9000)
£1294 $2303   (1-Dec-91 HOR.H266) Birch on the shore (88x65cm-35x26in) s.d.1950
  (F.M 10000)
£1391 $2448   (12-Apr-92 HOR.H258) Clear autumn day (72x56cm-28x22in) s.d.1946
  (F.M 11000)
£1552 $2763   (1-Dec-91 HOR.H267) Winter evening (72x56cm-28x22in) s.d.1947 (F.M 12000)
£1643 $2893   (12-Apr-92 HOR.H259) Birches (56x65cm-22x26in) s.d.1926 (F.M 13000)
£2070 $3684   (1-Dec-91 HOR.H265/R) By the window (65x54cm-26x21in) s.d.1934
  (F.M 16000)

WISBY, Jack (19th C?) American
£1711 $3250   (24-Jun-92 B.SF6302/R) Mount Tamalpais (51x91cm-20x36in) s.
£2368 $4500   (24-Jun-92 B.SF6278/R) Yosemite Valley (61x71cm-24x28in) s.

WISER, Josef Leopold (18th C) Yugoslavian
£745 $1274   (18-Mar-92 D.V343/R) Quodlibet (35x21cm-14x8in) s. W/C indian ink gold
  (A.S 15000)

WISHART, Peter (1852-1932) British
£800 $1448   (4-Dec-91 S194/R) Sketching by river bank (29x40cm-11x16in) s.

WISINGER-FLORIAN, Olga (1844-1926) Austrian
£2441 $4150   (24-Oct-91 D.V52) Stream in landscape (28x19cm-11x7in) board (A.S 50000)
£19980 $35964   (21-Nov-91 D.V5/R) Fish market, Venice (28x41cm-11x16in) mono.d.92
  (A.S 400000)
£45000 $80100   (27-Nov-91 S153/R) Apple orchard (131x181cm-52x71in) s.
£77557 $141154   (26-May-92 D.V40/R) Field with sunflowers (134x176cm-53x69in) s.i.verso
  (A.S 1600000)

WISSEL, Abraham van der (1865-1926) Dutch
£608 $1058   (17-Sep-91 CH.AM229) A farmer steering a punt in a stream towards a
  drawbridge by a farm (47x66cm-19x26in) s. (D.FL 2000)

WISSELINGH, Johannes Pieter van (1812-1899) Dutch
£621 $1075   (24-Mar-92 VN.R105) Wooded landscape (24x39cm-9x15in) s. panel
  (D.FL 2000)

WISSING, Willem (1653-1687) Dutch
£5400 $9666   (13-Nov-91 S138/R) Portrait of Lady Lisburn wearing dress with robes
  (74x61cm-29x24in) i. i.verso painted oval
£6000 $10560   (8-Apr-92 S19/R) Portrait of lady with daughter, seated in landscape,
  child holding posy (45x36cm-18x14in)
£6000 $10740   (13-Nov-91 S30/R) Portrait of lady seated wearing brocade dress with
  chemise (122x99cm-48x39in)
£10000 $17900   (13-Nov-91 S27/R) Portrait of Queen Mary seated wearing ermine lined
  robes (170x108cm-67x43in) i.

WISSING, Willem (after) (1653-1687) Dutch
£850 $1513   (31-Oct-91 B143) Portrait of Queen Mary II, seated, holding sprig of
  orange blossom (47x37cm-19x15in)

WISSING, Willem (circle) (1653-1687) Dutch
£1000 $1720   (8-Oct-91 PH28) Portrait of a gentleman, wearing a white lace stock
  (75x62cm-30x24in) oval

WISSING, Willem (circle) (1653-1687) Dutch-cont.
£1500	$2640	(8-Apr-92 S145/R) Portrait of gentleman, standing in landscape (124x99cm-49x39in)
£3800	$6840	(19-Nov-91 PH13/R) Portrait of Mary II when Princess of Orange seated with ermine coat (56x45cm-22x18in)
£3800	$6650	(27-Feb-92 B153/R) Portrait of a lady, member of the Arundell Family with her young daughter (125x103cm-49x41in)
£4651	$8000	(9-Oct-91 CH.NY138/R) Portrait of lady said to be Mrs. James and daughter, seated by tree (127x103cm-50x41in)

WISSING, Willem (studio) (1653-1687) Dutch
| £3000 | $5400 | (19-Nov-91 PH12/R) Portrait of Lady Elizabeth Felton seated holding monkey (127x100cm-50x39in) |

WISSING, Willem (style) (1653-1687) Dutch
| £2000 | $3580 | (13-Nov-91 S149/R) Portrait of Anne, Lady Crewe (64x56cm-25x22in) i.d.1689 i.d.1690verso painted oval |

WISTEHUFF, Revere F (1900-1971) American
| £787 | $1400 | (2-Nov-91 IH.NY119/R) Reclining girl writing love letter to soldier (58x43cm-23x17in) s. |
| £977 | $1700 | (15-Apr-92 SY.NY231/R) Through the hoop (52x43cm-20x17in) s. |

WISZNIEWSKI, Adrian (1958-) ?
| *£2400* | *$4368* | *(29-May-92 PHG64 a) Young man with book (152x101cm-60x40in) chl* |

WIT, Jacob de (1695-1754) Dutch
£3200	$6144	(7-Jul-92 PH157/R) Putti with shells and fishing nets holding medallion of head of Neptune (61x174cm-24x69in) s. canvas on board en grisaille
£5086	$9308	(13-May-92 LC.P11/R) Deux amours a la guirlande (87x110cm-34x43in) s.d.1728 (F.FR 50000)
£600	*$1092*	*(11-Dec-91 PH78/R) Three putti playing with fruit amongst classical statuary (13x11cm-5x4in) s. pen wash htd.white*
£720	*$1253*	*(13-Apr-92 S290/R) Head of putto (21x17cm-8x7in) black red chk wash*
£1199	*$2062*	*(11-Oct-91 AW.H1024/R) Ceiling design with scene of gods and putti (20x28cm-8x11in) wash W/C pen over pencil oval (DM 3500)*
£1242	*$2211*	*(25-Nov-91 CH.AM186/R) Allegory with five putti (21x25cm-8x10in) s.i. chk pen wash htd.white (D.FL 4000)*
£1304	*$2322*	*(25-Nov-91 CH.AM185/R) Allegory of autumn - the infant Bacchus with putti by vase (23x17cm-9x7in) s.d.1747verso chk pen wash htd.white arched top (D.FL 4200)*
£1646	*$2979*	*(5-Dec-91 SY.MO29/R) Groupe de personnages bibliques comprenant moise, David et Abraham (37x221cm-15x87in) s.d.1748 pen wash (F.FR 16000)*

WIT, Jacob de (attrib) (1695-1754) Dutch
| £16227 | $28560 | (10-Apr-92 AT.P61/R) Pymagalion contemplant sa statue (45x52cm-18x20in) traces sig. (F.FR 160000) |
| *£528* | *$940* | *(25-Nov-91 CH.AM188) Allegory of Africa. Design for allegory (18x23cm-7x9in) i. chk oval double-sided (D.FL 1700)* |

WIT, Jacob de (circle) (1695-1754) Dutch
| £2778 | $4972 | (12-Nov-91 SY.AM34) Grisaille overdoor depicting allegory (85x120cm-33x47in) (D.FL 9000) |
| *£447* | *$818* | *(3-Jun-92 DO.H2446/R) Allegory of winter (15x20cm-6x8in) indian ink brush grisaille oval (DM 1300)* |

WIT, Jacob de (studio) (1695-1754) Dutch
| £4800 | $8544 | (1-Nov-91 S367/R) Putti playing (63x95cm-25x37in) grisaille pair |

WIT, Jacob de (style) (1695-1754) Dutch
£3000	$5340	(1-Nov-91 S352/R) Putti with greyhound and hunting trophies (78x178cm-31x70in) grisaille irregular shape
£3200	$5600	(27-Feb-92 CSK173/R) Vanitas still lives (24x21cm-9x8in) panel pair
£3600	$6408	(1-Nov-91 S372/R) Putti at rest. Putti dancing with female figure playing trumpet (74x114cm-29x45in) grisaille pair

WIT, Prosper Joseph de (1862-1951) Belgian
£500	$881	(7-Apr-92 C.A436) Landscape (33x39cm-13x15in) s. (B.FR 30000)
£662	$1199	(23-May-92 KV.L116) Estaminet a Grimbergen (45x55cm-18x22in) s. (B.FR 40000)
£829	$1517	(12-May-92 C.A88/R) A drink on the sly (36x27cm-14x11in) s. panel (B.FR 50000)
£1027	$1858	(3-Dec-91 C.A81/R) The veteran (28x36cm-11x14in) s. panel (B.FR 60000)
£2488	$4552	(12-May-92 C.A89/R) View of La Calamine (40x65cm-16x26in) s.d.1888 (B.FR 150000)

WITHAM, J (19th C) ?
| £1000 | $1850 | (12-Jun-92 TE625/R) A feat of seamnship (61x107cm-24x42in) s.d.1881 |

WITHAM, J W (19/20th C) British?
| £1050 | $1817 | (24-Mar-92 PHC432/R) Follow Leader-Liverpool Pilot Boat No.2 leading 12 ships into Mersey (39x69cm-15x27in) s.d.1900 |

WITHERINGTON, William Frederick (1785-1875) British
£10000 $18800   (19-Dec-91 C188/R) Midsummer, ye verdant trees and underwood, where the poetic birds rejoice (70x90cm-28x35in) s.d.1851
£18000 $30600   (25-Oct-91 C38/R) Dinner time (88x117cm-35x46in) s.

WITHERS, Augusta Innes (fl.1829-1865) British
£720 $1282   (27-Nov-91 B125/R) Canaries on ledge with bowl (35x30cm-14x12in) s. W/C arched top
£3600 $6876   (13-Jul-92 PH60/R) Family of partridges (42x55cm-17x22in) s.d.1864 W/C

WITHERS, Walter (1854-1914) Australian
£3965 $7137   (24-Nov-91 SY.S459/R) Haystooks, Eltham (23x34cm-9x13in) s. board (A.D 9000)
£6000 $10680   (28-Nov-91 C15/R) Timber carting (46x30cm-18x12in) s.d.06 canvas on board
£6197 $11030   (28-Apr-92 CH.ME110/R) Sheep grazing in clearing (23x33cm-9x13in) s.d.06 i.verso board (A.D 14500)
£6452 $11226   (16-Sep-91 CH.ME119/R) Greensborough Lane (25x35cm-10x14in) s. i.verso academy board (A.D 14000)
£7489 $13330   (26-Nov-91 J.M3/R) Approaching storm (34x43cm-13x17in) s. (A.D 17000)
£7500 $13350   (28-Nov-91 C16/R) Sheep grazing (51x41cm-20x16in) s.
£8889 $15200   (17-Mar-92 JRL.S219/R) Eltham Road (29x49cm-11x19in) s. (A.D 20000)
£18779 $31362   (19-Aug-91 SY.ME237/R) Figures on beach (24x44cm-9x17in) s.d.1910 (A.D 40000)
£28169 $47042   (19-Aug-91 SY.ME261/R) Allegory to spring - portrait of Gladys Manifold (116x107cm-46x42in) s.d.1902 (A.D 60000)
£855 $1521   (27-Apr-92 J.M126/R) The milkmaid (21x31cm-8x12in) s. W/C (A.D 2000)
£940 $1674   (27-Apr-92 J.M38) Autumn glow (21x31cm-8x12in) s. W/C (A.D 2200)
£1145 $2062   (24-Nov-91 SY.S15) Valley Orchard (23x30cm-9x12in) init. W/C (A.D 2600)

WITHOOS, Matthias (1627-1703) Dutch
£7716 $13812   (14-Nov-91 CH.AM125/R) Vanitas still lives with flowers and ruins in Italianate gardens (66x57cm-26x22in) s.d.1665 pair (D.FL 25000)

WITHOOS, Matthias (circle) (1627-1703) Dutch
£8951 $16022   (12-Nov-91 SY.AM123/R) Birds nest surrounded by butterflies in trunk of tree (63x51cm-25x20in) panel (D.FL 29000)

WITHOOS, Pieter (1654-1693) Dutch
£870 $1548   (25-Nov-91 CH.AM172/R) Studies of three butterflies and two insects. Study of butterflies (17x22cm-7x9in) pen W/C two (D.FL 2800)

WITJENS, Adrianus Hendrikus see WITJENS, Jacques Stephen

WITJENS, Jacques Stephen (1881-1956) Dutch
£989 $1800   (11-Dec-91 RO.BA44) Botes en la Orilla (18x24cm-7x9in) s.
£1105 $1900   (9-Oct-91 RO.BA590) Pescadores (50x60cm-20x24in) s.
£1154 $2100   (11-Dec-91 RO.BA259) La playa (40x60cm-16x24in) s.
£1190 $2000   (1-Sep-91 PO.BA27) Grises y colores (40x60cm-16x24in) s.
£1319 $2400   (11-Dec-91 RO.BA261) Parvas (30x40cm-12x16in) s.
£1344 $2500   (16-Jun-92 RO.BA75) El viejo molino (35x51cm-14x20in) panel
£1389 $2500   (20-Nov-91 V.BA115/R) Paisaje con gallinas (36x56cm-14x22in)
£1453 $2500   (9-Oct-91 RO.BA764) Marina (40x50cm-16x20in) s.
£1676 $3000   (6-May-92 V.BA114/R) Paisaje holandes (50x60cm-20x24in)
£2043 $3800   (16-Jun-92 RO.BA74) Paisaje lacustre (45x60cm-18x24in)
£2258 $4200   (16-Jun-92 RO.BA96) En la playa (44x75cm-17x30in) panel

WITJENS, Willem (1884-1962) Dutch
£608 $1058   (17-Sep-91 CH.AM372) Winter in Maastricht (30x41cm-12x16in) s. i. verso canvas laid down on board (D.FL 2000)
£673 $1191   (5-Nov-91 SY.AM424/R) Turnershill, Sussex (83x112cm-33x44in) s.i.d.1953 (D.FL 2200)

WITKIEWICZ, Stanislaw (1851-1915) Polish
£418 $720   (13-Oct-91 REM.W37) Peasants (27x21cm-11x8in) s. W/C (P.Z 8000000)

WITKIEWICZ, Stanislaw Ignacy (1885-1939) Polish
£1290 $2310   (17-Nov-91 REM.W35) Portrait of young woman (64x50cm-25x20in) s (P.Z 25000000)
£1308 $2264   (7-Sep-91 AL.W7) Portrait of Sophie Lipinska (61x45cm-24x18in) s. pastel (P.Z 25000000)
£1450 $2725   (21-Dec-91 HO.P8) Portrait of Maria Jackowska-Wojciehowskab (67x47cm-26x19in) s. pastel (P.Z 28000000)
£1561 $2685   (20-Oct-91 UNI.W9) Portrait of Matylda Mach (74x54cm-29x21in) s. pastel (P.Z 30000000)
£1663 $2826   (26-Oct-91 AL.W5) Portrait of girl with red ribbons (64x46cm-25x18in) s.pastel (P.Z 32000000)
£1674 $2879   (13-Oct-91 REM.W35) Portrait of young woman (64x50cm-25x20in) pastel (P.Z 32000000)
£1755 $3141   (17-Nov-91 REM.W36) Portrait of Zofia Szuman (66x47cm-26x19in) s. pastel (P.Z 34000000)
£1831 $3149   (13-Oct-91 REM.W36) Portrait of P W (64x49cm-25x19in) pastel (P.Z 35000000)
£1831 $3149   (13-Oct-91 REM.W34) Portrait of Janina Leszczynska (64x51cm-25x20in) s. pastel (P.Z 35000000)

WITKIEWICZ, Stanislaw Ignacy (1885-1939) Polish-cont.
£1864 $3504 (21-Dec-91 PSA.W23) Portrait of Stefania Tuwim (65x49cm-26x19in) s. W/C
(P.Z 36000000)
£2041 $3531 (8-Sep-91 REM.W44) Portrait of a man (85x45cm-33x18in) s. pastel
(P.Z 39000000)
£2601 $4475 (20-Oct-91 UNI.W8) Portrait of Leon Reynel (65x47cm-26x19in) s. pastel
(P.Z 50000000)

WITKOWSKI, Karl (1860-1910) American
£2235 $4000 (14-Nov-91 CE.NY94/R) Peeling apple (56x46cm-22x18in) s.d.1900
£2394 $4500 (18-Dec-91 SY.NY119/R) Boy with parrot (61x50cm-24x20in) s.
£4094 $7000 (12-Mar-92 CH.NY54/R) Playing a tune (53x38cm-21x15in) init.
£6471 $11000 (25-Oct-91 S.W2749/R) Knucks down (61x71cm-24x28in) s.

WITMAN, C F (?) ?
£803 $1469 (3-Jun-92 R.T93/R) Saturday night (102x171cm-40x67in) with sig. i.
(C.D 1750)

WITMONT, Heerman (1605-?) Dutch
£14500 $25810 (30-Oct-91 S4/R) Shipping off the coast (50x72cm-20x28in) s. panel

WITSEN (?) Dutch?
£1049 $1836 (25-Feb-92 VN.R381) Still life (48x39cm-19x15in) (D.FL 3400)

WITT, Hans (1891-1966) Austrian
£485 $864 (29-Apr-92 D.V633/R) Fair at the Floridsdorfer Brucke (21x30cm-8x12in) s.
W/C (A.S 10000)

WITTE, Gaspar de (attrib) (1624-1681) Flemish
£2920 $5226 (6-May-92 GD.B1360/R) View of town with arched bridge and figures
(55x97cm-22x38in) s.d.1665 panel (S.FR 8000)

WITTE, O (?) ?
£1399 $2420 (25-Mar-92 KM.K1528/R) English harbour town with figures and shipping in
choppy seas (47x101cm-19x40in) s. (DM 4000)

WITTEL, Gaspar van (1653-1736) Dutch
£40775 $75841 (18-Jun-92 SY.MO36/R) L'Arc de Titus a Rome (63x48cm-25x19in)
(F.FR 400000)
£44852 $83425 (18-Jun-92 SY.MO16/R) Vue de la Villa Aldobrandini aux environs de Rome
(27x41cm-11x16in) vellum (F.FR 440000)
£140000 $245000 (31-Mar-92 PH127/R) View of Chiaia with tower looking up Strada de
Pozzuoli towards Margellina, Naples (50x65cm-20x26in)
£239873 $436569 (28-May-92 F.M139/R) Veduta di piazza San Pietro (52x107cm-20x42in)
mono.d.1721 (I.L 530000000)
£3080 $5544 (22-Nov-91 AGS.P142/R) Paysage du Lac Majeur pres de Pallanza
(23x34cm-9x13in) i. pen W/C (F.FR 30000)

WITTEL, Gaspar van (after) (1653-1736) Dutch
£7200 $12600 (3-Apr-92 C5/R) View of Vaprio and Canonica, with Villa Melzi, looking
north-west (66x108cm-26x43in)

WITTEL, Gaspar van (circle) (1653-1736) Dutch
£950 $1691 (30-Apr-92 CG879) Shipping anchored in Dutch port with figures on
quayside (46x60cm-18x24in)
£4631 $8012 (25-Mar-92 CH.R1/R) Veduta di Castel Sant'Angelo della sponda sinistra
del Tevere (13x35cm-5x14in) (I.L 10000000)

WITTEL, Gaspar van (style) (1653-1736) Dutch
£1677 $3102 (13-Jun-92 CH.AM197/R) Shepherdess with flock on path in Italianate
landscape, Tivoli beyond (51x61cm-20x24in) indis.s.d.763 panel
(D.FL 5500)
£2907 $5000 (10-Oct-91 SY.NY196/R) The Piazza Navona, Rome (20x26cm-8x10in) copper
£6853 $12129 (7-Nov-91 D.V305/R) Entrance to Farnesian Gardens, Rome (33x47cm-13x19in)
(A.S 140000)

WITTENBERG, Jan (1886-1963) Dutch
£851 $1481 (17-Sep-91 CH.AM225) A maraboe standing in a niche (60x43cm-24x17in) s.i.
(D.FL 2800)

WITTEVRONGEL, Roger (1933-) Belgian
£500 $881 (7-Apr-92 C.A667) Nude (65x50cm-26x20in) s. colour dr. (B.FR 30000)

WITTKAMP, Arnold (1827-1900) Dutch
£608 $1058 (17-Sep-91 CH.AM557) A wooded landscape with ducks in a pond, a farm
beyond, at sunset (45x59cm-18x23in) s. (D.FL 2000)

WITTLICH, Josef (1903-1982) ?
£859 $1460 (26-Oct-91 WK.M750/R) Queen in uniform (89x62cm-35x24in) s.d.1968 gouache
(DM 2500)

WITTMER, Johann Michael (1802-1880) German
£7200 $13392 (19-Jun-92 C23/R) Four Latin Fathers of the Church - St.Gerome,
St.Gregory, St.Ambrose, St.Augustine (56x90cm-22x35in) s.i.d.1864 panel
four in one frame

WITTMER, Johann Michael (1802-1880) German-cont.
£30717 $55597   (21-May-92 L.K502/R) Murnau family Kottmuller with saint by fountain in southern landscape (135x98cm-53x39in) s.d.1866 (DM 90000)

WITTNER, Gerhard (1926-) German
£1684 $3032   (19-Nov-91 L.K1225) Composition (73x73cm-29x29in) s.i.d.1974verso acrylic panel (DM 4800)

WITTWER-GELPKE, Martha (1875-1959) Swiss
£1275 $2308   (4-Dec-91 G.Z196/R) View of Zurich in morning fog (34x70cm-13x28in) mono. board (S.FR 3200)
£1901 $3536   (19-Jun-92 G.Z101/R) Harvest fruits (65x48cm-26x19in) (S.FR 5000)

WIVEL, Niels (1855-1914) Scandinavian
£758 $1303   (15-Oct-91 RAS.K299) Church mice (33x55cm-13x22in) s.d.1902 (D.KR 8500)

WIZON, Tod (20th C) American?
£670 $1200   (9-May-92 CE.NY217/R) Clots (91x102cm-36x40in) init.i.d.verso acrylic panel

WOCHER, Marquard (1760-1830) Swiss
£2993 $5028   *(27-Aug-91 RAS.K687/R) Swiss landscape (41x56cm-16x22in) pen W/C (D.KR 34000)*

WOCHER, Tiberius Dominikus (1728-1799) Swiss
£5500 $10010   (10-Dec-91 PH11/R) Daughter of Jephthah (78x113cm-31x44in) mono.
£667 $1193   *(12-Nov-91 GF.L5158/R) Pastoral landscape (16x6cm-6x2in) d.1745 indian ink pen wash grisaille (S.FR 1700)*

WOELFLE, Arthur William (1873-1936) American
£1596 $3000   (18-Dec-91 SY.NY120/R) Lady in white (101x76cm-40x30in) s.

WOENSAM, Anton von Worms (style) (1500-1541) German
£3200 $5600   (3-Apr-92 C70/R) Portrait of jeweller, standing, in tunic and hat, holding five rings (50x39cm-20x15in) panel

WOENSEL, Petronella van (1785-1839) Dutch
£13372 $23000   (10-Oct-91 SY.NY163 a/R) Still life of fruit and flowers all on a draped ledge (56x44cm-22x17in) s.

WOESTIJNE, Gustave van de (1881-1947) Belgian
£4500 $7965   (14-Feb-92 C51/R) Portrait de la Duchesse de Faiye (266x117cm-105x46in) s.d.MCM VII
£2649 $4795   *(23-May-92 KV.L424/R) The blind violin player (24x17cm-9x7in) s. chk. (B.FR 160000)*

WOHLOFF, J H (?) ?
£710 $1285   (4-Dec-91 DS.W29/R) Leuvehaven, Rotterdam Inner Harbour (39x48cm-15x19in) s. (NZ.D 2300)

WOHNER, Louis (1888-) German
£515 $897   (19-Sep-91 N.M2842/R) Village street in Oberstdorf (60x50cm-24x20in) s. i.verso (DM 1500)
£1963 $3750   *(3-Jul-92 S.W3121/R) Extensive Alpine mountain view (117x140cm-46x55in) s.*

WOJNAROWICZ, David (20th C) American?
£1397 $2500   *(12-Nov-91 CE.NY146/R) Time (122x244cm-48x96in) s.i.d.1982verso apray enamel masonite*

WOJNARSKI, Jan (1879-1937) Polish
£407 $741   *(15-Dec-91 REM.W49) Woman at her toilet (43x29cm-17x11in) crayon W/C (P.Z 8000000)*

WOJNIAKOWSKI, Kazimierz (1771-1812) Polish
£2036 $3705   (15-Dec-91 REM.W50) Portrait of Mrs Wlodek (62x51cm-24x20in) (P.Z 40000000)

WOJTKIEWICZ, Witold (1879-1911) Polish
£757 $1363   *(24-Nov-91 AG.W17) In a stall (17x13cm-7x5in) s. W/C (P.Z 15000000)*

WOLCOTT, James (19th C) American
£718 $1300   (5-Dec-91 GRO.B432) Fantasy in colour (61x91cm-24x36in)

WOLD, Roar (1926-1990) Norwegian
£702 $1208   *(10-Oct-91 BU.O113/R) Garden in Vence (78x106cm-31x42in) s. s.i.verso W/C (N.KR 8000)*

WOLD-TORNE, Oluf (1867-1919) Norwegian
£2726 $4799   (8-Apr-92 GWP.O81/R) Afternoon (37x46cm-15x18in) s. i.verso panel (N.KR 31000)

WOLF, Friedrich (19th C) Austrian
£2200 $3916   (28-Nov-91 CSK67) Deer hunters returning home (51x66cm-20x26in) s.d.1869

WOLF, Georg (1882-1962) German
£874	$1495	(19-Mar-92 N.M2861/R) Four cows grazing (36x50cm-14x20in) s. (DM 2500)
£1573	$2722	(25-Mar-92 KM.K1533) Cattle grazing in shade of tree (55x81cm-22x32in) s. (DM 4500)
£1706	$3089	(21-May-92 L.K503/R) Shepherd with flock (65x90cm-26x35in) s. (DM 5000)
£1724	$2966	(16-Oct-91 KM.K1455/R) Peasant girl with cattle and sheep on path lined by flowering fruit trees (64x80cm-25x31in) s. (DM 5000)
£1748	$3024	(25-Mar-92 KM.K1532/R) Peasant boy and animals resting in shade of tree (60x80cm-24x31in) s. (DM 5000)

WOLF, Hamilton Achille (1883-1967) American
| £526 | $1000 | (24-Jun-92 B.SF6529/R) Atomic landscape (63x48cm-25x19in) s. board |
| £1316 | $2500 | (24-Jun-92 B.SF6528/R) Bridge (107x76cm-42x30in) s. masonite |

WOLF, Joseph (?-1899) German
£900	$1548	(4-Mar-92 S76/R) Robin's nest (28cm-11ins circular)
£420	*$735*	*(25-Feb-92 C3) Studies of gulls (35x25cm-14x10in) black white chk*
£1600	*$2800*	*(25-Feb-92 C64/R) Storks (49x65cm-19x26in) s.d.1879 W/C*
£1700	*$3026*	*(28-Apr-92 S252/R) Arctic hares in the snow (24x19cm-9x7in) s.d.1876 W/C*

WOLF, Raimund Anton (1865-1924) Austrian
| *£1500* | *$2790* | *(17-Jun-92 S397/R) Lady reading in summer landscape (76x98cm-30x39in) s. pastel* |

WOLFAERTS, Artus (attrib) (1581-c.1641) Flemish
| £6790 | $12154 | (14-Nov-91 CH.AM113/R) Study of young woman's head (23x18cm-9x7in) paper on canvas (D.FL 22000) |

WOLFAERTS, Artus (circle) (1581-c.1641) Flemish
| £1958 | $3465 | (7-Nov-91 D.V256/R) Jupiter and Merkur with Philemon and Baucis (29x36cm-11x14in) copper (A.S 40000) |

WOLFE, Edward (1897-1982) British
£650	$1151	(23-Apr-92 CSK47) Portrait of Dorothy Phillips (58x47cm-23x19in) s.
£900	$1692	(18-Dec-91 C126/R) Portrait of soldier (54x47cm-21x19in) s. board
£1000	$1750	(27-Sep-91 C145/R) Still life (33x46cm-13x18in) s.d.1920 i. label verso
£1200	$2076	(2-Oct-91 S123/R) From Government House, Portmeirion (35x46cm-14x18in) s. s.i.verso canvasboard
£1200	$2148	(14-Jan-92 PH140) Italian fisherman, Ischia (55x45cm-22x18in) s. s.i.verso canvasboard
£1800	$3114	(2-Oct-91 S62) Still life of flowers and frog (40x50cm-16x20in) s.
£2319	$4104	(4-Nov-91 SY.J239/R) Shipping in harbour, Algiers (48x59cm-19x23in) s. board (SA.R 11500)
£2500	$4275	(16-Mar-92 LW1720) Thames barges below Tower Bridge (61x86cm-24x34in) s. d.1960 verso
£3200	$5504	(6-Mar-92 C45/R) The little Mexican (61x47cm-24x19in) s.
£3400	$5950	(27-Sep-91 C19/R) Taxco Landscape (53x77cm-21x30in) s.
£650	*$1222*	*(18-Dec-91 C174/R) Portrait of young boy (51x38cm-20x15in) s. pastel W/C*
£800	*$1504*	*(18-Dec-91 C96/R) Jamieson's Farm, Ardmore, Ireland (46x61cm-18x24in) s. s.i.verso pastel*
£900	*$1692*	*(18-Dec-91 C128/R) Two Mexican boys (84x63cm-33x25in) s. pastel*
£1000	*$1880*	*(18-Dec-91 C127/R) North African dream (99x70cm-39x28in) pencil pastel*
£1100	*$2013*	*(15-May-92 TE313/R) Head of man (33x23cm-13x9in) s. pencil*

WOLFE, George (1834-1890) British
| *£1700* | *$3043* | *(6-May-92 MMB202) Bristol Harbour (25x36cm-10x14in) s.i.d.1856 W/C htd.white* |

WOLFENSBERGER, Johann Jakob (1797-1850) Swiss
| *£3000* | *$5340* | *(29-Nov-91 C47/R) View of Athens with the Acropolis beyond (52x75cm-20x30in) s.indist.i. pencil W/C paper laid down on canvas* |

WOLFF, E (1802-1879) German
| £596 | $1020 | (13-Mar-92 FN.S2625) Interior with coffe table and view of garden (50x39cm-20x15in) s. (DM 1700) |

WOLFF, Eugen (1873-1937) German
| £887 | $1615 | (27-May-92 PH.DU152/R) In the garden (84x65cm-33x26in) s.d.09 (DM 2600) |
| £1404 | $2400 | (13-Mar-92 FN.S3023) Elegant figures in interior of Schloss Lindich (56x75cm-22x30in) s. (DM 4000) |

WOLFF, Henrik (19th C) Danish
| £3297 | $6000 | (28-May-92 SY.NY267/R) Still life with potted bluebells, dahlias and hollyhocks on marble ledge (36x44cm-14x17in) s.d.1837 |

WOLFLE, F X (1896-) Austrian
| £1220 | $2220 | (12-Dec-91 N.M2853/R) Old hunter with rifle (24x17cm-9x7in) s. panel (DM 3500) |

WOLFLE, Franz Xavier (1896-1989) Austrian
£500	$905	(21-May-92 CSK290) Neopolitan folk by fountain (29x39cm-11x15in) s.d.23
£802	$1452	(5-Dec-91 D.V253/R) Table with flowers (35x29cm-14x11in) s. i.verso panel (A.S 16000)
£1257	$2200	(18-Feb-92 CE.NY91/R) Recital (51x42cm-20x17in) s. panel
£2200	$3982	(22-May-92 C163/R) Game of chess (46x50cm-18x20in) s. panel

WOLFLE, Franz Xavier (1896-1989) Austrian-cont.
£2286	$4000	(18-Feb-92 CE.NY155/R) Letter (48x42cm-19x17in) s. panel
£2881	$5473	(26-Jun-92 CSC.P133/R) La lettre (47x42cm-19x17in) s. panel (F.FR 28000)
£1468	$2599	(7-Nov-91 D.V358/R) Bunch of flowers with parrott (69x52cm-27x20in) s. gouache (A.S 30000)

WOLFLI, Adolf (1864-1930) Swiss
£1916	$3314	(23-Mar-92 AB.L105/R) Praa,-Ala (11x37cm-4x15in) i.verso pencil col.pencil fragment (S.FR 5000)
£2682	$4640	(23-Mar-92 AB.L103/R) Gritt (34x21cm-13x8in) s.verso col.pencil pencil fragment (S.FR 7000)
£2682	$4640	(23-Mar-92 AB.L96/R) Santtajda and S.Roosali (16x32cm-6x13in) s.d.1917 i.verso pencil (S.FR 7000)
£3448	$5966	(23-Mar-92 AB.L97/R) Helldi-Veetia (32x25cm-13x10in) d.1917 i.verso (S.FR 9000)
£3448	$5966	(23-Mar-92 AB.L95/R) Der Licht-Falter und der Krohnen-Falter (31x23cm-12x9in) mono.i. col.crayon pencil (S.FR 9000)
£4215	$7291	(23-Mar-92 AB.L100/R) Kaiser Barbarossa (23x36cm-9x14in) i.verso col.pencil pencil (S.FR 11000)
£4981	$8617	(23-Mar-92 AB.L99/R) Magglingen, Leubringen (30x51cm-12x20in) s.d.1927verso col.crayon pencil (S.FR 13000)
£5364	$9280	(23-Mar-92 AB.L98/R) Das Konigs-Schloss in Bellgrad (37x49cm-15x19in) s.i.verso col.crayon pencil (S.FR 14000)
£8429	$14582	(23-Mar-92 AB.L106/R) Beschuttipumpper-Polka (36x71cm-14x28in) s.i.d.1917 i.verso pencil inkpen (S.FR 22000)
£15326	$26513	(23-Mar-92 AB.L102/R) Nach-Ruef, Marsch-Lied (50x37cm-20x15in) s.i.d.verso pencil col.pencil (S.FR 40000)
£16475	$28502	(23-Mar-92 AB.L107/R) Die Heilige Dreieinigkeit vom Ziller-Thal (67x72cm-26x28in) s.i.d.1915 i.verso pencil (S.FR 43000)
£22222	$38444	(23-Mar-92 AB.L104/R) Die Beatenberg-St.Adolf-Schatz'l-Fahne (99x70cm-39x28in) d.1918 i.verso collage col.pencil pencil (S.FR 58000)
£28736	$49713	(23-Mar-92 AB.L101/R) Der Grund-Riesen-Fonttaine-Strahl. St Adolf-Eewigkeits-Ring (92x75cm-36x30in) s.d.1913 pencil col.pencil double-sided (S.FR 75000)

WOLFRAM, Joseph (19th C) Austrian
£602	$1089	(5-Dec-91 D.V144) Roebuck (15x20cm-6x8in) s.d.873 board (A.S 12000)

WOLFSEN, Aleijda (1648-1690) Dutch
£1500	$2625	(1-Apr-92 S114/R) Portrait of gentleman (48x39cm-19x15in) s.i.d.1680
£1500	$2625	(25-Feb-92 PH73/R) Portrait of lady standing by fountain holding rose (41x35cm-16x14in)

WOLFSEN, Aleijda (attrib) (1648-1690) Dutch
£1698	$3039	(14-Nov-91 CH.AM205/R) Group portrait of six children on draped balcony with landscape beyond (46x38cm-18x15in) (D.FL 5500)

WOLFSON, William (1894-) American
£541	$1000	(10-Jun-92 CE.NY434/R) Miners (74x66cm-29x26in) s. oil gouache paperboard

WOLKERS, Jan (1925-) Dutch
£727	$1316	(19-May-92 CH.AM355/R) Abstract composition (61x52cm-24x20in) s.d.1980 oil on wooden relief (D.FL 2400)

WOLLASTON, John (?-1770) British
£1163	$2000	(9-Oct-91 CH.NY77/R) Portrait of gentleman said to be John Swift, holding tricorn hat (76x63cm-30x25in) painted oval
£2326	$4000	(9-Oct-91 CH.NY76/R) Portrait of officer, in military uniform (76x63cm-30x25in) painted oval
£4000	$7160	(15-Nov-91 C20/R) Portrait of Sir Rowland Alston, of Odell Castle, Bedfordshire (126x102cm-50x40in)

WOLLEN, William Barns (1857-1936) British
£520	$993	(16-Jul-92 CSK1) Waif of battle field (61x91cm-24x36in) s. s.i.verso pencil W/C htd white
£900	$1548	(4-Mar-92 S316/R) Patrol (52x44cm-20x17in) s.d.1906 W/C

WOLLHEIM, Gert (1894-1974) German/American
£1408	$2549	(6-Dec-91 GB.B7245/R) Portrait of lady wearing cap, gloves and fur-trimmed coat (48x33cm-19x13in) s. panel (DM 4000)
£859	$1572	(3-Jun-92 L.K465/R) Self portrait of artist drawing (31x24cm-12x9in) pencil (DM 2500)

WOLMARK, Alfred (1877-1961) British
£600	$1098	(4-Jun-92 CSK102/R) Mother's love (38x33cm-15x13in) mono.d.1914
£600	$1098	(4-Jun-92 CSK98/R) Bright red and yellow flowers (37x29cm-15x11in) s.d.1935 panel
£700	$1218	(19-Sep-91 B77/R) Bust portrait of woman (41x33cm-16x13in) s.
£880	$1531	(19-Sep-91 CSK39/R) Still life with summer flowers in vase (76x61cm-30x24in) init.
£900	$1557	(4-Sep-91 BT249/R) Portrait of girl (43x36cm-17x14in) panel

WOLONSKA (19th C) French
£2039	$3792	(18-Jun-92 SY.MO502/R) Vase de fleurs (45x34cm-18x13in) s. W/C vellum (F.FR 20000)

WOLS (1913-1951) German
£3058	*$5688*	*(15-Jun-92 GL.P9/R) Untitled (14x9cm-6x4in) s. ink W/C (F.FR 30000)*
£3568	*$6636*	*(15-Jun-92 GL.P13/R) Symphonie rose et bleue (18x12cm-7x5in) s. W/C (F.FR 35000)*
£7339	$13651	(15-Jun-92 GL.P11/R) Untitled (17x12cm-7x5in) s. ink W/C (F.FR 72000)
£11000	$21010	(2-Jul-92 S1/R) Deux tetes (20x14cm-8x6in) s. W/C ink
£13000	$23530	(5-Dec-91 S1/R) Untitled (24x31cm-9x12in) s. W/C ink
£13000	$24830	(2-Jul-92 S2/R) Composition (29x19cm-11x7in) s. gouache W/C ink

WOLSELEY, Garnet (1884-?) British
£1800	$3222	(5-May-92 SWS458/R) The dandelion clock (29x21cm-11x8in)

WOLSKI, Stanislaw (1859-1894) Polish
£1910	$3418	(17-Nov-91 REM.W31) In a steppe (56x97cm-22x38in) s. (P.Z 37000000)

WOLSTENHOLME, Charles Dean see WOLSTENHOLME, Dean (jnr)

WOLSTENHOLME, Dean (circle) (18/19th C) British
£2300	$4209	(12-May-92 H365) Hunting scene with figures and hounds in full pursuit (66x155cm-26x61in)

WOLSTENHOLME, Dean (jnr) (1798-1883) British
£1700	$3026	(21-Jan-92 PH70/R) Burial of Tom Moody (30x40cm-12x16in)
£1951	$3395	(19-Sep-91 D.V236/R) Path across ford near Highgate (23x44cm-9x17in) s. i.verso (A.S 40000)
£9836	$18000	(5-Jun-92 SY.NY102/R) Party of anglers fishing for pike and perch (40x56cm-16x22in) s. panel
£14368	$25000	(16-Sep-91 B.SF2014/R) Queen Elizabeth and Royal entourage riding to hunt (147x211cm-58x83in)

WOLSTENHOLME, Dean (snr) (1757-1837) British
£7000	$13370	(21-Jul-92 PH265/R) Colonel Jolliffe's hounds meeting at Chipstead Church (46x59cm-18x23in) s.indist.d.

WOLTER, Franz (1865-1932) German
£722	$1335	(13-Jun-92 WK.M375/R) Self portrait (96x75cm-38x30in) (DM 2100)

WOLTER, Hendrik Jan (1873-1952) Dutch
£912	$1587	(17-Sep-91 CH.AM417) Enkhuizen buitenhaven (35x44cm-14x17in) s. i. verso panel (D.FL 3000)
£917	$1596	(14-Apr-92 SY.AM316) The little dancer (177x83cm-70x33in) s. (D.FL 3000)
£917	$1633	(30-Oct-91 CH.AM226 c) Girl stringing beads (32x22cm-13x9in) s. panel (D.FL 3000)
£1194	$2125	(25-Nov-91 W.T1968/R) Against the sun, St Ives s. (C.D 2400)
£1667	$2950	(22-Apr-92 CH.AM28) Moored yachts and rowing boats in a harbour (25x30cm-10x12in) s. panel (D.FL 5500)
£14679	$25541	(14-Apr-92 SY.AM176/R) Pond in Laren near the 'Hut Van Mie' (83x98cm-33x39in) s. (D.FL 48000)

WOLTERS, Eugene (1844-?) Belgian
£2055	$3926	(1-Jul-92 FB.P142) Marine (77x104cm-30x41in) s.d.89 (F.FR 20000)

WOLTZE, Berthold (1829-1896) German
£2560	$4633	(21-May-92 L.K505/R) Traveller unable to pay in tavern interior (46x34cm-18x13in) s. (DM 7500)
£6977	$12000	(17-Oct-91 SY.NY254/R) Off to America (74x58cm-29x23in) s.

WOLTZE, Peter (1860-1925) German
£411	$707	(11-Oct-91 AW.H1386/R) View of Schloss Heidelberg (30x36cm-12x14in) s.d.1904 W/C bodycol over pencil (DM 1200)

WOLVECAMP, Theo (1925-) Dutch
£671	$1221	(10-Dec-91 RAS.K114) Composition (50x61cm-20x24in) s.verso (D.KR 7500)
£3704	$6741	(12-Dec-91 SY.AM262/R) Paysage en vert (120x95cm-47x37in) s. s.d.66-67 verso (D.FL 12000)
£4630	$8426	(11-Dec-91 CH.AM381/R) Abstract composition (155x100cm-61x39in) s.d.54 (D.FL 15000)

WOLVENS, Henri Victor (1896-1977) Belgian
£1242	$2248	(23-May-92 KV.L392) Chez Siska (16x26cm-6x10in) s. panel (B.FR 75000)
£1671	$2840	(22-Oct-91 C.A333) Still life with grapes (50x70cm-20x28in) s.d.1966 (B.FR 100000)
£4106	$7432	(7-Dec-91 KV.L479/R) The Vissershof (50x80cm-20x31in) s.d.1974 (B.FR 240000)
£6015	$10226	(22-Oct-91 C.A330/R) Entrance of the Brangwyn Museum in Brugge (55x80cm-22x31in) s.d.1943 (B.FR 360000)
£401	*$682*	*(22-Oct-91 C.A335) Terrace in Knokke (23x30cm-9x12in) s. W/C (B.FR 24000)*

WONG, Brent (1945-) New Zealander
£2239	$4007	(6-May-92 DS.W25/R) Ranges and clouds (68x73cm-27x29in) s.d.1976 i.verso acrylic (NZ.D 7500)
£4630	$8380	(4-Dec-91 DS.W26/R) Mirage (62x103cm-24x41in) s.d.72 i.verso acrylic (NZ.D 15000)

WONNER, Paul (20th C) American
£1176 $2000   (23-Oct-91 B.SF3729/R) Landscape (114x122cm-45x48in) s.
£2793 $5000   (7-May-92 SY.NY285/R) Untitled (99x70cm-39x28in) s. acrylic paper
£588 $1000   (23-Oct-91 B.SF3725/R) Garden with lawn glider (46x60cm-18x24in) s.
         gouache pencil

WOOD, C (?) ?
£500 $865   (6-Sep-91 BW279/R) Beached sailing boat (25x36cm-10x14in) init. W/C

WOOD, C Dudley (1905-) Australian
£881 $1568   (26-Nov-91 J.M61) Fishing cove (59x74cm-23x29in) s.d.60 board (A.D 2000)

WOOD, Catherine M (19/20th C) British
£2200 $3828   (12-Sep-91 CSK229/R) Books (20x41cm-8x16in) s. s.i.label verso

WOOD, Christopher (early 20th C) (1901-1930) British
£855 $1471   (12-Oct-91 SY.MO17/R) Monte Carlo (19x24cm-7x9in) s.d.1926 scraperboard
         (F.FR 8500)
£4000 $7080   (7-Nov-91 C26/R) Girl with bread (41x33cm-16x13in) canvasboard
£5500 $10065   (13-May-92 S53/R) The Pink House (33x41cm-13x16in) s. board
£7545 $12978   (12-Oct-91 SY.MO13/R) Breton seascape. Costume designs for two male
         dancers - Luna Park (40x28cm-16x11in) board double-sided (F.FR 75000)
£13000 $23400   (20-Nov-91 S124 a/R) Self portrait (40x30cm-16x12in)
£23139 $39799   (12-Oct-91 SY.MO11/R) Breton seascape. Costume design for show man,
         another and study of decor (41x56cm-16x22in) oil pencil double-sided
         two boards (F.FR 230000)
£26000 $47580   (13-May-92 S50/R) Evening, Brittany (56x81cm-22x32in) s.i.d.1929 verso
         board
£800 $1392   (19-Sep-91 CSK192/R) Study for Hell Floaters (25x20cm-10x8in) W/C pencil
£960 $1661   (4-Sep-91 PHK55) Study of nude seated (46x32cm-18x13in) red chk chl
£1000 $1770   (5-Nov-91 PH142) Self portrait. Farm landscape with peasants
         (28x24cm-11x9in) pencil two
£1500 $2565   (11-Mar-92 S117/R) Walkers on cliff-tops, Brittany (29x37cm-11x15in)
         pencil
£1811 $3115   (12-Oct-91 SY.MO16/R) Costume design for box-office attendant - Luna Park
         (20x15cm-8x6in) gouache W/C (F.FR 18000)
£4527 $7787   (12-Oct-91 SY.MO15/R) Design for decor - Luna Park (25x32cm-10x13in)
         gouache pencil htd silver paint (F.FR 45000)
£5634 $9690   (12-Oct-91 SY.MO18/R) Boris Kochno and Vladmir Dukelsky (35x26cm-14x10in)
         i. pen paper on card (F.FR 56000)
£8551 $14708   (12-Oct-91 SY.MO14/R) Designs for costumes and box-office telephonist.
         Design for decor - Luna Park (54x40cm-21x16in) oil pencil photomontage
         double-sided board (F.FR 85000)
£11066 $19034   (12-Oct-91 SY.MO12/R) Costume design for three-legged juggler and man
         with six arms -Luna Park (30x40cm-12x16in) gouache over pencil
         (F.FR 110000)

WOOD, Edmund L (19th C) British?
£1550 $2682   (26-Mar-92 RB709) Lady seated on balustrade with small dog
         (91x137cm-36x54in) s.d.1891

WOOD, Frank (?) ?
£400 $732   (14-May-92 TL215/R) H.M.S. Birmingham sinking German submarine U15
         (23x71cm-9x28in) s.d.1914 W/C
£800 $1416   (6-Nov-91 S252/R) Border link, Berwick on Tweed (24x34cm-9x13in) s.d.1902
         W/C

WOOD, Frank Watson (1862-1953) British
£580 $1003   (24-Mar-92 CG713) Berwick-upon-Tweed (14x57cm-6x22in) s.d.1922 W/C
         htd.bodycol.
£600 $1086   (20-May-92 S260/R) The Great Silver Jubilee Review, the salute
         (30x63cm-12x25in) s.i.d.1935 W/C
£600 $1068   (21-Jan-92 SWS1264) Berwick-on-Tweed (25x35cm-10x14in) s.d.1902 W/C
£1600 $2848   (30-Apr-92 CG816/R) Berwick-upon-Tweed from Tweedmouth (22x58cm-9x23in)
         s.d.1922 W/C htd white
£1900 $3382   (30-Apr-92 CG817/R) The Old Bridge, Berwick-upon-Tweed (31x74cm-12x29in)
         s.d.1923 W/C htd white

WOOD, George Albert (?) American?
£1167 $2100   (22-Nov-91 S.BM180/R) Clams served at all hours (56x91cm-22x36in) i.

WOOD, John (1801-1870) British
£650 $1190   (14-May-92 TL54) Portrait of Mrs Robert McMullin wearing black dress with
         shawl (89x69cm-35x27in) s.indist.d.

WOOD, Lawson (1878-1957) British
£400 $732   (14-May-92 B294) Urgent message - soldier with horses in landscape
         (43x63cm-17x25in) s.i.d.08 pencil W/C
£480 $869   (20-May-92 BT111) By Jove, I don't half want share (38x28cm-15x11in)
         s.d.20 i.verso W/C
£600 $1086   (20-May-92 BT113/R) Tiff (20x15cm-8x6in) s.d.20 s.i.verso W/C
£1000 $1830   (13-May-92 CBB39) Stratford Mop s.i.d.1908 wash dr.
£1100 $1991   (20-May-92 BT115/R) Moonlight serenade (46x38cm-18x15in) s. W/C
£1600 $2896   (20-May-92 BT110/R) One in the eye (43x33cm-17x13in) s. W/C
£1750 $3168   (20-May-92 BT112/R) Pack up your troubles (43x36cm-17x14in) s. W/C

WOOD, Lawson (1878-1957) British-cont.
£2000 $3620   (20-May-92 BT116/R) D'ye ken Gran'pop' (46x36cm-18x14in) s.i. W/C

WOOD, Lewis John (1813-1901) British
£650 $1118   (8-Oct-91 PH95) Ruen St Thomas (25x21cm-10x8in) board
£1714 $3033   (4-Nov-91 SY.J222/R) L'eglise, St Vulfram, Abbeyville (51x41cm-20x16in) panel (SA.R 8500)
£2100 $3738   (28-Nov-91 B180/R) Abbeville Cathedral (62x46cm-24x18in) s.
£520 $941   (19-May-92 PH68) Market day in continental square (34x24cm-13x9in) s.d.1878 W/C htd.white

WOOD, Peter M (1914-) British
£700 $1267   (20-May-92 S259/R) Schooner running down wind (50x75cm-20x30in) s.

WOOD, Robert W (1889-1979) American
£698 $1200   (20-Oct-91 HG.C47) Pond (64x76cm-25x30in) s.
£1143 $2000   (31-Mar-92 MOR.P115) Coastal, wood's cove (56x81cm-22x32in) s.
£1184 $2250   (24-Jun-92 B.SF6433/R) Scrub brush in bloom (36x46cm-14x18in) s. st.verso
£1271 $2250   (12-Feb-92 B.SF550/R) Incoming tide (36x46cm-14x18in) s. artist's st.verso
£1412 $2500   (12-Feb-92 B.SF564/R) Mountain lake (63x76cm-25x30in) s.
£1649 $3100   (18-Dec-91 SY.NY390/R) Rocky coastal hillside (63x76cm-25x30in) s.
£2907 $5000   (7-Mar-92 LAE.L69/R) Landscape with cactus flowers (61x76cm-24x30in) s.
£3409 $6000   (10-Apr-92 DM.D2004/R) Blue bonnets spring in texas (41x51cm-16x20in) artist's st.verso

WOOD, Thomas Waterman (1823-1903) American
£2890 $5000   (24-Mar-92 GRO.B56/R) Stitch in time (30x25cm-12x10in) s.
£2890 $5000   (6-Sep-91 S.BM194/R) Portrait of a woman in a shawl (46x36cm-18x14in) s.d.1858

WOOD, William (1769-1810) British
£741 $1341   (21-May-92 GK.Z1731) Portrait of young nobleman wearing blue coat with black collar (8x6cm-3x2in) min. oval gold medaillon hair compartment verso (S.FR 2000)
£1500 $2745   (2-Jun-92 S697) Sir Robert Townsend-Farquhar wearing dark blue coat (9x?cm-4x?in) min.s.i.verso oval gilt metal frame
£1700 $2975   (24-Sep-91 CSK29/R) Major General Sir Charles Bruce K C B in scarlet and green uniform (7x?cm-3x?in) min.i.verso oval rec.leather case
£1900 $3477   (2-Jun-92 S702) Walter Minto Townsend-Farquhar wearing blue coat (9x?cm-4x?in) min.s.i.verso oval gilt metal frame
£2500 $4450   (27-Nov-91 C251/R) Portrait of James Fletcher (8x?cm-3x?in) min. gold frame oval hair verso

WOOD, William (attrib) (1769-1810) British
£980 $1754   (15-Jan-92 BT16/R) Gentleman with short powdered hair (8x?cm-3x?in) min.gilt frame enamel hair plait verso oval

WOOD, William Thomas (1877-1958) British
£2600 $4706   (20-May-92 B265/R) August flowers s.

WOODBURY, Charles (1864-1940) American
£718 $1300   (5-Dec-91 GRO.B550) Midwinter, Ogunquit (43x53cm-17x21in) s.
£1111 $1900   (22-Mar-92 LIT.L161) Rocky shore (43x53cm-17x21in) s.i.
£1130 $2000   (25-Apr-92 YFA.M305/R) Midwinter, Ogunquit (43x53cm-17x21in) s. estate st.i.verso
£1271 $2250   (25-Apr-92 YFA.M307) Heavy swell (43x53cm-17x21in) s.
£1314 $2300   (22-Feb-92 YFA.M208/R) Summer-Castine (30x48cm-12x19in) s. board
£2235 $4000   (14-Nov-91 CE.NY338/R) Rushing wave (74x91cm-29x36in) s. st.init.i. verso
£2260 $4000   (25-Apr-92 YFA.M306/R) Dawn over fishing cove (25x51cm-10x20in) s.d.89 W/C

WOODHOUSE, Frederick (19/20th C) Australian
£940 $1674   (27-Apr-92 J.M555) The Assyrian (29x39cm-11x15in) board (A.D 2200)

WOODHOUSE, Frederick (snr) (1820-1909) Australian
£1496 $2662   (28-Apr-92 CH.ME135) Flying buck and jockey, Flemington (33x48cm-13x19in) s.d.1859 (A.D 3500)

WOODHOUSE, H J (19th C) British
£3488 $6000   (14-Oct-91 H.C42/R) Bird dog and pheasant (61x46cm-24x18in) s.

WOODHOUSE, William (1857-1939) British
£559 $950   (25-Oct-91 S.W2364/R) Still life - after hunt (30x41cm-12x16in) s.
£1100 $2013   (15-May-92 TE373/R) Shooting gulls (41x36cm-16x14in) s.d.1889
£2747 $5000   (27-May-92 CH.NY260/R) The blacksmith's shop (76x63cm-30x25in) s.

WOODLEY-BROWN, Rev R see BROWN, Rev R Woodley

WOODLOCK, D (1842-1929) British
£500 $890   (1-Nov-91 BW17) Eastern market scene (36x15cm-14x6in) s.

WOODLOCK, David (1842-1929) British
£600 $1038   (25-Mar-92 AH158) Cottage door near Wellington Salop (20x30cm-8x12in)

WOODLOCK, David (1842-1929) British-cont.

£1200	$2196	(3-Jun-92 S14/R) The salute from the Giudecca, Venice (29x44cm-11x17in) s. board
£480	*$888*	*(12-Jun-92 C44/R) A frugal meal (27x22cm-11x9in) s.i. W/C htd.white*
£480	*$859*	*(5-May-92 SWS178/R) In the garden (48x33cm-19x13in) s. W/C over pencil*
£500	*$890*	*(27-Nov-91 B203) Girl in cottage garden (28x20cm-11x8in) s. W/C bodycol*
£600	*$1032*	*(10-Oct-91 B192) Choirboy feeding pigeons, St. Mark's, Venice (23x14cm-9x6in) s. W/C*
£750	*$1410*	*(19-Dec-91 C52/R) Roadside cottage near Sevenoaks, Kent (25x18cm-10x7in) s.i. pencil W/C*
£820	*$1574*	*(29-Jul-92 PHC326/R) Cottage in Shakespeare country (24x17cm-9x7in) s.i.verso W/C*
£1000	*$1720*	*(10-Oct-91 B191/R) Flower sellers, Venice (23x14cm-9x6in) W/C htd white*
£1200	*$2196*	*(3-Jun-92 S285/R) Under a parasol (23x16cm-9x6in) s. W/C*
£1200	*$2256*	*(19-Dec-91 C21/R) Old cottage at Sutton Courtney, Berkshire (30x20cm-12x8in) s. i.verso W/C htd white*
£1500	*$2670*	*(29-Oct-91 C73/R) Anne Hathaway's Cottage (36x30cm-14x12in) s. i.verso pencil W/C htd white*
£1600	*$2832*	*(6-Nov-91 S275/R) Amidst the blossoms (71x48cm-28x19in) s.d.97 W/C*
£2457	*$4250*	*(29-Mar-92 MY.F75/R) Morning in Venice (76x51cm-30x20in) s. W/C board*
£2900	*$5307*	*(3-Jun-92 S235/R) The Ducal Palace, Venice (49x34cm-19x13in) s. W/C htd. bodycol.*
£3000	*$5340*	*(29-Oct-91 C62/R) Springtime (42x25cm-17x10in) s. i.verso pencil W/C htd white*

WOODSIDE, John Archibald (snr) (1781-1852) American

£2983	$5250	(9-Apr-92 FA.PH697) Still life with fruit (38x51cm-15x20in) s.d.1824

WOODWARD, A T (19/20th C) British?

£560	*$1002*	*(14-Jan-92 SWS93/R) The tennis player (62x45cm-24x18in) s.d.85 W/C*

WOODWARD, Mabel (1877-1945) American

£532	$1000	(18-Dec-91 SY.NY165/R) First Baptist Meeting House, Providence, Rhode Island (33x25cm-13x10in) s. canvas on board
£552	$1000	(24-May-92 JRB.C130/R) Dutch woman (74x53cm-29x21in) s.
£663	$1200	(24-May-92 JRB.C128/R) Tree sumphony (41x51cm-16x20in) s. masonite
£730	$1300	(26-Jan-92 JRB.C12) Self, Boston (58x53cm-23x21in) s.d.1936 canvas on board
£884	$1600	(24-May-92 JRB.C129/R) In the garden (51x41cm-20x16in) s.
£939	$1700	(24-May-92 JRB.C127/R) Winter landscape (41x51cm-16x20in) s. board
£957	$1800	(18-Dec-91 SY.NY392/R) Monterey Coast, California (40x50cm-16x20in) canvasboard
£1000	$1800	(22-Nov-91 S.BM197/R) Rockport Pier (25x30cm-10x12in) s. masonite
£1345	$2300	(22-Mar-92 LIT.L176) Autumnal scene (41x51cm-16x20in) s. canvasboard
£1768	$3200	(24-May-92 JRB.C125/R) Fisherman Waterfront, Provincetown, Massachusetts, Cape Cod (25x33cm-10x13in) s. i.verso board
£2527	$4750	(18-Dec-91 SY.NY175/R) Polperro. Venice (25x33cm-10x13in) s. canvas on board pair
£12571	$22000	(26-Sep-91 CH.NY111/R) Afternoon at beach (39x49cm-15x19in) s. canvas on masonite
£13812	*$25000*	*(6-Dec-91 CH.NY200/R) An afternoon on the beach (38x56cm-15x22in) s. W/C pencil board*

WOODWARD, Nathan (18th C) British?

£9000	$15840	(10-Apr-92 C68/R) Hunting scenes i. one s. two d.1769 and 1770 panel set of four

WOODWARD, Stanley W (1890-1970) American

£939	*$1700*	*(24-May-92 JRB.C66/R) Florida nude (48x38cm-19x15in) s. W/C*

WOODWARD, Thomas (1801-1852) British

£850	$1522	(14-Jan-92 SWS172/R) Prize cow in landscape (44x60cm-17x24in) bears i.d.1840stretcher
£14000	$24920	(1-May-92 PHE86/R) Gone to earth (70x95cm-28x37in) mono.d.1843 1844

WOOL, Christopher (1955-) American

£3911	$7000	(5-May-92 CH.NY161/R) Untitled (188x95cm-74x37in) s.d.1990 alkyd paper
£2514	$4500	(9-May-92 CE.NY274/R) Untitled (98x62cm-39x24in) st.sig alkyd
£3400	$6494	(2-Jul-92 C20/R) Untitled (127x97cm-50x38in) alkyd paper
£3429	$6000	(27-Feb-92 CH.NY120/R) Untitled (168x91cm-66x36in) alkyd
£5028	$9000	(5-May-92 CH.NY121/R) Untitled (168x91cm-66x36in) alkyd
£5587	$10000	(13-Nov-91 CH.NY327/R) Untitled (127x97cm-50x38in) s.d.1988verso alkyd
£9143	$16000	(25-Feb-92 SY.NY220/R) Untitled study no 13 (122x61cm-48x24in) s.i.d.87verso alkyd flashe aluminum
£10286	$18000	(27-Feb-92 CH.NY94/R) Untitled (122x81cm-48x32in) s.d.88verso alkyd flashe aluminum
£22346	$40000	(5-May-92 CH.NY110/R) Untitled (183x122cm-72x48in) s.i.d.87verso alkyd aluminum
£25000	$47750	(2-Jul-92 C21/R) Untitled - W6 (274x183cm-108x72in) s.i.d.W 6 1990 verso enamel aluminium
£27933	$50000	(14-Nov-91 SY.NY189/R) Untitled (206x152cm-81x60in) s.d.1988 verso alkyd flashe aluminium steel

WOOLF, Samuel Johnson (19/20th C) American

£8242	$15000	(28-May-92 CH.NY172/R) In the morning (157x108cm-62x43in) s.

WOOLF, Samuel Johnson (19/20th C) American-cont.
£30387 $55000   (6-Dec-91 CH.NY205/R) The Lower East Side (110x152cm-43x60in) s.

WOOLLASTON, Sir Mountford Tosswill (1910-) New Zealander
£3241 $5866   (4-Dec-91 DS.W25/R) Landscape (59x59cm-23x23in) s. (NZ.D 10500)
£3433 $6145   (6-May-92 DS.W40/R) New Plymouth power station (90x135cm-35x53in) s.
         (NZ.D 11500)
£5326 $8895   (21-Aug-91 DS.W40/R) Riwaka Wharf (55x77cm-22x30in) s. (NZ.D 15500)
£6186 $10330   (21-Aug-91 DS.W35/R) Brownacre and Mt Arthur (90x120cm-35x47in) s.d.86
         (NZ.D 18000)
£6186 $10330   (21-Aug-91 DS.W48/R) New Plymouth Power Station (90x135cm-35x53in) s.
         (NZ.D 18000)
£7113 $11879   (21-Aug-91 DS.W20/R) Above Wellington (90x120cm-35x47in) s.d.86
         (NZ.D 20700)
£617   *$1117*   *(4-Dec-91 DS.W36) Landscape, Bayly's Hill, Taranaki (25x36cm-10x14in)*
         s.d.62 ink (NZ.D 2000)
£741   *$1341*   *(4-Dec-91 DS.W6) Portrait of David Fowler (44x30cm-17x12in) s.d.79 W/C*
         (NZ.D 2400)
£1718   *$2869*   *(21-Aug-91 DS.W21/R) Above Wellington (29x44cm-11x17in) s. W/C pencil*
         (NZ.D 5000)

WOOLLETT, H C (fl.1851-1872) British
£600 $1086   (4-Dec-91 AH146) Shepherd and lady on horseback in landscape
         (36x20cm-14x8in)

WOOLLETT, Henry Charles (fl.1851-1872) British
£500 $855   (17-Mar-92 SWS1165) Outside an Inn (29x44cm-11x17in) s.

WOOLMER, Alfred Joseph (1805-1892) British
£1300 $2288   (8-Apr-92 S219/R) Young poet reciting (70x90cm-28x35in) s.

WOOLMER, Alfred Joseph (circle) (1805-1892) British
£750 $1335   (31-Oct-91 D90/R) Woman with cat in interior (58x43cm-23x17in)

WOOLNOTH, Thomas A (1785-1857) British
£650 $1118   (4-Mar-92 DR188) Portrait of Sir Edward Conroy, Bt., standing in naval
         attache's uniform (99x63cm-39x25in) s.d.1842

WOOSTER, Austin C (19/20th C) American
£791 $1400   (22-Apr-92 D.NY98) Macintosh apples spilling from basket
         (36x46cm-14x18in) s.d.1908

WOOSTER, Austin C (attrib) (19/20th C) American
£2260 $4000   (22-Apr-92 D.NY99/R) Strawberries spilling from bowl (38x66cm-15x26in)
         bears sig.

WOOTTON, Frank (1911-) British
£500 $855   (18-Mar-92 B58/R) Young boy and girl speeding along cliff road in rapier
         automobile (78x103cm-31x41in) s.
£1500 $2640   (7-Apr-92 EH4) Foal resting (48x58cm-19x23in) s.
£2000 $3520   (7-Apr-92 EH5/R) Alciston, Sussex (53x74cm-21x29in) s.d.1971
£2800 $5376   (28-Jul-92 SWS153/R) Chestnut, grey and black (59x75cm-23x30in) s.
         i.verso
£2800 $4760   (22-Oct-91 SWS409/R) Going out with hounds (101x70cm-40x28in) s. i.d.1971
         verso
£5600 $10752   (28-Jul-92 SWS152/R) Arkle with Pat Taffe up (79x89cm-31x35in) s.d.1966

WOOTTON, John (1686-1765) British
£1800 $3222   (13-Nov-91 S218/R) Match on Newmarket Heath (61x73cm-24x29in)
£7200 $12672   (10-Apr-92 C48/R) Roman capriccio with the Arch of Constantine, St
         Peter's and figures (112x125cm-44x49in)
£18000 $34560   (7-Jul-92 PH73/R) Herdsman and companion watching over livestock.
         Washerwomen on riverbank by ruins, shepherd to fore (127x180cm-50x71in)
         pair

WOPFNER, Joseph (1843-1927) Austrian
£1573 $2691   (18-Mar-92 N.M690/R) Chiemsee landscape (9x44cm-4x17in) s. canvas on
         board (DM 4500)
£4530 $8244   (11-Dec-91 N.M665/R) Fisher folk in boat gathering nets on lake Chiemsee
         (6x11cm-2x4in) mono. panel (DM 13000)
£6993 $11958   (18-Mar-92 N.M689/R) Chiemsee landscape with fishermen gathering nets
         (52x86cm-20x34in) s. (DM 20000)
£12544 $22829   (11-Dec-91 N.M664/R) Fisher folk in Chiemsee landscape (54x75cm-21x30in)
         s. (DM 36000)
£14777 $25711   (21-Sep-91 SA.A1801/R) Fishermen gathering nets in Chiemsee landscape
         (56x101cm-22x40in) s.i. (DM 43000)
£22337 $38866   (18-Sep-91 N.M752) Hay boat on shore of Lake Chiemsee (28x36cm-11x14in)
         s.i. panel (DM 65000)

WORES, Theodore (1859-1939) American
£526 $1000   (24-Jun-92 B.SF6284/R) View from archway (30x23cm-12x9in) s. canvasboard

WORMS, Jules (1832-1924) French
£562   *$1000*   *(22-Jan-92 SY.NY370/R) Femme a la fontaine (35x25cm-14x10in) s. W/C*

WORMS, Jules (1832-1924) French-cont.
£684 $1273   *(19-Jun-92 G.Z131/R) Manoeuvre militaire (30x39cm-12x15in) s. W/C (S.FR 1800)*

WORMS, Roger (1907-1980) French
£801 $1402   *(5-Apr-92 ZZ.F249/R) Le modele (80x54cm-31x21in) s. (F.FR 7700)*

WOROBIEFF, Maxim (school) (1787-1855) Russian
£2800 $4984   *(28-Nov-91 S444/R) View of St. Petersburg showing Egyptian steps on Neva, palace and pavilion (55x95cm-22x37in) bears sig.*

WORP, Hendrik van der (1840-1910) Dutch
£486 $846   *(17-Sep-91 CH.AM352) A summer landscape with a peasantwoman feeding chickens near a farm (31x45cm-12x18in) s.d.1879 (D.FL 1600)*

WORRELL, Abraham Bruiningh van (attrib) (18/19th C) Dutch
£1700 $2941   *(24-Mar-92 CG771/R) Drover and cattle on a hill. Woman spinning wool in a river landscape panel two*

WORSEY, Thomas (1829-1875) British
£500 $860   *(18-Oct-91 CBB100/R) Nest and flowers with mossy background (25x20cm-10x8in) s.d.1861*
£650 $1222   *(19-Dec-91 C208) Violets and bird's nest on mossy bank (26x21cm-10x8in) s.*
£1400 $2408   *(4-Mar-92 S92/R) Still life of primulas, pansies and bird's nest (28x33cm-11x13in) s.d.1861 s.indist.i.stretcher*
£1500 $2580   *(11-Oct-91 C25/R) Azaleas (36x29cm-14x11in) s.d.1863 panel*
£2000 $3440   *(11-Oct-91 C23/R) Roses, fuchsia, rhododendrons and other flowers on grassy bank (41x33cm-16x13in) s.*
£2500 $4575   *(3-Jun-92 S205/R) Pelargoniums and azaleas (33x41cm-13x16in) s.d.1872*
£2600 $4472   *(11-Oct-91 C24/R) Primroses, polyanthus, apple blossom and bird's nest on mossy bank (41x33cm-16x13in) s.d.1856*

WORSLEY, Charles N (?-1923) New Zealander
£687 $1148   *(21-Aug-91 DS.W100) Italian landscape (24x33cm-9x13in) s. W/C (NZ.D 2000)*
£2469 $4469   *(4-Dec-91 DS.W27/R) Otira Gorge scene with horseman (70x49cm-28x19in) s. W/C (NZ.D 8000)*
£2749 $4591   *(21-Aug-91 DS.W65/R) Coastal landscape with sheep drover (37x59cm-15x23in) s. W/C (NZ.D 8000)*

WOTRUBA, Fritz (1907-) Austrian
£436 $794   *(26-May-92 D.V180/R) Seated female nude (29x21cm-11x8in) pen (A.S 9000)*
£485 $882   *(26-May-92 D.V179/R) Seated female nude (29x21cm-11x8in) s.d.1944 pen indian ink (A.S 10000)*
£3635 $6617   *(26-May-92 D.V196/R) Architectural composition of figures (41x29cm-16x11in) s.d.1965 pen brush indian ink W/C (A.S 75000)*

WOU, Claes Claesz (1592-1665) Dutch
£3671 $6498   *(7-Nov-91 D.V297/R) Dutch three-master in choppy sea (36x47cm-14x19in) panel (A.S 75000)*
£7099 $12707   *(12-Nov-91 SY.AM92/R) Shipping in stormy sea (48x93cm-19x37in) s. panel pair (D.FL 23000)*

WOUTERMAERTENS, Edouard (1819-1897) Belgian
£699 $1210   *(25-Mar-92 KM.K1534) Two sheep grazing in landscape (22x27cm-9x11in) s. panel (DM 2000)*

WOUTERS, Frans (1614-1659) Flemish
£3779 $6500   *(10-Oct-91 SY.NY59/R) Aeneas fleeing Troy (56x40cm-22x16in) coper*
£1065 $1938   *(25-May-92 ARC.P60/R) Jupiter, Diane et Junon recevant faune et jaunesse (14x24cm-6x9in) pen wash (F.FR 10500)*

WOUTERS, Frans (attrib) (1614-1659) Flemish
£2762 $5000   *(21-May-92 CH.NY156/R) Madonna and child with infant Saint John the Baptist and putti (43x62cm-17x24in) panel*

WOUTERS, Frans (circle) (1614-1659) Flemish
£1600 $2800   *(27-Feb-92 CSK34/R) The Madonna and child with the infant Saint John and Putti in a landscape (36x57cm-14x22in) panel*

WOUTERS, Jan Ludewick de (1731-?) Flemish
£1613 $2855   *(6-Nov-91 LT.P31) Pecheurs en barque au claie du lune (28x41cm-11x16in) s. panel (F.FR 16000)*

WOUTERS, Rik (1882-1916) Belgian
£2649 $4795   *(23-May-92 KV.L472/R) Sketch of woman grooming cat (43x34cm-17x13in) pen (B.FR 160000)*
£2815 $5094   *(23-May-92 KV.L408/R) Woman in a wood (61x46cm-24x18in) i. brush ink (B.FR 170000)*
£25489 $43585   *(21-Mar-92 KV.L458/R) Femme accoudee (33x29cm-13x11in) s. W/C (B.FR 1500000)*

WOUW, Anton van (1862-1945) South African
£1392 $2421   *(13-Apr-92 SY.J297/R) Student (40x30cm-16x12in) s. W/C (SA.R 7000)*

WOUWERMAN (17th C) Dutch
£2000 $3460   (2-Oct-91 RBB811) Continental landscape with numerous figures, horses and travellers (56x66cm-22x26in)

WOUWERMAN, Philips (1619-1668) Dutch
£12000 $21840   (13-Dec-91 C193/R) Winter landscape with a grey feeding and peasants loading faggots (31x43cm-12x17in) panel
£50000 $91000   (10-Dec-91 PH77/R) Extensive landscape with cavalier seated on grey horse about to give alms to poor woman (31x33cm-12x13in) mono. panel
£54000 $93960   (15-Apr-92 C121/R) Stable with travellers resting their mounts (29x38cm-11x15in) mono.init.i. panel
£234807 $425000   (22-May-92 SY.NY106/R) Elegant hawking party heading out (48x64cm-19x25in) mono. panel

WOUWERMAN, Philips (after) (1619-1668) Dutch
£932 $1602   (7-Mar-92 CH.AM263/R) Cavalrists taking refreshments at booth, army encampment beyond (42x50cm-17x20in) (D.FL 3000)
£1183 $2140   (19-May-92 AB.S4391/R) Landscape with men on horseback (42x53cm-17x21in) (S.KR 12500)
£1698 $3039   (14-Nov-91 CH.AM6) Officers on horseback in occupied village and prisoners led away nearby (54x42cm-21x17in) (D.FL 5500)
£3395 $6077   (14-Nov-91 CH.AM190/R) Elegant party departing for the chase (49x67cm-19x26in) (D.FL 11000)

WOUWERMAN, Philips (attrib) (1619-1668) Dutch
£3495 $6397   (12-May-92 SY.AM57/R) Peasant saddling horse in cave (13x19cm-5x7in) mono. panel (D.FL 11500)
£16500 $28875   (1-Apr-92 S52/R) Dune landscape (51x66cm-20x26in) bears mono.

WOUWERMAN, Philips (circle) (1619-1668) Dutch
£1124 $2000   (30-Oct-91 D.NY55) At the horse fair (46x61cm-18x24in) bears sig. panel
£1742 $3171   (12-Dec-91 L.K215) Skirmish before dark sky (30x37cm-12x15in) (DM 5000)
£2616 $4500   (9-Oct-91 CH.NY70 a/R) Figures in dune landscape (36x30cm-14x12in) indist.init. panel
£4942 $8500   (9-Oct-91 CH.NY98/R) Elegant figures returning from hunt (36x52cm-14x20in) panel

WOUWERMAN, Philips (school) (1619-1668) Dutch
£1117 $2000   (13-Nov-91 B.SF2114/R) Horsemen bargaining with fishermen on seashore with castle beyond (15x18cm-6x7in) copper
£8172 $14545   (28-Apr-92 F.R77/R) Cavalli al guado. Sosta all'osteria (52x60cm-20x24in) pair (I.L 18000000)

WOUWERMAN, Philips (studio) (1619-1668) Dutch
£6458 $11043   (18-Mar-92 D.V384/R) Rest on the falcon hunt (30x42cm-12x17in) mono. panel (A.S 130000)

WOUWERMAN, Philips (style) (1619-1668) Dutch
£750 $1440   (9-Jul-92 CSK171/R) At the water trough (32x24cm-13x9in) panel
£917 $1679   (3-Jun-92 R.T184/R) Encampment with soldiers and horses (41x58cm-16x23in) (C.D 2000)
£950 $1663   (2-Apr-92 CSK84/R) Hunting party at inn (32x27cm-13x11in) panel
£1152 $2084   (3-Dec-91 AB.S4767/R) Riders at rest (34x30cm-13x12in) panel (S.KR 12000)
£1300 $2314   (31-Oct-91 B102) Battle scene (23x65cm-9x26in)
£1327 $2348   (10-Feb-92 GL.P39/R) Le depart pour la chasse (57x75cm-22x30in) (F.FR 13000)
£1400 $2520   (21-Nov-91 C32) Hawking party (35x41cm-14x16in) panel
£1468 $2599   (7-Nov-91 D.V303/R) Riders outside tavern (25x31cm-10x12in) panel (A.S 30000)
£1500 $2700   (22-Nov-91 SWS41) Revellers and figures on horseback in a barn outside an Inn (48x59cm-19x23in)
£1657 $3000   (22-May-92 S.BM23/R) Hunting party (69x107cm-27x42in)
£1800 $3150   (31-Mar-92 PH129/R) Figures with horses at river crossing before inn (49x60cm-19x24in)
£1800 $3150   (2-Apr-92 CSK95) Rest at inn (34x46cm-13x18in) panel
£1900 $3325   (25-Feb-92 PH70/R) Horseman preparing to depart from barn with other horses stabled (27x35cm-11x14in) panel
£2400 $4200   (31-Mar-92 PH131/R) Soldiers resting before military encampment (52x75cm-20x30in)
£2500 $4575   (12-May-92 SWS659/R) Landscape with horses watering at ford by wooded bridge, travellers resting (58x68cm-23x27in)
£3000 $5760   (10-Jul-92 C129/R) Cavalry at booth (49x44cm-19x17in) with mono. panel
£3448 $6000   (16-Sep-91 B.SF2006/R) Hunting party (37x48cm-15x19in) copper

WOUWERMAN, Pieter (1623-1682) Dutch
£3626 $6454   (28-Nov-91 BU.S79/R) Soldiers resting (50x66cm-20x26in) mono. (S.KR 38000)
£6272 $11415   (12-Dec-91 L.K217/R) Animals and figures before tavern (35x29cm-14x11in) mono. panel (DM 18000)
£11719 $20742   (5-Nov-91 GF.L2040/R) The rabbit hunt (26x35cm-10x14in) mono. copper (S.FR 30000)

WOUWERMAN, Pieter (after) (1623-1682) Dutch
£480 $840   (25-Feb-92 CSK26) Camp de Carolus (10x?cm-4x?in) min. gilt frame ribbon surmount rectangular

WOUWERMAN, Pieter (attrib) (1623-1682) Dutch
£4500 $8595   (21-Jul-92 PH234/R) Riders watering horses at fountain pool before sand dune (36x48cm-14x19in) panel
£5658 $10242   (7-Dec-91 CH.MO14/R) Une halte de Cavaliers (37x48cm-15x19in) panel (F.FR 55000)

WOUWERMAN, Pieter (circle) (1623-1682) Dutch
£1600 $3040   (23-Jun-92 CG661/R) Peasants unloading wagon. Figures at farriers (37x36cm-15x14in) pair
£2000 $3560   (29-Oct-91 PH92/R) Travellers on horseback outside an inn (26x34cm-10x13in) bears init. panel
£2393 $4188   (1-Apr-92 CSC.P24/R) La halte de cavaliers dans l'echope du barbier (40x52cm-16x20in) panel (F.FR 23000)

WOUWERMAN, Pieter (style) (1623-1682) Dutch
£820 $1492   (11-Dec-91 ZZ.B135) Interior of barn with horses, riders and grooms (62x75cm-24x30in)

WRETMAN, Fredrik (1953-) Scandinavian
£1200 $2171   (3-Dec-91 AB.S5179/R) Composition (125x250cm-49x98in) s.d.86verso diptych aluminium (S.KR 12500)

WRIGHT OF DERBY, Joseph (1734-1797) British
£14000 $24640   (8-Apr-92 S62/R) Vesuvius from Posillipo (43x57cm-17x22in)
£16000 $28160   (8-Apr-92 S33/R) Portrait of Master Curzon, seated in landscape, holding dove (51x42cm-20x17in)

WRIGHT OF DERBY, Joseph (style) (1734-1797) British
£1200 $2136   (29-Oct-91 HB590) Moonlit landscape with carriage and horses passing lake (61x74cm-24x29in)
£1890 $3250   (10-Oct-91 SY.NY201/R) Landscape with the rock of ages, Burrington Gorge, Burrington, Somerset (64x87cm-25x34in)
£3800 $6688   (10-Apr-92 C97/R) Portrait of two boys with tennis racquet and bow and arrow in landscape (157x102cm-62x40in)

WRIGHT, Alice Maud (fl.1911-1927) British
£420 $748   (27-Nov-91 ZZ.B173) Madonna and Child (42x28cm-17x11in) s. W/C

WRIGHT, Ferdinand von (1822-1906) Finnish
£8850 $15575   (12-Apr-92 HOR.H263/R) Chaffinches on branch (38x32cm-15x13in) s. d.1900verso (F.M 70000)
£29077 $51176   (12-Apr-92 HOR.H262/R) Cockerels fighting (48x64cm-19x25in) s.d.1872 (F.M 230000)

WRIGHT, George (1860-1942) British
£520 $998   (28-Jul-92 SWS130/R) Huntsman and hounds (19x14cm-7x6in) s.
£600 $1098   (12-May-92 LV239) Old mill on the Annan, with angler and figures (38x58cm-15x23in) s.d.1891
£1400 $2408   (4-Mar-92 S166/R) At Red Lion (40x61cm-16x24in) s. en grisaille
£1450 $2683   (9-Jun-92 LW1801/R) Army stable hand with chestnut hunter and three hounds in stableyard (38x58cm-15x23in) s.
£1500 $2580   (16-Oct-91 PHL344) Boarding coach outside Swan Inn (42x62cm-17x24in) s. monochrome
£1525 $2700   (9-Nov-91 W.W114/R) The fox hunt (36x51cm-14x20in) s.
£2186 $4000   (5-Jun-92 SY.NY307/R) Jack Russell terriers (33x43cm-13x17in) s.
£2186 $4000   (5-Jun-92 SY.NY306/R) Border collie puppies (33x43cm-13x17in) s.
£2295 $4200   (5-Jun-92 SY.NY200/R) Full cry (50x76cm-20x30in) s.
£2459 $4500   (5-Jun-92 SY.NY174/R) Full cry (30x40cm-12x16in) s.
£3005 $5500   (5-Jun-92 SY.NY175/R) Breaking cover (35x50cm-14x20in) s.
£7000 $12250   (2-Apr-92 HB626/R) Drawing gorse (33x48cm-13x19in) s.i.
£7650 $14000   (5-Jun-92 SY.NY277/R) Before the polo match (17x25cm-7x10in) s.
£7923 $14500   (5-Jun-92 SY.NY176/R) Let off lightly. Over the fence (31x41cm-12x16in) s. pair
£8721 $15000   (16-Oct-91 CH.NY245/R) Hunting scenes (41x61cm-16x24in) both s.
£8743 $16000   (5-Jun-92 SY.NY206/R) A cub hunting morning (40x61cm-16x24in) s.
£506 $900   (2-Nov-91 IH.NY124/R) Group of people around gondola in Venice (43x28cm-17x11in) s. chl W/C

WRIGHT, George F (1828-1881) American
£550 $957   (17-Sep-91 FN.S2617) Peasant with horses shying and farmhouse beyond (30x35cm-12x14in) s.d.1878 board (DM 1600)

WRIGHT, George H B (20th C) British
£5200 $8736   (26-Aug-91 S1025/R) Hilltop church (51x61cm-20x24in) s.d.1938

WRIGHT, Gilbert Scott (1880-1958) British
£1500 $2685   (15-Jan-92 BT202/R) The Charge of the 21st Lancers, Omdurman, 2nd September 1898 (38x48cm-15x19in) s.
£1900 $3477   (4-Jun-92 CSK133) Morning ride (58x48cm-23x19in) s. board
£2200 $3762   (12-Mar-92 CSK149/R) The master's footsteps (36x50cm-14x20in) s.
£2500 $4300   (4-Mar-92 S167/R) Horse thieves (46x66cm-18x26in) s.
£4000 $7520   (19-Dec-91 C157/R) Taking the fence (61x91cm-24x36in) s.
£11000 $20130   (3-Jun-92 S121/R) Outside the Crown Inn (61x91cm-24x36in) s.

WRIGHT, John (19th C) American
£13000 $22880   *(9-Apr-92 S166/R) Portrait of young boy, with curling fair hair, in blue coat (7x?cm-3x?in) min. s.i.verso gold frame oval*

WRIGHT, John Michael (1623-1700) British
£20000 $38200   *(15-Jul-92 S15/R) Portrait of young boy, possibly Philip Herbert, later Earl of Pembroke (127x104cm-50x41in)*

WRIGHT, John Michael (after) (1623-1700) British
£850 $1624   *(17-Jul-92 C51/R) Portrait of lady in lace trimmed dress (75x62cm-30x24in) feigned oval*

WRIGHT, John Michael (circle) (1623-1700) British
£3800 $6802   *(15-Nov-91 C155/R) Portrait of Cecilia Mildmay, daughter of Sir Humphrey Mildmay of Banbury Place (74x62cm-29x24in) i.*

WRIGHT, Joseph (fl.1880-1927) British
£741 $1298   *(20-Feb-92 D.V499) Landscape (40x60cm-16x24in) s. (A.S 15000)*
£27473 $50000   *(28-May-92 CH.NY16/R) Portrait of Benjamin Franklin (80x63cm-31x25in)*

WRIGHT, Margaret (fl.1906-1940) British
£850 $1428   *(26-Aug-91 S1027/R) Chillin by bank of Clyde (24x29cm-9x11in) W/C laid down on board*
£900 $1557   *(24-Mar-92 CG738) Girl wearing a blue dress playing marbles (51x41cm-20x16in) s. W/C*

WRIGHT, Percy J (?) British?
£550 $1018   *(11-Jun-92 CSK152/R) Tranquil river (55x45cm-22x18in) s.*

WRIGHT, Richard Henry (1857-1930) British
£540 $967   *(5-May-92 SWS101) Street in Verona, Italy (25x18cm-10x7in) s. W/C htd bodycol.*
£1100 $1958   *(29-Oct-91 C125/R) The Fish Market, Venice (20x26cm-8x10in) s. pencil W/C*

WRIGHT, Robert W (fl.1880-1900) British
£1600 $2928   *(15-May-92 TE415/R) Family meal (18x23cm-7x9in) s.d.1887 board*

WRIGHT, Rufus (1832-?) American
£1729 $3250   *(18-Dec-91 SY.NY48/R) Still life of peaches (55x40cm-22x16in) s.d.1870*

WROBLEWSKI, Andrzej (1927-1957) Polish
£3054 $5558   *(15-Dec-91 REM.W51) Nude on blue background (87x58cm-34x23in) (P.Z 60000000)*

WU CHANGSHUO (1844-1927) Chinese
£1695 $3000   *(7-Nov-91 B.SF1242/R) Gourds (135x39cm-53x15in) s. ink colour scroll*
£6780 $12000   *(7-Nov-91 B.SF1210/R) Flowering peony plants (178x47cm-70x19in) s. ink colour scroll*
£7345 $13000   *(7-Nov-91 B.SF1231/R) Berries and Narcissus (178x47cm-70x19in) s.d.1915 ink colour scroll*
£7396 $12944   *(30-Mar-92 CH.HK140/R) Red plum blossoms (137x53cm-54x21in) s.i.d.1921 ink W/C hanging scroll (HK.D 100000)*

WU CHANGSHUO and SHEN ZENGZHI (19/20th C) Chinese
£1849 $3236   *(30-Mar-92 CH.HK381/R) Plum blossoms and calligraphy (18x51cm-7x20in) s.i.d.1920 ink W/C two fans hanging scroll (HK.D 25000)*

WU CHENG-YEN (1921-) Chinese
£10115 $17297   *(22-Mar-92 SY.TA20/R) Peonies (60x72cm-24x28in) s.d.79 (T.D 440000)*

WU GUANZHONG (1919-) Chinese
£15678 $26810   *(22-Mar-92 SY.TA21/R) Poplars (45x30cm-18x12in) s.d.1976 chinese board (T.D 682000)*
£42989 $73510   *(22-Mar-92 SY.TA7/R) Staying home on winter evening (60x45cm-24x18in) s.d.1964 board (T.D 1870000)*
£45517 $77834   *(22-Mar-92 SY.TA54/R) Palace garden (72x53cm-28x21in) s.d.75 (T.D 1980000)*
£5917 $10355   *(30-Mar-92 CH.HK167/R) Spring and autumn (49x57cm-19x22in) d.1985 ink W/C scroll (HK.D 80000)*
£22189 $38831   *(30-Mar-92 CH.HK323/R) Hong Kong at night (69x138cm-27x54in) s.d.1991 ink W/C scroll (HK.D 300000)*

WU HAO (1931-) Chinese
£15172 $25945   *(22-Mar-92 SY.TA58/R) Autumn (73x100cm-29x39in) s.d.1991 (T.D 660000)*

WU HSUAN-SAN (1942-) Chinese
£9609 $16432   *(22-Mar-92 SY.TA60/R) Spanish church (53x65cm-21x26in) s.d.1977 verso (T.D 418000)*
£20230 $34593   *(22-Mar-92 SY.TA10/R) Oasis (98x117cm-39x46in) s.d.91 (T.D 880000)*

WU HUFAN (1894-1968) Chinese
£4068 $7119   *(30-Mar-92 CH.HK313/R) Landscapes after Old Masters (15x22cm-6x9in) s.d.1936 ink W/C album eight leaves (HK.D 55000)*

WU ZHENG (1876-1949) Chinese
£2367 $4142   (30-Mar-92 CH.HK351/R) Monk in tree (135x50cm-53x20in) s.i.d.1922 ink W/C
                    hanging scroll (HK.D 32000)

WU ZHENG and FENG CHAORAN (20th C) Chinese
£1701 $2977   (30-Mar-92 CH.HK352/R) Horse and groom (104x50cm-41x20in) s.i.d.1938 ink
                    W/C hanging scroll (HK.D 23000)

WUCHTERS, Abraham (1610-1682) Danish
£9884 $17000   (10-Oct-91 SY.NY21/R) Portrait of a an old woman wearing a fur hat
                    (70x50cm-28x20in) s.d.1652 panel

WUERMER, Carl (1900-1982) American
£1989 $3600   (4-Dec-91 D.NY79/R) December afternoon (48x74cm-19x29in) s. i.verso

WUNDER, Wilhelm Ernst (1713-1787) Dutch
£6395 $11000   (10-Oct-91 SY.NY105/R) Still life with fruit in a blue bowl and other
                    objects on a table (37x42cm-15x17in) s.

WUNDERLICH, Edmund (1902-1985) Swiss
£730 $1307   (6-May-92 GD.B1366/R) Silsersee landscape (69x80cm-27x31in) s.d.1949
                    (S.FR 2000)

WUNDERLICH, Paul (1927-) German
£3027 $5480   (19-May-92 AB.S5348/R) Woman composition (91x73cm-36x29in) s.d.1972
                    (S.KR 32000)
£4196 $7469   (25-Nov-91 WK.M1109/R) Black torso (81x65cm-32x26in) s.d.1969 i.stretcher
                    (DM 12000)
£7338 $13355   (25-May-92 WK.M1328/R) The feet (162x130cm-64x51in) s.d.1968 s.i.d.verso
                    (DM 21500)
£7719 $13895   (19-Nov-91 L.K1226/R) Der Ideologe und seine Frau V (99x81cm-39x32in)
                    s.d.1973 acrylic pencil (DM 22000)
£1579 $2842   (19-Nov-91 L.K1227) Afterwards (100x65cm-39x26in) s.d.63 graphite wash
                    board (DM 4500)
£2448 $4357   (30-Nov-91 VG.B318/R) Man and woman (100x70cm-39x28in) s.d.1964 wash
                    spray technique acrylic (DM 7000)
£2576 $4662   (21-May-92 SY.AM367/R) Untitled (88x68cm-35x27in) s.d.69 W/C pencil
                    collage (D.FL 8500)
£3147 $5601   (30-Nov-91 VG.B319/R) Facing the wall (86x68cm-34x27in) s.d.1972 col.chk
                    acrylic spray technique board (DM 9000)

WUNNEBERG, Walther (1818-1900) German
£2749 $4784   (18-Sep-91 N.M753/R) Burg Stolzenfels in Rhine landscape with view of
                    Oberwerth and Koblenz (66x95cm-26x37in) s. (DM 8000)

WUNNENBERG, Carl (1850-1929) German
£1040 $1809   (14-Apr-92 SY.AM265) Sorting the linen (49x39cm-19x15in) s.d.73
                    (D.FL 3400)

WUNNENBERG, Walther (1818-?) German
£1379 $2372   (16-Oct-91 KM.K1457/R) Cattle grazing in mountain landscape and village
                    beyond (70x100cm-28x39in) s. (DM 4000)

WURFFEL, Hans (1884-) German
£756 $1315   (18-Sep-91 N.M754/R) Peasant with horse-drawn cart (49x70cm-19x28in) s.
                    canvas on panel (DM 2200)

WURTZEN, Carl (1825-1880) Danish
£2600 $4732   (26-May-92 DUR.M7/R) Lago noruego con fondo de montanas
                    (135x200cm-53x79in) s. (S.P 475000)

WUSTLICH, Otto (1818-1886) German
£986 $1785   (3-Dec-91 FN.S451/R) Portrait of Queen Cleopatra dipping pearl in glass
                    of wine (13x10cm-5x4in) min.s.d.1843 porcellain gold metal frame
                    (DM 2800)

WUTKY, Michael (circle) (1739-1823) Austrian
£2981 $5097   (18-Mar-92 D.V279/R) Moonlit seascape with fishing boats
                    (64x84cm-25x33in) i. (A.S 60000)

WUTTKE, Carl (1849-1927) German
£2234 $3887   (21-Sep-91 SA.A1772/R) Porto San Lorenzo near Cestius pyramid in Rome
                    (39x54cm-15x21in) s.i.d.1912 i.verso canvas on board (DM 6500)
£2289 $4143   (6-Dec-91 GB.B6071/R) Morning at holy lake of Karnak (106x163cm-42x64in)
                    s.i.d.1910 (DM 6500)
£2577 $4716   (2-Jun-92 FN.S2816/R) View of Tokio temple with figures (40x54cm-16x21in)
                    s.i. canvas on board (DM 7500)
£4545 $7864   (25-Mar-92 KM.K1535/R) View of Bab Scherun with figures, Damascus
                    (106x80cm-42x31in) s.d.1911 (DM 13000)

WYANT, A H (1836-1892) American
£654 $1250   (19-Jul-92 LIT.L22) Pond landscape (41x30cm-16x12in) s.

WYANT, Alexander H (1836-1892) American
£649 $1200   (10-Jun-92 CE.NY162/R) Wooded clearing (47x62cm-19x24in) panel

WYANT, Alexander H (1836-1892) American-cont.

£805	$1400	(13-Sep-91 S.W2789/R) Landscape with castle ruins (30x18cm-12x7in) s. board
£805	$1400	(20-Sep-91 DM.D2172/R) Landscape with two cows (38x33cm-15x13in) s.
£1118	$1900	(25-Oct-91 S.W2763/R) Bear Creek, Jefferson County, New York (25x36cm-10x14in) s.
£1374	$2500	(13-Dec-91 S.W2614/R) Autumn landscape with running brook (43x61cm-17x24in) s.
£1657	$3000	(4-Dec-91 D.NY11/R) New England landscape (69x104cm-27x41in) s. canvas on masonite
£2348	$4250	(7-Dec-91 LAE.L74/R) Woodland stream (51x41cm-20x16in) s.
£4396	$8000	(28-May-92 CH.NY61/R) Path to the river (57x76cm-22x30in)
£11050	$20000	(6-Dec-91 CH.NY37/R) Autumn landscape (46x76cm-18x30in) s.
£1081	*$2000*	*(10-Jun-92 CE.NY220) Around country door (30x40cm-12x16in) s.i. W/C*

WYATT, Benjamin Dean (19th C) British

| *£1400* | *$2464* | *(7-Apr-92 C40/R) Project for North-East front of Duke of Wellington's Palace (51x91cm-20x36in) s.i.d.1815 pencil pen wash htd white pair* |

WYATT, Henry (1794-1840) British

| £800 | $1528 | (15-Jul-92 S145/R) Portrait of Mr John Thornton (75x62cm-30x24in) s.d.1828 |

WYATT, Lewis William (19th C) British

| *£3400* | *$6086* | *(14-Nov-91 S39/R) Perspective view of design for South front, Tatton Park, Cheshire (45x68cm-18x27in) W/C over pencil* |

WYATVILLE, Sir Jeffry (1766-1840) British

| *£3000* | *$5280* | *(7-Apr-92 C35/R) Designs for villa (28x40cm-11x16in) s.i.d.1799 pencil pen W/C pair* |

WYBURD, Francis John (1826-?) British

| £19000 | $33820 | (27-Nov-91 S167/R) Harem (71x91cm-28x36in) init.d.1873 |

WYCK (circle) (17th C) Dutch

| £3200 | $5600 | (27-Feb-92 B191/R) Landscape with a stag hunt and a castle beyond (69x119cm-27x47in) |

WYCK, Jan (1640-1702) Dutch

£1698	$3039	(14-Nov-91 CH.AM83/R) Italianate wooded landscape with bathers by lake (22x20cm-9x8in) s. (D.FL 5500)
£2575	$4840	(18-Dec-91 AT.P158/R) Apres la bataille (69x84cm-27x33in) s. (F.FR 25000)
£4086	$7273	(28-Apr-92 F.R46/R) Prima della battaglia (37x50cm-15x20in) (I.L 9000000)
£6600	$11616	(8-Apr-92 S116/R) William III at Battle of Boyne, July 1st 1690 (87x109cm-34x43in)
£13374	$25412	(26-Jun-92 AT.P94/R) Alchimiste dans son interieur (40x36cm-16x14in) s. (F.FR 130000)
£44155	$79921	(3-Dec-91 SY.MI256/R) Assedio di Vienna (276x247cm-109x97in) s.d.1695 (I.L 95000000)

WYCK, Jan (style) (1640-1702) Dutch

| £1760 | $3062 | (13-Sep-91 C31/R) Wooded Italianate landscape with castle on hill above waterfall (34cm-13ins circular) copper |

WYCK, Thomas (1616-1670) Dutch

£1216	$2067	(23-Oct-91 GD.B1346/R) Slaughtered pig hanging from ladder (68x39cm-27x15in) s. panel (S.FR 3100)
£5119	$9266	(21-May-92 L.K179/R) Street scene with figures in Italian town (53x70cm-21x28in) s.d.1644 panel (DM 15000)
£5500	$9625	(1-Apr-92 S47/R) Peasants in Italianate courtyard (35x46cm-14x18in) panel
£9215	$16679	(21-May-92 L.K178/R) Allegory of winter with couple in sledge. Summer with harvest scene (18x31cm-7x12in) mono panel (DM 27000)
£24000	$42720	(30-Oct-91 S73/R) Troop of cavalrymen and other figures outside inn with hill fort beyond (108x91cm-43x36in) s.
£977	*$1681*	*(10-Oct-91 D.V29/R) Riverside town (9x13cm-4x5in) indian ink brush (A.S 20000)*
£2160	*$3867*	*(12-Nov-91 SY.AM279/R) Italian courtyard with muleteers (17x19cm-7x7in) brush wash over chk (D.FL 7000)*

WYCK, Thomas (circle) (1616-1670) Dutch

| £7600 | $13680 | (30-Jan-92 TL85/R) Coastal scenes with figures, vessels and ruins (47x62cm-19x24in) indist.s. pair |

WYCK, Thomas (style) (1616-1670) Dutch

| £2200 | $3850 | (31-Mar-92 PH52/R) Travellers resting outside town walls of Mediterranean port (60x75cm-24x30in) |
| £4200 | $7350 | (3-Apr-92 C117) Italianate peasants at tables by Undercrofts (21x28cm-8x11in) pair |

WYCKAERT, Maurice (1923-) Belgian

£935	$1598	(21-Mar-92 KV.L375) Clouds (18x24cm-7x9in) s. (B.FR 55000)
£2506	$4261	(22-Oct-91 C.A337/R) Out of bounds (65x80cm-26x31in) s.d.1981 (B.FR 150000)
£3670	$6459	(7-Apr-92 C.A275/R) Vue insolite (100x122cm-39x48in) s.d.1967 (B.FR 220000)

WYCKAERT, Maurice (1923-) Belgian-cont.

£3837	$6752	(7-Apr-92 C.A274/R) Composition (80x120cm-31x47in) s.d.1974 (B.FR 230000)
£6291	$11387	(23-May-92 KV.L461/R) Violet sur les bords (100x120cm-39x47in) s.d.1987 (B.FR 380000)
£9167	$15767	(12-Oct-91 KV.L421/R) L'Action de la chlorophyle (100x120cm-39x47in) s. s.i.d.1967 verso (B.FR 550000)
£850	$1453	(21-Mar-92 KV.L373) Composition (52x70cm-20x28in) s.d.1957 W/C (B.FR 50000)

WYCZOLKOWSKI, Leon (1852-1936) Polish

£3140	$5433	(8-Sep-91 REM.W46) Zakopane landscape (47x63cm-19x25in) s. board (P.Z 60000000)
£4292	$7725	(24-Nov-91 AG.W18) An angler (24x29cm-9x11in) s. (P.Z 85000000)
£4676	$7949	(26-Oct-91 AL.W6) Digging beetroot (46x67cm-18x26in) s. board (P.Z 90000000)
£877	$1571	(17-Nov-91 REM.W32) Flowers in a vase (44x61cm-17x24in) s. W/C (P.Z 17000000)
£1047	$1811	(8-Sep-91 REM.W45) Irises (64x50cm-25x20in) W/C (P.Z 20000000)
£1277	$2312	(7-Dec-91 AL.W8) Orthodox church in the Ukraine (54x72cm-21x28in) s. pastel (P.Z 25500000)
£1753	$3174	(6-Dec-91 UNI.W6) Fog in the Tatra Mountains (40x49cm-16x19in) s. W/C (P.Z 35000000)
£2081	$3580	(20-Oct-91 UNI.W10) Debnicki Bridge in Cracow in winter (45x56cm-18x22in) s. W/C (P.Z 40000000)

WYDEVELD, Arnoud (19th C) Dutch

| £5525 | $10000 | (5-Dec-91 FA.PH553) Floral still life (76x56cm-30x22in) s.i. |

WYETH, Andrew (1917-) American

| £11404 | $19500 | (11-Mar-92 SY.NY107/R) Study of pine, Maine (37x52cm-15x20in) s.i. ink wash paperboard |

WYETH, Caroline (1909-) American

| £3191 | $6000 | (18-Dec-91 SY.NY302/R) A stand of fir trees (76x91cm-30x36in) s. |

WYETH, James (1946-) American

| £18129 | $31000 | (11-Mar-92 SY.NY105/R) Raven (152x183cm-60x72in) s. |

WYETH, N C (1882-1945) American

| £3933 | $7000 | (2-Nov-91 IH.NY115/R) Man with butterfly net standing in field (76x99cm-30x39in) s. |
| £7602 | $13000 | (11-Mar-92 SY.NY106/R) Garden meeting (58x123cm-23x48in) i. canvas on board |

WYETH, Newell Convers (1882-1945) American

| £6453 | $11550 | (14-Nov-91 GRO.B89/R) Attack on stockade (58x76cm-23x30in) s.d.1905 en grisaille |

WYETH, Newell Convers (after) (1882-1945) American

| £964 | $1735 | (23-Nov-91 YFA.M313) Good ship Rose (76x51cm-30x20in) |

WYGRZYWALSKI, Feliks (1875-1944) Polish

£777	$1360	(3-Apr-92 BM.B805/R) Cockfight (46x79cm-18x31in) s.i.d.1933 (DM 2200)
£853	$1553	(27-May-92 PH.DU190) Female nude by the sea (52x69cm-20x27in) s.i. (DM 2500)
£2260	$4091	(18-May-92 SY.MI3/R) Le bagnanti (91x147cm-36x58in) s.i. (I.L 5000000)

WYGRZYWALSKI, Tadeusz (1904-1963) Polish

| £465 | $831 | (17-Nov-91 REM.W33) Street theatre (60x79cm-24x31in) s. board (P.Z 9000000) |
| £1047 | $1811 | (8-Sep-91 REM.W47) Street theatre (76x99cm-30x39in) s. (P.Z 20000000) |

WYK, Henri van (1833-) Dutch

| £657 | $1195 | (26-May-92 DUR.M121/R) Arabes (20x40cm-8x16in) s. panel (S.P 120000) |

WYK, van (?) Dutch

£838	$1491	(28-Apr-92 RAS.K249) Musketeer music making in inn (35x28cm-14x11in) s. (D.KR 9500)
£970	$1727	(28-Apr-92 RAS.K248/R) From an artist's studio (35x28cm-14x11in) s.d.08 (D.KR 11000)
£1375	$2392	(18-Sep-91 N.M755/R) Arabs on horsebacks in mountain landscape (21x41cm-8x16in) s. panel (DM 4000)

WYLD, William (1806-1889) British

£614	$1050	(13-Mar-92 WOL.C433) Venice (38x30cm-15x12in) s. panel
£1200	$2088	(15-Apr-92 HAR483/R) Market place with figures (46x28cm-18x11in) s.
£410	$738	(2-Feb-92 ZZ.F246/R) Quais animes (32x24cm-13x9in) s.d.1876 Indian ink (F.FR 4000)
£660	$1181	(5-May-92 SWS63/R) View of Campo in Venice (13x8cm-5x3in) W/C over pencil htd white
£1361	$2600	(3-Jul-92 S.W3780/R) Santa Maria della Salute (28x41cm-11x16in) W/C
£1600	$2864	(14-Nov-91 S127) Honfleur, Northern France (22x16cm-9x6in) W/C over pencil

WYLER, Otto (1887-) Swiss
£1020	$1733	(23-Oct-91 GD.B811/R) Flowers by window (81x65cm-32x26in) s.d.50 (S.FR 2600)
£1765	$3159	(15-Nov-91 ZOF.Z1924) Aare landscape (64x76cm-25x30in) canvas laid down (S.FR 4500)

WYLIE, Kate (fl.1902-1940) British
£780	$1412	(5-Dec-91 CG209/R) Honeysuckle (46x36cm-18x14in) s.
£1000	$1780	(28-Apr-92 S286/R) Auricula (26x31cm-10x12in) s. s.i.verso board
£1000	$1810	(4-Dec-91 S369/R) Summer flowers in blue vase (28x35cm-11x14in) s. canvasboard
£2600	$4368	(26-Aug-91 S1148/R) Still life of flowers in vase (51x61cm-20x24in) s.

WYLLIE, Charles William (1853-1923) British
£2000	$3800	(23-Jun-92 PH180/R) The road by the shore (76x126cm-30x50in) s.d.1889
£2600	$4602	(6-Nov-91 S17/R) At Bosham, Sussex (36x60cm-14x24in) canvas on board
£800	$1360	(22-Oct-91 SWS144/R) Coming in (35x25cm-14x10in) s. W/C htd bodycol

WYLLIE, Harold (1880-?) British
£900	$1512	(15-Aug-91 B407/R) Battle of Barfleur (61x91cm-24x36in) s. bears i.verso
£3000	$5040	(15-Aug-91 B399/R) H.M.S. Hornet, with other shipping (45x81cm-18x32in) s.
£720	$1296	(9-Jan-92 B144/R) H M S Implacable, sailing into Plymouth Sound (26x37cm-10x15in) s. W/C

WYLLIE, William Lionel (1851-1931) British
£940	$1626	(1-Oct-91 SWS1696/R) Barges on river (18x37cm-7x15in) s.
£950	$1653	(14-Apr-92 CSK172/R) Stern-wheel gunboats Tamai, Abu Klea and Metemmeh firing (30x46cm-12x18in) s.d.1899
£5000	$9000	(22-Nov-91 C54/R) HMS Shannon and the Second Battle Squadron (69x109cm-27x43in) s.d.1911 s.i.verso
£7000	$12390	(6-Nov-91 S26/R) On the lower Thames (45x81cm-18x32in) s.
£420	$777	(11-Jun-92 CSK63) Portsmouth Harbour (8x28cm-3x11in) s. pencil W/C
£500	$870	(14-Apr-92 CSK98) Cape de Gallo (21x33cm-8x13in) s.i. pencil W/C
£550	$924	(15-Aug-91 B351/R) Entrance to Lough Swilly (11x38cm-4x15in) s.i. W/C
£650	$1164	(11-Nov-91 PH175) Ras-El-Tin (13x51cm-5x20in) s. W/C
£660	$1142	(3-Oct-91 DLY152/R) Canal (25x30cm-10x12in) s. W/C
£700	$1176	(15-Aug-91 B258/R) Fleet off Portsmouth, 1912 (15x37cm-6x15in) s. W/C
£720	$1289	(5-May-92 SWS115/R) Off the Yorkshire coast (22x40cm-9x16in) s.i.
£800	$1344	(26-Aug-91 S1133/R) Anderstron Quay, Glasgow (22x32cm-9x13in) s.i. W/C over pencil
£980	$1646	(15-Aug-91 B358/R) Gillingham, Kent (20x16cm-8x6in) s. W/C
£1000	$1910	(30-Jun-92 SWS1714) Vilean Point (18x32cm-7x13in) s.i. W/C
£1200	$2148	(5-May-92 SWS114/R) Yachts racing offshore (26x43cm-10x17in) s. W/C pencil
£1300	$2340	(22-Nov-91 C12/R) Battle of Jutland with HMS Calliope, HMS Constance and HMS Comus, 1916 (14x43cm-6x17in) s.d.1917 pencil W/C dr.of battle plan verso
£3400	$6120	(9-Jan-92 B249/R) Midway Shrimpers and barges (22x33cm-9x13in) s.i. W/C bodycol.
£5200	$9412	(20-May-92 S193/R) End of the day at the beach (25x41cm-10x16in) s. W/C
£6000	$10200	(22-Oct-91 C11/R) Barbados (26x41cm-10x16in) s.i. W/C

WYMAN, M A (20th C) American
£1006	$1800	(6-May-92 B.P143/R) Summer play (25x38cm-10x15in) s.d.1915 board

WYNANTS, Jan (1630-1684) Dutch
£5995	$11151	(16-Jun-92 SY.B200/R) Travellers in wooded landscape (68x84cm-27x33in) (B.FR 360000)
£13000	$24960	(10-Jul-92 C187/R) Wooded landscape with horseman on track approaching manor house (47x56cm-19x22in) s.d.1660
£33000	$58740	(1-Nov-91 C125/R) River landscape with horseman and peasants on path, house beyond (49x64cm-19x25in) s.d.1672

WYNANTS, Jan (style) (c.1630-1684) Dutch
£800	$1440	(21-Nov-91 C25) Wooded landscape with sportsmen and seated peasant (26x35cm-10x14in) bears sig. panel
£1200	$2100	(27-Feb-92 CSK124/R) Figures and goats in a river landscape (30x35cm-12x14in) with sig.
£4500	$8640	(8-Jul-92 S232/R) Landscape with figures on path and river valley beyond (70x73cm-28x29in)

WYNEN, Dominicus van (attrib) (1661-?) Dutch
£23743	$42500	(17-Jan-92 SY.NY43/R) A scene of sorcery (73x57cm-29x22in)

WYNEN, Oswald (1736-1790) Dutch
£1519	$2750	(21-May-92 GRO.B1/R) Vase of flowers on marble entablature (48x36cm-19x14in) s. W/C

WYNGAARDEN, D van (19th C) Dutch
£4255	$7319	(12-Oct-91 CH.AM204/R) Wooded river landscapes with townsfolk. Figures and cattle on road (40x53cm-16x21in) s.d.1823 pair (D.FL 14000)

WYNGAERDT, Anthonie Jacobus van (1808-1887) Dutch
£690 $1186   (16-Oct-91 KM.K1441) Stream in landscape and view of villlage with church beyond (18x28cm-7x11in) s. panel (DM 2000)
£1209 $2200   (26-May-92 CE.NY273/R) Cows grazing in open field (23x36cm-9x14in) s. panel
£2050 $3648   (26-Nov-91 VN.R137/R) Windmill beside a river (22x34cm-9x13in) s. panel (D.FL 6600)
£3704 $6704   (19-May-92 GF.L2196/R) Cattle and sheep grazing (27x43cm-11x17in) s. panel (S.FR 10000)

WYNGAERDT, Petrus Theodorus van (1816-1893) Dutch
£1500 $2670   (28-Nov-91 CSK176/R) The letter (29x19cm-11x7in) s.d.1859 panel
£3143 $5500   (18-Feb-92 CE.NY202/R) Blowing bubbles (53x39cm-21x15in) s.d.1846 panel

WYNGAERT, Ch van (19th C) ?
£2000 $3620   (22-May-92 C189/R) Amourous advance (45x34cm-18x13in) s.d.1872 indist.s.i.verso panel

WYNNE, Arthur (19th C?) British?
£1600 $2752   (11-Oct-91 C81/R) Near Pangbourne-on-Thames (50x76cm-20x30in) s. s.i.verso

WYNNEN, Domenicus van (circle) (?) ?
£1870 $3254   (13-Sep-91 C136/R) Dante and Virgil at entrance to hell (49x46cm-19x18in)

WYNTER, Bryan (1915-1975) British
£950 $1815   (16-Jul-92 B121) Double (101x81cm-40x32in) i.d.1970 verso
£2200 $4070   (11-Jun-92 C80 b/R) Beggar (76x63cm-30x25in) i.stretcher
£2100 $3570   (22-Oct-91 SWS239/R) Landscape with flowers (19x29cm-7x11in) s.d.49 gouache

WYRSCH, Charles (1920-) Swiss
£1533 $2651   (23-Mar-92 AB.L35/R) El Gran Culo (32x44cm-13x17in) s.i.d.verso (S.FR 4000)
£431 $772   (12-Nov-91 GF.L5395) Reclining female nude seen from behind (37x55cm-15x22in) s.d.1982 chl (S.FR 1100)

WYRSCH, Johann Melchior (1732-1798) Swiss
£8271 $15135   (4-Jun-92 SY.Z301/R) Portrait of Conrad Wirz-Nuscheler. Portrait of his wife (83x66cm-33x26in) i. s.i.d.1760verso canvas on panel pair (S.FR 22000)

WYSMULLER, Jan Hillebrand (1855-1925) Dutch
£500 $855   (17-Mar-92 PH17) Figures beside canal (38x56cm-15x22in) s. board
£673 $1171   (14-Apr-92 SY.AM397) Winter landscape with farm (59x39cm-23x15in) s. (D.FL 2200)
£979 $1732   (5-Nov-91 SY.AM256) Winter te Abcoude (80x123cm-31x48in) s. (D.FL 3200)

WYSPIANSKI, Stanislas (1869-1907) Polish
£12424 $23358   (21-Dec-91 PSA.W24) Young man and the Muses (76x53cm-30x21in) s. (P.Z 240000000)
£955 $1709   (17-Nov-91 REM.W34) Sketch of woman's head (27x21cm-11x8in) s. pastel (P.Z 18500000)
£967 $1760   (15-Dec-91 REM.W52) Young girl with plaits (41x39cm-16x15in) s. crayon gouache (P.Z 19000000)
£1450 $2725   (21-Dec-91 HO.P6) Portrait of Jacek Malczewski (42x29cm-17x11in) s. (P.Z 28000000)

WYSS, Caspar (1762-1798) German
£593 $1067   (19-Nov-91 GS.B4725/R) Ruins near Goldiwil with view of Schloss Thun (27x44cm-11x17in) s.d.1785 gouache (S.FR 1500)
£1265 $2277   (19-Nov-91 GS.B4724/R) View of the Habsburg with figures and animals (27x44cm-11x17in) s.d.1785 gouache (S.FR 3200)

WYTSMAN, Rodolphe (1860-1927) Belgian
£4078 $6974   (21-Mar-92 KV.L453/R) Derniers Rayons, Knocke (46x61cm-18x24in) s. d.1895 verso (B.FR 240000)
£2833 $4873   (12-Oct-91 KV.L450/R) Beside the river (33x41cm-13x16in) s. W/C (B.FR 170000)

XAVERY, Franciscus (18th C) Dutch
£2840 $5083   (12-Nov-91 SY.AM13/R) Ships in breezy sea (37x49cm-15x19in) s.d.1765 panel (D.FL 9200)

XCERON, John (1890-1967) American
£698 $1200   (12-Oct-91 SY.NY238/R) Abstract composition (21x28cm-8x11in) s.d.58 W/C gouache ink paper on board

XENAKIS, Constantin (1931-) Egyptian
£811 $1477   (25-May-92 D.P234) A contre sens 1988 (76x56cm-30x22in) s. ink W/C (F.FR 8000)

XIE ZHILIU (1910-) Chinese

£1849	$3236	(30-Mar-92 CH.HK350/R) Peach blossoms and bamboo (87x52cm-34x20in) s.i. ink W/C hanging scroll (HK.D 25000)
£2515	$4401	(30-Mar-92 CH.HK275/R) Flower and butterfly (20x55cm-8x22in) s.d.1955 ink folding fan (HK.D 34000)
£3107	$5436	(30-Mar-92 CH.HK346/R) Butterfly and red leaves (85x32cm-33x13in) s.d.1939 ink W/C hanging scroll (HK.D 42000)
£3550	$6213	(30-Mar-92 CH.HK257/R) Lotus (118x45cm-46x18in) s.i. ink W/C hanging scroll (HK.D 48000)
£4438	$7766	(30-Mar-92 CH.HK205/R) Mount Dan Xia (102x42cm-40x17in) s. ink W/C scroll (HK.D 60000)
£14053	$24593	(30-Mar-92 CH.HK110/R) Landscapes in mist (27x28cm-11x11in) one i. ink ten album leaves (HK.D 190000)

XIMENES, Bruno (1883-1921) Italian

£921	$1676	(10-Dec-91 F.R137/R) La modella (29x28cm-11x11in) s.d.1920 panel (I.L 2000000)

XU BEIHONG (1895-1953) Chinese

£126437	$216207	(22-Mar-92 SY.TA30/R) Yugong moving mountain (46x106cm-18x42in) (T.D 5500000)
£2737	$4789	(30-Mar-92 CH.HK311/R) Two magpies (32x32cm-13x13in) s.d.1945 ink W/C hanging scroll (HK.D 37000)
£4802	$8500	(7-Nov-91 B.SF1223/R) The summer day hangs heavy (103x55cm-41x22in) s.d.1936 ink colour
£11834	$20710	(30-Mar-92 CH.HK124/R) Examining horses (35x83cm-14x33in) s.d.1930 ink W/C silk scroll (HK.D 160000)
£13314	$23299	(30-Mar-92 CH.HK314/R) Horse eating grass (102x55cm-40x22in) s.i.d.1934 ink W/C hanging scroll (HK.D 180000)
£14793	$25888	(30-Mar-92 CH.HK253/R) Plum blossoms and bamboo (79x54cm-31x21in) s.i.d.1942 ink W/C hanging scroll (HK.D 200000)

XU GU (1824-1896) Chinese

£19231	$33654	(30-Mar-92 CH.HK260/R) Loquats (85x44cm-33x17in) s.i. ink W/C hanging scroll (HK.D 260000)
£25888	$45303	(30-Mar-92 CH.HK157/R) orchids (141x39cm-56x15in) s. ink W/C hanging scroll (HK.D 350000)
£40680	$71191	(30-Mar-92 CH.HK310/R) Flowers and fruits of New Year (182x62cm-72x24in) s. ink W/C hanging scroll (HK.D 550000)

XU LELE (1955-) Chinese

£1479	$2589	(30-Mar-92 CH.HK380/R) Ladies sitting in pavilion (43x42cm-17x17in) s. ink W/C scroll (HK.D 20000)

XU XI (20th C) Chinese

£2219	$3883	(30-Mar-92 CH.HK329/R) Moored fishing boats (46x69cm-18x27in) s.d.1991 ink W/C scroll (HK.D 30000)
£5917	$10355	(30-Mar-92 CH.HK325/R) Small neighbourhood in Suzhou (97x89cm-38x35in) s.d.1991 ink W/C scroll (HK.D 80000)

XUL SOLAR, Alejandro (1887-1963) Argentinian

£2247	$4000	(28-Apr-92 PO.BA32) Avis por siempre (30x21cm-12x8in) tempera
£17778	$32000	(19-Nov-91 CH.NY58/R) La sombra del caminante (21x21cm-8x8in) s. panel
£5525	$10000	(18-May-92 CH.NY133/R) Nitra (51x42cm-20x17in) s.d.1954 W/C ink
£6667	$12000	(20-Nov-91 V.BA116/R) Arbol de la vida (24x34cm-9x13in) d.1954 ink tempera
£6977	$12000	(9-Oct-91 RO.BA37/R) Las cinco torres (100x34cm-39x13in) s.d.1952 W/C
£7222	$13000	(18-Nov-91 SY.NY30/R) Careo (17x30cm-7x12in) init.d.1922 W/C
£27624	$50000	(18-May-92 CH.NY30/R) Fecha Patria (28x38cm-11x15in) init.d.1925 W/C pen

YA MING (1924-) Chinese

£1849	$3236	(30-Mar-92 CH.HK403/R) Village houses in Xiangxi (117x65cm-46x26in) s.d.1979 ink W/C hanging scroll (HK.D 25000)

YAKOVLEV, Andrey (1934-) Russian

£1462	$2558	(24-Sep-91 ARC.P217/R) Regards sur le fjord (90x104cm-35x41in) s. (F.FR 14500)
£1512	$2646	(24-Sep-91 ARC.P216/R) Le nouveau ne et le chien (110x106cm-43x42in) s. (F.FR 15000)
£2319	$4057	(24-Sep-91 ARC.P218/R) Pres du village (74x97cm-29x38in) s. (F.FR 23000)
£2456	$4373	(25-Nov-91 ARC.P90/R) Les premiers pas au printemps (80x120cm-31x47in) s. (F.FR 24000)
£2823	$4940	(24-Sep-91 ARC.P215/R) Les premiers pas au printemps (70x100cm-28x39in) s. (F.FR 28000)

YAN WENLIANG (1893-1990) Chinese

£8092	$13837	(22-Mar-92 SY.TA4/R) Houses of Parliament. Roman Forum (18x25cm-7x10in) s. board pair (T.D 352000)

YANEZ, Ferrando (fl.1506-1560) Spanish
£387919 $678858   (20-Feb-92 EP.M4/R) Cristo resucitado con los redimidos del Limbo ante la Virgen (128x172cm-50x68in) panel (S.P 70000000)

YANG DENGXIONG (1957-) Chinese
£1391 $2378   (22-Mar-92 SY.TA77/R) Self-portrait as fish (60x60cm-24x24in) s.d.90 s.d.1990 verso (T.D 60500)

YANG HSING-SHENG (1938-) Chinese
£12644 $21621   (22-Mar-92 SY.TA59/R) Suzhou (90x117cm-35x46in) s.d.1988 (T.D 550000)

YANG SAN-LANG (1907-) Chinese
£18966 $32431   (22-Mar-92 SY.TA57/R) Mexican-style street in America (27x35cm-11x14in) s. (T.D 825000)
£40460 $69186   (22-Mar-92 SY.TA23/R) Spanish village (63x75cm-25x30in) s. (T.D 1760000)

YANG SHANSHEN (1913-) Chinese
£2071 $3624   (30-Mar-92 CH.HK120/R) Cat (67x30cm-26x12in) s.i.d.1976 ink scroll (HK.D 28000)
£2219 $3883   (30-Mar-92 CH.HK400/R) Crane and peaches (129x58cm-51x23in) s.d.1976 ink W/C hanging scroll (HK.D 30000)
£2589 $4530   (30-Mar-92 CH.HK117/R) Bamboo, morning glories and tree (100x24cm-39x9in) s.d.1952 ink W/C scroll (HK.D 35000)
£5178 $9061   (30-Mar-92 CH.HK116/R) Egret under moonlight (143x39cm-56x15in) s. ink W/C scroll (HK.D 70000)
£19970 $34948   (30-Mar-92 CH.HK121/R) Tiger (102x52cm-40x20in) s. ink W/C hanging scroll (HK.D 270000)

YANG YANWEN (1939-) Chinese
£1627 $2848   (30-Mar-92 CH.HK379/R) Cactus flowers (69x68cm-27x27in) s.d.1991 ink W/C scroll (HK.D 22000)
£2663 $4660   (30-Mar-92 CH.HK318/R) Willow beside palace wall (89x90cm-35x35in) s.i. ink W/C scroll (HK.D 36000)
£4808 $8413   (30-Mar-92 CH.HK338/R) Flying swallows in spring (112x82cm-44x32in) s.d.1987 ink W/C hanging scroll (HK.D 65000)

YANKEL, Jacques (1920-) French
£589 $1026   (14-Apr-92 ZZ.F52) Les oliviers (60x60cm-24x24in) s. (F.FR 5800)
£618 $1162   (18-Dec-91 PR.P115) Monsieur Loyal (60x30cm-24x12in) s. (F.FR 6000)
£650 $1118   (5-Mar-92 CSK169) Fleus dans salon bleu (65x47cm-26x19in) s.
£800 $1376   (5-Mar-92 CSK170) Le Phare (46x65cm-18x26in) s.
£950 $1634   (5-Mar-92 CSK168/R) Le poisson rouge (94x65cm-37x26in) s.
£1119 $2048   (17-May-92 GL.P244/R) Paysage rouge (73x54cm-29x21in) s. (F.FR 11000)
£1389 $2528   (11-Dec-91 CH.AM432/R) Decor pour artiste peintre (90x90cm-35x35in) s.i.verso (D.FL 4500)
£1453 $2600   (9-May-92 CE.NY97/R) L'atelier de l'artiste (100x100cm-39x39in) s.

YAOUANC, Alain le (c.1940-) French
£405 $734   (20-May-92 FB.P175/R) L'elemental (48x64cm-19x25in) mixed media collage (F.FR 4000)
£829 $1476   (29-Nov-91 D.P234) Composition et personnages dans l'espace (33x23cm-13x9in) s.d.71 collage (F.FR 8100)

YARBER, Robert (20th C) ?
£1600 $2800   (27-Feb-92 CE.NY280/R) Untitled (76x112cm-30x44in) s.d.86 col.chk

YARD, Sidney Janis (1855-1909) American
£743 $1300   (31-Mar-92 MOR.P83) Landscape (36x53cm-14x21in) s. W/C
£1130 $2000   (12-Feb-92 B.SF419/R) Sheep grazing (38x56cm-15x22in) s. W/C

YARNOLD, George B (19th C) British
£628 $1150   (4-Jun-92 GOM.M23) Falls on the Chapel, North Wales (46x36cm-18x14in) s.
£628 $1150   (4-Jun-92 GOM.M24) Falls on the Chapel, North Wales (46x36cm-18x14in) s.

YARTSEV, Grigorii Fedorovich (1858-1918) Russian
£1500 $2670   (26-Nov-91 PH151) View of mountain village (54x90cm-21x35in) s.d.95

YASHINE, Pavel (1920-) Russian
£717 $1291   (27-Jan-92 ARC.P203/R) Rue de village (53x66cm-21x26in) s. (F.FR 7000)
£820 $1475   (27-Jan-92 ARC.P201) L'ombrelle rouge (69x59cm-27x23in) s. (F.FR 8000)

YATCHENKO, Youri (1928-) Russian
£748 $1346   (27-Jan-92 ARC.P215) La punition (59x80cm-23x31in) (F.FR 7300)

YATES, Cullen (1866-?) American
£714 $1200   (14-Aug-91 B.P83/R) Floral still life (41x51cm-16x20in) s.
£879 $1600   (15-Dec-91 LIT.L272) Incoming tide (30x41cm-12x16in)
£3924 $6750   (10-Oct-91 FA.PH914/R) Marigolds in blue vase (102x91cm-40x36in) s.

YATES, Fred (1922-) British
£700 $1211   (3-Oct-91 DLY752) Story of Mrs Pratt John (122x91cm-48x36in) board

YATES, Thomas Brown (1882-?) British
£1531 $2740   (5-May-92 ZEL.L1590/R) Portrait of young Spanish woman holding fan (183x76cm-72x30in) (DM 4500)

YATES, W (?) ?
£1000 $1850   (11-Jun-92 CSK117/R) River landscape with figures crossing bridge
                  (49x40cm-19x16in) s.

YATES, W (jnr) (19/20th C) British
£601 $1100   (5-Feb-92 D.NY91) Woodcutters (51x76cm-20x30in) s.

YBANEZ, Miguel (20th C) ?
£531 $971   (12-May-92 C.A410) Composition (100x100cm-39x39in) s.d.1987 (B.FR 32000)
£668 $1136   (22-Oct-91 C.A338/R) La caide del dolar III (150x130cm-59x51in) s.d.1987
                  (B.FR 40000)
£1078 $1973   (12-May-92 C.A409/R) Animal escondido en el envierno (130x80cm-51x31in)
                  s.d.1987 (B.FR 65000)

YEATS, Jack Butler (1871-1957) British
£6383 $11298   (26-Apr-92 SY.ME224/R) Tall low house (22x35cm-9x14in) s. board
                  (A.D 15000)
£16514 $30716   (17-Jun-92 A.D72/R) Poetic morning - 1945 (23x36cm-9x14in) s. board
                  (E.P 18000)
£17000 $30600   (20-Nov-91 S124/R) The Stevedore (38x28cm-15x11in) s. panel
£17500 $30975   (7-Nov-91 C119/R) The dark path (35x53cm-14x21in) s. i.stretcher
£21000 $36120   (6-Mar-92 C15/R) Sligo Bay (23x33cm-9x13in) s. i.verso panel
£23000 $39560   (6-Mar-92 C14/R) The country gentleman (35x23cm-14x9in) s. i.verso panel
£24074 $43815   (11-Dec-91 A.D84/R) Old Timers from Frisco (23x36cm-9x14in) s. panel
                  (E.P 26000)
£25000 $45000   (20-Nov-91 S179/R) Smoke (46x61cm-18x24in) s.
£33000 $60390   (13-May-92 S29 a/R) Dawn, Holyhead (35x45cm-14x18in) s. i.verso
£40000 $73200   (13-May-92 S30/R) The Handcuff Queen (45x61cm-18x24in) s. i.verso
£44000 $75680   (6-Mar-92 C12/R) The police sergeant (35x22cm-14x9in) s. i.verso panel
£45000 $77400   (6-Mar-92 C13/R) The minister (35x23cm-14x9in) s. i.verso panel
£80000 $146400   (13-May-92 S29/R) The 'Haute Ecole' Act (61x91cm-24x36in) s.
£694 $1264   (11-Dec-91 A.D9/R) The last request (10x13cm-4x5in) s. ink dr (E.P 750)
£833 $1517   (11-Dec-91 A.D85/R) Rhymes of the Gitano's (13x15cm-5x6in) mono. ink
                  (E.P 900)
*£2617 $4527   (25-Mar-92 A.D149) Loading the Currach (20x28cm-8x11in) s. pen col.wash
                  (E.P 2800)*
£2800 $4872   (18-Sep-91 CG9/R) Sailors come ashore (17x23cm-7x9in) s. pen W/C
£3364 $5821   (25-Mar-92 A.D49/R) A western man (25x18cm-10x7in) s. W/C (E.P 3600)
£4500 $8100   (20-Nov-91 S123/R) Before the start (47x30cm-19x12in) s.d.97 chk W/C
*£14500 $25665   (7-Nov-91 C120/R) To make a reputation (16x90cm-6x35in) s. W/C
                  bodycol.htd.white joined paper*

YEGOROV, Andrei (1878-1954) Russian
£600 $1116   (16-Jun-92 S62 a) Winter's day (35x50cm-14x20in) s. gouache

YELLAND, Raymond D (1848-1900) American
£1000 $1900   (23-Jun-92 MOR.P20) Yosemite (30x25cm-12x10in) s.
£29240 $50000   (11-Mar-92 SY.NY34/R) Yosemite (100x182cm-39x72in) s.d.1883

YENS, Karl Julius Heinrich (1868-1945) American
£1836 $3250   (12-Feb-92 B.SF427/R) Half dome, Yosemite (84x105cm-33x41in) s.d.1919
                  board
£2119 $3750   (12-Feb-92 B.SF520/R) Sacred solitude, divine retreat (127x152cm-50x60in)
                  s.
£5367 $9500   (12-Feb-92 B.SF424/R) Boys of Yosemite (137x112cm-54x44in) s.d.1919
                  s.i.verso cotton

YEPES, Tomas (1600-1674) Spanish
£43776 $77921   (29-Oct-91 EP.M13/R) Naturaleza muerta con frutas en una canastilla,
                  flores y hojas de parra (76x101cm-30x40in) (S.P 8000000)
£52646 $92131   (20-Feb-92 EP.M7/R) Naturaleza muerta con frutas, panes en un cestillo,
                  pasteles y una horchatera sobre una mesa (75x111cm-30x44in)
                  (S.P 9500000)
£55000 $100100   (29-May-92 C326/R) Jar, bottle, pot of cherries, pieces of cake on salver
                  and plate on ledge (74x95cm-29x37in) s.i.
£103967 $185062   (29-Oct-91 EP.M12/R) Naturaleza muerta con un florero, alcachofa, frutas
                  y salmon (87x127cm-34x50in) (S.P 19000000)

YGART, L (19th C) Austrian
£2105 $3789   (22-Nov-91 SA.A1576/R) Park of Ville d'Este in Tivoli (103x73cm-41x29in)
                  s. (DM 6000)

YIP, Richard (1919-1981) American
£734 $1300   (12-Feb-92 B.SF630/R) Walk along coast (37x55cm-15x22in) s. W/C

YKENS, Frans (1601-1693) Flemish
£4065 $7073   (15-Apr-92 CB.P4/R) Nature morte aux huitres et fleurs dans un vase sur
                  une table (24x34cm-9x13in) s. panel (F.FR 40000)
£23457 $41988   (14-Nov-91 CH.AM151/R) Shrimps, chicken and oysters on plate with fruit
                  on draped table (85x115cm-33x45in) indis.s. (D.FL 76000)

YKENS, Frans (circle) (1601-1693) Flemish
£8942 $15291   (18-Mar-92 D.V148/R) Garland of flowers surrounding Madonna with Child
                  and infant St John (123x90cm-48x35in) (A.S 180000)

YKENS, Frans (style) (1601-1693) Flemish
£7500 $13350   (30-Oct-91 S10/R) Still life of flowers in glass vase and oysters on wooden ledge (25x35cm-10x14in) bears sig. panel

YNFANTE, G L (20th C) Spanish?
£1105 $2077   (3-Jan-92 DUR.M2/R) Dama con mantilla (79x79cm-31x31in) s.d.1912 (S.P 200000)

YOAKUM, Joseph E (1886-1973) American
£464 $850   (17-May-92 DU.E1218) Home on the range Montana (23x30cm-9x12in) s.i. W/C dr.

YOHN, Frederick Caffrey (1875-1933) American
£787 $1400   (2-May-92 IH.NY53/R) Couple on steps, man wearing red coat (48x30cm-19x12in) s. gouache

YON, Edmond (1836-1897) French
£941 $1600   (23-Oct-91 GD.B1347/R) Autumn landscape (12x30cm-5x12in) s. d.1893verso canvas on panel (S.FR 2400)
£1126 $2004   (27-Nov-91 AT.P206) Ferme a Villerville (28x45cm-11x18in) s.i. (F.FR 11000)
£1626 $2829   (13-Apr-92 PLF.P79/R) Traversee du village (32x41cm-13x16in) s. panel (F.FR 16000)
£2220 $3818   (20-Oct-91 I.N96/R) Rue de village (50x73cm-20x29in) s.i. (F.FR 22000)
£3125 $5531   (5-Nov-91 GF.L2116/R) River landscape with fisherman and peasant (40x64cm-16x25in) s. (S.FR 8000)

YORKE, William Hoard (fl.1858-1903) British
£1600 $2896   (20-May-92 S131/R) Maria Margretha of Timra, Capt H.Holmcrin (51x76cm-20x30in) s.i.d.1889
£2660 $5000   (18-Dec-91 SY.NY28/R) The Ship Mobile (47x66cm-19x26in) s.d.1862
£2784 $4900   (9-Apr-92 FA.PH648/R) Ship-Holme Force (30x46cm-12x18in) s.
£3000 $5220   (15-Apr-92 PHL210/R) Portrait of Annie fully rigged off shore (49x74cm-19x29in) s.i.d.1882
£3333 $6000   (11-Jan-92 S.BM60/R) Portrait of barque Mertola, heading up coast (51x76cm-20x30in) s.d.87
£3600 $6516   (20-May-92 S154/R) Ship Henrietta (53x81cm-21x32in) s.i.d.1875
£4500 $8145   (20-May-92 S115/R) Claudia of Marstal, Capt C.I.Simonsen (50x75cm-20x30in) i.
£6000 $10860   (20-May-92 S114/R) The ship Ceferina, Capt Hein off Holyhead (61x91cm-24x36in) s.i.d.1873

YOSHIDA, H (20th C) Japanese
£2326 $4000   (12-Oct-91 DU.E526) Oriental landscape (61x76cm-24x30in) s. W/C

YOSHIDA, R (19/20th C) Japanese
£694 $1200   (6-Sep-91 S.BM268/R) An Oriental Genre scene (36x58cm-14x23in) s. panel

YOUNG, Alexander (fl.1883-1920) British
£600 $1038   (4-Oct-91 RS141) Busy port (38x61cm-15x24in) s.
£780 $1388   (1-Nov-91 PHE42) On the quayside (59x44cm-23x17in) s.
£1500 $2520   (26-Aug-91 S969/R) Fishing harbours (30x46cm-12x18in) s. pair
£1600 $2848   (28-Apr-92 S159/R) Unloading the catch, Kircaldy (61x40cm-24x16in) s. i.stretcher
£2200 $3696   (26-Aug-91 S971/R) Fife Harbour. Fishing boats (51x76cm-20x30in) s.d.1902 pair
£2500 $4450   (28-Apr-92 S160/R) Fife harbour. Fishing boats (51x76cm-20x30in) s.d.1902 pair
£2500 $4200   (26-Aug-91 S812/R) Loading a wagon (51x76cm-20x30in) s.
£2600 $4368   (26-Aug-91 S811/R) Watering a team (51x76cm-20x30in) s.d.1903
£3200 $5728   (14-Jan-92 SWS183/R) Shipping off North Shields (60x75cm-24x30in) s.d.96

YOUNG, Charles Morris (1869-1964) American
£814 $1400   (10-Oct-91 FA.PH935/R) September landscape (56x91cm-22x36in) s.d.1893

YOUNG, J (19th C) British
£612 $1089   (30-Oct-91 CH.AM106) Portrait of man in armour with sword holding bible seated in landscape (111x85cm-44x33in) s.indis.d. (D.FL 2000)

YOUNG, Mabel (?) ?
£880 $1601   (11-Dec-91 A.D41) Forest under snow (30x41cm-12x16in) s. (E.P 950)

YOUNG, Michael (20th C) American
£4000 $7000   (25-Feb-92 SY.NY221/R) Rhizome (208x198cm-82x78in) s.i.d.1986verso sand earth acrylic

YOUNG, Murat (1901-1973) American
£421 $750   (2-Nov-91 IH.NY154/R) Dagwood's grandma objects to the marriage (10x46cm-4x18in) s. pen W/C

YOUNG, W (?) ?
£586 $1119   (29-Jun-92 AAA.S190) The wool team (54x77cm-21x30in) s. W/C (A.D 1500)

YOUNG, W B (20th C) Australian
£441 $784   (26-Nov-91 J.M1282) Landscape (13x19cm-5x7in) s. W/C (A.D 1000)

YOUNG, William (19th C) British
£400 $684   (17-Mar-92 JRL.S27) Returning home (29x46cm-11x18in) s.d.1925 W/C
        (A.D 900)
£650 $1092   (26-Aug-91 S1056/R) Scotch firs (24x35cm-9x14in) s. W/C

YOUNG, William Blamire (1862-1935) Australian
£622 $1064   (17-Mar-92 JRL.S18) Grazing cattle (24x32cm-9x13in) s. W/C (A.D 1400)
£655 $1146   (30-Mar-92 AAA.S110) Street scene, Canongate (35x42cm-14x17in) s. W/C
        (A.D 1500)
£881 $1568   (26-Nov-91 J.M151) Landscape (21x27cm-8x11in) s. W/C (A.D 2000)
£1702 $3013   (26-Apr-92 SY.ME247/R) Still life of flowers with Moorcroft vase
        (23x28cm-9x11in) s. W/C (A.D 4000)
£2979 $5272   (26-Apr-92 SY.ME243/R) Portrait of artist's daughter, Lalage Hall
        (46x59cm-18x23in) W/C (A.D 7000)
£2991 $5325   (27-Apr-92 J.M226) On the banks of the Wentworth (52x74cm-20x29in) s. W/C
        (A.D 7000)

YOUNG, William S (fl.1850-1870) American
£1286 $2250   (22-Feb-92 YFA.M216/R) Hudson River landscape (61x104cm-24x41in)
        s.indist.d.

YOUON, Konstantin (1875-1958) Russian
£1100 $1958   (28-Nov-91 S405/R) Novgorod (26x33cm-10x13in) s. canvas on board
£4500 $8010   (28-Nov-91 S404/R) Church across river (46x54cm-18x21in) s.

YOUSSOUFBAIEV, Ramil (1956-) Russian
£1041 $1821   (30-Mar-92 ZZ.F252/R) La maison de mon enfance (110x350cm-43x138in)
        s.verso (F.FR 10000)

YPEREN, Gerrit Willem van (1882-1955) Dutch
£969 $1764   (26-May-92 D.V121/R) Summer (35x43cm-14x17in) mono.d.1910 (A.S 20000)

YSERN Y ALIE, Pedro (1876-?) Spanish
£2964 $5277   (29-Nov-91 GAB.G2911/R) Elegantes au restaurant (36x50cm-14x20in) s.
        panel (S.FR 7500)

YSEWIJN, Marcel (1921-) Belgian
£596 $1079   (23-May-92 KV.L394) Southern landscape (55x75cm-22x30in) s.d.87
        (B.FR 36000)

YTHJALL, Terje (20th C) Norwegian?
£709 $1255   (15-Feb-92 BU.O162) From a dreamer's zoo (50x45cm-20x18in) s. (N.KR 8000)

YU CHENG-YAO (1898-?) Chinese
£7586 $12972   (22-Mar-92 SY.TA80/R) Landscape (60x120cm-24x47in) s. seal hanging scroll
        ink colour (T.D 330000)
£156782 $268097   (22-Mar-92 SY.TA47/R) Landscape (292x362cm-115x143in) s. ink four hanging
        scrolls (T.D 6820000)

YU FEIAN (1888-1959) Chinese
£1331 $2330   (30-Mar-92 CH.HK399/R) Hibiscus and fish swimming (122x46cm-48x18in)
        s.i.d.1936 ink W/C scroll (HK.D 18000)
£2959 $5178   (30-Mar-92 CH.HK111/R) Mynah bird on cherry branch (68x34cm-27x13in)
        s.i.d.1946 ink W/C scroll (HK.D 40000)
£6657 $11649   (30-Mar-92 CH.HK113/R) Peonies and birds (107x53cm-42x21in) s.i.d.1947
        ink W/C scroll (HK.D 90000)
£15533 $27182   (30-Mar-92 CH.HK256/R) Pigeons (54x71cm-21x28in) s. ink W/C scroll
        (HK.D 210000)

YU, Jackson (1911-) Chinese
£5057 $8648   (22-Mar-92 SY.TA8/R) Church over flowering field (124x94cm-49x37in)
        s.d.90 (T.D 220000)

YUAN, S C (20th C) American
£1184 $2250   (24-Jun-92 B.SF6349/R) Tidal pools (30x41cm-12x16in) s. board

YULE, William James (19th C) British
£2000 $3560   (1-May-92 PHE56/R) Spanish children (63x83cm-25x33in) i.

YUZBASIYAN, Arto (1948-) Canadian
£459 $839   (1-Jun-92 W.T1098) Houses on Dundas (41x30cm-16x12in) s.i.d.1979verso
        board (C.D 1000)
£731 $1337   (14-May-92 SY.T174/R) Dundas St. near Parliament Street (30x39cm-12x15in)
        s. board (C.D 1600)
£822 $1496   (26-May-92 JOY.T192) Eglise Saint-Georges vue du chateau
        (45x60cm-18x24in) s. (C.D 1800)
£1098 $1976   (19-Nov-91 FP.M193) Plateau Mont-Royal (56x71cm-22x28in) s. (C.D 2250)
£3000 $5310   (6-Nov-91 SY.T76/R) Queen Street East (60x85cm-24x33in) s. s.d.1980 verso
        (C.D 6000)
£913 $1662   (26-May-92 JOY.T245/R) Queen Street East at Degrassi (55x74cm-22x29in) s.
        W/C (C.D 2000)

YVON, Adolphe (1817-1893) French
£824 $1500   (28-May-92 SY.NY181/R) Portrait d'une femme (55x46cm-22x18in) s.d.1867
        painted oval

YVON, Adolphe (1817-1893) French-cont.
£1300 $2210   (23-Oct-91 S44/R) Whirling dervish (18x19cm-7x7in) s. indis.i.verso panel

ZABALETA, Rafael (20th C) Spanish
£41040 $74692   (11-Dec-91 FER.M170 a/R) Maternidad (100x81cm-39x32in) s. (S.P 7500000)
£776 $1373   (12-Feb-92 ANS.M46/R) Retrato de dama (67x44cm-26x17in) s.d.1949 pencil
                   dr (S.P 140000)
£1163 $2093   (28-Jan-92 EP.M61/R) Desnudo (48x34cm-19x13in) s. ink (S.P 210000)
£2599 $4731   (11-Dec-91 FER.M45/R) Terraza de un cafe parisino (35x25cm-14x10in)
                   s.d.1950 Indian ink dr (S.P 475000)

ZABEHLITZKY, Alois (1883-1969) Austrian
£540 $1026   (25-Jun-92 D.V624/R) Still life of flowers (100x70cm-39x28in) s. canvas
                   on board oval (A.S 11000)
£561 $1005   (5-May-92 ZEL.L1592/R) Still life of different vessels on drape
                   (48x58cm-19x23in) s.d.1930 board (DM 1650)

ZACCO, G (18/19th C) Italian
£1050 $2006   (14-Jul-92 DR365) Veduta della citta di Catania dalla parte Meridionale
                   (38x80cm-15x31in) s.d.1807 W/C

ZACHO, Christian (1843-1913) Danish
£617 $1048   (8-Aug-91 RAS.V1006/R) View of Silkeborg Islands (53x80cm-21x31in)
                   s.d.1886 (D.KR 7000)
£713 $1226   (15-Oct-91 RAS.K300/R) Avenue of palm trees near the Mediterranean
                   (64x58cm-25x23in) s.d.1909 (D.KR 8000)
£1058 $1884   (27-Apr-92 BU.K17/R) View of Cannes (64x59cm-25x23in) s.d.1909
                   (D.KR 12000)
£1233 $2097   (8-Aug-91 RAS.V1007/R) Wooded landscape with deer by river
                   (88x124cm-35x49in) s.d.1907 (D.KR 14000)
£1249 $2323   (16-Jun-92 RAS.K278/R) Wooded summer landscape with river
                   (85x125cm-33x49in) s.d.1876 (D.KR 14000)
£1346 $2341   (14-Apr-92 SY.AM337/R) Woman having tea in garden (40x55cm-16x22in)
                   s.d.1912 (D.FL 4400)

ZACK, Leon (1892-1980) Russian
£712 $1238   (17-Sep-91 RAS.K10/R) Composition (40x27cm-16x11in) s. (D.KR 8000)
£900 $1638   (12-Dec-91 CSK210/R) Abstract composition in cream and grey
                   (61x49cm-24x19in) s.d.60
£1800 $3096   (17-Oct-91 C35/R) Hommage a Guardia (81x116cm-32x46in) s. s.i.stretcher
£1945 $3462   (27-Nov-91 AT.P207) Deux garcons (93x73cm-37x29in) s.d. (F.FR 19000)
£1976 $3518   (29-Nov-91 GAB.G2913/R) Composition bleue (92x73cm-36x29in) s.d.73
                   (S.FR 5000)
£2047 $3644   (27-Nov-91 AT.P208/R) Sans titre (73x92cm-29x36in) s.d.62 (F.FR 20000)
£2200 $3784   (17-Oct-91 C2/R) Composition (60x73cm-24x29in) s.d.59
£3162 $5628   (29-Nov-91 GAB.G2912/R) Abstraction lyrique (100x81cm-39x32in) s.d.77
                   (S.FR 8000)
£3561 $6516   (14-May-92 BG.P27/R) Composition (81x65cm-32x26in) s.d.64 (F.FR 35000)
£3708 $6340   (22-Mar-92 I.N44/R) Composition (60x73cm-24x29in) s. (F.FR 36000)
£4094 $7288   (1-Dec-91 I.N30) Hommage a Guardia (81x116cm-32x46in) s. (F.FR 40000)
£4125 $7095   (12-Oct-91 GL.P46/R) Composition (81x116cm-32x46in) s.d.1959 (F.FR 41000)
£5242 $9069   (4-Oct-91 CSC.P87/R) Sans titre (92x73cm-36x29in) s.d.71 (F.FR 52000)
£495 $852   (4-Mar-92 KH.K222) Form noire sur form rouge, Paris (47x30cm-19x12in) s.
                   W/C crayon (D.KR 5500)
£514 $915   (29-Nov-91 GAB.G2914) Composition en noir (29x21cm-11x8in) s.d.76 W/C
                   (S.FR 1300)
£532 $947   (1-Dec-91 I.N22) Composition (32x23cm-13x9in) s.d.1969 W/C (F.FR 5200)
£560 $1025   (3-Jun-92 CSC.P48) Grand Signe (38x31cm-15x12in) s.d.74 W/C (F.FR 5500)
£907 $1570   (4-Oct-91 CSC.P88) Composition (43x36cm-17x14in) s. Indian ink wash
                   (F.FR 9000)

ZADEMACK, Siegfried (1952-) German
£481 $895   (20-Jun-92 BM.B1158) Theatre (61x92cm-24x36in) d.1980 col.chk pencil
                   indian ink pen (DM 1400)

ZADKINE, Ossip (1890-1967) French
£395 $750   (28-Jun-92 LIT.L378) Study for sculpture (43x25cm-17x10in) s.d.42 W/C
£432 $800   (12-Jun-92 SY.NY44/R) Embracing figures (24x20cm-9x8in) s.inits.
                   ballpoint pen board
£967 $1770   (3-Jun-92 CSC.P34) Trois personnages (25x21cm-10x8in) init. pencil
                   (F.FR 9500)
£1649 $2854   (23-Mar-92 GL.P151/R) Paysage de montagne (53x73cm-21x29in) s.d.1944
                   gouache (F.FR 16000)
£3757 $6500   (2-Oct-91 SY.NY57/R) Quatre figures (63x48cm-25x19in) s.d.51 gouache
£4200 $7266   (25-Mar-92 S193/R) Les Saltimbinques (65x45cm-26x18in) s.d.27 W/C gouache
£4573 $7957   (14-Apr-92 CSC.P37/R) Les baigneuses (29x40cm-11x16in) s.d.1919 W/C
                   (F.FR 45000)
£4645 $8500   (14-May-92 SY.NY307/R) L'homme et le cheval (72x56cm-28x22in) s.d.32 W/C
                   gouache
£5429 $9500   (25-Feb-92 CH.NY42/R) Meditation - portrait of Carol (65x55cm-26x22in)
                   s.d.37 gouache

ZADKINE, Ossip (1890-1967) French-cont.
£7377 $13279   (2-Feb-92 CSC.P62/R) Deux figures (73x55cm-29x22in) s.d.32 gouache
                      (F.FR 72000)
£10000 $19100   (1-Jul-92 S179/R) Tete d'homme (49x35cm-19x14in) s.d.21 indist.i. pencil
                      crayon
£10000 $19100   (1-Jul-92 S246/R) Couple buvant (63x48cm-25x19in) s.d.63 gouache

ZADOR, Istvan (1882-?) Hungarian
£2224 $3893   (19-Feb-92 D.V115/R) Female nude before mirror (110x70cm-43x28in) s.
                      (A.S 45000)

ZAGANELLI, Francesco (?-1531) Italian
£20112 $36000   (17-Jan-92 SY.NY14 b/R) The Madonna and child at a parapet
                      (51x41cm-20x16in) tempera oil panel
£27624 $50000   (21-May-92 CH.NY78/R) Madonna and child before parapet and canopy,
                      landscape beyond (63x54cm-25x21in) canvas transferred from panel

ZAGERIS, Peter (20th C) ?
£881 $1568   (26-Nov-91 J.M195 a/R) Robert Hawke (152x121cm-60x48in) s.d.1981
                      (A.D 2000)

ZAGO, Erma (1880-1942) Italian
£1859 $3365   (3-Dec-91 SY.MI78) Scorci di Venezia (19x26cm-7x10in) s. pair
                      (I.L 4000000)
£2299 $4116   (14-Nov-91 CH.R220) Gondola e Veezia. Vita veneziana (19x27cm-7x11in) s.
                      panel pair (I.L 5000000)
£635 $1182   (16-Jun-92 F.M19) Incrocio di canali veneziani (36x30cm-14x12in) s. W/C
                      paper on board (I.L 1400000)
£681 $1266   (16-Jun-92 F.M18) Angolo veneziano (35x30cm-14x12in) s. W/C paper on
                      board (I.L 1500000)
£726 $1351   (16-Jun-92 F.M20) Veduta di canale veneziano (36x30cm-14x12in) s. W/C
                      paper on board (I.L 1600000)

ZAHN, Friedrich (19th C) ?
£728 $1296   (29-Apr-92 D.V910/R) Mountain lake landscape (41x65cm-16x26in) s.d.1874
                      (A.S 15000)

ZAHND, Johann (1854-1934) Swiss
£3059 $5475   (15-Nov-91 ZOF.Z1925/R) Shepherd couple with flock in Roman campagna
                      (59x112cm-23x44in) s.i. (S.FR 7800)

ZAHRTMANN, Kristian (1843-1917) Danish
£626 $1140   (12-Dec-91 RAS.V802) Before church (39x26cm-15x10in) s.d.70 (D.KR 7000)
£673 $1211   (30-Jan-92 RAS.V694/R) Matteo and his wife (42x49cm-17x19in) (D.KR 7500)
£1083 $1949   (19-Nov-91 RAS.K312/R) Portrait of Miss Thora Lund, aged fifteen
                      (68x52cm-27x20in) mono.d.1874 (D.KR 12000)
£1102 $1962   (28-Apr-92 RAS.K650/R) Artist's self portrait (23x19cm-9x7in) mono.d.1867
                      (D.KR 12500)
£1440 $2635   (5-Feb-92 KH.K147/R) Zantippe and Socrates (72x59cm-28x23in) mono.
                      (D.KR 16000)
£1587 $2825   (28-Apr-92 RAS.K489/R) Peace - interior with woman seated with prayerbook
                      (51x45cm-20x18in) mono.d.1914 (D.KR 18000)
£1890 $3459   (5-Feb-92 KH.K148/R) Young girl smelling a rose (58x45cm-23x18in)
                      mono.d.1868 (D.KR 21000)
£2166 $3704   (10-Mar-92 RAS.K105/R) Adam and Eve with mountains and sea in background
                      (66x55cm-26x22in) mono.d.1892 (D.KR 24000)
£3081 $5176   (28-Aug-91 KH.K226/R) Civita d'Antino - family joy (110x103cm-43x41in)
                      mono.d.1889 (D.KR 35000)
£3103 $5338   (16-Oct-91 KM.K1459/R) Fra en Fyrreskov (113x105cm-44x41in) mono.d.1896
                      (DM 9000)

ZAIS, Giuseppe (circle) (1709-1784) Italian
£4144 $7500   (21-May-92 CH.NY175/R) Mountainous river landscape with figures fishing
                      by (54x71cm-21x28in)
£6800 $11900   (2-Apr-92 CSK81/R) Shepherd and shepherdess with sheep in wooded
                      Italianate landscape (122x80cm-48x31in)

ZAIS, Giuseppe (style) (1709-1784) Italian
£1200 $2100   (28-Feb-92 C115) Italianate landscape with peasant woman and child
                      fishing (37x29cm-15x11in) panel
£1300 $2340   (21-Nov-91 CSK114/R) Peasant travellers approaching farm in Italianate
                      landscape (73x86cm-29x34in)
£2200 $3960   (21-Nov-91 C57/R) Italianate landscape with peasant fishing in rocky pool
                      (51x61cm-20x24in)
£2400 $4320   (21-Nov-91 C56/R) Capriccio of Venetian Lagoon with couple embarking
                      (35x45cm-14x18in)
£8500 $14875   (1-Apr-92 S239/R) Hilly landscape with figures near path in foreground
                      (32x45cm-13x18in)

ZAJICEK, Carl Wenzel (1860-1923) Austrian
£890 $1557   (20-Feb-92 D.V528/R) View of Kurrentgasse (23x16cm-9x6in) s. W/C
                      (A.S 18000)
£1221 $2101   (10-Oct-91 D.V257/R) Chapel near Nussdorferlinie (20x15cm-8x6in) s. pen
                      indian ink W/C (A.S 25000)

ZAJICEK, Carl Wenzel (1860-1923) Austrian-cont.
£1466 $2521   (10-Oct-91 D.V259/R) The old Hofoper, Vienna (11x16cm-4x6in) s. W/C (A.S 30000)
£1697 $3088   (27-May-92 D.V689/R) The Kartnerthor Theater, Vienna (10x14cm-4x6in) s. pen indian ink W/C (A.S 35000)
£1710 $2941   (10-Oct-91 D.V260/R) Burgtheater, Vienna (11x16cm-4x6in) s. W/C (A.S 35000)
£1942 $3456   (29-Apr-92 D.V673/R) Moonlit Danube canal (14x19cm-6x7in) s. W/C paper on board (A.S 40000)
£1954 $3361   (10-Oct-91 D.V263/R) Karmelitermarkt (11x16cm-4x6in) W/C (A.S 40000)
£3641 $6481   (29-Apr-92 D.V674/R) Der Graben in Wien (14x19cm-6x7in) s. W/C paper on board (A.S 75000)

ZAK, Eugene (1884-1926) Polish
£6411 $11412   (3-Nov-91 PSA.W18) Head of a woman (33x27cm-13x11in) s. board (P.Z 125000000)
£26402 $49635   (21-Dec-91 PSA.W25) Woman and clown (92x65cm-36x26in) (P.Z 510000000)
£1035 $1946   (21-Dec-91 HO.P7) Study of a woman (27x21cm-11x8in) s. pastel (P.Z 20000000)
£4571 $8000   (26-Sep-91 SY.I46/R) Portrait of woman in profile (72x57cm-28x22in) s. gouache chl board

ZAKARINE, Vladimir (1909-) Russian
£533 $959   (27-Jan-92 ARC.P108/R) Promenade en barque (68x78cm-27x31in) s. (F.FR 5200)

ZAKHAROV, Fiodor (1919-) Russian
£507 $917   (20-May-92 ARC.P14) Roses d'automne (80x80cm-31x31in) s. isorel (F.FR 5000)
£510 $948   (17-Jun-92 ARC.P31/R) Lilas en fleurs (48x76cm-19x30in) s. board (F.FR 5000)
£559 $973   (13-Apr-92 ARC.P57) Les roses blanches (80x80cm-31x31in) s. (F.FR 5500)
£608 $1100   (20-May-92 ARC.P15) Les branches d'amandier (80x80cm-31x31in) s. isorel (F.FR 6000)
£663 $1232   (17-Jun-92 ARC.P32/R) Les branches de lilas (86x103cm-34x41in) s. board (F.FR 6500)
£691 $1202   (13-Apr-92 ARC.P58/R) Roses d'automne (80x80cm-31x31in) s. (F.FR 6800)
£1067 $1857   (13-Apr-92 ARC.P59/R) Les lilas dans l'atelier (86x104cm-34x41in) s. board (F.FR 10500)
£2026 $3668   (20-May-92 ARC.P13/R) Les lilas de Yalta (79x100cm-31x39in) s. (F.FR 20000)

ZALCE, Alfredo (1908-) Mexican
£3860 $6600   (21-Mar-92 W.W61/R) Boat landing (61x81cm-24x32in) masonite

ZALOPANY, Michele (20th C) ?
£3179 $5500   (3-Oct-91 SY.NY191 a/R) Untitled (233x246cm-92x97in) chl.pastel

ZAMACOIS Y ZABALA, Eduardo (1842-1871) Spanish
£2743 $4800   (19-Feb-92 CH.NY119/R) Court jester (41x28cm-16x11in) s.d.67 W/C over pencil

ZAMACOIS, Eduardo (?) Spanish
£518 $892   (16-Oct-91 FER.M141/R) Dia de verano en la playa de Biarritz (16x27cm-6x11in) s. W/C (S.P 95000)

ZAMBELETTI, Ludovico (1881-1966) Italian
£3021 $5166   (19-Mar-92 F.M30) Val Vigezzo (100x133cm-39x52in) s. (I.L 6500000)
£1208 $2066   (19-Mar-92 F.M55) Conversazione (24x17cm-9x7in) s. W/C cardboard (I.L 2600000)

ZAMPIERI, Domenico see DOMENICHINO

ZAMPIGHI, Emiliano (19th C) Italian
£1923 $3500   (26-May-92 CE.NY133 a/R) Two and two are four (50x62cm-20x24in) s.

ZAMPIGHI, Eugenio (1859-1944) Italian
£3800 $6764   (28-Nov-91 B198/R) A good story (30x40cm-12x16in) s.
£3947 $7500   (26-Jun-92 WOL.C469/R) Frugal meal (53x76cm-21x30in) s.
£4286 $7800   (26-May-92 CE.NY139/R) Mandolin player (45x36cm-18x14in) s.
£4374 $7610   (13-Apr-92 SY.J263/R) Doting grandfather. Centre of attraction (25x35cm-10x14in) s. pair (SA.R 22000)
£4700 $7990   (22-Oct-91 SWS341/R) Love riddle (58x44cm-23x17in) s.
£5300 $9276   (3-Apr-92 BM.B739/R) The pleasures of old age (44x58cm-17x23in) s. (DM 15000)
£5814 $10000   (17-Oct-91 SY.NY331/R) Musicians and dancer (77x56cm-30x22in) s.
£6500 $11765   (22-May-92 C238/R) First steps (56x76cm-22x30in) s. canvas on board
£7303 $13000   (1-Dec-91 DU.E1144/R) Blowing bubbles (56x76cm-22x30in) s.
£7418 $13500   (28-May-92 BG.M553/R) Interior scene with grandmother, daughter and grandson with chickens (56x76cm-22x30in) s.
£9000 $16740   (19-Jun-92 C55/R) Another drink (55x76cm-22x30in) s.
£12209 $21000   (17-Oct-91 SY.NY375/R) happy days (72x105cm-28x41in) s.
£16092 $28000   (10-Sep-91 BG.M635/R) Italian family (48x107cm-19x42in) s.
£22857 $40000   (20-Feb-92 SY.NY100/R) Grandfather's visit (76x127cm-30x50in) s. canvas on panel

ZAMPIGHI, Eugenio (1859-1944) Italian-cont.
£3141	$6000	(16-Jul-92 SY.NY582/R) Preparing the the Baby's bath (38x55cm-15x22in) s. W/C
£4077	$7542	(8-Jun-92 CH.R529) Idillio in cucina (54x36cm-21x14in) s. W/C (I.L 9000000)
£5800	$10498	(22-May-92 C234/R) Centre of attraction (46x63cm-18x25in) s. pen W/C
£5888	$10893	(8-Jun-92 CH.R528/R) Il gomitolo (54x36cm-21x14in) s. W/C (I.L 13000000)

ZANCHI, Antonio (1631-1722) Italian
£9259	$16759	(4-Dec-91 CB.P11/R) Hercule et Omphale (128x113cm-50x44in) (F.FR 90000)
£13014	$23556	(4-Dec-91 CH.R61/R) Diogene (100x170cm-39x67in) (I.L 28000000)

ZANCHI, Antonio (circle) (1631-1722) Italian
£8500	$16320	(10-Jul-92 C239/R) Abraham amd Isaac (103x85cm-41x33in)

ZANCOLLI, Giuseppe (1888-?) Italian
£2222	$4022	(19-May-92 GF.L2529/R) Verona, Piazza delle Erbe (82x71cm-32x28in) s.indis.d. (S.FR 6000)

ZANDINI (19th C) Italian
£4571	$8000	(20-Feb-92 SY.NY321/R) Piazza San Marco la Notte (72x102cm-28x40in) s.indist.d.

ZANDLEVEN, Jan Adam (1868-1923) Dutch
£612	$1064	(14-Apr-92 SY.AM376) Still life with orange flowers (39x59cm-15x23in) s.d.09 (D.FL 2000)
£617	$1080	(18-Feb-92 CH.AM134) Blossoming tree (40x32cm-16x13in) s.d.1912 canvas laid down on board (D.FL 2000)
£1061	$1920	(19-May-92 CH.AM102) Tree by a wall (49x34cm-19x13in) s.d.1914 canvas on panel (D.FL 3500)
£1080	$1966	(11-Dec-91 CH.AM9) Mushrooms (33x43cm-13x17in) s.d.1917 (D.FL 3500)

ZANDOMENEGHI, Federico (1841-1917) Italian
£23949	$43588	(12-Dec-91 F.M22/R) Poires (34x31cm-13x12in) s.d.1914 (I.L 52000000)
£97606	$166907	(19-Mar-92 F.M85/R) Vaso di fiori e guanti (72x47cm-28x19in) s. (I.L 210000000)
£471429	$825000	(20-Feb-92 SY.NY117/R) En promenade (73x92cm-29x36in) s.
£2416	$4422	(16-May-92 F.L131/R) Donna che si stira (40x23cm-16x9in) s. chl (S.FR 6500)
£4606	$8382	(12-Dec-91 F.M35/R) Figura femminile allo specchio (35x24cm-14x9in) chl (I.L 10000000)
£11628	$20000	(16-Oct-91 CH.NY205/R) Study for Signora All'Aperto (55x44cm-22x17in) studio st. pastel chl.

ZANDT, William Thompson van (19th C) ?
£2186	$4000	(9-Feb-92 LIT.L206) First sorrow (79x64cm-31x25in) s.

ZANDT, William van (19th C) American
£1868	$3250	(15-Apr-92 SY.NY53/R) Sulky and rider (48x67cm-19x26in) s.d.87

ZANETTI, Giuseppe Miti (1859-1929) Italian
£7410	$12819	(24-Mar-92 CH.R56/R) In riva al Brenta (102x120cm-40x47in) s.d.1926 (I.L 16000000)

ZANGS, Herbert (1924-) German
£1232	$2218	(19-Nov-91 FB.P203/R) Nails (20x41cm-8x16in) s. d.52verso oil nails wood (F.FR 12000)

ZANGUIDI, Jacopo (1544-1574) Italian
£7500	$14400	(7-Jul-92 C131/R) Madonna and Child with Sts Jerome, Matthew and angels. Putto (22x19cm-9x7in) i. chk pen wash double-sided

ZANGUIDI, Jacopo (circle) (1544-1574) Italian
£550	$1001	(11-Dec-91 PH244/R) Orlando Rossi liberates Borgo San Donnino (54x42cm-21x17in) pen wash htd.white

ZANIN, Francesco (19th C) Italian
£13000	$24180	(17-Jun-92 S536/R) Paddle steamer in Bacino, Venice (73x109cm-29x43in) s.d.1869

ZANKOVSKII, Ilia Nikolaevich (?) Russian?
£600	$1074	(14-Nov-91 CSK296) Woodcutter's settlement in Dagestan (36x84cm-14x33in) s.

ZANNONI, Giuseppe (1849-1903) Italian
£1478	$2571	(18-Sep-91 N.M756/R) Girl sewing (40x24cm-16x9in) s. (DM 4300)
£2038	$3771	(9-Jun-92 F.R50/R) La cucitrice (40x25cm-16x10in) s. (I.L 4500000)

ZAO-WOU-KI (1920-) Chinese
£3168	$5766	(26-May-92 SY.MI114/R) Composizione (23x31cm-9x12in) s. s.d.1961 (I.L 7000000)
£4024	$6922	(12-Oct-91 GL.P45/R) Pecheurs et filet (28x34cm-11x13in) s. i.d.1952verso wood (F.FR 40000)
£17137	$29647	(4-Oct-91 CSC.P89/R) Composition (81x65cm-32x26in) s. d.31.03.86 verso (F.FR 170000)

ZAO-WOU-KI (1920-) Chinese-cont.

£25458	$46589	(3-Jun-92 CSC.P85/R) Composition (100x80cm-39x31in) s. s.d.16-3-88 verso (F.FR 250000)
£30345	$51890	(22-Mar-92 SY.TA52/R) Abstract street scene (49x65cm-19x26in) s. (T.D 1320000)
£850	$1471	(26-Mar-92 C7) Untitled (37x28cm-15x11in) s.d.51 ink wash
£1220	$2122	(13-Apr-92 GL.P93) Projet d'affiche (50x47cm-20x19in) W/C (F.FR 12000)
£1955	$3500	(13-Nov-91 B.SF2411/R) Composition (48x47cm-19x19in) s.i.d.54 W/C
£2216	$3766	(24-Oct-91 CSC.P64/R) Composition (18x28cm-7x11in) s.d.58 W/C (F.FR 22000)
£2749	$5031	(2-Jun-92 L.K1062/R) Flowers in vase (52x34cm-20x13in) s.d.1953 W/C pen (DM 8000)
£4634	$7925	(17-Mar-92 FB.P64/R) Paysage aux cerfs (28x36cm-11x14in) s.d.52 ink W/C (F.FR 45000)
£4791	$8911	(15-Jun-92 GL.P30/R) Untitled (48x64cm-19x25in) s.d.1960 W/C ink (F.FR 47000)
£5629	$10020	(30-Nov-91 FB.P27/R) Sans titre (121x123cm-48x48in) s.d.82 ink wash (F.FR 55000)

ZAPOROGETZ, Boris (1935-) Russian

£605	$1058	(24-Sep-91 ARC.P141/R) Sur les rochers (94x75cm-37x30in) s. (F.FR 6000)
£815	$1491	(3-Jun-92 ARC.P198/R) A table (79x60cm-31x24in) s. (F.FR 8000)
£866	$1584	(3-Jun-92 ARC.P200/R) Jeunes filles au cafe (79x69cm-31x27in) s. (F.FR 8500)
£928	$1587	(13-Mar-92 ARC.P213) Les voiles (86x69cm-34x27in) s. (F.FR 9000)
£958	$1676	(24-Sep-91 ARC.P142/R) Avant le bain (99x80cm-39x31in) s. (F.FR 9500)
£1018	$1864	(3-Jun-92 ARC.P199/R) Le vent de la mer (79x59cm-31x23in) s. (F.FR 10000)
£1076	$1936	(27-Jan-92 ARC.P197) Portrait de jeune fille (63x51cm-25x20in) s. (F.FR 10500)
£1119	$1958	(24-Sep-91 ARC.P139/R) La baignade (100x80cm-39x31in) s. (F.FR 11100)
£1178	$2121	(27-Jan-92 ARC.P198/R) Sur la plage (63x51cm-25x20in) s. (F.FR 11500)
£1443	$2468	(13-Mar-92 ARC.P212/R) Les jours d'ete (80x62cm-31x24in) s. (F.FR 14000)
£2254	$4057	(27-Jan-92 ARC.P196/R) Le bain (86x60cm-34x24in) s. (F.FR 22000)

ZARAGOZA, Jose (1874-1949) Spanish

£2061	$3710	(19-Nov-91 DUR.M48/R) La dama de la rosa (216x100cm-85x39in) s.d.1910 (S.P 375000)

ZARATE (?) Mexican

£16667	$30000	(18-Nov-91 SY.NY2/R) Monja coronada - retrato de la Hermana Francisca Leal y Bidrio (200x119cm-79x47in) s.i.d.1840

ZARCO, Antonio (1930-) Spanish

£970	$1717	(12-Feb-92 ANS.M104/R) Paisaje con un transformador (70x90cm-28x35in) s. (S.P 175000)

ZARDO, Alberto (1876-1959) Italian

£765	$1300	(25-Oct-91 S.W2368/R) Horses at water's edge in mountain landscape (30x43cm-12x17in) s. i.verso board
£1279	$2200	(15-Oct-91 CE.NY431/R) A fishing village at sunset (55x44cm-22x17in) s.i.
£1585	$2933	(8-Jun-92 CH.R549) Pastorella con gregge al pascolo (70x90cm-28x35in) s. (I.L 3500000)

ZARITSKY, Joseph (1891-1985) Israeli

£2703	$5000	(8-Jun-92 GG.TA160/R) Untitled (60x73cm-24x29in) s.
£2919	$5400	(8-Jun-92 GG.TA159/R) Untitled (54x65cm-21x26in) s.
£3085	$5800	(5-Jan-92 GG.TA213/R) Brush strokes in green (39x41cm-15x16in) s.d.1966
£4571	$8000	(26-Sep-91 SY.I119/R) Abstract composition (108x108cm-43x43in) s.d.1973
£5946	$11000	(9-Jun-92 GG.TA274/R) Yechiam (48x40cm-19x16in) s. paper
£6111	$11000	(6-Jan-92 GG.TA412/R) Red touch (89x92cm-35x36in) s.
£4255	$8000	(5-Jan-92 GG.TA214/R) Evirons of Jerusalem (35x37cm-14x15in) s.d.1928 W/C pencil
£5135	$9500	(8-Jun-92 GG.TA158/R) Tel Aviv, pole above roofs (49x69cm-19x27in) s. W/C
£6216	$11500	(9-Jun-92 GG.TA335/R) Tel Aviv, view from roof (53x73cm-21x29in) s. W/C pencil
£6383	$12000	(5-Jan-92 GG.TA215/R) View of Tel Aviv from the roof (52x70cm-20x28in) s. W/C
£6486	$12000	(8-Jun-92 GG.TA157/R) Woman on roof (52x72cm-20x28in) s. W/C pencil
£8378	$15500	(9-Jun-92 GG.TA334/R) Eagle over Temple Mount (32x40cm-13x16in) s. W/C

ZARRAGA, Angel (1886-1946) Mexican

£2572	$4887	(24-Jun-92 GL.P162/R) Panier de fruits (35x65cm-14x26in) s. (F.FR 25000)
£10497	$19000	(19-May-92 SY.NY86/R) Paisaje con figuras (36x27cm-14x11in) s.
£12222	$22000	(19-Nov-91 CH.NY55/R) Jugada de futbol (100x80cm-39x31in) s.

ZATZKA, Hans (1859-1949) Austrian

£1890	$3459	(2-Jun-92 FN.S2817) Still life of flowers with plants and mushrooms between rocks and roots (35x52cm-14x20in) s. canvas on panel (DM 5500)
£2171	$3800	(18-Feb-92 CE.NY236/R) Ornate still life on ledge (76x63cm-30x25in) s. i.verso
£2500	$4525	(22-May-92 C172/R) Mondfee (81x49cm-32x19in) s. s.i.verso
£2921	$5082	(21-Sep-91 SA.A1956/R) Classical scene with reclining woman and attendants in landscape (45x58cm-18x23in) s. (DM 8500)
£3158	$5684	(22-Nov-91 SA.A1727/R) Zur Abkuhlung (47x31cm-19x12in) s. grisaille panel (DM 9000)

ZATZKA, Hans (1859-1949) Austrian-cont.
£3265 $5680   (21-Sep-91 SA.A1958/R) Female playing flute and maid seated on fountain (82x50cm-32x20in) s. (DM 9500)
£3448 $5931   (16-Oct-91 KM.K1460) Women by pond in park landscape (50x65cm-20x26in) s. (DM 10000)
£3652 $6500   (22-Jan-92 SY.NY279/R) Still life of flowers (77x63cm-30x25in) s.
£3714 $6500   (20-Feb-92 SY.NY234/R) Sea nymphs (56x78cm-22x31in) s. s.i.verso
£3796 $7250   (16-Jul-92 SY.NY428/R) Sleeping beauty (58x78cm-23x31in) s.
£3988 $7139   (16-Jan-92 D.V81/R) The welcome intruder (59x36cm-23x14in) s. (A.S 80000)
£4000 $6840   (18-Mar-92 S70/R) The Nymphs' garden (77x57cm-30x22in) s.
£4286 $7500   (20-Feb-92 SY.NY233/R) Lady in waiting (69x48cm-27x19in) s. s.i.verso
£4995 $8991   (21-Nov-91 D.V73/R) Fauns and nymphs (79x58cm-31x23in) s. (A.S 100000)
£8430 $14500   (12-Oct-91 DU.E92/R) Wood nymphs blowing bubbles (51x81cm-20x32in) s.

ZAUGG, Hans (1894-) Swiss
£1255 $2334   (19-Jun-92 ZOF.Z2139/R) Late summer evening, Emmental (59x49cm-23x19in) s. i.verso board (S.FR 3300)

ZBUKVIC, Joseph (?) Australian?
£855 $1521   (27-Apr-92 J.M348) Between the flags (51x70cm-20x28in) s.d.86 W/C (A.D 2000)

ZEEMAN, Abraham Johannes (1811-1842) German
£1970 $3486   (22-Apr-92 CH.AM88/R) A lad of great promise (87x69cm-34x27in) s. (D.FL 6500)

ZEEMAN, Regnier Nooms see   NOOMS, Reinier

ZEGELAAR, Gerrit (1719-1794) Dutch
£4000 $6960   (15-Apr-92 C129/R) Haymaker and wife resting outside farmhouse (24x19cm-9x7in) s. panel pair

ZEHENDER, Karl Ludwig (1751-1814) Swiss
£1049 $1867   (29-Nov-91 ZEL.L1123/R) Peasants merrymaking and river landscape, evening (27x34cm-11x13in) s. panel (DM 3000)

ZEILEISSEN, Rudolf von (1897-1970) Austrian
£497 $884   (28-Nov-91 D.V217/R) At the beach (28x42cm-11x17in) pencil W/C gouache (A.S 10000)

ZEIZIG, Johann Eliazar see   SCHENAU, Johann Eleazar

ZELENINE (20th C) ?
£558 $982   (8-Apr-92 FB.P73/R) Composition (100x81cm-39x32in) s. (F.FR 5500)
£558 $982   (8-Apr-92 FB.P74) Femme et papillons (100x81cm-39x32in) s.d.3.79 (F.FR 5500)

ZELGER, Jakob Joseph (1812-1885) Swiss
£926 $1676   (19-May-92 GF.L2591/R) Mountain landscape with stream (26x36cm-10x14in) s. board (S.FR 2500)
£5000 $8700   (16-Apr-92 PHX394/R) Swiss mountain landscape with cattle near chalets. Swiss mountain village (46x64cm-18x25in) s. pair

ZELLER, Fred (20th C) ?
£721 $1233   (22-Mar-92 LT.P200) Les ballons (40x60cm-16x24in) s. panel (F.FR 7000)
£1648 $2818   (22-Mar-92 LT.P124) La vague (54x81cm-21x32in) s. (F.FR 16000)

ZELLER, Magnus (1888-1973) Polish
£874 $1556   (30-Nov-91 VG.B1058/R) Im Rausch. Figurenskizze (23x16cm-9x6in) s. pencil board double-sided (DM 2500)
£1224 $2178   (30-Nov-91 VG.B1059/R) The runner (32x35cm-13x14in) s. W/C over pencil (DM 3500)
£1224 $2178   (30-Nov-91 VG.B1061/R) Der Traumtanzer (26x18cm-10x7in) s. pencil board (DM 3500)

ZELTER, Georges (20th C) French?
£565 $1080   (3-Jul-92 GL.P203) Honfleur, le bassin (65x92cm-26x36in) s.i.d.1991verso (F.FR 5500)
£1767 $3393   (6-Jul-92 HC.P50/R) La jetee de Trouville (73x54cm-29x21in) s. (F.FR 17000)

ZEMPLENYI, Tividar (1864-1917) Hungarian
£791 $1384   (20-Feb-92 D.V358) Feeding the ducks (17x31cm-7x12in) s. board (A.S 16000)

ZENAKEN (20th C) ?
£614 $1093   (1-Dec-91 I.N12) Composition (115x88cm-45x35in) s. (F.FR 6000)
£624 $1198   (6-Jul-92 HC.P33/R) Composition abstraite (89x116cm-35x46in) s. acrylic (F.FR 6000)

ZENATTI, Jacques (1952-) ?
£615 $1107   (2-Feb-92 CSC.P132) Composition (100x100cm-39x39in) s. d.91verso acrylic (F.FR 6000)
£965 $1680   (14-Apr-92 CSC.P76) Lorenne (100x100cm-39x39in) s. acrylic (F.FR 9500)

ZENATTI, Jacques (1952-) ?-cont.
£467 $849   (25-May-92 D.P235) Composition abstraite (100x81cm-39x32in) s. s.d.12-89 mixed media (F.FR 4600)

ZENDER, Rudolf (1901-1988) Swiss
£519 $939   (19-May-92 GF.L2912) Portrait of Jamalo Staub (45x33cm-18x13in) mono (S.FR 1400)
£757 $1370   (4-Dec-91 G.Z1320) Cello player (55x33cm-22x13in) s. (S.FR 1900)
£1185 $2145   (20-May-92 GK.Z5147) Seine landscape (74x100cm-29x39in) s.d.1963 (S.FR 3200)

ZENNSTROM, Petter (1945-) Scandinavian
£954 $1698   (27-Nov-91 BU.S9/R) Composition (58x48cm-23x19in) init.d.1988 paper (S.KR 10000)
£1193 $2123   (27-Nov-91 BU.S91/R) Composition (73x48cm-29x19in) init.d.1988 paper (S.KR 12500)

ZENO, Jorge (1956-) Puerto Rican
£5525 $10000   (18-May-92 CH.NY220/R) Lluvia (100x85cm-39x33in) s. s.i.d.89 verso
£7778 $14000   (19-Nov-91 CH.NY183/R) Silencio (122x91cm-48x36in) s.

ZENONI (19th C) Italian
£1400 $2394   (17-Mar-92 PH202/R) Venice from the lagoon (50x65cm-20x26in) s.

ZERBE, Karl (1903-1974) German/American
£541 $1000   (10-Jun-92 CE.NY583) Dog under table (91x61cm-36x24in) s. i.d.1946 verso
£601 $1100   (6-Jun-92 LAE.L132/R) Marion Square, Charleston (81x76cm-32x30in) s. d.1941 verso

ZERILLI, Francesco (?-1837) Italian
£3200 $5664   (14-Feb-92 C152/R) Temple of Segesta in the Girgenti, Sicily (30x44cm-12x17in) mono. pencil bodycol.paper laid down on board
£3500 $6195   (14-Feb-92 C148/R) The Temple of Segesta in the Girgenti, Sicily (30x44cm-12x17in) pencil bodycol.paper laid down on board
£4200 $7434   (14-Feb-92 C153/R) Agrigento (30x45cm-12x18in) init. pencil bodycol.paper laid down on board
£5200 $9204   (14-Feb-92 C150/R) Taormina, Sicily (30x44cm-12x17in) mono. pencil bodycol.paper laid down on board
£5500 $9735   (14-Feb-92 C146/R) View of Marsala with figures collecting salt, and a sportsman (30x44cm-12x17in) init. pencil bodycol.paper laid down on board
£6000 $10620   (14-Feb-92 C143/R) Panoramic view of Palermo (30x45cm-12x18in) init. pencil bodycol.paper laid down on board
£6500 $11505   (14-Feb-92 C147/R) Messina (30x44cm-12x17in) init. pencil bodycol.paper laid down on board
£6500 $11505   (14-Feb-92 C151/R) Theatre at Taormina with Mount Etna beyond (30x44cm-12x17in) init. pencil bodycol.paper laid down on board
£7000 $12390   (14-Feb-92 C149/R) The Temple of Segesta, Sicily (30x44cm-12x17in) init. pencil bodycol.paper laid down on board
£7000 $12390   (14-Feb-92 C142/R) Panoramic view of Palermo, Sicily (29x44cm-11x17in) init. pencil bodycol.paper laid down on board
£7200 $12744   (14-Feb-92 C134/R) View of Palermo from Bocca de Falco (30x44cm-12x17in) init. bodycol.
£7800 $13806   (14-Feb-92 C145/R) Fishermen in Bay of Palermo (29x44cm-11x17in) init. bodycol.paper laid down on board
£7800 $13806   (14-Feb-92 C144/R) Panoramic view of Palermo from Bocca di Falco (30x44cm-12x17in) init. pencil bodycol.paper laid down on board
£9000 $15930   (14-Feb-92 C154/R) View of Catania with Mount Etna beyond (30x44cm-12x17in) bodycol.paper laid down on board

ZERRITSCH, Fritz (jnr) (1888-?) Austrian
£878 $1520   (3-Oct-91 D.V192/R) Landscape with two horses (65x100cm-26x39in) s. (A.S 18000)

ZETSCHE, Eduard (1844-1927) Austrian
£501 $907   (5-Dec-91 D.V183) View of Gogsheim, France (24x17cm-9x7in) s. W/C (A.S 10000)
£583 $1037   (29-Apr-92 D.V702/R) View of chapel (18x12cm-7x5in) s.d.921 pen indian ink W/C (A.S 12000)
£728 $1296   (29-Apr-92 D.V701/R) View of hilltop castle (31x41cm-12x16in) s. W/C (A.S 15000)
£777 $1383   (29-Apr-92 D.V703/R) Village square (34x25cm-13x10in) s.d.907 W/C (A.S 16000)
£969 $1764   (27-May-92 D.V691/R) The edge of the wood (18x12cm-7x5in) s.d.915 pen indian ink W/C (A.S 20000)

ZETTERBERG, Nisse (1910-1986) Swedish
£520 $942   (19-May-92 AB.S5349/R) Beach and low tide (60x73cm-24x29in) s.d.48 (S.KR 5500)

ZETTERWALL, Eva H (1941-) Swedish
£1466 $2654   (19-May-92 AB.S5352/R) Lovers (90x56cm-35x22in) s. (S.KR 15500)
£2933 $5308   (19-May-92 AB.S5351/R) Composition with figures (213x128cm-84x50in) s. (S.KR 31000)

ZETTERWALL, Eva H (1941-) Swedish-cont.
£759 $1389   *(13-May-92 BU.S218/R) Untitled (26x21cm-10x8in) s. mixed media collage (S.KR 8000)*

ZETTLER, Max (20th C) German
£517 $916   *(6-Nov-91 N.M1195/R) Summer evening (30x42cm-12x17in) s.i.d.1922 board (DM 1500)*

ZEUTHEN, Christian Olavius (1812-1890) Danish
£802 $1380   *(15-Oct-91 RAS.K307/R) From Toldboden (28x40cm-11x16in) (D.KR 9000)*

ZEUTHEN, Ernst (1880-1938) Danish
£632 $1080   *(12-Mar-92 RAS.K714) Fishingboat on green ocean (81x106cm-32x42in) s.d.1932 (D.KR 7000)*

ZEVENBERGHEN, Georges van (1877-1968) Belgian
£834 $1468   *(7-Apr-92 C.A639) In the studio (27x22cm-11x9in) s.d.1915 panel (B.FR 50000)*

ZEWY, Karl (1855-1929) Austrian
£2457 $4300   *(18-Feb-92 CE.NY310/R) White lillies (107x69cm-42x27in) s.*
£6786 $12351   *(27-May-92 D.V527/R) In the church on Sunday (32x24cm-13x9in) s.d.1896 panel (A.S 140000)*

ZEZZOS, Alessandro (1848-1914) Italian
£750 $1433   *(29-Jun-92 PHB153) Portrait of young Italian girl (40x29cm-16x11in) s. W/C*

ZHANG DAQIAN (1899-1983) Chinese
£1130 $2000   *(7-Nov-91 B.SF1224/R) Boating on the river (87x34cm-34x13in) s. ink scroll*
£1627 $2848   *(30-Mar-92 CH.HK198/R) Plum blossoms and butterflies (69x34cm-27x13in) s.i.d.1946 ink W/C painted with four artists (HK.D 22000)*
£2684 $4750   *(7-Nov-91 B.SF1225/R) Lotus (129x42cm-51x17in) s.d.1924 ink colour scroll*
£4438 $7766   *(30-Mar-92 CH.HK178/R) Peony (109x47cm-43x19in) s.i.d.1945 ink W/C scroll (HK.D 60000)*
£5178 $9061   *(30-Mar-92 CH.HK173/R) Qingke Ping of Mount Hua (108x32cm-43x13in) s.i. ink W/C hanging scroll (HK.D 70000)*
£6287 $11002   *(30-Mar-92 CH.HK177/R) Dove standing on pear blossom branch (102x43cm-40x17in) s.i.d.1948 ink W/C hanging scroll (HK.D 85000)*
£7396 $12944   *(30-Mar-92 CH.HK300/R) Lotus (38x92cm-15x36in) s. ink W/C scroll (HK.D 100000)*
£7396 $12944   *(30-Mar-92 CH.HK232/R) Bird standing on cherry branch (43x71cm-17x28in) s.i.d.1934 ink W/C hanging scroll (HK.D 100000)*
£8136 $14238   *(30-Mar-92 CH.HK237/R) Eggplant, melon and chillis (46x66cm-18x26in) s. ink W/C scroll (HK.D 110000)*
£8136 $14238   *(30-Mar-92 CH.HK295/R) Scholar fishing on boat waiting for moon (33x66cm-13x26in) s.i.d.1947 ink W/C hanging scroll (HK.D 110000)*
£8136 $14238   *(30-Mar-92 CH.HK236/R) Landscape of Qipan Pass (131x66cm-52x26in) s.i.d.1940 ink W/C hanging scroll (HK.D 110000)*
£8876 $15533   *(30-Mar-92 CH.HK174/R) Landscape after Zhao Mengfu (111x39cm-44x15in) s.i.d.1941 ink W/C hanging scroll (HK.D 120000)*
£8876 $15533   *(30-Mar-92 CH.HK239/R) Self-portrait (44x36cm-17x14in) s.i.d.1965 ink scroll (HK.D 120000)*
£8876 $15533   *(30-Mar-92 CH.HK172/R) View of Taihua Mountain (100x36cm-39x14in) s.i.d.1938 ink W/C hanging scroll (HK.D 120000)*
£9615 $16827   *(30-Mar-92 CH.HK181/R) Blue and green landscapes (19x39cm-7x15in) s. ink W/C scrolls pair (HK.D 130000)*
£11095 $19416   *(30-Mar-92 CH.HK238/R) Po-Mo landscape (56x76cm-22x30in) s.d.1973 ink W/C scroll (HK.D 150000)*
£11834 $20710   *(30-Mar-92 CH.HK179/R) Lotus (137x46cm-54x18in) s.i.d.1968 ink W/C hanging scroll (HK.D 160000)*
£11834 $20710   *(30-Mar-92 CH.HK170/R) Waterfall landscapes (59x39cm-23x15in) one s. one s.i. ink W/C board scroll pair (HK.D 160000)*
£12574 $22004   *(30-Mar-92 CH.HK182/R) Landscape (45x60cm-18x24in) s.d.1965 ink W/C scroll (HK.D 170000)*
£19231 $33654   *(30-Mar-92 CH.HK240/R) Peonies (90x58cm-35x23in) s.i.d.1966 ink W/C hanging scroll (HK.D 260000)*
£22189 $38831   *(30-Mar-92 CH.HK233/R) Lotus (68x135cm-27x53in) s.d.1976 ink W/C scroll (HK.D 300000)*
£22189 $38831   *(30-Mar-92 CH.HK292/R) Dragon peak of Mount Hua (141x74cm-56x29in) s.i.d.1965 ink W/C hanging scroll (HK.D 300000)*
£23669 $41420   *(30-Mar-92 CH.HK171/R) Lofty pines amidst clouds (45x60cm-18x24in) s.i. ink W/C scroll (HK.D 320000)*
£25148 $44009   *(30-Mar-92 CH.HK293/R) Red trees in autumn mountains (106x45cm-42x18in) s.i. ink gold W/C board (HK.D 340000)*
£26627 $46598   *(30-Mar-92 CH.HK169/R) Po-Mo landscape (56x98cm-22x39in) s. ink W/C scroll (HK.D 360000)*
£38462 $67308   *(30-Mar-92 CH.HK297/R) Cloudy mountains (30x165cm-12x65in) s.i. ink handscroll (HK.D 520000)*
£92456 $161797   *(30-Mar-92 CH.HK180/R) Sunny peaks after Juran - 10th century (168x85cm-66x33in) s.i. ink W/C hanging scroll (HK.D 1250000)*
£118343 $207101   *(30-Mar-92 CH.HK288/R) Lotus (155x350cm-61x138in) s.d.1958 ink six panel folding screen (HK.D 1600000)*

ZHANG DAQIAN (1899-1983) Chinese-cont.
£207101 $362426   (30-Mar-92 CH.HK241/R) *Landscape of Wu Gorge* (151x97cm-59x38in)
         s.i.d.1973 ink W/C scrolls four (HK.D 2800000)

ZHANG SHANZI (1882-1940) Chinese
£2219 $3883   (30-Mar-92 CH.HK387/R) *Two tigers* (134x67cm-53x26in) s.i.d.1931 ink W/C
         scroll (HK.D 30000)

ZHAO CHUNXIANG (1912-1991) Chinese
£7080 $12108   (22-Mar-92 SY.TA38/R) *Birds* (92x61cm-36x24in) s. ink acrylic paper on
         canvas (T.D 308000)
£10621 $18161   (22-Mar-92 SY.TA69/R) *Seven star lights* (186x94cm-73x37in) s.d.1972 ink
         acrylic paper on canvas (T.D 462000)

ZHAO SHAOANG (1904-) Chinese
£2219 $3883   (30-Mar-92 CH.HK348/R) *Sparrow catching bee* (132x33cm-52x13in) s.i. ink
         W/C hanging scroll (HK.D 30000)
£2811 $4919   (30-Mar-92 CH.HK298/R) *Cabbage and radish* (43x55cm-17x22in) s.d.1946 ink
         W/C hanging scroll (HK.D 38000)
£4068 $7119   (30-Mar-92 CH.HK274/R) *Cicada on branch* (19x50cm-7x20in) s.d.1958 i.verso
         ink W/C folding fan (HK.D 55000)
£4237 $7500   (7-Nov-91 B.SF1220/R) *Pheasant and wisteria* (107x49cm-42x19in) s.d.1930
         ink colour scroll
£4237 $7500   (7-Nov-91 B.SF1211/R) *Cicadas* (149x32cm-59x13in) s. ink colour scroll
£7027 $12297   (30-Mar-92 CH.HK307/R) *Carp* (105x45cm-41x18in) s.i. ink W/C hanging
         scroll (HK.D 95000)

ZHAO ZHUNWANG (1944-) Chinese
£395 $700   (7-Nov-91 B.SF1237/R) *Night view of Jiangnan village* (70x70cm-28x28in) s.
         ink colour

ZHENG XIAOXU and QI BAISHI (19/20th C) Chinese
£2825 $5000   (7-Nov-91 B.SF1229/R) *Wisteria and calligraphy* (?x53cm-?x21in) s.i.d.1925
         ink colour fan double-sided

ZHENG XIE (1693-1765) Chinese
£7910 $14000   (7-Nov-91 B.SF1245/R) *Bamboo and rocks* (138x77cm-54x30in) s. ink colour

ZHOU LUYON (1924-) Chinese
£5547 $9708   (30-Mar-92 CH.HK337/R) *Infinite landscape* (181x97cm-71x38in) ink W/C
         scroll (HK.D 75000)

ZHU QIZHAN (20th C) Chinese
£1627 $2848   (30-Mar-92 CH.HK366/R) *Narcissus* (97x57cm-38x22in) s. ink W/C hanging
         scroll (HK.D 22000)
£2367 $4142   (30-Mar-92 CH.HK197/R) *Loquats* (96x60cm-38x24in) s.d.1981 ink W/C hanging
         scroll (HK.D 32000)
£4438 $7766   (30-Mar-92 CH.HK312/R) *Red cliffs and blue river* (66x66cm-26x26in)
         s.i.d.1983 ink W/C scroll (HK.D 60000)

ZICHY, Count Mihaly von (1827-1906) Hungarian
£660 $1267   (28-Jul-92 SWS231 a/R) *Boy wiping his eyes* (16x12cm-6x5in) s.d.1863
         crayon
£2593 $4693   (21-May-92 SY.G14/R) *Portrait of Empress Maria Feodorovna* (4x?cm-2x?in)
         min.oval (S.FR 7000)

ZICK, Januarius (1730-1797) German
£3953 $7036   (29-Nov-91 GAB.G3115/R) *La descente de Croix. La mise au tombeau*
         (79x61cm-31x24in) pair (S.FR 10000)
£36000 $65520   (11-Dec-91 S126/R) *Peasant family in interior* (43x57cm-17x22in) s.
£40223 $72000   (16-Jan-92 CH.NY63/R) *Two shepherds wooing shepherdess, with children*
         quarelling, fountain in landscape (67x82cm-26x32in)

ZICK, Januarius (circle) (1730-1797) German
£1600 $2912   (10-Dec-91 PH187/R) *Portrait of Swiss guard* (16x13cm-6x5in) metal oval
£3584 $6486   (21-May-92 L.K180) *Shepherd couple before ruins on river banks*
         (36x49cm-14x19in) i.verso (DM 10500)

ZICK, Januarius (style) (1730-1797) German
£1980 $3445   (13-Sep-91 C82/R) *Witch conjuring up ghost before potenate at night*
         (49x60cm-19x24in)

ZICK, Johann (1702-1762) German
£4895 $8664   (7-Nov-91 D.V69/R) *Portrait of bearded man* (75x57cm-30x22in) (A.S 100000)

ZIDLICKY, Vladimir (1945-) Czechoslovakian
£497 $884   (29-Nov-91 D.V144/R) *Dramatic figure 32* (90x75cm-35x30in) d.1987/90 mixed
         media board (A.S 10000)

ZIEGLER, Henry Bryan (1793-1874) British
£1500 $2670   (28-Nov-91 B137/R) *Cider Mill, Hertfordshire* (31x42cm-12x17in) s.
         s.i.verso board
£7500 $13425   (13-Nov-91 S69/R) *Views of Bedgebury Park, Kent, seat of the Law Family*
         (24x33cm-9x13in) i.verso board pair

ZIEGLER, Nellie Evelyn (20th C) American
£1836 $3250   (12-Feb-92 B.SF556/R) Arroyo (63x76cm-25x30in) s.

ZIEGLER, Richard (1891-1992) German
£702 $1200   (13-Mar-92 FN.S2628/R) Fortified castle, Aargau (15x21cm-6x8in) mono. pastel over indian ink (DM 2000)

ZIEM, Felix (1821-1911) French
£700 $1239   (13-Feb-92 CSK254) On the Venetian Lagoon - a sketch (17x25cm-7x10in) s. paper
£1228 $2112   (16-Oct-91 FER.M137/R) Lavando en el rio en un paisaje oriental (24x33cm-9x13in) s. (S.P 225000)
£1598 $2764   (29-Mar-92 FE.P75) Bateau et gondoles dans la lagune paper laid down (F.FR 15500)
£1951 $3511   (20-Nov-91 CN.P223) Le Bosphore (21x41cm-8x16in) s. panel (F.FR 19000)
£2058 $3909   (22-Jun-92 AT.P101 b) Bastide aupres d'un grand pin parasol (22x27cm-9x11in) s. panel (F.FR 20000)
£2316 $3938   (24-Oct-91 CJ.N92/R) Bouquet de fleurs (38x60cm-15x24in) studio st. board (F.FR 23000)
£2674 $4600   (20-Oct-91 HG.C62) Canal scene (33x46cm-13x18in) s. board
£2747 $4917   (13-Nov-91 PIC.P93/R) Florence, vue de Fiesole (17x30cm-7x12in) s. paper laid down on canvas (F.FR 27000)
£2875 $5175   (18-Nov-91 AT.P385/R) La baie d'Alger (27x46cm-11x18in) s. panel (F.FR 28000)
£2930 $4980   (24-Oct-91 D.V141/R) View of Constantinople (28x35cm-11x14in) s. (A.S 60000)
£3052 $5463   (17-Nov-91 FB.P203) Vues de Canal de Venise (18x27cm-7x11in) s. panel (F.FR 30000)
£3488 $6000   (15-Oct-91 CE.NY103/R) A view of the Piazza San Marco (38x56cm-15x22in) s. panel
£3571 $6500   (28-May-92 SY.NY164/R) Drapeaux sur un canal a Venise (64x41cm-25x16in) s. panel
£4000 $6840   (17-Mar-92 PH115/R) Coastal landscape (53x65cm-21x26in) s. panel
£4144 $7500   (22-May-92 S.BM83/R) Along the Grand Canal (46x56cm-18x22in) s. panel
£4883 $8301   (24-Oct-91 D.V23/R) View of Venice (35x53cm-14x21in) s. (A.S 100000)
£5144 $9774   (22-Jun-92 AT.P101/R) Effet de soleil sur la Royale (72x55cm-28x22in) s. (F.FR 50000)
£5223 $9350   (14-Nov-91 GRO.B64/R) Venice (28x43cm-11x17in) s. panel
£5500 $9955   (22-May-92 C259/R) Bacine, Venice (68x102cm-27x40in) s.
£6294 $10762   (18-Mar-92 N.M691/R) View of Bacino di S.Marco with shipping, Venice (54x82cm-21x32in) s. (DM 18000)
£6385 $10919   (22-Mar-92 LT.P60/R) La traversee du Grand Canal au crepuscule pres de la place Saint-Marca Venise (38x46cm-15x18in) s. panel (F.FR 62000)
£7560 $13155   (18-Sep-91 N.M757/R) View of Venice with Doge's Palace, Piazza S.Marco and Canale Grande (47x65cm-19x26in) s. (DM 22000)
£8242 $15000   (28-May-92 SY.NY98/R) Le Grand Canal, Venice (55x86cm-22x34in) s.
£8257 $14367   (14-Apr-92 SY.AM309/R) The Venetian Lagoon (82x115cm-32x45in) s. (D.FL 27000)
£8721 $15000   (16-Oct-91 CH.NY6/R) Jour de fete sur le Grand Canal (58x71cm-23x28in) s.
£9341 $17000   (27-May-92 CH.NY12/R) A Venetian regatta (37x74cm-15x29in) s. panel
£10286 $18000   (19-Feb-92 CH.NY19/R) Venetian scene with view of Piazza San Marco at sunset (54x84cm-21x33in) s.
£10909 $19309   (22-Apr-92 CH.AM180/R) Vue de Venise (56x74cm-22x29in) s. panel (D.FL 36000)
£11429 $20000   (19-Feb-92 CH.NY17/R) Departure for Mecca (55x80cm-22x31in) s.
£13187 $24000   (27-May-92 CH.NY8/R) Les Eaux Douces, Constantinople (62x107cm-24x42in) s.
£13714 $24000   (19-Feb-92 CH.NY16/R) Venetian regatta (54x85cm-21x33in) s.
£16484 $30000   (27-May-92 CH.NY13/R) Panorama of Venice showing Doge's Palace and Campanile (68x113cm-27x44in) s.
£17442 $30000   (16-Oct-91 CH.NY7/R) A view of Venice (75x106cm-30x42in) s.
£18286 $32000   (19-Feb-92 CH.NY18/R) Venetian scene with view of Piazza San Marco and Santa Maria d.Salute (55x90cm-22x35in) s.
£26749 $50823   (22-Jun-92 AT.P110/R) Venise (65x80cm-26x31in) s. (F.FR 260000)
£31250 $56250   (2-Feb-92 ZZ.F68/R) Vue de Venise (75x105cm-30x41in) s. (F.FR 305000)
£528 $920   (15-Apr-92 PLF.P89/R) Gondoles devant le parc (13x20cm-5x8in) studio st. d.1874 pen dr (F.FR 5200)
£1094 $1980   (4-Dec-91 NA.BA48) Le Bosphore (21x32cm-8x13in) s. W/C
£1233 $2356   (1-Jul-92 CD.P9/R) Vue de Venise (10x18cm-4x7in) s. W/C gouache (F.FR 12000)

ZIEM, Felix (attrib) (1821-1911) French
£1111 $2011   (19-May-92 GF.L2533/R) Constantinopel at sunset (17x22cm-7x9in) bears sig canvas on panel (S.FR 3000)

ZIEMERT (20th C) ?
£865 $1582   (14-May-92 BG.P5 b/R) Concours de circonstances 1978 (67x97cm-26x38in) s.d.1978 (F.FR 8500)

ZIER, Francois Edouard (1856-1924) French
£1058 $1873   (5-Nov-91 ZZ.F133/R) Cycliste, asise sur le rebord d'une fenetre (39x33cm-15x13in) s. board (F.FR 10500)
£1648 $3000   (26-May-92 CE.NY46/R) The young scholar (45x33cm-18x13in) s.d.

ZIESENIS, Johan Georg (attrib) (1716-1776) Danish
£766 $1363   *(22-Jan-92 SY.NY237/R) Portrait of gentleman (70x56cm-28x22in)*

ZIGLDRUM, Fred Arnus (1941-1984) German
£722 $1270   *(11-Apr-92 AW.H2457) View of Pellheim (29x40cm-11x16in) s.i.d.1977 W/C over chk (DM 2100)*

ZILLA, Vettore Zanetti (1866-1945) Italian
£2556 $4627   *(3-Dec-91 SY.MI81/R) Reti e barche di pescatori (54x54cm-21x21in) panel (I.L 5500000)*

ZILLE, Heinrich (1858-1929) German
£378 $699   *(12-Jun-92 HN.H854) Woman gathering skirt seen from behind (17x9cm-7x4in) st.sig. chl col.chk (DM 1100)*
£401 $719   *(6-May-92 GD.B1546/R) Girl with baby (26x21cm-10x8in) s. chl (S.FR 1100)*
£410 $741   *(23-May-92 GB.B7410) Bust of woman (13x10cm-5x4in) col.chk (DM 1200)*
£412 $763   *(12-Jun-92 HN.H855) Man with bowler (17x9cm-7x4in) st.sig. chl col.chk (DM 1200)*
£481 $890   *(12-Jun-92 HN.H856) Woman carrying pannier (14x10cm-6x4in) st.sig. chl col.chk (DM 1400)*
£702 $1263   *(21-Nov-91 L.K520) Female dancer (29x17cm-11x7in) st.sig. chl pastel (DM 2000)*
£877 $1579   *(21-Nov-91 L.K517) Studies of women (47x29cm-19x11in) st.sig. sold with dr.of male nude (DM 2500)*
£1375 $2543   *(12-Jun-92 HN.H858) Dicke Mamsell (18x9cm-7x4in) st.sig. chl col.chk (DM 4000)*
£1474 $2653   *(21-Nov-91 L.K509/R) Young woman with green cardigan (17x12cm-7x5in) col.chk (DM 4200)*
£1474 $2653   *(21-Nov-91 L.K510/R) Girl wearing coat with fox collar (21x11cm-8x4in) col.chk (DM 4200)*
£2200 $3982   *(2-Dec-91 CSK51/R) Junges Madchen mit Kind (18x13cm-7x5in) s. pen two*
£3158 $5684   *(21-Nov-91 L.K508/R) Organ grinder in back yard (24x33cm-9x13in) s. pen paper on board (DM 9000)*
£9474 $17053   *(21-Nov-91 L.K507/R) Eene, meene, ming-mang s. s.i.d.1928verso pen W/C bodycol (DM 27000)*
£11000 $19910   *(2-Dec-91 CSK52/R) Drei junge Madchen (16x24cm-6x9in) s.i.d.1922 pencil gouache crayon*
£12628 $22983   *(30-May-92 VG.B130/R) Sommer im Grunewald bei Krausens (23x17cm-9x7in) i.d.05 W/C indian ink pen over pencil board (DM 37000)*

ZILLEN, Johannes Wilhelm (1824-1870) Danish
£628 $1130   *(30-Jan-92 RAS.V695/R) Feeding cows, ducks and chickens in farmyard (27x42cm-11x17in) s.d.1861 (D.KR 7000)*
£704 $1183   *(27-Aug-91 RAS.K607/R) Milking place near Vingsted (100x159cm-39x63in) s.d.1868 (D.KR 8000)*

ZIMMER, Bernd (1948-) German
£6529 $11948   *(2-Jun-92 L.K1068/R) In the olive grove (130x160cm-51x63in) s.i.d.1964 acrylic cotton (DM 19000)*
£7719 $13895   *(19-Nov-91 L.K1233/R) Summer (156x205cm-61x81in) s.i.d.1979 dispersion cotton (DM 22000)*

ZIMMER, H P (1939-) German
£12238 $21783   *(26-Nov-91 KF.M1157/R) Greta Garbo (82x50cm-32x20in) s.i.d.1965 (DM 35000)*
£850 $1547   *(10-Dec-91 RAS.K108/R) Composition (46x34cm-18x13in) s.i.d.62 W/C (D.KR 9500)*
£1678 $2987   *(26-Nov-91 KF.M1159/R) An der Borse (55x75cm-22x30in) s.i.d.1989 mixed media (DM 4800)*

ZIMMER, Hans Peter (1936-) German
£1486 $2557   *(4-Mar-92 KH.K106/R) Composition (48x36cm-19x14in) paper (D.KR 16500)*
£721 $1240   *(4-Mar-92 KH.K223) Bei einem Sammler (44x62cm-17x24in) s.d.75 W/C collage (D.KR 8000)*

ZIMMER, Wilhelm Carl August (1853-1937) German
£16783 $28699   *(18-Mar-92 N.M692/R) Der Sieger des Schweine-Auskegelns (72x109cm-28x43in) i. s.d.1882 (DM 48000)*

ZIMMERMAN, Jan W G (1816-1887) Dutch
£4070 $7000   *(17-Oct-91 SY.NY273/R) Deerhound in landscape (76x100cm-30x39in) s.i.*

ZIMMERMANN, Adolf (1799-1859) German
£1553 $2765   *(29-Apr-92 D.V915/R) Bay of Naples, morning (58x76cm-23x30in) (A.S 32000)*

ZIMMERMANN, August Albert (1808-1888) German
£699 $1196   *(18-Mar-92 N.M693/R) Wooded mountain landscape in alpine glow (91x60cm-36x24in) i. (DM 2000)*
£1220 $2220   *(14-Dec-91 BOD.P770/R) Torrent in valley and snow covered mountains beyond (90x130cm-35x51in) (DM 3500)*
£1236 $2163   *(20-Feb-92 D.V437/R) Sunset in lake landscape with riding falconers (26x40cm-10x16in) mono.d.1849 panel (A.S 25000)*
£1941 $3396   *(19-Feb-92 D.P36/R) Le torrent (59x49cm-23x19in) s. panel (F.FR 19000)*
£2062 $3588   *(21-Sep-91 SA.A1808/R) Torrent in Alpine landscape (71x58cm-28x23in) s. (DM 6000)*

ZIMMERMANN, August Albert (1808-1888) German-cont.
£2062 $3588   (21-Sep-91 SA.A1807/R) Water fall in high mountains (72x58cm-28x23in) s.
     (DM 6000)
£2493 $4462   (16-Jan-92 D.V43/R) Pass Lueg (59x49cm-23x19in) s.i.d.1884 panel
     (A.S 50000)

ZIMMERMANN, Carl (1863-1930) German
£1045 $1902   (11-Dec-91 N.M669/R) Stag with herd by the edge of the wood
     (80x70cm-31x28in) s.d.1888 (DM 3000)
£1203 $2093   (18-Sep-91 N.M759/R) Stag and deer by the edge of woods (80x70cm-31x28in)
     s.d.1888 (DM 3500)

ZIMMERMANN, Ernst (1852-1901) German
£862 $1483   (16-Oct-91 KM.K1461/R) Portrait of gentleman with stick and tophat seated
     in Alpine landscape (26x21cm-10x8in) s.indis.d.18.. panel (DM 2500)

ZIMMERMANN, Friedrich (1823-1884) German
£593 $1067   (19-Nov-91 GS.B3691) Moor landscape, evening (45x64cm-18x25in) s.
     (S.FR 1500)
£859 $1521   (5-Nov-91 GF.L2609/R) Lake landscape with view of mountains
     (35x52cm-14x20in) s. (S.FR 2200)
£1255 $2133   (23-Oct-91 GD.B819/R) View of Weisshorn and Matterhorn (71x50cm-28x20in)
     s.i.d.1880 (S.FR 3200)

ZIMMERMANN, Friedrich August (1805-1876) German
£1500 $2655   (13-Feb-92 CSK194/R) Visit to the fortune teller (76x66cm-30x26in)
     s.d.1851

ZIMMERMANN, Julius (1824-1906) German
£977   *$1681*   *(10-Oct-91 D.V216/R) Lakeside town (28x42cm-11x17in) s.d.75 pen indian*
     ink W/C (A.S 20000)

ZIMMERMANN, Mac (1912-) German
£632   *$1137*   *(23-Nov-91 N.M713/R) Two dancing furies (65x50cm-26x20in) s.indis.d.1972*
     gouache (DM 1800)

ZIMMERMANN, Reinhard Sebastian (1815-1893) German
£782 $1400   (13-Nov-91 B.SF2304/R) Jilted (32x23cm-13x9in)
£4530 $8244   (11-Dec-91 N.M670/R) The broken jug (60x76cm-24x30in) s. (DM 13000)
£8247 $14351   (17-Sep-91 FN.S2623/R) Children preparing meal in peasant interior
     (50x40cm-20x16in) s.d.1853 (DM 24000)
£20619 $35876   (17-Sep-91 FN.S2662/R) Councillors seated round table taking part in
     official celebrations (81x116cm-32x46in) s.d.1865 (DM 60000)

ZINCKE, Christian Friedrich (1683-1767) German
£400   *$720*   *(19-Nov-91 CSK187/R) Gentleman, in brown coat, white shirt and cravat,*
     full-bottomed wig (4x?cm-2x?in) enamel gold frame oval
£432   *$800*   *(10-Jun-92 SY.NY4/R) Portrait of Frederick, Prince of Wales (4x?cm-2x?in)*
     min. enamel silver/gold frame oval
£541   *$1000*   *(10-Jun-92 SY.NY2/R) Portrait of J.Bernard (5x?cm-2x?in) min. enamel*
     gilt-metal frame oval
£720   *$1238*   *(4-Mar-92 C58/R) Lady, in decollete blue dress with white underslip*
     (4x?cm-2x?in) min. enamel gold frame oval
£750   *$1343*   *(11-Nov-91 PH80/R) Portrait of gentleman wearing blue coat, shirt and*
     lace cravat (4x?cm-2x?in) min.enamel gold frame oval
£800   *$1432*   *(11-Nov-91 PH82/R) Portrait of gentleman wearing coat with lace cravat*
     (5x?cm-2x?in) min.i.verso enamel gold frame oval
£900   *$1611*   *(11-Nov-91 PH79/R) Portrait of gentleman wearing coat, shirt and cravat*
     (5x?cm-2x?in) min.oval gold brooch frame pierced scroll border
£1020   *$1948*   *(30-Jun-92 SWS2370/R) Portrait of the Honourable Thomas Caulifield*
     (5x?cm-2x?in) min. enamel oval gold frame i.verso
£1750   *$3115*   *(27-Nov-91 C208/R) Sir Thomas Frederick in crimson coat and lace jabot*
     (5x?cm-2x?in) min. enamel gold frame reeded border oval
£5500   *$9680*   *(9-Apr-92 S125/R) Portrait of Elizabeth Crew, later Countess of Arran*
     (?x7cm-?x3in) min. enamel gold bezel silver-gilt back oval

ZINFORNITI, E (?) ?
£643 $1100   (13-Mar-92 WOL.C1123) Young woman on the steps (61x91cm-24x36in) s.

ZINGG, Adrian (1743-1816) Swiss
£405   *$733*   *(6-Dec-91 GB.B5639) Wooded landscape (31x23cm-12x9in) pen wash (DM 1150)*
£410   *$741*   *(22-May-92 GB.B5717) Schandau on Elbe (17x25cm-7x10in) s. pen indian ink*
     wash (DM 1200)
£1045   *$1902*   *(12-Dec-91 L.K499/R) Mountainous river landscape with peasant and two*
     children (48x65cm-19x26in) pen indian ink brush sepia (DM 3000)
£1045   *$1902*   *(12-Dec-91 L.K500/R) Peasant with oxen team in river landscape with mill*
     beyond (48x65cm-19x26in) pen indian ink brush sepia (DM 3000)

ZINGG, Jules (1882-1942) French
£1767 $3393   (7-Jul-92 ARC.P99) paysage aux toits rouges (33x40cm-13x16in) s. panel
     (F.FR 17000)
£1874 $3393   (18-May-92 AT.P162) Gardeuse de vaches (38x55cm-15x22in) s. panel
     (F.FR 18500)
£4299 $7652   (27-Nov-91 AT.P210/R) Paysage de Doubs (48x71cm-19x28in) s. panel
     (F.FR 42000)

ZINGG, Jules (1882-1942) French-cont.
£4532 $7704   (24-Oct-91 D.P143/R) Village sous la neige (46x66cm-18x26in) s. board
    (F.FR 45000)
£4743 $8443   (29-Nov-91 GAB.G3216/R) Village sous la neige (65x45cm-26x18in) s. panel
    (S.FR 12000)
£563 $1002   (27-Nov-91 AT.P68) Voiliers au port (16x23cm-6x9in) s. W/C (F.FR 5500)

ZINKEISEN, Anna (1901-) British
£600 $1032   (5-Mar-92 CSK21/R) Summer blooms in large white bowl (76x63cm-30x25in)
    init.
£1800 $3024   (26-Aug-91 S1031/R) Highland lass (76x63cm-30x25in) s.

ZINKEISEN, Doris (1898-1991) British
£500 $890   (30-Apr-92 T80/R) Stable companions (51x61cm-20x24in) s.
£500 $915   (4-Jun-92 CSK34) Hat maker (51x41cm-20x16in) s.
£550 $935   (22-Oct-91 HS3) Tea in the garden (64x74cm-25x29in) s.
£650 $1118   (5-Mar-92 CSK69/R) Cafe in Champs Elysees (63x76cm-25x30in) s.
£750 $1305   (19-Sep-91 CSK24/R) In the paddock (51x64cm-20x25in) s.
£1462 $2792   (19-Jul-92 SY.ME37/R) Colombo (44x34cm-17x13in) s. (A.D 3800)
£1800 $3132   (14-Apr-92 GA105) Visitors for Christmas - carriage scenes, figures in
    19th century dress (51x76cm-20x30in) s. pair

ZINNER, Robert (1904-) Austrian
£976 $1689   (3-Oct-91 D.V209/R) Morsbachalm with Schoberspitze beyond
    (60x70cm-24x28in) s.i.verso panel (A.S 20000)

ZITKO, Otto (20th C) ?
£971 $1778   (5-Feb-92 FB.P250) Bez Nazvu (140x160cm-55x63in) (F.FR 9500)

ZITO (20th C) ?
£811 $1477   (25-May-92 AT.P156/R) Josephine devant son Hispano (62x31cm-24x12in)
    s.d.28 gouache silver (F.FR 8000)

ZIVERI, Alberto (1908-) Italian
£3109 $5846   (19-Dec-91 F.M79/R) Vaso di fiori (45x35cm-18x14in) s.d.1957
    (I.L 6700000)
£3109 $5846   (19-Dec-91 F.M111/R) Natura morta con fiasco e pesce (40x50cm-16x20in)
    s.d.1956 (I.L 6700000)
£3538 $6475   (12-May-92 F.R184/R) Autoritratto (25x19cm-10x7in) s.d.1937 s.d.verso
    (I.L 7800000)
£6961 $13087   (19-Dec-91 F.M206/R) Ragazzi (62x52cm-24x20in) s.d.1933 (I.L 15000000)

ZIX, Ferdinand (1864-?) German
£951 $1721   (3-Dec-91 FN.S2539) Bunch of flowers with tulips (35x25cm-14x10in) s.
    board (DM 2700)

ZMURKO, Francois (1859-1910) Polish
£942 $1630   (8-Sep-91 REM.W48) Study of a Roman Patrician (93x57cm-37x22in) s.
    (P.Z 18000000)

ZOBEL, Fernando (1924-1987) Spanish
£4073 $7250   (29-Nov-91 MFA.C151/R) Interior Sevillano (79x79cm-31x31in) s.d.1967
    acrylic
£4200 $7644   (29-May-92 C444/R) Saeta 50 (46x92cm-18x36in) s.i.d.58verso
£1374 $2419   (9-Apr-92 ANS.M123/R) Serie gestos Hockey sobre hielo (24x38cm-9x15in)
    s.i.d.1979 W/C (S.P 250000)
£1522 $2602   (17-Mar-92 FER.M180/R) Orilla del Jucar (27x35cm-11x14in) s.i.d.1978verso
    ink W/C (S.P 275000)

ZOCCHI, Antonio (style) (?) ?
£2800 $4900   (28-Feb-92 C13/R) An Italianate landscape with pilgrims resting by a
    cascade (79x89cm-31x35in)

ZOCCHI, Giuseppe (attrib) (1711-1767) Italian
£6085 $10710   (11-Apr-92 AT.P28/R) Glaucus et Scylla (77x57cm-30x22in) (F.FR 60000)
£11888 $20329   (18-Mar-92 N.M476/R) Capriccio of classical ruins and two travellers
    (80x112cm-31x44in) (DM 34000)

ZOCCHI, Guglielmo (1874-?) Italian
£1792 $3100   (6-Sep-91 S.BM279/R) Seated nude with mirror and pearl necklace
    (38x30cm-15x12in) s. panel
£2700 $4833   (5-May-92 SWS415/R) Mummy's darling (71x57cm-28x22in) s.

ZOFF, A (1852-1927) Austrian
£1443 $2511   (19-Sep-91 N.M2849) Coastal landscape with cliffs, Capri
    (38x53cm-15x21in) s. i.verso board (DM 4200)

ZOFF, Alfred (1852-1927) Austrian
£1878 $3287   (19-Feb-92 D.V25/R) Rocks in water (29x39cm-11x15in) s. i.verso canvas on
    panel (A.S 38000)
£2181 $3970   (26-May-92 D.V43/R) Shipyard in Chioggia (39x50cm-15x20in) s. i.verso
    canvas on board (A.S 45000)
£2427 $4320   (28-Apr-92 D.V96/R) Promenade, Nervi (41x52cm-16x20in) s. i.verso canvas
    on panel (A.S 50000)

ZOFFANY, Johann (1733-1810) British
£10000 $19100   (15-Jul-92 S34/R) Portrait of William Henry, 1st Duke of Gloucester
                      (60x49cm-24x19in)
£1568 $2854   (12-Dec-91 L.K501 a/R) Caritas. Aeneas saving his father Anchises from
                      burning Troy s. pastel two (DM 4500)

ZOFFANY, Johann (circle) (1733-1810) British
£1047 $1800   (14-Oct-91 H.C25/R) Interior with oyster eaters (64x76cm-25x30in)

ZOFREA, Salvatore (1946-) Italian
£1145 $2062   (24-Nov-91 SY.S148) Children at play III (100x121cm-39x48in) s.
                      (A.D 2600)
£1878 $3136   (19-Aug-91 SY.ME276/R) Dancer (151x101cm-59x40in) s. (A.D 4000)
£469 $895   (29-Jun-92 AAA.S291) Reclining nude (54x77cm-21x30in) s. W/C (A.D 1200)

ZOIA (1903-) Russian/Swedish
£2846 $5209   (13-May-92 BU.S219/R) Tulips and daffodils in pottery jar
                      (61x50cm-24x20in) s. panel (S.KR 30000)

ZOIA, Krukowskaja (1903-) Russian/Swedish
£477 $839   (11-Apr-92 FAL.M428/R) Flowers in vase (40x33cm-16x13in) s. panel
                      (S.KR 5000)
£589 $1025   (13-Apr-92 AB.S286) Woman with parasol (36x21cm-14x8in) s. panel
                      (S.KR 6200)

ZOIR, Emil (1867-1936) Swedish
£527 $949   (19-Nov-91 GO.G199) Coastal landscape with sailingboat (67x81cm-26x32in)
                      s. (S.KR 5500)
£1376 $2518   (14-May-92 BU.S106/R) By evening lamplight (44x54cm-17x21in) s.d.1897 W/C
                      (S.KR 14500)

ZOIR, Hildegard (1876-1935) Swedish
£425 $751   (5-Nov-91 BA.S252/R) A gorgeous garden (42x50cm-17x20in) s. W/C
                      (S.KR 4500)

ZOLL, Kilian (1818-1860) Swedish
£3422 $6125   (16-Nov-91 FAL.M373/R) Children picking flowers (37x28cm-15x11in) s.
                      (S.KR 36000)
£15000 $28800   (10-Jul-92 C207/R) Dolgoruki and Golowin laying down arms before King
                      Charles XII of Sweden after Battle of Narva (148x207cm-58x81in)
                      s.d.1858

ZOMMER, Richard Karlovich (1866-1939) Russian
£500 $915   (5-Feb-92 ZZ.B209) Camel riders in mountainous landscape
                      (42x70cm-17x28in) s.

ZONA, Antonio (1813-1892) Italian
£4571 $8000   (19-Feb-92 CH.NY95/R) Neopolitan beauty (141x103cm-56x41in) s.d.1875

ZONARO, Fausto (1854-1929) Italian
£6000 $10200   (23-Oct-91 S237) Istanbul from the Bosphorus s. board

ZOPF, Julius (1838-1897) Austrian
£732 $1273   (19-Sep-91 D.V130/R) Landscape with stone bridge (53x79cm-21x31in) s.
                      (A.S 15000)

ZOPPI, Antonio (1860-1926) Italian
£6559 $11151   (22-Oct-91 DUR.M43/R) Escena galante (102x71cm-40x28in) s. (S.P 1200000)

ZORACH, Marguerite (1887-1968) American
£5028 $9000   (6-May-92 B.P113/R) Lonely campfire (51x76cm-20x30in) s. i.stretcher
£20468 $35000   (12-Mar-92 CH.NY236/R) The sisters (76x56cm-30x22in) s.d.1922
£2321 $3900   (14-Aug-91 B.P144/R) Mountain sunset (33x25cm-13x10in) s. W/C

ZORACH, William (1887-1966) American
£22099 $40000   (5-Dec-91 SY.NY111/R) Springtime in the High Sierras (116x100cm-46x39in)
£447 $850   (24-Jun-92 D.NY82) View of coastline (28x38cm-11x15in) s. W/C
£833 $1400   (14-Aug-91 B.P139/R) Autumn, Maine (28x38cm-11x15in) s. W/C
£838 $1500   (14-Nov-91 CE.NY429/R) Cottages near woodland path (35x46cm-14x18in)
                      s.d.1937 W/C
£1229 $2200   (14-Nov-91 CE.NY455) Family at rest (26x36cm-10x14in) s.d.15 W/C
£1862 $3500   (18-Dec-91 SY.NY182/R) New England village (25x34cm-10x13in) s.d.1917 W/C
                      graphite

ZORD, Arnold (1887-?) Hungarian
£444 $804   (19-May-92 GF.L2604/R) View of the Reformed Church in Arosa with view of
                      Schafrucken und Erzhorn (66x77cm-26x30in) s.d.1920 (S.FR 1200)

ZORKOCZY, Gyula (1873-1932) Hungarian
£499 $892   (15-Jan-92 D.V25) Rest by the edge of the field (40x50cm-16x20in) s.
                      (A.S 10000)
£727 $1323   (27-May-92 D.V644/R) Huntsmen in snow covered forest (80x120cm-31x47in)
                      s. (A.S 15000)

ZORN, Anders (1860-1920) Swedish

£3774	$6755	(7-May-92 RAS.S51/R) Coastal landscape from Mora (10x17cm-4x7in) s.d.96 panel (S.KR 40000)
£18975	$34725	(11-May-92 NOR.S33/R) Country girl (35x52cm-14x20in) s.d.1903 (S.KR 200000)
£20341	$36816	(19-May-92 AB.S4295/R) Svardsjo - portrait of girl (53x35cm-21x14in) s.d.1918 (S.KR 215000)
£36053	$65977	(11-May-92 NOR.S30/R) Woodland nymph (52x34cm-20x13in) s.d.1894 (S.KR 380000)
£48387	$88548	(11-May-92 NOR.S42/R) 'Smalandskan' - nude on beach (100x64cm-39x25in) s.d.1916 (S.KR 510000)
£49336	$90285	(14-May-92 BU.S79/R) Nude by open fire (91x60cm-36x24in) s.d.1916 (S.KR 520000)
£56604	$101321	(7-May-92 RAS.S22/R) Two nudes on rocks by the sea (52x32cm-20x13in) s.d.1902 (S.KR 600000)
£150000	$279000	(17-Jun-92 S322/R) Dalaro (101x68cm-40x27in) s.d.1892
£227704	$416698	(11-May-92 NOR.S52/R) Nude under pine trees (100x78cm-39x31in) s.d.1892 (S.KR 2400000)
£246679	$451423	(11-May-92 NOR.S22/R) After bathing (57x83cm-22x33in) s.d.1888 (S.KR 2600000)
£274725	$500000	(28-May-92 SY.NY117/R) Portrait of daughters of Ramon Subercasseaux (81x65cm-32x26in) s.d.92
£1805	$3249	(19-Nov-91 RAS.K541/R) Portrait of Mrs. Dora Wheeler Keith (20x16cm-8x6in) s. pencil dr (D.KR 20000)
£15180	$27780	(14-May-92 BU.S107/R) Miss Law (23x17cm-9x7in) s. W/C paper on panel (S.KR 160000)
£36053	$65977	(11-May-92 NOR.S27/R) The boy Falbe - young boy on bed, St Bernard nearby (67x51cm-26x20in) s.d.1884 W/C (S.KR 380000)
£58491	$104698	(7-May-92 RAS.S16/R) Spanish lady with fan (54x39cm-21x15in) s.d.84 W/C (S.KR 620000)
£86372	$156334	(3-Dec-91 AB.S4684/R) The boy Falbe, portrait of Danish Minister Falbe's two year old son (67x51cm-26x20in) s. W/C (S.KR 900000)
£283822	$513718	(19-May-92 AB.S4296/R) Boat-race, Dalaro (29x44cm-11x17in) s.d.86 W/C (S.KR 3000000)

ZORN, Anders (attrib) (1860-1920) Swedish

£1268	$2283	(19-Nov-91 FP.M82/R) Young girl disrobing behind bushes (40x60cm-16x24in) init.d.89 (C.D 2600)
£571	$1000	(3-Apr-92 S.W1980/R) Portrait of young girl (30x23cm-12x9in) bears sig. W/C pastel

ZORNES, Milford (1908-) American

£368	$700	(24-Jun-92 B.SF6521/R) South from Dana Point (51x71cm-20x28in) s.d.68 W/C
£368	$700	(24-Jun-92 B.SF6523/R) El Salvador (56x72cm-22x28in) s.d.79 W/C
£395	$750	(24-Jun-92 B.SF6520/R) Mining town (55x74cm-22x29in) s.d.50 W/C
£500	$950	(24-Jun-92 B.SF6525/R) Crater Lake (55x71cm-22x28in) s.d.64 s.verso W/C
£579	$1100	(24-Jun-92 B.SF6524/R) Arch, Laguna (51x71cm-20x28in) s.d.73 s.verso W/C
£734	$1300	(12-Feb-92 B.SF629/R) Rocky coast (49x71cm-19x28in) s.d.70 W/C
£791	$1400	(12-Feb-92 B.SF628/R) Treasure Island (49x71cm-19x28in) s.d.70 W/C
£895	$1700	(24-Jun-92 B.SF6522/R) Morro Beach (53x74cm-21x29in) s.d.61 W/C

ZSCHIMMER, Emil (1842-1917) German

£879	$1494	(24-Oct-91 D.V57/R) Heath landscape, autumn (87x145cm-34x57in) s.d.1911 (A.S 18000)

ZUBER, Henri (1844-1909) French

£1420	$2499	(10-Apr-92 AGS.P37/R) Les rochers (40x59cm-16x23in) s. (F.FR 14000)
£8615	$15422	(19-Jan-92 CSC.P98/R) Jonque chinoise dans la baie de Ting-Hae (142x200cm-56x79in) s. (F.FR 84000)

ZUBER-BUHLER, Fritz (1822-1896) Swiss

£1203	$2093	(18-Sep-91 N.M760/R) Girl washing feet in tub (34x28cm-13x11in) s. panel (DM 3500)
£2174	$3913	(22-Nov-91 EA.Z739/R) Girl with cat (33x24cm-13x9in) s. (S.FR 5500)
£3846	$7000	(26-May-92 CE.NY47/R) Mother and child (147x113cm-58x44in) s.
£4314	$7722	(15-Nov-91 ZOF.Z1929/R) Girl by window (45x36cm-18x14in) s. i.stretcher (S.FR 11000)
£4651	$8000	(17-Oct-91 SY.NY269 a/R) La toilette (35x27cm-14x11in) s.
£5464	$10000	(17-May-92 DU.E1119/R) Mother and children with nurse (71x61cm-28x24in) s. panel

ZUBIAURRE, R de (1882-1969) Spanish

£663	$1246	(3-Jan-92 DUR.M20/R) Tamborilero (30x25cm-12x10in) bears sig. (S.P 120000)

ZUBIAURRE, Ramon de (1882-1969) Spanish

£610	$1079	(12-Feb-92 ANS.M159/R) Retrato de nina (55x46cm-22x18in) s. (S.P 110000)
£2738	$5230	(2-Jul-92 ANS.M51/R) Retrato de Dama (84x65cm-33x26in) s. (S.P 500000)

ZUBRICZKY, Lorand (1869-?) Hungarian

£1764	$3139	(28-Apr-92 RAS.K145/R) Hunting party resting by foot of cliff (60x91cm-24x36in) s.d.93 (D.KR 20000)
£3713	$6646	(17-Nov-91 FB.P175/R) Scene de parc (37x48cm-15x19in) s.d.1909 panel (F.FR 36500)

ZUCCARELLI, Francesco (1702-1788) Italian

£25000	$45500	(13-Dec-91 C96/R) Washerwoman and beggars by fortified bridge, town beyond (52x69cm-20x27in)
£38268	$65055	(24-Oct-91 D.P20/R) Caprices animes (66x84cm-26x33in) (F.FR 380000)
£40733	$74134	(28-May-92 F.M117/R) Paesaggio arcadico con pastori presso un torrente (54x70cm-21x28in) (I.L 90000000)
£57613	$104280	(7-Dec-91 CH.MO6/R) Paysage avec des bergers pres d'une riviere (113x143cm-44x56in) (F.FR 560000)
£60000	$115200	(7-Jul-92 PH90/R) Traveller and peasants at well in Italianate wooded river landscape (70x103cm-28x41in)
£4000	*$7280*	*(11-Dec-91 PH167/R) Elegant figures fishing from river bank (18x31cm-7x12in) pen chk wash htd.white*
£6500	*$12480*	*(7-Jul-92 C207/R) Wooded river landscape with fisherfolk, drover and town beyond (20x31cm-8x12in) mono.i.verso chk pen wash htd white*

ZUCCARELLI, Francesco (after) (18th C) Italian

| £2484 | $4247 | (18-Mar-92 D.V224/R) Italian landscape with riders (70x101cm-28x40in) (A.S 50000) |

ZUCCARELLI, Francesco (attrib) (1702-1788) Italian

| £5200 | $9984 | (9-Jul-92 CSK280) Stormy Italianate landscape with drover, cattle and sheep (39x51cm-15x20in) |
| £30000 | $52500 | (2-Apr-92 CSK91/R) Italianate river landscapes with anglers and other figures on river bank (57x42cm-22x17in) pair |

ZUCCARELLI, Francesco (style) (18th C) Italian

£1000	$1830	(12-May-92 SWS751/R) Capriccio landscape with figures beside lakeside buildings (36x85cm-14x33in)
£1211	$2083	(16-Oct-91 AT.P3) Abraham et les trois anges (37x59cm-15x23in) (F.FR 12000)
£1500	$2745	(12-May-92 SWS656/R) Landscape with figures on path by stream (71x104cm-28x41in)
£1852	$3315	(14-Nov-91 CH.AM103) Italianate river landscape at sunset with peasants resting by wood (72x92cm-28x36in) (D.FL 6000)
£3500	$6300	(21-Nov-91 C46/R) Italianate landscapes with ostler teaching horse. Animals leaving village (28x14cm-11x6in) pair
£5247	$9392	(12-Nov-91 SY.AM32/R) Maids in Italianate landscape (83x117cm-33x46in) (D.FL 17000)
£6686	$11500	(10-Oct-91 SY.NY194/R) Rocky landscape with shepherds by a winding river (49x75cm-19x30in)
£8200	$14596	(30-Oct-91 S20/R) Pastoral landscape with figures and cattle (36x55cm-14x22in) pair
£12500	$24000	(8-Jul-92 S90/R) Mountainous river landscape with figures fishing (55x71cm-22x28in)

ZUCCARO, Federico (1540-1609) Italian

£3800	*$7296*	*(7-Jul-92 C130/R) St John the Baptist preaching (23x17cm-9x7in) chk pen wash*
£5000	*$9600*	*(7-Jul-92 C18/R) The Submission of the Emperor Frederick Barbarossa to Pope Alexander III (53x46cm-21x18in) chk pen wash oiled paper*
£5000	*$9600*	*(7-Jul-92 C19/R) Fra Stefano, Abbot of Camaldoli as St Romuald (27x16cm-11x6in) i. chk*
£5028	*$9000*	*(14-Jan-92 SY.NY3/R) Allegorical figure, seated, holding book, other figures seated behind (22x17cm-9x7in) i. pen wash oval*

ZUCCARO, Federico (attrib) (1540-1609) Italian

| *£1400* | *$2436* | *(13-Apr-92 S152/R) Copy of Masaccio's Sagra (8x18cm-3x7in) bears i.verso black chk* |
| *£4749* | *$8500* | *(14-Jan-92 SY.NY9/R) St. Agnes (27x17cm-11x7in) pen htd white over black chk* |

ZUCCARO, Federico (circle) (1540-1609) Italian

| *£2800* | *$4872* | *(14-Apr-92 C92/R) The Entombment (32x25cm-13x10in) i. chk pen wash* |

ZUCCARO, Taddeo (1529-1566) Italian

| *£2400* | *$4368* | *(10-Dec-91 C115/R) Abstinence (20x7cm-8x3in) i. ink wash* |

ZUCCARO, Taddeo (attrib) (1529-1566) Italian

| *£1542* | *$2945* | *(3-Jul-92 SD.P75) La presentation du Butin de guerre (26x40cm-10x16in) ink wash htd white (F.FR 15000)* |

ZUCCHERI, Luigi (1904-1974) Italian

| £1390 | $2475 | (29-Nov-91 F.F165) Pesce nel laghetto di montagna (25x30cm-10x12in) s. panel (I.L 3000000) |
| £1529 | $2722 | (29-Nov-91 F.F164/R) Tartaruga (25x30cm-10x12in) s. panel (I.L 3300000) |

ZUCCHI, Antonio (1726-1795) Italian

| £700 | $1225 | (3-Apr-92 C79/R) Hebe (45x35cm-18x14in) paper on canvas |
| *£1900* | *$3648* | *(7-Jul-92 C212/R) Adoration of the Shepherds (31x25cm-12x10in) chk pen wash htd white* |

ZUCCHI, Jacopo (c.1541-1590) Italian

| *£10000* | *$18200* | *(10-Dec-91 C122/R) The Calydonian boar hunt (23x36cm-9x14in) blk.chk.ink wash* |

ZUCKERBERG, Stanley (1919-) American?
£674 $1200   (2-Nov-91 IH.NY64/R) Man drying woman's tears (38x56cm-15x22in) s. gouache

ZUGEL, Heinrich von (1850-1941) German
£976 $1865   (1-Jul-92 FB.P77) Le jeune veau (26x39cm-10x15in) s. (F.FR 9500)
£1020 $1733   (23-Oct-91 GD.B1353) Ram mono.d.94 i.verso panel (S.FR 2600)
£1404 $2400   (13-Mar-92 FN.S3032/R) Bekass II, dog seated (40x30cm-16x12in) s. board (DM 4000)
£1754 $3000   (13-Mar-92 FN.S3031/R) Dead pheasant (20x29cm-8x11in) s. (DM 5000)
£5361 $9810   (2-Jun-92 FN.S2821/R) Sheep on hillside (21x7cm-8x3in) panel (DM 15600)
£6000 $10620   (14-Feb-92 C66/R) The artist's dachsunds (46x69cm-18x27in) s.d.1909verso
£8741 $15559   (29-Nov-91 ZEL.L1125) Cattle resting (40x54cm-16x21in) s.d.1913 (DM 25000)
£11189 $19916   (26-Nov-91 KF.M282) Cattle grazing (36x46cm-14x18in) s.indis.d.190. (DM 32000)
£12195 $22195   (11-Dec-91 N.M673/R) Shepherd with flock beneath trees (48x70cm-19x28in) s. (DM 35000)
£13572 $24702   (27-May-92 D.V571/R) Sheep (43x42cm-17x17in) s. (A.S 280000)
£18900 $34588   (2-Jun-92 FN.S2820/R) Sheep watering in landscape (16x25cm-6x10in) s.i. panel (DM 55000)
£19298 $33000   (13-Mar-92 FN.S3030/R) Sheep by gate in landscape and hills beyond, spring (60x80cm-24x31in) s.d.1928 (DM 55000)
£35211 $63732   (3-Dec-91 FN.S2540/R) Shepherd girl with sheep by gate before shed (87x71cm-34x28in) s. (DM 100000)
£45714 $80000   (20-Feb-92 SY.NY30/R) Young shepherd (72x95cm-28x37in) s.i.
£55233 $95000   (16-Oct-91 CH.NY126/R) At the stable door (35x54cm-14x21in) s.i. panel
£55749 $101463   (11-Dec-91 N.M672/R) Shepherd with flock (92x122cm-36x48in) s.d.1931 (DM 160000)

ZUGNO, Francesco (1709-1787) Italian
£2652 $4800   (21-May-92 CH.NY137/R) Vision of Saint Teresa of Avila (66x34cm-26x13in)
£3953 $7036   (29-Nov-91 GAB.G3116/R) Le Martyre de Saint-Laurent (91x45cm-36x18in) (S.FR 10000)

ZUGNO, Francesco (attrib) (1709-1787) Italian
£3462 $6612   (15-Jul-92 CH.S764/R) Apollo and Muses - modello for ceiling decoration (40x55cm-16x22in) shaped (A.D 9000)

ZUHR, Hugo (1895-1971) Swedish
£584 $1039   (28-Oct-91 AB.S269) Fruit farm, Greek landscape (49x60cm-19x24in) s.d.30 (S.KR 6200)
£902 $1570   (13-Apr-92 AB.S288) Greek landscape with wines (64x80cm-25x31in) mono. (S.KR 9500)

ZUIDEMA BROOS, Jan Jacob (1833-1877) Dutch
£1576 $2789   (22-Apr-92 CH.AM302/R) Royal arrival (32x41cm-13x16in) s.d.1877 W/C htd.white (D.FL 5200)

ZUKOWSKI, Stanislaw see JOUKOVSKI, Stanislav

ZULOAGA, Ignacio (1870-1945) Spanish
£14000 $25480   (29-May-92 C385/R) Fish, maize, vegetables and herbs in basket leaning against wall (54x72cm-21x28in) s.
£220000 $400400   (29-May-92 C408/R) Baile Gitano, en una terraza de Granada (198x200cm-78x79in) s.

ZULOAGA, Ignacio (attrib) (1870-1945) Spanish
£8201 $14598   (28-Apr-92 RAS.K97 a/R) Aquadores (60x100cm-24x39in) i. (D.KR 93000)

ZULOW, Franz von (1883-1963) Austrian
£1396 $2499   (15-Jan-92 D.V93/R) Still life with earthenware (29x32cm-11x13in) s.d.31 board (A.S 28000)
£437 $778   (28-Apr-92 D.V56/R) Hansel and Gretel (26x26cm-10x10in) pen brush indian ink W/C (A.S 9000)
£485 $864   (28-Apr-92 D.V55/R) Rose (21x20cm-8x8in) s. pen indian ink W/C (A.S 10000)
£589 $1119   (25-Jun-92 D.V694) Chapel (14x23cm-6x9in) s.d.1920 brush pen indian ink W/C (A.S 12000)
£727 $1323   (26-May-92 D.V30/R) Orchard (29x18cm-11x7in) s. paste technique (A.S 15000)
£874 $1555   (28-Apr-92 D.V147/R) Dream city II (35x47cm-14x19in) i.verso pen indian ink col.pencil chk (A.S 18000)
£883 $1678   (25-Jun-92 D.V695) House by telephone mast. Village view (17x23cm-7x9in) s.d.1919 mixed media pair (A.S 18000)
£890 $1557   (19-Feb-92 D.V36) Heads (29x44cm-11x17in) s.d.1919 paste technique (A.S 18000)
£890 $1557   (19-Feb-92 D.V35/R) Moonlit landscape (21x35cm-8x14in) s.d.1919 mixed media (A.S 18000)
£1066 $1941   (26-May-92 D.V96/R) Cow shed (23x28cm-9x11in) mixed media (A.S 22000)
£1214 $2160   (28-Apr-92 D.V54/R) Village (20x20cm-8x8in) s.indis.i.d.1915 pen indian ink W/C (A.S 25000)
£1214 $2160   (28-Apr-92 D.V148/R) Courtyard (34x49cm-13x19in) s.d.24 W/C (A.S 25000)
£1357 $2470   (26-May-92 D.V94/R) Outside the shop. Village street (20x17cm-8x7in) s.d.1920 mixed media two (A.S 28000)

ZULOW, Franz von (1883-1963) Austrian-cont.
£1357 $2470   (26-May-92 D.V95/R) Tableware (29x39cm-11x15in) s.d.36 brush indian ink
                       W/C (A.S 28000)
£2483 $4419   (28-Nov-91 D.V29/R) Children, chicken, pigs (44x32cm-17x13in) s.d.1903
                       pen W/C (A.S 50000)

ZUMPF, Christoph Ludwig (18th C) ?
£1563 $2689   (10-Oct-91 D.V327/R) Trompe l'oeuil of stag resting in woodlands
                       (13x18cm-5x7in) s.d.1778 gouache (A.S 32000)

ZUMSANDE, Josef (1806-1865) German
£728 $1296   (29-Apr-92 D.V730/R) Portrait of young woman wearing shawl
                       (15x12cm-6x5in) s. W/C ivory (A.S 15000)

ZUND, Robert (1827-1909) Swiss
£2778 $5028   (19-May-92 GF.L2277/R) Study of tree (33x25cm-13x10in) mono (S.FR 7500)
£8889 $16089   (19-May-92 GF.L2274/R) Haslistrand (24x44cm-9x17in) s.d.1853 (S.FR 24000)
£17188 $30422   (5-Nov-91 GF.L2250/R) Schellenmatt (13x17cm-5x7in) mono. (S.FR 44000)
£29197 $52263   (6-May-92 GD.B1383/R) View of lake and Pilatus from Vorder-Meggen
                       (74x99cm-29x39in) s. (S.FR 80000)

ZUND, Robert (attrib) (1827-1909) Swiss
£781 $1383   (5-Nov-91 GF.L2615/R) Wooded landscape with stream (11x13cm-4x5in) bears
                       sig. grisaille canvas on panel (S.FR 2000)

ZUND, Robert (school) (1827-1909) Swiss
£692 $1245   (19-Nov-91 GS.B3345) Wooded landscape (36x31cm-14x12in) panel (S.FR 1750)

ZUNIGA, Francisco (1913-) Costa Rican
£1657 $3000   (19-May-92 SY.NY184/R) Desnudo de frente (65x50cm-26x20in) s.d.1972 chl
                       pastel
£2210 $4000   (19-May-92 SY.NY97/R) Mujer acostada (58x89cm-23x35in) s.d.1973 pastel
                       chl
£2229 $3900   (22-Feb-92 YFA.M218/R) Three seated women by candlelight
                       (56x74cm-22x29in) mono.d.1968 chl
£2326 $4000   (12-Oct-91 SY.NY193/R) Seated old woman (50x65cm-20x26in) s.d.1965 pen
                       board
£2333 $4200   (19-Nov-91 CH.NY106/R) Mestiza dormida (56x72cm-22x28in) s.d.1976 chl
£2762 $5000   (18-May-92 CH.NY158/R) Desnudo reclinado (50x72cm-20x28in) s.d.1978 chl
£2941 $5000   (25-Oct-91 S.W2768/R) Mujer sentada (56x74cm-22x29in) s.d.1977 chl htd
                       pastel
£3039 $5500   (18-May-92 CH.NY159/R) Mujer sentada (50x65cm-20x26in) s.d.1964 chl
                       sanguine
£3052 $5250   (12-Oct-91 SY.NY192/R) Study of women (50x65cm-20x26in) s.d.1966 chl
                       pastel
£3235 $5500   (23-Oct-91 B.SF3785/R) Mujer sentada (61x48cm-24x19in) s.d.1969 chl
£3315 $6000   (19-May-92 SY.NY95/R) Mujer sentada (50x65cm-20x26in) s.d.1966 chl
£3333 $6000   (18-Nov-91 SY.NY90/R) Seis comadres (50x65cm-20x26in) s.d.1965 chl pastel
                       paper laid down on board
£3333 $6000   (19-Nov-91 CH.NY195/R) Dos mujeres sentadas (56x76cm-22x30in) s.d.1977
                       chl
£3867 $7000   (18-May-92 CH.NY160/R) Mujer con naranjas (49x65cm-19x26in) s.d.1967
                       sanguine chl
£4118 $7000   (23-Oct-91 B.SF3786/R) Dos mujeres (48x63cm-19x25in) s.d.1969 chl pastel
£4167 $7500   (18-Nov-91 SY.NY119/R) Mujer sentada (50x70cm-20x28in) s.d.1979 pastel
£4444 $8000   (19-Nov-91 CH.NY197/R) Sin titulo (48x67cm-19x26in) s.d.1979 pastel chl
£4444 $8000   (18-Nov-91 SY.NY118 a/R) Tehuana en una silla (50x65cm-20x26in) s.d.1972
                       chl pastel
£4696 $8500   (18-May-92 CH.NY97/R) Chamulas (67x101cm-26x40in) s.d.1981 chl pastel
£4722 $8500   (18-Nov-91 SY.NY163/R) Dos mujeres (65x50cm-26x20in) s.d.1963 ink W/C
£4972 $9000   (18-May-92 CH.NY98/R) Madre y Nino (65x48cm-26x19in) s.d.1966 W/C crayon
                       white chk
£5556 $10000   (18-Nov-91 SY.NY119 a/R) Dos mujeres sentadas (50x65cm-20x26in) s.d.1972
                       chl W/C

ZUOREN, Wu (1908-) Chinese
£2367 $4142   (30-Mar-92 CH.HK376/R) Two pandas (39x36cm-15x14in) s.d.1972 ink scroll
                       (HK.D 32000)
£8136 $14238   (30-Mar-92 CH.HK229/R) Eagles perched on cliff (97x85cm-38x33in) s.d.1990
                       ink W/C scroll (HK.D 110000)
£11095 $19416   (30-Mar-92 CH.HK114/R) Various subjects (25x32cm-10x13in) s. ink W/C
                       album 11 leaves various artists (HK.D 150000)
£13314 $23299   (30-Mar-92 CH.HK123/R) Camels (57x127cm-22x50in) s.d.1987 ink scroll
                       (HK.D 180000)
£13314 $23299   (30-Mar-92 CH.HK109/R) Camels (129x68cm-51x27in) s.d.1987 ink W/C scroll
                       (HK.D 180000)

ZURBARAN, Francisco (1598-1664) Spanish
£70000 $127400   (29-May-92 C319/R) Ruy Velazquez (185x94cm-73x37in)
£145000 $263900   (29-May-92 C318/R) St Agnes (140x106cm-55x42in)

ZURBARAN, Francisco (circle) (1598-1664) Spanish
£1531 $2709   (10-Feb-92 GL.P44/R) Saint Francois adorant la croix (140x53cm-55x21in)
                       panel (F.FR 15000)

ZURBARAN, Francisco (studio) (1598-1664) Spanish
£10465 $18000   (10-Oct-91 SY.NY5/R) Saint Margaret (84x56cm-33x22in)

ZURBARAN, Francisco (style) (1598-1664) Spanish
£750 $1350   (21-Nov-91 CSK17) The Madonna Immaculate with Christ (146x102cm-57x40in)
£3300 $5742   (13-Sep-91 C109/R) Warrior martyr saint (112x86cm-44x34in)
£3511 $6250   (22-Jan-92 SY.NY190/R) Still life with pears (60x80cm-24x31in)

ZURBARAN, Juan de (1620-1649) Spanish
£80000 $145600   (29-May-92 C317/R) Figs on pewter plate on ledge (34x42cm-13x17in)

ZURCHER, Antonie Frederik (1825-1876) Dutch
£549 $1021   (16-Jun-92 VN.R331) Mother and child in a Larens interior
                      (22x31cm-9x12in) s. panel (D.FL 1800)

ZURCHER, Frederik Willem (1835-1894) Dutch
£1463 $2546   (19-Sep-91 D.V210/R) Shepherd with cattle (11x13cm-4x5in) s. panel
                      (A.S 30000)

ZURICH SCHOOL, 17th C Swiss
£3800 $6916   (10-Dec-91 PH144/R) Portrait of lady, wearing ornate headpiece and dress,
                      holding carnation (91x76cm-36x30in)

ZURKINDEN, Irene (1909-1987) Swiss
£588 $1000   (23-Oct-91 GD.B824/R) Woman wearing big hat beside painting
                      (49x34cm-19x13in) s. indian ink W/C (S.FR 1500)
£665 $1238   (19-Jun-92 ZOF.Z2151/R) Horse and rider performing in circus
                      (20x28cm-8x11in) indian ink pen (S.FR 1750)

ZURSTRASSEN, Yves (20th C) Belgian?
£770 $1393   (3-Dec-91 C.A488) Extase (125x175cm-49x69in) s.d.1988 (B.FR 45000)
£1112 $2013   (3-Dec-91 C.A490/R) Composition (200x215cm-79x85in) s.d.1985 verso
                      (B.FR 65000)

ZUSI, A (?) ?
£1620 $2900   (15-Nov-91 DM.D2015/R) Russian troika pulling officer (20x25cm-8x10in)
                      s.indis.d.

ZUSTERS, Reinis (1918-) Australian
£1586 $2855   (19-Nov-91 JRL.S351) Sydney (122x211cm-48x83in) s. board (A.D 3600)

ZWAAN, Cornelisz C (1882-1964) Dutch
£2049 $3750   (17-May-92 DU.E1136/R) Story time (66x91cm-26x36in) s.

ZWAAN, Cornelisz C (attrib) (1882-1964) Dutch
£789 $1500   (22-Jun-92 SG.M629) Mother and children in an interior (71x56cm-28x22in)
                      s.
£842 $1600   (22-Jun-92 SG.M628/R) The sewing lesson (51x38cm-20x15in) s.

ZWART, Arie (1903-1981) Dutch
£547 $952   (17-Sep-91 CH.AM231) Aan de plassen bij Vinkeveen (40x80cm-16x31in) s. i.
                      verso (D.FL 1800)
£610 $1134   (16-Jun-92 VN.R327/R) Ducks on a river in a polder landscape
                      (48x71cm-19x28in) s. (D.FL 2000)
£612 $1083   (5-Nov-91 SY.AM361) Boats in harbour (48x69cm-19x27in) s.d.38 (D.FL 2000)
£642 $1143   (29-Oct-91 VN.R318/R) View of farmhouse with pond (40x50cm-16x20in) s.
                      (D.FL 2100)
£734 $1306   (29-Oct-91 VN.R320) Farmhouse (94x93cm-37x37in) s. (D.FL 2400)
£870 $1504   (24-Mar-92 VN.R107/R) Mother child before a farmhouse (50x60cm-20x24in)
                      s. (D.FL 2800)

ZWART, Willem de (1862-1931) Dutch
£586 $1026   (18-Feb-92 CH.AM66) Farm in landscape (29x114cm-11x45in) s. panel
                      (D.FL 1900)
£612 $1083   (5-Nov-91 SY.AM332) Summer landscape (13x21cm-5x8in) s.panel (D.FL 2000)
£917 $1624   (5-Nov-91 SY.AM142) Polder landscape with farmhouse on sunny day
                      (25x43cm-10x17in) init. panel (D.FL 3000)
£1835 $3248   (5-Nov-91 SY.AM49/R) Peeling potatoes (22x23cm-9x9in) s. panel
                      (D.FL 6000)
£1970 $3486   (22-Apr-92 CH.AM37/R) A cow-market (39x50cm-15x20in) s. (D.FL 6500)
£3636 $6436   (22-Apr-92 CH.AM166/R) Cattle on a farm yard (33x48cm-13x19in) s. panel
                      (D.FL 12000)
£20795 $36807   (5-Nov-91 SY.AM120/R) Carriages on Loosduinseweg, Hague (54x98cm-21x39in)
                      s. (D.FL 68000)

ZWENGAUER, Anton (1810-1884) German
£893 $1555   (18-Sep-91 N.M763/R) Moor landscape, evening (10x26cm-4x10in) s. board
                      (DM 2600)
£1056 $1912   (3-Dec-91 FN.S2541/R) Fishermen in boat gathering nets in wooded lake
                      landscape, evening (44x103cm-17x41in) s. (DM 3000)
£2062 $3588   (18-Sep-91 N.M762/R) Sunset in high mountains with view of valley
                      (73x88cm-29x35in) s.d.1850 (DM 6000)

ZWENGAUER, Anton (younger) (1850-1928) German
£839 $1452   (28-Mar-92 BOD.P1048) Heath landscape with ducks (16x33cm-6x13in)
                      s.i.1891 board (DM 2400)

ZWILLER, Marie Augustin (1850-1939) French
£2261 $3889   (4-Mar-92 AT.P214/R) Modele au drap rouge (26x35cm-10x14in) s.
                      (F.FR 22000)

ZYL, Gerard Pietersz van (1607-1665) Dutch
£4500 $8190   (10-Dec-91 PH83/R) Elegant women and courtiers seated around table on
                      terrace (70x86cm-28x34in)

ZYSSET, Philippe Aurele (1899-) Swiss
£586 $1037   (5-Nov-91 GF.L2600/R) By the bridge (65x93cm-26x37in) s. (S.FR 1500)

Index

Sculpture, bronzes and three dimensional
works of art sold during the auction season
are covered by this book.

Sculptors A - Z

STARTING PRICES

Sculpture or 3 dimensional - £750

A P M (?) ?
£1411 $2498   (7-Nov-91 AT.P78) Monkey (20cm-8in) s. pat.bronze (F.FR 14000)

AARONS, George (1896-1980) American
£1600 $2736   (20-Mar-92 S159/R) Martha Graham (35cm-14in) s.d.1941 num.4/12 brown
              pat.bronze i.Modern Art
£2072 $3750   (24-May-92 JRB.C9/R) Female nude (86cm-34in) s.d.1930 green pat bronze

ABAKANOWICZ, Magdalena (1930-) Polish
£2314 $3980   (7-Oct-91 RY.P10/R) The back bronze (F.FR 23000)

ADAM, Francois Gaspard Balthasar (style) (1710-1761) French
£4500 $8640   (7-Jul-92 C75/R) Apollo holding drapery and wreath standing by altar
              (72cm-28in) marble

ADAMS-ACTON, John (1831-1910) British
£1500 $2610   (17-Sep-91 PH268/R) Bust of Pharaoh's daughter wearing headband, earrings
              and necklace (67cm-26in) s.i.d.1864 marble

ADAMSSON, Bo Ake (1941-) Swedish
£1139 $2083   (13-May-92 BU.S227/R) The dancer (29cm-11in) init.num.32/70, gilded
              bronze (S.KR 12000)

ADOLPH (?) ?
£850 $1624   (2-Jul-92 CSK125/R) Young girl walking holding hem of dress in right hand
              (28cm-11in) s. silvered bronze onyx base

AGAM, Yaacov (1928-) Israeli
£1221 $2234   (17-May-92 GL.P252/R) Sens - presence - sens (20cm-8in) s.num.131/245
              metal plexiglass (F.FR 12000)
£1676 $3000   (7-May-92 SY.NY253/R) Beating heart - moods (14cm-6in) gold plated brass
              nine elements
£2762 $4750   (12-Oct-91 SY.NY368/R) Multispace star of David (45cm-18in) s.d.1969
              polished steel
£14451 $25000   (3-Oct-91 SY.NY31/R) Open space (274cm-108in) stainless steel sculpture
              in four parts

AGASIAS (after) (1st C B.C.) Greek
£7602 $13000   (13-Mar-92 WOL.C635 a/R) The Borghese gladiator (170cm-67in) bronze
              Cast.c.1780-1810

AGRICOLA, Rudolf Alexander (1912-) Russian
£2921 $5345   (3-Jun-92 L.K11/R) Girl seated (45x28x40cm-18x11x16in) s.d.1933 bronze
              (DM 8500)
£7018 $12632   (21-Nov-91 L.K5/R) Boy standing (103cm-41in) i.d.1937 bronze
              st.f.G.Schmake Dusseldorf (DM 20000)

AHEARN, John (20th C) American
£3911 $7000   (7-May-92 SY.NY218/R) Clyde with folded arms (66x51cm-26x20in) painted
              cast plaster

AITKEN, Robert Ingersoll (1878-1949) American
£1714 $3000   (26-Sep-91 CH.NY127/R) Bookends of reclining figures (19cm-7in) mono.i.
              green/brown pat.bronze f.i. pair
£2632 $4500   (11-Mar-92 SY.NY90/R) Allegorical group of satyr and mermaid (69cm-27in)
              i. brown pat.bronze f.i.Roman Bronze Works

AIZELIN, Eugene (1821-1902) French
£1345 $2300   (13-Mar-92 WOL.C762 a/R) Bust of a woman (56cm-22in) s.f.Barbedienne
              bronze br.pat.

AKELEY, Carl Ethan (1864-1926) American
£2000 $3500   (25-Sep-91 SY.NY60/R) Stung (23cm-9in) i. dark brown pat.bronze f.i.Roman
              Bronze Works

AKERS, Benjamin Paul (1825-1861) American
£1061 $1900   (14-Nov-91 CE.NY239) Bust of gentleman (58cm-23in) s. white marble

ALECHINSKY, Pierre (1927-) Belgian
£926 $1676   (4-Dec-91 LD.P99/R) Visage (24cm-9in) s.num.98/150 gilded bronze
              Cast.Valsuani (F.FR 9000)

ALFIERI, Edoardo (19th C) Italian
£7500 $13050   (17-Sep-91 PH270/R) Figure of naked maiden holding drape. Naked maiden
              with small boy s. marble pair

ALGARDI, Alessandro (circle) (1602-1654) Italian
£4190 $7500   (14-Jan-92 CH.NY141/R) Figures formed as mounts - partially draped seated
              male figures (36cm-14in) black patin. copper pair
£5607 $10428   (19-Jun-92 CN.P116/R) Buste de femme, les cheveux noues (60cm-24in)
              terracotta (F.FR 55000)

ALLEGRAIN (17/18th C) French
£928 $1587   (9-Mar-92 AT.P254/R) Baigneuse (85cm-33in) s. Carrare marble (F.FR 9000)

ALLEGRAIN, C G (1710-1795) French
£819 $1400   (9-Mar-92 B.LA740) Figure of Venus (53cm-21in) i. dark brown pat.bronze
                         f.i.F.Barbedienne

ALLEN, Charles John (1863-1956) British
£4000 $7240   (21-May-92 C61/R) Cupid and mermaid standing on rocky pedestal
                         (53cm-21in) c.1890 bronze on marble socle

ALLIOT, L C E (1877-1967) French
£1249 $2223   (27-Nov-91 CB.P247/R) La cymbaliere (33cm-13in) blue gilded pat.bronze
                         ivory base onyx marble (F.FR 12200)

ALLIOT, Lucien Charles Edouard (1877-1967) French
£995 $1771   (21-Jan-92 DUR.M269/R) Pierrot (36cm-14in) s. gilded bronze ivory on
                         marble base (S.P 180000)
£1224 $2117   (25-Mar-92 KM.K1787/R) Phaleno (68cm-27in) i. bronze (DM 3500)

ALONIS, D (?) Belgian
£766 $1425   (16-Jun-92 GM.B1080/R) Chatelaine sur escalier d'Albatre s. bronze ivory
                         (B.FR 46000)

ALONZO, D (20th C) French
£1640 $2788   (23-Oct-91 DUR.M647/R) Aguadora oriental (20cm-8in) s. polychrome bronze
                         ivory (S.P 300000)

ALONZO, Dominique de (20th C) French
£1000 $1830   (12-May-92 SWS370/R) Flamenco dancer (30cm-12in) gilt-bronze ivory
£2200 $3762   (20-May-92 S196/R) At the top of the steps (41cm-16in) s. gilt bronze
                         ivory
£2226 $4050   (12-Dec-91 D.V132/R) Half nude young girl standing (27cm-11in) s.num.6590
                         gold bronze ivory st.foundry (A.S 45000)

ALVIANI, Getulio (1939-) Italian
£1358 $2471   (26-May-92 SY.MI14/R) Composizione (70x70x23cm-28x28x9in) metal mirror
                         (I.L 3000000)

AMBROSI, Gustinus (1893-1975) Austrian
£1689 $3006   (27-Nov-91 BL.P214) Le desespoir (40cm-16in) s. pat.bronze (F.FR 16500)
£13000 $22230   (20-Mar-92 S200/R) Phaedrus (180cm-71in) s.d.1953 green pat.bronze

AMERICAN SCHOOL, 19th C
£2105 $4000   (23-Jun-92 CE.NY84/R) Stag (163x139cm-64x55in) painted iron

ANDRAUN, F (19th C) ?
£847 $1500   (13-Feb-92 SY.NY48/R) Figure of Diana (102cm-40in) i. marble

ANDRE, Carl (1935-) American
£8000 $13840   (26-Mar-92 S76/R) Copper-copper dipole - N-S (100x100cm-39x39in) copper
£19553 $35000   (14-Nov-91 SY.NY183/R) Cascade (175x240x490cm-69x94x193in) gas-beton
                         blocks 550 unit stepped stack
£55866 $100000   (13-Nov-91 SY.NY34/R) 8003 Monchengladbach Square
                         (1x300x300cm-0x118x118in) hot-rolled steel 36-unit square
£86592 $155000   (13-Nov-91 SY.NY103/R) Inverted henge, Meditation on the year 1960
                         (180x150x30cm-71x59x12in) timber s.i.d.1971 on certificate

ANDRES VILELLA, Mariano (1930-) ?
£1125 $2058   (3-Feb-92 HH.P30/R) Sans titre (48x27x18cm-19x11x7in) s. Belgian
                         blk.marble (F.FR 11000)

ANDRIESSEN, Mari Silvester (1892-?) Dutch
£848 $1536   (19-May-92 CH.AM106) Musicians (11cm-4in) mono. bronze (D.FL 2800)
£988 $1798   (11-Dec-91 CH.AM69) Musicians (11cm-4in) mono. bronze (D.FL 3200)
£1698 $3090   (11-Dec-91 CH.AM71/R) Seated nude (17cm-7in) mono. sandstone (D.FL 5500)
£2160 $3932   (12-Dec-91 SY.AM109/R) Adriaan Roland Holst (27cm-11in) mono. bronze
                         (D.FL 7000)

ANFRIE, Charles (19th C) French
£1180 $2100   (30-Apr-92 CE.NY42/R) Allegorical group - Esperance (75cm-30in) i.
                         gilt-bronze

ANGHIK, Abraham Apakark (1951-) North American
£688 $1259   (1-Jun-92 W.T855) Spirit polar bear reaching for the sky (69cm-27in)
                         mottled soapstone (C.D 1500)

ANGLES, Joaquin (20th C) French
£1102 $1918   (19-Sep-91 GK.Z537/R) Premier Triomphe (51cm-20in) green brown pat.bronze
                         (S.FR 2800)

ANGLO-ITALIAN SCHOOL, 19th C
£3500 $6720   (7-Jul-92 C80/R) Bust of La Zingara crowned by bejewelled tiara and veil
                         (55cm-22in) i. marble

ANGUIER, Michel (1612-1686) French
£34156 $64897   (26-Jun-92 AGS.P147/R) Pluton et Cerbere (56cm-22in) brown pat.bronze
                         (F.FR 332000)

ANGUIER, Michel (circle) (1612-1686) French
£112637 $205000   (26-May-92 SY.NY117/R) Figure of Jupiter, thunderbolts in raised right hand (72cm-28in) rich olive-brown pat.bronze

ANTES, Horst (1936-) German
£2105 $3789   (19-Nov-91 L.K530) Figure 1000 (220x90x70cm-87x35x28in) s.num.1/1000 steel (DM 6000)
£2281 $4105   (19-Nov-91 L.K531/R) Head (45x46x14cm-18x18x6in) i.num.124/1000 pat.iron (DM 6500)
£2378 $4232   (25-Nov-91 WK.M20 a/R) Head (45x47x13cm-18x19x5in) s.num.37/1000 rust pat.iron indis.st.foundry (DM 6800)

ANTHOONS, Willy (1911-1983) Belgian
£911 $1648   (23-May-92 KV.L15/R) Mother and child (54x27cm-21x11in) s.f.Verbeyst num.2/3 bronze dk.br.pat. (B.FR 55000)

ANZINGER, Siegfried (1952-) Austrian
£2302 $4213   (2-Jun-92 L.K480/R) Horse (32x18cm-13x7in) mono.num.1/6 brown pat.bronze (DM 6700)

AOUARD, H A (?) French
£2105 $3600   (13-Mar-92 WOL.C1024/R) Father scolding his young son (74cm-29in) s. bronze

APPEL, Karel (1921-) Dutch
£22699 $40404   (29-Apr-92 F.F118/R) Clown Fleur (100x117x30cm-39x46x12in) s. num.9/Nverso acrylic wood (I.L 50000000)

ARCHIPENKO, Alexander (1887-1964) Russian
£6873 $12096   (10-Apr-92 KM.K308/R) Torso (37cm-15in) i.d.1922 silvered bronze marble socle (DM 20000)
£6993 $12448   (30-Nov-91 VG.B227/R) Standing woman combing her hair (32cm-13in) i.d.1915 black brown pat.bronze marble socle (DM 20000)
£18000 $32580   (4-Dec-91 S159/R) Hollywood-torso (70cm-28in) i.d.1936 num.5/6 st. bronze
£18000 $34380   (30-Jun-92 C150/R) La negresse (49cm-19in) num.1/2 green pat.bronze
£18286 $32600   (25-Feb-92 SY.NY70/R) Figure (51cm-20in) terracotta
£27119 $48000   (6-Nov-91 CH.NY280/R) Torse (38cm-15in) s. brown pat.bronze
£39548 $70000   (6-Nov-91 CH.NY278/R) La mere dans les roches, Madonna of the Rocks (52cm-20in) s.d.1912 num.6/6 brown green pat.bronze
£41000 $78310   (30-Jun-92 C148/R) Negresse assise (55cm-22in) s. black marble

ARGENTI, Antonio (19/20th C) Italian
£3315 $6000   (6-Dec-91 GC.M139/R) Carmen (120cm-47in) s. Carrara marble on granite socle

ARMAN, Fernandez (1928-) French
£1088 $1969   (19-May-92 AB.S5126/R) Tubes de coleur (40x29cm-16x11in) s.indist.num.26/30, colouring tubes in plexiglas (S.KR 11500)
£1155 $1987   (8-Mar-92 BU.M506) 'Bok' (27cm-11in) s.num.20/100, pat bronze (S.KR 12000)
£1270 $2324   (12-May-92 F.R3/R) Accumulazione - rasoi (40x25x40cm-16x10x16in) s.num.25/40 razors perspex (I.L 2800000)
£1613 $2952   (12-May-92 GO.G206/R) Object (80x65cm-31x26in) s. red paint tubes (S.KR 17000)
£1634 $2909   (29-Apr-92 F.F116/R) Senza titolo (78x110x10cm-31x43x4in) s.num.XV/XX mixed media (I.L 3600000)
£1789 $3256   (10-Dec-91 RAS.K79/R) Violin (36cm-14in) s. bronze (D.KR 20000)
£1992 $3646   (12-May-92 GO.G305/R) Cut teapot (40cm-16in) s.num.1/2, gilded brass marble base (S.KR 21000)
£2034 $3682   (21-May-92 F.M263/R) Violino (54x22cm-21x9in) s. bronze (I.L 4500000)
£2126 $3869   (25-May-92 RAS.K122/R) Pistols (107x72cm-42x28in) s. acrylic serigraf in plexiglass (D.KR 24000)
£2273 $4114   (19-May-92 CH.AM309/R) Venus (33cm-13in) s.num.48/100 bronze (D.FL 7500)
£2364 $4515   (30-Jun-92 ZZ.F76/R) Violon (61x24x7cm-24x9x3in) s.num.23/150 cut violin inclusion (F.FR 23000)
£2369 $4050   (21-Mar-92 AT.P101/R) Crosses de violons (41x11x8cm-16x4x3in) s.base num.21/50 gilt bronze Cast.Bocquel (F.FR 23000)
£2480 $4514   (25-May-92 RAS.K100/R) The camera (31x60x23cm-12x24x9in) s.num.35/45, painted bronze (D.KR 28000)
£2483 $4495   (23-May-92 KV.L499/R) Venus (32x11cm-13x4in) s.f.Bocquel num.37/100 bronze dk.br.pat. (B.FR 150000)
£2672 $4756   (27-Nov-91 BU.S4/R) Accumulation de violons (114x113cm-45x44in) s.num.1/50, welded bronze (S.KR 28000)
£2817 $4845   (12-Oct-91 GL.P67/R) Poppers (15x15x15cm-6x6x6in) s. poppers in plexiglass (F.FR 28000)
£2823 $5082   (19-Nov-91 FB.P211/R) Cameras decoupees dans une boite de plexiglass (20x25x10cm-8x10x4in) s.d.71 cameras plexiglass box (F.FR 27500)
£4111 $7852   (30-Jun-92 ZZ.F75/R) Clubs de golf (38cm-15in) s. num.H.C. nickel-plated metal (F.FR 40000)
£4370 $7604   (16-Apr-92 FB.P223/R) Tete dcoupee (65cm-26in) s. num.EA 2/3 brn.pat.bronze Cast.Bocquel (F.FR 43000)
£6000 $10380   (26-Mar-92 C46 a/R) Accumulation brisee (70x90x8cm-28x35x3in) s. broken plates in polyester plexiglass box
£6826 $12423   (29-May-92 VG.B85/R) Multiplication (37x33cm-15x13in) s.i.d.1960 object box with clock movements (DM 20000)

ARMAN, Fernandez (1928-) French-cont.

£7500	$12900	(17-Oct-91 S51/R) Untitled (69x29x7cm-27x11x3in) s.d.66 burnt violin in polyester
£7700	$13860	(19-Nov-91 FB.P242/R) Violon calcine (80x40x5cm-31x16x2in) s.d.69 broken violin plexiglass block (F.FR 75000)
£8945	$16279	(10-Dec-91 RAS.K66/R) Differences of opinion (77x103cm-30x41in) s.i.d.86verso accumulation of paint tubes (D.KR 100000)
£9568	$17414	(12-Dec-91 SY.AM214/R) Violin (80x40x5cm-31x16x2in) s.d.69 burnt violin plexiglass (D.FL 31000)
£9697	$17552	(21-May-92 SY.AM259/R) Untitled (120x90cm-47x35in) s.d.1988 match boxes in polyester resin (D.FL 32000)
£9697	$17552	(21-May-92 SY.AM270/R) Untitled (120x90cm-47x35in) d.1988 s. match boxes in polyester resin (D.FL 32000)
£9859	$16958	(8-Oct-91 CC.P71/R) Violons at cadrans (62x26x19cm-24x10x7in) s. base num.4/4 gilded pat.bronze Cast.Bocquel (F.FR 98000)
£11066	$19034	(8-Oct-91 CC.P72/R) Sans titre (70x45x50cm-28x18x20in) s. bronze sculpture (F.FR 110000)
£11066	$19034	(12-Oct-91 GL.P66/R) Sans titre (52x43x20cm-20x17x8in) s. coffee set cut and soldered (F.FR 110000)
£13078	$22495	(12-Oct-91 GL.P53/R) Big string (170x87x59cm-67x34x23in) s.num.2/8 bronze Cast.Bocquel (F.FR 130000)
£15000	$25950	(26-Mar-92 C44/R) Venus au Violon (93cm-37in) s. broken violins polyester
£15000	$27150	(5-Dec-91 S31/R) Poubelle (139x51x12cm-55x20x5in) refuse in plexiglass
£15152	$27424	(21-May-92 SY.AM258/R) Cello (120cm-47in) s.num.1/8 wooden cello bronze (D.FL 50000)
£16461	$31276	(26-Jun-92 FB.P42/R) Frozen in the dark (120x120cm-47x47in) s.d.70verso collection of crayons in plexiglass (F.FR 160000)
£18519	$35185	(26-Jun-92 FB.P78/R) Maternite - violon et violoncelle decoupes (114x97x25cm-45x38x10in) s.num.2/8 brown pat.bronze (F.FR 180000)
£19697	$35652	(21-May-92 SY.AM257/R) Tranche de lagoya (100cm-39in) c.1985 s.i.num.2/2 bronze wooden guitar (D.FL 65000)
£20112	$36000	(14-Nov-91 SY.NY323/R) Souvenir de Geneve (58x35x35cm-23x14x14in) broken charred glued violins plexiglass
£21127	$36338	(12-Oct-91 GL.P63/R) Accumulation de violons (56x95x40cm-22x37x16in) s. violons (F.FR 210000)
£21277	$38511	(21-May-92 CC.P84/R) Untitled (121x65x10cm-48x26x4in) s. charred cello in plexiglass block (F.FR 210000)
£22000	$42020	(2-Jul-92 S54/R) Violoncelle brule (160x120cm-63x47in) s.d.69 burnt broken cello in plexiglass
£22518	$40082	(30-Nov-91 FB.P62/R) Violon (91x61x10cm-36x24x4in) s. pieces of violon in plexiglass block (F.FR 220000)
£25140	$45000	(14-Nov-91 SY.NY300/R) Colere d'accordeon (120x120x20cm-47x47x8in) s.d.1971 broken accordions in plexiglass
£30000	$57300	(2-Jul-92 C38/R) XXIVeme Caprice de Paganini (82x64cm-32x25in) s.d.1962 cut violin painted board
£36000	$65160	(5-Dec-91 S26/R) Les batteurs - kill chicken in egg (58x38x10cm-23x15x4in) egg beaters whisks in wood perspex box

ARMITAGE, Kenneth (1916-) British

£3500	$6685	(16-Jul-92 B178/R) The Legend of Skedar (41cm-16in) init.d.1965num.4/6 bronze bl.pat.
£5500	$10175	(11-Jun-92 C123/R) Seated figure with arms raised (34cm-13in) black pat.bronze f.st.Valsuani
£22857	$40000	(25-Feb-92 SY.NY72/R) Sprawling woman (249cm-98in) green pat.bronze

ARP, Jean (1887-1966) French

£847	$1500	(5-Nov-91 CE.NY150/R) Homme vu par une fleur (11cm-4in) polished bronze
£6857	$12000	(25-Feb-92 CH.NY83/R) Decoupage No. 13 Meditation (41cm-16in) s.num.verso 5/5 polished bronze
£13143	$23000	(25-Feb-92 CH.NY74/R) Echo de torse (33cm-13in) mono.num.5/5 polished bronze f.st.Susse Fres
£15254	$27000	(7-Nov-91 SY.NY178/R) Silencieux (34cm-13in) mono. num.3/5 gold pat.bronze
£15254	$27000	(6-Nov-91 CH.NY285/R) Piece d'echec (48cm-19in) mono.i.num.2/5 polished bronze i.Susse Fond
£28000	$50680	(4-Dec-91 S154/R) Du pays des lutins (25x20cm-10x8in) bronze
£28249	$50000	(7-Nov-91 SY.NY179/R) Outrance d'une outre - mystique No.2 (43cm-17in) gold pat.bronze
£77160	$139660	(2-Dec-91 CC.P22/R) Groupe Mediterranee (78x92x50cm-31x36x20in) num.0/3 polished bronze (F.FR 750000)

ARROYO, Edouard (1937-) Spanish

| £16402 | $30016 | (13-May-92 FER.M220/R) Cabeza con chistera (46cm-18in) bronze copper iron wood (S.P 3000000) |

ARTSCHWAGER, Richard (1924-) American

£8380	$15000	(13-Nov-91 CH.NY330/R) Mirror (59x52x10cm-23x20x4in) s.i.d.88verso formica on wood
£15896	$27500	(3-Oct-91 SY.NY127/R) Soviet accelerator (127x94x6cm-50x37x2in) s.i.d.80verso acrylic celotex formica wood
£22346	$40000	(14-Nov-91 SY.NY142/R) Handle (105x33x30cm-41x13x12in) formica wood
£27933	$50000	(6-May-92 SY.NY40/R) Chair (150x46x77cm-59x18x30in) formica on wood
£41908	$72500	(3-Oct-91 SY.NY95/R) Mirror (155x110x10cm-61x43x4in) formica
£55866	$100000	(6-May-92 SY.NY38/R) Book II, Nike (188x116x117cm-74x46x46in) formica construction

ARTSCHWAGER, Richard (1924-) American-cont.
£67039 $120000   (13-Nov-91 SY.NY64/R) Long table with two pictures s.d.63-64 verso
                acrylic celotex formica on wood

ASPETTI, Tiziano (after) (c.1565-1607) Italian
£3500 $6720   (9-Jul-92 S110) Statuette of Mars, in classical armour brandishing shield
                (47cm-19in) dark red brown lacquer bronze

ASPETTI, Tiziano (studio) (c.1565-1607) Italian
£17877 $32000   (14-Jan-92 CH.NY132/R) Figures of Venus and Mars (45cm-18in) bronze pair

AUBE, Paul (1837-1916) French
£1300 $2314   (29-Nov-91 S106/R) Peinture (61cm-24in) s.i. brown/green pat.bronze

AUBLET, Annick (1943-) French?
£1110 $1909   (20-Oct-91 I.N71/R) La fierte (27cm-11in) num.1/4 brn.pat.bronze cire
                perdue (F.FR 11000)
£1145 $2096   (3-Feb-92 HH.P68/R) Caline (18x18x12cm-7x7x5in) s.num.2/8 brn.pat.bronze
                Cast.Delval (F.FR 11200)
£1207 $2076   (7-Oct-91 HH.P3/R) Meditation (20x21x13cm-8x8x5in) s.num.2/8 brn.green
                pat.bronze (F.FR 12000)

AUGUSTIN, Edgar (1936-) German?
£769 $1315   (21-Mar-92 WK.M29/R) Figure standing wearing long flowing dress
                (56x15x10cm-22x6x4in) s. brown pat.bronze (DM 2200)

AUPALUKTUK, Moses (1924-1983) North American
£872 $1595   (1-Jun-92 W.T785 a) Inuit hunter wearing parka standing about to hurl
                harpoon at seal (38cm-15in) s.d.1973 mottled soapstone (C.D 1900)

AUSTRIAN SCHOOL (?) Austrian
£5200 $9464   (12-Dec-91 S241/R) Bust of St. Cecilia (98cm-39in) with i. repousse
                silver

AUSTRIAN SCHOOL, 18th C
£2091 $3805   (10-Dec-91 N.M62/R) Bishop standing with church by his feet, probably St
                Wolfgang (105cm-41in) wood (DM 6000)
£2400 $4608   (9-Jul-92 S175/R) Statue of St. Florian, wearing armour and billowing
                cloak (50cm-20in) polychrome giltwood

AYRTON, Michael (1921-1975) British
£1700 $2907   (11-Mar-92 S184/R) Icarus (38cm-15in) bronze
£1802 $3100   (12-Oct-91 SY.NY177/R) Minotaur revealed (71cm-28in) greenish-brown
                pat.bronze
£4200 $7770   (11-Jun-92 C120/R) Figure on wall (43cm-17in) green/brown pat.bronze
£8000 $14800   (11-Jun-92 C118/R) Web (176cm-69in) num.5/9 verso dark brown pat.bronze
                steel

BACKSTROM, Barbro (1939-1990) Swedish
£1008 $1824   (3-Dec-91 AB.S5191/R) 'Vagrorelse' (17x18cm-7x7in) s.d.66 aluminium
                (S.KR 10500)
£1328 $2431   (13-May-92 BU.S25/R) Composition (23x40cm-9x16in) oil, metal net wooden
                box (S.KR 14000)
£2467 $4514   (13-May-92 BU.S24/R) Torso (40x20cm-16x8in) init.d. net iron (S.KR 26000)
£5344 $9511   (27-Nov-91 BU.S58/R) Three torsos (20x23cm-8x9in) iron cloth (S.KR 56000)

BACON, John (younger) (?) British
£5000 $8900   (1-Nov-91 S293/R) Bust of Lady Ribblesdale (75cm-30in) s. marble

BAIER, Jean (1932-) ?
£2107 $3646   (23-Mar-92 AB.L140/R) Composition (130x130cm-51x51in) s.d.1967verso
                cellulose paint metal diagonal (S.FR 5500)

BAILEY, Ruby Levick (19/20th C) British
£1150 $2093   (27-May-92 SWS398) Figure of boy, seated naked on rocky outcrop
                (68cm-27in) s.d.1927 lead

BAJ, Enrico (1924-) Italian
£927 $1650   (26-Nov-91 SY.MI73) The Baj Rolling General (64x70x14cm-25x28x6in)
                s.num.19/180 wood collage foamrubber objects (I.L 2000000)

BALDINI, R (?) ?
£967 $1750   (6-Dec-91 GC.M141/R) Nina Napolitana tanendo la mandolina (80cm-31in) s.
                Carrara marble on granite pedestal

BALL, Percival (19th C) British
£10000 $18100   (21-May-92 C56/R) Figure of Bacchus seated holding cup of wine
                (79cm-31in) s.d.1879 marble

BALL, Thomas (1819-1911) American
£2047 $3500   (18-Mar-92 GRO.B76/R) Daniel Webster (76cm-30in) i.d.1853 brown
    pat.bronze
£2660 $5000   (18-Dec-91 SY.NY152/R) Portrait bust of Napoleon (82cm-32in) i.d.1856
    marble

BALLA, Giacomo (1871-1958) Italian
£13714 $24000   (25-Feb-92 SY.NY44/R) Rose (33cm-13in) s. painted plywood
£14857 $26000   (25-Feb-92 SY.NY43/R) Tree (32cm-13in) s. painted plywood

BALLESTER BESALDUCH, Agustin (?) ?
£984 $1801   (13-May-92 FER.M241/R) Desnudo femenino (33cm-13in) s. bronze
    (S.P 180000)

BALZICO, Alfonso (1820-1901) Italian
£2299 $4116   (14-Nov-91 CH.R226) Cavallo (69cm-27in) s.d.1864 bronze (I.L 5000000)

BANDINI, Giovanni (studio) (1540-1599) Italian
£27473 $50000   (26-May-92 SY.NY36/R) Bust of Architecture, head turned, wavy hair tied
    back (48cm-19in) marble

BANNINGER, Otto Charles (1897-1973) Swiss
£4781 $8653   (5-Dec-91 SY.Z157/R) Man with horse (62cm-24in) mono.i.d.1939 num.8 gold
    pat.bronze st.Ruetschi (S.FR 12000)

BARBEDIENNE, F (19/20th C) French
£802 $1380   (15-Oct-91 RAS.K639/R) Venus de Milo (86cm-34in) i. pat bronze
    Cast.Barbedienne (D.KR 9000)
£1083 $1949   (21-Nov-91 RAS.K966/R) Woman wearing classical dress (67cm-26in) i.
    silvered gold bronze (D.KR 12000)

BARBEDIENNE, Ferdinand (19/20th C) French
£1777 $3252   (13-May-92 FER.M217/R) Mercurio (90cm-35in) s. pat.bronze on marble base
    (S.P 325000)

BARBELLA, Constantino (1852-1925) Italian
£1323 $2354   (30-Apr-92 RAS.K998) Seated female model (59cm-23in) s.i. white marble
    (D.KR 15000)

BAREAU, Georges (1866-1931) French
£1573 $2800   (30-Apr-92 CE.NY47/R) Call to arms - allegorical figure (50cm-20in) i.
    parcel-gilt bronze
£2299 $4000   (13-Sep-91 SY.NY49/R) Seated female nude (60cm-24in) i. parcel gilt
    bronze st.f.F.Barbedienne

BARKER, Clive (?) ?
£1300 $2301   (8-Nov-91 C372/R) American beauty (37cm-15in) s.base gold pat.bronze

BARLACH, Ernst (1870-?) German
£1527 $2779   (15-Dec-91 REM.W53) Statue of God of the Father (53cm-21in) stone
    (P.Z 30000000)
£2062 $3814   (12-Jun-92 HN.H24/R) Death mask of Theodor Daubler (35x18x11cm-14x7x4in)
    d.1934 brown pat.bronze (DM 6000)
£3413 $6177   (23-May-92 GB.B6208/R) Kopf eines vergnugten Einbeins (11x9x5cm-4x4x2in)
    brown pat.bronze (DM 10000)
£5088 $9158   (21-Nov-91 L.K26/R) Mask of Christ (17x7cm-7x3in) i.pat.bronze st.f.Noack
    Berlin (DM 14500)
£5986 $10835   (6-Dec-91 GB.B6218/R) Kissing group III (17x12x7cm-7x5x3in) s.i.d.1921
    bronze st.f.H.Noack Berlin (DM 17000)
£6529 $12079   (12-Jun-92 HN.H21/R) Der Spazierganger (51x25x17cm-20x10x7in) brown grey
    stucco (DM 19000)
£6826 $12355   (23-May-92 GB.B6207/R) Russian beggar woman II (24x43x18cm-9x17x7in) s.
    terracotta (DM 20000)
£7679 $13899   (23-May-92 GB.B6206/R) Kiss group (18x17x8cm-7x7x3in) s.d.1929 yellow
    brown plaster (DM 22500)
£7692 $13692   (30-Nov-91 VG.B168/R) Monks reading (15cm-6in) s.d.1921 brown pat.bronze
    st.f.Noack Berlin (DM 22000)
£7719 $13895   (21-Nov-91 L.K25/R) Figures kissing (16cm-6in) i. bronze brown pat.bronze
    st.f.Noack Berlin (DM 22000)
£12587 $22406   (30-Nov-91 VG.B170/R) Blind beggar woman with child (36cm-14in) d.1907
    brown plaster (DM 36000)
£13986 $24895   (30-Nov-91 VG.B171/R) The flute player (60cm-24in) brown plaster shellack
    (DM 40000)
£24055 $44502   (12-Jun-92 HN.H22/R) Der Racher (43x59x19cm-17x23x7in) s.d.1914 bronze
    (DM 70000)
£26224 $46678   (28-Nov-91 SY.BE47/R) The doubter (51cm-20in) s. gold brown pat.bronze
    st.f.H.Noack Berlin (DM 75000)
£192440 $356014   (12-Jun-92 HN.H20/R) The flame (115x41x20cm-45x16x8in) s.d.1934 wood
    (DM 560000)

BARON, Hannelore (1926-1987) Swiss?
£1725 $3089   (15-Nov-91 GK.Z5653) Untitled (12x10x2cm-5x4x1in) d.1984 collage wood
    painted (S.FR 4400)

BARRIAS (?) French
£1287 $2201   (18-Mar-92 ARC.P67/R) Buste de jeune oriental (18cm-7in) s. gilt bronze
   Cast.Susse Freres (F.FR 12500)

BARRIAS, Louis Ernest (1841-1905) French
£1010 $1788   (26-Apr-92 SY.MO271) La nature se devoilant devant la science (43cm-17in)
   gilt pat.bronze Cast.Susse Freres (F.FR 10000)
£1500 $2565   (20-Mar-92 S142/R) Children playing with tortoise (13cm-5in) s.d.1877
   brown pat.bronze i.F.Barbedienne
£1724 $3000   (13-Sep-91 SY.NY111/R) Figure of Joan of Arc (51cm-20in) i. gilt silvered
   bronze ivory st.f.Susses Freres
£2180 $3750   (20-Oct-91 HG.C101) Figure of winged victory (86cm-34in) bronze turquoise
   stones
£2917 $5192   (27-Nov-91 CB.P240/R) La nature se devoilant devant la Science
   (43cm-17in) s.num.P gilded pat.bronze Cast.Susse Freres (F.FR 28500)
£3000 $5340   (29-Nov-91 S98/R) Mozart (70cm-28in) s.d.1883 brown pat.bronze
   i.f.F.Barbedienne
£4121 $7500   (27-May-92 CH.NY126/R) La Nature se devoilant devant la Science
   (58cm-23in) i.f.Susse Freres bronze
£5085 $9000   (13-Feb-92 SY.NY12/R) Nature revealing herself to science (74cm-29in) i.
   gilt pat.bronze
£6481 $11731   (4-Dec-91 LD.P197/R) La nature se devoilant devant la science (73cm-29in)
   s. brn.gold pat.bronze Cast.Susse Freres (F.FR 63000)
£6500 $11375   (20-Feb-92 C183/R) Nature unveiling herself before Science (65cm-26in)
   s.i. pat.bronze marble socle Cast.Susse Fres.
£7863 $13917   (6-Nov-91 BL.P14/R) La nature se devoilant devant la science (74cm-29in)
   s.d.27 mai 1914 gilded bronze (F.FR 78000)
£8140 $14000   (17-Oct-91 SY.NY28/R) Nature unveiling herself before science (58cm-23in)
   i. gilt-bronze marble lapis lazuli f.seal
£8642 $16420   (24-Jun-92 AT.P209/R) La nature se devoilant devant la Science
   (73cm-29in) s. gilded/silvered pat.bronze Carrara marble (F.FR 84000)
£17816 $31000   (13-Sep-91 SY.NY59/R) La renomee, allegory of fame (86cm-34in) i. gilt
   silver bronze i.f.Susse Freres

BARSANTI, P (19th C) ?
£10270 $19000   (8-Jun-92 B.LA1264/R) Nude figure of Aphrodite (173cm-68in) i. marble

BARTELS, Wera von (1886-1922) German
£1900 $3382   (29-Nov-91 S30/R) Panther (38cm-15in) s. brown pat.bronze on marble base

BARTHE, Richmond (1901-1989) American
£1429 $2600   (28-May-92 CH.NY213/R) The Black Madonna (34cm-13in) i.bronze bl.br.pat.
   on marble cube

BARTHELEMY, L (19/20th C) French
£1108 $1962   (12-Feb-92 ANS.M369/R) Dama (18cm-7in) s. bronze ivory on marble base
   (S.P 200000)

BARTLETT and HAYWARD (19th C) American
£9474 $18000   (23-Jun-92 CE.NY68/R) Sailor, Newfoundland dog (92x166cm-36x65in) painted
   iron figure

BARTLETT, Jennifer (1941-) American
£41899 $75000   (14-Nov-91 SY.NY172/R) 22 East 10 Street (96x328cm-38x129in) enamel
   silkscreen grid 12 square steel plates

BARTLETT, Paul Wayland (1881-1925) American
£2261 $4250   (18-Dec-91 SY.NY157/R) Preparedness (31cm-12in) i.d.1916 black green pat.
   bronze

BARTOLINI, Lorenzo (attrib) (1777-1850) Italian
£1800 $3276   (12-Dec-91 S262/R) Bust of Lord Byron (34cm-13in) marble

BARWIG, Franz (1868-1931) Austrian
£825 $1410   (9-Mar-92 AT.P263/R) La gazelle dansante (56cm-22in) mono. blk.pat.bronze
   (F.FR 8000)

BARYE (?) French?
£920 $1619   (8-Apr-92 CSK104) Equestrian group of Gaston de Foix, cuirassed knight
   astride steed (36cm-14in) s. green pat.bronze
£989 $1731   (3-Apr-92 BM.B1545) Big cat with prey (60cm-24in) i. green pat.bronze
   (DM 2800)
£1236 $2163   (21-Feb-92 LC.P116/R) Tigre et Antilope (28x48x17cm-11x19x7in) s.base
   pat.bronze (F.FR 12100)

BARYE (after) (?) French
£1200 $2088   (17-Sep-91 PH251/R) Rearing bull (25cm-10in) s. bronze i.Barbedienne

BARYE, Alfred (19th C) French
£769 $1400   (13-Dec-91 S.W3026/R) Standing lion (25cm-10in) s. green pat.bronze
£1724 $3000   (13-Sep-91 SY.NY83/R) Equestrian group of mounted Indian (70cm-28in) i.
   green brown pat.bronze on stepped plinth
£2486 $4500   (5-Dec-91 SY.NY63/R) Racehorse (49x66cm-19x26in) i.d.1868 dk.brown
   pat.bronze

BARYE, Antoine-Louis (1796-1875) French

£737	$1320	(14-Nov-91 GRO.B86/R) Walking lion (25cm-10in) i. greenish-brown pat.bronze f.i.F.Barbedienne
£750	$1335	(29-Nov-91 S4) Pointer (8cm-3in) s. brown pat.bronze
£750	$1335	(29-Nov-91 S5) Stag (16cm-6in) s. green pat.bronze
£765	$1400	(5-Jun-92 SY.NY122/R) Wounded pheasant (12cm-5in) s. bronze br.pat.
£847	$1500	(13-Feb-92 S.W2779/R) Standing lion (20x36cm-8x14in) s. brn.yellow pat.bronze
£870	$1548	(29-Nov-91 GAB.G2027 a) Lion devorant un marcassin (17cm-7in) s. brn.green pat.bronze (S.FR 2200)
£900	$1575	(20-Feb-92 C167/R) Stag with leg raised (19cm-7in) s.i. bronze Cast.F Barbedienne
£1000	$1750	(20-Feb-92 C168/R) Stag feeding (28cm-11in) s.i. bronze Cast.Susse Freres
£1000	$1750	(20-Feb-92 C173/R) The elephant of Cochin China (14cm-6in) s. bronze
£1053	$1800	(13-Mar-92 DM.D1026/R) Tiger devouring gazelle (33cm-13in) s.base brn.green pat.bronze Cast.Barbedienne
£1067	$1900	(30-Apr-92 CE.NY87/R) Walking tiger (21cm-8in) i. dark brown pat.bronze f.i.F. Barbedienne
£1093	$2000	(5-Jun-92 SY.NY133/R) Panthere attaquant un cerf (33x48cm-13x19in) i.f.Susse Fres bronze gr.br.pat.
£1100	$2013	(12-May-92 PH105/R) Lion crushing serpent with its paw (86cm-34in) s. brown pat.bronze
£1130	$2000	(13-Feb-92 S.W2785/R) Lion attacking wild boar (25x48cm-10x19in) s. brn.pat.bronze
£1148	$2100	(5-Jun-92 SY.NY138/R) Lion qui marche (22x39cm-9x15in) f.Barbedienne bronze gr.bl.pat.
£1149	$2000	(13-Sep-91 SY.NY106/R) Standing basset (15x28cm-6x11in) i. golden brown pat.bronze
£1149	$2000	(13-Sep-91 SY.NY107/R) Standing basset (15x21cm-6x8in) i. green brown pat.bronze
£1400	$2450	(20-Feb-92 C172/R) Two cavalier King Charles Spaniels (10x18cm-4x7in) bronze
£1429	$2600	(27-May-92 CH.NY108/R) Tigre qui marche (21cm-8in) i.f.Barbedienne bronze green brown pat.
£1437	$2500	(13-Sep-91 SY.NY104/R) Figural group of panther attacking stag (51cm-20in) i. gilt bronze st.f.Susse Freres Paris
£1475	$2700	(5-Jun-92 SY.NY137/R) Tigre qui marche (41x21cm-16x8in) i. bronze gr.bnl.pat.
£1484	$2700	(27-May-92 CH.NY105/R) Tigre qui marche (21cm-8in) i.f.Barbedienne bronze brown pat.
£1512	$2600	(16-Oct-91 CH.NY145/R) Panther attacking a civet cat (11cm-4in) i. red brn.pat.bronze
£1600	$2800	(20-Feb-92 C169/R) Stag rubbing his antlers against a tree (22cm-9in) s.i. bronze Cast.F Barbedienne
£1600	$2736	(20-Mar-92 S26/R) Walking lion (21cm-8in) s. brown pat.bronze i.f.Barbedienne
£1600	$2848	(29-Nov-91 S8) Seated cat (9cm-4in) s. brown,green pat.bronze
£1648	$3000	(27-May-92 CH.NY101/R) Aigle pres d'un heron mort (31cm-12in) i.f.Barbedienne bronze green brown pat.
£1758	$3200	(27-May-92 CH.NY99/R) Dromadaire d'Algerie (19cm-7in) i. bronze green brown pat.
£1776	$3250	(5-Jun-92 SY.NY119/R) Aigle tenant un heron (31cm-12in) i. bronze bronze gr.br.pat.
£1913	$3500	(5-Jun-92 SY.NY139/R) Tigre qui marche (21x39cm-8x15in) f.Barbedienne bronze dk.br.pat.
£1967	$3600	(5-Jun-92 SY.NY124/R) Panthere surprenant un zibeth (22x45cm-9x18in) i. bronze
£2000	$3420	(20-Mar-92 S3/R) Eagle (28cm-11in) s. brown pat.bronze
£2000	$3560	(29-Nov-91 S35/R) Seated lion (21cm-8in) s. brown pat.bronze sold with plaster cast
£2088	$3800	(27-May-92 CH.NY106/R) Lion qui marche (27cm-11in) i. bronze red green brown pat.
£2090	$3887	(21-Jun-92 LT.P100/R) Lionne a l'affut (14x46cm-6x18in) s. brown pat.bronze on marble socle (F.FR 20500)
£2200	$3762	(20-Mar-92 S18/R) Theseus fighting the centaur (41cm-16in) s. brown pat.bronze
£2500	$4450	(29-Nov-91 S14) Pointer and setter searching out grouse (12cm-5in) s. brown pat.bronze
£2688	$5000	(16-Jun-92 RO.BA115) Panthere de Tunis (13x27cm-5x11in) pat.bronze
£2869	$5250	(5-Jun-92 SY.NY135/R) Lion et serpent (26x34cm-10x13in) i. bronze br.pat.
£3000	$5340	(29-Nov-91 S13) Stag, doe and fawn (23cm-9in) s. dk.brown pat.bronze i.f.F.Barbedienne
£3005	$5500	(5-Jun-92 SY.NY129/R) Elephant d'Afrique (13cm-5in) i. bronze red br. pat.
£3297	$6000	(27-May-92 CH.NY104/R) Ours debout (24cm-9in) i. bronze red green brown pat.
£3488	$6000	(16-Oct-91 CH.NY144/R) Elephant du Senegal (13cm-5in) i. num.6 Cast.Barbedienne green brn.pat.bronze
£3500	$6230	(29-Nov-91 S15) Pointer, retriever and pheasant (16cm-6in) s.num.8 brown pat.bronze
£4222	$7938	(16-Dec-91 AGS.P30/R) Brque en arret devant un faisan (85x21cm-33x8in) num.5 bronze (F.FR 41000)
£4500	$8010	(29-Nov-91 S26/R) Tiger and gavial (20x50cm-8x20in) s. brown pat.bronze i.f.V.P.
£4598	$8000	(13-Sep-91 S.W2630/R) Le cheval turc (28cm-11in) s. silvered bronze

BARYE, Antoine-Louis (1796-1875) French-cont.
£4800 $8544   (29-Nov-91 S25/R) Running elephant (25cm-10in) s. brown pat.bronze
     i.f.F.Barbedienne
£6385 $12004   (16-Dec-91 AGS.P32/R) Thesee combattant le Centaure Bienor
     (72x70cm-28x28in) s. base brn.blk.pat.bronze Cast.Barbedienne
     (F.FR 62000)
£6593 $12000   (27-May-92 CH.NY114/R) Cerf attaque par deux chiens (42cm-17in) i. bronze
     red brown pat.
£10920 $19000   (13-Sep-91 SY.NY43/R) Figure of buck deer (96cm-38in) i. green pat.bronze
     st.f.Susse Freres Paris
£24286 $42500   (20-Feb-92 SY.NY56/R) Roger and Angelica borne by Hippogriff (51cm-20in)
     i. greenish brown pat.bronze red highlights

BARYE, Antoine-Louis (after) (1796-1875) French
£819 $1400   (13-Mar-92 DM.D1027/R) Elephant (18cm-7in) s. brn.pat.bronze wood base
£2236 $3890   (13-Apr-92 PLF.P103/R) Tigre devorant une antilope (34x55cm-13x22in)
     green pat.bronze (F.FR 22000)

BARZAGHI, Francesco (1839-1892) Italian
£1200 $2052   (20-Mar-92 S118/R) Beethoven (46cm-18in) s.d.1886 alabaster
£15000 $26700   (29-Nov-91 S154/R) The fisherboy (203cm-80in) s.i. white marble
     incl.ebonised wood column

BARZANTI, Peter (19/20th C) Italian
£2907 $5000   (10-Oct-91 FA.PH789) Bust of female (48cm-19in) s.i. white marble

BASCOM, Earl W (20th C) American
£11436 $21500   (18-Dec-91 SY.NY386/R) Turk Greenough on Five Minutes to Midnight
     (47cm-19in) i.d.1982 black pat bronze
£17553 $33000   (18-Dec-91 SY.NY387/R) Cochise (73cm-29in) i.d.1981 num.13/75 brown pat.
     bronze

BASETTI, A (19th C) Italian
£1404 $2500   (30-Apr-92 CE.NY26/R) Figure of boy climbing tree (117cm-46in) s. white
     marble

BASKIN, Leonard (1922-) American
£1117 $2100   (18-Dec-91 SY.NY348/R) Male torso (22cm-9in) mahogany

BATACCHI, A (19th C) Italian
£5376 $10000   (16-Jun-92 RO.BA127) Ninfa (120cm-47in) Carrara marble on pedestal

BATTIGLIA, E (19th C) Italian
£90000 $153900   (20-Mar-92 S131/R) Cleopatra (160cm-63in) s.i. marble

BAUERMEISTER, Mary (1934-) German
£1714 $3000   (27-Feb-92 CE.NY276/R) Untitled (27x27x17cm-11x11x7in) s.d.31/1990
     optical glass painted wood
£2400 $4200   (27-Feb-92 CE.NY180/R) Break-off (57x50x14cm-22x20x6in) s.d.1969 acrylic
     wood stones sand epoxy panel
£6704 $12000   (9-May-92 CE.NY368/R) Pictionary (54x99x24cm-21x39x9in) init.i.d.1967
     s.i.d.verso mixed media on wood

BAUR, Theodore (1835-1898) American
£22000 $38500   (27-Sep-91 S53/R) Indian lion huter on horseback (178cm-70in) silvered
     bronze marble plinth marble column

BAYENS, Hans (1924-) Dutch
£802 $1460   (11-Dec-91 CH.AM66) Pregnant woman standing (28cm-11in) st.init. bronze
     (D.FL 2600)

BAZCARDO, Juan de (17th C) Spanish
£1915 $3486   (11-Dec-91 FER.M212/R) Santa Catalina de Siena (65cm-26in) polychrome
     gilded wood (S.P 350000)
£3010 $5477   (11-Dec-91 FER.M211/R) Santa Catalina de Alejandria (70cm-28in)
     polychrome gilded wood (S.P 550000)

BAZZANTI, P (19th C) Italian?
£1031 $1794   (21-Sep-91 SA.A2455/R) Florentine girl (44x31x24cm-17x12x9in) i. marble
     (DM 3000)

BEAUFILS (20th C) French
£4494 $8000   (30-Apr-92 CE.NY32/R) Allegorical female figures of four continents
     (140cm-55in) i. walnut four

BEAUMONT, Cyril W (20th C) American
£15254 $27000   (7-Nov-91 SY.NY9/R) Dancing figures of the Diaghilev Ballet gouache wood
     silver paint wood base twelve

BECK, Gerlinde (1930-) German
£1614 $2905   (19-Nov-91 L.K556/R) Lichtfugenstelle (46cm-18in) d.1969 steel (DM 4600)

BECKMANN, Curt (1901-1970) German
£1375 $2419   (10-Apr-92 KM.K321/R) Female figure kneeling (105cm-41in) mono. bronze
     st.f.Kittel Dusseldorf (DM 4000)

BEELER, Joe Neil (1931-) American
£1105 $2000   (4-Dec-91 D.NY48/R) Praying for rain (46cm-18in) s. num.19/30 brown
      pat.bronze

BEGAS, Reinhold (1831-1911) German
£1890 $3289   (21-Sep-91 SA.A485/R) Torso (35cm-14in) black brown pat.bronze (DM 5500)
£7692 $13692   (30-Nov-91 VG.B111/R) Centaur and nymph (90cm-35in) d.1881/86 green-brown
      pat.bronze st.f.Gladenbeck (DM 22000)

BEGUINE, Michel Leonard (1855-1929) French
£828 $1423   (16-Oct-91 KM.K1632) Singing young woman with lute seated in chair
      (57cm-22in) i. bronze (DM 2400)
£2771 $4849   (18-Feb-92 DUR.M431/R) Ninfa tocando doble caramillo griego (81cm-32in)
      s. bronze (S.P 500000)

BEHN, Fritz (1878-?) Austrian
£1158 $1980   (13-Mar-92 FN.S1378) Water buffalo (37cm-15in) mono. bronze
      st.f.A.Brandstetter Munchen (DM 3300)
£2448 $4357   (25-Nov-91 WK.M72/R) Female nude squatting (50x19x33cm-20x7x13in)
      mono.d.1918 marble (DM 7000)

BEHRENS, William (20th C) ?
£33668 $56563   (16-Aug-91 ZZ.F46/R) Le joueur de polo (180x127cm-71x50in) s.num.6/6
      green brn.pat.bronze marble base (F.FR 335000)

BELL, John (19th C) British
£11000 $19250   (20-Feb-92 C148/R) The Octoroon (160cm-63in) s.i. bronze

BELLEGHEM, Gilbert van (20th C) Belgian
£2039 $3487   (21-Mar-92 KV.L294) Kneeling nude (82x88cm-32x35in) marble (B.FR 120000)

BELLING, Rudolf (20th C) ?
£7714 $13500   (25-Feb-92 SY.NY24/R) The boxer Max Schmeling (54cm-21in) i. dark brown
      pat.bronze st.f.H.Noack Berlin
£12587 $22406   (29-Nov-91 VG.B54/R) Fabeltier, sog. Horchtier, Kuhlerfigur fur Autofirma
      Horch (10cm-4in) s.d.1923 dark brown pat.bronze (DM 36000)

BELLINI, Paolo (1941-) Italian
£4790 $8671   (7-Dec-91 KV.L490/R) Figura verticale (91cm-36in) s.d.79 num.1/3 bronze
      brown pat. (B.FR 280000)

BELLONI, Jose (?) ?
£1235 $2100   (9-Aug-91 GC.M210) El Gausquero (27cm-11in) bronze on wood socle

BELMONDO, Paul (1898-1982) French?
£2569 $4419   (4-Mar-92 AT.P98/R) Baigneuse (18cm-7in) s.num.2/7 pat.bronze
      Cast.Valsuani cire perdue (F.FR 25000)

BEN (1935-) Swiss
£2026 $3668   (21-May-92 CC.P99) La couleur est rouge mais passe vite au brun puis au
      noir (35x44cm-14x17in) s.d.1978 acrylic mouse-traps panel (F.FR 20000)

BENATOV, Leonardo (1899-) Russian
£2866 $5101   (27-Nov-91 AT.P72/R) L'armenien (41cm-16in) s.num.EA II/IV green
      pat.bronze Cast.Valsuani (F.FR 28000)
£4606 $8199   (27-Nov-91 AT.P73/R) Femme au bras leve (66cm-26in) s.num.4/8 pat.bronze
      Cast.Valsuani (F.FR 45000)

BENGLIS, Linda (1941-) American
£3911 $7000   (13-Nov-91 CH.NY218/R) Tukki (34x99x31cm-13x39x12in) bronze vapourized
      aluminium copper coating
£6286 $11000   (25-Feb-92 SY.NY249/R) Pankh, wing (125x24x29cm-49x9x11in) gold leaf over
      plaster metal wire

BENK, Johannes (1844-?) Austrian
£2700 $4806   (29-Nov-91 S92/R) Young woman, Cupid and doves (60cm-24in) s. brown
      pat.bronze

BENLLIURE Y GIL, Mariano (1862-1947) Spanish
£1228 $2112   (16-Oct-91 FER.M314/R) Velazquez (63cm-25in) s. bronze (S.P 225000)
£1663 $2943   (12-Feb-92 ANS.M372/R) Toro (23x49x20cm-9x19x8in) s.d.1943 num.2/2 bronze
      (S.P 300000)
£2353 $4236   (28-Jan-92 EP.M26/R) Toro (22cm-9in) s.d.1947 num.1/6 pat.bronze
      (S.P 425000)
£3876 $6977   (28-Jan-92 EP.M27/R) Ensalzando la naranja (67cm-26in) s.i.d.1946
      escayola (S.P 700000)

BEOTHY, Etienne (1876-1961) Hungarian
£3360 $6150   (3-Jun-92 CSC.P2/R) Suzanne II (47x6x7cm-19x2x3in) s.num.4/6 brown
      pat.bronze f.st.Thinot Paris (F.FR 33000)
£4500 $8595   (30-Jun-92 C147/R) Suzanne, Opus 33 (47cm-19in) s. num.2/8 green/brown
      pat.bronze f.st.E Godard
£4888 $8945   (3-Jun-92 CSC.P8/R) Attitude, opus 90, 1945 (71cm-28in) s.num.6/6 brown
      pat.bronze f.st.Blanchet (F.FR 48000)

BEOTHY, Etienne (1876-1961) Hungarian-cont.
£4990 $9131   (3-Jun-92 CSC.P11/R) Couple IV (51x28x10cm-20x11x4in) s.num.2/6 brown
    pat.bronze f.st.Blanchet (F.FR 49000)

BERG, Christian (20th C) Swedish
£1608 $2911   (19-May-92 AB.S5130/R) The shell (19cm-7in) s.num.5, polished bronze
    incl.stone base (S.KR 17000)
£3690 $6678   (19-May-92 AB.S5129/R) Shell shape (32cm-13in) s.num.1, polished bronze
    incl.stone base (S.KR 39000)

BERGE, Edward Henry (1876-1924) American
£1215 $2200   (4-Dec-91 D.NY51/R) Duck mother (56cm-22in) s. greenish-brown pat.bronze
    f.st.Roman Works
£6316 $12000   (23-Jun-92 CE.NY63/R) Nymph sitting on vine covered tree stump
    (71x64cm-28x25in) i. pat.bronze i.f.Roman Bronze Works
£7182 $13000   (4-Dec-91 D.NY52/R) Wild flower (107cm-42in) s. greenish-brown pat.bronze
    f.st.Roman Works

BERGMAN (?) ?
£1200 $2292   (30-Jun-92 PH93/R) Harem dancer standing on covered plinth (40cm-16in) s.
    s. cold painted bronze
£1350 $2579   (30-Jun-92 PH92/R) Snake charmer on carpet covered circular base
    (44cm-17in) s. cold painted bronze

BERGMAN, Franz (19/20th C) Austrian
£1100 $1958   (29-Nov-91 S237/R) North African cooking scene (20cm-8in) st.num.3412
    cold-painted polychrome bronze
£1400 $2492   (29-Nov-91 S236/R) Elephant tiger hunt (24cm-9in) st. cold-painted
    polychrome bronze
£2400 $4272   (29-Nov-91 S239/R) The oasis (70cm-28in) s. cold-painted polychrome
    pat.bronze

BERGMANN (?) ?
£2000 $3520   (8-Apr-92 CSK111/R) Model of cockerel (29cm-11in) mono. num.7018 cold
    painted bronze glass

BERKE, Hubert (20th C) German?
£1614 $2905   (19-Nov-91 L.K557) Untitled (42x26cm-17x10in) s.i.d.1959 wood nails
    (DM 4600)
£1754 $3158   (19-Nov-91 L.K558/R) Untitled (36x30cm-14x12in) s.d.1959 wood nails
    (DM 5000)
£2807 $5053   (19-Nov-91 L.K559) Constallation in black-white (85x25x18cm-33x10x7in)
    s.i.d.1959verso wood nails (DM 8000)

BERLINGERI (?) Italian?
£1361 $2532   (16-Jun-92 F.M15) Bambino con cesto di frutta (42cm-17in) s. bronze
    (I.L 3000000)

BERNARD, Joseph (1864-1933) French
£12320 $22177   (20-Nov-91 CN.P67/R) Femme au bain (68cm-27in) s.num.7 pat.bronze cire
    perdue Cast.Valsuani (F.FR 120000)

BERNINI (after) (?) Italian
£3670 $6312   (7-Oct-91 CH.E28/R) Busts (102cm-40in) one i. marble on wooden plinth
    pair (E.P 4000)
£7000 $12460   (1-Nov-91 S322/R) Bust of Monsignor Pedro de Montoya (67cm-26in) white
    marble

BERROCAL (attrib) (?) ?
£1018 $1884   (11-Jun-92 ARC.P21) Romeo et Julietta gilt pat.bronze (F.FR 10000)

BERROCAL, Miguel (1933-) Spanish
£722 $1300   (22-Nov-91 S.BM221/R) Abstract figure study (15x23cm-6x9in) s. num.1902
    gold pat.bronze
£1083 $1863   (12-Oct-91 KV.L17) Mini David (13x5cm-5x2in) s. 2346/10000 aluminium
    alloy (B.FR 65000)
£1094 $2079   (23-Jun-92 DUR.M313/R) Torso masculino (27cm-11in) s. num.338/2000 bronze
    (S.P 200000)
£1203 $2201   (2-Jun-92 L.K501/R) Goliath (20x14x10cm-8x6x4in) i.num.595/2000 brass 79
    parts st.f.Reischauer (DM 3500)
£1250 $2150   (12-Oct-91 KV.L16) Richelieu (19x15cm-7x6in) s.num.696/2000 polished
    brass (B.FR 75000)
£1486 $2600   (27-Feb-92 CE.NY187/R) Mini-David (14x6x6cm-6x2x2in) st.sig.num.000101
    000103 gold plated bronze two
£1573 $2847   (23-May-92 KV.L22) Torero (28x22cm-11x9in) s.num.30/2000 polished bronze
    (B.FR 95000)
£1622 $3000   (12-Jun-92 SY.NY283/R) Torso (27cm-11in) s. polished bronze
£1640 $2788   (23-Oct-91 DUR.M646/R) Torso masculino (26cm-10in) s.num.329/2000 bronze
    (S.P 300000)
£1918 $3376   (7-Apr-92 C.A2/R) Torero (27cm-11in) s. bronze (B.FR 115000)
£2033 $3537   (13-Apr-92 GL.P168/R) Romeo e Giulietta (21x12x9cm-8x5x4in) s.num.918 16
    pieces iron soldered polished (F.FR 20000)
£2046 $3520   (16-Oct-91 FER.M301/R) Torso de torero (28cm-11in) s. num.780/2000 gilded
    bronze (S.P 375000)

BERROCAL, Miguel (1933-) Spanish-cont.
£2548 $4740 (15-Jun-92 GL.P93 b/R) Romeo e Julietta (21x12x9cm-8x5x4in) s.num.36 articulated polished iron (F.FR 25000)

BERSTAMM, Leopold Bernard (1859-1910) Russian
£1813 $3082 (24-Oct-91 CJ.N111/R) Victor Hugo (53cm-21in) s. pat.bronze. Cast.Barbedienne (F.FR 18000)

BERTELLI, R G (20th C) ?
£7003 $13166 (18-Dec-91 FB.P182 b) Buste de Mussolini (27cm-11in) s.d.1935 num.2/10base brn.pat.bronze (F.FR 68000)

BERTHOLD, Joachim (?) ?
£914 $1600 (28-Feb-92 SY.NY333/R) Mother and child (22cm-9in) i. num.3/9 dark brown pat.bronze

BERTOIA, Harry (1915-1978) American
£1047 $1800 (10-Oct-91 FA.PH794/R) Bush (15x25x8cm-6x10x3in) welded phosphorous bronze
£1892 $3500 (12-Jun-92 SY.NY281/R) Multiplane construction (107x273cm-42x107in) bronze gold pat.
£2200 $3806 (26-Mar-92 C67/R) Tree (80cm-31in) stainless steel wires
£2400 $4128 (17-Oct-91 S12/R) Tonal (107cm-42in) bronze phosphorus bronze rods
£2674 $4600 (10-Oct-91 FA.PH795/R) Sounding sculpture (61cm-24in) beryllium copper rods
£3143 $5500 (28-Feb-92 SY.NY328/R) Winds (93cm-37in) berillium copper
£4070 $7000 (12-Oct-91 SY.NY310/R) Wire sculpture (94cm-37in) steel wires slate base
£4215 $7250 (12-Oct-91 SY.NY312/R) Multiplane construction (189cm-74in) gold pat.bronze
£6800 $11696 (17-Oct-91 S15/R) Bush (46cm-18in) bronze
£6977 $12000 (10-Oct-91 FA.PH793/R) Sonambient - sounding sculpture (114cm-45in) 16 rods on square base phosphorous bronze rods
£7821 $14000 (14-Nov-91 SY.NY326/R) Bush (33cm-13in) bronze
£11919 $20500 (10-Oct-91 FA.PH796/R) Willow tree (183cm-72in) stainless steel wires

BERTOS, Francesco (attrib) (fl.1693-1733) Italian
£8500 $15470 (12-Dec-91 S155/R) Figures of naked dancing children (46cm-18in) bronze pair

BESI, G (19th C) Italian
£800 $1376 (3-Mar-92 SWS499/R) Bust of a child (99cm-39in) indist.s. alabaster waisted socle

BEURDEN, Alphonse van (1854-1938) Flemish
£850 $1454 (10-Mar-92 PH31/R) Bust of laughing young boy wearing tasselled cap (60cm-24in) s.i.d.1886verso marble
£1235 $2198 (30-Apr-92 RAS.K1070/R) Mother seated nursing baby (158cm-62in) s. marble incl.base (D.KR 14000)
£1450 $2639 (27-May-92 SWS367/R) Figure of child - la Toilette (210cm-83in) s. white marble
£1499 $2788 (16-Jun-92 SY.B117/R) Seated boy resting head on raised leg (213cm-84in) marble (B.FR 90000)
£2165 $4027 (16-Jun-92 SY.B109/R) Naked boy (210cm-83in) marble (B.FR 130000)

BEUYS, Joseph (1921-1986) German
£1296 $2345 (3-Dec-91 AB.S5190/R) Wirtschaftswert - DDR-Tute (28x19cm-11x7in) s.d.1979 bag with tea in wooden box (S.KR 13500)
£1538 $2754 (19-Jan-92 CC.P42) Bidon d'huile F I U (53cm-21in) s.num.9/50 metal olive oil (F.FR 15000)
£8421 $15158 (22-Nov-91 SA.A460/R) Green violin (61cm-24in) st.sig. (DM 24000)
£24000 $45840 (2-Jul-92 C26/R) Handkreuz (20x15x2cm-8x6x1in) light brown pat.bronze chased
£28000 $53480 (2-Jul-92 C24/R) Wurfkreuz mit uhr (19x13cm-7x5in) st.verso dark brown pat.bronze stop watch

BICKERTON, Ashley (20th C) American?
£11732 $21000 (14-Nov-91 SY.NY209/R) Uuehh (76x219x35cm-30x86x14in) acrylic silver paint plywood aluminium

BIGONET, Charles (?-1935) French
£1235 $2235 (4-Dec-91 LD.P189) La metisse (45cm-18in) s. brn.pat.bronze Cast.Siot cire perdue (F.FR 12000)

BILL, Max (1908-) Swiss
£3200 $5504 (17-Oct-91 S125/R) Unity of 3 equal volumes (20x25x33cm-8x10x13in) gilt brass
£56000 $96320 (17-Oct-91 C32/R) Hexagonal surface in form of column (315cm-124in) s.d.1953 polished gold pat.bronze

BISSELL, George Edwin (1839-1920) American
£1564 $2800 (14-Nov-91 CE.NY242) Bust of Abraham Lincoln (45cm-18in) i. reddish brown pat.bronze f.Gorham Founders

BJERG, Johannes C (20th C) Danish
£758 $1303   (16-Oct-91 KH.K27/R) Abessinier (55cm-22in) s. st.DK7, one of ten bronze
                      (D.KR 8500)
£1610 $2930   (10-Dec-91 RAS.K238) Abessinier (67cm-26in) s.d.1914-15 pat bronze
                      incl.marble base (D.KR 18000)
£11271 $20063   (25-Nov-91 BU.K47/R) Dawn (172cm-68in) s.d.41-42 num.4, pat.bronze stone
                      base (D.KR 125000)

BLAY, Miguel (19th C) Spanish
£1368 $2490   (11-Dec-91 FER.M242/R) Busto de dama (20cm-8in) s. pat.terracotta
                      (S.P 250000)

BLOCH, Elisa (19th C) Scandinavian
£759 $1389   (17-May-92 BU.M425) On one's knee (45cm-18in) s. dark pat bronze
                      (S.KR 8000)

BLOCHE, Roger (1865-?) French
£1331 $2368   (27-Nov-91 BL.P174/R) Leon Lhermitte dessinant (39cm-15in) s.i.d.1898
                      pat.bronze (F.FR 13000)

BLOCK, Emiel de (1941-) Belgian
£1501 $2642   (7-Apr-92 C.A18/R) Eva (70cm-28in) s.num.2/6 bronze (B.FR 90000)
£1504 $2556   (22-Oct-91 C.A32) Torso (77cm-30in) mono. bronze (B.FR 90000)

BLONDAT, Max (1879-1926) French
£2214 $3786   (18-Mar-92 ARC.P65/R) Le baiser des naiades (33x51cm-13x20in) s.num.1753
                      tin Cast.Siot Decauville, Paris (F.FR 21500)

BLUMENTHAL, Hermann (1905-1942) German
£2281 $4105   (21-Nov-91 L.K42/R) Standing figure with arms raised (28cm-11in) i. brown
                      pat.bronze marble socle (DM 6500)
£15700 $28416   (23-May-92 GB.B6261/R) Male figure kneeling with raised arms
                      (63x23x22cm-25x9x9in) mono brown pat.bronze (DM 46000)

BLUNDSTONE, Ferdinand-Victor (1882-?) Swiss
£2300 $3933   (20-Mar-92 S176/R) Diana and greyhound (46cm-18in) s.d.1931 green brown
                      pat.bronze on marble base

BOCK, Arthur (1875-?) German
£962 $1761   (2-Jun-92 FN.S1306) Squatting female nude (78cm-31in) s.i. stone
                      (DM 2800)

BODINI, Floriano (1933-) Italian
£2497 $4444   (29-Apr-92 F.F236/R) Nike (40cm-16in) s.d.1987 num.4/6 bronze
                      (I.L 5500000)

BODIOU, Yves (1954-) ?
£869 $1590   (3-Feb-92 HH.P46/R) Le taureau mythique (21x34x11cm-8x13x4in) s.num.2/8
                      brn.pat.bronze Cast.Centri Or (F.FR 8500)

BOEHM, J E (?) ?
£1200 $2088   (18-Sep-91 PHS122) Grenadier Guardsman (58cm-23in) i. bronze on plinth
                      st.Elkington

BOERO, Jacques (19th C) Italian
£4200 $7350   (27-Sep-91 S19/R) French Noblewoman (86cm-34in) s. Carrara marble

BOHEMIAN SCHOOL, 18th C
£3072 $5560   (21-May-92 L.K212/R) St Johannes von Nepomuk standing holding crucifix
                      (127cm-50in) i. wood (DM 9000)

BOISSEAU, Emile Andre (1842-1923) French
£1600 $2848   (29-Nov-91 S194/R) Cupid (63cm-25in) s. marble
£3200 $5472   (20-Mar-92 S77/R) Psyche with two children (64cm-25in) s. marble

BOLOGNESE SCHOOL, 18th C Italian
£2308 $4408   (15-Jul-92 CH.S496/R) Group of Madonna and child (34cm-13in) terracotta
                      (A.D 6000)

BOLOTOWSKY, Ilya (1907-1984) Russian
£1117 $2000   (12-Nov-91 CE.NY93/R) Untitled (76x18x18cm-30x7x7in) i.num.XXI/XXV
                      acrylic silkscreen plexiglas

BOLTANSKI, Christian (1944-) French
£17877 $32000   (6-May-92 CH.NY228/R) Vitrine of Reference (12x73x110cm-5x29x43in)
                      vitrine tin wood plastic wax wire photos cloth
£36313 $65000   (5-May-92 CH.NY67/R) Reliquaire (220x241x91cm-87x95x36in) 8 columns 118
                      tin boxes photographs 8 lamps

BOLTEN, Arent van (after) (17th C) Dutch
£1300 $2496   (7-Jul-92 C164/R) Grotesque beast with bird-like legs and snail like body
                      (17cm-7in) bronze oil lamp on marble base

BOLZ, Hans (1887-1918) German
£7368 $13263   (21-Nov-91 L.K44/R) Head (37x20cm-15x8in) green pat.bronze (DM 21000)

BONE, Phyllis Mary (1896-1972) British
£850 $1513   (29-Apr-92 CG303/R) Study of foal (27cm-11in) i.d.1935 bronze

BONEVARDI, Marcelo (1929-) Argentinian
£2778 $5000   (19-Nov-91 CH.NY168/R) Table with objects (122x76cm-48x30in) s.d.68
              i.verso oil gesso wood construction
£4444 $8000   (18-Nov-91 SY.NY177/R) Astrolabio II (105x118cm-41x46in) s.i.d.64verso
              painted canvas wood construction

BONHEUR, I (1827-1901) French
£1400 $2506   (13-Nov-91 CSK71/R) Bull (21cm-8in) s. bronze

BONHEUR, Isidore (1827-1901) French
£800 $1368   (20-Mar-92 S54/R) Baying stag (23cm-9in) s. brown pat.bronze st.f.Peyrol
£820 $1402   (10-Mar-92 PH65/R) Model of prowling lioness (31cm-12in) s. bronze
£920 $1600   (15-Apr-92 B.SF3201) Equestrian group (74x61cm-29x24in) i. brown
              pat.bronze
£1000 $1710   (20-Mar-92 S49/R) Panther beside stream (11cm-4in) s. brown pat.bronze
              st.f.Peyrol
£1283 $2310   (18-Nov-91 AT.P312) Cavalier arabe au fusil (32cm-13in) s.base
              brn.pat.bronze (F.FR 12500)
£1475 $2700   (5-Jun-92 SY.NY113/R) Hen investigating a snail. Goose drinking from
              bucket (7cm-3in) i. bronze br.pat. pair
£1700 $3026   (29-Nov-91 S6) Pigs (14cm-6in) s. red/brown pat.bronze on marble base
£1769 $3096   (30-Mar-92 ZZ.F136/R) Le taureau a la patte levee (30x34cm-12x13in)
              brn.pat.bronze (F.FR 17000)
£1900 $3249   (20-Mar-92 S62/R) Walking racehorse (21cm-8in) s. brown pat.bronze
£1982 $3428   (1-Oct-91 SY.AM172/R) Horse and jockey (87cm-34in) s. pat.bronze
              (D.FL 6500)
£2081 $3642   (30-Mar-92 ZZ.F142/R) Le postillon (33x35cm-13x14in) s.base brn.green
              pat.bronze (F.FR 20000)
£2198 $4000   (27-May-92 CH.NY112/R) Milkmaid and cow (30cm-12in) i.f.Peyrol red brown
              pat.
£2400 $4104   (20-Mar-92 S69/R) Standing bull (31cm-12in) s.i. brown pat.bronze
£3088 $5250   (25-Oct-91 S.W2637) Prince of Wales, King Edward VII on horseback
              (41cm-16in) s. silvered bronze f.st.Paval, London
£3415 $6250   (5-Jun-92 SY.NY111/R) Standing ram (27x34cm-11x13in) i. bronze br.pat.
£4121 $7500   (27-May-92 CH.NY96/R) A pointer (33x73cm-13x29in) i.f.Peyrol bronze red
              brown pat.
£4396 $8000   (27-May-92 CH.NY111/R) Postillion and two carriage horses (36cm-14in)
              i.f.Peyrol bronze red brown pat.
£4500 $8010   (29-Nov-91 S33/R) Standing bull (38cm-15in) s. brown pat.bronze
              st.f.Peyrol

BONHEUR, Isidore (after) (1827-1901) French
£3700 $6290   (23-Oct-91 B98 a/R) Horse with jockey up (94cm-37in) bronze

BONHEUR, Rosa (1822-1899) French
£843 $1500   (30-Apr-92 CE.NY80/R) Figure of grazing ewe (14cm-6in) i. medium brown
              pat.bronze
£900 $1539   (20-Mar-92 S64/R) Reclining bull (15cm-6in) s. brown pat.bronze
              st.f.Peyrol
£955 $1700   (30-Apr-92 CE.NY64/R) figure of bull (18cm-7in) i. reddish brown
              pat.bronze st.
£1047 $1800   (16-Oct-91 CH.NY138/R) Figure of a sheep (13cm-5in) i. st.Peyrol
              brn.pat.bronze
£1600 $2736   (20-Mar-92 S41/R) Walking bull (18cm-7in) s. brown pat.bronze st.f.Peyrol
£1969 $3425   (19-Sep-91 GK.Z539/R) Bull walking (31x17cm-12x7in) s. dark pat.bronze
              st.f.Peyrol (S.FR 5000)

BONNARD, Pierre (1867-1947) French
£5866 $10500 (9-May-92 CE.NY6/R) Baigneuse (27cm-11in) init.num.15/24 dark brown
              pat.bronze

BONTECOU, Lee (1931-) American
£3073 $5500   (13-Nov-91 CH.NY129/R) Untitled (24x20x10cm-9x8x4in) oil canvas welded
              steel in artist frame

BORATON, A (20th C) French
£1000 $1710   (20-Mar-92 S6/R) Two chicks and a duckling (15x46cm-6x18in) s.i. brown
              green pat.bronze st.f.Susse Freres

BORGLUM, J Gutzon (1867-1941) American
£2261 $4250   (18-Dec-91 SY.NY153/R) Isadora Duncan (31cm-12in) i. brown black pat.
              bronze

BOROFSKY, Jonathan (1942-) American
£6286 $11000 (27-Feb-92 CH.NY97/R) Pencil head (91x53x16cm-36x21x6in) i. acrylic
              sixteen pencils canvas
£11173 $20000 (14-Nov-91 SY.NY257/R) Motor mind at 2,559,701 (188x119cm-74x47in) dayglo
              paint masonite aluminium relief motor

BORRAS, Jorge (1952-) French
£1030 $1761   (22-Mar-92 LT.P110/R) Jeue fille a la natte (24cm-9in) s.num.11/1V i.EA
              brn.pat.bronze Cast.Blanchet (F.FR 10000)

BORRAS, Jorge (1952-) French-cont.

£1107	$1903	(7-Oct-91 HH.P82/R) Le soir (35x20x17cm-14x8x7in) s.d.1952 num.6/8 green pat.bronze Cast.Landowski (F.FR 11000)
£1460	$2482	(27-Oct-91 LT.P81/R) Reverie (41cm-16in) s.i.num.2/8 brn.pat.bronze cire perdue (F.FR 14500)
£1529	$2844	(21-Jun-92 LT.P92/R) Printemps (42x20x21cm-17x8x8in) s.num.2/8 grn.pat.bronze st.f.Fond.de la Plaine (F.FR 15000)
£1529	$2844	(21-Jun-92 LT.P93/R) Porteuse d'eau (42x21x21cm-17x8x8in) s.num.2/8 brn.pat.bronze st.f.Fond.de la Plaine (F.FR 15000)
£1545	$2642	(22-Mar-92 LT.P109/R) Le baiser (26cm-10in) s.num.7/8 brn.green pat.bronze Cast.Landowski (F.FR 15000)
£2249	$4117	(3-Feb-92 HH.P4/R) Reverie (37x25x26cm-15x10x10in) s.num.4/8 brn.pat.bronze Cast.Landowski (F.FR 22000)

BOTERO, Fernando (1932-) Colombian

£37500	$67500	(18-Nov-91 SY.NY44/R) Cabeza de mujer (38cm-15in) s.d.75 white marble
£44199	$80000	(18-May-92 CH.NY33/R) Bailarina (34cm-13in) s.num.1/9 brown pat.bronze
£55249	$100000	(18-May-92 CH.NY59/R) El Obispo (120cm-47in) s.num.1/6 polychromed polyester
£82873	$150000	(19-May-92 SY.NY58/R) Desnudo reclinado (91cm-36in) s.num.5/6 black pat.bronze st.f.Fonderia M

BOTTIGLIERI, Matteo (attrib) (1684-1757) Italian

£5578	$10095	(4-Dec-91 CH.R81/R) Cristo deposto (16x18x46cm-6x7x18in) terracotta polychrome (I.L 12000000)

BOUCHARDON (after) (18th C) French

£923	$1763	(30-Jun-92 SY.AM476/R) Satyr leaning forward to kiss nymph with child and young satyr at feet (49cm-19in) s.i. green pat.bronze (D.FL 3000)

BOUCHER, Alfred (1850-1934) French

£1868	$3250	(13-Sep-91 SY.NY53/R) Figure of violin player (65cm-26in) i. gilt bronze on black pat.socle

BOURAINE (20th C) ?

£850	$1624	(2-Jul-92 CSK80/R) Nubian slave presenting Salome with the head of St John the Baptist (43cm-17in) marble vase and white chequered floor

BOURAINE, Marcel (20th C) French

£1600	$2848	(29-Nov-91 S222/R) Warrior (34cm-13in) i. green/brown pat.bronze
£2200	$4026	(15-May-92 S328/R) Penthesilia Queen of the Amazons (49cm-19in) i.f.Susse Freres Editeurs silvered bronze

BOURDELLE, Antoine (1861-1929) French

£1892	$3500	(12-Jun-92 SY.NY13/R) Petite nymphe (13cm-5in) i. greenish-black pat.bronze st.f.A.Valsuani
£2863	$5239	(3-Feb-92 HH.P18/R) Sourire (24x31cm-9x12in) s.base painted plaster (F.FR 28000)
£4469	$8000	(9-May-92 CE.NY9/R) Torse de l'urne (38cm-15in) i.num.2 green pat.bronze st.Clementi
£4749	$8500	(9-May-92 CE.NY7/R) Eve (28cm-11in) s.i.num.IV d.1908 brown pat.bronze st.f.Valsuani
£5464	$10000	(13-May-92 CH.NY218/R) Beethoven, etude de buste (29cm-11in) s.i.num.1 golden brown pat.bronze f.i.
£8571	$15000	(25-Feb-92 CH.NY18/R) Femme au compas - Mme Bourdelle (43cm-17in) s. brown pat.bronze f.i.Converset Fondeur Paris
£9714	$17000	(25-Feb-92 CH.NY24/R) La sieste (41cm-16in) s.i.num.VI green brown pat.bronze f.st.
£12022	$22000	(13-May-92 CH.NY211/R) Bacchante portant Eros (59cm-23in) s.i.num.IV dark brown pat.bronze f.i.Paris
£22599	$40000	(6-Nov-91 CH.NY279/R) Portrait de Mlle Markovitch, eleve russe (64cm-25in) s.i.num.III brown pat.bronze i.f.M.Hohwiller
£81716	$143003	(24-Feb-92 ARC.P34/R) Herakles archer (71x58cm-28x23in) s.i.d.janvier 1921 pat.bronze Cast.Rudier (F.FR 800000)
£87432	$160000	(12-May-92 CH.NY101/R) La victoire (123cm-48in) s. dark brown pat.bronze f.i. Alexis Rudier

BOURET (19th C) French

£850	$1556	(15-May-92 CBS181) Seated tambourine girl dressed in lion skin cape (25cm-10in) s. gilt bronze

BOURET, Eutrope (1833-1906) French

£739	$1300	(6-Apr-92 B.LA2621) Wind blown maiden with arms crossed wearing mandolin on back (53cm-21in) i. brown pat.bronze on marble base

BOURGEOIS, Louise (20th C) French

£100559	$180000	(12-Nov-91 CH.NY38/R) Untitled (165cm-65in) painted wood

BOUVAL, M (1863-1920) French

£850	$1624	(2-Jul-92 CSK119/R) Female nude cloaked in flowing robe standing with casket held to breast (36cm-14in) s. pat.bronze
£906	$1541	(25-Oct-91 PLF.P104/R) Saliere (6cm-2in) s. gilded pat.bronze (F.FR 9000)

BOUVAL, Maurice (1863-1920) French
£1556 $2816   (19-May-92 GF.L483/R) Female figure standing holding her dress
   (27cm-11in) s. gold pat.bronze st.f.Jollet Cie Paris (S.FR 4200)
£6687 $12104   (4-Dec-91 LD.P207/R) Ophelie (35cm-14in) s. gilded bronze Cast.E Colin
   and Cie, Paris (F.FR 65000)

BOUVAL, Maurice (after) (1863-1920) French
£855 $1530   (17-Nov-91 LT.P5/R) Un buste de femme dans des feuillages (36cm-14in)
   s.i.C.A pat.bronze (F.FR 8400)

BOYLE, Mark (20th C) ?
£1700 $3145   (11-Jun-92 C86/R) Lorry park study (30x30x6cm-12x12x2in) s.i.d.1974 verso
   mixed media construction

BOYLES, N (?) ?
£760 $1300   (13-Mar-92 WOL.C1108/R) Two goldfish swimming through seaweed (91cm-36in)
   s.d.84 bronze

BRACH, Malvina (19/20th C) French
£1700 $3026   (29-Nov-91 S105/R) Undressing (67cm-26in) s. brown pat.bronze
£3491 $6178   (5-Nov-91 BA.S253/R) Girl with slippers (69cm-27in) s. green pat bronze
   (S.KR 37000)

BRACKEN, Clio Hinton (1870-1926) American
£798 $1500   (18-Dec-91 SY.NY159/R) Nymph with drapery (14cm-6in) i. brown green pat.
   bronze

BRACQUEMOND, E L (20th C) French
£1318 $2400   (26-May-92 FB.P52) Panthere (36cm-14in) s. brown pat.bronze (F.FR 13000)

BRACQUEMOND, Emile Louis (20th C) French
£916 $1602   (3-Apr-92 CB.P100/R) Panthere (23cm-9in) s. gilt pat.bronze blk.marble
   base (F.FR 8800)

BRAQUE, Georges (1882-1963) French
£7650 $14000   (13-May-92 CH.NY274/R) Le Nil (27x31cm-11x12in) init.num. 2/6 grey green
   pat.bronze

BRAVO, Claudio (1936-) Chilean
£14444 $26000   (19-Nov-91 CH.NY129/R) Pan (24cm-9in) s.d.MCMLXXIV painted bronze

BREHMER, K P (20th C) German?
£838 $1500   (13-Nov-91 SY.NY126/R) Elly (159x95x10cm-63x37x4in) s.i.d.1965 num.732
   mixed media box with light

BREKER, Arno (1900-) German
£1049 $1867   (25-Nov-91 WK.M116/R) Grazie (25x18x16cm-10x7x6in) s.num.102/300 bronze
   st.f.Venturi arte (DM 3000)
£1134 $1996   (11-Apr-92 AW.H1056/R) Kneeling grace (18x22cm-7x9in) s.d.1979
   num.124/300 green gold pat.bronze st.f. (DM 3300)
£10398 $19339   (19-Jun-92 ARC.P51/R) Richard Wagner (63cm-25in) s.d.1939 green/brown
   pat.bronze. Cast.A.Rudier (F.FR 102000)

BRENNER, Victor David (1871-1924) American
£1341 $2400   (14-Nov-91 CE.NY253) Abraham Lincoln and Gettysburg Address - relief
   (55x73cm-22x29in) i. brown pat.bronze f.i.Gorham Co

BREUER, Peter (1856-1930) German
£4240 $7420   (3-Apr-92 BM.B1550/R) Statue of Kaiser Wilhelm II in parade uniform
   (36cm-14in) i. pat.bronze st.f.H.Gladenbeck (DM 12000)

BRIGAUD, Florentin (20th C) French
£6077 $11000   (5-Dec-91 SY.NY76/R) Standing figure of Cape buffalo (47x61cm-19x24in)
   i.num.I/VII golden-grn.pat.bronze st.f.Valsuani

BRINDESI, Olympio (1897-1965) American
£714 $1300   (13-Dec-91 S.W3022/R) Portrait of American Indian man (46cm-18in)
   s.d.1920 brown pat.bronze

BRITISH SCHOOL, 18th C
£8500 $15470   (27-May-92 SWS348/R) Lion (114x195cm-45x77in) coade stone
£66000 $115500   (24-Sep-91 SWS306/R) Four figures representing the seasons (186cm-73in)
   st.sig. stone designed by John Bacon

BRITISH SCHOOL, 19th C
£2300 $3956   (15-Oct-91 SWS532/R) Figure of a horse and jockey (30cm-12in) bronze gilt
   bronze red marble plinth
£2600 $4498   (30-Sep-91 PHG40/R) Venus (92cm-36in) marble circular base

BROCHET, Francois (20th C) French
£1118 $1945   (16-Apr-92 FB.P65/R) Jeune fille au tournesol (55cm-22in) s.d.61 num.3/5
   brn.pat.bronze (F.FR 11000)

BRONSON, Clark (1939-) American
£3177 $5750   (5-Dec-91 SY.NY68/R) The big boys (81cm-32in) i.num.13/17 d.1984 brown pat.bronze

BROODTHAERS, Marcel (1924-1976) Belgian
£14000 $26740   (2-Jul-92 C73/R) Pelle (115x19x5cm-45x7x2in) wood iron wallpaper felt
£38000 $72580   (2-Jul-92 C75/R) Language de fleurs s.i.d.65 verso oil panel plastic flowers
£44000 $84040   (2-Jul-92 C76/R) Petite cage avec oeufs (24x23x16cm-9x9x6in) metal rods wood egg-shell rope
£52000 $99320   (2-Jul-92 C71/R) Femur de l'homme belge (8x47x10cm-3x19x4in) painted bone
£80000 $152800   (2-Jul-92 C72/R) Panneau de moules (80x60cm-31x24in) panel encrusted mussel shells painted
£120000 $229200   (2-Jul-92 C79/R) Une echelle de briques (230x55x40cm-91x22x16in) ladder brick cement
£160000 $305600   (2-Jul-92 C74/R) Triomphe de moule I - Moules Casserole (50x40x40cm-20x16x16in) painted casserole mussel shells
£170000 $324700   (2-Jul-92 C78/R) La malediction de Magritte (78x62x32cm-31x24x13in) s.i.d.66 verso wood paper glass cotton wool
£360000 $687600   (2-Jul-92 C77/R) Armoire blanche et table blanche (100x100x40cm-39x39x16in) wood oil egg-shells cabinet table

BROOKS, Richard Edwin (1865-1919) American
£806 $1370   (25-Oct-91 PLF.P111/R) Claude Monet a la palette (36cm-14in) s.d.1919 plaster (F.FR 8000)
£4857 $8500   (3-Apr-92 S.W2272/R) John Hanson, first President of United States in Congress assembled (64cm-25in) s.i. bronze f.i.Paris

BROWN, Henry Kirke (1814-1866) American
£1564 $2800   (14-Nov-91 CE.NY244/R) Portrait relief of Thomas Jefferson (25cm-10in) i. brown pat.bronze

BROWN, Joe (1909-1985) American
£1637 $2800   (12-Mar-92 CH.NY117/R) Counter punch, two boxers (25cm-10in) i.d.1949 num.3 green-brown pat.bronze

BRUN, Pierre (?) French?
£1227 $2245   (3-Feb-92 HH.P74/R) La messagere (61x43x29cm-24x17x11in) s.num.2/8 blk.pat.bronze (F.FR 12000)
£1509 $2596   (7-Oct-91 HH.P32/R) L'enigme (54x28x7cm-21x11x3in) s.num.3/8 blue pat.bronze green marble base (F.FR 15000)

BRUTT, Adolf Karl Johannes (1855-?) German
£862 $1483   (16-Oct-91 KM.K1633/R) Female dancer with castanetes (47cm-19in) i.bronze st.f.H.Gladenbeck (DM 2500)

BUECKELAER, Joachim (1530-1573) Flemish
£5115 $9616   (18-Dec-91 GM.B4099/R) Les poissonniers (108x66cm-43x26in) wood (B.FR 300000)

BUENTELLO, Humberto (20th C) ?
£2113 $3634   (7-Oct-91 HH.P30/R) Le bonhomme qui marche (48x34x16cm-19x13x6in) mono.num.1/8 brn.pat.bronze (F.FR 21000)

BUGATTI, Rembrandt (1885-1916) Italian
£7223 $13218   (13-May-92 LC.P62/R) Faon (33x38x11cm-13x15x4in) s. num.10 bronze f.st.A.A.Hebrard (F.FR 71000)
£8065 $14274   (7-Nov-91 AT.P83/R) Biche d'Amerique (22cm-9in) s.num.3 pat.bronze cire perdue Cast.Hebrard (F.FR 80000)
£12097 $21411   (7-Nov-91 AT.P84/R) Femelle jaribu (35cm-14in) s.num.7 blk.pat.bronze cire perdue Cast.Hebrard (F.FR 120000)
£14113 $24980   (7-Nov-91 AT.P81/R) Le reveil (33cm-13in) s. pat.bronze Cast.Hebrard cire perdue (F.FR 140000)
£15121 $26764   (10-Nov-91 ZZ.F153/R) Petites antilopes - La caresse (25x51cm-10x20in) s. brn.pat.bronze Cast.A A Hebrard cire perdue (F.FR 150000)
£19000 $34390   (4-Dec-91 S111/R) Petites antilopes - la mere malade (22x33cm-9x13in) i.num.6 bronze f.st.A.A.Hebrard cire perdue
£20576 $37243   (4-Dec-91 LD.P210/R) Panthere marchant, la patte arriere en bord de terrasse (22x52cm-9x20in) s.base brn.pat.bronze Cast.A A Hebrard (F.FR 200000)
£32000 $61120   (1-Jul-92 S117/R) Panthere marchant (51cm-20in) i.num.E.2 st.f.A.A.Hebrard cire perdue
£42339 $74940   (7-Nov-91 AT.P82/R) La mere blessee, les trois antilopes (60x137cm-24x54in) s.i.d.1911 pat.bronze Cast.Hebrard wood base (F.FR 420000)

BUHOT, C (19th C) ?
£994 $1700   (13-Mar-92 WOL.C1280) Abduction of Helie with Zeus as an eagle (53cm-21in) s. bronze gold br.pat.

BUHOT, Louis Charles Hippolyte (1815-1865) French
£1124 $2000   (30-Apr-92 CE.NY50/R) Group of Hebe abd Jupiter (67cm-26in) s. medium brown pat.bronze

BUIRETTE, Jacques (attrib) (1631-?) French
£28000 $53760   (9-Jul-92 S162/R) River gods allegorical of Tiber and Nile - male figures
                    reclining on drapery (26x45x22cm-10x18x9in) st. bronze pair

BUISSON, Nicole (20th C) French
£1431 $2620   (3-Feb-92 HH.P65/R) A l'infini (41x17x17cm-16x7x7in) s.verso num.1/8
                  brn.pat.bronze Cast.Chapon (F.FR 14000)

BUREAU (after) (?) ?
£3274 $5632   (16-Oct-91 FER.M315/R) Pareja de mosqueteros (91cm-36in) s. bronze pair
                  (S.P 600000)

BURTON, Scott (20th C) American?
£44693 $80000   (5-May-92 CH.NY55/R) Two-part chairs, right angle
                    (107x51x77cm-42x20x30in) polished verde mergozzo granite pair

BURY, Pol (20th C) ?
£4154 $7519   (21-May-92 CC.P112/R) Ponctuation (70x61x20cm-28x24x8in) s.i.d.1973verso
                  wood nylon (F.FR 41000)
£7429 $13000   (27-Feb-92 CH.NY12/R) Septante deux boules, grosses, petites et moyennes
                  (87x62x28cm-34x24x11in) s.i.d.1964verso wood balls wire motor on board

BUTENSKY, J L (1871-?) Russian
£1047 $1800   (20-Oct-91 HG.C102) Figure of man carrying child s.i. bronze f.i.Roman
                  Bronze Works NY

BUTLER, James (1931-) British
£4000 $7080   (5-Nov-91 PH75/R) The young ballet dancer (63cm-25in) s.d.90 num.IX/X
                  bronze

BUTLER, Reg (1913-) British
£1400 $2478   (5-Nov-91 PH78/R) Archaic head (26cm-10in) bronze
£4000 $7400   (11-Jun-92 C121/R) Standing girl (53cm-21in) init.num.6/8 black
                  pat.bronze f.st.Susse Paris
£15000 $26550   (8-Nov-91 C369/R) Seated girl (121x97cm-48x38in) s.d.62 num.2/8
                  blk.pat.bronze base
£22951 $42000   (13-May-92 CH.NY332/R) Figure falling (141x107x109cm-56x42x43in) st.mono.
                  num.2/8 grey green pat.bronze

C W (?) ?
£2600 $4420   (22-Oct-91 C63 a/R) Boer farmer (46cm-18in) i. bronze

CACHEUX, Francois (1923-) French
£5123 $9221   (2-Feb-92 ZZ.F192/R) Aphrodite dansant (46cm-18in) s.num.7/8
                  brn.pat.bronze (F.FR 50000)

CAESAR, Doris (20th C) American?
£857 $1500   (23-Sep-91 S.SL403) Seated woman (23cm-9in) brn.pat.bronze marble plinth

CAFFIERI (after) (?) French?
£3600 $6408   (1-Nov-91 S328/R) Bust of Corneille van Cleve (69cm-27in) marble

CAFFIERI, Jean Jacques (after) (1725-1792) French
£1400 $2534   (21-May-92 C10/R) Le Fleuve (60cm-24in) i.d.1759 terracotta

CAIN, Auguste (1822-1894) French
£1081 $1849   (22-Mar-92 LT.P108) Le coq Francais chantant (46cm-18in) s. pat.bronze
                  (F.FR 10500)
£1236 $2200   (30-Apr-92 CE.NY89/R) Group of two hunting dogs, Seduisant and Lumineau
                  (32cm-13in) i. greenish-brown pat.bronze
£3825 $7000   (5-Jun-92 SY.NY123/R) Lioness with cubs and peacock (61x101cm-24x40in)
                  i.f.Susse Freres bronze dk.br.pat.

CALDER, Alexander (1898-1976) American
£2907 $5000   (12-Oct-91 SY.NY180/R) Horse II (11x20cm-4x8in) bronze
£4469 $8000   (7-May-92 SY.NY232/R) Horse I (20cm-8in) mono. num.5/6 bronze
£4571 $8000   (25-Feb-92 SY.NY191/R) Untitled (8x46x34cm-3x18x13in) init. gouache
                  fiberglass
£5000 $9550   (2-Jul-92 C45/R) Untitled (10x6x5cm-4x2x2in) standing mobile painted
                  sheet metal
£5028 $9000   (9-May-92 CE.NY325/R) Arrows (192cm-76in) s. gouache fiberglass maquette
                  for DC 8
£5028 $9000   (7-May-92 SY.NY236 a/R) Horse II (21cm-8in) init.num.4/6 bronze
£6286 $11000   (25-Feb-92 SY.NY192/R) Untitled (8x46x34cm-3x18x13in) init.i. gouache
                  fiberglass
£8571 $15000   (25-Feb-92 SY.NY190/R) Untitled (8x46x34cm-3x18x13in) init. gouache
                  fiberglass
£10615 $19000   (13-Nov-91 CH.NY137/R) Untitled (9x8cm-4x3in) painted metal mobile
£12346 $23457   (24-Jun-92 FB.P73/R) Untitled (10cm-4in) painted metal iron
                  stabile-mobile (F.FR 120000)

CALDER, Alexander (1898-1976) American-cont.

£14000	$26740	(2-Jul-92 C43/R) Untitled (12x19x9cm-5x7x4in) standing mobile painted sheet metal rod
£14403	$27366	(24-Jun-92 FB.P74/R) Untitled (20x38cm-8x15in) mono. painted metal iron stabile-mobile (F.FR 140000)
£15000	$25800	(17-Oct-91 S48/R) Standing mobile (21x20cm-8x8in) init. painted metal
£15000	$28650	(2-Jul-92 C44/R) Untitled (7x16x4cm-3x6x2in) standing mobile painted sheet metal rod
£17877	$32000	(6-May-92 CH.NY323/R) Untitled (22x28cm-9x11in) init. mobile painted sheet metal brass wire
£18000	$31140	(26-Mar-92 S78/R) Cactus (40cm-16in) init.d.59 metal
£20000	$34400	(17-Oct-91 C71/R) Untitled (20x50cm-8x20in) init.d.71 mobile painted sheet metal rod
£20112	$36000	(6-May-92 CH.NY292/R) Untitled (36x26cm-14x10in) with init. mobile painted metal brass wire rod
£21678	$38587	(29-Nov-91 VG.B62/R) Mobile in Form eines Seehundes (36cm-14in) mono.d.58 welded bronze panel wire (DM 62000)
£22346	$40000	(14-Nov-91 SY.NY269/R) Untitled (34x33x18cm-13x13x7in) painted metal mobile
£26286	$46000	(25-Feb-92 SY.NY99/R) Lantern (32x53x25cm-13x21x10in) init. painted metal standing mobile
£28004	$51808	(13-Jun-92 AT.P70/R) Untitled (80cm-31in) painted steel mobile (F.FR 275000)
£33520	$60000	(6-May-92 CH.NY287/R) Untitled (43x62x25cm-17x24x10in) init. standing mobile painted sheet metal wire
£44000	$84040	(2-Jul-92 C53/R) Untitled (92x118cm-36x46in) standing mobile painted sheet metal rod
£45000	$81450	(5-Dec-91 C32/R) Untitled (123x170cm-48x67in) init.d.66 mobile painted sheet metal rod
£55866	$100000	(6-May-92 SY.NY5 a/R) Red crescent with orange and black (53x152x76cm-21x60x30in) init. painted hanging metal mobile
£55866	$100000	(14-Nov-91 SY.NY285 a/R) Ritou I (81x79x48cm-32x31x19in) painted metal hanging mobile
£60109	$110000	(13-May-92 SY.NY22/R) The arrow (122cm-48in) init.d.61 painted metal hanging mobile
£61453	$110000	(5-May-92 CH.NY31/R) Jaune perse sur rouge (87x95x38cm-34x37x15in) init.d.63 painted sheet metal rod mobile
£64246	$115000	(14-Nov-91 SY.NY295/R) Black flower in seventeen (85x103cm-33x41in) init.d.59 painted metal hanging mobile
£67039	$120000	(7-May-92 SY.NY251/R) Untitled (264x95cm-104x37in) num.I-XII painted metal hanging mobile
£69832	$125000	(7-May-92 SY.NY243/R) Untitled (74x103cm-29x41in) init. painted metal hanging mobile
£83799	$150000	(13-Nov-91 CH.NY134/R) Disque blanc croissant bleu (142x190cm-56x75in) init.d.60 hanging mobile sheet metal rod
£92179	$165000	(6-May-92 SY.NY9 a/R) Carroi (208x132x102cm-82x52x40in) init.d.66 painted metal standing mobile
£94972	$170000	(12-Nov-91 CH.NY43/R) Five white discs with colour tail (216cm-85in) init.d.70 mobile painted sheet metal rod
£106145	$190000	(12-Nov-91 CH.NY61/R) Hanging mobile with two crescents (188x307cm-74x121in) mobile painted sheet metal rod
£110000	$210100	(2-Jul-92 S17/R) Whose breast have you hooked on to (130x170cm-51x67in) painted metal
£120000	$217200	(5-Dec-91 C35/R) Nantes (205x277cm-81x109in) init.d.71 mobile painted sheet metal rod
£122857	$215000	(27-Feb-92 CH.NY15/R) Untitled (212x249x157cm-83x98x62in) init.d.67 standing mobile of painted steel
£201117	$360000	(5-May-92 CH.NY38/R) Roxbury Front (167x292cm-66x115in) init.d.65 painted sheet metal rod hanging mobile
£474860	$850000	(12-Nov-91 CH.NY29/R) Bougainvillea (198x218cm-78x86in) standing mobile paint sheet metal rod wire stone

CALMELS, Celestin Anatole (1822-1906) French

| £1876 | $3526 | (18-Dec-91 GM.B4109) Groupe equestre (47cm-19in) polychrome pat.bronze ivory (B.FR 110000) |

CALVI, Pietro (1833-1884) Italian

£2473	$4500	(28-May-92 SY.NY328/R) Bacchante (71cm-28in) i. marble
£12308	$23508	(19-Jul-92 SY.ME46/R) Bust of Selika (86cm-34in) s.d.1879 bronze marble on marble column (A.D 32000)
£21154	$40404	(19-Jul-92 SY.ME45/R) Bust of Othello (76cm-30in) s.d.1879 bronze marble on marble column (A.D 55000)
£23000	$39330	(20-Mar-92 S121/R) Arab man (69cm-27in) s.i. bronze marble
£105000	$183750	(27-Sep-91 S17/R) Othello (93cm-37in) s.i. Carrara marble brn.pat.bronze

CAMBI, A (19th C) Italian

| £1676 | $3000 | (15-Nov-91 DM.D1334/R) Bust of young girl wearing bead necklace and summer dress (61cm-24in) s.i. white marble |

CAMMILLI, E (19/20th C) French

| £699 | $1300 | (16-Jun-92 RO.BA122) Maternite (48cm-19in) pat.bronze |

CAMPAGNA, Girolamo (studio) (1550-c.1623) Italian

| £7821 | $14000 | (14-Jan-92 CH.NY131/R) Figure of amor, formed as handle of door knocker (33cm-13in) rich dark brown pat.bronze |

CAMPAGNA, Girolamo (style) (1550-c.1623) Italian
£7821 $14000   (14-Jan-92 CH.NY125/R) Candlebearing angels, looking upwards (40cm-16in) reddish brown pat.bronze pair

CAMPAGNE, Pierre Etienne Daniel (1851-?) French
£2889 $4940   (21-Mar-92 KV.L31/R) Draped female nude (85x46cm-33x18in) s. bronze br.pat. (B.FR 170000)

CAMPBELL, Thomas (style) (1790-1858) British
£6200 $11904   (9-Jul-92 S231/R) Bust of soprano Angelica Catalani, with ringlets and coiled plait (54cm-21in) marble

CAMUS, Jean (?) French
£1093 $1912   (31-Mar-92 AT.P82) Baigneuse aux voiles (64cm-25in) s. pat.bronze Cast.Bisceglia cire perdue (F.FR 10500)

CANE, Louis (1943-) French
£811 $1477   (25-May-92 ZZ.F107/R) Les Trois Graces (15x21x6cm-6x8x2in) s.num.1/8 blue pat.bronze st.f.Bocquel (F.FR 8000)
£1744 $3121   (19-Jan-92 CC.P49/R) Balancoire bambou (39x36x22cm-15x14x9in) s.num.1/8 bronze (F.FR 17000)
£2160 $3910   (2-Dec-91 CC.P49/R) Petite femme au tabouret (35x15x12cm-14x6x5in) s.num.5/8 green pat.bronze Cast.Susse Freres (F.FR 21000)
£2650 $4930   (15-Jun-92 GL.P104/R) Femme torse (59x17x17cm-23x7x7in) s.d.82 num.5/6 Cast.Capelli (F.FR 26000)
£4913 $8745   (30-Nov-91 FB.P87/R) Menine espagnole (67x35x34cm-26x14x13in) s.num.1/8verso bronze (F.FR 48000)
£5149 $8805   (17-Mar-92 FB.P77/R) Menine Espagnole (67x35x34cm-26x14x13in) s. num.5/8verso bronze (F.FR 50000)
£5322 $9474   (30-Nov-91 FB.P86/R) Menine du Benin (64x38x35cm-25x15x14in) s.num.1/8base bronze Cast.Susse (F.FR 52000)
£5629 $10020   (30-Nov-91 FB.P88/R) Menine Japonaise (59x36x35cm-23x14x14in) s.num.1/8verso bronze (F.FR 55000)

CANNEEL, Eugene (1882-1966) Belgian
£833 $1433   (12-Oct-91 KV.L31) Motherhood (46x25cm-18x10in) s. bronze green pat. marble socle (B.FR 50000)

CANONICA, Pietro (1869-?) Italian
£1411 $2470   (23-Sep-91 D.L2/R) Dopo il voto (34cm-13in) s. chryselephantine bronze ivory marble base (F.FR 14000)

CANOVA (after) (1757-1822) Italian
£877 $1500   (13-Mar-92 WOL.C952/R) Hercules (41cm-16in) bronze bl.pat.
£1100 $1925   (24-Sep-91 SWS368) Figure of Venus standing (153cm-60in) green pat.bronze

CANOVA, Antonio (after) (1757-1822) Italian
£1152 $1982   (7-Oct-91 SY.J811/R) Statue of Pauline Borghese Bonaparte reclining on chaise longue (50x90cm-20x35in) marble (SA.R 5600)
£2059 $3500   (25-Oct-91 S.W2639/R) Napoleon on rearing horse (53cm-21in) s. bronze
£2200 $3982   (21-May-92 C21/R) Three graces (44cm-17in) alabaster
£2211 $4200   (23-Jun-92 CE.NY13/R) Venus Italica (168x72cm-66x28in) marble
£4200 $8064   (7-Jul-92 C3/R) Three graces embracing (22cm-9in) ivory

CANOVA, Antonio (studio) (1757-1822) Italian
£1910 $3285   (16-Oct-91 FER.M287/R) Busto de Afrodita (64cm-25in) marble (S.P 350000)

CANTRE, Jozef (1890-1957) Belgian
£1500 $2610   (14-Apr-92 GM.B1048/R) Pleureuse s.num.III/VI bronze (B.FR 90000)

CAPPELLO, Carmelo (1912-) Italian
£1946 $3464   (29-Nov-91 F.F148/R) Centro Cosmico (43cm-17in) num.4/5 gold bronze (I.L 4200000)

CARADOSSI, Vittorio (19/20th C) Italian
£850 $1624   (30-Jun-92 PH39/R) Conch shell with reclining naked maiden within (55cm-22in) s. alabaster lamp
£3500 $6125   (20-Feb-92 C146/R) Reclining maiden (23x61cm-9x24in) i. bronze green marble socle

CARBONELL, Manuel (20th C) American?
£3714 $6500   (28-Feb-92 SY.NY91/R) Model for modern dancer (47cm-19in) i. num.1/8 d.1974 polished bronze

CARDENAS, Augustin (1927-) Cuban
£2546 $4633   (15-Dec-91 P.V71/R) Couple (58cm-23in) s.num.1/8base brn.pat.bronze (F.FR 25000)
£4350 $7743   (1-Dec-91 I.N75/R) Jeune femme allongee (16x44x19cm-6x17x7in) s.num.2/8 blk.pat.bronze Cast.Oceane (F.FR 42500)

CARLIER, E (?) French
£2170 $3732   (20-Oct-91 PLF.P111/R) Homme aile sur Bleriot XI (35cm-14in) pat.bronze (F.FR 21500)

CARLIER, Emile Joseph Nestor (1849-1927) French
£1037 $1877   (19-May-92 GF.L296/R) La bonne recette (68cm-27in) s.i. brown pat.bronze (S.FR 2800)

CARO, Anthony (1924-) British
£4571 $8000   (25-Feb-92 SY.NY178/R) Table piece CVII (43x65x45cm-17x26x18in) steel
£5143 $9000   (25-Feb-92 SY.NY119/R) Table piece (56x71x84cm-22x28x33in) num.LXXXIII stainless steel
£7514 $13000   (3-Oct-91 SY.NY49/R) Table piece Z-10 (91x77x88cm-36x30x35in) steel rusted and varnished
£8939 $16000   (13-Nov-91 CH.NY156/R) Writing piece - Div (37x56x15cm-15x22x6in) oil welded steel
£11000 $19030   (26-Mar-92 C73/R) Table piece Z-56 (66x117x38cm-26x46x15in) rusted varnished sheet steel
£11000 $19030   (26-Mar-92 C70/R) Evening (47x46x22cm-19x18x9in) cast welded bronze brass
£16760 $30000   (14-Nov-91 SY.NY316/R) Index (121x140x91cm-48x55x36in) painted steel
£17341 $30000   (3-Oct-91 SY.NY36/R) Jester (99x107x66cm-39x42x26in) painted steel
£20112 $36000   (14-Nov-91 SY.NY305/R) Water street Whow (152x101x61cm-60x40x24in) welded bronze with copper

CARPEAUX, Jean Baptiste (1827-1875) French
£874 $1662   (24-Jun-92 AT.P214) La frileuse (40cm-16in) s. brown pat.bronze. Cast.Susses Freres (F.FR 8500)
£1580 $2750   (13-Sep-91 SY.NY98/R) Bust of fisherboy (49cm-19in) i. brown pat.bronze
£1749 $3166   (4-Dec-91 CB.P83/R) Le pecheur Napolitain (35cm-14in) s.base pat.bronze (F.FR 17000)
£1821 $3296   (23-May-92 KV.L48/R) Pecheur Napolitain (34x19cm-13x7in) s.d.1857 bronze br.pat. (B.FR 110000)
£2187 $4002   (13-May-92 FER.M218/R) Nino con barretina (53cm-21in) st. pat.bronze (S.P 400000)
£3022 $5500   (27-May-92 CH.NY135/R) La Frileuse (40cm-16in) i. bronze red brown pat.
£3529 $6000   (22-Oct-91 CE.NY27/R) Jeune pecheur a la coquille (62cm-24in) i. parcel-gilt polychrome bronze f.st.
£4115 $7819   (26-Jun-92 AGS.P27/R) Etude de femme debout, ou 'L'abondance' (16cm-6in) terracotta on marble socle (F.FR 40000)
£5948 $10527   (7-Nov-91 AT.P85/R) L'amour moqueur (71cm-28in) s. pat.bronze cire perdue Cast.Susse Freres (F.FR 59000)
£6212 $11368   (3-Jun-92 PIC.P36/R) Son Altesse le Prince Imperial et son chien Negro (66cm-26in) s.d.1865 terracotta (F.FR 61000)
£7692 $14000   (27-May-92 CH.NY130/R) Frere et Soeur (64cm-25in) i. bronze red brown pat.
£8172 $14300   (19-Feb-92 D.P38/R) Ugolin et ses fils (48cm-19in) s. pat.bronze (F.FR 80000)
£8287 $15000   (5-Dec-91 SY.NY58/R) Jeune fille a la coquille (93cm-37in) i. st.num.1284 terracotta
£11593 $20519   (7-Nov-91 AT.P86/R) Femme allongee (12cm-5in) s. wax figures plaster base (F.FR 115000)
£26163 $45000   (17-Oct-91 SY.NY80/R) Three Graces (75cm-30in) i.d.1873 terracotta st. atelier seal

CARRIER-BELLEUSE (19/20th C) French
£9357 $16000   (13-Mar-92 WOL.C680 a/R) The Four Seasons (79cm-31in) i. bronze marble base four

CARRIER-BELLEUSE (after) (19th C) French
£1300 $2223   (10-Mar-92 PH30/R) Bust of young woman with eyes closed and locks trailing over shoulder (59cm-23in) marble

CARRIER-BELLEUSE (circle) (19th C) French
£1501 $2581   (16-Oct-91 FER.M291/R) Ninfa tanendo la lira (80cm-31in) bronze on marble base (S.P 275000)

CARRIER-BELLEUSE, A (1824-1887) French
£2400 $4104   (10-Mar-92 PH53/R) Liseuse, figure dressed in 16th century costume (65cm-26in) i. bronze ivory on marble plinth
£2500 $4275   (10-Mar-92 PH49/R) Figures of royal guardsmen holding staff (77x64cm-30x25in) s. bronze pair

CARRIER-BELLEUSE, Albert (1824-1887) French
£730 $1300   (30-Apr-92 CE.NY44/R) Figure of medieval lady (65cm-26in) i. reddish brown pat.bronze
£750 $1335   (29-Nov-91 S115/R) La liseuse (40cm-16in) s.i. golden brown pat.bronze
£829 $1559   (16-Dec-91 ANS.M462/R) Doncella y cupido (70cm-28in) s. bronze (S.P 150000)
£950 $1739   (2-Jun-92 S455) Flora and putto (50cm-20in) s. lacquered brown pat.bronze
£980 $1715   (20-Feb-92 C139/R) Minerva (39cm-15in) s. bronze green marble socle Cast.Valsuani
£1108 $1950   (9-Apr-92 FA.PH256) Woman standing in fine gown holding skein of wool (33cm-13in) s. gilt bronze ivory on marble base
£1400 $2492   (29-Nov-91 S111/R) Medieval maiden with jewel casket (66cm-26in) s. brown pat.bronze
£1500 $2670   (1-Nov-91 S300/R) Allegory of summer - classically draped figure holding aloft wheat sheaf (79cm-31in) s. bronze
£1550 $2837   (2-Jun-92 S485) Flora (48cm-19in) s. marble

2052

CARRIER-BELLEUSE, Albert (1824-1887) French-cont.
£1758	$3200	(27-May-92 CH.NY120/R) Bust of a lady (48cm-19in) i. terracotta marbelized wood base
£1900	$3249	(20-Mar-92 S124/R) La cigale (69cm-27in) s.i. brown pat.bronze
£1903	$3635	(4-Jul-92 BOD.P80) Female nude standing with corn and overturned water jug (56cm-22in) s. bronze (DM 5500)
£1950	$3354	(15-Oct-91 SWS535/R) Soldiers in Renaissance dress (66cm-26in) s. brn.pat.bronze pair
£2000	$3560	(29-Nov-91 S84/R) Albert Durer (51cm-20in) s. brown parcel gilt pat.bronze marble plinth
£2100	$3738	(29-Nov-91 S145/R) Young girl with plaited hair (42cm-17in) s. marble on red marble socle
£2200	$3762	(20-Mar-92 S156/R) Comedy and Tragedy (52cm-20in) s. brown pat.bronze pair
£2353	$4000	(22-Oct-91 CE.NY21/R) Female figures (61cm-24in) i. silvered bronze pair
£2448	$4234	(28-Mar-92 BOD.P726) La fileuse (52cm-20in) s. gold pat.bronze marble socle st.f.Chardon (DM 7000)
£2610	$4750	(28-May-92 BG.M438/R) Two standing maidens in classical drapery reading book with seated child (69cm-27in) s. bronze marble base
£3200	$5696	(29-Nov-91 S134/R) Undine (56cm-22in) s. brown pat.bronze
£3448	$6000	(13-Sep-91 SY.NY101/R) Group of Herme and Bacchante (70cm-28in) i. gilt pat.bronze
£4469	$8000	(11-Nov-91 B.LA1639/R) Caresse de l'Amour (91cm-36in) i. green-brown pat.bronze
£5000	$9050	(21-May-92 C11/R) Venus and cherubs (67cm-26in) s. white marble
£6000	$10860	(21-May-92 C14/R) La bonne mere (67cm-26in) s. bronze on ormolu socle
£9890	$18000	(27-May-92 CH.NY122/R) Diane Victorieuse (66cm-26in) i.bronze marble socle
£12000	$21000	(20-Feb-92 C189/R) Diana victorious (80cm-31in) i. pat.bronze revolving marble socle

CARRIER-BELLEUSE, Louis (1848-1913) French
| £1050 | $1869 | (29-Nov-91 S233/R) Melodie (30cm-12in) s. silvered brown pat.bronze ivory |

CARRILERO, Jose (1928-) Spanish
| £1776 | $3020 | (23-Oct-91 DUR.M637/R) Mujer (64cm-25in) s. bronze (S.P 325000) |

CARROLL, Lawrence (20th C) American
£2312	$4000	(3-Oct-91 SY.NY161/R) Yellow rose - for Elizabeth (71x61x35cm-28x24x14in) s.i.d.1988verso oil wax staples mixed media
£3911	$7000	(7-May-92 SY.NY184/R) Empty cup (206x122x25cm-81x48x10in) oil wax fabric canvas
£5714	$10000	(27-Feb-92 CH.NY74/R) Greying eyes (273x120x30cm-107x47x12in) s.i.d.1989verso oil wax canvas glass wood

CARTIER, F (19th C) French
| £1011 | $1800 | (30-Apr-92 CE.NY88/R) Group of lion and lioness (31cm-12in) i. gilt-bronze |

CASINI, Ernest (19/20th C) French
| £950 | $1815 | (30-Jun-92 PH38/R) Young girl seated on bench cradling young child (41cm-16in) s. alabaster |

CASORATI, Felice (1886-1963) Italian
| £2971 | $5645 | (23-Jun-92 F.M46/R) Testa appoggiata (25cm-10in) mono.num.3/6 bronze (I.L 6500000) |

CASTANEDA, Felipe (1933-) Mexican
£4972	$9000	(18-May-92 CH.NY167/R) Felicidad (63cm-25in) s.i.d.1984 brown green pat.bronze
£6667	$12000	(19-Nov-91 CH.NY199/R) Mujer arrodillada (72cm-28in) s.d.1985 num.III/VII green pat.bronze
£8840	$16000	(19-May-92 SY.NY93/R) Maternidad (48x78cm-19x31in) s.num.I/III d.1983 dark green pat.bronze
£8889	$16000	(18-Nov-91 SY.NY153/R) Flor (91cm-36in) s.d.1986 num.VI/VII green pat.bronze

CASTLE, Wendell (20th C) American
| £45322 | $77500 | (14-Mar-92 SY.NY42/R) Illusions coat rack (182cm-72in) s.d.78 laminated carved mahogany |

CASTOR, Christian (1953-) French
| £1099 | $1967 | (17-Nov-91 R.P95/R) Sculpture carree (150cm-59in) s. wood polychrome (F.FR 10800) |

CAUER, Friedrich (1874-1945) German
| £871 | $1585 | (10-Dec-91 N.M143/R) Nude girl walking with raised head and holding hoop (54cm-21in) s.d.1904 black pat.bronze marble socle (DM 2500) |

CAUSSE (?) ?
| £1400 | $2464 | (8-Apr-92 CSK91/R) Figure of demure young woman standing barefoot on rocky promontory (71cm-28in) s. bronze |

CAVACEPPI, Bartolomeo (attrib) (c.1716-c.1799) Italian
£7500 $14400   (7-Jul-92 C94/R) Bust of Bacchus with ribbons and grape vine entwined through hair (54cm-21in) marble

CAVAROC, F (19th C) French
£100000 $178000   (29-Nov-91 S83/R) Sphinx and Cupids (188x158x70cm-74x62x28in) s. marble green pat.bronze incl.plinth pair

CAVELIER, Pierre Jules (1814-1896) French
£2000 $3500   (20-Feb-92 C178/R) Penelope (35cm-14in) i. gilt bronze Cast.F Barbedienne

CECCOBELLI, Bruno (1952-) Italian
£2123 $3800   (9-May-92 CE.NY265/R) Vanitas (166x99x16cm-65x39x6in) init.i.d.1988verso oil wax lead paper on wood

CECIONI, Adriano (1836-1886) Italian
£794 $1413   (30-Apr-92 RAS.K1263/R) Small girl holding cockerel in her arms and crying (30cm-12in) s. pat bronze (D.KR 9000)
£1649 $2821   (9-Mar-92 AT.P267/R) L'enfant au coq (58cm-23in) s. brn.pat.bronze Cast.Martin (F.FR 16000)
£2637 $4800   (27-May-92 CH.NY129/R) Bambino col gallo (38cm-15in) i.f.G Martin bronze green brown pat.
£2714 $4750   (20-Feb-92 SY.NY149/R) Child with cock (79cm-31in) i. dark brown pat.bronze golden highlights

CEMIN, Saint Clair (1951-) American
£914 $1600   (27-Feb-92 CE.NY271/R) Reader (12x8x7cm-5x3x3in) with sig. d.87 num.1/7 bronze
£1508 $2700   (9-May-92 CE.NY246/R) Family (10x24x17cm-4x9x7in) s.d.1985 terracotta
£1714 $3000   (27-Feb-92 CE.NY266/R) Utopia (53x18x28cm-21x7x11in) s.d.87 num.4/5 terracotta
£1788 $3200   (12-Nov-91 CE.NY161/R) Double handle (16x35x35cm-6x14x14in) s.num.1/1 brown pat.bronze st.foundry
£2000 $3500   (27-Feb-92 CH.NY77/R) Legend of Cruz Alta (10x34x21cm-4x13x8in) s.i.d.87 num.2/5 lead black pat.bronze
£8939 $16000   (5-May-92 CH.NY184/R) Standing man (77x41x28cm-30x16x11in) s.num.3/3 bronze

CERIBELLI, Cesar (1841-?) French
£785 $1500   (3-Jul-92 S.W3142/R) Portrait bust of lady (38cm-15in) s. gilt bronze

CESAR (1921-) French
£979 $1694   (29-Mar-92 P.V96) Poule (34x23x20cm-13x9x8in) s.num.12/100 black epoxy resin (F.FR 9500)
£1747 $3337   (30-Jun-92 ZZ.F74/R) Compression plexiglas (30x20x20cm-12x8x8in) s. num.138/150 plexiglass (F.FR 17000)
£2014 $3585   (28-Oct-91 GL.P194/R) Compression (30x21x21cm-12x8x8in) s.num.144/150 plexiglass (F.FR 20000)
£2256 $4039   (19-Jan-92 CC.P48) Compression (30x20x21cm-12x8x8in) s.num.117/150 compression transparent plexi (F.FR 22000)
£2300 $3956   (17-Oct-91 S14/R) Pouce (8cm-3in) s.num.6/10 bronze f.st.A. Valsuani
£2881 $5214   (6-Dec-91 GL.P288/R) Personnage fantastique (32x17x24cm-13x7x9in) s.base num.5/8 bronze (F.FR 28000)
£3292 $6255   (26-Jun-92 FB.P104/R) Compression Coca-Orangina (35x14x14cm-14x6x6in) s. compressed aluminium cans (F.FR 32000)
£3600 $6192   (17-Oct-91 S45/R) Compression (28x27cm-11x11in) s.
£4119 $7044   (19-Mar-92 CSC.P81/R) Compression de boites Coca, Kronenbourg, Orangina, Perrier (32x15x15cm-13x6x6in) s. compressed boxes (F.FR 40000)
£4582 $8478   (12-Jun-92 AT.P46/R) Poulette No.1 (19cm-7in) num.H.C.2/2 pat.bronze (F.FR 45000)
£5658 $10242   (5-Dec-91 BG.P45/R) Compression (29x28x28cm-11x11x11in) white iron (F.FR 55000)
£7716 $13966   (6-Dec-91 GL.P285/R) Eiffel engage (56x28x22cm-22x11x9in) s.base num.5/8 bronze (F.FR 75000)
£8056 $13696   (27-Oct-91 P.V64/R) Autoportrait au cadre ovale (47x24x24cm-19x9x9in) s.num.2/2 brn.pat.bronze Cast.Venturi Arte (F.FR 80000)
£8258 $14038   (27-Oct-91 P.V63/R) Autoportrait au miroir (38x16x28cm-15x6x11in) s.num.2/2 brn.green pat.bronze Cast.Venturi Arte (F.FR 82000)
£9054 $15573   (12-Oct-91 GL.P62/R) Expansion (14x30cm-6x12in) Roger Vivier shoe polyurethane (F.FR 90000)
£11000 $19030   (26-Mar-92 C42/R) Insecte (26x35x28cm-10x14x11in) s.num.5/8 gold pat.bronze
£12085 $20544   (27-Oct-91 P.V68/R) Compression murale de velomoteurs (63x45x13cm-25x18x5in) s.d.1970 (F.FR 120000)
£13000 $22490   (26-Mar-92 C43/R) Compression (51x51x22cm-20x20x9in) s. compressed bicycle
£13374 $25412   (26-Jun-92 FB.P89/R) Nadine (63x30x23cm-25x12x9in) s.num.HC 1/2 bronze. Cast.Bocquel (F.FR 130000)
£14208 $26000   (11-May-92 CH.NY84/R) Le dindon (41x25x49cm-16x10x19in) with sig. num. bronze
£17486 $32000   (11-May-92 CH.NY83/R) Composition (34x22x9cm-13x9x4in) bronze
£22119 $42027   (26-Jun-92 FB.P61/R) Plaque Tesconi (81x50x20cm-32x20x8in) s.num.1/8 bronze (F.FR 215000)
£36660 $66721   (15-Dec-91 P.V65/R) Nu de la belle de mai (95x25x31cm-37x10x12in) s.num.8/8base brn.pat.bronze (F.FR 360000)

CESAR (1921-) French-cont.

£39095	$74280	(26-Jun-92 FB.P43/R) L'insecte (26x23x23cm-10x9x9in) s.d.56 iron (F.FR 380000)
£41152	$78189	(26-Jun-92 FB.P40/R) La sauterelle (36x49x26cm-14x19x10in) iron (F.FR 400000)
£46296	$87963	(26-Jun-92 FB.P51/R) La rambaud (95x90x65cm-37x35x26in) s.num.3/8 bronze (F.FR 450000)
£58763	$101660	(29-Mar-92 P.V92/R) Les Patins de Gilles (95x100x50cm-37x39x20in) s.num.6/8 brn.pat.soldered bronze st.f.Bocquel (F.FR 570000)
£120846	$205438	(24-Oct-91 CSC.P15 a/R) Nu assis (101x49x52cm-40x19x20in) s.num.2/8 brn.pat.bronze Cast.Bocquel (F.FR 1200000)

CESAR, Baldaccini (1921-) French

£816	$1486	(25-May-92 ZZ.F96) Expansion (32x25x15cm-13x10x6in) chromed jar resin (F.FR 8050)
£1745	$3142	(19-Nov-91 FB.P223/R) Portrait de compression (44x33x5cm-17x13x2in) s.d.1977 steel wool oil crayon panel (F.FR 17000)
£2846	$5209	(13-May-92 BU.S228/R) Compression (20cm-8in) s. aluminium on plexiglas box (S.KR 30000)
£6385	$10919	(17-Mar-92 FB.P74/R) Compression Marlboro (123x103cm-48x41in) s. compressed cigarette packets drawing crayon (F.FR 62000)
£6936	$12000	(3-Oct-91 SY.NY74 a/R) Untitled (81x71x5cm-32x28x2in) s. pencil collage pennies board
£56295	$100205	(30-Nov-91 FB.P63/R) Pouce (140cm-55in) s.num.5/8base gilded pat.bronze Cast.Bocquel (F.FR 550000)

CHADWICK, Lynn (1914-) British

£950	$1682	(8-Nov-91 C343/R) Miniature Lion IV (13cm-5in) init.num.7/30 blk.brn.pat.bronze
£1900	$3363	(8-Nov-91 C344/R) Miniature Figure III (10cm-4in) init.num.22/30 blk.brn.pat.bronze
£2400	$4248	(8-Nov-91 C342/R) Lion (25cm-10in) init.num.7/9head blk.pat.bronze
£2793	$5000	(6-May-92 CH.NY275/R) Cloaked figure VI (24x13x22cm-9x5x9in) st.mono. d.77 753 num.2/8 bronze
£2800	$5180	(11-Jun-92 C140/R) Maquette VI sitting woman (15cm-6in) init.d.1986 num.4/9 black/blue pat.bronze
£3500	$6195	(8-Nov-91 C340/R) Winged figure (20cm-8in) init.num.2/4 blk.brn.pat.bronze
£4000	$7080	(8-Nov-91 C341/R) Maquette VII sitting woman (20cm-8in) d.num.9/9base blk.brn.pat.bronze
£4000	$7080	(8-Nov-91 C366/R) Seated cloaked couple (10cm-4in) brn.pat.bronze polished faces
£4200	$7266	(26-Mar-92 S46/R) Cloaked figure V (26cm-10in) st.mono.i.d.76 num.3/8 bronze
£4324	$8000	(12-Jun-92 SY.NY161/R) Maquette II Stranger (26cm-10in) i.num.1/4 bronze bl.pat.
£4335	$7500	(6-Sep-91 S.BM326/R) Untitled (46cm-18in) s.d.451 brn.gold pat.bronze
£4982	$8669	(18-Sep-91 KH.K15/R) Standing woman (26cm-10in) init.d.45 num.4/9, bronze (D.KR 56000)
£5028	$9000	(12-Nov-91 CE.NY94/R) No 703 (21x23x19cm-8x9x7in) st.sig.d.75 703 num.3/8 black pat.bronze
£5200	$8996	(26-Mar-92 S45/R) Sitting watchers I (22cm-9in) i. num.3/8 bronze
£5500	$9460	(17-Oct-91 S13/R) Girl V (37cm-15in) st.init.i.d.73 num.5/6 bronze
£6000	$10620	(8-Nov-91 C356/R) Standing figure (33cm-13in) d.1956 num.1/9 blk.pat.bronze
£6200	$10974	(8-Nov-91 C364/R) Girl V (37cm-15in) init.d.72 num. blk.pat.bronze polished head
£8000	$13840	(26-Mar-92 C39/R) Sitting couple (22x25x28cm-9x10x11in) st.sig.d.num.7/8 brn.pat.bronze
£8197	$15000	(14-May-92 SY.NY325/R) Trigon V (51cm-20in) i.num.3/6 green pat.bronze
£9000	$15930	(8-Nov-91 C365/R) Paper hat (60cm-24in) s.num.0/4base Cast.Singer blk.green pat.bronze
£9714	$17000	(25-Feb-92 SY.NY73/R) Maquette for fountain (45cm-18in) i. brown pat.bronze
£10056	$18000	(6-May-92 CH.NY373/R) Seated couple IV (37x30x30cm-15x12x12in) st.mono.d.74 677S num.1/8 bronze
£11173	$20000	(13-Nov-91 CH.NY116/R) Watcher (53x16x18cm-21x6x7in) sig.d.61 num.651 0/4 bronze
£13661	$25000	(13-May-92 SY.NY221/R) Beast IX (95cm-37in) i.num.2/6 green oxidized pat.bronze
£14124	$25000	(7-Nov-91 SY.NY185/R) Walking couple IV (46cm-18in) i. num.4/9 brown pat.bronze f.st.Pangolin
£16975	$30895	(11-Dec-91 CH.AM323/R) Maquette diamond wing (70cm-28in) s.d.1970 num.4/6 bronze (D.FL 55000)
£19000	$33630	(8-Nov-91 C354/R) Pair of sitting figures V (48cm-19in) s.d.86 num.658S grey blk.pat.bronze
£21229	$38000	(13-Nov-91 CH.NY136/R) 606 (72x30x20cm-28x12x8in) st.sig.d.70 num.606 5/6 bronze
£49133	$85000	(2-Oct-91 SY.NY64 a/R) Square (219cm-86in) i. st.num.68 568 1/4 black pat.bronze

CHAISSAC, Gaston (1910-1964) French

£8105	$14671	(21-May-92 CC.P75/R) Os peint (27cm-11in) painted shoulder-blade (F.FR 80000)

CHALON, Louis (1687-1741) French
£1453 $2500   (20-Oct-91 HG.C107) Figure of Valkyrie - Kara (71cm-28in) bronze

CHAMBARD, Louis Leopold (after) (1811-1895) French
£1200 $2088   (17-Sep-91 PH219/R) Figure of le bucheron (88cm-35in) bronze

CHAMBERLAIN, John (1927-) American
£4857 $8500   (25-Feb-92 SY.NY205 b/R) Any minute man (15x20x9cm-6x8x4in) painted
                 stainless steel
£7263 $13000   (13-Nov-91 CH.NY166/R) Sinclair (15x10x8cm-6x4x3in) welded painted steel
£16185 $28000   (3-Oct-91 SY.NY110/R) Tintinnabulary (98x91x78cm-39x36x31in) steel
£28571 $50000   (25-Feb-92 SY.NY212/R) The Arch of Lumps, tribute to act of unclarity,
                 Vietnam War (360x162x146cm-142x64x57in) painted chromium plated steel
£33520 $60000   (7-May-92 SY.NY300/R) Ruby-Ruby (89x94x73cm-35x37x29in) painted
                 chromium-plated steel
£53073 $95000   (6-May-92 SY.NY19/R) Untitled (183x122x106cm-72x48x42in) painted chromium
                 plated steel

CHAPU, Henri Michel Antoine (1833-1891) French
£850 $1454   (20-Mar-92 S105/R) Joan of Arc (46cm-18in) s. brown pat.bronze
                s.F.Barbedienne
£1293 $2250   (13-Sep-91 SY.NY50/R) Figure of grieving woman (74cm-29in) i. parcel gilt
                bronze i.F.Barbedienne
£1536 $2750   (11-Nov-91 B.LA1647/R) Muse of Literature seated at bench (86cm-34in) i.
                brown pat.bronze relief plaque
£1800 $3150   (20-Feb-92 C176/R) La Pensee (86cm-34in) s.i. bronze
£2201 $3697   (28-Aug-91 RAS.K1157/R) Seated young woman, Pallas Athene in background
                (42x25cm-17x10in) s.i. gilt bronze green onyx (D.KR 25000)

CHARDIGNY (18/19th C) French?
£13388 $22894 (20-Mar-92 ZZ.F54/R) Couple de Bacchants allonges (44x59cm-17x23in)
                s.d.1802 terracotta oblong base two (F.FR 130000)

CHARPENTIER, Felix (1858-1924) French
£2528 $4500   (30-Apr-92 CE.NY37/R) Les Lutteurs (64cm-25in) i. greenish-brown
                pat.bronze

CHATEAU, Ludwig (1906-1975) German
£1237 $2264   (3-Jun-92 L.K79) Great bear (31x45x27cm-12x18x11in) i. brown pat.bronze
                st.f.Fussel Berlin (DM 3600)

CHAUVIN, Jean (1889-1976) French
£2600 $4550   (26-Feb-92 MMB221/R) Standing figure (56cm-22in) bronze
£3008 $5113   (22-Oct-91 C.A16) Standing figure (55cm-22in) s. bronze (B.FR 180000)

CHEERE, John (attrib) (18th C) British
£16500 $28050 (22-Oct-91 S333/R) Figures of Farnese Flora and Capitoline Flora, each
                holding pendant lamp (221cm-87in) bronzed plaster on mahogany plinth
                pair

CHEMIN, Joseph Victor (1825-1901) French
£1093 $2000   (5-Jun-92 SY.NY116/R) The stork and the wolf (38cm-15in) i. bronze
                br.pat.
£1100 $1881   (20-Mar-92 S44/R) Scratching greyhound (15cm-6in) s. brown pat.bronze

CHERC (?) ?
£909 $1600   (6-Apr-92 B.LA2626/R) Bust of maiden (60cm-24in) c.1900 brown pat.bronze
                st.F.Goldscheider

CHERKI, Sabine (20th C) French?
£1143 $2195   (6-Jul-92 HC.P68) Le matin (50cm-20in) s. num.3/8 bronze (F.FR 11000)

CHEVALIER, Miguel (20th C) French
£1134 $1962   (23-Mar-92 CC.P81) Vecteurs (84x100x15cm-33x39x6in) s.i.d.1988-89verso
                chrome plexiglass aluminium (F.FR 11000)

CHEVERTON, B (1794-1876) British
£3100 $5518   (29-Nov-91 S129/R) Patroclus (28cm-11in) s.d.1840 ivory on marble plinth

CHIA, Sandro (1946-) Italian
£12849 $23000   (6-May-92 CH.NY224/R) Bacco (65x34x33cm-26x13x13in) with sig.d.83 bronze
£19553 $35000   (7-May-92 SY.NY208/R) Boy with ram (152x140x76cm-60x55x30in) s.d.83
                 bronze
£61453 $110000 (7-May-92 SY.NY142 a/R) Poet-painter (183x76x137cm-72x30x54in) st.s. d.83
                 bronze f.st.

CHILLIDA, Eduardo (20th C) ?
£22518 $40082   (30-Nov-91 FB.P11/R) Albatre (33x30cm-13x12in) s. alabaster (F.FR 220000)
£26000 $47320   (29-May-92 C471/R) Lurra (39x28x28cm-15x11x11in) st.mono. fired clay
£163132 $290375 (28-Apr-92 EP.M4/R) Deseoso (96cm-38in) iron (S.P 30000000)

CHINARD, Joseph (after) (1756-1813) French
£1235 $2210   (14-Nov-91 D.V238/R) Portrait bust of Madame Recamier (63cm-25in) white
                marble (A.S 25000)

CHINARD, Joseph (attrib) (1756-1813) French
£2884	$4931	(20-Mar-92 ZZ.F45/R) Projet d'un mausolee (15cm-6in) terracotta (F.FR 28000)

CHINARD, Joseph (style) (1756-1813) French
£3911	$7000	(14-Jan-92 CH.NY159/R) Figure of Cupid, naked and leaning against pedestal (48cm-19in) terracotta

CHIPARUS (1888-1950) Rumanian
£800	$1360	(23-Oct-91 LJ228) Figure of woman with raised arm (39cm-15in) s. bronze ivory
£3600	$6876	(2-Jul-92 CSK128/R) The squall, young woman dressed in fur scarf and muff shieling from wind (30cm-12in) s.i. cold painted bronze ivory onyx base

CHIPARUS, D (1888-1950) Rumanian
£3500	$6230	(29-Apr-92 C78/R) Ayouta (28cm-11in) s. bronze ivory sold with figure by Joe Descomps
£5000	$8900	(29-Apr-92 C77/R) Mother and child (54cm-21in) s. silver pat.bronze ivory

CHIPARUS, Demetre (1888-1950) Rumanian
£900	$1647	(15-May-92 S351/R) The little sad one (17cm-7in) i. gilt bronze ivory marble
£1100	$2013	(15-May-92 S349/R) Dancer of Olynthus (38cm-15in) i. bronze onyx
£1481	$2681	(19-May-92 GF.L480/R) Little sad one (30cm-12in) i.pat.bronze on marble socle st.f.Etling Paris (S.FR 4000)
£1500	$2670	(29-Apr-92 C82/R) Girls dressed in short gowns (19cm-7in) s. ivory on onyx base pair
£1719	$3042	(5-Nov-91 GF.L427/R) Pierette (23cm-9in) i. pat.bronze ivory marble socle st.f.Etling (S.FR 4400)
£2525	$4470	(26-Apr-92 SY.MO276/R) Pierrot a la mandoline (41cm-16in) pat.bronze ivory (F.FR 25000)
£3200	$5856	(15-May-92 S343/R) Oriental dancer (40cm-16in) i. painted bronze onyx
£3204	$5800	(6-Dec-91 GC.M122/R) Pierrot Trovador (67cm-26in) s. green/brown pat.bronze ivory
£3486	$6100	(30-Mar-92 ZZ.F67/R) La petite tristounnette (30cm-12in) s. ivory gilded bronze veined marble base (F.FR 33500)
£3800	$6954	(15-May-92 S332/R) Scarf dancer (67cm-26in) i. silvered bronze onyx
£4400	$8052	(15-May-92 S342/R) Nimble dancer (47cm-19in) gilt bronze ivory onyx marble
£6897	$11862	(16-Oct-91 KM.K1506/R) Female Hindu dancer (61cm-24in) i. green pat.bronze ivory marble socle (DM 20000)
£7000	$11900	(25-Oct-91 S357/R) Les amis de Toujours (41cm-16in) i.num.135 gilded cold painted bronze ivory onyx
£8000	$14640	(15-May-92 S345) Testris (43cm-17in) i. painted bronze ivory onyx
£11696	$20000	(21-Mar-92 SY.NY214/R) Figural group - Les Amis de Toujours - maiden petting flanking borzoi (63x65cm-25x26in) i. gilt silver copper pat.bronze ivory
£40936	$70000	(21-Mar-92 SY.NY213/R) Figure of dancer in jewelled revealing costume, arms outstretched (67cm-26in) i. gilt silvered bronze ivory
£49000	$83300	(25-Oct-91 S359/R) Antinea (68cm-27in) i.c.1925 silvered bronze ivory marble onyx

CHIPARUS, Demetre (after) (1888-1950) Rumanian
£1162	$2069	(29-Oct-91 VN.R1705) Dancer (45cm-18in) bronze ivory (D.FL 3800)
£1800	$3294	(11-May-92 HS485/R) Three children wearing raincoats sheltering underneath umbrella (23cm-9in) i.num.6361 bronze ivory st.Fabrication Francais

CHIRICO, Giorgio de (1888-1978) Italian
£1390	$2475	(26-Nov-91 SY.MI156/R) Oreste (26x10cm-10x4in) s.i. num.9/100 bronze (I.L 3000000)
£3200	$5536	(25-Mar-92 S199/R) Il Castore (27cm-11in) i.num.21/50 silver pat.bronze Cast.Cavallari
£6704	$12000	(9-May-92 CE.NY68/R) Ettore e Andromaca (44cm-17in) s.num.8/8 brown pat.bronze st.f.Tesconi
£7429	$13000	(25-Feb-92 CH.NY78/R) Ettore e Andromaca (44cm-17in) s.num.5/8 dark brown pat.bronze f.st.
£8197	$15000	(14-May-92 SY.NY285/R) La musa (30cm-12in) i.num.12/50 polished bronze st.f.Cavallari, Roma
£8626	$15354	(29-Apr-92 F.F237/R) Cavallo e palafreniere (32cm-13in) s.num.2/8 bronze (I.L 19000000)
£13714	$24000	(25-Feb-92 SY.NY50/R) Cavallo (36cm-14in) i. gold pat.bronze st.f.Bonvicini Verona
£14451	$25000	(2-Oct-91 SY.NY55/R) Ettore E Andromaca (51cm-20in) i. num.6/9 gold pat.bronze f.st.Esse Verona
£17143	$30000	(25-Feb-92 SY.NY48/R) Il grande metafisico (48cm-19in) gold pat.bronze
£27143	$47500	(25-Feb-92 SY.NY52/R) Le muse (94cm-37in) i.num.0/0 black-blue pat.bronze st.Gogarte
£31421	$57500	(14-May-92 SY.NY279/R) Il poeta solitario (51cm-20in) i. silver pat.bronze st.f.Artistica Gi.Bi.Esse
£40000	$72400	(4-Dec-91 S164/R) Il grande metafisico (100cm-39in) i. num.1/5 gold pat.bronze f.st.Bonvicini Italy
£60694	$105000	(2-Oct-91 SY.NY56/R) Il grande travatore (75cm-30in) i. num.4/9 silver pat.bronze f.st.Cavallari

CHOPIN, F (20th C) ?
£1200 $2292   (2-Jul-92 CSK116/R) Male figure standing holding ship (53cm-21in) s.
   pat.bronze onyx base

CHRISTO (1935-) Rumanian
£8571 $15000   (27-Feb-92 CH.NY34/R) Package 1963 (30x13x11cm-12x5x4in) wall relief
   s.d.63 fabric rope twine
£11856 $20510   (29-Mar-92 P.V90/R) Packed tree (57x72x4cm-22x28x2in) s.i.d.1968 jute
   plastic string ink plexiglass (F.FR 115000)

CHRISTOPHE (?) ?
£941 $1600   (22-Oct-91 CE.NY50/R) Equestrian group of World War I cavalryman
   (48cm-19in) i. rich reddish brown pat.bronze

CHRISTOPHE, Pierre Robert (1880-1971) French
£1200 $2052   (20-Mar-92 S153/R) First World War cavalryman (52cm-20in) s. brown
   pat.bronze on marble plinth

CHRYSSA (1933-) American/Greek
£5780 $10000   (3-Oct-91 SY.NY53/R) Untitled (188x124x61cm-74x49x24in) alminium blue
   neon

CIMIOTTI, Emil (1927-) German
£1237 $2164   (3-Apr-92 BM.B1552/R) Mannequin (43cm-17in) i. bronze (DM 3500)

CIPRIANI (attrib) (?) Italian
£955 $1700   (30-Apr-92 CE.NY20) Bust of girl (44cm-17in) indist.s. alabaster

CIPRIANI, A (?) Italian?
£756 $1300   (9-Oct-91 RO.BA596) Busto de joven (72cm-28in) s. sculpture on base
£3000 $5340   (29-Nov-91 S198/R) The flower picker (81cm-32in) s.d.1881 alabaster on
   socle beaded bronze rim
£13978 $26000   (16-Jun-92 RO.BA130) Primavera (160cm-63in) Carrara marble
£87079 $155000   (30-Apr-92 CE.NY28 a/R) Venus in vulcan's net (279cm-110in) s. marble
   incl.veined marble base

CIPRIANI, G (?) Italian
£995 $1771   (21-Jan-92 DUR.M640/R) Venus de Milo (89cm-35in) s. white marble
   (S.P 180000)

CLAEYS, Jean (1941-) French?
£2815 $5094   (23-May-92 KV.L507/R) Rider falling from a horse (32x46cm-13x18in)
   num.1/8 bronze brown pat. (B.FR 170000)

CLARA (?) ?
£1244 $2339   (18-Dec-91 DUR.M1063/R) Ay, que me quita la merienda (28cm-11in) bears
   sig. bronze on black marble base (S.P 225000)

CLARA, Jose (1878-?) Spanish
£1016 $1768   (16-Apr-92 FB.P70/R) Femme aux bras leves (37cm-15in) s.base num.6/8
   brn.pat.bronze (F.FR 10000)
£1093 $1858   (23-Oct-91 DUR.M629/R) Una joven desnuda (44cm-17in) s.num.VI/VIII bronze
   st.f.A.Valsuani (S.P 200000)
£1230 $2091   (23-Oct-91 DUR.M638/R) Una joven desnuda (37cm-15in) s.num.7/8 bronze
   st.f.A.Valsuani (S.P 225000)
£1321 $2299   (16-Apr-92 FB.P110/R) Femme a la tete penchee et au drap tombant
   (45cm-18in) s.base num.2/8 brn.pat.bronze (F.FR 13000)
£1503 $2555   (23-Oct-91 DUR.M639/R) Una joven desnuda (33cm-13in) s.num.4/8 brown
   pat.bronze st.f.A.Valsuani (S.P 275000)
£1503 $2555   (23-Oct-91 DUR.M630/R) Heureux age (27cm-11in) s.i. bronze st.f.La Casa
   de Bellas Artes (S.P 275000)
£3354 $5835   (16-Apr-92 FB.P62/R) La diosa (37cm-15in) s.base num.5/8 brn.pat.bronze
   (F.FR 33000)
£5081 $8841   (16-Apr-92 FB.P1/R) L'Esclave (81cm-32in) s.num.1/8 green pat.bronze
   Cast.Valsuani (F.FR 50000)

CLARA, Juan (1875-?) Spanish
£774 $1455   (18-Dec-91 DUR.M1067/R) El acrobata (14cm-6in) s.num.20R bronze
   (S.P 140000)
£1244 $2339   (18-Dec-91 DUR.M1060/R) Este zapato no me entra (24cm-9in) s.num.256
   bronze (S.P 225000)
£1500 $2670   (29-Nov-91 S232/R) Ummm (33cm-13in) s.i.num.352 brown pat.bronze
£1800 $3132   (17-Sep-91 PH231/R) Small girl standing on stool holding boot in left
   hand (34cm-13in) bronze st.f.Goldscheider
£2100 $3591   (20-Mar-92 S192/R) Struggling in a chair (23cm-9in) s.num.119/1308 brown
   pat.bronze st.Goldscheider
£2200 $3762   (20-Mar-92 S193/R) Lolotte et Fifi (35cm-14in) s.i.st.num.13CA brown
   pat.bronze

CLARK, Allan (c.1897-1950) American
£829 $1500   (21-May-92 GRO.B87/R) Yang Kwei Fei (20cm-8in) i. silvered bronze marble
   base st.f.Gorham Co
£977 $1700   (15-Apr-92 SY.NY122/R) Dancing male figure (48cm-19in) i.d.1920 black
   pat.bronze

CLARK, Allan (c.1897-1950) American-cont.
£2047 $3500   (11-Mar-92 SY.NY88/R) Charmion (38cm-15in) i. turquoise pat.bronze
                    f.i.Roman Bronze N.Y

CLARK, James Lippitt (1883-1957) American
£3297 $6000   (28-May-92 CH.NY99/R) A rhinoceros (15cm-6in) i. bronze red brown pat.
£3571 $6500   (28-May-92 CH.NY100/R) African Cape Buffalo (32cm-13in) i. bronze green
                    brown pat.

CLATWORTHY, Robert (1928-) British
£1200 $2220   (11-Jun-92 C156/R) Study for equestrian monument (19cm-7in) init.d.1988
                    num.4/12 black/green pat.bronze
£2800 $5348   (16-Jul-92 B183/R) Horse (56cm-22in) num.4/12 br.pat. bronze

CLAUDEL, Camille (1856-c.1920) French
£6425 $11500   (9-May-92 CE.NY67/R) Chienne affamee (26cm-10in) s. brown pat.bronze
                    st.f.Siot Decauville Paris
£12220 $22607   (12-Jun-92 AT.P11/R) La jeune fille a la gerbe (35cm-14in) s.num.5/8
                    pat.bronze. Cast.Coubertin (F.FR 120000)
£17312 $31680   (3-Jun-92 CSC.P91/R) L'homme penche (42cm-17in) s.num.1/4 brown
                    pat.bronze f.i. (F.FR 170000)

CLAUS, Eric (20th C) ?
£909 $1645   (19-May-92 CH.AM110 a) Cavalry skirmish (23cm-9in) bronze (D.FL 3000)

CLEMECIN, A (?) French
£1007 $1793   (28-Oct-91 AT.P125/R) Celuy quy fut pris (38cm-15in) s.i. gold silver
                    pat.bronze base (F.FR 10000)

CLEREN, Jean Paul (1940-) French
£1098 $1965   (15-Nov-91 GK.Z5525) Visage voile (34x24x40cm-13x9x16in) s.num.3/25
                    bronze stone socle (S.FR 2800)

CLERGERIE, Yvonne (20th C) French
£3347 $5723   (22-Mar-92 LT.P112/R) Le rayon de soleil (61cm-24in) s.num4/8 green
                    pat.bronze Cast.Cappelli (F.FR 32500)

CLERICI, L (19/20th C) ?
£800 $1464   (12-May-92 SWS373) Bust of Caesar Augustus (56cm-22in) s.d.1876 marble

CLESINGER, J (1814-1883) French
£850 $1539   (20-May-92 CSK256/R) Figure of Grecian maiden (69cm-27in) s. bronze
£2848 $5099   (13-Nov-91 CD.P20/R) Deux taureaux s'affrontant au dessus de ruines
                    (69x34x16cm-27x13x6in) pat.bronze Cast.Maison Marnyac red marble base
                    (F.FR 28000)
£28836 $49310   (20-Mar-92 ZZ.F62/R) Sapho tenant sa lyre (175cm-69in) s. white marble
                    wooded sculpted base (F.FR 280000)

CLESINGER, Jean Baptiste (1814-1883) French
£767 $1464   (2-Jul-92 ANS.M288/R) Ecce Homo (40cm-16in) s.d.1858 bronze (S.P 140000)
£1210 $2141   (10-Nov-91 ZZ.F164/R) Le buste d'Helene (31cm-12in) s. brn.pat.bronze
                    Cast.Barbedienne (F.FR 12000)
£1300 $2223   (20-Mar-92 S108/R) Sapho (42cm-17in) s.i. brown pat.bronze marble socle
                    i.f.Mainyhae
£1310 $2320   (10-Nov-91 ZZ.F162/R) La Zingara ou la danseuse Napolitaine (54cm-21in)
                    s. brn.pat.bronze (F.FR 13000)

CLEVE, Corneille van (attrib) (1645-1735) French
£22000 $42240   (9-Jul-92 S151/R) Group of Venus and Cupid, with Venus seated on grassy
                    bank, startled by Cupid (48cm-19in) i. st. bronze

CLODION (after) (1738-1814) French
£912 $1669   (12-May-92 GM.B1517) Bacchants sur un Bouc bronze (B.FR 55000)
£1100 $1958   (1-Nov-91 S334/R) Group of Bacchante riding satyr (36cm-14in) bears sig.
                    terracotta
£1724 $3000   (13-Sep-91 SY.NY103/R) Figural group (48cm-19in) i. green brown
                    pat.bronze
£1803 $3210   (25-Nov-91 BU.K121/R) Faun and nymph (46cm-18in) pat bronze marble base
                    (D.KR 20000)
£2730 $4750   (13-Sep-91 SY.NY28/R) Figural group on oriental style base (122cm-48in)
                    i. brown pat.bronze

CLODION (style) (1738-1814) French
£3652 $6500   (21-Jan-92 CE.NY78/R) Bacchanalian scenes (58cm-23in) bronze red marble
                    socle square base pair

CLODION, Claude-Michel (1738-1814) French
£806 $1500   (16-Jun-92 RO.BA116) Owls and Satyr (32cm-13in) bronze
£1279 $2200   (20-Oct-91 HG.C96) Bacchantes de Clodion (66cm-26in) bronze
£1397 $2500   (11-Nov-91 B.LA1635/R) Two Bacchantes and baby satyr (55cm-22in) s. brown
                    pat.bronze on red marble base

CLODION, Claude-Michel (after) (1738-1814) French
£2303 $4169   (3-Dec-91 AB.S4578/R) Figure group (86cm-34in) dark pat bronze
                    (S.KR 24000)

CLODION, P (after) (19th C) French
£2998 $5575   (16-Jun-92 SY.B173/R) Putti playing (190cm-75in) terracotta painted wooden base (B.FR 180000)

CLOUTIER, Francois (1922-) French
£2045 $3742   (3-Feb-92 HH.P54/R) La femme en courbes (31x16x14cm-12x6x6in) s.num.4/8 green pat.bronze Cast.Landowski (F.FR 20000)
£2414 $4153   (7-Oct-91 HH.P66/R) Seishin (21x16x16cm-8x6x6in) s.num.2/8 green pat.bronze (F.FR 24000)

COCK, Jan de (after) (?) Flemish
£1050 $1869   (1-Nov-91 S331/R) Bust of Negro page (37cm-15in) plaster

COGNE, Francois (20th C) French
£2586 $4500   (13-Sep-91 SY.NY41/R) La Marne (122cm-48in) i. gilt bronze

COINCHON, Jacques Antoine Theodore (1814-1881) French
£850 $1462   (3-Mar-92 SWS515/R) Seated Pan (43cm-17in) s. green pat.bronze
£1200 $2052   (20-Mar-92 S150/R) Pan (67cm-26in) s. green brown pat.bronze on marble plinth

COLINET (?) French
£1309 $2330   (28-Oct-91 AT.P128/R) La jongleuse aux trois balles (52cm-20in) s. pat.bronze blk.marble socle (F.FR 13000)
£2200 $4202   (2-Jul-92 CSK121/R) Corinthian dancer poised on top of pile of roses (30cm-12in) s. gilt bronze ivory

COLINET, Claire Jeanne Roberte (19/20th C) French
£3600 $6588   (15-May-92 S334/R) Figural lamp (58cm-23in) i. pat.bronze marble
£4688 $8297   (5-Nov-91 GF.L428/R) Egyptian dancer seated on socle with arms raised (26x30cm-10x12in) i. pat.bronze ivory (S.FR 12000)
£16000 $28000   (27-Sep-91 S7/R) Valykrie (72x67cm-28x26in) s. brn.gilt pat.bronze silver gilt ivory marble

COLLA, Ettore (1896-1968) Italian
£5884 $10708   (26-May-92 SY.MI153/R) Rilievo (35x45x15cm-14x18x6in) bronze (I.L 13000000)
£13014 $23556   (3-Dec-91 F.R267/R) Rilievo con anello (30x44x5cm-12x17x2in) d.1958/59 iron (I.L 28000000)

COLLIN, Alberic (1886-1962) Belgian
£1249 $2185   (30-Mar-92 ZZ.F82) Panthere penchant (44x86x24cm-17x34x9in) pat.plaster (F.FR 12000)

COLLOT, Marie (18th C) French
£2037 $3768   (10-Jun-92 ZZ.F104/R) Portrait de femme, les cheveuz boucles retenus par un ruban (48cm-19in) s.d.1755 terracotta (F.FR 20000)

COLOGNE SCHOOL German
£6000 $10920   (10-Dec-91 C49/R) Group of Virgin and Child (37cm-15in) polychrome oak c.1380-1400

COLOMBO, P (19th C) ?
£1200 $2112   (8-Apr-92 CSK89/R) Bust of Napoleon, as emperor (36cm-14in) s.d.1885 bronze

COMBAS, Robert (1957-) French
£722 $1248   (29-Mar-92 P.V7000) Untitled (30cm-12in) acrylic paintbrush (F.FR 7000)
£1231 $2203   (19-Jan-92 CC.P50/R) Figure de prou pierral (27cm-11in) painted sculpture (F.FR 12000)

COMBAY, Alponse de (19th C) Belgian
£1050 $1869   (29-Nov-91 S108/R) Neapolitan fisherboy with lute (72cm-28in) s. brown pat.bronze i.H.Luppens

COMOLERA, F (?) French
£767 $1381   (21-Nov-91 RAS.K1089) Chanteclair (70cm-28in) s. brown pat bronze (D.KR 8500)

COMOLERA, Paul (1818-1897) French
£1236 $2200   (30-Apr-92 CE.NY72/R) Figure of whippet (37cm-15in) i. st. reddish brown pat.bronze
£1383 $2572   (16-Jun-92 RAS.V317/R) Cockerel (64cm-25in) s. pat bronze (D.KR 15500)

CONSAGRA, Pietro (1920-) Italian
£3168 $5766   (26-May-92 SY.MI155/R) Composizione (40x30cm-16x12in) s. bronze (I.L 7000000)
£5233 $9000   (12-Oct-91 SY.NY302/R) Untitled (48cm-19in) i.d.61 golden dark brown pat.bronze welded
£7677 $13664   (30-Nov-91 FB.P9/R) Colloquio con la Speranza (70x56cm-28x22in) s.d.57base soldered gilded brn.pat.bronze (F.FR 75000)
£9012 $15500   (12-Oct-91 SY.NY301/R) Colloquio (60cm-24in) i.d.53 black gold pat.bronze
£9259 $17593   (26-Jun-92 FB.P5/R) Colloquio Libero No.5 (73x71cm-29x28in) s.d.61 gilded pat.bronze (F.FR 90000)

CONSTANT, Joseph (1892-1969) French
£1297 $2400   (8-Jun-92 GG.TA237/R) Tiger (93cm-37in) s. wood
£2128 $4000   (5-Jan-92 GG.TA331/R) Ram and two dogs (87cm-34in) s. wood

CONTI, Primo (1900-1989) Italian
£7264 $12929   (29-Apr-92 F.F235/R) Testa di Cristo (51x22x17cm-20x9x7in) bronze
                  (I.L 16000000)

CONTINENTAL SCHOOL (?) European
£824 $1500   (13-Dec-91 S.W3037/R) Two wrestlers (74cm-29in) brown pat.bronze
£1484 $2700   (13-Dec-91 S.W3045/R) Cupid feeding doves (74cm-29in) white marble
£1955 $3500   (11-Nov-91 B.LA1927/R) Figure of Cupid looking at butterfly on right arm
                  (94cm-37in) s. c.1900 marble fountain

CONTINENTAL SCHOOL, 18th C
£2485 $4250   (9-Mar-92 B.LA815/R) Mythical female figure - human head and shoulders,
                  lion front feet and scale tail (44x55cm-17x22in) carved wood gesso
                  paint

CONTINENTAL SCHOOL, 19th C
£2155 $3750   (15-Apr-92 B.SF3170/R) Figure of cavalier standing holding standard
                  (102cm-40in) bronze
£6180 $11000   (27-Apr-92 S.SL474/R) Allegorical bust of satyr (203cm-80in) cast iron
                  marble term
£18500 $31635   (20-Mar-92 S115/R) North African dancer torcheres (197cm-78in) pat. cold
                  painted cast iron pair

CONTINENTAL SCHOOL, 19th/20th C
£5263 $10000   (23-Jun-92 CE.NY15/R) Bearded satyr with lion skin and grape vines in
                  hair. Bacchante (193cm-76in) marble pair

COPER, Hans (?) ?
£5000 $9150   (4-Jun-92 DLY596/R) Spade form (20cm-8in) stoneware

COQUELIN, Gabriel Eugene (20th C) French
£817 $1445   (8-Nov-91 LGB.P116) Baigneuse (30x80x10cm-12x31x4in) s.num.3/8 pat.bronze
                  (F.FR 8100)

CORBUSIER, le (1887-1965) French
£2263 $4097   (5-Dec-91 BG.P44/R) Sculpture en bois et verre (45x35x25cm-18x14x10in)
                  wood glass (F.FR 22000)

CORDIER, Charles Henri Joseph (1827-1905) French
£4440 $7637   (14-Oct-91 CB.P165/R) Buste d'une jeune juive d'Algerie (57cm-22in)
                  s.d.1862 brn.red pat.bronze red marble socle (F.FR 44000)
£7800 $13884   (29-Nov-91 S130/R) The Jewess of Algiers (45cm-18in) s.d.1862 silvered
                  bronze gilt enamel
£10000 $17500   (27-Sep-91 S66/R) The Jewess of Algiers (50cm-20in) s.d.1862 silvered
                  bronze polychrome enamel
£12000 $21000   (20-Feb-92 SY.NY146/R) Nubian busts - male and female (43cm-17in) i. dark
                  brown pat.bronze pair
£25000 $43750   (27-Sep-91 S13/R) Fortuna (166cm-65in) s. brn.pat.bronze onyx purple
                  green white marble

CORDIER, Henri Louis (1853-1926) French
£1500 $2625   (20-Feb-92 C182/R) Prestige (43cm-17in) s.i. bronze

CORNELISSEN, Remy (?) ?
£3676 $6249   (22-Oct-91 C.A25/R) Rider on horseback (145cm-57in) mono. metal
                  (B.FR 220000)

CORNELL, Joseph (1903-1973) American
£15714 $27500   (25-Feb-92 SY.NY147/R) Untitled (34x22x13cm-13x9x5in) s. wood box glass
                  cork sand
£25140 $45000   (14-Nov-91 SY.NY322/R) Untitled (24x38x10cm-9x15x4in) wood collage glass
                  ceramic pipe construction
£26536 $47500   (14-Nov-91 SY.NY277/R) Constellation (25x39x11cm-10x15x4in) s.verso wood
                  collage cork glass shell metal

CORNU, Vital (1851-?) French
£1366 $2432   (26-Nov-91 SY.AM61/R) Le Reveille du Genie (98cm-39in) s. bronze
                  f.i.Societe des Bronzes de Paris (D.FL 4400)
£3017 $5250   (13-Sep-91 SY.NY63/R) Excelsior, figural group (119cm-47in) i. brown
                  pat.bronze

CORTOT, Jean-Pierre (1787-1843) French
£1000 $1710   (20-Mar-92 S95/R) Soldat spartiate (38cm-15in) s. brown green pat.bronze
                  i.F.Barbedienne Paris

COUDRAY, Georges Charles (20th C) French
£800 $1528   (2-Jul-92 CSK60) Bust of maiden with flowers in flowing hair (64cm-25in)
                  i. marble
£1800 $3078   (20-Mar-92 S126/R) Tahoser (67cm-26in) s.i.num.543 brown green pat.bronze
                  st.f.Societe

COUSTOU, Guillaume (after) (18th C) French
£3158 $6000   (23-Jun-92 CE.NY55/R) Horse trainers of Marly (56x53cm-22x21in) i. bronze pair

COUSTOU, Nicolas (1658-1733) French
£3304 $5550   (1-Sep-91 PO.BA32) Caballos de Marli (60cm-24in) s. pat.bronze pair

COUTURIER, Robert (1905-) French
£4527 $7787   (7-Oct-91 HH.P50/R) Couple (38x22x13cm-15x9x5in) s.num.2/6 brn.pat.bronze Cast.Susse (F.FR 45000)

COUZIJN, Wessel (1912-) Dutch
£1212 $2194   (19-May-92 CH.AM202/R) First sketch - Corporate Entity (15cm-6in) bronze wooden base (D.FL 4000)
£1364 $2468   (19-May-92 CH.AM204/R) Struggle (20cm-8in) s.num.5/5 bronze wooden base (D.FL 4500)
£2121 $3839   (19-May-92 CH.AM203/R) Tobias (30cm-12in) s.num.2/7 bronze wooden base (D.FL 7000)

COUZO, D A and POLLET, Joseph Michel-Ange (19th C) French
£1500 $2745   (15-May-92 S317) Art Nouveau bronzes (33cm-13in) i. pat.bronze pair

COYSEVOX, Antoine (after) (1640-1720) French
£2155 $3750   (13-Sep-91 SY.NY112/R) Allegorical figural group (55cm-22in) i. gilt bronze i.f.F.Barbedienne

COYSEVOX, Antoine (studio) (1640-1720) French
£276243 $500000   (5-Dec-91 SY.NY23/R) Stallion in trotting posture (84x86cm-33x34in) copper-brown pat.bronze varnish lacquer

COYSEVOX, Antoine (style) (1640-1720) French
£2400 $4248   (13-Feb-92 TL27) Trotting stallion (17cm-7in) bronze rectangular base

CRAGG, Tony (1949-) American?
£10000 $19100   (2-Jul-92 C7/R) Small window 1 (122x120cm-48x47in) painted wood
£20571 $36000   (27-Feb-92 CH.NY69/R) Japanese couple, Mr and Mrs Otani (165x150cm-65x59in) plastic found objects
£25258 $43696   (23-Mar-92 CC.P58/R) Cader Idris (115x170x170cm-45x67x67in) two bikes table plastic (F.FR 245000)
£28000 $53480   (2-Jul-92 C9/R) Palette (236x310cm-93x122in) painted wood plastic carpet record paper
£53073 $95000   (5-May-92 CH.NY20/R) Three cast bottles (99x99x99cm-39x39x39in) cast iron

CREEFT, Jose de (1884-1983) Spanish
£1754 $3000   (12-Mar-92 CH.NY119/R) Clair de lune, head of woman (23cm-9in) s. green steatite on marble base
£2637 $4800   (28-May-92 CH.NY214/R) Guatamalateca (41cm-16in) s. ebony
£3297 $6000   (28-May-92 CH.NY215/R) Female nude (113cm-44in) s. snakewood

CRISTESCO, Constantin (fl.1911) French
£1800 $3078   (20-Mar-92 S36/R) Two horses leaping fence (26cm-10in) s.i. brown green pat.bronze st.f.Susse Freres

CRISTOBAL, Juan (1898-1961) Spanish
£1246 $2243   (28-Jan-92 EP.M31/R) Busto de mujer (29cm-11in) s.d.1934 bronze (S.P 225000)

CROISSANT, Michael (1928-) German
£2116 $3851   (25-May-92 WK.M237 b) Head I (23x18x15cm-9x7x6in) brown pat.bronze on wooden socle (DM 6200)
£3413 $6212   (25-May-92 WK.M237 a) Head of horse I (41x16x17cm-16x6x7in) brown pat.bronze on wooden socle (DM 10000)

CROISY, Aristide-Onesime (1840-1899) French
£1231 $2241   (11-Dec-91 FER.M231/R) Soldado con estandarte (41cm-16in) s. bronze st.f.Susse Freres (S.P 225000)

CRUZ-DIEZ, Carlos (1923-) Venezuelan
£5000 $9000   (18-Nov-91 SY.NY178/R) Physichrome No.2073 (100x100cm-39x39in) s.i.d.1982verso painted sheet metal construction

CSAKY, Josef (1888-1971) Hungarian/French
£2240 $4145   (12-Jun-92 AT.P7/R) Les deux amies (28cm-11in) s.num.1/8 pat.bronze.Cast.C.Valsuani (F.FR 22000)
£2469 $4469   (6-Dec-91 GL.P243/R) Jeune fille agenouillee (23x5x9cm-9x2x4in) studio st.num.2/8 blk.pat.bronze Cast.Blanchet (F.FR 24000)
£2658 $4865   (3-Feb-92 HH.P105/R) Femme agenouillee (24x14x23cm-9x6x9in) s.num.1/8base brn.pat.bronze (F.FR 26000)
£2846 $4951   (13-Apr-92 GL.P164/R) Adam et Eve (50x30x19cm-20x12x7in) s.num.HC 1base brn.pat.bronze Cast.Blanchet (F.FR 28000)
£3800 $6536   (16-Oct-91 S109/R) Femme nue (29cm-11in) s.i.num.1/8 bronze st.Landowski Fondeur
£4090 $7485   (3-Feb-92 HH.P92/R) Tete de femme (30x15x20cm-12x6x8in) s.num.6/8 brn.pat.bronze (F.FR 40000)

CSAKY, Josef (1888-1971) Hungarian/French-cont.

£4312	$7762	(20-Nov-91 CN.P68/R) Femme bras croise dans le dos (51cm-20in) s.d.47 num.22/8 brn.pat.bronze (F.FR 42000)
£7599	$13754	(24-May-92 GL.P39/R) Tete de femme, ou Tete perlee (29cm-11in) s.num.E/A/2 gold/silver pat.bronze st.f.Blanchet (F.FR 75000)
£8247	$14268	(23-Mar-92 GL.P166/R) Figure abstraite debout (73x16x13cm-29x6x5in) studio st.s.num.EA2 pat.bronze Cast.Blanchet (F.FR 80000)
£8763	$15160	(23-Mar-92 GL.P162/R) Figure habillee (80x21x19cm-31x8x7in) studio st.s.num.1/8 blk.pat.bronze Cast.Blanchet (F.FR 85000)
£9485	$16408	(23-Mar-92 GL.P171/R) Tete architectonique (33x26x33cm-13x10x13in) s.num.8/8 blk.pat.bronze Cast.Blanchet (F.FR 92000)
£11145	$20172	(24-May-92 GL.P42/R) L'etudiante (168cm-66in) s.num.H.C.2 brown pat.bronze st.f.Blanchet (F.FR 110000)
£40692	$72838	(17-Nov-91 GL.P22/R) L'etudiante (164x49x46cm-65x19x18in) s.num.3/8 green pat.bronze Cast.Landowski (F.FR 400000)

CUCCHI, Enzo (1950-) Italian

£15000	$25950	(26-Mar-92 C109/R) Untitled (290x245cm-114x96in) iron rubber on iron stretcher

CUMBERWORTH, Charles (1811-1852) French

£1229	$2200	(14-Nov-91 GRO.B121/R) Venus clipping wings of Cupid (41cm-16in) i. golden brown pat.bronze
£2567	$4620	(18-Nov-91 AT.P324) Couple de noirs (45cm-18in) s.base brn.pat.bronze Cast.Susse marble base two (F.FR 25000)

CZESCHKA, Carl Otto and HOFFMANN, Josef (19/20th C) Austrian

£25000	$45750	(15-May-92 S225/R) Pair of Caryatid figures (47cm-19in) gilt wood ebony mother of pearl ivory

DAGONET, Ernest (1856-1926) French

£2000	$3580	(13-Nov-91 CSK107/R) Two stags in combat (49cm-19in) s. bronze

DALI, Salvador (1904-1989) Spanish

£877	$1579	(22-Nov-91 SA.A484/R) Double Nike (18cm-7in) s.i.num.16/175 gold bronze (DM 2500)
£878	$1520	(3-Oct-91 D.V304/R) Venus a la girafe (56cm-22in) s.num.194/1500B pat.bronze st.f.Venturi Arte (A.S 18000)
£1107	$1970	(29-Nov-91 GAB.G2655) Le matador aux ciseaux (45cm-18in) s. brn.pat.bronze (S.FR 2800)
£1300	$2483	(29-Jun-92 CSK134/R) Alice au Pays des Merveilles (91cm-36in) st.num.d.64/350 1984 green gold pat.bronze
£1306	$2272	(21-Sep-91 SA.A494/R) Doppelnike (18cm-7in) s.indis.num.17/175 gold pat.bronze (DM 3800)
£1329	$2365	(25-Nov-91 WK.M213/R) Venus a la girafe (56x27x9cm-22x11x4in) s.d.1974 num.182/1000 silver bronze st.f.Venturi (DM 3800)
£1488	$2692	(3-Dec-91 AB.S5193/R) The Birdman (27cm-11in) s.num.18/350, green gold pat bronze inc.base (S.KR 15500)
£1500	$2715	(2-Dec-91 CSK97/R) Venus a la giraffe (56cm-22in) s. num.863/1000 silvered bronze st.Euro Art
£1569	$2667	(23-Oct-91 GD.B2500/R) Venus a tete de rose (43cm-17in) s.i.d.1981 bronze electrified acrylic shaft (S.FR 4000)
£1987	$3596	(23-May-92 KV.L70) Hommage a Newton (32x15cm-13x6in) s.num.509/1000 polished bronze marble socle (B.FR 120000)
£2397	$4314	(19-Nov-91 GO.G300) Reclining woman (23cm-9in) s.num.55/330, sterling silver (S.KR 25000)
£2400	$4128	(16-Oct-91 S125/R) Yang et Yen (13cm-5in) s.num.4/8 bronze
£2800	$5348	(29-Jun-92 CSK138/R) L'Ange Surrealiste (56cm-22in) st. num.1014/1500 dark brown pat.bronze
£3200	$5536	(25-Mar-92 S198/R) Le cabinet anthropomorphique (25cm-10in) i.num.072/300 sterling silver Cast.Mibrosa
£3551	$6427	(3-Dec-91 AB.S5192/R) Antropomorphique cabinet (32x58cm-13x23in) s.num.104/330, dark pat bronze Cast.Milbrosa (S.KR 37000)
£3800	$6878	(2-Dec-91 CSK98/R) Anthropomorphic cabinet (12x23cm-5x9in) i.num.B-108/330 gilt pat.bronze st.f.Mibrosa
£4333	$7453	(12-Oct-91 KV.L47/R) L'escargot et L'ange (44x62cm-17x24in) s.num.87/350 bronze marble base (B.FR 260000)
£5098	$8717	(21-Mar-92 KV.L414/R) Space elephant (85x44cm-33x17in) s.f.Venturi Arte num.244/350bronze plexi marble (B.FR 300000)
£5464	$9889	(23-May-92 KV.L492/R) Femme en flamme (84x34cm-33x13in) s.f.Venturi Artenum.222/350 polished bronze (B.FR 330000)
£5464	$9889	(23-May-92 KV.L68/R) La Noblesse du temps (59x38cm-23x15in) st.sig.num.62/350 bronze gr.br.pat. (B.FR 330000)

DALLIN, Cyrus Edwin (1861-1944) American

£2793	$5000	(13-Nov-91 B.SF2727/R) Pretty eagle (74cm-29in) bronze

DALOU, Aime Jules (1838-1902) French

£1350	$2471	(2-Jun-92 S499) Labourer with hoe at his feet (30cm-12in) s.i.bronze i.f.Susse Freres Paris

DALOU, Aime Jules (1838-1902) French-cont.

£1546	$2644	(9-Mar-92 AT.P268/R) La toilette (32cm-13in) s. brn.green pat.bronze (F.FR 15000)
£1573	$2847	(23-May-92 KV.L72/R) Le semeur (47x17cm-19x7in) st.sig.f.Susse Fres bronze br.pat. (B.FR 95000)
£1657	$3000	(5-Dec-91 SY.NY59/R) La verite meconnue (13cm-5in) i. dk.brown pat.bronze st.f.Susse Freres
£2800	$4984	(29-Nov-91 S211/R) The woman of Boulogne (67cm-26in) s. brown pat.bronze on marble plinth
£3500	$6335	(21-May-92 C48/R) Head of peasant wearing open necked shirt (34cm-13in) s.num.5 bronze st.f.Hebrard
£4000	$7000	(20-Feb-92 C150/R) Group of a Satyr embracing a nymph (41cm-16in) s. bronze marble base Cast.A A Hebrard
£4684	$8525	(13-Dec-91 ZZ.F63/R) Etude pour le triomphe de la Republique, cote droit (49cm-19in) s.base brn.pat.bronze Cast.Susse (F.FR 46000)
£5635	$10143	(2-Feb-92 ZZ.F193/R) Torse nu (48cm-19in) s. brn.pat.bronze Cast.Susse cire perdue (F.FR 55000)
£6110	$11303	(10-Jun-92 LD.P152/R) Tete d'enfant regardant sur la droite (40cm-16in) s. black pat.bronze on marble socle st.f.Hebrard (F.FR 60000)
£6129	$10725	(21-Feb-92 LT.P10/R) Faune et jeune femme (41cm-16in) s. brn.pat.bronze Cast.Hebrard cire perdue (F.FR 60000)
£8784	$15373	(24-Feb-92 ARC.P33/R) Enfant aux fleurs (54cm-21in) s.num.6 pat.bronze Cast.Hebrard cire perdue (F.FR 86000)

D'ALTRI, Arnold (20th C) Swiss?

| £6667 | $12067 | (22-May-92 EA.Z121/R) Torso (182cm-72in) c.1937 sand stone (S.FR 18000) |

DAMER, Anna Seymour (1749-1828) British

| £16000 | $29120 | (10-Dec-91 C91/R) Portrait bust of Mary Berry (46cm-18in) s. bronze |

DAMISCH, Gunter (1958-) Austrian

| £2098 | $3734 | (25-Nov-91 WK.M2004/R) Das Zwergenholz (150x90x7cm-59x35x3in) s.d.1982/83 oil panel board cork canvas (DM 6000) |

D'ANGERS, David (19th C) ?

| £1044 | $1900 | (27-May-92 CH.NY115/R) General Bonchamp (19cm-7in) i. bronze green brown pat. |
| £1500 | $2715 | (21-May-92 C25/R) Figure of Philopoemen (66cm-26in) s.d.1837 bronze |

DANNHAUSER, Johan Eduard (1869-?) German

| £1413 | $2473 | (3-Apr-92 BM.B1553/R) Polo player (50cm-20in) i.d.1908 pat.bronze st.f.H.Noack Friedenau (DM 4000) |

DANZINGER, Itzhak (1916-1977) Israeli

| £13143 | $23000 | (26-Sep-91 SY.I120/R) King of the shepherds (78cm-31in) polished brass |

DASHWOOD, Jeffrey (1947-) British

| £6500 | $11505 | (8-Nov-91 C327/R) Female torso (81cm-32in) s. num.7/12 green pat.bronze |

DASSON, Henry (after) (19th C) French

| £1573 | $2800 | (21-Jan-92 CE.NY75/R) Cupid restraining a duck (56cm-22in) i. bronze stepped oval red marble base |

DAUMIER, Honore (1808-1879) French

£1609	$2800	(13-Sep-91 S.W2628/R) L'avocat (25cm-10in) s.num.3/9 bronze f.st.C.Valsuani Cire Perdue
£3162	$5628	(29-Nov-91 GAB.G3139/R) L'Elegant (17cm-7in) st.mono.num.14/30 bronze Cast.Valsuani (S.FR 8000)
£3162	$5628	(29-Nov-91 GAB.G3138/R) Le roi Minos (18cm-7in) green pat.bronze cire perdue Cast.Valsuani (S.FR 8000)
£3601	$6842	(22-Jun-92 AT.P17/R) Le provincial a Paris (18cm-7in) init.num.26/30 pat.bronze f.st.C Valsuani Paris (F.FR 35000)
£4150	$7387	(29-Nov-91 GAB.G3141/R) L'Avocat (26cm-10in) num.3/30 green pat.bronze Cast.Valsuani (S.FR 10500)
£4150	$7387	(29-Nov-91 GAB.G3140/R) Le comte d'Argoul (29cm-11in) num.4/30 green pat.bronze Cast.Valsuani (S.FR 10500)
£4938	$9383	(22-Jun-92 AT.P16/R) L'elegante ou l'amoureux (17cm-7in) init.num.2/30 pat.bronze f.C.Valsuani Paris (F.FR 48000)
£5658	$10751	(22-Jun-92 AT.P18/R) Le valet de chambre (13cm-5in) init.num.4/30 pat.bronze f.st.C Valsuani Paris (F.FR 55000)
£22000	$42020	(30-Jun-92 C116/R) Ratapoil (43cm-17in) brown pat.bronze f.st.Alexis Rudier Paris
£26986	$49384	(3-Jun-92 PIC.P54/R) Daumier par lui-meme (73cm-29in) num.E.1 pat.bronze. Cast.C.Valsuani cire perdue (F.FR 265000)

DAVID, Jose Maria (20th C) ?

| £3582 | $6377 | (27-Nov-91 LGB.P79 b/R) Elephant d'Asie (74x38cm-29x15in) num.3/8 brn.pat.bronze Cast.Valsuani (F.FR 35000) |

DAVID, Pierre Jean (1788-1856) French

| £1700 | $3043 | (13-Nov-91 CSK146/R) Bust of General Foy (47cm-19in) mono. bronze stepped plinth with ormolu trophies |

DAVIES, John (?) ?
£2890 $5000   (3-Oct-91 SY.NY80/R) Head with wire (169cm-67in) init.d.72 painted
                      acrylic

DAVIS, Edward (19th C) British
£3500 $6230   (29-Nov-91 S96/R) Busts of Victorian lady and gentleman (201cm-79in) one
                      s.d.1849 marble incl.column pair

DEBAY, Auguste Hyacinth (1804-1865) French
£11628 $20000   (16-Oct-91 CH.NY149/R) Le Berceau primitif - Eve et ses deux enfants
                      (104cm-41in) white marble green marble wood pedestal

DEBUT, Marcel (1865-?) French
£719 $1374   (1-Jul-92 FB.P156/R) Le forgeron (40cm-16in) s. brown/silvered pat.bronze
                      on marble base (F.FR 7000)
£843 $1500   (30-Apr-92 CE.NY73/R) Figure of borzoi (41cm-16in) i. rich brown
                      pat.bronze
£900 $1602   (29-Nov-91 S185) Medieval maiden (58cm-23in) s. gilt bronze
£1300 $2223   (20-Mar-92 S101/R) Young hunter (67cm-26in) s. brown pat.bronze
£1800 $3078   (20-Mar-92 S102/R) The successful hunter (88cm-35in) s. brown green
                      pat.bronze

DECKER, Jos de (?) ?
£833 $1433   (12-Oct-91 KV.L62) Joy of life (26x20cm-10x8in) s. bronze (B.FR 50000)

DEFERNEX, Jean Baptiste (1729-1783) French
£1400 $2548   (10-Dec-91 C88/R) Bust of Madame de Fondville (39cm-15in) s.d.1760 bronze

DEGAS, Edgar (1834-1917) French
£21858 $40000   (13-May-92 CH.NY202/R) Danseuse s'avancant, les bras leves (35cm-14in)
                      st.sig. num.19/O black pat.bronze f.st.Hebrard
£36847 $65589   (28-Nov-91 FB.P23 c/R) Baigneuse assise se sechant le cou (31cm-12in)
                      s.num.44F brn.pat.bronze Cast.A A Hebrard (F.FR 360000)
£43716 $80000   (14-May-92 SY.NY225/R) Arabesque ouverte sur la jambe droite, le bras
                      gauche en avant (20cm-8in) i.num.1/4 brown pat.bronze st.f.A.A.Hebrard
£45000 $81450   (3-Dec-91 S13/R) Cheval en marche (27x21cm-11x8in) st.num.10/O bronze
                      f.st.A A Hebrard
£81967 $150000   (13-May-92 SY.NY1/R) Arabesque sur la jambe droite, la main droite pres
                      de terre (42cm-17in) i. green black pat.bronze st.f.A.A.Hebrard
£96045 $170000   (6-Nov-91 SY.NY11/R) Grande arabesque, premier temps (48cm-19in) i.
                      st.18/0 Cast.A A Hebrard cire perdue bronze
£103825 $190000   (13-May-92 SY.NY2/R) Danseuse attachant le cordon de son maillot
                      (43cm-17in) i. brown pat.bronze st.A.A.Hebrard

DEJEAN, Louis (attrib) (1872-?) French
£920 $1600   (15-Sep-91 JRB.C29/R) Standing female (114cm-45in) s. bronze
                      f.st.F.Barbedienne Fondeur, Paris

DELABRIERE, Paul Edouard (1829-1912) French
£800 $1368   (20-Mar-92 S4/R) Chiens braque et epagneau sur faisan (28cm-11in) s.i.
                      green-brown pat.bronze
£1600 $2848   (29-Nov-91 S31/R) Pointer and rabbit (38cm-15in) s. green/black
                      pat.bronze

DELESALLE (19th C) French
£1000 $1790   (13-Nov-91 CSK108) Figure of uniformed bugler with sword slung at back
                      (46cm-18in) s.i. bronze

DENECHEAU, Seraphin (1831-1912) French
£10000 $17500   (27-Sep-91 S62/R) Femme caressant une chimere (224cm-88in) s.
                      brn.pat.bronze marble socle marble column

D'EPINAY, Prosper (1836-?) French
£21627 $36982   (20-Mar-92 ZZ.F60/R) Jeune femme ajustant une ceinture, une urne a ses
                      cotes (176cm-69in) marble base (F.FR 210000)

DERAIN, Andre (1880-1954) French
£3429 $6000   (28-Feb-92 SY.NY41/R) Le vieux gaulois (20x11cm-8x4in) i. reddish brown
                      pat.bronze
£6857 $12000   (27-Feb-92 CE.NY70/R) La femme a la coiffe (28cm-11in) with i.sig.
                      num.4/11 golden brown pat.bronze

DERUJINSKY, Gleb W (20th C) Russian
£860 $1540   (14-Nov-91 GRO.B122/R) Woman with whippet (20cm-8in) i.num.1
                      greenish-brown pat.bronze f.i.Roman NY

DESCHAMPS, Gerard (1937-) French
£7049 $11984   (27-Oct-91 P.V61) Paella aux fraises (65x75x17cm-26x30x7in)
                      s.i.d.1962verso tissue canvas in plexiglass box (F.FR 70000)
£8157 $13867   (27-Oct-91 P.V60/R) Retroviseur balayette (78x100x13cm-31x39x5in)
                      s.i.d.1962verso plastic objects in plexiglass (F.FR 81000)

DESCOMPS, J (1869-1950) French
£820 $1500   (3-Jun-92 D.NY663) Group of female nude and satyr (58cm-23in) s. bronze
                      marble

DESCOMPS, Joe (1869-1950) French
£3500 $6230   (29-Apr-92 C78/R) Oriental dancer (28cm-11in) s.bronze ivory sold with figure by Chiparus

DESPIAU, Charles (1874-1946) French
£3107 $5500   (5-Nov-91 CE.NY152/R) Mlle Bianchini (37cm-15in) s. black pat.bronze st.f.C.Valsuani
£3429 $6000   (28-Feb-92 SY.NY31/R) Tete de l'actrice Maria Lani (37cm-15in) i. black pat.bronze f.st.Valsuani/Perdue
£7000 $12110   (24-Mar-92 C58/R) La jeune, buste de Mme Paul Louis Weiller (63cm-25in) i.st.num.4/10 gold pat.bronze
£9714 $17000   (25-Feb-92 CH.NY19/R) La bacchante (57cm-22in) s.num.3/5 black pat.bronze f.st.C.Valsuani

DETRIER, Pierre-Louis (1822-1897) French
£934 $1700   (27-May-92 CH.NY128/R) Mother and child (41cm-16in) i. bronze marble base

DEUTSCHMANN, Joseph (attrib) (1717-1787) German
£2682 $4800   (14-Jan-92 CH.NY118/R) Cherubs (33cm-13in) polychrome wood pair

DEXTER, Henry (1806-1876) American
£838 $1500   (14-Nov-91 CE.NY238) Bust of man (69cm-27in) s. white marble

D'HAESE, Reinhoud (1928-) Swiss
£1810 $3276   (4-Dec-91 KH.K8/R) Do you want to fight.. (24cm-9in) copper (D.KR 20000)
£3422 $6193   (7-Dec-91 KV.L443/R) Le nez au vent (34x30cm-13x12in) pewter stone socle (B.FR 200000)
£3667 $6307   (12-Oct-91 KV.L427/R) L'Oisivete n'est pas mon fort (36x53cm-14x21in) copper stone socle (B.FR 220000)

DICK, Sir William Reid (1879-1961) British
£2000 $3560   (29-Nov-91 S214/R) The slingboy (33cm-13in) s. brown pat.bronze on green marble plinth
£7000 $11970   (20-Mar-92 S173/R) The slingboy (67cm-26in) s. green pat.bronze on marble plinth

DIEDERICH, Wilhelm Hunt (1884-1953) American
£4678 $8000   (21-Mar-92 SY.NY218/R) Group of Diana and hound (63x72cm-25x28in) mono. blackish-green pat.iron

DIETZ, Ferdinand (after) (1708-1777) German
£2200 $4224   (9-Jul-92 S197/R) Putti representing hunting and fishing (19cm-7in) Rococo wood pair

DINE, Jim (1935-) American
£8380 $15000   (6-May-92 CH.NY314/R) Tampa tools (68x73x83cm-27x29x33in) with sig. cast aluminium five panels
£44693 $80000   (12-Nov-91 CH.NY20/R) The yellow painting (160x117x12cm-63x46x5in) s.i.d.1972-3verso oil crayon chl.tools
£55866 $100000   (13-Nov-91 CH.NY225/R) Double Venus (162x46x58cm-64x18x23in) cast bronze

DING, Henri Marius (1844-1898) French
£1412 $2400   (22-Oct-91 CE.NY34/R) Figure of woman playing harp (46cm-18in) i. rich golden brown pat.bronze f.st.

DOBSON, Frank (1888-1963) British
£1500 $2610   (19-Sep-91 B55/R) Ann - artist's daughter (27cm-11in) s. bronze oxidised silver

DOKOUPIL, Jiri Georg (1954-) Czechoslovakian
£9714 $17000   (27-Feb-92 CH.NY71/R) Blue songs about love (99x99x99cm-39x39x39in) init.d.1982verso oil canvas and bronze two parts

DOMINGUEZ, Oscar (1906-1958) Spanish
£19547 $35381   (2-Dec-91 CC.P10/R) Tete de taureau (67x41x13cm-26x16x5in) wood polychrome (F.FR 190000)

DONATELLO (after) (19th C) Italian
£2492 $4262   (10-Mar-92 SY.AM138) Equestrian statue of Gattamelata (182cm-72in) bronze (D.FL 8000)

D'ORS, Esperanza (1949-) Spanish
£1020 $1743   (21-Mar-92 KV.L108) Aphrodite 8 (49x28cm-19x11in) num.2/4 bronze green pat. (B.FR 60000)
£1167 $2007   (12-Oct-91 KV.L93) Aphrodite (43x22cm-17x9in) s.num.2/6 bronze green pat. (B.FR 70000)

DROUOT, Edouard (1859-1945) French
£1034 $1800   (13-Sep-91 SY.NY110/R) Female figure (61cm-24in) i. brown pat.bronze
£1075 $2000   (16-Jun-92 RO.BA121) La defenseuse (79cm-31in) pat.bronze
£1100 $2101   (30-Jun-92 SWS570/R) Muse des bois, naked to the waist blowing pipes (73cm-29in) s.i.c.1890 black brown pat.bronze
£1200 $2292   (30-Jun-92 PH91/R) Echo, bare breasted young woman standing amongst clump of reeds (63cm-25in) s.i. brown pat.bronze

DROUOT, Edouard (1859-1945) French-cont.
£1916	$3488	(10-Dec-91 N.M140/R) Lutte pour la vie (57cm-22in) black-brown pat.bronze marble socle (DM 5500)
£2567	$4620	(18-Nov-91 AT.P334/R) Chamelier a l'assaut (56cm-22in) s.base pat.bronze (F.FR 25000)
£2874	$5000	(13-Sep-91 SY.NY117/R) Indian on horseback (52x62cm-20x24in) i. brown green pat.bronze st.Bronze France

DRURY, A (19/20th C) British
| £3200 | $5536 | (25-Mar-92 PHI704/R) Bust of young girl wearing dress with puffed sleeves (40cm-16in) pat.bronze on marble plinth |

DRURY, Alfred (1856-1944) British
| £2800 | $4984 | (29-Nov-91 S207/R) The age of innocence (41cm-16in) s. golden brown pat.bronze black marble plinth |

DRYER, Moira (1957-) American
| £782 | $1400 | (9-May-92 CE.NY208/R) Megaphone (43x40x59cm-17x16x23in) s.i.d.1986verso casein wood |

DUBOIS, E (?) ?
| £2118 | $3600 | (22-Oct-91 CE.NY19/R) Allegorical group (61cm-24in) i. rich brown pat.bronze |

DUBOIS, Paul (1829-1905) French
£1628	$2800	(9-Oct-91 RO.BA56) Tribunal (68cm-27in) s. pat.bronze f.F.Barbedienne
£1629	$2900	(30-Apr-92 CE.NY48/R) Figure of Florentine lute player (89cm-35in) i. brown pat.bronze
£2050	$3506	(20-Mar-92 S163/R) Le courage militaire (62cm-24in) s. brown pat.bronze marble plinth i.Barbedienne
£10000	$17500	(27-Sep-91 S61/R) Charity (195cm-77in) s.i. pat.bronze marble plinth Cast.Barbedienne

DUBUCAND, A (1828-1894) French
| £2135 | $3800 | (30-Apr-92 CE.NY39/R) Picador. Matador (51cm-20in) i. parcel-gilt bronze pair |

DUBUCAND, Alfred (1828-1894) French
£714	$1300	(27-May-92 CH.NY98/R) Stag and doe (21cm-8in) i. bronze red brown pat.
£850	$1624	(30-Jun-92 PH88/R) Nubian huntsman seated on horse with pair of hounds at his feet (25cm-10in) s. brown pat.bronze
£924	$1663	(18-Nov-91 AT.P340) Jeune fellah et son ane (32cm-13in) s. brn.pat.bronze green marble base (F.FR 9000)
£1232	$2218	(18-Nov-91 AT.P341) Mule et enfant (34cm-13in) s.base pat.bronze (F.FR 12000)
£2035	$3500	(16-Oct-91 CH.NY147/R) Partridges with their chicks both i. brn.pat.bronze pair
£3200	$5856	(12-May-92 SWS371/R) Cavalier et femme arabe a la fontaine (73cm-29in) s. pale-brown pat.bronze
£8140	$14000	(16-Oct-91 CH.NY148 a/R) Le Trait du Parthe (89cm-35in) i. red brn.pat.bronze

DUBUFFET, Jean (1901-1985) French
£20950	$37500	(14-Nov-91 SY.NY286 a/R) Paysage aux plantes (26x52x57cm-10x20x22in) init.d.69 epoxy paint on polyurethane 3 parts
£24565	$43726	(30-Nov-91 FB.P31/R) L'arbre no.5 (80cm-31in) num.5base fibreglass epoxy resin (F.FR 240000)
£33520	$60000	(5-May-92 CH.NY35/R) Element bleu IV (88x115x11cm-35x45x4in) init.d.67 num.44 acrylic on cast polyester resin
£50279	$90000	(7-May-92 SY.NY266/R) Arbre au chef touffu (142cm-56in) init.d.69 polyester resin
£118644	$210000	(6-Nov-91 SY.NY66/R) Le lunatique (181cm-71in) init.d.72 acrylic klegecell polyester fibreglass

DUCHOISELLE (19th C) French
| £866 | $1507 | (19-Sep-91 GK.Z536/R) Young woman seated threading pearls from box (31cm-12in) s. bronze marble socle (S.FR 2200) |
| £5000 | $8750 | (27-Sep-91 S11/R) Indian squaw in canoe (22x93cm-9x37in) s. brn.pat.bronze |

DUFF, John (1925-) Canadian
| £6704 | $12000 | (14-Nov-91 SY.NY214/R) Green curved wedge (188x29x37cm-74x11x15in) s.d.83 fibreglass paint resin tin cans masonite |

DUMAIGE, Etienne-Henri (1830-1888) French
£820	$1435	(20-Feb-92 C145/R) Muse (33cm-13in) s. bronze
£1044	$1900	(13-Dec-91 S.W3036/R) Return from fields - allegory of harvest (56cm-22in) s.i. gilt bronze
£1100	$1881	(20-Mar-92 S135/R) The family (53cm-21in) s. brown pat.bronze

DUMOULIN, Leonce (19th C) French
| £12000 | $20520 | (20-Mar-92 S197/R) The sunflower girl (122cm-48in) s. marble |

DUQUESNOY (after) (18th C) Italian
£1100 $2002   (12-Dec-91 S131) Statuette of executioner, standing naked with head of victim in hand (28cm-11in) bronze

DUQUESNOY, Francois (attrib) (1594-1643) Flemish
£45296 $82439   (10-Dec-91 N.M93/R) Allegory of winter depicting nude young boy seated on tree stump (21cm-8in) ivory (DM 130000)

DUQUESNOY, Francois (style) (1594-1643) Flemish
£1923 $3500   (26-May-92 SY.NY110/R) Group of Madonna and Child, seated upon bank of clouds (14cm-6in) gilt bronze
£2998 $5575   (16-Jun-92 SY.B134/R) The Flagellation (21cm-8in) ivory wooden base (B.FR 180000)

DURBAN, Arne (1912-) Scandinavian
£1063 $1934   (14-Dec-91 BU.O24/R) Mother and baby (56cm-22in) s. bronze (N.KR 12000)

DURET, Francisque-Joseph (1804-1864) French
£958 $1695   (10-Nov-91 ZZ.F160/R) La tragedie (40cm-16in) s. brn.blk.pat.bronze (F.FR 9500)
£1008 $1784   (10-Nov-91 ZZ.F161/R) La comedie (40cm-16in) s. brn.blk.pat.bronze (F.FR 10000)
£1700 $2907   (20-Mar-92 S109/R) Commedy and Tragedy (40cm-16in) i. gilt bronze pair
£5814 $10000   (9-Oct-91 RO.BA52/R) Mercure inventant la lyre (100cm-39in) s. pat.bronze f.Delafontaine

DURHAM, J (1814-1877) British
£1150 $2024   (8-Apr-92 CSK90/R) Group of boating pair, holding boater and oar (42cm-17in) s. bronze

DURST, Alan (1883-1970) British
£4800 $8496   (5-Nov-91 PH79/R) Reclining female form (66cm-26in) init.d.1935 Hopton wood stone

DUSSART, Gustave (1875-?) French
£1237 $2300   (16-Jun-92 RO.BA119) Inconsciente (66cm-26in) bronze

DUTCH SCHOOL (?) Dutch
£2060 $3750   (26-May-92 SY.NY60/R) Group of Madonna and child, with child supported on right hip (44cm-17in) walnut traces polychromy c.1700

DUTCH SCHOOL, 17th C
£4500 $8190   (12-Dec-91 S253/R) Statue of Venus, holding vase and dolphin at side (81cm-32in) marble

DUTTMANN, Hermann (19th C) German
£1203 $2093   (21-Sep-91 SA.A2480/R) Putto holding rose riding on lion (62x76x25cm-24x30x10in) i. green black pat.bronze (DM 3500)

DYSON-SMITH (fl.1919-1940) British
£1250 $2288   (12-May-92 H150/R) Nude dancer with head back, her arms outstretched balancing on one leg (33cm-13in) s.d.1920 bronze slate base
£1250 $2288   (12-May-92 H149/R) Nude dancer with head down, her arms outstretched balancing on one leg (33cm-13in) s.d.1925 bronze slate base
£1250 $2288   (12-May-92 H148/R) Nude dancer with hands crossed over her head (33cm-13in) s.d.1925 bronze slate base

EBERLE, Abastenia St Leger (1878-1942) American
£1475 $2640   (14-Nov-91 GRO.B128/R) L'Isolee (18cm-7in) i. greensih-brown pat.bronze

EDGCUMBE, Ursula (1900-1985) British?
£1250 $2313   (11-Jun-92 C111/R) Three horses, Keystone (39x34x21cm-15x13x8in) stone

EFTIMIADI, Frosso (1916-) Greek
£1086 $1900   (27-Feb-92 CE.NY182/R) Bird (122x115x35cm-48x45x14in) st.sig. hammered brass

EGGENHOFER, Nick (1897-?) American
£939 $1700   (4-Dec-91 D.NY49/R) Bison (15cm-6in) s. num.22/30 dark brown pat.bronze

EGYPTIAN SCHOOL (?) Egyptian
£12232 $22752   (19-Jun-92 CB.P178/R) Statuette d'Ibis (12x13cm-5x5in) bronze ivory (F.FR 120000)

ELDH, Carl (1873-1955) Swedish
£770 $1324   (8-Mar-92 BU.M330) Mother's sorrow (18cm-7in) s. gold pat bronze Cast.H.Bergman (S.KR 8000)
£940 $1570   (25-Aug-91 BU.M318) Seated girl (26cm-10in) s.d.1904 pat bronze Cast.H. Bergman (S.KR 10000)
£1044 $1910   (14-May-92 BU.S108/R) Brita (20cm-8in) s.d.1908 brown pat bronze Cast.H.Bergman (S.KR 11000)

ELDH, Carl (1873-1955) Swedish-cont.
£1898	$3472	(14-May-92 BU.S109/R) Self criticism (14cm-6in) s. brown pat bronze Cast.H Bergman (S.KR 20000)
£2176	$3939	(19-May-92 AB.S4553/R) Seated nude woman (25cm-10in) s.d.1904 dark pat bronze Cast.Bergman (S.KR 23000)
£4800	$8544	(29-Nov-91 S220/R) The slipped robe (102cm-40in) s. marble

ENGLISH SCHOOL, 17th C
£5060	$8704	(15-Oct-91 CH.R172/R) Personaggi su sfondo di paesaggi campestri (79x110cm-31x43in) painted copper panels on cabinet drawers (I.L 11000000)

ENGLISH SCHOOL, 18th C
£3600	$6912	(8-Jul-92 PH122/R) Bust of bearded emperor Caracalla wearing drapes fastened by fibula (70cm-28in) marble
£4600	$8372	(10-Dec-91 C66/R) Figure of reclining putto, resting on left arm, other arm on leg (44x62cm-17x24in) marble

ENGLISH SCHOOL, 19th C
£1000	$1830	(2-Jun-92 S483) John Milton (53cm-21in) marble
£2400	$4104	(20-Mar-92 S78/R) Diana the huntress (89cm-35in) marble
£4500	$8190	(10-Dec-91 C65/R) Busts of children, draped (46cm-18in) white marble
£5400	$9234	(20-Mar-92 S177/R) Sirens of the wave (68cm-27in) marble

ENGLISH SCHOOL, 20th C
£1800	$3150	(20-Feb-92 C144/R) Allegorical maiden, possibly justice (29cm-11in) bronze stained wooden socle
£5100	$9078	(29-Nov-91 S42/R) Clydesdale (36cm-14in) mono.d.1942 bronze on marble base

EPSTEIN, Sir Jacob (1880-1959) British
£2260	$4000	(5-Nov-91 CE.NY153/R) Head of young girl (23cm-9in) green pat.bronze
£2335	$4250	(13-Dec-91 S.W3049/R) Seated nude (48x30cm-19x12in) s. green pat.bronze
£2616	$4997	(21-Jul-92 JRL.S171/R) Lydia (50cm-20in) bronze (A.D 6750)
£2700	$4779	(5-Nov-91 PH71/R) Fourth portrait of Dolores (24cm-9in) brn.pat.bronze
£2700	$4779	(5-Nov-91 PH72/R) Third portrait of Jackie (23cm-9in) gold pat.bronze
£3000	$5310	(8-Nov-91 C323/R) Isobel Hughes (31cm-12in) s. light green pat.bronze
£3200	$5664	(8-Nov-91 C320 a/R) Epstein's left hand (19cm-7in) brn.pat.bronze
£3200	$5664	(8-Nov-91 C322/R) Fourth portrait of Leda (20cm-8in) s. brn.pat.bronze
£3800	$7030	(11-Jun-92 C104/R) First portrait of Jackie (42cm-17in) brown pat.bronze
£4360	$7500	(12-Oct-91 SY.NY178/R) Maquette for St. Michael and Devil (53cm-21in) golden brown pat.bronze
£6286	$11000	(26-Sep-91 SY.I67/R) Betty Peters (60cm-24in) bronze
£6500	$12025	(11-Jun-92 C101/R) First portrait of Louise (56cm-22in) brown pat.bronze
£6538	$12488	(19-Jul-92 SY.ME42/R) Head of a woman (30cm-12in) bronze (A.D 17000)
£8000	$14160	(8-Nov-91 C321/R) Third portrait of Sunita (58cm-23in) gold brown pat.bronze
£14000	$25900	(11-Jun-92 C99/R) Second portrait of George Bernard Shaw (43x24cm-17x9in) s. black pat.bronze

ERIKSSON, Christian (1858-1935) Swedish
£1044	$1910	(14-May-92 BU.S110/R) 'Elof' (19cm-7in) s.d.1901 brown pat bronze Cast.H Bergman (S.KR 11000)

ERIKSSON, Liss (1919-) Swedish
£882	$1615	(12-May-92 GO.G308) Figure of man (30cm-12in) s.i.d.1947-51 num.5/8, pat bronze Cire Perdue (S.KR 9300)

ERNST, Max (1891-1976) German
£3093	$5351	(23-Mar-92 CC.P36/R) Le Grand Ignorant (183x164cm-72x65in) mono. oi wood collage lithograph three parts (F.FR 30000)
£3764	$6813	(7-Dec-91 KV.L416/R) Fontaine D'Amboise la Tortue (31x20cm-12x8in) s. marble (B.FR 220000)
£4190	$7500	(9-May-92 CE.NY73/R) Le roi, la reine et le fou (30cm-12in) s.num.12/35 black pat.bronze
£9827	$17000	(2-Oct-91 SY.NY84/R) Sedona relief (38cm-15in) i. st. dark brown pat.bronze
£26230	$48000	(13-May-92 CH.NY311/R) La tourangelle (26cm-10in) s. num.VI/VIII black pat.bronze f.i.
£28000	$50680	(4-Dec-91 S158/R) Deux assistants (36x40cm-14x16in) i.num.II/VI bronze f.i.Susse Fondeur Paris

ERTE, Romain de Tirtoff (1892-1990) Russian
£1143	$2000	(23-Sep-91 S.SL408) Amazon (43cm-17in) s. num.219-375 gilt bronze polychrome
£1257	$2200	(23-Sep-91 S.SL413) The masque (46cm-18in) s. num.51/375 blk.gilt pat.bronze
£1371	$2400	(23-Sep-91 S.SL417) Coquette (46cm-18in) s. num.240/375 polychrome silver gilt pat.bronze
£1497	$2500	(25-Aug-91 JRB.C138) Deco figure (46x18cm-18x7in) num.228/375 bronze
£1771	$3100	(23-Sep-91 S.SL419) The wedding (41x46cm-16x18in) s. num.295/375 silver pat.bronze polychrome
£1913	$3500	(15-May-92 DM.D2049/R) Je t'aime (48cm-19in) s.d.1988 bronze
£2093	$3600	(14-Oct-91 H.C218/R) Egyptian Queen (48cm-19in) i. polychrome bronze st.f.Sevenarts Ltd.

ERTE, Romain de Tirtoff (1892-1990) Russian-cont.
£2317	$4194	(3-Dec-91 R.T60/R) Fire bird (41cm-16in) s.i.d.1980 num.16/250 brown pat.bronze i.Parker (C.D 4750)
£2442	$4200	(14-Oct-91 H.C216/R) Le Soleil (46cm-18in) i.st. polychrome bronze gold tone beading
£2459	$4500	(15-May-92 DM.D2048/R) Dreambirds (46cm-18in) s.d.1988 bronze
£2596	$4750	(15-May-92 DM.D2041/R) Aphrodite (48cm-19in) s.d.1986 bronze
£2778	$4750	(13-Mar-92 DM.D2191/R) Flowers of love (43cm-17in) s.base bears mono. brn.gilt pat.bronze
£3005	$5500	(15-May-92 DM.D2040/R) Chinese legend (56cm-22in) s.d.1988 bronze

ESCALER MILA, Lambert (1874-?) Spanish
£2215	$3833	(24-Mar-92 DUR.M215/R) Una joven vestida con traje largo de amplio vuelo que sujeta con ambas manos (56cm-22in) s. polychrome terracotta (S.P 400000)

ESCOFFIER, Beatrice (1954-) French?
£1125	$2058	(3-Feb-92 HH.P84/R) Les deux joyeux (28x20x15cm-11x8x6in) s.num.EA 1 base blue pat.bronze Cast.Clement (F.FR 11000)

ETROG, Sorel (1933-) Canadian/Rumanian
£2682	$4800	(12-Nov-91 CE.NY95/R) Untitled, bacarole (56x46x13cm-22x18x5in) st.sig.num.2/6 brown pat.bronze
£2857	$5000	(25-Feb-92 SY.NY194/R) Antitete (44x57cm-17x22in) st.sig. num.5/7 bronze

ETUNGAT, Abraham (1911-) ?
£688	$1259	(1-Jun-92 W.T889) Bird standing with outstretched wings (30cm-12in) mottled green serpentine carving (C.D 1500)

EVALUARDJUK, Henry (1923-) North American
£688	$1259	(1-Jun-92 W.T842) Polar bear stretching to sniff for scents in the air (30cm-12in) mottled serpentine carving acrylic base (C.D 1500)
£1743	$3190	(1-Jun-92 W.T836/R) Polar bear standing embracing dancing seal (41cm-16in) s.d.1974 mottled soapstone (C.D 3800)

EZEKIEL, Moses (1844-1917) American
£847	$1500	(13-Feb-92 SY.NY106/R) Figure of winged Victory breaking chains (229cm-90in) i. marble

FABBRI, Agenore (1911-) Italian
£4171	$7424	(26-Nov-91 SY.MI212/R) Composizione (37x39x12cm-15x15x5in) s. bronze (I.L 9000000)
£4171	$7424	(26-Nov-91 SY.MI11/R) Crocifissione (51cm-20in) s. painted terracotta (I.L 9000000)

FAGUAYS, Pierre le (20th C) French
£1279	$2200	(14-Oct-91 H.C214/R) Diane (66cm-26in) i. green pat.bronze st.f.Susse Freres
£2600	$4420	(25-Oct-91 S345/R) Dancer with Thyrsus (56cm-22in) i. cold painted bronze marble
£4500	$8235	(15-May-92 S331) The huntswoman (35cm-14in) i. silvered bronze ivory

FAGUAYS, le (20th C) French
£939	$1700	(6-Dec-91 GC.M123/R) Joven atleta (26cm-10in) s. gilded bronze ivory on onyx socle
£1309	$2330	(28-Oct-91 AT.P131) Diane chasseresse (65cm-26in) s. silver gold pat.bronze Cast.Susse Freres (F.FR 13000)

FALCONET (after) (18th C) French
£1000	$1720	(15-Oct-91 SWS492/R) Figure of Venus (94cm-37in) white marble
£2027	$3750	(10-Jun-92 SY.NY201/R) The Bronze Horseman (24cm-9in) i. gilded bronze on malachite pedestal
£2082	$3872	(16-Jun-92 SY.B143/R) Venus at her toilet (40cm-16in) s. bronze br.pat. pair (B.FR 125000)

FALCONET, Etienne Maurice (1716-1791) French
£1453	$2500	(9-Oct-91 RO.BA61) Cupido (47cm-19in) s. bronze on marble base

FALCONET, Etienne Maurice (after) (1716-1791) French
£733	$1400	(3-Jul-92 S.W3902) Seated nude (20cm-8in) bears sig. bronze

FALCONET, Etienne Maurice (studio) (1716-1791) French
£6000	$11520	(7-Jul-92 C74/R) Venus seated on tree stump proferring breast to cupid (34cm-13in) marble

FALGUIERE, A (1831-1900) French
£1150	$1955	(23-Oct-91 LJ221) Figure of running youth holding cockerel (80cm-31in) bronze f.i.Belmanivey and Carter, New Bond St.

FALGUIERE, Alexandre (1831-1900) French
£1648 $3000   (27-May-92 CH.NY124/R) Diane (46cm-18in) i.f.Thiebaut Freres bronze green brown pat.
£1754 $3000   (13-Mar-92 DM.D2193/R) Classical style boy holding a rooster s. brn.pat.bronze

FALK, Lars-Erik (1922-) Scandinavian
£946 $1712   (19-May-92 AB.S5136) Modul sculpture in colour 24 (49cm-19in) s.d.1984 black varnished metal incl.white base (S.KR 10000)
£1708 $3125   (11-May-92 NOR.S103/R) Ascending forms (90cm-35in) s.d.1964 painted sheet metal (S.KR 18000)

FANELLI, Francesco (attrib) (19th C) Italian
£8500 $16320   (7-Jul-92 C154/R) Group of St George and the Dragon (22cm-9in) bronze on wood socle
£15000 $28800   (7-Jul-92 C155/R) Group of cupid on horseback drawing bow and dog barking at horse (16cm-6in) bronze
£21000 $38220   (10-Dec-91 C98/R) Group of Cupid on horseback, drawing bow and dog underneath barking (16cm-6in) bronze

FANNY (1944-) French?
£1509 $2596   (7-Oct-91 HH.P8/R) Cathie (50cm-20in) s.num.2/8 brn.green pat.bronze Cast.Clementi (F.FR 15000)

FANTACCHIOTTI, Cesare (1844-1922) Italian
£3000 $5340   (29-Nov-91 S133/R) Egyptian dancer (97cm-38in) s. brown pat.bronze i.f.Firenze Fond.Galli

FARNHAM, Sally James (1876-1943) American
£865 $1600   (10-Jun-92 CE.NY374/R) Group of two elephants (9cm-4in) i. rich brown pat.bronze
£1520 $2600   (12-Mar-92 CH.NY113/R) Two elephants (20cm-8in) i. dark brown pat.bronze
£6593 $12000   (28-May-92 CH.NY103/R) Will Rogers on his horse (54cm-21in) i. bronze dark brown pat.

FAUSTO, Biggi (19th C) Italian
£5000 $8900   (29-Nov-91 S203/R) Cupid and Psyche (81cm-32in) s.i. marble on yellow marble plinth

FAVRE, Maurice (19/20th C) French
£1777 $3252   (13-May-92 FER.M215/R) Joven dama con partitura (32cm-13in) s. gilded bronze ivory (S.P 325000)

FAYDHERBE, Lucas (attrib) (1617-1697) Flemish
£9500 $17290   (12-Dec-91 S229/R) Group of Virgin and Child - Virgin seated on stool supporting Child (23cm-9in) boxwood

FAZZINI, Pericle (1913-) Italian
£1676 $3000   (9-May-92 CE.NY72/R) Acrobata (13cm-5in) s. brown pat.bronze
£3352 $6000   (9-May-92 CE.NY70/R) Ginnasta (22cm-9in) s.indis.i.d.1937 brown pat.bronze
£5670 $10377   (12-May-92 F.R261/R) Ritratto della Baronessa Anita Blanc (21x20x12cm-8x8x5in) s.i.d.1938 wood (I.L 12500000)

FEGER, Stefan (attrib) (1726-1770) Austrian
£2787 $5073   (10-Dec-91 N.M109/R) St Mary. St Joseph (99x99x99cm-39x39x39in) wood bone (DM 8000)
£2787 $5073   (10-Dec-91 N.M110/R) St Joachim and St Anna (99x99x99cm-39x39x39in) wood (DM 8000)

FEI MINGJIE (1949-) Chinese
£7080 $12108   (22-Mar-92 SY.TA13/R) Pear (48x23cm-19x9in) s.d.90 bronze green brown (T.D 308000)

FENOSA, Apelles (1899-1989) Spanish
£2616 $4499   (7-Oct-91 HH.P47/R) Femme les mains jointes (17x6x6cm-7x2x2in) mono. terracotta (F.FR 26000)
£3119 $5364   (7-Oct-91 HH.P48/R) Femme les bras ouverts (16x6x4cm-6x2x2in) s. brn.pat.bronze Cast.Busato (F.FR 31000)

FENTON, Beatrice (1887-?) American
£44199 $80000   (5-Dec-91 SY.NY62/R) Nereid fountain (274cm-108in) i.d.1928 weathered pat.bronze i.f.Bureau Bros.

FERAUD, Albert (20th C) ?
£1007 $1793   (28-Oct-91 GL.P196/R) Sans titre (65x72x27cm-26x28x11in) s.d.1972base soldered iron steel (F.FR 10000)

FERGUSSON, John Duncan (1874-1961) British
£900 $1629   (4-Dec-91 S260/R) Trousers - goat (10cm-4in) brass

FERNANDEZ, Gregorio (studio) (16th C) Spanish
£1173 $2018   (16-Oct-91 FER.M282/R) Cristo (55cm-22in) sculpture (S.P 215000)

FERRARA, Jackie (1929-) American
£9497 $17000   (6-May-92 CH.NY358/R) A209 Zogg (286x80x105cm-113x31x41in) pine with drawing s.d.6-80 col.felt-tip pen

FERRERIRA, Carlos (attrib) (?) Spanish
£985 $1793   (27-May-92 DUR.M484/R) Nike de esbeltas proporciones y elegante torso de suaves curvaturas (193cm-76in) bronze on black marble plinth (S.P 180000)

FERVILLE-SUAN, Charles (19th C) French
£1765 $3000   (22-Oct-91 CE.NY31/R) Fauconniere - figure (103cm-41in) i. brown pat.bronze
£2167 $3770   (14-Apr-92 GM.B1059/R) Bergere s. bronze Cast.H Luppens marble column (B.FR 130000)

FEUCHERE, Jean-Jacques (1807-1852) French
£1744 $3000   (16-Oct-91 CH.NY148/R) Amazone domptant un cheval sauvage (44cm-17in) i. brn.blk.pat.bronze

FEUERMAN, Carole Jeane (20th C) American
£3243 $6000   (12-Jun-92 SY.NY286/R) Blue beret (40cm-16in) init.d.83 num.4/6 polyester resin

FIACHI, Professor (19/20th C) Italian
£12712 $22500   (14-Feb-92 DM.D2150/R) The Goddess - Sappho in meditation (76cm-30in) i. white marble bronze

FIASCHI, E (19th C) Italian
£772 $1389   (22-Nov-91 SA.A2397/R) Mother and child (54cm-21in) s. alabaster (DM 2200)
£1453 $2500   (7-Mar-92 LAE.L7/R) Elegante de la Renaissance (81cm-32in) s. Carrara marble

FIASCHI, L E (19/20th C) Italian
£7796 $14500   (16-Jun-92 RO.BA129) Pudor (123cm-48in) Carrara marble

FIASCHI, P C E (19/20th C) Italian
£1600 $2736   (20-Mar-92 S194/R) Young woman seated in chair (36cm-14in) brown pat.bronze alabaster marble

FIEVRE, Yolande (1907-) French
£1336 $2552   (3-Jul-92 GL.P62) Mon chateau pour un reve (24x24cm-9x9in) s. pebbles debris wood mirror (F.FR 13000)

FIORAVANTI, Jose (1896-1977) Argentinian
£1075 $2000   (16-Jun-92 RO.BA117) Dr.Alejandro Bustillo (46cm-18in) bronze

FIORI, Ernesto di (1884-1945) German
£2632 $4737   (21-Nov-91 L.K142/R) Standing youth holding cloth (14x18cm-6x7in) mono.d.1930 dark brown pat.bronze (DM 7500)

FIOT (?) French
£765 $1400   (3-Jun-92 D.NY756) Sculpture of lion (46cm-18in) s. bronze

FISCHER, Lothar (1933-) German
£1296 $2359   (11-Dec-91 CH.AM404/R) Torso (84cm-33in) s.d.73 num.4 terracotta (D.FL 4200)
£1329 $2365   (25-Nov-91 WK.M305/R) Head with helmet (58x45x26cm-23x18x10in) s.d.1980 num.3/6 black pat.iron (DM 3800)
£1718 $3144   (2-Jun-92 L.K622/R) Female figure (47x12cm-19x5in) s.d.197verso terracotta (DM 5000)
£2028 $3468   (21-Mar-92 WK.M150 a/R) Head with armour (58x47x30cm-23x19x12in) s.d.1980 num.E.A. rust pat.iron (DM 5800)

FISKE, J W (19th C) American
£18421 $35000   (23-Jun-92 CE.NY69/R) Hounds standing on ground facing in opposing directions (122x118cm-48x46in) i. painted zinc pair

FLAMEN, Anselme and MARSY, Gaspard (after) (17th C) French
£52486 $95000   (20-May-92 SY.NY53/R) The Rape of Orithyia by Boreas. The Rape of Proserpine by Pluto (78cm-31in) 2nd.sculp.after Girardon bronze on Boulle base

FLANAGAN, Barry (1941-) British
£20000 $35000   (27-Feb-92 CH.NY67/R) Elephant (62x42x28cm-24x17x11in) init.i. bronze wood base
£25140 $45000   (14-Nov-91 SY.NY207/R) Unicorn (80x75x25cm-31x30x10in) num.5/7 gilded bronze limestone base
£47486 $85000   (5-May-92 CH.NY1/R) Acrobats (305x94x65cm-120x37x26in) init.num.4/5 bronze
£52000 $99320   (2-Jul-92 C10/R) Leaping hare on crescent and bell (116x94x60cm-46x37x24in) num.6 green light brown pat.bronze f.st.

FLATH, Otto (1906-) Russian
£3436 $5979   (21-Sep-91 SA.A487/R) Light and shade (16cm-6in) wood (DM 10000)

FLAVIN, Dan (1933-) American
£16760 $30000   (14-Nov-91 SY.NY156/R) Untitled no.5 - to Donna (244x244cm-96x96in) yellow pink blue fluorescent light
£26012 $45000   (3-Oct-91 SY.NY99/R) Four red horizontals (244cm-96in) red fluorescent light
£34682 $60000   (3-Oct-91 SY.NY1112/R) Untitled Jan 22 1964 (762cm-300in) flourescent lights in five sections
£50279 $90000   (13-Nov-91 SY.NY63/R) Monument for V. Tatlin (310cm-122in) cool white fluorescent light
£75419 $135000   (13-Nov-91 SY.NY116/R) The diagonal of May 25, 1963 to Brancusi (244x244cm-96x96in) yellow fluorescent light s.d.1963 on certificate

FLEMISH SCHOOL, 17th C
£2000 $3640   (12-Dec-91 S215/R) Group of Virgin and Child (20cm-8in) pedestal with mono. boxwood
£2060 $3750   (26-May-92 SY.NY43/R) Figure of Virgin, with long cloak over dress (86cm-34in) wood
£2400 $4296   (11-Nov-91 S50/R) Allegorical figure of naked woman (48cm-19in) alabaster
£12849 $23000   (11-Nov-91 B.LA1901/R) Mars and Diana with attendants in landscapes (133x65cm-52x26in) painted panels on cabinet

FLEMISH SCHOOL, 18th C
£37000 $64750   (24-Sep-91 SWS301/R) Figure of Minerva standing with owl at her feet (183cm-72in) white marble on stone plinth

FLORENTINE SCHOOL, 17th C Italian
£70000 $134400   (9-Jul-92 S147/R) Knifegrinder - muscular man naked but for cloak over shoulder (33cm-13in) num.14 bronze

FLORENTINE SCHOOL, 19th C Italian
£3000 $5730   (30-Jun-92 PH97/R) Figure of Rebecca at the Well leaning on water jug (98cm-39in) s. marble

FOCHT, Frederic (1879-?) French
£5848 $10000   (21-Mar-92 SY.NY217/R) Figure - Spirit of Flight, cast as Icarus astride star beam over waves (86cm-34in) i. gilt bronze

FOGGINI (after) (?) Italian
£9500 $16910   (1-Nov-91 S16/R) Figures of manacled seated slaves (58cm-23in) bronze gilt-bronze pair

FOGGINI, Giovanni Battista (studio) (1652-1725) Italian
£3571 $6500   (26-May-92 SY.NY65/R) Bust of Grand Duke Ferdinando II d'Medici (81cm-32in) marble

FONSECA, Gonzalo (1922-) Uruguayan
£25000 $45000   (18-Nov-91 SY.NY55/R) House of the Foot (56cm-22in) limestone with carved elements

FONTANA, Lucio (1899-1968) Italian
£2486 $4500   (21-May-92 F.M262/R) Concetto spaziale (70x70cm-28x28in) i.num,22/75 s.verso multiple (I.L 5500000)
£9052 $16474   (26-May-92 SY.MI156/R) Concetto spaziale natura (26cm-10in) s.num.46/500 polished bronze pair (I.L 20000000)

FORD, Edward Onslow (1852-1901) British
£3415 $6146   (19-Nov-91 FP.M81/R) Tete de jeune fille (37cm-15in) s.d.1884 pat.bronze (C.D 7000)
£6000 $10860   (21-May-92 C60/R) Bust of girl wearing turban headdress (44cm-17in) s.d.1884 num.5 bronze

FORG, Gunther (1952-) American
£7263 $13000   (14-Nov-91 SY.NY225/R) Untitled (99x60x6cm-39x24x2in) bronze

FRAMPTON, Sir George James (1860-1928) British
£800 $1392   (19-Sep-91 B51/R) Head of young woman (26cm-10in) mono.d.1915 bronze

FRANCHISEY (20th C) ?
£920 $1684   (3-Feb-92 HH.P82/R) Les droits de l'homme (25x19x17cm-10x7x7in) s.d.1988num.3/8 green blue pat.bronze (F.FR 9000)

FRANCK, Myriam (20th C) ?
£1006 $1730   (7-Oct-91 HH.P20/R) Aleph (20x16x16cm-8x6x6in) s.num.3/8 blk.pat.bronze Cast.Landowski (F.FR 10000)

FRANCO-FLEMISH SCHOOL, 18th C
£2400 $4368   (12-Dec-91 S160/R) Figure of carousing pageboy (21cm-8in) dark brown pat.bronze

FRANK, Mary (1933-) American
£3631 $6500   (9-May-92 CE.NY306 a/R) Flower woman (67x43x57cm-26x17x22in) two parts terracotta

FRASER, James Earle (1876-?) American
£1429 $2400   (14-Aug-91 B.P103/R) End of the Trasail (71cm-28in) s. base bronze

FRASER, James Earle (1876-?) American-cont.
£3315 $6000   (6-Dec-91 CH.NY102/R) End of the trail (31cm-12in) i.f.Kunst Foundry red brown pat. bronze

FRATIN, Christopher (1800-1864) French
£950 $1634   (3-Mar-92 SWS533/R) Mare and foal (20cm-8in) s. brn.pat.bronze oval base
£1200 $2052   (20-Mar-92 S11/R) Two eagles attacking goat (49cm-19in) s. gold-brown pat.bronze
£1500 $2565   (20-Mar-92 S65/R) Lion and wild boar (25cm-10in) s.i. brown pat.bronze
£1900 $3629   (30-Jun-92 PH89/R) Mare and foal (28cm-11in) s. bronze
£4000 $7120   (29-Nov-91 S34/R) Mare and foal (36cm-14in) s. brown pat.bronze
£6686 $11500   (16-Oct-91 CH.NY143/R) A bear selling baptismal documents (19cm-7in) st. brn.pat.bronze

FRECHILLA, Lorenzo (?) ?
£821 $1494   (11-Dec-91 FER.M248/R) Torsion (42cm-17in) stone (S.P 150000)

FREDDIE, Wilhelm (1909-) Danish
£2643 $4784   (20-May-92 KH.K23/R) Tete (36cm-14in) s.d.1953 brass (D.KR 30000)

FREEMAN, Augusta (19th C) American
£843 $1500   (30-Apr-92 CE.NY22/R) Figure of recumbent child in cradle (32cm-13in) s. white marble

FREMIET, E (1824-1910) French
£950 $1672   (8-Apr-92 CSK101/R) Group of dachshunds, one with head lowered (15cm-6in) s. bronze

FREMIET, Emmanuel (1824-1910) French
£730 $1300   (30-Apr-92 CE.NY40/R) Group of St. Michael and devil (56cm-22in) i. gilt-bronze
£774 $1300   (1-Sep-91 PO.BA34) Dos perros (25cm-10in) s. pat.bronze. Cast.Barbedienne
£820 $1460   (28-Apr-92 SWS494/R) Model of regimental charger (31cm-12in) s. silver plated bronze
£1000 $1710   (20-Mar-92 S63/R) Norse warrior on horseback (40cm-16in) s.num.429 brown pat.bronze
£1554 $2750   (13-Feb-92 S.W2777/R) Louis d'Orleans (46cm-18in) s. c.1800 brn.pat.bronze
£3022 $5500   (27-May-92 CH.NY109/R) Horse and jockey (45cm-18in) i. bronze red brown pat.
£9605 $17000   (13-Feb-92 SY.NY11) Equestrian group of Roman warrior (38cm-15in) i. brown pat.bronze

FRENCH SCHOOL (?) French
£5000 $9100   (10-Dec-91 C19/R) Group of Anna Selbdritt, veiled saint standing (105cm-41in) polychrome limestone c.1500
£9000 $16380   (10-Dec-91 C81/R) Figure of Venus de'Medici, dolphin at feet (55cm-22in) bronze c.1700

FRENCH SCHOOL, 17th C
£2100 $3738   (1-Nov-91 S311/R) Bust of satyr, with leering expression and short curled hair (23cm-9in) marble
£16495 $28536   (27-Mar-92 CN.P104/R) Deux groupes de trois figures (104x49cm-41x19in) pat.bronze one after G.Marsy other F.Girardon (F.FR 160000)
£104972 $190000   (5-Dec-91 SY.NY135/R) Busts of the Continents - Africa, America, Asia, Europe (100cm-39in) white marble four

FRENCH SCHOOL, 17th/18th C
£46344 $79248   (20-Mar-92 ZZ.F56/R) Neptune et .. (43x52cm-17x20in) terracotta pair (F.FR 450000)

FRENCH SCHOOL, 18th C
£2210 $4000   (20-May-92 SY.NY22/R) Putti on a column with female figure beside it (21cm-8in) ormolu marble
£2500 $4800   (9-Jul-92 S169) Bust of Socrates (58cm-23in) bronze white marble socle
£2968 $5284   (29-Nov-91 ARC.P38/R) Tete d'homme (45cm-18in) terracotta marble base (F.FR 29000)
£8287 $15000   (5-Dec-91 SY.NY127/R) Bust of young woman (63cm-25in) i. white marble on marble socle
£8939 $16000   (11-Nov-91 B.LA1802/R) Figure of maiden wearing laced bodice and long skirt (189cm-74in) terracotta incl.pedestal
£13966 $25000   (14-Jan-92 CH.NY158/R) Bust of gentleman, wearing open jacket and stock, hair en queue (75cm-30in) s. terracotta

FRENCH SCHOOL, 19th C
£2000 $3620   (21-May-92 C44/R) Bust of Charles V crowned with laurel wearing robes of office (63cm-25in) bronze
£2423 $4337   (14-Nov-91 ANS.M214/R) Joven con cestas (80cm-31in) indist.s. bronze on marble base (S.P 440000)
£2500 $4525   (20-May-92 CSK237/R) Model of Napoleon's Column (44cm-17in) bronze marble stand
£2600 $4732   (27-May-92 SWS166/R) Fountain with water putto seated on upturned ewer (132cm-52in) cast iron
£2600 $4446   (20-Mar-92 S91/R) Ganymede (61cm-24in) brown pat.bronze
£2800 $4984   (29-Nov-91 S70/R) Moses (63cm-25in) brown pat.bronze i.f.F.Barbedienne

FRENCH SCHOOL, 19th C-cont.

£2800	$4984	(1-Nov-91 S261/R) Model of parrot, perched on palm (61cm-24in) bronze
£3000	$5490	(2-Jun-92 S473) Allegorical figure of night (135cm-53in) pat.spelter marble porphery plinth
£3200	$6144	(7-Jul-92 C81/R) Bust of Bacchus with jovial expression (60cm-24in) marble
£3200	$5472	(20-Mar-92 S92/R) Milo of Croton (76cm-30in) brown pat.bronze on mahogany pedestal
£3400	$6188	(27-May-92 SWS168/R) Fountain, with scallop-shaped bowl on volute supports, putto on top (176cm-69in) carved stone
£3490	$5968	(10-Mar-92 CH.R179/R) Ercole ricoperto dalla pelle di leone nell'atto di trattenere Detanira (89cm-35in) s.Rancoulet pat.bronze (I.L 7500000)
£3509	$6000	(13-Mar-92 FN.S1401/R) Oriental couple (50x48cm-20x19in) dark and gold pat.bronze marble socle (DM 10000)
£4500	$7875	(24-Sep-91 SWS347/R) Figures of putti representing hunting and fishing (129cm-51in) cast iron pair
£4600	$8188	(29-Nov-91 S73/R) Marly horse (104cm-41in) s.d.1721 brown,green pat.bronze
£5500	$9625	(28-Feb-92 S51/R) Female torch bearer (190cm-75in) c.1880 cast iron pair attrib.to Val D'Osne F.
£6661	$12390	(16-Jun-92 SY.B119) Bust of Ceres with corn in her hair (71cm-28in) bronze (B.FR 400000)
£6800	$12104	(29-Nov-91 S69/R) Allegorical figures of summer and winter (92cm-36in) white marble pair
£9200	$16376	(29-Nov-91 S127/R) Allegorical torcheres of North Africa and North America (156cm-61in) cast iron i.Coalbrookdale pair
£9500	$16625	(28-Feb-92 S60/R) Female figures with putti and torch, the other with sheaf of corn (60cm-24in) c.1870 ivory pair
£11000	$19250	(27-Sep-91 S69/R) Sea Goddess (55cm-22in) ivory silver gilt ebonised wood socle
£15500	$28210	(27-May-92 SWS167/R) Fountain, with circular bowl supported by three putto with dolphins (170cm-67in) traces gilding bronze marble
£17500	$30625	(28-Feb-92 S50/R) Draped female figure holding drinking horn (161cm-63in) c.1880 pat.bronze pair
£24000	$42000	(27-Sep-91 S68/R) Dawn and Dusk i. ivory shagreen ivory plinth pair

FRENCH SCHOOL, 20th C

£937	$1639	(30-Mar-92 ZZ.F110/R) Ours polaire (26x23cm-10x9in) brn.pat.bronze alabaster (F.FR 9000)
£1724	$3000	(15-Sep-91 JRB.C31/R) Mercury (152cm-60in) s. bronze f.mark F.Barbedienne Fondeur, Paris
£4000	$6840	(20-Mar-92 S205/R) Japanese maiden (120cm-47in) st.seal dark brown pat.bronze

FRENCH, Daniel Chester (1850-1931) American

£737	$1320	(14-Nov-91 GRO.B131/R) Bust of woman (20cm-8in) i. greenish-brown pat.bronze f.st.B.Zoppo NY

FRILLI, A (19th C) Italian

£1176	$2000	(22-Oct-91 CE.NY7/R) Bust of laughing girl (102cm-40in) s. alabaster
£2100	$3738	(29-Apr-92 CG257) Peasant cradling wine flask in his arms (53x106cm-21x42in) i. white marble
£2431	$4400	(6-Dec-91 GC.M140/R) Venus del Cantaro (90cm-35in) s. sculpture on granite pedestal

FRINK, Elizabeth (1930-) British

£900	$1593	(10-Feb-92 B83/R) Study for Standard VI (42cm-17in) s. bronze
£3600	$6372	(10-Feb-92 B84/R) Dead hen (16x58cm-6x23in) bronze
£3976	$6918	(13-Apr-92 SY.J282/R) Bird with wing (50cm-20in) s.num.4/6 bronze (SA.R 20000)
£4500	$7965	(8-Nov-91 C349/R) Small winged figure (44cm-17in) s.num.4/10 brn.pat.bronze
£6000	$11100	(11-Jun-92 C124/R) Small eagle (23cm-9in) s.num.8/9 brown pat.bronze
£6000	$11100	(11-Jun-92 C127/R) Bird with wing (52cm-20in) s.num.5/6 brown pat.bronze
£7000	$11970	(11-Mar-92 S188/R) Assassins I (56cm-22in) s.num.5/8 bronze
£7500	$14325	(16-Jul-92 B174/R) Horse and rider (59cm-23in) s.num.7/9 bronze br.pat.
£8000	$14160	(8-Nov-91 C353/R) Water Buffalo (33cm-13in) s.i. green pat.bronze
£8000	$14800	(11-Jun-92 C158/R) Horse in rain (26cm-10in) s.num.7/9 brown pat.bronze
£9500	$17575	(11-Jun-92 C159/R) Chinese horse I (48cm-19in) s.num.6/8 green/brown pat.bronze
£13000	$23400	(20-Nov-91 S202/R) Goggled head II, teeth (65cm-26in) bronze
£13000	$24830	(2-Jul-92 S63/R) Goggled Head I (65cm-26in) s.num.6/6 bronze
£20000	$36000	(20-Nov-91 S201/R) In memoriam I (127cm-50in) d.1981 num.5/6 bronze

FRISENDAHL, Carl (1886-1948) Swedish

£901	$1649	(13-May-92 BU.S237/R) Wild boar (24cm-9in) s.num.4/12, dark pat bronze Cast.Valsuani (S.KR 9500)

FRISHMUTH, Harriet Whitney (1880-1980) American

£1724	$3000	(15-Apr-92 SY.NY113/R) Star (49cm-19in) i.d.1918 dark brown pat.bronze f.i.Gorham
£2400	$4200	(26-Sep-91 CH.NY134/R) Greek dancers - bookends (22cm-9in) i. mid brown pat.bronze pair
£3143	$5500	(26-Sep-91 CH.NY133/R) Allegra - figure of nymph (29cm-11in) i. greenish brown pat.bronze f.st.Gorham QGNZ

FRISHMUTH, Harriet Whitney (1880-1980) American-cont.

£3297	$6000	(28-May-92 CH.NY197/R) The vine (30cm-12in) i.f.Gorham Co. bronze red gr.pat. marble base
£3390	$6000	(9-Nov-91 W.W232/R) The vine (30cm-12in) s.d. brn.pat.bronze Cast.Gorham Co.
£3571	$6250	(23-Sep-91 S.SL272) Crest of the Wave (53cm-21in) s. bronze Cast.QFHL
£3801	$6500	(11-Mar-92 SY.NY85/R) Crest of Wave (54cm-21in) i. greenish-brown pat.bronze f.st.Gorham Co
£4144	$7500	(5-Dec-91 SY.NY53/R) Speed (25x31cm-10x12in) i. brown pat.bronze incl.black marble base
£4396	$8000	(28-May-92 CH.NY198/R) Crest of the wave (53cm-21in) i.f.Gorham Co. bronze gr.pat. marble base
£4469	$8000	(15-Nov-91 DM.D2101/R) The vine, figure of nymph (28cm-11in) s.d.1921 num.3609 pat.bronze i.f.Gorham
£4696	$8500	(6-Dec-91 CH.NY183/R) Crest of the wave (53cm-21in) i.f.Gorham Co. green brown pat. bronze
£5307	$9500	(13-Nov-91 B.SF2656/R) Crest of wave (157cm-62in) s. pat.bronze
£8000	$14000	(26-Sep-91 CH.NY136/R) Pas de deux (38x70cm-15x28in) i. dark brown pat.bronze f.st.Gorham QBCS
£9945	$18000	(5-Dec-91 SY.NY56/R) Crest of the wave (55cm-22in) i. greenish brown pat.bronze st.f.Gorham Co.
£24862	$45000	(6-Dec-91 CH.NY184/R) Reflections (146cm-57in) i.f.Gorham Co. bronze fountain figure
£42857	$75000	(25-Sep-91 SY.NY49/R) Crest of wave (170cm-67in) i. weathered pat.bronze f.st.Gorham Co Founders

FUCHS, Emile (1866-?) Austrian

£1300	$2223	(20-Mar-92 S38/R) Great dane (14cm-6in) s. brown pat.bronze st.f.G.Nisini Roma

FUCHS, Ernst (1930-) Austrian

£825	$1509	(2-Jun-92 FN.S2297 a) Sphinx (35x20x16cm-14x8x6in) s.num.685/1000 pat.bronze st.f.Arte Venturi (DM 2400)
£859	$1598	(20-Jun-92 BM.B649 a) Female nude with fan (44cm-17in) i.dark pat.bronze with gold i.Euro Art Ventini (DM 2500)

FUGERE, Henry (1872-?) French

£756	$1300	(9-Oct-91 RO.BA60) Il est quatre heures (55cm-22in) s. pat.bronze

FUJITA, Kenji (1955-) ?

£1143	$2000	(27-Feb-92 CE.NY255/R) Untitled (76x55x31cm-30x22x12in) s.d. 1985 verso acrylic wood

FURST, Else (1673-?) German

£1034	$1800	(13-Sep-91 SY.NY61/R) Group of male and female nude (77cm-30in) i. dark brown pat.bronze

GABINO, Amadeo (1922-) Spanish

£1385	$2452	(12-Feb-92 ANS.M370/R) Proel (35x26x26cm-14x10x10in) mono.d.1981 num.28/92 iron stainless steel (S.P 250000)

GAHAGAN, Lawrence (18/19th C) British

£950	$1824	(7-Jul-92 C138/R) Bust of Wellington wearing Roman armour (30cm-12in) i.d.1811 bronze

GALLELLI, S (19th C) Italian

£15000	$26700	(29-Nov-91 S149/R) Wood nymph (213cm-84in) s.i.d.1875 marble incl.grey marble plinth

GALLO, Frank (1933-) American

£847	$1500	(9-Nov-91 W.W335/R) Prima Vera (56cm-22in) s.i. num.80/300 polychromed epoxy resin
£3352	$6000	(12-Nov-91 CE.NY66/R) Winged figure (194cm-76in) polished bronze on plexiglas base
£4651	$8000	(12-Oct-91 SY.NY311/R) Standing female beach figure (160cm-63in) i.d.65 num.3/5 polyester resin

GALLO, Vincent (1961-) American

£1117	$2000	(12-Nov-91 CE.NY156/R) Yes I'm lonely (122x76x4cm-48x30x2in) s.i.d.1985verso oil graphite steel

GAMBARTES, Leonidas (1909-1963) Argentinian

£2473	$4500	(11-Dec-91 RO.BA246) Paye (70x40cm-28x16in) s. chrome plaster

GARBE, Herbert (19/20th C) German

£750	$1433	(2-Jul-92 CSK12/R) Elephant (46cm-18in) s.num.2 pat.bronze

GARBE, Richard (1876-1957) British

£4200	$7602	(21-May-92 C58/R) Lionesses, one resting on paws the other licking forepaw (35x66x47cm-14x26x19in) s.d.1945 carved stone pair

GARDET, Georges (1863-1939) French
£956 $1750   (5-Jun-92 SY.NY115/R) Panther (33x44cm-13x17in) i. bronze gr.pat.
£1200 $2052   (20-Mar-92 S48/R) Tiger and tortoise (20cm-8in) s. green brown pat.bronze
£2326 $4000   (9-Oct-91 RO.BA53/R) Combat de cerfs (53cm-21in) s. pat.bronze on wood base f.F.Barbedienne
£2326 $4000   (9-Oct-91 RO.BA54/R) Famille des cerfs (57cm-22in) s. pat.bronze on wood base f.F.Barbedienne

GARELLA, A (19th C) Italian?
£2335 $4250   (13-Dec-91 S.W3040/R) Portrait of woman (81cm-32in) s.d.1891 white marble

GARELLI, Franco (1909-) Italian
£1358 $2471   (26-May-92 SY.MI7/R) Composizione (61cm-24in) enamelled iron (I.L 3000000)

GARGALLO, Pablo (1881-1934) Spanish
£70000 $126700   (2-Dec-91 C22/R) La tragedie (35cm-14in) s.d.1915 sheet iron

GASPAR, Jean Marie (1861-1931) Belgian
£5000 $8600   (12-Oct-91 KV.L372/R) Walking elephant (49x85cm-19x33in) s.d.1908 bronze green pat. (B.FR 300000)

GASQ, Paul Jean Baptiste (1860-1944) French
£829 $1500   (2-Dec-91 S.SL272/R) Female allegorical bust figure (61cm-24in) s. golden brown pat.bronze
£1618 $2750   (25-Oct-91 S.W2652/R) Kiss (71cm-28in) s.i. brown pat.bronze f.i.F. Barbedienne

GAUDEZ, Adrien Etienne (1845-1902) French
£917 $1679   (3-Jun-92 R.T75/R) Marguerite (80cm-31in) s.i. num.16368 gold pat.bronze (C.D 2000)
£1395 $2400   (9-Oct-91 RO.BA57) Forgeron, hors concours (59cm-23in) s. pat.bronze
£2730 $4750   (13-Sep-91 SY.NY27/R) Tresoric Generale d'Alger (173cm-68in) i. brown pat.bronze on grey marble pedestal

GAUGUIN, Paul (1848-1903) French
£3800 $7258   (29-Jun-92 CSK45/R) Stele au Christ (49cm-19in) init.i. brown pat.bronze f.st.C Valsuani
£6000 $11460   (30-Jun-92 C144/R) L'apres-midi d'un faune (35cm-14in) i. num.6/10 brown pat.bronze f.st.C Valsuani

GAUL, August (1869-1921) German
£842 $1516   (22-Nov-91 SA.A368/R) Goose (16cm-6in) i. dark brown pat.bronze marble socle (DM 2400)
£1195 $2174   (25-May-92 WK.M433/R) Three piglets galloping (8x22x8cm-3x9x3in) s.monod.1913 brown pat.bronze st.f.H.Noack (DM 3500)
£1579 $2842   (23-Nov-91 N.M105/R) Goose running (12cm-5in) s.d.1901 black pat.bronze st.f.H.Noack Berlin (DM 4500)
£2048 $3727   (30-May-92 VG.B124/R) Two sheep standing (14cm-6in) i.d.1902 brown pat.bronze marble socle (DM 6000)
£2062 $3814   (12-Jun-92 HN.H271/R) Otter with fish (19x8x13cm-7x3x5in) s. dark brown pat.bronze st.f.H.Noack Berlin (DM 6000)
£2386 $4295   (23-Nov-91 N.M104/R) Bear standing (30cm-12in) s.d.1914/15 brown pat.bronze st.f.Noack Berlin (DM 6800)
£2405 $4402   (3-Jun-92 L.K153/R) Goose standing (7cm-3in) s. silver on marble socle st.f.H.Noack Berlin (DM 7000)
£2749 $5113   (20-Jun-92 BM.B650/R) Cat standing (21cm-8in) i.pat.bronze stone socle st.f.Noack Berlin (DM 8000)
£3072 $5590   (30-May-92 VG.B123/R) Young lion seated (14cm-6in) i.d.1898 brown pat.bronze marble st.f.H.Noack (DM 9000)
£3780 $6993   (12-Jun-92 HN.H272/R) Penguin standing (27x15x14cm-11x6x6in) s.c.1918 brown pat.bronze st.f.H.Noack (DM 11000)
£4211 $7579   (23-Nov-91 N.M103/R) Trumpeting elephant (41cm-16in) s.d.1905 brown pat.bronze st.f.H.Noack Berlin (DM 12000)
£5245 $9336   (30-Nov-91 VG.B117/R) Penguin standing (24cm-9in) s.c.1918 dark brown pat.bronze st.f.Noack Berlin (DM 15000)
£5498 $10227   (20-Jun-92 BM.B651/R) Two pelicans, one resting the other arranging feathers (30x34cm-12x13in) s.pat.bronze st.f.H.Noack Berlin (DM 16000)
£7719 $13200   (13-Mar-92 FN.S2487/R) Standing penguin (26cm-10in) s. black gold painted bronze (DM 28000)

GAUQUIE, Henri (1858-1927) French
£1800 $3258   (21-May-92 C16/R) Struggling nymph and satyr (97cm-38in) s. bronze

GAUTIER, J (?) French
£1018 $1853   (15-Dec-91 REM.W54) Mephistopheles on a rock (85cm-33in) s. bronze (P.Z 20000000)

GAUTIER, Jacques Louis (1831-?) French
£800 $1368   (20-Mar-92 S160/R) Mephistopheles (66cm-26in) s. brown black pat.bronze i.Duplan et Salles Ft

GAZAN (?) ?
£7000 $12250   (27-Sep-91 S28/R) The water carrier (66cm-26in) s. silvered brn.red pat.bronze marble plinth

GAZZERI, Ernesto (19/20th C) Italian
£5376 $10000   (16-Jun-92 RO.BA131) Afrodita (124cm-49in) Carrara marble

GECHTER, Jean Francois Theodore (1796-1844) French
£843 $1500   (30-Apr-92 CE.NY77/R) Figure of workhorse (41cm-16in) i. greenish-black
        pat.bronze
£1350 $2376   (8-Apr-92 CSK106/R) Group of fallen Amazonian warrior (38cm-15in) s.
        bronze
£1547 $2800   (2-Dec-91 S.SL277/R) Battle scene depicting Joan of Arc mounted, with
        trampled opponent (69cm-27in) s. light brown pat.bronze f.i.

GEEFS, Josef (1808-1885) Belgian
£1118 $1990   (26-Nov-91 SY.AM62) Bust of bacchante (46cm-18in) s. marble (D.FL 3600)

GEILING, C M (19/20th C) German
£988 $1700   (9-Oct-91 RO.BA226) Le forgeron (59cm-23in) s. pat.bronze f.Bronce Bild
        Giessere G.M.B.H.

GEISER, Karl (1898-1957) Swiss
£2891 $5175   (5-May-92 ZEL.L2018/R) Standing female nude (53cm-21in) s.d.1933 bronze
        (DM 8500)
£3077 $5846   (25-Jun-92 GK.B347) Head of girl (33cm-13in) s.c.1930 bronze st.f.Pastori
        Geneva (S.FR 8000)

GEMITO, Vincenzo (1852-1929) Italian
£726 $1351   (16-Jun-92 F.M60) Pescatorello (26cm-10in) s. metal (I.L 1600000)
£782 $1399   (14-Nov-91 CH.R30) Busto di scugnizzo (18cm-7in) s. bronze st.foundry
        (I.L 1700000)
£906 $1541   (25-Oct-91 PLF.P108) Etude pour le buste de Meissonier (15cm-6in) s.
        plaster (F.FR 9000)
£1361 $2532   (16-Jun-92 F.M59) Acquaiolo (55cm-22in) i. metal (I.L 3000000)
£2200 $3982   (21-May-92 C49/R) Bust of bearded philosopher (53cm-21in) s. bronze on
        marble base st.foundry
£3488 $6000   (17-Oct-91 SY.NY227/R) Water vendor - figural fountain (56cm-22in) i.
        greenish brown pat.bronze

GEMITO, Vincenzo (attrib) (1852-1929) Italian
£3429 $6000   (20-Feb-92 SY.NY151/R) Bust of Domenico Morelli (71cm-28in) brown
        pat.bronze

GENNARELLI, Amedeo (20th C) Italian
£1600 $2736   (20-Mar-92 S161/R) Spring awakening (47cm-19in) s.st. bronze

GENRYUSAI (19th C) Japanese
£6000 $10680   (1-Nov-91 S265/R) Pacing camel (53cm-21in) s. bronze marble base

GENTILS, Vic (1919-) Belgian
£2172 $3693   (22-Oct-91 C.A173/R) Assemblage of piano keys (30x30cm-12x12in) s.d.1967
        verso wood (B.FR 130000)
£2506 $4261   (22-Oct-91 C.A172/R) Brutus (120x35cm-47x14in) s.d.1964 wood
        (B.FR 150000)
£3336 $5872   (7-Apr-92 C.A134/R) Composition (73x58cm-29x23in) s. d.1961 verso
        assemblage (B.FR 200000)

GENZKEN, Isa (1948-) German?
£3093 $5660   (2-Jun-92 L.K641/R) Small pavillon (34x45x39cm-13x18x15in) d.1989
        concrete roof tiles on stand (DM 9000)

GERDAGO (20th C) French
£800 $1360   (25-Oct-91 S364/R) Kneeling female figure (17cm-7in) i. cold painted
        bronze ivory onyx
£1600 $3056   (2-Jul-92 CSK110/R) Exotic dancer wearing head dress and harem pants
        (36cm-14in) cold painted bronze ivory pen tray with 2 pens
£4138 $7117   (16-Oct-91 KM.K1507/R) Female dancer wearing costume with pointed hat and
        train (31cm-12in) i. gold pat.bronze ivory (DM 12000)

GERHARD, Hubert (style) (1540-1620) Flemish
£110000 $200200   (12-Dec-91 S128/R) Statuette of St. Sebastian (47cm-19in) gilt bronze

GERMAIN (18-20th C) French
£2300 $4002   (17-Sep-91 PH234/R) Pair of mythological lovers wearing shepherd's
        costume (72cm-28in) s. bronze

GERMAIN, Jean-Baptiste (1910-) French
£2400 $4104   (20-Mar-92 S154/R) Young girl and lute (70cm-28in) s. rubbed green
        pat.bronze
£2824 $4800   (22-Oct-91 CE.NY22/R) Le printemps d'amour (77cm-30in) i. parcel-gilt
        bronze
£3161 $5500   (13-Sep-91 SY.NY26/R) Allegorical figure group on pedestal (175cm-69in)
        i. brown pat.bronze on marble

GERMAN SCHOOL (?) German
£4800 $8736   (10-Dec-91 C82/R) Heraldic lions, roaring, with front paws on orbs
        (12x35cm-5x14in) bronze c.17th-18th C pair

GERMAN SCHOOL, 17th C
£9165 $16680   (11-Dec-91 LD.P264/R) Faucon de chasse perche sur un rameau (54x37x21cm-21x15x8in) forged and sheet iron wooden base (F.FR 90000)

GERMAN SCHOOL, 18th C
£2265 $4122   (10-Dec-91 N.M64/R) St Sebastian standing with hands tied to tree (200cm-79in) wood (DM 6500)

GERMAN-AUSTRIAN SCHOOL, 18th C
£4121 $7500   (26-May-92 SY.NY88/R) Figure of angel, head bowed and arms crossed at chest (102cm-40in) gilt painted wood

GEROME, Jean Leon (1824-1904) French
£1031 $1763   (9-Mar-92 AT.P270) Femme au cerceau (32cm-13in) s.num.Y208 gilt bronze onyx base Cast.Siot (F.FR 10000)
£2933 $5308   (19-May-92 AB.S4555/R) 'Joueuse de boules' (27cm-11in) s.num.0453, gold pat bronze Cast.S Decauville (S.KR 31000)
£3800 $6650   (27-Sep-91 S9/R) Jules Cesar traversant le Rubicon (38x46cm-15x18in) s.i.num.64D green brn.pat.bronze gilt Cast.Siot
£5233 $9000   (16-Oct-91 CH.NY152/R) Joueuse de Boules (53cm-21in) i. num.154F gilt bronze ormolu marble base
£5814 $10000   (17-Oct-91 SY.NY31/R) Bathsheba (31cm-12in) i. gilt-bronze f.st.Siot Decauville
£10440 $19000   (28-May-92 SY.NY56/R) Victoire marchant (55cm-22in) i. gilt bronze f.i.F.Barbedienne Paris
£11494 $20000   (13-Sep-91 SY.NY62/R) Figure of Selene (79cm-31in) i.num.5214 bronze st.f.Siot Tiffany and Co
£12000 $21000   (27-Sep-91 S10) La fuite en Egypte (77cm-30in) s.num.E143 brn.red silver pat.bronze Cast.Siot
£18000 $31500   (27-Sep-91 S12/R) Allegory of speed (58x95cm-23x37in) s.i. two tone gilt bronze Cast.Siot
£27473 $50000   (28-May-92 SY.NY55/R) Tanagra (75cm-30in) i. pewter f.st.Siot-Decauville

GEYTON, G (19th C) French
£2000 $3560   (29-Nov-91 S99/R) Mozart (66cm-26in) s.i. brown pat.bronze

GHENT, Maurice de (?) ?
£872 $1500   (20-Oct-91 HG.C92) Bust of Marie Antoinette (56cm-22in) bronze marble

GIACOMETTI, Alberto (1901-1966) Swiss
£6857 $12000   (25-Feb-92 CH.NY82/R) Lampe au forme geometrique (47cm-19in) green pat.bronze
£163934 $300000   (12-May-92 CH.NY151/R) Tete de Diego (25cm-10in) s.num.2/6 dark brown pat.bronze f.i.Susse Paris
£197740 $350000   (5-Nov-91 CH.NY46/R) Annette X (44cm-17in) s.i.num.7/8 brown pat.bronze st.f.Susse Fondeur
£225989 $400000   (5-Nov-91 CH.NY42/R) Diego (59cm-23in) s.i.num.2/8 brown pat.bronze st.f.Susse Fondeur
£314208 $575000   (13-May-92 SY.NY92/R) Buste d'Annette (46cm-18in) i.num.3/6 brown pat.bronze i.Susse Fondeur Paris
£320000 $579200   (3-Dec-91 S50/R) Tete de Diego (39cm-15in) i. num.2/6 bronze f.st.Susse Fondeur Paris
£464481 $850000   (11-May-92 CH.NY47/R) Buste de Diego (39cm-15in) s.num.6/6 dark brown pat.bronze f.indist.i.
£634615 $1205769   (26-Jun-92 GK.B30/R) Le nez (81x37x46cm-32x15x18in) s.num.d.1947 bronze iron construction (S.FR 1650000)

GIAMBOLOGNA (c.1529-1608) Italian
£33520 $60000   (14-Jan-92 CH.NY130/R) Statuette of Flying Mercury - messenger of the Gods (33cm-13in) olive brown pat.bronze gilt. Cast.A.Susini

GIAMBOLOGNA (after) (c.1529-1608) Italian
£950 $1824   (7-Jul-92 C157) Bull standing. Horse trotting (9x11cm-4x4in) bronze pair
£1100 $2002   (12-Dec-91 S140) Statuette of Venus after the bath (12cm-5in) polished bronze
£1250 $2150   (15-Oct-91 SWS544/R) The rape of the Sabines (84cm-33in) bronze Cast.H Luppens green marble base
£1500 $2610   (17-Sep-91 SWS507/R) Figure of Mercury supported by allegory of the North Wind (183cm-72in) lead
£1600 $2768   (30-Sep-91 PHG45/R) Mercury and Fortuna (87cm-34in) dark green pat.bronze circular bases pair
£1700 $3264   (9-Jul-92 S125) Figure of Corpus Christi (23cm-9in) gilt bronze
£1754 $3000   (9-Mar-92 B.LA746/R) Figure of Mercury, naked with winged helmet and poised on one foot (114cm-45in) pat.bronze
£2200 $3982   (20-May-92 CSK283/R) Rape of Sabine (104cm-41in) bronze
£2400 $4608   (7-Jul-92 C158/R) Figure of Fiorenza standing naked resting foot on urn at her side (66cm-26in) bronze
£3200 $5856   (15-May-92 TE460/R) Mars, standing naked, left hand outstretched (41cm-16in) wood
£3500 $6335   (21-May-92 C23/R) Figure of nymph, head crowned with flowers and foot supported by urn (75cm-30in) white marble on marble column
£4119 $7745   (16-Dec-91 AGS.P79/R) Statuette de Mercure (64cm-25in) pat.gilded bronze column base red marble bronze (F.FR 40000)
£5028 $9000   (14-Jan-92 CH.NY144/R) Figure of walking bull (22cm-9in) reddish green brown pat.bronze lacquer

GIAMBOLOGNA (after) (c.1529-1608) Italian-cont.
£7821 $14000   (14-Jan-92 CH.NY142/R) Figure of walking horse (22cm-9in) brown pat.bronze gilding lacquer
£9800 $17150   (24-Sep-91 SWS314/R) Mercury. Fortuna (190cm-75in) green pat.bronze on stone plinth pair
£16575 $30000   (5-Dec-91 SY.NY132/R) Nessus and Deianira (52cm-20in) bronze sold with sculpture after Girardon

GIAMBOLOGNA (circle) (c.1529-1608) Italian
£2100 $3822   (12-Dec-91 S142) Corpus Christi - Cristo Morto (42cm-17in) gilt bronze

GIAMBOLOGNA (studio) (c.1529-1608) Italian
£38674 $70000   (5-Dec-91 SY.NY130/R) Venus after the bath (25cm-10in) olive-brown pat.bronze lacquer

GIBRAN, Kahlil George (1922-) American
£819 $1400   (13-Mar-92 S.BM331/R) Job (36cm-14in) s.verso black pat.bronze
£2083 $3750   (24-Nov-91 JRB.C286/R) St John the Baptist (224cm-88in) s.base welded steel cement base

GIBSON (after) (?) ?
£1250 $2188   (24-Sep-91 SWS334/R) Bust of Venus (69cm-27in) c.1870 white marble

GIES, Ludwig (1887-1966) German
£4211 $7579   (21-Nov-91 L.K151/R) Mother with child (30cm-12in) brown pat.bronze (DM 12000)

GILARDI, Piero (1924-) Italian
£927 $1650   (26-Nov-91 SY.MI105/R) Mele e susine (29x29x11cm-11x11x4in) s.init.d.1991verso foam rubber (I.L 2000000)

GILIOLI, Emile (1911-1977) French
£1955 $3538   (6-Dec-91 GL.P284 b) Fecondite (15x20x15cm-6x8x6in) s. num.2/5 blk.pat.bronze (F.FR 19000)
£3862 $6720   (16-Apr-92 FB.P156/R) Quart de soleil (27cm-11in) s.num.1/3base polished gilt pat.bronze (F.FR 38000)
£4800 $8304   (26-Mar-92 C40/R) Saint Martin (42cm-17in) granite
£4835 $8752   (4-Dec-91 LD.P110/R) Tabernacle (38cm-15in) s.d.1960 polished white marble (F.FR 47000)
£8056 $14340   (28-Oct-91 GL.P193/R) Soleil sur la colline (47x40x10cm-19x16x4in) s.d.1972 white marble (F.FR 80000)

GILL, Eric (1882-1940) British
£1400 $2674   (16-Jul-92 B173) Adam (18cm-7in) i. wood

GINOTTI, Giacomo (1837-1897) Italian
£10225 $18508   (4-Dec-91 SY.MI401/R) La schiava, mora nuda seduta su roccia, mani e piede in catene (154cm-61in) i.d.1878 marble (I.L 22000000)

GIOVANNI DA BOLOGNA (after) (14th C) Italian
£1146 $2041   (30-Apr-92 RAS.K874/R) Neptune (45cm-18in) pat gilded bronze marble base (D.KR 13000)

GIRARDON (after) (18th C) French
£16575 $30000   (5-Dec-91 SY.NY132/R) Rape of Sabine Woman (48cm-19in) bronze sold with sculpture after Giambologna

GIRARDON, Francois (after) (1628-1715) French
£968 $1656   (13-Mar-92 FN.S1399/R) The rape of Proserpina (45x92cm-18x36in) i. bronze (DM 2760)
£8500 $16320   (7-Jul-92 C127) Equestrian figure of Louis XIV (110cm-43in) bronze on painted wood pedestal base
£52486 $95000   (20-May-92 SY.NY53/R) The Rape of Orithyia by Boreas. The Rape of Proserpine by Pluto (78cm-31in) 1st.sculp after Marsy and Flamen bronze

GIRARDON, Francois (studio) (1628-1715) French
£21605 $41049   (22-Jun-92 PIC.P70/R) Cheval au pas (80x62cm-31x24in) brown pat.bronze on tortoiseshell/copper socle (F.FR 210000)

GIRAUD, Alice (19th C) ?
£1359 $2325   (21-Mar-92 KV.L133) Bachannte (56x26cm-22x10in) s.f.Valsuani bronze gold pat. marble socle (B.FR 80000)

GIRELLI, A (?) ?
£1076 $1936   (2-Feb-92 ZZ.F198/R) Mathilde (123cm-48in) s.i.base wood stone (F.FR 10500)

GIRONCOLI, Bruno (1936-) Austrian
£4847 $8822   (26-May-92 D.V275/R) Untitled (95x40cm-37x16in) polyester painted gold bronze (A.S 100000)

GIRONIERE, Yves Benoist (20th C) French
£2758 $4826   (30-Mar-92 ZZ.F105/R) Le Trotteur (38x80x27cm-15x31x11in) s.base brn.pat.bronze (F.FR 26500)

GLEICHEN, Countess Feodora von (1861-1922) British
£750 $1283   (20-Mar-92 S116/R) Edward VII (77cm-30in) s.d.1913 marble
£950 $1691   (29-Nov-91 S138/R) Edward VII (80cm-31in) init.d.1879 marble
£4500 $8010   (29-Nov-91 S140/R) Disraeli (81cm-32in) init.d.1880 marble

GOBER, Robert (1954-) American
£61453 $110000   (5-May-92 CH.NY10/R) Sink (66x71x61cm-26x28x24in) s.i.d.1984-8verso
   enamel plaster wire lath wood
£92179 $165000   (13-Nov-91 SY.NY79/R) Split up conflicted sink (206x209x63cm-81x82x25in)
   semi-glass enamel plaster wood steel wire lathe
£100559 $180000   (5-May-92 CH.NY18/R) Bed (112x180x99cm-44x71x39in) s.i.d.1988 enamel wood
   cotton wool

GODARD, A (?) ?
£4000 $7320   (15-May-92 S346/R) Charm of the Orient (49cm-19in) i. silvered painted
   bronze ivory marble

GODET, Henri (1863-?) French
£1600 $2736   (20-Mar-92 S104/R) La glaneuse (76cm-30in) s. green brown pat.bronze
   st.Bronze Garanti seal

GOLDSCHEIDER, Friedrich (19/20th C) ?
£3100 $5518   (28-Apr-92 SWS440/R) Bust of Nubian girl holding wicker basket on her
   head (74cm-29in) s.st. cold painted pottery

GOLDSCHEIDER, Vienne (19/20th C) ?
£1118 $1945   (13-Apr-92 AT.P188/R) Grand buste de nomade (70cm-28in) polychrome
   terracotta (F.FR 11000)
£1220 $2122   (13-Apr-92 AT.P187/R) Bedouin de Syrie (70cm-28in) s. polychrome terracotta
   (F.FR 12000)

GOMES, Karel (1930-) Dutch
£1030 $1865   (19-May-92 CH.AM108) Standing girl (68cm-27in) init. bronze (D.FL 3400)

GONZALEZ, Julio (1876-1942) Spanish
£20000 $36400   (29-May-92 C413/R) Tete aigue (42cm-17in) i.num.6/9 brown pat.bronze
   st.f.C.Valsuani

GOOD, John Willis (19th C) British
£2637 $4800   (27-May-92 CH.NY97/R) A harnessed horse (39cm-15in) i.f.Elkington bronze
   red brown pat.

GORI, A (after) (?) ?
£1639 $3000   (3-Jun-92 D.NY688/R) Fashionably dressed lady descending staircase
   (43cm-17in) bronze ivory marble

GORMAN, R C (1933-) American
£2131 $3900   (8-Feb-92 S.BM59/R) Tasha - seated figure (61cm-24in) s.indist.i.verso
   bronze wool wood

GORMLEY, Anthony (20th C) ?
£22346 $40000   (7-May-92 SY.NY148/R) Fill (183x203x23cm-72x80x9in) lead fibreglass
   plaster

GORY, Affortunato (1895-1925) ?
£998 $1767   (5-Nov-91 GF.L425/R) Female nude kneeling holding ball in raised hand
   (23cm-9in) s. gold pat.bronze marble socle (S.FR 2555)

GOSSER, Wilhelm (1881-?) Austrian
£1600 $2736   (20-Mar-92 S167/R) Mutter Erde (48cm-19in) s.num.908 brown pat.bronze

GOSSIN, Louis (19th C) French
£12994 $23000   (13-Feb-92 SY.NY100/R) Allegorical group (43cm-17in) i. gilt-bronze ivory

GOTZ, Johannes (1865-?) German
£1378 $2412   (3-Apr-92 BM.B1562/R) Female nude carrying water bucket on her shoulder
   (74cm-29in) pat.bronze stone socle (DM 3900)
£1800 $3294   (2-Jun-92 S491) Balancing boy on ball (78cm-31in) s.num.D3070 brown
   pat.bronze marble plinth st.f.

GOUDIE, Alexander (19th C) British
£1000 $1790   (13-Nov-91 CG650/R) The embrace (33cm-13in) s. brn.pat.bronze ebonised
   plinth

GOWER, Lord Ronald Sutherland (?-1915) British
£977 $1700   (20-Sep-91 DM.D2129/R) La garde meurt etne se rend pas (48cm-19in) s.
   dark brown pat.bronze

GRAHAM, Richard D (1940-) American
£1176 $2106   (15-Nov-91 GK.Z5701/R) Soft fold (34x22x22cm-13x9x9in) num.Vd.1975 white
   carrara marble (S.FR 3000)

GRAHAM, Robert (1938-) American
£33424 $56820   (23-Oct-91 B.SF3817/R) Fountain figure 2 (188cm-74in) painted bronze
   pat.bronze base

GRAHAM, Robert (1938-) American-cont.
£33424 $56820   (23-Oct-91 B.SF3816/R) Fountain figure 3 (249cm-98in) painted bronze
        pat.bronze base

GRANDI, Giuseppe (1843-1897) Italian
£2500 $4525   (21-May-92 C42/R) Figure of Cesare Beccaria standing holding quill and
        papers (49cm-19in) s.i. bronze on marble socle
£4462 $7630   (19-Mar-92 F.M64/R) Il Maresciallo Ney (59cm-23in) mono.d.1875 plaster
        (I.L 9600000)

GRARD, Georges (1901-1984) Belgian
£2039 $3487   (21-Mar-92 KV.L406/R) Two girls on a bench (17x15cm-7x6in) s.num.II/VII
        bronze br.pat. (B.FR 120000)
£2333 $4013   (12-Oct-91 KV.L129/R) Femme debout (58cm-23in) s. terracotta
        (B.FR 140000)
£3311 $5993   (23-May-92 KV.L422/R) Printemps (28x25cm-11x10in) s.num.2/9 bronze
        br.pat. (B.FR 200000)
£7333 $12613   (12-Oct-91 KV.L406/R) Young girl with plaits (61x18cm-24x7in) s.num.9/9
        polished bronze (B.FR 440000)
£15398 $27870   (7-Dec-91 KV.L418/R) Plenitude (114x31cm-45x12in) s. bronze brown pat.
        (B.FR 900000)

GRATCHEFF, Alexei Petrovitch (1780-1850) Russian
£824 $1400   (22-Oct-91 CE.NY44/R) Group of rifleman and horse (12cm-5in) i. brown
        pat.bronze
£880 $1479   (28-Aug-91 RAS.K1030) Farewell kiss (24cm-9in) s.i. bronze (D.KR 10000)
£882 $1500   (22-Oct-91 CE.NY49/R) Group of hunters returning from hunt
        (16x30cm-6x12in) i. medium brown pat.bronze
£1000 $1700   (22-Oct-91 CE.NY45/R) Troika group (11x26cm-4x10in) i. brown pat.bronze
£1294 $2200   (22-Oct-91 CE.NY40/R) Group of returning huntsmen (15cm-6in) i. rich
        brown pat.bronze
£1294 $2200   (22-Oct-91 CE.NY47/R) Group of cossack kissing girl (22cm-9in) i.
        greenish brown pat.bronze

GRATCHEV, Vassily (1831-1905) Russian
£934 $1700   (13-Dec-91 SY.NY256/R) Old woman with cane feeding fish to two dogs
        (16cm-6in) s. bronze i.f.Woerffel
£2088 $3800   (13-Dec-91 SY.NY253/R) Mounted cossack lifting his sweetheart in embrace
        (24cm-9in) s. bronze i.f.Woerffel

GRATE, Eric (1896-1983) Swedish
£1246 $2244   (19-Nov-91 GO.G302) Woman with veil (51cm-20in) num.7, Bergman cire
        perdue, gold pat bronze (S.KR 13000)
£1536 $2779   (3-Dec-91 AB.S5196/R) Bird (27cm-11in) s.num.5/6, gold pat bronze
        Cast.Bergman (S.KR 16000)
£1703 $3082   (19-May-92 AB.S5139/R) Jetsam (43cm-17in) s.num.1/5, br pat bronze
        incl.base cire perdue (S.KR 18000)
£2176 $3939   (19-May-92 AB.S5140/R) The wanderer (31cm-12in) s.XXXI, brown pat bronze
        incl.base cire perdue (S.KR 23000)
£2399 $4343   (3-Dec-91 AB.S5195/R) Apollon and Antinea (35cm-14in) s.num.4/6, gold pat
        bronze inc.marble base (S.KR 25000)

GRATH, Anton (1881-?) Austrian
£3000 $5130   (20-Mar-92 S203/R) Lady Godiva (66cm-26in) s. black pat.bronze on marble
        plinth

GRAVES, Nancy (1940-) American
£10615 $19000   (14-Nov-91 SY.NY358/R) Byrd (52x18x23cm-20x7x9in) s.d.7/83 TX polychrome
        pat.bronze

GRECO, Emilio (1913-) Italian
£25714 $45000   (25-Feb-92 CH.NY59/R) Olympian victory (70cm-28in) s.d.1961 brown
        pat.bronze

GREGOIRE, J L (1840-1890) French
£763 $1389   (15-Dec-91 REM.W55) Dancing woman with tambourine (66cm-26in) s. bronze
        (P.Z 15000000)

GREGOIRE, Jean-Louis (1840-1890) French
£1824 $3100   (22-Oct-91 CE.NY20/R) Figure of nymph (114cm-45in) i. brown pat.bronze
£2500 $4450   (29-Nov-91 S97/R) Mozart (79cm-31in) s.num.6657 brown pat.bronze
        i.f.Gervais
£3768 $6970   (12-Jun-92 ARC.P90/R) L'allegro (92cm-36in) s. brown pat.bronze
        (F.FR 37000)
£4213 $7500   (30-Apr-92 CE.NY52/R) Group of Perseus and Andromeda (90cm-35in) i.
        reddish-brown pat.bronze marble column

GREVIN, Alfred (1827-1892) French
£1550 $2666   (3-Mar-92 SWS531/R) Une fille d'Eve (60cm-24in) s. brn.pat.bronze Cast.E
        Tassel

GROOMS, Red (1937-) American
£1453 $2600   (12-Nov-91 CE.NY35/R) The kiss (71x54cm-28x21in) oil cardboard canvas
        collage on plastic tray

GROOMS, Red (1937-) American-cont.
£5714 $10000   (27-Feb-92 CH.NY142/R) Harvard Yale bowl (43x63x35cm-17x25x14in) s.
                         bronze

GROSS, Chaim (1904-1991) American
£1228 $2100   (13-Mar-92 S.BM327/R) Acrobat (13cm-5in) init.i. brown pat.bronze
£3216 $5500   (12-Mar-92 CH.NY120/R) Dancing girls (31cm-12in) i. bronze on revolving
                         wood base st.f.Bedi-Makky

GROSSBACH, Peter (1934-1988) German
£1389 $2486   (15-Nov-91 KM.K168/R) Young Senegalese woman (30cm-12in) mono.d.1971
                         bronze (DM 4000)

GRUPPE, Karl Heinrich (1893-1982) American
£4000 $7000   (26-Mar-92 CH.NY135/R) Goose girl (55cm-22in) i. mid brown pat.bronze
                         f.st.Valsuani

GRZIMEK, Waldemar (20th C) ?
£1748 $3112   (30-Nov-91 VG.B326/R) Standing female nude with right arm raised
                         (44cm-17in) i. brown gold pat.bronze (DM 5000)
£1748 $3112   (30-Nov-91 VG.B325/R) Traumende (33cm-13in) mono.num.1/14 green brown
                         pat.bronze (DM 5000)

GUAYASAMIN, Oswaldo (1913-) Ecuadorian
£4094 $7000   (21-Mar-92 W.W108/R) Young motherland (216x140x48cm-85x55x19in) s.num.2/3
                         moulded copper red painted cast iron

GUIET, A (19th C) ?
£1050 $1900   (21-May-92 S.W3285/R) Polo player, closing (10cm-4in) s. green pat.bronze
£2072 $3750   (21-May-92 S.W3286/R) Polo player preparing to score (10x15cm-4x6in)
                         st.sig.i. brown-green pat.bronze

GUILLEMIN, Emile Coriolan Hippolyte (1841-1907) French
£2210 $4000   (2-Dec-91 S.SL278/R) Figure - what a fly (74cm-29in) s. metal
£20000 $35600   (29-Nov-91 S128/R) Japanese courtesans (241cm-95in) s.parcel gilt,brown
                         pat.bronze incl.column pair
£65000 $113750   (27-Sep-91 S32/R) Japanese courtesans s.i.d.1875 num.227 228 gilt
                         pat.bronze pair

GUILLOT, Anatole Jean (1865-1911) French
£1344 $2419   (19-Nov-91 GS.B7266) Centaur attacked by lion (50cm-20in) s.c.1890
                         pat.bronze (S.FR 3400)

GUINO, Richard (1890-1973) French
£1235 $2346   (24-Jun-92 GL.P144/R) Petite Venus a la pomme (28cm-11in) s.num.IV/VIII
                         brown/green pat.bronze f.Valsuani (F.FR 12000)

GUINO, Richard and RENOIR, Pierre Auguste (20th C) French
£9836 $18000   (14-May-92 SY.NY239/R) Buste de Coco (28cm-11in) i. brown pat.bronze
                         st.f.Valsuani

GUIRAUD-RIVIERE, Maurice (1881-?) French
£1170 $2000   (21-Mar-92 SY.NY216/R) Figure of athlete (46x62cm-18x24in) i.
                         greensih-brown pat.bronze

GULUCHE, J le (19/20th C) French
£1027 $1848   (18-Nov-91 AT.P362) Portrait deCaid (56cm-22in) s.under bust bronze
                         (F.FR 10000)

GURDJAN, Akop (20th C) Armenian
£1000 $1710   (20-Mar-92 S136/R) Isadora Duncan (45cm-18in) s. brown pat.bronze st.f.Le
                         Blanc Barbedienne

GUTFREUND, Otto (1889-1927) Czechoslovakian
£7059 $12635   (15-Nov-91 GK.Z5561/R) The toilet (43cm-17in) mono. bronze (S.FR 18000)

GUTTERO, Alfredo (1882-1932) Argentinian
£29070 $50000   (9-Oct-91 RO.BA199 b) Descendimiento (180x121cm-71x48in) s.d.1929 plaster

HABBAH (1928-) French?
£805 $1384   (7-Oct-91 HH.P33/R) Le bordel (13x30x5cm-5x12x2in) twisted forks english
                         metal (F.FR 8000)

HACKER, Dieter (1942-) German
£1308 $2250   (12-Oct-91 SY.NY303/R) Windsbraut (60cm-24in) i.num.1/10 brownish-black
                         pat.bronze f.st.

HAERENS-ROBELUS, Louise (19/20th C) Belgian
£3333 $5733   (12-Oct-91 KV.L369/R) Three cats (17x41cm-7x16in) s.f.Batardy Bruxelles
                         bronze dk brown pat. (B.FR 200000)

HAFELFINGER, Eugen (1898-1979) Swiss
£717 $1298   (4-Dec-91 G.Z85/R) Angel (33cm-13in) metal (S.FR 1800)
£3150 $5417   (16-Oct-91 G.Z69/R) Untitled (51cm-20in) metal (S.FR 8000)

HAFNER, Charles Andrew (1888-?) American
£11696 $20000   (11-Mar-92 SY.NY91/R) Peter Pan (150cm-59in) i. greenish brown pat.bronze weathered

HAGENAUER (20th C) ?
£1000 $1910   (2-Jul-92 CSK58/R) Mask of female head with curly hair (23cm-9in) st. wood copper wire
£1300 $2483   (2-Jul-92 CSK87/R) Figure of bare breasted dancer (30cm-12in) silvered bronze wood
£2000 $3660   (15-May-92 S231) Standing female figure (54cm-21in) mono. bronze

HAGENAUER, Franz (20th C) Austrian
£750 $1335   (29-Apr-92 C113/R) Female nude walking two greyhounds (20cm-8in) st.studio i. silvered brass
£1465 $2592   (22-Apr-92 ZZ.F271/R) Tete stylisee (42cm-17in) s. gilt brass (F.FR 14500)
£1800 $3204   (29-Apr-92 C112/R) Nude woman walking panther (25cm-10in) st.sig.i. silvered metal wood
£1923 $3423   (30-Nov-91 VG.B651/R) Fruitbowl in the shape of bird (22cm-9in) ca.1955 mono.i.chromium plated metal (DM 5500)
£1987 $3398   (20-Mar-92 D.V358/R) Bust of negroe woman (35cm-14in) s.c.1930 wood (A.S 40000)
£2235 $3823   (20-Mar-92 D.V355/R) Bust of negroe woman (27cm-11in) c.1930 dark brown pat.bronze (A.S 45000)
£2800 $4984   (29-Apr-92 C11/R) Bust of man (77cm-30in) st.sig.i. brass
£3600 $6408   (29-Apr-92 C110/R) Bust of woman (74cm-29in) st.sig.i. brass
£4946 $9001   (12-Dec-91 D.V158/R) Two female heads (47cm-19in) i.studio num.1334 brass (A.S 100000)
£7509 $13666   (30-May-92 VG.B276/R) Female head (41cm-16in) st.i.num. silvered sheet metal (DM 22000)
£9891 $18002   (12-Dec-91 D.V159/R) Adam and Eve (83cm-33in) c.1950/60 i.studio brass (A.S 200000)
£13910 $23785   (20-Mar-92 D.V361 v/R) Two heads (40cm-16in) s.i.d.1936 brass (A.S 280000)

HAGENAUER, Karl (20th C) Austrian
£1000 $1830   (15-May-92 S229/R) Sitting woman (30cm-12in) mono. mahogany

HAGER, Albert (1857-1940) Belgian
£4139 $7492   (23-May-92 KV.L402/R) Two elephants and rider (42x102cm-17x40in) s.d.1919 f.J Petermann bronze dk.br.pat. (B.FR 250000)

HAHN, Hermann (1868-1945) German
£866 $1507   (19-Sep-91 GK.Z546) Standing female nude (64x67cm-25x26in) s. brown pat.bronze marble socle (S.FR 2200)
£1024 $1781   (19-Sep-91 GK.Z544/R) Manneken Piss (80cm-31in) bronze (S.FR 2600)

HAJDU, Etienne (1907-) French
£3000 $5160   (17-Oct-91 C31/R) Untitled (35cm-14in) i. alabaster
£6237 $10728   (7-Oct-91 HH.P28/R) Les deux oiseaux (51x46x12cm-20x18x5in) s.num.2/3 d.1974 pat.polished bronze (F.FR 62000)
£7263 $13000   (9-May-92 CE.NY377/R) Tete de femme (69x42x22cm-27x17x9in) s. s.d.1965 black marble

HAJEK, Otto Herbert (1927-) German?
£2797 $4979   (30-Nov-91 VG.B652/R) Plastik 62 (16cm-6in) s.d.1962 num.1/5 brown pat.bronze (DM 8000)

HALL, Maja van (1937-) Dutch?
£926 $1685   (11-Dec-91 CH.AM79) The prelate (27cm-11in) s. bronze (D.FL 3000)

HALLER, Erwin (?) ?
£1207 $2076   (16-Oct-91 KM.K1639/R) Boy with two turtles (80cm-31in) i. bronze st.f.Bentsch and Kleefisch (DM 3500)

HALLER, Hermann (1880-1950) Swiss
£1692 $3215   (25-Jun-92 GK.B372) Nude girl standing with hands on her back (60cm-24in) mono.i.d.1918 brown pat.bronze (S.FR 4400)

HALNON, F (?) ?
£850 $1471   (25-Mar-92 PHI703/R) Bust of winged goddess her banded hair swept back (37cm-15in) s. bronze on marble plinth

HALONEN, Arttu (1885-1965) Finnish
£948 $1669   (12-Apr-92 HOR.H97) Mother and child (76cm-30in) s.d.1937 bronze (F.M 7500)
£1682 $2994   (1-Dec-91 HOR.H90) Seated girl (55cm-22in) s.d.1913 bronze (F.M 13000)

HAMAND, G (?) ?
£1312 $2256   (20-Oct-91 PLF.P112/R) Victoire portee par une helice (38x50cm-15x20in) polished bronze (F.FR 13000)

HAMMOND, Stanley S (1913-) Australian
£1057 $1882   (26-Nov-91 J.M381) Standing nude (65cm-26in) i.num.1/9 dark brown
     pat.bronze (A.D 2400)

HARING, Keith (1958-1990) American
£2235 $4000   (12-Nov-91 CE.NY185/R) Untitled (28x31x3cm-11x12x1in) s.d.83 dayglo
     felt-tip pen carved wood
£3073 $5500   (12-Nov-91 CE.NY186/R) Untitled (30x30x8cm-12x12x3in) s.i.d.1982verso
     enamel sheet metal
£3400 $5882   (26-Mar-92 C101/R) Untitled (28x41x3cm-11x16x1in) s.i.d.83verso acrylic
     enamel paint marker wood
£3400 $5882   (26-Mar-92 C102/R) Untitled (30x58x3cm-12x23x1in) s.i.d.83verso acrylic
     enamel marker carved wood
£17877 $32000   (5-May-92 CH.NY188/R) Capuera dancers (71x67x63cm-28x26x25in) s.d.86
     num.1/3 baked enamel aluminium

HARMSWORTH, Margaret (1928-) British
£755 $1298   (7-Oct-91 HH.P4/R) Les amants (29x25x18cm-11x10x7in) s.num.1/5 pat.bronze
     Cast.Landowski (F.FR 7500)

HARTLEY, Jonathan Scott (attrib) (1845-1912) American
£1117 $2000   (14-Nov-91 CE.NY251/R) Nearing goal - figure of football player
     (39cm-15in) st. reddish brown pat.bronze

HARTWELL, Charles Leonard (1873-1951) British
£1600 $2736   (20-Mar-92 S191/R) Naked fisher boy (30cm-12in) s. brown pat.bronze on
     marble plinth

HARVEY, Eli (1860-1957) American
£865 $1600   (10-Jun-92 CE.NY366/R) Figure of bull elk (42cm-17in) i. reddish brown
     pat.bronze f.st.Gorham G.435
£1200 $2100   (23-Sep-91 S.SL275) Figures of a bear (23cm-9in) s. brn.pat.bronze green
     marble plinth

HASELTINE, Herbert (1877-1962) American
£2088 $3800   (28-May-92 CH.NY209/R) The thoroughbred horse (9cm-4in) i.f.Valsuani
     bronze marble base

HASSELBERG, Per (1850-1894) Swedish
£1583 $2866   (3-Dec-91 AB.S4560/R) 'Grodan' (30cm-12in) s. brown pat.bronze
     (S.KR 16500)
£1708 $3125   (14-May-92 BU.S111/R) 'Grodan' (37cm-15in) s. white marble (S.KR 18000)

HASSELRIIS, Ludwig (1844-1912) Danish
£2207 $3995   (3-Dec-91 AB.S4561/R) Satyrs dancing and drinking (56cm-22in) s. green
     pat bronze (S.KR 23000)

HAUGEN-SORENSEN, Jorgen (20th C) Danish
£901 $1550   (4-Mar-92 KH.K147/R) Bridge that's biting (32x30x37cm-13x12x15in)
     travertin (D.KR 10000)
£905 $1638   (4-Dec-91 KH.K30/R) Figure (27x40cm-11x16in) mono.d.60 bronze
     (D.KR 10000)
£991 $1705   (4-Mar-92 KH.K99) Him on the stool (34cm-13in) bronze (D.KR 11000)
£1081 $1859   (4-Mar-92 KH.K149/R) The blue crawling over the red (36cm-14in) travertin
     (D.KR 12000)
£1712 $2944   (4-Mar-92 KH.K148/R) Portrait of it shutting (48cm-19in) travertin
     (D.KR 19000)

HAUSER, Simon and Joseph Philipp (18th C) German
£1916 $3488   (10-Dec-91 N.M53/R) St John the Evangelist holding book and pointing up
     with left hand (84cm-33in) i.d.1722verso silvered wood (DM 5500)

HAYDON, Samuel James Bouverie (1815-1891) British
£750 $1313   (20-Feb-92 C159/R) Portrait bust of a Gentleman (80cm-31in) s.d.1842
     white marble moulded socle

HEATHCOTE, Lucy H (18th C) British
£1600 $2800   (24-Sep-91 SWS369/R) Figure of naked child (55cm-22in) s.d.1936 lead on
     circular base

HEBALD, Milton (20th C) American
£760 $1300   (12-Mar-92 CH.NY121/R) Pressed flower, figure of woman (91cm-36in)
     i.d.1959 num.3 parcel silvered gilt bronze

HEBERT, Henri (1884-1950) Canadian
£3171 $5707   (19-Nov-91 FP.M177/R) Le tireur d'epine (53cm-21in) s.d.1913 pat.bronze
     f.i.Roman Bronze Works NY (C.D 6500)

HEBERT, Louis Philippe (1850-?) Canadian
£732 $1317   (19-Nov-91 FP.M158/R) Buste d'homme (32cm-13in) s.d.1912 pat.bronze
     f.i.Hohwiller Fondeur Paris (C.D 1500)
£860 $1590   (9-Jun-92 FB.M34) A la nage (53cm-21in) s.d.1910 plaster (C.D 1900)

HEERICH, Erwin (1922-) German
£5965 $10737   (19-Nov-91 L.K784/R) Untitled (78x30cm-31x12in) brown cardboard
         (DM 17000)

HEERUP, Henry (1907-) Danish
£1068 $1858   (18-Sep-91 KH.K36) Bird bath (22x40cm-9x16in) granite (D.KR 12000)
£1171 $2014   (4-Mar-92 KH.K47/R) Goblin cap (18cm-7in) stone (D.KR 13000)
£1354 $2315   (12-Mar-92 RAS.K656/R) Untitled (38x43cm-15x17in) cut granite
         (D.KR 15000)
£2162 $3719   (4-Mar-92 KH.K134/R) Figure (33x34cm-13x13in) stone (D.KR 24000)
£2262 $4095   (4-Dec-91 KH.K58/R) Bear (40cm-16in) stone (D.KR 25000)
£2347 $4013   (12-Mar-92 RAS.K655/R) The motor man (29x39cm-11x15in) cut granite red
         painted helmet (D.KR 26000)
£2580 $4489   (18-Sep-91 KH.K13/R) Cat thinking (33cm-13in) s.d.50 granite (D.KR 29000)
£3965 $7176   (20-May-92 KH.K78/R) The flower 1949 (37x32cm-15x13in) Gotland sandstone
         (D.KR 45000)
£4525 $8190   (4-Dec-91 KH.K45/R) Bird (60cm-24in) stone (D.KR 50000)
£6335 $11466   (4-Dec-91 KH.K137/R) Woman 1951 (110cm-43in) stone (D.KR 70000)

HEILIGER, Bernhard (1915-) German
£5965 $10737   (23-Nov-91 N.M130) Figure with arms raised (26cm-10in) s.num.d.1949 brown
         pat.bronze st.f.Rich.Barth (DM 17000)

HEIZER, Michael (1944-) American
£4469 $8000   (14-Nov-91 SY.NY170/R) Brazil (150x213cm-59x84in) ebony aluminium base

HENDRIKZ, Willem de Sanderes (1910-1959) South African
£847 $1499   (4-Nov-91 SY.J343/R) Mother and child (40cm-16in) dark brown pat.bronze
         (SA.R 4200)

HENNING, Gerhard (1880-1967) Swedish
£891 $1533   (16-Oct-91 KH.K10/R) Reclining girl (23x17cm-9x7in) s.d.1914 Cast.Schmidt
         bronze (D.KR 10000)
£894 $1628   (12-Dec-91 RAS.V363/R) Young girl drying her feet (28cm-11in) s.d.1923
         Cire perdue (D.KR 10000)
£980 $1686   (16-Oct-91 KH.K9/R) Seated girl (45x38cm-18x15in) leather (D.KR 11000)
£1248 $2146   (16-Oct-91 KH.K11/R) Head of girl (30cm-12in) s.d.1929 num.V,
         Cast.Rasmussen bronze (D.KR 14000)
£1337 $2299   (16-Oct-91 KH.K7/R) Girl drying her feet (31x25cm-12x10in) studio
         st.num.II/VI DBB cire perdue bronze (D.KR 15000)
£1362 $2384   (1-Apr-92 KH.K31/R) Girl standing (35cm-14in) s.d.1924 num.IV, bronze
         (D.KR 15000)
£1417 $2579   (25-May-92 RAS.K221/R) Youth (28x37cm-11x15in) s.d.1922 pat bronze cire
         perdue (D.KR 16000)
£1783 $3066   (16-Oct-91 KH.K8/R) Reclining nude (45x22cm-18x9in) s.d.1948 num.I,
         Cast.Rasmussen bronze (D.KR 20000)
£2228 $3832   (16-Oct-91 KH.K5/R) Seated girl (45x38cm-18x15in) s.d.1944 num.III,
         Cast.Rasmussen bronze (D.KR 25000)
£2317 $3986   (16-Oct-91 KH.K3/R) Standing girl (46cm-18in) s.num.I, Cast.Rasmussen
         bronze (D.KR 26000)
£2496 $4292   (16-Oct-91 KH.K2/R) Adam and Eve (40x27cm-16x11in) s.num.I,
         Cast.Rasmussen bronze (D.KR 28000)
£2669 $4644   (17-Sep-91 RAS.K153/R) Nude woman standing (46cm-18in) s.num.III,
         green,brown pat bronze (D.KR 30000)
£2669 $4644   (17-Sep-91 RAS.K154/R) Seated woman drying her feet (30x51cm-12x20in)
         s.Cast.L.Rasmussen bronze (D.KR 30000)
£6952 $11957   (16-Oct-91 KH.K1/R) Seated girl plaiting her hair (40x39cm-16x15in)
         s.num.III, bronze Cast.Rasmussen (D.KR 78000)

HEPWORTH, Dame Barbara (1903-1975) British
£4000 $7000   (25-Feb-92 CH.NY73/R) Small hieroglyph (11cm-4in) num.8/10 polished
         bronze
£4651 $8000   (12-Oct-91 SY.NY181/R) Sphere and hemisphere (10cm-4in) num.2/6 polished
         bronze
£10286 $18000   (25-Feb-92 SY.NY74/R) Small sun (33cm-13in) i.num.9/9 gold pat.bronze
         string
£136612 $250000   (14-May-92 SY.NY301/R) The family of man, figure 1, ancestor 1
         (277cm-109in) i. brown green pat.bronze

HERBERT, Emile (19th C) ?
£874 $1600   (3-Jun-92 D.NY470/R) Oedipe - standing figure next to sphinx (53cm-21in)
         s. bronze

HEROLD, Georg (20th C) American?
£8939 $16000   (14-Nov-91 SY.NY220/R) Little Dipper (109x270x150cm-43x106x59in) sewn
         canvas over wood

HESCHLER, David (after) (1611-1677) German
£5500 $10560   (9-Jul-92 S242/R) Statuette of St. Roch (30cm-12in) ivory

HESSE, Eva (1936-1970) American
£58659 $105000   (13-Nov-91 SY.NY59/R) Sequel (76x81cm-30x32in) latex 91 spheres one latex
         sheet

HIETZ, Matthias (1923-) Austrian?
£978 $1740   (31-Oct-91 D.V220/R) Pair (51cm-20in) c.1960 iron (A.S 20000)

HIQUILY, Philippe (1925-) French
£3242 $5868   (20-May-92 FB.P12 a) Femme au balancier (73cm-29in) s.num.1/1 iron
                      (F.FR 32000)
£5876 $10636   (20-May-92 FB.P11 a/R) La femme qui marche (128cm-50in) st.sig. brass
                      electric motor (F.FR 58000)
£6212 $11305   (15-Dec-91 P.V75/R) Femme totem (92x20x40cm-36x8x16in) s.d.1959verso
                      hammered iron (F.FR 61000)
£6495 $11236   (29-Mar-92 P.V101/R) Mimi Patte en l´air (110x66x18cm-43x26x7in)
                      s.num.7/8 brown pat.bronze st.f.Bocquel (F.FR 63000)

HJORTH, Bror (1894-1968) Swedish
£2372 $4341   (11-May-92 NOR.S88/R) Girl with dog s.num.1/35, polycrome cement
                      (S.KR 25000)
£3879 $7021   (19-May-92 AB.S5143/R) Girl with violin (40cm-16in) s. dark pat bronze
                      Cast.Bergman cire perdue (S.KR 41000)

HODIN, Daniel (1918-) French?
£1329 $2433   (3-Feb-92 HH.P97/R) Duo (37x8x8cm-15x3x3in) s.num.1/8base brn.pat.bronze
                      Cast.Ducros (F.FR 13000)
£1710 $2942   (7-Oct-91 HH.P52/R) Tendresse (22x14x12cm-9x6x5in) s.num.3/8
                      brn.pat.bronze marble base Cast.Ducros (F.FR 17000)

HOEHME, Gerhard (1920-1990) German
£5842 $10691   (2-Jun-92 L.K678/R) Schnittlinien mit Spiegel (76x61x6cm-30x24x2in) i.
                      s.i.d.1964verso mixed media collage (DM 17000)

HOETGER, Bernhard (1874-?) German
£2807 $5053   (21-Nov-91 L.K208/R) Le mendiant (26cm-10in) i. brown pat.bronze
                      (DM 8000)

HOFFMAN, Malvina (1887-1966) American
£2730 $4750   (15-Apr-92 SY.NY112/R) Struggle-elemental man (64cm-25in) i. greenish
                      brown pat.bronze f.i.Bedi-Rassy NY
£2857 $5000   (25-Sep-91 SY.NY58/R) Breton wrestlers (50cm-20in) i. brown pat.bronze
£17045 $30000   (6-Apr-92 B.LA2618/R) Bacchanale Russe (103cm-41in) i.d.1917 black green
                      pat.bronze i.f.Rom.Bronze

HOFFMANN, Anker (1904-) Danish
£758 $1303   (16-Oct-91 KH.K13) Lovers (32x28cm-13x11in) mono.d.79 bronze (D.KR 8500)
£891 $1533   (16-Oct-91 KH.K25/R) Kneeling girl (43x27cm-17x11in) mono.d.60 bronze
                      (D.KR 10000)

HOFFMANN, Josef and CZESCHKA, Carl Otto (19/20th C) Austrian
£25000 $45750   (15-May-92 S225/R) Pair of Caryatid figures (47cm-19in) gilt wood ebony
                      mother of pearl ivory

HOFFMANN, O (20th C) ?
£1600 $2928   (2-Jun-92 S415) Exotic dancer (33cm-13in) i.pat.bronze ivory marble base
                      i.f.R.M

HOFNER, Otto (?) Austrian
£3800 $6764   (29-Nov-91 S1/R) Rearing stallions (54cm-21in) s. brn.pat.bronze st.f.A G
                      Wien pair

HOGOMMAT (1925-) ?
£869 $1590   (3-Feb-92 HH.P44/R) Cheval cabre (27x28x12cm-11x11x5in) s.num.3/8
                      brn.pat.bronze (F.FR 8500)

HOGOMMAT, Andre (1925-) ?
£1207 $2076   (7-Oct-91 HH.P98/R) Le penseur (32x22x20cm-13x9x8in) s.num.6/8
                      brn.pat.bronze (F.FR 12000)

HOLMENS, Gerard (1934-) Belgian
£1105 $1889   (21-Mar-92 KV.L148) Silence (74x11cm-29x4in) wood marble socle
                      (B.FR 65000)
£6117 $10460   (21-Mar-92 KV.L418/R) Form (200x70cm-79x28in) polished marble
                      (B.FR 360000)

HOLMSKOV, Helge (20th C) Dutch
£850 $1547   (10-Dec-91 RAS.K132) Artists (63cm-25in) mono.d.63 pat iron (D.KR 9500)
£1246 $2167   (18-Sep-91 KH.K134/R) Mother and child (39cm-15in) mono. bronze
                      (D.KR 14000)

HOLZER, Jenny (1950-) American?
£15642 $28000   (6-May-92 CH.NY196/R) Living series - more than once
                      (44x91x46cm-17x36x18in) bethel white granite bench
£33520 $60000   (5-May-92 CH.NY66/R) Untitled (24x448x11cm-9x176x4in) electronic LED sign
                      three color diodes

HORTER, Ernst (20th C) ?
£1500 $2565   (20-Mar-92 S206/R) Young nude woman stretching (67cm-26in) s.i. white
                      marble

HOTTOT, Louis (1834-1905) French
£3198 $5500   (10-Oct-91 FA.PH786/R) Arab woman with jar and Arab warrior with gun (74x76cm-29x30in) s. bronze enamel polychrome pair
£6500 $11570   (29-Nov-91 S243/R) Nubian serving girl (145cm-57in) s.num.A10520 cold-painted spelter

HOUDON (?) French
£877 $1500   (13-Mar-92 WOL.C641/R) The kiss (48cm-19in) s. bronze br.pat.

HOUDON (after) (20th C) French?
£800 $1424   (1-Nov-91 S327) Bust of Rousseau (38cm-15in) white marble
£1050 $1838   (24-Sep-91 SWS325/R) Bust of la frileuse (70cm-28in) c.1880 white marble

HOUDON, Jean Antoine (1741-1828) French
£7677 $13664   (25-Nov-91 GL.P55/R) La fileuse (170cm-67in) bronze base (F.FR 75000)
£40722 $70448   (26-Mar-92 PIC.P83/R) Buste representant Voltaire age (47cm-19in) s.d.1778 white marble (F.FR 395000)

HOUDON, Jean Antoine (after) (1741-1828) French
£1600 $2800   (20-Feb-92 C140/R) Diane Chasseresse (73cm-29in) i. bronze square base
£2060 $3750   (26-May-92 SY.NY83 a/R) Bust of Marquis de Condorcet (63cm-25in) tinted terracotta

HOVI, Mikko (1879-1962) Finnish?
£970 $1727   (1-Dec-91 HOR.H97) The magistrate (24cm-9in) s. bronze (F.M 7500)

HOWARD (?) ?
£822 $1570   (3-Jul-92 SD.P41) Pierrot, Arlequin et Colombine (24x23x17cm-9x9x7in) s. painted plaster (F.FR 8000)

HOWES, Edgar Allan (1888-?) British
£805 $1400   (13-Sep-91 SY.NY88/R) Group of peasant couple mounted on working horse (38cm-15in) i. brown pat.bronze

HRDLICKA, Alfred (1928-) Austrian
£825 $1435   (17-Sep-91 FN.S2011/R) Sappho (27x35x35cm-11x14x14in) s.num.372 bronze (DM 2400)
£825 $1435   (21-Sep-91 SA.A502/R) Sappho (28cm-11in) s.num.195/282 pat.bronze (DM 2400)
£1474 $2520   (13-Mar-92 FN.S2517/R) Sappo (27x35x35cm-11x14x14in) s.d.1972 num.220 bronze (DM 4200)

HSU, Ti-Shan (20th C) ?
£1714 $3000   (27-Feb-92 CE.NY269/R) Two blues (212x118x13cm-83x46x5in) s.d.86 verso alkyd acrylic wood
£4335 $7500   (3-Oct-91 SY.NY152/R) R E M (152x152x10cm-60x60x4in) acrylic alkyd compound on wood

HUBACHER (?) ?
£2200 $3916   (28-Apr-92 SWS478/R) Nude female torso with drape around her legs (122cm-48in) s. green pat.bronze indis.st.f.M.Pa..ori

HUGARD (20th C) French
£2113 $3634   (7-Oct-91 HH.P80/R) L'interieur de la carriere (50x41x34cm-20x16x13in) s.num.1/8 brn.green pat.bronze Cast.Capelli (F.FR 21000)

HUGGLER, Arnold (1894-?) Swiss
£2091 $3890   (19-Jun-92 G.Z442/R) Poodle (74x71x25cm-29x28x10in) s. bronze (S.FR 5500)

HUNT, Bryan (1947-) American
£9497 $17000   (14-Nov-91 SY.NY336 a/R) Dancers (234cm-92in) s.d.85 num.2/4 IX bronze limestone base
£13714 $24000   (27-Feb-92 CH.NY125/R) Untitled (151x53x28cm-59x21x11in) s.d.82 num.3/6 bronze limestone base
£15607 $27000   (3-Oct-91 SY.NY140/R) Neptune (231x51x51cm-91x20x20in) s.num.1/3 d.1987 bronze copper
£16000 $28000   (27-Feb-92 CH.NY62/R) Double niche (145x69x33cm-57x27x13in) i. bronze limestone base

HUNTINGTON, Anna Hyatt (1876-1973) American
£819 $1400   (13-Mar-92 DM.D68/R) Cougar on tree trunk (15cm-6in) num.7 bronze Cast.Gorham Co.
£894 $1600   (6-May-92 D.NY42/R) Napoli (25cm-10in) s.i. red brown pat.bronze st.f.Gorham Co
£894 $1600   (14-Nov-91 CE.NY256/R) Grizzly - figure of bear cub (8cm-3in) i. reddish brown pat.bronze f.st.Gorham Co
£1222 $2200   (22-Nov-91 S.BM155/R) Yawning tiger (33cm-13in) s.i. green pat.bronze f.st.Gorham
£1381 $2500   (21-May-92 S.W3282/R) Panther on rock (6cm-2in) s. brown pat.bronze st.f.Gorham Co
£1538 $2800   (28-May-92 CH.NY211/R) Kangaroo (26cm-10in) i.f.Roman Bronze Works aluminum
£1714 $3000   (26-Sep-91 CH.NY125/R) Figure of stag (48cm-19in) i. green/brown pat.bronze f.st.Gorham

HUNTINGTON, Anna Hyatt (1876-1973) American-cont.
£1923 $3500   (28-May-92 CH.NY212/R) Bull and cape (34cm-13in) i.f.Roman Bronze Works aluminum
£2299 $4000   (15-Apr-92 SY.NY111/R) Yawning tiger (34cm-13in) i. num.270 dark brown pat.bronze f.st.Gorham
£5780 $10000   (6-Sep-91 S.BM287/R) Yawning tiger (20x71cm-8x28in) s. brn.pat.bronze Cast.Gorham Co Q509 GAC 6
£6044 $11000   (28-May-92 CH.NY210/R) Leve-toi Mam j'ai faim (52x66cm-20x26in) i.f.Roman Bronze Works aluminum

HUSSMANN, Albert Heinrich (1874-?) German
£900 $1539   (20-Mar-92 S53/R) Buck (18cm-7in) s. brown pat.bronze mono.f.N.W

IBBESON, Graham (20th C) ?
£1649 $2854   (23-Mar-92 CC.P153) Hero in y fronts (151x36x37cm-59x14x15in) s.i.base fibre wooden base (F.FR 16000)

IMMENDORF, Jorg (1945-) German
£31579 $56842   (19-Nov-91 L.K818/R) Flag (255x8x20cm-100x3x8in) wood col.string (DM 90000)

INJALBERT, Jean Antoine (1845-1933) French
£1105 $1900   (14-Oct-91 H.C211/R) Cupid riding rampant lion (48cm-19in) i. greenish brown pat.bronze
£1152 $2084   (3-Dec-91 AB.S4562/R) Buste d'adolescent (48cm-19in) s. dark pat bronze (S.KR 12000)

IOMMI, Enio (20th C) ?
£1744 $3000   (12-Oct-91 SY.NY213/R) Observation (75x40cm-30x16in) s.d.87 stainless steel marble

IPOUSTEGUY, Jean (c.1920-) French
£1646 $2979   (2-Dec-91 CC.P19/R) Duguesclin (24x30x30cm-9x12x12in) s.num.4/6 blk.pat.bronze Cast.Attilio Valsuani (F.FR 16000)
£2819 $5103   (20-May-92 KH.K176/R) Tete d l'homme (54cm-21in) s.d.1966 num.3/9, bronze (D.KR 32000)

IRGANG, Rainer (20th C) German
£881 $1595   (20-May-92 KH.K229/R) Untitled (49x72cm-19x28in) marble (D.KR 10000)

ISELI, Rolf (1934-) Swiss
£2555 $4573   (6-May-92 GD.B2603/R) Composition in red and blue (29x32cm-11x13in) s.d.69 polychrome painted wood (S.FR 7000)

ITALIAN SCHOOL (?) Italian
£2600 $4732   (9-Dec-91 PH123/R) Bacchus (30cm-12in) c.1700 bronze rectangular marble plinth
£3853 $6628   (7-Oct-91 CH.E27/R) Busts of Roman Emperors, possibly Hadrian and Trajan (73cm-29in) black mottled yellow marble pair (E.P 4200)
£6500 $11830   (10-Dec-91 C89/R) Busts of Achilles and Ajax, helmeted and facing right (39cm-15in) i. bronze c.1800 pair

ITALIAN SCHOOL, 16th/17th C
£2800 $5096   (12-Dec-91 S134) Statuette of John the Baptist standing as if preaching (23cm-9in) gilding brown pat.bronze c.1600
£4974 $9500   (3-Jul-92 S.W3141/R) Standing nymph (48cm-19in) bronze gilt bronze
£6552 $11467   (25-Sep-91 CSC.P46/R) Hercule brandissant une massue (44cm-17in) pat.bronze (F.FR 65000)

ITALIAN SCHOOL, 17th C
£2000 $3840   (8-Jul-92 PH67/R) Youth standing wearing drapery (77cm-30in) carved and polychrome
£2335 $4250   (26-May-92 SY.NY108/R) Figure of dead Christ (34cm-13in) gilt copper
£3022 $5500   (26-May-92 SY.NY56/R) Figure of angel, clad with fur-lined cloak over wind-swept gown (124cm-49in) painted wood
£3631 $6500   (14-Jan-92 CH.NY136/R) Figure of Jupiter Tonans, partially draped with eagle at feet (31cm-12in) golden brown pat.bronze black lacquer
£9000 $17280   (7-Jul-92 C70/R) Bust of Perseus crowned with fantastic beast helmet wearing tunic (84cm-33in) marble
£17000 $32640   (9-Jul-92 S174/R) Venus. Belvedere Antinous (52cm-20in) golden pat.bronze pair
£23000 $40940   (1-Nov-91 S303/R) Head of emperor (81cm-32in) marble
£58011 $105000   (5-Dec-91 SY.NY129/R) Busts of Roman Emperors (95cm-37in) marble on variegated marble socle two

ITALIAN SCHOOL, 17th/18th C
£5405 $10000   (8-Jun-92 B.LA1262/R) Bust of bearded nobleman (90cm-35in) marble
£7500 $14400   (9-Jul-92 S216/R) Bust of Caracalla (51cm-20in) white col.marble

ITALIAN SCHOOL, 18th C

£1923	$3500	(26-May-92 SY.NY64/R) Pair of Cherubim, heads touching (32x46cm-13x18in) marble
£1955	$3500	(14-Jan-92 CH.NY146/R) Bust of Saint Peter (28cm-11in) rich brown pat.bronze red lacquer
£2345	$4361	(19-Jun-92 CN.P79/R) Femme avec des fleurs et des perles, symbolisant la deesse Flore (93x64cm-37x25in) white marble (F.FR 23000)
£2485	$4250	(9-Mar-92 B.LA810/R) Figure of infant satyr (140cm-55in) weathered pine
£2874	$5000	(10-Sep-91 BG.M583/R) Figures of cherubs, with outstretched wings (198cm-78in) polychromed oak fluted column pedestals pair
£4800	$8544	(1-Nov-91 S294/R) Figure of Callipygian Venus, looking over right shoulder (95cm-37in) bronze
£6178	$10564	(12-Mar-92 GK.Z829/R) Bust of Roman lady (49cm-19in) marble (S.FR 16000)
£7602	$13000	(9-Mar-92 B.LA800/R) Bust of nobleman (89cm-35in) marble
£17033	$31000	(26-May-92 SY.NY90/R) Figure of Aphrodite, nude with piece drapery to side (122cm-48in) marble

ITALIAN SCHOOL, 19th C

£1900	$3268	(15-Oct-91 CSK213/R) Naked cradling a dove (64cm-25in) white marble stand detachable stepped plinth
£1913	$3500	(3-Jun-92 D.NY749) Two children playing (69cm-27in) figure group
£1963	$3750	(3-Jul-92 S.W3173/R) Venus (109cm-43in) white marble
£2300	$4186	(27-May-92 SWS349/R) Group of two children (92cm-36in) white marble
£2300	$4393	(30-Jun-92 PH106/R) Slave girl seated on rush mat with shawl loosely draped over lower body (66cm-26in) marble
£2390	$4327	(5-Dec-91 SY.Z185/R) Figure of Minerva wearing armour and lancet (81cm-32in) s. bronze marble socle (S.FR 6000)
£2400	$4608	(9-Jul-92 S165) Group of Marcus Aurelius, with robed emperor riding prancing horse (35cm-14in) bronze marble pedestal
£2874	$5000	(16-Sep-91 B.SF2025/R) Figure of Nubian attendant, in native dress and plumed headdress (160cm-63in) parcel gilt polychrome painted
£3000	$5430	(21-May-92 C24/R) Figure of Germanicus standing naked with cloak draped over arm (81cm-32in) white marble on column
£3652	$6500	(21-Jan-92 CE.NY61/R) Classical female nude (112cm-44in) white marble stepped circular base
£3800	$6612	(17-Sep-91 PH267/R) Young naked mother seated on stump cradling two infant boys asleep (60cm-24in) marble
£3997	$7434	(16-Jun-92 SY.B174/R) Spinario (146cm-57in) ma (B.FR 240000)
£4500	$8145	(21-May-92 C22/R) Figure of Venus Marina with truncated arms and head (76cm-30in) white marble on marble column
£4800	$8208	(20-Mar-92 S122/R) Desdemona (71cm-28in) i. white marble
£5000	$8900	(1-Nov-91 S305/R) Bust of Emperor Augustus (60cm-24in) marble
£5263	$10000	(23-Jun-92 CE.NY7/R) Flora wearing wreath of roses holding posie at her chin (152cm-60in) marble
£6200	$11036	(29-Nov-91 S68/R) Venus and Mars (102cm-40in) marble wood spear
£6800	$12376	(27-May-92 SWS370/R) Group of Venus and Cupid (116cm-46in) white marble
£7600	$12996	(20-Mar-92 S76/R) Pauline Borghese (51x98cm-20x39in) parcel gilt marble
£8818	$15697	(30-Apr-92 RAS.K818/R) Blackamoors (163cm-64in) polycrome wood pair (D.KR 100000)
£10000	$17800	(1-Nov-91 S312/R) Groups of hound and stag, and lion and horse (25cm-10in) marble pair
£12500	$22250	(29-Nov-91 S76/R) Venus unveiling (151cm-59in) marble
£13966	$25000	(11-Nov-91 B.LA1929/R) Discus thrower (267cm-105in) marble incl.mottled marble pedestal
£13966	$25000	(11-Nov-91 B.LA1930/R) Wrestlers (198cm-78in) white marble incl.grey marble pedestal
£16000	$28000	(3-Apr-92 S18/R) Figures with spear and shields, each of knight in armour (270cm-106in) parcel-gilt walnut pair
£23000	$39330	(20-Mar-92 S79/R) Venus (172cm-68in) marble on column after Antonio Canova

ITALIAN SCHOOL, 19th/20th C

£2688	$5000	(16-Jun-92 RO.BA128) Desnudo femenino con cantaro (65cm-26in) Carrara marble

ITALIAN SCHOOL, 20th C

£1170	$2000	(9-Mar-92 B.LA742/R) Figure of infant Hercules, on lion skin (47cm-19in) dark brown pat.bronze
£2000	$3800	(23-Jun-92 CE.NY8/R) Bacchante (166x72cm-65x28in) marble
£8000	$14560	(27-May-92 SWS165/R) Fountain with three cherubs holding shell with dolphin spouts (180cm-71in) marble
£8621	$15000	(15-Sep-91 JRB.C4/R) Head (71cm-28in) s. bronze f.st.C.Valsuani after Modigliani
£13500	$23625	(3-Apr-92 S27/R) Busts of a Roman Emperor (197cm-78in) porphyry verde antico col.marble pair

ITALIAN-FLEMISH SCHOOL, 19th C

£2200	$3916	(1-Nov-91 S260/R) Group of Silenus with five putti (32cm-13in) bronze

ITALIAN-FRENCH SCHOOL, 17th C

£4000	$7680	(9-Jul-92 S144) Rearing stallion (20cm-8in) bronze wooden pedestal

ITZYKSON, Anne (1963-) ?

£1431	$2620	(3-Feb-92 HH.P5/R) Eveil (24x23x14cm-9x9x6in) s.num.6/8 d.1990 pat.bronze Cast.Mariani Pietra (F.FR 14000)

JACKSON, Harry (1924-) American

£1105	$2000	(4-Dec-91 D.NY50/R) Seeker (36cm-14in) s.d.1978 num.564 dark brown pat.bronze
£4000	$7000	(25-Sep-91 SY.NY44/R) Frontiersman (52cm-20in) mono.i. painted bronze polychrome
£5495	$10000	(28-May-92 CH.NY102/R) Cowboy's meditation (56cm-22in) i. bronze marble base
£9945	$18000	(6-Dec-91 CH.NY105/R) John Wayne - model for unfinished monument (95cm-37in) i. brown pat. bronze

JACKSON, Hazel B (1894-?) American

£1106	$1980	(14-Nov-91 GRO.B88/R) Pampalune (51cm-20in) i. golden brown pat.bronze

JACOBSEN, Robert (1912-) Danish

£1222	$2211	(4-Dec-91 KH.K11/R) Two figures (14x22cm-6x9in) init.num.7/9, bronze (D.KR 13500)
£2147	$3907	(10-Dec-91 RAS.K63/R) The golden rider. The small constructor (16cm-6in) init.num.28/75, bronze pair (D.KR 24000)
£2480	$4514	(25-May-92 RAS.K70/R) Spontan construction (20x30x19cm-8x12x7in) mono. iron (D.KR 28000)
£2534	$4586	(4-Dec-91 KH.K9/R) Figures (27x31cm-11x12in) init. iron (D.KR 28000)
£2888	$4939	(12-Mar-92 RAS.K516/R) Miao (16x17x13cm-6x7x5in) s. black painted iron (D.KR 32000)
£3069	$5247	(12-Mar-92 RAS.K503/R) Huochezhan (19x17x12cm-7x7x5in) s. black painted iron (D.KR 34000)
£3249	$5556	(12-Mar-92 RAS.K502/R) Tan (20x21x11cm-8x8x4in) init. black painted iron (D.KR 36000)
£3366	$6126	(25-May-92 RAS.K111/R) Untitled (32cm-13in) mono. pat iron (D.KR 38000)
£3430	$5865	(12-Mar-92 RAS.K513/R) Hutong (19x14x14cm-7x6x6in) init. black painted iron (D.KR 38000)
£3430	$5865	(12-Mar-92 RAS.K508/R) Shan (21x14x9cm-8x6x4in) s. black painted iron (D.KR 38000)
£3430	$5865	(12-Mar-92 RAS.K507/R) Liu (19x13x10cm-7x5x4in) init. black painted iron (D.KR 38000)
£3610	$6173	(12-Mar-92 RAS.K511/R) Shier (18x16x12cm-7x6x5in) init. black painted iron (D.KR 40000)
£3610	$6173	(12-Mar-92 RAS.K506/R) Si (24x16x15cm-9x6x6in) init. black painted iron (D.KR 40000)
£3620	$6552	(4-Dec-91 KH.K60/R) Don Quixote (30cm-12in) init. iron (D.KR 40000)
£3791	$6482	(12-Mar-92 RAS.K501/R) Theme Chinois - O (17x15cm-7x6in) init. black painted iron (D.KR 42000)
£3791	$6482	(12-Mar-92 RAS.K505/R) Men-Er (18x15x10cm-7x6x4in) s. black painted iron (D.KR 42000)
£3982	$7207	(4-Dec-91 KH.K158/R) The possessed dream (44cm-17in) init. iron (D.KR 44000)
£4061	$6945	(12-Mar-92 RAS.K519/R) Shigi (21x18x12cm-8x7x5in) init. black painted iron (D.KR 45000)
£4152	$7099	(12-Mar-92 RAS.K515/R) Canting (22x17x11cm-9x7x4in) init. black painted iron (D.KR 46000)
£4332	$7408	(12-Mar-92 RAS.K517/R) Wan (20x15x11cm-8x6x4in) s. black painted iron (D.KR 48000)
£4513	$7717	(12-Mar-92 RAS.K518/R) Men (18x15x10cm-7x6x4in) s. black painted iron (D.KR 50000)
£4562	$8302	(10-Dec-91 RAS.K32/R) Untitled (52x62cm-20x24in) init. black painted iron (D.KR 51000)
£4693	$8025	(12-Mar-92 RAS.K510/R) Yi-Er-San (23x19x11cm-9x7x4in) init. black painted iron (D.KR 52000)
£5415	$9260	(12-Mar-92 RAS.K509/R) Dian (24x22x13cm-9x9x5in) s. black painted iron (D.KR 60000)
£5415	$9260	(12-Mar-92 RAS.K504/R) Shi (20x14x12cm-8x6x5in) init. black painted iron (D.KR 60000)
£5783	$10062	(17-Sep-91 RAS.K130/R) Untitled (45x60cm-18x24in) s.verso iron on wooden panel (D.KR 65000)
£5856	$10072	(4-Mar-92 KH.K10/R) Sculpture 101, Paris 1950 (14cm-6in) init.num.101, black painted iron (D.KR 65000)
£5866	$10032	(12-Mar-92 RAS.K514/R) Ershi (19x15x12cm-7x6x5in) init. black painted iron (D.KR 65000)
£5866	$10032	(12-Mar-92 RAS.K520/R) Theme Chinois - Fin (22x21x12cm-9x8x5in) init. black painted iron (D.KR 65000)
£6050	$10527	(17-Sep-91 RAS.K44/R) Zwei winkeln (31x25cm-12x10in) init. black painted iron (D.KR 68000)
£6318	$10803	(12-Mar-92 RAS.K527/R) Untitled (69x146x52cm-27x57x20in) init. black painted iron (D.KR 70000)
£6643	$12090	(25-May-92 RAS.K140/R) Untitled (26x26x19cm-10x10x7in) mono. black painted iron (D.KR 75000)
£6673	$11610	(17-Sep-91 RAS.K45/R) Telefax 1986 (40cm-16in) init. black painted iron (D.KR 75000)
£7086	$12896	(25-May-92 RAS.K137/R) Composition with iron wire (61x40x42cm-24x16x17in) mono. black, blue red painted iron (D.KR 80000)
£7671	$13118	(12-Mar-92 RAS.K512/R) Hong (20x14x10cm-8x6x4in) init. black painted iron (D.KR 85000)
£8249	$14189	(7-Oct-91 RY.P64/R) Sans titre (47x34x30cm-19x13x12in) painted steel (F.FR 82000)
£9025	$15433	(12-Mar-92 RAS.K528/R) Untitled (80x118x51cm-31x46x20in) init. black painted iron (D.KR 100000)

JACOBSEN, Robert (1912-) Danish-cont.
£11121 $19351 (17-Sep-91 RAS.K73/R) John Coltrane (54x47cm-21x19in) init. black painted iron (D.KR 125000)
£11733 $20063 (12-Mar-92 RAS.K522/R) Untitled 1987 (107x114x69cm-42x45x27in) init. black red painted iron (D.KR 130000)
£11733 $20063 (12-Mar-92 RAS.K523/R) Untitled (108x80x53cm-43x31x21in) init. black, red blue painted iron (D.KR 130000)
£12635 $21606 (12-Mar-92 RAS.K524/R) Tribute to Torgbo (90x73x75cm-35x29x30in) init. black red blue painted iron (D.KR 140000)
£13538 $23150 (12-Mar-92 RAS.K529/R) Untitled (103x79x87cm-41x31x34in) init. red black painted iron (D.KR 150000)
£14440 $24693 (12-Mar-92 RAS.K525/R) Untitled (157x79x69cm-62x31x27in) init. black painted iron (D.KR 160000)
£16216 $27892 (4-Mar-92 KH.K169/R) Construction (45cm-18in) init. black painted iron (D.KR 180000)
£16290 $29484 (4-Dec-91 KH.K99/R) Construction (44cm-17in) init.d.49 black painted iron (D.KR 180000)
£18953 $32410 (12-Mar-92 RAS.K530/R) Untitled (107x106x43cm-42x42x17in) init. black blue painted iron (D.KR 210000)
£20758 $35496 (12-Mar-92 RAS.K521/R) Friendship (54x42x31cm-21x17x12in) init. black painted iron (D.KR 230000)
£24368 $41670 (12-Mar-92 RAS.K526/R) Untitled (108x70x60cm-43x28x24in) init. black painted iron (D.KR 270000)
£26834 $48837 (10-Dec-91 RAS.K16 a) Jean Billancourt (133cm-52in) iron (D.KR 300000)

JACQUEMART, Alfred (1824-1896) French
£4000 $6840 (20-Mar-92 S19/R) Seated bloodhound (81cm-32in) s.i. brown pat.bronze

JAEGER, Gotthilf (1871-?) German
£849 $1453 (12-Mar-92 GK.Z838) Shepherdess with goat (37x27cm-15x11in) s.c.1900 bronze on marble socle (S.FR 2200)

JANENSCH, Gerhard Adolf (1860-?) German
£777 $1360 (3-Apr-92 BM.B1565/R) Walking girl reading in book and holding another under her arm (68cm-27in) pat.bronze stone socle (DM 2200)

JANSSEN, Ulfert (1878-?) German
£1053 $1800 (13-Mar-92 FN.S1384/R) Bust of man wearing vine leaves and grapes (53cm-21in) s. bronze marble socle (DM 3000)

JARL, Otto (1856-1915) Swedish
£1000 $1830 (2-Jun-92 S434) Group of Hippopotami (23cm-9in) s.i.num.23 brown pat.bronze marble base

JARL-LORENZL, Karin (20th C) Austrian
£795 $1359 (20-Mar-92 D.V369/R) Diana (46cm-18in) s.c.1925 green pat.bronze on onyx socle (A.S 16000)

JEANCLOS, Georges (1933-) French
£5040 $8921 (7-Nov-91 AT.P66/R) Adam et Eve VII (94x67x23cm-37x26x9in) s. terracotta (F.FR 50000)

JENNEWEIN, Carl Paul (19/20th C) American
£2128 $4000 (18-Dec-91 SY.NY208/R) Repose (30cm-12in) i.d.1920 black pat. bronze

JENNEY, Neil (1945-) American
£18156 $32500 (14-Nov-91 SY.NY178/R) Morning (45x82x7cm-18x32x3in) s.d.1977-78 verso s.d.1985 frame oil wood

JERICHAU, Jens Adolf (1816-1883) Danish
£2452 $4292 (1-Apr-92 KH.K45/R) Man and woman (23cm-9in) one of three bronze (D.KR 27000)

JESPERS, Floris (1889-1965) Belgian
£1389 $2528 (11-Dec-91 CH.AM297/R) The witch-doctor (48cm-19in) s. iron mixed media concrete base (D.FL 4500)

JESPERS, Oscar (1897-1970) Belgian
£855 $1548 (7-Dec-91 KV.L181) Head of a girl (40x18cm-16x7in) s. terracotta (B.FR 50000)
£1250 $2150 (12-Oct-91 KV.L160) Head of a girl (23x13cm-9x5in) s. terracotta wooden base (B.FR 75000)
£1667 $2867 (12-Oct-91 KV.L461/R) Bather I (32cm-13in) s. terracotta (B.FR 100000)
£3008 $5113 (22-Oct-91 C.A45/R) Reclining figure (50cm-20in) s. patinated plaster (B.FR 180000)

JEWETT, Maude Sherwood (1873-1953) American
£3022 $5500 (28-May-92 CH.NY199/R) Flower holder (26cm-10in) i.d.1924 f.Kunst Foundry bronze gr.br.pat.

JOHNSON, Grace Mott (1882-1967) American
£1229 $2200 (14-Nov-91 CE.NY257/R) Figure of lamb (29cm-11in) i. brown pat.bronze cast Griffoul, Newark NJ

JONES, Allen (1937-) British
£1620 $2900   (7-May-92 SY.NY315/R) Hat's off (118x27x27cm-46x11x11in) painted steel
£9249 $16000   (3-Oct-91 SY.NY77/R) Headstand (246x122x109cm-97x48x43in) painted steel
£12000 $21240   (8-Nov-91 C270/R) L A sheer (229x152cm-90x60in) s.i.d.1969 primed canvas
     plastic steps

JONES, Arne (1914-1976) ?
£1431 $2548   (27-Nov-91 BU.S33/R) Piazza (50x42cm-20x17in) s.d.1971 bronze plywood
     (S.KR 15000)
£1488 $2692   (3-Dec-91 AB.S5201/R) Composition (16cm-6in) s.num.47, metal black base
     (S.KR 15500)
£1708 $3125   (13-May-92 BU.S238/R) Triad (27cm-11in) s.num.18/65, dark pat bronze
     (S.KR 18000)
£2099 $3737   (27-Nov-91 BU.S57/R) Triad (27cm-11in) s.d.1954 num.5/65, silvered bronze
     (S.KR 22000)

JORGENSEN, Anita (20th C) Danish
£1354 $2315   (10-Mar-92 RAS.K175/R) Curued figure with double glasstairs
     (48x165x180cm-19x65x71in) lead covered furniture panels (D.KR 15000)

JORGENSEN, Borge (20th C) Scandinavian
£914 $1600   (27-Feb-92 CE.NY181/R) Abstract form (138x42x17cm-54x17x7in) init.d.71
     welded iron glass
£1171 $2014   (4-Mar-92 KH.K77/R) Untitled (64x60x12cm-25x24x5in) s.d.1973 stainless
     steel (D.KR 13000)
£1690 $2941   (18-Sep-91 KH.K142/R) The human gate (50x58x13cm-20x23x5in) s.d.90
     stainless steel blue acrylic (D.KR 19000)
£2262 $4095   (4-Dec-91 KH.K170/R) Untitled (170cm-67in) s.d.82 stainless steel
     incl.base (D.KR 25000)

JOSEPH, A M (20th C) ?
£1374 $2500   (13-Dec-91 DM.D2130/R) Deco girl in bathing suit (71cm-28in) marble on
     onyx base

JOULIA, Elisabeth (1925-) French?
£806 $1395   (6-Oct-91 BG.P37/R) Sans titre (78x44x32cm-31x17x13in) s. sandstone
     anthropomorphe (F.FR 8000)

JOUSSEAUME, Dominique (1950-) ?
£1022 $1871   (3-Feb-92 HH.P73/R) Meteorite (50x30x26cm-20x12x10in) s.num.1/8 brn.red
     pat.bronze (F.FR 10000)

JOUVE, Georges (1910-1964) French
£7863 $13603   (6-Oct-91 BG.P100/R) Le couple (102x60x12cm-40x24x5in) sculpture metal
     iron copper (F.FR 78000)

JU MING (1938-) Chinese
£8092 $13837   (22-Mar-92 SY.TA12/R) Lady and attendant (37cm-15in) s.d.1987 wood
     carving Living World series (T.D 352000)
£42989 $73510   (22-Mar-92 SY.TA68/R) T'Ai Chi (77x125cm-30x49in) s.d.1990 wood carving
     (T.D 1870000)

JUDD, Don (1928-) American
£773 $1338   (23-Mar-92 CC.P76/R) Corner chair (75x50x50cm-30x20x20in) mono.num.14 90
     painted aluminium (F.FR 7500)
£4305 $7791   (23-May-92 KV.L180) Wallpiece (71x71cm-28x28in) s.num.40/40 aluminium
     plexiglas (B.FR 260000)
£6704 $12000   (6-May-92 CH.NY346/R) Untitled (53x43x5cm-21x17x2in) s.num.2.76 r.8/85.JC
     verso cadmium red oil wood
£9497 $17000   (7-May-92 SY.NY168 a/R) Juddbox (30x60x30cm-12x24x12in) st.s.d.87 pulver
     aluminium
£16760 $30000   (6-May-92 CH.NY205 a/R) Untitled (25x183x66cm-10x72x26in) st.verso
     brushed aluminium
£16760 $30000   (6-May-92 CH.NY360 a/R) Untitled (15x69x61cm-6x27x24in) with sig. st.
     copper
£17877 $32000   (7-May-92 SY.NY161/R) Untitled (30x179x30cm-12x70x12in) st.d.85-11
     painted aluminium
£33520 $60000   (7-May-92 SY.NY153/R) Untitled (13x102x23cm-5x40x9in) galvanized iron
£33520 $60000   (5-May-92 CH.NY60/R) Untitled (84x122x173cm-33x48x68in) s.i.d.77 clear
     anodized aluminum plexiglas
£47486 $85000   (14-Nov-91 SY.NY173/R) Untitled (23x102x79cm-9x40x31in) st. stainless
     steel anodized aluminium ten unit
£61453 $110000   (7-May-92 SY.NY157/R) Untitled (150x150x150cm-59x59x59in) stainless steel
     nickel four units
£83799 $150000   (13-Nov-91 SY.NY41/R) Untitled (91x152x152cm-36x60x60in) copper light
     cadmium red enamel on aluminum

KACK, H (20th C) German
£866 $1507   (19-Sep-91 GK.Z542) Nude woman with ball (28x21cm-11x8in) s. pat.bronze
     marble socle (S.FR 2200)

KAESBACH, Rudolph (1873-?) German
£730 $1300   (30-Apr-92 CE.NY15/R) Figure of kneeling Amazon (36cm-14in) s. alabaster parcel-gilt bronze

KALISH, Max (1891-1945) American
£1383 $2600   (18-Dec-91 SY.NY158/R) The family (30cm-12in) i.d.1906 marble

KAOL, Claude (20th C) ?
£1831 $3278   (17-Nov-91 R.P144/R) Andorgine du 1er Mai (146cm-57in) s.verso epoxterre (F.FR 18000)

KAPOOR, Anish (20th C) ?
£9714 $17000   (27-Feb-92 CH.NY68/R) Untitled (99x92x29cm-39x36x11in) wall relief acrylic pigment polystyrene

KARLSSON, C Goran (20th C) Scandinavian
£859 $1529   (27-Nov-91 BU.S34/R) 'Semafor' (74cm-29in) init.d.1977 num.16/25, plexiglass on base (S.KR 9000)

KASPER, Ludwig (1893-1945) German
£839 $1494   (30-Nov-91 VG.B764/R) Child's head, Ursula (26cm-10in) d.1931 grey stucco wooden socle (DM 2400)

KAUBA, Carl (1865-1922) Austrian/American
£790 $1414   (14-Nov-91 D.V82/R) Couple dressed in festive costumes (31cm-12in) i. gold pat.bronze plastic marble socle (A.S 16000)
£889 $1591   (14-Nov-91 D.V83/R) Courting couple (22cm-9in) i. gold pat.bronze plastic bronze marble socle (A.S 18000)
£1176 $2000   (23-Oct-91 GD.B2513/R) Rodeo (37cm-15in) s. bronze on stone socle (S.FR 3000)
£1293 $2250   (13-Sep-91 SY.NY87/R) Indian child on mule (33cm-13in) i. polychrome bronze on onyx base
£1779 $3238   (26-May-92 DUR.M289/R) Bailarina (36cm-14in) s. gilded black pat.bronze (S.P 325000)
£2235 $4000   (13-Nov-91 B.SF2726/R) Frontier justice (56cm-22in) s. polychromed bronze
£3600 $6588   (15-May-92 S319) Femme Papillon automaton (26cm-10in) i. bronze enamel marble base

KEIL, Christian (1826-1890) German
£767 $1395   (14-Dec-91 BOD.P428) Equestrian statue of Kaiser Wilhelm I (58cm-23in) s.i.d.1882 bronze wooden socle (DM 2200)

KELETY, Alexander (20th C) French
£1724 $2966   (16-Oct-91 KM.K1508/R) Pas-de-deux with pierrot taking mask off female dancer (49cm-19in) i. bronze ivory marble socle (DM 5000)

KEMENY, Zoltan (1907-1965) Swiss
£8500 $14705   (26-Mar-92 S44/R) Association de deux optiques (68x83cm-27x33in) s.num.132 verso copper tubes zinc on board

KENWORTHY, Jonathan (1943-) British
£3000 $5160   (5-Mar-92 CSK191/R) Cheetahs (18cm-7in) s.d.66 num.1/5 dark brown pat.bronze

KERANEN, Veikko (1935-) Finnish
£1803 $3299   (13-May-92 BU.S240/R) Spool-shaped figure (98cm-39in) one of eight, gold pat.bronze (S.KR 19000)

KERN, Leonhard (1588-1662) German
£6969 $12683   (10-Dec-91 N.M89/R) Huckepack, young boy carrying smaller young boy on his back (12cm-5in) c.1635-45 brown pat.bronze (DM 20000)

KEYSER, Ephraim (1850-1937) American
£4971 $8500   (12-Mar-92 CH.NY111/R) Little girl feeding dove (86cm-34in) s.d.1878 white marble

KEYSER, Hendrick de (circle) (16/17th C) Dutch
£1400 $2688   (9-Jul-92 S115/R) Putto astride sea monster's shell, wrestling with dolphin (8cm-3in) bronze

KIECOL, Hubert (1950-) German
£4124 $7546   (2-Jun-92 L.K730/R) Red house on square (35x10x10cm-14x4x4in) concrete 3 parts on base (DM 12000)

KIENHOLZ, Edward (1927-) American
£874 $1583   (5-Dec-91 BG.P38) The billionaire Deluxe (27x37x35cm-11x15x14in) s.d.1977 num.7/56 verso portable television (F.FR 8500)

KING, Inge (20th C) Australian
£1210 $2250   (21-Jun-92 SY.ME127) Lookout (61x96x33cm-24x38x13in) painted steel (A.D 3000)

KING, William (18th C) British
£2235 $4000   (9-May-92 CE.NY307/R) After (225x81x53cm-89x32x21in) i.d.1982 dacron aluminum

KINSBURGER, Sylvain (1855-?) French
£2800 $4788   (20-Mar-92 S148/R) The lullaby (117cm-46in) s.i.d.1891 brown pat.bronze
               on marble socle

KIRKEBY, Per (1938-) Danish
£1404 $2526   (19-Nov-91 L.K833) Model (20x7x6cm-8x3x2in) d.1988 brown black pat.bronze
               (DM 4000)

KLEIN, Yves (1928-1962) French
£8230 $14897   (6-Dec-91 GL.P290/R) Venus bleue (70x31x23cm-28x12x9in) blue pigment
               I.K.B. on resin (F.FR 80000)
£12860 $23277   (2-Dec-91 CC.P45/R) Venus d'Alexandrie pigment IKB on plaster
               (F.FR 125000)
£14000 $24220   (26-Mar-92 C45/R) Victoire de Samothrace (51cm-20in) init.num.82/175
               pigment resin plaster cast stone

KLIMSCH, Fritz (1870-1960) German
£1300 $2379   (2-Jun-92 S454) Crouching femle nude (42cm-17in) s. brown pat.bronze
£1754 $3158   (23-Nov-91 N.M164/R) Siesta (24cm-9in) mono.d.1955 brown pat.bronze
               st.f.Strassacker (DM 5000)
£2740 $4712   (8-Oct-91 ZEL.L2306/R) Female nude kneeling (34cm-13in) i. green
               pat.bronze (DM 8000)
£2749 $5086   (12-Jun-92 HN.H431/R) Blick von der Hohe (21x33x14cm-8x13x6in)
               mono.c.1950 brown pat.bronze (DM 8000)
£3427 $6099   (25-Nov-91 WK.M589/R) Reclining nude (9x15x5cm-4x6x2in) s.c.1913 brown
               pat.bronze st.f.H.Noack Friedenau (DM 9800)
£5155 $9536   (12-Jun-92 HN.H430/R) Beschaulichkeit (32x20x32cm-13x8x13in) mono black
               green pat.bronze st.f.H.Noack Berlin (DM 15000)
£5614 $10105   (23-Nov-91 N.M163/R) Before the mirror (72cm-28in) mono.d.1941 green
               pat.bronze st.f.H.Noack Berlin (DM 16000)
£7560 $13155   (21-Sep-91 SA.A495/R) Girl holding mirror (46cm-18in) s. pat.bronze
               (DM 22000)
£8421 $14400   (13-Mar-92 FN.S2524/R) Female figure walking (36cm-14in) mono.d.1936
               bronze (DM 24000)
£12000 $21720   (3-Dec-91 C247/R) Der Abend (49cm-19in) mono. green pat.bronze Cast.H
               Noack, Berline
£15734 $28007   (28-Nov-91 SY.BE11/R) In wind and sunshine (148cm-58in) s. brown-green
               pat.bronze (DM 45000)

KLINGER, Max (1857-1920) German
£3200 $5472   (20-Mar-92 S166/R) Bathing woman (54cm-21in) init.brown pat.bronze
               i.Akt.Ges.Vorm.Gladenbeck

KLIPPEL, Robert (1920-) Australian
£1692 $3232   (19-Jul-92 SY.ME25/R) Acrobatic study (21cm-8in) init.d.88 num.744 gold
               (A.D 4400)
£2722 $5063   (21-Jun-92 SY.ME110/R) Construction (151x31x27cm-59x12x11in) d.1984
               painted wood (A.D 6750)
£3269 $6244   (19-Jul-92 SY.ME35/R) Opus 253A - Metal construction (23cm-9in)
               init.d.1970 num.253 metal sections (A.D 8500)
£3462 $6612   (19-Jul-92 SY.ME24/R) Untitled (32cm-13in) init.d.88num.726 gold
               (A.D 9000)
£3617 $6402   (26-Apr-92 SY.ME389/R) Opus 258 metal construction, 1970 (48cm-19in)
               brazed welded steel geometric sections objects (A.D 8500)
£5507 $9912   (24-Nov-91 SY.S395) Sentinel - RK421, 1981 (170cm-67in) bronze
               (A.D 12500)

KLOTZ, Edmund (19/20th C) Austrian
£3600 $6408   (29-Nov-91 S93/R) The dancing faun (118cm-46in) s. brown pat.bronze

KNOPPEL, Arvid (1893-1970) Swedish
£815 $1467   (19-Nov-91 GO.G307/R) Baby deer suckling (20cm-8in) s. pat bronze
               (S.KR 8500)
£959 $1726   (19-Nov-91 GO.G309) Elk calf (24cm-9in) s. pat bronze (S.KR 10000)
£1055 $1898   (19-Nov-91 GO.G310) Bison oxe (38cm-15in) s. pat bronze (S.KR 11000)
£1104 $1998   (3-Dec-91 AB.S4563/R) Lynx crawling along (17x20cm-7x8in) s. pat bronze
               (S.KR 11500)
£1246 $2244   (19-Nov-91 GO.G306/R) Lynx (22cm-9in) s. pat bronze (S.KR 13000)
£1486 $2675   (19-Nov-91 GO.G305/R) Standing bear (33cm-13in) s. pat bronze
               (S.KR 15500)
£1518 $2778   (14-May-92 BU.S112/R) Female elk (22cm-9in) s. dark pat bronze Cast.H
               Bergman (S.KR 16000)

KOGAN, Moissey (1879-1942) Russian
£1053 $1895   (23-Nov-91 N.M168/R) Head of girl (13cm-5in) mono.c.1920 dark brown
               pat.bronze (DM 3000)

KOLAR, Jiri (20th C) French
£1612 $2934   (9-Dec-91 CH.R54/R) Nikdo-Nikde (40x30cm-16x12in) s.i.d.1982 collage and
               discs vinyl on cardboard (I.L 3500000)

KOLBE, Georg (1877-1947) German
£2730 $4942   (23-May-92 GB.B6714/R) Head of Giovanni (16x14x14cm-6x6x6in) brown
               pat.bronze marble socle (DM 8000)

KOLBE, Georg (1877-1947) German-cont.
£4021 $7157   (30-Nov-91 VG.B246/R) Nude girl seated with arms raised (25cm-10in)
     terracotta (DM 11500)
£4706 $8000   (25-Oct-91 S.W2654/R) Sitzende (28cm-11in) init. brown pat.bronze
£5000 $8650   (25-Mar-92 S23/R) Die Sitzende (28cm-11in) mono. bronze
£5286 $9250   (23-Sep-91 S.SL412) Crouching girl (28cm-11in) mono. golden
     brn.pat.bronze
£7719 $13895   (23-Nov-91 N.M174/R) Female nude standing (41cm-16in) mono.d.1921
     red-brown pat.bronze st.f.H.Noack (DM 22000)
£11429 $20000   (25-Feb-92 CH.NY60/R) Kniende (55cm-22in) mono. brown pat.bronze f.st.
£13652 $24846   (29-May-92 VG.B60/R) Klagende (40cm-16in) mono brown pat.bronze
     (DM 40000)
£26000 $44720   (16-Oct-91 S46/R) Javanische Tanzerin (73cm-29in) mono. bronze
     st.f.H.Noack Berlin Friedenau

KOLLWITZ, Kathe (1867-1945) German
£8741 $15559   (26-Nov-91 KF.M780/R) Die Klage (25x25cm-10x10in) s. bronze st.f.H.Noack
     Berlin (DM 25000)
£19672 $36000   (13-May-92 CH.NY271/R) Pieta (38cm-15in) s. brown pat.bronze f.st. Noack
     Berlin
£22308 $42385   (26-Jun-92 GK.B72/R) Pieta (38x27x39cm-15x11x15in) s. brown pat.bronze
     (S.FR 58000)
£24476 $43566   (29-Nov-91 VG.B13/R) Die Klage (26cm-10in) s. brown pat.bronze (DM 70000)

KONTI, Isidore (1862-1938) Austrian/American
£1754 $3000   (11-Mar-92 SY.NY83/R) Dancing girl (30cm-12in) i. brown pat.bronze
     f.i.Roman Bronze Works N.Y

KOONING, Willem de (1904-) American/Dutch
£72626 $130000   (13-Nov-91 SY.NY12/R) Head III (51cm-20in) st.s. num.9/12 bronze

KOONS, Jeff (1955-) American
£8939 $16000   (6-May-92 CH.NY197/R) Inflatable flowers (41x61x35cm-16x24x14in) plastic
     plexiglas mirror vinyl flowers
£67039 $120000   (5-May-92 CH.NY15/R) Three ball total equilibrium tank
     (154x124x34cm-61x49x13in) glass iron water sodium chloride 3
     basketballs
£78212 $140000   (14-Nov-91 SY.NY200/R) Two ball 50/50 tank - Spalding Dr. J. Silver
     Series, Spalding Dr.J241 Series (159x93x34cm-63x37x13in) glass steel
     tank 2 basketballs distilled water
£89385 $160000   (5-May-92 CH.NY8 a/R) Stacked (140x152x65cm-55x60x26in) s.i. painted wood
£100559 $180000   (14-Nov-91 SY.NY184/R) New Shelton wet/dry triple decker
     (316x71x71cm-124x28x28in) 3 vacuum cleaners plexiglass fluorescent
     lights

KOPER, Tadeusz (1913-) ?
£784 $1404   (15-Nov-91 GK.Z5721) Untitled (70x60x5cm-28x24x2in) c.1966 marble
     (S.FR 2000)
£980 $1755   (15-Nov-91 GK.Z5723) Abstract figure II (46x79x36cm-18x31x14in) d.1973/87
     marble (S.FR 2500)
£1294 $2316   (15-Nov-91 GK.Z5720) Untitled (55x50x27cm-22x20x11in) c.1965 white
     carrara marble (S.FR 3300)

KORBEL, Mario Joseph (1882-1954) American
£1648 $3000   (28-May-92 CH.NY201/R) Female nude (39cm-15in) i.f.Roman Bronze Works
     bronze marble base

KORSHANN, H (?) ?
£1050 $1922   (13-May-92 CBB346) Feeding time (41x28cm-16x11in) bronze

KOSTA, Alex (20th C) ?
£1571 $2750   (28-Feb-92 SY.NY331/R) Homme au chapeau (53cm-21in) i.d.32 black
     pat.bronze

KOUNELLIS, Jannis (1936-) Greek
£55866 $100000   (12-Nov-91 CH.NY65/R) Untitled (200x183x27cm-79x72x11in) burlap steel

KOWALSKI, Piotr (20th C) ?
£3927 $6677   (27-Oct-91 P.V83) La Bas (82x56cm-32x22in) s.i.d.1969verso wood objects
     in plexiglass (F.FR 39000)

KRANEWITTER, Franz Josef (1893-1974) Austrian
£1454 $2647   (26-May-92 D.V33/R) The amourous faun (34cm-13in) s.d.20 wood (A.S 30000)

KRAUSE, Karl Heinz (20th C) German
£1025 $1793   (3-Apr-92 BM.B1566/R) Male nude (31cm-12in) mono. bronze (DM 2900)

KRICKE, Norbert (1922-1984) German
£22526 $40997   (29-May-92 VG.B80/R) Raumplastik (27cm-11in) stainless steel bronze on
     socle (DM 66000)

KRUSE, Max (1854-1942) German
£1045 $1902   (10-Dec-91 N.M145/R) Young love, standing male nude holding hand of
     female nude seated on rock (38cm-15in) s.num.47 black pat.bronze
     st.f.Gladenbeck Berlin (DM 3000)

KUDO, Tetsumi (1935-) Japanese
£1017	$1862	(14-May-92 BG.P59/R) Cultivation (20x13x23cm-8x5x9in) s.d.1971 mixed media (F.FR 10000)
£2987	$5107	(21-Mar-92 AT.P56/R) Portrait d'artiste (25x27x18cm-10x11x7in) s.base i. various objects in cage (F.FR 29000)

KUMPF, Gottfried (1930-) Austrian
£1562	$2702	(3-Oct-91 D.V305/R) Der Asoziale (19cm-7in) s.num.58/44 pat.bronze (A.S 32000)

KUNA, Henri (1885-?) Polish
£1714	$3000	(28-Feb-92 SY.NY32/R) Tete de femme (37cm-15in) i. blackish brown pat.bronze f.st.A.Valsuani

LACOMBE, Georges (1868-1916) French
£9714	$17776	(3-Feb-92 HH.P80/R) L'etreinte (54x30x24cm-21x12x9in) s.num.08 brn.pat.bronze (F.FR 95000)

LADD, Anna Coleman (1878-1939) American
£2105	$4000	(23-Jun-92 CE.NY71/R) St Elizabeth of Hungary. St Helena of Constantinople (156x155cm-61x61in) i. bronze pair

LAGOS, Alberto (1885-1960) Argentinian
£2088	$3800	(11-Dec-91 RO.BA70/R) Cabeza de nina (20cm-8in) s.d.1912 pat.bronze on marble base

LAGRIFFOUL, Henri Albert (1907-) French
£1710	$2942	(7-Oct-91 HH.P7/R) Femme nue se coiffant (60x24x11cm-24x9x4in) s.base brn.pat.bronze (F.FR 17000)

LAIB, Wolfgang (1950-) ?
£12000	$21000	(27-Feb-92 CH.NY115/R) Maison de Riz (15x64x13cm-6x25x5in) s.d.86 enamel rice wood
£16760	$30000	(5-May-92 CH.NY151/R) Maison de Riz (17x125x20cm-7x49x8in) s.d.89 marble with rice

LALIBERTE, Alfred (1878-1953) Canadian
£814	$1507	(9-Jun-92 FB.M35) Le minot de Ble (14cm-6in) s. pat.bronze (C.D 1800)

LAMBEAUX, Jef (1852-1908) Belgian
£775	$1402	(3-Dec-91 FN.S933) Bust of young woman wearing low cut dress (49cm-19in) s. marble (DM 2200)
£917	$1577	(12-Oct-91 KV.L179) Victory (60x22cm-24x9in) s. bronze brown/green pat. (B.FR 55000)
£1100	$1881	(20-Mar-92 S117/R) Bust of young bacchante woman (63cm-25in) s. green pat.bronze
£1500	$2580	(12-Oct-91 KV.L178/R) Wrestlers (74x50cm-29x20in) s. bronze black pat. (B.FR 90000)
£1600	$2784	(17-Sep-91 PH228) Two wrestlers in athletic pose the bearded pugilist throwing opponent (106cm-42in) bears sig. i.f.R.Debraz Bruxelles
£2653	$4856	(12-May-92 C.A609) Brabo (163cm-64in) s. bronze (B.FR 160000)

LAMBERT-RUCKI (1888-1967) French
£2058	$3909	(24-Jun-92 AT.P220/R) Masque (21x15cm-8x6in) s.num.7/8 polychrome pat.bronze cire perdue (F.FR 20000)

LAMBERT-RUCKI, Jean (1888-1967) French
£1216	$2201	(18-May-92 AT.P42/R) L'homme a la feuille (64cm-25in) s. polychrome plaster (F.FR 12000)
£1829	$3183	(14-Apr-92 CSC.P29/R) La ronde (17x40x25cm-7x16x10in) s.num.EA 1/2 bronze polychrome Cast.Clementi (F.FR 18000)
£1890	$3250	(12-Oct-91 SY.NY175/R) Figure with horse (42cm-17in) i. num.3/8 gold pat.bronze f.st.Fondeur Plaine
£2033	$3537	(14-Apr-92 CSC.P22/R) Masque (21x15x10cm-8x6x4in) s.num.EA 1/2 bronze polychrome (F.FR 20000)
£2456	$4373	(1-Dec-91 I.N73/R) Maternite (150x35x21cm-59x14x8in) painted plaster (F.FR 24000)
£2642	$4598	(14-Apr-92 CSC.P21/R) Portrait (44cm-17in) s.num.EA 1/24 bronze polychrome (F.FR 26000)
£2846	$4951	(14-Apr-92 CSC.P23/R) Le baiser (97x36x22cm-38x14x9in) s.num.EA 1/1 bronze polychrome (F.FR 28000)
£3049	$5305	(14-Apr-92 CSC.P25/R) L'effort (95x15cm-37x6in) s.base num.EA 1/1bronze polychrome (F.FR 30000)
£3049	$5305	(14-Apr-92 CSC.P19/R) Le reve du chat (52x23cm-20x9in) s.num.EA1 bronze polychrome Cast.Clementi (F.FR 30000)
£3150	$5482	(14-Apr-92 CSC.P20/R) Masque no.1 (21x15x7cm-8x6x3in) s.num.EA 1/1 bronze polychrome Cast.Blanchet (F.FR 31000)
£3219	$5537	(7-Oct-91 HH.P95/R) Masque no.3 (21x9x18cm-8x4x7in) s.num.3/8 bronze polychrome Cast.Blanchet (F.FR 32000)
£3354	$5835	(14-Apr-92 CSC.P24/R) Saint Francois d'Assise (68x50x20cm-27x20x8in) s. num.EA 1, EA 1 bronze polychrome (F.FR 33000)

LAMBERT-RUCKI, Jean (1888-1967) French-cont.

£3760	$6543	(14-Apr-92 CSC.P27/R) Couple au chapeau gibus (27x7cm-11x3in) s.base num.EA 1/1 blk.pat.bronze Cast.Blanchet (F.FR 37000)
£3862	$6720	(14-Apr-92 CSC.P31/R) Acrobate (115x15cm-45x6in) s.num.EA 1/1 bronze polychrome Cast.Clementi (F.FR 38000)
£4330	$7708	(28-Oct-91 GL.P190/R) Tete a la tresse (44x18x17cm-17x7x7in) s.base num.7/8 bronze polychrome Cast.Laplaine (F.FR 43000)
£4684	$8525	(15-Dec-91 P.V21/R) Couple aux masques (51x15x11cm-20x6x4in) s.num.5/8 bronze polychrome Cast.Blanchet (F.FR 46000)
£5041	$9325	(10-Jun-92 LD.P158/R) Couple au chapeau gibus (55x11x10cm-22x4x4in) s.num.7/8 black pat.bronze st.f.Blanchet (F.FR 49500)
£5231	$8998	(7-Oct-91 HH.P68/R) Saint-Francois d'assise (86x59x26cm-34x23x10in) s.num.2/8 bronze polychrome Cast.Blanchet (F.FR 52000)
£7771	$14221	(3-Feb-92 HH.P42/R) Le songeur (79x40x16cm-31x16x6in) s.num.1/8 bronze polychrome Cast.Blanchet (F.FR 76000)

LANCERAY (19/20th C) Russian

| £1415 | $2633 | (16-Jun-92 SY.B164/R) Russian cavalier with horses (45cm-18in) bronze marble base (B.FR 85000) |

LANCERAY (after) (?) Russian

| £874 | $1600 | (3-Jun-92 D.NY723) Horse drawn cart with three figures (61cm-24in) s. bronze |

LANCERAY, Eugene Alexandro (1848-1886) Russian

£753	$1296	(8-Oct-91 ZEL.L2307/R) Two cossacks performing on galopping horses (50cm-20in) bronze st.f.Staatl.Eisengiesserei Tula (DM 2200)
£931	$1601	(16-Oct-91 KM.K1649/R) Mounted cossack kissing girl (41cm-16in) i. bronze (DM 2700)
£931	$1601	(16-Oct-91 KM.K1650/R) Peasant woman and child riding horse and foal (31cm-12in) i. bronze (DM 2700)
£1000	$1700	(22-Oct-91 CE.NY42/R) Equestrian group (26cm-10in) i. dark brown pat.bronze
£1000	$1910	(30-Jun-92 PH67/R) Warrior seated on horse holding long spear (41cm-16in) s. brown pat.bronze
£1000	$1830	(2-Jun-92 S449) Young boy with pack mules (20cm-8in) s. brown pat.bronze st.foundry
£1086	$1900	(21-Feb-92 BG.M324/R) Chasseur au depart (25x25cm-10x10in) s.st.i.d.1870 bronze
£1593	$2900	(13-Dec-91 SY.NY251/R) The kiss (42cm-17in) s. bronze
£2088	$3800	(13-Dec-91 SY.NY248/R) The bugler (39cm-15in) s. bronze i.f.Chopin
£2304	$4125	(14-Nov-91 GRO.B84/R) Taming wild horse (64cm-25in) i. golden brown pat.bronze
£2353	$4000	(22-Oct-91 CE.NY46/R) Equestrian group of medieval knight (39cm-15in) i. black pat.bronze

LANCERAY, Yevgeni (1875-1946) Russian

| £3256 | $5600 | (10-Oct-91 FA.PH778/R) Three Cossack soldiers with horses and packhorse travelling over snow (38x53cm-15x21in) s. bronze white marble |

LANDOWSKI, Paul Maximilien (1875-1961) French

| £3801 | $6500 | (21-Mar-92 SY.NY223/R) Figure of Icarus (154cm-61in) s. green-black pat.bronze f.i.F.Barbedienne |
| £5464 | $9889 | (23-May-92 KV.L400/R) Young girl with two peacocks (58x141cm-23x56in) s.f.A A Hebrard bronze gr.br.pat. (B.FR 330000) |

LANIAU, Jean (1931-) French

£1112	$1991	(10-May-92 LT.P101) Arabesque (21x9cm-8x4in) s.num.3/8 black pat.bronze f.st. (F.FR 11000)
£1158	$1969	(27-Oct-91 LT.P83/R) Pont (13x27cm-5x11in) s.i.num.EA 3/4 brn.pat.bronze cire perdue (F.FR 11500)
£1339	$2289	(22-Mar-92 LT.P106) Femme-papillon (18cm-7in) s.num.5/8 green pat.bronze Cast.Cappelli (F.FR 13000)
£1339	$2289	(22-Mar-92 LT.P107/R) Horizon (22cm-9in) s.num.2/4 brn.pat.bronze Cast.Capelli (F.FR 13000)
£1376	$2560	(21-Jun-92 LT.P95 b) Coiffure IV (26cm-10in) brown pat.bronze (F.FR 13500)
£1427	$2654	(21-Jun-92 LT.P95/R) Reverie (25cm-10in) s.num.4/4 green pat.bronze i.f.Cappelli (F.FR 14000)

LAPICQUE, Charles (1898-1988) French

| £1453 | $2600 | (9-May-92 CE.NY117/R) Saint Georges terrasant le dragon (57cm-22in) s.num.9/9 joined metal cutouts |
| £1876 | $3302 | (8-Apr-92 FB.P109) Xerxes (40cm-16in) s.num.8/9 onyx (F.FR 18500) |

LAPINI, C (1848-?) Italian

| £2025 | $3401 | (28-Aug-91 RAS.K881) El primo Dispiacere (73cm-29in) s.i.d.1893 white marble (D.KR 23000) |

LAPINI, Cesare (1848-?) Italian

£714	$1300	(13-Dec-91 S.W3023/R) Little Red Riding Hood (66cm-26in) s.d.1889 white marble
£850	$1454	(20-Mar-92 S134/R) Young woman wearing lace shawl (66cm-26in) s.d.1889 alabaster on marble socle
£1500	$2670	(29-Nov-91 S147/R) Bust of gypsy (56cm-22in) s.d.1887 marble

LAPINI, Cesare (1848-?) Italian-cont.
£6250 $11000   (10-Apr-92 DM.D2109/R) Gli Addirati - depicts two children (84cm-33in)
s.d.1883 marble

LAPLANCHE, Pierre-Albert (1854-?) French
£1600 $2736   (20-Mar-92 S9/R) Stag and doe beside stream (45cm-18in) s. brown green
pat.bronze on marble plinth

LAPORTE (?) ?
£3801 $6500   (13-Mar-92 WOL.C1126/R) Young girl playing with a cat (94cm-37in) bronze
br.pat.

LAPORTE-BLAIRSY, Leo (1865-1923) French
£4678 $8000   (21-Mar-92 SY.NY219/R) Figural lamp - maiden in flowing gown (31cm-12in)
i.num.57283/26 brown-black pat.bronze

LARA, Laetitia (1957-) ?
£1943 $3555   (3-Feb-92 HH.P3/R) Femme accroupie (33x25x25cm-13x10x10in) s.num.8/8base
pat.bronze Cast.Pesaredona (F.FR 19000)

LARCHE, Raoul (1860-1912) French
£1000 $1830   (15-May-92 S318) Naked female figure supporting dish (16cm-6in) i.
pat.bronze
£1031 $1763   (9-Mar-92 AT.P272) Jesus au milieu des docteurs (70cm-28in) s. green
pat.bronze (F.FR 10000)

LASSAW, Ibram (1913-) American/Egyptian
£1744 $3000   (12-Oct-91 SY.NY363/R) Enclave (33cm-13in) gold bronze pat. bronze

LAURENS, Henri (1885-1954) French
£16888 $30061   (27-Nov-91 LGB.P80/R) Femme accroupie a la draperie (33cm-13in)
terra-cotta (F.FR 165000)
£18000 $32580   (3-Dec-91 C290/R) La jeune soeur (30cm-12in) init.num.2/6 blk.pat.bronze
Cast.C Valsuani
£21000 $40110   (30-Jun-92 C149/R) Le compotier de raisins (46x60cm-18x24in) mono.
num.4/6 brown pat.bronze f.st.C Valsuani
£27322 $50000   (13-May-92 CH.NY239/R) Femme a l'eventail (51x39cm-20x15in) init. st.
num.2/6 brown pat.bronze
£38251 $70000   (12-May-92 CH.NY144/R) Femme couchee (23x54cm-9x21in) terracotta
£40183 $71928   (17-Nov-91 GL.P21/R) Femme a la draperie (47x40x5cm-19x16x2in)
init.num.5/6 bronze Cast.C.Valsuani cire perdue (F.FR 395000)
£73446 $130000   (7-Nov-91 SY.NY165/R) L'Espagnol (41cm-16in) mono. num.0/6 golden-brown
pat.bronze f.st.

LAVATELLI, Carla (20th C) Italian
£1111 $1900   (21-Mar-92 W.W77/R) Dancing rhythm (284x117cm-112x46in) s.d.1970 greenish
brown pat.bronze

LAVERGNE (?) ?
£1700 $3111   (15-May-92 CBS111) Figure of young boy - Charmeur de Lezards (38cm-15in)
s. bronze

LAVIER, Bertrand (20th C) French
£15353 $27329   (30-Nov-91 FB.P68/R) Paragon (276x153x7cm-109x60x3in) liquitex on
table-tennis table diptych (F.FR 150000)

LAWLOWSKI, L (20th C) French
£1609 $2800   (15-Sep-91 JRB.C30/R) Male athlete (69cm-27in) s. bronze f.st.Leblanc
Barbedienne and Fils

LEBOURG, C (19th C) French
£874 $1669   (1-Jul-92 CD.P125/R) Buste de femme, in dress decorated with roses
terracotta marble column (F.FR 8500)

LEBROC, Jean-Baptiste (1825-1870) French
£1184 $2250   (25-Jun-92 BG.M483) Bacchants with satyr and child (91cm-36in) s. marble

LECOMTE, Felix (after) (1737-1817) French
£2730 $4750   (13-Sep-91 S.W2631/R) Bust of Marie Antoinette (89cm-35in) s. brown
pat.bronze

LECOURTIER, Prosper (1855-1924) French
£1300 $2483   (30-Jun-92 PH79/R) Seated terrier (48cm-19in) s. brown pat.bronze
£3258 $5800   (30-Apr-92 CE.NY38/R) Group of racing charioteer (61cm-24in) i.
parcel-gilt bronze

LEDERER, Hugo (1871-?) German
£1474 $2653   (21-Nov-91 L.K264/R) The archer (55cm-22in) i.indis.st.num.8 brown-green
pat.bronze (DM 4200)

LEE, Arthur (1881-1961) American
£920 $1600   (15-Apr-92 SY.NY116/R) Philosopher (43cm-17in) black pat.bronze f.i.Kunst
Fdy NY

EESER, Titus (1903-) Dutch
£669 $1164   (17-Sep-91 CH.AM129) Standing nude, three quarters length (48cm-19in) init. chamotte clay (D.FL 2200)

EGER, Fernand (1881-1955) French
£12022 $22000   (13-May-92 CH.NY275/R) Visage aux deux mains (46x31cm-18x12in) s. num.4/8 brown pat.bronze f.st.Valsuani

EHMANN, Kurt (1905-) German
£1215 $2175   (15-Nov-91 KM.K173/R) Flute player (23cm-9in) i. brown pat.bronze st.f.Barth Berlin (DM 3500)

EHMBRUCK, Wilhelm (1881-1919) German
£5461 $9939   (27-May-92 PH.DU61/R) Head of woman (42cm-17in) rem.sig. plaster (DM 16000)
£24476 $43566   (28-Nov-91 SY.BE5/R) The little thinker (53cm-21in) s. brown pat.bronze st.H.Noack Berlin Friedenau (DM 70000)

EINFELLNER, Heinz (1911-1973) Austrian
£1939 $3529   (26-May-92 D.V195/R) Reclining fisherman (26x45cm-10x18in) green pat.bronze (A.S 40000)

EISEK, Georg (1869-?) Austrian
£889 $1591   (14-Nov-91 D.V202/R) Bust of Kaiser Franz Joseph (28cm-11in) i. dark brown pat.bronze plastic (A.S 18000)

LEMOYNE, Jean Baptiste (after) (18th C) French
£1481 $2592   (24-Feb-92 ARC.P51/R) Buste de Fontenelle (61cm-24in) terracotta pedestal (F.FR 14500)

LEMOYNE, Jean Baptiste (younger) (1704-1778) French
£3475 $5942   (12-Mar-92 GK.Z841/R) Bust of Madame de Vendeuil (60cm-24in) s.d.1770 terracotta on marble socle (S.FR 9000)

LENOIR, Alfred Charles (1850-1920) French
£1294 $2200   (22-Oct-91 CE.NY30/R) Portrait figure of Hector Berlioz (53cm-21in) i. reddish brown pat.bronze f.i.Alexis Rudier

LENORDEZ, Pierre (19th C) French
£1150 $2047   (29-Nov-91 S61/R) The steeplechase (24x39cm-9x15in) s. brown pat.bronze
£1400 $2492   (29-Nov-91 S3/R) Royal Quand Meme (34cm-13in) s. dk.brown pat.bronze

LEONARD, Agathan (1841-?) French
£4129 $7349   (28-Oct-91 AT.P120/R) Buste (60cm-24in) gilded bronze red marble socle Cast.Susse Freres (F.FR 41000)
£5041 $9124   (4-Dec-91 LD.P199/R) Danseuse au tambourin (58cm-23in) s. gilded bronze Cast.Susse Freres (F.FR 49000)
£6036 $10382   (13-Oct-91 SY.MO368/R) Joueuse de flute et joueuse de tambourin (56cm-22in) gilded bronze Cast.Susse Freres pair (F.FR 60000)
£6173 $11173   (4-Dec-91 LD.P200/R) La cothurne (54cm-21in) s. gilded bronze Cast.Susse Freres (F.FR 60000)
£6173 $11173   (4-Dec-91 LD.P201/R) Danseuse au tambourin (55cm-22in) s. gilded bronze Cast.Susse Freres (F.FR 60000)

LEONCILLO (1915-1968) Italian
£2263 $4119   (26-May-92 SY.MI145/R) Composizione (41x15x15cm-16x6x6in) s. terracotta polychrome enamel (I.L 5000000)
£8679 $15101   (14-Apr-92 F.M119/R) San Sebastiano (54cm-21in) s.d.1959 terracotta (I.L 19000000)

LEPCKE, Ferdinand (1866-1909) German
£976 $1776   (10-Dec-91 N.M144) Nude girl seated (16x19x13cm-6x7x5in) s.d.1890 black brown pat.bronze st.f.Lauchhammer (DM 2800)

LEQUESNE (20th C) French
£917 $1604   (24-Sep-91 GM.B186) Satyr aux instruments de musique bronze (B.FR 55000)

LEQUESNE, Eugene L (1815-1887) French
£800 $1528   (30-Jun-92 PH52/R) Figure of dancing faun playing pipe standing on tasseled cushion (52cm-20in) s. black silver gilt pat.bronze st.f.Susse

LEROUX, Colon (19th C) ?
£4094 $7000   (9-Mar-92 B.LA745/R) Bust of Othello, wearing cape (91cm-36in) i. green black brown pat.bronze

LEROUX, Gaston (1854-?) French
£3371 $6000   (30-Apr-92 CE.NY17/R) Figure of Aida (75cm-30in) s. white marble

LEROY, Hippolite (1857-?) Belgian
£9000 $15750   (28-Feb-92 S75/R) Attendant in mediaeval tunic holding lantern with borzoi at his feet (250cm-98in) s.c.1890 marble gilt-bronze electrified

LETOURNEAU, Edouard (?-1907) French
£1657 $3000   (2-Dec-91 S.SL279/R) Indian on horseback (58cm-23in) s. dark brown pat.bronze

LEVASSEUR, Henri (1853-?) French
£850 $1624   (30-Jun-92 PH62/R) Model of huntress sitting astride on eagle on rocky base (56cm-22in) s. pat.bronze marble plinth
£1300 $2223   (20-Mar-92 S180/R) Diane chasseresse (72cm-28in) s.i. brown pat.bronze
£3200 $5472   (20-Mar-92 S149/R) The beautiful peacock (80cm-31in) s. brown pat.bronze

LEVEQUE, Edmund Louis Auguste (1814-1875) French
£1018 $1864   (2-Jun-92 AT.P207) Les deux esclaves (47x23x17cm-19x9x7in) pat.bronze (F.FR 10000)

LEVKOVITCH, Leon (1936-) Polish
£905 $1557   (7-Oct-91 HH.P38/R) Nu couche (16x26x18cm-6x10x7in) s.d.1987 num.1/8 brn.green pat.bronze (F.FR 9000)

LEVY, Charles-Octave (?-1899) French
£1161 $2124   (12-May-92 C.A610) The sower (80cm-31in) s. bronze (B.FR 70000)
£2600 $4446   (20-Mar-92 S125/R) Salome (83cm-33in) s.i. brown pat.bronze

LEVY, Michel (19th C) ?
£1663 $3193   (6-Jul-92 HC.P67/R) Athanor (41cm-16in) s.num.4/8 bronze cire perdue (F.FR 16000)
£2980 $5693   (3-Jul-92 GL.P97/R) Le printemps (80x18x26cm-31x7x10in) s.mono.d.1986 num.1/8 bronze. Cast.Susse (F.FR 29000)

LEWERS, Gerald Francis (20th C) Australian
£1322 $2379   (24-Nov-91 SY.S108) Untitled (29x68cm-11x27in) wood (A.D 3000)

LEWIS, Edmonia (1843-?) American
£34341 $62500   (27-May-92 SY.NY36/R) Marriage of Hiawatha (74cm-29in) i. white marble

LEWITT, Sol (1928-) American
£1375 $2516   (3-Jun-92 CSC.P174/R) Forme brisee (38x34x24cm-15x13x9in) s.num.11/12 metal (F.FR 13500)
£4938 $8938   (5-Dec-91 BG.P46/R) Sculpture (38x56x56cm-15x22x22in) templon (F.FR 48000)
£10286 $18000   (25-Feb-92 SY.NY210/R) 1-2-3-4-5-4-3-2-1 (33x214x42cm-13x84x17in) painted aluminum
£16201 $29000   (13-Nov-91 CH.NY223/R) Incomplete cube (107x107x107cm-42x42x42in) aluminium painted white
£17490 $33230   (26-Jun-92 FB.P79/R) Paravent (174x74cm-69x29in) mixed media canvas screen 5 double-sided panels (F.FR 170000)
£19487 $34882   (19-Jan-92 CC.P53/R) Sans titre (137x46x46cm-54x18x18in) painted iron enamel (F.FR 190000)
£19553 $35000   (5-May-92 SY.NY61/R) Column with geometric figures within a square (290x100x100cm-114x39x39in) wood painted white
£20231 $35000   (3-Oct-91 SY.NY100/R) Serial project No.1 Seta (24x91x91cm-9x36x36in) baked enamel on steel
£41899 $75000   (7-May-92 SY.NY163/R) Serial project No.1 - set C (230cm-91in) baked enamel on aluminium
£41899 $75000   (13-Nov-91 SY.NY109/R) Modular piece (278x141x140cm-109x56x55in) painted aluminum
£64246 $115000   (13-Nov-91 SY.NY58/R) All variations of incomplete open cubes 122 wood sculptures 131 framed photos drawings

LEYSALLE, Pierre Emile (1847-?) French
£912 $1650   (23-May-92 G.SB115/R) L'age d'or (55cm-22in) s. brown pat.bronze (F.FR 9000)

LHOSTE, Claude (20th C) French
£2045 $3742   (3-Feb-92 HH.P56/R) La petite poule (26x32x14cm-10x13x6in) s.num.5/6base blk.pat.bronze Cast.Godard (F.FR 20000)

LIBERICH, Nicolai Ivanovich (1828-1882) Russian
£1647 $2800   (22-Oct-91 CE.NY41/R) Group of huntsman after hunt (29cm-11in) i. greenish brown pat.bronze

LIBERMAN, Alexander (1912-) American
£872 $1500   (12-Oct-91 SY.NY367/R) Chrome VI (24cm-9in) init.num.3/3 chrome-plated metal
£3634 $6250   (12-Oct-91 SY.NY305/R) Passage (29cm-11in) i.num.3/3 black pat.bronze
£33520 $60000   (12-Nov-91 CH.NY41/R) Gyre (361x422x325cm-142x166x128in) init.d.66 welded steel painted blk.

LICHTENSTEIN, Roy (1923-) American
£1221 $2234   (14-May-92 BG.P55/R) Sculpture en plexi (42cm-17in) s.num.160/200 multiple (F.FR 12000)
£16760 $30000   (13-Nov-91 CH.NY173/R) Brushstroke (66x107x4cm-26x42x2in) enamel steel
£22346 $40000   (12-Nov-91 CH.NY33/R) Small wall explosion (55x53x18cm-22x21x7in) s.d.65 num.4/6verso enamel on steel
£83799 $150000   (6-May-92 SY.NY24/R) Surrealist head (201x72x42cm-79x28x17in) s.num.1/6 d.86 painted bronze

LIEBERMANN, Ferdinand (1883-?) German
£4211 $7200   (13-Mar-92 FN.S1385/R) Female nude dancing (61cm-24in) s. dark green pat.bronze stepped socle (DM 12000)

LIEBMANN, Hans Harry (1876-?) German
£1440 $2606   (3-Dec-91 AB.S4565) Diana with bow and cows (83cm-33in) s. black pat
       bronze (S.KR 15000)
£1452 $2513   (2-Sep-91 BU.K118/R) Diana standing (59cm-23in) s. pat bronze marble base
       (D.KR 16500)

LIMBACH, Hans Jorg (1928-1990) Swiss
£6742 $12000   (29-Apr-92 G.Z100/R) Dancer (80cm-31in) s.d.1979 bronze (S.FR 18000)

LINDSAY, Norman Alfred Williams (1879-1970) Australian
£2558 $4886   (21-Jul-92 JRL.S169/R) Aphrodite (46cm-18in) num.8/10 bronze (A.D 6600)
£3295 $6293   (21-Jul-92 JRL.S174/R) The Balinese dancer (60cm-24in) bronze (A.D 8500)

LIPA (1907-1976) French
£1022 $1871   (3-Feb-92 HH.P55/R) Pingouin (47x20x7cm-19x8x3in) s.num.2/8 pat.bronze
       (F.FR 10000)

LIPCHITZ, Jacques (1891-1973) French
£2866 $5101   (27-Nov-91 LGB.P79/R) Nu (21x12cm-8x5in) s. bronze (F.FR 28000)
£3000 $5250   (23-Sep-91 S.SL406) Towards the new world (18x20cm-7x8in) s. num.2/1
       bronze cire perude Cast.Busato
£8475 $15000   (7-Nov-91 SY.NY164/R) Mother and child I (44cm-17in) i. num.5/7 st. brown
       pat.bronze
£16571 $29000   (25-Feb-92 SY.NY71 a/R) Study for Return of the Child (30cm-12in)
       s.thumbprint num.1/7 pat.bronze st.f.Modern Art
£31730 $56479   (28-Nov-91 FB.P12/R) Figure with guitar (19x26cm-7x10in) s.
       brn.pat.bronze (F.FR 310000)
£152542 $270000   (5-Nov-91 CH.NY49/R) Homme assis a la clarinette I (75cm-30in)
       s.i.num.2/7 green pat.bronze st.f.Modern Art

LIPCHITZ, Samuel (19/20th C) ?
£1400 $2492   (29-Oct-91 SWS2067/R) 1920'S figure, standing poised on right foot,
       holding ball and stick (37cm-15in) s. bronze ivory
£1800 $3204   (29-Oct-91 SWS2068/R) Figure of 1920's female juggler, holding three
       balls (34cm-13in) s. gilt-bronze ivory

LIPTON, Seymour (20th C) American
£16760 $30000   (7-May-92 SY.NY237/R) Viking (81cm-32in) nickel-silver on Monel metal

LIVI, G (?) French
£908 $1526   (27-Aug-91 GM.B1527) Scene galante d.1889 white marble (B.FR 55000)

LOBO, Balthazar (1911-) Spanish
£4587 $8532   (15-Jun-92 GL.P69 b) Femme revant (25x12x8cm-10x5x3in) s.num.1/8 brown
       pat.bronze (F.FR 45000)

LOMBARDI, Giovanni Battista (19/20th C) Italian
£35000 $62300   (29-Nov-91 S82) The surprised Egyptian bather (208cm-82in) s.d.1875
       marble incl.plinth with socle
£52000 $88920   (20-Mar-92 S80/R) The surprised bather (132x76cm-52x30in) s.d.1873 marble
       on column pair

LOMBARDO, Antonio I (style) (1458-1516) Italian
£35000 $67200   (8-Jul-92 PH98/R) Head of young woman (12cm-5in) bronze

LONGO, Robert (1953-) American
£4000 $7000   (27-Feb-92 CE.NY225/R) Swing (52x95x12cm-20x37x5in) cast aluminium
£5714 $10000   (27-Feb-92 CH.NY89/R) New York Athletic Club (96x122x35cm-38x48x14in)
       lacquer on cast aluminum bonding
£13295 $23000   (3-Oct-91 SY.NY123/R) American soldier (66x33x5cm-26x13x2in) s.num.1
       d.1977verso enamel on cast aluminium

LORCHER, Alfred (1875-1962) ?
£1228 $2100   (13-Mar-92 FN.S2548/R) Silen drunk (9cm-4in) d.1955-56 terracotta
       (DM 3500)
£1404 $2400   (13-Mar-92 FN.S2547/R) Two boys drunk (13x9x10cm-5x4x4in) d.1941-43
       bronze (DM 4000)
£2632 $4500   (13-Mar-92 FN.S2550/R) Seated girl plaiting her hair (15cm-6in) d.1923-24
       terracotta (DM 7500)
£2632 $4500   (13-Mar-92 FN.S2551/R) Female squatting (8cm-3in) d.1924 terracotta
       (DM 7500)

LORENZ (?) ?
£1058 $1884   (30-Apr-92 RAS.K1224) Woman with dog (33x36cm-13x14in) s. silvered metal
       green onyx base (D.KR 12000)

LORENZL (20th C) ?
£1200 $2292   (2-Jul-92 CSK75/R) Diana pulling back bow with two dogs running at her
       side (46cm-18in) silver pat.bronze on onyx base
£2000 $3400   (25-Oct-91 S370/R) The archer (58cm-23in) i. silvered cold painted bronze
       wood
£3000 $5730   (2-Jul-92 CSK101/R) Dancing nude balanced on foot with arms outflung and
       head thrust back (76cm-30in) s. silvered bronze on onyx columns
£3700 $6290   (25-Oct-91 S371/R) Female figure with hounds (35cm-14in) i.silvered
       pat.cold painted bronze marble

LORENZL, Josef (1928-) Austrian
£742 $1314   (5-Nov-91 GF.L426/R) Dancer (35cm-14in) s. pat.zinc ivory marble socle
                    (S.FR 1900)

LORRAIN, Fernand (after) (19th C) French
£914 $1600   (27-Sep-91 S.BM626) Figure of beggar (56cm-22in) i. bronze

LOVET-LORSKI, Boris (1891-?) Russian/American
£737 $1320   (14-Nov-91 GRO.B130/R) Prancing poodle i. silvered bronze
£35714 $65000   (28-May-92 CH.NY204 a/R) Melpomene (100cm-39in) s. marble
£41436 $75000   (5-Dec-91 SY.NY61/R) Polynesia (44cm-17in) i. slate

LOYER, Christophe (1956-) French?
£971 $1778   (3-Feb-92 HH.P61/R) L'exploration des profondeurs (90cm-35in) s.num.1/8
                    pat.bronze (F.FR 9500)

LUCCHESI, Bruno (19/20th C) American
£1453 $2600   (14-Nov-91 CE.NY263/R) Figure of girl washing windows (62cm-24in) i.
                    greenish brown pat.bronze
£2346 $4200   (14-Nov-91 CE.NY264/R) Orchard Street - group (46cm-18in) i. golden brown
                    pat.bronze

LUCHOW-NIELSEN, Henry (?) ?
£3737 $6502   (17-Sep-91 RAS.K150/R) Nude woman (165cm-65in) s. Cast.Grage, bronze
                    (D.KR 42000)

LUCKE, Carl August (elder) (17th C) German
£4800 $9216   (9-Jul-92 S240/R) Bust of nobleman, wearing military uniform (8cm-3in) s.
                    ivory

LUDLOW, Henry Stephen (1861-?) British
£2800 $5348   (16-Jul-92 CG54/R) Figure of Harry Vardon (22cm-9in) i.d.1905-6 bronze
                    ebonised plinth

LUGERTH, Ferdinand (fl.1885-1915) ?
£847 $1500   (13-Feb-92 SY.NY21/R) Figure of stag (56cm-22in) s. greenish-black
                    pat.bronze

LUNDBERG, Theodor (1852-1925) Swedish
£1514 $2740   (19-May-92 AB.S4556) Nude blowing bubbles (46cm-18in) s. green pat bronze
                    Cast.O Meyer (S.KR 16000)

LUNDGREN, Tyra (1897-1979) Swedish
£949 $1736   (13-May-92 BU.S242/R) Swan (50cm-20in) dark pat bronze Cast.H Bergman
                    (S.KR 10000)

LUTHER, Adolf (1912-1990) German
£7560 $13835   (2-Jun-92 L.K777/R) Untitled (92x92x9cm-36x36x4in) mirror boxes set of
                    four (DM 22000)

MACDONALD, Chris (1957-) American
£800 $1400   (27-Feb-92 CE.NY292/R) Untitled - Pasing No. 2 (45x56x29cm-18x22x11in)
                    s.d.3-4 1991 acrylic plywood

MACKARNESS, C (19/20th C) American
£1400 $2450   (20-Feb-92 CC165/R) Three terriers (21x29cm-8x11in) s.d.1912 bronze
                    Cast.Roman Bronze Works

MACKENNAL, Sir Edgar Bertram (1862-1931) Australian
£1500 $2670   (29-Nov-91 S217/R) Model for the Victoria 60 year Memorial (57cm-22in)
                    s.i.d.1897 brown pat.bronze i.f.E.Gruet Jeune
£3846 $7346   (19-Jul-92 SY.ME20/R) Bust of young woman (48cm-19in) plaster maquette
                    (A.D 10000)

MACMONNIES, Frederick William (1863-1937) American
£1111 $1900   (12-Mar-92 CH.NY114/R) Pan of Rohallion (26cm-10in) i.indis.d.1890 brown
                    pat.bronze st.f.E.Gruet
£1486 $2600   (26-Sep-91 CH.NY128/R) Bacchante and infant faun (39cm-15in) i. greenish
                    brown pat.bronze f.i.Roman Works NY
£2261 $4250   (18-Dec-91 SY.NY154/R) Bacchante and infant faun (40cm-16in) i.d.1899
                    green black pat. bronze
£6630 $12000   (6-Dec-91 CH.NY179/R) Boy and heron (69cm-27in) i. green brown pat.
                    bronze
£7143 $13000   (28-May-92 CH.NY86/R) Diana the huntress (78cm-31in) i.f.Jaboueuf and
                    Rouard bronze gr.br.pat.

MACNEIL, Hermon Atkins (1866-1947) American
£1955 $3500   (13-Nov-91 B.SF2658/R) Abraham Lincoln (71cm-28in) s. bronze f.st.Roman
                    Bronze Works

MADRASSI, Luca (1848-1919) Italian
£2000 $3560 (29-Nov-91 S175/R) Pax Libertas Mundi (88cm-35in) s.i. brown pat.bronze on green marble plinth
£2360 $4200 (30-Apr-92 CE.NY53/R) Pax Liberas Mundi (98cm-39in) i. natural pat.bronze

MAIGNAN, M (?) ?
£1287 $2200 (13-Mar-92 WOL.C1170/R) En peril (43cm-17in) s. bronze

MAILLARD, Auguste (1864-?) French
£791 $1400 (13-Feb-92 SY.NY2/R) Figure of boy with cat (62cm-24in) i. brown pat.bronze

MAILLOL, Aristide (1861-1944) French
£16949 $30000 (7-Nov-91 SY.NY109/R) Tete de Dina (25cm-10in) mono. st.num 1/6 light brown pat.bronze f.st.
£22000 $38060 (25-Mar-92 S22/R) Nu allonge (20x16cm-8x6in) mono.num.4/6 bronze Cast.Alexis Rudier
£35519 $65000 (13-May-92 SY.NY55/R) Grande femme assise, femme assise a la draperie (30cm-12in) mono.num.2/6 brown pat.bronze st.f.Alexis Rudier
£38251 $70000 (13-May-92 SY.NY54/R) Baigneuse a l'echarpe (34cm-13in) mono.num.3/6 green pat.bronze st.f.Alexis Rudier
£131148 $240000 (12-May-92 CH.NY112/R) Petite flore nue (66cm-26in) mono.num.5/6 green brown pat.bronze f.i.Rudier
£296610 $525000 (6-Nov-91 SY.NY30/R) Nymph (154cm-61in) mono.num.6/6 Cast.Alexis Rudier green pat.bronze
£1129944 $2000000 (6-Nov-91 SY.NY28/R) Monument a Paul Cezanne (226cm-89in) i.num.1/6 Cast.Georges Rudier, Paris lead
£1129944 $2000000 (6-Nov-91 SY.NY26/R) Les trois nymphes (157cm-62in) mono. green blk.pat.bronze

MALAUSSENA, Jean Pierre (1935-) French
£971 $1778 (5-Feb-92 FB.P184) La Grand Soeur (56cm-22in) s.num.1/8 green pat.bronze (F.FR 9500)

MALFRAY, Charles Alexandre (1887-1940) French
£4597 $8044 (24-Feb-92 ARC.P35/R) Sur les cimes de l'olympe (28x41x13cm-11x16x5in) s.num.1/8 i. green pat.bronze htd.gold (F.FR 45000)

MALISSARD, Georges (1877-1942) French
£2976 $5000 (1-Sep-91 PO.BA35) Biribi (42x52cm-17x20in) s.d.1926 bronze. Cast.Valsuani cire perdue

MAN-RAY (1890-1976) American
£877 $1500 (13-Mar-92 S.BM325/R) Herma (25cm-10in) s.i.num.145/350 d.1975 brass pat.bronze
£1322 $2352 (26-Nov-91 J.M271/R) Landscape with cow (49x69cm-19x27in) s.verso leather board (A.D 3000)
£2060 $3522 (21-Mar-92 AT.P106/R) Plume (15cm-6in) s.num.5/12 silver metal (F.FR 20000)
£4115 $7819 (24-Jun-92 FB.P76/R) Cadeau (16x9x10cm-6x4x4in) iron upholstery-tacks altuglass wood (F.FR 40000)
£4115 $7819 (24-Jun-92 FB.P75/R) Perpetual motif, Object to be destroyed, Indestructible object (23x11cm-9x4in) s.d.1970 num.11/40 metronome wood indicator (F.FR 40000)
£14124 $25000 (7-Nov-91 SY.NY210/R) Optical hopes and illusions (73cm-29in) i. num.st.5/9 wood rope magnifying glass
£19429 $34000 (25-Feb-92 SY.NY45/R) New York (42cm-17in) i.d.1917 num.1/9 bronze chrome plated metal
£28249 $50000 (6-Nov-91 CH.NY283/R) New York (41cm-16in) s.i.d.1917 st.init. silver with metal clamp

MANE KATZ (1894-1962) French
£1622 $3000 (8-Jun-92 GG.TA189/R) Young rabbi (44cm-17in) s.num.verso bronze
£5714 $10000 (26-Sep-91 SY.I36/R) Horse head (70x80cm-28x31in) s. bronze

MANOLO (1872-1945) Spanish
£3073 $5500 (9-May-92 CE.NY115/R) Maternidad (29cm-11in) s.i.num.3 rown pat.bronze st.Fundicion Bechini
£4362 $8113 (16-Jun-92 EP.M40/R) Maternidad (29cm-11in) s. terracotta (S.P 800000)

MANSHIP, Paul Howard (1885-1966) American
£7692 $14000 (28-May-92 CH.NY208/R) A shoebill stork (35cm-14in) i.f.Pressman Bauer bronze granite base
£8791 $16000 (27-May-92 SY.NY34/R) Abraham Lincoln, the Hoosier Youth (47cm-19in) i. green pat.bronze
£37088 $67500 (27-May-92 SY.NY92/R) Indian. Pronghorn antelope (35cm-14in) s.d.1914 greenish brown pat.bronze f.st. pair

MANTYNEN, Jussi (1886-1978) Finnish
£1518 $2778 (14-May-92 BU.S122/R) Seated lynx (28cm-11in) s.d.1923 dark pat bronze (S.KR 16000)
£1552 $2763 (1-Dec-91 HOR.H163) Lynx (11cm-4in) s.d.1950 bronze (F.M 12000)
£1613 $2952 (14-May-92 BU.S120/R) Elk preparing to fight (22cm-9in) s.d.1948 bronze (S.KR 17000)

MANTYNEN, Jussi (1886-1978) Finnish-cont.

£1708	$3125	(14-May-92 BU.S121/R) Lioness (38x13cm-15x5in) s.d.1957 brown pat bronze (S.KR 18000)
£2170	$3841	(5-Nov-91 BA.S264/R) Lynx (20cm-8in) s.d.1940 brown pat bronze (S.KR 23000)
£2642	$4675	(5-Nov-91 BA.S263/R) Female elk and calf (32cm-13in) s.d.1930 gold pat bronze (S.KR 28000)
£3239	$5669	(25-Sep-91 HOR.H72) Lynx (20cm-8in) bronze (F.M 23000)
£3416	$6250	(14-May-92 BU.S123/R) Cranes (42cm-17in) s. green pat bronze Cast.A Pettersson (S.KR 36000)
£3793	$6675	(12-Apr-92 HOR.H177) Lynx (34cm-13in) s.d.1936 bronze (F.M 30000)
£4744	$8681	(14-May-92 BU.S119/R) Excelsior (55cm-22in) s.d.1940 green pat bronze (S.KR 50000)
£7780	$14237	(14-May-92 BU.S117/R) Coquet lynx (47cm-19in) s.d.1931 black granite (S.KR 82000)

MANZONI, Piero (1933-1963) Italian

| £11585 | $20621 | (26-Nov-91 SY.MI194/R) Pacco (30x30cm-12x12in) packing paper string wax seals on canvas (I.L 25000000) |

MANZU, Giacomo (1908-1991) Italian

£23752	$41329	(14-Apr-92 F.M209/R) Striptease (62cm-24in) s. bronze (I.L 52000000)
£24324	$45000	(12-Jun-92 SY.NY163/R) Sedia (33cm-13in) bronze br.pat.
£39548	$70000	(6-Nov-91 CH.NY310/R) Busto di Inge (50cm-20in) st.sig. green pat.bronze
£62147	$110000	(6-Nov-91 CH.NY309/R) Ballerina (65cm-26in) st.sig. brown pat.bronze i.Fonderia MAF Milano
£62842	$115000	(13-May-92 CH.NY287/R) Pittore e modella (55x63x28cm-22x25x11in) st.sig. brown pat.bronze
£64972	$115000	(7-Nov-91 SY.NY213/R) Bust of Inge (82cm-32in) st. brownish gold pat.bronze

MARATTI, Francesco (style) (17th C) Italian

| £23000 | $44160 | (9-Jul-92 SY.S204/R) Angels kneeling on banks of clouds, in prayer and arms clasped to chest (40cm-16in) terracotta pair |

MARCH, Sidney (19/20th C) British

| £800 | $1368 | (20-Mar-92 S179/R) Study for Europa and the bull (29cm-11in) s. brown pat.bronze |
| £6000 | $10500 | (20-Feb-92 C164/R) Field Marshall Lord Kitchener (121cm-48in) s.d.1911 bronze |

MARCKS, Gerhard (1889-) ?

£962	$1636	(25-Oct-91 BM.B1854/R) Swan feeding (7cm-3in) s.num.5/10 bronze st.f.Barth Berlin (DM 2800)
£1371	$2400	(23-Sep-91 S.SL405) Prayer (28cm-11in) gilt pat.bronze st.Barth BLN stone plinth
£2560	$4659	(30-May-92 VG.B263/R) Teacher with pupil (35cm-14in) s. brown pat.bronze st.f.Schmacke Dusseldorf (DM 7500)
£4467	$8265	(12-Jun-92 HN.H560/R) Kleine verhullte Eos (80x16x15cm-31x6x6in) mono gold brown pat.bronze (DM 13000)
£6143	$11181	(26-May-92 KF.M1042/R) Rider trotting (18x19x6cm-7x7x2in) d.1934 zinc (DM 18000)
£10309	$17526	(25-Oct-91 BM.B1854 a/R) Graziella, female nude (98cm-39in) mono. bronze st.f.Barth Rinteln (DM 30000)
£13372	$23000	(12-Oct-91 SY.NY173/R) Kleine drei grazen (58cm-23in) mono.num.2/8 gold black pat.bronze f.st.Barth

MARCOUSSIS, Louis (1883-1941) French

| £30286 | $53000 | (25-Feb-92 CH.NY41/R) Objet III (71x58cm-28x23in) s.d.27 oil sand glass |

MARCUSE, Rudolf (1878-?) German

| £1474 | $2683 | (25-May-92 WK.M834/R) Tennis player (39x39x17cm-15x15x7in) s.d.1910 gold pat.bronze on marble socle (DM 4320) |
| £1813 | $3100 | (13-Mar-92 WOL.C1181/R) Two semi-clad women (43x69cm-17x27in) s. marble |

MARCY, Gaspard (after) (?) ?

| £5263 | $9000 | (13-Mar-92 WOL.C1094/R) The Rape of Orithea by Boreas (91cm-36in) bronze dk.br.pat. |

MARIN (?) ?

| £7010 | $12128 | (26-Mar-92 PIC.P61/R) Buste de jeune bacchante (26x11cm-10x4in) terracotta on marble/bronze socle (F.FR 68000) |

MARIN, Joseph Charles (1759-1834) French

| £7087 | $12331 | (19-Sep-91 GK.Z527) Nude nymph leaning on wine barrel and satyr (28cm-11in) s.d.1790 terracotta (S.FR 18000) |

MARIN, Joseph Charles (attrib) (1759-1834) French

| £5155 | $8918 | (27-Mar-92 CN.P98/R) Stauette de Flore (51cm-20in) painted terrracotta (F.FR 50000) |

MARINI, Marino (1901-1980) Italian

| £8000 | $15280 | (1-Jul-92 S240/R) Piccola figura (18cm-7in) bronze |
| £20571 | $36000 | (25-Feb-92 SY.NY42/R) Bust de Grit Kallin Fischer (39cm-15in) st.sig. brown-gold pat.bronze |

MARINI, Marino (1901-1980) Italian-cont.
£21858 $40000   (14-May-92 SY.NY290/R) Composition (40cm-16in) init.num.1/6 black green
    pat.bronze
£36000 $68760   (1-Jul-92 S221/R) Composition (40cm-16in) st.inits. partly painted bronze
£54477 $96970   (29-Apr-92 F.F238/R) Composizione (21x19x40cm-8x7x16in) d.1956/1957 mono
    polychrome bronze (I.L 120000000)
£98870 $175000   (7-Nov-91 SY.NY186/R) Cavallo e cavaliere (41cm-16in) st.init. grey brown
    pat.bronze

MARINO DI TEANA, Francesco (1920-) Italian
£1804 $3121   (29-Mar-92 P.V110/R) Untitled (32x18cm-13x7in) st.sig.num.2/5 d.72-88
    steel (F.FR 17500)

MARINUS, Ancieto (19th C) Spanish
£882 $1500   (22-Oct-91 CE.NY36/R) Seated figure of Diego Velaquez (41cm-16in) i. rich
    brown pat.bronze

MARION, R (1934-) French
£2616 $4499   (7-Oct-91 RY.P83/R) Hatchepsout (40x20x18cm-16x8x7in) Balarue marble
    (F.FR 26000)

MARIOTON, E (1854-1925) French
£824 $1400   (9-Aug-91 GC.M208) Campesina Oteando el Horizonte (64cm-25in) bronze

MARIOTON, Eugene (1854-1925) French
£805 $1400   (15-Apr-92 B.SF3204) Standing figure with toga and one foot on pile of
    weapons (69cm-27in) i.c.1900 brown pat.bronze
£1118 $1900   (25-Oct-91 S.W2651/R) Goddess of music (81cm-32in) s. brown pat.bronze
£2000 $3420   (20-Mar-92 S157/R) Viking family (81cm-32in) s. brown pat.bronze
£2000 $3420   (20-Mar-92 S103/R) Fascinator (84cm-33in) s.i. brown pat.bronze
£2059 $3500   (22-Oct-91 CE.NY32/R) Figure of nymph playing pipes (81cm-32in) i.
    greenish brown pat.bronze
£2494 $4364   (18-Feb-92 DUR.M433/R) Fascinator (84cm-33in) s.i. bronze (S.P 450000)
£3200 $5472   (20-Mar-92 S186/R) The pipe player (81cm-32in) s.num.175 brown pat.bronze

MARIOTON, Eugene (after) (1854-1925) French
£840 $1470   (24-Feb-92 SY.J757) Figure of Diana, naked huntress looking dexter, right
    hand to breast (63cm-25in) pale brown pat.bronze (SA.R 4200)

MARQUET, Rene-Paul (1875-?) French
£3136 $5707   (14-Dec-91 BOD.P430) Pageboy with greyhounds (37cm-15in) s. bronze ivory
    marble socle st.foundry (DM 9000)

MARROY (20th C) Belgian?
£1003 $1704   (22-Oct-91 C.A54/R) Hernia (26cm-10in) s.d.1975 bronze (B.FR 60000)

MARSY, Gaspard and FLAMEN, Anselme (after) (17th C) French
£52486 $95000   (20-May-92 SY.NY53/R) The Rape of Orithyia by Boreas. The Rape of
    Proserpine by Pluto (78cm-31in) 2nd.sculp after Girardon bronze on
    Boulle base

MARTEL, Jan and Joel (1896-?) French
£1616 $2861   (24-Apr-92 CN.P315) Christ (77x33cm-30x13in) s. silver pat.bronze
    Cast.Valsuani cire perdue (F.FR 16000)
£3593 $6468   (20-Nov-91 CN.P72/R) Femme au liver (145cm-57in) s. stone (F.FR 35000)

MARTIN, Etienne (1913-) French
£2567 $4620   (19-Nov-91 FB.P158/R) Petit nu (25cm-10in) s.d.1935verso bronze
    (F.FR 25000)

MARTINI, Arturo (1889-1947) Italian
£4139 $7409   (14-Nov-91 F.M31/R) Deposizione (14x21x13cm-6x8x5in) s. terracotta
    (I.L 9000000)
£9282 $17450   (19-Dec-91 F.M138/R) La Scoccombrina (32x23x18cm-13x9x7in) s.num.3/4
    bronze (I.L 20000000)
£11602 $21812   (19-Dec-91 F.M165/R) La Fede - La Luce (69x59x70cm-27x23x28in) bronze
    (I.L 25000000)

MARTINS, Maria (1900-) Brazilian
£6630 $12000   (19-May-92 SY.NY104/R) Samba flows in her veins (133cm-52in) s.d.1941
    jacaranda wood

MARTINUS, Elsa (20th C) Dutch/American
£2632 $4500   (13-Mar-92 DM.D1009/R) Boy with a towell wrapped around his waist
    (112cm-44in) bronze

MASCHERINI, Marcello (1906-1983) Italian
£2529 $4527   (14-Nov-91 F.M19/R) Figura femminile (43cm-17in) s. bronze (I.L 5500000)

MASSON, Andre (1896-1988) French
£3608 $6242   (23-Mar-92 GL.P185/R) Bacchantes (11x12x4cm-4x5x2in) s.num.4/6 pat.bronze
    Cast.Valsuani (F.FR 35000)

MASSON, Jules-Edmond (1871-1932) French
£1075 $2000   (16-Jun-92 RO.BA120) Le grand cerf (52cm-20in) pat.bronze

MASSON, Jules-Edmond (1871-1932) French-cont.

£1461	$2600	(30-Apr-92 CE.NY84/R) Group of two deer (34cm-13in) i. reddish-brown pat.bronze
£3933	$7000	(30-Apr-92 CE.NY83/R) Figure of stag (78cm-31in) i. rich brown pat.bronze

MASTROIANNI, Umberto (1910-) Italian

£3787	$6741	(30-Nov-91 FB.P8/R) Sans titre (62cm-24in) bronze base white marble (F.FR 37000)
£15338	$27762	(3-Dec-91 F.R254/R) Senza titolo (90x90cm-35x35in) s.d.1961 bronze (I.L 33000000)

MATARE, Ewald (1887-1965) German

£5155	$9433	(3-Jun-92 L.K310/R) Zeichen eines Pferdes (9x9cm-4x4in) st.mono 1/3 gold brown pat.bronze (DM 15000)
£5155	$8763	(26-Oct-91 WK.M435/R) Maulwurfskuh (7x11x5cm-3x4x2in) mono.c.1936 brown pat.bronze (DM 15000)
£6873	$12715	(12-Jun-92 HN.H571/R) Eingekauertes Rind I (9x15x5cm-4x6x2in) mono brown pat.bronze (DM 20000)

MATHIESON (?) ?

£800	$1528	(2-Jul-92 CSK6/R) Naked woman kneeling face down (46cm-18in) s. pat.bronze marble base

MATISSE, Henri (1869-1954) French

£5670	$9809	(23-Mar-92 GL.P177/R) La faune (14x12x9cm-6x5x4in) init.num.9/10 blk.pat.bronze Cast.Valsuani (F.FR 55000)
£8000	$15280	(30-Jun-92 C143/R) Tete de faune (14cm-6in) init. num.4/10 brown pat.bronze f.st.C Valsuani
£8743	$16000	(11-May-92 CH.NY5/R) Petit torse accroupi (8cm-3in) init. num.1/10 dark brown pat.bronze
£20809	$36000	(2-Oct-91 SY.NY37/R) Small head with pompadour (13cm-5in) i.num.2/10 dark brown pat.bronze
£37158	$68000	(13-May-92 CH.NY217/R) Nu assis appuye sur les mains (24cm-9in) init. num.3/10 brown pat.bronze
£131148	$240000	(13-May-92 SY.NY13/R) Jeanette I (33cm-13in) init.num.3 brown pat.bronze st.f.C.Valsuani
£131148	$240000	(13-May-92 SY.NY11/R) Nu assis, bras sur la tete (35cm-14in) st.init.num.1/10 black pat.bronze st.f.Valsuani

MATTA (1911-) Chilean

£6630	$12000	(19-May-92 SY.NY195/R) Personnage I (55cm-22in) s.num.1/6 black pat.bronze st.f.Susse

MAULIN, E (?) French?

£1744	$3000	(18-Oct-91 DM.D1276/R) Classical female nude (102cm-40in) bronze

MAVAMBU, N'Dangani (1959-) ?

£1534	$2807	(3-Feb-92 HH.P47/R) Desir (62x28x20cm-24x11x8in) s.num.1/8 blk.pat.bronze Cast.Clementi (F.FR 15000)

MAYER, C (?) ?

£5495	$10000	(27-May-92 SY.NY37/R) Enchained slave (69cm-27in) s. brown pat.bronze f.st.Janitschek-Ruquet NY

MBOMIO, Leandro (1938-) Guinean

£4433	$7758	(19-Feb-92 DUR.M1081/R) Maternidad (173cm-68in) bronze incl.pedestal (S.P 800000)

McCARTAN, Edward (1879-1953) American

£3757	$6800	(6-Dec-91 CH.NY181/R) Figure of Pan (38cm-15in) i.f.Roman Bronze Works green brown pat. bronze

McCOLLUM, Allan (1944-) French

£5587	$10000	(5-May-92 CH.NY111/R) Colored surrogates (62x173x4cm-24x68x2in) s.d.1986 num.1/5-5/5 acrylic enamel hydrostone
£6704	$12000	(7-May-92 SY.NY179/R) Coloured surrogates (51x172cm-20x68in) s.d.1986 num.8619 five enamel acrylic plaster
£7821	$14000	(14-Nov-91 SY.NY258/R) Perfect vehicle (50cm-20in) s.i.d.88 enamel five cast plaster units
£8939	$16000	(5-May-92 CH.NY106/R) Perfect vehicle (203x91x91cm-80x36x36in) MoorGlo on concrete
£8939	$16000	(13-Nov-91 CH.NY303/R) Colou7red surrogates (51x184x4cm-20x72x2in) s.num.1/5-5/5verso acrylic enamel hydrostone 5
£10056	$18000	(7-May-92 SY.NY177/R) Perfect vehicles (49cm-19in) s.d.1987 num. five cast plaster enamel paint
£11173	$20000	(13-Nov-91 CH.NY331/R) Perfect vehicle (203x91x91cm-80x36x36in) MoorGlo on concrete
£13873	$24000	(3-Oct-91 SY.NY147/R) 25 perfect vehicles (45x122x122cm-18x48x48in) each s.num.d.1987base 25 plaster enamel wood
£30726	$55000	(14-Nov-91 SY.NY202/R) Surrogates s.d. num.verso 240 works cast plaster enamel

McKENZIE, Robert Tait (1867-1938) American

£17143	$30000	(25-Sep-91 SY.NY108 a/R) Plunger (67cm-26in) i. brown pat.bronze f.i.Roman Bronze Works N.Y

McWILLIAM, F E (1909-) British

£1800	$3330	(11-Jun-92 C144/R) Legs professional (43cm-17in) init. num.1/5 gold pat.bronze
£1900	$3629	(16-Jul-92 B180/R) Judo wrestlers (53cm-21in) init.num.1/5 br.pat. bronze
£2000	$3700	(11-Jun-92 C143/R) Crossed legs (42cm-17in) init.num.3/5 dark gold pat.bronze f.st.Fiorini
£4200	$7434	(8-Nov-91 C367/R) Girl rising (28cm-11in) init.num.3/5 brn.pat.bronze polished
£5000	$8850	(8-Nov-91 C351/R) Standing relief VI (76cm-30in) init.num.1/3 brn.pat.bronze

MEAD, Larkin Goldsmith (1835-1910) American

| £2299 | $4000 | (15-Apr-92 SY.NY4/R) Venezia (64cm-25in) i. white marble |

MEADMORE, Clement (1929-) American?

| £806 | $1500 | (21-Jun-92 SY.ME26) Sophisticated lady (25x20x5cm-10x8x2in) d.1977 bronze (A.D 2000) |
| £838 | $1500 | (9-May-92 CE.NY310/R) Untitled (33x17x6cm-13x7x2in) s.num.2/12 brown pat.bronze st.f.Morris Singer |

MEADOWS, Bernard (1915-) British

| £2200 | $4070 | (11-Jun-92 C131/R) Crab (46cm-18in) black pat.bronze |
| £2400 | $4440 | (11-Jun-92 C129/R) Mother and child (38cm-15in) black pat.bronze |

MEIER-DENNINGHOFF, Brigitte (1923-) German

| £2982 | $5368 | (19-Nov-91 L.K940/R) Ast I (33x31x27cm-13x12x11in) mono.i.d.1978 metal brass pewter slate socle (DM 8500) |
| £5965 | $10737 | (19-Nov-91 L.K939/R) Untitled (24x11x4cm-9x4x2in) mono.i.num.62/2 pewter brass slate socle (DM 17000) |

MELOTTI, Fausto (1901-1986) Italian

| £10195 | $18146 | (29-Nov-91 F.F147/R) Composizione (60cm-24in) copper (I.L 22000000) |

MENCONI, D (19th C) Italian

| £2500 | $4300 | (10-Oct-91 FA.PH788/R) Bust of George Washington (76x53cm-30x21in) s.d.1862 marble |
| £3600 | $6552 | (27-May-92 SWS366/R) Figure of Andromeda, standing scantily draped and manacled to outcrop (105cm-41in) s.d.1879 white marble |

MENE, P J (1810-1879) French

£838	$1500	(6-May-92 B.P101/R) After hunt in Scotland (28x38cm-11x15in) s. bronze
£874	$1600	(3-Jun-92 D.NY672/R) Figure of horse tied to tree (36cm-14in) s.d.1877 bronze
£1202	$2200	(3-Jun-92 D.NY730/R) Scotsman holding quarry, hunting dog by side (46cm-18in) s. bronze
£1500	$2865	(30-Jun-92 PH74 a) Iron figure of ram (24cm-9in) s. black pat.bronze
£2200	$4224	(8-Jul-92 CSK4/R) Mare and rearing foal (49cm-19in) i. bronze

MENE, Pierre Jules (1810-1879) French

£698	$1200	(16-Oct-91 CH.NY136/R) An Elk feeding (38cm-15in) i. brn.pat.bronze wooden base
£824	$1500	(13-Dec-91 S.W3024/R) Setter (15x33cm-6x13in) s. bronze
£850	$1454	(20-Mar-92 S43/R) Tethered bloodhound (24cm-9in) s. brown pat.bronze
£872	$1500	(16-Oct-91 CH.NY139/R) Setter pointing (17cm-7in) i. brn.pat.bronze
£900	$1602	(29-Nov-91 S60/R) Whippets playing (16cm-6in) s. black, red/brown pat.bronze
£900	$1539	(20-Mar-92 S37/R) Greyhound and King Charles spaniel (15cm-6in) s. brown pat.bronze
£900	$1539	(20-Mar-92 S39/R) Greyhound and whippet (15cm-6in) s. brown pat.bronze
£935	$1598	(21-Mar-92 KV.L211) Greyhound (26x38cm-10x15in) s. bronze gr.pat. marble socle (B.FR 55000)
£937	$1639	(30-Mar-92 ZZ.F161/R) Le cheval cabre (28x36x18cm-11x14x7in) s. brn.pat.bronze (F.FR 9000)
£1000	$1780	(29-Nov-91 S29/R) Chasse au lapin (20cm-8in) s. brown pat.bronze
£1000	$1780	(29-Nov-91 S29/R) Retriever standing on bank (21cm-8in) s. brown pat.bronze
£1011	$1800	(30-Apr-92 CE.NY82/R) Equestrian group of eastern hunter with game (46cm-18in) i. reddish brown pat.bronze
£1017	$1800	(13-Feb-92 S.W2786/R) Gone to earth (20x36cm-8x14in) s. brn.pat.bronze
£1050	$1869	(29-Nov-91 S12) Two whippets (15cm-6in) s. brown pat.bronze
£1149	$2000	(13-Sep-91 SY.NY113/R) Panther attacking crocodile (18x42cm-7x17in) i. golden pat.bronze on red marble base
£1150	$2047	(29-Nov-91 S40/R) Retriever (14cm-6in) s. brown pat.bronze
£1250	$2225	(29-Nov-91 S10) Whippet and King Charles Spaniel (16cm-6in) s. dk.brown pat.bronze
£1337	$2300	(16-Oct-91 CH.NY135/R) Two foxes fighting over a pheasant (18cm-7in) i.d.1865 brn.pat.bronze
£1361	$2409	(5-Nov-91 GGL.L2/R) Cheval a la barriere (38cm-15in) s.base pat.bronze dim.length (F.FR 13500)
£1437	$2500	(13-Sep-91 SY.NY114/R) Morrocan falconer (67cm-26in) i.d.1873 brown pat.bronze
£1500	$2565	(10-Mar-92 PH77/R) Huntswoman (24cm-9in) bronze
£1500	$2565	(20-Mar-92 S50/R) Mare and foal (16cm-6in) s. brown pat.bronze
£1570	$2700	(10-Oct-91 FA.PH781/R) Four dogs attacking wild boar (46cm-18in) bronze
£1600	$2848	(29-Nov-91 S41/R) Pointer and retriever (13cm-5in) s. brown pat.bronze

MENE, Pierre Jules (1810-1879) French-cont.

£1914	$3502	(13-May-92 FER.M216/R) El cazador (49cm-19in) s. pat.bronze (S.P 350000)
£2000	$3560	(29-Nov-91 S21/R) Cheval a la barriere (29cm-11in) s. brown pat.bronze
£2700	$4617	(20-Mar-92 S45/R) The stag hunt (38x70cm-15x28in) s.i. brown pat.bronze st.f.Suss Frs Edts
£2941	$5000	(25-Oct-91 S.W2634/R) Mare and foal (46cm-18in) s. golden brown pat.bronze
£3600	$6408	(29-Nov-91 S19) Vainquer du Derby (42cm-17in) s. brown pat.bronze
£3696	$6653	(20-Nov-91 CN.P76/R) L'accolade (33cm-13in) s. pat.bronze (F.FR 36000)
£3867	$7000	(5-Dec-91 SY.NY64/R) Horse and jockey (42cm-17in) i. golden-brown pat.bronze st.f.Susse Freres
£4000	$6840	(20-Mar-92 S23/R) Mare and foal (46cm-18in) s. brown pat.bronze
£4500	$8010	(29-Nov-91 S18) Vanquer du Derby (42cm-17in) s.i.d.1863 brown pat.bronze on wooden plinth
£4800	$8688	(21-May-92 C32/R) The Accolade, Arab mare and stallion with necks interlocked (34cm-13in) s.c.1850 bronze

MENE, Pierre Jules (after) (1810-1879) French

£824	$1500	(13-Dec-91 DM.D2241) Stallion near fence (28cm-11in) bronze
£904	$1600	(13-Feb-92 S.W2787/R) Derby winner (74cm-29in) bears sig. brn.pat.bronze wood base
£1038	$1900	(5-Jun-92 SY.NY109/R) Deux chiennes (24x44cm-9x17in) i. bronze br.pat.

MERCIE, Marius Jean Antonin (1845-1916) French

£1392	$2380	(9-Mar-92 AT.P281) David vainqueur de Goliath (75cm-30in) s. brn.gold pat.bronze Cast.Barbedienne (F.FR 13500)
£1700	$2907	(20-Mar-92 S138/R) David with the head of Goliath (74cm-29in) s.num.82 brown pat.bronze st.f.F.Barbedienne
£1900	$3249	(20-Mar-92 S145/R) David with the head of Goliath (74cm-29in) s. brown pat.bronze i.F.Barbedienne Fondeur
£2000	$3420	(20-Mar-92 S128/R) David avant le combat (80cm-31in) s. brown pat.bronze i.f.Barbedienne Paris
£2300	$3933	(10-Mar-92 PH81/R) David after combat standing naked resting one foot on head of Goliath (44cm-17in) s. brown pat.bronze i.f.Barbedienne Paris
£2600	$4628	(29-Nov-91 S117/R) David apres le combat (91cm-36in) s. brown pat.bronze i.f.F.Barbedienne
£3093	$5289	(9-Mar-92 AT.P282 b) David vainqueur de Goliath (46cm-18in) s. brn.pat.bronze Cast.Barbedienne (F.FR 30000)
£3311	$5993	(23-May-92 KV.L221/R) Gloria Victis (104x60cm-41x24in) s.f.Barbedienne bronze gr.br.pat. (B.FR 200000)
£3600	$6156	(20-Mar-92 S155/R) David with the head of Goliath (75cm-30in) s.i.brown parcel gilt pat.bronze i.F.Barbedienne
£5233	$9000	(9-Oct-91 RO.BA51/R) David Vainqueur (110cm-43in) s. pat.bronze f.F.Barbedienne
£6137	$10495	(12-Mar-92 RAS.V403/R) Gloria Victis (104cm-41in) s. pat.bronze Cast.F.Barbedienne (D.KR 68000)
£7692	$14000	(28-May-92 SY.NY109/R) Gloria Victis (109cm-43in) i. brown pat.bronze gilt f.i.Barbedienne
£12000	$21360	(29-Nov-91 S143/R) Gloria Victis (122cm-48in) s.num.935 brown/gilt pat.bronze i.f.Barbedienne
£14000	$23940	(20-Mar-92 S158/R) Gloria Victis (123cm-48in) s.num.902 parcel gilt pat.bronze i.F.Barbedienne
£25000	$44500	(29-Nov-91 S144/R) Gloria Victis (250cm-98in) s.i. brown/gilt pat.bronze incl.pedestal

MERCULIANO, Giacomo (1859-?) French

| £1500 | $2565 | (20-Mar-92 S1/R) Lioness on rock (38cm-15in) s. green pat.bronze marble |

MERRIFIELD, Tom (20th C) Australian

£800	$1392	(17-Sep-91 PH59) Terry Gilbert (30cm-12in) init. num.5/30 bronze
£800	$1392	(17-Sep-91 PH58) Julia en arabesque (29cm-11in) init. num.5/30 bronze
£1100	$1925	(27-Sep-91 C40/R) Anthony Dowell (43cm-17in) s.i.num.3/10 blk.pat.bronze
£1400	$2506	(14-Jan-92 PH145) L'arabesque (63cm-25in) s.num.1/9 brown pat.bronze
£1900	$3325	(27-Sep-91 C39/R) Faune (38cm-15in) s.i.num.6/10 blk.pat.bronze
£2400	$4200	(27-Sep-91 C37/R) John Curry (46cm-18in) s.i.num.1/10 blk.pat.bronze length
£2400	$4200	(27-Sep-91 C41/R) Anthony Dowell (28cm-11in) s.i.num.2/10 blk.pat.bronze
£4000	$7000	(27-Sep-91 C38/R) Natalia Makarowa (46cm-18in) s.i.num.6/10 blk.pat.bronze

MESSER, Guido (1941-) Argentinian

| £982 | $1680 | (13-Mar-92 FN.S2562/R) State visit (37x15x133cm-15x6x52in) painted bronze steel on high socle (DM 2800) |
| £982 | $1680 | (13-Mar-92 FN.S2563) Family (15x31x134cm-6x12x53in) s.i.d.1969 painted bronze india rubber on socle (DM 2800) |

MESSINA, Francesco (1900-?) Italian

£7358	$13171	(14-Nov-91 F.M124/R) San Sebastiano (64cm-25in) s. bronze (I.L 16000000)
£9211	$16765	(9-Dec-91 CH.R95/R) Aurelia (59cm-23in) s. green pat.bronze (I.L 20000000)
£14256	$25519	(14-Nov-91 F.M114/R) Vittoria (34cm-13in) s.d.1923 bronze (I.L 31000000)

MESTROVIC, Ivan (1883- ?) Balkan

| £6951 | $12373 | (28-Nov-91 D.V171/R) Figure of girl, possibly from Kosovo (37cm-15in) mono. dark pat.bronze wooden socle (A.S 140000) |

METZLER, Kurt Laurenz (1941-) Swiss
£787 $1354   (16-Oct-91 G.Z34/R) Standing figure (95cm-37in) mono.d.1982 metal (S.FR 2000)

MEUNIER, C (19th C) Belgian
£1408 $2549   (3-Dec-91 FN.S3452) Fisherman (48cm-19in) s. dark green pat.bronze (DM 4000)

MEUNIER, Constantin (1831-1905) Belgian
£1271 $2250   (13-Feb-92 SY.NY6/R) Minor on horse (61cm-24in) i. dark greenish-black pat.bronze f.st.Lefshoul
£1337 $2272   (22-Oct-91 C.A55) Miner with a shovel (48cm-19in) s. bronze (B.FR 80000)
£2326 $4000   (16-Oct-91 CH.NY151/R) The Hammersmith (48cm-19in) i. Cast.Verbeyot Bruxelles brn.pat.bronze

MEYER, Marcus (-1732) Dutch?
£5500 $10010   (12-Dec-91 S256/R) Bust of young woman, allegorical of spring (65cm-26in) s.d.1731 marble

MICHELANGELO (after) (1475-1564) Italian
£1724 $3000   (13-Sep-91 SY.NY31) Figure of Moses (71cm-28in) brown pat.bronze
£3600 $6264   (17-Sep-91 PH238/R) The dying slave (151cm-59in) bronze s.F.Barbedienne Paris

MIDDLE RHINE SCHOOL (?) German
£11000 $21120   (8-Jul-92 PH75/R) Crucifixion with six horsemen, Mary and St John and other figures (31cm-12in) wood

MILANESE, Rocco (1852-?) Italian
£2286 $4000   (20-Feb-92 SY.NY152/R) Nymph (80cm-31in) i. white marble

MILLER, Carol (1933-) American/Mexican
£1934 $3500   (18-May-92 CH.NY103/R) Pantera (36cm-14in) s. dark green pat.bronze
£2222 $4000   (19-Nov-91 CH.NY103/R) Mixcoatl y su perro (59cm-23in) s. dark green pat.bronze

MILLES, Carl (1875-1955) American
£1423 $2604   (14-May-92 BU.S116/R) The water carrier (11cm-4in) s. brown pat bronze Cast.H Bergman (S.KR 15000)
£1711 $3063   (16-Nov-91 FAL.M214/R) Girl and cat (21cm-8in) s. bronze (S.KR 18000)
£1749 $3323   (24-Jun-92 AT.P223) Petite paysanne (25cm-10in) s.num.128 brown-green pat.bronze (F.FR 17000)
£2087 $3820   (14-May-92 BU.S115/R) Horse (22cm-9in) s. dark pat bronze (S.KR 22000)
£2486 $4500   (5-Dec-91 SY.NY25/R) The milk carrier (22cm-9in) i. brown pat.bronze i.f.Holland,Herman Bergman
£2762 $5000   (5-Dec-91 SY.NY21/R) Playing elephants (20cm-8in) i. golden brown pat.bronze
£2762 $5000   (5-Dec-91 SY.NY11/R) Girl with cat (21cm-8in) i. brown pat.bronze
£2762 $5000   (5-Dec-91 SY.NY12/R) The female beggar (30cm-12in) i. brown pat.bronze i.f.Andro
£2879 $5211   (3-Dec-91 AB.S4567/R) Female head (35cm-14in) s.num.7-12, green pat bronze (S.KR 30000)
£3019 $5404   (7-May-92 RAS.S63/R) Jacob's fight with the angel (29x19x18cm-11x7x7in) green pat bronze (S.KR 32000)
£3039 $5500   (5-Dec-91 SY.NY40/R) Hunting dogs (21cm-8in) i.st. green pat.bronze
£3039 $5500   (5-Dec-91 SY.NY36/R) Boy with two fish - a fountain (33cm-13in) i.num.1-19 green pat.bronze st.f.H.Bergman
£3591 $6500   (5-Dec-91 SY.NY16/R) Family against the wind (41cm-16in) i. brown pat.bronze
£3591 $6500   (5-Dec-91 SY.NY20/R) American bison (37cm-15in) i. brown pat.bronze i.f.Herman Bergman
£4144 $7500   (5-Dec-91 SY.NY27/R) Horse being watered (11cm-4in) i. brown pat.bronze i.f.Herman Bergman
£4144 $7500   (5-Dec-91 SY.NY1/R) Nach dem cafe (32cm-13in) i. brown pat.bronze st.f.PGB
£4396 $8000   (28-May-92 CH.NY207/R) Boar (25cm-10in) st.sig. bronze green pat.
£4696 $8500   (5-Dec-91 SY.NY15/R) Girl with apple (33cm-13in) reddish brown pat.bronze i.f.Herman Bergman
£4730 $8562   (19-May-92 AB.S5151/R) Jonah and the whale (49cm-19in) s. green pat bronze incl.stone base (S.KR 50000)
£4972 $9000   (5-Dec-91 SY.NY6/R) Eagle on globe (32cm-13in) i.d.1947 green pat.bronze st.f.H.Bergman
£4972 $9000   (5-Dec-91 SY.NY9/R) Tarantella (34cm-13in) i. black pat.bronze
£5249 $9500   (5-Dec-91 SY.NY23/R) Female bust, detail of sunshine (20cm-8in) i. green pat.bronze st.f.L.Rasmussen
£5660 $10132   (7-May-92 RAS.S49/R) Europa (57x18x4cm-22x7x2in) green pat bronze (S.KR 60000)
£5676 $10274   (19-May-92 AB.S5150/R) Poseidon (59cm-23in) s. green pat bronze Cast.E Pettersson incl.base (S.KR 60000)
£6415 $11483   (7-May-92 RAS.S62/R) Dancer with plaits (25x15x8cm-10x6x3in) white marble (S.KR 68000)
£6906 $12500   (5-Dec-91 SY.NY4/R) The serpentine dancer (37cm-15in) i. brown pat.bronze st.f.H.Bergman
£7191 $12943   (19-Nov-91 GO.G313/R) Poseidon (55cm-22in) s. pat bronze (S.KR 75000)

MILLES, Carl (1875-1955) American-cont.

£8157	$14765	(3-Dec-91 AB.S4566/R) Dutch fisherwomen in the wind (24x40cm-9x16in) s. dark pat bronze (S.KR 85000)
£8287	$15000	(5-Dec-91 SY.NY14/R) The wings (60cm-24in) i. brown pat.bronze i.f.Herman Bergman
£8287	$15000	(5-Dec-91 SY.NY31/R) Female bust - detail of Europa and the Bull (42cm-17in) st. green pat.bronze st.f.L.Rasmussen
£8840	$16000	(5-Dec-91 SY.NY2/R) Struggle for existence (19cm-7in) i. greenish brown pat.bronze i.f.Andro
£9434	$16887	(7-May-92 RAS.S48/R) Singing to the sun (40x23x9cm-16x9x4in) bronze (S.KR 100000)
£11505	$20709	(19-Nov-91 GO.G312/R) Sisters reunion (85cm-33in) s. green pat bronze (S.KR 120000)
£12431	$22500	(5-Dec-91 SY.NY39/R) Angel on stem (79cm-31in) i.num.6/12 greenish black pat.bronze st.f.PGB
£13260	$24000	(5-Dec-91 SY.NY5/R) The sisters (83cm-33in) i. green pat.bronze st.f.L.Rasmussen
£15094	$27019	(7-May-92 RAS.S78/R) The flying horse (54x86x17cm-21x34x7in) one of twelve, green pat bronze (S.KR 160000)
£21226	$37995	(7-May-92 RAS.S64/R) Europa and the bull (57x46x27cm-22x18x11in) Ekeberg marble (S.KR 225000)
£22770	$41670	(14-May-92 BU.S114/R) Flying horse (47cm-19in) s. green pat bronze Cast.G Pettersson (S.KR 240000)
£27624	$50000	(5-Dec-91 SY.NY10/R) Dancing Maenad, a relief (71cm-28in) green pat.bronze i.f.Herman Bergman
£30387	$55000	(5-Dec-91 SY.NY22/R) Bathing women (72cm-28in) greenish brown pat.bronze st.f.Herman Bergman
£77348	$140000	(5-Dec-91 SY.NY32/R) Europa and the Bull (72cm-28in) st. green pat.bronze st.f.L.Rasmussen

MILLES, Ruth (1873-?) Swedish

£1183	$2140	(19-May-92 AB.S4558) Girl sewing (20cm-8in) s.d.1911 dark pat bronze Cast Bergman (S.KR 12500)
£1198	$2157	(19-Nov-91 GO.G314) Girl with flowers (22cm-9in) s. pat bronze (S.KR 12500)
£1200	$2171	(3-Dec-91 AB.S4568) Dutch girl with bouquet of flowers (21cm-8in) s. dark pat bronze (S.KR 12500)
£1514	$2740	(19-May-92 AB.S4557) Dutch girl standing (48cm-19in) s. dark pat bronze Cast. E Blot (S.KR 16000)

MILLS, Clark (c.1810-1883) American

£3867	$7000	(6-Dec-91 CH.NY56/R) General Jackson on horseback (61cm-24in) i. metal grey pat.

MILNE, John E (1931-) British

£800	$1424	(28-Nov-91 L231/R) Project 1969 (56cm-22in) init.d.1970 cold cast aluminium on slate base

MINNE, G (19/20th C) Belgian

£2500	$4350	(14-Apr-92 GM.B1084) Homme agenouille plaster (B.FR 150000)

MINNE, George (1866-1941) Belgian

£1454	$2632	(7-Dec-91 KV.L243/R) Head of Eva I (16x12cm-6x5in) s. bronze brown pat. (B.FR 85000)
£2339	$3977	(22-Oct-91 C.A60/R) The labourer (80cm-31in) s.d.1913 bronze (B.FR 140000)
£2901	$5251	(23-May-92 GB.B6918) L'adolescent agenouille (77cm-30in) s.c.1897 bronze (DM 8500)
£4200	$7266	(25-Mar-92 S25/R) Le petit blesse II (26cm-10in) i.d.98 st.mono. bronze Cast.J Petermann
£4282	$7750	(21-May-92 GRO.B91/R) La baigneuse I (38cm-15in) i.num.3/8 brown pat.bronze st.f.DeGroeve
£4321	$7864	(11-Dec-91 CH.AM303/R) L'adolescent, de jongeling (42cm-17in) i. green pat.bronze (D.FL 14000)
£6000	$10320	(16-Oct-91 S45/R) Tete de Debardeur (60cm-24in) s. bronze
£11696	$19883	(22-Oct-91 C.A59/R) Le grand blesse (45cm-18in) s.d.1894 marble (B.FR 700000)

MIRANDA, Sebastian (1885-1975) Spanish

£1107	$1893	(17-Mar-92 FER.M220/R) Gitana peinando a su hija (47x32x26cm-19x13x10in) s. pat.bronze (S.P 200000)

MIRKO (1910-1969) Italian

£2171	$3800	(27-Feb-92 CE.NY71/R) Composizione astratta (22cm-9in) s.d.53 golden pat.bronze wood base

MIRKO, Basaldella (1910-1969) Italian

£1627	$2944	(3-Dec-91 F.R212/R) Ragazzo con serpente (35x24x12cm-14x9x5in) d.1935 bronze (I.L 3500000)

MIRO, Joan (1893-1983) Spanish

£16000	$28960	(4-Dec-91 S157/R) Oiseau - solaire (13x19cm-5x7in) i.num.8/8 bronze f.i.V.Gimeno-Fundit Barna
£87432	$160000	(14-May-92 SY.NY299/R) Femme (113cm-44in) i.num.4/4 bronze st.f.Clementi

MIRO, Joan (1893-1983) Spanish-cont.
£133880 $245000   (14-May-92 SY.NY300/R) Projet pour un monument a Los Angeles (49cm-19in) i.num.2/6 painted bronze
£214689 $380000   (6-Nov-91 SY.NY67/R) Personnage (190cm-75in) painted synthetic resin

MISERONI, Ottavio (style) (16/17th C) Italian
£3022 $5500   (26-May-92 SY.NY186/R) Diogenes, philosopher seated by tree trunk, lantern behind, bowl to side (7cm-3in) agate carving wood base

MITORAJ, Igor (20th C) ?
£1628 $2979   (14-May-92 BG.P8/R) Visage bande (32cm-13in) s. bronze (F.FR 16000)

MODIGLIANI, Amedeo (1884-1920) Italian
£29532 $54043   (3-Jun-92 CSC.P90/R) Tete (72cm-28in) s.num. black pat.bronze f.st.Valsuani (F.FR 290000)
£32421 $58683   (24-May-92 GL.P36/R) Tete d'homme (72cm-28in) s.num.EMJ 1 brown pat.bronze st.f.Valsuani (F.FR 320000)
£33951 $61451   (6-Dec-91 GL.P246/R) Tete (71x30x21cm-28x12x8in) s.num.5/9 brn.pat.bronze Cast.Valsuani (F.FR 330000)
£44845 $77582   (23-Mar-92 GL.P181/R) Tete (71x30x21cm-28x12x8in) s.base brn.pat.bronze Cast.Valsuani cire perdue (F.FR 435000)
£65856 $119200   (24-May-92 GL.P40/R) Tete de femme (50cm-20in) s.num.MJ brown pat.bronze st.f.Valsuani (F.FR 650000)

MOELLER, Edmund (1885-?) German
£2105 $3600   (13-Mar-92 FN.S2569/R) Two figures wrestling (70cm-28in) s.d.1920 bronze (DM 6000)

MOIGNIEZ, J (1835-1894) French
£811 $1500   (8-Jun-92 B.LA1162/R) Ewe resting and lamb standing on grassy meadow (16x33cm-6x13in) i. gilt bronze encrier
£843 $1500   (21-Jan-92 CE.NY84) Four sheep on a rocky knoll (41x25cm-16x10in) i. bronze brass base
£872 $1500   (20-Oct-91 HG.C103) Figure of eagle, with talon clutching tree stump (74cm-29in) s. bronze

MOIGNIEZ, Jules (1835-1894) French
£800 $1368   (20-Mar-92 S46/R) Retriever with pheasant (30cm-12in) s. brown pat.bronze
£814 $1400   (16-Oct-91 CH.NY146/R) A silvered bronze figure of a pheasant (32x77cm-13x30in) i. bronze
£850 $1454   (20-Mar-92 S52/R) Two partridges with corn (23cm-9in) s. brown pat.bronze on wooden plinth
£874 $1600   (5-Jun-92 SY.NY108/R) Setter pointing (20x30cm-8x12in) i. bronze br.pat.
£1163 $2000   (10-Oct-91 FA.PH779/R) Cock pheasant (58cm-23in) bronze
£1350 $2403   (29-Nov-91 S57/R) Merinos nes a Wideville (24cm-9in) s.i. brown pat.bronze
£2049 $3750   (5-Jun-92 SY.NY117/R) Pheasant (33cm-13in) i. bronze gr.br.pat.
£2473 $4500   (27-May-92 CH.NY110/R) Retour au Pesage (33cm-13in) i.bronze brown pat.
£2600 $4446   (20-Mar-92 S59/R) Boar hunt (32cm-13in) s. brown pat.bronze
£4310 $7500   (13-Sep-91 SY.NY85/R) Equestrian group of Prince Albert (62cm-24in) i. brown pat.bronze

MOIGNIEZ, Jules (after) (1835-1894) French
£857 $1500   (3-Apr-92 S.W2295/R) Eagle on branch (76cm-30in) bears sig. brown pat.bronze

MOLLERBERG, Nils (1892-1954) Scandinavian
£1892 $3425   (19-May-92 AB.S5152/R) Galathea (60cm-24in) s. gold pat bronze (S.KR 20000)

MOLTENI, F (20th C) Italian
£1250 $2213   (5-Nov-91 GF.L242/R) Bust of woman (87cm-34in) s.d.1959 green pat.bronze stone socle indis.st. (S.FR 3200)

MONDINO, Aldo (1938-) ?
£9731 $17322   (29-Nov-91 F.F146/R) Chitarra cubista (100x65cm-39x26in) d.1989 num.8/8 mixed media (I.L 21000000)

MONGINOT, C (1872-?) French
£820 $1500   (3-Jun-92 D.NY698) Gentleman pushing lady on sleigh (53cm-21in) s. bronze

MONOGRAMMIST D B (?) ?
£1236 $2113   (20-Mar-92 ZZ.F44/R) Petit faune (27cm-11in) terracotta round base (F.FR 12000)

MONTEYNE, Roland (1932-) Belgian
£2506 $4261   (22-Oct-91 C.A63/R) Self-crucifixion (59x95x70cm-23x37x28in) s. bronze (B.FR 150000)

MONTINI, Tullio (attrib) (1878-?) Italian
£1257 $2200   (23-Sep-91 S.SL632) Dante (58cm-23in) s. marble plinth

MOON SHIN (1923-) Korean
£2213 $3807   (7-Oct-91 RY.P107/R) Olympic 88 (80cm-31in) stainless steel (F.FR 22000)

MOORE, Christopher (1790-1863) Irish
£1800 $3276   (12-Dec-91 S265/R) Bust of girl (47cm-19in) s.d.1849 marble

MOORE, Henry O M (1898-1986) British
£1923 $3500   (13-Dec-91 S.W3038/R) Small maquette for two figures (15x8cm-6x3in) s.num.5/9 bronze
£2432 $4500   (12-Jun-92 SY.NY164/R) Boat form (10cm-4in) bronze gr.br.pat.
£2800 $4956   (8-Nov-91 C335/R) Head (11cm-4in) s.num.9/9base light brn.pat.bronze
£3514 $6500   (12-Jun-92 SY.NY162/R) Two standing figures - concretions (23cm-9in) i.num.7/9 bronze br.pat.
£3600 $6876   (29-Jun-92 CSK153/R) Head (14cm-6in) i.num.1/7 gold pat.bronze f.st.Noack Berlin
£3800 $6726   (8-Nov-91 C332/R) Seated figure on a log (18cm-7in) s.st.num.7/9 brn.pat.bronze bronze base
£3838 $6794   (24-Apr-92 CN.P213/R) Torso shoulders (19cm-7in) num.7/9 bronze (F.FR 38000)
£4000 $7080   (8-Nov-91 C334/R) Girl (20cm-8in) s.num.4/9base blk.brn.pat.bronze bronze base
£4700 $8319   (8-Nov-91 C333/R) Bonnet figure (18cm-7in) s.num.4/9base blk.pat.bronze bronze base
£5200 $9204   (8-Nov-91 C336/R) Reclining figure - holes (13cm-5in) s.st.num.4/9base brn.pat.bronze
£5233 $9000   (12-Oct-91 SY.NY172/R) Seated figure - cross hatch (13cm-5in) i.num.6/9 greenish-brown pat.bronze f.st.
£6000 $11100   (11-Jun-92 C112/R) Standing figurine (11cm-4in) s.num.3/9 dark green pat.bronze
£6000 $11100   (11-Jun-92 C113/R) Two bulb forms (11cm-4in) s.num.1/9 brown/green pat.bronze
£6000 $10380   (24-Mar-92 C84/R) Reclining figure, hollows (20cm-8in) s.num.4/9 brown pat.bronze on wood base
£6000 $11460   (1-Jul-92 S229/R) Female torso (17cm-7in) i.num.4/9 bronze
£7000 $12950   (11-Jun-92 C115/R) Upright motive - maquette no.3 (24cm-9in) brown pat.bronze
£7000 $12390   (8-Nov-91 C337/R) Maquette for reclining figure - circle (15cm-6in) s.num.3/9base dark green pat.bronze
£8197 $15000   (14-May-92 SY.NY324/R) Mother and child (26cm-10in) i.num.9/12 brown pat.bronze st.f.H.Noack
£9000 $15930   (8-Nov-91 C330/R) Mother and child with tree trunk (23cm-9in) s. num.3/9 green pat.bronze
£9249 $16000   (2-Oct-91 SY.NY66/R) Head of girl (25cm-10in) greenish brown pat.bronze
£10857 $19000   (25-Feb-92 SY.NY71/R) Maquette for reclining figure, circle (15cm-6in) i.num.2/9 dark green pat.bronze
£11494 $19885   (28-Mar-92 F.L92/R) Standing figure (26cm-10in) num.3/6 bronze (S.FR 30000)
£11877 $20548   (28-Mar-92 F.L93/R) Standing figure (26cm-10in) d.1960 num.3/6 bronze (S.FR 31000)
£12994 $23000   (7-Nov-91 SY.NY221 a/R) Reclining figure - wing (15cm-6in) i. st.num.3/9 brown pat.bronze
£13115 $24000   (13-May-92 CH.NY317/R) Reclining torso (22cm-9in) s.num.9/9 brown pat.bronze
£14208 $26000   (13-May-92 SY.NY219/R) Small mother and child (13cm-5in) i.num.3/9 brown pat.bronze
£15000 $28650   (1-Jul-92 S230/R) Maquette for two piece reclining figure - cut (21cm-8in) i.num.6/9 bronze
£15928 $28990   (25-May-92 WK.M896/R) The matron (21x7x7cm-8x3x3in) s.num.4/9 d.1975 brown pat.bronze (DM 46670)
£17000 $30090   (8-Nov-91 C325 a/R) Bird (38cm-15in) green pat.bronze
£18579 $34000   (14-May-92 SY.NY294/R) Maquette for standing figure (26cm-10in) black pat.bronze
£22000 $39820   (4-Dec-91 S185/R) Animal head (21x28cm-8x11in) bronze
£23224 $42500   (13-May-92 SY.NY220/R) Reclining figure, right angels (20cm-8in) i.num.3/9 brown pat.bronze
£28000 $53480   (1-Jul-92 S226/R) Maquette for reclining figure no.7 (20cm-8in) i.num.7/9 bronze
£38251 $70000   (13-May-92 SY.NY21/R) Mother with child on knee (17cm-7in) green pat.bronze
£45198 $80000   (6-Nov-91 CH.NY315/R) Armless figure against round wall (28cm-11in) green brown pat.bronze on stone base
£46448 $85000   (14-May-92 SY.NY292/R) Head and ball (50cm-20in) cumberland alabaster on limestone base
£46448 $85000   (13-May-92 CH.NY299/R) Seated woman in chair (27cm-11in) s.num.4/6 brown pat.bronze
£76271 $135000   (7-Nov-91 SY.NY183/R) Working model for reclining figure (44cm-17in) black pat.bronze
£140000 $253400   (2-Dec-91 C35/R) Seated figure (25cm-10in) plaster
£200000 $354000   (5-Nov-91 PH86/R) Figures (24cm-9in) ebony
£423729 $750000   (6-Nov-91 SY.NY31/R) Goslar warrior (249cm-98in) i.num.5/7 brn.pat.bronze

MORALES, Dario (1944-1988) Colombian
£15470 $28000   (18-May-92 CH.NY62 a/R) Mujer banandose (19x39x36cm-7x15x14in) s.d.80 num.2/6 greenish brown pat.bronze f.st.

MOREAU (style) (?) French
£775 $1325   (17-Mar-92 FER.M242/R) La toilette (62cm-24in) calamine on wood base (S.P 140000)

MOREAU, A (?) French
£2154	$4114	(30-Jun-92 SY.AM472) Cupid (99x99x99cm-39x39x39in) s.i.c.1890 dark pat.bronze (D.FL 7000)

MOREAU, Auguste (19th C) French
£750	$1283	(20-Mar-92 S190) The wandering cupid (24cm-9in) s. brown pat.bronze on marble socle
£799	$1430	(14-Nov-91 GRO.B119/R) Wood nymph (51cm-20in) i. brown pat.bronze
£1100	$1881	(20-Mar-92 S119/R) L'amour enchainant la fortune (51cm-20in) s.i. bronze stripped patination
£1124	$2000	(30-Apr-92 CE.NY49/R) Jeune femme a l'oiseau - figure of nymph (42cm-17in) s. reddish-brown pat.bronze
£1500	$2565	(20-Mar-92 S152/R) The slave trader (70cm-28in) s. spelter cold painted polychrome
£1500	$2670	(29-Nov-91 S231/R) The bee (43cm-17in) s. brown/green pat.bronze
£1700	$3111	(2-Jun-92 S487) Vici (61cm-24in) s.i.d.1897 brown pat.bronze wired f.electricity
£1900	$3382	(29-Nov-91 S178/R) Venus attended by cupids (165cm-65in) s. brown pat.bronze incl.green marble plinth
£1996	$3553	(25-Nov-91 GL.P20/R) Un amour aile, un oiseau pose sur son bras droit (45cm-18in) pat.bronze (F.FR 19500)
£2200	$3762	(20-Mar-92 S189/R) Blowing a kiss (44cm-17in) s. rubbed pat.bronze on marble plinth
£2586	$4500	(10-Sep-91 BG.M582/R) Venus disarming Cupid (86cm-34in) with sig. bronze
£3032	$5791	(1-Jul-92 FB.P150) Le char de l'Aurore (80cm-31in) s. brown pat.bronze (F.FR 29500)
£3200	$5696	(29-Nov-91 S184) Two children (51cm-20in) s. brown pat.bronze on swivel stand
£3400	$5814	(20-Mar-92 S183/R) Aurore (67cm-26in) s.i. brown pat.bronze
£3485	$6168	(22-Apr-92 ZZ.F274/R) Depart des hirondelles (93cm-37in) s.i. brn.pat.bronze green marble base (F.FR 34500)
£3800	$6498	(20-Mar-92 S143/R) L'aurore (79cm-31in) s.i. brown polished pat.bronze
£4000	$6800	(22-Oct-91 CE.NY23/R) Groups of putti with urns (59cm-23in) i. bronze pair

MOREAU, H F (19/20th C) American
£1651	$2939	(29-Oct-91 VN.R1706) Hunter with two dogs (80cm-31in) s. bronze st.foundry (D.FL 5400)

MOREAU, Hippolite (19th C) French
£1131	$1900	(14-Aug-91 B.P106/R) Woman holding a bird (81cm-32in) s. base green brn.pat.bronze

MOREAU, Hippolyte Francois (1832-1927) French
£1400	$2492	(29-Nov-91 S114/R) Dans d'Azur (51cm-20in) s.i. red/brown pat.bronze

MOREAU, Louis (?) French
£1685	$3000	(30-Apr-92 CE.NY51/R) Les Adieux - metal group (90cm-35in) i. brown pat. green marble metal
£4200	$7182	(20-Mar-92 S182/R) Nuit d'ete (87x10cm-34x4in) s.i.d.1894 green pat.bronze on marble plinth

MOREAU, M (?) ?
£1538	$2938	(30-Jun-92 SY.AM473/R) Statue of winged woman as Artes Liberales leaning on column (77cm-30in) s.num.5224E pat.parcel gilt bronze marble column (D.FL 5000)

MOREAU, Mathurin (1822-1912) French
£872	$1492	(10-Mar-92 SY.AM136) Shepherdess with goat (42cm-17in) bronze (D.FL 2800)
£949	$1708	(19-Nov-91 GS.B7281) Young woman with basket seated on rocks (60cm-24in) i.c.1900 pat.bronze (S.FR 2400)
£958	$1744	(10-Dec-91 N.M149/R) Young fisherwoman with children waiting on rock for the returning boats (57cm-22in) brown pat.bronze (DM 2750)
£1000	$1780	(29-Nov-91 S165/R) Aurore (46cm-18in) s. brown pat.bronze
£1443	$2511	(17-Sep-91 FN.S635/R) Young female nude with drape seated after bath (73cm-29in) s. bronze (DM 4200)
£1520	$2600	(13-Mar-92 WOL.C1257/R) L'Ete (53cm-21in) s.f.Susse Freres bronze br.gr. pat.
£1573	$2800	(30-Apr-92 CE.NY25/R) Figure of girl by spring (62cm-24in) s. white marble gilt-bronze reliefs
£2000	$3560	(29-Nov-91 S162/R) La source (61cm-24in) s. brown pat.bronze st.f.E.Colin
£2035	$3642	(17-Nov-91 LT.P1/R) Un amour offrant a boire dans une coquille a une jeune fille assise (56cm-22in) s.d.1872 brn.pat.terracotta red marble base (F.FR 20000)
£2300	$4094	(29-Nov-91 S176/R) La rosee (67cm-26in) s. brown pat.bronze
£2443	$4250	(13-Mar-92 SY.NY30) Female figure raised on stepped plinth (84cm-33in) i. gilt bronze
£2586	$4500	(13-Sep-91 SY.NY97/R) Female nude with water jug (61cm-24in) i. brown pat.bronze on marble base
£2759	$4745	(16-Oct-91 KM.K1653/R) Godess of victory (115cm-45in) i. bronze st.f.Colinsch Paris (DM 8000)
£2800	$4984	(29-Nov-91 S160/R) Young woman seated on wall (70cm-28in) s.i. brown pat.bronze on swivelling base
£3345	$6055	(3-Dec-91 FN.S935/R) Peasant maid holding chicken and wicker basket (66cm-26in) s.i. bronze marble socle (DM 9500)

MOREAU, Mathurin (1822-1912) French-cont.
| £6098 | $10976 | (19-Nov-91 FP.M97/R) Les glaneuses (84cm-33in) pat.bronze (C.D 12500) |
| £13500 | $24030 | (29-Nov-91 S164/R) La source (99cm-39in) s. brown,green pat.bronze i.Susse Freres |

MOREAU-VAUTHIER, Paul (1871-?) French
| £1073 | $1900 | (13-Feb-92 SY.NY9/R) Allegorical figure (83cm-33in) i. gilt-bronze f.i.F. Barbedienne |

MOREAUX, Louis Auguste (1817-1877) French
| £908 | $1688 | (16-Jun-92 F.M14) Bambino con brocca (60cm-24in) s. bronze (I.L 2000000) |

MORGROVE (?) ?
| £1873 | $3278 | (31-Mar-92 AT.P87/R) Les espadons (40x80cm-16x31in) s. blk.pat.bronze Cast.Susses Freres cire perdue (F.FR 18000) |

MORIS, Louis Marie (1818-1883) French
| £2514 | $4500 | (11-Nov-91 B.LA1629/R) Equestrian figure of Napoleon Bonaparte (63cm-25in) i. bronze |
| £3846 | $7000 | (28-May-92 SY.NY108/R) Napoleon on horseback (63cm-25in) i. golden pat.bronze |

MORIS, Louis Marie (after) (1818-1883) French
| £938 | $1594 | (23-Oct-91 EA.M505) Equestrian portrait of Emperor Napoleon I (61cm-24in) s. brown pat.bronze (C.D 1800) |

MORLEY, Malcolm (1931-) British
| £162011 | $290000 | (13-Nov-91 SY.NY55/R) S.S. France (204x153x8cm-80x60x3in) init. oil canvas objects two panels aluminum |

MORRIS, Robert (1931-) American
£9143	$16000	(25-Feb-92 SY.NY205/R) Untitled (292x370cm-115x146in) grey felt
£9827	$17000	(3-Oct-91 SY.NY106/R) Untitled (173x183x66cm-68x72x26in) nine strips of felt
£10615	$19000	(14-Nov-91 SY.NY160/R) Untitled (244cm-96in) felt
£15363	$27500	(14-Nov-91 SY.NY137/R) Untitled (111x65x15cm-44x26x6in) s.d.1964 verso lead wood plaster

MOSMAN, Warren T (1908-) American
| £1053 | $1800 | (11-Mar-92 SY.NY81/R) Oriental lady (46cm-18in) i. dark green pat.bronze |

MOSS, L V (20th C) ?
| £1471 | $2500 | (22-Oct-91 CE.NY37/R) Head of Leon Tolstoy (42cm-17in) s.d.1919 stone |

MOULIN (?) ?
| £1100 | $1870 | (23-Oct-91 LJ222) Figure of prancing youth (80cm-31in) bronze f.i.Belmanivey and Carter, New Bond St. |

MOULIN, Hippolyte (1832-1884) French
| £2217 | $3879 | (18-Feb-92 DUR.M432/R) Un hallazgo en Pompeya (82cm-32in) bronze (S.P 400000) |

MOZIER, Joseph (1812-1870) American
| £1229 | $2200 | (14-Nov-91 CE.NY237/R) Bust of lady (75cm-30in) s. white marble |
| £8840 | $16000 | (21-May-92 GRO.B33/R) Pocahontas (124cm-49in) s.i.d.1867 white marble |

MULLER, Hans (?) German
| £890 | $1620 | (12-Dec-91 D.V130/R) Standing female figure reading beneath lantern (83cm-33in) s. electric table lamp (A.S 18000) |
| £1250 | $2213 | (5-Nov-91 GF.L234/R) Female nude leaning forward (55cm-22in) s. brown pat.bronze marble socle (S.FR 3200) |

MULLER, Karl (1818-1893) German
| £1294 | $2200 | (22-Oct-91 CE.NY6/R) Early rising (72cm-28in) s.i. marble |

MULLER, Rudolf (1816-1904) Austrian
| £784 | $1333 | (23-Oct-91 GD.B2515/R) Walking girl from Ticino carrying bowl on head (74cm-29in) bronze (S.FR 2000) |

MUNICH SCHOOL, 18th C German
| £5200 | $9984 | (9-Jul-92 S179/R) Figure of putto, with swirling drapery attached by ribbon (53cm-21in) giltwood |

MUNOZ, Juan (20th C) ?
£4749	$8500	(7-May-92 SY.NY199/R) Square at bottom (100x58x30cm-39x23x12in) wood plaster graphite
£6704	$12000	(6-May-92 CH.NY227/R) Perfect balcony (86x88x44cm-34x35x17in) welded steel switchblade
£20000	$38200	(2-Jul-92 C18/R) Bailarinas en apartemento (60x67x57cm-24x26x22in) green pat.bronze wood

MURER, Augusto (1922-1985) Italian
| £1612 | $2934 | (9-Dec-91 CH.R37/R) Don Chisciotte (35x16x12cm-14x6x5in) s.d.1978 bronze (I.L 3500000) |

MURER, Augusto (1922-1985) Italian-cont.
£6719 $11960   (29-Nov-91 F.F149/R) Donna sdraiata (26cm-10in) s.d.1971 bronze
   (I.L 14500000)

MYRON (after) (fl.480-440 B.C.) Greek
£9064 $15500   (13-Mar-92 WOL.C1328/R) Figure of the Discobolus (163cm-64in) bronze
   Cast.c.1780-1810

NAKIAN, Reuben (1897-) American
£1351 $2500   (12-Jun-92 SY.NY156/R) Europa and the Bull (40cm-16in) i.num.2/9 bronze
   br.pat.

NANCY SCHOOL, 18th/19th C French
£4179 $7774   (19-Jun-92 ARC.P131/R) Deux amours (49x43cm-19x17in) terracotta
   (F.FR 41000)

NANIM, R (?) ?
£941 $1600   (9-Aug-91 GC.M209/R) La Cosecha de Trigo (45x65cm-18x26in) s. bronze

NAPS (19th C) ?
£4121 $7500   (13-Dec-91 SY.NY257/R) Bear attacking man, with peasant wife wielding axe
   to drive it off (49cm-19in) s. bronze i.f.Woerffel

NARVAEZ, Francisco (1905-1982) Venezuelan
£12222 $22000   (19-Nov-91 CH.NY88/R) Maternidad (29x58cm-11x23in) s. polished wood

NASH, David (1945-) British
£8380 $15000   (13-Nov-91 CH.NY285/R) From nature to nature (98x80cm-39x31in) s.d.86
   chl.three drawings charred wood three

NAUDET, Francoise (1928-) French
£2117 $3662   (6-Oct-91 E.LA139) Gabrielle assise s.num.1/4 brn.pat.bronze
   (F.FR 21000)

NAUMAN, Bruce (1941-) American
£9497 $17000   (14-Nov-91 SY.NY216/R) Untitled - cross beams (25x217x217cm-10x85x85in)
   cast iron two parts
£11173 $20000   (13-Nov-91 CH.NY273/R) Untitled - cross beams (25x217x217cm-10x85x85in)
   two beams cast iron grit blast finish
£16760 $30000   (14-Nov-91 SY.NY256/R) Double poke in eye II (61x91x28cm-24x36x11in) neon
   construction
£64246 $115000   (13-Nov-91 SY.NY47/R) Untitled (10x120x120cm-4x47x47in) lead plates
   painted steel wedge
£81006 $145000   (13-Nov-91 SY.NY52/R) Three dead end adjacent tunnels, not connected
   (53x292x264cm-21x115x104in) cast iron

NEAPOLITAN SCHOOL, 18/19th C Italian
£6704 $12000   (14-Jan-92 CH.NY120/R) Equestrian creche groups depicting two tartars in
   period costume (58cm-23in) polychrome terracotta wood pair

NEAPOLITAN SCHOOL, 18th C Italian
£8500 $16320   (7-Jul-92 C49/R) Two moor under coconut palm with monkey perched on top
   holding coconut (180cm-71in) polychrome giltwood mother-of-pearl ebony

NEGRET, Edgar (1920-) Colombian
£2326 $4000   (12-Oct-91 SY.NY214/R) Metamorfosis (71cm-28in) s.d.1983 painted
   aluminium

NEGRI, Mario (1916-) Italian
£4942 $8500   (12-Oct-91 SY.NY306/R) Composizione (39cm-15in) st.init. num.2/3
   golden-brown pat.bronze

NEGRO, Pietro (19th C) Italian
£2600 $4550   (24-Sep-91 SWS328/R) Figure of child holding dress over her head
   (94cm-37in) s.i.d.1878 white marble

NELLEMOSE, Knud (20th C) Danish
£787 $1433   (10-Dec-91 RAS.K136/R) Soren Kierkegaard (44cm-17in) s. pat bronze
   (D.KR 8800)
£802 $1380   (16-Oct-91 KH.K19/R) Seated woman (37cm-15in) s. st.DBB Cire perdue
   bronze (D.KR 9000)
£891 $1533   (16-Oct-91 KH.K18/R) Pregnant (49cm-19in) bronze (D.KR 10000)

NEVELSON, Louise (1900-1988) American
£1892 $3500   (12-Jun-92 SY.NY289/R) Female head (37cm-15in) pink marble
£2626 $4700   (9-May-92 CE.NY340/R) Untitled (56x46x3cm-22x18x1in) s.d.80 wood collage
   on panel

NEVELSON, Louise (1900-1988) American-cont.

£2793	$5000	(9-May-92 CE.NY339/R) Study for large wall (23x25x11cm-9x10x4in) maquette brass
£5882	$10000	(23-Oct-91 B.SF3738/R) Night column 2 (38cm-15in) s.num.9/11 painted bronze
£6704	$12000	(7-May-92 SY.NY258/R) Royal organ (121x25cm-48x10in) gold painted wood
£6857	$12000	(27-Feb-92 CH.NY11/R) City space scape XIII (42x41x10cm-17x16x4in) sig.d.68 wood formica painted black
£6857	$12000	(25-Feb-92 SY.NY188/R) Uja federation edition D (80x46x24cm-31x18x9in) s.num.3/10 wood painted black
£8929	$15000	(14-Aug-91 B.P140/R) Untitled (102x81x20cm-40x32x8in) wood paper metal
£8939	$16000	(13-Nov-91 CH.NY127/R) Moon garden series s. wood box plaster figure three
£10615	$19000	(7-May-92 SY.NY238/R) Untitled (30x25x18cm-12x10x7in) init. bronze wood base
£14525	$26000	(7-May-92 SY.NY255/R) End of day XXXVI (88x48cm-35x19in) black painted wood construction
£16760	$30000	(14-Nov-91 SY.NY273/R) Dancer (37x35x20cm-15x14x8in) s. bronze wood base
£17143	$30000	(25-Feb-92 SY.NY102/R) Untitled (222cm-87in) painted wood construction
£17877	$32000	(13-Nov-91 CH.NY162/R) Dawwn's landscape XX (107x110x16cm-42x43x6in) wood painted white
£30347	$52500	(3-Oct-91 SY.NY33/R) Black light Zag 5 (118x125x19cm-46x49x7in) blk.painted wood with formica frame
£30726	$55000	(7-May-92 SY.NY230/R) Undermarine scape (73x43x43cm-29x17x17in) s. wood construction glass metal case
£53073	$95000	(12-Nov-91 CH.NY24/R) Moon garden reflections (204x76x26cm-80x30x10in) three boxes and base wood painted blk.
£83799	$150000	(6-May-92 SY.NY15/R) Untitled (26x241x43cm-10x95x17in) s.d. wood painted black

NICOLA (20th C) ?

£2016	$3488	(6-Oct-91 BG.P117/R) Femme television (170x93x85cm-67x37x33in) female shape furnishing TV receiver (F.FR 20000)
£3831	$6627	(6-Oct-91 BG.P114/R) Femme television (170x93x85cm-67x37x33in) female shape furnishing leather TV receiver (F.FR 38000)

NIEDERHAUSERN-RODO (1863-1913) Swiss

£8765	$15865	(5-Dec-91 SY.Z61/R) L'offrande a Bacchus (73cm-29in) s. bronze st.f.M.Pastori Geneve (S.FR 22000)

NIELSEN, Kay (1868-?) Danish

£805	$1465	(10-Dec-91 RAS.K225/R) My girl Nina (53cm-21in) s.num.1, bronze incl.base (D.KR 9000)
£894	$1628	(10-Dec-91 RAS.K281/R) Girl bending touching her toes (18cm-7in) s.num.16 gilded bronze (D.KR 10000)
£939	$1709	(10-Dec-91 RAS.K280/R) Seated woman (21cm-8in) s.d.1910 num.15, gilded bronze (D.KR 10500)
£1565	$2849	(12-Dec-91 RAS.V854/R) Naval war memorial (98x71cm-39x28in) plaster (D.KR 17500)

NIEUWERKERKE, Comte de Alfred-Emilien (1811-1892) French

£1800	$3096	(15-Oct-91 SWS550/R) Combat du Duc de Clarence (53cm-21in) s. blk.pat.bronze marble plinth
£2921	$5082	(17-Sep-91 FN.S637/R) Wilhelm I von Oranien mounted on horse wearing rennaissance costume (57cm-22in) s.d.1843 bronze i.Susse F.Res (DM 8500)

NOACK, Astrid (1888-?) Swedish?

£770	$1324	(8-Mar-92 BU.M332) Girl standing (57cm-22in) s. dark pat bronze (S.KR 8000)

NOBLE, Matthew (1818-1876) British

£1000	$1760	(8-Apr-92 CSK71/R) Bust of Alexander Halley, shoulders draped in plaid (66cm-26in) i.d.1849 white marble

NOGUCHI, Isamu (1904-) American

£6857	$12000	(26-Sep-91 CH.NY138/R) Suzanne Ziegler - portrait bust (35cm-14in) whitewashed wood
£17877	$32000	(6-May-92 CH.NY341/R) Appalachian spring - rocking chair (102x39x77cm-40x15x30in) with sig.d.44-85 num.4/6 bronze
£18497	$32000	(3-Oct-91 SY.NY12/R) Okame (33cm-13in) cast iron
£72626	$130000	(14-Nov-91 SY.NY283/R) Sinai (91cm-36in) cats iron

NOLL, Alexandre (1890-1970) French

£3528	$6104	(6-Oct-91 BG.P60/R) Sculpture (70cm-28in) elm-tree sculpture hollowed ball (F.FR 35000)
£3528	$6104	(6-Oct-91 BG.P190/R) Abstraction (102cm-40in) s. ebony (F.FR 35000)
£5040	$8720	(6-Oct-91 BG.P178/R) Totem (117x32cm-46x13in) ebony sculpture (F.FR 50000)
£29234	$50575	(6-Oct-91 BG.P97/R) Bar (140cm-55in) s.verso beech sculpture (F.FR 290000)
£58468	$101149	(6-Oct-91 BG.P154/R) Armoir a magnum (110cm-43in) s.verso sculpture ebony door opening (F.FR 580000)

NOLLEKENS, Joseph (1737-1823) British
£1800 $3456   (7-Jul-92 C69/R) Naked young god standing beside tree stump (12cm-5in)
           i.d.1944 terracotta

NONAS, Richard (20th C) American
£2286 $4000   (27-Feb-92 CH.NY61/R) Untitled (10x121x10cm-4x48x4in) steel
£5429 $9500   (27-Feb-92 CH.NY43/R) North slope I (152x152x5cm-60x60x2in) s.i.d.1973
           steel four pieces

NORTH ITALIAN SCHOOL, 17th/18th C
£13000 $24960   (7-Jul-92 C45/R) Group of three putti, possibly representing music on
           rocky base (94cm-37in) giltwood

NUNZIO (20th C) American
£2346 $4200   (9-May-92 CE.NY204/R) Centauro (129x55x15cm-51x22x6in) lead wood chl chk
£3714 $6500   (27-Feb-92 CE.NY267/R) Armata (118x159x4cm-46x63x2in) charred wood lead
           four parts

NYMAN, Olle (1909-) Swedish
£2099 $3737   (27-Nov-91 BU.S71/R) 'Kore-parafras' (105cm-41in) s. cement stone
           (S.KR 22000)
£2751 $5035   (13-May-92 BU.S245/R) Statue of a King (34cm-13in) scrap iron
           (S.KR 29000)

OJANSIVU, Juha (1948-) Scandinavian
£1294 $2303   (1-Dec-91 HOR.H180/R) Break through (80cm-31in) s. stainless steel
           (F.M 10000)

OLAFSSON, Sigurjon (1908-1982) Icelandic
£3604 $6198   (4-Mar-92 KH.K61/R) Man and woman (150cm-59in) wood (D.KR 40000)

OLAFSSON, Tove (20th C) ?
£891 $1533   (16-Oct-91 KH.K32/R) Standing girl (37cm-15in) init.d.1960 num.2/10,
           St.JTS bronze (D.KR 10000)
£1362 $2384   (1-Apr-92 KH.K158/R) Mother nursing baby (39cm-15in) init.d.1960
           num.10/10, bronze (D.KR 15000)

OLDENBURG, Claes (1929-) American
£1390 $2475   (27-Nov-91 F.M107/R) Tea bag (100x70cm-39x28in) s.num.110/125 mixed media
           plastic (I.L 3000000)
£11732 $21000   (7-May-92 SY.NY307/R) Soft screw (120cm-47in) st.sig.i. rubber revolving
           wooded base
£26816 $48000   (5-May-92 CH.NY30/R) Fragments de glace (41x24x13cm-16x9x5in) enamel on
           plastic oer wire mesh on board
£50279 $90000   (13-Nov-91 SY.NY38/R) Giant soft Swedish light switches
           (132x132x38cm-52x52x15in) black vinyl filled kapok

OLOFSSON, Pierre (1921-) ?
£883 $1598   (3-Dec-91 AB.S5206/R) Abstract composition (64cm-25in) s.num.4/5, copper
           (S.KR 9200)

OLSON, Eric H (1909-) Swedish
£2207 $3995   (3-Dec-91 AB.S5209/R) Optochromi (18cm-7in) s. glass filter (S.KR 23000)
£3167 $5732   (3-Dec-91 AB.S5208/R) Optochromi -R6 (30cm-12in) s.d.65 glass filter
           (S.KR 33000)

OMERTH (fl.1895-1925) French
£1724 $3000   (13-Sep-91 SY.NY102/R) Equestrian group (53cm-21in) i. gilt bronze

OPIE, Julian (1958-) British
£503 $900   (9-May-92 CE.NY248/R) Open can (35x14x13cm-14x6x5in) s.d.83verso oil
           sheet metal
£800 $1400   (27-Feb-92 CE.NY251/R) Blues (47x32x1cm-19x13x0in) s.d.83 verso oil sheet
           metal
£2793 $5000   (5-May-92 CH.NY175/R) Please do not touch (124x120x24cm-49x47x9in)
           s.d.83verso oil sheet metal
£3143 $5500   (27-Feb-92 CH.NY135/R) Do you feel the same (103x71x21cm-41x28x8in) i.
           sheet metal
£6145 $11000   (5-May-92 CH.NY186/R) Serenade and Relax (163x106x49cm-64x42x19in)
           init.d.1985 oil sheet metal

OQUTAQ, Sheokjuk (1920-1982) North American
£963 $1763   (1-Jun-92 W.T902/R) Swimming bird (36cm-14in) marbled serpentine carving
           (C.D 2100)

ORLOFF, Chana (1888-1968) French
£1081 $2010   (21-Jun-92 LT.P101/R) Le chien (16x15cm-6x6in) s.d.1941 brown pat.bronze
           (F.FR 10600)
£4000 $7000   (26-Sep-91 SY.I55/R) Liseuse II (48cm-19in) s.d.60 bronze st.f.Susse
           Fondeur Paris
£5405 $10000   (9-Jun-92 GG.TA303/R) Pensee Accoudee II (40cm-16in) s. bronze f.st.

ORLOFF, Chana (1888-1968) French-cont.

£5714	$10000	(26-Sep-91 SY.I37/R) Baigneuse-nu couche (21x47cm-8x19in) s.d.1930 bronze st.f.Susse Fondeur Paris
£6215	$11000	(5-Nov-91 CE.NY243/R) Jeune fille a la balle (87cm-34in) s.i.d.66 num.2/8 black pat.bronze
£9143	$16000	(26-Sep-91 SY.I38/R) Cheval au galop (80cm-31in) s.d.65 bronze st.f.Susse Fondeur Paris
£12208	$22340	(17-May-92 GL.P184/R) Suzy - 1930 (76cm-30in) s.num.2/8 black pat.bronze f.i.Susse, Paris (F.FR 120000)
£12571	$22000	(26-Sep-91 SY.I68/R) Deborah poetess (47cm-19in) s.d.42 wood
£12628	$22731	(20-Nov-91 CN.P69/R) Maternite (51cm-20in) s.base wood (F.FR 123000)
£15198	$27508	(24-May-92 GL.P37/R) Nu assis (41cm-16in) s.d.1927 num.3/8 brown pat.bronze.Cast.Susse (F.FR 150000)
£42857	$75000	(26-Sep-91 SY.I103/R) Baigneuse accroupie (118cm-46in) s.d.1925 bronze st.f.Susse Fondeur Paris
£88866	$153738	(23-Mar-92 GL.P182/R) Grande baigneuse accroupie (115x70x60cm-45x28x24in) s.d.1925 num.5/8 brn.pat.bronze Cast.Susse (F.FR 862000)

ORSKOV, Willy (20th C) Danish

£1351	$2324	(4-Mar-92 KH.K224) Untitled (56x65cm-22x26in) bronze (D.KR 15000)

ORTIZ MONASTERIO, Luis (1906-) Mexican

£4420	$8000	(19-May-92 SY.NY100/R) Pareja (34cm-13in) inits.num.III d.81 dark green pat.bronze

OSSORIO, Alfonso (1916-) American

£4571	$8000	(28-Feb-92 SY.NY354/R) Garden enclosed (32x93cm-13x37in) s.d.1967 num.7 verso assemblage masonite

OTTERSON, Joel (20th C) American

£3073	$5500	(6-May-92 CH.NY259/R) Designer nucleic acid (250x41x41cm-98x16x16in) init.d.1986 copper steel brass aluminium

OWEN, William Harold (1897-1971) British

£950	$1634	(4-Mar-92 DR126/R) Standing nude (150cm-59in) white stone

PAIK, Nam June (20th C) American?

£22346	$40000	(7-May-92 SY.NY221/R) Hommage to Jules Verne (180x171x51cm-71x67x20in) four antique televisions four videos

PAILES, Isaac (1895-1978) French

£865	$1582	(17-May-92 GL.P207/R) Tete de femme (41cm-16in) s.num.2/6 brown pat.bronze f.st.Lebel (F.FR 8500)

PAJOU, Augustin (1730-1809) French

£85599	$145519	(21-Oct-91 ARC.P39/R) Nathalie de Laborde, future Duchesse de Mouchy (63cm-25in) s. terracotta marble pedestal (F.FR 850000)

PAKCIARZ (20th C) ?

£1585	$2900	(3-Feb-92 HH.P8/R) Femme (25x38x30cm-10x15x12in) s.verso Carrare marble (F.FR 15500)

PALADINO, Mimmo (1948-) Italian

£3000	$5190	(26-Mar-92 C112/R) Untitled (23cm-9in) s.i.d.86 bronze base
£66000	$126060	(2-Jul-92 C2/R) Giardino chiuso (270x190x170cm-106x75x67in) with sig.d.1982 painted bronze
£67039	$120000	(5-May-92 CH.NY2/R) Red horse (221x403x18cm-87x159x7in) init.d.1984 s.d.verso oil painted wood canvas

PALERMO, Blinky (1943-1977) German

£5155	$9433	(2-Jun-92 L.K847/R) Blue triangle (64x50cm-25x20in) s.d.num.8/50 brush and tube in box (DM 15000)

PALLANDT, Charlotte van (1898-?) Dutch

£1698	$3090	(12-Dec-91 SY.AM189/R) Staande met opgeheven handen (22x9x7cm-9x4x3in) init. bronze (D.FL 5500)
£1852	$3370	(12-Dec-91 SY.AM186/R) Zittende met linker opgetrokken knie (13x11x12cm-5x4x5in) bronze (D.FL 6000)
£1852	$3370	(12-Dec-91 SY.AM187/R) Zittende met armen omhoog (18x13x12cm-7x5x5in) s. bronze (D.FL 6000)

PALLENBERG, Joseph Franz (1882-1946) German

£1027	$1900	(10-Jun-92 CE.NY368/R) Figure of bison (37cm-15in) i. rich medium brown pat.bronze

PANGNARK, John (1920-1980) North American

£757	$1385 •	(1-Jun-92 W.T720) Standing Inuit figure wearing parka (19cm-7in) soapstone (C.D 1650)

PANOVA (after) (?) ?
£6179 $10566   (20-Mar-92 ZZ.F63/R) Paire de danseuses (81cm-32in) white marble round base pair (F.FR 60000)

PANT, Theresia van der (1924-) Dutch
£1212 $2194   (19-May-92 CH.AM103/R) A camel (24cm-9in) s. bronze (D.FL 4000)
£1296 $2359   (11-Dec-91 CH.AM82) Bison (15cm-6in) s. bronze (D.FL 4200)

PAOLINI, Giulio (1940-) Italian
£27933 $50000   (13-Nov-91 SY.NY122/R) Mimesi (162cm-64in) resin marble wood two parts

PAOLOZZI, Eduardo (1924-) British
£900 $1665   (11-Jun-92 C139/R) Head (12cm-5in) s.num.1/V brown/gold pat.bronze
£1714 $3000   (27-Feb-92 CE.NY192/R) Acila (112x30x44cm-44x12x17in) chrome-plated steel
£3000 $5550   (11-Jun-92 C142/R) Newtonian figure (21cm-8in) s.d.1988 num.3/3 black/brown pat.bronze
£3400 $6018   (8-Nov-91 C376/R) Alpha (37x102x80cm-15x40x31in) chromium-plated steel

PAPINI, Prof (19/20th C) Italian
£14286 $26000   (28-May-92 SY.NY54/R) Donna nuda (142cm-56in) s.i. white carrara marble

PARIS, Rene (1881-1970) French
£3226 $6000   (16-Jun-92 RO.BA126) Cheval de course avec son jockey, Biribi (18x23cm-7x9in) bronze cire perdue

PARIS, Roland (1894-?) French
£850 $1624   (2-Jul-92 CSK141/R) Figure playing the lute wearing cape, tights and plumed cap (36cm-14in) s. gilt bronze ivory
£962 $1790   (20-Jun-92 BM.B662) Mephisto (47cm-19in) s. pat.bronze (DM 2800)
£1400 $2562   (15-May-92 S352/R) Devil and girl (40cm-16in) i. painted bronze ivory marble

PARR, Lenton (20th C) Australian
£1694 $3150   (21-Jun-92 SY.ME68) Scorpio (233x73x75cm-92x29x30in) d.1981 painted steel (A.D 4200)

PARTY (?) ?
£2298 $4022   (21-Feb-92 LC.P117/R) Scaramouche (194cm-76in) s.base pat.bronze Cast.Graux (F.FR 22500)

PASSAGE, Comte Arthur Marie Gabriel du (1838-1909) French
£2011 $3500   (13-Sep-91 SY.NY84/R) Mounted huntsman (56cm-22in) i. brown pat.bronze

PASSAVANT, Lucile (1910-) French
£820 $1500   (3-Jun-92 D.NY100) Seated nude (36cm-14in) s.num.3/6 green/brown pat.bronze

PATSOGLOU, Aristide (c.1941-) Greek?
£2616 $4499   (7-Oct-91 HH.P10/R) Jambes croisees (70x31x20cm-28x12x8in) s.num.1/8 brn.green pat.bronze (F.FR 26000)

PAUSCHINGER, Rudolf (1882-?) German
£756 $1315   (17-Sep-91 FN.S638) Running panther (60cm-24in) s. bronze marble base (DM 2200)

PAUTROT, F (19th C) French
£760 $1338   (8-Apr-92 CSK105) Group of startled cockerel surveying lizard (15cm-6in) s. bronze

PAUTROT, Ferdinand (19th C) French
£877 $1500   (13-Mar-92 DM.D2194/R) Standing pheasant (56cm-22in) s. brn.pat.bronze
£1124 $2000   (30-Apr-92 CE.NY67/R) Figure of hunting dog softmouthing by pheasant (30cm-12in) i. reddish brown pat.bronze
£1639 $3000   (5-Jun-92 SY.NY122 a/R) Fowl and chicks playing with butterfly (54x45cm-21x18in) i. bronze golden pat.

PECH, Gabriel Edouard Baptiste (1854-1930) French
£2941 $5000   (22-Oct-91 CE.NY33/R) Puss 'n Boots (57cm-22in) i. reddish brown pat.bronze f.st.Siot-Paris

PECHSTEIN, Max (1881-1955) German
£5155 $9588   (20-Jun-92 BM.B1060/R) Idol (5x13x9cm-2x5x4in) mono silvered copper on wooden box (DM 15000)

PEGRAM, Alfred Bertram (1873-1941) British
£800 $1528   (30-Jun-92 PH102/R) Figure of a piperfrom the land of dreams (68cm-27in) s. green pat.bronze marble plinth

PEIDES, Patricia (20th C) ?
£9557 $16439   (7-Oct-91 HH.P13/R) La grande Zoa (37x36x18cm-15x14x7in) mono.num.5/8 polished bronze blk.marble base (F.FR 95000)

PEINTE, Henri (1845-1912) French
£2500 $4275   (20-Mar-92 S114/R) Orpheus and Cerberus (88cm-35in) s. brown pat.bronze st.Siot Paris V.605

PENALBA, Alicia (1918-1982) Argentinian
£2236 $3890   (13-Apr-92 GL.P167/R) Sans titre (44x17cm-17x7in) s.num.4/6 bronze
                          Cast.Valsuani (F.FR 22000)
£2361 $4250   (18-Nov-91 SY.NY168/R) Untitled (51cm-20in) s.num.2/6 brown pat.bronze
                          st.f.A.Valsuani
£29006 $52500   (19-May-92 SY.NY66/R) Apocalyptic childhood (180cm-71in) s.num.1/4 green
                          pat.bronze i.f.E.Godard

PENCK, A R (1939-) German
£2126 $3869   (25-May-92 RAS.K108/R) Woman (21cm-8in) s.d.1987 num.1/6, bronze
                          Cast.Jerotka (D.KR 24000)
£5155 $9072   (10-Apr-92 KM.K503/R) Idol (27cm-11in) i.num.1/7 bronze two parts
                          (DM 15000)
£9000 $15480   (17-Oct-91 C110/R) ALS (58cm-23in) st.init. num.2/6 brown pat.bronze

PEPPER, Beverly (1924-) American
£4070 $7000   (12-Oct-91 SY.NY309/R) Untitled (84cm-33in) cast iron

PEROT, Robert (1931-) French
£971 $1778   (3-Feb-92 HH.P21/R) Petit voilier (28x11x10cm-11x4x4in) s.num.1/8
                          brn.pat.bronze Cast.Anpire (F.FR 9500)

PERTOLDI, G (19th C) Italian
£5000 $8500   (23-Oct-91 LJ218) Cleopatra seated on rocky plinth covered by deerskin
                          (122cm-48in) s.d.1874 carrara marble

PERU, Michel (?-1670) French
£4200 $7644   (12-Dec-91 S246/R) Statuette of Farnese Hercules (27cm-11in) s.d.1635
                          wood

PETER, Victor (1840-1918) French
£1300 $2223   (20-Mar-92 S68/R) Deux amis (26cm-10in) s.i. brown pat.bronze st.f.Susse
                          Freres

PETERSEN, Nielsine Caroline (1851-1916) Danish
£3122 $5807   (16-Jun-92 RAS.K724/R) Portrait bust of Bertel Thorvaldsen
                          (71x43cm-28x17in) s.d.1882 white marble (D.KR 35000)

PETERSSON, Axel (1868-1925) Danish
£2111 $3821   (3-Dec-91 AB.S4558/R) Concertina player (32cm-13in) st.sig. polycrome
                          wood (S.KR 22000)
£2214 $3808   (8-Mar-92 BU.M124) Dear Mother at milkingtime (20cm-8in) s.d.1918
                          polycrome wood pair (S.KR 23000)
£3605 $6598   (11-May-92 NOR.S44/R) Playing chess s. polycrome wood three pieces
                          (S.KR 38000)
£3985 $7292   (11-May-92 NOR.S43/R) The marriage (34x26cm-13x10in) s.d.1918 polycrome
                          wood (S.KR 42000)
£4175 $7639   (11-May-92 NOR.S46/R) The christening (28cm-11in) s.d.1919 polycrome wood
                          three figures (S.KR 44000)
£4934 $9028   (11-May-92 NOR.S49/R) The wedding (26cm-10in) s.d.1919 five figures
                          (S.KR 52000)
£5028 $9202   (11-May-92 NOR.S47/R) The auction (28cm-11in) s.d.1919, 1920 polycrome
                          wood three figures (S.KR 53000)
£5598 $10244   (11-May-92 NOR.S62/R) The auction st.sig. polycrome wood seven figures
                          (S.KR 59000)
£7116 $13022   (11-May-92 NOR.S50/R) The funeral (28cm-11in) s.d.1919 polycrome wood
                          eight figures (S.KR 75000)

PETERSSON, Axel (attrib) (1868-1925) Danish
£1085 $1920   (25-Aug-92 SO.S688/R) Thoroughbred horse (39x31cm-15x12in) wood
                          (S.KR 11500)

PFAEFFEL (20th C) German
£775 $1402   (3-Dec-91 FN.S936/R) Girl dancing in long flowing dress (47cm-19in) s.
                          gold pat.bronze st.foundry (DM 2200)

PHILIPPE, P (1900-1930) French
£1710 $2942   (13-Oct-91 SY.MO369/R) Danseuse (28cm-11in) s. gilded bronze ivory marble
                          base (F.FR 17000)

PHILIPPE, Paul (?) ?
£1800 $3060   (25-Oct-91 S339/R) Russian dancer (57cm-22in) i. pat.cold painted bronze
                          marble

PIAT, Frederic Eugene (1827-1903) French
£2200 $3916   (29-Nov-91 S121/R) The vine cherub chariot (40cm-16in) s. brown
                          pat.bronze

PICARD, F (?) ?
£2443 $4250   (13-Sep-91 SY.NY42/R) St George and dragon (130cm-51in) s.i. bronze

PICASSO, Pablo (1881-1973) Spanish
£1220 $2122   (13-Apr-92 GL.P166/R) Visage (31x10cm-12x4in) painted earthenware
                          (F.FR 12000)

PICASSO, Pablo (1881-1973) Spanish-cont.

£6395	$11000	(12-Oct-91 SY.NY182/R) Face of bearded man (8cm-3in) num.2/2 golden pat.bronze
£8743	$16000	(11-May-92 CH.NY67/R) Faune (19x9cm-7x4in) s.d.18.6.57 col.crayons terracotta
£11351	$21000	(12-Jun-92 SY.NY160/R) Joueur de Cymballes (14cm-6in) i.num.3/6 gold
£13295	$23000	(2-Oct-91 SY.NY36/R) Tete de femme (12cm-5in) i. dark brown pat.bronze
£16393	$30000	(11-May-92 CH.NY6/R) Tete de femme (12cm-5in) s. dark brown pat.bronze
£27429	$48000	(25-Feb-92 CH.NY77/R) Priape (5cm-2in) brown gold pat.bronze
£40000	$76400	(1-Jul-92 S162/R) Tete de femme (18cm-7in) i.d.1908 num.2/6 bronze st.f.C.Valsuani
£62000	$112220	(3-Dec-91 C278 a/R) Femme arrangeant ses Cheveux (42cm-17in) num.10/10 base brn.pat.bronze Cast.C Valsuani
£76503	$140000	(14-May-92 SY.NY282/R) Le hibou blanc et noir (35cm-14in) s.d.52 painted unglazed terracotta
£120000	$210000	(25-Feb-92 CH.NY99/R) Tete de taureau (37cm-15in) num.2/2 black pat.bronze f.st.E.Godard

PICAULT, E (1839-?) French

| £929 | $1700 | (3-Jun-92 D.NY725/R) La nuit en dormant la nature il d'Ischia - two allegorical figures (46cm-18in) s. bronze |
| £1202 | $2200 | (3-Jun-92 D.NY716) Standing winged male figure (79cm-31in) s. bronze |

PICAULT, Emile (1839-?) French

£756	$1285	(25-Oct-91 BM.B1856/R) Virtutes civicae-ense et Labore (61cm-24in) i. pat.bronze (DM 2200)
£1500	$2670	(29-Nov-91 S79/R) Perseus and Pegasus with the head of Medusa (50cm-20in) s. brown pat.bronze i.Salon des Beaux Arts
£1580	$2750	(13-Sep-91 SY.NY40/R) Figure of wine merchant (71cm-28in) i. green-brown pat.bronze
£1977	$3400	(10-Oct-91 FA.PH782/R) Medieval soldiers, one with sword and banner, one with cross bow, sword (79x69cm-31x27in) s.bronze
£1986	$3574	(21-Nov-91 RAS.K962) Youth with wings standing on cloud (97cm-38in) s.i. pat.bronze (D.KR 22000)
£2000	$3560	(29-Nov-91 S103/R) Le jour naissant (85cm-33in) s.i. brown pat.bronze
£3000	$5130	(20-Mar-92 S127/R) La victoire (97cm-38in) s.i. brown pat.bronze i.F.Susse Fres Edts
£3800	$6498	(10-Mar-92 PH50/R) Scantily clad maiden seated on eagle with outstretched wings (103cm-41in) s.i. bronze on marble plinth

PICAULT, Emile (after) (1839-?) French

| £1414 | $2700 | (3-Jul-92 S.W3151/R) Reveil de la nature (86cm-34in) s. brown pat.bronze |
| £1437 | $2500 | (13-Sep-91 S.W2643) David (165cm-65in) s. brown pat.bronze |

PICCIRILLI, Attilio (1868-1945) American

| £1092 | $1900 | (15-Apr-92 SY.NY109/R) Outcast (16cm-6in) i. dark brown pat.bronze |

PIENOTTI (19th C) ?

| £1293 | $2250 | (10-Sep-91 B.SF299/R) Bust of 18th Century woman, with rose in pompadour hairstyle (71cm-28in) i. marble |

PIGALLE (after) (18/19th C) French

| £900 | $1638 | (27-May-92 SWS373/R) Figure of Mercury seated on rocky outcrop (58cm-23in) weathered green pat.bronze |
| £1121 | $2086 | (19-Jun-92 CN.P78/R) Le Marechal de Saxe (84cm-33in) plaster (F.FR 11000) |

PIGALLE, Jean Baptiste (after) (1714-1785) French

| £1789 | $3400 | (23-Jun-92 CE.NY9/R) L'amour et l'Aamitie, allegorical group (147x74cm-58x29in) i.d.1758 terracotta |

PILON, Germain (after) (c.1533-1590) French

| £1871 | $3200 | (13-Mar-92 WOL.C873/R) The Three Graces (71cm-28in) bronze |

PINA, Alfredo (1883-?) Italian

£1124	$2000	(30-Apr-92 CE.NY78/R) Figure of workhorse (33cm-13in) i. reddish-brown pat.bronze
£2800	$4844	(25-Mar-92 S26/R) Nudo seduto (29cm-11in) i. bronze cire perdue Cast.A G 13
£5200	$8892	(20-Mar-92 S175/R) Beethoven (79cm-31in) s. bronze on marble plinth st.f.A.G.Paris

PINAZO MARTINEZ, Ignacio (1883-1970) Spanish

| £2765 | $5198 | (16-Dec-91 ANS.M467/R) Enigma (44x56cm-17x22in) s. bronze on marble base (S.P 500000) |

PINEDO (19th C) French

| £1202 | $2200 | (3-Jun-92 D.NY591/R) Woman looking in mirror (36cm-14in) s. bronze |

PINEDO, Emile (19th C) French

| £802 | $1380 | (15-Oct-91 RAS.K674/R) Arab with knife in his belt (60cm-24in) s. brown pat bronze (D.KR 9000) |

PIQTOUKUN, David Ruben (1950-) North American

| £1376 | $2518 | (1-Jun-92 W.T728/R) Flying spirit bird with head of chanting shaman with inset eyes (46cm-18in) s. mottled soapstone (C.D 3000) |

PITER, Riccardo (20th C) Italian
£907 $1660   (12-May-92 F.R137) La vanita (61x23x13cm-24x9x5in) s.d.1938 brown
                  pat.bronze (I.L 2000000)

PLAZZOTTA, Enzo (1921-) Italian
£853 $1629   (21-Jul-92 JRL.S173/R) Pieta (62cm-24in) st.sig.num.6/9 bronze (A.D 2200)
£1200 $2292   (2-Jul-92 CSK14 a/R) Naked girl with pony tail standing with one hand
                  raised to mouth (58cm-23in) s.num.8/9 pat.bronze
£1200 $2292   (2-Jul-92 CSK14 b) Kneeling naked girl bronze
£1357 $2591   (21-Jul-92 JRL.S170/R) Acquavella Fountain (115cm-45in) st.sig.num.1/8
                  bronze (A.D 3500)
£1714 $3000   (28-Feb-92 SY.NY332/R) Joni - crouching position (32cm-13in) st.sig.
                  num.5/12 brown pat.bronze f.st.Mariani
£1744 $3000   (12-Oct-91 SY.NY174/R) Swimmer (30cm-12in) i.num.6/9 greenish-black
                  pat.bronze f.st.
£1900 $3325   (27-Sep-91 C44/R) Anthony Dowell (46cm-18in) s.num.1/9 front
                  brn.pat.bronze stone base
£2500 $4375   (27-Sep-91 C45/R) Anthony Dowell (46cm-18in) s.i.num.1/12 base
                  brn.pat.bronze bronze base
£3800 $6650   (27-Sep-91 C43/R) Sibley in repose (39cm-15in) s.num.6/9 base
                  brn.pat.bronze stone base
£4200 $7644   (27-May-92 SWS395/R) Figure of Adam (167cm-66in) s.d.1967 white marble
£4500 $8325   (11-Jun-92 C106/R) Summer dream (66x112cm-26x44in) s.num.6/9 green/blue
                  pat.bronze f.st.
£7364 $14066   (21-Jul-92 JRL.S163/R) Ballet shoes (175cm-69in) st.sig.num.5/9 bronze
                  (A.D 19000)

PLE, Henri Honore (1853-1922) French
£4200 $7182   (20-Mar-92 S112/R) Fisherwoman in boat (83cm-33in) s.d.1886 brown
                  pat.bronze

PLENSA, Jaume (20th C) ?
£3850 $6969   (21-May-92 CC.P88/R) Suite del Silenci II (106x46x37cm-42x18x15in) bronze
                  (F.FR 38000)
£5982 $10647   (28-Apr-92 EP.M31/R) Cabeza de Pajaro (19x34x21cm-7x13x8in) iron
                  (S.P 1100000)

POELS, Albert (1903-1984) Belgian
£2649 $4795   (23-May-92 KV.L417/R) Reinaert en Tijl (60x30cm-24x12in) s. wood marble
                  socle (B.FR 160000)

POERTZEL, Otto (1876-?) German
£825 $1435   (17-Sep-91 FN.S639/R) Butterfly dancer (19cm-7in) s. gold bronze marble
                  base (DM 2400)
£1500 $2550   (25-Oct-91 S368/R) Snake charmer (27cm-11in) cold painted bronze ivory
                  onyx

POHL, Adolf Josef (1872-?) Austrian
£994 $1699   (20-Mar-92 D.V365/R) Squatting female nude (14cm-6in) s.c.1900/10 gold
                  brown pat.bronze f.A.Rubinstein (A.S 20000)

POISSON, Pierre Marie (1876-1953) French
£3080 $5544   (18-Nov-91 AT.P369/R) Danseuse Ouled Nail (23x13cm-9x5in) s.base num.4
                  bronze Cast.Valsuani cire perdue (F.FR 30000)

POITEVIN, Philippe (1831-1907) French
£4000 $7120   (1-Nov-91 S26/R) Torchere, support in form of greyhound, seated on
                  haunches (98cm-39in) s. spelter

POLET, Johan (1894-?) Dutch
£2576 $4662   (21-May-92 SY.AM160/R) Reclining nude (86cm-34in) s. bronze (D.FL 8500)

POLI, Paolo de (20th C) ?
£1100 $1870   (25-Oct-91 S365/R) Peacock (61cm-24in) i.d.1965 enamelled copper wood

POLLET, Joseph Michel-Ange (1814-1870) French
£950 $1691   (29-Nov-91 S86/R) Une heure de la nuit (33cm-13in) s. brown pat.bronze

POLLET, Joseph Michel-Ange and COUZO, D A (19th C) French
£1500 $2745   (15-May-92 S317) Art Nouveau bronzes (33cm-13in) i. pat.bronze pair

POLLOCK, Jackson (1912-1956) American
£4581 $8200   (6-May-92 CH.NY269/R) Self-portrait (11cm-4in) st.num.3/7 bronze

POMMEREULLE, Daniel (1937-) French
£757 $1302   (14-Oct-91 AT.P207/R) Objet de premonition (16x14x5cm-6x6x2in) s.num.3/8
                  Cast.Blanchet bronze (F.FR 7500)

POMODORO, Arnaldo (1926-) Italian
£2429 $4250   (28-Feb-92 SY.NY326/R) Bozzatto (21x17cm-8x7in) s.d.1966 silver mounted
                  on wood
£4000 $6880   (17-Oct-91 C52/R) Lettera (45x35cm-18x14in) s.i.d.77 num.1/2 gold
                  pat.bronze
£30000 $57300   (2-Jul-92 S65/R) La Colonna del Viaggiatore (134cm-53in) s.d.61 bronze
                  copper

POMODORO, Arnaldo (1926-) Italian-cont.
£35000 $60550   (26-Mar-92 S43/R) Stele (250x26x18cm-98x10x7in) s.d.59 num.1/2 bronze

POMODORO, Gio (1930-) Italian
£2088 $3926   (19-Dec-91 F.M60) Progetto per monumento (30x43x43cm-12x17x17in) num.3/12 bronze (I.L 4500000)
£2907 $5000   (12-Oct-91 SY.NY304/R) Radial G (18cm-7in) st.init.d.66 num.5/6 polished bronze

POMPON, Francois (1855-1933) French
£772 $1397   (4-Dec-91 CB.P2) Hippopotame (14cm-6in) plaster (F.FR 7500)
£772 $1397   (4-Dec-91 CB.P3) Tourterelle (23cm-9in) plaster (F.FR 7500)
£2669 $4805   (20-Nov-91 CN.P75/R) L'hippopotame (16cm-6in) s.base pat.bronze marble base (F.FR 26000)
£3086 $5586   (4-Dec-91 CB.P4) Coq, girouette (54cm-21in) soldered copper (F.FR 30000)
£5355 $9158   (18-Mar-92 PIC.P87 b/R) Le coq (22cm-9in) s. pat.bronze. Cast A.Hebrard cire perdue (F.FR 52000)
£8230 $14897   (2-Dec-91 CC.P3/R) Jeune oie (24cm-9in) s.base num.4/12 blk.pat.bronze Cast.Valsuani (F.FR 80000)
£28498 $51581   (4-Dec-91 CB.P1) Grand Duc (54cm-21in) s. marble (F.FR 277000)

PONIATOWSKI, Prince Josef Antoni (1763-1813) ?
£1852 $3296   (30-Apr-92 RAS.K1072/R) Polish nobleman and soldier (49cm-19in) ivory incl.wooden base (D.KR 21000)

PONSIN-ANDARAHY, Charles (1835-1885) French
£1955 $3500   (16-Nov-91 WOL.C378/R) Semi-nude North African figure wearing a fez (64cm-25in) bronze marble base

POPE, Nicholas (1949-) British
£420 $743   (10-Feb-92 B88) Model for the Grandes (54x43x30cm-21x17x12in) chk polyphant

PORTA, della (after) (16/17th C) Italian
£33000 $63360   (9-Jul-92 S77/R) Statuette of Farnese Hercules (62cm-24in) terracotta

POTTER, Louis McClellan (1873-1912) American
£1330 $2500   (18-Dec-91 SY.NY156/R) The backpacker (38cm-15in) i.d.1904 brown pat. bronze

POWERS, Hiram (1805-1873) American
£3191 $6000   (18-Dec-91 SY.NY151/R) Proserpine (61cm-24in) i. marble
£16575 $30000   (6-Dec-91 CH.NY46/R) Hope (71cm-28in) s. white marble
£17000 $30260   (1-Nov-91 JH1) Busts of young ladies (66cm-26in) white marble pair
£32000 $57920   (21-May-92 C41/R) Bust of Prosperpine rising from bed of leaves (53cm-21in) s. white marble on wood socle

POWERS, Hiram (after) (1805-1873) American
£787 $1400   (21-Jan-92 CE.NY65/R) Persephone (61cm-24in) white marble circular socle

PRADIER, Jean Jacques (1792-1852) French
£862 $1500   (13-Sep-91 SY.NY116/R) Figure of woman dressing (25cm-10in) i. golden brown pat.bronze
£1050 $1869   (29-Nov-91 S80/R) Femme nue endormie (5x18cm-2x7in) s.d.1842 brown pat.bronze st.f.Susse Freres
£2800 $4900   (20-Feb-92 C177/R) Pandora (41cm-16in) s.i. bronze Cast.E de Labroue
£3000 $5130   (20-Mar-92 S110/R) Seated lady undressing (23cm-9in) s. brown pat.bronze on wooden plinth
£3000 $5340   (29-Nov-91 S88/R) Phryne (66cm-26in) s. brown pat.bronze st.Susse Freres
£4500 $7875   (20-Feb-92 C188/R) La Toilette (52cm-20in) s.i. bronze Cast.Duplan and Salles
£5000 $8900   (29-Nov-91 S64) Zephyr and Flora (42cm-17in) s.i. brown pat.bronze

PRANTL, Karl (1923-) Austrian
£1564 $2784   (31-Oct-91 D.V69/R) Untitled (20x7x6cm-8x3x2in) mono. pat.bronze (A.S 32000)

PRATT, Bela Lyon (1867-1917) American
£3994 $7150   (14-Nov-91 GRO.B129/R) Nathan Hale (89cm-35in) i.num.257 greenish-brown pat.bronze f.st.NY
£6857 $12000   (26-Sep-91 CH.NY123/R) Nathan Hale (89cm-35in) i. brown pat.bronze f.st.Roman Works NY
£8791 $16000   (27-May-92 SY.NY33/R) Nathan Hale (89cm-35in) s.i. brown pat.bronze f.st.Roman Works NY

PREISS, F (1882-1943) German
£1000 $1830   (2-Jun-92 S417) Standing female nude (42cm-17in) i. col painted bronze onyx base
£1150 $2105   (11-May-92 HS487/R) Charleston dancer (39cm-15in) i. bronze ivory on marble socle
£3000 $5340   (29-Oct-91 SWS2062/R) Bathers clock group, with two kneeling figures, one male and one female (41cm-16in) bronze ivory

PREISS, Ferdinand (1882-1943) German

£900	$1719	(2-Jul-92 CSK72/R) The Spring, female nude standing beside gargoyle fountainhead (18cm-7in) pat.bronze ivory watch case
£1100	$2101	(2-Jul-92 CSK104/R) Sonny Boy, young boy standing with hands in pockets and red book i. cold painted bronze ivory onyx base
£1277	$2286	(6-May-92 GD.B2610/R) Awakening (23cm-9in) s. ivory bronze stone socle st.f.PK (S.FR 3500)
£1400	$2492	(29-Apr-92 C93/R) Aphrodite (22cm-9in) s. bronze ivory on onyx base
£1500	$2550	(25-Oct-91 S356/R) Sonny boy (21cm-8in) i. cold painted bronze ivory onyx
£1800	$3060	(25-Oct-91 S353/R) Sonny boy (21cm-8in) i. cold painted bronze ivory onyx
£1900	$3629	(2-Jul-92 CSK127/R) Russian dancer with tambourine (30cm-12in) s. silvered bronze ivory stone base
£1900	$3629	(2-Jul-92 CSK137/R) Maiden leaning forward holding torch (28cm-11in) s. silvered pat.bronze ivory
£2266	$4147	(2-Jun-92 SY.MI2/R) Figura femminile (35cm-14in) s.c.1925 bronze ivory on marble base (I.L 5000000)
£2400	$4080	(25-Oct-91 S349/R) Grecian with torch (29cm-11in) i. cold painted bronze ivory
£2732	$4672	(20-Mar-92 D.V374/R) Dancer Ekstase (44cm-17in) s.c.1930 ivory on onyx socle (A.S 55000)
£2800	$4984	(29-Apr-92 C102/R) Young woman golfer (21cm-8in) s. bronze ivory onyx base
£3000	$5730	(2-Jul-92 CSK97/R) Cabaret girl in short costume and skull cap (38cm-15in) s. silvered bronze ivory on onyx base
£3400	$6052	(29-Apr-92 C97/R) Moth girl (40cm-16in) s. bronze ivory on onyx base
£3500	$6230	(29-Apr-92 C94/R) Torch dancer (39cm-15in) s. bronze ivory on gilded base
£3534	$6184	(3-Apr-92 BM.B1574/R) Female dancer holding glass of champagne (41cm-16in) i. bronze (DM 10000)
£3534	$6184	(3-Apr-92 BM.B1575/R) Charleston dancer (41cm-16in) i. bronze marble socle (DM 10000)
£3600	$6120	(25-Oct-91 S369/R) Ecstasy (56cm-22in) i. cold painted bronze ivory marble onyx
£3600	$6408	(29-Apr-92 C100/R) Ecstasy, naked girl standing with arms raised (34cm-13in) s. ivory on onyx dish
£3600	$6588	(15-May-92 S339/R) Golfer (23cm-9in) i. painted bronze ivory marble
£4000	$6800	(25-Oct-91 S352/R) Beach dancer (39cm-15in) i. cold painted bronze ivory onyx
£4400	$8052	(15-May-92 S337/R) Javelin thrower (28cm-11in) i. painted bronze ivory onyx
£4550	$7735	(25-Oct-91 S350/R) Balancing (38cm-15in) i. cold painted bronze ivory marble
£5200	$9516	(15-May-92 S338/R) Con Brio (38cm-15in) i. painted bronze ivory onyx
£6500	$12415	(2-Jul-92 CSK142/R) The red dancer (41cm-16in) s. cold painted bronze ivory onyx base
£7400	$12580	(25-Oct-91 S351/R) Autumn dancer (36cm-14in) i. cold painted bronze ivory onyx marble
£17000	$31110	(15-May-92 S336/R) The archer (46cm-18in) i. painted bronze ivory onyx

PRIEUR, Barthelemy (attrib) (1540-1611) French

£2000	$3640	(10-Dec-91 C80/R) Model of stag, shown trotting forward (20cm-8in) reddish-gold pat.bronze
£2500	$4800	(9-Jul-92 S101/R) Statuette of peasant, with sickle tucked in belt, carrying basket (14cm-6in) black lacquer over dark brown pat.bronze

PRINNER, Anton (1902-1983) French

£1636	$2994	(3-Feb-92 HH.P10/R) Jeune femme en buste (28x9x5cm-11x4x2in) s.num.2/8 pat.bronze Cast.Landowski (F.FR 16000)
£1636	$2994	(3-Feb-92 HH.P94/R) Jeune femme a la tresse (31x9x10cm-12x4x4in) s.num.4/8 brn.pat.bronze Cast.Landowski (F.FR 16000)
£1933	$3537	(14-May-92 BG.P79/R) Femme allongee (79cm-31in) s.num.6/8 bronze Cast.Bocquel (F.FR 19000)

PRINZ'IVALLI, Michel (1956-) ?

£855	$1471	(7-Oct-91 HH.P60/R) Fifty Fifty (177x84x45cm-70x33x18in) s.d.1991verso wood acrylic vegetable paints (F.FR 8500)

PROCTOR, Alexander Phimister (1860-1950) American

£4396	$8000	(27-May-92 SY.NY35/R) Polar bear (20cm-8in) s. brown pat.bronze f.i.H.Bonnard NY
£4396	$8000	(28-May-92 CH.NY98/R) Stalking panther (96cm-38in) i. bronze red green brown pat.
£4420	$8000	(5-Dec-91 SY.NY42/R) The Indian warrior (48cm-19in) i. brown pat.bronze st.f.Gorham Co.

PUECH, Denis (1854-1942) French

£3568	$6636	(19-Jun-92 ARC.P27) La Seine - Grand nu couche (70x130cm-28x51in) s. white marble (F.FR 35000)
£75000	$131250	(27-Sep-91 S33/R) La Sirene (153cm-60in) s.d.1903 Carrara marble

PUGI, G (19th C) Italian

£1108	$2116	(30-Jun-92 SY.AM464/R) Lady seated on sofa (64x49cm-25x19in) s. marble alabaster (D.FL 3600)

PURYEAR, Martin (1941-) American
£18436 $33000   (5-May-92 CH.NY115/R) Untitled (46x35x25cm-18x14x10in) d.1987 i.num.2/5
                      bronze wall relief

QUEROL, Agustin (attrib) (1863-1909) Spanish
£1366 $2323   (23-Oct-91 DUR.M967/R) Busto de joven (47cm-19in) white marble
                      (S.P 250000)

RADECKER, Antoon (1887-1960) Dutch
£1970 $3565   (19-May-92 CH.AM109/R) Mask (27cm-11in) init. stone (D.FL 6500)

RADECKER, John (1885-1956) Dutch
£1152 $2084   (19-May-92 CH.AM105/R) Standing woman (29cm-11in) init. bronze
                      (D.FL 3800)
£4938 $8988   (12-Dec-91 SY.AM110/R) Madonna met kind (64cm-25in) init.d.1928 bronze
                      wood base (D.FL 16000)

RANCOULET, Ernest (19th C) French
£928 $1587   (9-Mar-92 AT.P292/R) A Trouville (57cm-22in) s.i. brn.pat.bronze
                      (F.FR 9000)
£1027 $1900   (8-Jun-92 B.LA1160/R) Young maiden holding cornucopia standing on winged
                      wheel (81cm-32in) i. green brown pat.bronze
£3800 $6498   (20-Mar-92 S147/R) Triumphator (108cm-43in) s.i. brown pat.bronze
                      swivelling socle

RATHSACK, Svend (1885-1941) Danish
£1984 $3531   (25-Nov-91 BU.K45/R) Two boys dancing (104cm-41in) mono.d.23-24 bronze
                      (D.KR 22000)

RAUSCHENBERG, Robert (1925-) American
£8380 $15000   (7-May-92 SY.NY298/R) Personal box (6x14x8cm-2x6x3in) assemblage paper
                      collage bone fabric wood box
£10056 $18000   (7-May-92 SY.NY299/R) Personal box (4x12x6cm-2x5x2in) assemblage paper
                      collage bone string fabric box
£122905 $220000   (13-Nov-91 SY.NY56/R) Untitled - Venezuela painting
                      (201x251x49cm-79x99x19in) acrylic collage panels objects
£698324 $1250000   (13-Nov-91 SY.NY32/R) Small red painting (70x53x12cm-28x21x5in) combine
                      painting

RAYNAUD, Jean Pierre (1939-) French
£2572 $4887   (26-Jun-92 FB.P94/R) Untitled (25cm-10in) s. terracotta pot (F.FR 25000)
£4938 $9383   (26-Jun-92 FB.P72/R) Mur Lampe (55x45cm-22x18in) s.i.d.1971verso
                      assemblage panel (F.FR 48000)
£5761 $10947   (26-Jun-92 FB.P46/R) Extincteur N.1 (55x45cm-22x18in) s.d.1968 assemblage
                      panel (F.FR 56000)
£21000 $36330   (26-Mar-92 C46/R) Psycho Objet (103x122cm-41x48in) s.d.61verso ceramic
                      tiles, metal screenprints
£23663 $44959   (26-Jun-92 FB.P47/R) Psycho-objet (187x122cm-74x48in) s.d.1966
                      photos.gravel crutches case panel (F.FR 230000)
£32000 $55040   (17-Oct-91 S60/R) Psycho-objet 27 B2 (122x183x10cm-48x72x4in) init.d.66
                      v. photos plaques tileboard hardware

REBEYROLLE, Paul (1926-) French
£808 $1430   (24-Apr-92 CN.P210/R) Lezard et son nid (13x27x40cm-5x11x16in) bronze
                      (F.FR 8000)

REINHAREZ, Magdalena (20th C) French?
£1610 $2769   (7-Oct-91 HH.P91/R) La corrida (29x47x26cm-11x19x10in) s.num.1/8
                      brn.green pat.bronze Cast.Capelli (F.FR 16000)

REINHOUD (20th C) ?
£1852 $3352   (5-Dec-91 BG.P82/R) Sculpture (39cm-15in) pewter (F.FR 18000)
£2932 $5336   (11-Dec-91 CH.AM395/R) Avocette (34cm-13in) welded copper (D.FL 9500)

REMINGTON, Frederic (1861-1909) American
£1190 $2000   (14-Aug-91 B.P101/R) Coming through the Rye (71x71x41cm-28x28x16in) s.
                      base bronze
£1898 $3472   (17-May-92 BU.M562) Mounted Indian below steep cliff (70cm-28in) s.i.
                      brown pat bronze marble base (S.KR 20000)
£142857 $260000   (27-May-92 SY.NY39/R) Mountain man (72cm-28in) s.i. num.10 brown
                      pat.bronze f.st.Roman Work NY

REMINGTON, Frederic (after) (1861-1909) American
£800 $1464   (13-May-92 CBB371) The bear hunt (46cm-18in) bronze
£850 $1556   (13-May-92 CBB389) Bucking bronco (56cm-22in) bronze marble base
£900 $1548   (4-Mar-92 CBB384) Cowboy on horseback (49cm-19in) bronze oval base
£916 $1750   (17-Jul-92 DM.D2162) Bronco Buster (81cm-32in) brown pat.bronze

REMINGTON, Frederic (after) (1861-1909) American-cont.
£2267 $3900   (10-Oct-91 FA.PH797) Outlaw (58cm-23in) i. green pat.bronze f.i.Roman
                  Works N.Y.

RENAUD, Francis (1887-?) French
£1050 $2006   (2-Jul-92 CSK136/R) Naked young butterfly girl rising up from flowing
                  robe (28cm-11in) s. bronze

RENDA (?) ?
£1071 $1800   (1-Sep-91 PO.BA36) Nino (42cm-17in) s. pat.bronze on marble base

RENOIR, Pierre Auguste (1841-1919) French
£7500 $14325   (29-Jun-92 CSK16/R) Tete de danseuse (17cm-7in) with sig. num.2/4 dark
                   green pat.bronze f.st.
£9000 $16290   (2-Dec-91 CSK34/R) Tete de femme (39cm-15in) i. green pat.bronze
                   st.f.Alexis Rudier Paris

RENOIR, Pierre Auguste and GUINO, Richard (20th C) French
£9836 $18000   (14-May-92 SY.NY239/R) Buste de Coco (28cm-11in) i. dark brown pat.bronze
                   st.f.Valsuani

RENS, Roland (1952-) Belgian
£795 $1438   (23-May-92 KV.L277) Verteller (22x24cm-9x9in) bronze (B.FR 48000)
£821 $1486   (7-Dec-91 KV.L265) Dreaming (27x37cm-11x15in) bronze brown pat.
                  (B.FR 48000)

REUTER, Fritz Ernst (1911-) German
£1195 $2162   (23-May-92 GB.B7145) Female torso (95cm-37in) plaster (DM 3500)

RICCIO, Andrea (school) (1470-1532) Italian
£1397 $2500   (14-Jan-92 CH.NY138/R) Figure of Caesar Augustus, standing wearing togo
                  and laurel wreath (33cm-13in) brown pat.bronze black lacquer

RICHEFEU, Charles Ed (1868-1945) French
£1461 $2600   (22-Jan-92 SY.NY420/R) Hands up (63cm-25in) i.d.1919 dark brownish green
                  pat.bronze f.i.

RICHIER, Germaine (1904-1959) French
£6701 $11593   (23-Mar-92 GL.P158/R) Weiblicher Akt (67cm-26in) init.num.21/30 cast
                   cement (F.FR 65000)
£20765 $38000   (13-May-92 CH.NY312/R) Personnage menacant (32cm-13in) lead coloured
                   glass
£21000 $40110   (30-Jun-92 C205/R) L'Epi (44cm-17in) s. dark brown pat.bronze
                   f.st.Valsuani
£52632 $94737   (21-Nov-91 L.K423/R) Don Quichotte a l'aile de moulin (53cm-21in) i. gold
                   pat.bronze st.f.Thinot (DM 150000)
£67210 $122994   (3-Jun-92 PIC.P88/R) Don Quichotte a l'aile de moulin (56cm-22in) s.
                   gilded pat.bronze. Cast.Thinot (F.FR 660000)

RICKEY, George (1907-) American
£1105 $1900   (12-Oct-91 SY.NY366/R) Moving blade 1964 (24cm-9in) num.33 metal
£3123 $5621   (19-Nov-91 L.K1044/R) Mobile (47cm-19in) s.num.2/5 steel wooden socle
                   (DM 8900)
£4286 $7500   (27-Feb-92 CE.NY234/R) One vertical, one horizontal line diagonal
                   (59x59x7cm-23x23x3in) with sig. num.1/3 d.1984 stainless steel
£5152 $9324   (19-May-92 CH.AM328/R) Unstable Square I (77x61cm-30x24in) s.d.71 num.66
                   stainless steel mobile (D.FL 17000)
£6069 $10500   (3-Oct-91 SY.NY46/R) Four lines in a square with diagonal
                   (75x61x7cm-30x24x3in) s.d.70 stainless steel
£6145 $11000   (14-Nov-91 SY.NY334 a/R) Column with six lines (34x33x18cm-13x13x7in)
                   s.d.1975 num.3/3 stainless steel
£8191 $14908   (30-May-92 VG.B404/R) Two lines up eccentric (142cm-56in) s.d.1975 mobile
                   out door-plastic stainless steel (DM 24000)
£14525 $26000   (13-Nov-91 CH.NY205/R) Two lines leaning, gyratory
                   (244x209x209cm-96x82x82in) sig.num.1/3 d.1981base stainless steel
£32961 $59000   (13-Nov-91 CH.NY194/R) Two open triangles up gyratory
                   (312x330x89cm-123x130x35in) sig.num.2/3 d.1982base stainless steel
£55866 $100000   (7-May-92 SY.NY277/R) Two lines oblique down (518cm-204in) stainless
                   steel

RIGANELLI, Agustin (1890-1949) Argentinian
£1437 $2500   (19-Sep-91 V.BA87/R) El pionero (34x20x20cm-13x8x8in) plaster
£1648 $3000   (11-Dec-91 RO.BA73/R) Cabeza de nina (38cm-15in) s. bronze on marble base
£2473 $4500   (11-Dec-91 RO.BA72/R) Cabeza de nina (46cm-18in) s. quebracho on marble
                  base
£3488 $6000   (9-Oct-91 RO.BA218 b) Serenidad (56cm-22in) s. pat.bronze on marble base

RIGHETTI, Francesco (1738-1819) Italian
£1923 $3500   (26-May-92 SY.NY115/R) Figure of Apollo Belvedere, barely draped with
                  left hand outstretched (34cm-13in) i.d.1787 brown pat.bronze beneath
                  green lacquer

RINALDI, Rinaldo (1793-1873) Italian
£13000 $23140   (29-Nov-91 S74/R) Spring and winter (153cm-60in) s. marble pair

RINEHART, William Henry (1825-1874) American
£4678 $8000   (12-Mar-92 CH.NY110/R) Penserosa (61cm-24in) s.d.1870 white marble

RINEHART, William Henry (attrib) (1825-1874) American
£3846 $7000   (28-May-92 CH.NY85/R) Bust of Juno (66cm-26in) bears.sig. marble

RIVERA, Jose de (1904-) American
£4571 $8000   (25-Feb-92 SY.NY103/R) Untitled (53x102cm-21x40in) st.sig.d.1951 brass
£8939 $16000   (7-May-92 SY.NY242 a/R) Construction no.2 (44x56x51cm-17x22x20in) stainless steel

ROBERT, Louis Valentin Elias (1821-1874) French
£2589 $4350   (1-Sep-91 PO.BA33) Figuras clasicas sosteniendo anforas (50cm-20in) s. bronze two

ROBUS, Hugo (19/20th C) American
£957 $1800   (18-Dec-91 SY.NY346/R) Meditating girl (19cm-7in) i. bronze gold pat.
£977 $1700   (15-Apr-92 SY.NY124/R) Meditating girl (20cm-8in) i. silver

ROCCATAGLIATA, Niccolo (attrib) (16/17th C) Italian
£6500 $12480   (7-Jul-92 C139/R) Andiron of bearded satyr's mask flanked by winged horses with satyrs (45x69cm-18x27in) bronze
£12000 $23040   (7-Jul-92 C152/R) Cupid holding conch shell on knees seated on gnarled tree trunk (16cm-6in) bronze inkwell

ROCCATAGLIATA, Niccolo (studio) (16/17th C) Italian
£56701 $98093   (26-Mar-92 PIC.P63/R) Putti jouant de la flute, de la mandoline, de la trompette et du tambour (36cm-14in) dark pat.bronze on marble socles four (F.FR 550000)

ROCCHI, Francesco de (1902-) Italian
£905 $1647   (26-May-92 SY.MI31/R) Testa (29cm-11in) s. terracotta (I.L 2000000)

RODIN, Auguste (1840-1917) French
£1163 $2000   (12-Oct-91 SY.NY4/R) Tete de Damnee (9cm-4in) i. num.7 brown pat.bronze f.st.Susse Paris
£1366 $2459   (19-Nov-91 FP.M118/R) Main No. 30 (11cm-4in) s. pat.bronze f.i.G.Rudier, France (C.D 2800)
£1657 $3000   (5-Dec-91 SY.NY57/R) Head of a muse (11cm-4in) i. greenish black pat.bronze i.f.Alexis Rudier
£1744 $3000   (12-Oct-91 SY.NY1/R) Bust of Andrieu d'Andres (8cm-3in) i.d.1985 num.4/8 black pat.bronze f.st.E.Godard
£2348 $4250   (5-Dec-91 SY.NY56/R) Petite masque d'Iris (10cm-4in) i. greenish black pat.bronze i.f.C.Rudier
£2907 $5000   (12-Oct-91 SY.NY3/R) Tete de femme au nez retroussee (13cm-5in) i.d.1965 greenish-black pat.bronze f.st.Rudier
£2973 $5500   (12-Jun-92 SY.NY10/R) Tete de l'homme au nez casse (9cm-4in) i. green pat.bronze i.f.G.Rudier
£3500 $6020   (16-Oct-91 S15/R) Tete coupee de St Jean Baptiste (27x20x15cm-11x8x6in) s.st.sig. bronze i.Alexis Rudier Fondeur Paris
£3620 $6552   (4-Dec-91 KH.K175/R) Psyche-Pomone (32cm-13in) s. Cast.Georges Rudier bronze (D.KR 40000)
£3779 $6500   (12-Oct-91 SY.NY2/R) Main No 19 (9cm-4in) i. brownish-black pat.bronze f.st.G. Rudier
£3825 $7000   (13-May-92 SY.NY202/R) L'homme assis, les jambes etendues (15cm-6in) s.i.num.7 d.1965 brown pat.bronze st.f.G.Rudier
£4469 $8000   (9-May-92 CE.NY8/R) Main no 1 (11cm-4in) s.i.d.1960 green brown pat.bronze i.f.G.Rudier
£4571 $8000   (25-Feb-92 CH.NY3/R) Main no. 1 (12cm-5in) s. dark brown pat.bronze f.i.A.Rudier, Paris
£5714 $10000   (25-Feb-92 CH.NY2/R) Main no. 35 (14cm-6in) s.i. brown pat.bronze f.i.Georges Rudier, Paris
£6301 $10963   (15-Apr-92 CB.P8/R) Iris messagere des dieux (40cm-16in) s. terracotta (F.FR 62000)
£6500 $11180   (16-Oct-91 S16/R) Masque de Hanako (18cm-7in) s. bronze st.f.Alexis Rudier Paris
£6993 $12448   (30-Nov-91 VG.B110/R) L'homme au nez casse (26cm-10in) i.brown pat.bronze alabaster socle st.f.A.Rodier (DM 20000)
£7000 $12040   (16-Oct-91 S19/R) Petit torse feminin (18cm-7in) s.num.9 d.1979 bronze st.f.Coubertin
£7509 $13666   (30-May-92 VG.B108/R) L'homme au nez casse (26cm-10in) i.d.1864 green black pat.bronze st.f.A.Rudier (DM 22000)
£8000 $14240   (29-Nov-91 S136/R) Suzon (39cm-15in) s. brown pat.bronze on socle on marble plinth
£10929 $20000   (13-May-92 CH.NY203/R) Mercure debout (35cm-14in) s.i.num.12 dark brown green pat.bronze f.i.
£11000 $21010   (1-Jul-92 S113/R) Polypheme (24cm-9in) st.sig.i. bronze i.f.Alexis Rudier
£11000 $18920   (16-Oct-91 S13/R) Mouvement de danse I (13x23cm-5x9in) s.i.d.1963 num.1 bronze st.George Rudier
£11200 $19376   (25-Mar-92 S24/R) La toilette de Venus (43cm-17in) s.indist.i. plaster
£11429 $20000   (25-Feb-92 CH.NY25/R) Ombre se peignant (17cm-7in) s. brown green pat.bronze f.i.A.Rodin Rudier
£13595 $23112   (27-Oct-91 LT.P80/R) Le baiser (25cm-10in) s. brn.green pat.bronze Cast.Alexis Rudier (F.FR 135000)
£14208 $26000   (13-May-92 SY.NY205/R) Torse d'homme (16cm-6in) i.num.2 green pat.bronze

RODIN, Auguste (1840-1917) French-cont.

£16500	$29865	(4-Dec-91 S109/R) L'homme au nez casse (25cm-10in) i. bronze f.st.Alexis Rudier Fondeur Paris
£18519	$33519	(2-Dec-91 CC.P7/R) Torse d'Adele (44cm-17in) blk.pat.bronze Cast.Alexis Rudier (F.FR 180000)
£19000	$34390	(4-Dec-91 S110/R) Camille Claudel au bonnet (25cm-10in) i. bronze f.st.Alexis Rudier Fondeur Paris
£19429	$34000	(25-May-92 SY.NY1/R) Mouvement de danse B (31cm-12in) i.num.1 black green pat.bronze
£20765	$38000	(13-May-92 SY.NY203/R) Etude pour Iris, messagere des dieux (19cm-7in) i.num.3 d.1958 bronze
£21858	$40000	(13-May-92 SY.NY201/R) Mouvement de danse, exercise pour le port d'armes (33cm-13in) i.num.2 d.1958 brown pat.bronze
£22000	$42020	(30-Jun-92 C115/R) Tete de Saint Jean Baptiste (20x38x28cm-8x15x11in) i. marble
£26000	$49660	(1-Jul-92 S114/R) Jules Dalou (53cm-21in) st.sig.i.bronze i.f.Alexis Rudier
£26612	$47369	(28-Nov-91 FB.P22/R) Pierre de wiessant (45cm-18in) s. bronze Cast.Alexis Rudier (F.FR 260000)
£27322	$50000	(14-May-92 SY.NY229/R) Titans (99x99x99cm-39x39x39in) terracotta on plaster bases set of four
£30220	$55000	(11-Dec-91 RO.BA77/R) Le baiser (25cm-10in) s. pat.bronze f.F.Barbedienne
£31000	$53320	(16-Oct-91 S18/R) La jeunesse triomphante (52cm-20in) s. bronze
£38251	$70000	(14-May-92 SY.NY235/R) La main crispee (46cm-18in) s.i. black green pat.bronze st.f.Alexis Rudier
£38571	$67500	(25-Feb-92 SY.NY2/R) L'eternelle idole (29cm-11in) s.i. black pat.bronze st.f.Georges Rudier Paris
£42308	$80808	(19-Jul-92 SY.ME44/R) L'Athlete (43cm-17in) s.foundry George Rudier bronze (A.D 110000)
£43716	$80000	(14-May-92 SY.NY226/R) Le baiser (40cm-16in) i.num.23 gold brown pat.bronze st.f.Barbedienne
£45000	$85950	(1-Jul-92 S116/R) Deux enfants s'embrassant (35cm-14in) marble
£45000	$81450	(4-Dec-91 S107/R) L'Eternel printemps (39cm-15in) i. bronze f.st.F. Barbedienne Fondeur
£50000	$95500	(1-Jul-92 S115/R) Les Metamorphoses d'Ovide (32cm-13in) st.sig.i.bronze i.f.Alexis Rudier
£54527	$103601	(24-Jun-92 AT.P224/R) Le baiser (72cm-28in) s. brown-green pat.bronze. Cast.Barbedienne (F.FR 530000)
£54645	$100000	(14-May-92 SY.NY236/R) Venus (96cm-38in) i.num.6 d.1977 black pat.bronze st.f.E.Godard
£88571	$155000	(25-Feb-92 SY.NY25/R) L'athlete (39cm-15in) i. dark brown pat.bronze st.f.Alexis Rudier
£437158	$800000	(13-May-92 SY.NY67/R) Le penseur (72cm-28in) s.i. brown pat.bronze i.f.Alexis Rudier Paris

RODIN, Auguste (after) (1840-1917) French

£781	$1313	(28-Aug-91 EA.M669/R) Eternal Spring (48cm-19in) s. brn.pat.bronze marble base (C.D 1500)
£911	$1549	(23-Oct-91 EA.M470/R) Praying hands (58cm-23in) s. green pat.bronze (C.D 1750)

ROEDER, Emy (1890-1971) German

£1754	$3158	(21-Nov-91 L.K424/R) Young female carrying basket (44cm-17in) brown pat.bronze (DM 5000)

ROGERS, Randolph (1825-1892) American

£1429	$2500	(3-Apr-92 S.W2285/R) Bust portrait of gentleman, possibly Nathaniel Currier (79cm-31in) s.i. white marble
£10497	$19000	(5-Dec-91 SY.NY41/R) The last arrow (112x145cm-44x57in) i. brown pat.bronze i.f.Nelli

ROLAND, Philippe Laurent (1746-1816) French

£6626	$12324	(19-Jun-92 ARC.P132/R) Jeune Prince (35x29x18cm-14x11x7in) s.d.1774 ocre patina terracotta (F.FR 65000)

ROMAN SCHOOL, 17th C Italian

£1676	$3000	(14-Jan-92 CH.NY137/R) Bust of Lucius Verus (30cm-12in) brown pat.bronze black lacquer
£2000	$3640	(12-Dec-91 S147) Triton supporting figure blowing on conch shell (25cm-10in) bronze

ROMAN SCHOOL, 18th C Italian

£2235	$4000	(14-Jan-92 CH.NY143/R) Group of lion attacking horse (30cm-12in) greenish brown pat.bronze
£6200	$11284	(12-Dec-91 S248) Bust of Bacchic faun (60cm-24in) marble
£9000	$17280	(9-Jul-92 S206/R) Bacchic faun, carrying wine sack over shoulder and thyrsus in hand (51cm-20in) marble
£10000	$17800	(1-Nov-91 S292/R) Figure of Apollo Belvedere, by tree stump entwined with serpent (103cm-41in) bronze
£16733	$30287	(5-Dec-91 SY.Z37/R) Figures of negroes in flowing dress holding cornucopia (120cm-47in) wood painted and gilded porte-torcheres (S.FR 42000)

ROMANELLI, R (19/20th C) Italian
£4678 $8000   (13-Mar-92 WOL.C923 b/R) Figure of woman with roses in her hair (94cm-37in) s. marble
£5263 $9000   (13-Mar-92 WOL.C923 a/R) Figure of woman with upswept hair and holding a flower (104cm-41in) s. marble
£6579 $12500   (26-Jun-92 WOL.C824 a/R) Five putti seated on a bench looking at a sheet of music (76x97cm-30x38in) marble

ROMANELLI, Romano (1882-1958) Italian
£2557 $4500   (10-Apr-92 DM.D2110/R) Shepherd boy with flute (99cm-39in) s. marble

ROSATI, James (20th C) ?
£1676 $3000   (12-Nov-91 CE.NY22/R) Floating figure (162x114x28cm-64x45x11in) plaster wire mesh metel on wood base
£1890 $3250   (12-Oct-91 SY.NY308/R) Untitled (127cm-50in) i.d.74-80 cor-ten steel

ROSSET, Michel (1951-) French?
£1247 $2283   (3-Feb-92 HH.P48/R) La pensee (32x13x10cm-13x5x4in) s.num.1/8 brn.green pat.bronze Cast.Godard (F.FR 12200)

ROSSETTI, Antonio (1819-?) Italian
£12500 $21375   (20-Mar-92 S168/R) The shy nymph (124x52cm-49x20in) s. white marble on pillar

ROSSI, J N O (19th C) ?
£750 $1365   (27-May-92 SWS357) Bust of Diana, wearing diadem (61cm-24in) indist.s. white marble

ROSSI, Prof (19/20th C) ?
£1149 $2000   (13-Sep-91 SY.NY90/R) Girl standing next to tree (91cm-36in) i. marble figure i.f.Galeria Artistica Pero

ROSSO, M (19th C) Italian
£1360 $2488   (4-Jun-92 F.M239) Testa di ragazzo (35cm-14in) s. bronze (I.L 3000000)

ROSSO, Medardo (1858-1928) Italian
£16129 $28548   (7-Nov-91 AT.P80/R) Gavroche (31x15cm-12x6in) pat.bronze red marble base (F.FR 160000)
£34274 $60665   (7-Nov-91 AT.P79/R) L'enfant juif (24cm-9in) s.i. pat.wax (F.FR 340000)

ROTH, Frederick George Richard (1872-1944) American
£1514 $2800   (10-Jun-92 CE.NY372/R) Figure of reclining dog (19cm-7in) i. reddish brown pat.bronze

ROUSSEAU, Victor (attrib) (1865-1954) Belgian
£1771 $3100   (23-Sep-91 S.SL635) L'humanite arretant la guerre (81cm-32in) s. brn.gold pat.bronze green octagonal plinth

ROUX, Constant (1865-1929) French
£1124 $2000   (21-Jan-92 CE.NY72) Classical nude boy (94cm-37in) i. white marble

RUCKRIEM, Ulrich (1938-) German
£1117 $2000   (13-Nov-91 SY.NY110/R) Untitled (157x1x1cm-62x0x0in) felt tip paper two iron bars
£4211 $7579   (19-Nov-91 L.K1056/R) Untitled (100x50x50cm-39x20x20in) num.1/10 Alfanger granite (DM 12000)

RUNER, Johan (1861-1945) Swedish
£2554 $4623   (19-May-92 AB.S4559/R) Senta - nude woman standing (98cm-39in) s.d.1914 Carerra marble (S.KR 27000)

RUSTHOLLKARHU, Seija (1932-) Scandinavian
£776 $1382   (1-Dec-91 HOR.H194) The cat (16cm-6in) s. silver (F.M 6000)

RUTHENBECK, Reiner (1937-) German
£3158 $5684   (19-Nov-91 L.K1057/R) Triangle (50x29x1cm-20x11x0in) black metal (DM 9000)

RYBACK, Issachar (1897-1935) Russian
£798 $1500   (5-Jan-92 GG.TA359/R) The chicken vendor (27cm-11in) s. bronze

RYMAN, Robert (1930-) American
£67039 $120000   (14-Nov-91 SY.NY180/R) Converter (264x91x9cm-104x36x4in) s.d.84 verso oil aluminium

SAINT-GAUDEN, Augustus (1848-1907) American
£121547 $220000   (6-Dec-91 CH.NY57/R) Diana of the Tower (93cm-37in) i. red brown pat. bronze

SAINT-MARCEAUX, Rene (1845-1915) French
£2000 $3560   (29-Nov-91 S183/R) The Harlequin (68cm-27in) s.d.1879 gilt bronze
i.f.F.Barbedienne

SAINT-PHALLE, Niki de (1930-) French
£923 $1680   (25-May-92 ZZ.F102) Nana gonflable (46x38cm-18x15in) s. plastic
impression (F.FR 9100)
£2448 $4185   (21-Mar-92 WK.M547/R) La vache (14x25x12cm-6x10x5in) s.i. painted plaster
(DM 7000)
£2732 $4726   (23-Mar-92 CC.P152) Nana (25x36x30cm-10x14x12in) st.sig.num.489 polyester
polychrome (F.FR 26500)
£4424 $8007   (4-Dec-91 LD.P97/R) Femme aux formes genereuses (16cm-6in) s. plaster
(F.FR 43000)
£8000 $13760 (17-Oct-91 S47/R) Stool (50cm-20in) st.sig. num.3/10 acrylic on
fibreglass
£12000 $20640 (17-Oct-91 S44/R) Table (73cm-29in) st.sig. num.3/20 acrylic fibreglass
£14933 $25536 (17-Mar-92 FB.P79/R) Tabouret, table et vase num.EA 11/V polyester
polychrome (F.FR 145000)
£18004 $32587 (4-Dec-91 LD.P98/R) Danseuse (64cm-25in) s.d.21/9/66base plaster
(F.FR 175000)

SALY, Jacques Francois Joseph (after) (1717-1776) French
£2200 $3916   (1-Nov-91 S323/R) Bust of young girl (42cm-17in) terracotta

SAMARAS, Lucas (1936-) American
£8571 $15000 (25-Feb-92 SY.NY161/R) Box no 49 (32x30x28cm-13x12x11in) box wood wool
glass beads plexiglass plastic
£9249 $16000 (3-Oct-91 SY.NY122/R) Chicken wire box no.21 (35x30x41cm-14x12x16in)
painted wire construction
£11173 $20000 (14-Nov-91 SY.NY369/R) Box No 82 (26x30x28cm-10x12x11in) wood box
construction pins plaster paint
£15084 $27000 (7-May-92 SY.NY302/R) Self-portrait box (9x15x11cm-4x6x4in) wood box wool
nails steel pins photographs
£16760 $30000 (14-Nov-91 SY.NY359/R) Box no.83 (27x35x20cm-11x14x8in) mixed media wood
box
£23743 $42500 (7-May-92 SY.NY312/R) Sculpture table (106x132x89cm-42x52x35in) s.d.81
num.2/4 silver plated bronze
£23743 $42500 (6-May-92 SY.NY23/R) Box no 94 (33x33x66cm-13x13x26in) wood construction
wool yarn steel pins knives

SAMUEL, Charles (1862-?) Belgian
£1244 $2276   (12-May-92 C.A614) Tijl Uilenspiegel en Nele (64cm-25in) s. bronze
(B.FR 75000)

SANCHEZ, Jose Luis (1926-) Spanish
£1637 $2962   (20-May-92 ANS.M504/R) Mikonos (59x39cm-23x15in) s.d.1984 s.i.verso
marble (S.P 300000)

SANDOZ, Edouard-Marcel (1881-1971) Swiss
£1061 $1877   (22-Apr-92 ZZ.F279) Poisson sur la vague (14cm-6in) s. pat.bronze
(F.FR 10500)
£1181 $2125   (20-Nov-91 CN.P86/R) Vase carpe (28cm-11in) s. brn.pat.bronze Cast.F
Rosseni cire perdue (F.FR 11500)
£1901 $3250   (21-Mar-92 SY.NY222/R) Figure of hare (11x12cm-4x5in) i. marble
£2047 $3500   (21-Mar-92 SY.NY221/R) Figure of fish (18cm-7in) i. greenish-brown
pat.bronze f.st.Valsuani
£2990 $5112   (9-Mar-92 AT.P295) Rascasse (25x44cm-10x17in) s. brn.gold pat.bronze
Cast.Valsuani cire perdue (F.FR 29000)
£4800 $8160   (25-Oct-91 S360/R) Fish (25cm-10in) init.i.pat.silvered bronze

SANMARTINO, Giuseppe (style) (1720-1793) Italian
£5000 $9100   (12-Dec-91 S254/R) Group of two putti, allegorical of winter (66cm-26in)
marble

SARET, Alan (1944-) American
£3911 $7000   (13-Nov-91 CH.NY212/R) Spirit of the full born (91x69x56cm-36x27x22in)
copper col.plastic-coated wire

SARTEEL, Leon (1882-1942) Belgian
£1189 $2034   (21-Mar-92 KV.L251/R) Mother and child embracing (48x32cm-19x13in) s.
bronze br.pat. (B.FR 70000)
£1821 $3296   (23-May-92 KV.L286/R) Kneeling bather (96x34cm-38x13in) s. plaster beige
pat. (B.FR 110000)

SAULO, Georges Ernest (1865-?) French
£828 $1498   (23-May-92 KV.L288) Bust of young woman (26x32cm-10x13in) s. bronze
br.pat. (B.FR 50000)

SAUTNER, F (19/20th C) Austrian
£1130 $2000   (13-Feb-92 SY.NY7/R) Figure of man holding eagle (51cm-20in) i. black
pat.bronze

SAZIKOV (19/20th C) Russian
£4189 $7750   (10-Jun-92 SY.NY178/R) Horse and sled driven by Izvoshchik with companion
(26cm-10in) silver on silver marble base

SCAILLIET, Emile Philippe (1846-1911) French
£12000 $21000   (27-Sep-91 S71/R) Water Nymph (62cm-24in) s. ivory mirror plate calla
lillies ebony socle

SCHEEMAECKERS (style) (?) ?
£4400 $8008   (12-Dec-91 S212/R) Allegorical female figure, draped and holding poppies
or pomegranates (54cm-21in) terracotta

SCHEIBE, Richard (1879-1964) German
£1986 $3416   (8-Oct-91 ZEL.L2168/R) Portrait head of Paul Hindemith (32cm-13in) mono.
panel (DM 5800)

SCHERER, Hermann (1893-1927) Swiss
£2444 $4472   (4-Jun-92 SY.Z596/R) Pieta (110x61x71cm-43x24x28in) s. plaster
(S.FR 6500)

SCHMIDT (?) ?
£2025 $3401   (28-Aug-91 RAS.K1155/R) Woman dancing (38cm-15in) s.i. gilt bronze bone,
onyx base (D.KR 23000)

SCHMIDT-KESTNER, Erich (1877-?) German
£792 $1331   (28-Aug-91 RAS.K1181) Dancing model (37cm-15in) s. pat bronze marble base
(D.KR 9000)

SCHMIDT-ROTTLUFF, Karl (1884-) German
£5944 $10580   (25-Nov-91 WK.M898/R) Adorant (30x16x9cm-12x6x4in) st.sig. bronze
(DM 17000)

SCHNABEL, Julian (1951-) American
£47486 $85000   (5-May-92 CH.NY113 a/R) Stephen Janson known to some as Stephen Gluck
(182x152x8cm-72x60x3in) oil ceramic Bondo wood
£58659 $105000   (7-May-92 SY.NY143/R) Joe Glasco (183x152x13cm-72x60x5in) oil plates
bondo epoxy wood
£117318 $210000   (6-May-92 SY.NY45/R) Stella Maris (274x366x25cm-108x144x10in) oil plates
bondo on wood in five parts
£162011 $290000   (6-May-92 SY.NY37/R) Bob's worlds (248x371x30cm-98x146x12in) oil wax
bondo horns wood canvas

SCHNAUDER, Reinhard (1856-1923) German
£966 $1661   (16-Oct-91 KM.K1656/R) Female rider watering horse (75cm-30in) i.d.1920
bronze marble socle (DM 2800)

SCHOENENERK (19th C) ?
£26777 $45788   (20-Mar-92 ZZ.F61/R) L'Amour endormi porte par deux enfants (105cm-41in)
s.d.1863 marble wooden base (F.FR 260000)

SCHOENHOLTZ, Michael (1937-) German
£1297 $2360   (30-May-92 VG.B956/R) Man with landscape (79cm-31in) mono.d.1973 brown
pat.brown (DM 3800)

SCHOONHOVEN, Jan J (1914-) Dutch
£5455 $9873   (19-May-92 CH.AM332/R) R 71-32 (53x53cm-21x21in) s.i.d.1971 verso papier
mache relief (D.FL 18000)

SCHOTT, Walter (1861-1938) German
£1375 $2543   (13-Jun-92 WK.M382/R) Kugelspielerin (25cm-10in) s.c.1900 gold bronze
ivory on onyx marble socle (DM 4000)
£2577 $4485   (21-Sep-91 SA.A2454/R) Bust of Friedrich Wilhelm II (112x78cm-44x31in) s.
bronze (DM 7500)
£2800 $4984   (29-Nov-91 S142/R) Kaiser Wilhelm II (118cm-46in) s.i. marble

SCHRIEBER, Ludwig Gabriel (1907-1973) German
£3072 $5590   (30-May-92 VG.B283/R) Head of girl (34cm-13in) d.1951 wood (DM 9000)

SCHULZ, Moritz (1825-1904) German
£3000 $5430   (21-May-92 C12/R) Bust of Psyche (57cm-22in) s.d.69 white marble

SCHWAIGER, Rudolf (1924-1979) Austrian
£969 $1764   (26-May-92 D.V194/R) Man and woman (38cm-15in) s.d.1948 terracotta on
wooden socle (A.S 20000)
£1097 $1963   (15-Jan-92 D.V183/R) Female nude standing (46cm-18in) mono. terracotta
(A.S 22000)
£1297 $2360   (25-May-92 WK.M1141/R) Gaia (25x58x25cm-10x23x10in) d.1971 wood (DM 3800)

SCHWANTHALER, Franz Jakob (1760-1801) Austrian
£1742 $3171   (10-Dec-91 N.M66/R) Christ standing at the flagellation post (140cm-55in)
wood (DM 5000)

SCHWARZ, Heinz (1920-) Swiss
£711 $1266   (29-Nov-91 GAB.G2874) Suzanne (20cm-8in) olive pat.bronze (S.FR 1800)

SCHWITTERS, Kurt (1887-1948) German
£38251 $70000   (14-May-92 SY.NY293/R) C.68 Wanteeside (15x18cm-6x7in) s.i.d.1945
i.d.1946verso oil assemblage wood

SCIALOJA, Toti (1914-) Italian
£2759 $4939   (14-Nov-91 F.M121/R) Composizione (71x101cm-28x40in) cement on cardboard
                                (I.L 6000000)

SCOTT, Tim (20th C) ?
£1000 $1730   (26-Mar-92 S102/R) Shruti XI (49x45cm-19x18in) welded steel
£1500 $2580   (17-Oct-91 S124/R) Nrtta VI (62x44x47cm-24x17x19in) welded steel
£2800 $4956   (8-Nov-91 C380/R) Counterpoint (122x153x80cm-48x60x31in) perspex metal

SCUDDER, Janet (1873-1940) American
£2629 $4600   (26-Sep-91 CH.NY137/R) Frog baby (32cm-13in) i. black pat.bronze
                                f.st.Griffoul Newark N.J
£6630 $12000   (6-Dec-91 CH.NY182/R) Frog baby (31cm-12in) i. green brown pat. bronze

SCUDERI, J (?) ?
£835 $1428   (9-Mar-92 AT.P300/R) Carpe et grenouille (40x33cm-16x13in) s.
                                blk.pat.bronze Cast.Susse Freres cire perdue (F.FR 8100)

SEARS, Philip Shelton (1867-1953) American
£2339 $4000   (13-Mar-92 S.BM301/R) The diver (71cm-28in) s.i.d.1928 brown green
                                pat.bronze

SEAVER, Elizabeth A (fl.1930-1940) American
£2229 $3900   (26-Sep-91 CH.NY139/R) Adagio - figure of dancer (73cm-29in) i. brown
                                pat.bronze f.st.Antioch Art

SEGAL, George (1924-) American
£1486 $2750   (12-Jun-92 SY.NY284/R) Nude female torso (71x31cm-28x12in) s.d.82
                                num.22/30 verso plaster
£3831 $6628   (28-Mar-92 F.L101/R) Fragment girl resting (37cm-15in) s.d.1970 num.65/75
                                plaster (S.FR 10000)
£13966 $25000   (7-May-92 SY.NY331/R) jacket (190x56x18cm-75x22x7in) painted plaster wood

SEGER, Ernst (1868-?) German
£2657 $4569   (19-Oct-91 UA.U422/R) Dancer (183cm-72in) white marble on column
                                (S.KR 28000)

SEGRELLES, Eustaquio (19/20th C) Spanish
£1366 $2323   (24-Oct-91 DUR.M1340/R) Pescadoras (45cm-18in) s.num.6/50 d.90 bronze
                                (S.P 250000)

SEIFERT, V H (1870-1953) German
£2905 $4880   (28-Aug-91 RAS.K1156/R) Young woman with drinking cup (29cm-11in) s.i.
                                gilt bronze bone marble base (D.KR 33000)

SEIFERT, Victor Heinrich (1870-1953) German
£667 $1207   (19-May-92 GF.L476/R) Female nude with fishing rod standing on rock
                                (36cm-14in) i.c.1905 yellow pat.bronze (S.FR 1800)

SEITZ, Gustav (1906-1969) German
£1818 $3236   (30-Nov-91 VG.B990/R) Woman standing (26cm-10in) i.d.1951 brown
                                pat.bronze (DM 5200)
£3505 $6414   (3-Jun-92 L.K429/R) Female torso (20x10cm-8x4in) d.1955 brown pat.bronze
                                (DM 10200)

SERGEFF (?) ?
£1000 $1780   (29-Apr-92 C109/R) Nude woman with head to one side touching her long
                                hair (114cm-45in) s. wood

SERGEL, Johan Tobias (1740-1814) Swedish
£768 $1390   (3-Dec-91 AB.S4572) Portrait of Anna Maria Lenngren (63cm-25in) plaster
                                (S.KR 8000)
£787 $1424   (3-Dec-91 AB.S4573/R) Portrait of Gustav Fredrik Gyllenborg (63cm-25in)
                                plaster (S.KR 8200)
£816 $1476   (3-Dec-91 AB.S4575/R) Portrait of Karl Gustav of Leopold (63cm-25in)
                                plaster (S.KR 8500)
£931 $1685   (3-Dec-91 AB.S4574/R) Portrait of Johan Gabriel Oxenstierna (63cm-25in)
                                plaster (S.KR 9700)

SERRA, Richard (1939-) American
£39106 $70000   (13-Nov-91 SY.NY61/R) Balanced (246x157x2cm-97x62x1in) hot rolled steel
£111732 $200000   (13-Nov-91 SY.NY76/R) Kitty Hawk (242cm-95in) corten steel two plates

SERRANO, Pablo (c.1910-) Spanish
£1245 $2129   (17-Mar-92 FER.M221/R) El caballo (33cm-13in) iron (S.P 225000)
£1385 $2452   (12-Feb-92 ANS.M371/R) Corazon entre dos manos (17cm-7in) s.d.1981
                                num.47/92verso bronze (S.P 250000)
£2106 $3727   (12-Feb-92 ANS.M373/R) Tauromaquia (19x22x28cm-7x9x11in) s.num.25/68
                                bronze (S.P 380000)
£8186 $14079   (16-Oct-91 FER.M319/R) Ponce de Leon (43cm-17in) s. bronze
                                st.f.Codina-Madrid (S.P 1500000)

SEVERINI, Gino (1883-1966) Italian
£5285 $9195   (13-Apr-92 GL.P165/R) Sculpture (35x15x12cm-14x6x5in) s.base polychrome
                                plaster (F.FR 52000)

SEVERO DA RAVENNA (after) (15th C) Italian
£1900 $3458   (9-Dec-91 PH105/R) Kneeling satyr - inkstand (23cm-9in) bronze circular plinth

SEVERO DA RAVENNA (attrib) (15th C) Italian
£10500 $20160   (9-Jul-92 S114/R) Inkwell of dragon (10x25cm-4x10in) bronze

SEVERO DA RAVENNA (studio) (15th C) Italian
£6704 $12000   (14-Jan-92 CH.NY135/R) Inkstand, formed as kneeling satyr, brandishing club (27cm-11in) brown pat.bronze black lacquer

SHAPIRO, Joel (1941-) American
£6704 $12000   (6-May-92 CH.NY361/R) Untitled (24x27x17cm-9x11x7in) with sig.d.1987-1988 num.5/6 bronze metal base
£9000 $15570   (26-Mar-92 C100/R) Untitled (6x7x5cm-2x3x2in) s.num.1/3d.78-86 bronze
£12849 $23000   (7-May-92 SY.NY168/R) Untitled (8x15x8cm-3x6x3in) s.d.78 bronze
£29330 $52500   (14-Nov-91 SY.NY179/R) Untitled (60x33x20cm-24x13x8in) cast bronze
£47486 $85000   (7-May-92 SY.NY150/R) Untitled (7x60x44cm-3x24x17in) s.d.78 num.ap bronze
£48883 $87500   (7-May-92 SY.NY191/R) Untitled (146x86x89cm-57x34x35in) bronze
£64246 $115000   (5-May-92 CH.NY147/R) Untitled (122x130x80cm-48x51x31in) s.d.82/83 num.3/3 bronze
£86592 $155000   (14-Nov-91 SY.NY206/R) Untitled (147x173x152cm-58x68x60in) bronze
£111732 $200000   (6-May-92 SY.NY28/R) Untitled JSS 866 (178x203x76cm-70x80x30in) d.1989 num.2/4 bronze
£122905 $220000   (5-May-92 CH.NY12/R) Untitled (229x17x56cm-90x7x22in) d.1988-1989 num.3/4 bronze

SICARD, Francois Leon (1862-1934) French
£4802 $8500   (13-Feb-92 SY.NY18/R) Oedipus and sphinx - allegorical group (69cm-27in) i. brown pat.bronze

SIGNORET-LEDIEU, Lucie (1858-1904) French
£1100 $1881   (20-Mar-92 S162/R) Source (47cm-19in) s.i. brown pat.bronze
£1200 $2052   (20-Mar-92 S184/R) Nymphe de Diane (62cm-24in) s.num.9821 brown pat.bronze st.f.Paris A.B.

SILBERSTEIN, Fany (20th C) ?
£1534 $2807   (3-Feb-92 HH.P71/R) Esther debout (50cm-20in) s.num.2/8 blue green pat.bronze Cast.Clementi (F.FR 15000)

SILVERMAN, Martin (20th C) American
£1163 $2000   (12-Oct-91 SY.NY364/R) Bag man (38cm-15in) mono.num.5 painted bronze

SILVESTRE, Paul (1884-?) French
£2632 $4500   (21-Mar-92 SY.NY220/R) Leda and swan (34x79cm-13x31in) i. brown-black pat.bronze f.st.Susse Fes Paris

SIMMONDS, William George (1876-1968) British
£4800 $8784   (5-Feb-92 C201/R) Old English Rabbit (37cm-15in) painted wooden sculpture

SINDING, Stephan (1846-1922) Norwegian
£803 $1493   (16-Jun-92 RAS.V867 a) Two figures (27x32cm-11x13in) s. pat bronze (D.KR 9000)
£878 $1510   (7-Oct-91 B.O122/R) Man and woman embracing (24cm-9in) s. marble (N.KR 10000)
£1700 $2975   (20-Feb-92 C161/R) Brunhilda on horseback (52cm-20in) s.i. bronze Cast.Gladenbeck-Berlin
£1977 $3500   (13-Feb-92 SY.NY19/R) Figural group - to Mennesker (48cm-19in) i. brown pat.bronze
£7036 $12383   (8-Apr-92 GWP.O65/R) Two figures (50cm-20in) s. bronze (N.KR 80000)

SINTENIS, Renee (1888-1965) German
£1203 $2201   (3-Jun-92 L.K433/R) Young billy goat (6x8x5cm-2x3x2in) d.1916 1/25 mono brown pat.bronze (DM 3500)
£2048 $3727   (30-May-92 VG.B197/R) Self portrait (33cm-13in) i. brown pat.bronze stone socle st.f.H.Noack (DM 6000)
£2048 $3706   (23-May-92 GB.B7249/R) Fawn kneeling (8cm-3in) pat.bronze (DM 6000)
£2260 $4000   (5-Nov-91 CE.NY151/R) Liegender Hund (10cm-4in) st.init. brown pat.bronze st.f.Noack Berlin
£2542 $4500   (5-Nov-91 CE.NY154/R) Selbstportrait (28cm-11in) cast metal st.f.H.Noack Berlin
£2641 $4780   (6-Dec-91 GB.B7124/R) Foal standing (11x11cm-4x4in) mono. black brown pat.bronze (DM 7500)
£2749 $5086   (12-Jun-92 HN.H782/R) The boxer Erich Brandl (40x16x16cm-16x6x6in) d.1925 stucco on wooden socle (DM 8000)
£3123 $5621   (21-Nov-91 L.K465/R) Dog sitting up (13cm-5in) i. brown pat.bronze st.f.Noack Berlin Friedenau (DM 8900)
£3147 $5601   (30-Nov-91 VG.B252/R) Self portrait (28cm-11in) mono. dark brown pat.bronze marble socle (DM 9000)
£3684 $6632   (21-Nov-91 L.K466/R) Sleeping fawn (4x11cm-2x4in) i. brass pat.bronze st.f.Noack Berlin (DM 10500)
£3955 $7000   (5-Nov-91 CE.NY149/R) Springendes Fohlen (14cm-6in) st.init. brown pat.bronze st.f.RS H.Noack
£4054 $7500   (12-Jun-92 SY.NY12/R) Foal (13cm-5in) i. greenish-brown pat.bronze

SINTENIS, Renee (1888-1965) German-cont.
£4386 $7895   (23-Nov-91 N.M296/R) Foal grazing (8cm-3in) mono.d.1919 brown pat.bronze
                (DM 12500)
£4895 $8713   (28-Nov-91 SY.BE37/R) Galopping foal (15cm-6in) mono. dark brown
                pat.bronze (DM 14000)
£5594 $9958   (28-Nov-91 SY.BE36/R) The boxer Erich Brandl (40cm-16in) mono. brown
                pat.bronze st.f.H.Noack Berlin (DM 16000)
£56701 $103763 (3-Jun-92 L.K434/R) Foal standing (105x80x31cm-41x31x12in) i.d.1932
                bronze st.f.Noack Berlin (DM 165000)

SKEAPING, John (1901-1980) British
£8500 $14705 (2-Oct-91 S149/R) Sleeping hog (23cm-9in) green serpentine on wooden base

SKOOG, Karl Frederick (1878-1934) American
£3333 $6000   (22-Nov-91 S.BM163/R) Days of joy - fountain (122cm-48in) s. green
                pat.bronze f.i.P.B.u. Co. Munich

SMITH, David (1906-1965) American
£14525 $26000 (6-May-92 CH.NY267/R) Ritual (25x27x10cm-10x11x4in) with sig. forged
                steel
£44693 $80000 (12-Nov-91 CH.NY6/R) Albany IX (45x51x12cm-18x20x5in) s.i.d.7-4-60 oil on
                welded steel

SMITH, Richard (1931-) British
£4000 $7400   (11-Jun-92 C40/R) Malaya (244x198x36cm-96x78x14in) oil canvas

SMITH, Tony (1912-1980) American
£8939 $16000 (13-Nov-91 CH.NY229/R) Wall (41x92x13cm-16x36x5in) st.i.d.1963 num.1/9
                bronze
£11173 $20000 (14-Nov-91 SY.NY141/R) New piece (53x91x107cm-21x36x42in) bronze
£11317 $21502 (26-Jun-92 FB.P80/R) Tau (60x39x31cm-24x15x12in) s.d.1965 num.7/9 black
                pat.bronze (F.FR 110000)
£17877 $32000 (13-Nov-91 CH.NY153/R) Marriage (51x51x61cm-20x20x24in) st.sig.d.1961
                num.2/4 bronze

SMITH, Treania (1901-1990) Australian
£1498 $2696   (24-Nov-91 SY.S246) Kathleen (79cm-31in) s.d.1930-32 num.6/6 bronze
                (A.D 3400)

SMITHSON, Robert (1938-1973) American
£47486 $85000 (14-Nov-91 SY.NY159/R) Untitled (90x80x79cm-35x31x31in) coral rock mirror
                wood construction

SNELSON, Kenneth (1927-) American
£1486 $2600   (27-Feb-92 CE.NY235/R) Untitled (39x18x17cm-15x7x7in) aluminium wire
                sculpture

SOM CHAI (20th C) ?
£1875 $3188   (23-Oct-91 EA.M503) Group of seven flying swans s.d.1987 num.1/10 dark
                brown pat.bronze (C.D 3600)

SOMME, Theophile (1871-?) French
£1304 $2322   (26-Nov-91 SY.AM437/R) Dancer (32cm-13in) i. bronze ivory (D.FL 4200)

SORENSEN, Jens Flemming (20th C) Danish
£2715 $4914   (4-Dec-91 KH.K29/R) Double portrait (57x36cm-22x14in) marble (D.KR 30000)
£5727 $10366 (20-May-92 KH.K53/R) Female torso (85x40x30cm-33x16x12in) s.d.1986 marble
                (D.KR 65000)

SOTO, Jesus Raphael (1923-) Venezuelan
£6667 $12000 (19-Nov-91 CH.NY171/R) Tri-coloured vibration (106x106x15cm-42x42x6in)
                s.d.1965 painted wood metal construction
£11340 $19619 (29-Mar-92 P.V102/R) Cuervas interferentes azules y negras
                (142x142cm-56x56in) s.d.1975 nylon thread mobile metal shafts panel
                (F.FR 110000)
£15091 $25956 (8-Oct-91 CC.P39/R) Dos grandes barras (123x103cm-48x41in) s.i.d.1971
                verso wood painted metal (F.FR 150000)
£19337 $35000 (18-May-92 CH.NY54/R) Construccion en blanco (202x214cm-80x84in) s.d.1974
                verso painted wood nylon cord wires
£20121 $34608 (8-Oct-91 CC.P38/R) Relations jaune et argente (158x107cm-62x42in)
                s.i.d.1965 verso wood painted metal (F.FR 200000)

SOUDBININE, Seraphin (19/20th C) Russian
£1852 $3519   (24-Jun-92 AT.P233/R) Sirene au dauphin (92cm-36in) s.d.1924 plaster
                (F.FR 18000)

SOUKOP, Willi (?) ?
£950 $1758   (11-Jun-92 C132/R) Two figures (102cm-40in) init. wood

SOUTH GERMAN SCHOOL, 17th C
£2800 $5376   (9-Jul-92 S176/R) Figure of Angel Gabriel, with right hand raised
                (104cm-41in) polychrome giltwood
£4800 $8736   (10-Dec-91 C61/R) Figure of male saint, standing, arms gesturing outwards
                (103cm-41in) polychrome giltwood

SOUTH GERMAN SCHOOL, 17th C-cont.
£55249 $100000   (5-Dec-91 SY.NY131/R) Hound in crouching position (25cm-10in) gilt bronze
sold with another slightly smaller

SPANISH SCHOOL, 17th C
£2733 $4646   (23-Oct-91 DUR.M635/R) San Gregorio Magno (140cm-55in) polychrome wood
(S.P 500000)

SPERANDIO, Savelli (15th C) Italian
£2372 $4221   (29-Nov-91 GAB.G3104) Buste d'une jeune fille de Mantoue beige
terra-cotta (S.FR 6000)

SPOERRI, Daniel (20th C) ?
£4326 $7441   (12-Oct-91 GL.P64/R) Dejeuner, tableau piege (70x71x34cm-28x28x13in)
s.i.d.1972verso collage panel (F.FR 43000)
£4615 $8262   (19-Jan-92 CC.P45/R) Tableau piege (45x71cm-18x28in) s.d.1965verso dinner
objects mounted on panel (F.FR 45000)
£5800 $10034   (26-Mar-92 S97/R) Tableau piege (70x70cm-28x28in) s.i.d.1972 verso
assemblage
£8939 $16000   (13-Nov-91 SY.NY129/R) Untitled table (70x74x27cm-28x29x11in) assemblage
£10070 $17120   (27-Oct-91 P.V66/R) Embauchoirs de chaussures (100x145x25cm-39x57x10in)
s.d.1989 boot-trees shoes other objects (F.FR 100000)

SPRONKEN, Arthur (1930-) Dutch
£1818 $3291   (21-May-92 SY.AM291/R) Horse (18cm-7in) st.studio bronze (D.FL 6000)

STADLER, Toni (1888-1982) German
£3754 $6833   (25-May-92 WK.M1170/R) Reclining female nude (15x40x22cm-6x16x9in)
green-brown pat.bronze (DM 11000)

STAEBLER, Stephen de (20th C) American
£10286 $18000   (25-Feb-92 SY.NY181/R) Standing figure with blue shoulder
(192x38x44cm-76x15x17in) bronze

STANZANI, E (20th C) Italian
£1494 $2600   (15-Sep-91 JRB.C28/R) Harlequin (157cm-62in) s. painted bronze
f.st.Brotal, Mendrisio

STAPPEN, Charles van der (1843-1910) Belgian
£1178 $2250   (17-Jul-92 DM.D2174/R) St. Michael spearing Lucifer (94x48cm-37x19in) s.
black pat.bronze f.st.J Petermann, Bruxelles

STASIO, Stefano di (1948-) Italian
£3621 $6590   (26-May-92 SY.MI54/R) Intorno all'esserci (145x110cm-57x43in) s.d.1983
(I.L 8000000)

STEELL, Sir John Robert (1804-1891) British
£750 $1313   (20-Feb-92 C158/R) Bust of a Lady (76cm-30in) s.d.1853 white marble
moulded circular base

STEEN, Knut (1924-) Scandinavian
£746 $1387   (15-Jun-92 B.O148/R) Dance (140x80x40cm-55x31x16in) bronze iron
(N.KR 8500)

STEHLE, Alois (1854-1932) German
£850 $1513   (29-Nov-91 S228/R) Egyptian priestess (33cm-13in) s. bronze
st.f.J.Mayr,Moberndorfer

STEINBACH, Haim (1944-) American
£7263 $13000   (14-Nov-91 SY.NY260/R) No wires no power cord (142x142x61cm-56x56x24in)
wood trays basketball shoes formica on wood

STEINLEN (19/20th C) Swiss
£1108 $2084   (17-Dec-91 GM.B1502) Chat endormi cire perdue (B.FR 65000)

STELLA, Frank (1936-) American
£16760 $30000   (6-May-92 CH.NY362/R) La Columba ladra (83x75x48cm-33x30x19in)
init.d.1989 cast aluminium wall relief
£22346 $40000   (14-Nov-91 SY.NY332/R) Kamionka Strumilowa II (198x320x10cm-78x126x4in)
s.d.72 verso mixed media wood
£44693 $80000   (7-May-92 SY.NY310/R) Maquette I for Botafogo (91x138x12cm-36x54x5in)
lacquer oil aluminium
£47486 $85000   (13-Nov-91 CH.NY226/R) The cassock (160x226x80cm-63x89x31in) acrylic
enamel on aluminium
£61453 $110000   (7-May-92 SY.NY319/R) Shards III, 1X-D (116x102x25cm-46x40x10in) mixed
media aluminium

STEPHENS, Edward Bowring (1815-1882) British
£5500 $9625   (24-Sep-91 SWS335/R) Group of Euphrosyne holding dove and cupid standing
reaching up (153cm-60in) s.d.1868 white marble

STEPHENSON, Peter (1823-1860) American
£838 $1500   (14-Nov-91 CE.NY240) Bust of man (61cm-24in) s.

STERN, Rhona (20th C) South African?
£565 $999   (4-Nov-91 SY.J345/R) Madonna of the Rocks (87cm-34in) s.d.62 bronze (SA.R 2800)

STEVENS, Alfred (1823-1906) Belgian
£3800 $6878   (21-May-92 C53/R) Putti standing in profile holding foliate cornucopia (37cm-15in) pair

STOLL, Fredy (20th C) French?
£9000 $15300   (25-Oct-91 S372/R) Daphne (94cm-37in) i.c.1925 silvered bronze marble

STOREL, Sergio (c.1926-) Italian
£1585 $2900   (3-Feb-92 HH.P31/R) Nucleisme 1972-1978 Fleur 1977 (51cm-20in) s. soldered copper round (F.FR 15500)

STOTZER, Werner (1931-) German
£1910 $3418   (15-Nov-91 KM.K182/R) Werra. Saale (99x99x99cm-39x39x39in) mono. bronze st.f.Strassacker Sussen pair (DM 5500)

STRAETEN, George van der (1856-?) Belgian
£1254 $2283   (13-Dec-91 BM.B1414/R) Julie, bust of young woman wearing hooded cloak (45cm-18in) i.pat.bronze st.f.Societe des Bronces de Paris (DM 3600)

STRANDMAN, Otto (1871-1960) Swedish
£870 $1575   (19-May-92 AB.S4561/R) Three graces dancing (31cm-12in) s.d.1909 dark pat bronze incl.base Cast Berman (S.KR 9200)

STRASSER (?) ?
£1802 $3100   (9-Oct-91 RO.BA228) Retour de la fontaine (61cm-24in) s. pat.bronze

STRINDBERG, Tore (1882-1968) Swedish
£787 $1424   (3-Dec-91 AB.S5213/R) Crocus - Female head (37cm-15in) s. gold pat bronze (S.KR 8200)

STUCK, Franz von (1863-1928) German
£1923 $3423   (25-Nov-91 WK.M967/R) Athlete (65cm-26in) s. brown pat.bronze st.f.C.Leyrer Munchen (DM 5500)

STURSA, Jan (1880-1925) Czechoslovakian
£1754 $3158   (23-Nov-91 N.M362/R) Melancholic female nude kneeling (42cm-17in) s. brown pat.bronze st.f.FK (DM 5000)
£2401 $4250   (7-Nov-91 SY.NY2/R) Dancer (49cm-19in) i.base green pat.bronze

SUBIRACHS, Jose Maria (1927-) Spanish
£2249 $4117   (3-Feb-92 HH.P52/R) Sans titre (41x31x13cm-16x12x5in) s. bronze stone (F.FR 22000)
£2350 $4418   (17-Dec-91 BRO.B381) Espirales varias (55x33x18cm-22x13x7in) iron wood lance (S.P 425000)
£6840 $12175   (29-Oct-91 BRO.B369/R) Dos mujeres (30x39cm-12x15in) s. bronze (S.P 1250000)

SUDRE (19/20th C) French
£2200 $4202   (30-Jun-92 PH51/R) Figure of Mercury head bent to examine wings on left foot (96cm-38in) s. bronze st.f.

SUEUR, Hubert le (attrib) (?-1670) French/British
£50000 $91000   (12-Dec-91 S135/R) Figure of kneeling knight (28cm-11in) dark brown pat.bronze

SUMMERS, Charles (1827-1878) British
£38000 $68780   (21-May-92 C47/R) Figure of Ruth seated pensively on rocky outcrop (96cm-38in) s.i.d.1878 white marble on pedestal

SUSILLO Y FERNANDEZ, Antonio (1857-1896) Spanish
£1424 $2720   (2-Jul-92 ANS.M289/R) Cabeza de Cristo (36cm-14in) s. terracotta (S.P 260000)

SUSUMU SHINGU (1937-) Japanese
£1610 $2769   (7-Oct-91 RY.P108/R) Sans titre (130cm-51in) stainless steel (F.FR 16000)

SUVERO, Mark di (1933-) American
£6704 $12000   (7-May-92 SY.NY275/R) Untitled - puzzle (25x32x25cm-10x13x10in) s.i. stainless steel
£8939 $16000   (13-Nov-91 CH.NY148/R) Untitled (74x91x91cm-29x36x36in) welded steel stainless steel base
£11173 $20000   (14-Nov-91 SY.NY319/R) Feather touch (43x44cm-17x17in) welded steel two parts
£19553 $35000   (6-May-92 CH.NY334/R) Untitled (55x46x45cm-22x18x18in) s. welded steel two parts

SUZOR-COTE, Marc-Aurele de Foy (1867-1937) Canadian
£1244 $2302   (9-Jun-92 FB.M167) Calling moose (52cm-20in) s. pat.bronze (C.D 2750)
£1463 $2634   (19-Nov-91 FP.M169/R) Harry A Norton (29cm-11in) s.d.1924 pat.bronze f.i.Roman Bronze Works NY (C.D 3000)

SUZOR-COTE, Marc-Aurele de Foy (1867-1937) Canadian-cont.
£2055	$3760	(14-May-92 SY.T90/R) L'Iroquois (48cm-19in) s.d.1907 num.15/24 bronze
		f.st.Roman Works NY (C.D 4500)
£2073	$3732	(19-Nov-91 FP.M172) Le fumeur (47cm-19in) s. pat.bronze f.i.Roman Bronze
		Works Inc (C.D 4250)
£2511	$4596	(14-May-92 SY.T164/R) Marie Chapdelaine (25cm-10in) s.i.d.1925 bronze
		f.st.Roman Bronze Works NY (C.D 5500)
£4000	$7080	(6-Nov-91 SY.T112/R) Maria Chapdelaine (39cm-15in) s.i.d.1925 bronze
		f.st.Roman Bronze Works N.Y (C.D 8000)
£4338	$7938	(14-May-92 SY.T166/R) Le portageur (41cm-16in) s.i.d.1922 bronze
		f.st.Roman Bronze Works NY (C.D 9500)
£5000	$8850	(6-Nov-91 SY.T111/R) Le Portageur (42cm-17in) s.i.d.1922 bronze
		f.st.Roman Bronze Works N.Y (C.D 10000)
£5500	$9735	(6-Nov-91 SY.T114/R) Le vieux pionnier Canadien (39cm-15in) s.i.d.1912
		pat.bronze f.st.Roman Works N.Y (C.D 11000)
£6000	$10620	(6-Nov-91 SY.T113/R) Calling moose (53cm-21in) s. num.13 greenish
		pat.bronze f.st.N.Y (C.D 12000)

SYKES, Charles (20th C) ?
| £3415 | $6146 | (19-Nov-91 FP.M125/R) Spirit of Ecstasy (53cm-21in) s.num.28 pat.bronze |
| | | (C.D 7000) |

SZCZEBLEWSKI, V (19th C) European
£785	$1500	(3-Jul-92 S.W3144/R) Mousse Siffleur (58cm-23in) s.i. brown pat.bronze
		f.st.
£962	$1761	(2-Jun-92 FN.S1315) Mousse siffleur (56cm-22in) i.pat.bronze i.f.
		(DM 2800)

TACCA, Ferdinando (attrib) (1619-1686) Italian
| £2300 | $4186 | (10-Dec-91 C77/R) Figure of sleeping nymph, on rocky ground |
| | | (8x19cm-3x7in) bronze |

TACCA, Pietro (after) (1577-1640) Italian
| £2600 | $4992 | (8-Jul-92 PH114/R) Slaves with hands manacled behind back on basket of |
| | | fruit with dolphins (74cm-29in) bronze on iron base pair |

TADOLINI (19/20th C) Italian
| £47120 | $90000 | (3-Jul-92 S.W3140/R) Narcissus (193x97cm-76x38in) s.d.1853 marble bronze |

TADOLINI, Giulio (1849-1918) Italian
| £9357 | $16000 | (9-Mar-92 B.LA968/R) Figure of water bearer, carrying amphora on left |
| | | shoulder (205cm-81in) s.d.1889 marble |

TAJIRI, Shinkichi (1923-) Dutch
| £3348 | $6060 | (20-May-92 KH.K28/R) Fortress 11 (76cm-30in) s.d.64 bronze (D.KR 38000) |

TAKIS (1925-) Greek
£3800	$6574	(26-Mar-92 C41/R) Espace interior (40cm-16in) s.num.1/6 gold pat.bronze
		painted wood base
£5400	$9288	(17-Oct-91 C29/R) Standing figure (90cm-35in) green pat.bronze
£16000	$30560	(2-Jul-92 S66/R) Untitled (210cm-83in) s. metal copper cement

TAKIS, Vassilakis (1925-) Greek
£4119	$7044	(19-Mar-92 CSC.P107/R) Socle rouge (80x59cm-31x23in) s.d.1963-71verso
		magnet four switches (F.FR 40000)
£5455	$9655	(24-Apr-92 CN.P209/R) Signal (118cm-46in) bronze steel (F.FR 54000)
£7506	$13211	(7-Apr-92 C.A39) Signal with three arms (172cm-68in) mono.d.1978 metal
		(B.FR 450000)

TALBOT, Grace Helen (1901-) American
£2778	$4750	(21-Mar-92 SY.NY225/R) Figural candlesticks of standing nude maidens
		holding urns aloft (44cm-17in) i. brown pat.bronze f.i.Roman Works N.Y
		pair

TASSAERT (style) (?) ?
| £2600 | $4732 | (12-Dec-91 S257/R) Bust of girl (46cm-18in) marble |

TEGNER, Rudolph (1873-1950) Danish
£4000	$7280	(27-May-92 SWS169/R) Wellhead of dancers Emilie, Grethe Elna (75cm-30in)
		i. bronze st.
£8000	$14640	(15-May-92 S325) Aphrodite guiding the bow of Eros (89cm-35in) i.
		pat.bronze
£8363	$14467	(2-Sep-91 BU.K81/R) Diana standing on a half-moon (176cm-69in) green pat
		bronze, incl.wooden base (D.KR 95000)

TERESZCZUK, P (20th C) Austrian
£800	$1424	(29-Nov-91 S234/R) The fishergirl (31cm-12in) s. brown pat.bronze ivory
£800	$1360	(25-Oct-91 S366/R) Dancing (24cm-9in) i. ivory onyx
£852	$1500	(6-Apr-92 B.LA2622/R) Nymph wearing gown raising large shell in both arms
		(44cm-17in) i.c.1900 bronze shell lamp

TESHIGAHARA, Sofu (20th C) ?
£5307 $9500   (6-May-92 CH.NY271/R) Untitled (45x41x13cm-18x16x5in) brass nails wood
£7263 $13000   (6-May-92 CH.NY272/R) Untitled (52x42x44cm-20x17x17in) sheet metal nails wood

THEED, William (younger) (1804-1891) British
£800 $1368   (20-Mar-92 S98/R) Bust of young woman (62cm-24in) s.d.1846 marble

THOMAS, Mark (19/20th C) Belgian
£787 $1400   (30-Apr-92 CE.NY75/R) Figure of Borzoi (27cm-11in) i. brown pat.bronze

THOMAS, R (19th C) French
£1300 $2223   (20-Mar-92 S2/R) Walking lion (37cm-15in) s. green-brown pat.bronze st.f.C.H.Gautier

THOMAS-SOYER, Mathilde (1860-1940) French
£2000 $3560   (29-Nov-91 S155/R) En vedette (58cm-23in) s. brown pat.bronze st.f.Thiebaut Freres
£2072 $3750   (21-May-92 S.W3273/R) Russian wolfshounds (23x20cm-9x8in) s. brown pat.bronze st.f.Thiebaut Freres

THOREN, Esaias (1901-1981) Swedish
£787 $1424   (3-Dec-91 AB.S5214/R) Machine (33x23cm-13x9in) s.d.30 num.4/9, gold pat bronze Cast.Bergman (S.KR 8200)

THORNYCROFT, Hamo (1850-1925) British
£1300 $2327   (13-Nov-91 CSK103/R) General Gorden with bible, staff and field glasses, foot on broken cannon (37cm-15in) s.i.d.1888 bronze
£5800 $10324   (29-Nov-91 S208/R) Queen Victoria on horseback (56cm-22in) s.i.d.1853 brown pat.bronze
£10000 $17500   (20-Feb-92 C184/R) Mower (63cm-25in) s.i. bronze
£12000 $21000   (20-Feb-92 C142/R) Teucer (74cm-29in) s.d.1881 1904 num.22 bronze

THORVALDSEN, Bertel (after) (1770-1844) Danish
£900 $1629   (21-May-92 C26/R) Figure of Venus with apple (46cm-18in) i. bronze

TIKKANEN, Ulf (1920-1969) Finnish
£1081 $1968   (11-Dec-91 HOR.H116) Hares on the run (35cm-14in) s. bronze (F.M 8400)

TIKTAK, John (1916-1981) North American
£1193 $2183   (1-Jun-92 W.T733/R) Standing Inuit figure (18cm-7in) s. mottled soapstone (C.D 2600)

TILGNER, Victor Oskar (1844-1896) Austrian
£2400 $4368   (27-May-92 SWS170/R) Fountain, with scantily draped putto fighting with crocodile (100cm-39in) i. weathered green-brown pat.bronze

TINGUELY, Jean (1925-1991) Swiss
£22346 $40000   (13-Nov-91 CH.NY113/R) Plate sculpture (37x30x30cm-15x12x12in) painted metal wire electric motor
£30000 $57300   (2-Jul-92 S58/R) Santana No.6 (50x65x30cm-20x26x12in) iron bars wood electric motor
£85000 $162350   (2-Jul-92 S35/R) Isidor III (135x100x70cm-53x39x28in) iron metal wheels rubber belts electric motor

TOBIASS, Francine (1949-) French?
£905 $1557   (7-Oct-91 HH.P72/R) Femme flamme (36x9x9cm-14x4x4in) s.d.1989 num.2/8 green pat.bronze Cast.Blanchet (F.FR 9000)

TOLEDO, Francisco (1940-) Mexican
£2210 $4000   (19-May-92 SY.NY149/R) Tortuga (18cm-7in) green pat.bronze
£2762 $5000   (19-May-92 SY.NY151/R) Conejo en Columpio (19cm-7in) s.num.1/5 black pat.bronze
£3867 $7000   (19-May-92 SY.NY150/R) Figura de pajaro (26cm-10in) s.num.II/III black pat.bronze

TOROS (1934-) French?
£1022 $1871   (3-Feb-92 HH.P23/R) Pause (19x21x11cm-7x8x4in) s.num.5/8 polished bronze Cast.Crois Luizet (F.FR 10000)
£1227 $2245   (3-Feb-92 HH.P96/R) Couple (36x11x9cm-14x4x4in) s.num.4/8 green pat.bronze Cast.Crois Luizet (F.FR 12000)

TOURGUENEFF, P N (1854-1912) Russian/French
£1319 $2400   (13-Dec-91 SY.NY262/R) Mounted French officer astride his walking horse (61cm-24in) bronze

TOURGUENEFF, Pierre Nicolas (1854-1912) Russian/French
£785 $1500   (17-Jul-92 DM.D2140/R) Hunter with bow and arrow (74cm-29in) bronze
£955 $1700   (30-Apr-92 CE.NY74/R) Figure of alsatian (10cm-4in) i. greenish-brown pat.bronze f.st.Susse Freres
£2559 $4555   (29-Nov-91 ARC.P39) Hussard a cheval (61cm-24in) s. base red brn.pat.bronze (F.FR 25000)
£5376 $10000   (16-Jun-92 RO.BA123) Cheval Anglais (46x50cm-18x20in) pat.bronze

TREMONT, Auguste (1893-) ?
£928 $1587   (9-Mar-92 AT.P304) Heron (27cm-11in) brn.green pat.bronze Cast.Valsuani
cire perdue (F.FR 9000)

TRENTANOVE, Raimondo (1792-1832) Italian
£2500 $4525   (6-Dec-91 TE689) Young girl feeding dove held in one hand from stemmed
cup (89cm-35in) s.i.d.1830 white marble

TRIBOLO, Niccolo (studio) (1500-1550) Italian
£1788 $3200   (14-Jan-92 CH.NY133/R) Figure of satyr holding bowl (20cm-8in) blackish
brown pat.bronze

TRIMBLE, Gary (20th C) Irish?
£2545 $4404   (2-Oct-91 A.D183) Michael Collins (58x30cm-23x12in) init.d.1973 bronze
(E.P 2800)

TROGER, Simon (school) (1694-1768) Austrian
£966 $1797   (16-Jun-92 SY.B187/R) A beggar on crutches (23cm-9in) wood ivory
(B.FR 58000)

TROGER, Simon (style) (1694-1768) Austrian
£2800 $5096   (9-Dec-91 PH51/R) Mary with boy Jesus and St Joseph (35cm-14in) wood
ivory marble plinths pair

TROIANI, Troiano (1885-1963) Argentinian
£977 $1700   (19-Sep-91 V.BA105) Cabeza (50x52x32cm-20x20x13in) plaster
£1344 $2500   (16-Jun-92 RO.BA118) Extasis (59cm-23in) bronze
£1484 $2700   (11-Dec-91 RO.BA76/R) Ilusion (31cm-12in) s. bronze on marble base
f.Trivium
£2747 $5000   (11-Dec-91 RO.BA75/R) Desnudo (33cm-13in) s. pat.bronze f.Balsells
£3571 $6500   (11-Dec-91 RO.BA74/R) Walkiria (48cm-19in) s. bronze on wood base

TROUBETZKOY, Prince Paolo (1866-1938) Russian
£908 $1688   (16-Jun-92 F.M34) Domatore di cavalli (39cm-15in) s. bronze (I.L 2000000)
£968 $1800   (16-Jun-92 RO.BA124) Chien (29cm-11in) pat.bronze
£1089 $2026   (16-Jun-92 F.M32) Beduino a cavallo (42cm-17in) s. bronze (I.L 2400000)
£1290 $2347   (12-Dec-91 F.M61) Cane (31cm-12in) s. bronze (I.L 2800000)
£2038 $3771   (9-Jun-92 F.R43/R) La danzatrice (36cm-14in) s. bronze (I.L 4500000)
£2042 $3799   (16-Jun-92 F.M240/R) Tolstoj (35x28x29cm-14x11x11in) s. bronze
(I.L 4500000)
£6593 $12000   (27-May-92 CH.NY138/R) Campagne de Prusse (43cm-17in) i. bronze dark
brown pat.
£6704 $12000   (6-May-92 D.NY6 a/R) Bust of George Bernard Shaw (67cm-26in)
£16633 $29441   (7-Nov-91 AT.P87/R) Femme au levrier (60cm-24in) s.d.1914 num.1
pat.bronze Cast.Valsuani (F.FR 165000)

TROUBETZKOY, Prince Paolo (after) (1866-1938) Russian
£1374 $2500   (13-Dec-91 SY.NY326/R) Figure of Indian Chief holding staff in right hand
(48cm-19in) bronze
£1404 $2500   (30-Apr-92 CE.NY54/R) Figure of Samoyed (27cm-11in) i. greenish-brown
pat.bronze

TROVA, Ernest (1927-) American
£7821 $14000   (7-May-92 SY.NY328/R) Falling man overhead figure (83x25x25cm-33x10x10in)
st. num.2-2 d.1984-85

TUCKER, William (20th C) American
£2600 $4810   (11-Jun-92 C147/R) Meru I (196x58x76cm-77x23x30in) painted steel

TURNBULL, William (20th C) ?
£4400 $8140   (11-Jun-92 C149/R) Gate (216cm-85in) brushed stainless steel
£12000 $21600   (20-Nov-91 S71/R) Totem (165cm-65in) bronze

TUTTLE, Richard (1941-) American
£3911 $7000   (5-May-92 CH.NY149/R) Untitled (33x25x9cm-13x10x4in) wood metal rods wire
fabric paperboard W/C
£5028 $9000   (13-Nov-91 CH.NY230/R) Cardboard constructions (8x8x8cm-3x3x3in) six
units cardboard
£5587 $10000   (5-May-92 CH.NY117/R) Chinese fret (87x91x13cm-34x36x5in) acrylic
cardboard aluminum cut masonite paper
£8671 $15000   (3-Oct-91 SY.NY148/R) Monkey's recovery 1 - no.5 (81x71x13cm-32x28x5in)
mixed media
£9827 $17000   (3-Oct-91 SY.NY142/R) Monkey's recovoery 1 - no.1 (72x107x23cm-28x42x9in)
mixed media

UECHTRITZ-STEINKIRCH, Cuno von (1856-1908) German
£5498 $9347   (25-Oct-91 BM.B1861/R) Frederick the Great seated on horse (82cm-32in) i.
pat.bronze (DM 16000)

UECKER, Gunther (20th C) German

£11561	$20000	(3-Oct-91 SY.NY26/R) Untitled (81x81cm-32x32in) s.d.1966verso painted nails canvas over wood
£12982	$23368	(19-Nov-91 L.K1172/R) Circle circles (50x50cm-20x20in) s.i.d.1966 nails on panel (DM 37000)
£13287	$23650	(29-Nov-91 VG.B79/R) Untitled (40x39cm-16x15in) s.i.d.1965verso nails canvas on white panel (DM 38000)
£20979	$37343	(29-Nov-91 VG.B78/R) Spiral (70x70cm-28x28in) s.i.d.1966verso nails canvas on panel (DM 60000)

ULLBERG, Kent (?) Swedish

| £815 | $1467 | (19-Nov-91 GO.G321) Antilope (50cm-20in) s.num.6/12, pat bronze (S.KR 8500) |
| £863 | $1553 | (19-Nov-91 GO.G322) Mountain goats (35cm-14in) s.num.3/12, pat bronze (S.KR 9000) |

ULLMANN, Francis (1930-) ?

| £1125 | $2058 | (3-Feb-92 HH.P67/R) Laurence (23x21x23cm-9x8x9in) s.num.2/8 brn.green pat.bronze (F.FR 11000) |

UMLAUF, Charles (1911-) American

| £1117 | $2000 | (14-Nov-91 CE.NY261) Man in supplication (67cm-26in) i. greenish black pat.bronze indist.f.st. |

UNDERWOOD, Leon (1890-1975) British

| £1337 | $2300 | (12-Oct-91 SY.NY179/R) Prodigal son (30x28cm-12x11in) s.d.62 num.II/VII gold pat.bronze |
| £4200 | $7266 | (2-Oct-91 S212/R) The prophet (43cm-17in) bronze wooden base |

UPPER RHINE SCHOOL, 17th C German

| £8500 | $15470 | (12-Dec-91 S243/R) Memento Mori figure - skeletal, with snakes and rocks (28cm-11in) boxwood |

URBAN (after) (?) ?

| £806 | $1427 | (8-Nov-91 CN.P84/R) Saint Georges terrassant le dragon (49cm-19in) brn.pat.bronze marble base (F.FR 8000) |

USTINOV, Igor (1956-) ?

| £3579 | $6549 | (3-Feb-92 HH.P100/R) Le mathematicien (52x33x21cm-20x13x8in) s.num.5/8base green pat.bronze (F.FR 35000) |

VACCARO (attrib) (17/18th C) Italian

| £14525 | $26000 | (14-Jan-92 CH.NY116/R) Group of Saint Michael expelling rebel angels (18cm-7in) polychrome giltwood |

VAERE, Jean-Antoine de (1754-1830) Flemish

| £2235 | $4000 | (13-Jan-92 CE.NY12) Apollo (122cm-48in) s. white marble |

VAERENBERGH, G V (20th C) ?

| £1327 | $2428 | (12-May-92 GM.B1527/R) Pierrot au banjo bronze marble (B.FR 80000) |

VAISMAN, Meyer (1960-) American

| £12570 | $22500 | (14-Nov-91 SY.NY210/R) Live the dream (195x236x18cm-77x93x7in) s.d.1986 verso laminated inks clocks two panels |

VALENTA, Pierre (20th C) ?

| £1534 | $2807 | (3-Feb-92 HH.P62/R) Lac des cygnes (84cm-33in) s.d.1990num.EA1/4 EA2/4 blue pat.bronze pair (F.FR 15000) |

VALL, Louis (20th C) ?

| £926 | $1685 | (12-Dec-91 SY.AM188/R) Amazone (35cm-14in) init.num.1/6 bronze (D.FL 3000) |

VALLGREN, Ville (1855-1940) Scandinavian

| £798 | $1452 | (11-Dec-91 HOR.H119) Dancer (23cm-9in) s.d.1937 terracotta (F.M 6200) |

VALLMITJANA Y BARBANY, Agapit (1830-1905) Spanish

| £1237 | $2226 | (19-Nov-91 DUR.M382/R) Torero (20cm-8in) s.d.1878 marble (S.P 225000) |

VALTON, C (?) ?

| £1397 | $2500 | (11-Nov-91 B.LA1623/R) Figure of bulldog (46cm-18in) i. brown pat.bronze on ebonized wood base |

VALTON, Charles (1851-1918) French

£833	$1549	(16-Jun-92 SY.B125) Jockey on horseback (28cm-11in) i. bronze (B.FR 50000)
£872	$1500	(9-Oct-91 RO.BA62) Scene de ferme s. pat.bronze on marble base
£968	$1800	(16-Jun-92 RO.BA114) Scene de ferme pat.bronze
£1400	$2394	(20-Mar-92 S7/R) Two stags (53cm-21in) s. brown pat.bronze
£1437	$2500	(13-Sep-91 SY.NY86/R) Equestrian group of Picador (55cm-22in) i. brown pat.bronze

VALTON, Charles (1851-1918) French-cont.
£2542 $4500   (6-Nov-91 D.NY60 a/R) The seated lioness (28cm-11in) s.st.sig.i.brown
                  pat.bronze st.f.C.Valsuani

VALTON, Charles (after) (1851-1918) French
£3216 $5500   (9-Mar-92 B.LA747/R) Figure of wounded lioness, snarling and dragging a
                  back leg (53x89cm-21x35in) s. copper-brown pat.bronze

VANDERHOYDEN (after) (?) ?
£1167 $2030   (14-Apr-92 GM.B1008) Mere et enfants s. white marble (B.FR 70000)

VANNETTI, Antonio (19th C) ?
£2100 $3738   (28-Apr-92 SWS474/R) Napoleon with his charger (46cm-18in) s. brown
                  pat.bronze marble

VARELA, Abigail (1948-) Venezuelan
£6630 $12000   (18-May-92 CH.NY164/R) Caminadora Apurada III (73x54x82cm-29x21x32in)
                  brown pat.bronze
£9444 $17000   (19-Nov-91 CH.NY100/R) Mujer recostada (42x65x20cm-17x26x8in) s.num.5/6
                  golden brown pat.bronze
£22099 $40000   (18-May-92 CH.NY58/R) Las comrades (114x78x90cm-45x31x35in) num.5/6 brown
                  pat.bronze
£23333 $42000   (19-Nov-91 CH.NY35/R) Extasis (118cm-46in) golden brown pat.bronze

VASARELY, Victor (1908-) Hungarian
£2838 $5137   (19-May-92 AB.S5156/R) Kezdi (63cm-25in) s.num.28/175, polycrome wood
                  (S.KR 30000)
£3531 $6284   (27-Nov-91 BU.S51/R) 'Kezdi' (66x64cm-26x25in) s.num.151/175, multipel
                  (S.KR 37000)

VAUTIER, Benjamin (19/20th C) German/Swiss
£3018 $5191   (12-Oct-91 GL.P55/R) Portrait au balai (105x54x26cm-41x21x10in) s.d.1983
                  painted wood other objects (F.FR 30000)

VEDOVA, Emilio (1919-) Italian
£1090 $1939   (29-Apr-92 F.F117/R) Composizione (72x51x14cm-28x20x6in) s.num.51/99
                  mixed media on plexiglass (I.L 2400000)

VEDRES, Mark Weinberger (1871-?) Hungarian
£1600 $2736   (20-Mar-92 S172/R) Adam and Eve (41cm-16in) s. brown pat.bronze on marble
                  plinth

VEKENE, Nicolas van der (style) (1637-1704) Flemish
£6000 $10920   (12-Dec-91 S217/R) Group of Virgin and Child, with Virgin standing on
                  head of serpent (28cm-11in) boxwood

VENET, Bernar (1941-) French
£4381 $7580   (29-Mar-92 P.V105/R) Ligne indeterminee (31x45x45cm-12x18x18in)
                  s.num.3189 steel (F.FR 42500)
£6524 $12135   (15-Jun-92 GL.P86/R) Ligne indeterminee (45cm-18in) iron (F.FR 64000)
£16113 $27392   (27-Oct-91 P.V78/R) Ligne indeterminee (127x115x66cm-50x45x26in) steel
                  (F.FR 160000)

VENETIAN SCHOOL (?) Italian
£2703 $5000   (8-Jun-92 B.LA1299/R) Blackamoor youngster holding tray
                  (158x37cm-62x15in) c.1900 gilt bronze on wooden socle

VENETIAN SCHOOL, 18th C Italian
£4200 $7644   (12-Dec-91 S251/R) Statuette of Bacchus reclining, crowned with fruit
                  (23x46cm-9x18in) marble
£14041 $25977   (8-Jun-92 CH.R408/R) Due giovani fanciulle nell'atto di inchinarsi
                  (50cm-20in) wood pair (I.L 31000000)
£26000 $47320   (12-Dec-91 S153/R) Goddesses as seasons- Minerva as winter. Venus with
                  dolphin as autumn. Spring. Summer (26cm-10in) gilt bronze four

VENETIAN SCHOOL, 19th C Italian
£15000 $25650   (10-Mar-92 PH117/R) Blackamoor torcheres, male with turban and female
                  wearing headscarf (178cm-70in) c.1880 polychrome pair

VENETO SCHOOL, 18th C Italian
£13588 $25139   (8-Jun-92 CH.R226/R) Giovani donne simboleggianti l'Estate e l'Autunno
                  (173cm-68in) wood (I.L 30000000)

VERBANCK, Geo (1881-1961) Belgian
£1283 $2322   (7-Dec-91 KV.L344/R) Nude (28cm-11in) s.f.Vindevogel SA bronze brown pat.
                  (B.FR 75000)

VERBRUGGEN, Jan (18th C) Dutch
£12000 $21840   (12-Dec-91 S145/R) Statuette of William IV, Prince of Orange on horseback
                  (34cm-13in) s.d.1751 bronze

VERDUYN, Jacques (1946-) Belgian
£1000 $1720   (12-Oct-91 KV.L344) Standing nude (173cm-68in) s. polyester (B.FR 60000)

VERKADE, Kees (1941-) Dutch
£1852 $3370   (11-Dec-91 CH.AM78) Le cabotin (38cm-15in) s.d.90 num.2/6 bronze
            (D.FL 6000)
£8287 $15000   (5-Dec-91 SY.NY72/R) Invitation (172cm-68in) i.num.1/6 d.82 greenish
            black pat.bronze

VERROCCHIO (after) (?) Italian
£2400 $4368   (12-Dec-91 S176) Group of Bartolommeo Colleoni on horseback (59cm-23in)
            bronze

VERROCCHIO, Andrea (after) (15th C) Italian
£1579 $3000   (23-Jun-92 CE.NY62/R) Putto holding fish (72cm-28in) bronze fountain

VERSCHNEIDER, Jean (1872-1943) French
£2400 $4272   (29-Nov-91 S94/R) Gladiator and Lion (215cm-85in) s. green,brown
            pat.bronze incl.column

VERSTOCKT, Mark (1930-) Belgian
£1454 $2632   (7-Dec-91 KV.L349/R) Kubus (26x26cm-10x10in) metal plexi (B.FR 85000)

VIBERT, Alexandre (?-1909) French
£9563 $18362   (7-Jul-92 ARC.P210/R) Reine tenant un evangeliaire - peut-etre Reine
            Clothilde (63cm-25in) s. pat.bronze semi-precious stones marble base
            (F.FR 92000)

VICHI, F (19th C) Italian
£1600 $2800   (20-Feb-92 C157/R) Busts of Dante and Beatrice (47cm-19in) white red
            marble pair

VICHY, F (?) Italian
£881 $1559   (23-Apr-92 RAS.V331/R) Beatrice Portina (65cm-26in) s.num.11, white
            marble (D.KR 10000)

VICTORIAN SCHOOL (19th C) British
£2155 $3750   (15-Apr-92 B.SF3101/R) Young woman wearing gown standing barefoot in
            chilly blast (109cm-43in) white marble

VIDAL, Louis (1754-?) French
£765 $1400   (5-Jun-92 SY.NY136/R) Standing lion (17x30cm-7x12in) i. bronze br.pat.

VIE, Bernard (1947-) French
£1509 $2596   (7-Oct-91 HH.P39/R) Le recit de voyage (23x17x35cm-9x7x14in) s.num.5/8
            brn.green pat.bronze (F.FR 15000)

VIENNESE SCHOOL, 19th C Austrian
£3086 $5864   (22-Jun-92 PIC.P61/R) Cavaliers representant les empereurs Leopold I et
            Francois II pat.bronze on marble bases pair (F.FR 30000)

VIGELAND, Gustav (1869-1943) Norwegian
£3333 $6200   (15-Jun-92 B.O183/R) Woman and bear (33cm-13in) s. bronze (N.KR 38000)
£4035 $7505   (15-Jun-92 B.O182/R) The fetus (15cm-6in) s. bronze (N.KR 46000)

VIKAINEN, Jussi (1907-) Finnish
£809 $1424   (12-Apr-92 HOR.H247) Young woman (35cm-14in) s.d.1950 bronze (F.M 6400)

VILLANIS, Emmanuele (19th C) Italian
£1100 $1958   (29-Nov-91 S168/R) Bohemienne (48cm-19in) s. green,brown pat.bronze
£1200 $2040   (25-Oct-91 S338/R) The sculptress (47cm-19in) i.c.1900 pat.cold painted
            bronze
£2400 $4272   (29-Nov-91 S248/R) Enfant a la souriciere (30x49cm-12x19in) s.i. brown
            pat.bronze
£4485 $8343   (19-Jun-92 ARC.P50/R) La boite de Pandore (85cm-33in) s. pat.bronze on
            onyx socle (F.FR 44000)
£4500 $8235   (12-May-92 SWS351/R) L'Eclipse (229cm-90in) s. brn pat.bronze
            f.st.incl.wood pedestal

VILLAREAL, Victor (1944-) Mexican
£820 $1500   (17-May-92 DU.E1098) Ballet dancer putting on stockings (51cm-20in) s.

VINGTRI, Bayard de la (19th C) Belgian
£884 $1600   (6-Dec-91 GC.M126) Banista del Novecientos (80cm-31in) s. pat.bronze
£2500 $4450   (29-Nov-91 S137/R) La source (71cm-28in) s. golden/green brown pat.bronze
            on marble socle

VISSER, Carel (1928-) Dutch
£2727 $4936   (19-May-92 CH.AM329/R) Romeo and Julia (65cm-26in) iron sculpture
            (D.FL 9000)
£2727 $4936   (19-May-92 CH.AM330/R) Equilibrium II (90cm-35in) iron sculpture
            (D.FL 9000)
£2778 $5056   (11-Dec-91 CH.AM411/R) Gat - Hole (24x24x4cm-9x9x2in) iron (D.FL 9000)
£6364 $11518   (21-May-92 SY.AM289/R) Dubbel vorm 5 (151cm-59in) iron on wooden base
            (D.FL 21000)

VITAL-CORNU, Charles (1851-1927) French
£4839 $9000   (16-Jun-92 RO.BA125) Reveil du Genie (112cm-44in) pat.bronze

VOHLWASEN, Prof (?) German
£1329 $2299   (28-Mar-92 BOD.P725) Man kneeling with hands bound (33cm-13in) mono.i.
                      bronze (DM 3800)

VOLLMER, Ruth (1903-1982) American
£726 $1300   (12-Nov-91 CE.NY9/R) Musical forest (12x25x25cm-5x10x10in) s.num.4/5
                      bronze wood st.f.Modern Art
£1229 $2200   (12-Nov-91 CE.NY10/R) Sphere within a sphere (23cm-9in) s. brown
                      pat.bronze polished bronze

VOLTI (1915-) French
£6173 $11728   (24-Jun-92 GL.P224/R) Eva (30x11x7cm-12x4x3in) s.num.3/8 brown pat.bronze
                      f.Godard (F.FR 60000)

VOLTI, Antoniucci (1915-1990) French
£2817 $4845   (7-Oct-91 HH.P12/R) Leda et le cygne (12x14x9cm-5x6x4in) s.
                      blk.pat.bronze Cast.Bisceglia (F.FR 28000)
£5225 $9406   (27-Jan-92 GL.P85/R) Nu adosse (19x35x10cm-7x14x4in) s.num.6/8 green
                      pat.bronze Cast.Godard (F.FR 51000)
£5328 $9590   (27-Jan-92 GL.P86/R) Nu assis (22x15x14cm-9x6x6in) s.num.7/8 blue
                      pat.bronze Cast.Susse (F.FR 52000)
£6486 $12000   (12-Jun-92 SY.NY157/R) Reclining nude (35cm-14in) i.f.Guidard bronze
                      gr.br.pat.
£6746 $11535   (22-Mar-92 LT.P1115/R) Florence (11x28cm-4x11in) s.num.3/8 green
                      pat.bronze Cast.Cappelli (F.FR 65500)
£7848 $13419   (22-Mar-92 LT.P114/R) Liane (19x35cm-7x14in) s.num.3/8 blk.green
                      pat.bronze Cast.Godard (F.FR 76200)
£10082 $19156   (28-Jun-92 FE.P43) Daphne (28cm-11in) s.num.2/8 bronze f.Hevrard
                      (F.FR 98000)
£24390 $42439   (19-Apr-92 ZZ.F52 b/R) Litchi (60cm-24in) s.num.3/6 green pat.bronze
                      Cast.Susse, Paris (F.FR 240000)
£45327 $76149   (16-Aug-91 ZZ.F48/R) Florentine 1 (94cm-37in) s.num.1/6 blue pat.bronze
                      (F.FR 451000)

VOLZ, Mandy (1938-) Swiss
£1556 $2816   (19-May-92 GF.L304/R) Composition (36cm-14in) s.d.76 num.3/3 polished
                      bronze on stone socle (S.FR 4200)

VONNOH, Bessie Potter (1872-1955) American
£1429 $2500   (26-Sep-91 CH.NY130/R) Intruder - centrepiece (29cm-11in) i. natural
                      pat.bronze f.i.Roman Works N.Y.
£2857 $5000   (25-Sep-91 SY.NY55/R) Goodnight (23cm-9in) i. brown pat.bronze
                      f.i.MXXVIII Roman Bronze NY
£33149 $60000   (6-Dec-91 CH.NY180/R) L'Allegresse (119cm-47in) i.num.10 f.Roman Bronze
                      Works bronze

VOULKOS, Peter (20th C) ?
£12291 $22000   (7-May-92 SY.NY276/R) Stack (109x36x36cm-43x14x14in) glazed terracotta

VRUBEL, Mikhail Alexandrovich (1856-1910) Russian
£6800 $12104   (28-Nov-91 S410/R) Lion's head (26x41cm-10x16in) cast earthenware lustre
                      glaze

VRUYNELL (19th C) ?
£11299 $20000   (13-Feb-92 SY.NY155/R) Bust of woman (63cm-25in) i. gilt-bronze marble

WAAGEN (19th C) German
£730 $1300   (30-Apr-92 CE.NY94/R) Group of greyhound and cat (27cm-11in) cold-painted
                      bronze
£1437 $2500   (13-Sep-91 SY.NY44/R) Figure of woman with removable drapery and
                      tambourine (74cm-29in) i. white metal polychrome

WAGNER, Eugen (1871-?) German
£1034 $1779   (16-Oct-91 KM.K1509/R) Female nude wearing drape (27cm-11in) i. gold
                      bronze marble socle st.f.Gladenbeck (DM 3000)

WAKSVIK, Skule (1927-) Scandinavian
£1114 $1927   (23-Mar-92 B.O143/R) Duck (25cm-10in) s. bronze incl.base (N.KR 12500)

WALDMANN, Oscar (1856-1937) Swiss
£2200 $3916   (29-Nov-91 S46/R) Herd of deer (37x61cm-15x24in) s. green pat.bronze

WARHOL, Andy (1930-1986) American
£1237 $2140   (23-Mar-92 CC.P119/R) Boite Brillo (7x11x7cm-3x4x3in) s. Brillo box
                      (F.FR 12000)

WATERBECK, August (1875-?) German
£8200 $14350   (20-Feb-92 C163/R) Lifesize figure of an athlete (177cm-70in) s.d.1910
                      bronze

WAUER, William (20th C) ?
£1754 $3000   (13-Mar-92 FN.S965/R) The shepherd (28cm-11in) s. dark brown pat.bronze
            st.f.W Fussel Berlin (DM 5000)
£2389 $4348   (30-May-92 VG.B273/R) Der Blitzreiter (13cm-5in) i. silvered bronze
            (DM 7000)

WEAVER, John (1920-) Canadian
£721 $1262   (17-Feb-92 HO.ED62) Horse capture (41x33x25cm-16x13x10in) bronze
            (C.D 1500)
£3125 $5469   (17-Feb-92 HO.ED146/R) Indian skirmish (96x71x50cm-38x28x20in) d.1979
            num.4/6 two (C.D 6500)

WEIGELE, Henry (1858-1927) French
£23000 $40250   (27-Sep-91 S67/R) Diana (85cm-33in) s. Carrrara marble gilt bronze veined
            marble

WEINMAN, Adolph Alexander (1870-?) American
£3867 $7000   (5-Dec-91 SY.NY55/R) Rising day - male figure (68cm-27in) i. brown
            pat.bronze i.f.Roman Bronze Works

WEINMANN, Turi (1883-1950) German?
£1294 $2303   (25-Nov-91 WK.M1079/R) Loving couple (55x29x22cm-22x11x9in) s.i.d.1923
            brown pat.bronze (DM 3700)

WERNER, Nat (1910-) American
£1064 $2000   (18-Dec-91 SY.NY345/R) Female torso (30cm-12in) i. mahogany walnut base

WESSELMANN, Tom (1931-) American
£4571 $8000   (27-Feb-92 CH.NY141/R) Tiny dropped bra no 19 (15x21x11cm-6x8x4in)
            s.i.num.19twice liquitex board in lucite box
£4571 $8000   (25-Feb-92 SY.NY171/R) Maquette for tulip and smoking cigarette
            (23x29x19cm-9x11x7in) s.d.83 i.83-6 liquitex Bristol board wood
£8380 $15000   (7-May-92 SY.NY302 a/R) Maquette for still life no.57
            (32x46x28cm-13x18x11in) liquitex pencil cardboard wood construction
£11429 $20000   (27-Feb-92 CH.NY139/R) Dropped bra no 4, yellow (72x141x67cm-28x56x26in)
            st.sig.num.4verso enamel aluminum
£47486 $85000   (7-May-92 SY.NY325/R) Vivienne - 3-D (196x196x24cm-77x77x9in) s.d.87
            enamel cut-out aluminium

WEST, Franz (1947-) Austrian
£1842 $3352   (26-May-92 D.V305/R) Passtuck (100x6x10cm-39x2x4in) d.1981 iron paper
            mache varnished (A.S 38000)
£2181 $3970   (26-May-92 D.V306/R) Passtuck (125x40x15cm-49x16x6in) d.1981 iron plastic
            paper mache varnished (A.S 45000)

WESTERMAN, H C (1922-) American
£3631 $6500   (7-May-92 SY.NY321/R) California redwood - about the last of it
            (26x63cm-10x25in) st. d.1966 redwood brass plate mirror

WESTMACOTT, Sir Richard (1775-1856) British
£2081 $3642   (30-Mar-92 ZZ.F102/R) Buste d'homme (80cm-31in) s.base verso bronze
            (F.FR 20000)

WEVER, Auguste de (1836-?) Belgian
£767 $1342   (24-Sep-91 GM.B172) Mephisto s. bronze (B.FR 46000)
£1600 $2848   (29-Nov-91 S177/R) Ninette au la pie voleuse (61cm-24in) s. brown
            pat.bronze

WEYNS, Jules (1849-1925) Belgian
£2498 $4646   (16-Jun-92 SY.B110/R) Boy playing a flute (140cm-55in) marble
            (B.FR 150000)

WHEELER, Hughlette (1901-1954) American
£1105 $2000   (21-May-92 S.W3274/R) Hardheads (12cm-5in) s.i.d.1931 brown pat.bronze
£1189 $2200   (10-Jun-92 CE.NY371/R) Group of mare and foal (23cm-9in) i. greenish
            brown pat.bronze

WIEGAND, Don (20th C) American
£2099 $3800   (2-Dec-91 S.SL275/R) Figure of Mark Twain (41cm-16in) s.d.1985 brown
            pat.bronze

WIIG-HANSEN, Svend (1922-) Danish
£1176 $2129   (4-Dec-91 KH.K31/R) Woman standing (48cm-19in) stone (D.KR 13000)
£2669 $4644   (18-Sep-91 KH.K188/R) Reclining man (40cm-16in) init.num.6/7, bronze
            (D.KR 30000)

WILMARTH, Christopher (1943-1987) American
£20000 $35000   (27-Feb-92 CH.NY36/R) Split stream (72x71x5cm-28x28x2in) two glass panels
            steel wire

WILSON, Edward N (19/20th C) American
£1061 $1900   (14-Nov-91 CE.NY249/R) Group of two football players (34cm-13in) i.
            reddish brown pat.bronze

WIMMER, Hans (1907-) German
£2577 $4768 (12-Jun-92 HN.H843 a/R) Seated female nude (28x12x13cm-11x5x5in) s.
             bronze (DM 7500)

WOERFFEL, C F (?) Russian?
£1408 $2366 (28-Aug-91 RAS.K1273/R) Cossac on horseback resting with his dogs and
             smoking pipe (42x40cm-17x16in) i. pat.bronze (D.KR 16000)

WOLFF, Emil (after) (1802-1879) German
£750 $1343 (13-Nov-91 CSK88) Child draped in wolf skin cloak resting on inverted
            shepherd's crook (63cm-25in) white marble

WOLFF, Franz Alexander Friedrich Wilhelm (1816-1887) German
£995 $1900 (3-Jul-92 S.W3159/R) Russian peasant boy and girl on horseback
            (30x20cm-12x8in) s. brown pat.bronze

WOLKOWYSKI, Alexandre (1833-?) Russian
£3080 $5544 (20-Nov-91 CN.P71/R) Deux baigneuses (34cm-13in) s.num.2/6 pat.bronze
             Cast.Valsuani cire perdue (F.FR 30000)

WOOD, Francis Derwent (1871-1926) British
£2800 $5180 (11-Jun-92 C108/R) Nymph with satyr (56cm-22in) s.d.1907 green/grey
             pat.bronze

WOODROW, Bill (20th C) ?
£8380 $15000 (7-May-92 SY.NY220/R) Switch (143x187x300cm-56x74x118in) toy horse metal
              trunk car bonnet enamel acrylic

WOTRUBA, Fritz (1907-) Austrian
£878 $1520 (3-Oct-91 D.V266/R) Female seated (21cm-8in) s.num.229/1000 dark
            pat.bronze (A.S 18000)
£4895 $8713 (25-Nov-91 WK.M1106/R) Reclining male (17x39x15cm-7x15x6in)
             st.sig.num.18/30 brown pat.bronze st.f.A.Zottl (DM 14000)
£27491 $50309 (2-Jun-92 L.K1053/R) Torso (79x28cm-31x11in) s.d.1953/1954 brown
               pat.bronze (DM 80000)

WOUTERS, Rik (1882-1916) Belgian
£1501 $2642 (7-Apr-92 C.A46) Laughing mask (42cm-17in) s. plaster (B.FR 90000)
£2315 $4213 (11-Dec-91 CH.AM302/R) Portrait of Kapitein Stoett (26cm-10in) s. bronze
             (D.FL 7500)
£8007 $14092 (7-Apr-92 C.A45/R) Head of a woman (38cm-15in) s.d.1907 bronze
              (B.FR 480000)

WOUW, Anton van (1862-1945) South African
£5814 $10000 (16-Oct-91 CH.NY154/R) Dagga smoker (16x51cm-6x20in) i. brn.pat.bronze
              wood base
£6452 $11419 (4-Nov-91 SY.J257/R) Maquette for monument for President M.T.Steyn
              (52cm-20in) init.bronze (SA.R 32000)
£10465 $18000 (16-Oct-91 CH.NY153/R) Bushman hunting (48cm-19in) i.d.1902
               Cast.Nisini-Fuse Roma brn.pat.bronze
£30000 $51000 (22-Oct-91 C65/R) Die hamerwerker (63cm-25in) i. gold pat.bronze

WUNDERLICH, Paul (1927-) German
£909 $1645 (19-May-92 CH.AM312) Nike (47cm-19in) s.num.531/1000 bronze marble base
            (D.FL 3000)
£1170 $1988 (22-Oct-91 C.A83) Polmenleis (84cm-33in) s. marble (B.FR 70000)
£1500 $2580 (12-Oct-91 KV.L367/R) Shoe (19x13cm-7x5in) s. polished bronze
             (B.FR 90000)
£1546 $2691 (21-Sep-91 SA.A504/R) Nike with one wing (59cm-23in) s.num.298/1000
             pat.bronze st.f.Ceropersa Bologna (DM 4500)

WURM, Erwin (1954-) Austrian
£2199 $3915 (31-Oct-91 D.V198/R) Untitled (135cm-53in) s.d.1985 wood (A.S 45000)

WYATT, R J (1795-1850) British
£3400 $5882 (25-Mar-92 PHI712/R) Bust of nude young maiden her hair dressed in
             ringlets and chignon (60cm-24in) white marble

WYATT, Richard James (1795-1850) British
£950 $1824 (9-Jul-92 S224) Bust of man (156cm-61in) s. marble column
£11000 $20020 (10-Dec-91 C67/R) Bust of nymph, possibly Flora (55cm-22in) s. white
               marble

WYATT, Richard James (attrib) (1795-1850) British
£1346 $2450 (13-Dec-91 S.BM446/R) Shepherdess (89cm-35in) white marble

WYK, Charles van (1875-1917) Dutch
£1524 $2835 (16-Jun-92 VN.R902/R) Seated woman feeding her child (37cm-15in) s.
             bronze (D.FL 5000)

WYNANTS, Ernest (1878-?) Belgian
£10842 $19083 (7-Apr-92 C.A43/R) Rythmical movement (160cm-63in) s.d.1941 num.3/3
               bronze (B.FR 650000)
£13245 $23974 (23-May-92 KV.L469/R) Reflecting (155x47cm-61x19in) s. gilded bronze
               (B.FR 800000)

WYNNE, David (1926-) British
£1400 $2562   (14-May-92 C116/R) Diver (76cm-30in) mono. num.3/6 green pat.bronze
£2600 $4498   (2-Oct-91 S225/R) Sea lions (54cm-21in) s.i.d.1983 bronze

WYON, Edward William (1811-1885) British
£1250 $2313   (12-Jun-92 TE1341/R) Bust of Robert Stephenson (81cm-32in) s.i.d.1855
                        marble
£1300 $2223   (20-Mar-92 S90/R) St Michael and Satan (51cm-20in) i. green brown
                        pat.bronze after Flaxman

YANG YING-FENG (1926-) Chinese
£10115 $17297   (22-Mar-92 SY.TA14/R) Wind (29x35cm-11x14in) s.d.1974 bronze (T.D 440000)

YATES, Ruth (1896-1969) American
£6897 $12000   (15-Sep-91 JRB.C1/R) Joe Louis, 1940 (48cm-19in) s. marble

YENCESSE, Hubert (1900-) French
£3443 $6576   (1-Jul-92 FB.P154/R) Femme nue couchee (52cm-20in) s. brown pat.bronze.
                        Cast.A.Rudier (F.FR 33500)

YOURIEVITCH, Serge (20th C) French
£1200 $2052   (20-Mar-92 S198/R) La danseuse Nattova (39cm-15in) i. brown pat.bronze on
                        marble plinth

YRURTIA, Rogelio (1879-1950) Argentinian
£1744 $3000   (9-Oct-91 RO.BA47/R) Dr.Manuel B. Gonnet (56cm-22in) s.i. bronze on
                        marble base
£2198 $4000   (11-Dec-91 RO.BA71/R) Cabeza de nino (38cm-15in) s. pat.bronze on marble
                        base
£2326 $4000   (9-Oct-91 RO.BA48/R) Indiecito (35cm-14in) s.d.1921 bronze on marble base
                        f.H.Campalola
£6395 $11000   (9-Oct-91 RO.BA46/R) Serenidad (50cm-20in) s. bronze f.R.Buchhass

ZACH, Bruno (19/20th C) ?
£1000 $1780   (29-Nov-91 S227/R) The dancers (41cm-16in) cold painted bronze on onyx
                        plinth
£1150 $2047   (29-Nov-91 S226) The whip girl (45cm-18in) s. brown pat.bronze on marble
                        socle st.f.Broma
£1271 $2162   (25-Oct-91 BM.B1862/R) Female nude dancing (35cm-14in) i. pat.bronze
                        stone socle (DM 3700)
£1754 $3000   (21-Mar-92 SY.NY228/R) Figure of dancer, bare-breasted with outspread
                        arms (36cm-14in) s. cold-painted bronze
£2600 $4966   (2-Jul-92 CSK76/R) Young woman dressed in light chemise standing with
                        riding crop (46cm-18in) s. pat.bronze on marble base

ZADKINE, Ossip (1890-1967) French
£7216 $13206   (3-Jun-92 L.K468/R) Ariane (12x31x14cm-5x12x6in) i.num.9/10 brown
                        pat.bronze st.f.Susse F.Paris (DM 21000)
£20809 $36000   (2-Oct-91 SY.NY72/R) Figurine drapee a l'antique en pieds et de face
                        (63cm-25in) i. greenish black pat.bronze f.i.Alexis Rudier

ZAJAC, Jack (1929-) American
£1765 $3000   (23-Oct-91 B.SF3760/R) Split almond (69x48x23cm-27x19x9in) pat.bronze
                        marble
£2500 $4250   (23-Oct-91 B.SF3759/R) Swan IX (53x75x25cm-21x30x10in) white marble

ZELEZNY, Franz (1866-1936) Austrian
£1887 $3358   (28-Nov-91 D.V62/R) Adam and Eve as children (41cm-16in) s. wood
                        (A.S 38000)

ZETTLER, Emil Robert (1878-1946) American
£1149 $2000   (15-Apr-92 SY.NY114/R) Torso-female (44cm-17in) black pat.bronze
                        f.i.Gorham Co Founders QBNU

ZIMMERMANN, Eduard (1872-1949) Swiss
£1852 $3352   (19-May-92 GF.L293/R) The three graces (44cm-17in) s.c.1920 pat.bronze
                        (S.FR 5000)
£1972 $3569   (7-Dec-91 WK.M536/R) Standing female nude (159cm-63in) s.i.d.1909 stone
                        (DM 5600)

ZITMAN, Cornelis (1926-) Dutch/Venezuelan
£8889 $16000   (19-Nov-91 CH.NY155/R) Los cuatro ciclistas (20x23x45cm-8x9x18in)
                        init.d.70 num.6/6 brown pat.bronze
£9945 $18000   (18-May-92 CH.NY171/R) La Guerrera (48cm-19in) num.6/8 bronze

ZOI, D (?) Italian?
£2947 $5600   (26-Jun-92 WOL.C968/R) Female nude with dove (183cm-72in) d.1897 marble
on green marble column
£8130 $14146   (13-Apr-92 AT.P215/R) La porteuse d'eau (114cm-45in) marble bronze
(F.FR 80000)

ZORACH, William (1887-1966) American
£6077 $11000   (6-Dec-91 CH.NY185/R) Man with winged horse (36cm-14in) i.num.4/6 green
black pat. bronze
£28729 $52000   (6-Dec-91 CH.NY193/R) The family (50cm-20in) s. granite

ZORILLA DE SAN MARTIN, J L (1891-?) Uruguayan
£1492 $2700   (6-Dec-91 GC.M129/R) El Gaucho (57cm-22in) s. green/brown pat.bronze

ZSCHOKKE, Alexander (1894-1981) Swiss
£1316 $2408   (4-Jun-92 SY.Z595/R) The foolish virgins (37x25cm-15x10in) s. bronze
(S.FR 3500)

ZUNIGA, Francisco (1913-) Costa Rican
£6111 $11000   (18-Nov-91 SY.NY120/R) Dos mujeres (22cm-9in) s.d.1963 brown pat.bronze
£8235 $14000   (23-Oct-91 B.SF3787/R) Seated woman (28cm-11in) s.num.V/VI 1967 bronze
£8287 $15000   (19-May-92 SY.NY98/R) Dos mujeres sentadas (27cm-11in) s.num.I/III d.1977
black pat.bronze
£8889 $16000   (19-Nov-91 CH.NY74/R) La familia (25cm-10in) s.d.1962 brown pat.bronze
£9444 $17000   (19-Nov-91 CH.NY91/R) Madre e Hijo (25cm-10in) s.d.1971 num.IV/IV dark
brown pat.bronze
£11050 $20000   (18-May-92 CH.NY95/R) Nino en la Ventana (51cm-20in) s.d.1980 num.IV/VI
golden pat.bronze releif
£14917 $27000   (19-May-92 SY.NY27/R) Madre e hijo (45cm-18in) s.d.1962 granite
£15470 $28000   (18-May-92 CH.NY96/R) Mujer sentada (42cm-17in) s.d.1972 num.VI/VI brown
pat.bronze
£17778 $32000   (19-Nov-91 CH.NY92/R) Mujer Sentada (37cm-15in) s.d.1975 IV/IV brown
pat.bronze
£17778 $32000   (18-Nov-91 SY.NY68/R) Mujer con las manos al frente (60cm-24in) s.d.1971
num.I/VI brown pat.bronze
£18333 $33000   (18-Nov-91 SY.NY63/R) Yucateca en cuclillas (38cm-15in) s.d.1975
num.II/III black pat.bronze
£19444 $35000   (19-Nov-91 CH.NY107/R) Maternidad (68cm-27in) s.d.1965 num.516 golden
brown pat.bronze
£27778 $50000   (19-Nov-91 CH.NY40/R) Silvia Agachada (32cm-13in) s. black marble
£35912 $65000   (18-May-92 CH.NY15/R) Virginia Agachada (46x87x84cm-18x34x33in) s.d.1975
num.I/VI greenish pat.bronze
£55249 $100000   (19-May-92 SY.NY51/R) Mujer sentada (103cm-41in) s.num.II/II d.1960 green
pat.bronze i.f.
£58333 $105000   (18-Nov-91 SY.NY46/R) Desnudo reclinado de Dolores (107cm-42in) s.d.1976
grn.pat.bronze i.Fund.Moises del Aguila